# LIFE MATTERS

## Connecting Biology to Your World

**Dora Cavallo-Medved**
*University of Windsor*

**M. Brock Fenton**
*University of Western Ontario*

**Bill Milsom**
*University of British Columbia*

**Shelby Riskin**
*Brown University*

**Kenneth Wilson**
*University of Saskatchewan*

**NELSON EDUCATION**

**Life Matters: Connecting Biology to Your World**

by Dora Cavallo-Medved, M. Brock Fenton,
Bill Milsom, Shelby Riskin, and Ken Wilson

**Vice President, Editorial
Higher Education:**
Anne Williams

**Senior Publisher:**
Paul Fam

**Marketing Manager:**
Leanne Newell

**Developmental Editor:**
Candace Morrison

**Photo Researcher and
Permissions Coordinator:**
Kristiina Paul

**Senior Production
Project Manager:**
Natalia Denesiuk Harris

**Production Service:**
MPS Limited

**Substantive Editors:**
Rosemary Tanner,
Sharilynn Wardrop

**Copy Editors:**
Holly Dickinson, Carolyn Jongeward

**Proofreader:**
MPS Limited

**Indexer:**
Edwin Durbin

**Design Director:**
Ken Phipps

**Managing Designer:**
Franca Amore

**Art Coordinator:**
Suzanne Peden

**Interior Design:**
Dianna Little

**Interior Design Modifications:**
Nelson Gonzalez

**Cover Design:**
Courtney Hellam

**Cover Images:**
Eric Isselee/Shutterstock
(salamander, orange butterfly);
Ron and Joe/Shutterstock
(letter L); Evgeniya/Shutterstock
(peacock feather); Leigh
Prather/Shutterstock (letter F);
HandMadeFont.com/Shutterstock
(letter E); Prapann/Shutterstock
(white butterfly); Panachai
Cherdchucheep/Shutterstock
(monarch butterfly);
M.B. Fenton (bat)

**Compositor:**
MPS Limited

**Library and Archives Canada
Cataloguing in Publication Data**

Cavallo-Medved, Dora, 1971–,
author
    Life matters : connecting
biology to your world / Dora
Cavallo-Medved, M. Brock Fenton,
Bill Milsom, Shelby Riskin, Ken
Wilson.

Includes index.
ISBN 978-0-17-650517-2 (pbk.)

    1. Biology—Textbooks. 2. Life
sciences—Textbooks. I. Title.

QH308.2.C38 2015    570
C2015-901644-4

ISBN-13: 978-0-17-650517-2
ISBN-10: 0-17-650517-2

# BRIEF CONTENTS

# TABLE OF CONTENTS

## CHAPTER 5

### Harvesting and Utilizing Energy in Cells   100

## CHAPTER 6

### A Cell's Life   128

## CHAPTER 7

### Gaining Genetic Diversity   150

## CHAPTER 8

### Genes and Patterns of Inheritance   170

# ABOUT THE AUTHORS

DORA CAVALLO-MEDVED, Ph.D. Dora Cavallo-Medved received her Ph.D. in Biochemistry from the University of Windsor in 2000 (Windsor). Subsequently, she was awarded a Natural Sciences and Engineering Research Council of Canada (NSERC) Postdoctoral Fellowship to study the role of the cysteine protease cathepsin B in cancer progression and invasion at Wayne State University and Barbara Ann Karmanos Cancer Institute (Detroit, Michigan, USA). She returned to the University of Windsor in 2008 as a faculty member in the Department of Biological Sciences. Her main research interest is the development of three-dimensional co-culture models to study the tumour microenvironment. In addition to her research, she has developed a great interest in and passion for teaching biology. She currently teaches introductory biology for science majors and mentors undergraduate biology students. She has been awarded several pedagogical grants to work with undergraduate biology students to develop novel, investigative labs for introductory biology courses. She has found that involving undergraduate students in curriculum development is a successful way to engage and enrich their undergraduate experience. She is also a recipient of the Roger Thibert Teaching Excellence Award from the Faculty of Science at the University of Windsor.

University of Chicago Press). He has supervised the work of 46 M.Sc. students and 22 Ph.D. students who have completed their degrees. He currently supervises five M.Sc. students and two Ph.D. students. He continues his research on the ecology and behaviour of bats, with special emphasis on echolocation. In addition to teaching parts of first-year biology, he has taught vertebrate biology, animal biology, and conservation biology, as well as field courses in the biology and behaviour of bats. He has received numerous awards for his teaching (Carleton University Faculty of Science Teaching Award; Ontario Confederation of University Faculty Associations Teaching Award; and a 3M Teaching Fellowship, Society for Teaching and Learning in Higher Education), in addition to recognition of his work on public awareness of science (Gordin Kaplan Award from the Canadian Federation of Biological Societies; Honorary Life Membership, Science North, Sudbury, Ontario; Canadian Council of University Biology Chairs Distinguished Canadian Biologist Award; the McNeil Medal for the Public Awareness of Science of the Royal Society of Canada; and the Sir Sanford Fleming Medal for Public Awareness of Science, the Royal Canadian Institute). He also received the C. Hart Merriam Award from the American Society of Mammalogists for excellence in scientific research. Bats and their biology, behaviour, evolution, and echolocation are the topics of his research, which has been funded by NSERC. He serves as co-editor of the *Canadian Journal of Zoology* and is the academic editor for *PLOS ONE*. He is currently an emeritus professor of biology, University of Western Ontario.

M.B. (BROCK) FENTON, Ph.D. Brock Fenton received his Ph.D. from the University of Toronto in 1969 for work in the ecology and behaviour of bats. Since then he has held academic positions at Carleton University (Ottawa, 1969 to 1986), York University (Toronto, 1986 to 2003), and the University of Western Ontario (London, 2003 to present). He has published over 200 papers in refereed journals (most of them about bats), as well as numerous nontechnical contributions. He has written four books about bats intended for a general audience (*Just Bats*, 1983, University of Toronto Press; *Bats*, 1992, and its revised edition in 2001, Facts On File Inc; *The Bat: Wings in the Night Sky*, 1998, Key Porter Press; and, with Nancy B. Simmons, *Bats: A World of Science and Mystery*, 2015,

BILL MILSOM, Ph.D. Bill Milsom is a professor in the Department of Zoology at the University of British Columbia, where he has taught a variety of courses, including first-year biology, for over 30 years. His research interests include the evolutionary origins of respiratory processes and the adaptive changes in these processes that allow animals to exploit diverse environments. He examines respiratory and cardiovascular adaptations in vertebrate animals in rest, sleep, exercise, altitude, dormancy, hibernation, diving, and so on. This research contributes to our understanding of the mechanistic basis of biodiversity and the physiological costs of habitat selection. His research has been funded by NSERC, and he has received several academic awards and distinctions, including the Fry Medal of the Canadian Society of Zoologists, the August Krogh Award of the American Physiological Society, the Bidder Lecture of the Society for Experimental Biology, and the Izaak Walton Killam Award for Excellence in Mentoring. He has served as president of the Canadian Society of Zoologists and as president of the International Congress of Comparative Physiology and Biochemistry.

**SHELBY RISKIN, Ph.D.** Shelby Riskin received her Ph.D. from Brown University in 2013 (Rhode Island, USA). Broadly, Shelby's research interests are focused on global agricultural expansion, on the role of phosphorus in agriculture, particularly in tropical soils, and on water quality. Her dissertation work, a joint project between Brown University and the Marine Biological Laboratory in Woods Hole, Massachusetts, focused on the effects of land-use change in the Brazilian Amazon. More recently, she has worked as a research associate at McGill University. She has published in *BioScience, Global Change Biology, Philosophical Transactions of the Royal Society B*, and other journals. In addition to academic research, Shelby works to facilitate dialogue between scientists and citizens over scientific issues. She has conducted water quality research with citizen stakeholder input, and she has facilitated a multidisciplinary group at the Sustainable Phosphorus Summit at Arizona State University in 2011 with members from academia, industry, and elsewhere to address the issue of our use of phosphorus, a finite and irreplaceable natural resource.

**KENNETH WILSON, Ph.D.** Kenneth Wilson received his Ph.D. from the Department of Plant Sciences at the University of Western Ontario in 2001. He is currently a faculty member in the Department of Biology at the University of Saskatchewan. Since starting at the University of Saskatchewan in 2004, Ken has taught courses in genetics, plant physiology, plant diversity, photobiology, and the first-year introduction to cell biology and genetics. Based on comments from students and colleagues, he has been awarded the College of Arts and Sciences Excellence in Teaching Award and the Provost's Award for Outstanding Teaching. Ken is involved in a number of science outreach projects at the University of Saskatchewan aimed at communicating science to the community and attracting young students, especially young Aboriginal students, to study science at university. Funded by NSERC and the Canadian Foundation for Innovation, his research uses green algae as a model system for studying cellular energy balance under changing environmental conditions. The approaches he uses to answer research questions range from biotechnology to biophysics. Using the largest and most expensive research tool ever built in Canada, the Canadian Light Source synchrotron, his students can examine changes in the molecular makeup of living cells in real time.

# PREFACE

## Why We Wrote This Text

Biology, the study of living organisms, is as old as mankind, and each of us in one way or another has participated. You see, biology is not a field limited to scientists. Instead, we have all asked questions about the living world around us, explored biological explanations, and even experimented here and there. By nature we are biology, and the matters of life matter to us. In this book, we authors have tried to introduce key biological concepts—from the cell to whole organisms to entire ecosystems—in a way that we hope will connect with you. Of course, a biology textbook is mandated to deliver scientific facts. We explain cellular mechanisms and discuss biological concepts but have tried to do so by intertwining this information within other disciplines, including history, art, and political science. For example, in Chapter 3 we discuss the art of microscopy, and the beauty of microscopic images of cells and organisms. In Chapter 9, we share the history of the discovery of DNA and the story of the people involved. In Chapter 31, we discuss how public policies play a role in maintaining our natural ecosystems and biological diversity, and our role in the environment. By writing the book in this style, we intended for you, the reader, to see biology as more than an independent branch of science—as a connector of us all.

As you embark on your journey through this book, you will find that it does not begin in the traditional style of most biology textbooks. Rather than devote the first few chapters to the chemistry and physics that serve as a background to the study of biology, we dive into the biology in your life. We hope to capture you by exploring the biology that affects all of us every day. We placed the background reference material, the Building Blocks of Biology, in the Purple Pages in the middle of the book. These building blocks support the study of living organisms and apply to all chapters of the book. We highlight them by placing them in the centre of the book, where they are readily available to you whenever you need them, no matter what biological topic you are studying.

As you begin to explore the chapters, you will find that we start each one with Why It Matters. Here we tell a story, often a non-scientific one, about the chapter content, and we provide a sneak peak at what lies ahead. We end each chapter with Putting It in Perspective. Here we wrap up the material presented in the chapter in a way that relates to our everyday lives. This section provides relevance and significance and often connects back to Why It Matters. Throughout each chapter, you will also find some feature boxes. These are meant to momentarily take you away from the text and provide interesting examples, engaging stories, or current research on the chapter content. The Molecule behind the Biology boxes showcase specific molecules involved in a biological concept presented in the chapter or perhaps discuss the history of the molecule and the people who discovered it. In some examples, we describe how these molecules are being developed as therapies to cure diseases. The Biology Is Everywhere boxes are meant to demonstrate how we find biology in all aspects of life. In some examples, we discuss how biology plays a role in industry and commercialization, influences government policies, and may alter our behaviour. Finally, the Life on the Edge boxes are meant to feature extreme organisms or illustrate cutting-edge research in biology—such as designer babies, hyperthermophilic archaea that can survive temperatures over 120°C, and birds and mammals that can live at high altitude—and show how this research may change our lives. These boxes are meant to keep you thinking about biology even after you close the book. Finally, throughout each chapter, we provide study break questions that are intended to help you reflect on the chapter content, and at the end of each chapter you will find review questions for self-assessment.

We authors are excited about this new biology textbook and are eager to share it with you. Individually, we come from different scientific backgrounds in biology, but together we represent the entire field. From cell and molecular biology to evolution to systems to ecology, collectively we speak as one voice for the study of life and our passion for teaching it. But we could not have spoken alone. We acknowledge the dedicated efforts and critical guidance of our publishing team, the expert reviewers, and you, the student. We hope that together we tell the story of life in a way that matters in your world.

## Organizing Features of the Text

The content of the textbook has been organized into 33 chapters, each written with the intent to connect the reader to the field of biology. The first chapter initially engages readers by providing a plethora of examples on how biology relates to them. Chapter 1 is meant to draw in the readers by using everyday examples that help them feel comfortable with biology and that highlight how biology connects to other disciplines of study. Chapter 2 introduces biology by focusing on what life is and providing a general outline of the major biological concepts that will be discussed in more detail in the chapters that follow. Chapters 3–11 are focused on cell and molecular biology, with an emphasis on DNA and applications in biotechnology. Chapters 12–19 discuss the theory of evolution, mechanisms of speciation, and the classification of all living organisms; specific chapters are dedicated to the major groups of organisms. Chapters 20–28 describe the working systems within plants and animals, including anatomy and physiology, and how they function cooperatively for survival. Chapters 29–32 concentrate on ecology, conservation, and behaviour and the interactions among species within populations, communities, and ecosystems. Finally, Chapter 33 reconnects readers to biology by providing a concluding overview of how biology impacts them and how they in turn impact biology. Each chapter also includes various pedagogical features to enrich the content and provide readers with self-assessment tools.

## Features

### Why It Matters

Each chapter begins with a Why It Matters section, including the introduction of a recent and interesting publication or an example of a biological concept, presented in a manner that relates to readers. This section is meant to be used as the basis of conversation throughout the chapter.

### Study Break Questions

Each chapter includes Study Break questions at the end of the chapter's major sections. They contain questions written by the authors to identify some of the important features of the section.

### Biology Is Everywhere

The Biology Is Everywhere boxes contain stories connecting biological concepts and everyday life. Many of these stories describe how biologists and non-biologists alike have used their ingenuity and creativity to expand our knowledge of biology. Others describe how people use biology for purposes far removed from scientific inquiry.

### The Molecule behind the Biology

The Molecule behind the Biology boxes give readers a sense of the exciting impact of molecular research and how these impacts may affect them. A wide range of molecules are highlighted, including oxygen, testosterone, cholesterol, vitamin $K_2$, dopamine, and the HPV vaccine, Gardisil.

### Life on the Edge

Life on the Edge boxes provide accounts of biological extremes, including organisms thriving "on the edge" in unusual environmental conditions and novel biological applications that drive the future of biotechnology. These boxes also discuss how these biological extremes and their applications affect everyday life.

### Putting It in Perspective

This section at the end of every chapter is intended to personalize the chapter content by making links between the subject matter and daily life. It often relates to the Why It Matters section at the beginning of the chapter.

### The Purple Pages

The Purple Pages reference section, entitled Building Blocks of Biology, outlines background material, including basic chemistry and physics concepts that support the study of biology. This reference information is important for understanding the content of all chapters in the book. Therefore, instead of the traditional placing of this information in the first few chapters of the book, it is readily accessible in the middle of the book and highlighted with purple-edged pages.

### Key Concepts Review and Questions

Every chapter concludes with Key Concepts Review and Questions. This section includes a short description of key concepts from the chapter and questions—multiple choice, short answer, matching, and critical thinking—that test students' knowledge of the key concepts.

## Instructor Ancillaries

### About the Nelson Education Teaching Advantage (NETA)

The **Nelson Education Teaching Advantage (NETA)** program delivers research-based instructor resources that promote student engagement and higher-order thinking to enable the success of Canadian students and educators. Be sure to visit Nelson Education's **Inspired Instruction** website at http://www.nelson.com/inspired/ to find out more about NETA. Don't miss the testimonials of instructors who have used NETA supplements and seen student engagement increase!

All NETA and other key instructor ancillaries can be accessed through http://www.nelson.com/instructor, giving instructors the ultimate tools for customizing lectures and presentations.

**NETA Test Bank**: This resource was written by Laura Ambrose, University of Regina. It includes over 1000 multiple-choice questions written according to NETA guidelines for effective construction and development of higher-order questions. Also included are true/false and fill-in-the-blank questions.

The NETA Test Bank is provided in a new cloud-based platform. **Nelson Testing Powered by Cognero®** is a secure online testing system that allows you to author, edit, and manage test bank content from any place you have Internet access. No special installations or downloads are needed, and the desktop-inspired interface, with its drop-down menus and familiar, intuitive tools, allows you to create and manage tests with ease. You can create multiple test versions in an instant, and import or export content into other systems. Tests can be delivered from your learning management system, your classroom, or wherever you want. Nelson Testing Powered by Cognero for *Life Matters: Connecting Biology to Your World,* can be accessed through http://www.nelson.com/instructor. Printable versions of the Test Bank in Word and PDF formats are available upon request.

**NETA PowerPoint:** Microsoft® PowerPoint® lecture slides for every chapter have been created by Dora Cavallo-Medved, University of Windsor. There is an average of 40 slides per chapter, many featuring key figures, tables, and photographs from *Life Matters: Connecting Biology to Your World.* NETA principles of clear design and engaging content have been incorporated throughout, making it simple for you to customize the deck for your courses.

**Image Library:** This resource consists of digital copies of figures, short tables, and photographs used in the book. You may use these jpegs to customize the NETA PowerPoint or create your own PowerPoint presentations.

**NETA Instructor's Manual:** This resource was written by Martin Crozier, University of Windsor, and Sara McNorton, University of Windsor. It is organized according to the textbook chapters and addresses key educational concerns, such as typical stumbling blocks students face and how to address them.

**Day One:** Day One—Prof InClass is a PowerPoint presentation that you can customize to orient students to the class and their text at the beginning of the course.

### MindTap

**MindTap** for *Life Matters: Connecting Biology to Your World* has been developed by Sean Rogers, University of Calgary, and Andrew Hubberstey, University of Windsor. MindTap is a personalized teaching experience with relevant assignments that guide students to analyze, apply, and elevate thinking, allowing instructors to measure skills and promote better outcomes with ease. A fully online learning solution, MindTap combines all student learning tools—readings, multimedia, activities, and assessments—into a single Learning Path that guides the student through the curriculum. Instructors personalize the experience by customizing the presentation of these learning tools to their students, even seamlessly introducing their own content into the Learning Path.

## Student Ancillaries

 MindTap®

### MindTap

Stay organized and efficient with **MindTap**—a single destination with all the course material and study aids you need to succeed. Built-in apps leverage social media and the latest learning technology. For example,

- ReadSpeaker will read the text to you.

- Flashcards are pre-populated to provide you with a jump start for review—or you can create your own.

- You can highlight text and make notes in your MindTap Reader. Your notes will flow into Evernote, the electronic notebook app that you can access anywhere when it's time to study for the exam.

- Self-quizzing allows you to assess your understanding.

Visit http://www.nelson.com/student to start using **MindTap**. Enter the Online Access Code from the card included with your text. If a code card is *not* provided, you can purchase instant access at this location.

## Acknowledgements

We wish to sincerely and gratefully acknowledge the many people who have assisted and encouraged us throughout this endeavour. We would specifically like to acknowledge members of the science community, including our colleagues, mentors, assistants, and students who contributed ideas, figure images, research data, constructive feedback, and assistance. With your support we have been able to make this book more comprehensive, enriching, and engaging for our readers. A special thank-you to copyeditors Holly Dickinson and Carolyn Jongeward, who read the manuscript with an eye for accuracy. And to Paul Fam, our senior publisher and team strategist, who initiated and then guided the author team on an incredible journey to create a book that truly connects to the reader. Paul's enthusiasm and dedication to student learning as the fundamental purpose of our collective endeavour have been very much appreciated by the author team. Candace Morrison, our developmental editor, has worked patiently to keep the author team focused throughout the project and diligently on schedule. Natalia Denesiuk Harris, the senior production project manager, has eagerly worked with the author team to coordinate the book in its final stages. We also acknowledge the contributions of permissions and photo researcher Kristiina Paul and Lynn McLeod, Project Manager, Rights Acquisition & Policy, as well as the substantive editors, Rosemary Tanner and Sharilynn

Wardrop, who worked meticulously and cooperatively with the author team to produce a book that is both refined and engaging.

We are indebted to the reviewers of this book at several stages for their outstanding and invaluable advice on how to construct an effective book:

Catherine Glass, Langara College
Diana Fletcher, Mount Royal University
Jim Karagatzides, Georgian College
Laura Graham, University of Guelph
Mariola Janowicz, Concordia University College of Alberta
Robert Edwards, University of Calgary
Jiantee Jagessar, Centennial College
Frank Williams, Langara College
Gavin Park, Nipissing University
Leslie Dafoe, Sault College
Shanta Srivastava, Dawson College
Gerry De Iuliis, George Brown College and University of Toronto
Julie Smit, University of Windsor
Margot Wassenaar-Faber, Seneca College
Sean Rogers, University of Calgary
Michael Durrant, Champlain Regional College

The authors would also like to include personal acknowledgments.

Dora Cavallo-Medved thanks her husband, David, and her two daughters, Anna and Angelina, for their endless encouragement, inspiration, and patience. She also thanks her parents, Tony and Angela; her sister, Antonella; and all her family and friends for their constant care and support. Finally, she also thanks her students, who provide the energy that drives her passion for teaching and continual learning.

Brock Fenton thanks his late wife, Eleanor, for all of her help and support over many years. He also thanks Karen Campbell, Beth (E.L.) Clare, Michael Owen, and Naas Rautenbach for their discussions about text and photographs. He is also grateful to the many students who drew him more deeply into biology and teaching.

Bill Milsom would like to thank his wife, Bridget, for her patience and support, and his students, who fuel the passion to teach and to explore.

Shelby Riskin would like to thank her husband, Dan, for his help, support, and input. She would also like to thank her parents, Chris and Barb Hayhoe, for their unending support, particularly in the last few years. She would also like to thank Jennifer Gardy and Matthew Heard for help with content. She also thanks her children, Sam, Linnea, and Wallace Riskin for being so sweet.

Ken Wilson would like to thank his wife, Tricia, not only for her patience as deadlines approached but also for tolerating the endless chatter about fascinating (for him) biology stories. He would also like to thank the science teachers he has had during his life, beginning with the first ones—his parents, George and Sharon. Finally, he is especially thankful for the advice, friendship, and support of the professors emeriti from the Department of Biology at the University of Saskatchewan.

We would be most grateful if any readers of this book could send us any suggestions they might have for improvements.

We hope this book will be helpful as you learn about biology.

Dora Cavallo-Medved
Brock Fenton
Bill Milsom
Shelby Riskin
Ken Wilson

# Biology in Your Life

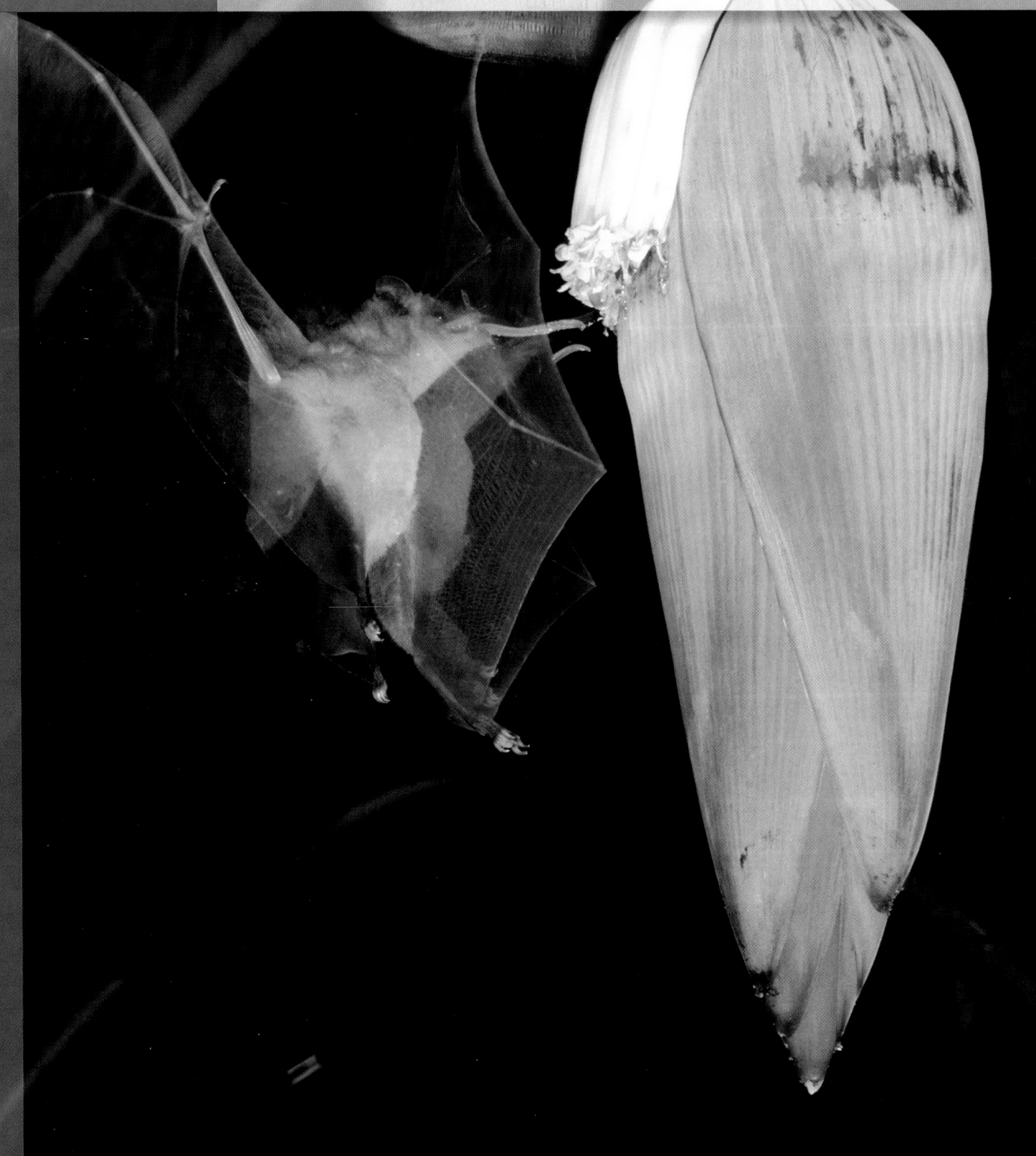

M.B. Fenton

## WHY IT MATTERS

On August 5, 2012, Usain Bolt sprinted 100 m in 9.63 s. He covered the distance in 41 strides, averaging 2.44 m per stride. How do sprinters run so fast? Are they different from other people? Why are some of them faster than others? These questions are basic ones about variation and raise other questions about the biological significance of **variation**.

Part of the answer about how sprinters run so fast emerged in 2012. Josh Baxter and a team from Pennsylvania State University reported that the **ankles** and feet of sprinters differed from those of non-sprinters. They drew this conclusion from data collected from 16 men, 8 sprinters and 8 non-sprinters. Using magnetic resonance imaging (MRI), the team demonstrated that the plantar flexor moment arms (pfMA; **Figure 1.1**) were shorter in sprinters than in non-sprinters. The difference was statistically significant; it could have happened by chance just once in 98.9 times (or $p=0.011$). Sprinters also have longer forefoot bones than non-sprinters. The centre of rotation (CoR) of the ankle joint accounted for most of the difference in the pfMA (99.9%). This combination means more movement with less work. We have known for some time that some foot bones (e.g., metatarsals) of adult humans vary considerably—8% to 17% of the mean value. The new work demonstrated the significance of the variation. Some people appear "born" to be sprinters. As we will see repeatedly in this book, variation is a central component of evolution—change over time. We expect variation at the population level **(Figure 1.2, p. 4)** within a species (the foot bones) or among species **(Figure 1.3, p. 4)**.

There are obvious differences in the foot skeletons of different species of Primates (the order including

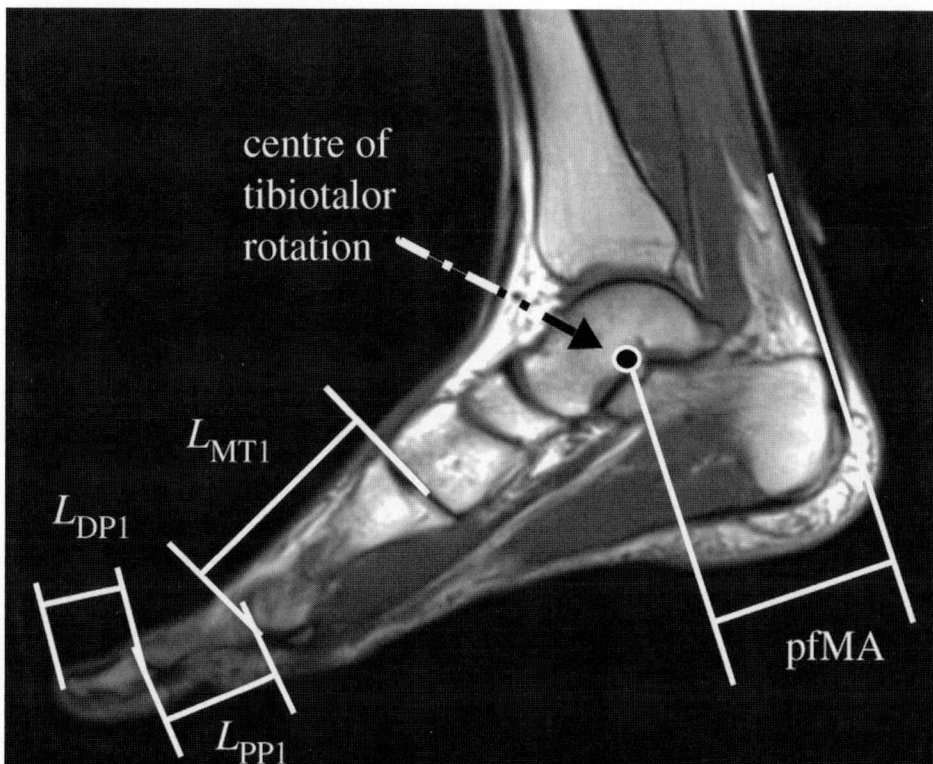

**FIGURE 1.1** Human ankle in neutral position showing the centre of tibiotalor rotation (CoR), the plantar flexor moment arms (pfMA), the length of the metatarsal 1 ($L_{MT1}$), the length of the first proximal phalanx ($L_{PP1}$), and the length of the first digital phalanx ($L_{DP1}$).

SOURCE: Baxter, J.R., T.A. Novack, H. Van Werkhoven, D.R. Pennell and S.J. Piazza, "Ankle joint mechanics and foot proportions differ between human sprinters and non-sprinters," *Proceedings of the Royal Society* B, 2012, Volume 279, Issue 1735, by permission of the Royal Society.

**FIGURE 1.2** Biologists on a field trip illustrate intraspecific variation.

humans), including clear differences in the size of the heels and the lengths of the feet. Similar patterns are evident among other mammals, but when species not designed for speed are considered (Figure 1.3), the level of variation increases dramatically.

When did bipedalism appear in the lineage leading to humans? The fossil record, specifically the structure of some foot bones **(Figure 1.4)**, indicates that the ~3 million-year-old fossil *Australopithecus afarensis* (also known as "Lucy") was bipedal. Other fossils (including fossilized footprints) suggest that by 4.4 million years ago, *Ardipithecus ramidus* was bipedal, revealing that this trait appeared early in the lineage leading to humans. Carol Ward and her colleagues published their findings about *A. afarensis* in 2011,

an important contribution to our understanding of the evolutionary history of our own species.

Does **bipedal** locomotion make humans faster than other animals? Imagine a foot race involving a sprinter such as Usain Bolt, an ostrich (*Struthio camelus*), another biped, and quadrupeds such as a cheetah (*Acinonyx jubatus*), a greyhound (*Canis familiaris*), and a horse (*Equus caballus*). In this grouping, the cheetah would be the fastest (32.5 m.s$^{-1}$), followed by the ostrich, the greyhound, and the horse (19.4 m.s$^{-1}$), all well ahead of Usain Bolt (10.4 m.s$^{-1}$). Bipedalism does not make humans the fastest of running animals. Being bipedal has many other advantages, as we will see below, and there are different approaches to bipedalism (see Chapter 22).

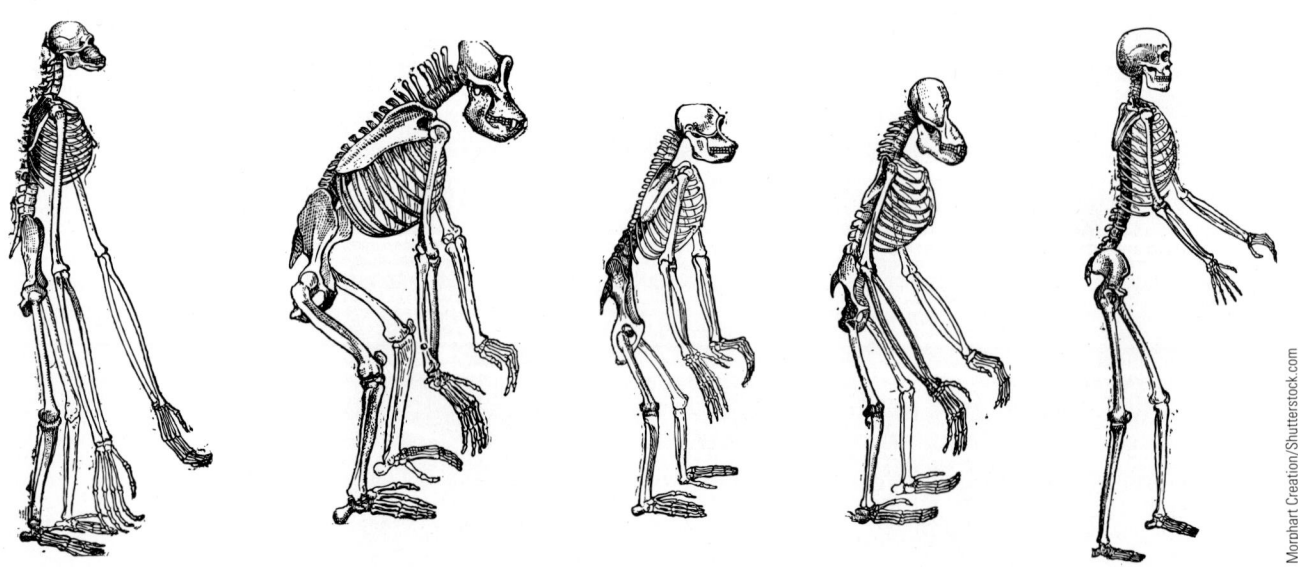

**FIGURE 1.3** A comparison of the skeletons of a gibbon (*Hydrobates* sp.), a gorilla (*Gorilla gorilla*), a chimpanzee (*Pan troglodytes*), an orangutan (*Pongo* sp.), and a human (*Homo sapiens*). Note the proportions of feet and ankles.

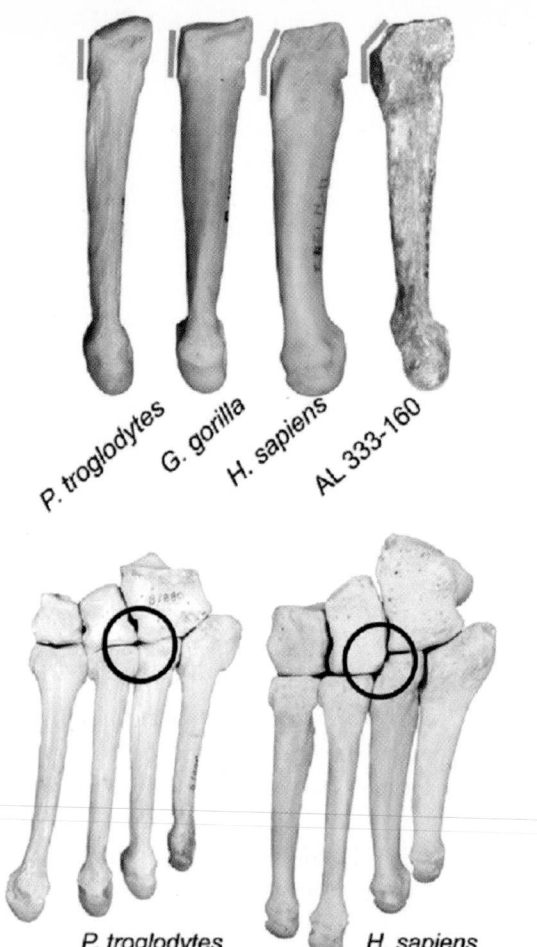

**FIGURE 1.4** A comparison of the left fourth metatarsals of a chimp (*Pan troglodytes*), a gorilla (*Gorilla gorilla*), a human (*Homo sapiens*), and an *Australopithecus afarensis*. The circled area shows articulated heads of foot bones (cuboid, lateral, and medial cuneiform and lateral metatarsals). Note the angles of articulation noted in the upper drawings.

SOURCE: From Ward, C.V., W.H. Kimbel and D.C. Johanson, "Complete fourth metatarsal and arches in the foot of Australopithecus afarensis," *Science*, vol. 331, 11 February 2011, pp. 750–753. Reprinted with permission from AAAS.

Bipedalism allows humans to use their hands to advantage. Our hands do not support body mass, particularly during locomotion, so our fingers are lightly built and our fingertips are very sensitive to touch. Combined with an opposable thumb, we have great ability to manipulate (from the Latin *manus* for hand) objects and use precision and power **grips (Figure 1.5)** to advantage.

Returning to the topic of variation, how and why do sprinters run so fast? Stride length is an important element in Usain Bolt's success **(Figure 1.6, p. 6)**, but training and conditioning are also involved. What else could be involved? At the Olympic Games in 2012, Jamaican sprinters won four gold, four silver, and four bronze medals in seven races. The population of Jamaica is about 3 million, and their record in running events is extraordinary. What is special about Jamaica when it comes to sprinters?

When thinking about variation, remember that it is uncommon to find simple relationships between variations (**polymorphisms**) in **genes** and in specific traits. Often complex traits are affected by complexes of causal genes. One example is the locus controlling the defensive chemistry protecting some plants from herbivores, specifically branched-chain methionine allocation (BCMA). Changes in BCMA influence the production of **glucosinolates**. These secondary compounds produced by plants inhibit feeding and **oviposition** by some herbivorous insects and provide protection for the plants against some microbial pathogens. Changes in BCMA determine the production of glucosinolates and thus influence the vulnerability of plants. Changes in the underlying genes are themselves influenced by ecological interactions in the variety of environments where the plants and their enemies occur. Evidence of this example of variation comes from assessments of geographic variation in BCMA at sites in Colorado and Montana.

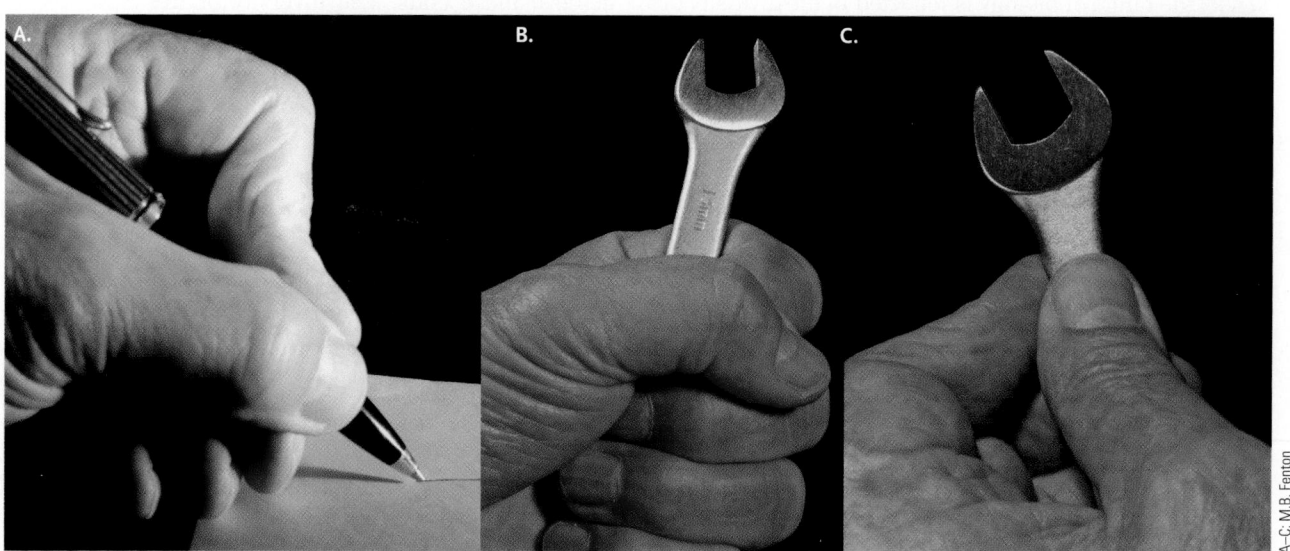

**FIGURE 1.5** The human hand can be used in a precision **(a)** or power **(b)** grip or in a combination **(c)**.

**FIGURE 1.6** Usain Bolt in mid-stride.

Ververidis Vasilis/Shutterstock.com

We introduce biology with a sampling of examples about various aspects of life. We progress from the capture of solar energy by photosynthesis, which typically occurs in chloroplasts (whether in plants or in animals), to the importance of nitrogen to plants. Some carnivorous plants acquire nitrogen from insects via fungi, whereas others catch and digest insects. Others have symbiotic relationships with animals. Farming is a behaviour known from a variety of animals, from social amoebae to ants, termites, beetles, snails, and damselfish, as well as from humans. In humans, farming includes domestication (selective breeding) of preferred species of plants or animals. By farming, animals (including people) gain access to more dependable and larger amounts of food. Genetic evidence helps us unravel the history of domestication and of a farming way of life in humans. We also use the role of **symbionts** in digestion as an illustration of diversity and interactions among species. Like many other (most? all?) animals, humans harbour a huge biota that is essential to digestion and other processes. Responses to changing conditions allow some organisms to benefit and expand their population and distribution. Our introductory examples include plants growing on the forest floor, butterflies, and moths. We also raise the topic of human effects on climate and the future of the planet. This initial sampling sets the stage for topics that are discussed in more detail later in the book. One goal is to underscore the reality that humans are like other living organisms, depending on the earth and its resources, including the diversity of life.

What advantages does variation confer? Please keep this question in mind as you proceed through the book.

Biology, the study of life, covers a wide range of topics, from interactions that take place within an organism to those among organisms in a habitat. In a sense, the range of biology is reflected in the diversity of life, from bacteria to birds, trees to tadpoles, mushrooms to mackerels. As intriguing as the organisms is the range of systems they contain, responsible for breathing, acquiring and using energy, and reproduction and many other functions. The control of life's processes is a central part of biology, across operations from reproduction and development to breathing and excretion.

The purpose of this book is to introduce you to the realm of biology by illustrating the many ways that our societies and way of life reflect our biology. To achieve this, we begin each chapter with a brief essay (Why It Matters) to illustrate some facet of biology. We finish each chapter by addressing basic questions about life that are central to our species, from the impact of *Clostridium difficile* to arguments about the use of **GMOs**, genetically modified organisms. This first chapter presents a sampling of topics to illustrate the nature and scope of biology.

## 1.1 A Sampling of Life

In one sense, life is about burning fuel to produce energy that an individual uses, ultimately to reproduce itself. The diversity of life reflects the myriad of ways that organisms achieve these ends. The diversity of the fossil record reminds us that the solutions we see today often have a long evolutionary history. In this book, we will explore the diversity of life and consider how our own species fits into the pattern of life on Earth.

Plants, especially green plants, usually begin the energy process by converting solar energy to chemical energy. This process, **photosynthesis** (see Chapter 5), also releases oxygen, which is vital to most forms of life on Earth. Some bacteria (photoautotrophs) also convert solar to chemical energy. The diversity of **photoautotrophs** **(Figure 1.7)** extends from bacteria to animals, illustrating the range of approaches that can be involved. **Chlorophyll**, the molecule directly involved in photosynthesis, occurs in different configurations, partly reflecting the range of light conditions over which the process occurs. In plants, chlorophyll is typically housed in chloroplasts **(Figure 1.7a)**, intracellular **organelles**.

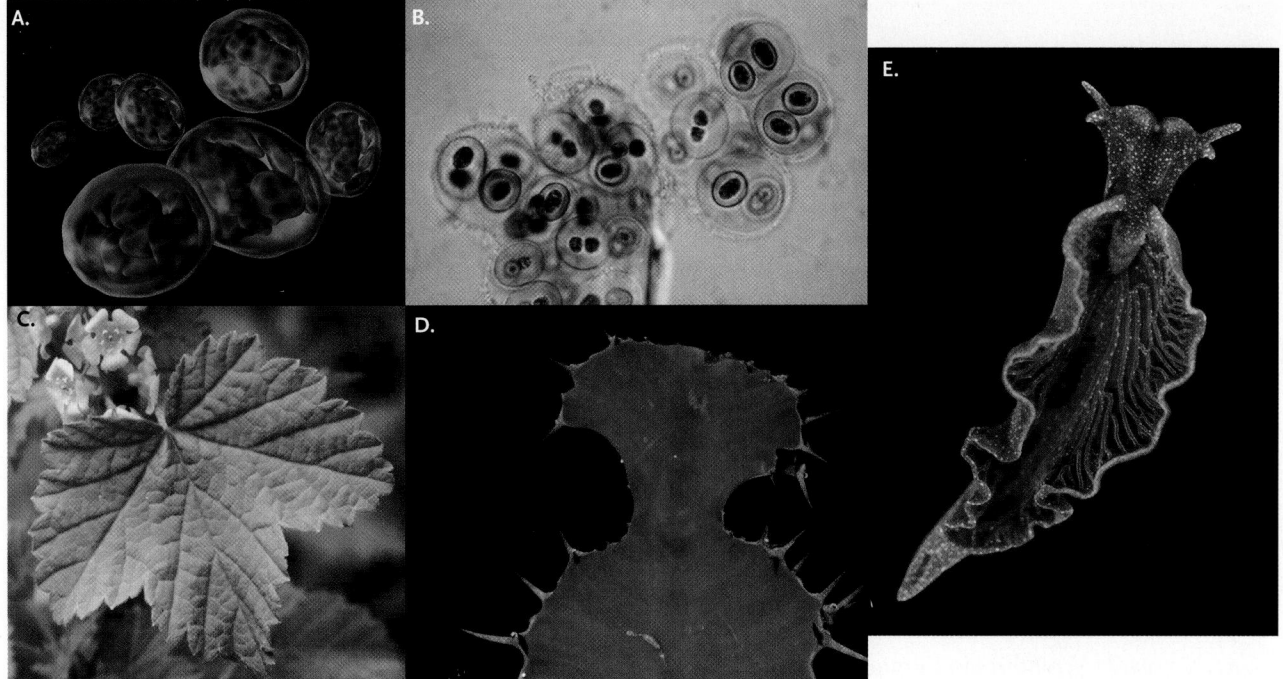

**FIGURE 1.7** Sites for photoconversion of carbon dioxide to energy: chloroplasts **(a)**, *Gloeocapsa* photoautotrophic bacteria **(b)**, a leaf from a vascular plant **(c)**, *Euphorbia grandicornis* **(d)**, and a solar sea slug (*Elysia chlorotica*) **(e)**. Not to scale.

SOURCE: Photos A–E: Knorre/Shutterstock.com; Ed Reschke/Photolibrary/Getty Images; Aleksandr Stepanov/Shutterstock.com; M.B. Fenton; Dr. Mary Tyler & Dr. Mary Rumpho, University of Maine, (2008). "Horizontal gene transfer of the algal nuclear gene psbO to the photosynthetic sea slug Elysia chlorotica," *PNAS*, 105 (46), 17868, Copyright (2008) National Academy of Sciences, U.S.A.

It may be surprising to learn that some animals are effectively "solar panels," capable of photosynthesis. This is usually achieved by obtaining chloroplasts and using them to generate energy. The sea slug, *Elysia chlorotica* **(Figure 1.7e)**, obtains chloroplasts from algae, and individuals can use them for at least 6 months. Quite amazing is the discovery that these sea slugs have genes allowing them to control the operations of the chloroplasts. Chloroplasts, like mitochondria, have DNA reflecting their origin as independent organisms (see Chapter 5). As discussed in Chapter 13, sea slugs are one of several examples of animals that short-circuit the usual food chain that starts with primary productivity (photosynthesis) by plants.

Control of chloroplasts is an example of the underlying role of genetics in life and life processes (see also Chapters 3, 5, and 10). Genetics plays a fundamental role whether the focus is the pattern of development of an organism from a fertilized egg, the control of a chloroplast, or the appearance of foot bones or hair colour. Improved and sophisticated genetic techniques have been responsible for many advances in biology, from understanding the process of evolution or using genetic manipulations to cure some diseases or human conditions.

As every gardener knows, plants need more than sunlight to thrive and reproduce. **Nitrogen** ($N_2$) is essential for most plants, and the **Haber–Bosch process** for fixing $N_2$ was instrumental in converting $N_2$ into a form usable by plants. This process involved mass synthesis of ammonia ($NH_3$), which was developed just before World War I, and led to huge advances in fertilizer production. The associated increase in plant productivity was central to supporting a growing human population (Chapter 29).

Nitrogen-fixing bacteria (Chapter 21) and decomposition of plant and animal material (usually by microbial decomposition) provide most species of plants with nitrogen. Michael Bidochka and colleagues from Brock University investigated the close symbiotic association between plants and endophytic fungi (*Metarhizium* spp.) that prevails in many ecosystems. These fungi, for example, *Metarhizium robertsii*, are insect pathogens and active transfer of nitrogen to plants from insects killed by the fungus. Haricot beans (*Phaseolus vulgaris*) and switchgrass (*Panicum virgatum*) are examples of plants that actively acquire nitrogen from insects via *M. robertsii*. Symbiotic relationships among leaf-cutter ants and other bacteria (see below) also provide a source of nitrogen in the ecosystems where they occur. Annually, each colony of leaf-cutter ants may contribute 1.8 kg of fixed nitrogen.

**Insectivorous plants (Figure 1.8, p. 8)** are another example of how plants can exploit animal sources of nitrogen. This approach to life has evolved at least six times among plants whose mature seeds are enclosed (also known as angiosperms). The best known carnivorous plants trap animals, usually insects, by pitfall traps (pitcher plants) or glue-like substances (sundews). In 2012, Caio Pereira and colleagues described how a plant (*Philcoxia minensis*) uses underground leaves to trap

**FIGURE 1.8** The insect-catching devices of a sample of carnivorous plants, including **(a)** venus flytrap (*Dionaea muscipula*), **(b)** sundew (*Drosera*), **(c)** pitcher plant (*Darlingtonia*), **(d)** butterwort (*Pinguicula*), and **(e)** bladderwort (*Utricularia*).

nematodes. Bladderworts (*Utricularia* spp.) trap plankton in negatively pressured bladders. By hitting a sensor, the prey opens the bladder, which draws in the prey. Active ion transport is involved in resetting the traps; in these plants, we see evidence of direct selection on subunit I of cytochrome *c* oxidase (COX) (see Chapter 5).

Another variant on the theme of carnivorous plants is a pitcher plant (*Nepenthes bicalcarata*) from Borneo that has a symbiotic interaction with the ant, *Camponotus schmitzi*. Vincent Bazile and his colleagues demonstrated that the wastes of the ant provided nitrogen to the plant and that plants with ants had more and larger pitchers than plants without ants. Symbiotic relationships between *Nepenthes* species and animals are not limited to ants. Also in Borneo, another species of *Nepenthes* benefits from the urine and feces of roosting woolly bats (*Kerivoula hardwickii*); still another exploits tree shrews (*Tupaia montana*).

How could you demonstrate that the plants acquire and use nitrogen from the animals? (For more details, see Chapters 17 and 21.)

Many other organisms are carnivorous, literally "meat eating." Cats, wolves, and other mammals of the order Carnivora are examples presented in Chapter 19. Also included are species of fungi, a marsupial lion, and many insects, molluscs, fish, amphibians, and birds.

**STUDY BREAK**

1. How can you measure variation?
2. What is the role of nitrogen in the lives of plants?
3. What are two examples of carnivorous plants?

## 1.2 Growing Your Food

### Animal Farmers

Being able to grow the food that we need was a major development in human history and a very large industry. It should come as no surprise, however, that other organisms also grow their own food. In 2011, Debra Brock and her colleagues from Rice University in Houston, Texas, reported that *Dictyostelium discoideum*, a **social amoeba**, exhibits a farming system that involves both dispersal and prudent harvesting of the crop. Approximately 33% of the clones they collected in the wild practised husbandry with bacteria. *D. discoideum* do not eat all of the bacteria in a patch, and they incorporate bacteria into their **fruiting bodies**. We do not know when this behaviour appeared in the evolutionary history of *D. discoideum*.

**Leaf-cutter ants** (**Figure 1.9**; tribe Attini, genera *Atta* and *Acromyrmex*) represent approximately 33% of the

**FIGURE 1.9** A leaf-cutter ant handling a piece of leaf for transport back to the nest. Note the vein in the leaf, the cut edges, and the way that the ant carries the piece of leaf.

**FIGURE 1.10** A damselfish, *Stegastes nigricans*, on its garden.

SOURCE: Paul Asman and Jill Lenoble, https://www.flickr.com/photos/pauljill/5800428420/. Licensed under Creative Commons Attribution 2.0 Generic (CC BY 2.0), https://creativecommons.org/licenses/by/2.0/

global biomass of insects. In forests along the Amazon River, leaf-cutter ants represent about four times the biomass of all land vertebrates. These ants are one of the most dominant herbivores of the New World (North, Central, and South America), and their leaf harvesting stimulates plant growth and plays a vital role in nutrient cycling. Cultivation of fungi on the plant material they harvest is the key to their success. The ants have a close symbiotic relationship with the fungi they grow and with bacteria (Actinobacteria in the genus *Pseudonocardia*). These bacteria produce antibiotics that help control parasites in the ants' fungal gardens. The fossil record indicates that leaf-cutter ants date back at least 50 million years.

In Africa, termites in one subfamily (Macrotermitinae) are symbiotic with fungi of the genus *Termitomyces*. Fungi are involved in the degradation of cellulose in plant material. The ants store their food in a comb made of fungus, a structure within the termites' nest. The termites add newly acquired plant material to the comb and consume older material from it. The family trees (phylogenies) of the termites and the fungi are very similar.

Ambrosia beetles are species of weevils (beetles) in two subfamilies (Scolytinae and Platypodinae). Ambrosia beetles carry fungal spores and mycelia in specialized glands (mycangia), moving them into the wood of living trees. Three genera of ophiostomatoid fungi (*Ophiostoma, Ceratocystis, Certaocystiopsis*) inhibit the defensive systems of the host trees, making them vulnerable to invasion by the fungus. This approach to symbiosis with fungi is probably as old as the one involving attine ants.

Another example, the marine snail (*Littoraria irrorata*), grazes on marsh grass (*Spartina alternifolia*). The snail's grazing prepares the surface of the grass's leaves for the growth of fungi, which the snails later eat. The combined actions of the snails and the fungi suppress the growth of the marsh grass.

Using their territorial defenses, individual damselfish (**Figure 1.10**; *Stegastes nigricans*) protect their algal "farms" from other damselfish. They also remove (weed) unpalatable algae, leaving their farms dominated by one species of *Polysiphonia*. At least three other species of algae in the genus *Polysiphonia* are farmed by damselfish.

Relatively recent confirmation of so many animal "farmers" suggests the promise of more discoveries of such interactions between animals and plants. The common feature emerging from these examples is the close relationships between species, with a clear nutritional benefit to the "farmer." How does this relate to our own species?

## People and Food

In **fossils** from ~1.8 million years ago, brain size is one feature distinguishing *Homo erectus* from *Homo habilis* (**Figure 1.11, p. 11**). This change emerged perhaps 0.7 million years after *Homo habilis* began to use tools. About 1.8 million years ago, at least at sites in modern-day Kenya, our ancestors ate fish and other marine life. This is "brain food" because it contains polyunsaturated fatty acids, which fuel the growth of the **cerebral cortex**. Does evidence of use of these foods at some sites indicate a widespread pattern?

**Cooking** is another important component in our relationship with food. Cooking requires controlled use of fire and, increasingly, utensils such as pots. A key point about cooking is rendering inedible, and even dangerous potential food materials edible. Cooking effectively increases the range of food available. In 2012, Francesco Berna and colleagues reported evidence of controlled use of fire 1 million years ago at a cave in the Northern Cape Province of South Africa.

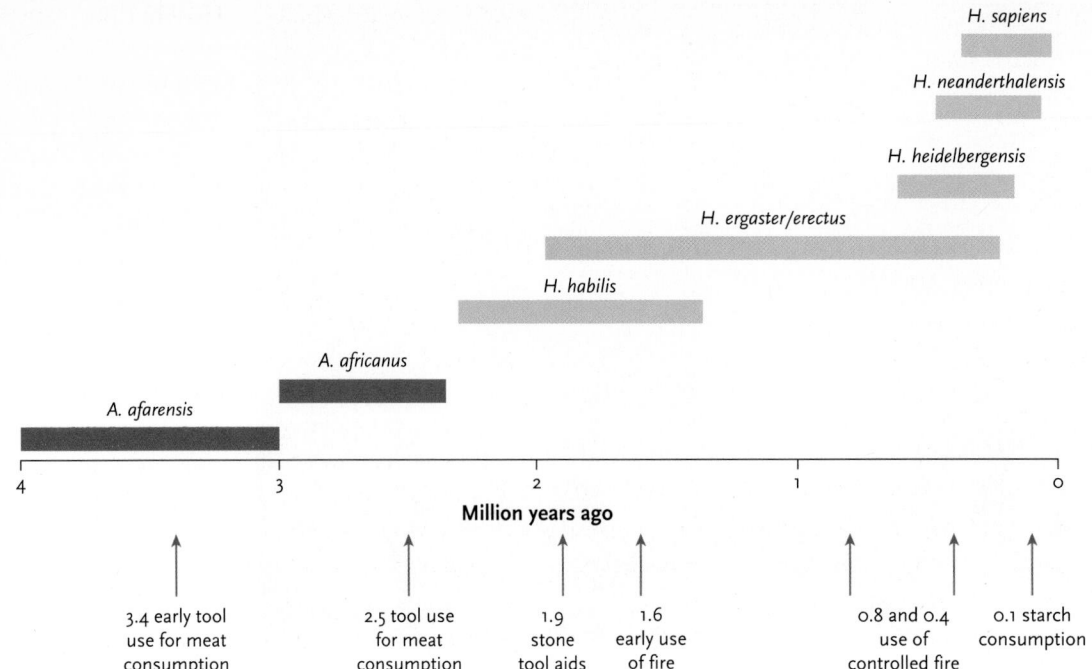

**FIGURE 1.11** Changes in diet across 4 million years of hominid history. Progression from using tools for meat consumption (3.4 and 2.5 million years ago) through using stone tools in the consumption of aquatic animals (1.9 million years ago) to the use of fire (1.6, 0.8, and 0.4 million years ago). Also shown is the consumption of catfish and other aquatic animals (0.19 million years ago) and then starches (0.5 million years ago). Brain size in hominids ranges from 385 cm³ in *Australopithecus* to 1350 cm³ in *Homo neanderthalensis* and *Homo sapiens*. A. = *Australopithecus*; H. = *Homo*.

There is considerable debate about the time when our ancestors began to show evidence of "culture." From southern Africa, some evidence suggests that the San (Bushman) material culture dates back to at least 40,000 years Before Present. The evidence includes weapons, tools, notched bones for notation, red ochre, and various ornaments made from marine shells and ostrich eggshells.

There is evidence of pottery from 20,000 to 19,000 years Before Present from a cave in China. Pottery, fired ceramic containers, differs considerably from objects made of baked clay. The appearance of pottery marks a basic shift in the way humans operated, from subsistence practices to various social and symbolic behaviours.

Another fundamental change in human behaviour was the move from hunting and gathering, typically a nomadic existence, to more permanent settlements, with attendant structures for living and storage. At this time, we began to rely more on cultivating other species, taking steps to enhance their availability as food (plants) or food and service (animals). The next stage in the process was selective breeding, the hallmark of domestication. The patterns and timing of domestication of animals and plants are illustrated in **Figure 1.12**.

From **Table 1.1**, it is clear that plants have been domesticated in several major areas of the world. The application of genetic techniques has often revealed that some plants, such as cotton (*Gossypium* spp.), or animals, such as pigs (*Sus scrofa*), were domesticated in more than one area. These data make it clear that no one group of

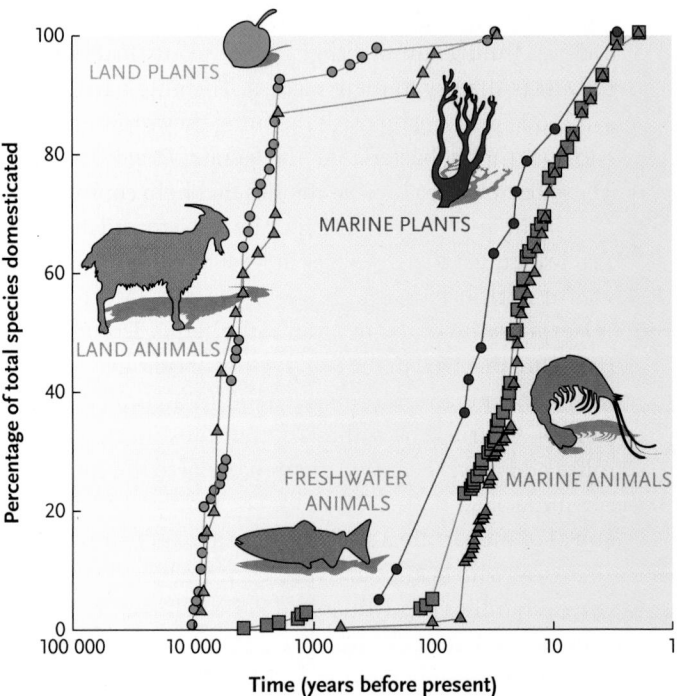

**FIGURE 1.12** Numbers of organisms (by group) domesticated over time shown as a percentage of total species domesticated (vertical axis) and over time in years (horizontal axis).

SOURCE: From M. Duarte, Nuria Marba, Marianne Holmer, "Rapid Domestication of Marine Species," *Science*, vol. 316, Apr 20, 2007, pp. 382–383. Reprinted with permission from AAAS.

people was responsible for domesticating other species, but areas closer to the equator have had more scope for domestication than those at higher latitudes.

| TABLE 1.1 | Approximate Numbers of Species of Plants Domesticated in Different Geographic Areas | |
|---|---|---|
| Area | | Numbers of Species Domesticated There |
| China | | 54 |
| India | | 74 |
| Inner Asia | | 35 |
| Asia Minor | | 41 |
| Mediterranean | | 54 |
| Ethiopia | | 22 |
| Southern Mexico, Central America | | 32 |
| South America (Peru, Ecuador, Bolivia) | | 26 |
| Chile | | 2 |
| Brazilia–Paraguay | | 8 |

Source: Based on Small, E. 2009. *Top 100 food plants: the world's most important culinary crops.* NRC Press, Ottawa, Canada.

Peoples that **domesticated** (selectively bred) other species typically benefitted from increased and more reliable availability of food, effectively fostering the growth of their populations (Chapter 29). On the island of New Guinea, a site at 2000 m elevation was occupied by people from 49,000 to 36,000 years ago. The record suggests that even then some people were modifying local habitat to promote the growth of beneficial plants. The evidence is stone **tools**, which were apparently used to fell trees, combined with consumption of an endemic nut (*Pandanus* spp.) and yams (*Dioscorea* spp.) as food. Habitat

modification to promote preferred plant species has also been reported from sites in South Africa and China.

One example of the origin and spread of a farming way of life comes from ~11,000 years ago in the Near East. From there, farming spread to Europe, where it arrived ~10,000 years ago and was widespread by ~5000 years ago. The arrival of farming coincided with displacement of groups of hunter–gatherers. In 2012, Pontus Skoglund and colleagues reported the results of analyses of genomic DNA recovered from the ~5000-year-old remains in Scandinavia of three hunter–gatherers and one farmer. The farmer was genetically most similar to southern Europeans and the hunter–gatherers to extant northern Europeans. This evidence suggests that the spread of agriculture involved dispersals of people.

This interpretation is supported by the work of Remco Bouckaert and his colleagues on the origins and expansion of Indo-European **languages (Figure 1.13)**. They used phylogeographic approaches combined with data about vocabulary from 103 ancient and contemporary languages. Their findings suggest an Anatolian origin and expansion from there starting 8000 to 9500 years Before Present. This interpretation augments the agricultural/ farming expansion presented by Skoglund and colleagues. An alternative explanation is that these languages originated in the Pontic Steppes (north shore of the Black Sea) about 6000 years ago.

Could dispersal of farmers account for the domestication events that occurred in the New World (North, South, and Central America)? Once again, genetic analysis may help begin to answer this question. In 2012, David Reich and 63 other authors used data from

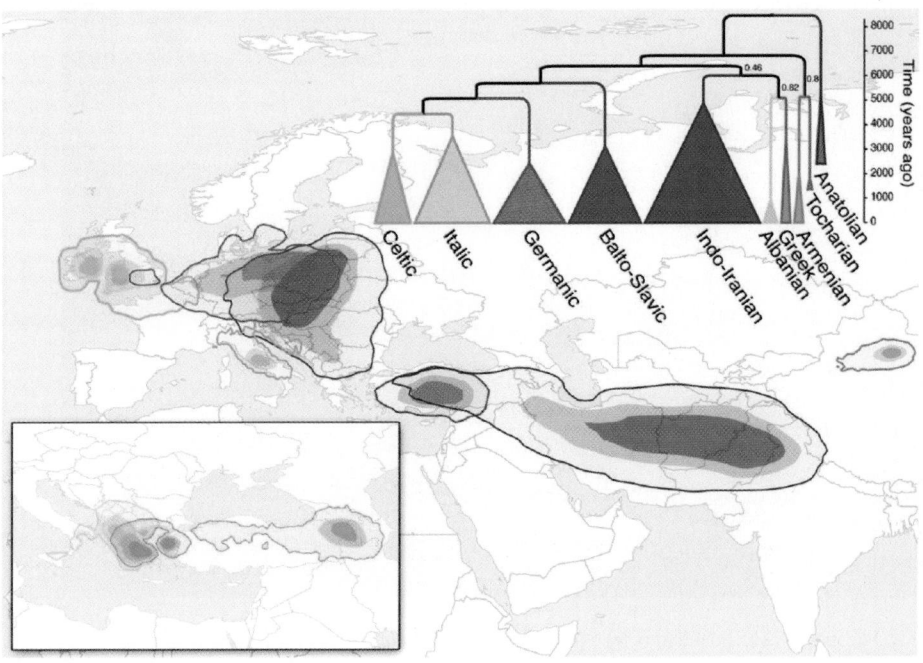

**FIGURE 1.13** The diversification of major Indo-European subfamilies of languages is shown as a family tree (phylogenetic) representation of the timing of their emergence superimposed on a map of the area. Colours match names and areas. The inset shows the inferred location for each subfamily.

SOURCE: From Bouckaert, R., P. Lemey, M. Dunn, S.J. Greenhill, A.V. Alekseyenko, A.J. Drummond, R.D. Gray, M.A. Suchard and Q. D. Atkinson, "Mapping the origins and expansion of the Indo-European language family," *Science*, vol. 337, 24 August 2012, pp. 957–960. Reprinted with permission from AAAS.

52 Native American and 17 Siberian groups of people to support the idea that Native Americans are descendants of 3 streams of gene flow from Asia. Most can be associated with the first dispersal event. But those speaking Eskimo–Aleut languages inherit ~50% of their ancestry from a second event. Chipewyan speakers of Na-Dene received ~10% of their ancestry from a third event.

Domestication events in the New World probably occurred among groups from the first dispersal. We do not know if this included experienced farmers who began to work with local species of plants and animals, such as corn (*Zea mays*) and turkeys (*Meleagris gallopavo*). It is clear, however, that social networking (Chapter 32) in at least some hunter–gatherer societies arises from interactions with both kin and non-kin individuals and is strongly based on a propensity to cooperate. Social networking appears to have been an ancient trait in our species.

## STUDY BREAK

1. What are three animals other than humans that have "farmed"?
2. Where have plants been domesticated?
3. What is domestication?

## 1.3 Interactions with Other Organisms

**Cellulose** is one of the principal structural elements in plants, and most species of animals cannot digest it and gain access to the energy stored there. This means that when we eat something with cellulose, most of it passes straight through the body without much chemical alteration (see Chapter 21). However, many species of animals eat and digest cellulose **(Figure 1.14)**. The list includes cattle and other ruminants, termites, rabbits, shipworms (gribbles), kangaroos, and many more (see Chapter 21). Most often the ability to digest cellulose results from the symbiotic fauna and flora living in the animal's digestive system.

Giant pandas (*Ailuropoda melanoleuca*) belong to the mammalian order Carnivora. These mammals are not normally known for their ability to digest cellulose. Therefore, it is not surprising that Lifeng Zhu and his colleagues found that pandas lacked genes responsible for enzymes that digest cellulose. They did, however, find 13 "species" of *Clostridium* coding at least two cellulose-digesting enzymes. These species are only known from the guts of giant pandas. This demonstrates that animals may step outside their "normal" range of diet, especially

**FIGURE 1.14** A sampling of animals that digest cellulose. Included is **(a)** a gribble (*Limnoria quadripunctata*), **(b)** an eastern cottontail (*Sylvilagus floridanus*), **(c)** termites (*Reticulitermes flavipes*), and **(d)** a cape buffalo (*Syncerus caffer*). Shown with the buffalo is a Red-Eyed Oxpecker (*Buphagus erythrorhynchus*), which is not able to digest cellulose. Pictures not to scale.

when they recruit the assistance of other organisms, usually microbiota.

Like other animals, we humans also harbour a rich biota of organisms in our guts. It is possible that our microbial communities contain at least 100 times as many genes as each of us has in our own genome. The population in a human gut is typically 100 trillion individual organisms. The community of **endosymbionts** includes bacteria, protozoans, and fungi. The populations and diversity of the gut biome increase as you progress further along the digestive tract (away from the mouth). This community is an important source of genetic and metabolic diversity.

Is there a "natural" human gut biota? The answer appears to be "no." Gut biomes in an individual can change over time, with age, and according to location and lifestyle. A number of pathways are regulated by signalling between host and microbiota. Furthermore, the biota physiologically connects gut, liver, muscle, and brain (**Figure 1.15**). Fungi play a crucial role in the gut microbiota of humans. The innate immune receptor dectin-1 is the portal of interaction between fungi and the immune system of the host. It appears that a suppressed fungal community increases susceptibility to chemically induced colitis.

The human **microbiota** is an ecosystem within an individual. Each of us is effectively a patch of habitat for microbiota. The composition of the biota, its relative numbers, and its activity can be understood through ecological processes (see Chapter 30) such as dispersal, community ecology, and environmental selection. Theories about metacommunities that ecologists use are also applicable to understanding our microbiota.

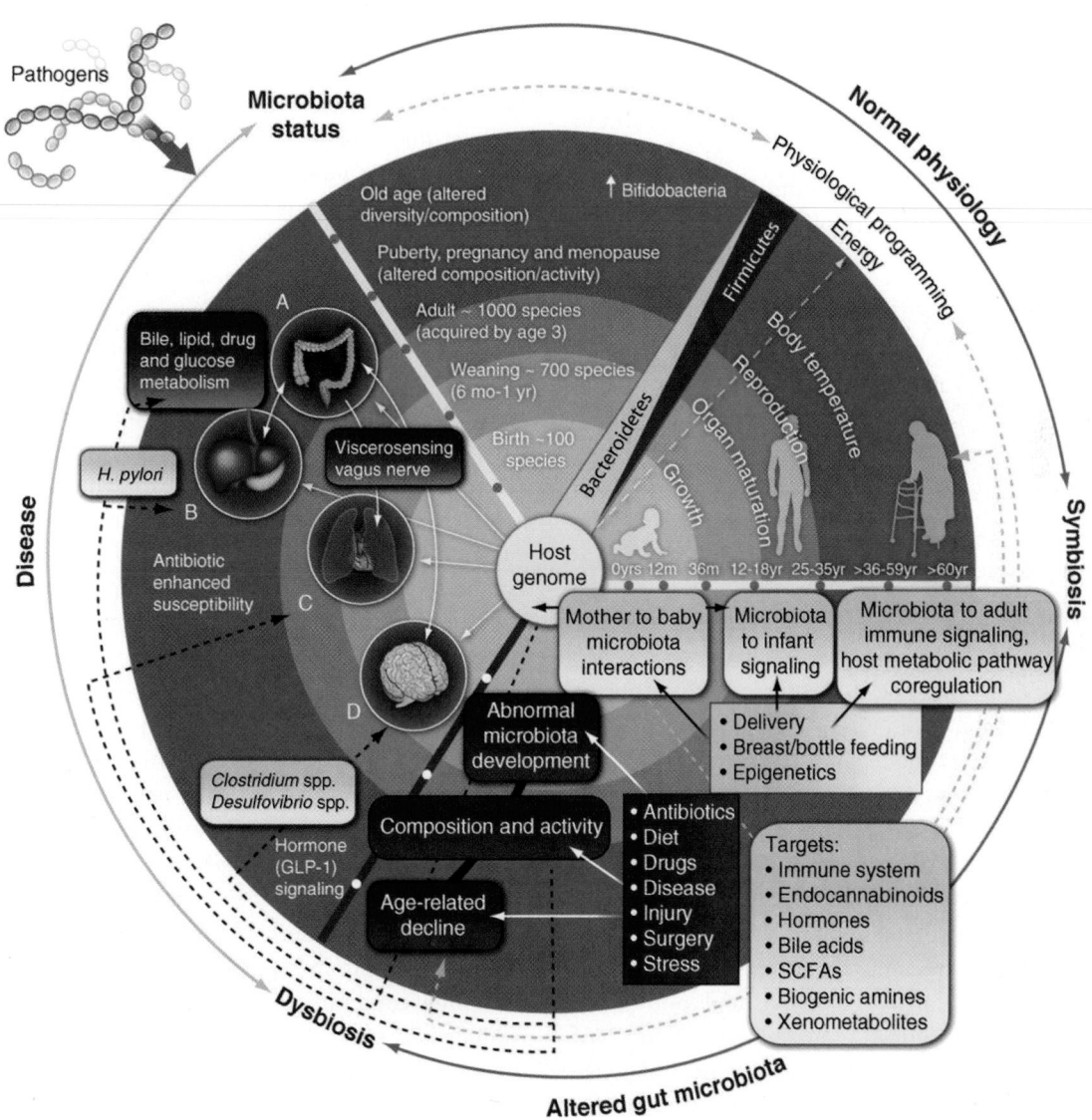

**FIGURE 1.15** This picture depicts the complex interactions associated with humans and our gut microbiota. Depicted are various patterns of interaction and feedback, including factors such as antibiotics, which can disrupt the system. SCFA = short-chain fatty acid.

SOURCE: From Nicholson, J.K., E. Holmes, J. Kinross, R. Burcelin, G. Gibson, W. Jia and S. Pettersson, "Host-gut microbiota metabolic interactions," *Science*, vol. 336, 8 June 2012, pp. 1262–1267. Reprinted with permission from AAAS.

Many people who have taken antibiotics have experienced the symptoms of a disrupted gut biome. Antibiotics can remove and/or change the variety of and balance between many symbionts, resulting in considerable intestinal discomfort. Anyone who has to take antibiotics should also ingest probiotics, live organisms that are beneficial either through direct interactions with the gut or its biota. People taking antibiotics should also eat prebiotics, ingredients in food that are beneficial to the gut biota.

*Clostridium difficile* **(Figure 1.16)** is a bacterium that is naturally part of your gut biota. Upsetting the natural equilibrium of the gut biota changes the situation and can lead to diarrhea and even to potentially lethal inflammation of the colon caused by the previously innocuous *C. difficile*. Outbreaks of what is now called "*C. difficile*" are all too common in hospitals and long-term care facilities, where they mainly affect older adults. These outbreaks usually occur after use of antibiotic medications. *C. difficile* too often illustrates how bacteria can spread through a population.

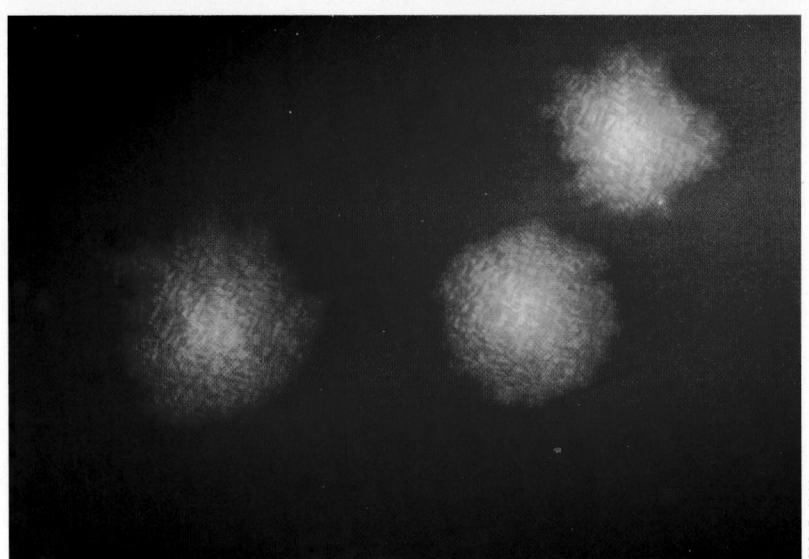

**FIGURE 1.16** *Clostridium difficile.*

## STUDY BREAK

1. What is the human microbiota?
2. What functions does the microbiota serve?
3. What is *C. difficile*?

## 1.4 Responses to Change

What factors can influence the success of one species invading the habitat of another? The canopy in deciduous forests provides shade, an important feature limiting the spread of other species of plants in the forest. Many plants of the forest floor, such as spring flowers in these woodlands, bloom in the spring before the canopy leafs out. Some successful invaders of deciduous forests in the eastern United States remain leafed well into the autumn after forest trees have shed their leaves. Jason Fridley showed that although native and non-native forest invaders have autumn growing seasons, those of non-native invaders are 4 weeks longer than those of native species. Most productivity (annual carbon assimilation) of non-native invaders occurs after forest trees have shed their leaves. Native invaders proved better at tracking year-to-year changes in spring temperatures than the non-native invaders.

Historically in the United Kingdom **(Figure 1.17)**, the brown argus butterfly (*Aricia agestis*) used one plant as its host (food for its caterpillars), namely the rockrose (*Helianthemum nummularium*). Now the pattern of **climate warming** that has resulted in *A. agestis* also exploits the more widespread geranium (*Geranium molle*) as food and has expanded its range considerably (Figure 1.17). Specifically, in Britain over the last 20 years, *A. agestis* has moved 79 km northward. The butterflies have benefitted from climate warming. Meanwhile, in the Netherlands, pied flycatchers (*Ficedula hypoleuca*) have experienced reduced reproductive success as a result of climate warming. As the climate warmed, these birds returned from their overwintering grounds earlier and earlier. Coinciding with earlier arrivals, the birds nested and laid eggs sooner than they had before. Unfortunately, the caterpillars that were their main source of food did not change their patterns of emergence with temperature because hatching of the insect eggs was determined by photoperiod, not by temperature. The net effect was many failed nests as parent pied flycatchers could not find enough caterpillars to feed their nestlings.

Many species of hawkmoths (family Sphingidae) visit flowers to obtain nectar and are important in the pollination of some species of plants. To explore flower choice by the hawkmoth *Manduca sexta*, researchers considered different species of *Nicotiana*. Under simulated moonlight conditions, Rainee Kaczorowski and colleagues scored visits to flowers by *M. sexta*, studying flowers of a species of *Nicotiana* apparently specialized for pollination by the hawkmoths. By comparing these data to those for *Nicotiana* pollinated by hummingbirds, they found that the moths preferred flowers specialized for sphingids **(Figure 1.18)**. The shape of the carolla of the flower affected the hawkmoths' choices and overall flower size.

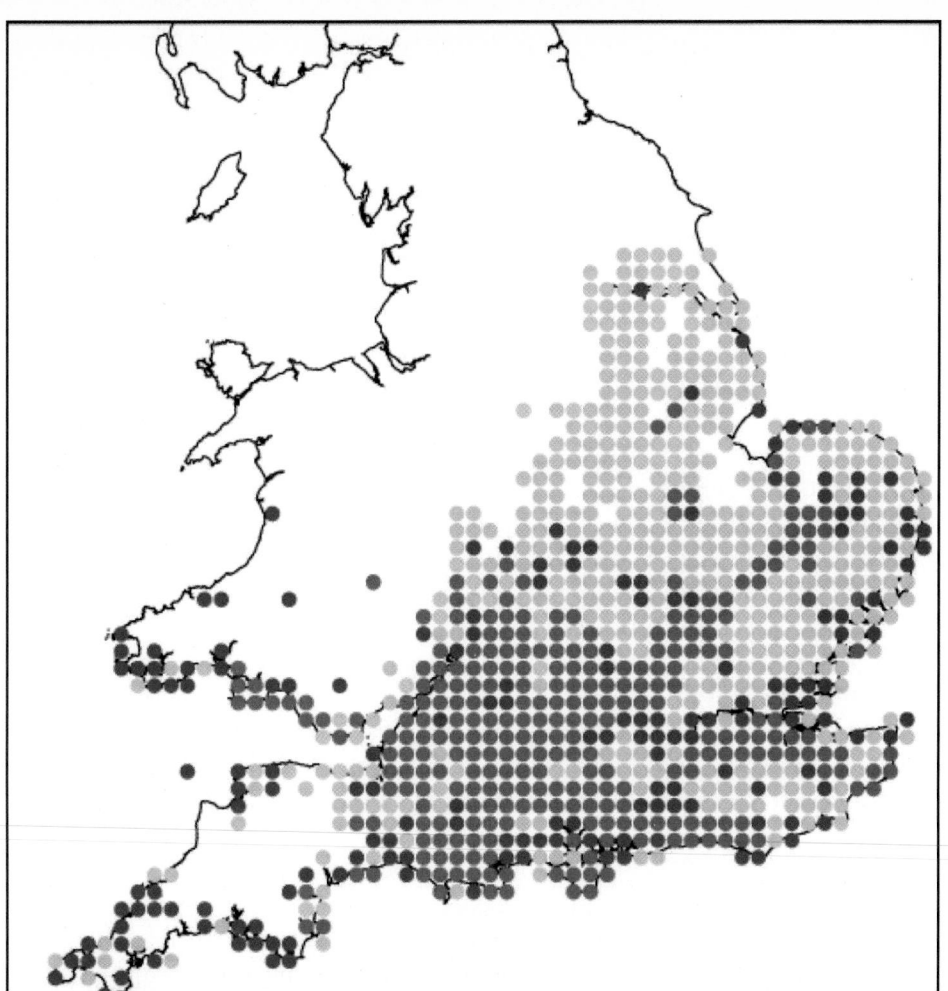

**FIGURE 1.17** Distribution and changes in density of *Aricia agestis* as indicated by 10 × 10 km grid squares with rockrose (*Helianthemum nummularium*—red) and geranium (*Geranium molle*—blue).

SOURCE: From Pateman, R.M., J.K. Hill, D.B. Roy, R. Fox and C.D. Thomas, "Temperature-dependent alterations in hose use drive rapid range expansion in a butterfly," *Science*, vol. 336, 25 May 2012, pp. 1028–1030. Reprinted with permission from AAAS.

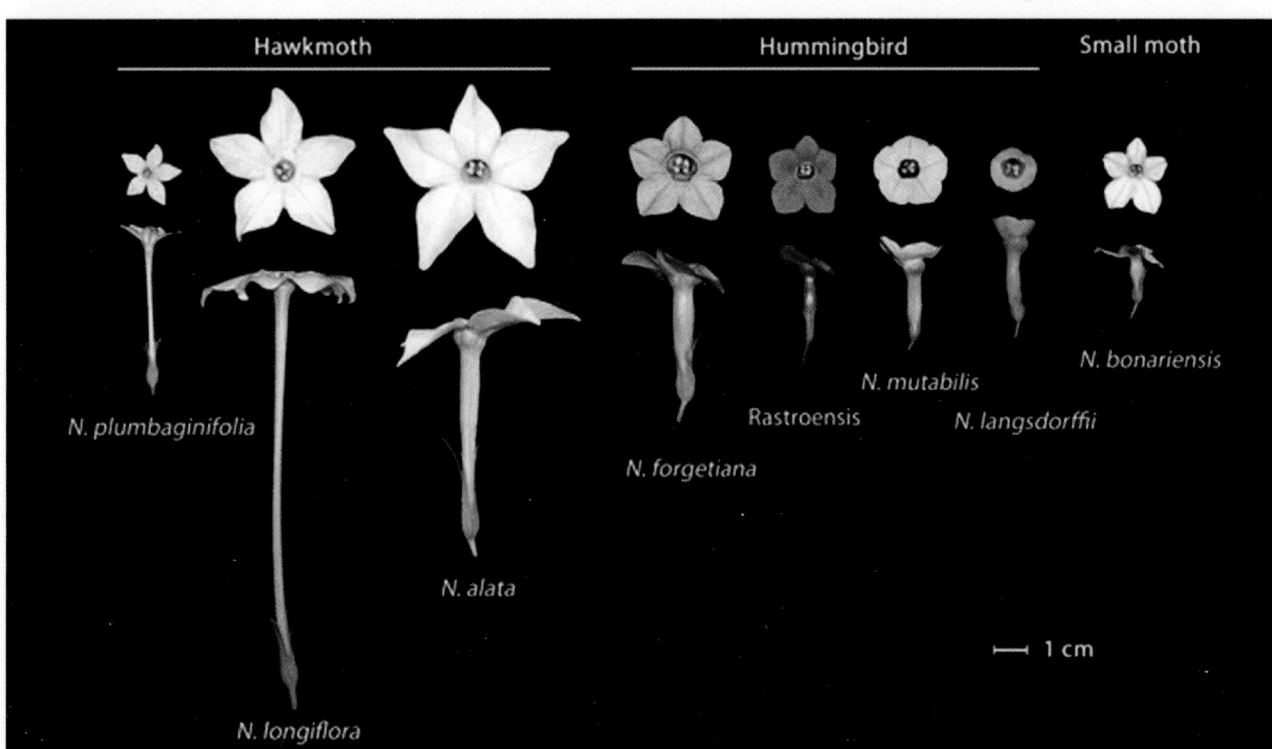

**FIGURE 1.18** A comparison of the flowers of different species of *Nicotiana* comparing those pollinated by hawkmoths, hummingbirds, and small moths.

SOURCE: Kaczorwski, R.L., A.R. Seliger, A.C. Gaskett, S.K. Wigsten and R.A. Raguso. 2012. "Corolla shape vs size in flower choice by a nocturnal hawkmoth pollinator," *Functional Ecology*, 26:577–587. John Wiley and Sons. © 2012 The Authors. Functional Ecology © 2012 British Ecological Society.

1. What is climate warming?
2. How can it affect organisms?

## 1.5 Humans and the Future of Planet Earth

To date, it appears that life is unique to Planet Earth. One extraordinary feature of life is its diversity. Diversity of life is a recurring theme throughout this book because it is central to the survival and prosperity of humans. Some biologists estimate that there are ~9 million types of living organisms on the planet, as well as about 7 billion people. The abundance, density, and impact of people threaten the future of Earth's biodiversity (see Chapter 31). Populations undergoing exponential growth **(Figure 1.19)** exert enormous negative pressures on the natural systems in which they occur. One important root of the problems generated by explosive growth is a rapid increase in the incidence of rare variants in the overall population. These often include complex diseases and traits resulting from genetic mutations. Alan Keinan and Andrew G. Clark explored this situation in their 2012 paper in *Science*, noting its implications for public health and the costs of health care.

It becomes increasingly clear that biodiversity is a key feature of ecosystems because of many positive interactive associations between the two features (biodiversity and ecosystems). This topic was addressed by Bradley Cardinale and 17 others in a review paper in *Nature* published in 2012. Among biologists studying ecosystems, there is general consensus that reductions in biodiversity severely affect the functioning of ecosystems. This negative effect increases over time. In turn, the health of multiple ecosystems is central to continued biodiversity. It also becomes increasingly clear that the history of life on Earth gives today's biologists a strong means of predicting the long-term outcomes of reducing biodiversity. We explore these situations in Chapter 31.

Around the world, the prosperity of humans depends on functioning ecosystems because of ecological processes controlling fluxes of energy, organic matter, and nutrients. This ranges from conversion of solar to chemical energy and to extensive natural recycling of resources. It also includes benefits, for example, providing renewable resources (food, wood, and fresh water). Regulation is another important facet of natural systems, including ameliorating changes associated with climate warming or the control of pests and diseases. We ignore these realities at our peril.

Too often we depend on our political leaders to lead in areas of environmental protection, providing the legal framework to ensure a stable future. Increasingly, however, we see evidence that people can rise up and effect change in the way their lives are regulated. Although concerns about the environment repeatedly emerge as

**FIGURE 1.19** Changes in the size of human population based on census rather than absolute numbers illustrate the explosive increase in the last 1000 years.

SOURCE: From Keinan, A. and A.G. Clark, "Recent explosive human population growth has resulted in an excess of rare genetic mutants," *Science*, vol. 336, 11 May 2012, pp. 740–743. Reprinted with permission from AAAS.

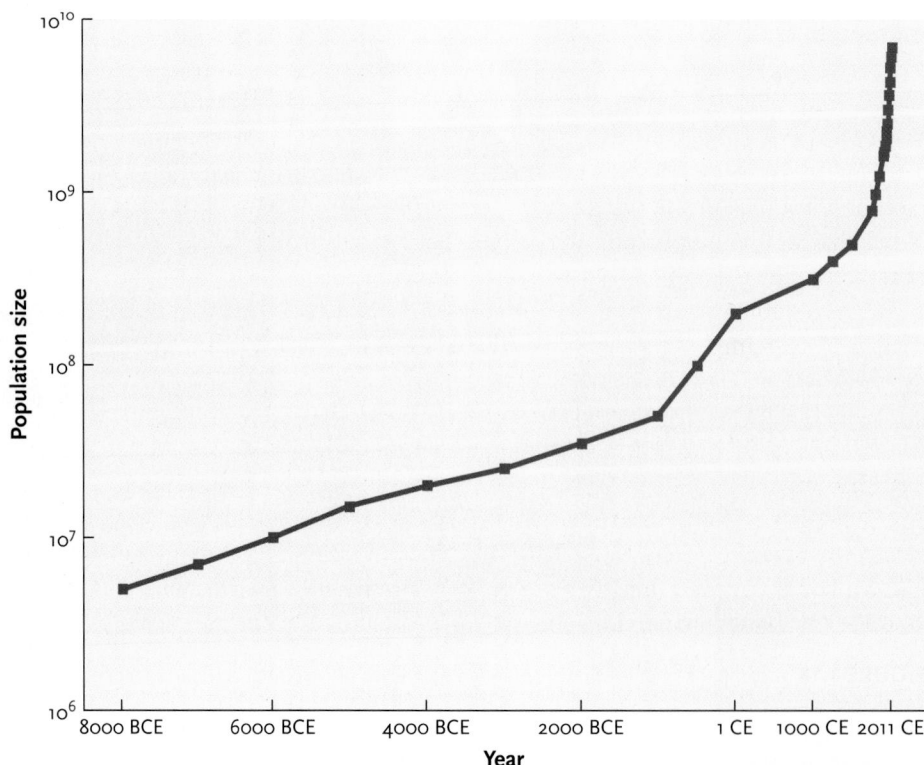

matters of wide concern among the citizens of many countries, this concern may not appear on the agendas of their governments.

In 2012, Berry J. Brosi and Eric G.N. Biber reminded us that citizen involvement can be crucial in identifying species that are at risk. Their analysis suggested that in the United States, at-risk species are more often effectively identified by citizen action than by the United States Fish and Wildlife Service (USFWS). In the United States and Canada, government agencies such as the **USFWS** and the Committee on the Status of Endangered Wildlife in Canada (**COSEWIC**) are specifically obliged to attend only to the factors that put a species at risk. Neither group is encouraged to consider the possible conflict with listing (protecting) a species and commercial or other development that might threaten the species. In the United States, citizens can petition the USFWS to list unprotected species, an important component in the system. Brosi and Biber argue that this situation has proved to be an effective way to identify at-risk species. They contend that efforts to curtail this aspect of the *Endangered Species Act* has drastic negative consequences.

Protecting resources that are not enclosed by national boundaries can be very challenging. Antarctica is an interesting example of an area that appears to be protected by the Antarctic Treaty System, which, to date, has proved to be a successful example of cooperative regulation around the use of a common space. A combination of exploration for mineral or other deposits and climate change puts new pressures on the system. Included among the threats are the introduction of non-native species and increased human activity, from tourism to exploration for resources. Over the next 50 years or so, the pressures on the Antarctic system will increase, requiring additional investment if the area is to be protected.

The global ocean system is another example of a common resource mostly lying outside territorial waters. Nearly half of the human population lives near a ocean coast. Humans depend on the oceans for food, employment, recreational activities, and regulation of the global climate. One example of a clear challenge is finding levels at which we can exploit marine resources (such as fish) while ensuring that the harvest is sustainable. Enforcing these levels may be an entirely different and more difficult challenge.

Biologists and other scientists should figure prominently in providing governments and international agencies with objective measures of critical factors. This could ensure that the levels of exploitation, for example, are, in fact, sustainable. Consumer pressure can be an important factor in the success of identifying and enforcing sustainable practice. But how could you know if the fish you have just purchased is what the label said? For more

on the challenge of identifying organisms (and parts of organisms), see Chapters 3, 16, 17, 18, and 19.

We will return to issues of conservation of biodiversity in Chapter 31.

## STUDY BREAK

1. What is explosive population growth?
2. What role does biodiversity play in our lives?

## 1.6 How Your Authors Got Hooked on Biology

### Dora Cavallo-Medved

Biology is the most diverse field of science. It involves the study of life but also incorporates physics, chemistry, and mathematics. And in today's technologically advanced world, it also includes computer science and engineering. However, biology is not limited to its relationships with other scientific disciplines because it is woven into our history, for example, the potato famine that triggered a mass immigration of Irish people to North America. It also influences our politics, for example, global public policy debates about the effects of greenhouse gases and climate change. Biology has also been the foundation of many globally successful businesses, such as the impact of major pharmaceutical and biotechnology companies on health care.

Biology has also been revealed in art as a medium for expression. This is clear in photomicrography and music as an innovative therapeutic strategy for cancer patients. Indeed, partnerships between biology and other disciplines are an intriguing feature of this science and one of the reasons for my passion for this field. In my early years, I was fascinated with the mysteries of life. Why are we made up of cells? How are we related to other species? What keeps us alive and what kills us? I was excited to search for pieces of information that would allow me to better understand. I wanted to be more educated. I wanted to be "in the know."

This knowledge has given me confidence in myself and yet humbled me to the complex world around me. It influenced my development and, in essence, played a role in shaping my identity. And it wasn't until I became a biologist, with a degree in hand to prove it, that I realized that I was a biologist all along **(Figure 1.20, p. 8)**. In fact, my desire for investigation and the discovery of the living world around me is shared by my scientific colleagues and by many other people. For example, when we don't feel well, we question the cause of our illness and explore pathways to reverse those effects. When a new family member is born, we investigate the mechanisms of

FIGURE 1.20 As autumn approaches, Dora's children examine the change in the colour of leaves from a burning bush plant.

of insects, over a million species. The pictures of a moth, a Virginia ctenucha (**Figure 1.21**; *Ctenucha virginica*), illustrate another aspect of insect diversity. The pictures show two parts of a four-part life cycle, namely larva (caterpillar) and adult (moth). Larval animals, for example, tadpoles and larval fish, are often strikingly different from adults. This poses one problem of associating adult and larva. It poses other interesting questions about ecology. Do specializations in life cycle represent a means of avoiding competition? How would we describe the niche of a species? How would we treat an animal in which the larvae fill a different feeding niche than the adults?

As an undergraduate student, I was introduced to bats in two ways. The first was a 1963 field experience, visiting a cave in December and finding bats hibernating there. The bats hung from the ceiling, entirely oblivious to us. This was not true of the porcupine sitting under them, which was alert and better avoided. The second was a 1965 essay assignment in a course about insects. I chose to write about bats and insects, focusing on the ears that allow moths to detect the echolocation calls of bats and take appropriate evasive action.

The bats, their insect prey, and the caves offered interesting opportunities for engagement and discovery. I became engrossed with the bats and began to try to study their movements between summer and winter sites. We did this by banding the bats, and each time we visited a summer roost (in the attic of a building) or a hibernation site (a cave or an abandoned mine), I was always looking

genetics by searching for physical similarities. And when we look up at the stars at night, we wonder if there is life as we know it beyond our planet. These types of questions are what bring biology, the study of life, into our daily lives, connect us as people, and make us all biologists by nature.

## Brock Fenton

I find the diversity of life one of the most alluring things about biology. Think of the diversity of birds—colourful, noisy, about 8000 species worth. But then ponder the variety

FIGURE 1.21 **(a)** A caterpillar and **(b)** an adult Virginia ctenucha (*Ctenucha virginiana*). This day-flying tiger moth (family Arctiidae) is bad tasting and brightly coloured to warn away predators. But this story involves more than just warnings. There is striking seasonal variation in the colour of the hairs on the caterpillars. Summer caterpillars are yellow; those in spring and autumn are black and yellow. The colour of the hairs influences the caterpillars' capacity for thermoregulation. From caterpillar to moth, there is more to this story than good (or bad) taste.

FIGURE 1.22 Brock Fenton photographing flying bats in a cave in Cuba. Note that much of him is coated with bat feces.

biology. For me, they are the gift that keeps on giving. The application of DNA barcoding to the challenge of identifying just what species of insects that bats eat is an example of a recent eye-opener. It was a former student, Dr. Beth Clare, who made this connection for me, tightening the link between bats and insects.

## Bill Milsom

I ended up a biologist not by forethought or good planning but by simply doing what interested me, with no thought to the future. In this respect, I have been incredibly lucky. As a child, I spent all of my free time outdoors, in the woods, swamps, and fields that surrounded wherever we happened to be living at the time **(Figure 1.23)**. I loved animals and brought home anything I could catch as a potential pet. Ironically, I avoided biology classes in school, finding them boring, and was attracted to physics instead. In hindsight, I think what appealed to me was problem solving and what bored me was rote memorization. It wasn't the subject matter so much as the way it was taught. I loved to take things apart to see how they worked—clocks, bicycles, toasters, you name it. It wasn't until I was at university that I discovered the science in biology and became fascinated trying to understand how animals "work." I fell in love with the relationship

for bands. This obsession raised other questions about how bats could find their way from one place to another.

From the outset, people were important in encouraging and challenging me. Professor Roland E. Beschel took me into my first cave. Professor Bev N. Smallman taught the entomology course and introduced me to Professor Kenneth D. Roeder, who studied moths listening to bats. Then Professor R.L. (Pete) Peterson accepted me as a graduate student. Somewhere along the line, bats and their diversity captured me.

In the interim, I have continued to study bats **(Figure 1.22)**—their evolution, ecology, behaviour, echolocation, and conservation. These animals opened my eyes to many fascinating questions in

FIGURE 1.23 Bill Milsom in one of his native habitats.

**FIGURE 1.24** Some of Bill Milsom's favourite study animals.

SOURCES: Left to right: Bill Milsom; Nature Picture Library / Britain On View / Getty Images; Ainars Aunins/Shutterstock.com

between form and function and in trying to understand the adaptations that allow animals to inhabit extreme environments. I came to the realization that we humans are not terribly adept at anything biological. Our senses (sight, hearing, smell) are mediocre compared to those of most other animals. There are species with better kidneys, hearts, lungs, athletic ability, etc. When my dog arises from sitting by the fire and heads out into the snow without putting on shoes or a coat, I realize how pathetic I am. If not for our opposable thumb and large brain, we would be in serious trouble competing in nature **(Figure 1.24)**.

We are generalists, and what fascinates me is unraveling the ways in which evolution has produced the specialized adaptations. Three examples of adaptations in different species that allow them to flourish in extreme environments include the diving ability of northern elephant seals, the ability of golden mantled ground squirrels to hibernate, and adaptations for high-altitude flight in barheaded geese.

With a love of nature, one can't help but be concerned about protecting and conserving the diversity of life on this planet. Paradoxically, the root cause of all the major threats we currently face is the growth of our own population, our inability to control our own biological urges. We vainly struggle to reduce our carbon footprint and greenhouse gas emissions while allowing our population to expand uncontrolled. The best way to combat this logical disconnect is through knowledge and education, and this is my other passion, to teach others about biology in a way that excites and challenges them and prepares them to deal with global environmental issues in a responsible way.

## Shelby Riskin

I didn't always think that I would be a biologist **(Figure 1.25)**. In fact, I went to university thinking I would study English and dance. I had always loved the outdoors and wildlife and had spent much of my life on a lake. I had even tried some ill-advised wildlife management, catching and transporting frogs by paddleboat to islands because I thought they were overrun with crickets. It never occurred

to me, however, that following my passion for all things wild could be my career.

During the most awkward of my awkward middle school years, I travelled on a sort of environmental stewardship trip, learning how to backpack, pulling out invasive plants, and encountering redwoods in California. When I started university, I joined the campus environmental group and started organizing a water-monitoring group. I loved wearing waders and figuring out how to use test strips and some basic chemistry kits. It still didn't occur to me that I could be a scientist or that all of that amazing stuff could play a large role throughout my life.

It wasn't until my second semester that I took my first biology class. Instead of a traditional class, where we had a broad introduction across the biological world (which is much of our intention with this book), this course was topic specific. The strategy was to introduce

**FIGURE 1.25** Shelby Riskin gets ready to measure water velocities in a stream in the Brazilian Amazon.

**FIGURE 1.26** Plants play many important roles in the biotic environment of the planet, some of which might surprise you. The trees of the Amazon, for example, are responsible for generating more than 30% of the precipitation that falls across the rainforest. And with roots that can extend more than 8 m into the soil (roots have been observed at depths of 18 m!), these trees can bring up water from deep soils to shallow soils, where it can be used by other plants and shallow soil organisms, a phenomenon especially important during the dry season. Many of these tropical trees, through activity by microbes living in root nodules, can take nitrogen from the atmosphere and turn this nutrient essential for life into forms that organisms can use.

students to the study of science and biology through a specific topic of interest. In my case, the topic was the effect of climate change on organisms. One day I found myself at the university's environmental research area, sitting by a stream. Our professor was reading a passage from Aldo Leopold's *A Sand County Almanac*. Aldo Leopold was a great naturalist and passionate environmentalist who lived, farmed, and studied the outdoors in Wisconsin in the first half of the 20th century. He is sometimes credited with founding the discipline of environmental ethics. I can't find the passage that I heard anymore (perhaps it has been too distorted by my memory), but the message that I took away from it was that ecosystems are more than a commodity to be consumed and that everyone has a responsibility to take action in conservation. I took that message to heart.

I never stopped taking biology classes after this one. I did my dissertation studying the consequences of the conversion of land to agriculture in the Amazon **(Figure 1.26)**. For me, studying and teaching biology and ecology are my way of taking action. For me, understanding biology makes the world around me a bigger, brighter place. My

job as a biologist helps me feel as if I am contributing to the greater good.

### Ken Wilson

I cannot remember ever making a conscious choice to become a biologist. However, growing up with a father who was a high school biology teacher and a mother who was a nurse certainly put me on a scientific trajectory. Looking back, I do not think that there was a time when I was not interested in biology. In elementary school, I read a lot about the natural world and loved animals, especially wild animals. We lived on a "hobby farm" in a rural area of southern Ontario, and our house backed onto a large cedar forest, which was slowly taking over our neighbour's neglected farmland **(Figure 1.27)**. That was my first lesson in the ecology of forest succession. My parents always encouraged me to ask questions, and I guess I was naturally curious. I would search milkweed plants for monarch butterfly caterpillars and try to raise them into butterflies in jars. When cleaning fish, we would dissect their stomachs to see what they had eaten **(Figure 1.28; p. 22)**. Finding crayfish claws in the stomach of a small mouth bass was an amazing discovery for me. I loved fishing, hiking, and learning as much as I could about the world around me. During high school, I took as many science courses as I

**FIGURE 1.27** Ken Wilson's childhood home was surrounded by "nature," with a lot of things to explore. In the upper part of the photograph, the cedar forest moving into the neighbour's farmland can be seen.

Ken Wilson

**FIGURE 1.28** Fish that made it home for lunch were also part of Ken's biology studies. Careful dissection of their digestive systems was not only fascinating but also provided clear insight into what type of bait to use on the next outing.

interacting with their environment keeps me asking questions. In fact, as my current career has evolved, I have come to love trying to communicate my fascination with the natural world. I find myself drawn back to using examples such as the milkweed plant and monarch butterfly to get my students asking questions and to encourage their curiosity.

## 1.7 Stories Behind the Cover

The picture on the back cover was taken in Belize in Central America. It shows a nectar-feeding bat (Pallas's long-tongued bat—*Glossophaga soricina*) visiting a banana flower. On the face of it, there is nothing unusual about this situation. Around the tropics, there are bats that visit and **pollinate** flowers and plants that depend on the pollination services of bats (see Chapter 28). But there is more to the bats and bananas story than meets the eye.

Bats visit banana flowers **(Figures 1.29** and **1.30)** because they produce considerable amounts of nectar (~100 mg per flower per day). Furthermore, individual banana flowers last for several days, opening new accesses to nectar every day for at least a week. In Belize in April 2014, an international group of biologists (Brock Fenton,

could; I loved the classes, and the scientific approach to solving problems just seemed to make sense to me. After high school, I enrolled in the Co-op Biochemistry program at the University of Waterloo. At the time, when people asked my why, I normally answered because I wanted to figure out how living things work. During my undergraduate program, I took more and more chemistry courses. Chemistry was more structured and gave clearer answers than biology. During my final work term placement, I was in a chemical research lab trying to make better fungicides, based on a plan my supervisor had developed. For 4 months I sent off samples to another branch of the company in Florida where they tested the potential fungicides for biological activity. As I received the results from these tests, I started to get quite jealous of the biologists doing the work. They got to try to figure out what the chemicals did. That quickly pushed me back to biology.

Although my research program at the University of Saskatchewan uses algae to study how plants detect stress, I love hiking and watching the things going on around me. A more in-depth knowledge of the biological and chemical processes that occur in the autumn may kill a bit of the romance of watching the leaves turn colour, but understanding how the plants and animals I see are

M.B. Fenton

**FIGURE 1.29** A banana flower with the bract partly raised to reveal the flower parts below. Some developing bananas are also visible.

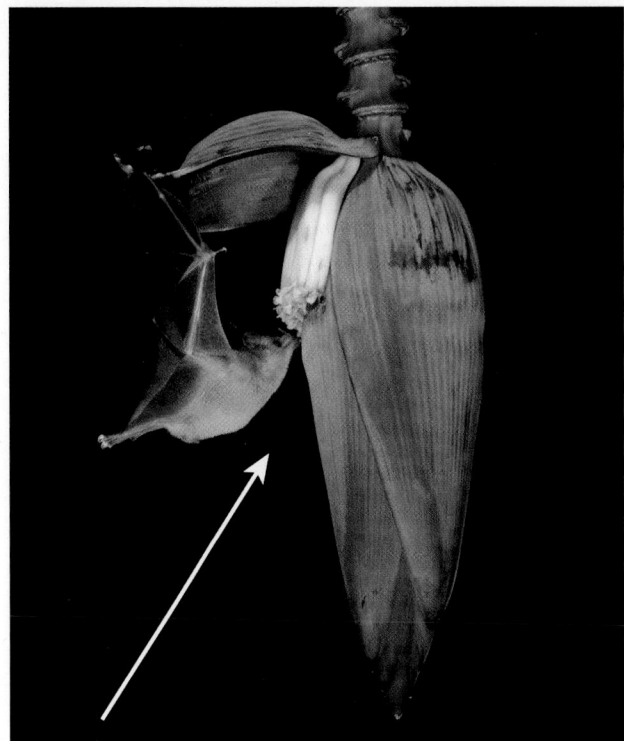

**FIGURE 1.30** Pallas's long-tongued bat drinking nectar. The arrow shows the flight trajectory of the bat. Note the position and shape of the bract.

Canada; Jens Rydell, Sweden; Ted Fleming and Meghan Murphy, United States; Yossi Yovel and Yonon Ba-ron, Israel; and Beth Clare, United Kingdom) spent some time observing Pallas's long-tongued bats visiting banana flowers. The bats always approached the flower on an upward trajectory (Figure 1.30) and only went to the flower structures under the bract (a modified leaf). Like the bat in the picture, Pallas's long-tongued bats produced echolocation calls as they approached. Broadcasting the bats' echolocation calls at the bract and recording and analyzing returning echoes revealed that a bat approaching the flower from below received a strong echo from the bract.

The **bract** appeared to serve as a beacon for the bats indicating on any night where on the flower the nectar was available **(Figure 1.31)**. To test this hypothesis, the biologists removed the bract. When they did so before dark, the bats flew by the flower but appeared to have trouble finding the nectar. Removing the bract an hour after dark did not appear to disrupt the bats' ability to find nectar because they had already learned its location. Thus, the bract of the banana plant is critical to the bats' feeding success.

Bananas are also very important to humans. Bananas are part of the day-to-day diet of millions of people around the world and have been for over 4000 years. Bananas originated in Melesia (including Malaya, Indonesia, the Philippines, Borneo, and Papua New Guinea). Today they are grown in virtually every humid tropical country and many subtropical ones. The tree-like plants range from about 2 to 9 m in height. There are over 500 varieties of bananas, but the main varieties are dessert bananas (yellow, 15 to 30 cm long) and apple bananas, which are also yellow but smaller and ripen faster. There are also baby bananas, 6 to 8 cm long and yellow in colour and known for their sweetness. Red bananas are reddish or pinkish. Cooking bananas or plantains are starchy and must be cooked before eating. Plantains are a staple food in West and Central Africa, where they are the source of about 25% of people's dietary needs.

In spite of large banana plantations, almost 85% of banana production comes from small plots such as kitchen and backyard gardens. This is impressive when we remember that world production of bananas in 2001 was estimated to have been 99 million tonnes. Countries such as Brazil and Uganda are the world's largest producers of bananas, but many other countries, such as India, the Philippines, Ecuador, Colombia, Honduras, Indonesia, Ivory Coast, Rwanda, and Vietnam, are also major producers. In Uganda, the annual per capita consumption of bananas was 243 kg in 1996, compared to 13 kg in Canada.

The picture of the bat at a banana flower illustrates several pervasive features in biology. First, humans exploit other species such as bananas to ensure our food supply. Second, reproduction of many plants involves interactions between animals and plants, and we have much more to learn about interactions that can be so

**FIGURE 1.31** A double exposure of a Pallas's long-tongued bat visiting a banana flower. Note the tongue extended for feeding.

important to us. On the matter of pollination, the loss of bees is a stark example. But in the case of the bat and the banana, domesticated bananas reproduce asexually by suckers from an underground stem. We can understand why bats visit banana flowers (to obtain nectar), but it is not clear that the banana plants benefit from these visits because pollination is not part of their reproduction. So the cover image of the bat at the banana flower leaves us with the question of just how does the plant benefit from feeding the bat? Unanswered questions such as this stimulate biological research and drive our understanding of life forward.

## PUTTING IT IN PERSPECTIVE

We have identified some of the range of topics that are part of biology. Not by accident, many of them reflect both variation and interactions among organisms. Life depends on interactions among species from matters of form and function to capture of energy and the means organisms use to acquire the resources they need. It should also be evident that these interactions extend well beyond eating and avoiding being eaten. You have also had a glimpse into the lives of the authors!

## KEY CONCEPTS REVIEW AND QUESTIONS

### 1.1 A Sampling of Life

Life is diverse. Consequently, there are many ways in which organisms acquire the energy and nutrients they need to survive and reproduce. Some organisms, such as plants and some bacteria, conduct photosynthesis to convert solar energy to chemical energy. Plants require nitrogen, and they obtain it with the help of nitrogen-fixing bacteria, from decomposition of other organisms, or other strategies involving animals. Many organisms consume other organisms to gain the energy or nutrition they require.

1. Where can photosynthesis occur? What is the significance of the solar sea slug?
2. Why are some plants insectivorous?

### 1.2 Growing Your Food

Many organisms exhibit some form of farming behaviour that results in a clear nutritional benefit to the farmer. Food consumption patterns of humans and our ancestors have changed over the course of our evolution. Our cooking of food has increased the range of food available. Human lifestyles change from nomadic hunting and gathering to permanent settlements and cultivation and selective breeding or domestication of plants and animals.

3. Name three kinds of animals that are "farmers."
4. What features of humans have allowed us to become such a dominant force in the world?

### 1.3 Interactions with Other Organisms

Most species of animals cannot digest cellulose. However, many species of animals can digest cellulose with the aid of symbiotic fauna and flora that live in their digestive system. Human bodies also contain an ecosystem containing microbiota.

5. Where do you find a very high diversity of organisms in a human body? What is the significance of this biota?

### 1.4 Responses to Change

Changes to an ecosystem could impact the species living there either positively or negatively. An initial change in the ecosystem could result in changes to some species, which in turn could impact others in a range of ways.

6. What is the difference between global warming and climate change? What are the implications of such changes for humans?

### 1.5 Humans and the Future of Planet Earth

There is a large diversity of life on Planet Earth. There are many positive interactions between biodiversity and ecosystems. Maintaining biodiversity is essential to continued health of ecosystems. Healthy ecosystems are needed by humans to prosper because we rely on ecological processes controlling fluxes of energy, organic matter, and nutrients. Conservation of the environment is therefore important, and people can play a range of roles to support sustainable practices.

7. How can we find a sustainable balance between opposing points of view on topics as fundamental as individuals' rights to access to essential resources? What about reproductive rights and our ability to feed our population?
8. How restricted can we be in our view of what species and individuals we need to protect?
9. Use the electronic library to find a recent publication (e.g., a paper or an editorial) about the impact of food prices on our society. What about their effect on people living in poverty?

# Life: Diverse, Complex, and Always Changing

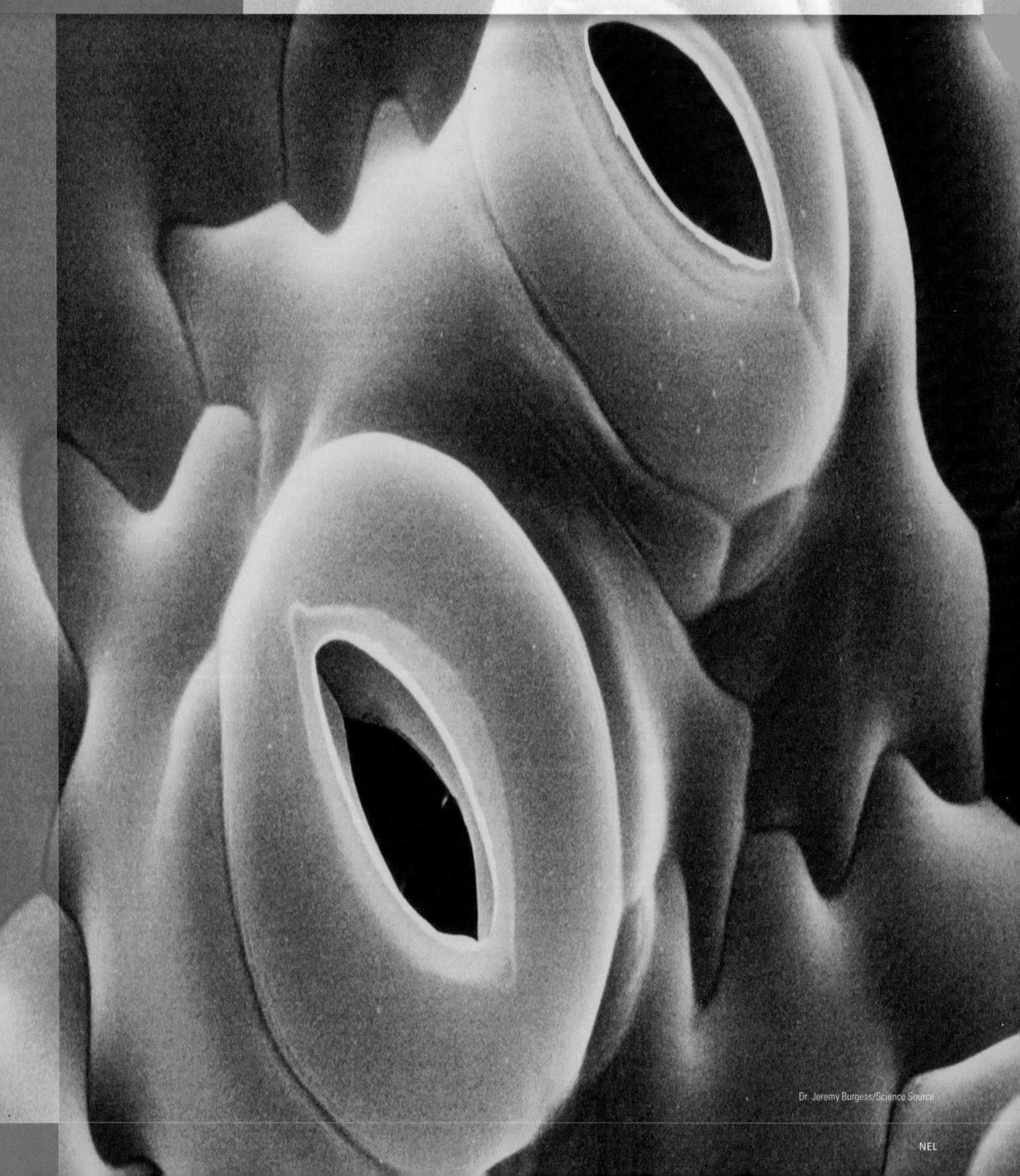

## WHY IT MATTERS

In Chapter 1, you were introduced to a few of the complex ways organisms interact and a diversity of organisms that use farming to obtain food. The role of pollination highlights both of these important biological phenomena.

Pollination takes place when pollen is transferred from the part of the plant that contains the sperm to the part of the plant that contains the eggs. This is done by a variety of animals and even by wind, depending on the type of plant. Many of the food, fibre, and feed crops on which humans depend are pollinated exclusively or in part by bees **(Figure 2.1)**. These crops include soybeans and other legumes; fruit trees as well as berries, squashes, and melons; many vegetables; cotton; and even coffee. In agriculture, bee pollination is worth billions of dollars each year. Worldwide for 2005, pollination services provided by honeybees were estimated to be worth US$217 billion. Loss of pollinators would result in the loss of crops and money to people around the world. In many places, managed bee populations are an important industry. Bee producers travel across North America annually with large trucks of beehives to provide enough pollinators for agricultural regions (see Box 2.1).

Currently, bee populations are in decline. This includes wild bees such as bumblebees (*Bombus* sp.) and both cultivated and wild honeybees (*Apis* sp.). No one knows exactly what is driving the decline. It appears that it is not attributable to a single cause but rather to a combination of insecticide use; infection by mites, fungi, and viruses; and habitat loss. Since 2006, colony collapse disorder (CCD), in which all bees in a hive except the queen disappear, has been observed in beehives in North America and Europe, and beekeepers can lose more than 50% of their bees over some winters.

The interactions among human activity, crops, pathogens, and bee populations are receiving increasing attention from scientists. Habitat loss is one likely contributor to pollinator declines. Crops provide food for bees during a short and intense period during the year. During the rest of the year, bees must forage on flowers found elsewhere. Development and land conversion have decreased the area and flowers available for foraging.

Experiments have suggested that a class of insecticides known as neonicotinoids may also be an important contributor to bee declines. These insecticides, often applied to plant seeds, are taken up by the crop plants as they grow and are then present in the plant's tissues, including in the nectar, which is subsequently consumed by pollinating bees. The amount of insecticide encountered by bees is typically not lethal, but it appears that even at low doses, the insecticide can affect bees, causing confusion and reducing reproductive output.

In one set of experiments, honeybees fed a mixture of sugar water and neonicotinoids were tagged with radio transmitters, released in fields, and tracked as they navigated back to their hives. If the area was familiar to the bees, 10% fewer bees were able to return to the hive compared to bees that were not exposed to the pesticides. If the area was unfamiliar to the bees, this number increased to about 30%. In another experiment, bumblebees fed a neonicotinoid–sugar–water solution not only saw decreased growth compared to control bees but also produced 85% fewer queens at the end of the season, suggesting that the number of new hives established for the following growing season

**FIGURE 2.1** Bees pollinate 80% of flowering plants. It is estimated that they are responsible for pollinating 30% of the plants that provide our food.

**FIGURE 1** Row upon row of honeybee hives provide enough pollinators for nearby agricultural crops.

In some regions, there are not enough native bees to effectively pollinate crops. In some of these places, beekeepers are paid to provide the bees, called migratory beekeeping **(Figure 1)**. The beekeepers drive truckloads of beehives from place to place, timed on when the different crops are flowering. Healthy hives, each with its tens of thousands of bees, are stacked on the trucks such that each truck can carry millions of bees. Each bee knows which hive is its own by smell; bee pheromones make each hive unique.

The largest pollination event in the world takes place each year in February and March in the Central Valley of California. An astounding 85% of the almonds produced worldwide come from this area, where approximately 2600 km² are planted in almond trees. The annual pollination requires more than a million hives and billions of bees, attracting beekeepers from across North America.

Migratory beekeeping operations can travel across many states and pollinate many crops each year. One beekeeper, Dave Heckenberg of Pennsylvania, USA, travels more than 18,000 km a year with his bee colonies. He spends February and March in California participating in the almond pollination event. From the middle of March through the middle of April, the insects are taken to Florida to pollinate citrus fruit, followed by a month in Pennsylvania pollinating apples, a month in Maine pollinating blueberries, and a month of honey extraction in New York. The bees spend the month between mid-July and mid-August pollinating pumpkins back in Pennsylvania, and finally the bees return to Florida for the remainder of the year to pollinate Brazilian peppers.

would also be reduced. Additional evidence suggests that pesticides and pathogens may be interacting. Honeybees exposed to low-level neonicotinoid doses and subsequently exposed to a common honeybee pathogen, the fungus *Nosema apis*, were infected significantly more than unexposed honeybees. In response to the mounting evidence of the effects of neonicotinoids on bees, the European Union banned their use in the spring of 2013.

No one yet knows the combined contributions of pesticides, pathogens, habitat loss, and other forces on pollinator losses. But our dependence on the pollination services of bees, in terms of both the economy and food production, makes it an important system to understand. Humans have exploited the biological world for things such as food, fibre, and energy for millennia. We are dependent on our relationships with other living things, just as other organisms, for example, honeybees and flowers, depend on each other. Understanding all of these complex interactions helps humans too.

In this chapter, you will be introduced to some of the basics of life on Earth. This includes defining what we mean when we describe something as "alive" and how we categorize life and describing some of the history of life on Earth. We will also introduce you to the fundamental lifestyles of the organisms that make up our biological world and will highlight some of the astounding ways in which these organisms interact.

From the earliest life in primordial seas to the most specialized interactions, the biological world is diverse, complex, and always changing.

## 2.1 What Is Life?

How do you know when something is alive? Intuitively, we know that a car is not alive, whereas the driver of that car is, or that a beaver and the tree it is gnawing on are both alive, whereas the water building up behind the beaver's dam is not **(Figure 2.2)**.

To be alive, something must be separated from the environment, self-contained. You can think of a cell

**FIGURE 2.2** A beaver (*Castor canadensis*) feeding.

**A. Display order:** All forms of life, including this flower, are arranged in a highly ordered manner, with the cell being the fundamental unit of life.

harmeet/StockXchng

**B. Harness and utilize energy:** Like this hummingbird, all forms of life acquire energy from the environment and use it to maintain their highly ordered state.

Mercury Freedom/Shutterstock.com

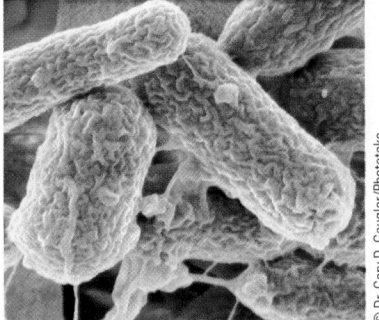

**C. Reproduce:** All organisms have the ability to make more of their own kind. Here, some of the bacteria have just divided into two daughter cells.

© Dr. Gary D. Gaugler/Phototake

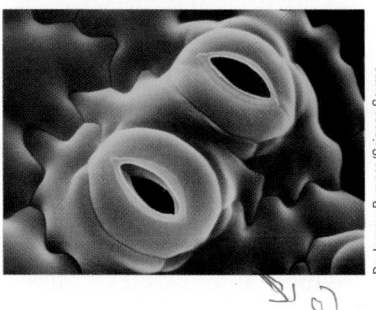

**D. Respond to stimuli:** Organisms can make adjustments to their structure, function, and behaviour in response to changes to the external environment. A plant can adjust the size of the pores (stomata) on the surface of its leaves to regulate gas exchange.

Dr. Jeremy Burgess/Science Source

(a leaf)

**E. Exhibit homeostasis:** Organisms are able to regulate their internal environment such that conditions remain relatively constant. Sweating is one way in which the body attempts to remove heat and thereby maintain a constant temperature.

© Tim Pannell/CORBIS

**F. Growth and development:** All organisms increase their size by increasing the size and/or number of cells. Many organisms also change over time.

© Karin Duthie/Alamy

**G. Evolve:** Populations of living organisms change over the course of generations to become better adapted to their environment. The snowy owl illustrates this perfectly.

Critterbiz/Shutterstock.com

**FIGURE 2.3** The seven characteristics of life.

and how it is separated from the environment by a membrane or wall. You will learn more about cells in Chapter 3. To be alive, however, takes much more than this. There are seven characteristics we will use to define life. To be alive, this self-contained object/thing/ organism must (1) display order, (2) harness and use energy, (3) reproduce (self-replicate), (4) respond to stimuli, (5) exhibit **homeostasis** (maintain relatively stable internal conditions), (6) grow and develop, and (7) evolve **(Figure 2.3)**.

Although it may be intuitive to us that a beaver is alive, whereas water is not, there are also a number of interesting phenomena on Earth that do not fit neatly into these categories of living or non-living. Viruses, for

example, display order and certainly evolve but must hijack the energy systems of other organisms' cells to reproduce. They are therefore not generally considered to be alive (see Chapter 14 for more information on viruses).

There are also prions (pronounced pree-ons), proteins that exhibit some of the characteristics associated with life and act as pathogens in animals, including humans, but are definitely not living. Prions are a group of proteins that misfold (see the Purple Pages for an overview of protein folding) and can cause a number of diseases. Proteins are definitely not alive: they are not separated from the environment, for example, nor do they harness energy or exhibit homeostasis.

However, the proteins are able to replicate, forming plaques that build up in brain tissue, causing a number of debilitating symptoms, including death. Many biologists studying diseases caused by prions were initially skeptical that they could be responsible. They did not realize that misfolding proteins could replicate, a key feature of living organisms, or that they could be spread from one infected animal to another. Kuru, a prion disease in humans, was first observed in Papua New Guinea among native people in the 1950s, where traditional cannibalism, specifically eating human brain during funeral ceremonies, was passing prion disease within the population. Kuru is the only known example of prion disease that is passed from human to human, although you may be familiar with another prion disease that affects humans, mad cow disease (otherwise known as bovine spongiform encephalopathy, or BSE). BSE was first observed in cattle that were being fed material that included animal body parts (including brains). BSE was then able to jump from cows to humans when humans consumed the diseased cows. Prion disease can remain dormant in people's bodies for many years, and now people in Canada, the United States, and elsewhere are not allowed to receive blood transfusions from anyone who received blood transfusions in the 1980s in Britain, where human cases of BSE originated.

Although viruses and prions are not alive, there are an incredible number of organisms on our planet that are. To understand those organisms and the interactions among them, we must first have a system by which to keep all of those living things organized.

FIGURE 2.4 Carolus Linnaeus (1707–1778), considered the father of modern taxonomy. It is interesting to note that Linnaeus is not the name he was given at birth. His original name was Carl von Linné, which he Latinized.

Alexander Roslin (1718–1793)

## 2.2 The Tree of Life

In this book, you will be introduced to the wide variety of organisms that make up the biosphere—the living, or biotic, world of our planet. Throughout the history of biology, we have tried to categorize these organisms into groups. Over time, the ways in which we do this have changed. As you will see, even today, there are different ways in which biologists think about all of the organisms on Earth and their relationships to one another.

The classification of organisms is called taxonomy, and the scientists that specialize in it are called taxonomists. Much of the historical classification system is based on the work of Carolus Linnaeus, a Swedish scientist (Figure 2.4).

Linnaeus introduced the concept of categorizing organisms in a hierarchy, starting with broad categories such as the "Plant Kingdom" and ending with very specific ones. Linnaeus also introduced the practice of binomial nomenclature, of defining individual species by both genus and species. For example, humans (*Homo sapiens*) are in the genus *Homo* and the species *sapiens*. Each combination of genus and species represents a unique species, but a group of organisms that share some traits are all included in the same genus, whereas genera (plural of genus) that share traits are grouped into families, families are grouped into orders, orders are grouped into classes, classes are grouped into phyla (the plural of phylum), and phyla are grouped into kingdoms. Since the time of Linnaeus, an additional level of organization has been added, with kingdoms grouped into domains. Genus and species levels are always written in italics or underlined, whereas higher levels of organization are not.

Scientists currently recognize three domains: Archaea, Bacteria, and Eukarya. Both Domain Archaea and Domain Bacteria contain exclusively single-celled organisms, whereas Domain Eukarya includes some single-celled protists and fungi but also includes the multicellular organisms you are familiar with, from humans and other vertebrate animals to plants, insects, and all other multicellular life.

At first, scientists categorized organisms exclusively by shared characteristics, such as body morphologies and habits. For example, the Ruby-throated Hummingbird (*Archilochus colubris*), the Mallard (*Anas*

**FIGURE 2.5** **(a)** Ruby-throated Hummingbird, **(b)** the American Wigeon, and **(c)** the Mallard.

*platyrhynchos*), and the American Wigeon (*Anas americana*) are all birds, in the domain Eukarya, the kingdom Animalia, the phylum Chordata (the chordates, all of which have a notochord, which becomes the backbone in many organisms), and the class Aves **(Figure 2.5)**.

However, this is where these birds diverge. The Ruby-throated Hummingbird is in the order Apodiformes. The Mallard and the American Wigeon are different in size and shape from the hummingbird, but they are more like each other. They have similar body orphologies and bills, live in similar habitats, reproduce in similar ways, and eat similar foods. These two organisms are both considered to be in the same order (Anseriformes) and even the same family, the Anatidae, which includes ducks, geese, and swans. In fact, they are so similar that they have been placed in the same genus, *Anas*, the group of dabbling ducks.

Looking at organisms in this way can give us the impression that we are looking at fully formed, "finished" organisms. It is like taking a snapshot of all the organisms we can find and sorting them into piles for a photo album. In fact, this is how Linnaeus understood the world when he invented the system around 1735. Although this can be convenient, especially if you are looking at a field guide while trying to identify ducks in a pond, it is not accurate to think of organisms as finished. In 1859, Charles Darwin published his book *On the Origin of Species* and introduced the theory of natural selection (see Chapter 13 for more information on natural selection and evolution). This fundamentally changed how we understand the tree of life. The Linnaean system now shows the relatedness of organisms to each other, with organisms in the same genus more closely related to one another than to organisms sharing only a family, and so forth.

With our understanding of evolution and selection, we know that the biological world is always changing, with organisms evolving all the time. The fossil record has also helped us understand life as an ongoing process—a movie (albeit a pretty slow-moving one) rather than a series of snapshots. Looking through the fossil record, we can see countless extraordinary organisms (see Chapter 18 for example). Some look similar to those we know today. But some are very different and are unlike any with which we are familiar.

The tree of life now groups organisms based not only on morphology and life history characteristics but also on relatedness. Many evolutionary biologists no longer use the hierarchy of classification long depended on by biologists. Instead, using genetic data from DNA (deoxyribonucleic acid; see Chapter 3) analysis, scientists construct hypotheses about the evolutionary histories of organisms. These hypotheses change over time as additional data are gathered and analyzed, so this categorizing based on evolutionary relationships changes and improves with time. Scientists construct evolutionary trees, or phylogenies, to show how groups of organisms are related to one another. Looking at a phylogeny, you can see that it shows the relationships between different groups of organisms **(Figure 2.6b, p. 32)**. Each fork in the tree shows you a divergence, when the organisms at the end of each branch of the fork last shared a common ancestor. Groups of organisms that share a common ancestor are called **clades**. Clades can be used to group organisms as an alternative to the traditional grouping of organisms into taxonomic hierarchies. Many scientists believe that this way of classifying organisms is more effective. A clade has a specific and biologically relevant definition, whereas separating organisms into families, orders, or even genera is more subjective. To get an idea of how to read or understand a phylogeny, let's once again consider the ducks. Here we will look at where birds fit in the phylogeny of eukaryotes (for more detailed information on phylogenies, see Chapter 13).

You may be surprised to see that birds share a common ancestor with reptiles that is not shared by other vertebrates, such as mammals, amphibians, or fish. Even more surprising, birds share a common ancestor with dinosaurs that is not shared by other reptiles **(Figure 2.6a, p. 32)**. So not only are birds closely related to dinosaurs, birds are actually dinosaurs.

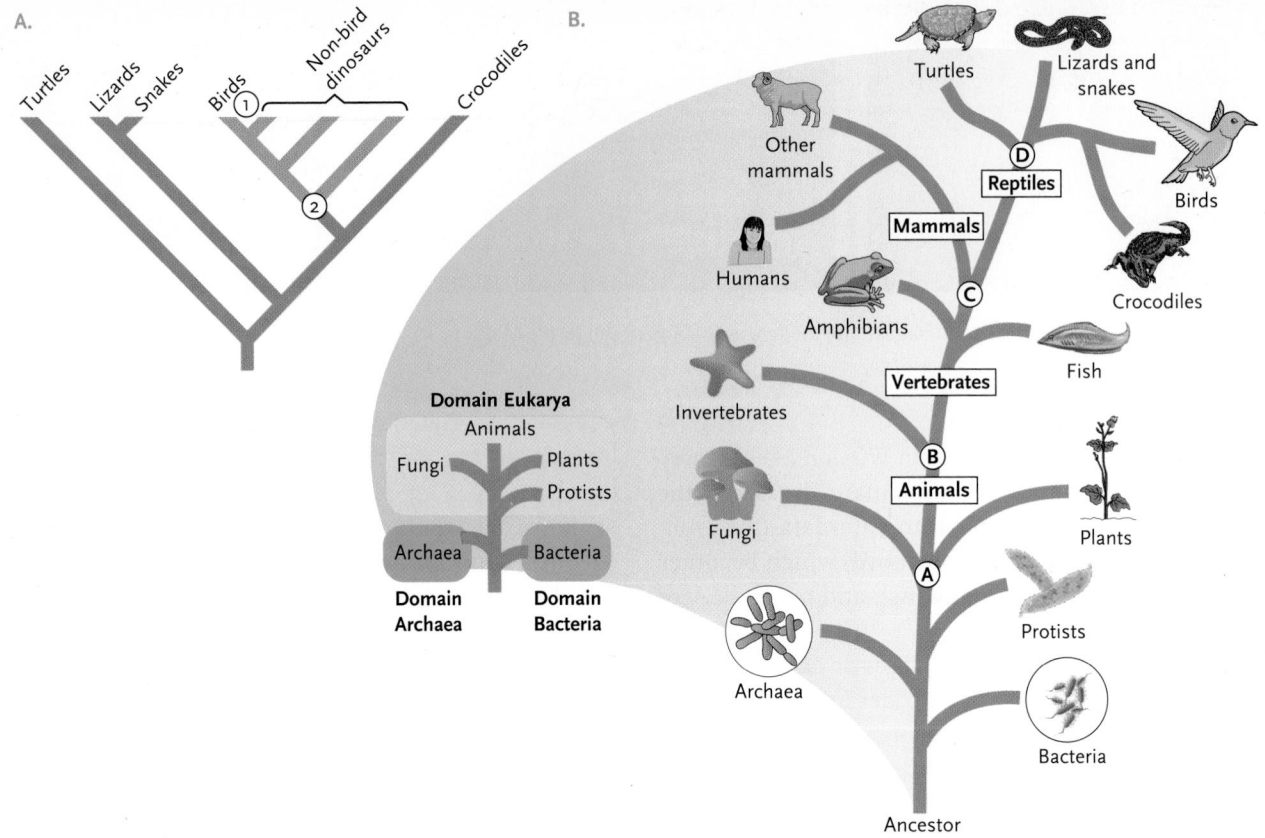

**FIGURE 2.6** Two examples of evolutionary trees. **(a)** Reptilian evolutionary tree showing that birds are the closest living relatives of non-bird dinosaurs and both birds and non-bird dinosaurs descended from a common ancestor. **(b)** The evolutionary tree of life showing that all organisms share a common ancestor.

SOURCE: From Noyd/Krueger/Hill, *Biology*, 1E. © 2014 Cengage Learning.

## STUDY BREAK

1. What characteristics do viruses have that make them seem alive?
2. What kinds of data do scientists use to construct phylogenies?
3. What is a clade?

## 2.3 How Life Began

No one knows exactly how life began. Life likely began in the oceans of the early Earth. The Earth formed approximately 4.6 billion years ago. It is hypothesized that the first precursors to life were organic molecules, amino and nucleic acids, the building blocks of proteins, DNA, and RNA (see the Purple Pages for an overview of amino and nucleic acids). In 1958, Stanley Miller conducted an experiment in which he simulated what was believed at the time to have been the early atmosphere on Earth and added electrical discharges as might be generated from lightning or during volcanic activity. With these experiments, he was able to generate amino acids. Meteorites (carbonaceous chondrites) found on Earth have also been shown to contain amino acids **(Figure 2.7)**.

Miller and his colleagues found the abundances of amino acids from these meteorites to be generally similar to those generated in the lab in simulations. Miller suggested that these same gases and electrical discharges

*Courtesy of Art Bromage*

**FIGURE 2.7** A fragment of the Murchison meteorite that fell to Earth in 1969 over Murchison, Australia, contained a number of amino acids.

may have led to organic molecules beyond Earth as well. Recently, scientists used modern technology to analyze archived lab samples from Miller's early experiments. They found many more amino acids than had previously been reported by Miller and even more similarity between the generated amino acid abundances in the samples and the abundances in several carbonaceous chondrites. These experiments all support the idea that organic molecules could have been generated on early Earth and elsewhere. However, no one has yet shown how these molecules formed the first protocells or exactly how they began the process of self-replication or metabolism.

Although we don't know exactly how life began, we have evidence for single-celled organisms as early as 3.5 billion years ago. Geological evidence suggests that life remained unicellular and in the early oceans for many millions, even billions, of years **(Figure 2.8)**.

So how did the first plants and animals move onto land? It has been hypothesized that terrestrial ecosystems (communities of organisms and their physical environments on land) evolved from the bottom up. That is, plants, capable of creating their own food through light energy, came first, followed by organisms that eat plants (**herbivores**), followed by organisms that feed on the plant-eating organisms (**consumers**). This is intuitive: herbivores would have nothing to eat on land without the arrival of plants there first. However, it's also possible that the first herbivores living on land might have fed in the ocean, like sea lions do today, for example, or on detritus washed up on the shore in coastal areas.

The oldest known terrestrial (land) animal fossils are of millipede footprints, estimated to be approximately 450 million years old. Fossilized millipede bodies come next, estimated at approximately 423 million years old **(Figure 2.9, p. 34)**.

The embryophytes, or land plants, make up the group of plants that includes most of the **primary producers** on Earth, including vascular plants (e.g., flowering plants and conifers), as well as ferns, mosses, liverworts, and hornworts.

The oldest fossils of embryophytes are estimated to be about 470 million years old, predating the earliest fossilized terrestrial animal evidence **(Figure 2.10, p. 34)**.

Recent analyses, however, suggest that the timing of plants and animals coming onto land might be much closer than suggested by the fossil evidence. Scientists can now estimate the age of groups of organisms using not only fossils but also molecular evidence from DNA analysis. Scientists begin with a phylogeny. Scientists can use fossil evidence to constrain the ages of branches in a phylogeny. For example, because we have fossilized millipede bodies from approximately 423 million years ago, we know that millipedes diverged from their closest

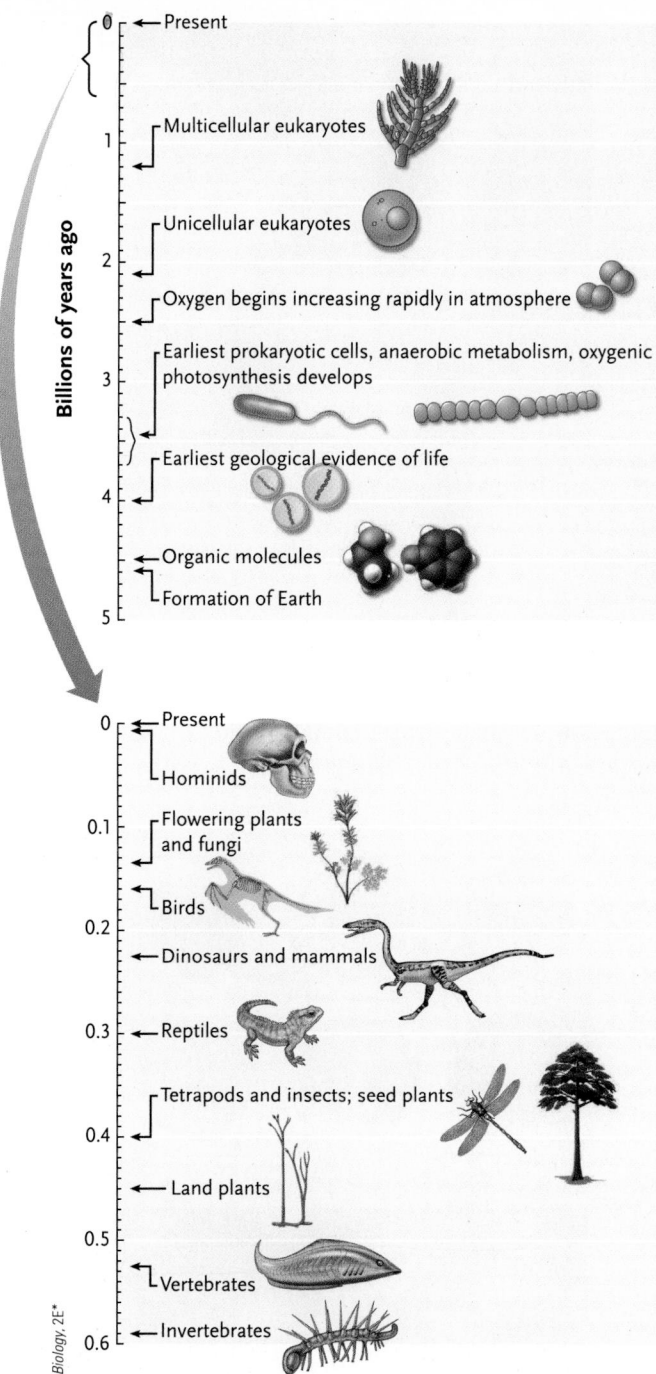

**FIGURE 2.8** A timeline for the evolution of major forms of life. The dates provided are derived mostly from geologic evidence.

aquatic ancestors at least 423 million years ago, and possibly much longer. Next, scientists look at DNA sequence data from organisms in the group they are interested in. We now have the technology to look at many millions of sequences of DNA relatively quickly, and we can compare these sequences among members of a group. We can look at the number of changes in these sequences over time and come up with a rate of change. This rate of change can then be used to estimate the times that the divergences observed in a phylogeny occurred. Using these methods, scientists have analyzed members of the Ecdy-

**FIGURE 2.9** A centipede, a member of the myriapods, the group that also includes millipedes. Fossils suggest that members of this group were among the first animals to colonize land.

Shelby Riskin

sozoa, a group that includes the millipedes and centipedes (the myriapods), as well as nematodes, arthropods, and their relatives. They showed that groups of terrestrial animals likely existed many millions of years before the earliest fossil evidence suggests. In agreement with the

**A.**

**B.**

**FIGURE 2.10 (a)** Cryptospores, found in Argentina, the oldest fossil evidence for land plants. They measure only about 30 μ (microns; 1 micron = 1 micrometre = $10^{-6}$ m) across. **(b)** Liverworts, a member of the embryophytes, are thought to be the closest living relative to the first terrestrial plants.

Bjorn van Lieshout, NiS/Minden Pictures

SOURCE: (A): Rubinstein, C.V.; Gerrienne, P.; de la Puente, G.S.; Astini, R.A. and Steemans, P., "Early Middle Ordovician evidence for land plants in Argentina (eastern Gondwana)," *New Phytologist* 188 (2): 365–369. John Wiley and Sons. © The Authors (2010). Journal compilation © New Phytologist Trust (2010).

fossil evidence, the myriapods appear to be the first animals to colonize land, between 544 and 457 million years ago. There has not been as extensive an analysis on the molecular evidence for embryophytes, but the most largest survey using both molecular and fossil evidence estimates that the first plants colonized land between 490 and 425 million years ago. These overlapping but offset estimates allow for animals to have lived on land prior to colonization by land plants. Although the timing remains uncertain, the hypothesis that terrestrial systems were built from the bottom up may not be correct.

It may surprise you that so much about early Earth remains uncertain, and it is undoubtedly true that much remains to be discovered. One of the wonderful things about biology, and indeed about all science, is the process. Biologists look at the living world and ask questions, perhaps some of the same questions that occur to you when you look at the world around you. Scientists then design experiments to try to answer some of these questions (as evidenced by the examples above). Over time, many scientists do different experiments that all address the same big questions. Evidence begins to accumulate that supports particular hypotheses, and we begin to understand how the living world works in more detail. Scientists are constantly adding to this understanding, correcting information that is incorrect or out of date, and collecting new data that weren't previously available. A scientist, it could be said, is never sure of anything. Instead, scientists come up with the best answers based on the data currently available, which have improved, and continue to improve, over time (see the Purple Pages for an overview of the scientific method).

## 2.4 Extinction and Diversification

Throughout the history of Earth, many species have evolved and have gone extinct. More than 99% of species that have lived on our planet are now extinct. Within the last 540 million years, there have been a number of mass extinction events, defined as time periods when more than 75% of species were lost in a relatively short time interval (less than 2 million years). There are five events that meet these criteria **(Table 2.1)**.

Although the drivers are still being debated, there are a number of different phenomena believed to be responsible for these large-scale decreases in global biodiversity (Table 2.1).

The existence of extinctions in geologic history does not mean that species extinctions today do not matter to the structure and function of Earth's ecosystems. Data suggest that there is a **background extinction rate** for species. This rate has been calculated in a number of ways and can vary but is often considered close to the loss of

| TABLE 2.1 | The "Big Five" Mass Extinction Events, When They Occurred, the Percentage of Genera and Species Lost, and the Hypothesized Causes of Extinction |
| --- | --- |
| Event | Proposed Causes |
| The Ordovician event ended ~443 Myr ago; within 3.3 to 1.9 Myr, 57% of genera were lost, an estimated 75% of species. | Onset of alternating glacial and interglacial episodes; repeated marine transgressions and regressions. Uplifted and weathering of the Appalachians, affecting atmospheric and ocean chemistry. Sequestration of $CO_2$. |
| The Devonian event ended ~359 Myr ago; within 29 to 2 Myr, 35% of genera were lost, an estimated 96% of species. | Global cooling (followed by global warming) possibly tied to the diversification of land plants, with associated weathering, pedogenesis, and the drawdown of global $CO_2$. Evidence of widespread deep-water anoxia and the spread of anoxic waters by transgressions. Timing and importance of bolide impacts still debated. |
| The Permian event ended ~251 Myr ago; within 2.8 Myr to 160 Kyr, 56% of genera were lost, an estimated 96% of species. | Siberian volcanism. Global warming, possibly tied to the diversification of land plants, with associated weathering pedogenesis and the drawdown of global $CO_2$. Evidence for widespread deep-water anoxia and the spread of anoxic waters by transgressions. Timing and importance of bolide impacts still debated. |
| The Triassic event ended ~200 Myr ago; within 8.3 Myr to 600 Kyr, 47% of genera were lost, an estimated 80% of species. | Activity in the Central Atlantic Magmatic Province (CAMP) thought to have elevated atmospheric $CO_2$ level, which increased global temperatures and led to a calcification crisis in the world oceans. |
| The Cretaceous event ended ~65 Myr ago; within 2.5 Myr to less than a year, 40% of genera were lost, an estimated 76% of species. | A bolide impact in the Yucatan is thought to have led to a global cataclysm and caused rapid cooling. Preceding the impact, biota may have been declining owing to a variety of causes; Deccan volcanism contemporaneous with global warming; tectonic uplifting altering biogeography and accelerating erosion, potentially contributing to ocean eutrophication and anoxic episodes. $CO_2$ spikes just before extinction and drops during extinction. |

Source: Reprinted by permission from Macmillan Publishers Ltd: *Nature*, Anthony D. Barnosky, Nicholas Matzke, Susumu Tomiya, Guinevere O. U. Wogan, Brian Swartz, Tiago B. Quental, "Has the Earth's sixth mass extinction already arrived?", copyright 2011.

one species every million years. Almost any way you calculate the background extinction rate, it appears to be much lower than our current rates of species loss. In our current era, often referred to as the Anthropocene (the age of humans), human behaviour is driving higher than average extinction rates. It has been suggested that we are now entering the sixth mass extinction event in history, driven by our own environmental degradation (see Chapter 31 for more information on biological conservation and extinction).

The counterpart to extinction is the process of speciation—the evolution of new species. Biodiversity has recovered following each of the mass extinction events of the past, although this happens over millions of years. In many cases, mass extinctions change the course of evolution, with some species types replaced or outcompeted by others. For example, the rise of mammals and birds followed the extinction of non-bird dinosaurs.

Two hypotheses describe what drives extinction and speciation, what drives evolution. One hypothesis is called the court jester hypothesis, named after the unpredictable and impulsive entertainer of royal courts. This hypothesis posits that large-scale, stochastic (unpredictable), and abiotic changes such as volcanic activity, meteor impacts, or climate change drive extinction and speciation and that these events occur infrequently. The other hypothesis is named after the Red Queen in *Alice Through the Looking Glass*, who says to Alice, "It takes all the running you can do, just to keep in the same place." This hypothesis posits that biotic selection pressure (see Chapter 13 for more information on natural selection and different types of selection pressure) drives evolution, including speciation and extinction. Although scientists have debated the primacy of these two hypotheses in driving evolutionary change, they are not mutually exclusive. It is likely that the importance of these two patterns of evolution varies across different scales of time and space. Local, biotic interactions are very important for driving evolutionary change over short timescales, whereas large-scale abiotic changes in the environment likely play a more important role over global and geologic timescales.

## STUDY BREAK

1. What type of organism would you hypothesize evolved to live on land first: plants or animals that eat plants?
2. What is the court jester hypothesis?

## 2.5 Fundamental Lifestyles

Organisms across the tree of life fill a few fundamental roles across the wide variety of ecosystems on Earth. You have probably heard of the circle of life; it is the stuff of songs and movies. We know that lions eat zebra and zebra eat grass. We can think of these organisms

Adwo/Shutterstock.com

Rigamondis/Shutterstock.com

Black Sheep Media/Shutterstock.com

**FIGURE 2.11** A food chain from the Serengeti.

as being connected by a food chain, beginning with grass, which is linked to zebra, which is then linked to lions **(Figure 2.11)**.

Thinking of the relationships among organisms in an ecosystem such as this, however, is an oversimplification. In the Serengeti, for example, zebra also eat

shrubs, and lions also eat wildebeest, gazelle, and even elephants. When lions die, scavengers such as vultures or hyenas may eat their bodies, and microorganisms such as bacteria and fungi decompose what remains. Once decomposed, the organic matter can be used again. Some is used directly in soils by the decomposers themselves, and some is taken up once again by the plants. Fungi play an important role here on both sides. Fungi can break down organic matter, even difficult material to break down, such as wood, and, as you will see, also help plants acquire soil nutrients as the cycle continues. Instead of thinking of trophic relationships as a linear chain, we can think of a food web, a branching representation of the trophic interactions among consumers and decomposers and those being consumed **(Figure 2.12)**.

We can still think about different trophic levels, however, with grass on the first level (primary producers), zebra on the second (primary consumers), and lions on the third (secondary consumers) (see Box 2.2).

## Primary Producers Make Up the Bottom of the Trophic Pyramid

Most life begins with light, with harvesting the light energy Earth receives from the Sun and converting that energy into forms that can fuel organisms. The first trophic level, from which all other levels ultimately feed, is called primary production and is performed by primary producers. Primary producers are **autotrophs**; that is, they produce their own food by converting carbon in the environment to carbohydrates—carbon molecules that store energy that organisms can use as fuel. This process is called carbon fixation. To fix carbon requires energy and a source of carbon from which the food is built. Most primary producers, such as plants and algae, are photoautotrophs. They fix carbon using a process called photosynthesis, using light from the Sun as the energy source and atmospheric carbon dioxide ($CO_2$) as the source of carbon (see Chapter 5 for details on carbon fixation and photosynthesis). Some autotrophs, however, such as microbes living in and around deep-sea hydrothermal vents, are chemoautotrophs, harnessing chemical energy to build organic (carbon-based) molecules.

The bottom trophic level is also the largest, containing more **biomass** (the weight, or mass, of the organisms) than any subsequent level. Primary producers are essential to life on Earth and in fact have profoundly changed Earth's atmosphere. Photosynthesis, which consumes $CO_2$ and releases oxygen, is the only reason we have the oxygenated atmosphere that we live in (and depend on) today. Cyanobacteria, a type of photosynthetic bacteria, were the first organisms to photosynthesize, and this began approximately 2.4 billion years ago.

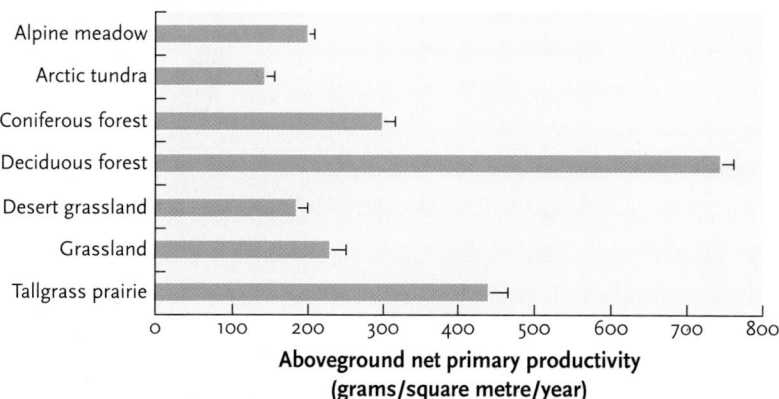

**FIGURE 2.12** An example of a food web in a terrestrial forest ecosystem. Energy and nutrients flow through food webs in most ecosystems. The food web includes primary producers, herbivores, and carnivores. The detrital part of the food web includes detritivores and decomposers. Each box in this diagram represents many species, and each arrow represents many arrows.

Sun

Solar energy

Tertiary consumers (carnivores)

Secondary consumers (carnivores)

Wastes

Primary consumers (herbivores)

Wastes

Primary producers

Wastes

Grazing food web

Detrital food web

Inorganic nutrients

Detritivores Decomposers

*Biology, 2E\**

Before that, the concentration of oxygen in the atmosphere was less than a thousandth of a percent of what it is today (see Box 2.3).

We define primary production as the rate that energy from the Sun is converted to organic compounds. Basically, this means the amount of plant material grown in a defined area in a defined amount of time. The amount of primary productivity can be very different in different types of ecosystems. You can imagine that there would be much more primary production in a square metre of tropical rainforest, for example, than in a square metre of desert or even prairie **(Figure 2.13)**.

In the Serengeti, average production rates have been measured as less than 400 g·m⁻²·yr⁻¹. In the Amazon, average production rates have been estimated to be

well over 1000 g·m⁻²·yr⁻¹, whereas in the Chihuahuan Desert of North America, average production rates are

Aboveground net primary productivity (grams/square metre/year)

Alpine meadow
Arctic tundra
Coniferous forest
Deciduous forest
Desert grassland
Grassland
Tallgrass prairie

0   100   200   300   400   500   600   700   800

**FIGURE 2.13** The average primary production across a range of ecosystems shows wide variation.

SOURCE: Based on http://www.globalchange.umich.edu/globalchange1/current/lectures/kling/energyflow/energyflow.html

BOX 2.2

# The Trophic Level of Humans

In this chapter, you have been introduced to the idea of trophic levels. Trophic levels help us understand the role of organisms in their ecosystems and how much energy different organisms require. The trophic levels of some organisms are intuitive: primary producers, for example, are on the first level, whereas an herbivore, an animal that eats only plants, is on the second. But what about organisms that have more complicated diets? For example, what is the trophic level of a bear?

Scientists have come up with ways to calculate the trophic level for different organisms. One way is to take the mean trophic level of all the items weighted by quantity and to add one. To use the herbivore example again, the mean trophic level of the food is 1, and 1 + 1 = 2 is the trophic level. Using this method, we can calculate the trophic level for any organisms, including humans.

This is exactly what Sylvain Bonhommeau and colleagues at Institut Français de Recherche pour l'Exploration de la Mer recently did. First, they collected data available from the Food and Agriculture Organization of the United Nations (FAO) on food consumed in countries across the world. They obtained data for 176 of the world's 198 countries, accounting for 98% of the calories eaten by people worldwide. They calculated the trophic level for each country and for each year between 1961 and 2009. Countries that consume more meat have higher trophic levels than countries that consume less meat. To come up with a global human trophic level, Bonhommeau and colleagues weighted the trophic level of each country by population and took the average. This resulted in a human trophic level of 2.21. This trophic level is equivalent to that of a fish such as anchoveta or a pig. This number increased over the 40 years analyzed in this study, suggesting that worldwide humans are eating more meat than we did several decades ago. This pattern, however, is driven entirely by China and India. When these two countries were removed from the analysis, the global average trophic level remained relatively steady between 1961 and 2009.

The researchers also looked at the trophic levels of individual countries over time. Doing this, they saw a number of interesting patterns. Based on these patterns, they separated the countries into five groups **(Figure 1)**. In one group, meat consumption increased over time, whereas in another, meat consumption decreased. In another group, characterized by the countries in sub-Saharan Africa, meat consumption remained low throughout the period of observation.

Data on human trophic levels can be used in a number of applications. They can help us understand the relationship between human diet and development, for example. They can be used by resource managers in consideration of human impacts through agriculture and by policy makers interested in changes in nutritional status.

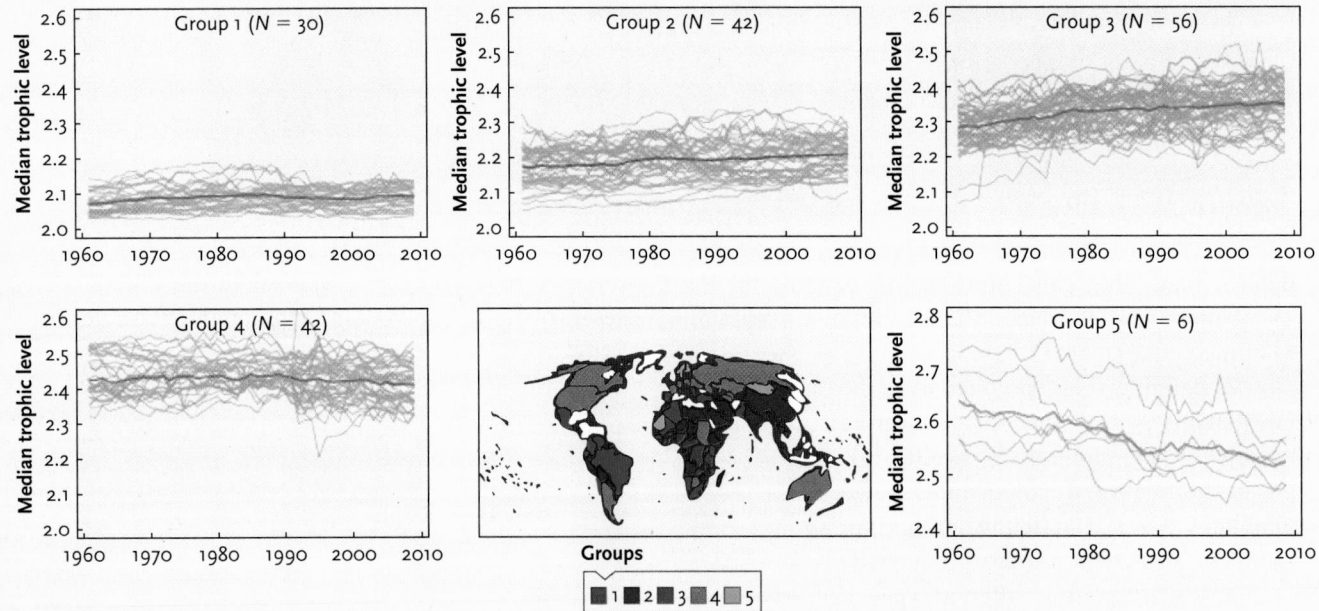

**FIGURE 1** The trophic level has changed for many countries over the past 40 years. Five general patterns emerged and are highlighted here. The colours of the group labels and lines correspond to the colours of the countries that fall into that group.

SOURCE: Bònhammeau et al., "Eating up the world's food web and the human trophic level," PNAS, vol. 110 no. 51: 20617–20620.

less than $60 \ g \cdot m^{-2} \cdot yr^{-1}$. These differences in the amount of energy available to be eaten control the amount of life at the second trophic level that can be supported. Rates of primary production are correlated with **biodiversity**, the number or abundance of different species or biological groups in an area. There are many more species in tropical forests, where primary productivity is very high, than in the Arctic, where primary production is much lower.

## THE MOLECULE BEHIND THE BIOLOGY 2.3
## Oxygen Both Sustains and Poisons Us

About 20% of Earth's atmosphere is oxygen, in the form of $O_2$. On early Earth, however, the atmosphere contained only a tiny amount of oxygen and likely much higher concentrations of methane, a greenhouse gas. Approximately 2.4 billion years ago, likely with the evolution of photosynthesis, in which water molecules are broken and oxygen is released as a waste product, the Great Oxidation Event began. During the Great Oxidation Event, the concentration of atmospheric oxygen rapidly increased to between 1% and 10% of modern-day oxygen concentrations. This is considered one of the most important events shaping the global climate. Because oxygen is not a greenhouse gas, the increase in atmospheric oxygen concentrations compared to methane concentrations likely caused a decrease in global temperatures. An oxygenated atmosphere also likely paved the way for the evolution

of most multicellular life. Using oxygen to fuel our respiration is 16 times more efficient than anaerobic respiration (respiration without oxygen, or fermentation).

However, oxygen is highly reactive. The newly oxygenated atmosphere would have been poisonous to many of the anaerobic bacteria (bacteria that require a non-oxygenated environment to live) that had previously made up much of life globally. These bacteria likely went extinct or were relegated to the places where oxygen could not reach, such as in some soils and sediments, where we still find anaerobic bacteria today. These are not the only organisms that suffered the poisonous effects of reactive oxygen, however. Oxygen is also a contributor to a number of chronic and degenerative conditions in humans (and other organisms), including cancer, heart disease, neurological disease, and aging.

Perhaps you have heard about the dangers of "free radicals." Many cosmetic products, particularly antiaging products, and foods rich in antioxidants are advertised as destroying the free radicals in your body that contribute to aging and disease. Radicals are molecules with an extra electron looking for a partner, and most of the free radicals on the loose in your body are oxygen. The oxygen can be in different forms: for example, as superoxide ($O_2^-$) or hydrogen peroxide ($H_2O_2$). These free radicals damage cells, including important cellular machinery such as DNA. Scientists estimate that oxygen radicals attach to each cell's DNA thousands of times each day. Much of the damage can be repaired, but you can imagine that over time, this repair might be unable to keep pace. The oxygenation of Earth's atmosphere facilitated the evolution of life, but oxygen also contributes to each individual's destruction.

## Consumers Eat Producers and Each Other

**Heterotrophs** are organisms that obtain energy from consuming other organisms. Heterotrophs known as primary consumers make up the second trophic level. These organisms feed on the primary producers: the plants on land and the algae in aquatic environments. This trophic level includes many invertebrates, such as insects, as well as larger herbivorous animals, such as sea urchins and some groups of fish and crabs in the oceans or rabbits and deer on land.

Just as plants do not successfully harness all light energy from the Sun, not all the energy in a plant is successfully harnessed by the organism that eats the plant. Generally, an animal must eat about 10 kg of plant material to build 1 kg of body mass, although this number can vary in different types of systems. Because of this, there is less biomass, the amount of biological material, with each step up in trophic level. Therefore, the relationship among trophic levels is often defined as a trophic pyramid **(Figure 2.14)**.

The transfer of energy between trophic levels generally follows the 10% rule described above, where 10 kg of biomass at one level are required to build 1 kg of biomass at the next. This means that between any two levels, about 90% of the energy is not directly harnessed by consumers. Some of the energy may remain in biomass left behind by consumers, such as the

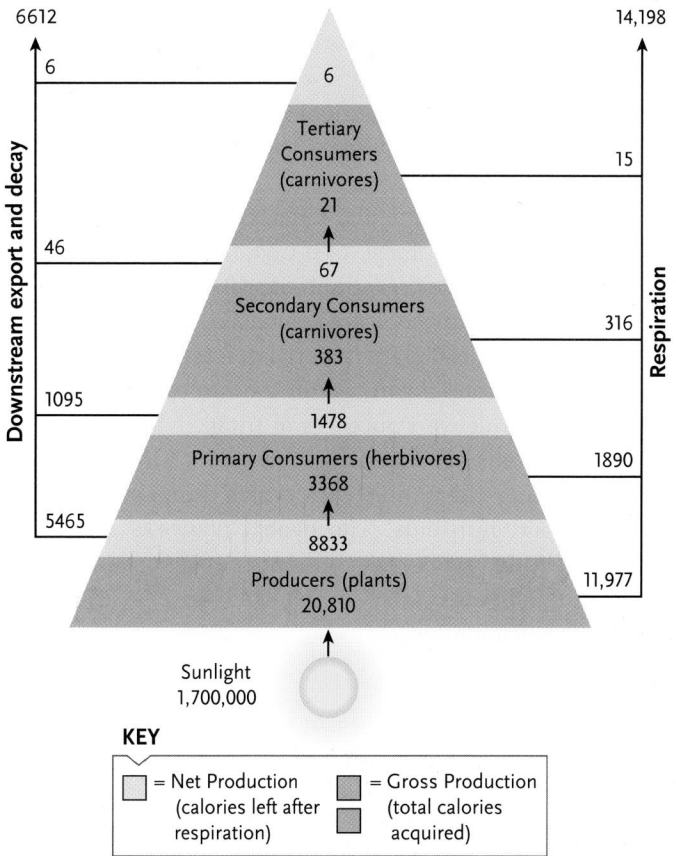

**FIGURE 2.14** Energy and biomass decrease with each step up a trophic pyramid.

SOURCE: From FENTON/DUMONT/OWEN. *Integrative Animal Biology*, 1E. © 2014 Nelson Education Ltd. Reproduced by permission. www.cengage.com/permissions

underground biomass of plants or animal body parts that are not edible to some consumers. Some energy is used by consumers to fuel metabolism and is thus lost from the biosphere.

Secondary consumers are predators, animals that eat other animals. Some secondary consumers are **omnivores**, eating both plants and animals, whereas others are **carnivores**, eating exclusively meat. Some ecosystems include additional levels, such as tertiary and quaternary consumers. Each of these levels is made up of predators that feed on prey on lower levels of the trophic pyramid, an act known as **predation**. This relationship describes those trophic relationships of the Serengeti between zebra and lion, for example, an ecosystem well known for dramatic predator–prey dynamics.

### Detritivores Break Down Dead Organic Matter

**Detritivores** are the decomposers. Rather than feeding on living organisms, these organisms feed on dead organic matter, or detritus. Most detritivores are microbes or fungi. Detritivores play an essential role in ecosystem functioning. By decomposing dead organic material, these organisms return organic material, including nutrients, to the soil as inorganic molecules, allowing them to be taken up by primary producers or other microbes and fungi again and recycled. All organisms, including autotrophs such as plants, require external sources of nutrients for growth. As you saw in Chapter 1, for example, nitrogen is one such nutrient essential for all organisms. Another is phosphorus (see Chapter 30 for more information on nutrient cycles).

Wood and some plant material can be particularly difficult to decompose (see Chapter 1 and the discussion of cellulose digestion). Saprotrophic fungi (fungi that are decomposers) are responsible for decomposing most of the dead plant material in forested ecosystems. The mushrooms you see on the forest floor are only the reproductive structures of fungi. Underneath the mushrooms are extensive networks of **hyphae** (thin, branching filaments) with which fungi absorb and transport nutrients. The hyphal networks are called **mycelium**. Fungal mycelium can be extensive and long lasting, living for thousands of years across many square kilometres.

### Energy and Nutrients Are Passed among Trophic Levels

One amazing example of nutrient cycling through a trophic pyramid is that of salmon along the western coast of North America **(Figure 2.15)**. Over the past 20 years, a number of experiments have traced nitrogen from a salmon through its recycling and reuse in for-

ested ecosystems. A number of salmon species (*Oncorhynchus* spp.) spend much of their lives in the nutrient-rich waters of the Pacific Ocean, returning to freshwater rivers along the west coast of Canada and Alaska to spawn and bringing marine-derived nitrogen with them.

Salmon carcasses are moved in great numbers, mostly by bears (*Ursus* spp.), from stream channels into the forests along the rivers and streams (riparian forest). In some cases, this can mean thousands of kilograms of salmon carcass per hectare of forest. Decomposers return the nitrogen from these carcasses to soils, which can then be taken up by riparian forest vegetation. Between 22% and 24% of the nitrogen in leaves of riparian trees and shrubs has been shown to be salmon derived. This nitrogen in fact acts as a fertilizer to riparian Sitka spruce trees (*Picea sitchensis*), increasing growth rates in comparison with trees in areas where there were no salmon-derived nitrogen inputs.

## STUDY BREAK

1. What is primary production?
2. Why does the biomass of each trophic level decrease upwards on the trophic pyramid?
3. What is the role of detritivores?

## 2.6 Interactions among Organisms

We instinctively think of many organisms in terms of **predators** and prey, but that's not the only type of interaction among organisms. **Symbioses** (singular = symbiosis) are interactions among organisms beyond the usual eating or being eaten. Symbioses are mutualistic when both partners benefit or commensal when one benefits and there is no cost (a neutral effect) to the other. Parasitic interactions are those in which one organism (the parasite) benefits at the expense of the other (the host).

### Mutualisms Benefit Both Partners

You yourself serve as host for many **mutualisms**. For example, as you saw in Chapter 1, you host microorganisms on your skin and in your gut. In fact, if you counted the trillions of cells that make up your body, there would be 10 times as many microbial cells as human cells! Although some of these relationships are not mutualistic, many are. We provide microorganisms with an easily available source of energy, and they contribute to the functioning of our digestive systems in addition to providing other services. We are learning more and more about how important these relationships are, playing a role in shaping even our behaviour and body

**FIGURE 2.15** Grizzly bears feed on spawning salmon, taking salmon carcasses from the rivers into the forests. The salmon carcasses fertilize the forests with the help of detritivores.

shapes. Laboratory mice, grown so that they have no gut microbiota (called germ-free mice), show less anxiety-associated behaviour than mice with normal microbiota, suggesting that bacteria in our guts affect our brain chemistry and development (possibly both positively and negatively). In addition, in both mice and humans, it appears that obesity is associated with different abundances of particular bacteria, specifically species in the phyla Firmicutes and Bacteroidetes. In humans, lean individuals tend to have larger numbers of Bacteroidetes compared to Firmicutes, whereas the opposite is true of obese individuals. Populations of Bacteroidetes increase almost immediately on restricting caloric intake, as when you embark on a low-carbohydrate diet or lose weight. Mice that are genetically predisposed to be obese also have larger numbers of Firmicutes species compared to lean mice, even when fed the same diet. When the microbiota of genetically obese mice is transferred to germ-free mice, the previously lean mice become obese. The exact relationships between particular diets, microbiota, and obesity remain unclear in humans, but we know that the trillions of microbes in our guts play important roles in our metabolic functioning.

In terrestrial ecosystems, mycorrhizal fungi are associated with plant roots, forming extensions from plant roots into the soil. This mutualistic relationship facilitates growth (primary production). The fungi penetrate the roots and either surround the cells of the plant roots or, in some cases, penetrate the root cells directly **(Figure 2.16, p. 42)**.

The fungus uses carbohydrates (i.e., carbon compounds) in the plant cells as an energy source. The plants benefit because the fungal hyphae extend the surface area of the plant's root network in the soil. This allows the uptake of more water and nutrients from the soil into the plant than would otherwise be possible. Although this might seem trivial, it is not. One study showed that 80% of plant species (92% of plant families) have mycorrhizal relationships. Mycorrhizae contribute substantial amounts of key plant nutrients and are able to exploit nutrient hot spots. For example, mycorrhizal hyphae are often found in shallow soils where organic material from dead plants and animals is actively being decomposed.

The relationship between plants and mycorrhizal fungi is hundreds of millions of years old and was long thought of as strictly mutualistic. In recent years, however, scientists have also discovered antagonistic relationships between mycorrhizal fungi and some plant species. For example, the energetic costs paid by plants to a mycorrhizal symbiont (partner in a symbiosis) can

### A. Mycorrhizal symbiosis between lodgepole pine and mycorrhizal fungus

### B. Mycorrhiza

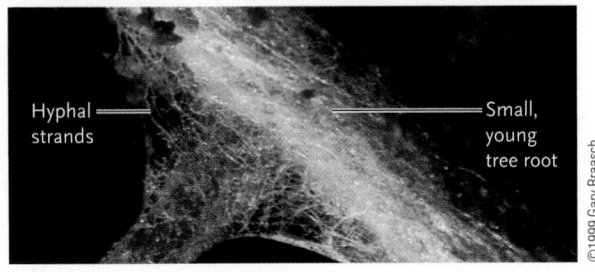

Hyphal strands

Small, young tree root

©1999 Gary Braasch

**FIGURE 2.16** Mycorrhizal fungi. **(a)** A lodgepole pine seedling (*Pinus contorta*) showing symbiosis with a mycorrhizal fungus. Notice the extent of the fungal mycelium compared to the above-ground portion of the seedling, which is only about 4 cm tall. **(b)** Mycorrhizal fungi of a hemlock tree.

Tony Moran/Shutterstock.com

ChameleonsEye/Shutterstock.com

**FIGURE 2.17** **(a)** The common milkweed (*Asclepias syriaca*) and **(b)** the specialist herbivore, the monarch butterfly caterpillar (*Danaus plexippus*).

outweigh the benefit of additional nutrients. For example, common milkweed (*Asclepias syriaca*) is colonized by two different species of mycorrhizal fungus (*Glomus etunicatum* and *Scutellospora pellucida*). Milkweed also produces several defensive compounds to deter and damage potential herbivores, including bitter-tasting compounds that can also affect the survival of the monarch butterfly (*Danaus plexippus*), whose caterpillar eats only milkweed **(Figure 2.17)**. These compounds are found in the latex produced by the plant and require large amounts of both energy and nutrients to produce. Colonization by one of the mycorrhizal species, *S. pellucida*, can be beneficial for both plant growth and the amount of latex produced. Colonization by *G. etunicatum*, however, can decrease both plant growth and latex production, and this effect

increases with increasing fungal colonization. This particular relationship between a common mycorrhizal fungi and its host appears to be of net benefit to the fungal symbiont but of net cost to the plant host—in other words, **parasitism**.

## Parasitism and Exploitative Relationships Benefit the Symbiont but Hurt the Host

In contrast to mutualisms, many interactions among organisms are not of mutual benefit and in fact harm one of the organismal partners. In general, these are called exploitative relationships. Herbivory, predation, and parasitism are all examples of exploitative relationships in which one organism benefits at a cost to another. Although any individual organism works hard to avoid being exploited, there are ecosystem benefits to exploitative relationships. Herbivory and predation are how

A.

Matthew Gilligan

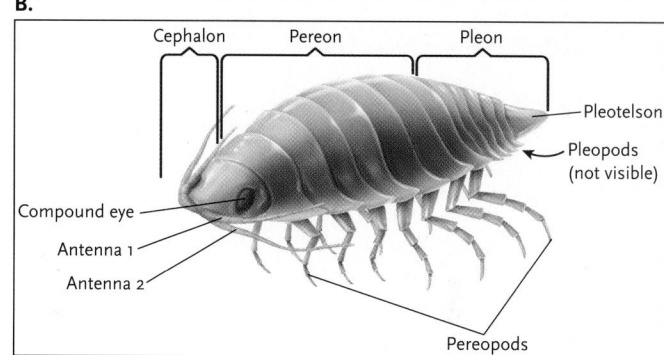

B.

**FIGURE 2.18** Certain marine isopods parasitize fish by killing and then replacing their tongues. **(a)** Although they do not infect humans, some of these isopods can be found in fish species that humans consume, such as this snapper. **(b)** The basic body plan of the isopod.

Cephalon    Pereon    Pleon

Pleotelson

Pleopods (not visible)

Compound eye

Antenna 1

Antenna 2

Pereopods

organisms on upper trophic levels survive by feeding on the levels below them.

Many human parasites are already familiar to us. Some, such as *Giardia* or tapeworms, are rarely fatal but are capable of doing considerable damage to our digestive systems. Others, such as the malaria parasite, are some of the greatest public health challenges facing the human population. Some animal and plant parasites, however, are some of the weirdest creatures out there. European mistletoe (*Viscum album*), which you might kiss someone under during the holidays, is a parasite of tree species. The roots of mistletoe are able to penetrate its host's tissues, from which it is able to draw water and nutrients.

Certain marine isopods (class Crustacea, family Cymothoidae) do something that is pretty astounding. These isopods, fish parasites, first reach adulthood as males. An isopod finds his way into the gills of a fish. If there are no isopods already parasitizing the fish, this first isopod becomes a female. Next, this now-female isopod attaches with its back legs to the fish's tongue and proceeds to drain the tongue of blood. Eventually, the tongue dies and falls out of the fish's mouth. The isopod then grabs onto the tissue that once held the fish tongue in place and holds on tight. The isopod feeds on blood and perhaps other material, such as mucus, and begins to grow. Her legs grow thick to help her hold on, and her eyes grow smaller until they disappear (she doesn't need to see now that she has a permanent home and food source). She becomes the tongue of the fish,

effectively doing the functions a normal fish tongue would do **(Figure 2.18)**.

Other male isopods may find their way into the fish's gills. They will not become females, however, and will not lose their eyesight or grow significantly in size. They may mate with the female, which gives birth to live isopods that seek out new fish to infect. Infection by these species has been shown to decrease the reproductive success of the fish. And there are 280 identified species in the family, and although not all are tongue eaters, many are, and likely many more will be discovered.

Other parasites can manipulate the behaviour of their hosts to their advantage. In 2011, an experiment used one such system found in many of our own backyards. Parasitoid wasps are wasps that spend a large portion of their life cycles inside or attached to another organism, an arrangement that typically leads to the death of the host organism. One parasitoid wasp (*Dinocampus coccinellae*) parasitizes the spotted lady beetle, or ladybug (*Coleomegilla maculata*) **(Figure 2.19, p. 44)**. Scientists in Quebec recently conducted an experiment that revealed the details of the interaction between these two species, as well as the costs and benefits of these interactions. A single egg is laid in the abdomen of the lady beetle by the parasitoid wasp. The larva that hatches feeds on the innards of the lady beetle until it is ready to emerge, at which time, it breaks through the lady beetle's abdomen. The larva then builds a cocoon between the lady beetle's legs.

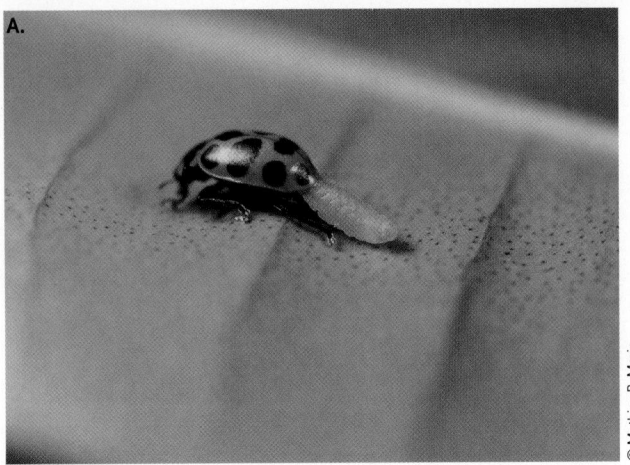

**FIGURE 2.19** **(a)** A fully grown larva of a parasitoid wasp (*Dinocampus coccinellae*) emerges from the abdomen of a spotted lady beetle (*Coleomegilla maculata*). **(b)** The larva builds a cocoon between the lady beetle's legs.

The lady beetle, at this point partially paralyzed, then keeps watch over the cocoon **(Figure 2.19b)**. The lady beetle twitches, moving irregularly and increasing its rate of movement when it is disturbed. Using experimentally manipulated cocoons and a natural parasitoid cocoon predator, the lace wing (*Chrysoperla carnea*), scientists were able to show that cocoons that were not guarded by lady beetles or that were guarded by lady beetles that were already dead were preyed on at higher rates than those protected by these zombie lady beetles. Unlike in a zombie movie, however, surprisingly, approximately 25% of zombie beetles were able to return to normal following the emergence of the adult parasitoid wasp.

It may seem that parasites are detrimental to an ecosystem, in that they decrease the health and fitness of individuals, but this may not be the case. It has been suggested that the parasite load of an ecosystem is an indicator of ecosystem health, with health increasing as parasite load increases. Ecosystem health is different from our definition of health for a single person or organism. Instead, we think about the qualities that support the healthy structure and functioning of the ecosystem as a whole, such as the number of species or productivity. Parasites might make up more than half of global biodiversity!

As amazing as many of these parasitic interactions are, some hosts have evolved equally amazing ways of avoiding and combatting parasites. In some species of birds, nest parasitism is common. In nest parasitism, a female of the parasitic bird species lays eggs in the nest of another species. Other birds then invest the energy and resources necessary to raise her brood, minimizing reproductive costs. Investing energy and resources to raise someone else's chicks is a cost to the host bird. These competing bird species are thus in a kind of evolutionary arms race. Through natural selection, parasitic species continue to evolve ways to trick host birds into taking care of their babies, and selection pressure drives parasitized species to develop new ways to identify intruder babies and get rid of them. This process of competing selection pressures affecting two species simultaneously is called **coevolution**.

The Superb Fairywren (*Malurus cyaneus*) in Australia is one such species whose nests are often parasitized, most commonly by the Horsfield's Bronze-Cuckoo (*Chalcites basalis*) **(Figure 2.20)**. The nestlings of the Superb Fairywren hatch after 15 days' gestation, whereas the eggs of Horsfield's Bronze-Cuckoo hatch after 12 days. This gives the Horsfield's Bronze-Cuckoo the opportunity to grow strong and to kick out the newborn wren hatchlings as they make their way out of their eggs. The baby Horsfield's Bronze-Cuckoos use a variety of begging calls until one causes its host parents to bring it food. Horsfield's Bronze-Cuckoos are generalists—that is, the species parasitizes a number of other species. Since an unhatched egg could be in a nest belonging to one of many different species, going through a wide repertoire of begging calls is a good strategy. On day 9 or 10 of the wren's gestation, however, the mother Superb Fairywren sings a particular song that is unique to each female and includes one particularly distinctive note. It appears that this distinctive note is like a password that the mother gives to her offspring. Once the baby wrens hatch, their begging calls also include the distinctive note, and the mother stops singing her unique song. The mother wren and her mate abandon a nest and begin again if the hatchlings call without using the password—in other words, if they identify an intruder that doesn't know the password. The Horsfield's Bronze-Cuckoo does not sing the

**FIGURE 2.20** **(a)** The Superb Fairywren (*Malurus cyaneus*) has evolved a unique system of teaching to identify nest intruders. **(b)** The most common nest parasitizer of the Superb Fairywren is the Horsfield's Bronze-Cuckoo (*Chalcites basalis*).

password in its repertoire of begging calls. Researchers do not yet know exactly why the cuckoo is unable to learn the password. It may be because the wrens hear the password for approximately 5 days (between days 10 and 15 of gestation) instead of only 2 (between days 10 and 12 of gestation for the cuckoos).

## PUTTING IT IN PERSPECTIVE

This chapter has given you an introduction to how we define life on Earth, what we know about how it began, and what we know about some of the complex interactions among organisms. These concepts are essential to the study of biology, but they are also important to our everyday lives. Strategies for battling the obesity epidemic, for example, may lie in a better understanding of the mutualism between humans and the microbiota we carry in our guts. And humans depend on primary production for food, fibre, animal feed, and biofuels. We appropriate about a third of global terrestrial primary production for our own use each year. This introduction to the development of and roles played by the organisms of our planet will help you contextualize the next chapters in which you will be introduced to the way living organisms function, beginning with the smallest unit of life, the cell.

## KEY CONCEPTS REVIEW AND QUESTIONS

### 2.1 What Is Life?

To be considered alive, an organism must exhibit a number of specific characteristics. First and foremost, it must be self-contained and separated from the external environment. It also must (1) display order, (2) harness and use energy, (3) reproduce (self-replicate), (4) respond to stimuli, (5) exhibit homeostasis (maintain relatively stable internal conditions), (6) grow and develop, and (7) evolve.

1. Multicellular organisms exhibit many of the characteristics of life at multiple levels. What are three levels at which multicellular organisms display order, respond to stimuli, and exhibit homeostasis?

2. How closely does human technology come to synthesizing living organisms? How many characteristics of life does such technology exhibit?

### 2.2 The Tree of Life

Traditionally, biologists have grouped organisms into a classification hierarchy. Groupings are based on shared morphological characters and, more recently, genetic data. This traditional classification system, however, is not always convenient. More and more evolutionary biologists classify animals according to clades, which are more biologically relevant than the traditional hierarchy. Biologists use evolutionary trees, or phylogenies, to understand how organisms are related to one another. Groups of organisms that share a common ancestor are called clades. Organisms within a clade share characteristics.

3. In the list of animals below, which are most closely related to one another? How would you show that graphically? Draw a phylogeny of these animals.
   a. Chimpanzee
   b. Gorilla
   c. Lion
   d. Nile crocodile
   e. Ostrich

4. Porcupines have evolved independently in both the Old World (Africa) and the New World (the Americas). Why might this phenomenon, known as convergent evolution, be problematic for morphology-based taxonomy?

## 2.3 How Life Began

Life began with single-celled organisms in the oceans of early Earth. All life on Earth evolved from a common ancestor. Scientists think that life began as organic molecules in the oceans came together and formed the first proteins and nucleic acids. Scientists don't yet know what the first organisms were to colonize land. The oldest fossils, however, suggest that the first land plant was related to liverworts and the first terrestrial animal was a myriapod (the group that includes centipedes and millipedes).

5. For evolution to begin, these clusters of organic molecules would have needed to begin to replicate. Based on the characteristics of life described in this chapter, what other characteristics would the first groups of organic molecules need to have to be alive?

6. Why would it make sense for plants to have moved onto land prior to the arrival of terrestrial animals?

## 2.4 Extinction and Diversification

Organisms are continuously evolving. This can result in new species being created, a process called speciation. The opposite of speciation is the death of a species, or extinction. Throughout the history of Earth, many species have gone extinct. More than 99% of species that once lived on Earth are no longer alive. During several events, a great number of species died more or less simultaneously. The extinction of the non-avian dinosaurs 65 million years ago is an example of one such event. Over time, different forces influence extinction and speciation.

There can be catastrophic disturbances, such as asteroid impacts or volcanic eruptions, or smaller-scale local evolutionary pressures from interactions among organisms. There is a background extinction rate for life on Earth, but recently, the impact of humans on organisms has created a much higher extinction rate.

7. If animals have always gone extinct, what are two reasons we still might worry about the current extinctions driven by human activities?

8. Are large extinction events likely to be driven mainly by large catastrophic disturbances or local-scale evolutionary pressures? Why?

## 2.5 Fundamental Lifestyles

Organisms across a wide variety of ecosystems fill fundamental trophic roles. Autotrophs are organisms that harness light or chemical energy to fuel themselves. Heterotrophs are organisms that must consume other organisms to obtain the energy they need. The trophic relationships in an ecosystem can be thought of as a pyramid. The autotrophic organisms, or primary producers, make up the base of the trophic pyramid. Because there is not a complete transfer of energy between one trophic level and another, the biomass of higher trophic levels is smaller than the biomass of lower trophic levels. There are often many trophic levels in an ecosystem. Herbivores are the primary consumers that feed on the primary producers. There are also both omnivorous and carnivorous consumers that feed on primary producers and other consumers.

9. Pelagic (open-water) freshwater ecosystems are full of life, despite often looking like nothing but water. Match the following types of pelagic organisms with their trophic role.
   a. Piscivore
   b. Zooplankton
   c. Phytoplankton
   d. Planktivore
   ___ Primary Producer
   ___ Primary Consumer
   ___ Secondary Consumer
   ___ Tertiary Consumer

10. Snowy owls weigh approximately 2 kg. They eat lemmings (approximately 1600 per year each), which in turn eat seeds. If the average square kilometre of tundra produces 800 kg of primary production per year, and you consider the 10% rule, what area would you need to support a single pair of snowy owls?

11. What takes the most land to produce: soybeans or cattle? Why?

12. Knowing that soybeans are typically used as an animal feed, whereas fruits are directly consumed by humans, would soybeans or strawberries occupy more agricultural land?

## 2.6 Interactions among Organisms

Symbioses are close ecological relationships between organisms. We typically define three types of symbioses, and these definitions depend on the costs and benefits for the symbiont and the host. In a parasitism, the host pays a cost, whereas the symbiont benefits. Mutualisms benefit both partners. Commensalisms are relationships that benefit the symbiont and do not affect the host either positively or negatively.

13. Describe an example of a mutualism and a parasitism not described in the chapter.

14. Can you think of a way that humans have exploited parasites?

Now that you have read and reviewed this chapter, we encourage you to attempt to build a concept map using these key concepts and indicate the connections between them. Please see Chapter 5 for examples of concept maps that could be developed for this chapter.

# CHAPTER 3

# The Cell Is the Basic Unit of Life

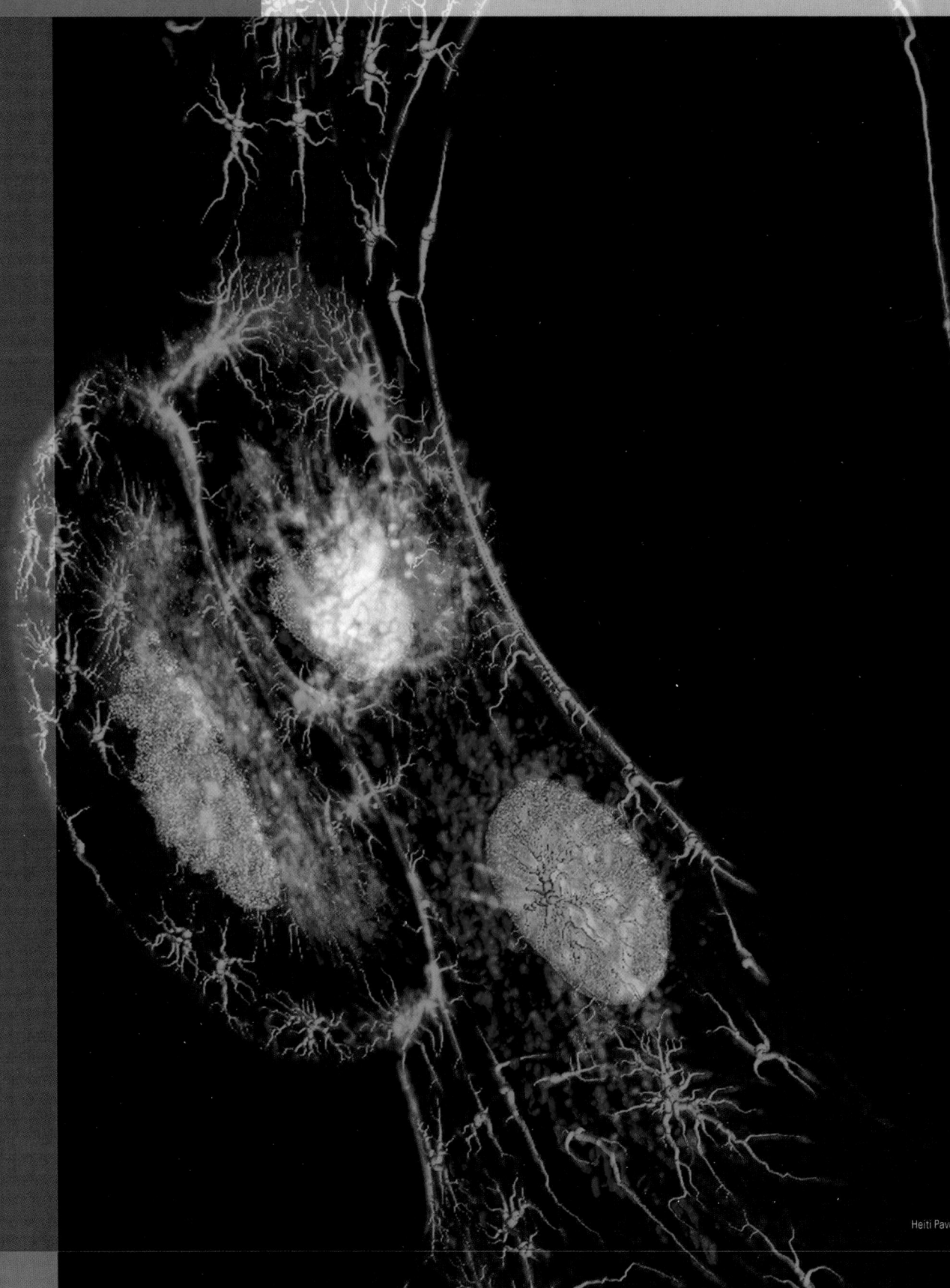

Heiti Paves/Shutterstock.com

## WHY IT MATTERS

We define a cell as the basic unit of life. The structural and functional properties of a cell are determined by the expression of its hereditary factors (genes) and by its environment. Mina Bissell from the Lawrence Berkley National Laboratory in California is a pioneer in the field of the cell microenvironment (the local microscopic environment outside the cell) and has spent her entire career using experiments to demonstrate that a cell's microenvironment can dictate both its structure and function. Her work, which is focused primarily on mammary gland development and breast cancer, clearly demonstrates that the molecular components of the cell's microenvironment and its interactions with neighbouring cells can alter the cell's structural and functional behaviour. For example, cells isolated from the human mammary gland grow as a flat monolayer of cells on the plastic surface of a tissue culture dish **(Figure 3.1a)**. However, if these dishes are first coated with a matrix made up of the same material (i.e., protein, complex carbohydrates, etc.) that is found surrounding mammary cells in the body, the mammary cells in the plate form three-dimensional (3D) cellular structures **(Figure 3.1, b and c)** that resemble the structural and functional subunits of the human mammary gland

**(Figure 3.1d)**. And even more surprising, when myoepithelial cells (contractile cells normally found lining glands) are added to the 3D mammary structures in the tissue culture dish, the mammary cells can produce and secrete milk proteins. Hence, it is clear from this example that cells are not simply free-floating independent units of life. Instead, they adhere to substances, communicate with one another, and respond to changes in their environment.

In this chapter, we will explore the major structural and functional components found in the two major groups of cells: prokaryotic and eukaryotic cells. We will also discuss the cell's microenvironment and the interactions with neighbouring cells. This chapter will serve as the basic foundation that we will build on in later chapters.

## 3.1 The Birth of Cell Biology

**Cell biology**, formerly called cytology, is a branch of biology that studies all aspects of cells, including their structural and physiological properties, life cycles, interactions with their environments, and even their death. Cell biology began with the invention of the microscope

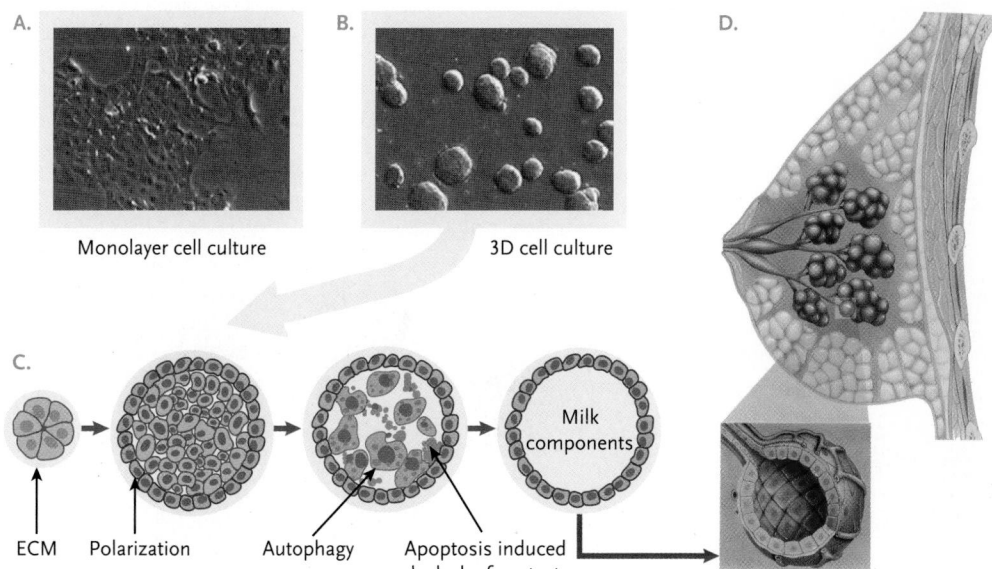

A.

Monolayer cell culture

B.

3D cell culture

C.

ECM    Polarization    Autophagy    Apoptosis induced by lack of contact with ECM (anoikis)

Milk components

D.

**FIGURE 3.1** Human mammary gland cells grown as a monolayer on plastic **(a)** and as three-dimensional (3D) structures on a matrix **(b)**. A schematic diagram depicting the 3D mammary structures **(c)** and the mammary glands in the human breast **(d)**. ECM = extracellular matrix.

SOURCE: (A–C): Immunology and Microbiology, *Autophagy – A Double-Edged Sword – Cell Survival or Death?*, book edited by Yannick Bailly, http://www.intechopen.com/books/autophagy-a-double-edged-sword-cell-survival-or-death-/autophagy-in-development-and-remodelling-of-mammary-gland, Published: April 17, 2013 under CC BY 3.0 license, http://creativecommons.org/licenses/by/3.0/; (D): Sophie Jacopin/Science Source

and is heavily interconnected with other scientific disciplines, such as genetics, molecular and developmental biology, and biochemistry.

## The Cell Theory Defines Cells

We discussed in Chapter 2 that life can exist within a single cell. In other words, cells are the basic unit of life. But what exactly are cells? The first observation of a cell was conducted in the mid-1600s by Robert Hooke, who was not a cell biologist but instead an English natural philosopher, architect, and polymath (an expert in many subject areas). Hooke applied thinly sliced cork as a biological sample under a newly invented inverted light microscope. What he saw through the microscope were tiny boxlike compartments that he named "cellulae," which in Latin means "small rooms." He thought that these biological compartments were similar to the small rooms that religious monks inhabited called cells. What Hooke did not realize at the time was that he was looking at the cell walls of dead cork plant cells **(Figure 3.2)**.

Anton van Leeuwenhoek, a Dutch shopkeeper, also used microscopes to observe cells such as sperm cells, protists, and bacteria. He termed these cells "animalcules" (little animals) and described their actions as "very prettily a-moving." Although these early findings contributed to the initiation of the field of cell biology, it would take quite some time before scientists would know what cells are made of, how they behave, and where they come from.

For nearly two centuries after Hooke coined the term cellulae, the inner components of cells remained a mystery. In the 1820s, Robert Brown, an English botanist, detected a distinct, spherical body inside cells. He named this cellular structure a nucleus. The function of the nucleus remained unknown until the late 1830s, when Matthias Schleiden, a German botanist, speculated that the nucleus was involved in the development of the cell. At about the same time, Theodor Schwann, a German zoologist, further suggested that all cells contain a nucleus and that cells are individual units of life, even if they are one of many cells within an organism. Moreover, in the late 1840s, Rudolf Virchow, a German physiologist, proposed that cells originate from pre-existing cells through cell division.

Thus, by the mid-1800s, the scientific work generated by many scientists using microscopes yielded three significant generalizations of cells, now known as the **cell theory**:

1. All organisms are composed of one or more cells.
2. The cell is the basic structural and functional unit of all living organisms.
3. Cells arise only from the division of pre-existing cells.

Although the cell theory is fundamental to all areas of biological science, these generalizations are the pillars of cell biology. In the next few chapters, we will discuss many aspects of cell biology, including metabolism, cell cycles, and genetics. But first we will explore the various structural parts of the cell and their functions and how they cooperatively give rise to the basic unit of life.

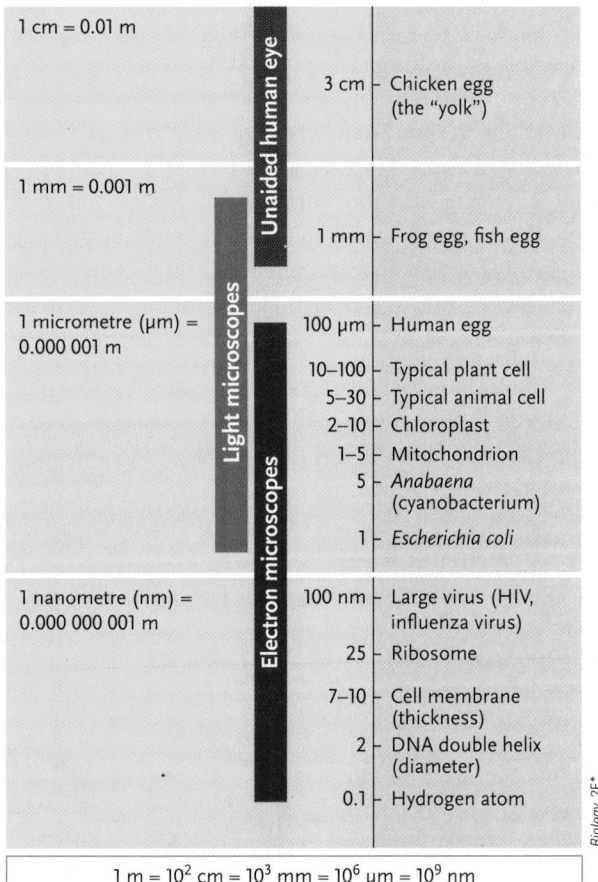

National Library of Medicine

Armed Forces Institute of Pathology

**FIGURE 3.2** The cork cells drawn by Robert Hooke and the compound microscope he used to examine them.

Biology, 2E*

| | | |
|---|---|---|
| 1 cm = 0.01 m | 3 cm | Chicken egg (the "yolk") |
| 1 mm = 0.001 m | 1 mm | Frog egg, fish egg |
| 1 micrometre (μm) = 0.000 001 m | 100 μm | Human egg |
| | 10–100 | Typical plant cell |
| | 5–30 | Typical animal cell |
| | 2–10 | Chloroplast |
| | 1–5 | Mitochondrion |
| | 5 | *Anabaena* (cyanobacterium) |
| | 1 | *Escherichia coli* |
| 1 nanometre (nm) = 0.000 000 001 m | 100 nm | Large virus (HIV, influenza virus) |
| | 25 | Ribosome |
| | 7–10 | Cell membrane (thickness) |
| | 2 | DNA double helix (diameter) |
| | 0.1 | Hydrogen atom |

Unaided human eye · Light microscopes · Electron microscopes

$$1\ m = 10^2\ cm = 10^3\ mm = 10^6\ μm = 10^9\ nm$$

**FIGURE 3.3** Units of measure and the ranges in which they are used in the study of molecules and cells. The vertical scale in each box is logarithmic.

## The Microscope Revolutionized How We Study Cells

Much of what we know today about cells stems from the advancements made in the field of microscopy. This important tool has been the foundation to our discovery of cells, their inner structures, and the roles that those structures play as a concerted effort to provide life to the cell. The invention of the microscope is truly the reason why the field of cell biology exists.

**Microscopy** is a technique that produces a magnified visual image of a specimen, including biological material, using an instrument called a **microscope**. Since most cells are too small to be seen by the unaided eye, ranging in diameter from 0.5 μm (the smallest bacteria), to 5 to 30 μm (an average animal cell), to 1 mm (a frog egg) **(Figure 3.3)**, a microscope is used to observe cells and their cellular components. Two common types of microscopes are the light microscope, which uses light to illuminate a specimen, and the electron microscope, which uses electrons

**A.** Light microscope $\to \simeq 2000$

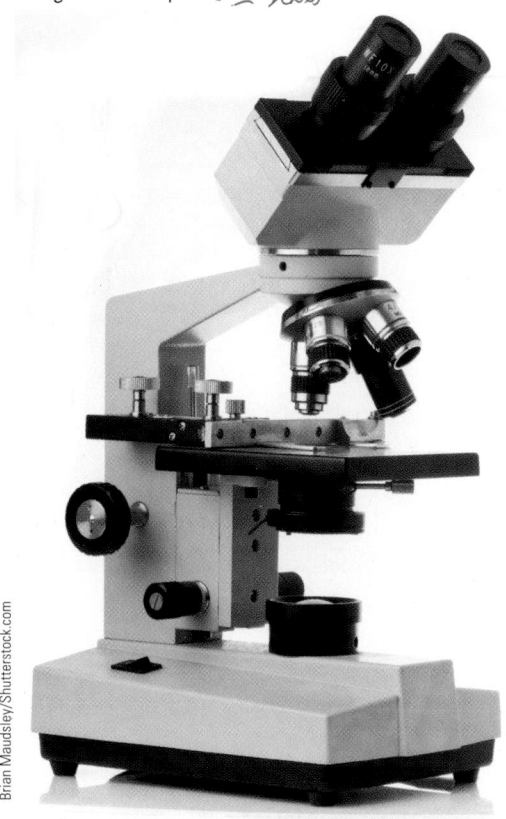

Brian Maudsley/Shutterstock.com

**B.** Electron microscope $\simeq 1{,}000{,}000$

Pan Xunbin/Shutterstock.com

**C.**

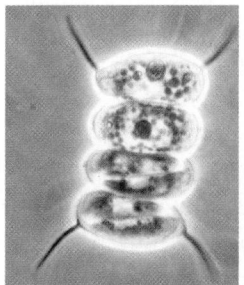 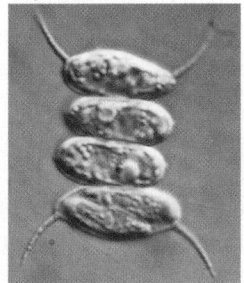  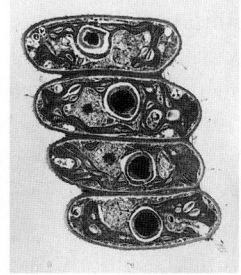 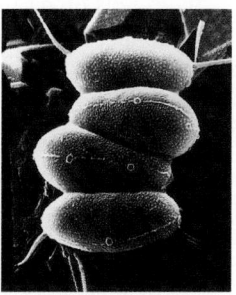

**i** Light micrograph. A phase-contrast microscope yields high-contrast images of transparent specimens. Dark areas have taken up dye.

**ii** Light micrograph. A reflected light microscope captures light reflected from specimens.

**iii** Fluorescence micrograph. This image shows fluorescent light emitted by chlorophyll molecules in the cells.

**iv** A transmission electron micrograph reveals fantastically detailed images of internal structures.

**v** A scanning electron micrograph shows surface details. SEMs may be artificially colored to highlight specific details.

**FIGURE 3.4** Microscopes. Different varieties of the **(a)** light microscope and the **(b)** electron microscope reveal **(c)** different characteristics of the same organism, a green alga (*Scenedesmus*).

SOURCE: (Photo i–ii, iv–v): © Jeremy Pickett-Heaps, School of Botany, University of Melbourne;(Photo iii): Tomasz Szul/Visuals Unlimited, Inc.

# BIOLOGY IS EVERYWHERE 3.1
## Photomicroscopy: The Beauty of Life

A photomicrograph is a photograph or digital image generated using a microscope and a camera. In 1877, Robert Koch published the first photomicrographs of bacteria. Today, this is a widely used method for recording images observed using a microscope for data analysis, publication, or even art. Indeed, many of today's cell biologists are also considered artists of the microscopic world. Dr. Larry Fowke, a retired University of Saskatchewan biology professor, is a world-renowned expert of plant biology. His research focus is on regulatory processes of plant cell division, and he has won many awards for his innovative development of tools for both forest regeneration and crop biotechnology. But there's another important and creative side to Fowke—his art. Throughout his life, Fowke has always been interested in the world's natural beauty. His passion for microscopes has enabled him to mesh science with art and capture some of nature's smallest and most intricate images using microscopes **(Figure 1a)**.

Today, with the aid of sophisticated computer software programs and specific dyes to highlight the various parts of the cell, photomicrographs can be turned into award-winning masterpieces. For the past 40 years, Nikon Corporation, a world leader in optics and imaging, has sponsored the international Small World Photomicrography Competition. The competition is the world's foremost forum for recognizing excellence in photography using the light microscope. Entries in this annual competition are judged on their originality, content, technical skill, and visual impact. Participants are creative in capturing their images using fluorescent dyes to tag specific proteins or structures within cells and entire cells within whole organisms. This is necessary as most parts of the cell are colourless. Furthermore, by playing around with brightness and contrast as well as shutter speeds, much like professional photographers do, these images of life literally appear out of this world. Past winners have included photomicrographs of the blood-brain barrier in a live zebrafish embryo, a portrait of a *Chrysopa* sp. (green lacewing) larva, and *Pleurosigma* (marine diatoms) **(Figure 1b)**. These photomicrographs are scientific treasures that provide a glimpse into the beauty of life.

A.

B.

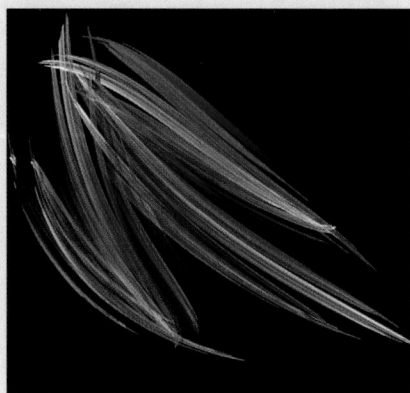

**FIGURE 1** Micrographs showing **(a)** a green alga (*Micrasterias*) and **(b)** marine diatoms *Pleurosigma* (200×).

SOURCE: (Photo A): Dr. Larry Fowke, University of Saskatchewan; (Photo B): Nikon Small World 2008 Photomicrography Competition, 1st Place, Michael J. Stringer, Westcliff-on-Sea, Essex, United Kingdom, Pleurosigma (marine diatoms) (200x).

---

to illuminate a specimen **(Figure 3.4, p. 51)**. Similar to the zoom lens on a camera, microscopes magnify the image of the specimen. **Magnification** is the ratio of a specimen's image size to its real size. In addition to magnifying an object, microscopes also increase the resolution, or amount of detail we can see. **Resolution** is the minimum distance by which two points in the specimen can be separated and still be distinguished as two points; in essence, it is a measure of clarity. The level of resolution is inversely related to the wavelength of light or electrons used to illuminate the specimen: the shorter the wavelength, the better the resolution. Since an electron beam has a shorter wavelength than light, an electron microscope provides a higher level of resolution than a light microscope **(Figure 3.4c)**.

Early scientists used light microscopes to observe cells of various organisms, and today it is still the most common type of microscope used in research and teaching laboratories around the world. The light microscope and a camera can be used to produce a **photomicrograph**, which is a photographic or digital image. Although photomicrographs are representations of biological specimen, surprisingly, they are also considered by many as works of art. (Read more about the art of photomicroscopy in Box 3.1.)

The electron microscope provides a higher level of magnification and resolution than the light microscope. However, due to its operation and maintenance cost, these microscopes are usually shared by many scientists. Keep in mind, however, that the type of microscope and the microscopic techniques used by scientists are dictated by the scientific questions they are asking. Sometimes those questions can be answered using the simplest of microscopes.

Advancements in the field of microscopy have also allowed us to visualize cellular function occurring within living cells in real time. Time-lapse microscopy has enabled us to visualize the molecular movement of cells, the interactions between cells, and the development of cellular structures in 3D. For example, using a confocal

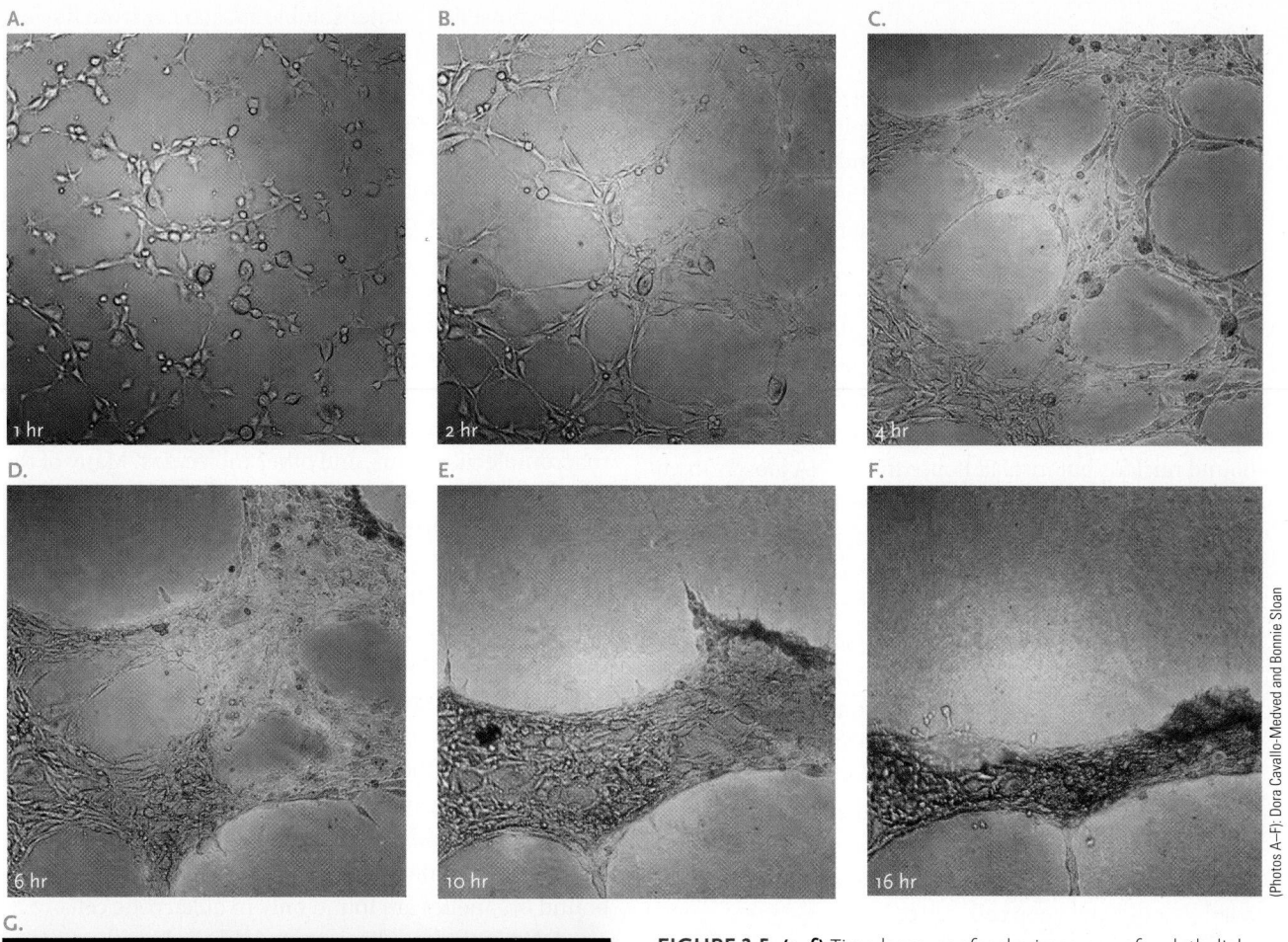

A. *1 hr*
B. *2 hr*
C. *4 hr*
D. *6 hr*
E. *10 hr*
F. *16 hr*

(Photos A–F): Dora Cavallo-Medved and Bonnie Sloan

G.

Dora Cavallo-Medved and Bonnie Sloan

1 Unit = 23.124052 μm

**FIGURE 3.5 (a–f)** Time-lapse, confocal microscopy of endothelial cells forming 3D tubular structures over 16 hours. Degradation products of the matrix protein collagen IV are observed as green. **(g)** Three-dimensional (3D) reconstructed image demonstrating tubular structure formation of live human umbilical vein endothelial cells (1 unit = 23.1 μm).

microscope (a type of light microscope that uses lasers to take images of numerous sections across a specimen), various time-lapse images of endothelial cells (cells that line blood vessels) forming tubular structures when grown in a matrix of collagen protein and other glycoproteins **(Figure 3.5, a–f)** can be acquired over a period of time. This cellular process mimics a natural process that occurs in the body called angiogenesis, which is the formation of new blood vessels. In the body, the entire framework of the circulatory system is developed by angiogenesis and occurs because of the interactions between the endothelial cells and the specific proteins in the matrix surrounding these cells. A sophisticated computer software program can also be used to create a 3D reconstruction of the captured microscopic images **(Figure 3.5g)**. A quick Internet search of YouTube videos will reveal many films of living cells in action using time-lapse microscopy.

## STUDY BREAK

1. What three generalizations constitute the cell theory?
2. Distinguish between a light microscope and an electron microscope.

## 3.2 The Basic Foundations of a Cell

All cells are categorized as either prokaryotic or eukaryotic. Prokaryotic cells constitute organisms that are classified in two of the domains of life—Archaea and Bacteria. Eukaryotic cells are found in organisms from the domain Eukarya. One of the most obvious distinguishing features between these two categories of cells is the presence or absence of a true nucleus. Eukaryotic cells (*eu* = true; *karyo* = nucleus) contain a prominent spherical body called a nucleus. The nucleus is surrounded by a membrane and contains the cell's hereditary material, DNA. Prokaryotic cells (*pro* = before; *karyo* = nucleus) do not contain a membrane-bound nucleus but instead house their DNA loosely in an unbound region within the interior of the cell called the nucleoid. Although there are other major structural and functional differences between prokaryotic and eukaryotic cells, the presence or absence of a nucleus is one of the key distinguishing characteristics. But before we talk more about the differences between these two basic cell types, let's first discuss some of their common features.

**Figure 3.6** shows a prokaryotic cell and two eukaryotic cells, one animal and one plant. Refer to these illustrations as you proceed through the chapter. In addition, see the Purple Pages for an overview of the macromolecules (i.e., carbohydrates, proteins, nucleic acids, and lipids) used to build and keep cells alive.

### All Cells Have Common Features

All cells are surrounded by a covering called the **plasma membrane,** built as a phospholipid bilayer (a two-layered structure consisting of lipids that contain phosphates) with embedded proteins. The plasma membrane acts as a protective and selectively permeable barrier between the cell and its environment. It has a hydrophobic, or water-repelling, lipid core that protects the inner contents of the cells by preventing water-soluble substances from flowing freely across the membrane. Transport of these substances across the membrane is instead directed through highly specialized membrane proteins that function under the strict control of the cell in response to its needs. For example, many plasma membranes allow for easy passage of gases such as oxygen and carbon dioxide across the membrane, whereas sugars and other large organic compounds can cross the membrane only with the help of membrane transport proteins. We'll describe membrane structure and function in more detail later.

The plasma membrane encloses a fluid or jellylike substance called the **cytoplasm,** which consists of water, macromolecules, ions, and other molecules. Many of the cell's metabolic reactions occur within the cytoplasm; therefore, the physiological conditions of the cytoplasm need to be optimally regulated. For example, the pH (acidity level; see the Purple Pages for an overview of pH) of the cytosol (the aqueous component of the cytoplasm) in most cells is about 7.4, an ideal condition for most cytoplasmic enzymes to function effectively (see Chapter 4 for an overview of enzyme function and regulation). In eukaryotic cells, the cytoplasm also houses internal membrane-bound organelles ("little organs"), which are specialized structural and functional subunits of the cell. With the exception of a few prokaryotic cells, membrane-bound organelles are found only in eukaryotic cells.

**DNA** is the hereditary material found in all cells (and even in some viruses) **(Figure 3.7, p. 56).** DNA is composed of two polynucleotide strands bound together by hydrogen bonding between the nucleotides. Double-stranded DNA is arranged as a twisted right-handed helix. (You will learn more about DNA in Chapter 9.) DNA and DNA proteins are bound together into larger structures called **chromosomes.** In eukaryotic cells, the DNA is contained primarily in the nucleus (there is a small amount of DNA inside mitochondria and plastids) and is organized into

**FIGURE 3.6** Diagrams of **(a)** a prokaryotic cell, **(b)** an animal eukaryotic cell, and **(c)** a plant eukaryotic cell, showing major structures and their locations. *(Continued)*

**A.**

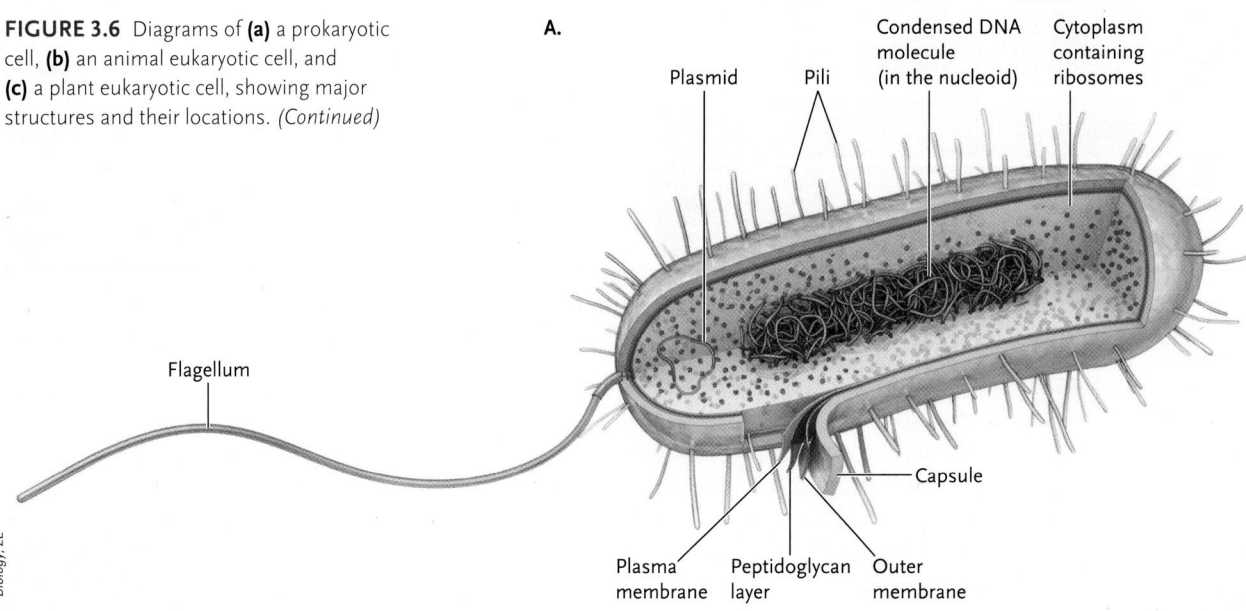

Plasmid · Pili · Condensed DNA molecule (in the nucleoid) · Cytoplasm containing ribosomes

Flagellum

Plasma membrane · Peptidoglycan layer · Outer membrane · Capsule

Biology, 2E*

**FIGURE 3.6** (*Continued*)

**B.**

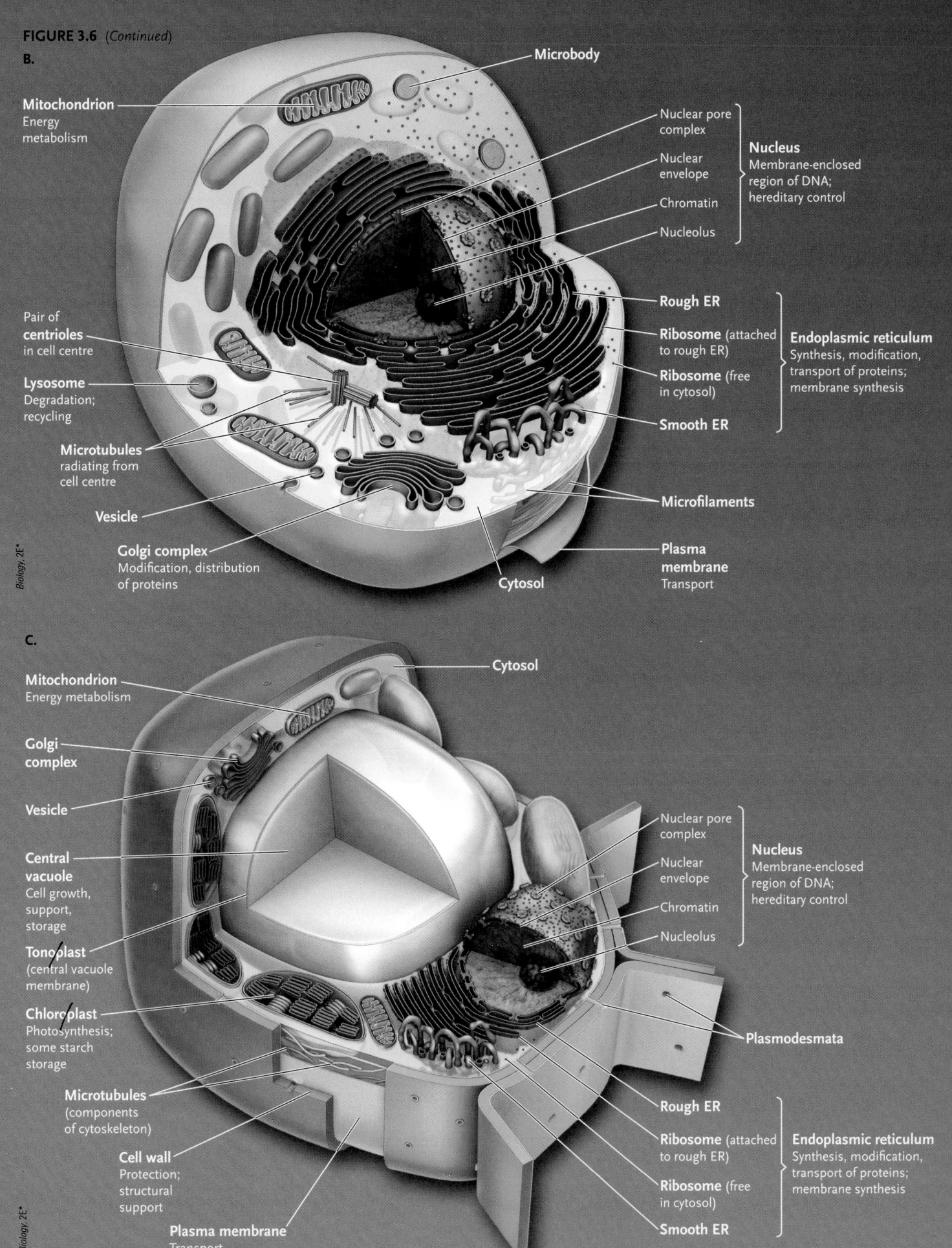

Microbody

**Mitochondrion**
Energy
metabolism

Nuclear pore
complex

Nuclear
envelope

Chromatin

Nucleolus

**Nucleus**
Membrane-enclosed
region of DNA;
hereditary control

**Rough ER**

Pair of
**centrioles**
in cell centre

**Ribosome** (attached
to rough ER)

**Endoplasmic reticulum**
Synthesis, modification,
transport of proteins;
membrane synthesis

**Lysosome**
Degradation;
recycling

**Ribosome** (free
in cytosol)

**Smooth ER**

**Microtubules**
radiating from
cell centre

**Microfilaments**

**Vesicle**

**Plasma
membrane**
Transport

**Golgi complex**
Modification, distribution
of proteins

Cytosol

*Biology, 2E\**

**C.**

Cytosol

**Mitochondrion**
Energy metabolism

**Golgi
complex**

**Vesicle**

Nuclear pore
complex

Nuclear
envelope

Chromatin

Nucleolus

**Nucleus**
Membrane-enclosed
region of DNA;
hereditary control

**Central
vacuole**
Cell growth,
support,
storage

**Tonoplast**
(central vacuole
membrane)

Plasmodesmata

**Chloroplast**
Photosynthesis;
some starch
storage

**Microtubules**
(components
of cytoskeleton)

**Rough ER**

**Cell wall**
Protection;
structural
support

**Ribosome** (attached
to rough ER)

**Endoplasmic reticulum**
Synthesis, modification,
transport of proteins;
membrane synthesis

**Ribosome** (free
in cytosol)

**Plasma membrane**
Transport

**Smooth ER**

*Biology, 2E\**

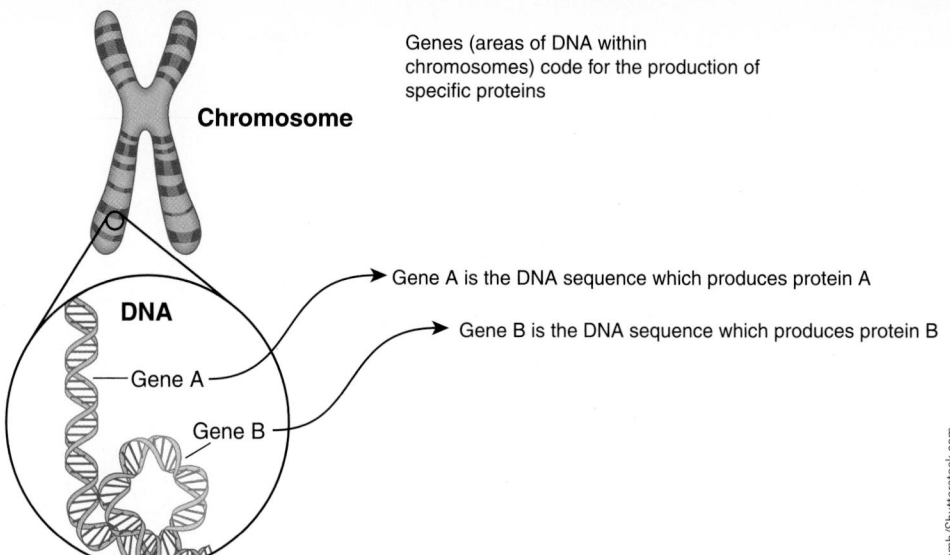

**FIGURE 3.7** Genes are unique sequences of nucleotides on DNA coiled into individual chromosomes.

**Chromosome**

Genes (areas of DNA within chromosomes) code for the production of specific proteins

**DNA**

Gene A

Gene B

Gene A is the DNA sequence which produces protein A

Gene B is the DNA sequence which produces protein B

Blamb/Shutterstock.com

several discrete linear chromosomes. In prokaryotic cells, the DNA is loosely suspended in the cytoplasm and organized into a single, circular chromosome.

**Genes** are individual hereditary units that are localized as unique DNA sequences on the chromosomes (Figure 3.7). Genes encode the information required to synthesize the various proteins and ribonucleic acid (RNA) (macromolecules that direct most of the cellular functions) needed by the cell. In essence, genes are analogous to the instruction manual on how to build a cell. You may be surprised to learn that 98% to 99% of the genes in your cells are the same as those found in closely related species such as chimpanzees or orangutans. So how can we have similar instruction manuals and yet appear so different? This is due to the slight variations in the genes we share and differences in how our cells express these genes. It's the same reason why you appear different from the person sitting next to you in class. In Chapter 10, we'll discuss in more detail how gene expression varies among different cell types and between different organisms.

All variety of proteins are the products of gene expression. They are also considered the "workhorses" of the cell as they are involved in carrying out many cellular functions. Proteins are synthesized by **ribosomes**, found either in the cytoplasm (free ribosomes) or on the surface of certain organelles (bound ribosomes). Ribosomes are small spherical structures that are composed of a large and a small subunit **(Figure 3.8)**. The large and small subunits of eukaryotic

ribosomes are different in structure from those found in prokaryotic cells, with the exception of ribosomes found in mitochondria and plastids. The ribosomes in these eukaryotic organelles are more similar to those found in prokaryotic cells. Below we will discuss how this similarity is evidence for the origin of these unique cellular organelles.

But how do we use genes to build protein? The information encoded in the DNA of a gene is initially transcribed into a complementary messenger RNA (mRNA) copy by a process called **transcription**. The copied information in the mRNA is later translated by ribosomes and used to build proteins by a process called **translation**. We will learn more about the mechanisms of transcription and translation in Chapter 10.

## Cellular Membranes Exhibit Structure and Function

As mentioned above, membranes are selectively permeable barriers surrounding each cell. The **fluid mosaic model** is the current view of the structural organization of membranes **(Figure 3.9)**. This model describes membranes as fluid structures composed of two layers of phospholipids (phospholipid bilayer) and containing a mosaic array of membrane proteins. Each phospholipid contains a polar head, which is hydrophilic, or water loving, and two fatty acid tails, which are hydrophobic, or water repelling. As a result of this amphipathic characteristic (containing both hydrophilic and hydrophobic properties), phospholipids will spontaneously organize themselves into a lipid bilayer structure in the presence of an aqueous solution. The bilayer is arranged so that the hydrophobic tails are sandwiched between the hydrophilic heads. In a cell, the lipid bilayer forms a spherical structure that encloses the cytoplasm and its contents. This membrane enclosure controls the transport of molecules into and out of the cell, which in turn helps maintain the proper balance of its internal physiological environment (e.g., pH level, sugar levels, ion

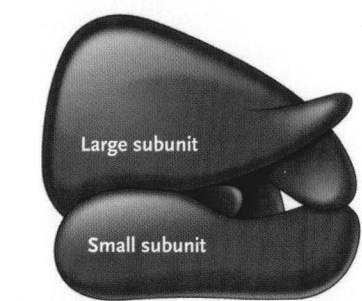

**Large subunit**

**Small subunit**

Biology, 2E*

**FIGURE 3.8** The two subunits of ribosomes and how they come together to form the whole ribosome.

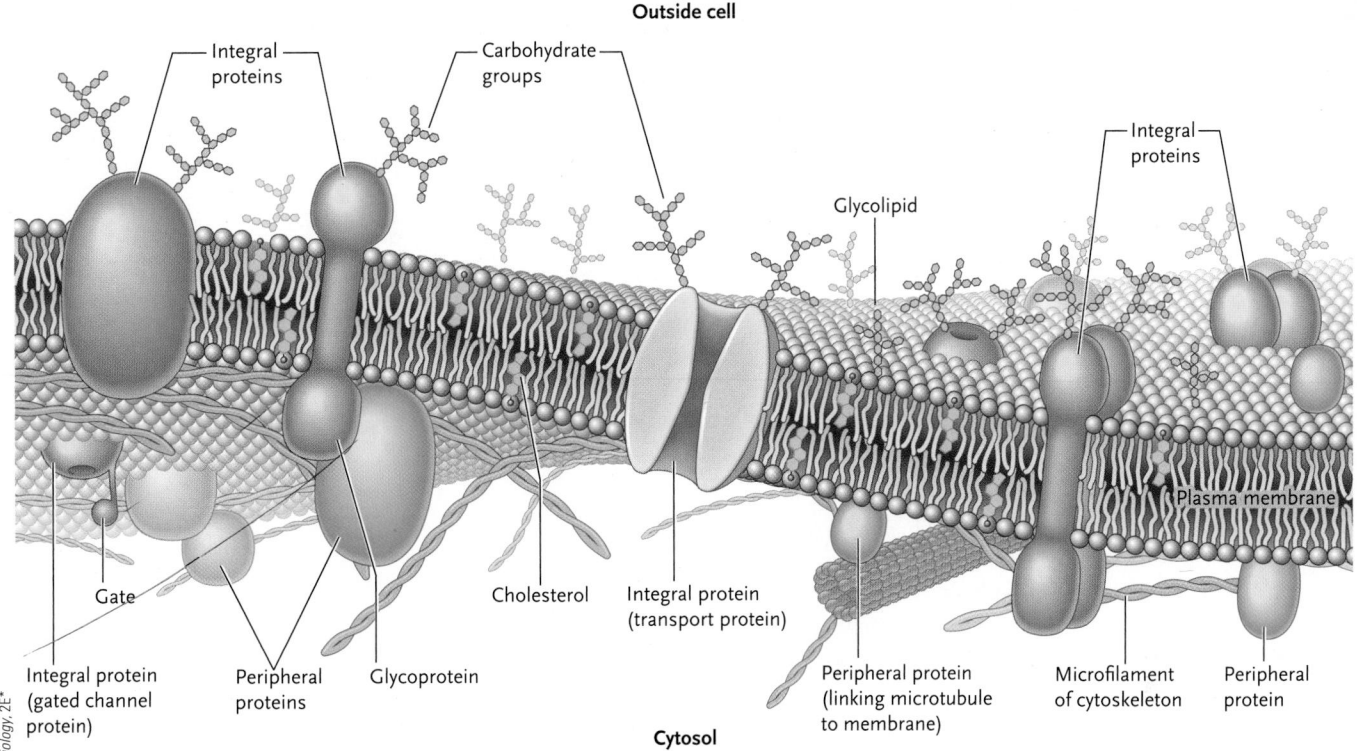

**Outside cell**

Integral proteins — Carbohydrate groups

Integral proteins

Glycolipid

Plasma membrane

Gate

Integral protein (gated channel protein)

Peripheral proteins

Glycoprotein

Cholesterol

Integral protein (transport protein)

Peripheral protein (linking microtubule to membrane)

Microfilament of cytoskeleton

Peripheral protein

**Cytosol**

Biology, 2E*

**FIGURE 3.9** Membrane structure according to the fluid mosaic model. The model proposes that integral membrane proteins are suspended individually in a fluid lipid bilayer. Peripheral proteins are attached to integral proteins or membrane lipids mostly on the cytoplasmic side of the membrane (the lower surface in the figure). Carbohydrate groups of membrane glycoproteins and glycolipids sit on the exterior of the membrane.

concentrations), despite the conditions of its external environment. We call this maintenance of internal balance homeostasis, and it is one of the properties that characterize life. Homeostasis can be observed in single cells and in an entire multicellular organism.

The fluidity of membranes is an important factor that determines membrane permeability. If a membrane is too fluid, as can happen under higher temperatures, it loses control over which molecules should be transported across it. These cell membranes could become leaky, resulting in the loss of vital molecules or the passage of dangerous pathogens into the cell. If a membrane is not fluid enough (too viscous), as it is under colder temperatures, then the molecules that would normally be transported across the membrane are impeded from doing so. Nutrients that are required for cell survival may be obstructed from entering into the cell, or waste products that need to be removed accumulate inside the cell, possibly causing damage.

One of the structural characteristics of membranes that dictate its fluidity under various conditions is the ratio of saturated versus unsaturated fatty acids in the hydrophobic tails of the phospholipids. You've probably heard a lot about saturated versus unsaturated fats with respect to diet, but how do these types of fats relate to membrane fluidity? Saturated fatty acids contain chains of hydrocarbons in which

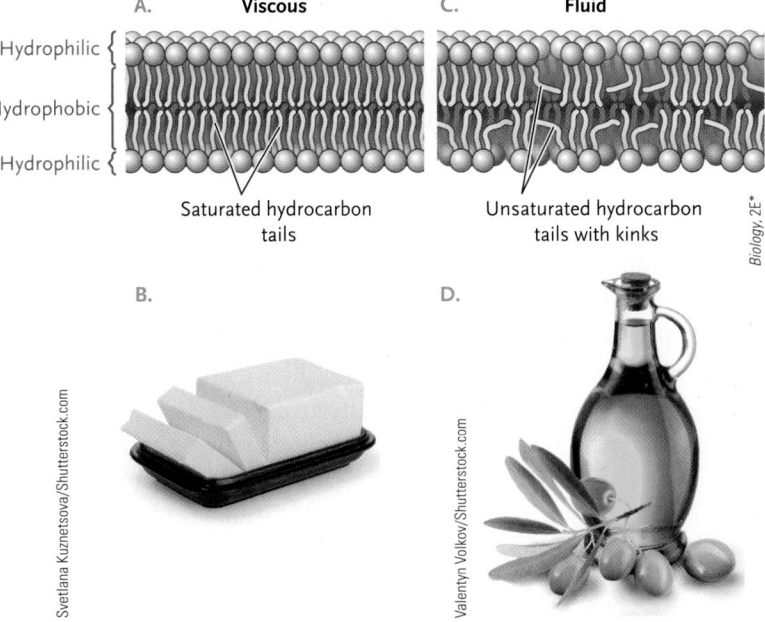

**FIGURE 3.10** Lipid molecule composition affects membrane density. **(a)** Some membranes contain phospholipids with saturated hydrocarbon tails that are closely packed. **(b)** Butter contains saturated fatty acids, thus making it a solid at room temperature. **(c)** Unsaturated hydrocarbon tails have kinks that prevent phospholipid molecules from packing closely together. **(d)** Olive oil contains unsaturated fatty acids, thus making it a liquid at room temperature.

each carbon atom is bound to as many hydrogen atoms as possible, thus making the tails straight or linear in structure **(Figure 3.10a)**. Due to this structural feature, phospholipids containing saturated fatty acid tails can pack tightly together within a given volume, thus increasing the density of phospholipids within a membrane and making the membrane less fluid (viscous). Butter contains more densely packed saturated fats such as stearic acid, which makes it solid at room temperature **(Figure 3.10b)**.

On the other hand, unsaturated fatty acids contain hydrocarbon tails in which some of the carbon atoms are double-bonded to one another (i.e., carbons are not bound to the maximal number of hydrogen atoms possible; see the Purple Pages for an overview of chemical bonds) **(Figure 3.10c)**. The double bonds cause kinks or bends in the structure of the phospholipid tails, which reduces the ability of these phospholipids to pack tightly together within a given volume. Less packing of phospholipids within a membrane means that the membranes are less dense and thus more fluid. Olive oil contains less densely packed unsaturated fats such as oleic acid making it a liquid at room temperature **(Figure 3.10d)**.

Maintaining proper fluidity within a membrane requires a proper balance of phospholipids. Under normal physiological conditions, the ratio of saturated versus unsaturated fatty acids in the phospholipids of the plasma membrane of most cells is approximately 1:1. These ratios may change when cells are exposed to different conditions in an effort to balance membrane fluidity. Organisms such as bacteria, fungi, plants, and fish whose internal temperatures vary according to the temperature in their environments can alter the ratio of saturated versus unsaturated fatty acids in the phospholipids of their plasma membrane to balance membrane fluidity. In colder temperatures, their membranes will contain more unsaturated fatty acids. In warmer temperatures, their membrane will contain more saturated fatty acids. This variability in saturated versus unsaturated fatty acid ratios in membranes is one reason why organisms such as sculpin fish can survive in the cold temperature of the Arctic Ocean or how salmon can adapt to differing temperatures as they migrate between oceans and streams.

Other lipids, including steroids, are also found in the phospholipid bilayer and play a role in maintaining membrane fluidity and permeability. Cholesterol is one such steroid found in animal cell membranes but not in those of plants or prokaryotes **(Figure 3.11)**. Although we often think of cholesterol as being harmful to us, this fat is naturally made in the body and plays many important physiological roles. For example, under conditions that cause membranes to become viscous (and therefore less fluid),

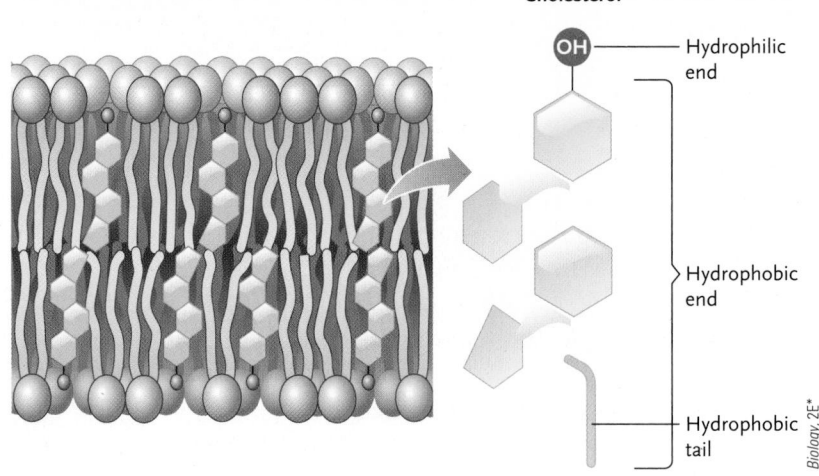

**FIGURE 3.11** The position taken by cholesterol within a membrane. The hydrophilic –OH group at one end of the molecule extends into the hydrophilic region of the bilayer; the ring structure extends into the hydrophobic membrane interior.

cholesterol in the membranes physically prevents the phospholipids from tightly packing. Hence, cholesterol aids in maintaining membrane fluidity and permeability. On the other end of the spectrum, cholesterol can also fill in the empty spaces created by less densely packed phospholipid tails in membranes that are too fluid. In this scenario, cholesterol acts by decreasing the fluidity of the membrane. Therefore, similar to saturated versus unsaturated ratios, the amount of cholesterol present within membranes is also important in maintaining proper

**A.** In a watery fluid, phospholipids spontaneously line up into two layers, tails to tails. This lipid bilayer spontaneously shapes itself into a sheet or a bubble. It is the basic structural and functional framework of all cell membranes. Many types of proteins intermingle among the lipids.

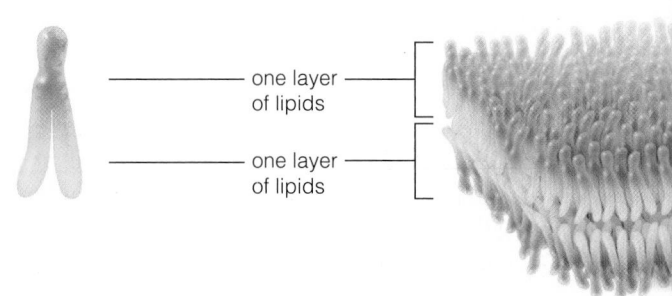

one layer of lipids

one layer of lipids

**FIGURE 3.12** The structure of cell membranes showing **(a)** the organization of phospholipids and **(b–e)** various types of embedded membrane proteins.

SOURCE: From Starr. *Biology*, 8E. © 2011 Brooks/Cole, a part of Cengage Learning, Inc. Reproduced by permission.www.cengage.com/permissions

membrane fluidity, which in turn is critical in maintaining homeostasis and proper cellular function. Take, for example, red blood cells that transport and deliver oxygen to cells and tissues. In the membranes of red blood cells, cholesterol content plays a role in cell deformation, a process that changes the shape of red blood cells from a round cushioned one into one that is flat. Deformation allows red blood cells to more easily squeeze through capillaries to transport oxygen to nearby tissue. Too much cholesterol in the red blood cell membranes, however, impedes deformation. In a recent study, the treatment of red blood cells with statins, drugs that reduce high cholesterol concentrations, increased cell deformation. These studies further support the contention that the proper balance of cholesterol content in red blood cell membranes is significant in reducing the risk of some cardiovascular diseases.

As previously mentioned, the mosaic portion of the fluid mosaic model describes a multiple array of diverse molecules that reside within or on the membrane. These include proteins, which are diverse in both their structure and function within the membrane. Structurally, the proteins are categorized as integral or peripheral membrane proteins. **Integral membrane proteins** are defined as proteins that interact with the hydrophobic core of membranes (Figure 3.9). Most of these proteins go completely through the membrane and are called **transmembrane proteins**. **Peripheral membrane proteins**, on the other hand, are not embedded within the membrane core but instead are associated with the membrane surface (Figure 3.9). As a result,

these proteins are often loosely, and thus temporarily, associated with the membrane.

The functions of membrane proteins are diverse and include recognition, attachment, transport, and enzymatic activity **(Figure 3.12)**. **Recognition proteins** on the cell membrane act as cellular identification tags. The proteins can distinguish one cell type from another and can also recognize cells of different species **(Figure 3.12b)**. Recognition of cell type is important in multicellular organisms, where cells need to work cooperatively. Identification of cells belonging to a different species is essential in detecting foreign invaders that may be harmful to the organism (see Chapter 27).

**Cell adhesion molecules** are typically transmembrane protein receptors that attach cells to one another or to components of the **extracellular matrix (ECM)**. Cell adhesion molecules have intracellular anchoring points that interact with the internal cytoskeleton. The physical connections made between neighbouring cells by cell adhesion molecules is the underlying structural basis that gives different tissue types their unique architectures, which in turn correlates with their specific functions. For example, epithelial tissue that makes up the outer surface of an animal's body and lines the internal organs is composed of cells that are connected to one another by cell adhesion molecules.

**Receptor proteins** bind specific molecules that can signal a particular cellular response, called **cell communication (Figure 3.12c)** (see Chapter 26). The signal

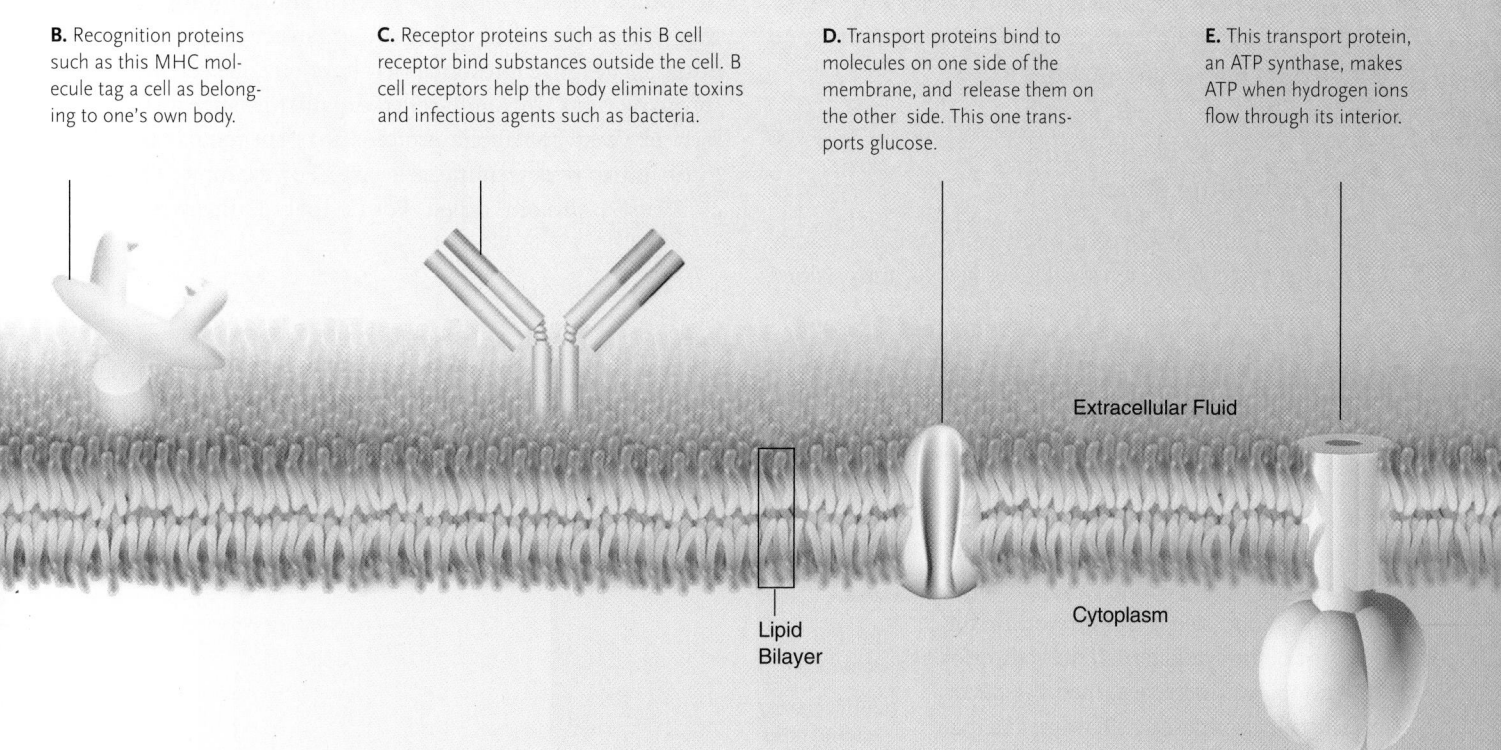

**B.** Recognition proteins such as this MHC molecule tag a cell as belonging to one's own body.

**C.** Receptor proteins such as this B cell receptor bind substances outside the cell. B cell receptors help the body eliminate toxins and infectious agents such as bacteria.

**D.** Transport proteins bind to molecules on one side of the membrane, and release them on the other side. This one transports glucose.

**E.** This transport protein, an ATP synthase, makes ATP when hydrogen ions flow through its interior.

Extracellular Fluid

Cytoplasm

Lipid Bilayer

molecule is usually sent by another cell. Cell communication can elicit responses such as cell growth and division, activation of specific metabolic pathways, or even cell suicide. Failure to send proper signals can lead to diseases such as atherosclerosis, diabetes, and even cancer.

**Transport proteins** are transmembrane proteins found on all cell membranes. They facilitate the transport of molecules such as sugars, proteins, and ions (charged atoms) across the membranes **(Figure 3.12, d** and **e)**. These molecules cannot easily penetrate the hydrophobic core of the lipid bilayer due to their size and/or their electric charge. Transport proteins provide a controlled passageway (like a toll road) through the phospholipid bilayer (see Chapter 4).

Many membrane proteins carry out more than one of these functions outlined. For example, some transport proteins are also enzymes that participate in cellular reactions at the membrane (Figure 3.12e). Which proteins are found on a particular membrane and which functions they perform depend on the type of membrane, the type of cell, and the specific needs of the individual cell. Recently, a team of Canadian scientists from several academic institutes across the country were the first to perform a global characterization of protein complexes on the membrane surfaces of yeast cells. This included a complete survey of 1590 integral, peripheral, and lipid-anchored membrane proteins. The described global topological landscape of membranes, called the membrane interactome, revealed numerous unexpected physical associations between membrane proteins. Their findings are important to better understand how a membrane's structure relates to its function. Moreover, this information can be used to develop novel strategies to deliver specific compounds into specific cells, such as drugs to combat a variety of diseases.

## Cell Size Is Dictated by Surface Area-to-Volume Ratios

The need for microscopes to study cell biology is simply because most cells are too small to be seen by the unaided eye. But why are cells so small? Is it possible to supersize our cells? Cell size is dictated by physical constraints. Remember that plasma membrane acts not only as a protective barrier but also as a permeable surface that allows the transport of substances into and out of the cell. Thus, the surface area of the plasma membrane must be able to supply all of the metabolic needs found within the volume of the cytoplasm. If the volume of the cytoplasm increases, then the needs of the cell also increase. This means that the surface area of the plasma membrane must increase accordingly to meet these

extra demands. Thus, the ratio of cell surface to cell volume—the surface area-to-volume ratio—is a critical component in maintaining a properly functioning and healthy cell. For simplicity, consider a cell shaped like a cube. The length, width, and height of the cell are all equal and can be denoted as x. Using geometrical formulae, we calculate the volume of the cell to be $x^3$. To calculate the surface area of the cube, we calculate the area of each side ($x^2$) and multiply by the number of sides ($6x^2$). Thus, the surface area-to-volume ratio would be $6/x$. If we insert values for x, then we can get a better idea of how this ratio changes as the cell becomes larger. From **Figure 3.13**, we can see how the volume increases faster than the surface area as a cell grows. This means that the plasma membrane has to work extra hard to bring in enough nutrients and remove waste fast enough from the cytoplasm to accommodate the increased metabolic needs of the larger cell. If the cell continues to increase in volume, at some point, the plasma membrane of that cell cannot work effectively enough to maintain balance or homeostasis in the cell. A loss in homeostasis leads to an unhealthy cell. Thus, the size of any cell is dictated by the optimal ratio between the plasma membrane area and the cytoplasmic volume.

Eukaryotic cells have the ability to become larger than prokaryotic cells because they have a series of internal membranes that aid in maintaining homeostasis as the size of the cell increases. We will see later in the chapter that some eukaryotic organelles have adaptations that greatly increase the amount of membrane surface area present in a specific volume. These allow critical biochemical reactions to occur at greater overall rates.

But how does a cell know when to stop growing? And why are some cells within an organism larger than others? These are questions that have puzzled scientists for many years. In single-celled organisms, such as bacteria or yeast, metabolic proteins that are regulated by diffusion may determine cell size. For example, yeast contains a protein called Pom1 that is involved in

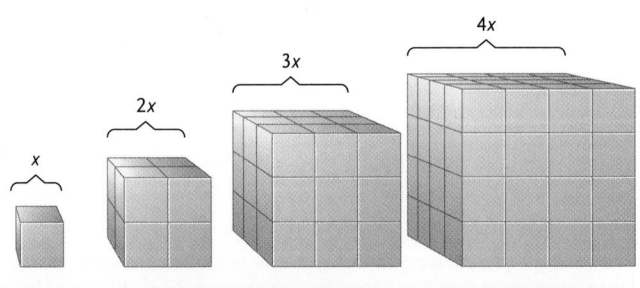

| | | | |
|---|---|---|---|
| **Total surface area** | $6x^2$ | $6(2x)^2 = 24x^2$ | $6(3x)^2 = 54x^2$ | $6(4x)^2 = 96x^2$ |
| **Total volume** | $x^3$ | $(2x)^3 = 8x^3$ | $(3x)^3 = 27x^3$ | $(4x)^3 = 64x^3$ |
| **Surface area/ volume ratio** | 6:1 | 3:1 | 2:1 | 1.5:1 |

*Biology, 2E\**

**FIGURE 3.13** Relationship between surface area and volume.

regulating cell division. As a yeast cell grows and lengthens, Pom1 becomes more concentrated in the cytoplasm at the lengthening ends of the cell. In the middle of the yeast cell, the Pom1 concentration becomes so low that it can no longer block the mechanism responsible for cell division. At this point, the cell has reached its maximum size and is triggered to divide.

In bacteria, cell growth is in part determined by how much food is available. The more food, the more energy is available for the bacteria to divide into two new cells and grow. In multicellular organisms, it was recently suggested that the growth of cells is regulated by both internal checkpoints and external factors. What exactly is the measuring stick used by these cells to measure this growth still remains unclear.

## 3.3 Prokaryotic Cell Structure and Function

All prokaryotes (the domains Bacteria and Archaea) are single-celled organisms that contain the basic features common to all cells—a cytoplasm bound by a plasma membrane, double-stranded DNA as their hereditary material, and ribosomes for protein synthesis. On a structural and organizational level, prokaryotic cells are smaller and less complex than eukaryotic cells; however, they can still carry out the same basic essential functions for survival and reproduction as any eukaryotic cell. And under some conditions, they do it better!

Prokaryotic cells range in size from 1 to 10 μm in length and by definition lack a membrane-bound nucleus and organelles (Figure 3.6a). Instead, their DNA is found coiled in the cytoplasm within an unbound region called the **nucleoid** (nucleuslike). This double-stranded DNA is arranged as a single, circular structure called the **prokaryotic chromosome** (in bacteria, it is often referred to as the **bacterial chromosome**). Genes, which are simply a unique arrangement of nucleotide sequences of DNA, are found within the chromosome. These genes are transcribed and their mRNA products are translated using prokaryotic ribosomes floating in the cytoplasm of the cell. Many bacterial cells also contain additional small, circular DNA molecules in their cytoplasm called **plasmids**. Plasmids are structurally and functionally independent of the bacterial chromosome and often contain a few genes. These extra genes make bacteria more genetically diverse, which in turn provides these organisms with a survival advantage. For example, bacterial cells that contain plasmids with antibiotic-resistant genes have the ability to survive even in the presence of antibiotics. We'll discuss genetic diversity and its evolutionary advantages in Chapters 7, 12, and 13.

Surrounding the plasma membrane of prokaryotic cells is a **cell wall**, a rigid structure that provides further protection and support to the cell. Unlike the cell wall of some eukaryotic cells, such as plants and fungi, the cell wall of prokaryotic cells is composed of either protein (in Archaeans) or polymers of peptides and polysaccharides called peptidoglycans (in bacteria). In addition, some bacteria also contain a sticky **capsule** consisting of polysaccharides that surround the cell wall. The capsule offers the cell additional protection against other cells. For example, the capsule surrounding the bacteria *Streptococcus pyogenes* protects the cells from being engulfed by the white blood cells of our immune system. The capsule also allows these cells to adhere to various surfaces.

Projecting from the plasma membrane of some prokaryotic cells are short, hairlike structures called **pili** (singular = pilus) and longer projections called **flagella** (singular = flagellum). Pili help the cells adhere to surfaces and to each other. One particular type of pilus, termed the sex pilus, attaches one bacteria cell to another during bacterial conjugation (a process where DNA from one bacterial cell is transferred to another; see Chapter 7). Unlike pili, flagella are longer structures that move in a propellerlike, rotational motion, which moves or propels bacteria around their environment. Flagella are especially important for bacteria that live in viscous environments, such as the ulcer-causing bacterium *Helicobacter pylori*, which use multiple flagella to migrate through the mucus lining of the stomach.

Prokaryotic cells also have diverse metabolic abilities. For example, they can obtain energy and carbon from various sources. Some use light and/or organic molecules for energy, whereas others use organic and/or inorganic compounds for carbon (see Chapter 14). This diversity allows prokaryotic cells to be versatile and adaptable to the changes they encounter within their environment. Indeed, this versatility has been the key to their success over the last 3.5 billion years!

### STUDY BREAK

1. List and describe some common features of all cell types.
2. What dictates the size of a cell?
3. In prokaryotes, how is the DNA organized and where is it located?

## 3.4 Eukaryotic Cell Structure and Function

Organisms of the domain Eukarya including animals, plants, fungi, and protists (eukaryotic microorganisms) are composed of one or more eukaryotic cells. It is hypothesized that the evolution of eukaryotic cells began approximately 2.1 billion years ago, a long time after the first prokaryotic cell appeared (~3.5 billion years ago). Eukaryotic cells exhibit a higher level of complexity, yet they carry out the same basic functions as prokaryotic cells, just in a more sophisticated and multifaceted manner (Figure 3.6, b and c). They also carry out some cellular processes not observed in prokaryotic cells. However, expressing this level of complexity does not necessarily mean that eukaryotic organisms have an advantage over prokaryotic cells because the diversity and versatility of prokaryotic cells have allowed these organisms to survive longer, in even more extreme harsh environments, and outnumber eukaryotic organisms on this ever-changing planet!

## The Nucleus Houses the Hereditary Material

One of the main distinguishing features of eukaryotic cells is the presence of membrane-bound organelles. One of those organelles is the **nucleus.** A double membrane called the **nuclear envelope** encloses the **nucleoplasm,** the inner thick fluid region of the nucleus **(Figure 3.14).** The nuclear envelope contains two phospholipid bilayers that are folded together. They act as a selectively permeable membrane that regulates the transport of certain substances into and out of the nucleus. These substances are transported through openings in the nuclear envelope called **nuclear pores.** The nuclear envelope is part of the cell's endomembrane system, which we will discuss in more detail later in the next section.

Within the nucleoplasm is nuclear DNA, the genetic material. Isolation of DNA within the nucleus, away from the metabolic activities and digestive enzymes found in the rest of the cell, reduces the risk of damage to the DNA. This is significant because DNA contains all the hereditary information required to build proteins and RNA. The nuclear DNA is organized through its binding with nuclear proteins to form **chromatin** (DNA plus its associated proteins). The degree of organization and the structure of the chromatin regulate DNA activity. For example, during cell division, the chromatin coils tightly, producing thick, rodlike structures that we can identify using a light microscope as chromosomes (see Chapter 6). The tight coiling of the chromatin prevents many of the DNA activities, such as DNA replication and transcription, from occurring during cell division. This ensures that the chromosomes are divided accurately and evenly between the two newly formed daughter cells.

Also in the nucleoplasm is the **nucleolus,** a dense, irregularly shaped region that is the site where the large and small ribosomal subunits are assembled (Figure 3.14). These subunits are composed of both **ribosomal RNA (rRNA)** and protein. Once produced in the nucleolus, the ribosomal subunits exit the nucleus via the nuclear pores and enter the cytoplasm, where they are used in protein synthesis. Free ribosomes are free-floating in the cytoplasm and are used to make cytoplasmic proteins,

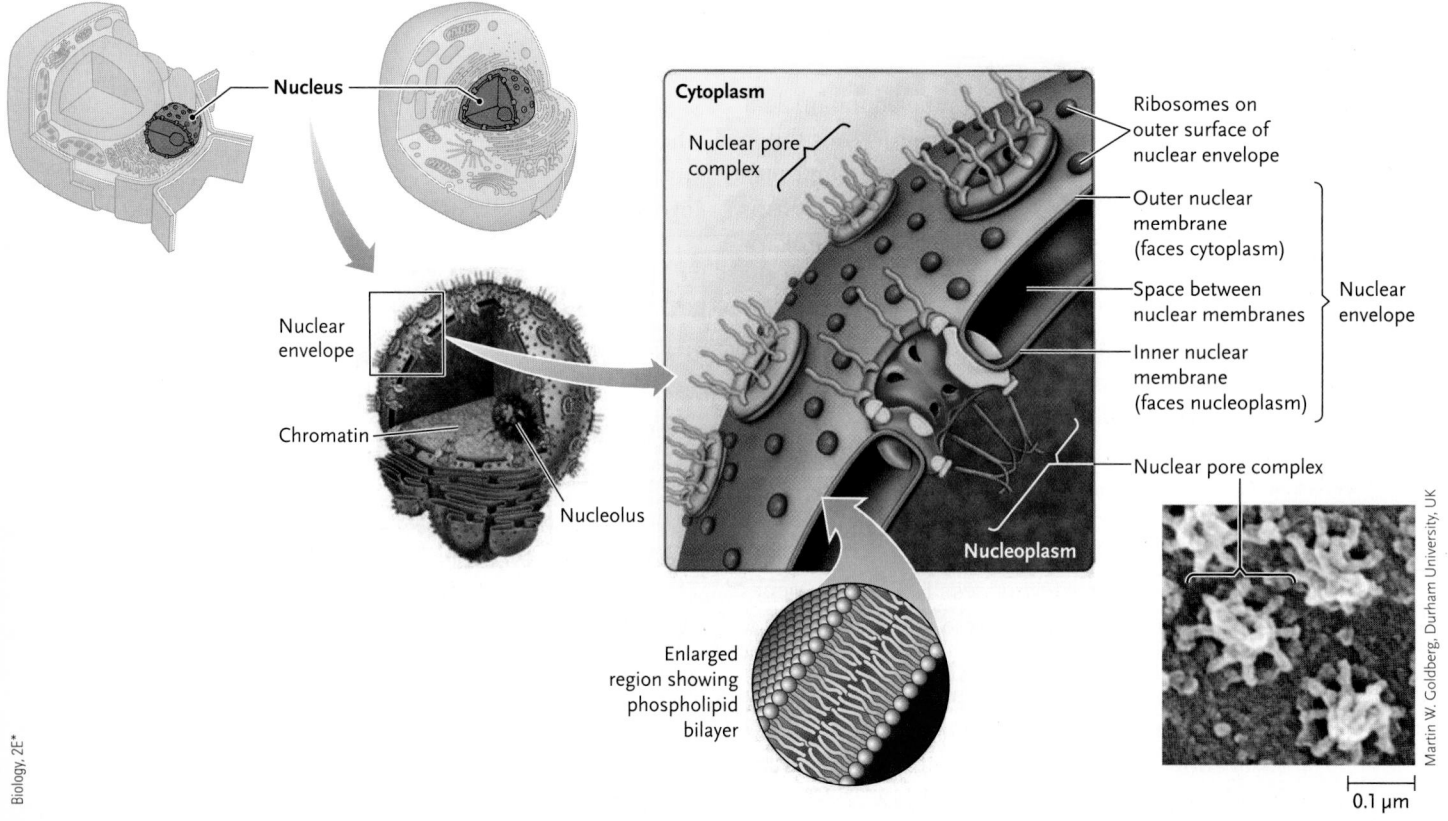

**FIGURE 3.14** The nuclear envelope, which consists of a system of two phospholipid bilayer membranes with nuclear pore complexes embedded. Nuclear pore complexes are octagonal symmetrical protein structures with a channel—the nuclear pore—through the centre. They control the transport of molecules between the nucleus and the cytoplasm.

Biology, 2E*

Martin W. Goldberg, Durham University, UK

whereas bound ribosomes are attached to the outer surface of certain organelles of the endomembrane system and are used to make two types of proteins: those that are part of the endomembrane system and those that will be secreted by the cell.

## The Endomembrane System Connects Many of the Cell's Organelles

The **endomembrane system** is composed of a series of membranes that are interconnected either directly or indirectly through tiny **vesicles** (membranous sacs). These membranes, which also include the plasma membrane and the nuclear envelope, enclose organelles, including the endoplasmic reticulum, the Golgi complex, lysosomes, and vacuoles. (They do not enclose mitochondria or chloroplasts; see below.) The collective functions of these organelles allow for more complexity in the eukaryotic cell. Also, as mentioned above, an increase in cellular membranes supports increased cytoplasmic volume and thus the greater metabolic needs of a larger-sized cell.

The **endoplasmic reticulum** (**ER**; *endoplasmic* = within the cytoplasm; *reticulum* = little net) is an extensive network of interconnected flattened sacs and tubes (**Figure 3.15**). The ER membrane is directly connected to the outer membrane of the nuclear envelope. There are two different compartments of the ER: the **smooth ER (SER)** and the **rough ER (RER)**. Since SER membranes lack ribosomes, under an electron microscope, the organelle's surface appears smooth. SER is the site for the assembly of lipids that are transported to the plasma membrane, the breakdown of lipids and carbohydrates, and the detoxification of poisons or drugs. Conversely, the membranes of the RER are studded with bound ribosomes, causing the surface of this organelle to appear rough under an electron microscope. The bound ribosomes are used to synthesize protein that will enter the RER and either become a resident of the endomembrane system or be secreted by the cell into the ECM.

The **Golgi complex**, named after the Italian biologist and physician Camillo Golgi, is a stack of flattened sacs that under an electron microscope appears as a stack of pancakes (**Figure 3.16, p. 64**). Unlike the ER, the sacs of the Golgi are not directly interconnected. Instead, the transport of molecules across the Golgi complex is

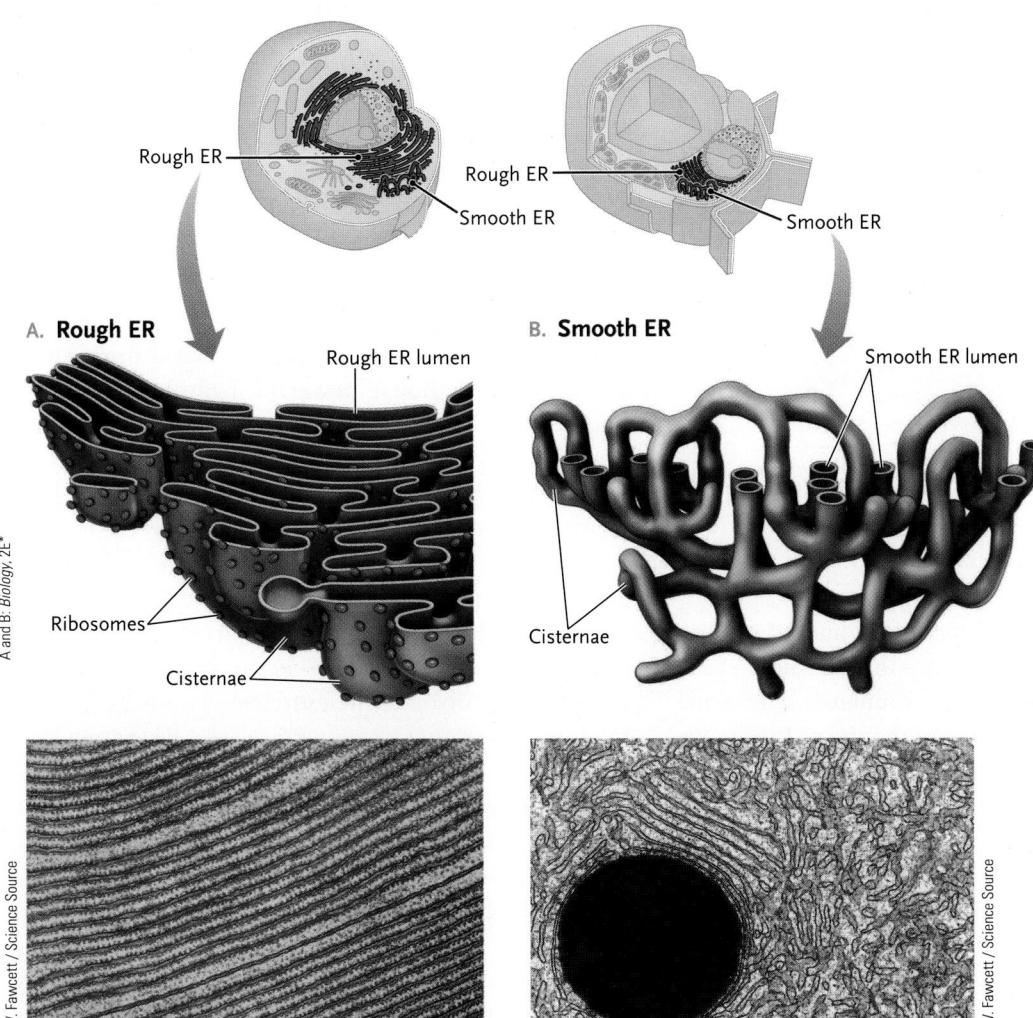

**A. Rough ER**

Rough ER lumen

Ribosomes

Cisternae

**B. Smooth ER**

Smooth ER lumen

Cisternae

A and B: *Biology, 2E*

Don W. Fawcett / Science Source

Don W. Fawcett / Science Source

**FIGURE 3.15** The endoplasmic reticulum (ER). **(a)** Rough ER showing the ribosomes that stud the membrane surfaces facing the cytoplasm. Proteins synthesized on these ribosomes enter the lumen of the rough ER, where they are modified chemically and then begin their path to their final destinations in the cell. **(b)** Smooth ER. Among their functions are the synthesis of lipids for cell membranes and enzymatic conversion of certain toxic molecules to safer molecules.

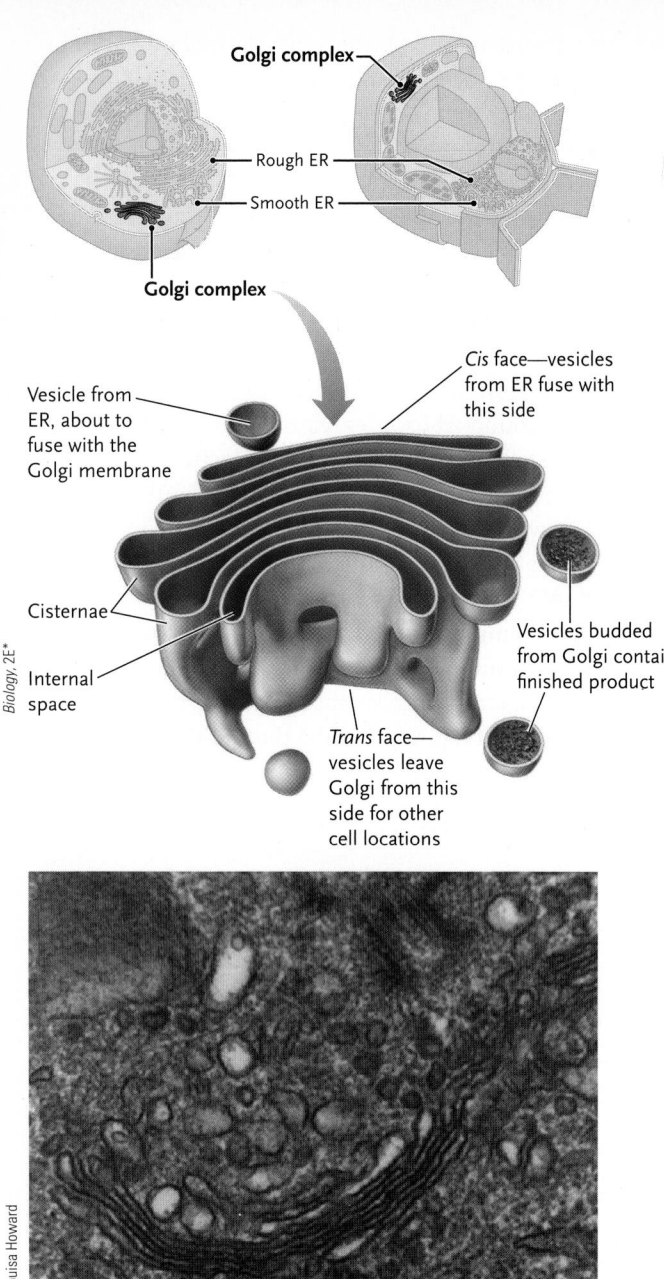

Golgi complex

Rough ER

Smooth ER

Golgi complex

*Cis* face—vesicles from ER fuse with this side

Vesicle from ER, about to fuse with the Golgi membrane

Cisternae

Internal space

Vesicles budded from Golgi containing finished product

*Trans* face—vesicles leave Golgi from this side for other cell locations

Biology, 2E*

Louisa Howard

0.25 μm

**FIGURE 3.16** The Golgi complex.

lipids are tagged by modification and sorted for their final destination. It works in a way that is analogous to a postal warehouse that receives and then sorts and delivers mail based on the postal/zip codes of the delivery addresses.

Modification of proteins may include adding and trimming carbohydrate groups or adding phosphate groups. These act as tags or identifying factors so they can be sorted and delivered to their proper destinations. Protein sorting within the endomembrane system may involve receptor proteins located on the surface of the membranes that can identify these tags. Specific tags serve to sort these proteins to lysosomes, vacuoles, or the plasma membrane. Some of the molecules may be secreted out of the cell via **secretory vesicles (Figure 3.17)** (see below for further discussion of vesicles). These secretory vesicles are formed as sacs budding off the membrane of the Golgi complex. The vesicles move toward the cell surface, where they fuse with the plasma membrane and release their contents to the outside of the cell into the ECM. The membrane portion of the secretory vesicles remains associated with the plasma membrane, operating as a mechanism to replenish the lipid bilayer of the plasma membrane and the membrane proteins. Plant cells contain many Golgi complexes, compared to the single Golgi complex found in most animal cells. The numerous Golgi complexes play a key role in producing the polysaccharide components required for the building of the plant cell wall (you'll read more about the plant cell wall in Section 3.5) and the subsequent transport of these materials to the cell exterior.

Proteins that are synthesized in the RER and modified in the Golgi complex may also be destined for **lysosomes**. Lysosomes are membrane-bound organelles, which primarily house powerful, hydrolytic enzymes (Figure 3.17). The internal environment of lysosomes is acidic, which is the optimum pH for the activity of these lysosomal enzymes. These enzymes are used to digest macromolecules that are ingested by the cell. In a process called **autophagy** (*auto* = self, *phagy* = to eat), these enzymes are used to recycle the cell's own damaged organelles that need to be cleared from the cell's cytoplasm (see Box 3.2 to learn more about how autophagy is involved in exercise). These functional roles for lysosomal enzymes are why lysosomes are often referred to as the "waste disposal" or "recycling centre" of the cell. However, lysosomal enzymes have also been shown to participate in other important functions, such as remodelling the ECM during cancer invasion and recognizing pathogens during an immune response.

The existence of lysosomes in plant cells is still heavily debated. The central vacuole in plants has long been thought to carry out many of the similar functions

guided through a series of vesicles that bud off one sac of the Golgi complex and then fuse into another nearby sac. It is believed that the Golgi complex is a dynamic structure in which entire sacs can mature as they move their cargo from the shipping to the receiving end of the Golgi complex. Proteins and lipids that are synthesized in the ER are transported to the Golgi complex via vesicles that bud off the surface of the RER. In the Golgi complex, these proteins and lipids are modified and sorted in preparation for further transport. Thus, the Golgi complex is often referred to as the sorting warehouse of the cell because it is here that arriving proteins and

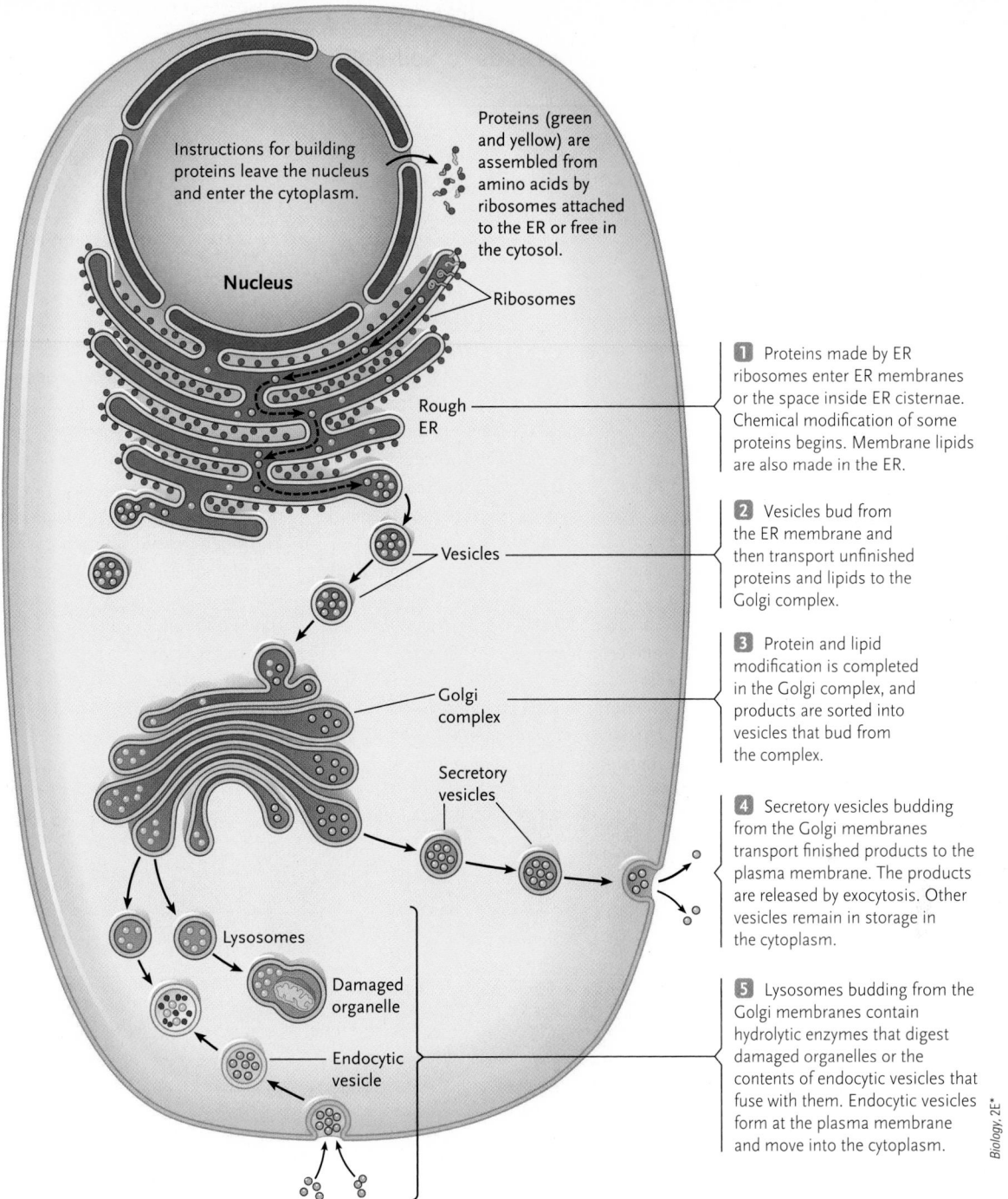

Instructions for building proteins leave the nucleus and enter the cytoplasm.

Proteins (green and yellow) are assembled from amino acids by ribosomes attached to the ER or free in the cytosol.

**Nucleus**

Ribosomes

Rough ER

Vesicles

Golgi complex

Secretory vesicles

Lysosomes

Damaged organelle

Endocytic vesicle

**1** Proteins made by ER ribosomes enter ER membranes or the space inside ER cisternae. Chemical modification of some proteins begins. Membrane lipids are also made in the ER.

**2** Vesicles bud from the ER membrane and then transport unfinished proteins and lipids to the Golgi complex.

**3** Protein and lipid modification is completed in the Golgi complex, and products are sorted into vesicles that bud from the complex.

**4** Secretory vesicles budding from the Golgi membranes transport finished products to the plasma membrane. The products are released by exocytosis. Other vesicles remain in storage in the cytoplasm.

**5** Lysosomes budding from the Golgi membranes contain hydrolytic enzymes that digest damaged organelles or the contents of endocytic vesicles that fuse with them. Endocytic vesicles form at the plasma membrane and move into the cytoplasm.

*Biology, 2E\**

**FIGURE 3.17** Vesicle traffic in the cytoplasm. The endoplasmic reticulum (ER) and Golgi complex are part of the endomembrane system, which releases proteins and other substances to the cell exterior and gathers materials from outside the cell.

observed in lysosomes of animal cells. More recent evidence, however, does suggest that there are lysosomal-like organelles that carry out digestive function in certain plant cells. These structures also play a role in autophagy in plants.

Vesicles are small, membranous sacs found within the cytoplasm that serve various functions (Figure 3.17). The phospholipid bilayer of vesicle membranes is similar to the plasma membrane, so these organelles can fuse with the plasma membrane to secrete their contents out of the cell. As well, these vesicles can be formed from the budding of the cell's plasma membrane. Vesicles can transport substances across the cell as a shuttle between different compartments of the endomembrane system. There are several types of vesicles within eukaryotic cells.

**Endocytic vesicles** transport substances from a cell's external environment into a cell (Figure 3.17). Once

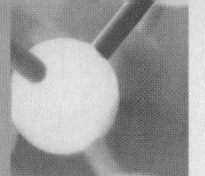

# THE MOLECULE BEHIND THE BIOLOGY 3.2
## Autophagosomes: Exercising Leads to Self-Eating

No one will argue that exercise is bad for you. It helps strengthen muscles, keeps you alert and energetic, and helps ward off or enhance those curves. It also helps offset diseases such as cancer, diabetes, Alzheimer disease, and cardiovascular disease. But what exactly is happening in our cells when we exercise? An Italian research team reported evidence that exercising induces autophagy in the skeletal muscles of mice. This observation was recently confirmed by another research group from Dallas, Texas, which further showed that autophagy is necessary to obtain the beneficial metabolic effects of exercising.

Autophagy is a cellular process in which cells are triggered to self-eat. The signal may come from defective organelles or other cellular molecules that are no longer required. The process may also be triggered by cellular starvation during exercise, as a mechanism for recycling nutrients in a hungry cell. During autophagy, membrane pockets called **phagophores** are formed in the cytoplasm, trapping cytoplasmic molecules and whole organelles **(Figure 1)**. These phagophores close to become **autophagosomes** (Figure 1). Autophagosomes deliver their material to lysosomes, where the material is digested and recycled by the lysosomal enzymes.

But where the membrane that is used to create a phagophore comes from remains controversial. Recent evidence supports four different possibilities: the ER, the Golgi, the plasma membrane, and the mitochondria. Four independent research groups have shown evidence that associates autophagosomes with all four of these organelles. For example, research from one group has localized autophagosomes to the ER surface as newborn vesicles. The ER seems a logical source as it is the source for membranes of all organelles of the endomembrane system. Another group has shown that autophagy requires a certain type of protein (called SNARE), which is released by vesicles budding off the Golgi complex. Although the plasma membrane appears at first to be an unlikely source, researchers recently speculated that the invagination of the plasma membrane, followed by endocytosis (recall from Figure 3.17), may supply the material to build the autophagosome membrane. Finally, a very recent study using live-cell microscopy showed that fluorescently tagged proteins on the outer surface of the mitochondria also appeared on nearby autophagosomes, suggesting a transfer of the membrane from the mitochondria to these organelles. But the question remains: which one of these possibilities is correct?

The answer may simply be "all of them." It is plausible that the cell would acquire membrane material from multiple sources within the cell to build autophagosomes. Indeed, it may simply come down to supply and demand. The stress related to cell starvation during exercise may initiate multiple pathways that mobilize membrane material from any place in the cell that can afford to donate it. As well, the reason for autophagy itself—starvation versus cell maintenance—may trigger different pathways. How these pathways are initiated and regulated remains to be determined. What is certain is that the next time you exercise, you will be triggering the formation of autophagosomes as a mechanism for cellular self-eating.

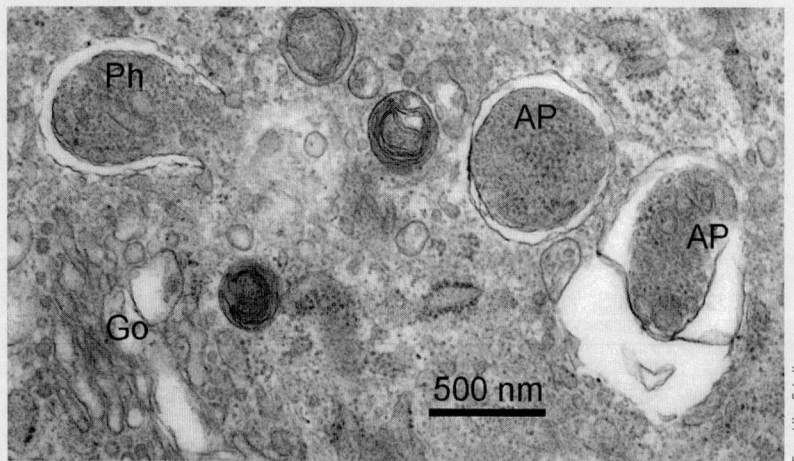

**FIGURE 1** An electron micrograph showing a phagophore (Ph) and two autophagosomes (AP) in normal rat kidney cells. Go = Golgi complex.

formed, these endocytic vesicles can fuse with lysosomes, thereby exposing its contents to digestive lysosomal enzymes. This process is called **endocytosis**. As mentioned above, secretory vesicles transport substances out of a cell (Figure 3.17), a process called **exocytosis**. These vesicles can originate by the budding membranes from the surface of the ER, Golgi complex, or lysosomes and then they fuse with the plasma membrane and release their contents outside the cell. Endocytosis and exocytosis are further discussed in Chapter 4.

**Vacuoles** are a type of vesicle used mainly as storage units. The **food vacuole** stores ingested food that is later digested by lysosomal enzymes. In plant cells, the main vacuole is the **central vacuole**, used to store carbohydrates, amino acids, ions, toxins, and pigments (Figure 3.6c). These toxins may be part of the plant's **defence mechanism** to ward off herbivores and pests.

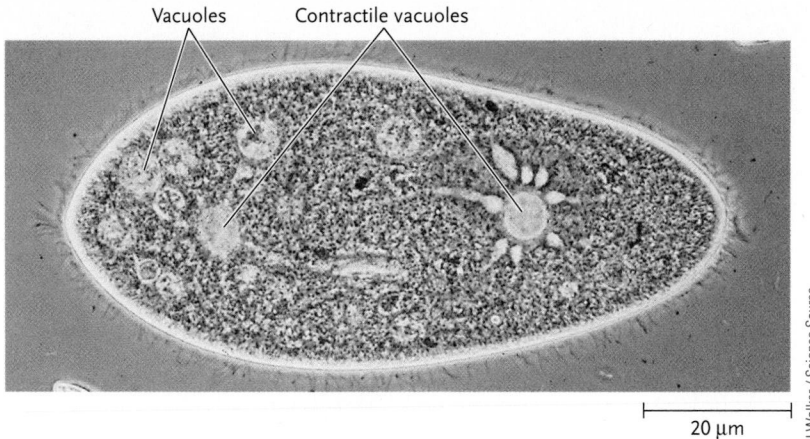

Vacuoles    Contractile vacuoles

20 µm

MI Walker / Science Source

**FIGURE 3.18** A *Paramecium*, showing the contractile vacuoles.

Stored pigments in the central vacuole (usually in flower petals) attract pollinators such as bees or hummingbirds. The central vacuole also contains hydrolytic enzymes and, like the lysosome, is a site for macromolecule digestion.

Another type of vacuole, a **contractile vacuole**, stores excess water that accumulates in the cell and can be found, for example, in the cytoplasm of the single-celled protist *Paramecium* **(Figure 3.18)**. Paramecia live in freshwater habitats, where the water is less concentrated than the organism's cytoplasm. As such, water from the environment will be transported into the Paramecia's cytoplasm (by osmosis) and collect within the contractile vacuole. Once full, the contractile vacuole moves to the cell surface and pumps the excess water out of the cell. This mechanism ensures that the excess water inside the cell does not build up in the cytoplasm, which would cause the cell to swell and burst.

## Mitochondria and Plastids Are Energy-Converting Organelles

All cells need energy to carry out the trillions of reactions that are required to keep them alive and healthy. **Plastids** and **mitochondria** (singular = mitochondrion) are organelles in eukaryotic cells that harvest energy and convert it into a form the cell can use. Similar to the nucleus, mitochondria and plastids are enclosed by a double membrane (i.e., two lipid bilayers, not part of the endomembrane system). In some protists, plastids may be enclosed by four membranes.

The main role of mitochondria **(Figure 3.19, p. 68)** is to convert the chemical energy that is found in macromolecules such as sugars into **adenosine triphosphate (ATP)** through a process called **cellular respiration**. ATP is a nucleotide that stores plenty of energy that is readily accessible to the cell when required. ATP is considered the energy currency of the cell. Cells hydrolyze (break down) ATP to release

the stored energy to carry out energy-consuming reactions (or work) in the cell. You will read more about how cells convert chemical energy in Chapter 5.

The double membrane of the mitochondria separates the organelle into two major compartments (Figure 3.19). The outer compartment, the intermembrane space, is the narrow space between the outer and inner membrane. The inner membrane encloses the **mitochondrial matrix**, the space inside the mitochondrion. The mitochondrial matrix is highly organized into multiple folds called **cristae**. In the mitochondrial matrix, the mitochondrial DNA is a single circular chromosome containing genes that primarily encode for mitochondrial protein. Ribosomes in the mitochondrial matrix are used to synthesize these mitochondrial proteins. In addition, many of the metabolic enzymes used in cellular respiration are in the mitochondrial matrix. The generation of ATP through the breakdown of glucose is the ultimate goal of this metabolic pathway. ATP synthesis occurs primarily on the inner mitochondrial membrane; thus, the highly folded cristae are a structural adaptation that increases the surface of this membrane and therefore the production of ATP (see Chapter 5). This is especially important in liver and muscle cells that carry out many metabolic reactions that require a high level of energy. In both of these cell types, we see much larger numbers of mitochondria, which in turn have more cristae, than what we observe in other cells with reduced metabolic demands.

Although not all eukaryotic cells contain plastids, these organelles are essential for aerobic (i.e., oxygen-essential) life on Earth. **Chloroplasts**, a common type of plastid found in plants and green algae, convert solar energy from the sun into chemical energy (in the form of organic molecules) through a process called photosynthesis (see Chapter 5). Organisms that do not have plastids, such as yourself, cannot carry out photosynthesis and, hence, rely on these primary-producing organisms to do the conversion for them.

Like mitochondria, chloroplasts are made up of multiple compartments separated by membranes **(Figure 3.20, p. 68)**. The thin space between the outer and inner membranes is called the **intermembrane space**. The inner membrane encloses a viscous fluid called the **stroma**. The stroma contains chloroplast DNA and ribosomes and many of the enzymes used during photosynthesis to catalyze or facilitate the production of carbohydrates from carbon dioxide. Inside the stroma is a network of interconnected sacs called **thylakoids** stacked together into **granum** (plural = grana). The space inside the thylakoids is called the **thylakoid lumen**. Pigment

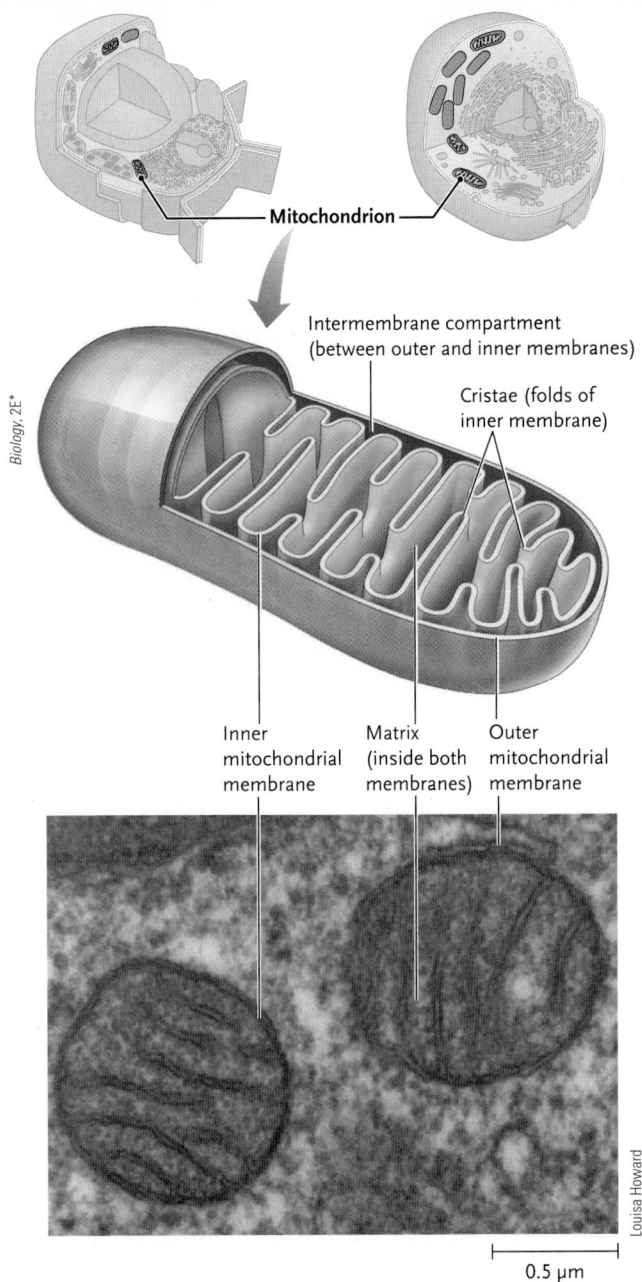

Mitochondrion

Intermembrane compartment (between outer and inner membranes)

Cristae (folds of inner membrane)

Inner mitochondrial membrane

Matrix (inside both membranes)

Outer mitochondrial membrane

Biology, 2E*

Louisa Howard

0.5 μm

**FIGURE 3.19** Mitochondria. The electron micrograph shows mitochondria from a mammalian lung. Folds extend from the inner mitochondrial membrane into the interior of the mitochondrion to form cristae.

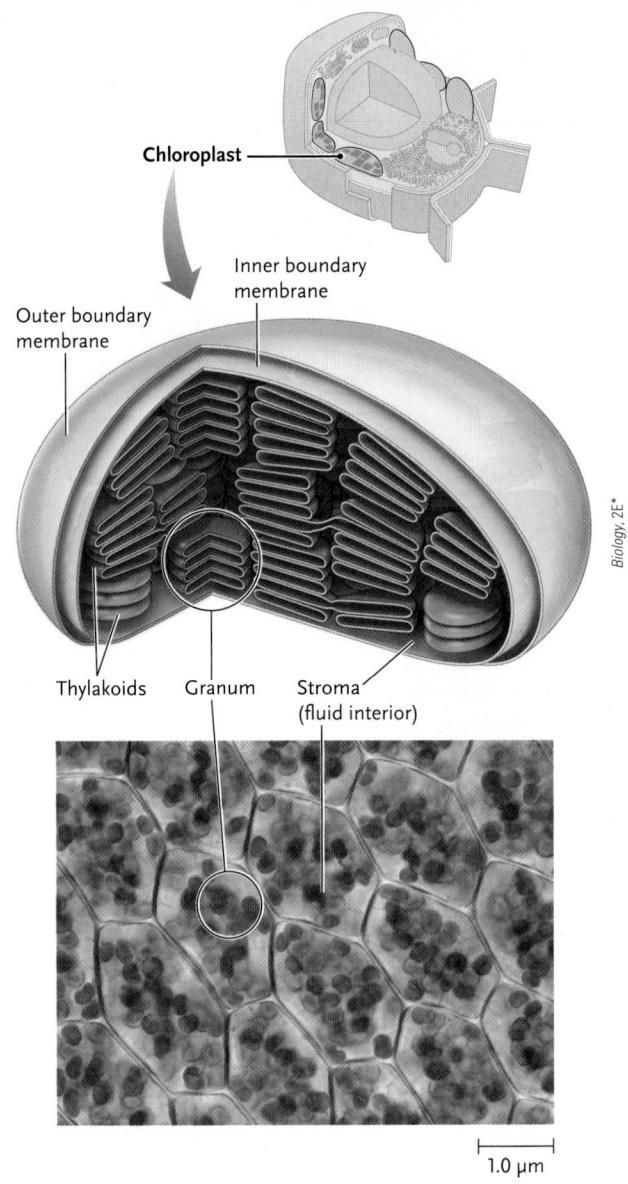

Chloroplast

Inner boundary membrane

Outer boundary membrane

Thylakoids   Granum   Stroma (fluid interior)

Biology, 2E*

1.0 μm

**FIGURE 3.20** Chloroplast structure. The electron micrograph shows chloroplasts in plant cells.

SOURCE: Kristian Peters – Fabelfroh, http://upload.wikimedia.org/wikipedia/commons/4/49/Plagiomnium_affine_laminazellen.jpeg. This file is licensed under the Creative Commons Attribution-Share Alike 3.0 Unported license, http://creativecommons.org/licenses/by-sa/3.0/deed.en

molecules such as chlorophylls located on the thylakoid membranes are used by the chloroplasts to harvest solar energy, similar to a set of solar panels found on many building rooftops. Much like the cristae of the mitochondria, the thylakoid membrane structures increase the surface area for light collection by the chloroplast. The harvested solar energy is then used to make ATP, which will then be used to make carbohydrates

If you examine mitochondria and plastids in more detail, you will find that these organelles share many similarities with prokaryotic cells. For example, the structural subunits of ribosomes within these organelles are more similar to those found in prokaryotes than those found within the

eukaryotic cytoplasm in which these organelles reside. In addition, most mitochondrial and plastid DNA is circular, and reproduction of these organelles is by a process similar to that of prokaryotic cells. Molecular analysis of mitochondria and plastid DNA also reveals relatedness to prokaryotes. Collectively, these pieces of evidence suggest that these organelles evolved from ancestral prokaryotic cells. This evidence is also the basis for the **theory of endosymbiosis (Figure 3.21)**. This theory hypothesizes that mitochondria and plastids are descendants of prokaryotic cells that were engulfed by, and formed a symbiotic relationship with, a larger host cell. In other words, engulfed prokaryotic cells remained alive and began living within the host cell as

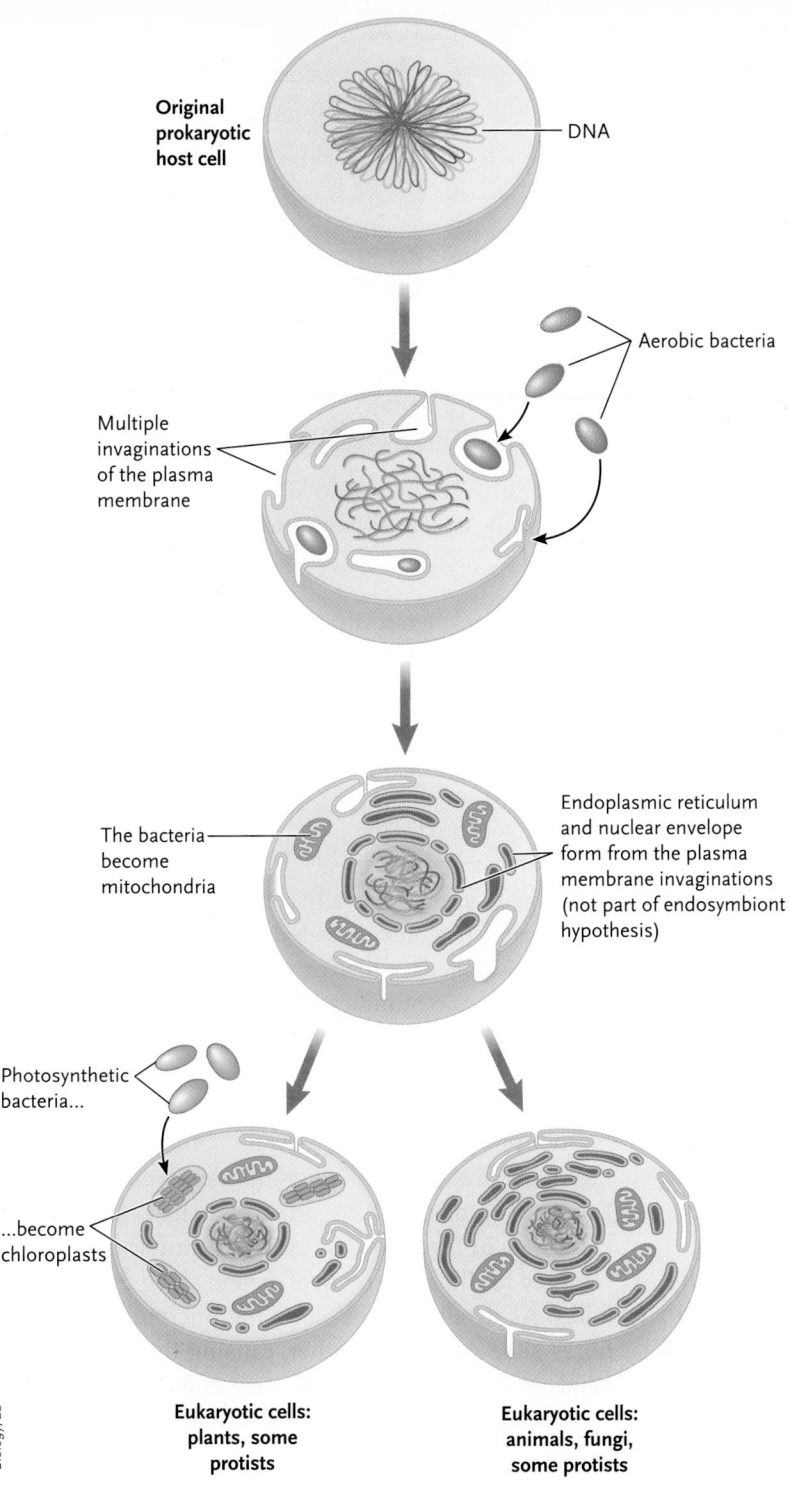

**Original prokaryotic host cell** — DNA

Aerobic bacteria

**Multiple invaginations of the plasma membrane**

**The bacteria become mitochondria**

Endoplasmic reticulum and nuclear envelope form from the plasma membrane invaginations (not part of endosymbiont hypothesis)

**Photosynthetic bacteria...**

**...become chloroplasts**

*Biology, 2E\**

**Eukaryotic cells: plants, some protists**

**Eukaryotic cells: animals, fungi, some protists**

**FIGURE 3.21** The theory of endosymbiosis. The mitochondrion is thought to have originated from an aerobic (requiring oxygen) prokaryote that lived as an endosymbiont within an anaerobic (not requiring oxygen) prokaryote. The chloroplast is thought to have originated from a photosynthetic prokaryote that became an endosymbiont within an aerobic cell that had mitochondria.

eukaryotic cells, mitochondria likely evolved first. Plastids likely arose from endosymbionts that could carry out photosynthesis. Since they are found in only some eukaryotic cells, they likely evolved later. This theory also helps explain why these organelles have a double membrane, one from the original plasma membrane of the engulfed prokaryotic cell and a second from the plasma membrane of the host cell as it engulfed it.

## The Cytoskeleton Acts as an Intracellular Network for Structure and Function

As we discussed at the opening of this chapter, the 3D organization of cells within tissues is partially in response to the extracellular environment of cells. This response of cell movement, adhesion, and arrangement involves the actions of an internal network of protein fibres, called the **cytoskeleton**, that extend from the nucleus to the plasma membrane of eukaryotic cells. The cytoskeleton also provides structural support to the cell, organizes organelles within the cytoplasm, and is involved in intracellular movement and the motility of whole cells across a surface. There are three main types of fibres that constitute the cytoskeleton: microtubules, intermediate filaments, and microfilaments. They differ with respect to their protein composition, thickness, and function within the cell.

**Microtubules** are the thickest of the three types of protein fibres of the cytoskeleton **(Figure 3.22a, p. 70)**. These fibres are composed of tubulin proteins arranged in a cylindrical hollow tube formation. Microtubules are often assembled and disassembled in response to the needs of the cell. The cell assembles microtubules by adding a pair of tubulin subunits to the microtubules; disassembly is carried out in the reverse manner. For example, during cell division, a spindle is formed in the cytoplasm by the assembly of microtubules, which is then quickly disassembled during the separation of chromosomes (see Chapter 6). Using motor proteins, microtubules often act as a structural transport system for the movement of organelles. These proteins "walk" along the microtubules transporting organelles throughout the cell. Microtubules are also found in flagella and cilia of eukaryotic cells—structures that move the cell within its

endosymbionts. Since this relationship was beneficial to both the endosymbiont and the host cell, over time, they became interdependent. This symbiotic relationship gave both the host and the endosymbiont such an evolutionary advantage that they eventually became one cell. Mitochondria likely arose from endosymbionts that could use oxygen in cellular respiration. Since they are found in almost all

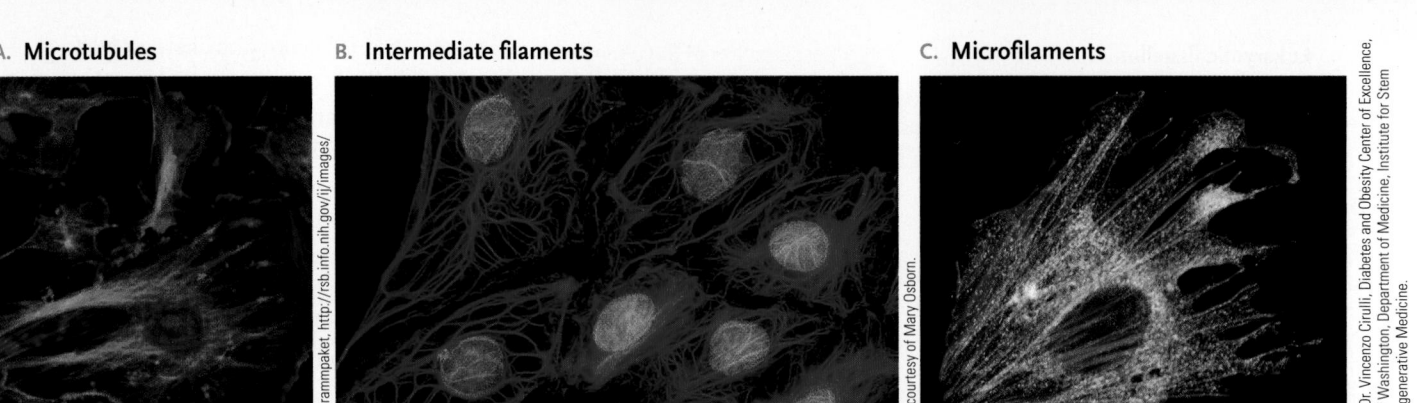

**A. Microtubules**　**B. Intermediate filaments**　**C. Microfilaments**

ImageJ-Programmpaket, http://rsb.info.nih.gov/ij/images/

Micrograph courtesy of Mary Osborn.

Courtesy of Dr. Vincenzo Cirulli, Diabetes and Obesity Center of Excellence, University of Washington, Department of Medicine, Institute for Stem Cells and Regenerative Medicine.

**FIGURE 3.22** Cytoskeletons of eukaryotic cells as seen in cells stained for light microscopy. **(a)** Microtubules (green) in endothelial cells. **(b)** Keratin intermediate filaments viewed by immunofluorescence microscopy in a rat kangaroo cell line Ptk2. **(c)** Microfilaments (red) in a motile mammalian cell.

environment. In animal cells, microtubules are synthesized from a main microtubule organizing centre called the **centrosome**. There is one centrosome per animal cell, composed of two centrioles that are arranged perpendicularly. Plant cells do not have a centrosome but instead have multiple microtubule organizing centres.

**Intermediate filaments** are composed of various proteins that are arranged in a ropelike manner **(Figure 3.22b)**. These filaments are of intermediate thickness between the other two protein fibres of the cytoskeleton. Intermediate filaments have a more permanent structure and thus do not assemble and disassemble as rapidly as microtubules. The fibres are used mainly to anchor certain organelles such as the nucleus and to reinforce the shape of the cell. For example, a layer of intermediate filaments called lamins underlies and supports the nuclear envelope. At the plasma membrane, intermediate filaments containing keratin protein participate in the cell adhesion between adjacent epithelial cells that make up your skin.

**Microfilaments** are the thinnest of the three fibres and are composed of subunits of globular actin protein **(Figure 3.22c)**. As such, microfilaments are also called **actin filaments**. Microfilaments are arranged as a twisted, double chain of actin subunits. They provide support to the shape of the cell by forming a 3D mesh network directly underneath the plasma membrane called the cell cortex. Microfilaments are also used in cell movement. The interaction of myosin, a motor protein, with the actin microfilaments allows cells such as muscle cells to contract and expand and allows cells such as amoeba or white blood cells to move in a crawling manner. Similar to microtubules, microfilaments are also essential to establishing the shape and movement of organelles such as the ER. Movement of the ER network in yeast cells relies heavily on its contacts with the actin cytoskeleton. If the actin proteins are damaged, the dynamic nature of the ER is halted. More recently, a similar relationship between the movement of ER and the actin cytoskeleton was identified in plant cells.

The cytoskeleton, along with interacting motor proteins, is also involved in the movement of flagella and cilia. As in prokaryotic cells, the eukaryotic flagellum causes a cell to move within a viscous environment. An example is the flagellum on a sperm cell, which moves the sperm through the viscous environment of the female reproductive tract. However, unlike prokaryotic flagella, which are composed mainly of **flagellin** protein, eukaryotic flagella are structurally composed of microtubules and motor proteins called **dynein (Figure 3.23, a–c)**. Eukaryotic flagella, which extend from the plasma membrane, have microtubules that are arranged in a "9 + 2 pattern," which describes a ring of nine pairs of microtubules (representing the "9" in the 9 + 2 pattern) arranged in a circular pattern around a central pair of microtubules (representing the "+ 2"). Dynein proteins project as "arms" from each pair of microtubules in the outer ring. Dynein is also an ATPase, an enzyme that catalyzes the hydrolysis or breakdown of ATP, which releases energy required for the movement of dynein along the microtubules. As dynein moves along the microtubules, these fibres slide past one another, causing the flagellum to bend. At the base of the innermost end of the flagellum is an anchoring structure called the **basal body**, which is composed of a ring pattern of nine microtubule triplets. The basal body acts as a foundation supporting the growth of the flagellum.

**Cilia** (singular = cilium) are short, hairlike projections that are structurally similar to flagella. However, the beating pattern of cilia differs from that of flagella **(Figure 3.23d)**. Flagella beat in a whiplike fashion, driving the movement of cells within a fluid environment (Figure 3.23d). Cilia, on the other hand, beat in a coordinated waving pattern to either propel cells through a fluid or stir fluids around a stationary cell. The cells of the respiratory system are lined with cilia that sweep mucus that contains trapped debris out of the lungs.

Other cellular structures are discussed in Box 3.3.

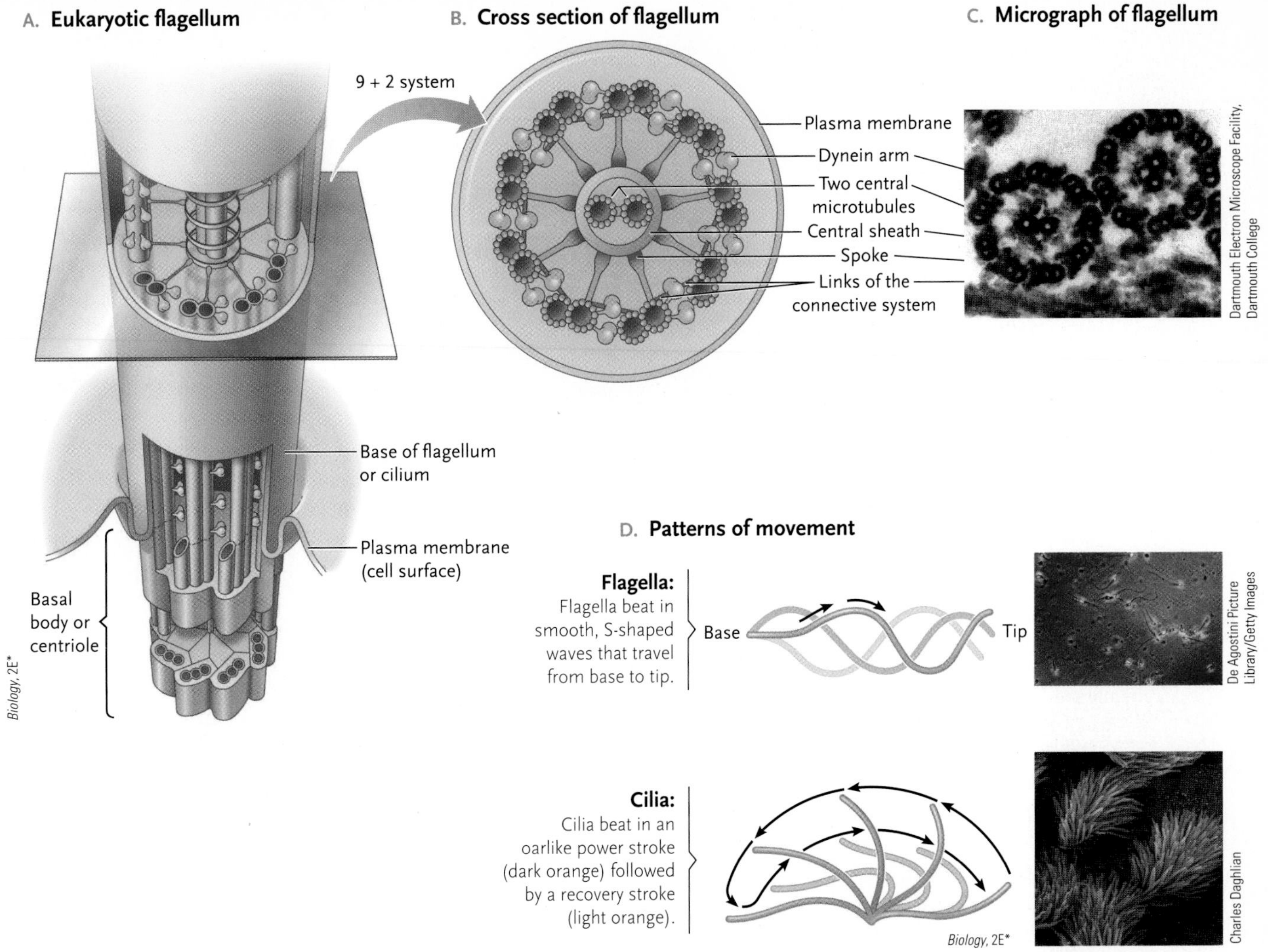

**A. Eukaryotic flagellum**

9 + 2 system

Base of flagellum or cilium

Plasma membrane (cell surface)

Basal body or centriole

*Biology, 2E\**

**B. Cross section of flagellum**

Plasma membrane
Dynein arm
Two central microtubules
Central sheath
Spoke
Links of the connective system

**C. Micrograph of flagellum**

Dartmouth Electron Microscope Facility, Dartmouth College

**D. Patterns of movement**

**Flagella:**
Flagella beat in smooth, S-shaped waves that travel from base to tip.

Base — Tip

De Agostini Picture Library/Getty Images

**Cilia:**
Cilia beat in an oarlike power stroke (dark orange) followed by a recovery stroke (light orange).

*Biology, 2E\**

Charles Daghlian

**FIGURE 3.23** Eukaryotic flagella and cilia. **(a)** The relationship between the microtubules and the basal body of a flagellum. **(b)** Diagram of a flagellum in cross section, showing the 9 + 2 system of microtubules. The spokes and connecting links hold the system together. **(c)** Electron micrograph of a flagellum in cross section; individual tubulin molecules are visible in the microtubule walls. **(d)** Beating patterns of flagella shown in human sperm and cilia from the lining of an airway in the lungs.

## STUDY BREAK

1. How is DNA organized and where is it located in (a) a prokaryote cell and (b) a eukaryote cell?
2. What is the function of the endomembrane system?
3. Compare the structures and functions of mitochondria and chloroplasts.
4. Describe the components of the cytoskeleton in eukaryotic cells.

## 3.5 Cooperation in Multicellular Organisms

In any multifaceted system, the various parts need to work together for the system to work successfully and efficiently. The same is true for multicellular organisms, which are composed of different cell types, each carrying out specific functions within the organism. Multicellularity allows for increased complexity in both the structure and function of organisms such as yourself. The ability for you to read and understand the words on this page is a result of a collection of different cells in your body working together to obtain, analyze, and respond to the information you are receiving.

### Cells Are Organized and Regulated on an Extracellular Matrix

Cells with a multicellular organism are surrounded by a non-living extracellular matrix (ECM) composed of fibrous proteins, polysaccharides (chains of sugars), and glycoproteins (proteins that contain sugars groups) that are produced and secreted by the cells. **Collagen** is the most abundant glycoprotein in the ECM. It forms strong fibres that are integrated into a network of other glycoproteins. Cells adhere to and organize themselves within the

Any cold case file contains old pieces of evidence, eye-witness accounts, and a bunch of clues that just don't add up to solve the case. The same is true of some cellular structures that have been observed by several scientists over the years, but no one knows what they are, let alone their function inside the cell. These small pieces of data (evidence) often end up tucked away in laboratory notebooks and computer files. Here are two cold case files on cellular structures that have recently been reopened and re-examined.

1. **Membrane nanotubes** are thin membranous filaments suspended between cells **(Figure 1a)**. In 2004, a German team concluded that membrane nanotubes could span the distance of several cells and could transport cytoplasmic material, including organelles, between cells. A British group later reported that immune cells could use nanotubes to send signals to each other. They also found that white blood cells could tether themselves to cancer cells using nanotubes in an effort to kill them. These nanotubes, they concluded, may be communication networks among cells.

2. **Vaults** are cytoplasmic ribonucleoproteins (protein that

A.

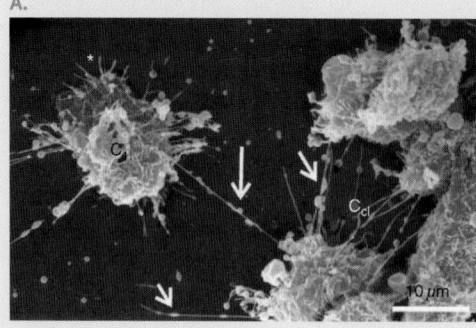

B.

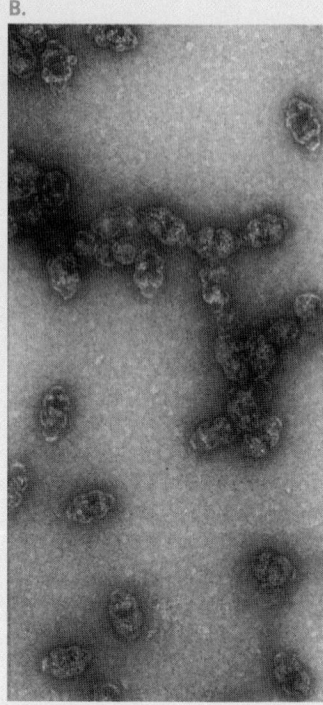

**FIGURE 1** Micrographs showing **(a)** membrane nanotubes running between two cells (arrows) and **(b)** vaults within the cytoplasm of a eukaryotic cell.

SOURCE: (A): Reprinted from *Advances in Planar Lipid Bilayers and Liposomes 10*, Lokar et al., Chapter 3 Membrane Nanotubes in Urothelial Cell Line T24, 65–94, Copyright (2009), with permission from Elsevier; (B):© 1990 KEDERSHA ET AL. *The Journal of Cell Biology*, Volume 110: 895-901. doi: 10.1083/jcb.110.4.895. By permission of Rockefeller University Press.

contains RNA). Discovered in the 1980s, these eukaryotic organelles are three times the size of ribosomes, and their structure resembles that of cathedral vaults **(Figure 1b)**. Although the function of these highly conserved organelles remains unknown, they have been associated with the nuclear pore complex and may function to transport RNA from the nucleus to the cytoplasm. More recent studies have suggested a role for vaults in multidrug resistance of cancer following chemotherapy. Hence, uncovering the secret behind the vaults could improve future cancer therapies.

ECM by using adhering proteins on the plasma membrane of the cells (Figure 3.9). **Integrins** are a group of transmembrane adhering proteins that bind to ECM glycoproteins extracellularly (outside the cell) and to the microfilaments of the cytoskeleton intracellularly (inside the cell). These proteins act as bridges between the intracellular and extracellular compartments of the cell and as such can transmit information between the ECM and the cytoskeleton. These interactions can result in the regulation of various cellular responses such as cell motility along the ECM, activation of metabolic enzymes, or expression of certain genes. Control of the cell's behaviour depends on which membrane proteins are found on

the cell's surface and the molecular composition of the ECM surrounding the cell.

The ECMs in different tissues within organisms have a unique mixture of proteins, polysaccharides, and glycoproteins. The composition of the ECM plays a significant role in the function of the tissues. For example, the ECM of bone tissue is composed of collagen that is hardened by mineral deposits, giving bone the rigidity to provide shape and support to the body. The ECM of **cartilage** tissue, on the other hand, contains collagen fibres that are embedded in an elastic matrix, making the tissue more flexible and responsive to different forces. Arthropods such as spiders, insects, and crabs secrete a polysaccharide called chitin into the ECM, resulting in the formation of a protective hard cuticle layer or exoskeleton (external skeleton). Fungi also secrete chitin and use it to produce a cell wall.

The ECM in plant cells is arranged as **cell walls** that provide protection, support, and shape to the plant cells **(Figure 3.24)**. Structurally different from the cell wall of prokaryotic cells or fungi, plant cell walls are composed mainly of cellulose, a complex polysaccharide that is embedded in a matrix of other polysaccharides and proteins. As plant cells grow, they continuously synthesize cellulose at the surface of the plasma membrane to form the **primary cell wall** that connects adjacent plant cells. This primary cell wall is thin and flexible, allowing for further growth and enlargement of the cell. At maturity, some plant cells stop increasing in size and begin depositing a layered **secondary cell wall** between the cell's plasma membrane and the primary cell wall. The layers of the secondary cell wall are strengthened by lignin, a rigid organic compound. Lignified plants such as trees are stronger, more waterproof, and more resistant to pathogens (see Chapter 17). Cells found on the exterior layer of a plant (i.e., epidermis) also secrete a wax containing lipids that forms the cuticle layer or covering that protects the plant's surface and reduces water evaporation.

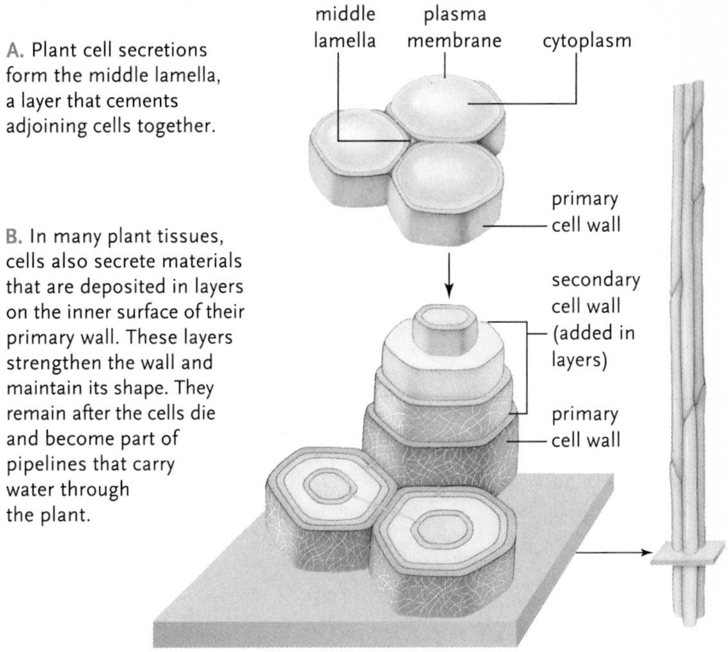

## Cells Are Connected to One Another through Cell Junctions

Cells of multicellular organisms are organized into complex structures such as tissue and organs. In some animal tissues, there are three types of cell junctions **(Figure 3.25, p. 74)** that are used to connect cells together and can also be used in the communication between adjacent cells.

**Tight junctions** occur between adjacent cells that are organized into rows or sheets. These junctions connect cells tightly to one another, ensuring that there is minimal space between the adjacent cells. This prevents the escape of fluids between these cells. For example, cells of the epithelium, which line body surfaces and internal cavities, are connected to one another through tight junctions.

**Anchoring junctions** are composed of adhesion proteins that are found on the plasma membranes of adjacent cells. As previously stated, adhesion proteins can fasten to each other and to molecules of the ECM. This results in the formation of strong sheets of cells that can withstand mechanical stress and stretching, as experienced in heart muscle and skin.

A. Plant cell secretions form the middle lamella, a layer that cements adjoining cells together.

B. In many plant tissues, cells also secrete materials that are deposited in layers on the inner surface of their primary wall. These layers strengthen the wall and maintain its shape. They remain after the cells die and become part of pipelines that carry water through the plant.

middle lamella — plasma membrane — cytoplasm
primary cell wall
secondary cell wall (added in layers)
primary cell wall

**FIGURE 3.24** Plant cell wall. In plants, the secondary cell wall is formed by material deposited in the plant cell in layers on the inner surface of their primary cell wall.

SOURCE: From Starr. *Biology*, 8E. © 2011 Brooks/Cole, a part of Cengage Learning, Inc. Reproduced by permission.www.cengage.com/permissions

**Gap junctions** are small channels that open and close between adjacent animal cells. The channels allow for small molecules such as ions to be transported from the cytoplasm of one cell to that of an adjacent cell. These small molecules can serve as signals in cell communication between adjacent cells. For example, the coordinated actions of heart muscle cells are regulated by the ions being transported between adjacent cells through these gap junctions.

Although plant cells do not have the cell junctions seen in animal cells, they do have channels that pass through the plant cell walls between adjacent cells. These channels, called **plasmodesmata** (singular = plasmodesma), allow water and small molecules to pass from one plant cell to another **(Figure 3.26, p. 74)**. Plasmodesmata, like gap junctions, are used as a tool in communication between adjacent plant cells.

## STUDY BREAK

1. What is the structure and function of the extracellular matrix in (a) animals and (b) plants?
2. How are cells in multicellular organisms connected to one another?

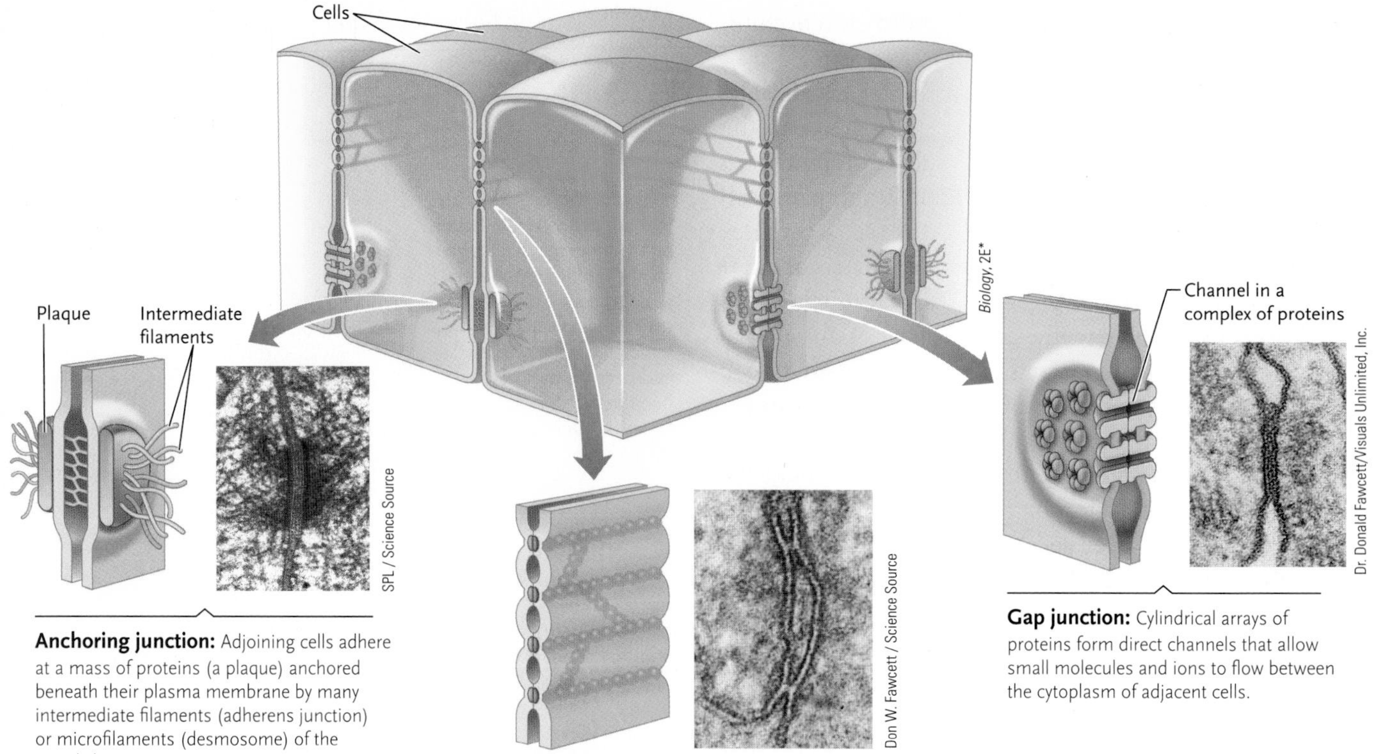

Cells

**Plaque**  **Intermediate filaments**

Channel in a complex of proteins

*Biology, 2E\**

SPL / Science Source

Dr. Donald Fawcett/Visuals Unlimited, Inc.

Don W. Fawcett / Science Source

**Anchoring junction:** Adjoining cells adhere at a mass of proteins (a plaque) anchored beneath their plasma membrane by many intermediate filaments (adherens junction) or microfilaments (desmosome) of the cytoskeleton.

**Tight junction:** Tight connections form between adjacent cells by fusion of plasma membrane proteins on their outer surfaces. A complex network of junction proteins makes a seal tight enough to prevent leaks of ions or molecules between cells.

**Gap junction:** Cylindrical arrays of proteins form direct channels that allow small molecules and ions to flow between the cytoplasm of adjacent cells.

**FIGURE 3.25** Anchoring junctions, tight junctions, and gap junctions, which connect cells in animal tissues.

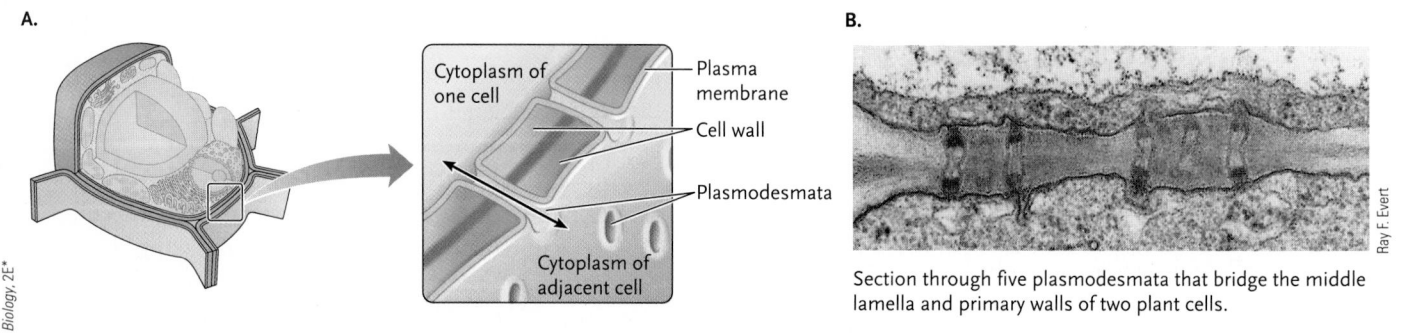

**A.**

*Biology, 2E\**

Cytoplasm of one cell

Plasma membrane

Cell wall

Plasmodesmata

Cytoplasm of adjacent cell

**B.**

Ray F. Evert

Section through five plasmodesmata that bridge the middle lamella and primary walls of two plant cells.

**FIGURE 3.26** **(a)** Cell wall structure in plants. **(b)** The electron micrograph shows plasmodesmata, which form openings in the cell wall that directly connect the cytoplasm of adjacent cells.

# PUTTING IT IN PERSPECTIVE

Cells are the basic units by which we define life on this planet. Knowing the composition, organization, and functions of cells is important in understanding how organisms develop, interact with each other, and respond to their environments in an effort to survive and reproduce. For example, knowing how cells will react to the decrease in oxygen at high altitudes is important to those who climb mountains, or how cells will respond to the enormous pressures of the oceans is critical to deep-sea divers. Furthermore, without the knowledge of the structure of bacterial cells, we wouldn't be able to determine an effective treatment strategy to combat infection. All of this information is crucial in our everyday lives.

Today, research in the area of synthetic biology is exploring ways to create cells artificially. These artificial cells, called "protocells," made of synthetic materials could theoretically function as a "living" cell. The first artificial cells were developed in the 1960s by Thomas Change at McGill University in Montreal, Canada. These cells were very simple, containing a semipermeable nylon membrane that housed several proteins, including enzymes. Protocells have come a long way since then. In 2010, researchers announced the development of a self-replicating bacterial protocell that contained an artificial cell wall and synthetic DNA. In 2013, eukaryotic protocells made of plastic that are capable of carrying out metabolic reactions using encapsu-lated compartments such as organelles were created. This research is aimed at better understanding the origins of life and strengthening the bridge between chemistry and biology. In addition, it may hold therapeutic value in the treatment against certain human diseases, although ethical concerns surrounding the creation and use of the artificial basic unit of life have also created much controversy.

In this chapter, we have laid a foundation for our understanding of the structural units of a cell, and in the next set of chapters, we will explore how the various parts of a cell are used to carry out basic and more intricate functions. Collectively, these functional properties are what define a cell as a basic unit of life.

## KEY CONCEPTS REVIEW AND QUESTIONS

### 3.1 The Birth of Cell Biology

The cell is defined as the basic unit of life and is characterized by the three generalizations of the cell theory. Cell biology is the study of all aspects of cells and relies heavily on microscopy as one of the primary investigative tools.

1. Describe the three generalizations of the cell theory.

2. Describe similarities and differences between the two types of microscopes used in cell biology.

### 3.2 The Basic Foundations of a Cell

All cells have a plasma membrane, DNA as the hereditary material, ribosomes, and cytoplasm. The plasma membrane serves as a selectively permeable barrier, and the ribosomes are used to synthesize protein. Cells are categorized as either prokaryotic or eukaryotic based on distinguishing character-istics. Eukaryotic cells contain membrane-bound organelles and house the DNA in a membrane-bound nucleus, a feature not seen in prokaryotic cells. In addition, eukaryotic cells are typically larger in size than prokaryotic cells due to their internal endomembrane system, which supports the larger cell size.

3. Describe the fluid mosaic model of cellular membrane.

4. Match the cellular component with its function.
   a. ATP production _____ Ribosome
   b. Photosynthesis _____ Chloroplast
   c. Lipid assembly _____ Nucleus
   d. Protein synthesis _____ Lysosome
   e. Acts as a selectively permeable barrier _____ Rough ER
   f. Protein sorting and shipping _____ Plasma membrane
   g. Store DNA _____ Mitochondria
   h. Synthesis of secretory proteins _____ Smooth ER
   i. Contains digestive enzymes _____ Golgi complex

5. The size of a cell is dictated primarily by which of the following factors?
   a. nuclear envelope area to nucleus volume ratio
   b. ribosome area to ribosome volume ratio
   c. membrane area to cytoplasm volume ratio
   d. organelle area to membrane volume ratio

### 3.3 Prokaryotic Cell Structure and Function

Prokaryotic cells do not contain membrane-bound organelles such as a nucleus, endomembrane system, mitochondria, and chloroplasts, which are found in eukaryotic cells.

6. Fill in the blanks.

   Prokaryotic cells house their DNA in the _____ region. The DNA is typically found in one _____ chromosome. In addition, prokaryotic cells have a _____ directly sur-rounding the outside of the plasma membrane. _____ are used by prokaryotic cells to move around in their environment.

7. True or False. Prokaryotic cells evolved before eukaryotic cells.

### 3.4 Eukaryotic Cell Structure and Function

Eukaryotic cells have a membrane-bound nucleus and other mem-brane-bound organelles. Eukaryotic cells also contain a network of specialized proteins that make up the internal cytoskeleton.

8. Which of the following is not a component of the cytoskeleton in eukaryotic cells?
   a. Microtubules
   b. Microfilaments

c. Actin

d. Cilia

e. Keratin

9. True or False. All eukaryotic cells have both mitochondria and chloroplasts.

## 3.5 Cooperation in Multicellular Organisms

Cellular responses are often dictated by the changes in their environment. In multicellular organisms, cells are surrounded by a microenvironment of proteins, polysaccharides, and glycoproteins that they adhere and respond to, and neighbouring cells that they interact with. These interactions help determine both the structural and functional basis of all cells.

10. Describe the difference between the extracellular matrix surrounding animal cells versus that surrounding plant cells.

11. Which of the following cell structures is found only in plant cells?

a. Adhering junctions

b. Gap junctions

c. Plasmodesmata

d. Tight junctions

Now that you have read and reviewed this chapter, we encourage you to attempt to build a concept map using these key concepts and indicate the connections between them. Please see Chapter 5 for examples of concept maps that could be developed for this chapter.

# Life Is a Transfer of Energy

## WHY IT MATTERS

In a January 2013 interview with Oprah Winfrey, Lance Armstrong openly discussed using banned performance-enhancing drugs throughout his cycling career. These drugs facilitated his win of seven consecutive Tour de France titles and an Olympic bronze medal. The worldwide attention to Lance Armstrong's interview heightened the very complex issue of doping in sports, raising questions about the manufacturing, availability, and testing of these drugs. In addition, ethical and safety concerns over the possibility of allowing the use of these drugs in competition are hotly debated. But how exactly do these drugs enhance athletic performance? Simply stated, they increase the efficiency by which energy is harnessed and used by cells to drive mechanical performance (see Box 4.1).

In all biological systems, cells need to work to stay alive, and this work requires energy. In this chapter, we will discuss energy, the fundamental laws surrounding energy transfer and use, and how they apply to living systems. In addition, we will describe how cell membranes are used to store the energy required to actively conduct reactions at the cell surface.

## 4.1 Transferring Energy in Cells

Work is an essential component of life. All the cells in your body are continuously working to keep you alive. Cellular work involves carrying out the trillions of chemical reactions that are needed to grow and develop, maintain homeostasis (consistent internal environment), and successfully reproduce. And it takes energy to do work. Cells must acquire the energy needed to stay alive and use it in an efficient and readily accessible manner. There are rules to follow in the harnessing and transferring of energy, called the laws of thermodynamics. And cells, like everything else in this universe, must abide by these rules.

### Cells Must Abide by the Laws of Thermodynamics

**Energy** is defined as the capacity to do work. But what does this mean? Energy is somewhat difficult to conceptualize, but, intuitively, we know that energy is all around

us, in various forms. For example, solar energy is evident on a sunny day, electrical energy powers your computer, thermal energy warms you up, and the energy of motion gets you to class every day. Moreover, energy can be converted from one form to another. The electrical energy in a light bulb is converted to light energy, and the chemical energy in gasoline is converted into mechanical energy in your car.

We classify energy into two major states: kinetic and potential. **Kinetic energy** is the energy of motion. In other words, it is the energy possessed by an object that is in motion. A moving object can perform work by transferring kinetic energy to another object. **Potential energy** is stored energy. The amount of potential energy stored in an object is governed by the object's location or chemical structure. When you hold an object in the air, the object has potential energy as a result of its elevation. Potential energy associated with the chemical structure of an object is called chemical energy and is stored energy available for release by breaking bonds during a chemical reaction. The specific arrangement of atoms in molecules such as glucose or gasoline allows them to store a specific amount of potential energy.

An example of the conversion of energy can be observed using a Newton's cradle, a desk toy you have probably seen in many offices **(Figure 4.1a, p. 81)**. When you hold the outer ball away from the device, it has potential energy due to its elevation **(Figure 4.1b)**. Releasing the ball causes its potential energy to be converted into kinetic energy during its drop in elevation **(Figure 4.1c)**. That kinetic energy associated with the moving ball is transferred to the next ball in the device, causing the second ball to move and transfer energy to the adjacent ball. This ball in turn transfers the energy to the next adjacent ball, and so on. The energy received by the final ball in the series is then used to elevate this ball, converting kinetic energy back to potential energy **(Figure 4.1d)**. The entire energy transformation process is now repeated, but in the opposite direction. In a cell, the potential energy in a glucose molecule can be released during a series of chemical reactions and converted to the kinetic energy needed to do work. In both living and non-living objects, the transfer

The use of performance-enhancing drugs or doping is not novel to sports. Even at the original Olympic Games in Ancient Greece, athletes were known to drink "magic" potions containing opium and eat exotic foods such as lizard meat to enhance their athletic performance in the pursuit of being crowned champions at their sport. Since those first Olympic Games, doping methods have evolved, and so have the mechanisms for their detection. At the 1968 Summer Olympics, Hans-Gunnar Liljenwall, a Swedish pentathlete, became the first Olympic athlete to test positive for the use of a performance-enhancing drug—alcohol—forcing him to relinquish his bronze medal. Today, the World Anti-Doping Agency (WADA) is the authoritative body on the use of performance-enhancing drugs and oversees the testing of athletes for several sports federations, including the International Olympic Committee.

One of the most common banned substances tested for is erythropoietin (EPO), a hormone also known as hematopoietin **(Figure 1)**. EPO enhances red blood cell production, which increases the ability of blood to deliver oxygen to muscle tissue. An increase in oxygen increases the amount of energy available to do work (see Section 4.1). Exogenous (originating outside the organism) EPO, however, can be detected in blood because its structure is slightly different from the endogenous (originating inside the organism) form. Autologous blood doping (transfusion of one's own blood), however, cannot be detected other than by an abnormally large number of red blood cells in circulation (an increased hematocrit). Recently, a formal athlete biological passport has been created for competitive athletes as a record of an individual's levels of selected biological markers (such as hematocrit), making it easier to detect unusual changes in these levels over time. However, there are problems associated with this

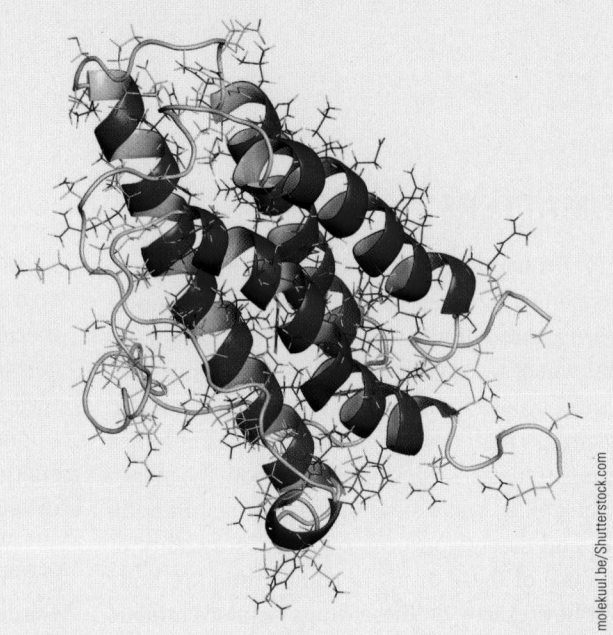

molekuul.be/Shutterstock.com

**FIGURE 1** Molecular structure of erythropoietin.

approach. For example, some variation in the levels of biological markers can be attributed to differences in an athlete's genotype (genetic makeup) and not to doping. In a recently published article, a group of Canadian researchers discuss the testing of genetic variations among athletes and the need to include this information in the athlete's biological passport. As such, the biological passport program would use intraindividual variability rather than population values to establish an athlete's acceptable physiological range.

An excellent example of the potential of genetic variants contributing to athletic excellence is the case of Finnish cross-country skier Eero Antero Mäntyranta, who won seven Olympic medals in the 1960s. Mäntyranta was a heterozygous carrier of a mutation in the gene that encodes for the erythropoietin receptor (EPOR), which initiates the hematological response to EPO. As a result, this athlete was "hyperresponsive" to his own EPO, resulting in greater blood oxygen–

carrying capacity and, presumably, endurance. Based on standard levels for hemoglobin concentration, Mäntyranta would be excluded from competition; however, if genotype information was available, a potential positive indication of blood doping would be revealed as a false positive and be attributed to nature, not cheating. Implementation of genetic data, however, inevitably raises many ethical concerns, including the fairness of the natural genetic advantages and disadvantages of athletes, correlations between performance and race, privacy of family medical information, and whether or not these tests are even effective in detecting novel doping strategies, including gene doping (alterations in the genotype of athletes through gene therapy). How these concerns will be addressed remains unclear. It is evident that the coevolution of doping and anti-doping strategies will become even more complex with the continued development of novel and more sophisticated technologies.

of energy from one form to another is governed by a set of rules called the laws of thermodynamics.

**Thermodynamics** is the study of energy and its transformations. This branch of science involves the physics of **matter** (anything that has a mass and volume), heat, work, energy, and **entropy** (measure of disorder). In the field of thermodynamics, scientists often use two terms: the "system" and the "surroundings." The system refers

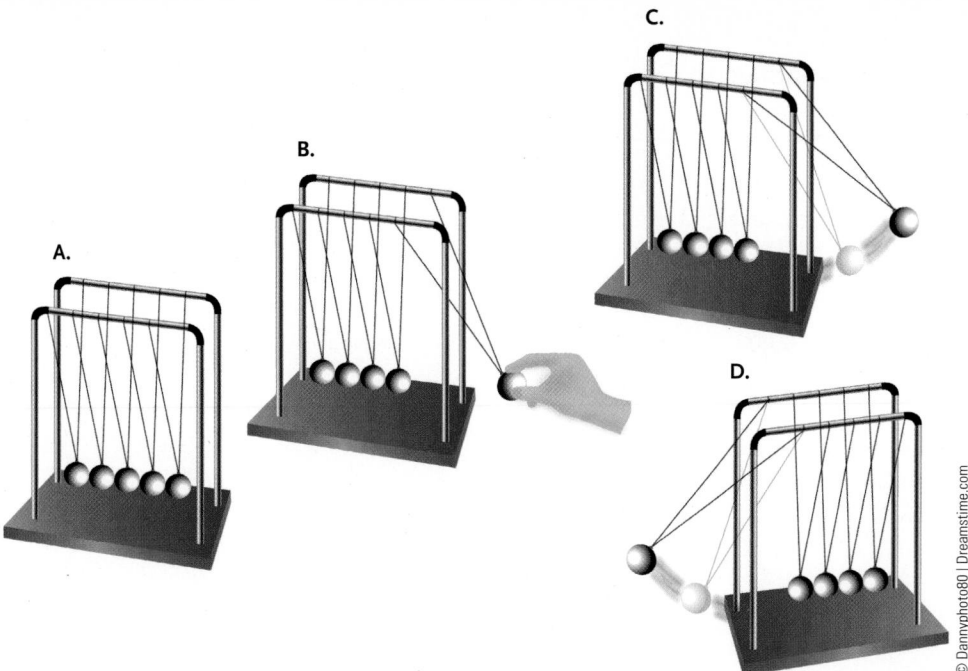

FIGURE 4.1 Energy transformation. **(a)** A Newton's cradle showing the balls at rest. **(b)** The elevated ball contains potential energy. **(c)** The elevated ball is released, and the potential energy associated with this ball is converted into kinetic energy during its drop. **(d)** The kinetic energy in the moving ball is transferred to adjacent balls in the device. Once this kinetic energy reaches the final ball in this device, it is used to elevate this ball, thereby converting this kinetic energy into potential energy.

© Dannyphoto80 | Dreamstime.com

to the object that is being studied, and the surroundings refer to everything outside that system. A system can be a cell, a car, or even an entire planet. Each cell in any organism is an open system. This means that both energy and matter are exchanged between the system (the cell) and its surroundings (the environment) **(Figure 4.2)**.

The **first law of thermodynamics**, also known as the law of energy conservation, states that *energy can be transformed from one form into another but cannot be created or destroyed.* Simply put, the amount of energy in the universe is constant. The only thing that changes is the form in which energy is found. For example, solar panels do not generate energy; they convert solar energy originating from the Sun into electrical energy that can be used as

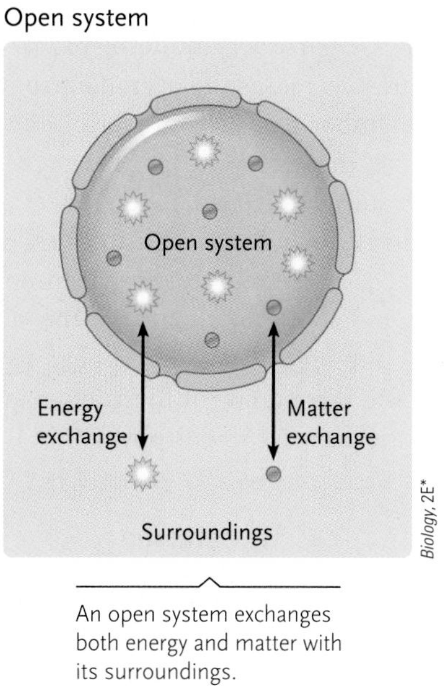

power. This is also true in life. When you walk across campus or move your eyes to read the words on this page, you are converting the chemical energy in the food you have consumed into mechanical energy (see Box 4.2 to read about energy transfer in cyborg animals).

This transfer of energy is what allows you to do work, and, remember, work is essential for life. However, the transfer of energy is not 100% efficient, so whenever energy is transferred, some of that energy is lost. The term "lost" in this context does not mean destroyed; it means that some of the energy is not used to do work. In most energy transformations, some energy is converted into heat and transferred to the surrounding environment. Since heat is energy associated with random molecular motion, this makes heat a disordered form of energy. Disorder, or randomness, can be measured and quantified as entropy, the amount of disorder within a system plus its surroundings. Since every transformation of energy creates molecular randomness (by the conversion of some of the energy into heat), our universe (system plus its surroundings) is becoming increasingly disordered as time goes on. Hence, the **second law of thermodynamics** states that *the total disorder (entropy) of an isolated system and its surroundings is always increasing.*

Let's discuss the second law of thermodynamics a bit further using examples. Gasoline is a source of energy used to power most combustion engines, such as those found in cars, boats, and airplanes **(Figure 4.3a, p. 83)**. Gasoline molecules have a high level of stored potential energy, and during the combustion of gasoline (i.e., the breaking of the chemical bonds in the gasoline molecules), the potential energy is transformed into mechanical energy, allowing the engine-driven machine to move **(Figure 4.3b)**. However, in this case, the transformation of energy is not very efficient. In fact, most engines are only 15% to 25%

## Open system

**Open system**

Energy exchange

Matter exchange

Surroundings

*Biology, 2E\**

An open system exchanges both energy and matter with its surroundings.

FIGURE 4.2 An open system in thermodynamics.

## LIFE ON THE EDGE 4.2
## From Energetic Cockroaches to Cyborg Humans

Although often considered vile and disgusting, cockroaches are now at the forefront of biofuel research. In a recent study by Rasmussen and colleagues from Case Western Reserve University in Cleveland, Ohio, cockroaches are among a group of newly created cyborg animals that have been implanted with biofuel cells and environmental sensors **(Figure 1)**. In this example, "biofuel" represents the conversion of the chemical energy in the cockroaches' food into electrical energy to power implanted sensors that transmit information about the insect's surroundings by radio antennae to the researchers. These biofuel cells tap into the creature's own metabolism to power implanted electronic devices.

In snails, biofuel cells have been able to provide a continuous stream of power for months at a time, eliminating the use of bulky and short-lived batteries. However, the rate at which biofuel cells can extract energy is limited by the size of the electrodes and the uptake of sugars and oxygen from the organism's circulatory system. Remember that even cyborgs need to follow that first law of thermodynamics: energy can be transformed from one form into another but cannot be created or destroyed.

To increase the potential of these cyborg organisms, the current objective is to downsize the extra weight of the biofuel cell while increasing the efficiency of energy transfer. The potential use of cyborg organisms is limitless, from monitoring environmental damage such as the nuclear disaster in Fukushima, Japan, to employing them on dangerous military reconnaissance missions. But could these technologies be applied to humans? Current research using cyborg mammals such as rats is part of a preliminary step toward using biocompatible fuel cells in humans to run low-power medical devices such as pacemakers or to drive low-power, low-energy cellular functions such as nerve cell stimulation.

© Mgkuijpers | Dreamstime.com

**FIGURE 1** Cockroach.

efficient in converting the potential energy in gasoline into mechanical energy. The remainder of the potential energy is converted to heat that is dissipated into the environment and hence increases the disorder of the universe.

All organisms work in a very similar manner to a combustion engine, but instead of burning gasoline, they digest food, which is full of high-energy macromolecules such as sugars, proteins, and fats. For example, during cellular respiration (see Chapter 5), cells break down glucose and convert the chemical energy stored in the glucose into chemical energy stored in ATP (adenosine triphosphate), a form of energy that is readily used to power our bodies. However, cellular respiration is only approximately 30% to 40% efficient as most of the potential energy in the foods we eat is converted to heat.

By now it may have occurred to you that the idea of living organisms following the second law of thermodynamics appears to go against one of the main characteristics defining life, which is that life displays order (for a review, see Chapter 2). How do cells display order and at the same time increase entropy (disorder)? Remember that cells are open systems, and to display order, cells must acquire chemical energy (e.g., glucose) from their surroundings. Then, through a series of reactions, they use this chemical energy to construct highly ordered cellular structures. For example, cells use the energy they have harnessed to assemble amino acids (low order) into proteins (medium order), which are then assembled into organelles (high order). Building highly ordered cellular structures decreases the overall entropy within the cell. But remember that the transfer of energy is never 100% efficient; therefore, during this process, some of the energy acquired by the cell is converted to heat. Since heat cannot be used by the cell to do work, it is released out of the cell and into the environment, thereby increasing the disorder or entropy of the surroundings **(Figure 4.4)**. Although it may not appear so at first, life does follow the second law of thermodynamics by contributing to the increase in entropy within the universe.

## In Cells, Energy Is Transferred through Chemical Reactions

Energy is required by all cells to do work. However, the acquisition and transfer of energy in a cell are not a simple one-step process. Instead, energy is transferred

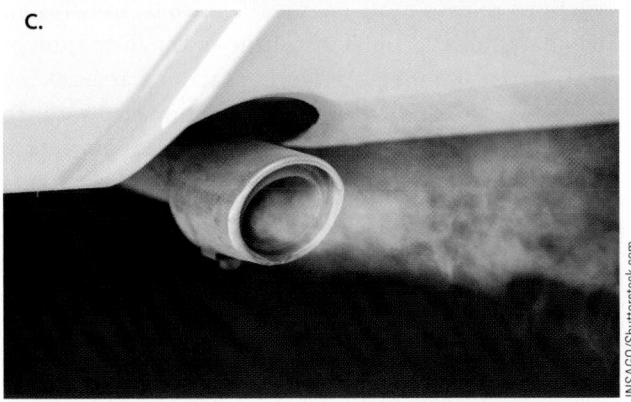

**FIGURE 4.3** Second law of thermodynamics. **(a)** Gasoline is a source of potential chemical energy used to power cars. **(b)** During the combustion of gasoline, potential chemical energy is converted into mechanical energy. **(c)** This transfer of energy is not very efficient.

through a series of **chemical reactions**. In these reactions, the atoms of one or more **reactants** (molecules that enter the reaction) are rearranged into one or more **products** (the molecules present at the end of the reaction; **Figure 4.5, p. 84**). Atoms are not lost or gained during a reaction; the atoms that enter into a reaction are the same atoms that come out, simply in a different arrangement. Reactions are written and described as "chemical equations," with reactants on the left side of the equation and products on the right side. Arrows indicate the direction of the reaction. Usually, just one right-pointing arrow is used; however, a reversible reaction has two arrows pointing in opposite directions.

Energy is stored in the chemical bonds between the atoms of a molecule. Chemical reactions that release energy are called **exergonic reactions**. This energy, called **free energy**, represents energy available to do work. Thus, the products of exergonic reactions have less free energy than the reactants **(Figure 4.6a, p. 84)**. For example, during cellular respiration, cells take the reactants glucose and oxygen and produce water and carbon dioxide. During this reaction, the free energy stored primarily within the chemical bonds of glucose is released.

$$\text{glucose} + O_2 \xrightarrow{\text{Energy released}} H_2O + CO_2$$

Reactants                       Products
(high energy)                 (low energy)

Releasing free energy during an exergonic reaction is "spontaneous," which in this context does not necessarily mean the reaction is going to happen quickly (like when you have an instantaneous reaction to a stimulus), but, instead, the reaction occurs without the input of free energy. The oxidation or breakdown of sugar is a spontaneous reaction, but it happens very slowly, which is why it doesn't just disintegrate overnight in the sugar bowl.

Chemical reactions in which the reactants have less free energy than the products are termed **endergonic reactions (Figure 4.6b)**. This means that during the

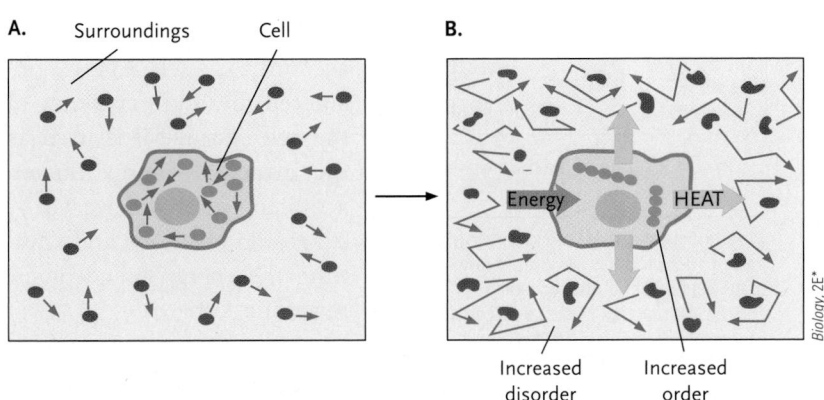

**FIGURE 4.4** A simple thermodynamic example of a living cell. **(a)** Molecules of both the cell and the surroundings are in a relatively disordered state. **(b)** The cell has taken in energy from the surroundings and used it to perform the work required to make molecules more ordered. This energy transformation releases heat, which increases the disorder (or entropy) of the surroundings.

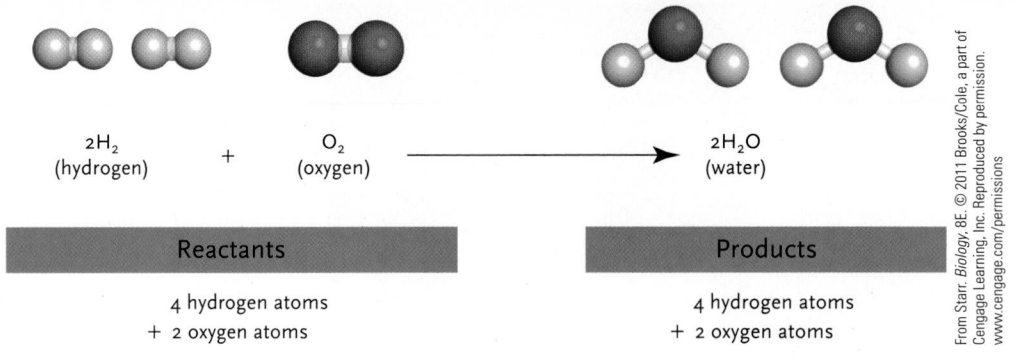

**FIGURE 4.5** A chemical equation outlines the reaction of hydrogen and oxygen (reactants) forming water (product). Arrows indicate the direction of the reaction. Usually, just one right-pointing arrow is used as shown here; however, a reversible reaction has two arrows pointing in opposite directions (not shown here).

$2H_2$
(hydrogen) + $O_2$
(oxygen) ⟶ $2H_2O$
(water)

| Reactants | Products |
|---|---|
| 4 hydrogen atoms + 2 oxygen atoms | 4 hydrogen atoms + 2 oxygen atoms |

reaction, energy must be absorbed, and this energy will be transferred and stored within the products. An example of an endergonic process is photosynthesis. The reactants water and carbon dioxide have less free energy than the products glucose and oxygen. The energy absorbed and transferred into the products comes from the sun.

Energy absorbed

$H_2O + CO_2$ ⟶ glucose + $O_2$
Reactants         Products
(low energy)       (high energy)

Most, although not all, endergonic reactions in a cell are non-spontaneous: they require an input of energy and usually result in the production of more highly ordered molecules that have more stored free energy than the reactants do.

All of the processes that take place in a living cell are due simply to the transfer of energy through a sequence of reactions. Some reactions release energy found within chemical bonds, whereas others acquire and store it within newly created chemical bonds. The interplay of exergonic and endergonic reactions is called **energy coupling**. In energy coupling, the energy released by a spontaneous exergonic reaction can be coupled with a non-spontaneous endergonic reaction. In a cell, the transfer of energy through energy coupling reactions is crucial for survival. For instance, the release of energy from the exergonic reactions associated with breaking down food molecules within the cell can be used to build the structural proteins required to construct new cells.

## ATP is the Primary Carrier Cells Use to Transfer Energy

During energy coupling reactions, some exergonic reactions release more energy than can be transferred to endergonic reactions, resulting in the formation of heat, whereas other exergonic reactions release too little energy to drive endergonic reactions forward. To make energy coupling reactions proceed more efficiently, the cell uses ATP (adenosine triphosphate), a small molecule composed of a ribose (a five-carbon sugar) bound to an adenine nitrogenous base and three negatively charged phosphate groups **(Figure 4.7a)**. The bonds in ATP contain just the right amount of energy for most purposes. Moreover, ATP can store free energy in a form that is readily available when required by the cell. It's analogous to your debit card allowing you efficient access to the money stored in your bank account. As such, ATP is considered the main currency of the cell because it is used as the principal energy carrier, acquiring energy released by exergonic reactions and shuttling the energy to endergonic reactions.

Most of the energy stored in ATP is found in the chemical

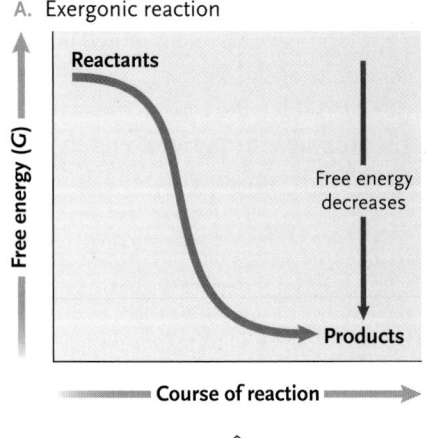

**A.** Exergonic reaction

Free energy (G)

Reactants

Free energy decreases

Products

Course of reaction

In an exergonic reaction, free energy is released. The products have less free energy than was present in the reactants, and the reaction proceeds spontaneously.

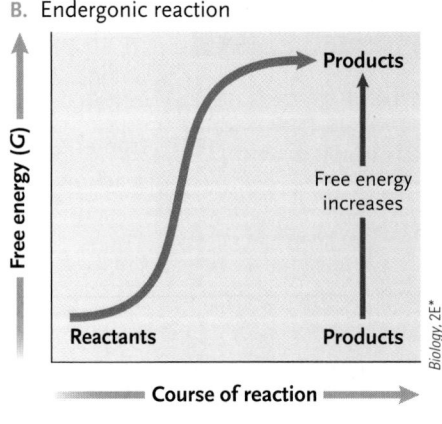

**B.** Endergonic reaction

Free energy (G)

Products

Free energy increases

Reactants       Products

Course of reaction

In an endergonic reaction, free energy is gained. The products have more free energy than was present in the reactants. An endergonic reaction is not spontaneous: it proceeds only if energy is supplied.

*Biology, 2E\**

**FIGURE 4.6** Metabolism consists of a combination of **(a)** exergonic and **(b)** endergonic reactions.

## A. Chemical structure of ATP

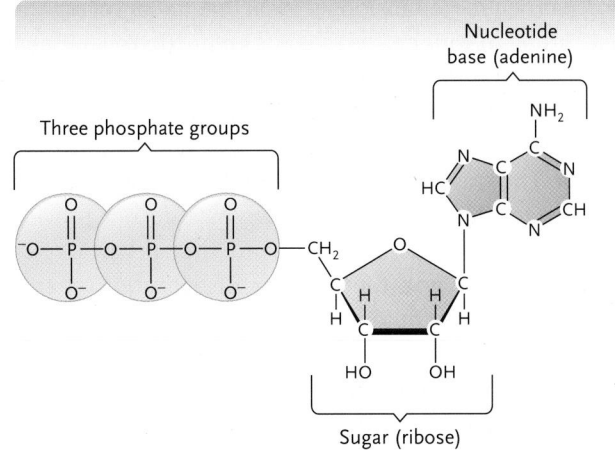

Three phosphate groups

Nucleotide base (adenine)

Sugar (ribose)

## B. Hydrolysis reaction removing a phosphate group from ATP

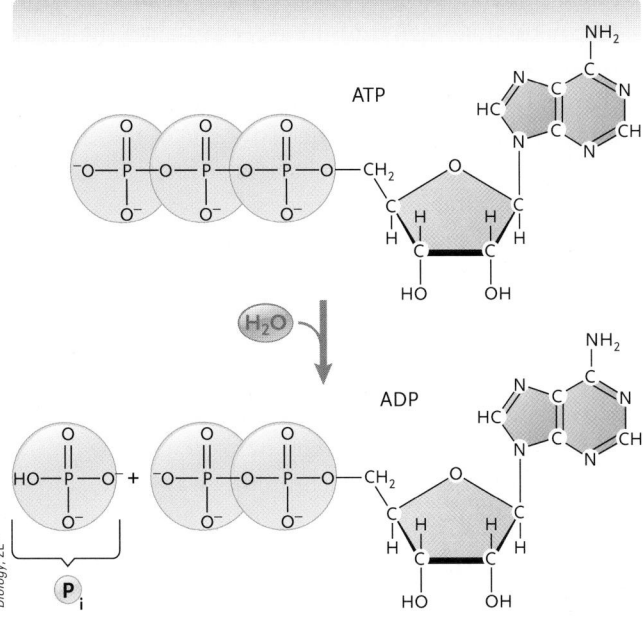

ATP

$H_2O$

ADP

$P_i$

**FIGURE 4.7** ATP, the primary molecule used to supply the energy for endergonic reactions. **(a)** Structure of one ATP molecule. **(b)** Reaction of ATP hydrolysis that releases energy. ADP = adenosine diphosphate.

*Biology, 2E\**

bonds between the three phosphate groups. Due to the negative charges of each of the phosphates, the bonds between them are highly unstable and therefore easily breakable **(Figure 4.7b)**. When these bonds break down, stored energy is released and can be used to drive endergonic reactions forward. This occurs through a process called **phosphorylation**, which involves the transfer of the terminal phosphate of ATP to a target molecule. Along with the phosphate, the energy released during ATP hydrolysis (breakdown) is also transferred to the target molecule. For example, the phosphorylation of glucose via the hydrolysis of ATP leads to the formation of glucose-6-phosphate, a more energized form of the sugar **(Figure 4.8)**. With the loss of a phosphate group, ATP becomes **ADP (adenosine diphosphate)**, a lower energy state molecule.

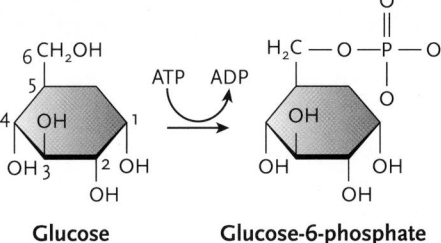

Glucose          Glucose-6-phosphate

**FIGURE 4.8** Phosphorylation of glucose to form glucose-6-phosphate.

Since cells are continually building and displaying order, they are in constant need of energy. As such, they are continuously breaking down ATP to drive endergonic reactions forward. The **ATP/ADP cycle** is used to ensure a continual supply of ATP **(Figure 4.9)**. In this cycle, the ADP formed during ATP hydrolysis is used to regenerate ATP using phosphate molecules and the energy released by other cellular exergonic reactions, such as those involved in the breakdown of sugars.

We should also note that organisms also store energy within macromolecules such as carbohydrates, proteins, nucleic acids, and lipids. In fact, long-term energy storage is primarily in the form of starch in plants and in the form of glycogen and lipid in animals. In Chapters 5 and 21, we will discuss further these cellular, long-term energy stores and how they can be tapped into when energy is required by cells.

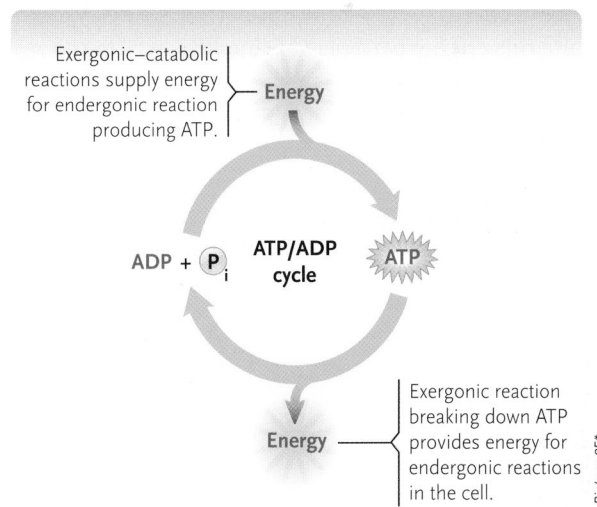

Exergonic–catabolic reactions supply energy for endergonic reaction producing ATP.

Energy

$ADP + P_i$     ATP/ADP cycle     ATP

Energy

Exergonic reaction breaking down ATP provides energy for endergonic reactions in the cell.

*Biology, 2E\**

**FIGURE 4.9** The ATP/ADP cycle couples reactions releasing free energy and reactions requiring free energy.

## STUDY BREAK

1. What are the first two laws of thermodynamics, and why are they relevant to biology?
2. Define and distinguish between endergonic and exergonic reactions. Give examples of each.
3. Why is ATP such an important molecule?
4. What is energy coupling?

## 4.2 Enzymes Are the Facilitators of Life

As just described, for cells to divide, grow, and survive, energy must be transferred through the coupling of spontaneous exergonic reactions with non-spontaneous endergonic reactions. But it only happens because of **enzymes**. Most of the reactions that need to occur within a cell occur at very slow rates. For example, the breakdown of glucose into carbon dioxide and water takes hundreds of years, and the phosphorylation of molecules takes even longer. However, with the help of enzymes inside your cells, these reactions can occur within milliseconds. Hence, enzymes are biological catalysts that function to facilitate the initiation of cellular reactions required to sustain life.

### Enzymes Lower the Energy Barriers of Cellular Reactions

Why is it that many cellular reactions happen so slowly? All reactions contain an energy barrier that must be overcome for the reaction to begin. The energy barrier, termed the **activation energy** ($E_A$), is the amount of energy that the reactants must absorb to distort or weaken their chemical bonds to bring them to their **transition state**—a state that is required to activate or initiate the reaction **(Figure 4.10)**. Even spontaneous reactions require an initial input of energy to overcome this barrier. One way to overcome this energy barrier is to supply energy to the reactants in the form of heat. For example, for you to use your gas barbecue, you need to initiate the combustion of propane by adding heat from a lit match. Once the reaction has begun, you no longer need that initial spark. The only problem with heat is that it is an uncontrollable and inefficient way to overcome an energy barrier. In a cell, an increase in temperature would help initiate all cellular reactions but ultimately destroy important organic molecules. Thus, as an alternative to heat, cells use proteins called enzymes. Unlike heat, enzymes do not provide energy to the reactants to overcome the energy barrier. Instead, they lower the amount of activation energy required to overcome this barrier (Figure 4.10). By lowering the energy required, the enzymes catalyze the initiation of reactions while remaining unchanged themselves.

Enzymes are biological catalysts whose three-dimensional structure binds specific reactant molecules called **substrates (Figure 4.11a)**. Substrates bind to a specific pocketlike region of the enzyme called the **active site**, which complements the substrate's shape, size, and charge. It is in the active site where the reaction occurs. As the substrate binds to the active site of the enzyme, this region of the enzyme changes shape to fit the substrate. This "induced fit" lowers the activation energy required and brings the reactant substrate(s) closer to initiating the reaction. This can be accomplished in different ways depending on the reaction **(Figure 4.11b)**. One mechanism is by bringing two reactants close together so that they are more likely to react. For example, the active site of hexokinase fits both glucose and ATP, which brings them close together to catalyze the formation of glucose-6-phosphate. Another way is to distort or strain the bonds in the substrate, making it more unstable and hence reactive. An example of this is the enzyme lysozyme, which binds to the peptidoglycan molecules in the cell wall of bacteria and distorts the molecules into an unstable, highly reactive shape. A third mechanism is by providing an environment within the active site that alters the charge of the substrates, making them more reactive. For example, the pH around the active site of certain enzymes promotes the breakdown of their substrates (see the Purple Pages for an overview of pH). Regardless of the mechanism, once reactions are complete, all enzymes are cleared of the reaction products, conform back to their original structure, and thus remain overall unchanged **(Figure 4.12)**. As such, enzymes can be recycled and reused many times within a cell. (See Box 4.3 on how enzyme replacement therapies are used to treat human metabolic disorders.)

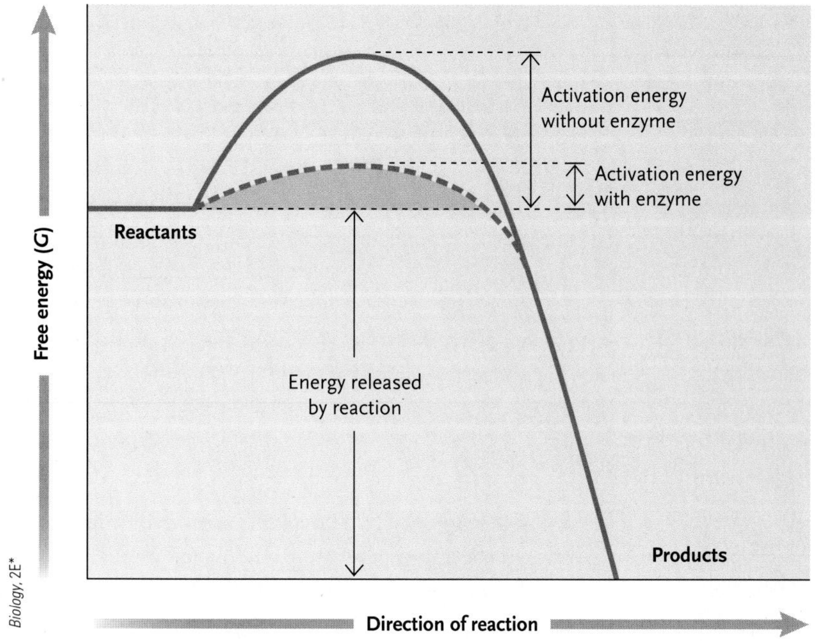

**FIGURE 4.10** Enzymes lower the activation energy ($E_a$) of a reaction. The reduction allows biological reactions to proceed rapidly at the relatively low temperatures that can be tolerated by living organisms.

*Biology, 2E**

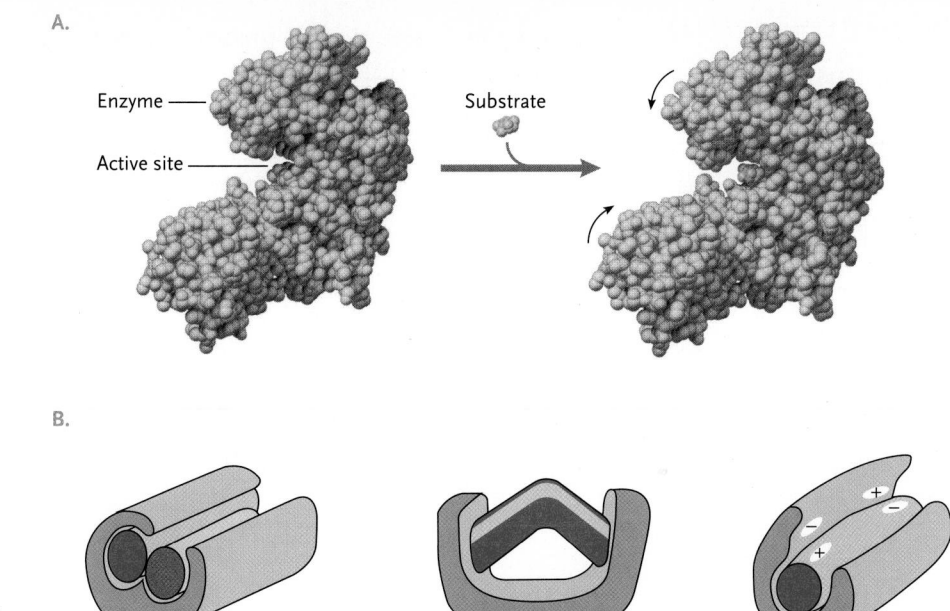

A.

Enzyme

Active site

Substrate

**FIGURE 4.11** Induced fit model. **(a)** Space-filling models showing the combination of an enzyme, hexokinase (in blue), with its substrate, glucose (in orange). Hexokinase catalyzes the phosphorylation of glucose to form glucose 6-phosphate. The phosphate group that enters the reaction is not shown. Note how the enzyme undergoes a conformational change, closing the active site more tightly as it binds the substrate. **(b)** Different mechanisms used during the binding of a substrate(s) to an active site that results in the substrate acquiring the transition state confirmation.

B.

Bring reacting molecules close together          Distort or strain substrate molecules          Charge interactions

*Biology, 2E\**

## Enzymes Require Optimal Working Conditions

Like all proteins in a cell, enzymes have an optimal set of conditions in which they function most effectively. These conditions include temperature, pH, and salinity. Less than optimal working conditions alter the three-dimensional structure of the enzyme, which in turn affects its overall function. High temperatures can destroy enzymes as heat can unravel or "denature" the 3D structures of the molecules and therefore inactivate them. Most human enzymes function within the range of 35°C to 40°C, which is ideal since our normal body temperature is 37°C **(Figure 4.13a, p. 89)**. All enzymes also have an optimal pH range. Most human enzymes function within an optimal pH range of 6.0 to 8.0, which coincides with cellular pH of approximately 7.4 **(Figure 4.13b)**. However, other enzymes have optimal pH levels that are more acidic or more basic. For example, lysosomal enzymes have an optimal pH level of about 5.5, which complements the acidic environment of the lysosome. In the digestive tract, the enzyme pepsin functions best in the acidic environment of the stomach, whereas the enzyme trypsin works best in the more basic pH conditions of the intestines (Figure 4.13b). The level of salinity is also important for enzyme function. Altering the concentration of salt around an enzyme can alter the enzyme shape or unfold the enzyme completely. Disruption in enzyme structure can lead to loss of function.

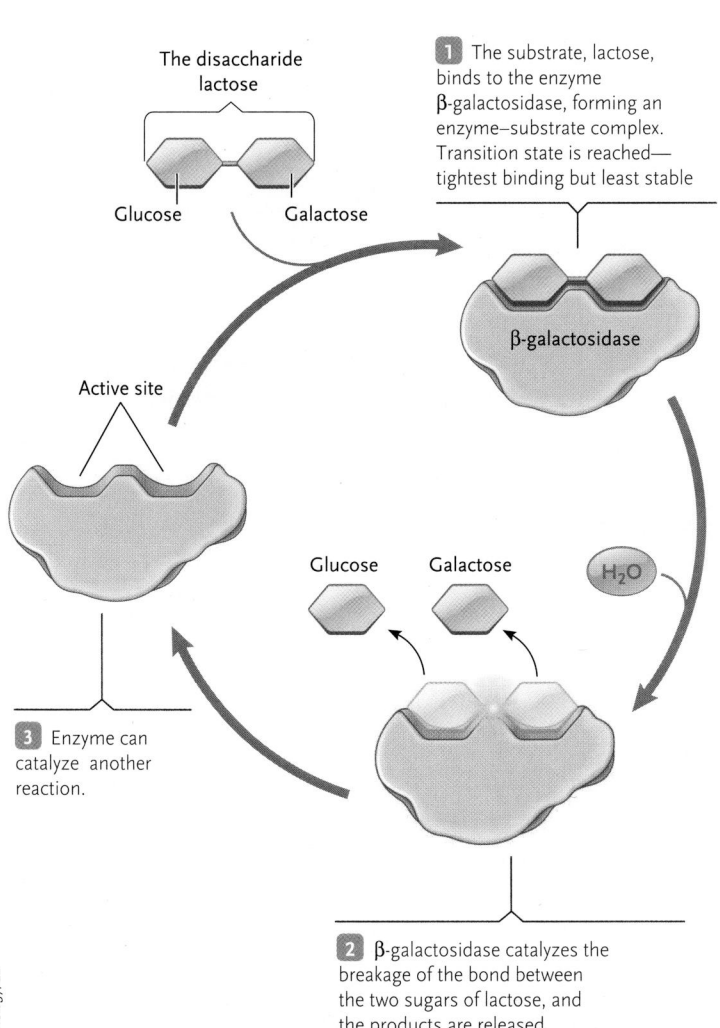

The disaccharide lactose

Glucose        Galactose

**1** The substrate, lactose, binds to the enzyme β-galactosidase, forming an enzyme–substrate complex. Transition state is reached—tightest binding but least stable

β-galactosidase

Active site

Glucose        Galactose        $H_2O$

**3** Enzyme can catalyze another reaction.

**2** β-galactosidase catalyzes the breakage of the bond between the two sugars of lactose, and the products are released.

*Biology, 2E\**

**FIGURE 4.12** The catalytic cycle of the enzyme β-galactosidase.

4.2 ENZYMES ARE THE FACILITATORS OF LIFE

One of the best things about summer is creamy, buttery corn on the cob. Corn or maize is the most widely grown grain crop in the Americas **(Figure 1)** and is used primarily for livestock feed and ethanol production. Transgenic maize (genetically modified corn) makes up the bulk of corn produced in both Canada and the United States, primarily due to its insect-resistant and herbicide-tolerant traits.

Corn is now being looked at as a potential producer of complex protein drugs for the treatment of lysosomal storage diseases, a group of inherent metabolic disorders caused by the malfunctioning of lysosomes as a result of deficient enzymes. Enzyme replacement therapy is one mechanism to treat these disorders. Traditionally, the production of human enzymes for replacement therapy has relied on systems derived from other mammal species. However, these mammalian systems are difficult to maintain as their optimal working conditions are restrictive and costly. Although bacteria have been used successfully to produce many different types of human protein (e.g., insulin produced in *Escherichia coli* to treat type 1 diabetes), they do not provide the proper sugar modification on proteins that need to be targeted to lysosome. Plants have also been used in the past to produce human enzymes to treat the disorder, but these enzymes are often modified with sugars in a plant-specific manner, making them functionally ineffective in animals. In more serious cases, they elicited a dangerous immune response when injected into patients.

Allison Kermode, a plant biologist at Simon Fraser University in Burnaby, British Columbia, has recently developed a novel way to manufacture the enzymes necessary for the treatment of the lysosomal storage disorder called mucopolysaccharidosis I (MPSI). MPSI is a genetic disorder that leads to slow growth, mental retardation, organ damage, and childhood death. Kermode's research uses transgenic maize to produce the lysosomal enzyme α-L-iduronidase, which is absent in patients with MPSI.

The enzyme is produced using a unique messenger RNA-based strategy that generates the native, unaltered form of the enzyme in the endosperm of the maize seeds without the addition of plant-specific sugar modifications. In other words, the enzymes produced using this system resemble those naturally found in humans, which makes them more effective in replacement therapy. Other plants have also shown potential for producing therapeutic enzymes, including carrots, duckweed, and tobacco. However, corn still remains an ideal plant organism for enzyme replacement therapies because the proteins are produced in the seeds, which are ideal for long-term storage.

Zeljko Radojko/Shutterstock.com

**FIGURE 1** Corn is a model for producing human protein to treat human diseases.

In addition to optimal environmental working conditions, some enzyme activity requires the support of other molecules. **Cofactors** are non-protein chemical compounds that associate with enzymes and assist in their proper functioning **(Figure 4.14)**. Cofactors can be metals such as zinc or magnesium, as seen in the example of matrix metalloproteinases, a set of enzymes that digest proteins in the extracellular matrix. Other cofactors can be organic molecules, such as vitamin C. Organic cofactors are specifically termed **coenzymes** and can be altered during cellular reactions. For example, coenzyme A, which is synthesized from vitamin $B_5$, is important in the synthesis and oxidation of fatty acids and pyruvate.

## Inhibitors and Activators Regulate Enzyme Activity

Inhibitors and activators are chemical compounds that influence the activities of enzymes by binding to them

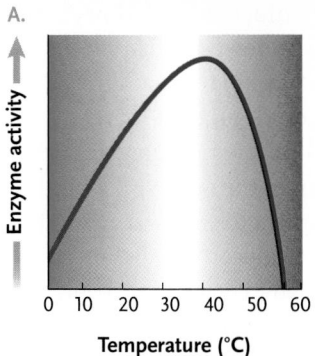

**A.**

Enzyme activity

Temperature (°C)
0 10 20 30 40 50 60

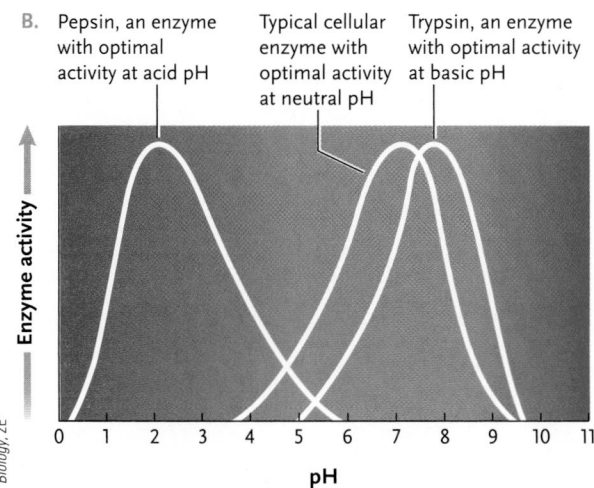

**B.**

Pepsin, an enzyme with optimal activity at acid pH

Typical cellular enzyme with optimal activity at neutral pH

Trypsin, an enzyme with optimal activity at basic pH

Enzyme activity

pH
0 1 2 3 4 5 6 7 8 9 10 11

*Biology. 2E*

**FIGURE 4.13** Effects of temperature and pH on enzyme activity. **(a)** As the temperature rises, the rate of the catalyzed reaction increases until the temperature reaches the point at which the enzyme begins to denature. The rate drops off steeply as denaturation progresses and becomes complete. **(b)** An enzyme typically has an optimal pH at which it is most active; at pH values above or below the optimum, the rate of enzyme activity drops off.

and altering their structure and therefore function. How and where inhibitors and activators bind to enzymes depend on the specific enzymes they regulate.

Some enzyme–inhibitor interactions are reversible, meaning that the bond between the inhibitor and the enzyme is weak. In this case, the inhibitor can be removed and the enzyme returned to its active state. Other interactions are irreversible, most often because the inhibitor binds to the active site of the enzyme.

Some inhibitors also exhibit **competitive inhibition** because they directly prevent the substrate from binding to the active site **(Figure 4.15a, p. 90)**. Competitive inhibition can be overcome by increasing the concentration of the substrate around the enzyme, thus increasing the probability of the substrate binding to the active site versus the inhibitor. Penicillin is an example of a competitive inhibitor of transpeptidase, an enzyme found in bacteria that catalyzes the synthesis of peptidoglycan, a key component of bacterial cell walls. Treatment of bacterial infection with penicillin inhibits the growth of bacteria by blocking the formation of its cell wall. Although penicillin was touted as a miracle drug when it was introduced in the 1940s, the overuse or misuse of penicillin over the years has led to the occurrence of antibiotic-resistant bacteria, "superbugs," which have an inherited ability to resist or overcome the actions of penicillin. Although non-resistant bacteria die during penicillin treatment, antibiotic-resistant bacteria survive and continue to propagate and spread. In essence, overtreatment has selected for antibiotic-resistant bacteria that over time have become the prominent bacteria within the population. For example, methicillin/multidrug-resistant *Staphylococcus aureus* is a type of "superbug" that is resistant to traditional penicillin-derived antibiotics and poses a major concern in hospitals, schools, and prisons, where the spread of bacterial infection through open wounds is more probable.

**Non-competitive inhibition** is a result of the inhibitor binding the enzyme at an "allosteric site" (a site on the enzyme other than the active site; **Figure 4.15b**). In this case, the inhibitor does not directly compete with the substrate for the active site. However, the inhibitor binding to the enzyme does change the shape of the enzyme, causing the active site to become less accessible to the substrate. This reduces the ability of the substrate to bind to the active site of the enzyme and decreases enzyme activity.

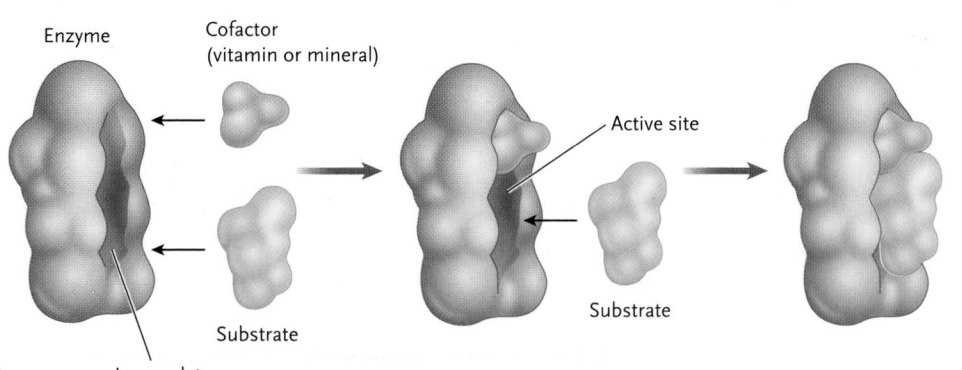

Enzyme

Cofactor (vitamin or mineral)

Active site

Substrate

Substrate

Incomplete active site

**FIGURE 4.14** Cofactors or coenzymes are non-protein molecules that bind to enzymes and aid in catalyzing reactions.

SOURCE: Based on Bernie Hobbs, "Vitamins: how do they work?" *ABC Science*, 13 October 2010, http://www.abc.net.au/science/articles/2010/10/13/3037285.htm

## A. Competitive inhibition

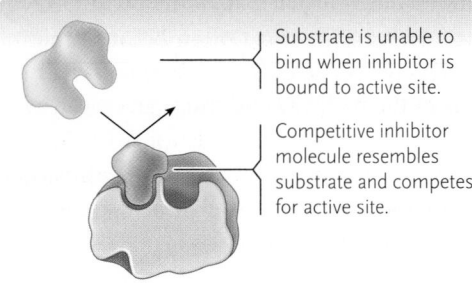

Substrate is unable to bind when inhibitor is bound to active site.

Competitive inhibitor molecule resembles substrate and competes for active site.

## B. Non-competitive inhibition

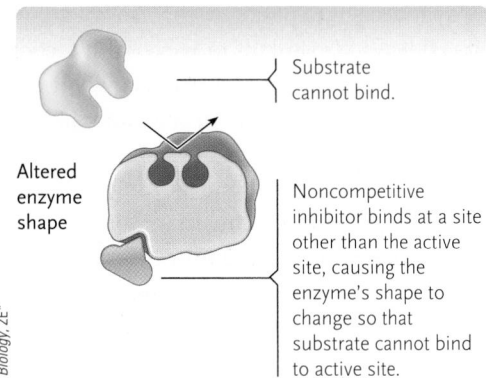

Altered enzyme shape

Substrate cannot bind.

Noncompetitive inhibitor binds at a site other than the active site, causing the enzyme's shape to change so that substrate cannot bind to active site.

*Biology, 2E\**

**FIGURE 4.15** How **(a)** competitive and **(b)** non-competitive inhibitors reduce enzyme activity.

Reaction products can also act to inhibit the enzymes that participate in the reactions. This mechanism of enzyme control is called **feedback inhibition** and occurs when the product of a metabolic reaction is overabundant. As a method to maintain efficiency in the cell, the excess product binds non-competitively and reversibly to an enzyme to either slow it down or turn it off completely. For example, ATP is used in feedback inhibition to regulate cellular respiration **(Figure 4.16, a and c)**. ATP is one of the products of cellular respiration, and when the ATP levels in a cell are high, the excess ATP binds to an allosteric site on phosphofructokinase-1, an enzyme that catalyzes an early step of glycolysis, the first metabolic pathway in cellular respiration. As a result, glycolysis is inhibited and the production of ATP is decreased and restored to cellular homeostatic levels.

Activators are regulatory molecules that bind to enzymes and increase enzyme activity. Since activators do not compete with substrates, they do not bind the active site of the enzyme but instead bind to an allosteric site. This binding alters the shape of the enzyme in a manner that promotes the substrate's accessibility to the active site and increases enzyme activity. ADP is an example of an allosteric activator of phosphofructokinase, which promotes cellular glycolysis and hence production of ATP **(Figure 4.16, a)**.

## STUDY BREAK

1. How do enzymes catalyze reactions?
2. Distinguish between competitive and non-competitive inhibitors.
3. What is allosteric regulation?
4. Give an example of feedback inhibition and describe the significance of this to a cell.

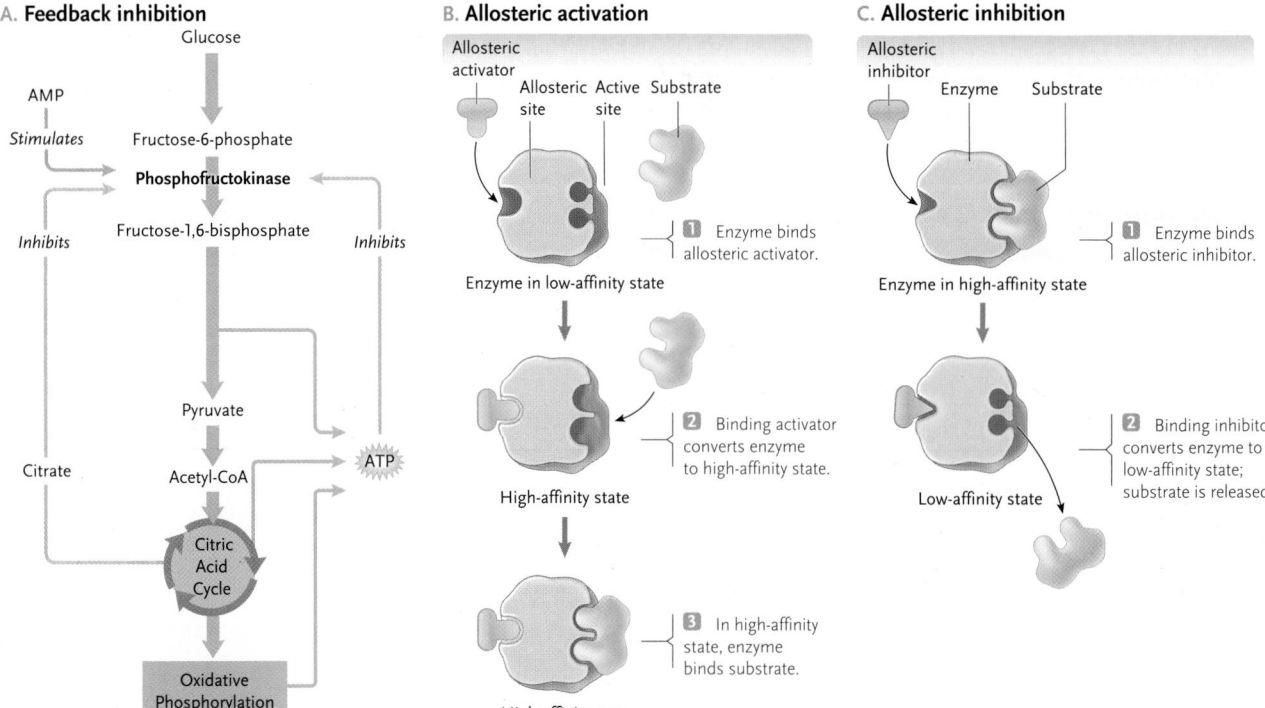

**FIGURE 4.16 (a)** Feedback inhibition, **(b)** allosteric activation, and **(c)** allosteric inhibition.

## 4.3 Metabolic Pathways Link Cellular Reactions

In a cell, thousands of endergonic and exergonic reactions are happening at any given time. Some of these reactions are linked to one another in sequence so that the products of one reaction become the reactants of the next reaction. These chains of enzyme-catalyzed reactions are called **metabolic pathways**. The total of all the metabolic pathways within an organism is called **metabolism,** and the net energy used by these reactions at any given time to sustain life is described as the metabolic rate.

### Energy Is Transferred via Anabolic and Catabolic Pathways

In any metabolic pathway, there is either absorption or release of free energy. Metabolic reactions that lead to the formation or building of complex molecules are called **anabolic pathways (Figure 4.17a)**. These pathways give rise to final products that have more free energy than the initial reactants. Since anabolic pathways as a whole are used to build complex molecules, energy input is required. Thus, overall, anabolic pathways are endergonic. In muscle tissue, both natural and synthetic anabolic steroids enhance anabolic pathways that lead to increased protein production and muscle mass. Because of this unfair advantage in athletic performance, these compounds are banned in sports.

Metabolic reactions that lead to the hydrolysis or breakdown of complex molecules are called **catabolic pathways (Figure 4.17b)**. Although these pathways are also composed of a series of endergonic and exergonic reactions, there is an overall release of free energy. Thus, these pathways are considered exergonic.

Metabolic pathways can be either linear or cyclic. A linear metabolic pathway runs straight through from reactant to product **(Figure 4.18a, p. 92)**. For example, glucose enters the glycolysis pathway, and after a sequence of reactions, pyruvate is produced as the final product In cyclic pathways, the last step regenerates one of the first reactants of the pathway and thus can readily be used to restart the cycle **(Figure 4.18b)**. The citric acid cycle is an example of a cyclic metabolic pathway. Oxaloacetate, one of the initial reactants in the citric acid cycle, is regenerated in the last step of the cycle.

### The Give and Take of Electrons Must Be Balanced through Redox Reactions

Many metabolic pathways transfer energy through the donation and acceptance of electrons (see the Purple Pages for an overview of electrons and atoms). Electrons are transferred from one molecule to another through electron transfer reactions called oxidation–reduction reactions, or **redox reactions** for short **(Figure 4.19, p. 92)**. During these reactions, **oxidation** occurs when one molecule donates electrons (is oxidized), and **reduction** occurs when the other molecule accepts electrons (is reduced). A simple mnemonic to remember the definitions of oxidation and reduction is LEO-GER. LEO is an acronym for "loss of electrons oxidation," and GER is an acronym for "gain of electrons reduction." In Chapter 5, we will illustrate many examples of redox reactions and the transfer of energy during both cellular respiration and photosynthesis.

### STUDY BREAK

1. Define and distinguish anabolic and catabolic metabolic pathways.
2. What occurs during a redox reaction?

**A. Anabolic pathway**

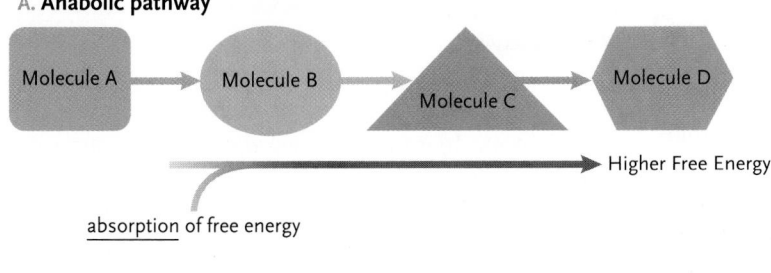

absorption of free energy

**B. Catabolic pathway**

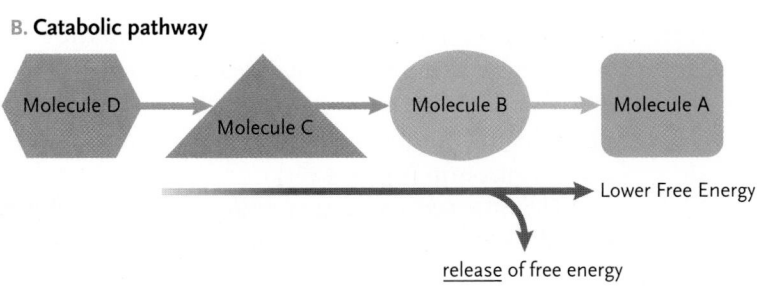

release of free energy

**FIGURE 4.17** Hypothetical examples of the two major types of metabolic pathways. **(a)** In the anabolic pathway, energy must be provided through a series of enzyme catalyzed reactions to convert the starting molecule A, which has lower free energy, to the molecule D, which has higher free energy. **(b)** In the catabolic pathway, energy is released through a series of enzyme-catalyzed reactions to convert the starting molecule D, which has higher free energy, to the molecule A, which has lower free energy.

**A. Linear metabolic pathway**　　**B. Cyclic metabolic pathway**

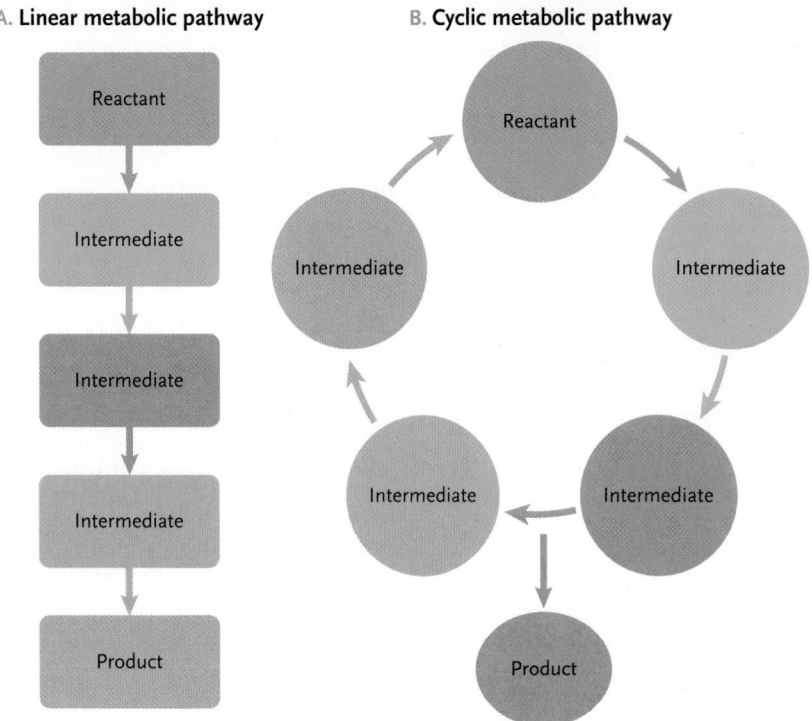

FIGURE 4.18 Examples of **(a)** linear and **(b)** cyclic metabolic pathways.

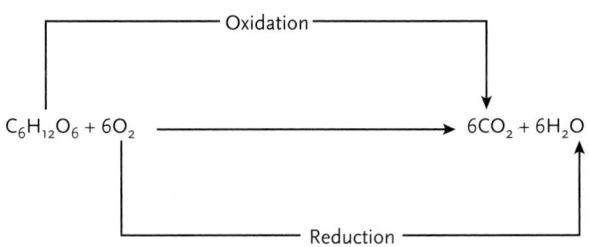

FIGURE 4.19 Combustion of glucose is an example of a redox reaction. During this reaction, glucose loses electrons (oxidation) and oxygen gains electrons (reduction).

## 4.4 Membrane Transport Requires Energy Transfer

As discussed in Chapter 3, cellular membranes act as a protective, selectively permeable barrier around cells or their internal compartments. Membranes are composed primarily of phospholipids and an array of proteins that provide structure, fluidity, and function. Transport of molecules across cellular membranes is influenced primarily by their size and charge. Here we will discuss the methods of transport across membranes and how the distribution of energy is both the cause of and the consequence of these transport mechanisms.

### Passive Transport across the Membrane Can Be Simple or Facilitated

Small, uncharged molecules such as oxygen or carbon dioxide can easily pass across the phospholipid bilayer of cellular membranes through a mechanism of **passive transport** called **diffusion**. The driving force for the diffusion of most molecules is a difference in concentration between the two sides of the membrane. This uneven distribution of molecules across the membrane is unstable. As such, molecules will spontaneously move from high concentrations to low concentrations (their concentration gradient) in an effort to reach stability or equilibrium. Since diffusion is a spontaneous event, it does not require an input of energy. Instead, free energy stored in the membrane is released during this process. You will see later in the chapter how this release of free energy can be used to drive endergonic reactions at the membrane.

Diffusion of some molecules across membranes requires the assistance of membrane proteins. The molecules are either small, charged molecules such as ions or larger molecules such as sugars. This method of passive transport is called **facilitated diffusion** because the membrane proteins facilitate the transport of these substances across the membrane. These membrane proteins, in the form of channel **(Figure 4.20a)** or carrier proteins **(Figure 4.20b)**, increase the rate of diffusion of these molecules by providing a more favourable route of transport across the membrane. Keep in mind that even in facilitated diffusion, substances move across the membrane along their concentration gradient and therefore do not require an input of energy but instead release energy.

The movement of water across membranes is called **osmosis,** and it is essential in maintaining homeostasis within a cell. During osmosis, water is transported across a membrane by diffusion in response to the concentration gradient of the substance(s) (solutes) dissolved in it. In other words, water moves across a membrane that is permeable to water but not to the solute, from a region of low-solute concentration to a region of high-solute concentration. Diffusion continues until either the concentration of the solute is balanced or the levels of free energy are in equilibrium, on both sides of the membrane. The diffusion of water is either simple (directly through the phospholipid bilayer) or facilitated through a specific water channel protein called **aquaporin (Figure 4.20c)**.

The transport of water across a cellular membrane is also influenced by the **tonicity** of the cell. Tonicity is the measure of "osmotic pressure" against a membrane. It is determined by the total concentration of solutes in the two solutions that are separated by a selectively permeable membrane. When a cell is placed in a hypotonic solution, a solution in which the concentration of solutes (e.g., sucrose) is less than that within the cell, the water molecules in the solution move across the plasma membrane and into the cell

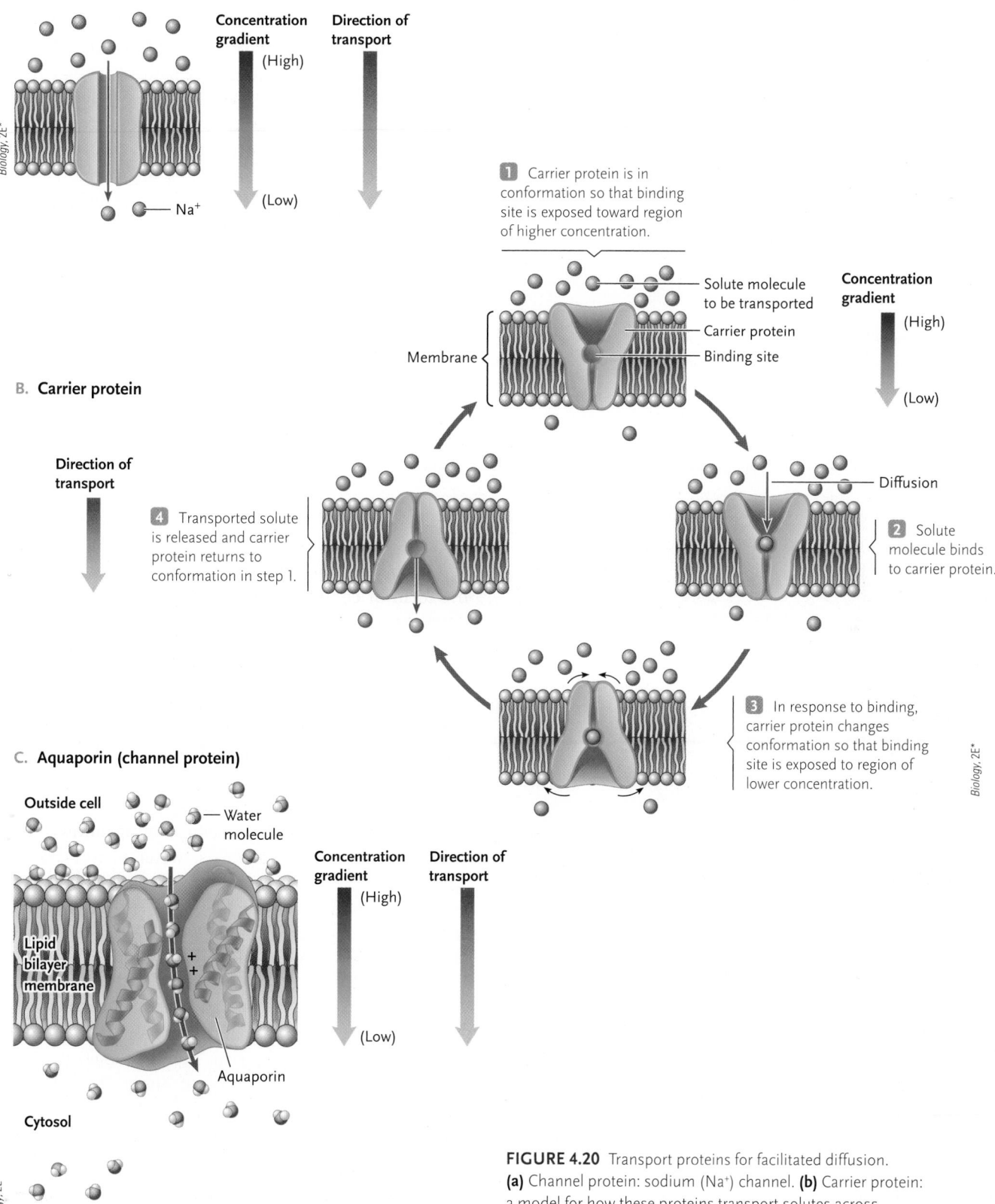

**A. Channel protein (sodium channel)**

Concentration gradient
(High)
(Low)

Direction of transport

Na⁺

1 Carrier protein is in conformation so that binding site is exposed toward region of higher concentration.

Membrane

Solute molecule to be transported

Carrier protein

Binding site

Concentration gradient
(High)
(Low)

**B. Carrier protein**

Direction of transport

4 Transported solute is released and carrier protein returns to conformation in step 1.

Diffusion

2 Solute molecule binds to carrier protein.

3 In response to binding, carrier protein changes conformation so that binding site is exposed to region of lower concentration.

**C. Aquaporin (channel protein)**

Outside cell

Water molecule

Lipid bilayer membrane

Concentration gradient
(High)
(Low)

Direction of transport

Aquaporin

Cytosol

**FIGURE 4.20** Transport proteins for facilitated diffusion. **(a)** Channel protein: sodium (Na⁺) channel. **(b)** Carrier protein: a model for how these proteins transport solutes across membranes. **(c)** The channel protein aquaporin.

**(Figure 4.21a).** As a result, the cell volume increases and the cell swells. In some cases, the increase in cell volume is so high that the membrane ruptures, thereby killing the cell. When a cell is placed in a hypertonic solution, a solution in which the concentration of solutes (e.g., sucrose) is greater than that within the cell, the water molecules inside the cell are transported out into the solution **(Figure 4.21b).** As a result, the cell's volume decreases and the cell shrivels up. Too much water loss can also lead to cell death. Finally, in an isotonic solution, a solution in which the solute (e.g., sucrose) concentration is the same both outside and within the cell, a cell remains unchanged with respect to overall water movement **(Figure 4.21c).** Although water is transported across the membrane, the rate of movement in either direction is equal, thus keeping the cell volume constant. An example is placing red blood cells in normal saline solution, which has relatively similar salt concentration as these cells. Normal saline also has the same salt concentration as blood plasma.

The maintenance of water balance, called **osmoregulation**, is a critical component of cellular homeostasis. The loss of osmoregulation can lead to an increase in concentration of solutes such as metabolic waste that is toxic to cells in high concentrations.

In organisms that have cell walls, such as plants, prokaryotes, fungi, and some protists, an increase in cytoplasmic volume can be resisted even in hypotonic environments. The rigid nature of the cell wall prevents the cells from overexpanding during osmosis. As a result, osmosis causes pressure, called **turgor,** to build up within the cell and against the external structures. Turgor prevents more water from diffusing into the cell and provides these organisms with structural support. For example, plants rely on turgid cells to resist gravity and remain upright. Many invertebrate animals, such as jellyfish or earthworms, depend on hydrostatic skeletons for support.

## Active Transport across the Membrane Requires Energy

The transport of any molecule across a membrane against their concentration gradient, from low concentration (stable) to high concentration (unstable), is called **active transport**. As such, active transport does not happen spontaneously and therefore requires an input of energy. The main source of energy to perform this task is through the hydrolysis or breakdown of ATP.

Active transport requires specific membrane proteins (often called pumps) that help move the molecules against their concentration gradient.

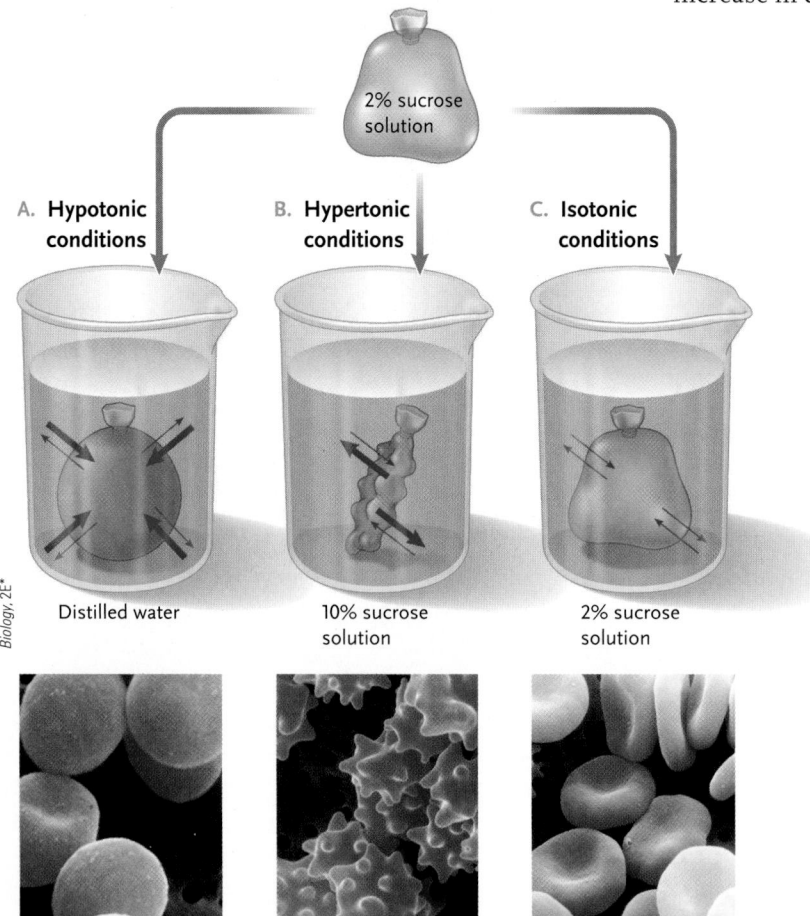

*Biology, 2E*

2% sucrose solution

A. **Hypotonic conditions** — Distilled water — Water diffuses inward; cells swell.

B. **Hypertonic conditions** — 10% sucrose solution — Water diffuses outward; cells shrink.

C. **Isotonic conditions** — 2% sucrose solution — No net movement of water; cells do not change in size or shape.

**FIGURE 4.21** Tonicity and osmotic water movement. The diagrams show what happens when a cellophane bag filled with a 2% sucrose solution is placed in **(a)** a hypotonic, **(b)** a hypertonic, or **(c)** an isotonic solution. The cellophane is permeable to water but not to sucrose molecules. The width of the arrows shows the amount of water movement. In the first beaker, the distilled water is hypotonic to the solution in the bag; net movement of water is into the bag. In the second beaker, the 10% sucrose solution is hypertonic to the solution in the bag; net movement of water is out of the bag. In the third beaker, the solutions inside and outside the bag are isotonic; there is no net movement of water into or out of the bag. The animal cell micrographs show the corresponding effects on red blood cells placed in hypotonic, hypertonic, or isotonic solutions.

SOURCE: Micrographs credit: © 1976 M. SHEETZ, R. PAINTER, and S. SINGER. *The Journal of Cell Biology,* Volume 70:193–302. By permission of Rockefeller University Press.

Figure 4.22 depicts a simple model for active transport. Active transport of a solute against this concentration gradient begins when a solute molecule on one side of the membrane binds to its specific transport protein on the membrane. ATP is hydrolyzed by the transport protein, and a phosphate group (along with energy) is transferred to the transport protein. As a result, the transport protein changes shape in a manner that allows the solute to be transported against its concentration gradient. Once the solute is released, the phosphate group is removed from the transport protein, causing it to resume its original shape.

Active transport can be used to maintain specific ion concentrations across cellular membranes (see the Purple Pages for an overview of ions). For example, active transport is used to maintain proper sodium (higher outside) and potassium (higher inside) levels across the plasma membrane of cells, and calcium pumps on the mitochondrial and endoplasmic reticulum membranes maintain high calcium stores inside these organelles. Sodium–potassium pumps are important to maintain cell volume and prevent cells from swelling up and bursting. Calcium pumps are important for relaying signals that stimulate cellular responses, as seen during the contraction of muscle cells.

## Membrane Transport Can Convert Kinetic Energy into Potential Energy Used to Drive Energy-Consuming Reactions

Pumping ions across a cellular membrane by active transport increases the concentration difference of these ions across the membrane, which in turn establishes a voltage difference across the membrane called a **membrane potential**. This membrane potential, similar to what you find in a battery, contains stored energy. And like a battery, this stored energy can be harnessed to drive endergonic, or energy-consuming reactions. In Chapter 5, we will describe how potential energy stored in the inner membrane of the mitochondria is used to drive the synthesis of ATP during cellular respiration.

## Membrane Trafficking Consumes Energy

Large, bulky molecules such as polysaccharides or proteins are too large to move across membranes by simply crossing the phospholipid bilayer or even through

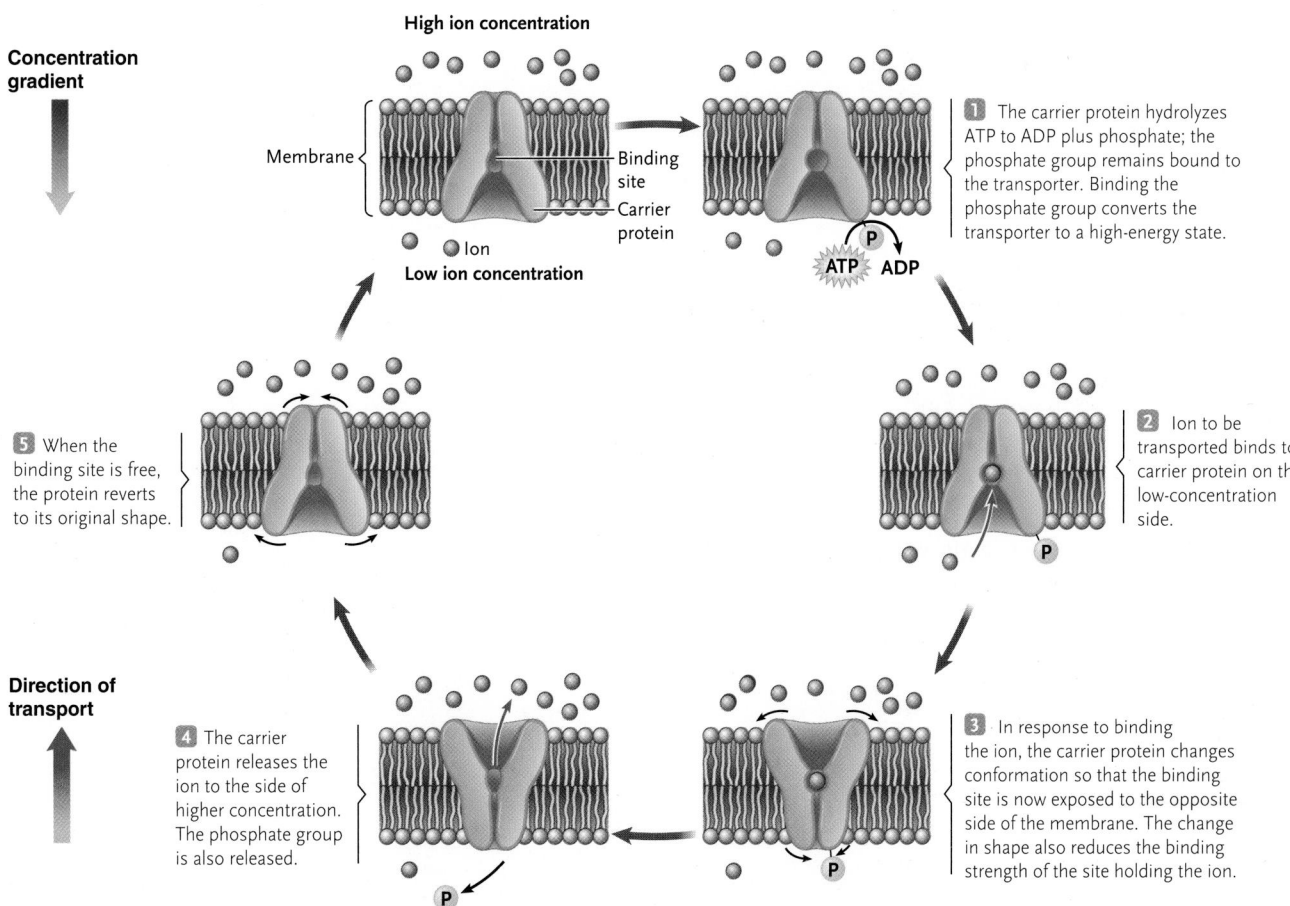

**FIGURE 4.22** Model for the operation of a primary active transport pump.

## A. Exocytosis: vesicle joins plasma membrane, releases contents

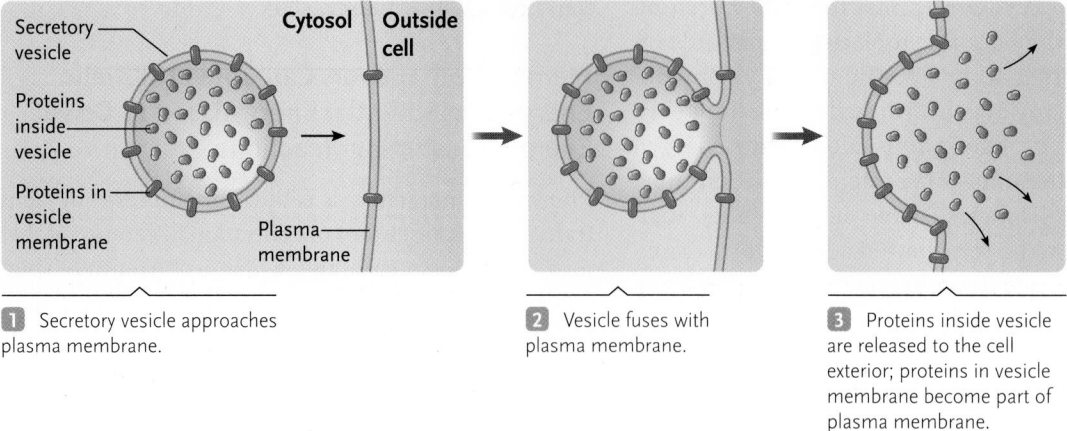

**1** Secretory vesicle approaches plasma membrane.

**2** Vesicle fuses with plasma membrane.

**3** Proteins inside vesicle are released to the cell exterior; proteins in vesicle membrane become part of plasma membrane.

## B. Bulk-phase endocytosis (pinocytosis): vesicle imports water and other substances from outside cell

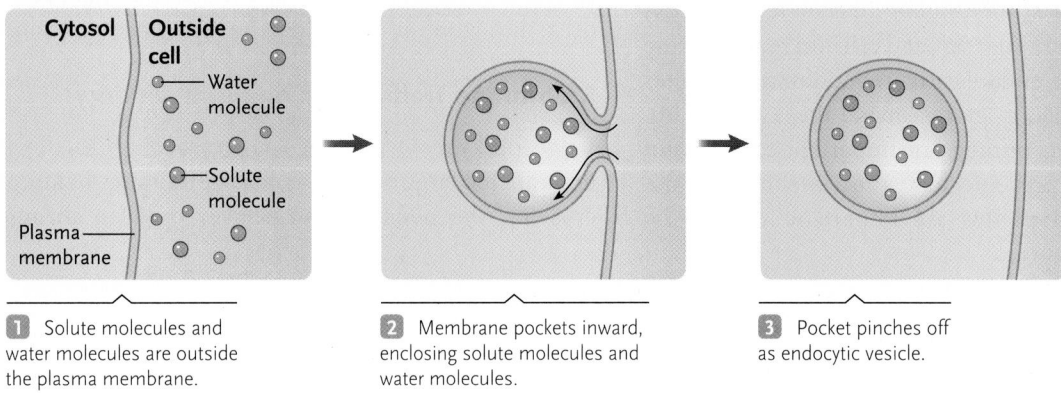

**1** Solute molecules and water molecules are outside the plasma membrane.

**2** Membrane pockets inward, enclosing solute molecules and water molecules.

**3** Pocket pinches off as endocytic vesicle.

## C. Phagocytosis: cytoplasmic lobes extend outward and engulf entire cells

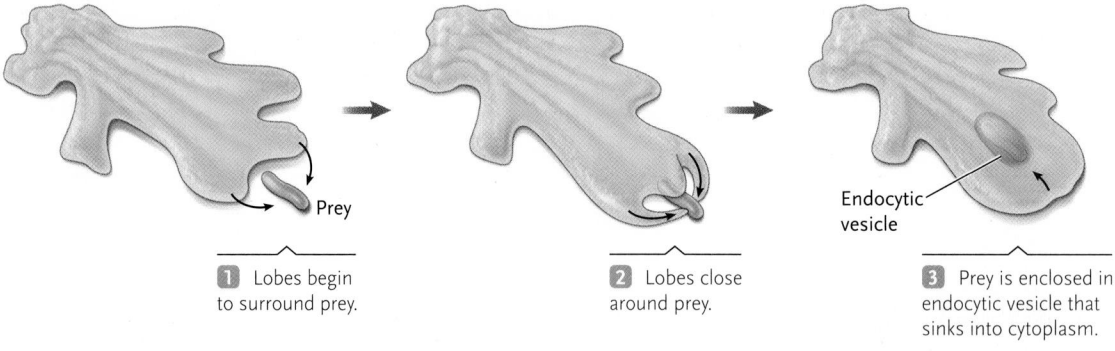

**1** Lobes begin to surround prey.

**2** Lobes close around prey.

**3** Prey is enclosed in endocytic vesicle that sinks into cytoplasm.

## D. Receptor-mediated endocytosis: vesicle imports specific molecules

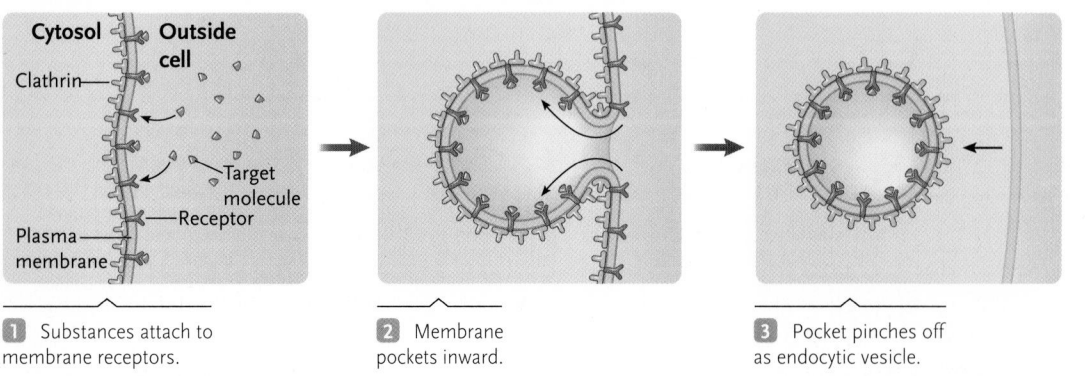

**1** Substances attach to membrane receptors.

**2** Membrane pockets inward.

**3** Pocket pinches off as endocytic vesicle.

*Biology, 2E\**

**FIGURE 4.23** Membrane trafficking showing **(a)** exocytosis, **(b)** pinocytosis, **(c)** phagocytosis, and **(d)** receptor-mediated endocytosis.

transport proteins. Instead, the cell forms membrane-bound vesicles to transport these substances into and out of the cell (for a review, see Chapter 3). Due to the work required to transport such large molecules, this is an energy-consuming process.

Exocytosis is the transport of large substances out of the cell (Latin: *ex* = out of; **Figure 4.23a**). The secretory pathway described in Chapter 3 uses exocytosis to transport waste material and secretory proteins such as collagen and fibronectin from the cell into the extracellular matrix. The membrane-bound vesicles transporting these proteins originate from a membrane budding off the Golgi apparatus. When these secretory vesicles reach the plasma membrane, they fuse with it and release their contents to the outside of the cell.

Endocytosis is transport of large substances into the cell. During endocytosis, the plasma membrane indents inward to form a pocket that engulfs the large substances immediately next to the outside of the membrane. The pocket pinches off from the surface of the cell, forming a membrane-bound vesicle inside the cell. This vesicle can then be transported to various regions inside the cell and deliver its contents. The three main forms of endocytosis are differentiated by the size of the transported substance and the use of specific receptor proteins.

The first two types of endocytosis, pinocytosis **(Figure 4.23b)** and phagocytosis **(Figure 4.23c)**, are not specific to any particular liquid or solute and do not involve receptor proteins. **Pinocytosis** is the endocytosis of small amounts of extracellular liquid and the small solutes contained within this liquid into a cell. **Phagocytosis** is the endocytosis of large particles and,

in some cases, entire cells. During phagocytosis, the cell extends its cytoplasm forward, forming structures called pseudopodia ("false feet") that wrap around and engulf the large particle. This leads to the formation of a large vesicle called a food vacuole, which transports its contents to lysosomes for digestion. The engulfment of bacteria by specialized white blood cells of the immune system called macrophages is through phagocytosis.

The third form of endocytosis is **receptor-mediated endocytosis (Figure 4.23d)** and involves membrane receptors that bind specific molecules. Once the molecule binds to its receptor on the surface of cells, the membrane indents inward to form a pit. The pit then pinches off from the plasma membrane to form a vesicle that is transported to specific areas within the cell. For example, the clearance of cholesterol from the blood is via receptor-mediated endocytosis using the low-density lipoprotein (LDL) receptor. A genetic defect in the LDL receptor disrupts cholesterol uptake, leading to increased levels of cholesterol in the blood. This condition, called familial hypercholesterolemia, can lead to atherosclerosis and heart disease.

## STUDY BREAK

1. What is the difference between passive and active transport? What is the driving force causing movement in each case?
2. Explain osmosis.
3. Define and distinguish between exocytosis and endocytosis.

---

## PUTTING IT IN PERSPECTIVE

By this point in your life, you probably have realized that it takes work to get yourself up in the morning and have a productive day. Your cells need energy to carry out the cellular functions required for survival. The work you carry out is powered by the energy you take into your body through eating and transform through metabolism within your cells. Hence, healthy food choices are important in increasing the efficiency of energy transformations within your body.

The transformation of energy through cellular reactions follows the rules of thermodynamics. Cells rely on many different enzymes to make those cellular reactions initiate more quickly and run more efficiently. We simply cannot afford the time it takes for reactions to occur without the aid of enzymes. Enzymes, however, work best under optimal conditions and

are regulated by inhibitors and activators. Regulation is important as an imbalance of enzyme activity (too much or too little) can be detrimental.

Membranes act as selectively permeable barriers to compartmentalize the contents of the cell and its organelles and to maintain cellular homeostasis. Some molecules, such as sugars, oxygen, and ions, move across membranes either passively or, in some cases, actively; this requires an input of energy. Some of this energy input is stored at the cell membrane and used at a later time to drive energy-consuming cellular reactions. In these cases, the membrane acts as a battery. You'll discover in Chapter 5 how this membrane "battery" is essential in the energy transfers in two major metabolic pathways, photosynthesis and cellular respiration. We will discuss the critical role of membranes in these events to make ATP in your cells. ATP is an essential molecule for life because it is the energy currency of the cell. ATP is what the cell spends to do the work that is required to get you up every morning and keep you alive.

# KEY CONCEPTS REVIEW AND QUESTIONS

## 4.1 Transferring Energy in Cells

Work is an essential component of life and requires the input of energy. Energy in a cell is transferred from one form to another through a series of spontaneous and non-spontaneous chemical reactions and is stored primarily in ATP. The mechanisms of energy transfer are continuously carried out in living cells while abiding by the laws of thermodynamics.

1. Determine if the statement is true or false. Rewrite the statement if it is false.
   a. Living organisms are open systems.
   b. The total amount of energy in the universe is always increasing.
   c. Cells display order by increasing the entropy inside the cell.
   d. The conversion of energy is never 100% efficient.
   e. An exergonic reaction requires the absorption of energy.
2. In ATP, where is most of the energy stored? How is this energy released?
3. In the ATP/ADP cycle that occurs in cells, where does the energy to build ATP come from?

## 4.2 Enzymes Are the Facilitators of Life

Enzymes catalyze cellular reactions by lowering the activation energy required to initiate the reactions and therefore bring reactants to their transition state faster. Enzymes interact with their substrates through an induced fit mechanism. Overall, enzymes are unaltered by the reaction. The activity of enzymes is regulated by pH and temperature as well as inhibitors and activators.

4. How are competitive inhibitors similar to the substrates of enzymes?
5. Which of the following is false about allosteric regulation of enzymes?
   a. An allosteric activator binds to the active site of the enzyme.
   b. An allosteric inhibitor binds to a site other than the active site of the enzyme.
   c. Feedback inhibition uses allosteric inhibitors to decrease the activity of enzymes.
   d. An enzyme that has an allosteric site will still have an active site.
6. Cathepsin B is an example of an enzyme that is found primarily in the acidic environment of lysosomes. If cathepsin B escapes the lysosome and enters the neutral environment of the cytoplasm, what will likely happen to the activity of this enzyme?

## 4.3 Metabolic Pathways Link Cellular Reactions

A cell's metabolism is a series of chemical reactions occurring in a sequential order. Metabolic pathways are either anabolic endergonic pathways that lead to the formation of complex molecules or catabolic exergonic pathways that lead to the breakdown of complex molecules. In metabolic pathways, energy is transferred through redox reactions by the donation and acceptance of electrons.

7. Fill in the blanks.
   Glycolysis is an example of a _____ pathway in which glucose is broken down to pyruvate through oxidation.
8. True or False? In an anabolic pathway, there are never any exergonic reactions.

## 4.4 Membrane Transport Requires Energy Transfer

How molecules are transported across membranes is dictated by the size and charge of the molecule and the direction of concentration and charge gradients. Smaller molecules can passively cross membranes by simple or facilitated diffusion along their concentration gradient. Active transport requires energy to transport these molecules across membranes against their concentration gradient, which in turn stores energy at the cell membrane. Transport of larger molecules requires membrane trafficking through exocytosis or endocytosis.

9. Which of the following statements does not apply to active transport across membranes?
   a. Requires ATP
   b. Transports molecules along their concentration gradient
   c. Requires membrane proteins
   d. Establishes an electrochemical gradient
10. How is pinocytosis different from receptor-mediated endocytosis?

Now that you have read and reviewed this chapter, we encourage you to attempt to build a concept map using these key concepts and indicate the connections between them. Please see Chapter 5 for some examples of concept maps.

# Harvesting and Utilizing Energy in Cells

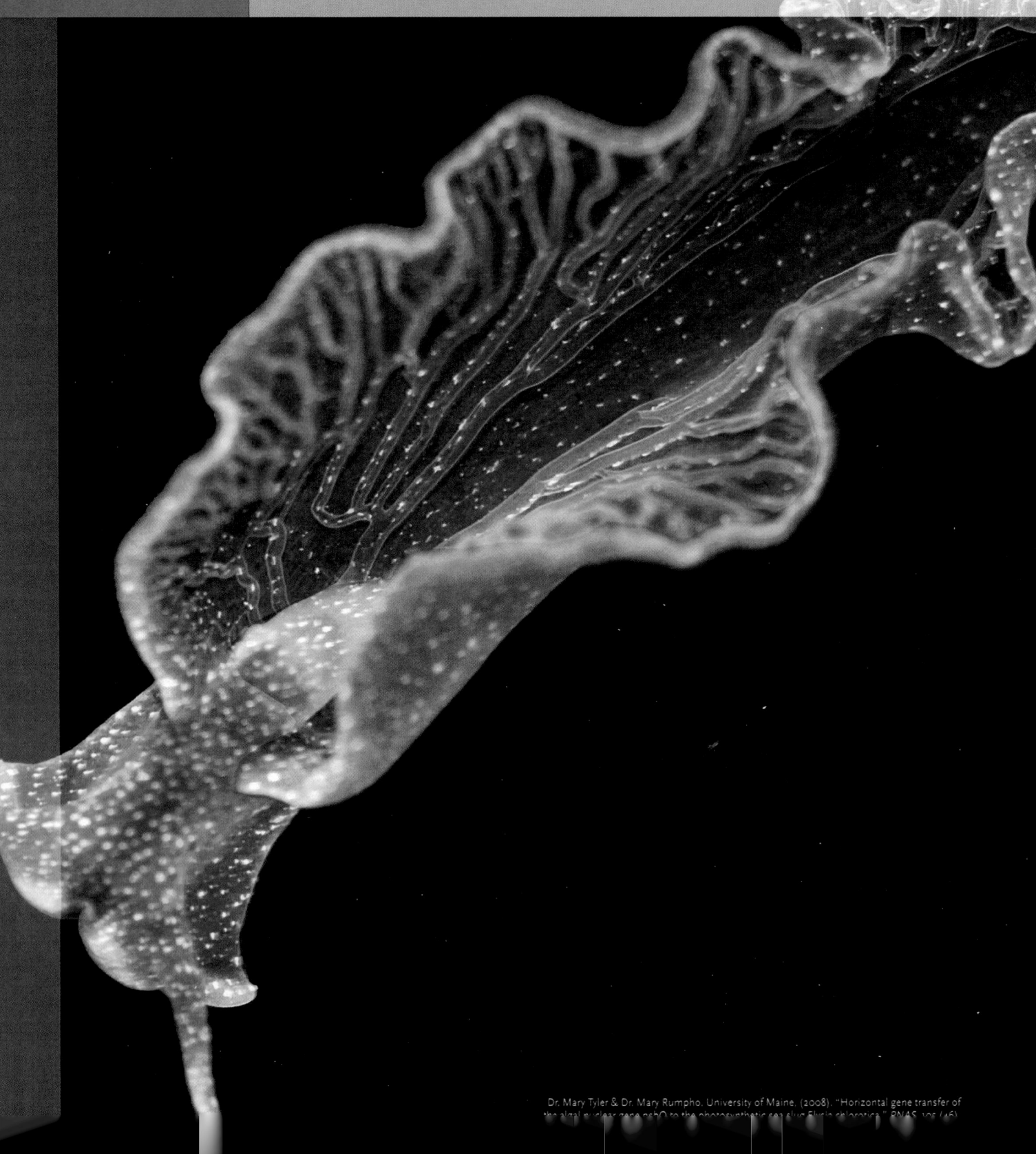

## WHY IT MATTERS

A picnic on the rolling hills of Tuscany on a warm summer day would not be complete without fresh bread, tasty cheeses, and a glass of fragrant wine **(Figure 5.1)**. These appetizing treats of life are the products of a process called fermentation—the same mechanism used by cells to ensure continued production of ATP (adenosine triphosphate) when oxygen is not available. The earliest evidence for the use of fermentation to make cheese and wine in Europe dates back about 7,500 years ago. Using gas chromatography and carbon–isotope ratios, scientists traced and dated dairy fat—isolated from the pores of ancient ceramic pottery vessels that were once used to strain milk—to the Neolithic period. During the cheese-making process, these specialized sieve pottery vessels were used by the people of this period to separate fatty milk curd from lactose-containing whey. Straining the milk is believed to have reduced the amount of lactose in the cheese, which would have been critical to the lactose-intolerant, farming societies of this time. More importantly, cheese making provided a method for preserving milk, a significant advancement in a prerefrigerator era. In turn, this increased the value in milk-producing animals and contributed to the evolution of livestock domestication.

Winemaking, or vinification, was likely initiated by farmers who had discovered alcohol—a product of fermentation—in decaying and damaged grapes. One of the most important organisms in winemaking is yeast, which resides on grape skin. Yeast is responsible for converting grape sugars into alcohol by a process called alcoholic fermentation. *Saccharomyces cerevisiae* is the common yeast type used in winemaking, and as you can imagine, the global multibillion dollar wine industry relies heavily on the fermentation mechanisms of

these single-celled fungi organisms. As such, winemakers are sensitive to the type or strain of yeast used in their wine manufacturing plants. Oenology, the study of winemaking, examines and compares the structural and functional genomes of various yeast strains to identify those that are ideal for making wine. Differing genetic

**FIGURE 5.1** Products of fermentation. Cheese, bread, and wine are all produced by the process of fermentation.

Thomas M Perkins/Shutterstock.com

yeast strains can generate distinguishing aromatic metabolites during fermentation that provide certain wines with their own unique bouquet.

In this chapter, we will further explore fermentation as an alternative mechanism of ATP production by oxidizing sugars in the absence of oxygen. We will also compare fermentation to cellular respiration, the process of oxidizing sugars using oxygen and a proton motive force for ATP production. But before we do that, we will begin the chapter by describing how sugars are actually created in the first place via photosynthesis, a process that requires water, carbon dioxide, and, most importantly, sunlight. As you go through this chapter, keep in mind the important concepts you learned in Chapter 4 regarding energy transformations, redox reactions, and metabolic pathways. You'll find applications to all of these concepts in photosynthesis, respiration, and fermentation. To help you organize these concepts and clarify their connections, we will construct a concept map, starting with photosynthesis, then respiration, and, finally, fermentation.

## 5.1 Photosynthesis: Capturing and Transforming Light Energy into Chemical Energy

Every year, school-aged children perform the basic bean plant experiment in their science class to determine the role of sunlight in plant growth **(Figure 5.2)**. The procedure is simple: plant bean seeds in a container of soil and grow the plants with water in the presence and absence of light. The results are always the same: the plants grown in the presence of sunlight are healthy, whereas the ones in darkness fail to develop successfully. This classic experiment illustrates that sunlight, or solar energy, is a main source of energy that is harnessed by plants and used to make the organic molecules, such as sugar, that plants require for survival (see the Purple Pages for an overview of organic molecules). This process, called photosynthesis, is carried out by photoautotrophs (primary producers) and is vital to most life today on this planet. As we discussed in Chapter 2, primary producers are positioned at the lowest trophic level and support all of the other organisms (primary, secondary, and tertiary consumers) above them in the food chain.

### Sunlight Is the Ultimate Source of Energy

Recall from Chapter 4 that cells need energy to carry out the work required for survival. But since we cannot create energy (remember the first law of thermodynamics), where does this energy come from? Simply put, the Sun is our ultimate source of energy. Energy from the Sun is delivered to Earth's surface mostly as light, a form of **electromagnetic radiation** (energy) that is transmitted in waves through space. The energy associated with these waves is inversely proportional to its **wavelength** (the distance between the crests of two consecutive waves)—the shorter the wavelength of light, the greater the energy it contains **(Figure 5.3a)**. The electromagnetic spectrum encompasses a wide range of electromagnetic wavelengths, each associated with a distinct amount of energy **(Figure 5.3b)**. Ultraviolet light, X-rays, and gamma rays are on the lower end of the electromagnetic spectrum with wavelengths of less than 400 nm, which means that they contain the highest amount of energy. Hence, these forms of radiation are extremely dangerous to cells because their high energy content can break the chemical bonds of biological molecules, thus destroying both the structures and functions of cells. At the other end of the spectrum are low-energy wavelengths such as radio waves, which are not harmful to cells. At the centre of the spectrum is visible light (380 to 700 nm),

Catalin Petolea/Shutterstock.com

**FIGURE 5.2** A child examines the growth of a bean plant.

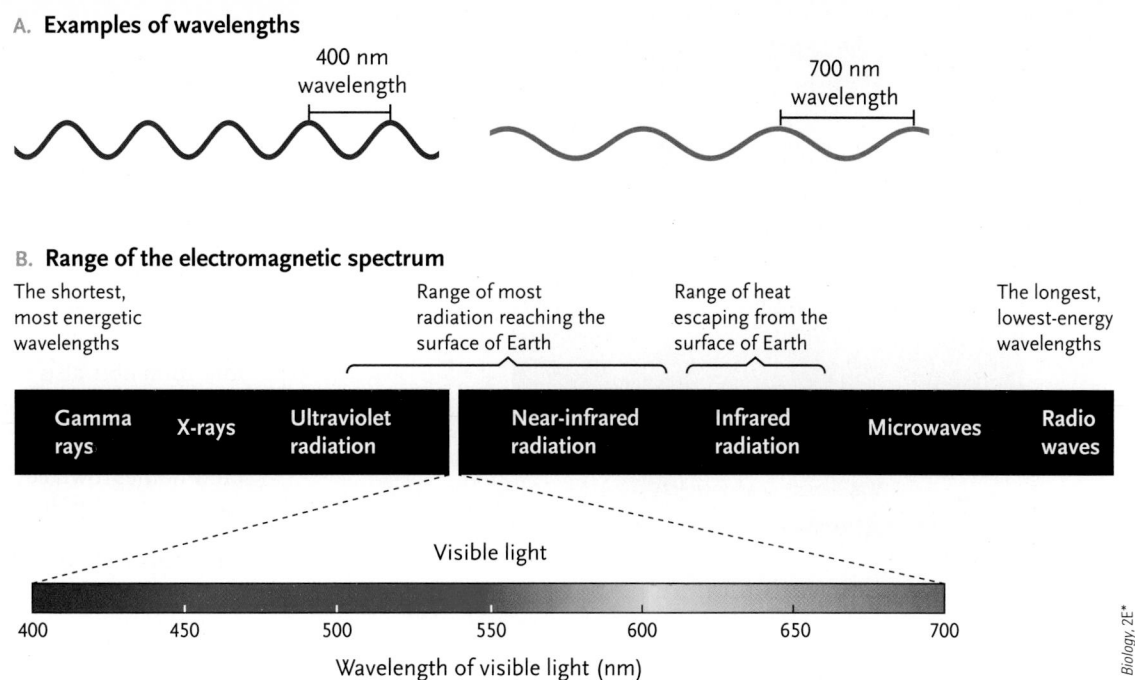

**A. Examples of wavelengths**

400 nm wavelength

700 nm wavelength

**B. Range of the electromagnetic spectrum**

The shortest, most energetic wavelengths

Range of most radiation reaching the surface of Earth

Range of heat escaping from the surface of Earth

The longest, lowest-energy wavelengths

| Gamma rays | X-rays | Ultraviolet radiation | Near-infrared radiation | Infrared radiation | Microwaves | Radio waves |

Visible light

400    450    500    550    600    650    700

Wavelength of visible light (nm)

*Biology, 2E\**

**FIGURE 5.3** The electromagnetic spectrum. **(a)** Examples of wavelengths, showing the difference between the longest and shortest wavelengths of visible light. **(b)** The electromagnetic spectrum ranges from gamma rays to radio waves. Visible light, which includes the wavelengths used for photosynthesis, occupies only a narrow band of the spectrum.

the radiation that you can see with your eyes as different colours. Most of the electromagnetic radiation that actually reaches Earth's surface is visible light, and as such, it is the main form of energy that drives photosynthesis.

But how is the energy in visible light used by living organisms here on Earth? When light reaches our planet's surface, special receptive molecules called **pigments** are able to capture or absorb this energy. In photoautotrophs such as plants and cyanobacteria, specialized pigments capture light energy, which will then be converted into chemical energy. This light energy is captured by the electrons within the pigment molecule (see the Purple Pages for an overview about electrons and atoms). These electrons gain just enough energy to move from their current energy shell within an atom of the pigment into a shell farther away from the pigment's atomic nucleus. This is described as an electron moving from a ground (low-energy) state to an excited (high-energy) state **(Figure 5.4)**. Different pigments require different amounts of energy to move the electrons in that particular pigment from their ground state to their excited state. In other words, each pigment absorbs a different wavelength of light and reflects or scatters the other wavelengths of light. Therefore, each pigment has a different characteristic colour—that of the wavelengths they reflect and do not absorb.

So what do these excited (high energy and unstable) electrons do with the energy they have captured? In

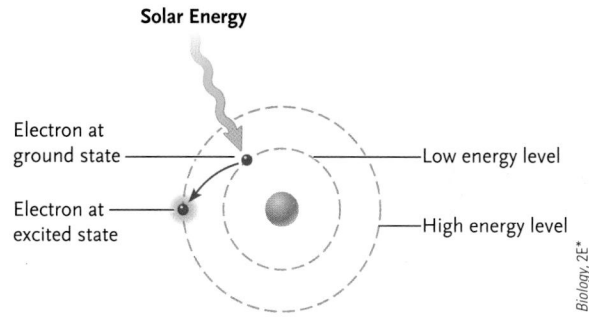

**Solar Energy**

Electron at ground state

Low energy level

Electron at excited state

High energy level

*Biology, 2E\**

**FIGURE 5.4** Solar energy is absorbed by an excitable electron that moves from a relatively low energy level to a higher energy level.

photoautotrophs, this energy will be released by these electrons, thereby initiating a series of events that make up photosynthesis. Photosynthesis converts light energy into chemical energy, which both primary producers and consumers require for survival.

**Chlorophylls** and **carotenoids** are pigment molecules that absorb light at the beginning of photosynthesis **(Figure 5.5a, p. 104)**. Chlorophylls, also called green pigments, are major photosynthetic pigments in cyanobacteria, green algae, and plants. Chlorophylls absorb both blue-violet and red light but not green light. Instead, the green wavelengths of light are reflected, thus giving these pigments their characteristic green colour that we detect with our eyes. The two most dominant types are chlorophyll *a* and *b*, which differ only slightly in their molecular structure. The carotenoids are **accessory pigments**, which absorb

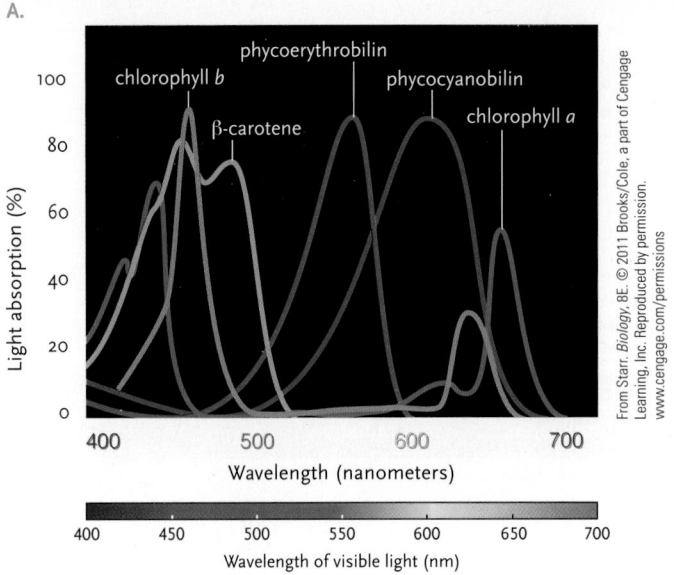

FIGURE 5.5 **(a)** Absorption spectra of a few photosynthetic pigments. Line colour is the characteristic colour of each pigment. **(b)** Changing colours of leaves in autumn. **(c)** An unevenly ripened tomato (left) and an evenly ripened tomato (right).

light and then transfer the energy to chlorophyll *a*. Carotenoids broaden the range of light absorbed; however, they do not absorb light in the yellow-orange wavelength range. Instead, these wavelengths of light are reflected, making these yellow-orange pigments. Other pigment molecules, such as phycobilins in protists and bacteria, absorb and reflect a diverse range of light.

Since the amount of chlorophyll in most plants is greater than that of other pigment molecules, the green colour reflected by these pigments dominates. However, during the autumn season when plants are preparing for dormancy, the chlorophylls break down at a faster rate than other pigment molecules, seen as the changing colours of the leaves **(Figure 5.5b)**. Pigment molecules, however, are not restricted to leaves but can also be found in the stems and fruits of plants. Take, for example, the tomato plant **(Figure 5.5c)**. Unequal distribution of chlorophylls and carotenoids in the tomato fruit causes them to ripen unevenly, a characteristic of homegrown tomatoes. Research on the modern tomato varieties, *Solanum lycopersicum*, has uncovered the *uniform ripening* gene

that, when mutated, is responsible for the uniform ripening of the fruit, which is an attractive selling feature of uniformly red, store-bought tomatoes. This effect involves the production and even distribution of chlorophylls and carotenoids in the tomato fruit, which give the characteristic red colour. Unfortunately, this mutation also inadvertently reduces sugar content, making these tomatoes less tasty than their homegrown counterparts.

## Chloroplasts Are Photosynthetic Factories

In photosynthetic prokaryotes such as cyanobacteria, the light-capturing pigments are primarily located on the cell surface. However, in photosynthetic eukaryotes such as plants and algae, these pigments are located on the surface of a group of organelles called plastids. Phylogenetic data suggest that all plastids today originated from cyanobacteria endosymbionts (recall from Chapter 3 the theory of endosymbiosis). The Plantae hypothesis, one of many working hypotheses on this subject, suggests that the evolutionary branch of Archaeplastida, which includes all land plants and the protist groups of green and red algae, have plastids that arose from only one cyanobacterial ancestor. In 2013, this hypothesis was strongly supported by several independent lines of evidence gained through the analysis of the most complete set of photosynthetic genomes available to date. These findings are significant because they allow scientists to better understand the evolutionary relationships of all photosynthesizing eukaryotes. Today, research into the evolution of photosynthesis is examining an amoeba-type protist named *Paulinella chromatophora*. This organism has two types of photosynthetic organelles that represent an earlier stage in the evolution of plastids. As such, they are an excellent research model to study the evolution of chloroplasts and photosynthesis in certain eukaryotic cells.

In this chapter, we will focus on **chloroplasts**, a type of plastid well specialized in photosynthesis and probably the plastid you are most familiar with. Found in the cytoplasm of plants and some other photosynthetic eukaryotic cells, chloroplasts are surrounded by two membranes (**Figure 5.6**). The double membrane is a unique feature as only a few other organelles, including the nucleus and mitochondria, share this characteristic. If you recall from Chapter 3, we discussed the significance of plastids having a double membrane—this double membrane is supportive evidence for the theory of endosymbiosis. The two membranes, termed the inner and **outer membranes**, separate the chloroplast into two compartments. The **intermembrane compartment** is found between the inner and outer membrane and the stroma, a semifluid matrix found within the inner membrane. Within the stroma are chloroplast DNA, ribosomes, and a third set of interconnected sacs of folded membranes called **thylakoid membranes** or thylakoids. These folded membranes contain the pigments that absorb light energy and are organized as stacks of discs called grana (singular = granum). The space within the thylakoids is called the **thylakoid lumen**.

These various components of the chloroplast work collectively to carry out photosynthesis. Although we often summarize photosynthesis into one neatly organized chemical equation, as shown here,

$$6CO_2 + 6H_2O \xrightarrow{\text{light energy}} C_6H_{12}O_6 + 6O_2$$

carbon dioxide    water              glucose    oxygen

the reality is that photosynthesis is a series of cellular reactions within a complex anabolic pathway. The pathway is divided into two stages: the **light-dependent reactions** followed by the **light-independent reactions**, also termed the **Calvin cycle (Figure 5.7, p. 106)**.

The thylakoids are the primary site for light-dependent reactions because the pigment molecules that capture light to drive these reactions are located on these membranes. During these reactions, the light energy that is captured by the pigments is converted into chemical energy in the form of ATP. These reactions also involve splitting water molecules and generating both the reduced form of nicotinamide adenine dinucleotide phosphate (**NADPH**) and oxygen. The products of these light-dependent reactions, namely NADPH and ATP, are then transferred to the stroma and, along with carbon dioxide, are used in light-independent reactions to produce sugar, which is simply another form of chemical energy. In the next sections, we will explore the light-dependent and light-independent reactions of photosynthesis in more detail while keeping

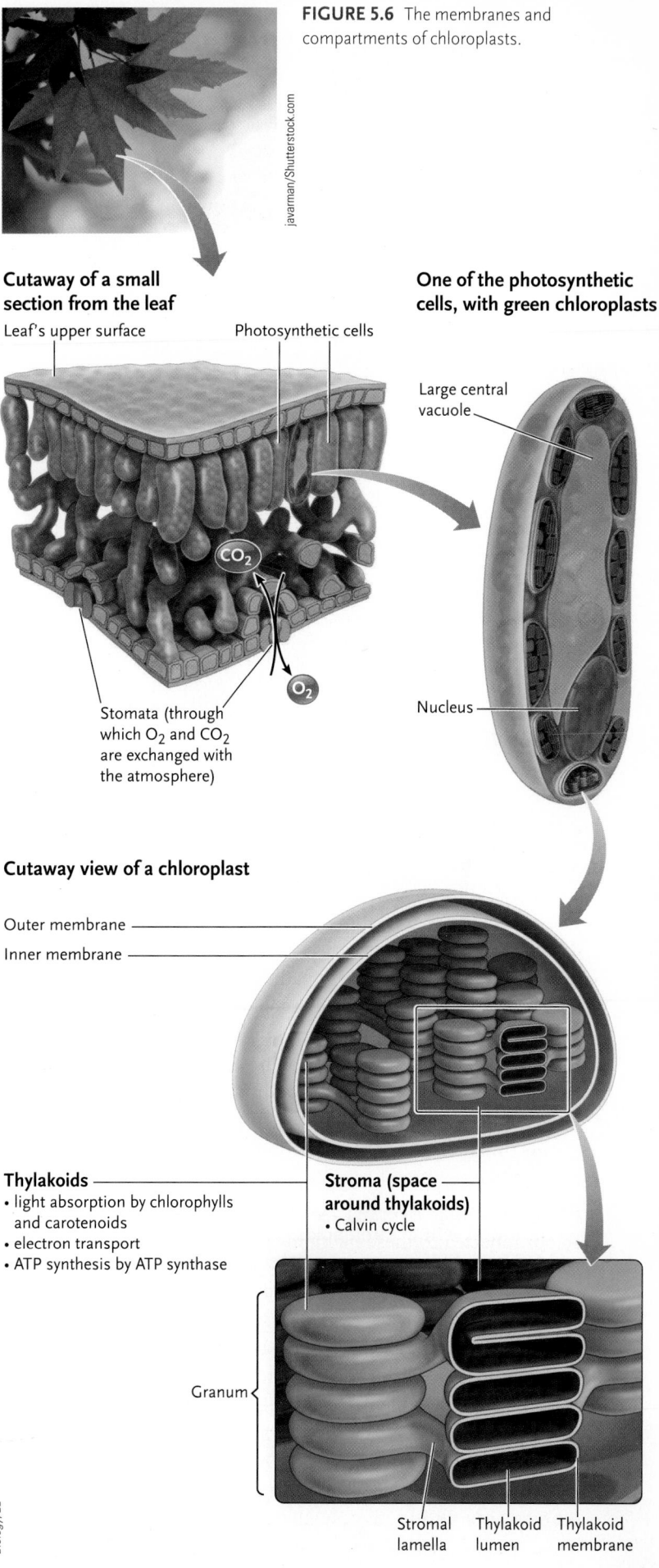

**FIGURE 5.6** The membranes and compartments of chloroplasts.

javarman/Shutterstock.com

**Cutaway of a small section from the leaf**

Leaf's upper surface

Photosynthetic cells

$CO_2$

$O_2$

Stomata (through which $O_2$ and $CO_2$ are exchanged with the atmosphere)

**One of the photosynthetic cells, with green chloroplasts**

Large central vacuole

Nucleus

**Cutaway view of a chloroplast**

Outer membrane

Inner membrane

**Thylakoids**
- light absorption by chlorophylls and carotenoids
- electron transport
- ATP synthesis by ATP synthase

**Stroma (space around thylakoids)**
- Calvin cycle

Granum

Stromal lamella

Thylakoid lumen

Thylakoid membrane

Biology, 2E*

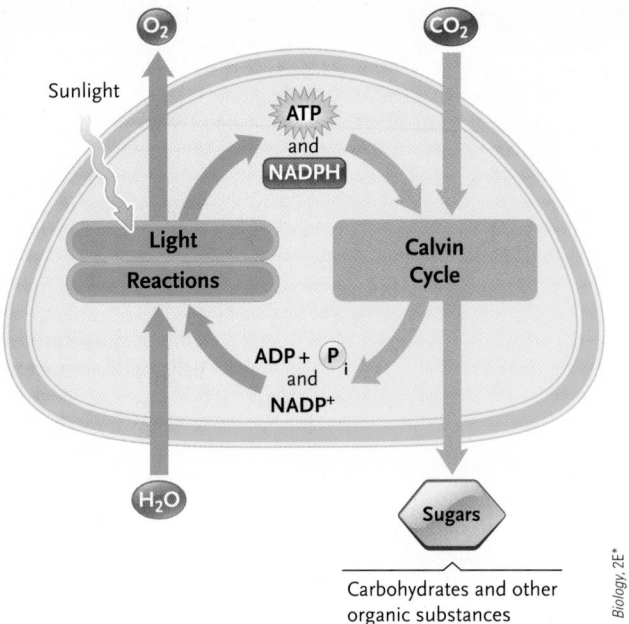

**FIGURE 5.7** The light reactions and the Calvin cycle are the two stages of photosynthesis. The two are linked together by reactants and products. Both processes occur in the chloroplasts of photoautotrophic eukaryotes (plants and algae) and in photosynthetic bacteria.

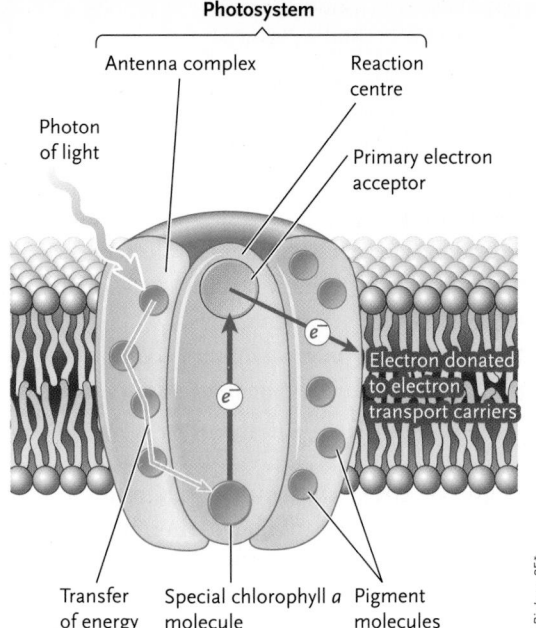

**FIGURE 5.8** Major components of a photosystem. A group of pigment proteins form an antenna complex that surrounds a reaction centre. Light energy absorbed anywhere in the antenna complex is conducted by inductive resonance to a special chlorophyll *a* molecule in the reaction centre. The absorbed light is converted to chemical energy when an excited electron from the chlorophyll *a* is transferred to a primary acceptor, also in the reaction centre. High-energy electrons are passed out of the photosystem to the electron transport system. The blue arrows show the path of energy flow.

in mind that these reactions, like many cellular reactions, are simply mechanisms to harness and transfer energy within the cell via the gain and loss of electrons (redox reactions).

## Light-Dependent Reactions Use Light and Water to Generate NADPH, ATP, and Oxygen

The light-dependent reactions can be subdivided into both the linear and cyclic pathways. We will first discuss the four main steps of the linear pathway to illustrate how light energy and water are used to generate NADPH, ATP, and oxygen. Then we will describe how the cyclic pathway is used as an alternative mechanism to generate supplemental ATP without producing additional NADPH and oxygen.

As mentioned above, initiation of photosynthesis requires the capture of solar or light energy by pigment molecules. In eukaryotes, pigments, including chlorophylls *a* and *b* and carotenoids, are arranged together within the **light-harvesting complex** of structures called **photosystems (Figure 5.8)**. Embedded within the thylakoid membrane are two types of photosystems: **photosystem I (PSI)** and **photosystem II (PSII)**. Although PSI was the first to be discovered, and hence named PSI, it is actually the second photosystem used in light-dependent reactions. PSII, which was discovered after PSI, is the first photosystem used in this pathway. Overall, the two photosystems share a similar structure and function and work cooperatively during photosynthesis. In both photosystems, the light-harvesting complex surrounds an inner

reaction centre containing a **specialized chlorophyll *a*** and a **primary electron acceptor** molecule. One distinguishing feature between the two photosystems is the type of specialized chlorophyll *a* pigment within the reaction centre. In PSII, the chlorophyll *a* in the reaction centre is termed P680 because it absorbs light maximally at a wavelength of 680 nm. On the other hand, in PSI, the chlorophyll *a* in the reaction centre is termed P700 because it absorbs light maximally at 700 nm.

### Step 1: Harvesting Light Energy and Gaining Electrons

So how do photosystems harness light energy, and where does this energy go? In the linear pathway, pigments within the light-harvesting complex of PSII absorb light, which, as described above, excites resident electrons within the pigment **(Figure 5.9, step 1)**. The increased energy associated with these excited electrons is transferred to other electrons in neighbouring pigment molecules, one by one, until the energy reaches the reaction centre, where P680 (specialized chlorophyll *a* molecule of PSII) accepts the remaining energy. The energy now excites an electron within P680, making it so unstable and highly reactive that it transfers the excited electron and its associated energy entirely to the primary electron acceptor. You may recall from Chapter 4

**1** Absorption of light energy by photosystem II results in the oxidation of P680. The liberated electron is used to reduce the primary acceptor. P680$^+$ is rapidly reduced back to P680 by an electron from $H_2O$ transferred from the oxygen evolving complex.

**2** From the primary acceptor, the electron is passed to the mobile carrier molecule plastoquinone (PQ). As it accepts an electron from photosystem II, it picks up a proton from the stroma. PQ diffuses through the membrane before binding to the cytochrome complex, at which point, it donates an electron and releases a proton into the thylakoid lumen. From the cytochrome complex, the electron is donated to plastocyanin.

**3** Absorption of light energy by photosystem I results in the oxidation of P700. The liberated electron is used to reduce the primary acceptor before being passed to ferredoxin. This single electron is then held by the NADP$^+$ reductase complex. P700$^+$ is reduced back to P700 by the electron that is coming from plastocyanin. Once a second electron travels along the chain and reaches NADP$^+$ reductase complex, NADP$^+$ is reduced to NADPH.

**4** Proton pumping by plastoquinone (red arrows) creates a concentration gradient of H$^+$ (a proton motive force) across the thylakoid membrane. The gradient is dissipated as H$^+$ diffuses back into the stroma through the ATPase complex, which drives the synthesis of ATP from ADP and Pi.

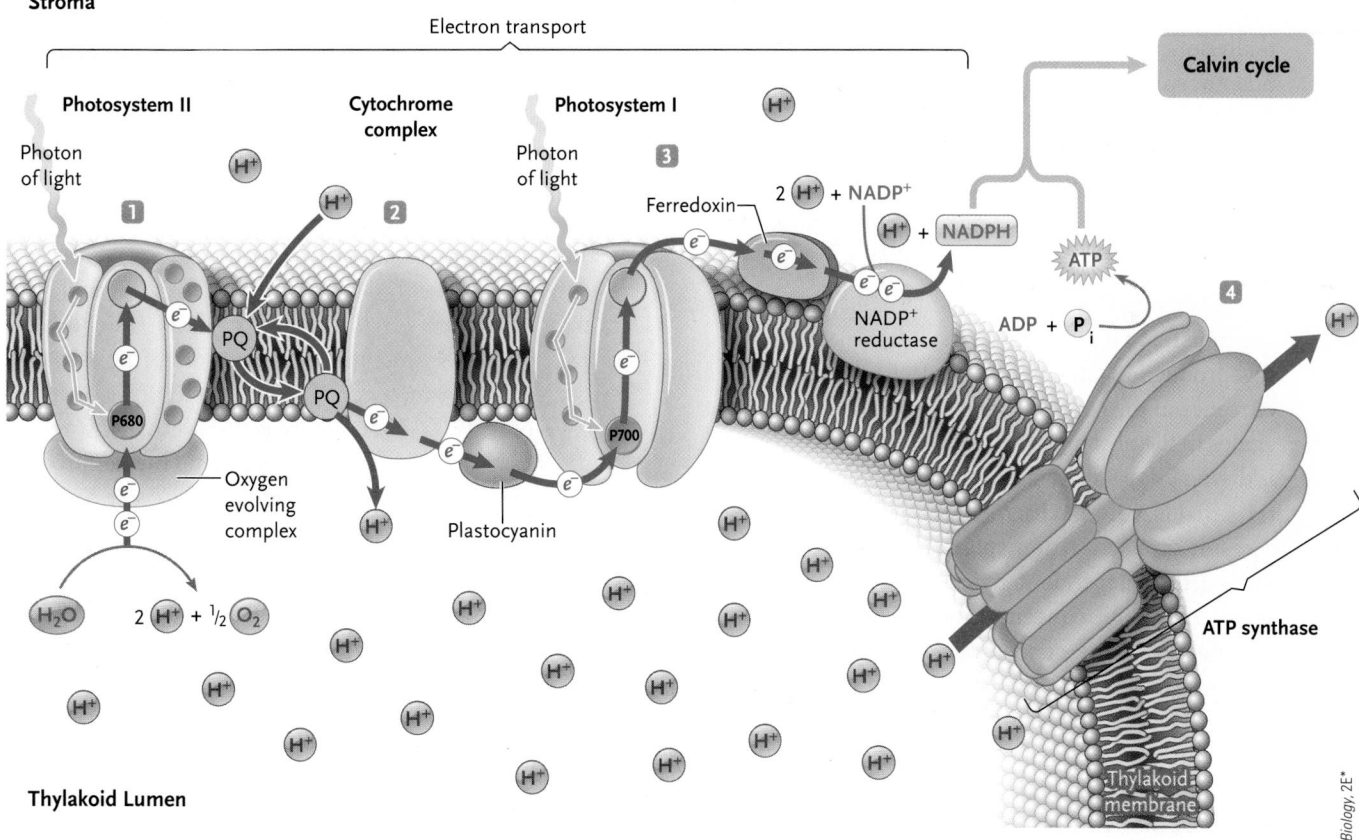

**FIGURE 5.9** The light-dependent reactions of photosynthesis. A model of the eukaryotic thylakoid membrane illustrating major protein and redox factors required for the transport of electrons, generation of NADPH, and synthesis of ATP.

that the transfer of electrons is a redox reaction. This is exactly what is occurring here: the primary electron acceptor is reduced (gain of electrons), whereas P680 is oxidized (loss of electrons). But how does the P680 replenish the electrons it loses to the primary electron acceptor during this redox reaction? Associated with PSII is an enzyme complex called an **oxygen-evolving complex** that splits water molecules into hydrogen and oxygen and releases electrons in the process. These electrons are donated to the P680 in PSII to replenish the electrons it lost to the primary electron acceptor. The hydrogen generated by splitting water accumulates in the thylakoid lumen, whereas the oxygen that is produced is released and accumulates in the atmosphere. We'll learn later in this chapter how oxygen is essential for the survival of aerobic organisms, such as yourself, to oxidize or break down organic molecules to make ATP.

*Step 2: Transferring Energized Electrons*

Now that we understand how photosystems harness light energy and transfer the energy via an excited electron to the primary electron acceptor, how is this energy transferred to the electron transport system and eventually converted into chemical energy? Recall that chemical energy is the form of energy that is used by all organisms for survival. The conversion begins when the primary electron acceptor in PSII donates the excited electron to an **electron transport chain** that is also on the thylakoid membrane **(Figure 5.9, step 2)**. This chain consists of multiple protein complexes containing non-protein cofactors and electron carriers. These cofactors and electron carriers accept (become reduced) and donate (become oxidized) electrons in a series of redox reactions that move or transfer the electrons down the chain.

## Step 3: Re-energizing the Transferring Electrons

During the transfer of electrons, energy is released (remember that the transfer of electrons is not 100% efficient), and by the time the electrons reach PSI, they have lost so much energy that they need to be re-energized. But how can electrons be re-energized? Re-energizing electrons requires capturing more light using pigments within the light-harvesting complex of PSI **(Figure 5.9, step 3)**. Similar to what occurs in PSII, the excited electrons are transferred completely to a primary acceptor electron in the PSI reaction centre. From here, the electrons are eventually donated to $NADP^+$ (nicotinamide adenine dinucleotide phosphate), a coenzyme located in the stroma. Once $NADP^+$ has gained electrons, it is reduced to NADPH, an electron carrier that will transfer these electrons to the light-independent reactions.

## Step 4: Using Stored Energy to Make ATP

In the last step of the light-dependent reactions, we finally see transfer of light energy into chemical energy through the production of ATP. Recall that ATP is the energy currency of the cell and is required to build organic molecules in the next phase of photosynthesis. ATP synthesis is driven by an electrochemical gradient of hydrogen ions ($H^+$) that is generated across the thylakoid membrane as a result of electron transport and NADPH production during light-dependent reactions. This gradient, composed of a high concentration of $H^+$ in the thylakoid lumen and a low concentration of $H^+$ in the stroma **(Figure 5.9, step 4)**, is created in three ways: (1) the pumping of $H^+$ across the thylakoid membrane, from the stroma to the thylakoid lumen, when electrons are transferred from PSII to PSI; (2) $H^+$ accumulation in the thylakoid lumen by the splitting of water in the lumen; and (3) the removal of $H^+$ in the stroma during NADPH production. Remember from Chapter 4, electrochemical gradients contain stored energy (like a battery) and are generally unstable. To reach stability, this stored energy must be released by diffusing $H^+$ from the thylakoid lumen (where $H^+$ concentration is high) toward the stroma (where $H^+$ concentration is low). However, $H^+$ are charged and do not move freely across the lipid bilayer of the membrane (recall membrane transport from Chapter 4). Instead, $H^+$ requires a transport protein to facilitate its movement across the membrane. One such protein embedded in the thylakoid membrane is **ATP synthase**. ATP synthase is also the enzyme that catalyzes the synthesis of ATP. Hence, when $H^+$ moves through ATP synthase from the thylakoid lumen to the stroma, the energy stored within the electrochemical gradient of the thylakoid membrane is released. This energy is harnessed by ATP synthase to catalyze ATP production in the stroma, which will be used to power light-independent reactions. The energy stored in ATP is now in the form of chemical energy.

## Light-Dependent Reactions Overview

Now let's recap. If you start at the beginning of the light-dependent pathway, from the capture of light energy by the pigment molecules in PSII, you can trace the transfer and conversion of light energy from the Sun into chemical energy in ATP. This process of generating ATP using light energy is called **photophosphorylation**. Later in the chapter, we will compare photophosphorylation to another mechanism of ATP production that also uses the energy stored in electrochemical gradients. However, in the latter mechanism, the initial input of energy does not come directly from sunlight but instead from the oxidation (or breakdown) of sugars such as glucose.

In some instances, the electron transport chain can be used to generate additional ATP in the absence of NADPH production. This process uses the cyclic pathway and occurs when there is an abundance of NADPH and oxygen in the cell. In this case, instead of being shuttled to $NADP^+$, electrons are cycled back and forth between PSI and electron carriers in the electron transport chain, independent of PSII. Since electrons are still moving down the chain, an electrochemical gradient is generated and drives the production of ATP. And since there is no splitting of water or transfer of electrons to $NADP^+$, there is no further production of oxygen or NADPH, respectively. The cyclic pathway, however, still relies on the input of light energy into PSI to excite the electrons that are cycling. **Figure 5.10** compares the energy flow between the linear and cyclic pathways of the light-dependent pathways of photosynthesis. Which of the two pathways is predominantly used in a cell depends on its current metabolic demands. During photosynthesis, additional ATP production without any further production of NADPH is important to maintain the optimal ATP-to-NADPH ratio (~1.5) required for efficient carbon fixation, which occurs during the light-independent reactions of photosynthesis. In essence, the cyclic pathway helps balance the energy output generated by light-dependent reactions (the first half of photosynthesis) with the energy input required to drive light-independent reactions (the second half of photosynthesis). This dominates even more during times of increased sugar production. On the other hand, during cold temperatures, when there is little production of sugar, the demand for NADPH decreases. As a result, NADPH accumulation in the cell inhibits the linear pathway, resulting in a switch toward using the cyclic pathway. This alternative pathway allows for the continued production of ATP required for other cellular metabolic reactions, without generating more NADPH.

## Light-Independent Reactions Use NADPH, ATP, and Carbon Dioxide to Generate Sugar

Carbon is the backbone of most organic molecules, including sugar. Thus, to build sugar, carbon must be acquired by the cell. In photosynthetic organisms, carbon can be harnessed from carbon dioxide (CO$_2$). The process of extracting carbon from an inorganic molecule, such as CO$_2$, to build an organic molecule, such as sugar, is called **carbon fixation**. Carbon fixation is the underlying principle of the second half of photosynthesis, the light-independent reactions (named so because these reactions do not require the direct input of light energy). Other names for this pathway include the Calvin–Benson–Bassham cycle (Calvin cycle for short), named for the three scientists who discovered the pathway, and the **C$_3$ pathway**, because the first organic intermediate formed during this pathway is a three-carbon molecule. There are three main phases to the Calvin cycle: carbon fixation, reduction, and regeneration.

### Phase 1: Carbon Fixation

Remember that for eukaryotic cells to use carbon from the environment, it has to be altered, or fixed, into a usable form. In eukaryotes, light-independent reactions occur in the stroma of the chloroplast and involve two initial reactants: CO$_2$, which is taken up by cells, and a five-carbon sugar called <u>ribulose-1-5-bisphosphate (RuBP)</u> **(Figure 5.11, phase 1, p. 110)**. An enzyme called **rubisco** is the catalyst that attaches CO$_2$ to RuBP in the first step of the Calvin cycle, the **carbon fixation** step. The product of this reaction is 3-phosphoglycerate (3-PGA), a three-carbon organic acid. The conversion of carbon from an inorganic to an organic form (carbon fixation) is critical in life. Heterotrophs, which will consume these photoautotrophs, can harness and use carbon only in the organic form.

### Phase 2: Reduction

Building organic molecules requires both energy and electrons. During the cycle, ATP and NADPH from the earlier light-dependent reactions donate energy and electrons, respectively **(Figure 5.11, phase 2)**. Energy and electrons are required to convert 3-PGA produced in phase 1 into <u>glyceraldehyde-3-phosphate (G3P)</u>, an essential starting material for sugar production. To produce sugar, G3P must exit the Calvin cycle. Therefore, to balance the number of carbon atoms coming into and going out of the cycle, three molecules of CO$_2$ and therefore three turns of the cycle are required. As a result, six G3P molecules are produced. One of the six G3P molecules will leave the cycle to be used in the production of glucose and other organic compounds and the remaining five G3P molecules remain in the cycle.

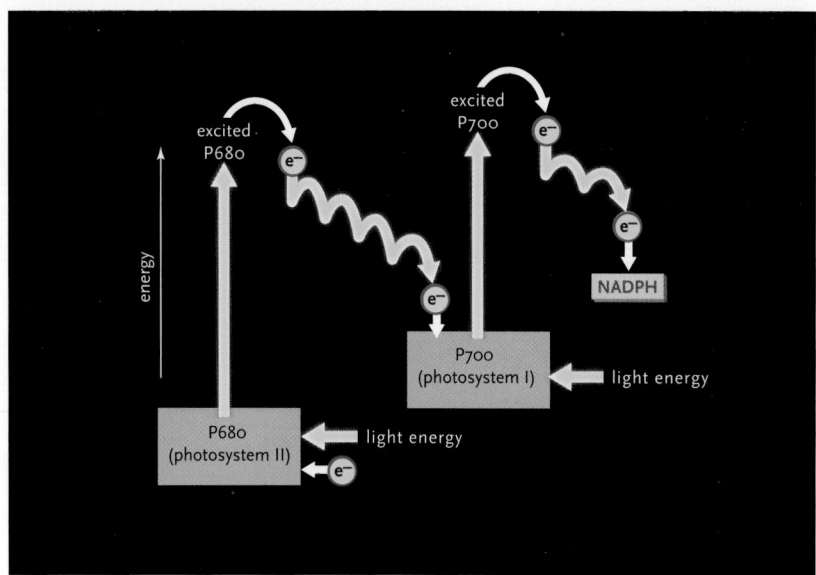

**A.** The noncyclic pathway is a one-way flow of electrons from water, to photosystem II, to photosystem I, to NADPH. As long as electrons continue to flow through the two electron transfer chains, H$^+$ continues to be carried across the thylakoid membrane, and ATP and NADPH keep forming. Light provides the energy boosts that keep the pathway going.

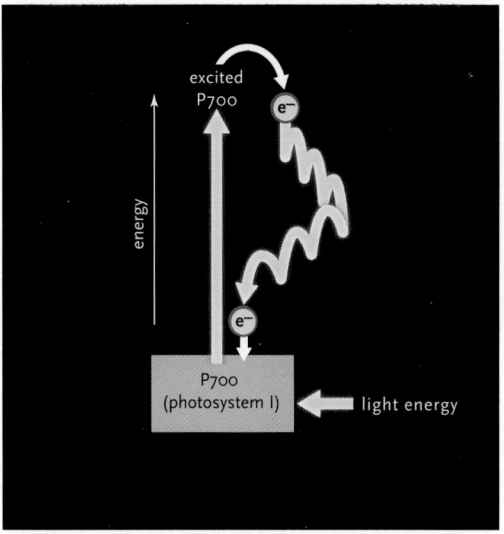

**B.** In the cyclic pathway, electrons ejected from photosystem I are returned to it. As long as electrons continue to pass through its electron transfer chain, H$^+$ continues to be carried across the thylakoid membrane, and ATP continues to form. Light provides the energy boost that keeps the cycle going.

**FIGURE 5.10** Energy flows in linear versus cyclic pathways. The graphs compare the input and flow of energy as electrons move through the linear versus the cyclic pathways of the light-dependent reactions of photosynthesis.

SOURCE: From Starr. *Biology*, 8E. © 2011 Brooks-Cole, a part of Cengage Learning, Inc. Reproduced by permission. www.cengage.com/permissions

### Phase 3: Regeneration

Recall from Chapter 4 that the final product of any cyclic metabolic pathway is also the initial reactant in the pathway (hence the term *cyclic*). Thus, regenerating RuBP completes the Calvin cycle now, making it available to be used again. So the five remaining G3P molecules produced in the second phase are used in the third phase through a series of reactions to regenerate the three initial RuBP used in the cycle **(Figure 5.11, phase 3)**. This regeneration phase also requires the hydrolysis of ATP.

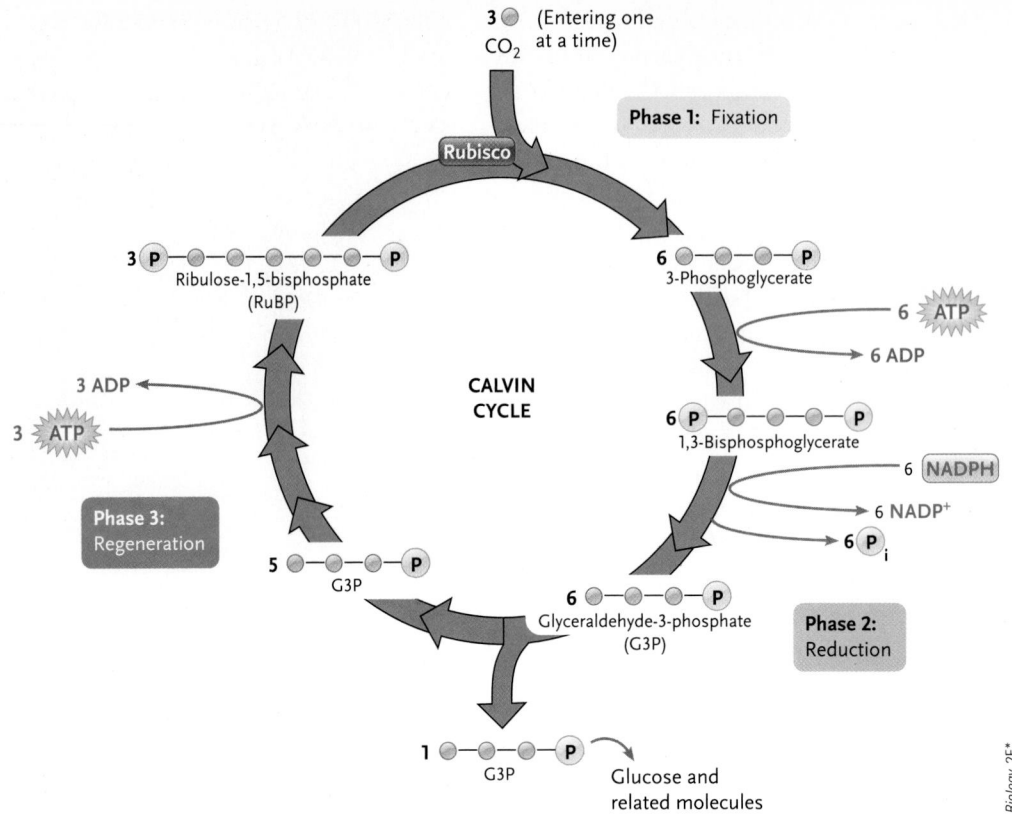

**FIGURE 5.11** The Calvin cycle. An overview of the three phases of the Calvin cycle showing the number of carbon atoms (red balls) at each step. For every three molecules of $CO_2$ that are fixed, six G3P molecules are generated. One G3P exits the cycle to make glucose and related molecules, and the other five are used to regenerate RuBP.

## Calvin Cycle Overview

In three turns of the Calvin cycle, three $CO_2$ are fixed using three RuBP molecules to generate six molecules of G3P. One G3P exits the cycle, and the remaining five G3P are used to regenerate the three initial RuBP. The cycle also requires six NADPH and nine ATP molecules (produced in light-dependent reactions).

## C₄ and CAM Pathways Are Adaptations That Minimize Photorespiration

When the ancestors of modern-day plants made the transition from water to land approximately 475 million years ago, they faced a number of challenges, including dehydration. The evaporation of water in the harsh land environment was overcome by some unique adaptations. Two of these adaptations are the waxy cuticle layer that coats the surface of plants and acts as a waterproof barrier and the stomata, which are pores on the surface of plants that can be closed to prevent evaporation. Although both of these adaptations are useful in preventing water loss, unfortunately, they also prevent efficient gas exchanges required for photosynthesis. For example, the closure of stomata on a hot, dry day reduces dehydration but also prevents

carbon dioxide from entering and oxygen from exiting the cell. As a result, the intracellular carbon dioxide levels decrease, whereas oxygen levels rise. This imbalance of gases reduces photosynthesis, which is required to build organic molecules, and instead promotes an inefficient and harmful process called **photorespiration (Figure 5.12)**.

Recall earlier the enzyme rubisco used in the Calvin cycle. Rubisco is an ancient enzyme and one of the most abundant proteins on this planet. Although rubisco binds carbon dioxide during carbon fixation, it also has an affinity for oxygen. During hot and dry conditions, oxygen accumulates in the cell and outcompetes carbon dioxide for rubisco's binding site. As a result, rubisco adds oxygen instead of carbon dioxide to RuBP, eventually leading to the formation of a harmful molecule called glycolate. To

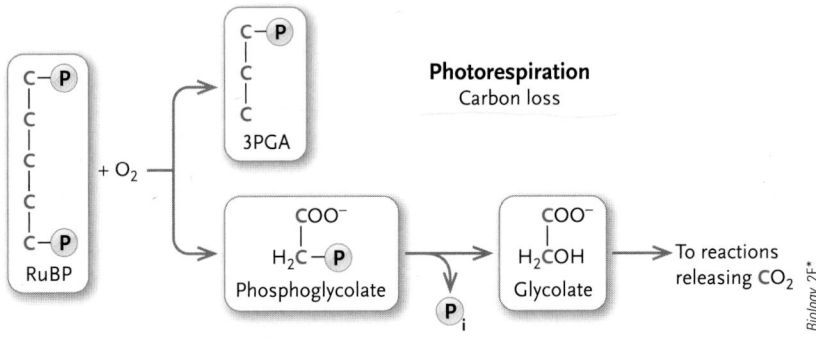

**FIGURE 5.12** Photorespiration. The oxygenase activity of rubisco leads to the production of only one molecule of 3PGA and the loss of carbon in the form of $CO_2$.

detoxify glycolate, the cell releases carbon from the molecule in the form of carbon dioxide. This process is called photorespiration. The disadvantage of photorespiration is that it reduces the cell's ability to fix carbon and instead results in the loss of carbon from the cell. Overall, this wasteful mechanism decreases the cell's efficiency to make sugars.

An alternative mechanism that plants have adapted to overcome photorespiration is the **C₄ pathway**. In **C₄ plants**, when the stomata are closed to conserve water, the carbon dioxide in the mesophyll cells found in the outer tissues of plants binds to an enzyme called **phosphoenolpyruvate (PEP) carboxylase (Figure 5.13a)**. PEP carboxylase has no affinity for oxygen and therefore does not function as an oxygenase. Instead, PEP carboxylase uses carbon dioxide to produce four-carbon intermediates (hence the name C₄ plant), which are shuttled to bundle sheath cells located deeper in the inner tissues of plants. In these cells, the oxygen levels are much lower; therefore, the risk of photorespiration is reduced. As a result, carbon is released from these intermediates within these cells and shuttled into the Calvin cycle for carbon fixation and G3P production.

In **CAM (Crassulacean acid metabolism) plants** such as cacti, pineapples, and other succulent plants, the C₄ pathway and Calvin cycle occur at different times of the

**A. C₄ pathway in C₄ plants**

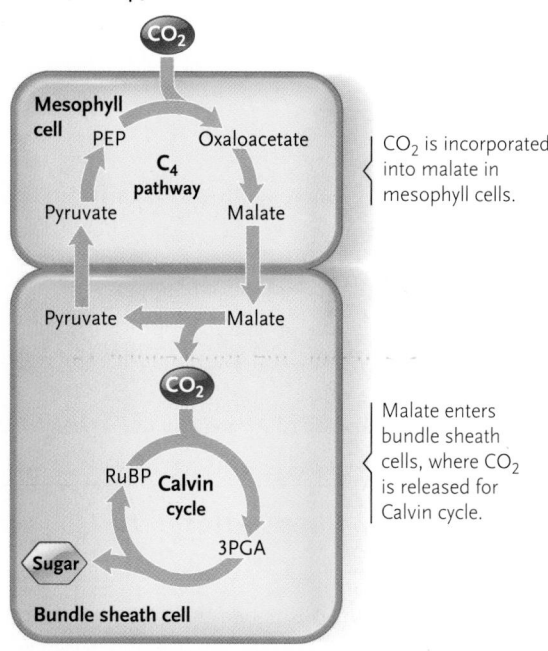

CO₂ is incorporated into malate in mesophyll cells.

Malate enters bundle sheath cells, where CO₂ is released for Calvin cycle.

**B. CAM pathway in CAM plants**

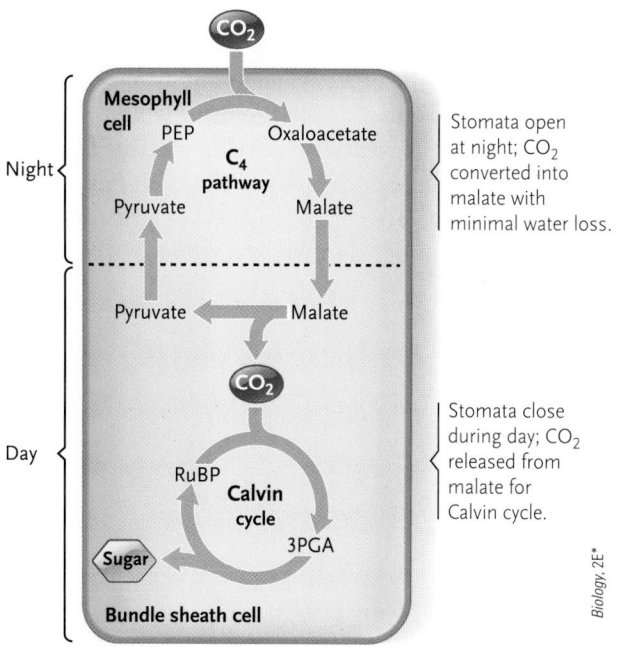

Stomata open at night; CO₂ converted into malate with minimal water loss.

Stomata close during day; CO₂ released from malate for Calvin cycle.

*Biology, 2E\**

*Zea mays* (corn)

Photodisk/Getty Images

*Opuntia basilaris*
(beavertail cactus)

Pixel Embargo/Shutterstock.com

**FIGURE 5.13** Two alternative processes of carbon fixation to minimize photorespiration. In each case, carbon fixation produces the four-carbon oxaloacetate, which is processed to generate the CO₂ that feeds into the Calvin (C₃) cycle. **(a)** In C₄ plants, carbon fixation and the Calvin cycle occur in different cell types: carbon fixation by the C₄ pathway takes place in mesophyll cells, whereas the Calvin cycle takes place in bundle sheath cells. **(b)** In CAM plants, carbon fixation and the Calvin cycle occur at different times in mesophyll cells: carbon fixation by the C₄ pathway takes place at night, whereas the Calvin cycle takes place during the day.

day **(Figure 5.13b)**. At night when temperatures are cooler, plants open their stomata to acquire carbon dioxide and release oxygen. The carbon dioxide is immediately shuttled into the $C_4$ pathway. During the day, when the stomata are closed to conserve water and oxygen levels are lower, the carbon is released from the $C_4$ pathway and shuttled into the Calvin cycle. Unlike the $C_4$ plants, both the Calvin cycle and the $C_4$ pathway occur in the same cells but at different times of the day. The outcome, however, is the same as in $C_4$ plants: photorespiration and carbon loss are minimized.

Photosynthesis is important to the maintenance of oxygen and carbon dioxide balance in the atmosphere. Indeed, today's atmosphere is very different from that of the primordial (primitive) Earth. Photoautotrophs such as cyanobacteria are predominantly responsible for this change, which saw a shift from the reducing (low in oxygen) atmosphere of the past to the oxidizing (high in oxygen) atmosphere of today. Their ability to split water as an electron source for photosynthesis and produce oxygen as a by-product is in part the reason for their long-term success, and it sparked the evolution of aerobic organisms. However, today, atmospheric oxygen is on the decline, whereas carbon dioxide in the atmosphere is increasing. Although it was initially thought that **deforestation** was a major cause of the oxygen decline, scientists now widely accept that only a relatively small amount of atmospheric oxygen comes from plants. Instead, most is produced by phytoplankton, small, drifting photoautotrophs within aquatic environments. But deforestation is a contributing factor to the increased accumulation of carbon dioxide in the atmosphere as a result of less carbon fixation on land. Along with the burning of fossil fuels, deforestation also promotes global warming by the greenhouse effect. Read more about global warming at the end of this chapter in "Putting It in Perspective."

Let's review the information on photosynthesis using a concept map **(Figure 5.14)**. In this map, we illustrate the light-dependent and light-independent pathways and highlight the reactants and products of these reactions.

## STUDY BREAK

1. Where does photosynthesis occur in eukaryotes versus prokaryotes?
2. How are the light-dependent and light-independent pathways connected to each other?
3. What is the role of water in photosynthesis?
4. How do $C_4$ and CAM plants reduce the risk of photorespiration?

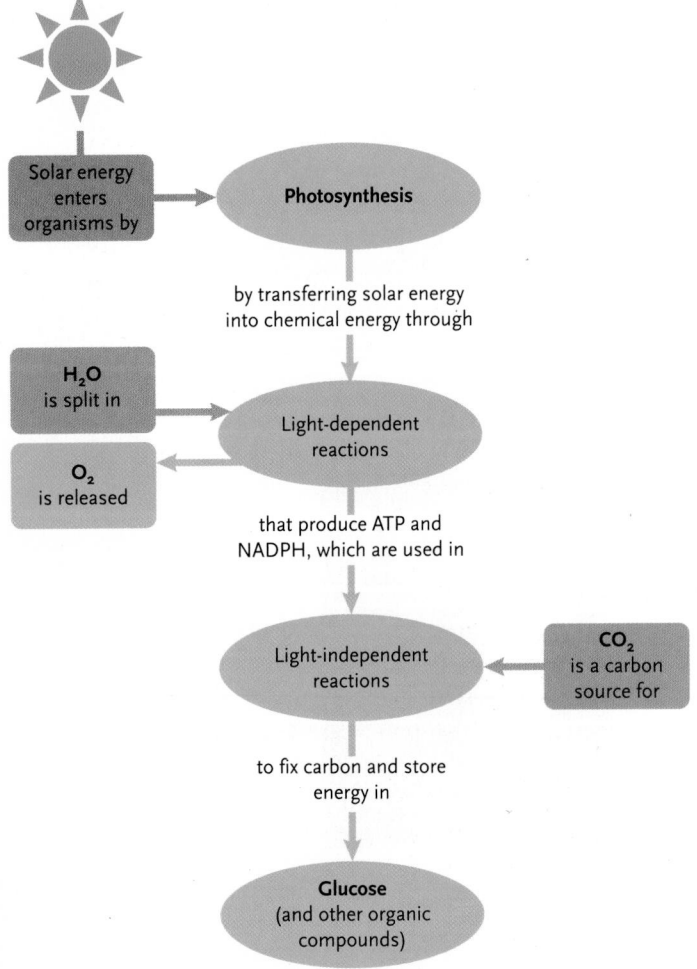

**FIGURE 5.14** A concept map of photosynthesis.

## 5.2 Cellular Respiration: Transferring Chemical Energy into ATP

In Chapter 4, we described ATP as the main energy currency of the cell and its importance for carrying out endergonic cellular reactions. In organisms, ATP is produced using solar energy and then used to produce sugars and other organic substances. In other words, the energy that reaches our planet from the Sun is initially transferred into small stores of chemical energy in ATP, which in turn is incorporated into larger stores in the bonds of more complex organic molecules. In this section, we will discuss how organisms, both photosynthetic and non-photosynthetic, can harness and use the chemical energy stored in these complex organic substances through a process called cellular respiration.

Cellular respiration is a pathway composed of a series of reactions that ultimately produce ATP. There are three major stages to cellular respiration: **glycolysis**, the **citric acid cycle**, and **oxidative phosphorylation**. A simple equation for cellular respiration is shown here.

$$C_6H_{12}O_6 + 6O_2 \longrightarrow 6CO_2 + 6H_2O + ATP$$

glucose    oxygen            carbon dioxide  water  energy

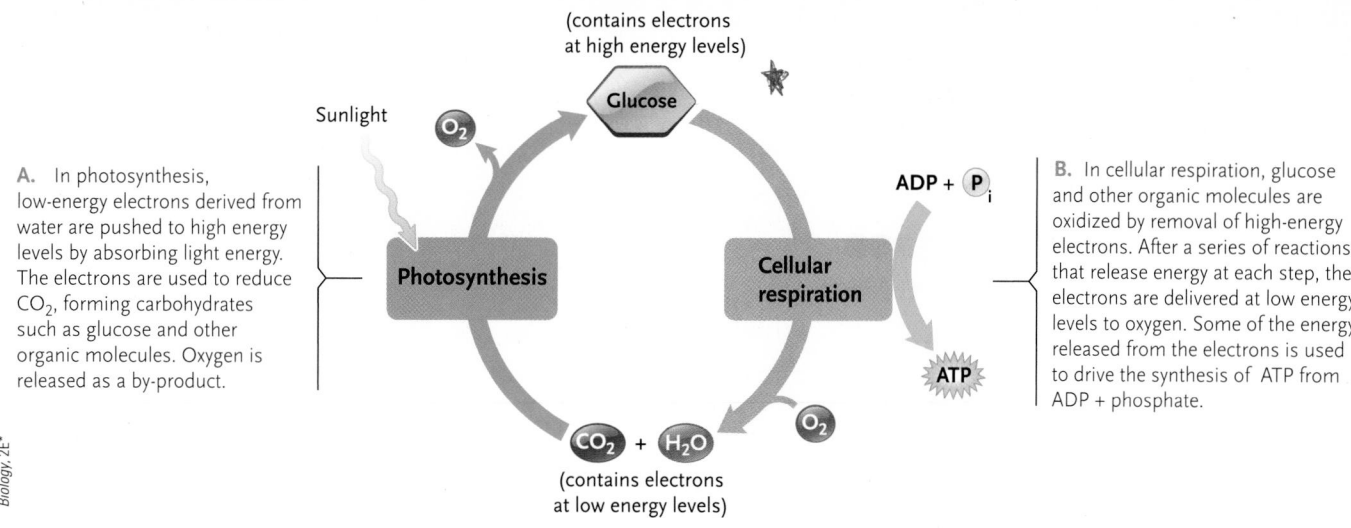

*Biology, 2E\**

**A.** In photosynthesis, low-energy electrons derived from water are pushed to high energy levels by absorbing light energy. The electrons are used to reduce $CO_2$, forming carbohydrates such as glucose and other organic molecules. Oxygen is released as a by-product.

(contains electrons at high energy levels)

Sunlight

$O_2$

**Glucose**

**ADP +** $P_i$

**Photosynthesis**

**Cellular respiration**

**B.** In cellular respiration, glucose and other organic molecules are oxidized by removal of high-energy electrons. After a series of reactions that release energy at each step, the electrons are delivered at low energy levels to oxygen. Some of the energy released from the electrons is used to drive the synthesis of ATP from ADP + phosphate.

**ATP**

$CO_2$ + $H_2O$

$O_2$

(contains electrons at low energy levels)

**FIGURE 5.15** Flow of energy linking photosynthesis and respiration. Photosynthesis uses light energy to convert carbon dioxide and water into energy-rich organic molecules such as glucose, which, in turn, are oxidized by cellular respiration.

Recall from Chapter 4 that ATP production is an endergonic reaction and thus requires energy. The energy comes from the free energy stored in the organic molecules, whose building blocks are generated during photosynthesis by primary producers. Indeed, the connection between photosynthesis and cellular respiration is significant. The products of one are the reactants of the other **(Figure 5.15)**. However, the balance between ATP production versus production of complex organic compounds depends on the current metabolic needs of the organism. When energy is in excess, it is stored away as complex organic compounds (such as starch in plants and glycogen in animals), and when it is scarce, the energy in these complex organic compounds is used to make ATP, a more readily usable form of chemical energy. Below we will discuss the production of ATP via the breakdown or oxidation of organic compounds through cellular respiration.

## Glycolysis Splits and Oxidizes Glucose

The first step in cellular respiration is glycolysis, which means "splitting of sugar." In both prokaryotes and eukaryotes, glycolysis occurs in the cytoplasm. The main goal of glycolysis is to oxidize and split the carbon–carbon bonds in glucose in a controlled, stepwise manner using a series of enzymes. Glycolysis is essentially controlled combustion of glucose, and as we discussed in Chapter 4, combustion of sugars releases an abundant amount of free energy that is stored in the hydrocarbon bonds of the carbohydrate (see the Purple Pages for an overview of carbohydrates). The energy is released through enzyme-catalyzed redox reactions, and this is the energy that will ultimately be used to produce ATP during cellular respiration. Glycolysis is divided into two main phases: an

energy investment phase and an **energy payoff phase (Figure 5.16)**.

### Phase 1: Energy Investment Phase Consumes ATP

First, the cell has to convert glucose to G3P, which is an intermediate form of the sugar that can be used in many metabolic pathways. This requires an investment of energy. The energy investment phase begins when glucose molecules enter the cytoplasm of the cell via the glucose transporter protein at the plasma membrane. In the first few steps of glycolysis, glucose is converted through intermediates to fructose-1,6-bisphosphate **(Figure 5.16, steps 1 and 2, p. 114)**. These steps require the hydrolysis or consumption of two ATP molecules—this is the "investment of energy." The high-energy phosphates associated with the fructose-1,6-bisphosphate produced make the molecule unstable, thus causing it to split into two, more stable G3Pmolecules (Figure 5.16, step 2).

### Phase 2: Energy Payoff Phase Generates ATP

In the second phase of glycolysis, the energy invested in the first phase pays off. First, the two G3Ps produced in phase 1 are oxidized, resulting in the loss and transfer of electrons and energy to two **NAD$^+$** (nicotinamide adenine dinucleotide) electron carrier molecules **(Figure 5.16, step 3)**. As a result, the NAD$^+$ is reduced to **NADH** (reduced form of NAD$^+$), a critical compound that will transport electrons collected during glucose oxidation to the final stage of cellular respiration, where most ATP is produced. The remaining steps involve the generation of two pyruvates, the final product of glycolysis. During these final steps, four ATP molecules are also produced: this is the "payoff of

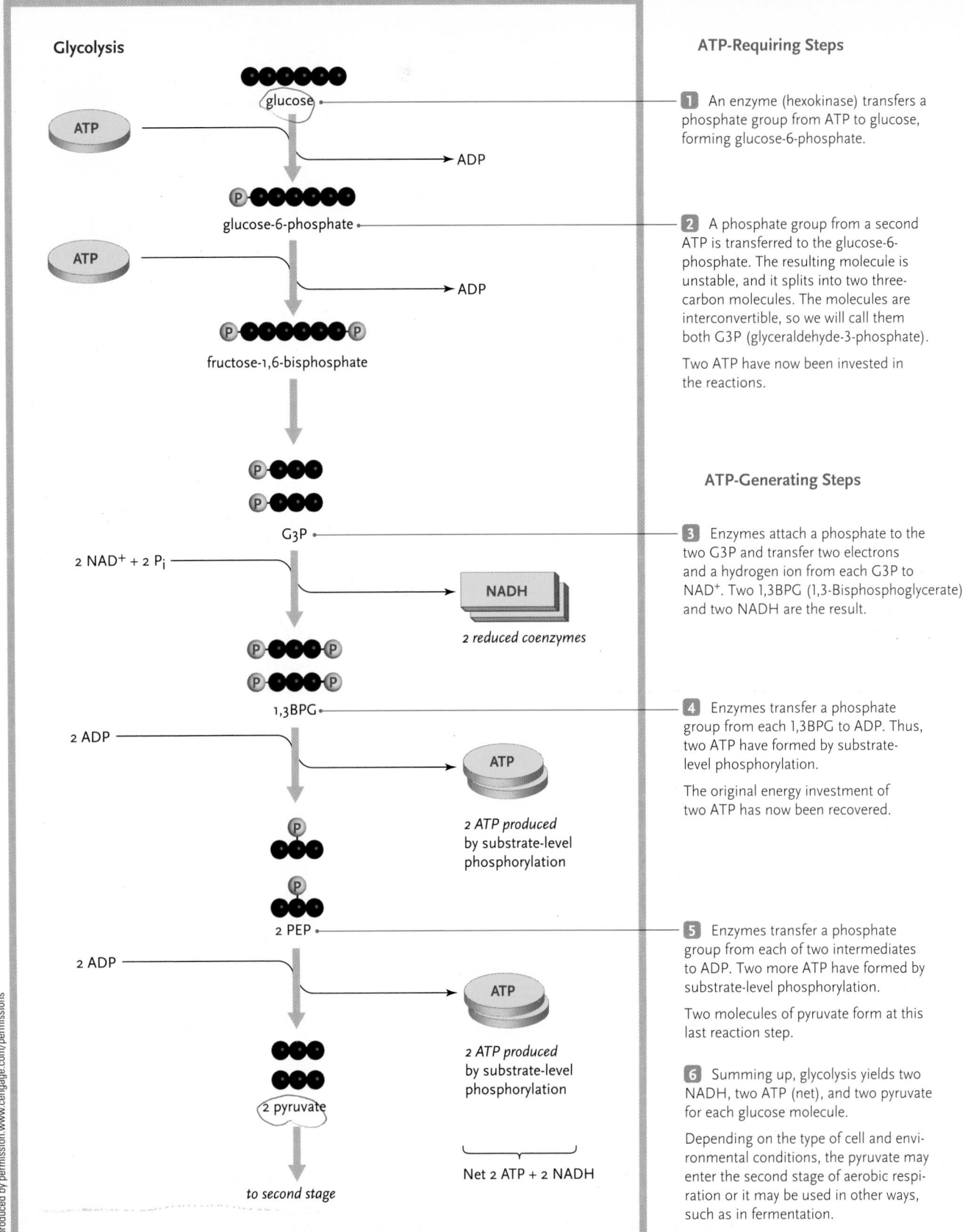

**Glycolysis**

**ATP-Requiring Steps**

glucose

ATP

ADP

**1** An enzyme (hexokinase) transfers a phosphate group from ATP to glucose, forming glucose-6-phosphate.

glucose-6-phosphate

ATP

ADP

**2** A phosphate group from a second ATP is transferred to the glucose-6-phosphate. The resulting molecule is unstable, and it splits into two three-carbon molecules. The molecules are interconvertible, so we will call them both G3P (glyceraldehyde-3-phosphate).

Two ATP have now been invested in the reactions.

fructose-1,6-bisphosphate

**ATP-Generating Steps**

G3P

2 NAD⁺ + 2 Pᵢ

NADH

*2 reduced coenzymes*

**3** Enzymes attach a phosphate to the two G3P and transfer two electrons and a hydrogen ion from each G3P to NAD⁺. Two 1,3BPG (1,3-Bisphosphoglycerate) and two NADH are the result.

1,3BPG

2 ADP

ATP

**4** Enzymes transfer a phosphate group from each 1,3BPG to ADP. Thus, two ATP have formed by substrate-level phosphorylation.

The original energy investment of two ATP has now been recovered.

*2 ATP produced by substrate-level phosphorylation*

2 PEP

2 ADP

ATP

**5** Enzymes transfer a phosphate group from each of two intermediates to ADP. Two more ATP have formed by substrate-level phosphorylation.

Two molecules of pyruvate form at this last reaction step.

*2 ATP produced by substrate-level phosphorylation*

2 pyruvate

Net 2 ATP + 2 NADH

*to second stage*

**6** Summing up, glycolysis yields two NADH, two ATP (net), and two pyruvate for each glucose molecule.

Depending on the type of cell and environmental conditions, the pyruvate may enter the second stage of aerobic respiration or it may be used in other ways, such as in fermentation.

**FIGURE 5.16** The reactions of glycolysis. The energy investment and the energy payoff phase of glycolysis are shown here.

From Starr, *Biology*, 8E. © 2011 Brooks/Cole, a part of Cengage Learning, Inc. Reproduced by permission. www.cengage.com/permissions

energy" **(Figure 5.16, steps 4 to 6)**. Here ATP is formed by **substrate-level phosphorylation**, which involves the direct transfer of a phosphate group from the intermediate molecules of glycolysis (substrates) to ADP. It is different from

the mechanism of ATP synthesis in the light-dependent pathway of photosynthesis and, as you'll soon learn, different from ATP synthesis at the end of cellular respiration.

## Glycolysis Overview

Now let's recap the events of glycolysis, keeping in mind the number of molecules involved: for every one glucose molecule that enters, is oxidized, and split during glycolysis, there are two pyruvates, two NADH, and a net gain of two ATP molecules generated.

## Mitochondria Are ATP Factories

In both prokaryotes and eukaryotes, the bulk of ATP production occurs after glycolysis during cellular respiration. In prokaryotes, this primarily occurs on the plasma membrane. In eukaryotes, cellular respiration occurs in the mitochondria. Like chloroplasts, mitochondria are double membrane organelles. The membranes divide the organelle into two compartments: the intermembrane compartment, found between the inner and the outer membrane, and the mitochondrial matrix, the aqueous environment found inside the inner membrane **(Figure 5.17)**. Mitochondrial DNA, ribosomes, and proteins are all in the mitochondrial matrix, the site for ATP production. Having mitochondria as dedicated organelles for ATP production is advantageous for eukaryotic organisms that require more energy to sustain their larger cell size and perform complex cellular functions. Below we will discuss the next stages of cellular respiration, citric acid cycle and oxidative phosphorylation, from a mitochondrial point of view.

## The Citric Acid Cycle Completes Glucose Oxidation

Recall that glycolysis is simply controlled combustion of glucose that releases stored free energy and produces pyruvate. Pyruvate, however, still has plenty of free energy stored within its chemical bonds that can be harnessed. As such, pyruvate will continue to be oxidized in the next stage of cellular respiration called the citric acid cycle. Since citric acid is a type of tricarboxylic acid (TCA), hence this cycle is also called the TCA cycle. In addition, it is also referred to as the Krebs cycle, named after Hans Adolf Krebs, who identified it in 1937.

Before the citric acid cycle can be used, pyruvate needs to be transported into the mitochondrial matrix, where the components of the citric acid cycle reside (in prokaryotes, components of the citric acid cycle are in the cytoplasm). Transport into the mitochondrial matrix occurs by simple diffusion through large pores on the outer mitochondrial membrane and via pyruvate-specific membrane transport proteins across the inner mitochondrial membrane **(Figure 5.18, p. 116)**.

Once transported into the mitochondrial matrix, pyruvate can be further oxidized. Pyruvate oxidation involves the removal of a carboxyl group (—COO⁻) from pyruvate by **decarboxylation**, a process that generates

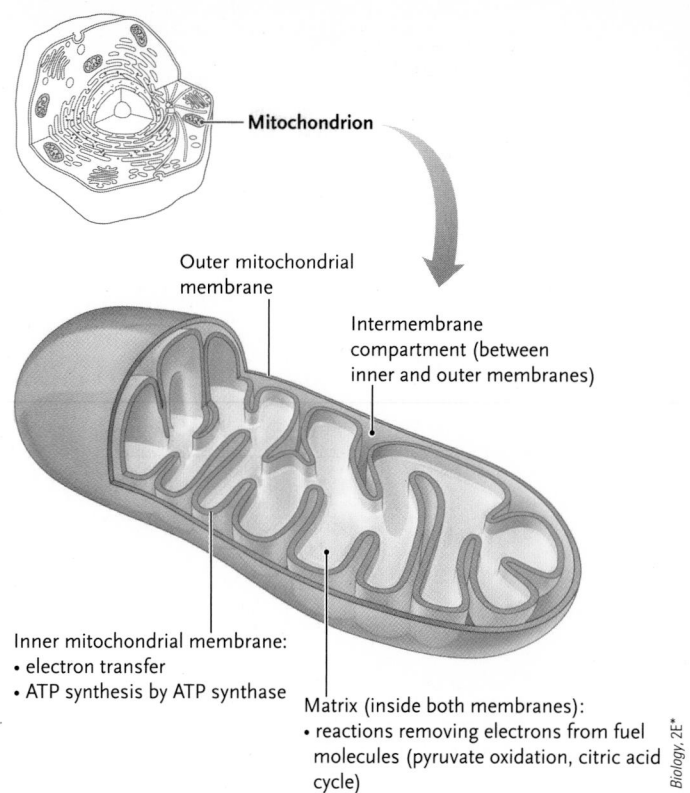

**FIGURE 5.17** Membranes and compartments of mitochondria. Label lines that end in a dot indicate a compartment enclosed by membranes.

carbon dioxide (Figure 5.18). Carbon dioxide is an inorganic, low energy–containing by-product of cellular respiration. It is released by the cell and ultimately excreted from the body. In addition to decarboxylation, pyruvate is also oxidized by the transfer of its electrons to NAD⁺, thus generating the electron carrier NADH. The final step is a reaction between the acetyl group and coenzyme A (CoA). A high-energy and unstable intermediate, acetyl–CoA, forms at this step, and it can enter directly into the citric acid cycle. Thus, for every pyruvate molecule that is oxidized, one NADH and one carbon dioxide are generated.

The citric acid cycle consists of seven major steps that ultimately oxidize the acetyl group in acetyl–CoA **(Figure 5.19, steps 1 to 7, p. 117)**. The cycle begins after pyruvate oxidation with the acetyl group (two-carbon) transfer from acetyl–CoA to oxaloacetate (Figure 5.19, step 1). During the citric acid cycle, electrons from the acetyl group will be donated to NAD⁺, producing NADH (Figure 5.19, steps 2 and 3). Carbon is released during these reactions in the form of carbon dioxide (Figure 5.19, steps 2 and 3), a waste product. Energy will also be harvested during this process to produce ATP by substrate-level phosphorylation (Figure 5.19, step 4). Further redox reactions lead to the donation of more electrons to another electron carrier, **FAD** (flavin adenine dinucleotide), and another molecule of NAD, thus reducing these molecules to **FADH₂** and NADH, respectively (Figure 5.19, steps 5 and 6). The electrons collected by

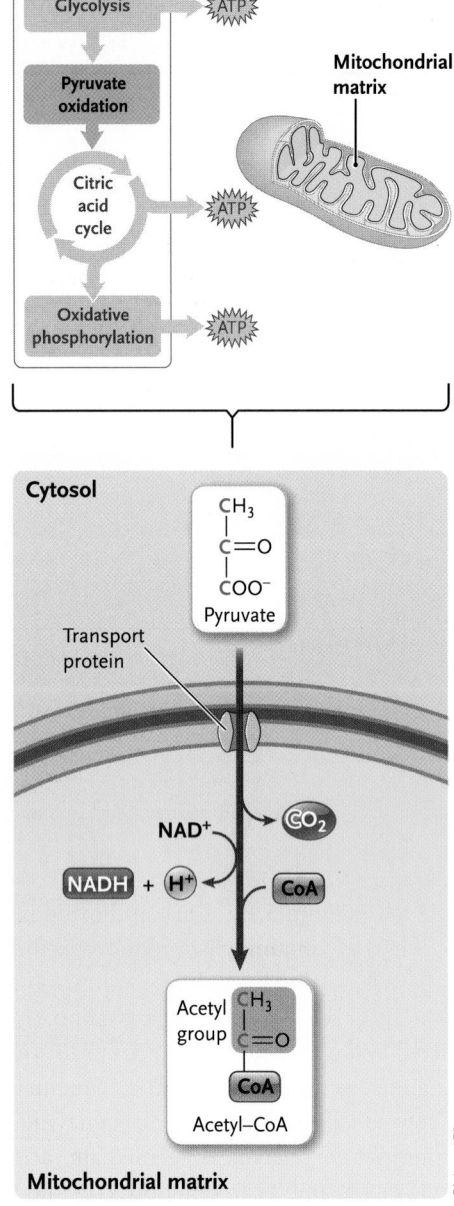

**FIGURE 5.18** Transport into the mitochondrial matrix occurs by simple diffusion through large pores on the outer mitochondrial membrane and via pyruvate-specific membrane transport proteins across the inner mitochondrial membrane. Once in the mitochondrial matrix, pyruvate is oxidized.

NADH and $FADH_2$ will be eventually donated to the electron transport chain in the third major phase of cellular respiration. The final step in the citric acid cycle is oxaloacetate regeneration, the first reactant of the cycle (Figure 5.19, step 7). Thus, for every turn of the citric acid cycle, there are three NADH, one $FADH_2$, one ATP, and two carbon dioxide molecules generated. Note that we will need to double the number of products generated from both pyruvate oxidation and the citric acid cycle if we take into consideration that one glucose molecule actually generates two pyruvates during glycolysis.

So let's take an inventory count of what has been generated thus far based on the complete oxidation (breakdown)

of one molecule of glucose through glycolysis, pyruvate oxidation, and the citric acid cycle: 4 ATP, 10 NADH, 2 $FADH_2$ and 6 $CO_2$ (Figures 5.17, 5.18, and 5.19). The ATP generated is stored until required by the cell, and the $CO_2$ is released by the cell. The electron carriers, NADH and $FADH_2$, will deliver the electrons they have collected to the final phase of cellular respiration, where most ATP is produced.

## Oxidative Phosphorylation Uses the Electron Transport Chain and Chemiosmosis to Make the Bulk of ATP

The overall goal of cellular respiration is to transfer the chemical energy stored in glucose, and other organic molecules, into ATP, a usable energy currency for the cell. However, so far, we have seen very little ATP produced during glycolysis and the citric acid cycle: only four ATP per glucose molecule oxidized. The bulk of ATP that is generated during cellular respiration occurs in the final phase, oxidative phosphorylation, which is actually divided into two major cooperative stages: the electron transport chain and **chemiosmosis (Figure 5.20)**.

The electron transport chain is the first stage of oxidative phosphorylation and is composed of four major protein complexes arranged in sequential order at the surface of the inner mitochondrial membrane (in prokaryotes, it is located at the plasma membrane). These protein complexes work together one by one through a series of redox reactions to transport electrons down the chain to a final electron acceptor.

### Stage 1: Electron Transport Chain Donates and Transfers Electrons

The donation and transport of electrons to the electron transport chain are critical in setting the stage for ATP production (stage 2), which is the ultimate goal of cellular respiration. The electrons are donated to the chain by the NADH and $FADH_2$, which collected these electrons during glycolysis, pyruvate oxidation, and the citric acid cycle **(Figure 5.20, step 1)**. Recall that these electrons originated from glucose. The electrons are then passed from each of the protein complexes in sequential order down the electron transport chain **(Figure 5.20, step 2)**. At the same time, $H^+$ accumulate in the intermembrane space. In aerobic respiration, the final electron acceptor at the end of the chain is oxygen. Oxygen drives the transport of electrons down the chain because of its high affinity for electrons. Once oxygen gains the electrons, the negative charge attracts hydrogen ions, resulting in the production of water **(Figure 5.20, step 3)**. The efficient addition of electrons and hydrogen is critical because failure to do so can lead to the production and accumulation of harmful reactive oxygen species in the cells. The harmful effects of these reactive

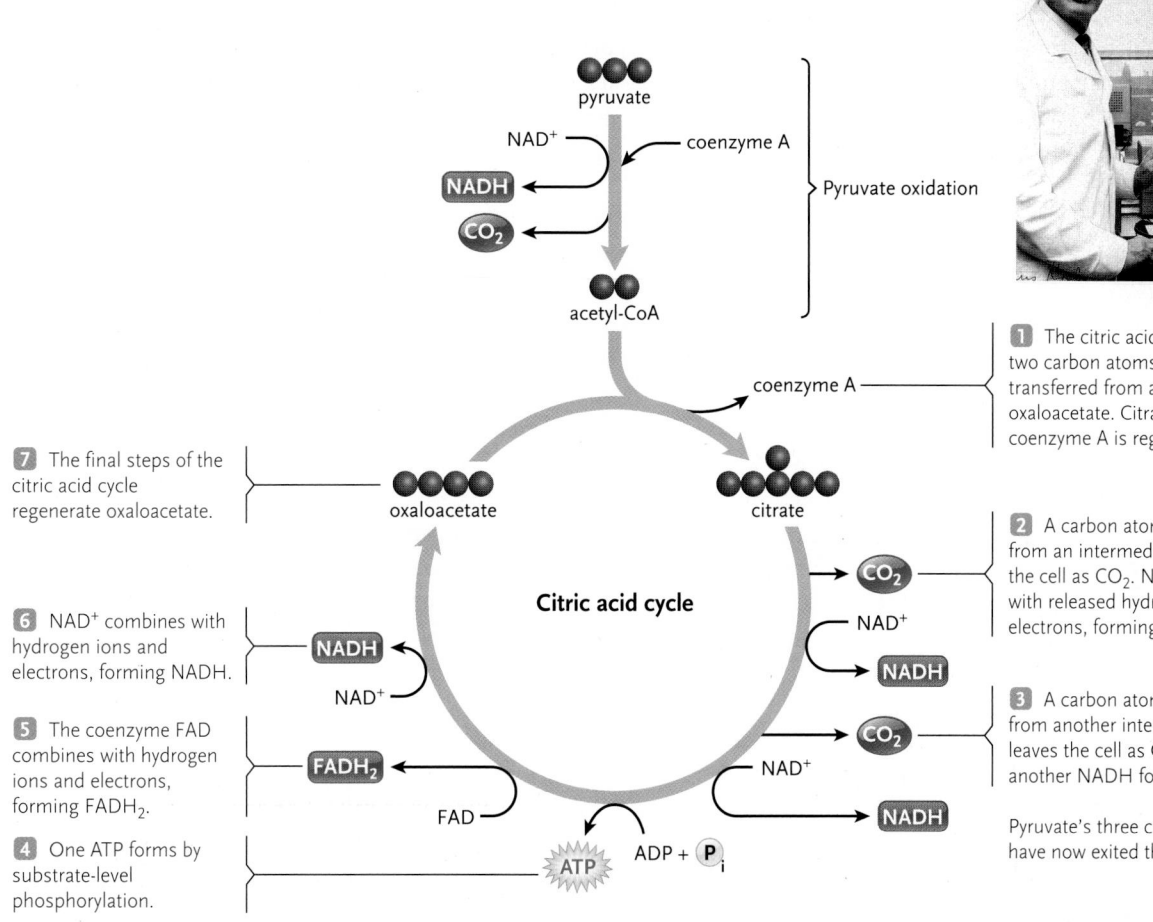

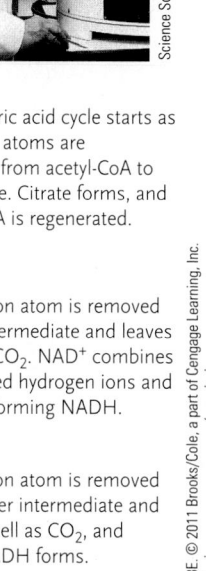

**1** The citric acid cycle starts as two carbon atoms are transferred from acetyl-CoA to oxaloacetate. Citrate forms, and coenzyme A is regenerated.

**2** A carbon atom is removed from an intermediate and leaves the cell as $CO_2$. $NAD^+$ combines with released hydrogen ions and electrons, forming NADH.

**3** A carbon atom is removed from another intermediate and leaves the cell as $CO_2$, and another NADH forms.

Pyruvate's three carbon atoms have now exited the cell, in $CO_2$.

**7** The final steps of the citric acid cycle regenerate oxaloacetate.

**6** $NAD^+$ combines with hydrogen ions and electrons, forming NADH.

**5** The coenzyme FAD combines with hydrogen ions and electrons, forming $FADH_2$.

**4** One ATP forms by substrate-level phosphorylation.

**FIGURE 5.19** The reactions of pyruvate oxidation and the citric acid cycle.

**Electron Transfer Phosphorylation**

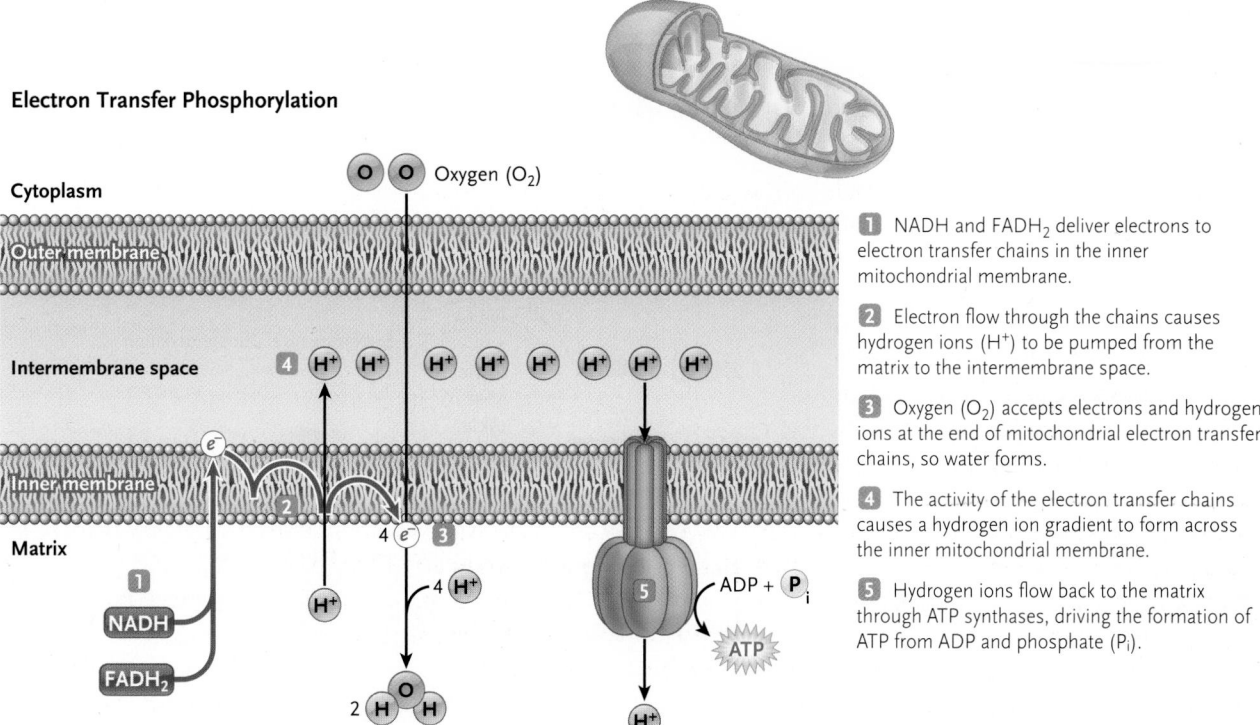

**1** NADH and $FADH_2$ deliver electrons to electron transfer chains in the inner mitochondrial membrane.

**2** Electron flow through the chains causes hydrogen ions ($H^+$) to be pumped from the matrix to the intermembrane space.

**3** Oxygen ($O_2$) accepts electrons and hydrogen ions at the end of mitochondrial electron transfer chains, so water forms.

**4** The activity of the electron transfer chains causes a hydrogen ion gradient to form across the inner mitochondrial membrane.

**5** Hydrogen ions flow back to the matrix through ATP synthases, driving the formation of ATP from ADP and phosphate ($P_i$).

**FIGURE 5.20** The third and final stage of cellular respiration, electron transport chain and chemiosmosis, leading to oxidative phosphorylation.

oxygen species (i.e., oxygen-centred free radicals) that can lead to neurological disorders and contribute to heart disease and cancer can be combatted with enzymes and antioxidants. Many foods, such as berries, fruits, and vegetables, contain beneficial antioxidants that clean up these types of free radicals and therefore help prevent disease.

## Stage 2: Chemiosmosis Drives the Production of ATP by Oxidative Phosphorylation

So how does the electron transport chain that transfers electrons to oxygen connect to the production of ATP? When electrons are transferred down the chain, free energy is released. This energy is not wasted but instead is used to actively transport $H^+$ from low concentration to high concentration across the inner mitochondrial membrane and into the intermembranous space **(Figure 5.20, step 4)**. This is conducted using pumps located within the protein complexes. As a result, an electrochemical gradient is established at the inner mitochondrial membrane.

As previously described in Chapter 4, electrochemical gradients contain stored potential energy (like a battery) and are highly unstable. To stabilize the membrane, the energy must be released by the spontaneous diffusion of $H^+$ across the inner mitochondrial membrane from high concentration to low concentration. But remember, $H^+$ is positively charged and cannot simply diffuse across the non-polar lipid bilayer of the membrane. Instead, $H^+$ is transported across the membrane through the membrane protein ATP synthase, which acts as both a transport protein and an enzyme. Please take note that this enzyme is similar to the ATP synthase found in chloroplasts and used during photosynthesis. The energy released during diffusion is harnessed by ATP synthase to catalyze the production of ATP in the mitochondrial matrix by a process called oxidative phosphorylation **(Figure 5.20, step 5)**. In this process of ATP production, phosphate groups located in the mitochondrial matrix are directly linked to ADP, a mechanism that differs from substrate-level phosphorylation observed in glycolysis and the citric acid cycle. Harnessing the stored energy in the electrochemical gradient to power the synthesis of ATP is called chemiosmosis. You may have noticed that chemiosmosis is similar to the mechanism that drives ATP production during photosynthesis. Hence, the connection

between the transfer of electrons and energy for the production of ATP is crucial for the success of both photosynthesis and cellular respiration and, ultimately, the cell.

So the big question now is how much ATP is generated by chemiosmosis? Theoretically, a total of 38 ATP are produced from the oxidation of one molecule of glucose during cellular respiration **(Figure 5.21)**. In reality, however, the actual number of ATP produced from cellular respiration is lower and varies depending on the cell type and the cellular conditions or extracellular environmental stresses that affect the efficiency of the cell and the mitochondria. Quality control systems in cells oversee the functional efficiency and maintenance of the mitochondria in response to these environmental changes and stresses. For example, under stressful conditions, such as starvation or accumulation of toxic reactive oxygen species, mitochondria often fuse together to maximize the capacity for ATP production. Fusion therefore allows functional mitochondria to complement and compensate for dysfunctional mitochondria. Alternatively, fission (or splitting) of mitochondria may also act as a quality control mechanism by allowing for the damaged segments of mitochondria to be removed through

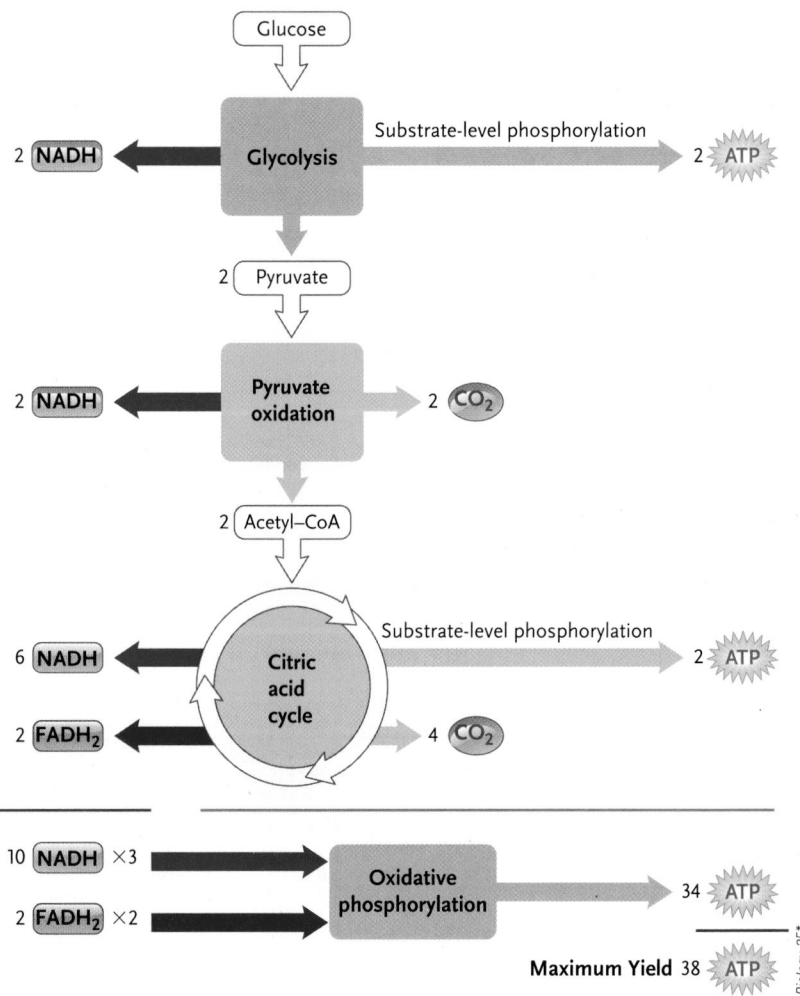

**FIGURE 5.21** ATP yield from the oxidation of glucose. The maximum possible ATP yield from the oxidation of one molecule of glucose is 38. However, this yield is rarely achieved.

# THE MOLECULE BEHIND THE BIOLOGY 5.1
## Vitamin K₂ to the Rescue

Parkinson disease is a neurodegenerative disorder of the central nervous system that causes movement-related symptoms of shaking, inflexibility, and difficulty walking. These symptoms are believed to be caused by the death of dopamine-producing cells within parts of the midbrain. At the cellular level, there appears to be a link with malfunctioning of mitochondria, the main power-producing units of the cell. Indeed, two genes, *pink1* and *parkin*, which are associated with mitochondrial quality control, have been shown to be mutated in individuals with Parkinson disease. *Pink1* codes for the protein PINK1, which is a protein kinase (an enzyme that phosphorylates proteins) that detects inefficiencies in mitochondrial membrane potential. *Parkin* codes for the cytoplasmic protein Parkin, which is recruited by PINK1 to malfunctioning mitochondria. Together PINK1 and Parkin direct the clearance of damaged mitochondria through autophagy as a quality control mechanism. Defects in the PINK1 and Parkin proteins result in deficient mitochondria remaining in the cell and thus a reduction in ATP (energy) production. Studies in the fruit fly, *Drosophila melanogaster*, revealed that this mitochondrial dysfunction is a result of inefficiencies in the electron transport chain and thus the transport of electrons across the mitochondrial membrane. Moreover, fruit flies with either the *pink1* or *parkin* mutation show an inability to fly due to these mitochondrial defects. However, promising research now shows that this loss of function may be rescued by vitamin K2, a fat-soluble vitamin **(Figure 1)**. Fruit flies with the *pink1* or *parkin* mutations that were treated with vitamin K₂ had increased ATP production and improved ability to fly. In prokaryotes, vitamin K₂ is an electron carrier in the plasma membrane. Studies now suggest that vitamin K₂ may also act as an electron carrier on the inner mitochondrial membrane of eukaryotic cells, contributing to the transport of electrons and establishment of the electrochemical gradient that drives ATP production in these organelles. Further studies are currently being conducted to validate a role for vitamin K₂ in the treatment of Parkinson disease in patients with PINK1 or Parkin deficiencies.

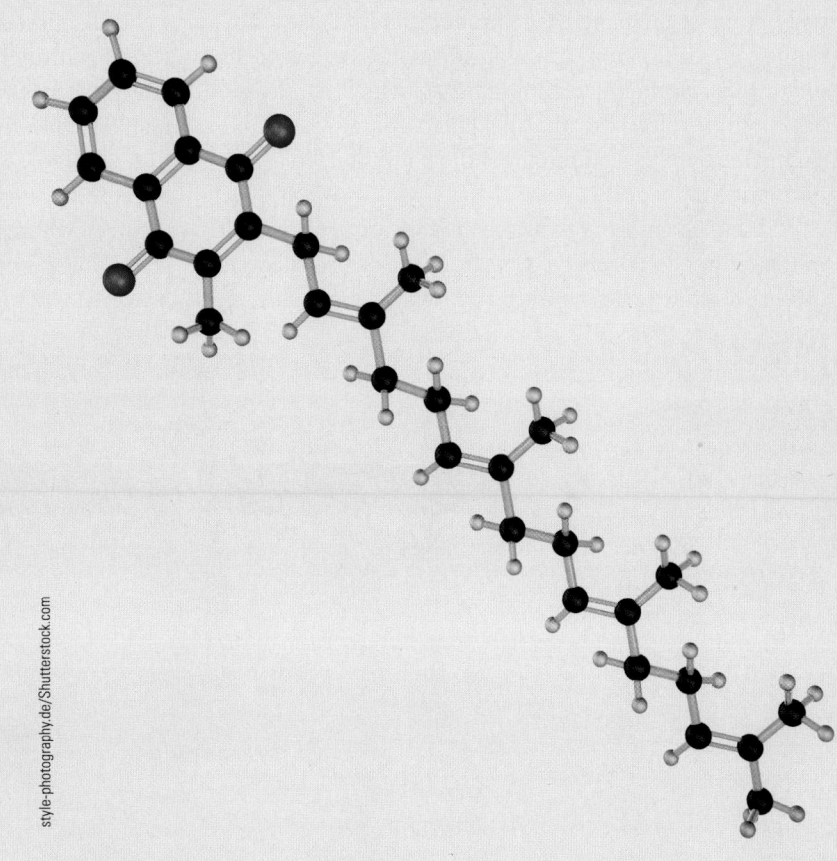

style-photography.de/Shutterstock.com

**FIGURE 1** Structural formula of vitamin K₂.

asymmetrical division. Failure to maintain proper mitochondrial function has been linked to several disorders, including Parkinson disease. In Box 5.1, we discuss how mutations in two genes whose protein products are involved in the removal of damaged mitochondria can lead to Parkinson disease and the potential use of vitamin K₂ as a treatment strategy.

## Cells Use Alternative Sources of Chemical Energy

We often use glucose as an example when we describe the process of cellular respiration because it is the initial reactant of glycolysis. However, there are other macromolecules, including other types of carbohydrates, proteins, and fats, which also contain chemical energy that can be harvested by cells **(Figure 5.22, p. 120)**. These alternative fuel sources are important as glucose may not always be around in sufficient amounts to support the growth and maintenance of cells. But how and when do we harness the energy from these alternative sources, and why do we store energy in these complex compounds to begin with?

Energy storage is an advantage because you, like other organisms, do not consume the same amount of energy continuously throughout the day. Thus, the amount of energy harvested and used by your body varies. The levels of glucose absorbed through the lining of the digestive tract and circulating through the bloodstream are constantly fluctuating depending on when you last ate. As a result, ATP production also fluctuates. When ATP levels are high in the animal cells, the first intermediate in glycolysis (glucose-6-phosphate) is redirected out of glycolysis and used to make glycogen. Glycogen is a multibranched polysaccharide that acts as an energy storage molecule in animal cells, namely liver and muscle cells. In plant cells, excess glucose is used to make starch. Converting glucose into glycogen in animals, or starch in plants, when energy is in excess is a significant mechanism for storing this energy that may be used when glucose levels drop in the body. For example, when you have not eaten in a while, glucose levels in the bloodstream will drop to levels that will stimulate the **pancreas** to produce and release a hormone called **glucagon**. Glucagon stimulates the liver cells to convert glycogen back into glucose, which is released back into the bloodstream. This glucose is now available for uptake by all cells throughout the body for cellular respiration to make ATP.

Excess glucose, or other carbohydrates, can also result in the redirection of acetyl–CoA from the citric acid cycle toward the fatty acid synthesis pathway. This results in

increased fat production, and, hence, carbohydrates are converted into fats. Fat is also an energy store that can be tapped into at a later time when energy levels in the body drop (see the Purple Pages for an overview of fats and other lipids). In animals, most of the energy reserves are found in the form of fat (or adipose) tissue. Fat is actually a more efficient energy store than carbohydrates since 1 g of fat contains over double the amount of calories that are in 1 g of sugar. This is important to mobile organisms as there is less burden of weight. Fat is also useful in insulating and protecting the body. Triglycerides make up the bulk of fat stored in the body. As the name indicates, triglycerides are three fatty acid chains attached to one glycerol molecule. The tails are made of hydrocarbons, and as we've discussed already, a high amount of energy can be stored within hydrocarbon bonds. The release of this energy occurs when glucose levels in the body drop. As a result, triglycerides in adipose tissue are broken down into the glycerol head and the three fatty acid tails **(Figure 5.22, steps 1** and **2)**. The glycerol is transported to the liver, where it is converted into an intermediate of glycolysis. The fatty acid tails are taken up by nearby cells and broken down into smaller fragments that are converted to

**FIGURE 5.22** Carbohydrates, fats, and proteins can act as alternative organic energy sources for cells. Oxidation of carbohydrates, fats, and proteins can generate intermediates that can enter cellular respiration at various stages.

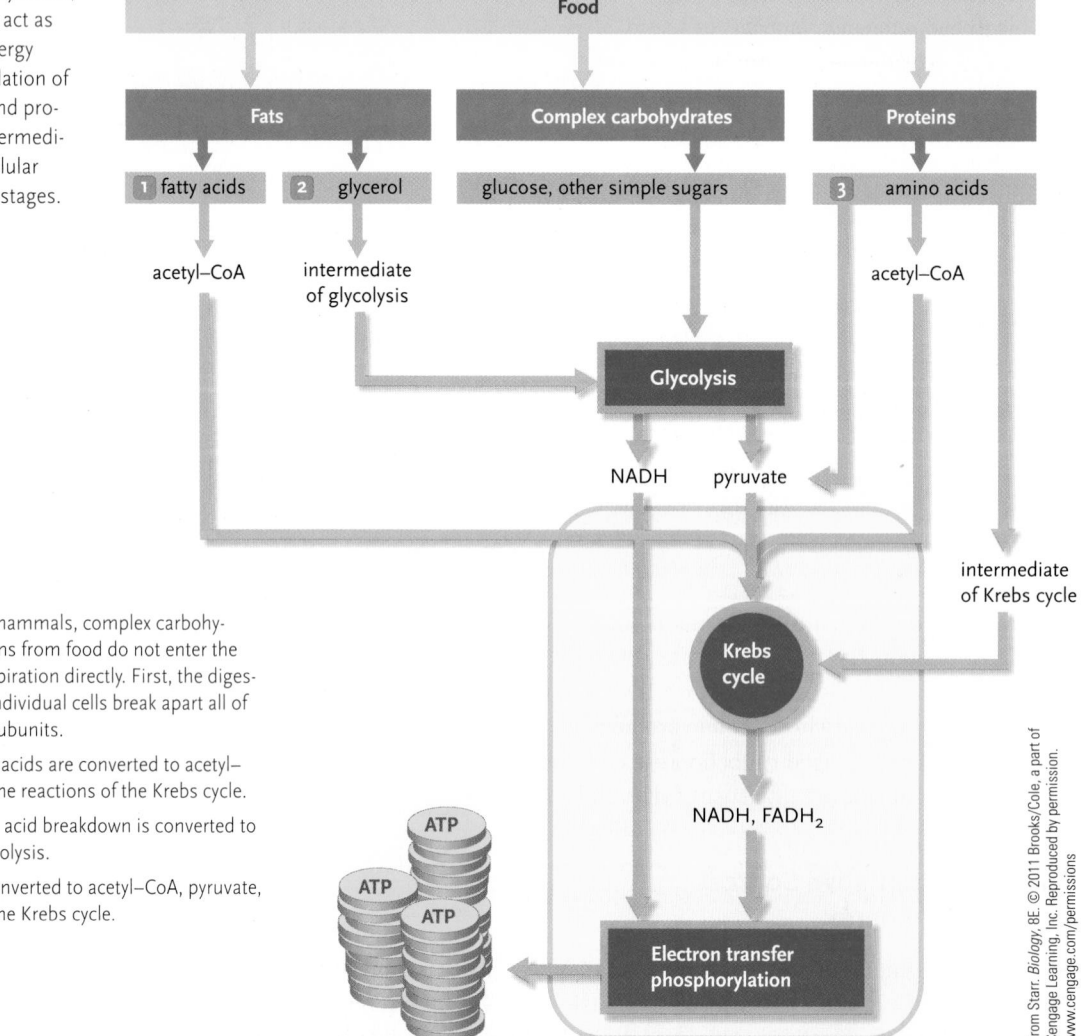

In humans and other mammals, complex carbohydrates, fats, and proteins from food do not enter the pathway of aerobic respiration directly. First, the digestive system and then individual cells break apart all of these molecules into subunits.

**1** Fragments of fatty acids are converted to acetyl–CoA, which can enter the reactions of the Krebs cycle.

**2** Glycerol from fatty acid breakdown is converted to an intermediate of glycolysis.

**3** Amino acids are converted to acetyl–CoA, pyruvate, or an intermediate of the Krebs cycle.

acetyl–CoA, which, as we learned already in this chapter, can enter freely into the citric acid cycle.

Proteins can also be digested into amino acid monomers **(Figure 5.22, step 3)**, which can be used by cells as building blocks to synthesize other proteins (see the Purple Pages for an overview of amino acids and proteins). Amino acids can also be further broken down when too much protein has been taken in. When amino acids break down, the amino group is removed and converted to ammonia, a waste product released through urine. The carbon backbone is split, and, depending on the type of amino acid, the products can enter cellular respiration as either pyruvate, acetyl–CoA, or intermediates of the citric acid cycle (Figure 5.22).

Before we continue, let's take a moment to review the information on cellular respiration using a concept map **(Figure 5.23)**. In this map, we illustrate glycolysis, the citric acid cycle, and oxidative phosphorylation and highlight the reactants and products of these reactions.

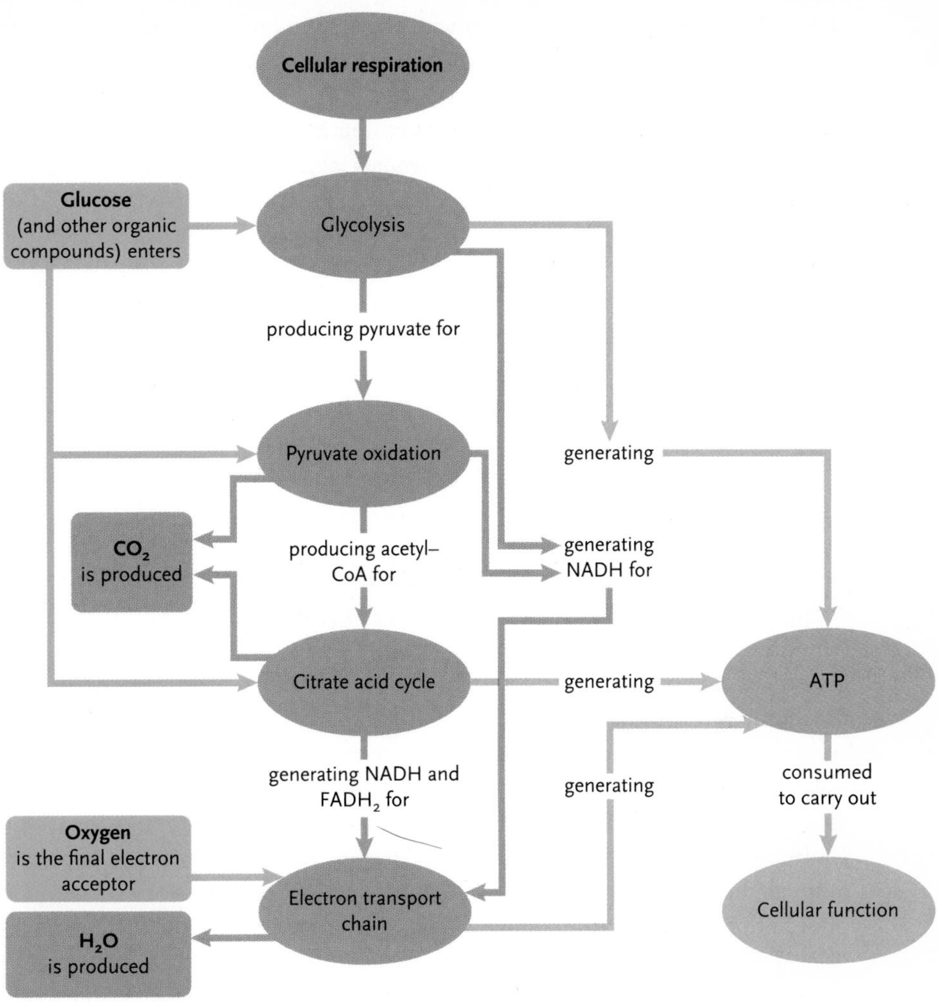

**FIGURE 5.23** A concept map of cellular respiration.

## STUDY BREAK

1. Describe the energy investment and energy payoff phases of glycolysis.
2. How are glycolysis and the citric acid cycle linked to each other?
3. Describe how the electron transport chain is connected to ATP synthase and the production of ATP.
4. What other organic molecules can be oxidized and used in cellular respiration?

## 5.3 Making ATP without Oxygen

In this chapter, we refer to oxygen as the final electron acceptor in the electron transport chain that acts as the driving force for the bulk of ATP production by chemiosmosis during cellular respiration. This type of respiration that uses oxygen as the final electron acceptor is also known as **aerobic respiration** and is carried out by aerobic organisms or **aerobes**. But what happens when oxygen is absent? Can cells still make ATP? In some cases, cells cannot produce enough ATP in the absence of oxygen, and they die. Therefore, these organisms are considered strict or **obligate aerobes**. However, there are many examples

where ATP is synthesized in the absence of oxygen by anaerobic (*an* = without; *aerobic* = air) organisms or **anaerobes**. Two such processes are called **anaerobic respiration** and **fermentation**, which we will discuss below. Some organisms actually cannot survive in the presence of oxygen because it is too toxic to them. These organisms are considered strict or **obligate anaerobes**. **Facultative aerobes** or **facultative anaerobes** are organisms that have the ability to switch between being an aerobe or an anaerobe, or vice versa, depending on the availability of oxygen. This diversity in metabolism with respect to the presence and absence of oxygen is in part what makes life on this planet so diverse and in turn what makes many places on this planet that are seemingly hostile actually habitable.

### In Anaerobic Respiration, Oxygen Is Not the Final Electron Acceptor

There are many bacteria and archaea that live in conditions where oxygen is unavailable, and as such, they have adapted mechanisms to harvest the energy from ingested macromolecules and convert it to ATP. Under these conditions, these organisms use molecules other than oxygen, such as ferric iron ($Fe^{3+}$), sulphate ($SO_4^{2-}$), or nitrate ($NO_3^-$), as the final electron acceptor at the end of the electron transport chain. Although the attraction for electrons by these molecules is not as strong as that of oxygen, these organisms can still use them in place of oxygen and produce ATP by chemiosmosis, although significantly less ATP than that produced during aerobic respiration. Since this process does not use oxygen, it is termed **anaerobic respiration**. For example, *Escherichia coli* that resides in the intestines of animals such as humans are facultative anaerobes that carry out anaerobic respiration and help animals digest and absorb food.

## During Fermentation, ATP Is Made Only by Glycolysis

Now let's return to the first scenario outlined in this chapter (Why It Matters) regarding the production of wine and cheese. These drink and food products are generated via fermentation, which is an alternative mechanism for oxidizing high-energy molecules in the absence of oxygen. However, unlike anaerobic respiration, fermentation processes do not use the electron transport chain and therefore do not generate ATP via chemiosmosis and oxidative phosphorylation. ATP is only made during glycolysis by substrate-level phosphorylation. Fermentation allows for the regeneration of $NAD^+$ from NADH, and glycolysis can continue to occur, thus producing ATP. Although it is not an efficient mechanism for harvesting energy compared to

respiration, it will at least generate enough ATP to keep certain cells (those with low energy demands) and organisms alive.

There are two modes of fermentation that occur in the cytoplasm of cells: **alcoholic fermentation**, which generates alcohol, and **lactate fermentation**, which generates lactate (the ionized form of lactic acid) **(Figure 5.24)**. In both processes, glucose is oxidized to pyruvate through glycolysis, $NAD^+$ is reduced to NADH, and ATP is generated via substrate-level phosphorylation. Since there is no cellular respiration in these cells, pyruvate accumulates and is reduced in the cytosol. Reduction of pyruvate by the transfer of electrons from NADH generated during glycolysis occurs through a series of reactions called fermentation. Oxidation of NADH is critical as it regenerates $NAD^+$ in the cytosol, which is important for further glycolysis. Without $NAD^+$, any new glucose molecules that enter the cell cannot be oxidized, and ATP production halts.

But which fermentation process, alcoholic or lactate, will occur in cells when oxygen is low or absent? This depends primarily on the cell type or organism. Lactate fermentation occurs in certain bacteria, yeast species, and even your own muscle cells. In this process, pyruvate generated through glycolysis is reduced to lactate **(Figure 5.24a)**. In the case of *Lactobacillus acidophilus*, these bacteria will use lactate fermentation to produce buttermilk and convert lactose in milk into cheese and yogurt. We can also use certain yeast cells to carry out lactate fermentation in the preservation of pickles and sauerkraut. In your muscle tissue, there are certain muscle fibres that have few mitochondria and thus

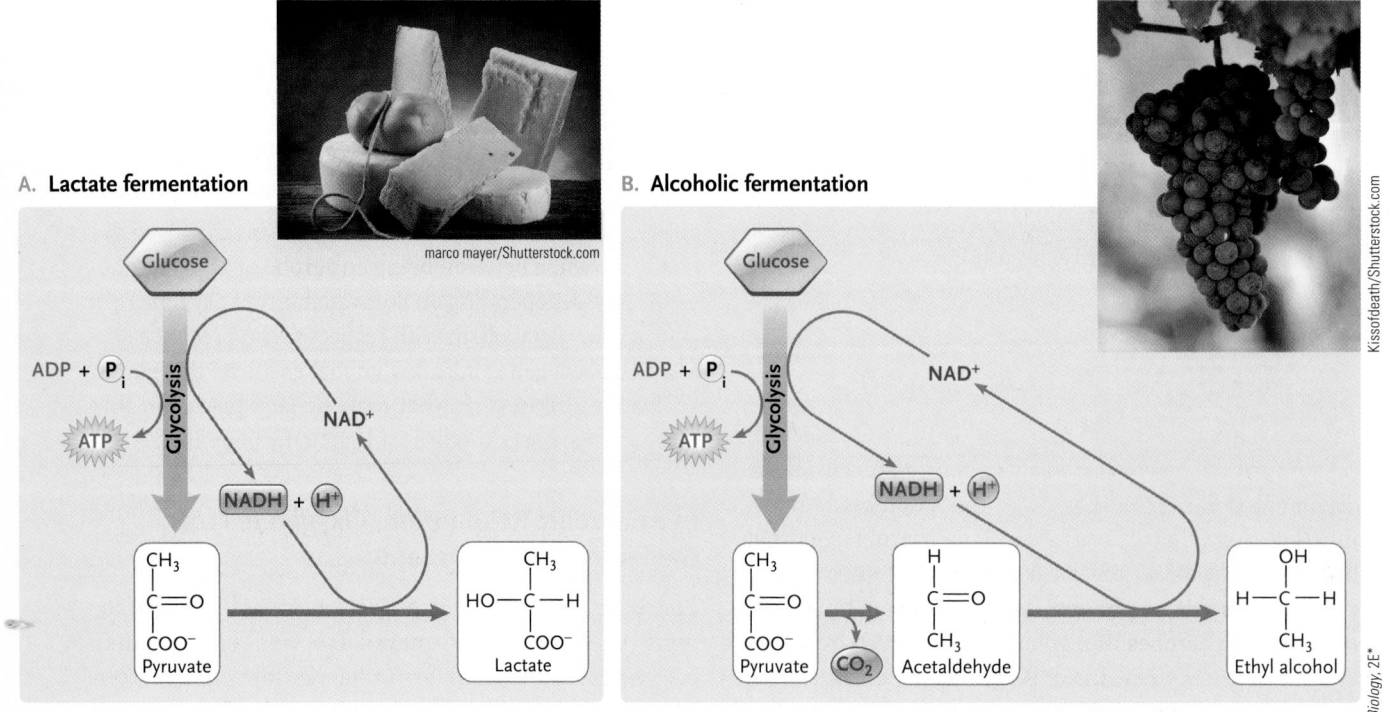

**A. Lactate fermentation**

marco mayer/Shutterstock.com

**B. Alcoholic fermentation**

Kissofdeath/Shutterstock.com

Biology, 2E*

**FIGURE 5.24** Fermentation reactions that produce **(a)** lactate and **(b)** ethyl alcohol. The fermentations, which occur in the cytosol, convert NADH to $NAD^+$, allowing the electron carrier to cycle back to glycolysis. This process keeps glycolysis running, with continued production of ATP.

## Chilled It through the Grapevine

Most winemakers collect their grape harvest in the early autumn, well in advance of the first frost, which may potentially destroy their crops unless they are a maker of ice wine. They instead harvest their crops in the middle of the winter, when the grapes are frozen and the sugar content is high. Unlike other dessert wines, the grapes used in the production of ice wine are frozen on the vine before fermentation , thus yielding a very sweet product **(Figure 1)**. However, the trick is for the freezing to occur when the grapes are still healthy, hence the grapes must be picked within hours of freezing. As a consequence, harvesting these frozen grapes is restricted to a small window of time, which makes production limited and expensive. In addition, since the sugar and other solute concentrations are high in frozen grapes, the yeast that carry out fermentation are under greater osmotic pressure. This results in altered metabolism, slow growth, and arrested fermentation in the yeast, which often leads to complications in ice wine production. For example, under osmotic stress, yeast will overproduce glycerol during fermentation, which will divert sugar metabolism away from ethanol synthesis and toward acetic acid (or vinegar) production. This is of major concern as the acetic acid content increases the risk that the ice wine will spoil. Although most ice wines do have a lower alcohol and higher acetic acid content compared to regular table wines, there are national standards that place an upper limit on the amount of allowable acetic acid content in retail ice wines. Current research is investigating the genetic variations and enzyme activities in yeast that undergo fermentation in ice wine production in an effort to better understand the balance between alcohol and acetic acid content. At Brock University in Ontario, Canada, the lab of Debra Inglis identified two enzymes—aldehyde dehydrogenase-3 and glycerol-3-phosphate dehydrogenase—that are associated with an increase in glycerol content and acetic acid production by yeast under stressful conditions. This study on Canadian ice wine is of particular economic significance as Canada is a leading player in the ice wine industry.

Due to the need for freezing, ice wine can be produced only in a few countries, where temperatures plunge well below 0°C. Although the first ice wine dates back to the 1700s in Germany, today's moderate European winters are not as consistently cold as those in Canada. Ice wine production relies on warm summers and cold winters, making Canada's international ice wine trade the largest in the Canadian wine industry. And the greatest production comes from the province of Ontario. In particular, ice wine producers from the Niagara Peninsula have received many global acclaims for the robust taste and balance between sweetness and acidity in their ice wine. Best served chilled, ice wine complements many desserts and cheeses and is often considered a delectable treat.

©iStock.com/ZU_09

**FIGURE 1** Ice wine grapes.

perform lactate fermentation in the absence of oxygen. This mechanism allows the cells to temporarily store the electrons harvested by high-energy molecules such as glucose during glycolysis while still regenerating $NAD^+$. When oxygen levels return to normal, lactate is converted back into pyruvate, and cellular (aerobic) respiration resumes. As you can see, fermentation, like anaerobic respiration, is an adaptation for survival in an environment lacking oxygen. And as a positive side effect, it generates many of the tasty products we enjoy on a daily basis.

Yeast cells, such as wild and cultivated strains of *Saccharomyces*, can carry out alcoholic fermentation. In this case, pyruvate is split into carbon dioxide (released and seen as bubbles) and acetaldehyde, which is then reduced to ethanol (ethyl alcohol) **(Figure 5.24b)**. Since ethanol is toxic to yeast cells, it is secreted by the cells into their environment—hence, the production of wine and other alcoholic beverages (read about alcoholic fermentation in the production of ice wine in Box 5.2). Alcoholic fermentation by yeast cells is also used in the baking of

On average, over 80% of today's college and university students consume alcohol. Although most students are moderate and responsible drinkers, overconsumption of alcohol, or "binge drinking," leads toward risky behaviours, such as drinking and driving, sexual abuse, and personal injury. Although the long-term effects on overall health are often not apparent until many years later, in the short term, heavy drinking leads to hangovers, with typical symptoms of nausea, headache, and lethargy **(Figure 1)**. New biotechnology research, however, may help combat the negative effects of alcohol consumption.

When alcohol is consumed, it is broken down by various metabolic pathways using enzymes found in the liver. However, the process to break down alcohol takes time, and some of the by-products are toxic to cells in the body. A research group from the UCLA Henry Samueli School of Engineering and Applied Science in California recently developed an enzyme nanocomplex that speeds up this process and quickly eliminates these toxic products. The nanocomplex is composed of two enzymes involved in alcohol metabolism: alcohol oxidase and catalase. These enzymes are enclosed within a thin polymer that acts as a capsule to keep them close to each other. This proximity is similar to how these enzymes are naturally found—compartmentalized in organelles within liver cells—thus making their actions more effective. Within the nanocomplex, the enzymes work collaboratively to break down and detoxify alcohol. Alcohol oxidase breaks down or oxidizes alcohol by removing electrons and generating aldehyde and hydrogen peroxide. Although aldehyde is further processed to acetate and acetic acid, hydrogen peroxide is toxic to cells. To detoxify this compound, the second enzyme, catalase, converts hydrogen peroxide into water and oxygen. But how effective is this enzyme nanocomplex? Testing revealed that the blood alcohol level of mice that were given the nanocomplex after alcohol consumption was approximately 35% lower after 3 hours compared to the control group of mice. Similar results were found when the nanocomplex was administered as a prophylactic at the same time as alcohol consumption. With further research, scientists believe that this enzyme nanocomplex could be available as a pill to combat alcohol intoxication, liver injury, and other negative side effects. How this pill will transform alcohol consumption and related behaviours among students across college and university campuses, however, remains to be seen.

**FIGURE 1** A man showing symptoms of a hangover from overconsumption of alcohol.

bread. In this case, the release of carbon dioxide causes the holes left behind in the bread, and the alcohol is evaporated during baking due to the hot temperatures of the oven. As mentioned, the alcohol produced during fermentation can be toxic to cells at high concentration. However, organisms have adapted mechanisms to break down alcohol and detoxify the by-products. But overconsumption of alcohol can stress organ systems in animals, leading to long-term health problems. In Box 5.3, learn about a novel synthetic approach involving biotechnology to combat the negative effects of alcohol consumption.

## STUDY BREAK

1. How are organisms characterized with respect to their tolerance to oxygen?
2. Describe two alternative mechanisms to produce ATP in the absence of oxygen.
3. Compare alcohol fermentation to lactate fermentation.

It is evident that photosynthesis and cellular respiration are two major cellular processes for harvesting

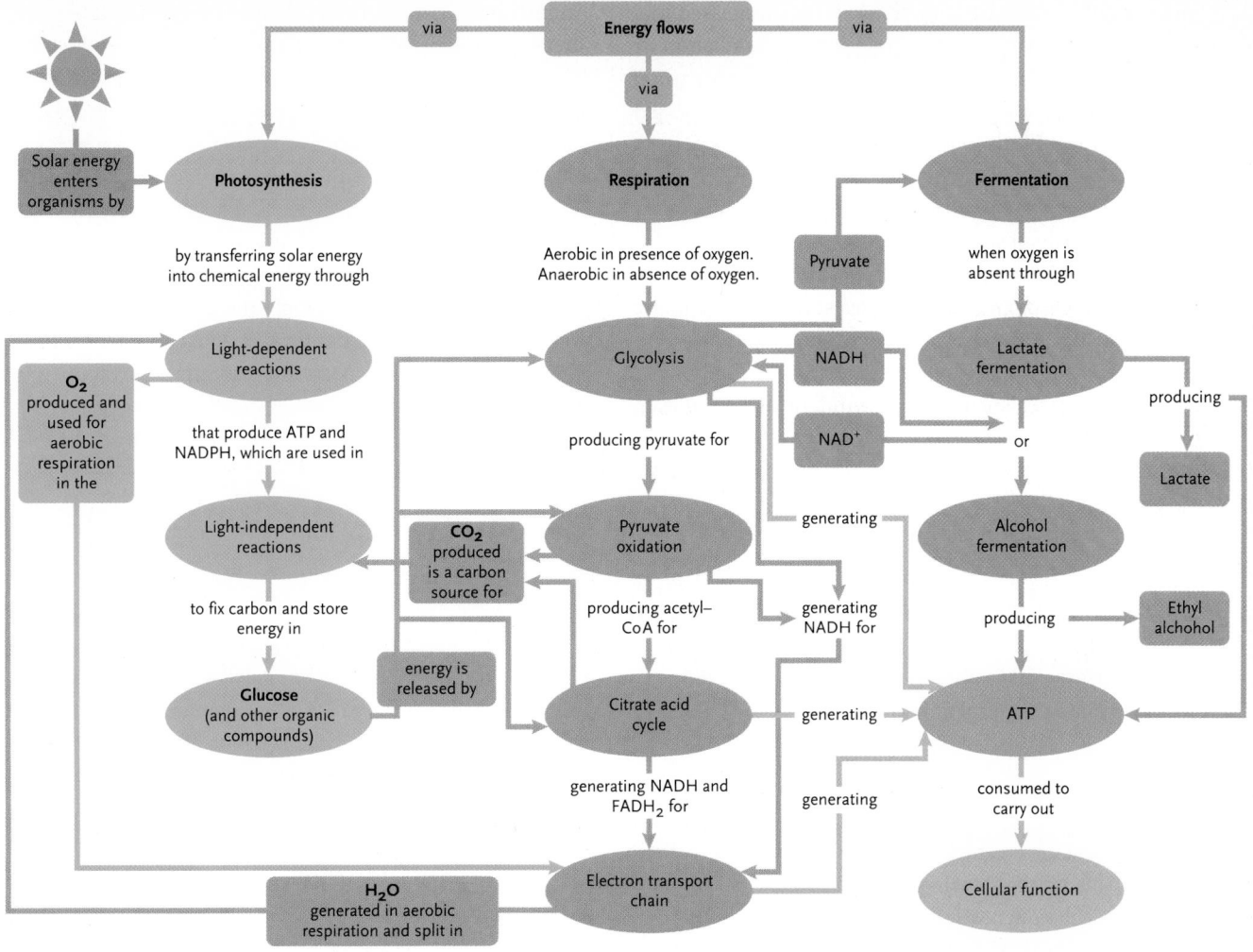

**FIGURE 5.25** A concept map of energy flow between photosynthesis, respiration (aerobic and anaerobic), and fermentation.

and using energy. Photosynthesis allows for the conversion of solar energy, originating from the Sun, into stored chemical energy such as carbohydrates, which is then transferred from primary producers to consumers through food webs. When consumed, these organic molecules are then broken down to release energy, which is used to make ATP, the main energy currency of the cell. These processes are interconnected through glucose, water, carbon dioxide, and oxygen, and they rely on each other as the products of one are the reactants of the other. In the absence of oxygen, anaerobic respiration and fermentation can also contribute to the production of ATP. In **Figure 5.25**, we take the two concept maps developed earlier in the chapter and combine them to show the overall picture of energy transfers in a cell and the interconnections between these processes.

## PUTTING IT IN PERSPECTIVE

In 1845, Jacques-Joseph Ebelmen, a French chemist and mining engineer, was one of the first scientists to describe the cycling of atmospheric oxygen and carbon dioxide in geological time. The connection between carbon dioxide and oxygen involves living organisms that produce these compounds through photosynthesis and cellular respiration, respectively. Moreover, the balance of carbon dioxide within the carbon cycle is essential for maintaining an environment that is favourable for life on Earth today. However, human actions have inadvertently caused major changes in the balance of these cycles. For example, excess burning of fossil fuels, which we heavily rely on to power the world, has caused an excess accumulation of carbon dioxide in our atmosphere. Deforestation has also contributed to this increased carbon dioxide accumulation by reducing global carbon fixation rates. It is believed that this accumulation is one of many factors contributing to the greenhouse effect and in turn global warming. Recall that most of the Sun's solar energy that reaches our planet is not harnessed and instead is reflected back into space either as radiation or heat. Excess greenhouse gases, such as atmospheric carbon dioxide, act as a blanket to trap this radiation (solar energy) and heat within Earth's atmosphere and return it back to Earth's surface, thereby increasing global temperatures. This may be harmful because increasing temperatures alter the global cycling of water, which is crucial to climate systems and the support of life on this planet. So how can we reduce the levels of greenhouse gases such as atmospheric carbon dioxide? There is a strong global campaign to decrease the burning of fossil fuels and instead use alternative energy sources such as solar, wind, or nuclear power.

Another mechanism is to convert the greenhouse gases already present in the atmosphere into a usable product. For example, researchers at the University of Texas at Arlington are conducting experiments in which sunlight is used in combination with photoactive copper oxide nanowires to convert excess carbon dioxide into methanol, a fuel that is also useful for making plastics and solvent, and in waste-water treatments. This mechanism is simpler and more efficient than previous methods of converting greenhouses gases into non-harmful products and is especially useful in areas where sunlight is plentiful. It is just another example of how important and powerful the Sun is to life on this planet.

# KEY CONCEPTS REVIEW AND QUESTIONS

## 5.1 Photosynthesis: Capturing and Transforming Light Energy into Chemical Energy

Solar energy is a main source of energy that is harnessed by photosynthetic organisms and, through photosynthesis, a two-step process involving water and carbon dioxide, is transferred to chemical energy, creating bonds in organic molecules, such as sugar. This process of energy conversion is vital to life on Earth as the subsequent release of this energy by carefully and enzymatically breaking these bonds delivers energy to organisms in an efficient and usable format. This process also delivers oxygen to the atmosphere. In addition, plants that live in warm, dry environments have also adapted alternative mechanisms to reduce both water loss and photorespiration.

1. What are the two molecules that link light-dependent with light-independent reactions of photosynthesis?

2. Describe the path taken by electrons through light-dependent reactions.

3. What does the linear pathway of light-dependent reactions produce that is not produced during the cyclic pathway?

4. Describe the effects on cellular carbon content when rubisco acts as an oxygenase in cells.

## 5.2 Cellular Respiration: Transferring Chemical Energy into ATP

The glucose produced during photosynthesis contains potential energy that can be harvested and transferred to ATP, the main energy currency of all cells. Cellular respiration is the process that involves the oxidation of glucose through an enzyme-controlled combustion and the transfer of this energy to ATP. It is divided into three main stages: glycolysis, the citric acid cycle, and oxidative phosphorylation. In the first two stages,

glucose is completely oxidized, and in the last stage, these electrons are used to drive ATP synthesis. Alternative sources of chemical energy come from the oxidation of other organic molecules, such as carbohydrates, proteins, and fats.

5. Match the term with the process. Each term may have more than one answer, and you may use each answer more than once.

a. Glycolysis        ___ Pyruvate

b. Pyruvate oxidation        ___ ATP synthase

c. Citric acid cycle        ___ Carbon dioxide

d. Electron transport chain        ___ NADPH

       ___ $FADH_2$

e. Chemiosmosis        ___ Proton gradient

       ___ Mitochondria

       ___ Acetyl–CoA

       ___ Oxygen

6. What would occur if a chemical compound that disrupts the inner mitochondrial membrane was added to cells?

7. Which of the following occurs during the citric acid cycle?

a. Substrate-level phosphorylation

b. ATP hydrolysis

c. Production of acetyl–CoA

d. Establishment of proton gradient

## 5.3 Making ATP without Oxygen

Organisms are categorized based on their tolerance for oxygen, which contributes to the diversity of organisms on our planet. In some cases, organisms require oxygen for aerobic respiration, and in other cases, organisms produce ATP in the absence of oxygen either through anaerobic respiration or fermentation.

In anaerobic respiration, the final electron acceptor in the electron transport chain is a molecule other than oxygen. In fermentation, glycolysis is followed by the reduction of pyruvate and oxidation of NADH. As a result, $NAD^+$ is recycled and one of two final products, alcohol or lactate, is generated.

8. Which of the following statements describes a facultative aerobe?

a. Cannot tolerate oxygen

b. Can survive in the presence and absence of oxygen

c. Cannot survive in the absence of oxygen

d. Can use oxygen only when light is present

9. Which of the following events occurs during alcoholic fermentation that does not occur during lactate fermentation?

a. Recycling of $NAD^+$

b. Oxidation of glucose

c. Production of ATP

d. Loss of $CO_2$

# A Cell's Life

## WHY IT MATTERS

Angelina Jolie made headline news in the spring of 2013 with her stunning announcement that she had undergone a double mastectomy, not because she had breast cancer, but because she carries the breast cancer 1 (*BRCA1*) gene mutation. Her mother had died of breast cancer at the early age of 56, and Jolie—who was 37 years old when she had the preventive surgery—decided to take a proactive role in reducing her chances of suffering the same fate. With the advancements made in DNA testing, many people now have the option to take these types of significant steps toward self-protection.

Cancer, like many other diseases, is initiated by one's own cells that are failing to reproduce normally within the body. Cancer cells grow at an accelerated rate, which eventually hinders the functions of neighbouring tissues and organs. Under normal conditions, the growth, development, and reproduction of cells are tightly regulated processes. Deregulation is often either through the overstimulation of cell growth or the loss of tumour suppressor proteins due to mutations in key regulatory genes such as *BRCA1* and *BRCA2*. In either case, deregulation leads to an imbalance in cell growth and death (read more about *BRCA1* and *BRCA2* genes in Box 6.1).

In this chapter, we will discuss the cellular events that lead to cancer and some novel therapeutic strategies that are being investigated. But to understand cancer, we need to first discuss the mechanisms for normal cell growth and division and the regulatory proteins that keep cells in check. Essentially, we will be discussing a cell's life and the key events that occur during this cell cycle. In addition to life, we will also discuss cellular aging (senescence) and death (apoptosis), processes that are programmed into the genetic makeup of the cell. We will learn how we can use cell aging and death to stop cancer.

## 6.1 Revisiting the Cell Theory

Reproduction is one of several defining characteristics of life (discussed in Chapter 2). At the organismal level, this refers to the creation of new individuals either asexually or sexually. In **asexual reproduction**, new individuals, or offspring, arise from a single parent **(Figure 6.1a)**. As such, the offspring inherits genetic information only from that single parent. In many organisms, such as bacteria and some fungi and protists, asexual reproduction is the only way species persist. In **sexual reproduction**, on the other

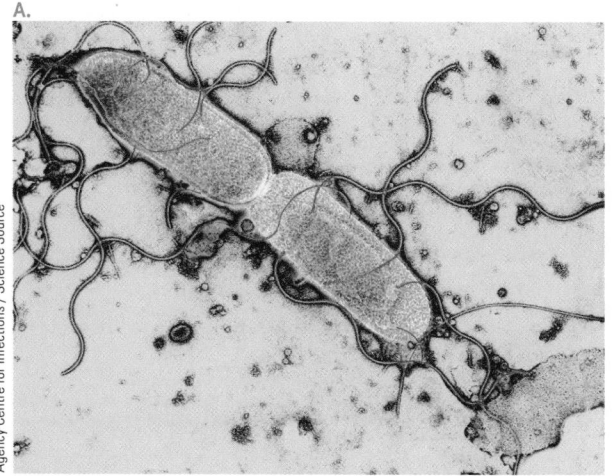

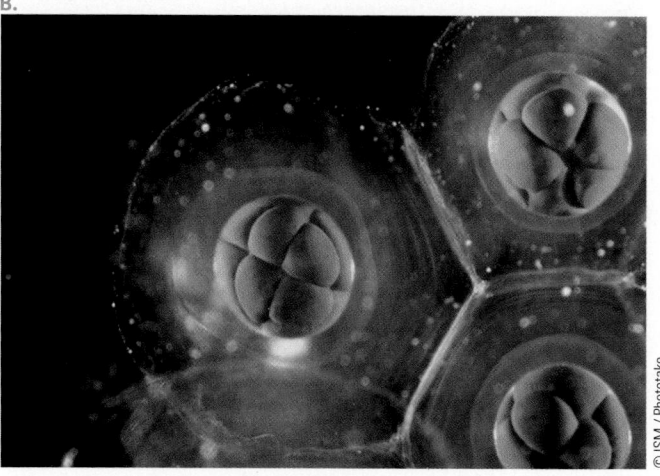

**FIGURE 6.1** Reproduction is a characteristic of life. **(a)** The bacterium *Escherichia coli* is actively reproducing asexually to create new bacterial cells and increase population size. **(b)** A frog embryo (multicellular eukaryotes) is growing and developing by reproducing cells through cell division.

Hazel Appleton, Health Protection Agency Centre for Infections / Science Source

© ISM / Phototake

Breast cancer is the most commonly diagnosed cancer in women worldwide, accounting for approximately 25% of all cancer cases in women. Although there are various subtypes of breast cancer, the overall general prognosis for the disease remains encouragingly high, with a 5-year survival rate of greater than 85%. Indeed, the enormous efforts directed toward breast cancer research and awareness over the past several decades have significantly contributed to this positive outcome.

Breast cancer cells arise from the cells of the mammary gland in the breast tissue. Although there are several different external and internal factors that can contribute to the onset of breast cancer, losing cell cycle control is a predominant characteristic of the disease. This results in a mass of cells (tumour) that not only grow at accelerated rates but also evade death. One of the reasons why this imbalance occurs is the loss of important regulatory proteins encoded by tumour suppressor genes. Two such genes are *BRCA1* and *BRCA2*, which encode for *BRCA1* and *BRCA2* tumour suppressor proteins, respectively **(Figure 1)**. These proteins are DNA repair proteins and as such function to suppress or inhibit tumour formation by repairing damaged or mutated DNA. Moreover, these proteins are also involved in stopping cell division and triggering cell death if the DNA damage is irreparable. In essence, their job is to maintain genomic stability and prevent the transfer of damaged DNA to the next generation of cells. But what happens when the DNA that is damaged or mutated is the tumour suppressor gene itself? In the case of *BRCA1* and *BRCA2* gene mutations, either *BRCA1* and *BRCA2* proteins are no longer produced or these proteins are produced but in a non-functional form. Losing the *BRCA1* and *BRCA2* tumour suppressor proteins and/or their activities means that damaged

DNA can escape surveillance and the cell can continue to divide and transfer its damaged DNA to future cells. If the damaged DNA involves genes that regulate the cell cycle, then the accumulation of these mutations in cells can increase rates of cell division, which can ultimately lead to cancer.

With the advancements in DNA technology, the *BRCA1* and *BRCA2* genes are the most commonly tested genes for breast and ovarian cancer. Individuals with a harmful mutation in either of these genes are considered to be predisposed to early-onset breast and/or ovarian cancers. Thus, these individuals, who have inherited these mutations either at birth (familial) or during their lifetime (sporadic), are at a higher risk for developing the disease (~60% to 85% risk for breast cancer and ~15% to 40% for ovarian cancer). Although familial breast cancer accounts for only 10% to 15% of breast cancer cases, currently, *BRCA1* and *BRCA2* gene mutations cause the majority of these hereditary cases. Harmful mutations in *BRCA1* and *BRCA2* genes have also

been linked to other cancers, such as colorectal, cervical, and pancreatic cancers.

Testing for gene mutations linked to cancer, such as in the case of *BRCA* genes, is performed in conjunction with a genetic counsellor. There are many ethical and social implications to genetic testing, with "genetic responsibility" and "genetic discrimination" being at the forefront. For example, is it the ethical responsibility of physicians to warn or inform a patient's family members of potential risks if that patient's *BRCA1* or *BRCA2* test comes back positive for a harmful mutation? Or does this violate patient–doctor confidentiality? Can information about genetic predisposition to breast cancer or other diseases be used in a discriminatory manner by society to reduce one's future potential? For example, will genetic information influence insurance rates or deny people insurance altogether? These are just a few of the ethical and social questions currently being investigated alongside scientific explorations.

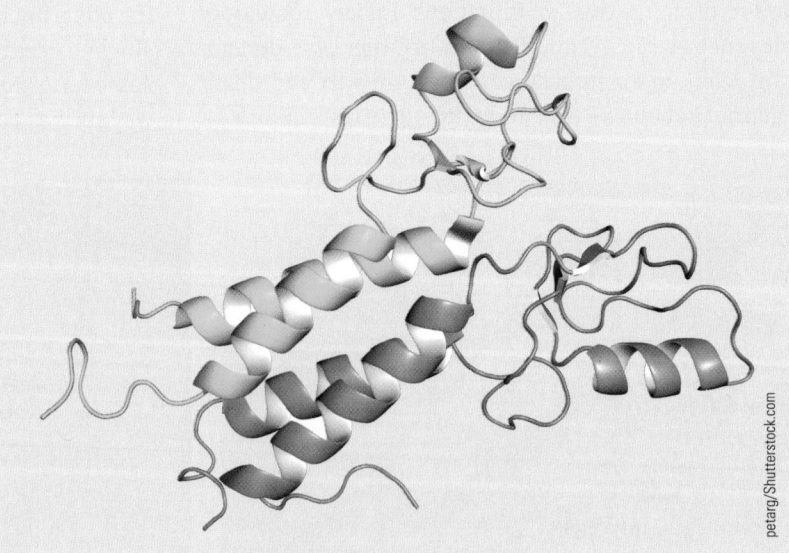

**FIGURE 1** The structure of *BRCA1*.

petarg/Shutterstock.com

hand, new individuals, or offspring, arise when two different cells from either a single parent or two different parents fuse, and the offspring inherits mixed genetic information from both of these cells. Sexual reproduction is common in animals, plants, fungi, and some protists.

Reproduction, however, does not always mean that an entirely new individual is created. Reproduction simply means "new life," and if you recall from the cell theory (discussed in Chapter 3), the basic unit of life is the cell. Thus, in multicellular eukaryotic organisms such as plants, animals, fungi, and some protists, reproduction of cells can occur within an organism without creating a new individual. Reproducing cells within multicellular organisms is the key to organismal growth, development, and tissue repair **(Figure 6.1b)**. But how do cells reproduce? Recall from the cell theory that new cells arise from pre-existing ones, and they do so by a process called **cell division**. Cell division is the final stage of the **cell cycle**, a series of events that also includes periods of cell growth, which includes RNA and protein production and DNA replication. The cell cycle essentially describes a cell's life.

In this chapter, we will first discuss cell division in prokaryotes and then follow with a more detailed explanation of the cell cycle in eukaryotic cells. In addition, we will discuss the regulation of the cell cycle, the initiation of programmed cell death, and how deregulation of the cell cycle can lead to cancer.

## STUDY BREAK

1. How does the cell theory describe where cells come from?
2. Describe the difference between asexual and sexual reproduction.

## 6.2 Reproduction in Prokaryotes by Binary Fission

In general, prokaryotes, which include bacteria and archaea, are unicellular organisms that contain a single copy of the genetic material (i.e., DNA) organized into a single circular chromosome. Reproduction in prokaryotes is asexual and occurs by **binary fission (Figure 6.2)**, a type of cell division. The rate of binary fission and thus cell division depends on the prokaryotic species and their surrounding environmental conditions, such as food availability, temperature, and salinity. For example, under ideal conditions, the bacteria *Clostridium perfringens* can double its population size in less than 10 minutes, twice as fast as *Escherichia coli*. This is particularly concerning because *C. perfingens* is a major cause of food poisoning. It grows in poorly prepared meats and poultry and is so common that you probably will encounter *C. perfingens*

 A bacterium has one circular chromosome that attaches to the inside of the plasma membrane.

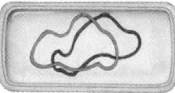 The cell duplicates its chromosome, attaches the copy beside the original, and adds membrane and wall material between them.

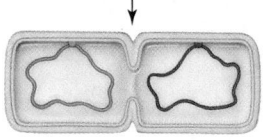 When the cell has almost doubled in size, new membrane and wall are deposited across its midsection.

 Two genetically identical cells result.

**FIGURE 6.2** Binary fission. The diagram depicts the main stages of cell division in prokaryotic cells.

SOURCE: From Starr. *Biology*, 8E. © 2011 Brooks/Cole, a part of Cengage Learning, Inc. Reproduced by permission.www.cengage.com/permissions

at least once in your lifetime. In most cases, eating these contaminated foods causes your immune system to produce antibodies within 24 hours to combat the majority of bacterial toxins it produces. However, if *C. perfingens* penetrates the skin barrier, infection can be deadly. It can cause gas gangrene, which results in muscle tissue necrosis, sepsis, and, ultimately, death.

Binary fission is a type of asexual reproduction (Figure 6.2). The main purpose of any type of asexual reproduction is to form new daughter cells that have inherited a complete and identical copy of the genome (an organism's entire hereditary information) from the parent cell. The term "daughter" here simply refers to offspring and does not refer to gender. This means that before cell division can occur, the chromosome (which houses the genome) within the parent cell must be duplicated by a DNA replication mechanism to ensure that one identical copy of the chromosome can be transferred to each newly formed daughter cell. You will learn more about how DNA is replicated in Chapter 9. In prokaryotic cells, once the single circular chromosome is duplicated by DNA replication, each copy of the chromosome attaches to the cell membrane and moves to the opposite side of the cell. During this time, the cell itself is stretching or elongating to make room for the chromosomes to separate. The plasma membrane surrounding the prokaryotic cell also begins to grow into the cell, between the two copies of the chromosome. Then a cell wall forms inward. It ultimately divides the prokaryotic cell into two new daughter cells, each containing a complete identical copy of the genome. The life of the parent cell is now complete, and the lives of the two new daughter cells have begun.

## 6.3 Exploring the Eukaryotic Cell Cycle

The cell cycle is a series of events that includes the growth of a cell, DNA replication, and nuclear (mitosis) and cytoplasmic division (cytokinesis). This is often referred to as the **mitotic cell cycle.** The mitotic cell cycle in eukaryotes can lead to either the creation of new individuals, as seen in unicellular protists, or to overall organism growth and development, as seen in animals and other multicellular eukaryotes. In addition, this process is important for cell replacement, tissue repair, and regeneration. For example, skin cells on the surface of the body are continuously being sloughed off and replaced by new cells via mitosis. Furthermore, when the skin is injured, mitosis is triggered and generates new cells to repair the damaged tissue. This process is called **wound healing.** In some cases, entire body parts, such as limbs or organs, can be regenerated by mitosis. Limb regeneration is evident in amphibians such as salamanders and newts following amputation.

A second type of nuclear division found in eukaryotes is **meiosis.** One of the major distinguishing features between mitosis and meiosis is the number of daughter cells produced and the distribution of genetic material. Mitosis results in the creation of two new daughter cells that each inherits a complete copy of the genome, thus making them genetically identical to each other. In meiosis, four new daughter cells are created, each inheriting half the genome. These daughter cells are therefore not genetically identical to one another. As such, meiosis is considered a mechanism of nuclear division that promotes genetic diversity within a species. Meiosis is also an important event in the sexual reproduction of eukaryotic organisms because newly formed daughter cells can mature into gametes (e.g., egg and sperm) that can fuse together during fertilization to produce a new offspring. In some organisms, such as plants, fungi, and some protists, meiosis results in the formation of spores that will germinate and grow into gamete-producing tissues (see Chapters 16, 17, and 18). These tissues produce gametes that will participate in sexual reproduction. In Chapter 7, we will discuss meiosis in more detail and the advantages of genetic diversity, but for now we will focus on mitosis.

### Cells Prepare for Cell Division during Interphase

The mitotic cell cycle of most eukaryotic cells has two major phases: **interphase** followed by **mitosis (Figure 6.3).** Interphase is essentially the time for the cell to grow and prepare for cell division, which includes DNA replication. Interphase is further divided into three main stages: **$G_1$ phase** (G stands for "gap"), **S phase** (S stands for

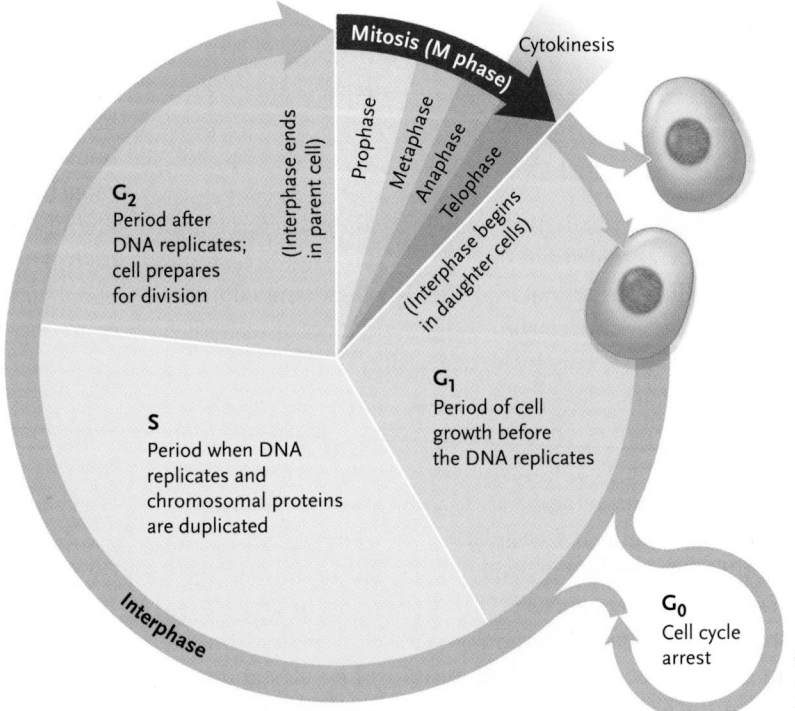

**FIGURE 6.3** The cell cycle. The length of $G_1$ varies, but for a given cell type, the timing of S phase, $G_2$ phase, and mitosis is usually relatively uniform. Cytokinesis (red segment) usually begins while mitosis is in progress and ends as mitosis ends. Cells in a state of division arrest are considered to enter a side loop (or shunt) from $G_1$ phase called $G_0$ phase.

Mitosis (M phase)

Cytokinesis

Prophase
Metaphase
Anaphase
Telophase

(Interphase ends in parent cell)

(Interphase begins in daughter cells)

**$G_2$**
Period after DNA replicates; cell prepares for division

**S**
Period when DNA replicates and chromosomal proteins are duplicated

**$G_1$**
Period of cell growth before the DNA replicates

**$G_0$**
Cell cycle arrest

Interphase

*Biology, 2E*

"DNA synthesis"), and **G₂ phase**. $G_1$ is the first interval in which cells are growing, making macromolecules such as RNA and protein and carrying out many of the cellular metabolic activities required for survival and growth (see the Purple Pages for an overview of macromolecules). The time a cell spends in $G_1$ depends on the cell type, the environmental conditions, and the requirements for cell division. For example, during the early stages of frog development, embryonic frog cells spend very little time in $G_1$; instead, most of their time is spent dividing by mitosis. The main objective at this point of the life cycle is simply to increase cell numbers and not to grow in size. This is in stark contrast to mature neurons that have stopped dividing altogether and have exited the cell cycle. Cells that exit the cell cycle are considered to be in **G₀ phase**, a state where cell division has stopped (Figure 6.3). Although cells in $G_0$ are considered to be in a resting phase (or cell cycle arrest), these cells are still carrying out many specialized cellular functions. For example, cardiac muscle cells are mature and differentiated muscle cells of the heart that are in the $G_0$ phase of the cell cycle. Although they are no longer actively dividing, they are still working dynamically to provide specialized functions, such as the coordinated contraction of the heart.

Once a cell has reached the end of $G_1$, it is now prepared for the next major phase: S phase or DNA synthesis (Figure 6.3). This is the critical stage in which the cell will make a duplicate copy of its genome, which will be inherited by future daughter cells. Thus, a cell's transition from $G_1$ to S phase is the first major commitment toward cell division. However, DNA replication in eukaryotic cells during S phase is not as simple as it is in prokaryotic cells. This is mainly because the genome in eukaryotes is arranged across more than one chromosome. For example, the common fruit fly (*Drosophila melanogaster* sp.) cell contains 8 chromosomes, and there are 46 chromosomes in a typical human cell. Since the complete genome of these cells is spread across multiple chromosomes, each of these chromosomes needs to be duplicated during S phase. We will discuss the mechanisms of DNA replication in more detail in Chapter 9. Here we will describe the bigger picture of DNA replication with respect to chromosomal duplication and cell division.

One of the critical outcomes of the mitotic cell cycle is the production of two daughter cells that are genetically identical to each other and to the original parent cell. As such, they all must contain the same genome. For this to occur, the genome in the parent cell must be accurately duplicated during S phase and then transferred effectively to each new daughter cell during mitosis. During S phase, DNA replication produces two identical double-stranded DNA molecules for each chromosome in the cell. The end result is two copies of each chromosome that remain tightly

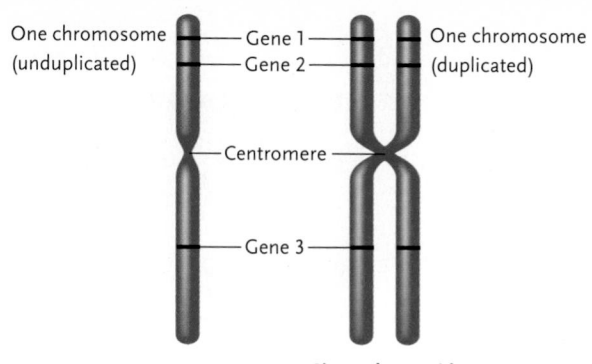

**Sister chromatids**

**FIGURE 6.4** Making new chromosomes during the cell cycle. During S phase, the DNA strands that make up chromosomes are duplicated. These duplicated strands remain together as sister chromatids, attached at their centromeres, until later in mitosis. By the end of mitosis, sister chromatids separate, and each sister chromatid is now considered an individual chromosome.

attached to one another at their **centromeres**. The centromere is a region of DNA within each identical DNA strand that links the two copies together **(Figure 6.4)**. Although the two identical DNA strands for each chromosome are attached to one another, they are called a pair of **sister chromatids** (Figure 6.4). It is not until they are separated during the later stages of mitosis that each of these sister chromatids will be considered an individual chromosome.

Another component of the cell that requires duplication during S phase is the pair of centrioles that make up the centrosome. Be careful not to confuse the term "centrosome" with the term "centromere"! The centrosome, if you recall from Chapter 3, is the main microtubule organizing centre found only in animal cells. Plants do not have centrosomes but instead have multiple microtubule organizing centres. In the next section, you will learn how doubling of the centrosome is critical to the separation of sister chromatids during mitosis. Once the entire genome of the cell and the centrosome has been duplicated, the cell can enter $G_2$, the next phase of the cell cycle. $G_2$ is a short-lived phase of the cell cycle in which RNA and protein continue to be synthesized in preparation for nuclear and cellular division.

## Mitosis Is a Form of Nuclear Division

After $G_2$, the cell is now ready to enter mitosis, the second major phase of the cell cycle. During mitosis, the nuclear material that has been duplicated in S phase will be divided up equally among the soon-to-be-formed daughter cells. Mitosis is divided into four different stages that proceed in the following order: prophase (*pro* = before), metaphase (*meta* = between), anaphase (*ana* = back), and telophase (*telo* = end) **(Figure 6.5, p. 134)**.

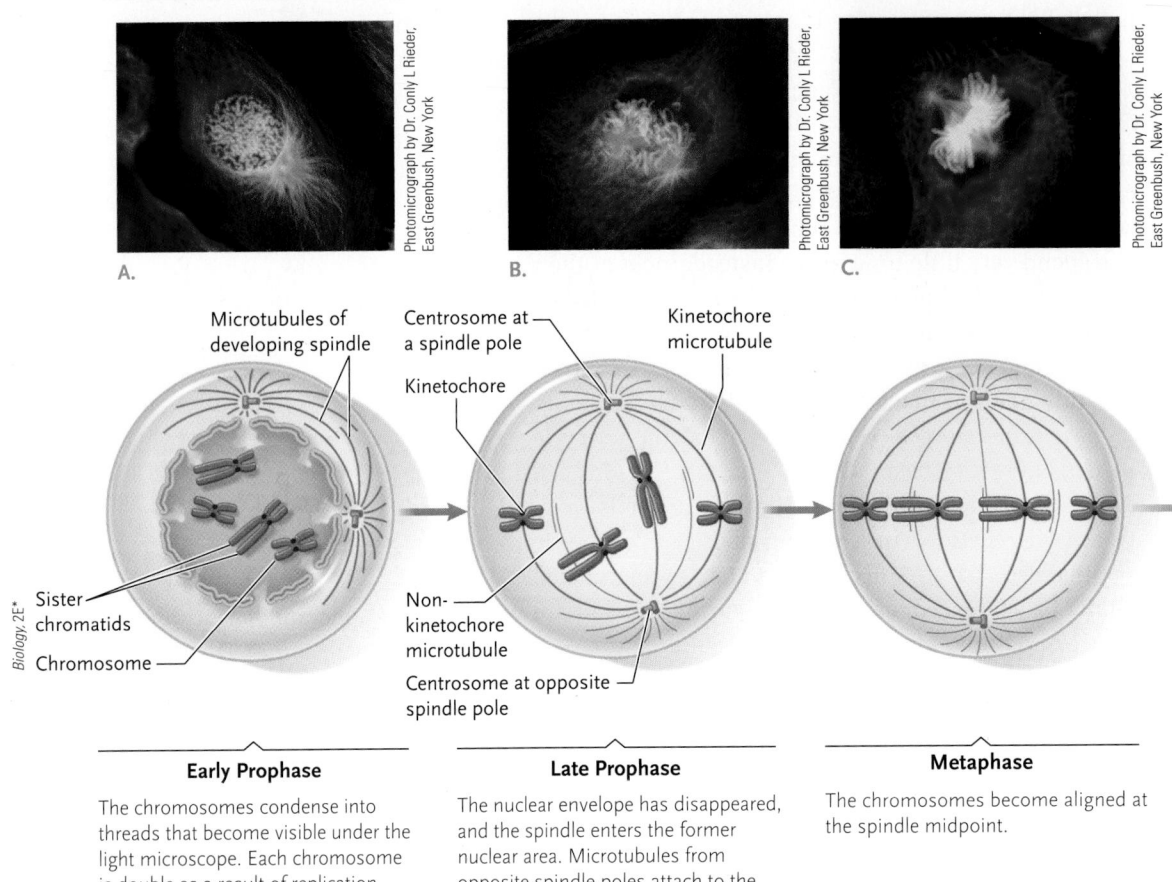

**Early Prophase**

The chromosomes condense into threads that become visible under the light microscope. Each chromosome is double as a result of replication. The centrosome has divided into two parts, which are generating the spindle as they separate.

**Late Prophase**

The nuclear envelope has disappeared, and the spindle enters the former nuclear area. Microtubules from opposite spindle poles attach to the two kinetochores of each chromosome.

**Metaphase**

The chromosomes become aligned at the spindle midpoint.

**FIGURE 6.5** The stages of mitosis. Immunofluorescent light micrographs show mitosis in an animal cell (salamander lung). The chromosomes are blue, the spindle and cytoplasmic microtubules are yellow-green, and the intermediate filaments are red. **(a)** Early prophase. Chromosomes are condensed, and the nuclear envelope is intact. **(b)** Late prophase. The nuclear envelope has broken down to allow the chromosomes to interact with the microtubules originating from two separate centrosomes. **(c)** Metaphase. All of the replicated chromosomes are aligned on the metaphase plate. **(d)** Anaphase/telophase. Chromosomes have been equally segregated and have decondensed to form two independent daughter nuclei. This cell has just begun cytokinesis. **(e)** The end result of mitosis: two genetically identical daughter cells.

## Prophase

Prophase is the first stage of mitosis. During early prophase, sister chromatids condense until they are rodlike structures that are visible under a light microscope **(Figure 6.5a)**. Also during this stage, the nuclear envelope surrounding the nucleus begins to break down and the nucleolus disappears, thus signifying a decrease in ribosomal RNA production and protein synthesis. Shutting down these processes is important because the cell must now focus its energy on dividing up the genetic material precisely and equally among the forming daughter cells. Failure to divide the genome accurately can lead to harmful and, in some cases, deadly consequences for the new cells.

By the end of prophase, the nuclear envelope has completely disappeared and the duplicated centrosomes have migrated to opposite ends, or poles, of the cell

**(Figure 6.5b)**. The microtubules will grow from the centrosomes (in plants, microtubules grow from the multiple microtubule organizing centres) and come together to form the **mitotic spindle**. You may recall from Chapter 3 that microtubules are cytoskeletal structures made of tubulin protein. The mitotic spindle is an important structure that directs the movement of chromosomes during nuclear division. The **kinetochore microtubules** of the mitotic spindle will first bind to the sister chromatids at their **kinetochores**. Kinetochores are protein complexes assembled and located on either side of the centromeres on the sister chromatids (Figure 6.5b). Motor proteins associated with the mitotic spindle then direct movement of the pairs of sister chromatids toward the centre of the cell. Also during this stage, **non-kinetochore microtubules**, microtubules not connected to sister chromatids, come together and overlap one another at the centre of the

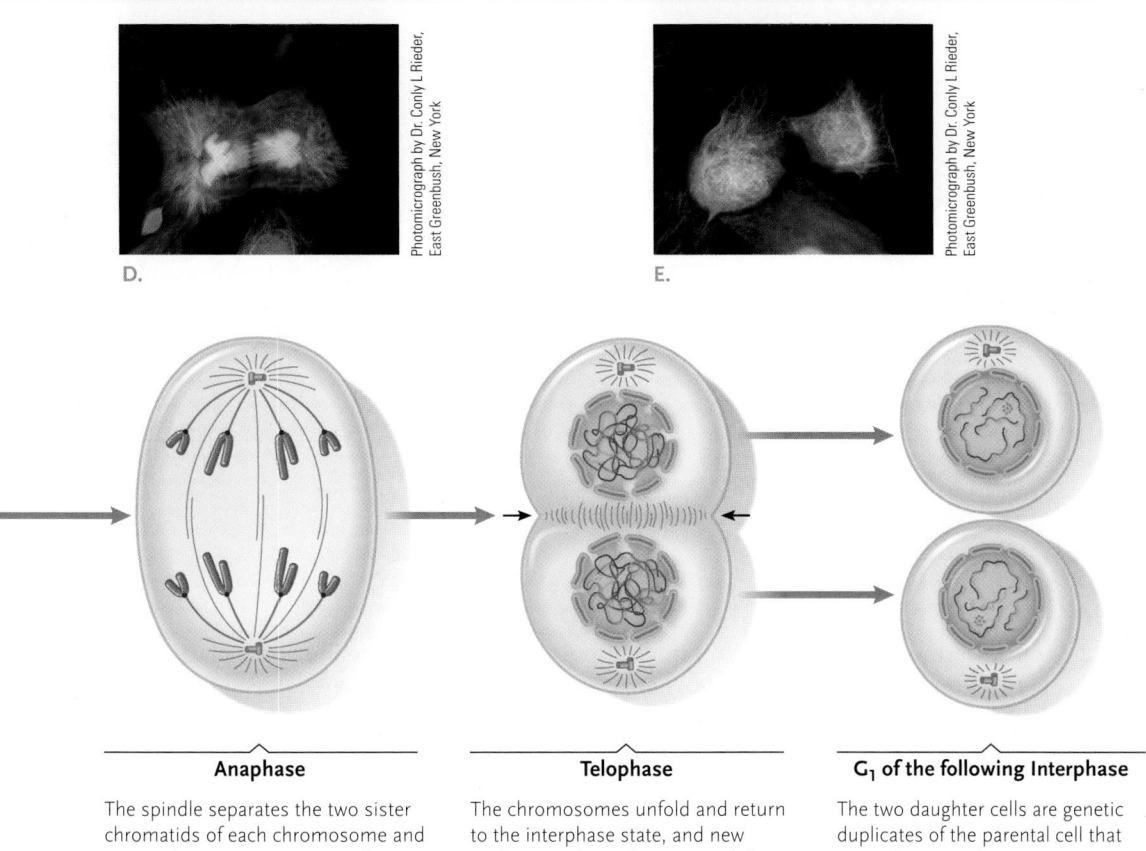

**D.**

Photomicrograph by Dr. Conly L Rieder, East Greenbush, New York

**E.**

Photomicrograph by Dr. Conly L Rieder, East Greenbush, New York

**Anaphase**

The spindle separates the two sister chromatids of each chromosome and moves them to opposite spindle poles.

**Telophase**

The chromosomes unfold and return to the interphase state, and new nuclear envelopes form around the daughter nuclei. The cytoplasm is beginning to divide by furrowing at the points marked by arrows.

**$G_1$ of the following Interphase**

The two daughter cells are genetic duplicates of the parental cell that entered mitotic division.

cell. They will be involved in ensuring that there is enough space in the cell for nuclear division to occur accurately.

### Metaphase

With the guidance of the kinetochore microtubules of the mitotic spindle, the sister chromatids align one by one at the centre of the cell across the metaphase plate (an imaginary plane equidistant from the opposing spindle poles) **(Figure 6.5c)**. The sister chromatids of each pair are facing opposite spindle poles. At this point, the sister chromatids are now ready to separate.

### Anaphase

During anaphase, the sister chromatids of each pair separate and move along their respective kinetochore microtubule toward the opposite spindle poles of the cell **(Figure 6.5d)**. Remember, once sister chromatids are separated from each other, they are now considered individual chromosomes. The chromosomes continue to separate until they reach the opposite poles of the cells. However, space is required within the cell to physically and accurately separate the chromosomes. As such, non-kinetochore microtubules that overlap each other begin to elongate at the centre of the cell,

causing the cell to stretch from opposite ends. This creates enough space to allows for complete segregation of chromosomes by the end of anaphase.

### Telophase

Telophase is the final stage of mitosis. During this stage, the mitotic spindle disappears and a new nuclear envelope forms around each set of chromosomes **(Figure 6.5e)**. The nucleolus reappears in each of the two new nuclei, and the chromosomes also decondense. These are both signs that the soon-to-be-formed daughter cells are preparing for growth in $G_1$, the first phase of a new cell cycle. In Chapter 9, you will learn how condensation and decondensation of DNA regulate expression of the genes found on the chromosomes and growth of the cell. Now that nuclear division is complete, the parent cell is ready to divide the cytoplasm and organelles and finalize the formation of the two new daughter cells.

## Cytokinesis Is Cytoplasmic Division

To complete cell division, the cytoplasm within the parent cell must separate to form two new daughter cells, each containing one of the two newly formed nuclei. This

**FIGURE 6.6** Cytokinesis by furrowing. The micrograph shows a furrow developing in the first division of a fertilized egg cell.

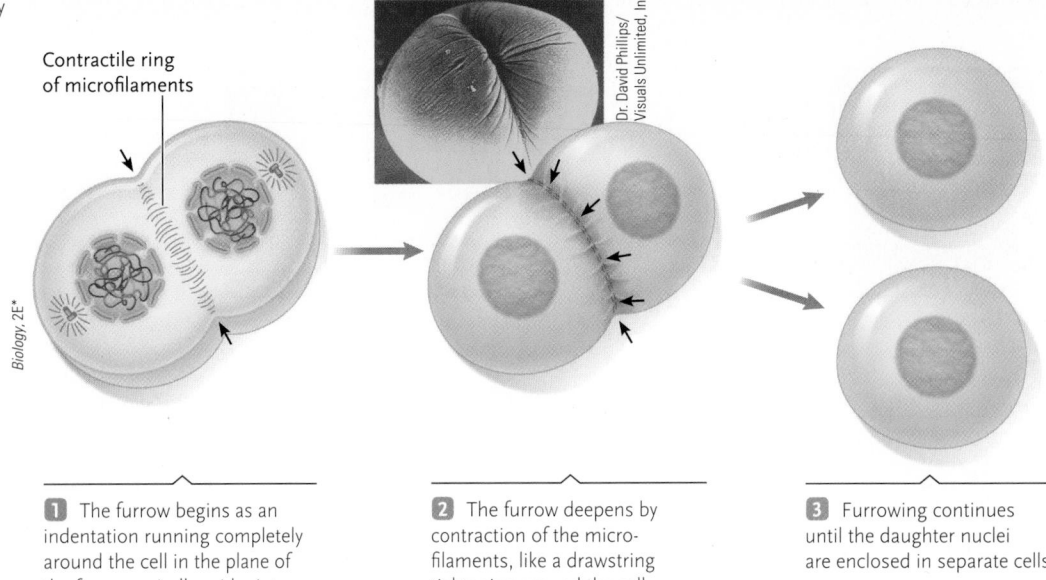

Contractile ring of microfilaments

Dr. David Phillips/ Visuals Unlimited, Inc.

Biology, 2E*

**1** The furrow begins as an indentation running completely around the cell in the plane of the former spindle midpoint.

**2** The furrow deepens by contraction of the microfilaments, like a drawstring tightening around the cell.

**3** Furrowing continues until the daughter nuclei are enclosed in separate cells.

process of cytoplasmic division is termed **cytokinesis** (*cyto* = cell, *kinesis* = movement). Cytokinesis often begins before mitosis is complete, usually during telophase. The mechanism of cytokinesis differs among eukaryotic cells.

In animal cells, a **cleavage furrow** or groove forms and wraps around the cell's midpoint between the two newly formed nuclei **(Figure 6.6)**. The furrow starts just underneath the plasma membrane, using a band of actin and myosin filaments called a contractile ring. As the ring contracts by using the power of motor proteins that consume ATP, it shrinks and pulls the plasma membrane inward. This appears as an indentation on the cell surface. The cleavage furrow deepens into the cytoplasm of the parent cell until the cell is pinched into two identical new daughter cells.

Plant cells have a stiff cell wall that does not move as fluidly as the plasma membrane. As such, plant cells undergo cytokinesis by forming a new cell wall between the two newly formed nuclei **(Figure 6.7)**. To begin, a set of microtubules forms on either side of the plane of the former spindle midpoint and the future site of the new cell wall. These microtubules will direct the movement of vesicles containing cell wall material from the Golgi complex toward this plane. Once the vesicles reach this plane, they will fuse together to form a **cell plate**. The cell plate extends to either edge of the cell and attaches at the cell membrane, dividing the cytoplasm. Eventually, the primary cell wall will merge with the parental cell wall and divide the cell into two new daughter cells.

At this point, let us recap the mitotic cell cycle. As we have already discussed, cells give rise to other cells through cell division. This occurs within a cell cycle that includes phases of growth and preparation (interphase), nuclear division (mitosis), and cytoplasmic division (cytokinesis). As a result, one parental cell gives rise to two genetically identical daughter cells that will enter the cell cycle at $G_1$ and thus renew life.

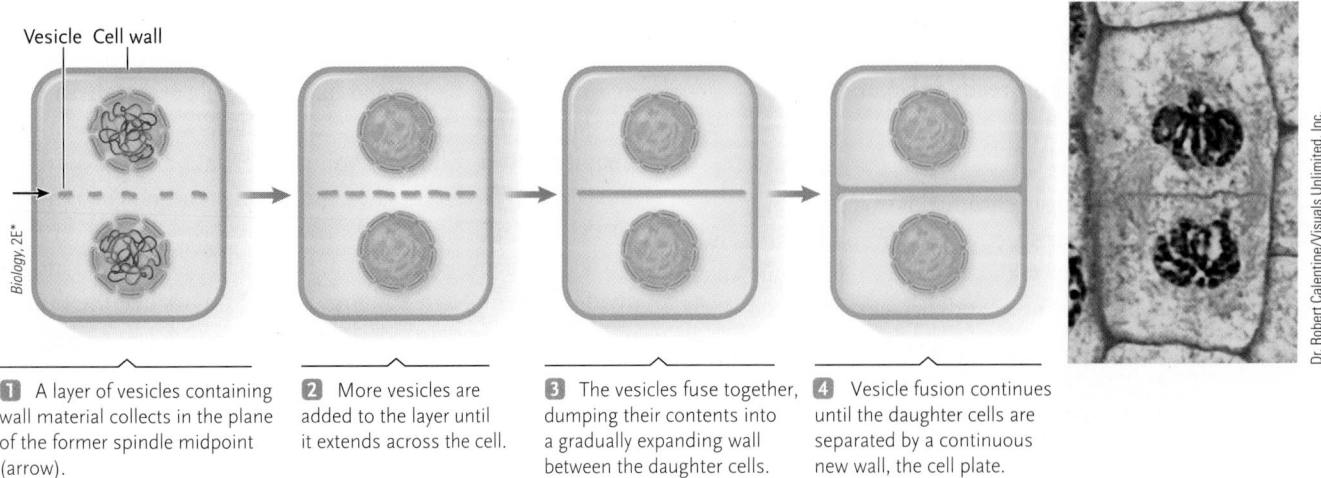

Vesicle  Cell wall

Biology, 2E*

Dr. Robert Calentine/Visuals Unlimited, Inc.

**1** A layer of vesicles containing wall material collects in the plane of the former spindle midpoint (arrow).

**2** More vesicles are added to the layer until it extends across the cell.

**3** The vesicles fuse together, dumping their contents into a gradually expanding wall between the daughter cells.

**4** Vesicle fusion continues until the daughter cells are separated by a continuous new wall, the cell plate.

**FIGURE 6.7** Cytokinesis by cell plate formation in plant cells.

1. Describe the two main phases of the mitotic cell cycle.
2. Describe the three phases of interphase and their purpose in the cell cycle.
3. Describe the stages of mitosis.
4. How does cytokinesis differ between animals and plants?
5. What is the end result of mitosis?

## 6.4 Controlling the Cell Cycle

The cell cycle is one of the most important cycles of life. And like anything in life that is vital for survival, regulatory mechanisms must be in place to ensure that the process occurs successfully and at the correct time. These are the checks and balances that must be met for life to proceed normally. The cell cycle is controlled primarily by a set of regulatory proteins. Some of these proteins promote cell growth and division, whereas others inhibit these processes. The balance between these actions is certainly complex. If these regulatory proteins do not function properly or are not produced in the right amounts, the result can range from premature cell death at one end of the spectrum to cancer on the other.

## Cells Must Pass Important Checkpoints Before Cell Division

Growth factors, as the name denotes, are a set of compounds that stimulate cell growth and division. Through this process, DNA is replicated and passed on to the new daughter cells. One main concern of this process is the inheritance of damaged DNA. Recall that DNA is the main information storage molecule of the cell. It is used to synthesize the RNA and protein required to build cell structure and carry out the cellular activities that are essential for life. Thus, damaging or altering DNA results in errors in the stored information—mistakes that in some cases can be harmful to the cell. There are several ways in which a cell's DNA can become damaged, including exposure of the cell to environmental assaults such as ultraviolet radiation or free radicals. Alterations or errors in the DNA can also occur during DNA synthesis (S phase) when chromosomes are undergoing duplication. Inheritance of these errors in the next generation of cells can be problematic.

The cell, however, is designed to check for many of these errors, repair damaged DNA, and halt the cell cycle as a protective measure. The cell cycle contains built-in checkpoints that control and direct the transition of cells from one phase to another **(Figure 6.8a)**. These checkpoints are critical for ensuring that the cell cycle proceeds accurately and efficiently. Two of the major checkpoints

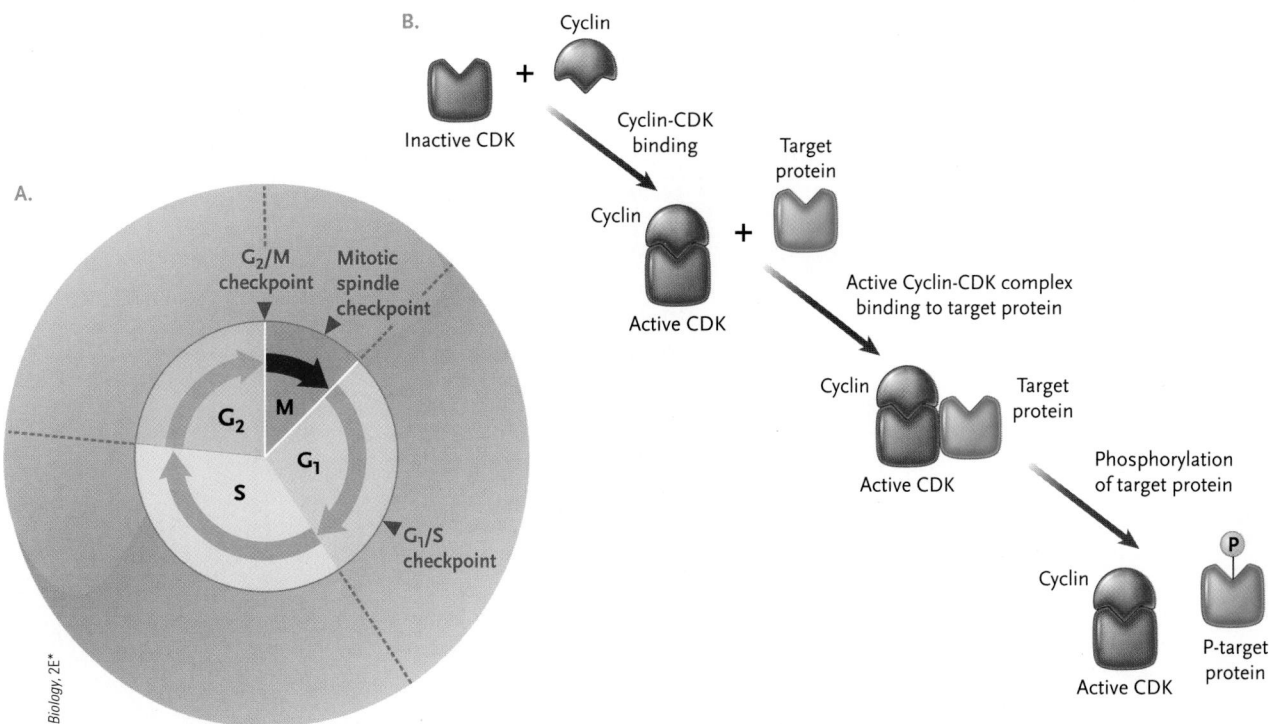

**FIGURE 6.8** Cyclin-CDK control of the $G_1/S$, $G_2/M$, and M checkpoints of the cell cycle. **(a)** A diagram highlighting the positions of three major checkpoints within the cell cycle. **(b)** An illustration of the mechanism of cyclin and CDK interactions.

in the cell cycle are between the $G_1$ and S phases—the $G_1$/S checkpoint—and between $G_2$ and mitosis—the $G_2$/M checkpoint (Figure 6.8a). A third major checkpoint is between metaphase and anaphase of mitosis, called the mitotic spindle (M) checkpoint (Figure 6.8a). The $G_1$/S checkpoint is often considered the most important barrier because passing this checkpoint commits the cell to divide. To initiate this transition, a cell will receive signals, usually in the form of growth factors, indicating that the intracellular and extracellular conditions of the cell are favourable for proliferation by cell division. It also indicates that any damage to the cell's DNA has been detected and repaired. The DNA is now ready for replication. The $G_2$/M checkpoint is also important for ensuring that DNA replication is complete and any errors or damage to the DNA acquired during DNA synthesis (S phase) have been corrected or repaired. Finally, the M checkpoint is a quality control mechanism that will block anaphase until all sister chromatids are stably attached to the mitotic spindle at their kinetochores during metaphase. Thus, the M checkpoint ensures that the sister chromatids separate accurately during anaphase, providing each new daughter with the correct number of chromosomes.

Cell cycle checkpoints are operated by sets of proteins that interact with one another. They integrate signals from within the cell and its environment to ensure that all the checks and balances are in place before the cell proceeds forward within the cell cycle. **Cyclins** are one such group of cell cycle proteins. Cyclins are named as such because their levels fluctuate or cycle, throughout the cell cycle. Cyclins bind to and activate another set of proteins called **cyclin-dependent kinases (CDKs)**, a group of enzymes that phosphorylate target proteins that regulate cell cycle events **(Figure 6.8b)**. The activities of these enzymes thus depend on the accumulation of cyclins during key points in the cell cycle. Phosphorylation by CDKs either activates or deactivates target proteins, which, in turn, can either direct the cell to the next phase of the cell cycle or prevent the cell from proceeding forward. As such, malfunctioning target proteins can lead to alterations in the regulation of the cell cycle and changes in the rates of cell division. And if left uncontrolled, increases in cell division can ultimately lead to cancer.

## Cells May Exit and Re-enter the Cell Cycle

After mitosis is complete, certain signaling molecules can promote **cell differentiation** in the newly formed cells. Cell differentiation is the maturation and specialization of cells. Let's take, for example, the differentiation of cardiac myocytes. Cardiac myocytes are specialized muscle cells of the heart. They are long and tubular and generate electrical impulses that contract the heart and control the heart rate **(Figure 6.9)**. During embryogenesis (early stage of animal development),

**FIGURE 6.9** Cardiac myocytes are the specialized muscle cells that make up the heart. **(a)** The gross anatomy of a human heart. **(b)** A microscopic view of cardiac myocytes, characterized by their tubular and branching structures.

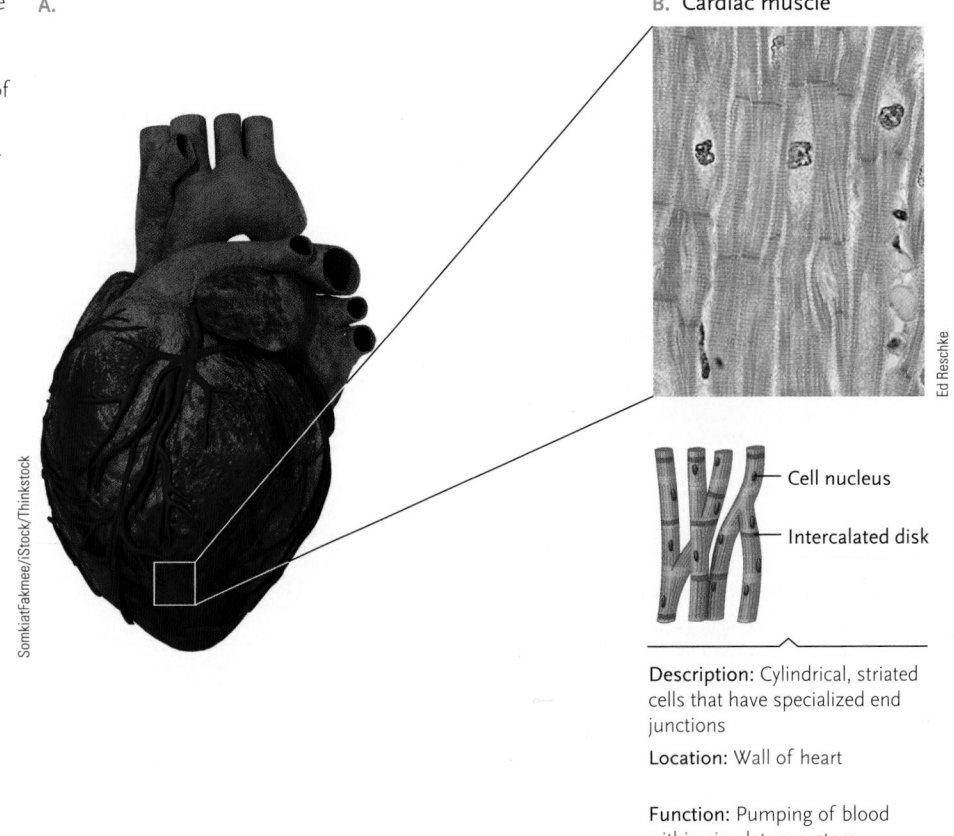

A.

B. Cardiac muscle

Cell nucleus

Intercalated disk

**Description:** Cylindrical, striated cells that have specialized end junctions

**Location:** Wall of heart

**Function:** Pumping of blood within circulatory system

SomkiatFakmee/iStock/Thinkstock

Ed Reschke

precursor myoblast cells, which are immature and thus not specialized, grow and divide by mitosis to build up an inventory of myoblast cells. This is stimulated by growth factors such as fibroblast growth factor and insulin-like growth factor. Both bind to specific receptors on the surface of the myoblast cells and direct their cell division. At some point during development, myoblast cells will receive signals to slow down cell division and begin differentiation. They can differentiate into various types of myocyte cells, including skeletal myocytes such as the cells found in your biceps or triceps, smooth muscle myocytes such as the cells found in the muscles that line your organs, and cardiac myocytes of the heart. Once differentiated, the rate of cell division in myocytes is dramatically reduced. Cells spend most of their time in either $G_1$ or, in some cases, $G_0$, depending on the specific muscle cell type. In fact, for many years, scientists believed that the cardiac myocytes exited the cell cycle completely after differentiation and remained in $G_0$ for the rest of the life of the heart. This hypothesis suggested that the cardiac myocytes that assembled to form your heart during embryonic development, before you were born, were the same cardiac myocytes you had in your heart as an adult. However, recent evidence contradicts that hypothesis. Research now shows that human cardiac myocytes do regenerate themselves through cell division during our lifetime. Although the rate of regeneration is limited, the data now suggest that up to 45% of the heart myocytes will be replaced by new cells during a typical human lifespan. This new scientific finding is a promising step toward developing new therapies to replace damaged cardiac tissue caused by heart attacks and/or coronary heart disease.

Even hepatocytes (differentiated cells of the liver), which typically are in $G_0$, can be stimulated to re-enter the cell cycle and proliferate to restore lost liver tissue. Once hepatocytes re-enter the cell cycle, their growth and cell division can restore up to 75% of lost liver tissue mass. However, even proliferating liver cells have to follow a highly regulated procedure for growth and must meet strict requirements before proceeding to cell division.

## STUDY BREAK

1. What are the three major checkpoints of the cell cycle, and what do they regulate?
2. What are cyclins and CDKs, and how do they work together in the cell cycle?

## 6.5 Cancer: Escaping the Regulatory Boundaries of the Cell Cycle

In most developed countries, cancer is one of the leading causes of death in both men and women. Inevitably, almost all of us will be affected by cancer in one way or another. But what exactly is cancer, and how does it start? Cancer is simply a group of cells that are growing and dividing via a deregulated cell cycle. Essentially, the cell cycle is the same as that followed by normal cells, however, the regulatory mechanisms that control the rate and accuracy of the cell cycle are disrupted **(Figure 6.10)**.

Cancers often begin when a cell undergoes a transformation that converts it from a normal cell to a cancerous one. These cancerous cells can grow to form a mass or lump of cells called **tumours** or **neoplasms**. Tumours that remain localized within their environment are referred to as **benign tumours (Figure 6.11, p. 140)**. Tumours that spread to nearby or distant organs are termed **malignant tumours** (Figure 6.11). Benign tumours

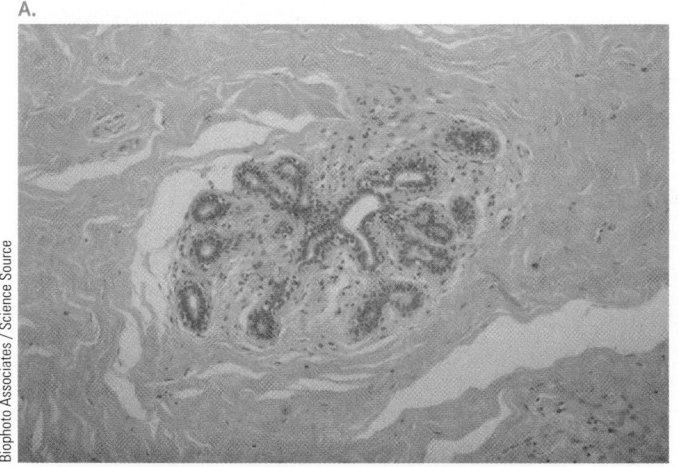

A.

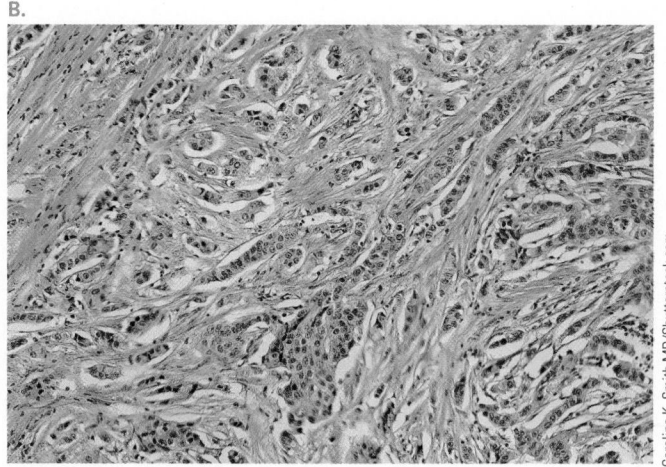

B.

Biophoto Associates / Science Source

Carolina K. Smith MD/Shutterstock.com

**FIGURE 6.10** Micrographs of **(a)** normal breast tissue and **(b)** breast adenocarcinoma (breast cancer) tissue. Breast epithelial cells (purple) in the normal breast tissue are growing at a regulated rate and are well organized compared to the cells (purple) in the breast cancer tissue that are growing uncontrollably and are disorganized into the adjacent supporting tissue (pink) of the breast.

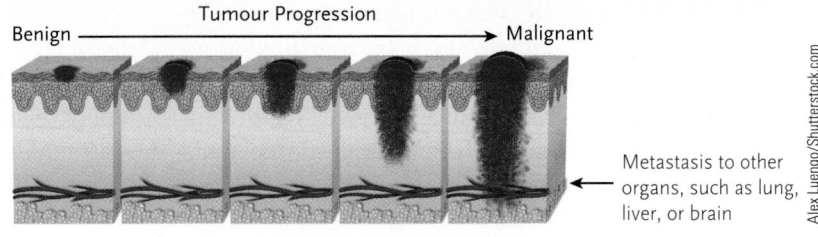

**FIGURE 6.11** Progression of skin cancer from a benign tumour to a malignant tumour that has invaded the blood vessels.

Tumour Progression

Benign ⟶ Malignant

Metastasis to other organs, such as lung, liver, or brain

Alex Luengo/Shutterstock.com

tend to be less dangerous than malignant tumours. They often grow slower, and the cells involved retain many of the adhesion proteins at the cell surface that anchor them to the extracellular matrix and to neighbouring cells within the tissue or organ. This ensures that they remain in place. Conversely, malignant tumours tend to grow faster and more abnormally, often due to a lack of cell cycle control, and are less anchored to their environment. As a result, these cells move more and are more invasive, thus promoting their ability to spread to distant organs. Although both benign and malignant tumours can physically and metabolically disrupt the structure and function of tissues and organs, the term "cancer" is used medically to describe only malignant tumours.

Cancers are named primarily by the organ in which the tumours began and are categorized into several groups. The four major categories are described here. **Carcinomas** are cancers that originate from cells that line the inner or outer surfaces of the body, such as the skin or lining of the digestive system. **Sarcomas** are cancers that originate from supportive tissue such as the bone or muscle. Cancers of the blood-forming tissues such as bone marrow and spleen are characterized as **leukemia**. **Lymphomas** involve cancers of the white blood cells of the immune system, including the lymph nodes.

The spread of cancer cells from their original site to other parts of the body is termed **metastasis (Figure 6.12)**. Metastasis first involves the recruitment of vessels from both the circulatory and lymphatic systems to the malignant tumour. From here, some of the malignant cells can detach from the original tumour and slip into the vessels, using the vessels to migrate through the body to distant locations. At these new sites, the migrating malignant cells can slip back out of the vessels and form a new or secondary tumour mass (Figure 6.12).

There are many facets to how a normal cell transforms into a cancerous one. One of the main causes for this transformation is the conversion of a **proto-oncogene** into an **oncogene**. A proto-oncogene is any gene in the cell that has the potential to become a cancer-causing gene (oncogene) if it is mutated or altered. Mutations in proto-oncogenes can occur during growth ($G_1$ phase) by exposure to cancer-causing environmental factors or because of an error in chromosome replication during DNA synthesis (S phase). Common proto-oncogenes are those that enhance or promote cell growth and development. For example, the family of *ras* genes (H-*ras*, K-*ras*, and N-*ras*) consists of proto-oncogenes whose protein products belong to a family of small GTPases—enzymes that break down guanosine triphosphate (GTP, an energy source and activator

**FIGURE 6.12** Cancer metastasis. An illustration of the various steps leading to the metastasis (spreading) of cancer cells through the circulatory system from a primary to a secondary site.

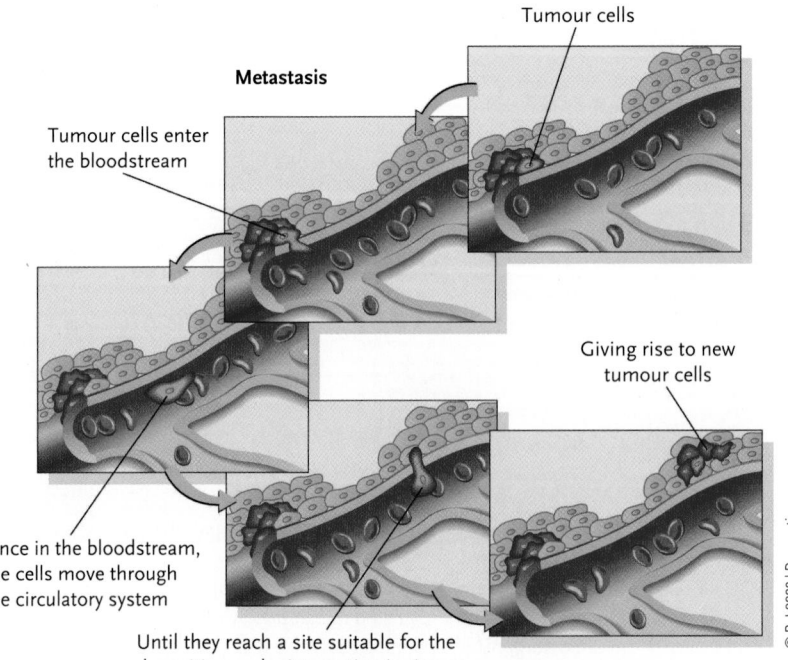

Tumour cells

Metastasis

Tumour cells enter the bloodstream

Giving rise to new tumour cells

Once in the bloodstream, the cells move through the circulatory system

Until they reach a site suitable for the deposition and reintegration in tissues

© Rob3000 | Dreamstime.com

molecule). By using the energy released when GTP breaks down, these enzymes can help transmit signals within cells that elicit certain cellular behaviours, such as growth and division. Ras proteins are activated when the cell receives a stimulus for growth (e.g., growth factor). As a result, the cell divides. Under normal conditions, when cells are not signalled to divide, ras proteins will be deactivated (turned off), and the cell remains in either $G_1$ or $G_0$. In certain cancerous cells, the *ras* proto-oncogene has been mutated and converted into a *ras*-oncogene. As a result, the ras protein that the oncogene encodes for is permanently activated. This means that the message to divide is continuously relayed to the cell, even in the absence of growth factors. In other words, the off switch (or deactivation of ras protein) is broken, and the cell continues to grow and divide indefinitely and out of control. The *ras* oncogenes have been implicated in many forms of cancer, including colorectal, breast, and pancreatic cancers.

Another major cause of cancer is mutated or deleted tumour suppressor genes. These genes encode for tumour suppressor proteins that reduce or inhibit cell division and thus are important in regulating the cell cycle. These proteins check and repair errors in the DNA and block DNA replication and cell division if DNA errors are not corrected. Mutations in these tumour suppressor genes can result in changes to the structure, and therefore function, of their protein products. In other words, those proteins that are supposed to ensure the rate and accuracy of cell division are themselves malfunctioning. One example is p53, a tumour suppressor protein encoded by the *TP53* gene. It is one of the most important regulators of the cell cycle. As such, it is often dubbed the "guardian of the genome." Its main function in the cell is to control the transition of cells from $G_1$ to S phase. If DNA is damaged within the genome, p53 can trigger DNA repair and block the cell from entering S phase until the DNA is repaired. If the DNA cannot be repaired, then p53 triggers **apoptosis**, also known as programmed cell death. Cell death is the last recourse used to ensure that the damaged DNA is not inherited by future daughter cells. When p53 is mutated, regulation of cell division is lost. In other words, any damaged DNA present in the parent cell is inherited by daughter cells. The accumulation of DNA mutations by future daughter cells can eventually lead to deregulated cell division and, ultimately, cancer. Indeed, almost 50% of cancers contain a *TP53* gene mutation. The *BRCA1* and *BRCA2* genes discussed in Box 6.1 are also tumour suppressor genes.

It is clear that cancer is an imbalance between cell growth and death. Oncogenes will tip the scale toward cancer, whereas tumour suppressor genes tip it toward apoptosis **(Figure 6.13)**. Hence, developing methodologies to restore this balance in the cell cycle is a

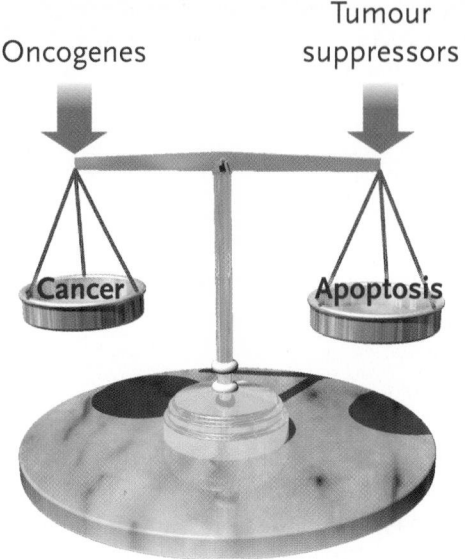

**FIGURE 6.13** Balance between cancer and apoptosis. Oncogenes promote cell growth and division, leading to cancer, whereas tumour suppressor proteins lead to apoptosis (programmed cell death), which inhibits cancer formation.

major focus of many cancer research studies. However, it should be noted that cancer is a progressive disease primarily based on the accumulation of DNA mutations either inherently acquired and/or through exposure to certain harmful environmental conditions. As such, the initiation and progression of cancer take time, and for most cancers, its incidence and onset are correlated with age. As we live longer, we accumulate more and more of these mutations in our cells, thus making our chances of acquiring cancer greater.

Although the reported incidence of cancer has increased over the last 50 years, the overall survival rates for many cancers have also improved. These trends are partly due to major advancements made in the early detection of the disease and in developing innovative and effective treatment strategies. Many cancers are being diagnosed at earlier stages, before metastasis, when treatments are more effective. However, many questions still remain about the most effective cancer treatments for patients. This is dependent on the tumour size and the location and stage of cancer progression. Surgery often remains the primary treatment option. Other treatments may also be administered in combination with surgery. These include radiation and chemotherapy.

High-energy radiation at the tumour site can kill cancer cells by damaging their DNA to the point where the cells can no longer divide. Radiation is often administered locally at the site of the cancer. For some cancers, such as prostate or testicular cancer, this may be the only form of effective treatment following surgery.

Chemotherapy involves the administration of drugs, either systemically (directly into the bloodstream) or orally, that can disrupt specific stages of the

FIGURE 6.14 **(a)** Paclitaxel is a chemotherapy drug molecule derived from a fungal endocyte living in the Pacific yew tree. **(b)** A small branch of the Pacific yew tree found on the West Coast of North America.

A.

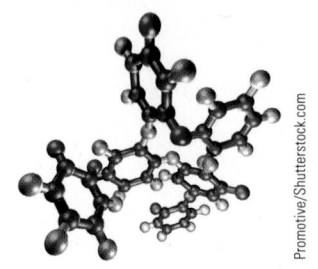

B.

cell cycle. For example, paclitaxel, also known commercially as Taxol (Bristol-Myers Squibb Company), is a common chemotherapeutic drug to treat breast cancer **(Figure 6.14a)**. Paclitaxel binds and stabilizes the microtubules that compose the mitotic spindle during mitosis, causing the cells to stay in metaphase and thus blocking passage through the M checkpoint. This triggers apoptosis, resulting in cell death. Interestingly, paclitaxel was originally isolated in 1967 from the Pacific yew tree, *Taxus brevifolia* **(Figure 6.14b)**. It was later discovered that the compound was not made by the plant itself but instead was made by an endophytic fungus (*Pestalotiopsis microspora* sp.), that lives in the bark of the tree.

Many chemotherapeutic drugs are aimed at stopping cells from dividing. Since cancer cells generally divide faster than normal cells, the effects of chemotherapy are therefore more devastating to cancer cells. However, one of the major disadvantages of most chemotherapeutic drugs is their inability to distinguish cancer cells from normal, rapidly dividing cells such as skin and intestinal cells. As a result, many of these normal cells are also susceptible to the actions of these chemotherapies, eliciting unfavourable side effects. For example, these drugs can affect hair follicles within the skin, resulting in hair loss. They can affect intestinal cells, resulting in nausea. They can affect white blood cells, compromising the immune system. All of these types of side effects reduce quality of life and increase the patient's mental anguish. Today, cancer research is heavily focused on developing targeted therapies that attack (or target) only the cancer cells, without damaging or affecting normal cells. To do this, scientists must identify major functional proteins that differ between cancer and normal cells to develop effective therapeutic strategies against these specific targets.

One common targeted chemotherapeutic drug is trastuzumab, commonly known as Herceptin (Genentech, Inc.). This drug is used to treat Her2-positive breast cancer patients. Since these types of breast cancers overexpress the cell surface growth factor receptor Her2, trastuzumab can bind specifically to the Her2 receptor on these cancer cells and inactivate it. This, in turn, stops the cells from growing and dividing out of control. Since trastuzumab is also an antibody, it can also trigger the immune system to destroy the cancer cell. Because normal cells do not overexpress Her2, they are protected against the actions of this chemotherapeutic drug.

Using the immune system to fight cancer is another current focus in cancer research. Immunotherapy uses the body's own immune system to fight specifically against cancer cells. The immune system is already designed to reject and destroy cancerous cells in the body. However, many cancers have evolved to produce an outer coating that masks their identifying characteristics. In other words, the immune cells cannot distinguish these cancer cells from normal cells and thus do not attack them. A novel immunotherapy drug that is currently under investigation removes this outer coating from the surface of cancer cells, exposing their unique features and triggering an immune response. As a result, the body's own immune system detects and destroys the cancerous cells with minimal side effects to the patient (read more about anti-cancer drug development and the pharmaceutical industry in Box 6.2).

## STUDY BREAK

1. What is the difference between a benign and a malignant tumour?
2. What is metastasis?
3. What is the difference between an oncogene and a tumour suppressor gene?
4. Describe some of the therapies used to treat cancer patients.

## 6.6 The End of a Cell's Life: Senescence and Apoptosis

**Cellular senescence** is the natural aging of a cell that ultimately leads to death. Accumulation of DNA mutations during the lifetime of a cell and decreased ability to repair these mutations may ultimately lead to an overall reduction

# BIOLOGY IS EVERYWHERE 6.2

## The Scientific, Social, and Economic Struggles of Drug Development

Mustine, sold under the brand name Mustargen (Lundbeck, LLC), was one of the first drugs used for the development of anti-cancer chemotherapeutics. Mustine is a nitrogen-based analogue of mustard gas, a chemical weapon used in both World War I and World War II. It functions by binding to the guanine nucleotides in DNA, causing the DNA strands of chromosomes to cross-link each other, and, consequentially, blocks cell division. Classified research on the effects of mustard gas on several lymphomas and leukemias (blood cancers) began in 1942 and was the basis for the development of mustine. Since that time, numerous new anti-cancer drugs with more effective properties have been designed and sent to market. But developing these drugs is not an easy task, and saving people's lives may not always be the driving force.

Each year, pharmaceutical companies spend billions of dollars on research and development of new drugs. But how do drugs go from the lab bench to the patient's bedside? Traditionally, the discovery of anti-cancer drugs has been either from isolating an active ingredient found within natural products or simply by chance. Currently, many drugs are discovered using modern biotechnological tools to elucidate the normal metabolic pathways and regulatory mechanisms of cells. Once discovered, researchers develop these compounds into a marketable drug based on appropriate formulation and dosing. The early stages of the discovery process occur in academic research labs, often funded by government research grants. However, the later stage of development, which includes clinical trials, requires an enormous amount of time and money, which are often accessible only to larger pharmaceutical companies. Indeed, the time from drug discovery to federal approval can take well over a decade. And with this large investment of money comes plenty of risk for these companies. A large fraction (up to 95% for anti-cancer drugs) of compounds identified as potential drugs fail in these late stages of development due to the frequency and severity of side effects to the patient, which could not be detected before human testing. Consequently, the cost of

discovering and developing the many drugs that fail is subsidized by the very few that succeed. With this large attrition rate, pharmaceutical companies feel the financial and social pressures to alter the process of drug development. In a recent perspective by the research-based charity Cancer Research UK, the authors propose that the future success of drug development lies with stronger collaborations between pharmaceutical companies and academics, who often have a more comprehensive and in-depth understanding of the biological mechanisms that underpin the disease. Indeed, both parties have their own unique yet complementary set of skills that can be used collaboratively to increase the success rate of drug development, which will ultimately better serve patients.

However, recent relationships between the pharmaceutical industry and academics have been strained. Most recently, over 100 leading cancer specialists, including cancer researchers, from 15 different countries condemned the enormous costs of anti-cancer drugs

in an article published in the journal *Blood*. Their view is that the cost of anti-cancer drugs is forcing many cancer patients to forgo treatment. Although the pharmaceutical industry reasons that the high cost of drug development is the cause of price increases, many of these cancer specialists, who have collaborative links to the industry, claim that these companies exaggerate the cost of development to fatten their bottom lines. In addition, the physicians maintain that the Hippocratic oath of *Primum non nocere* ("First, do no harm") compels them to advocate against high drug costs in an effort to save patient lives. On the other hand, these physicians and researchers now fear that their own scientific research, which in many cases is funded by the same industry that they are speaking out against, will suffer. In turn, this strain will inevitably affect the bigger relationship between the pharmaceutical industry and academics and, ultimately, the future of drug development in the treatment of cancer **(Figure 1)**.

**FIGURE 1** The balance between the production and the cost of pharmaceutical drugs.

# LIFE ON THE EDGE 6.3
## Cancer Stem Cells: The True Villain

The body you have today is not the same body you had at birth. Many of your the tissues and organs are being replenished by a unique set of cells called **stem cells**. Stem cells were first identified in 1961 by two Canadian scientists, James Till and Ernest McCulloch (later dubbed the "fathers of stem cell science"). They are self-renewing cells that have the ability to grow and divide continuously and differentiate into the specialized cells that make up the tissues and organs found throughout your body. But, like any other cell, errors in DNA can lead to deregulation of the structure and function of these stem cells. **Cancer stem cells** are malfunctioning stem cells that have the power to not only initiate tumour formation but also drive progression and, more importantly, recurrence.

The **cancer stem cell hypothesis** was brought to the scientific spotlight in the mid-1990s with the seminal work of another Canadian award-winning scientist, Dr. John Dick. He showed that in a population of leukemia (blood cancer) cells, there was a subpopulation of self-renewing cells that had "stem cell–like" properties. Today, cancer stem cells have been identified and isolated from many different types of cancers, including colon, prostate, breast, pancreatic, ovarian, and brain cancers. These cancer stem cells constitute only a small fraction of the cells within tumours. However, they have the unique capacity to initiate new tumours, which are characteristically similar to the original tumour they were isolated from. As such, they are also more accurately termed "tumour-initiating cells." The hypothesis thus suggests that all cells within a tumour are not alike and that the more potent ones, namely the cancer stem cells, are the driving force behind tumour initiation, progression, and metastasis. As such, cancer stem cells are the hot target of recent anti-cancer therapeutic strategy, especially in treatment resistance cancers.

It is evident that not all cancers are curable with chemotherapy or radiation treatments. Even if these treatments provide an initial response or bulk elimination of tumour cells, over time, some cancers develop resistance. As a result, the cancer either continues to progress (if it was not completely eliminated) or may recur at a later point in time. In either case, these recurring cells are faster growing and more aggressive, invasive, and resistant to conventional treatment. It is believed that these recurring cells are a propagation of cancer stem cells that were resistant and therefore not killed by initial treatment. Although initial treatments destroy non-resistant cancer cells, the treatment also inadvertently selects for the resistant cancer cells that could adapt and survive in the presence of the treatment (by means of artificial selection, which you can read more about in Chapter 13). These cells thus continue to propagate. Many scientists now believe that the one key approach to battling cancer is the initial elimination of these cancer stem cells **(Figure 1)**. But how can one identify a cancer stem cell?

One of the areas of main focus is the discovery of unique cancer stem cell biomarkers that could potentially identify cancer stem cells and be used as therapeutic targets. In addition, understanding the genetic defects that lead to resistance is important in developing new treatments. For example, recent efforts are using miRNA (micro-RNA) to combat cancer stem cells. These forms of RNA can bind to gene transcripts (messenger RNA) and block gene expression by inhibiting the production of the gene's protein product. This is significant in blocking

---

in cellular function. As a result, cells stop dividing and eventually die. Normal cells grown in a lab divide on average 50 times before they undergo cellular senescence.

However, unlike natural aging, death is also programmed within the genomes of eukaryotic cells and can be triggered by external or internal signals. Programmed cell death or apoptosis is an ancient mechanism common to all eukaryotic organisms studied thus far. In addition, it is an important part of development in multicellular eukaryotic organisms and can also be triggered to prevent cancer when there is an accumulation of DNA damage to genes associated with the cell cycle.

Apoptosis has been extensively studied in the roundworm nematode *Caenorhabditis elegans* **(Figure 6.15a, p. 146)**. This organism is ideal for studying programmed cell death because the number of cells that undergo apoptosis is constant throughout the development of the organism. This consistency has allowed researchers to study the signals that trigger apoptosis and the intracellular events that result in cell death. Two major groups of enzymes involved in carrying out apoptosis are caspases and nucleases **(Figure 6.15b)**. Caspases are proteases, or enzymes that degrade protein, that are activated during apoptosis and direct destruction of proteins, the major structural and functional macromolecules of the cell. Nucleases are enzymes that degrade nucleic acids such as RNA and DNA. Activating nucleases leads to destruction of the cellular information system. The actions of proteases and nucleases ultimately lead to cell death and the recycling of important cellular nutrients. During development, apoptosis is critical for removing surplus cells that are no longer required as development progresses. For example, the tips of the limb buds in a human fetus, which appear webbed, give rise to the

the expression of oncogenes or genes that promote self-renewal in these cancer stem cells, without attacking normal stem cells. Immunotherapy research is also investigating how to train the body's own immune system to attack cancer stem cells. Again, identifying cancer stem cell biomarkers would be essential for developing this type of therapy. Some laboratories are also investigating the tumour microenvironment for clues on how to stop cancer stem cells. Recall that we learned in Chapter 3 that cells are not autonomous but instead are organized in and interact with their microenvironment. This is also true of cancer stem cells. And the architecture and dynamic state of the cancer stem cell microenvironment, termed the "cancer stem cell niche," likely affect the decisions these cells make about growth and division and possibly even death. Targeting the unique components of the microenvironment that influences these decisions may lead to novel strategies that inhibit cancer stem cell growth and promote apoptosis. This should result in cancer regression and elimination.

As you can see, there is still an enormous amount of work to be done to learn more about cancer stem cells and their actions in cancer. As such, this requires multidisciplinary teams of scientists and clinicians. One such team that was recently formed is the Cancer Stem Cell Consortium, which is made up of experts from Canada and California who pioneered the discovery and knowledge of cancer stem cells. Founded in 2007, the Cancer Stem Cell Consortium is focused on accelerating cancer stem cell research by integrating the various specialties of the team members. They hope to facilitate the translation of basic scientific research from the lab bench to the clinic. And with the advancement in communication technologies, these types of team-focused approaches to global health issues will likely become more common.

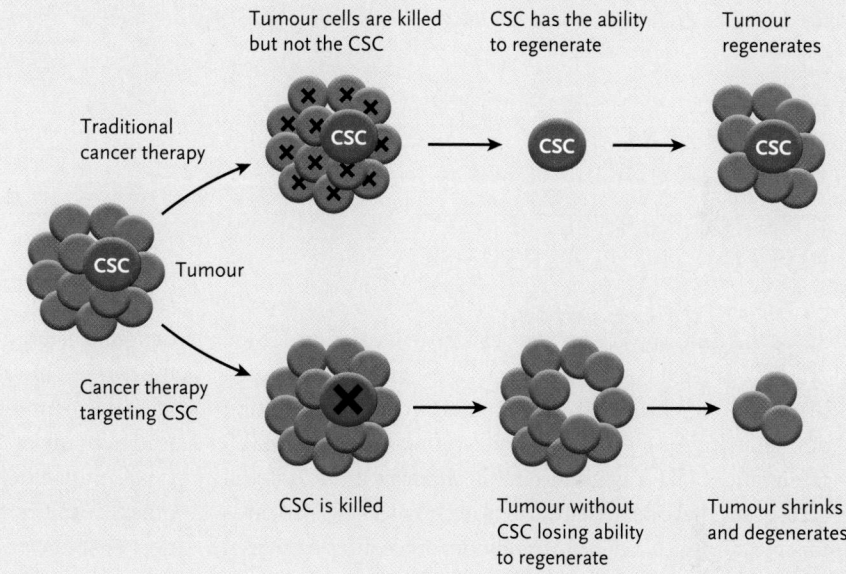

**FIGURE 1** Mechanism to treat cancer by targeting cancer stem cells (CSC).

hands and feet of the organism. To form the individual fingers and toes, the cells that make up the webbing characteristic must be eliminated. This is done by triggering apoptosis in these cells **(Figure 6.15c)**.

Apoptosis, like all other cellular events, is under tight control. Abnormalities can lead to increased or decreased apoptotic events. Too much apoptosis can lead to degenerative disorders such as Alzheimer or Parkinson disease. Excess neuronal cell death is a contributing factor in the progression of both of these diseases. Current research is investigating new strategies for inhibiting apoptosis in neural cells.

Apoptosis is also an important event that keeps cell division under control. When cells accumulate DNA damage that cannot be repaired, apoptosis is triggered in the cell. This event is often triggered by tumour suppressor proteins such as p53. In cancer cells, apoptosis is reduced or inhibited, resulting in a major defect in cell cycle regulation. Researchers are currently investigating mechanisms to target drug-resistant cancer cells, in particular cancer stem cells, by inducing apoptosis in these cells. Cancer stem cells are a small group of self-renewing cells within tumours that often are resistant to treatments. They are believed to be one of the leading causes of relapse and metastasis in many cancer patients (read more about cancer stem cells in Box 6.3).

## STUDY BREAK

1. What is the difference between cellular senescence and apoptosis?
2. Describe how caspases and nucleases carry out apoptosis.

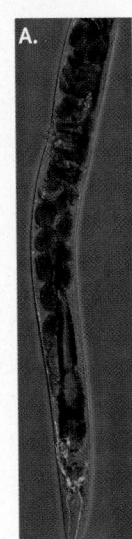

From Starr. *Biology*, 8E. © 2011 Brooks/Cole, a part of Cengage Learning, Inc. Reproduced by permission.www.cengage.com/permissions

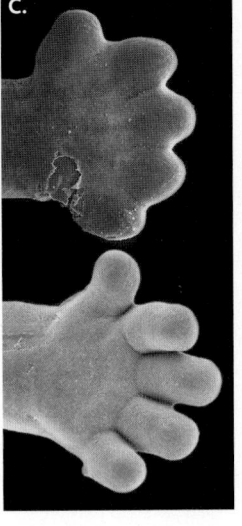

© Heiti Paves | Dreamstime.com

Courtesy of Dr.Kathleen K. Sulik, Bowles Center for Alcohol Studies, the University of North Carolina at Chapel Hill

**FIGURE 6.15** Apoptosis is programmed cell death. **(a)** A microscopic view of *C. elegans*, a model organism for studying apoptosis. **(b)** An artist's depiction of apoptosis, with enzymes shown as knifelike blades. **(c)** Formation of human fingers from 48 (top) to 51 (bottom) days after fertilization. Cells making up the tissue webs undergo apoptosis, resulting in the separation of digits.

## PUTTING IT IN PERSPECTIVE

Since the time you began your existence as a single-celled zygote (fertilized egg), your cells have been cycling through life. This cycle has been instrumental in your growth and development, tissue regeneration, wound healing, and differentiation. Like any important mechanism in life, the cell cycle events have been tightly regulated to meet the standards for accuracy and efficiency. In addition, procedures have been in place to correct any errors or mishaps. These regulatory checkpoints have ensured the success of newly formed daughter cells and the elimination of those that did not make the cut. But life as we know it is not perfect, and certain mistakes do go unnoticed. Unfortunately, these overlooked errors lead to many of the imbalances in a cell's life. Some simply cause minor defects within the whole organism, whereas others result in the end of the organism's existence. In the next chapter, we will continue to discuss a cell's life, but in the context of genetic diversity and how this diversity can lead to some major advantages for overall species survival.

## KEY CONCEPTS REVIEW AND QUESTIONS

### 6.1   Revisiting the Cell Theory

The cell theory states that cells arise from pre-existing cells. Reproduction can occur either asexually or sexually to produce a new individual or cell. This occurs through the cell cycle, which is made up of periods of cell growth and DNA replication and which culminates in cell division.

1.  True or False? Asexual reproduction results in offspring that are genetically identical to the parent.

2.  True or False? In multicellular eukaryotic organisms, cell reproduction occurs only for the purpose of generating new organisms.

### 6.2   Reproduction in Prokaryotes by Binary Fission

Prokaryotes, which include bacteria and archaea, reproduce asexually through binary fission. During this process, the single circular chromosome is duplicated, and each identical chromosome copy is transported to opposite poles of the cell. The plasma membrane and cell wall grow inward toward the centre of the cell and ultimately divide the cell into two new daughter cells, each containing an identical copy of the chromosome.

3.  If a bacterial cell has one copy of the chromosome prior to binary fission, how many copies does each newly formed daughter cell have?

    a. One

    b. Two

    c. Four

    d. Eight

4. Why is it important for the dividing cell to elongate during binary fission?

   a. To resume the correct cell shape

   b. To move to a more favourable environment

   c. To create more physical space for accurate separation of the two chromosome copies

   d. To ensure that the two copies of chromosomes have physical space to interact with each other

## 6.3 Exploring the Eukaryotic Cell Cycle

Most eukaryotic cells reproduce using a cell cycle that is divided into two main phases: interphase and mitosis (a type of nuclear division). The cell will grow during $G_1$ phase of interphase, duplicate its chromosomes by DNA replication during S phase, and prepare for cell division during $G_2$ phase. Cell division occurs during mitosis, which is broken down into four main stages: prophase, metaphase, anaphase, and telophase. During mitosis, chromosomes line up in the middle of the cell and interact with microtubules that will direct their movement to opposite ends of the cell, resulting in nuclear division. Beginning at the end of mitosis, cytokinesis will separate the cytoplasm, resulting in the formation of two new genetically identical daughter cells each, containing a complete set of chromosomes.

5. Prior to cell division, a typical human cell has 46 chromosomes. Following mitosis and cytokinesis, how many daughter cells will be produced, and how many chromosomes will each daughter cell contain?

   a. 1 daughter cell containing 46 chromosomes

   b. 2 daughter cells each containing 23 chromosomes

   c. 2 daughter cells each containing 46 chromosomes

   d. 4 daughter cells each containing 23 chromosomes

6. Match the term with the appropriate phrase.

   a. $G_0$ phase      ____ Cells can stay in this phase for an indefinite amount of time

   b. $G_1$ phase      ____ DNA replication

   c. $G_2$ phase      ____ Separation of sister chromatids

   d. S phase         ____ Mitotic spindle is completely formed

   e. Prophase        ____ Nuclear envelope reappears

   f. Metaphase       ____ Cytoplasmic division

   g. Anaphase        ____ Cell cycle arrest

   h. Telophase       ____ Chromatin condenses

   i. Cytokinesis

## 6.4 Controlling the Cell Cycle

The cell cycle is balanced by proteins that promote growth and proteins that inhibit growth. As such, cells must go through critical checkpoints strategically placed throughout the cell cycle before cell division finishes. These checkpoints are controlled by regulatory proteins such as cyclins and CDKs. These regulatory proteins interact with one another to activate or deactivate target proteins, which will either allow cells to proceed through the cell cycle or halt cells until they meet checkpoint standards.

7. Which of the following statements is incorrect?

   a. Cyclin levels fluctuate throughout the cell cycle.

   b. CDK levels fluctuate throughout the cell cycle.

   c. There are unique sets of cyclin-CDK interactions depending on the phase of the cell cycle.

   d. CDKs are enzymes that phosphorylate target proteins.

8. Which of the following checkpoints is critical in initiating the cell's first commitment for cell division?

   a. $M/G_1$ checkpoint

   b. $G_1/M$ checkpoint

   c. $G_1/S$ checkpoint

   d. $S/G_1$ checkpoint

   e. $G_2/M$ checkpoint

## 6.5 Cancer: Escaping the Regulatory Boundaries of the Cell Cycle

Cancers begin as benign tumours that advance to malignant stages with the potential to spread throughout the body by metastasis. Errors in the regulatory mechanisms of the cell cycle can lead to this uncontrolled cell growth and division, which is the basis for the initiation of cancer. This imbalance in cell growth and death is caused primarily by the transformation of proto-oncogenes into oncogenes and/or the functional mutation of tumour suppressor genes. Most anti-cancer therapeutic strategies are aimed at inhibiting the effects of oncogenes and/or promoting apoptosis. Novel approaches are also investigating more targeted therapies and a greater role for the immune system in combating the disease.

9. Why is p53 often dubbed the "guardian of the genome"?

   a. Because it is an oncogene that promotes genome inheritance

   b. Because it promotes genome division

   c. Because it can stimulate DNA repair mechanisms to stabilize the genome

   d. Because it is the main protein used to replicate the genome

10. Why are cancer stem cells significant in cancer progression?

    a. Because they are often resistant to conventional anti-cancer treatment

    b. Because they can differentiate into normal cells

c. Because they are present only at birth

d. Because they are not involved in recurrence of the disease

## 6.6 The End of a Cell's Life: Senescence and Apoptosis

Cells can die naturally either through the aging process, called senescence, or can be triggered to die by apoptosis. Certain signals can be received by cells that initiate apoptosis through the activation of enzymes that function to destroy protein and nucleic acids within the cell. This destruction ultimately leads to cell death.

11. True or False? In multicellular eukaryotes, apoptosis is not a favourable event and rarely occurs.

12. If you were a cancer researcher and wanted to develop an anti-cancer drug, what are the two effects that you would want the drug to have on cancer cells?

a. Promote both cell division and apoptosis

b. Promote cell division and inhibit apoptosis

c. Inhibit both cell division and apoptosis

d. Inhibit cell division and promote apoptosis

# Gaining Genetic Diversity

## WHY IT MATTERS

The world's largest lottery winning occurred on March 30, 2012, in the United States with a grand prize total of $656 million through the Mega Millions lottery. There were three winning tickets, each displaying the six numbers that matched the numbers on the balls drawn. But how did the winners know the right combination of numbers to choose? Although some believe they can use logic or superstition in choosing their lottery numbers, the reality is that winners simply use chance. They randomly choose variations of numbers they hope will be the winning combination **(Figure 7.1)**. The only way to increase the odds of success is to buy more tickets. In this way, the players generate a "diversity" of randomly chosen combinations.

In biology, having the right combination also influences the odds of success. But instead of shuffling numbers, organisms shuffle genes. **Genes**, specific sequences of DNA nucleotides, are the basic units of hereditary information that is required for survival. In a cell, a multitude of genes are found in various forms that we call **alleles**, some beneficial and others harmful. Within a species, having the right combination of alleles may

mean the difference between life and death. But similar to a lottery, the "winning" genetic combinations for the future success of a species are unknown. Since the environment around us is constantly changing, the genetic combinations that ensure today's successes may not be the right combinations for tomorrow. Thus, to help increase the odds for evolutionary success, many different combinations of alleles are generated within a species and passed on to the next generation. This occurs through genetic recombination (or shuffling) and fosters genetic diversity. And this may be of particular importance for endangered species, especially in small, isolated populations, where genetic diversity is typically low. But take, for example, the giant panda (*Ailuropoda melanoleuca* sp.), which is an endangered species with an approximate wild population of 1500. Scientists recently discovered that the genes involved in the organism's immune system are more diverse than in other endangered species. This high level of diversity means that these organisms are more readily able to protect themselves and better adapt to changing environments. Moreover, this high level of genetic diversity also suggests that the species of giant panda may be among the top candidates for effective captive breeding programs, more so than other endangered species. Thus, this diversity in the species' defence system in turn may be the key to the conservation of giant pandas and, more importantly, to its future prosperity.

Genetic recombination is also important in influencing the evolution of animal behaviour. Take, for example, honeybees, highly socialized members of the genus *Apis* that are best known for their collection of pollen and nectar and the production and storage of honey. In turn, their behaviours are also essential to the successful pollination of flowering plants, which is imperative for ecological stability. The rate of genetic recombination in honeybees is one of the highest in the

**FIGURE 7.1** A combination of seven lottery balls.

Edw/Shutterstock.com

Eusocial animals display the highest level of social organization within the animal kingdom. Their highly complex social behaviour is characterized by cooperative brood care (feeding and caring of young) and a division of labour between reproductive and non-reproductive members. As a result, members are divided into labour groups called castes. Each caste is distinguished by its unique combination of highly specialized behaviours that collectively is required to ensure the reproductive success and survival of the society. This type of social behaviour is clearly evident in an order of insects called Hymenoptera, which include bees, ants, and wasps.

True honeybees (genus *Apis*) have the highest order of social behaviour among bees **(Figure 1)**. Within a honeybee colony, the female worker bees are mainly responsible for the foraging of pollen and production of beeswax and honey, a role

**FIGURE 1** Honeybees working together in honey cells.

animal kingdom—10 times higher than that observed in humans. This high genetic recombination rate increases the rate of natural selection and evolution of honeybee behaviour, rendering these organisms highly successful. You can read more about how genetic recombination is key to the successful evolution of honeybee behaviour in Box 7.1.

In this chapter, we will discuss the mechanisms of genetic recombination in eukaryotic organisms during meiosis and sexual reproduction. We will also discuss other ways to achieve genetic diversity by altering chromosome structure and numbers. Finally, we will describe how prokaryotes achieve genetic diversity in the absence of meiosis and sexual reproduction. As you read through this chapter, keep in mind the significance of genetic diversity within a species as a whole and the importance of obtaining a suitable or "lucky" genetic combination to enhance a species' fitness and win the evolutionary "lottery."

## 7.1 Alleles: The Variant Forms of a Gene

When a baby is born into a family, we often look for similarities in the inherited features between the baby and other family members. These features, such as hair colour, nose shape, and height, are determined by the genes within the cells. Genes are specific nucleotide sequences within the DNA that makes up our chromosomes **(Figure 7.2)**. These nucleotide sequences contain the information or "blueprint" on how to build RNA and protein within the cell, which dictate the structural and functional features of cells and tissues. We observe these features as traits in the whole organism. Hence, any variation in the arrangement of the nucleotide sequences within a gene can result in variations in an organism's traits. These gene variants are called alleles, and for many genes there exists more than one type of allele. In some cases, alleles or gene variants encode for similar protein structure and function; thus, the variability in the gene is not obvious in the organism's traits. In other cases, however, even the most minor difference in nucleotide sequence between alleles of the same gene can result in a major variation in their protein products and therefore overall traits. These variations may be beneficial to the organism for survival. For example, the *CCR5* gene encodes for a CCR5 receptor protein that is found on the surface of immune cells and binds proteins that trigger inflammatory responses during infection. The CCR5 receptor protein is also used by the human immunodeficiency virus (HIV) to gain entry into these immune cells in an effort to propagate and spread within the body. A variant form of the *CCR5* gene, called the *CCR5-Δ32* allele, encodes for a version of CCR5 receptor that has an altered structural

critical to the success of the colony, which also includes the female queen bee and the male drones. As such, the worker bees have unique morphological features such as a corbiculum (pollen basket) and abdominal glands that produce wax. They also contain brood-feeding glands to nourish the young and a stinger for defence. Their highly skilled and specialized work practices also include a sophisticated dance used to communicate with each other the location and direction of pollen. All of these social characteristics have greatly contributed to the overall success of these species. But how have these organisms evolved into such effective collaborators? A scientific group headed by Dr. Amro Zayed from York University in Toronto, Ontario, is investigating that question by examining correlations between changes in the genomes of these organisms and their

well-developed working behaviours. In their recently published study, these researchers suggest that the behavioural success of honeybees is in part due to the high degree of genetic recombination observed in various segments of their genome. Dr. Zayed's lab discovered that the genes associated with high-level social behaviours are located in parts of the honeybee genome that have the highest degree of recombination. Their rate of gene shuffling, which is one of the highest in the animal kingdom, allows for the arrangement of novel combinations of genes responsible for work behaviour. These genetic variations have fostered evolutionary success by linking together the right combination of genes to elicit social behaviours that are most favourable for survival. Since these recombination events occur in the **ovaries** of the female queen bees, these new genetic

variations are inherited from generation to generation of female worker bees.

Dr. Zayed's lab is also exploring the correlation between high recombination frequencies and extremely complex social behaviours in other eusocial animals of the order Hymenoptera, such as ants and wasps. Thus far, the data they have collected support their hypothesis that higher recombination rates within the genomes of these organisms increase the diversity of genes associated with work behaviour and in turn enhance their overall success. How these increased recombination rates play a role in the evolution of caste specialization and the genes associated with the organization of the caste system in eusocial insects remains to be determined. But for now, as we enjoy the sweet products of their labour, these insects continue working forward on the path of evolutionary success.

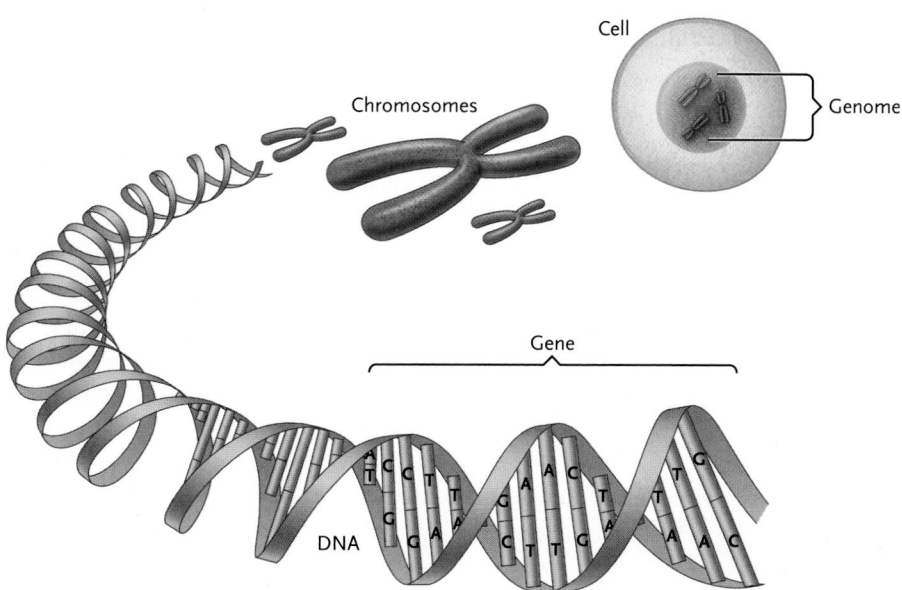

**FIGURE 7.2** The genome is the total DNA content of the cell organized into chromosomes. Genes are unique nucleotide sequences within the DNA that encode for protein or RNA.

SOURCE: From ROSCOE. *Introduction to Human Anatomy and Biology*, 1E. © 2015 Nelson Education Ltd. Reproduced by permission. www.cengage.com/permissions

strains. Thus, individuals expressing the *CCR5-Δ32* allele have been shown to have a greater resistance to HIV infection and delayed onset of acquired immune deficiency syndrome (AIDS). Current research is now aimed at mimicking the beneficial effects observed in patients containing the *CCR5-Δ32* allele by developing drugs that will block the interaction between HIV and the normal CCR5 receptor protein in patients containing the normal allele.

Alternatively, some genetic variants can be harmful to the organism. For example, the cystic fibrosis transmembrane conductance regulator (*CFTR*) gene encodes for the CFTR

form and does not bind to certain strains of HIV. Inhibition of HIV binding to the receptor therefore impedes the entry of the virus into immune cells that express this CCR5 protein variant. As such, this provides increased resistance for these immune cells against these HIV

protein, a membrane channel protein that is involved in the transport of chloride ions across the plasma membrane. The normal allele for this gene encodes for the normal structural and functional version of the CFTR protein **(Figure 7.3a, p. 154)**. However, patients with cystic fibrosis (CF) have a variant form of the gene, a mutated allele that contains a slightly different nucleotide sequence. Although there are thousands of alleles for the *CFTR* gene, one of the most common variants identified in CF patients is a mutated allele called *ΔF508* (Figure 7.3a). The *ΔF508* allele encodes for a different structural version of the CFTR protein, one that renders the protein non-functional. As a result, the transport of chloride ions across the plasma membrane is impeded, causing an accumulation of mucus in the lungs and ultimately leading to the symptoms associated with CF, such as shortness of breath, coughing, and frequent chest infections **(Figure 7.3b)**.

Thus, different alleles for each of the genes in an individual's genome and their varying combinations within cells are the reason why individuals within a species express differing characteristics or traits. The combined characteristics we observe in individuals are simply the result of a unique combination of the alleles they inherited from each of their parents. Whether this unique combination will provide an overall benefit or harm to the individual will also depend on the environment in which the organism finds itself throughout its lifetime. In the next section, we will discuss how unique combinations of alleles within eukaryotic individuals are generated in the parent cells during meiosis and how the shuffling of these alleles along with random fertilization leads to increased genetic diversity within species.

## 7.2 Gaining Genetic Diversity in Eukaryotes

Many eukaryotic organisms undergo sexual reproduction through the fusion of two reproductive cells termed **gametes** (i.e., egg and sperm) to form a **zygote**, the initial cell of a new individual offspring **(Figure 7.4)**. Each gamete generated by each of the two parental organisms delivers a copy of that parent's genetic information to the zygote. This genetic information is distributed in the form of chromosomes. Hence, each set of chromosomes in the zygote and all cells produced thereafter were originally inherited from each parent. For example, one of the two sets of chromosomes found in your cells was inherited from your mother and the other set from your father. This pattern of inheritance is what makes full siblings (i.e., siblings that share a similar biological mother and father) similar in their appearance, physiology, and even behaviour. But unless you are an identical twin, you will also note that there are many differences between you and your siblings. These differences are based on the fact that the gametes produced by parent organisms are not genetically identical to each other but instead contain differing combinations of alleles for the genes on the chromosomes that are passed on. The shuffling of these

**FIGURE 7.3** Variants of the *CFTR* gene. **(a)** Variations in the *CFTR* gene that result in the *ΔF508* mutation responsible for causing cystic fibrosis. **(b)** Comparison of a normal airway versus an airway affected by cystic fibrosis.

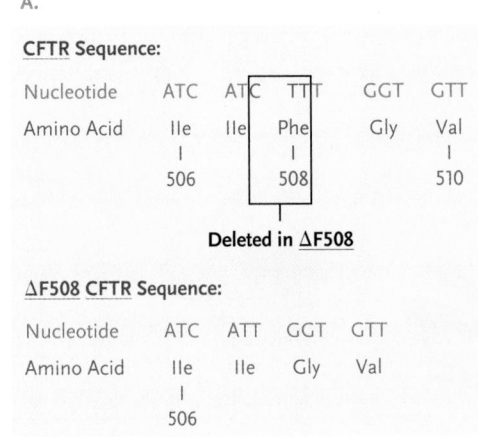

A.

**CFTR Sequence:**

| Nucleotide | ATC | ATC | TTT | GGT | GTT |
|---|---|---|---|---|---|
| Amino Acid | Ile | Ile | Phe | Gly | Val |
| | | | \| | | \| |
| | | | 506 | 508 | 510 |

**Deleted in ΔF508**

**ΔF508 CFTR Sequence:**

| Nucleotide | ATC | ATT | GGT | GTT |
|---|---|---|---|---|
| Amino Acid | Ile | Ile | Gly | Val |
| | \| | | | |
| | 506 | | | |

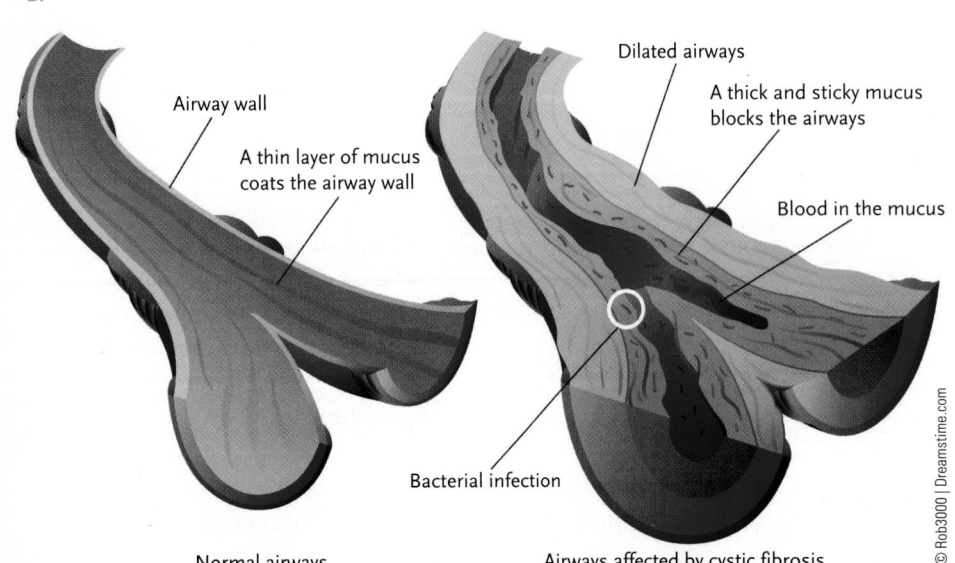

B.

Airway wall

A thin layer of mucus coats the airway wall

Dilated airways

A thick and sticky mucus blocks the airways

Blood in the mucus

Bacterial infection

Normal airways

Airways affected by cystic fibrosis

© Rob3000 | Dreamstime.com

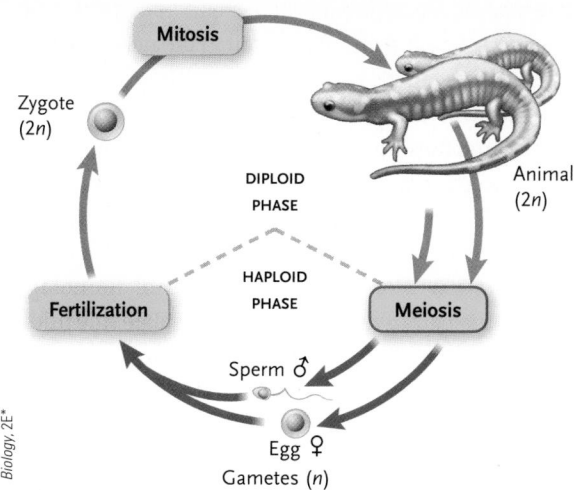

**FIGURE 7.4** Animal life cycle. Meiosis results in the formation of haploid gametes that fertilize to form a diploid zygote. Zygotes divide by mitosis. *n* refers to the haploid number of chromosomes; *2n* refers to the diploid number.

alleles (i.e., genetic recombination) occurs even before gametes are formed.

## Meiosis Generates Genetically Diverse Cells

Genetic recombination in eukaryotic cells occurs during meiosis, a form of cell division that occurs only in the immature reproductive **germ cells** (cells that give rise to gametes such as egg and sperm). As a result, the end stage of meiosis (meiosis II) produces genetically diverse

daughter cells that can mature into gametes. In addition to these genetic differences, gametes contain only half the number of chromosomes as the original parent cell. For example, most cells in the human body, including the germ cells, are **diploid (2n)**, meaning that they have 2 sets of chromosomes. These cells contain 23 pairs of chromosomes or, in other words, 2 sets of 23 chromosomes (46 chromosomes in total). Chromosomes within a matched pair are considered **homologous chromosomes** (or homologues) because they carry similar genes that are arranged in a similar physical order **(Figure 7.5)**. The physical location of an allele on a chromosome is called a **locus**. Although the genes between homologous chromosomes are the same, the versions of those genes (or the gene alleles) may differ.

Since sexual reproduction involves the fusion of gametes, only germ cells undergo meiosis to produce these specialized cells. Other cells in the body, which we term **somatic cells**, do not undergo meiosis and divide only by mitosis (see Chapter 6 for review). As germ cells divide during meiosis, homologous chromosomes within each pair separate from one other and are distributed to the newly formed daughter cells independent of their homologue. As a result, these daughter cells contain only one set of chromosomes (23 chromosomes in total; one from each pair of homologous chromosomes). We define cells with only one set of chromosomes as **haploid (n)** cells. Recall that the cells generated from meiosis can mature into gametes. It is not until two haploid gamete

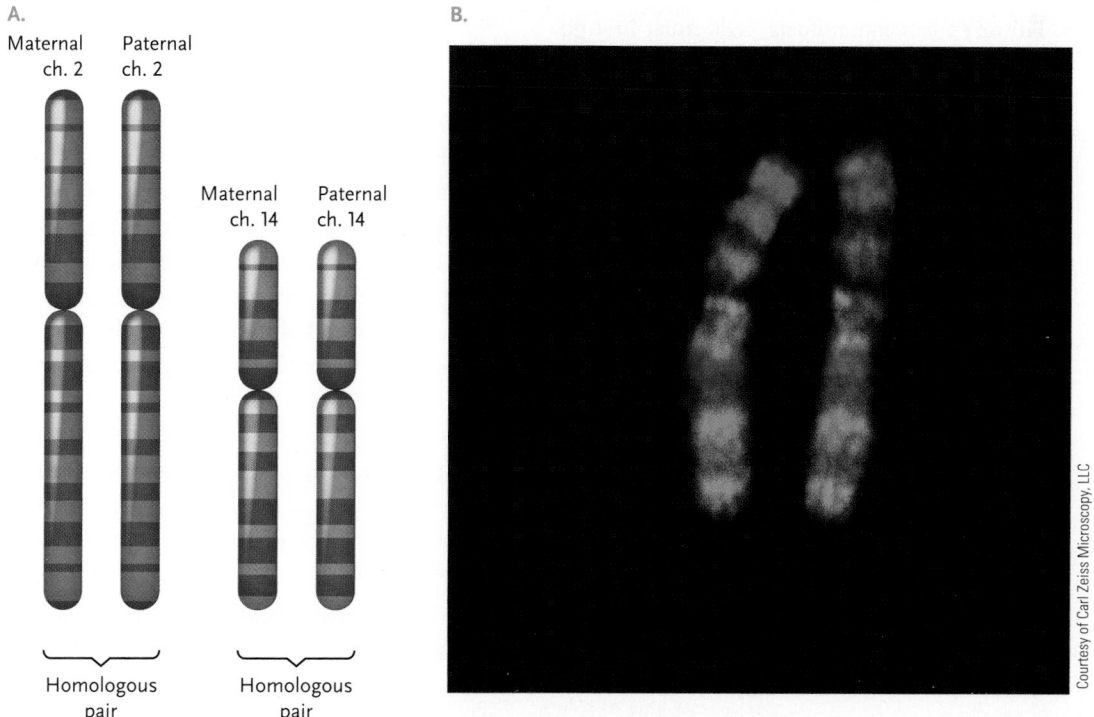

**FIGURE 7.5** Homologous chromosomes. **(a)** Schematic diagram illustrating two pairs of homologous chromosomes. Typically, one chromosome of each pair is inherited from the mother and the other from the father. **(b)** Coloured patches in the fluorescence micrograph indicate corresponding DNA sequences on the chromosome. These chromosomes carry the same series of genes, but the DNA sequence of any one of those genes might differ just a bit from that of its partner on the other chromosome. Different forms of a gene are called alleles.

cells fuse during **fertilization** that the diploid chromosome number is restored in the zygote (Figure 7.4). The reduction of chromosome numbers in gametes ensures that the correct chromosome numbers are maintained in species and prevents the doubling of chromosome numbers in each new generation.

As mentioned above, meiosis is a type of cell division observed in many eukaryotic organisms. The preparatory stages (i.e., interphase) prior to meiosis are similar to those leading up to mitosis (see Chapter 6 for review). For example, the initial period of growth, G1, is followed by S phase, where chromosomes double via DNA replication. The identical chromosome copies generated by DNA replication remain physically associated with one another as sister chromatids until the later stages of cell division. Following S phase, the cell enters $G_2$ phase in preparation for meiosis. Although many aspects of meiosis (in particular, the second stage of meiosis) are similar to the events that occur during mitosis, there are also some very unique activities that occur only in meiosis. These unique events contribute to the overall objective of this type of cell division: the formation of genetically diverse daughter cells (recall that in mitosis, the daughter cells produced are genetically identical to each other). Here we will discuss the genetic recombination events that occur during the first stage of meiosis that result in the genetic diversity found among gametes.

## Meiosis I

Meiosis is divided into two main stages: meiosis I and meiosis II. However, just like mitosis, cells must first go through S phase to duplicate their chromosomes and centrosome and then $G_2$ phase prior to entering meiosis. **Prophase I** is the first phase of meiosis I **(Figure 7.6, steps 1 to 3, p. 158)**. During this phase, the nuclear envelope within the cell begins to break down and the duplicated centrosomes move to the opposite poles of the cells. Microtubules growing out from the centrosomes begin to form the spindle apparatus (similar to that found in mitosis). In addition, the chromosomes condense and pair up with their homologue through a process called **synapsis.** Pairing of homologous chromosomes by synapsis forms a four-DNA stranded structure called a **tetrad.** Keep in mind that at this point, each chromosome is still in the form of sister chromatids as a result of DNA replication during S phase. As a tetrad, the homologous chromosomes are tightly aligned with one another, which allows them the opportunity to exchange corresponding or homologous segments of DNA. This process of DNA exchange is called **crossing over** and results in a shuffling or recombining of gene alleles. As a result, a new combination of alleles on one of each of the sister chromatids that make up the tetrad is generated. Note that crossing over does not occur during mitosis because the homologous chromosomes do not undergo synapsis. Hence, these events that promote genetic recombination are key

differentiating features between mitosis and meiosis. We'll discuss crossing over in more detail in the next section and how it leads to genetic diversity among gametes.

**Metaphase I** follows prophase I, and at this point, each chromosome is attached to spindle microtubules **(Figure 7.6, steps 4 and 5)**. Each chromosome within a homologous pair is connected to microtubules from opposing spindle poles. During this phase, the spindle microtubules will direct the alignment of homologous chromosome pairs along the metaphase plate (the midway point between the spindle poles). Homologous chromosomes align themselves on either side of the metaphase plate. It is important to note that how one pair of homologous chromosomes aligns at the metaphase plate is independent of how other pairs of chromosomes align at the plate. This random orientation of homologous chromosomes is referred to as independent assortment, which we will discuss further in the next section.

In **anaphase I**, the spindle microtubules begin to shorten, thereby pulling the chromosomes within homologous pairs away from each other and the metaphase plate **(Figure 7.6, step 6)**. They move toward the opposing spindle poles. As a result, each chromosome in a homologous pair is separated from its homologue. Keep in mind that the sister chromatids of each chromosome are still attached to one another at the centromere and thus do not separate from each other at this point. Their separation will not occur until later in meiosis II.

During **telophase I**, each set of chromosomes will reach opposing spindle poles, and in some cells, a new nuclear envelope will form around each chromosome set to form two haploid nuclei **(Figure 7.6, step 7)**. As well during this phase, the spindle apparatus disassembles, and two new centrosomes form in preparation for meiosis II. Next, the cytoplasm is divided through cytokinesis and results in the formation of two new haploid daughter cells. As a result of crossing over during prophase I, these haploid cells are genetically diverse, having a different combination of alleles from one another. In some cells, the end of meiosis I is followed by a period of rest called **interkinesis** (or interphase II) before entering meiosis II. Although the chromosomes may decondense or loosen during interkinesis, there is no DNA replication during this resting stage. Other cells skip this resting stage entirely and go directly into meiosis II.

## Meiosis II

Each daughter cell produced during meiosis I enters meiosis II, which begins with **prophase II**. During this phase, chromosomes recondense, and the nuclear envelope, if one was formed during telophase I, breaks down **(Figure 7.6, step 8)**. Microtubules from opposite spindle poles of the cells begin to form the spindle apparatus, which attaches to each sister chromatid within each chromosome.

During **metaphase II**, the spindle moves and aligns the sister chromatids on either side of the metaphase plate in preparation for division **(Figure 7.6, step 9)**. Keep in mind that how one pair of sister chromatids aligns at the metaphase plate is independent of how other sister chromatids align at the metaphase plate.

Separation of the sister chromatids occurs during **anaphase II**. Each sister chromatid within a chromosome moves away from the metaphase plate toward opposing spindle poles. This movement is directed by the shortening of the spindle microtubules **(Figure 7.6, step 10)**. Once sister chromatids are separated from each other, they are now considered individual chromosomes.

In **telophase II**, the two sets of chromosomes reach the opposite poles of the cell, and a new nuclear envelope forms around each set to form two new haploid nuclei **(Figure 7.6, step 11)**. This step is followed by cytokinesis and results in the formation of a total of four haploid daughter cells that are genetically diverse from one another. Each of these cells now has the potential to mature into a gamete and participate in fertilization, which will lead to the generation of a genetically unique individual offspring. In the next section, we will discuss in further detail the mechanisms of genetic recombination and other factors that contribute to these genetic variations.

## Crossing Over Generates New Genetic Combinations

As you can now see from the last section, two key events occur during meiosis that lead to genetic diversity in the newly formed cells. The first is crossing over, in which homologous chromosomes exchange corresponding DNA segments, leading to a new combination of alleles on these chromosomes. Crossing over occurs during prophase I of meiosis I and is initiated by the synapsis (or coming together) of homologous chromosomes to form a tetrad **(Figure 7.7, p. 160)**. In a tetrad, the homologous chromosomes are arranged one on top of the other so that one chromatid of one homologous chromosome is tightly aligned along its length with the one chromatid of the other homologous chromosome. This tight association allows for these chromatids to exchange corresponding DNA segments. If the alleles on the exchanged DNA segments are, in fact, a different version of the same gene, then the end result is a new combination of alleles in each of the two newly recombined chromatids. Note that although alleles are swapped between homologous chromosomes, the order of these alleles (the loci arrangement) remains the same.

Although the exchanges of DNA segments may occur randomly along any part of the homologous chromosomes, evidence shows that rates of crossing over along chromosomes are not uniform. As such, there are certain chromosomal regions or "hot spots" that tend to be more involved in crossing over events than other regions. Although the reason for this still remains largely

unknown, it is evident in honeybees that the regions of the chromosomes most active in crossing over are the ones that contain genes governing their highly complex work and social behaviour (see Box 7.1). Another important feature to note is that crossing over events may occur multiple times between the same pair of homologous chromosomes during prophase I. Moreover, the overall rate of crossing over within a cell is also highly dependent on the species. For example, the crossing over rate in humans is twice as much as that in mice and rats. Perhaps this explains the greater genetic diversity observed within the human species compared to rodents.

## Independent Assortment Contributes to Genetic Variation in Gametes

The second event that promotes genetic diversity is independent assortment, which represents the random alignment or orientation of homologous chromosomes across the metaphase plate. Earlier in this chapter, we stated that the two sets of chromosomes within cells of diploid organism were inherited, one from each of two parents. Hence, in homologous pairs of chromosomes, one member of each pair is a maternal chromosome, whereas the other member of the pair is a paternal chromosome. One member of each pair, whether it be maternal or paternal, is then passed on to daughter cells during meiosis. Each daughter cell therefore receives a full complement of chromosomes composed of a mixture of maternal and paternal chromosomes. The combination of maternal and paternal chromosomes each gamete inherits is random due to the independent assortment or alignment of homologous chromosomes at the metaphase plate during metaphase I of meiosis I. **Figure 7.8 (p. 160)** illustrates how independent assortment of homologous chromosomes results in various chromosome combinations that are passed on to daughter cells during meiosis. Random alignment of chromosomes initiates during prophase I, when each homologue within a pair of homologous chromosomes becomes attached to a spindle microtubule. Each homologue within a pair connects to spindle microtubules from opposite spindle poles (not shown in Figure 7.8). Once attached, each homologue within a pair is aligned on one side of the metaphase plate opposite to its homologue (recall that this occurs during metaphase I). Homologues are aligned on the same side of the metaphase plate as the spindle pole they are linked to. It is important to note that the random attachment of each homologue from one pair of homologous chromosomes to spindle microtubules is independent of the attachment of other pairs of homologous chromosomes. Due to this randomness, the alignment of homologous pairs of chromosomes across the metaphase plate is also arbitrary. Hence, maternal and paternal homologues for each pair of homologous chromosomes may not necessarily be

**Prophase I**

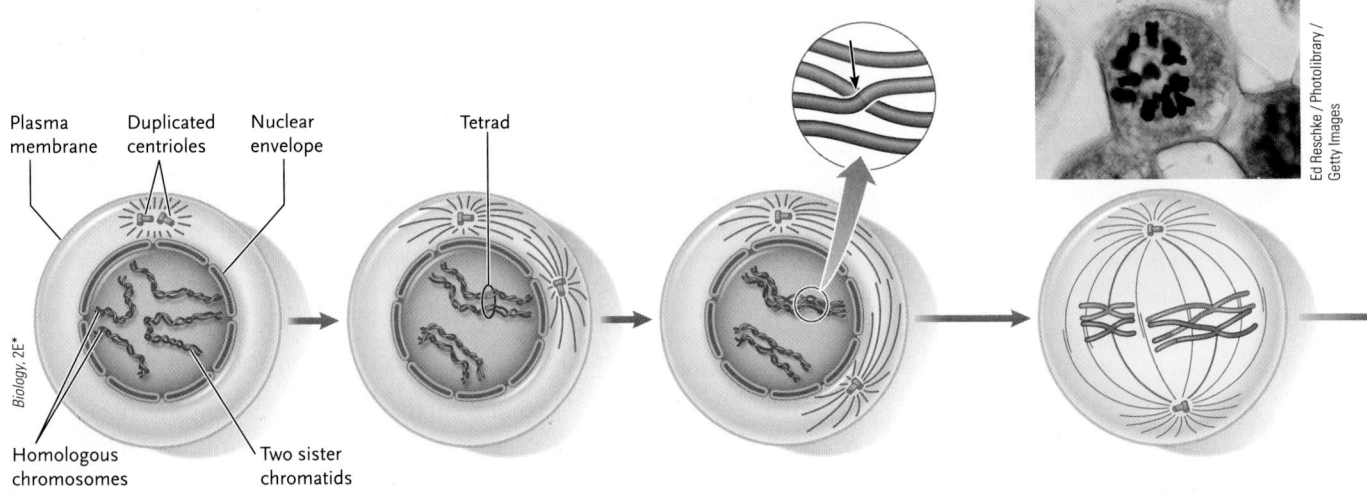

Plasma membrane | Duplicated centrioles | Nuclear envelope

Tetrad

*Biology, 2E**

Homologous chromosomes | Two sister chromatids

Ed Reschke / Photolibrary / Getty Images

### Condensation of chromosomes

**1** At the beginning of prophase I the chromosomes begin to condense into threadlike structures. Each consists of two sister chromatids, as a result of DNA replication during premeiotic interphase. The chromosomes of two homologous pairs, one long and one short, are shown.

### Synapsis

**2** Homologous chromosomes come together and pair.

### Recombination

**3** While they are paired, the chromatids of homologous chromosomes undergo recombination by exchanging segments. The enlarged circle shows a site undergoing recombination (arrow).

### Prometaphase I

**4** In prometaphase I, the nuclear envelope breaks down, and the spindle moves into the former nuclear area. Kinetochore microtubules connect to the chromosomes—kinetochore microtubules from one pole attach to both sister kinetochores of one duplicated chromosome, and kinetochore microtubules from the other pole attach to both sister kinetochores of the other duplicated chromosome.

## Second meiotic division

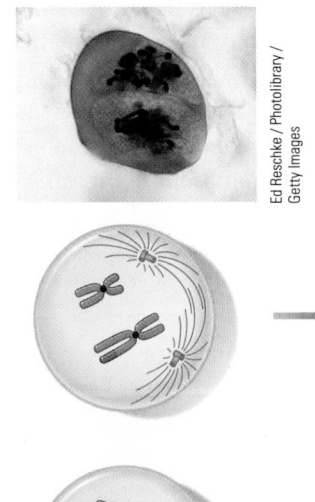

Ed Reschke / Photolibrary / Getty Images

*Biology, 2E**

### Prophase II

**8** The chromosomes condense and a spindle forms.

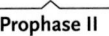

**FIGURE 7.6** The meiotic divisions. The behaviour of chromosomes.

Ed Reschke / Photolibrary / Getty Images
Ed Reschke / Photolibrary / Getty Images
Ed Reschke / Photolibrary / Getty Images
Metaphase plate
Homologous pair
Interkinesis: no DNA replication between first and second meiotic division
To prophase II in second meiotic division

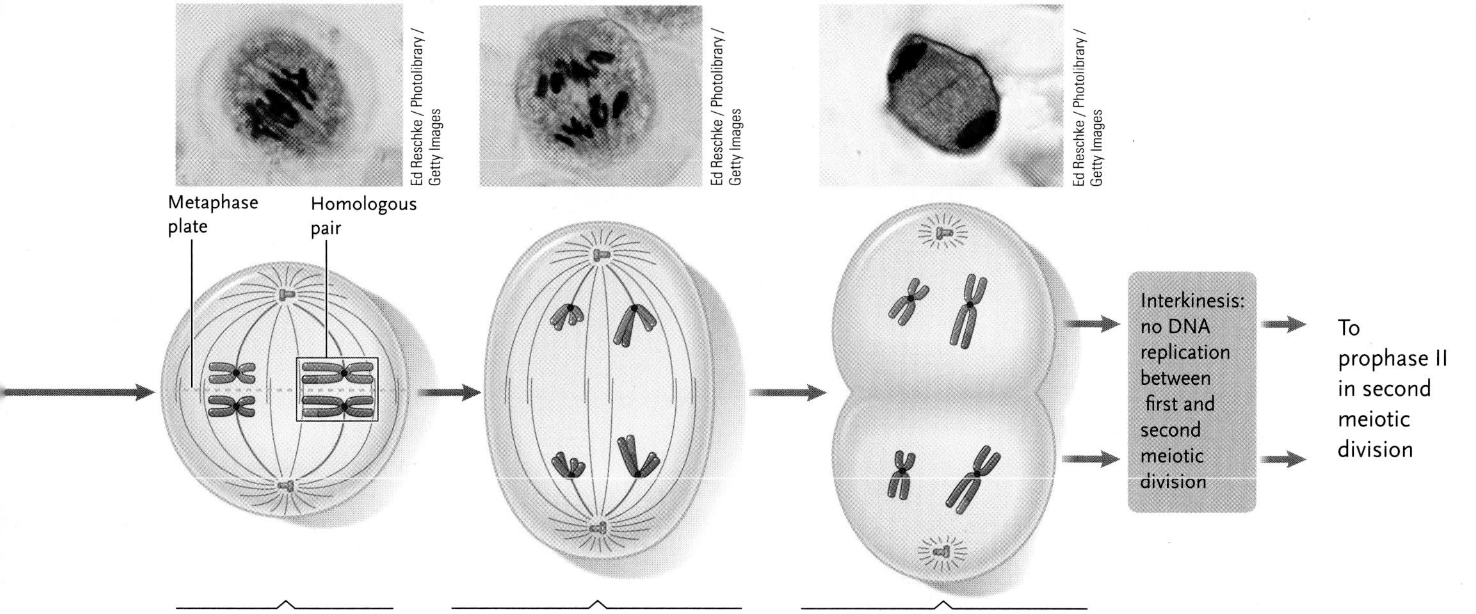

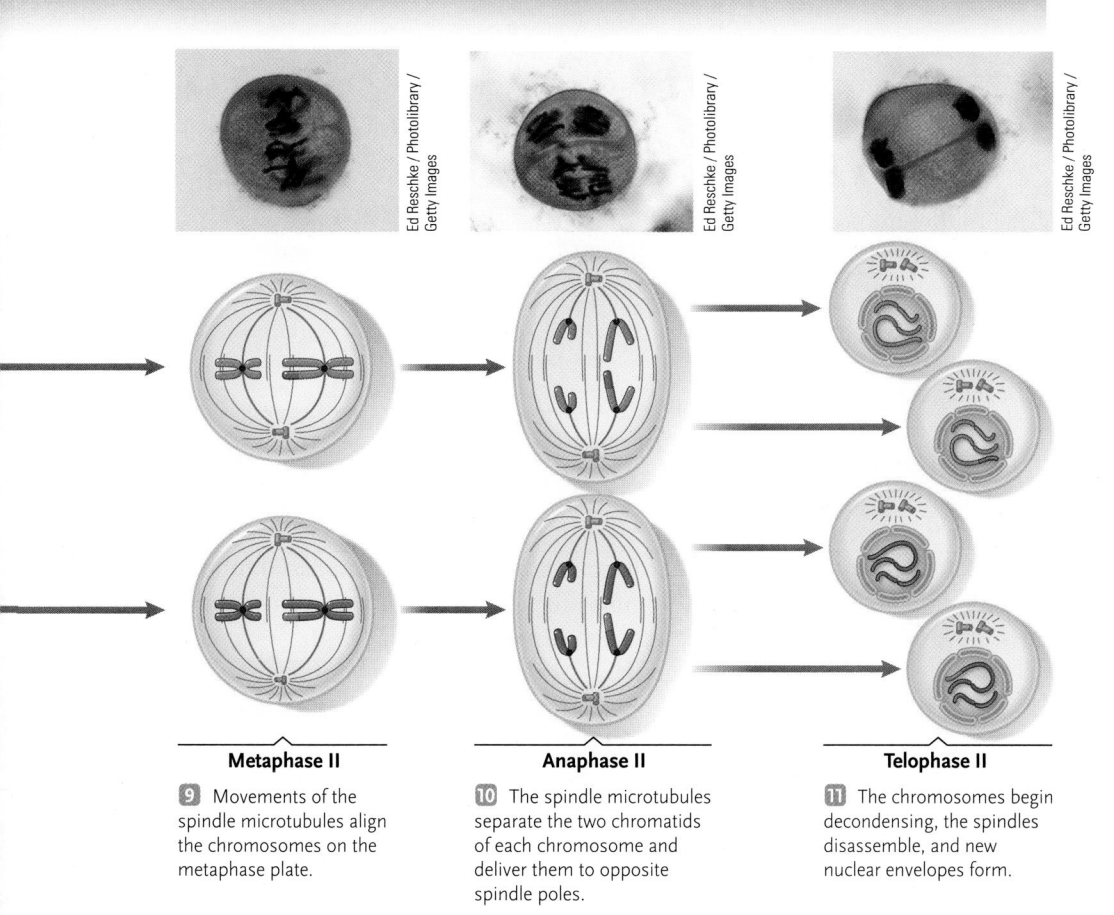

**Metaphase I**

5 Movements of the spindle microtubules align the tetrads in the equatorial plane—metaphase plate—between the two spindle poles.

**Anaphase I**

6 The spindle microtubules separate the two chromosomes of each homologous pair and move them to opposite spindle poles. The poles now contain the haploid number of chromosomes. However, each chromosome at the poles still contains two chromatids.

**Telophase I**

7 The chromosomes undergo little or no change except for limited decondensation or unfolding in some species. The spindle of the first meiotic division disassembles, and two new spindles form for the second division.

Ed Reschke / Photolibrary / Getty Images
Ed Reschke / Photolibrary / Getty Images
Ed Reschke / Photolibrary / Getty Images

**Metaphase II**

9 Movements of the spindle microtubules align the chromosomes on the metaphase plate.

**Anaphase II**

10 The spindle microtubules separate the two chromatids of each chromosome and deliver them to opposite spindle poles.

**Telophase II**

11 The chromosomes begin decondensing, the spindles disassemble, and new nuclear envelopes form.

A. Here we focus on only two of the many genes on a chromosome. In this example, one gene has alleles *A* and *a*; the other has alleles *B* and *b*.

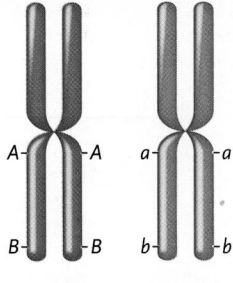

B. Close contact between homologous chromosomes promotes crossing over between nonsister chromatids. Paternal and maternal chromatids exchange corresponding pieces.

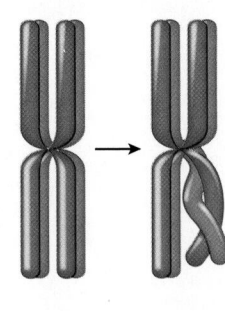

C. Crossing over mixes up paternal and maternal alleles on homologous chromosomes.

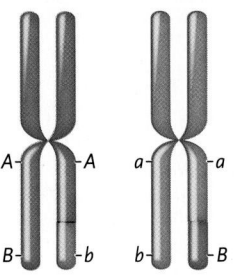

**FIGURE 7.7** Crossing over. Paternal chromosome and maternal homologues.

SOURCE: From Starr. *Biology*, 8E. © 2011 Brooks/Cole, a part of Cengage Learning, Inc. Reproduced by permission. www.cengage.com/permissions

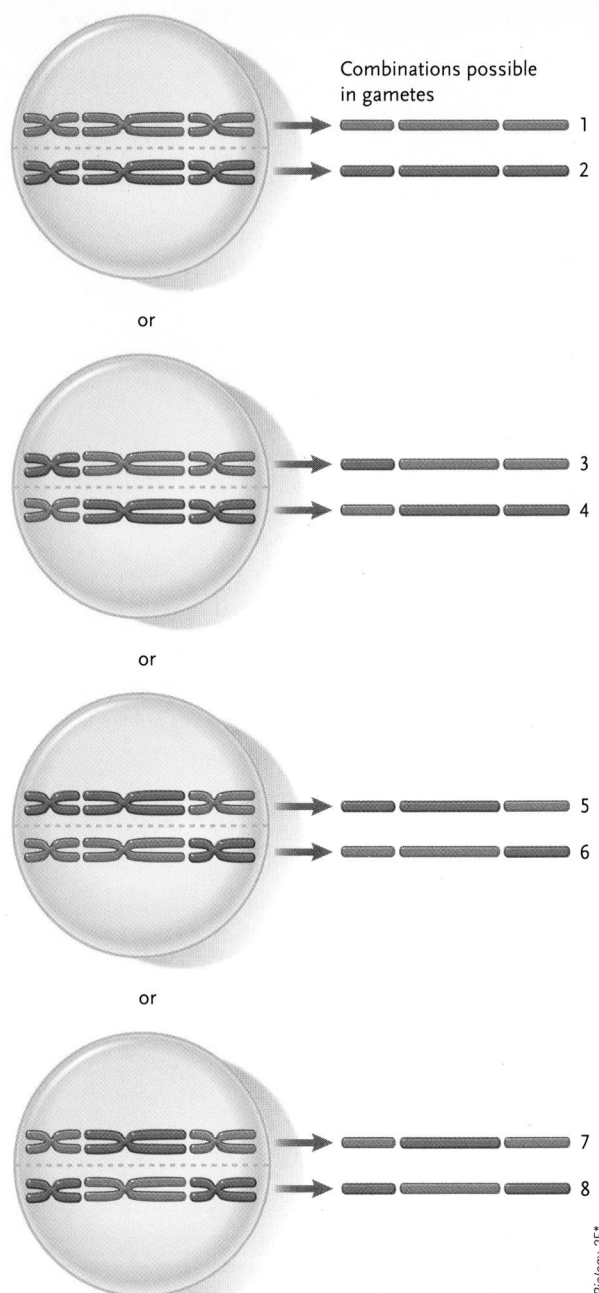

**FIGURE 7.8** Independent assortment. Possible outcomes of the random spindle connections of three pairs of chromosomes at metaphase 1 of meiosis.

arranged on the same side of the metaphase plates. This in turn results in a great number of different possible combinations of chromosomes on each side of the metaphase plate. This variability therefore translates into a great number of varying combinations of chromosomes that can be passed on to the gametes.

Thus, it is evident that both crossing over and independent assortment events contribute to the unique combination of alleles found within each new cell generated by meiosis. As these cells mature into gametes, these genetic variations can be passed on to the next generation of individuals within the species via sexual reproduction. In the next section, we will discuss how random fertilization during sexual reproduction further increases the genetic variability of offspring.

## Random Fertilization Generates Genetically Diverse Offspring

In addition to the genetic variability among gametes produced from each parent, genetic diversity is further increased with random fertilization. In essence, the fact that any two gametes of a species—which, recall, are already genetically diverse from one another—have the potential to fertilize means that the numbers of different combinations of alleles that can come together in a newly formed zygote are extraordinary. Take, for example, a human sperm and egg, each containing 23 chromosomes. Remember that each of these gametes was formed as a result of meiosis, where homologous pairs of chromosomes were separated from each other and independently assorted. This means that any combination of maternal and paternal chromosomes could have been distributed to the gametes. What is the number of different potential combinations? Over 8 million ($2^{23}$)! And when these gametes participate in fertilization, the number of different possible chromosome combinations inherited by the zygote expands to 64 trillion ($2^{23} \times 2^{23}$)! This is not even taking into account the crossing-over events of prophase I, which would make the number of genetic combinations limitless. These variations in genetics make each and every one of us unique, with the exception of identical twins, who inherit the same genetic combination because they arise after fertilization occurs.

## STUDY BREAK

1. Compare meiosis I and meiosis II, highlighting similarities and differences.
2. Explain how crossing over occurs between homologous chromosomes.
3. When does independent assortment occur during meiosis?
4. How does random fertilization increase genetic diversity?

## 7.3 Errors in Meiosis Increase Genetic Diversity

Cells, like anything in life, are not perfect. Sometimes errors occur in cells that result in either a beneficial or harmful outcome or simply cause no change. However, errors during meiosis can result in further increases in genetic diversity of a species and, in some cases, can even result in new species formation. These errors can occur during both crossing over and chromosomal separation.

### Altering Chromosomal Structure Results in Gain or Loss of Genes

Recall that during prophase I of meiosis I, homologous pairs of chromosomes come together and participate in crossing over events that lead to genetic recombination. This results in an alteration in the allele combinations within the sister chromatids of the chromosomes. Crossing over requires the physical breakage of the DNA that makes up the chromosome and then transfer of these DNA segments from one homologue to another. However, this mechanism may not always occur precisely; thus, errors in this process can lead to even greater diversity in the allele combinations within the chromosomes. Such errors can result in one homologue receiving an extra DNA segment, a process termed **duplication (Figure 7.9a)**, or losing a DNA segment, a process termed **deletion (Figure 7.9b)**. Duplication and

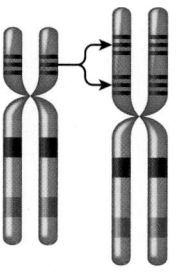 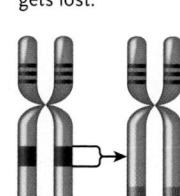

A. With a duplication, a section of a chromosome gets repeated.

B. With a deletion, a section of a chromosome gets lost.

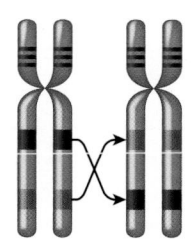

C. With an inversion, a section of a chromosome gets flipped so it runs in the opposite orientation.

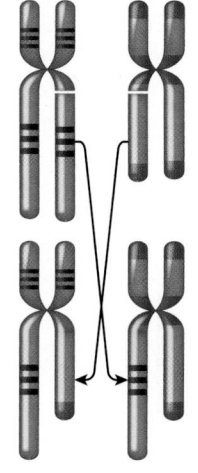

D. With a translocation, a broken piece of a chromosome gets reattached in the wrong place. This example shows a reciprocal translocation, in which two non-homologous chromosomes exchange chunks.

**FIGURE 7.9** Large-scale changes in chromosome structure including **(a)** duplication, **(b)** deletion, **(c)** inversion, and **(d)** translocation are depicted.

SOURCE: From Starr. *Biology*, 8E. © 2011 Brooks/Cole, a part of Cengage Learning, Inc. Reproduced by permission. www.cengage.com/permissions

deletion result in an abnormal number of alleles, either too many or not enough, respectively, on these particular chromosomes. And when these chromosomes are then distributed to the gametes, these new allele combinations can be inherited by the new offspring. Although the effects of these errors (either beneficial or harmful) are unclear at the time of inheritance, the one thing that is certain is that it will result in an increased genetic variability in the new generation.

Other alterations in chromosomal structure that can result during crossing over are **inversion (Figure 7.9c)** or **translocation (Figure 7.9d)**. In inversion, DNA segments that are switched between homologous chromosomes are inserted into the homologues in the reverse order. Although this does not change the overall number of alleles on the chromosome, it does cause the arrangement of alleles (i.e., the loci) within this DNA segment of the chromosomes to be inverted. In the case of translocation, a segment of DNA from one chromosome is removed and attached to a non-homologous chromosome. As a result, one chromosome loses alleles and the other chromosome (the non-homologue) ends up with alleles that don't normally belong there. Translocation events can also be reciprocal, in which there is a switch of DNA segments between two non-homologous chromosomes that results in both chromosomes obtaining completely atypical combination of genes. Again, the inheritance of these abnormal chromosomal structural changes leads to further genetic differences between the gametes that may or may not be beneficial to the next generation. It should also be noted that these chromosomal changes can also occur in somatic cells. In this case, these chromosomal changes may occur when these cells are undergoing mitosis and may alter the cells' genetics. In turn, this may result in significant changes within the organism itself; however, since these events are occurring in somatic cells that do not give rise to gametes, these genetic alterations will not be passed on to the next generation.

In some very extreme cases, altered chromosomal structures can lead to new species formation. Take, for example, human chromosome 2, the second largest chromosome in the human genome, which contains approximately 8% of the total DNA in a human cell (Figure 7.10). Scientists believe that human chromosome 2 arose from the fusion of two ancestral chromosomes, chromosomes that still remain separated in our closest living hominid relatives, chimpanzees, gorillas, and orangutans (collectively described as the family of great apes). The cells of these living relative species contain 24 pairs of chromosomes, one more pair than human cells. Indeed, the genes found on human chromosome 2 span across these two extra chromosomes found in these other hominids. As such, chromosome 2 provides strong evidence for the close evolutionary relationship between humans and these other hominids and, more importantly, suggests that these types of structural chromosome changes can initiate the formation of new species.

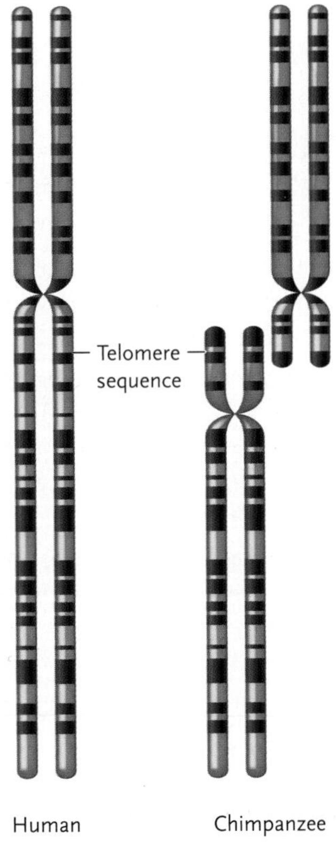

## Nondisjunction Leads to Altered Chromosome Numbers

Another error that can occur during meiosis is uneven distribution of chromosomes during anaphase I or anaphase II. Recall that the goal of anaphase in any type of cell division is to separate chromosomes (either homologous chromosomes in anaphase I or sister chromatids in anaphase II). This mechanism requires accuracy and precision to ensure that the resulting daughter cells obtain a full set of chromosomes and their associated genes. Failure to separate chromosomes properly during anaphase I or II is called **nondisjunction** and results in gametes with abnormal numbers of chromosomes (either too many or not enough) (Figure 7.11). If these gametes participate in fertilization, this abnormal number of chromosomes is then inherited by the resulting offspring. Although this does contribute to an increase in genetic variability within a species population, usually, abnormal chromosome numbers result in fatal outcomes for the offspring. However, trisomy 21, also known as Down syndrome, is one example where offspring do survive and can live well into adulthood. These individuals have inherited an extra copy of chromosome 21 (three copies instead of two) that can be detected in a **karyotype**, an organized microscopic picture profiling a person's chromosomes. It is caused by nondisjunction occurring during meiosis in one of the parent cells. As a result, one of the gametes from this parent inherits two copies of chromosome 21, which is then passed on to the offspring following fertilization of this gamete with a gamete from the other parent containing the normal number of

Telomere sequence

Human          Chimpanzee

**FIGURE 7.10** Human chromosome 2 compared to chimpanzee chromosomes 2A and 2B.

SOURCE: From STARR/TAGGART/Evers/Starr. *Biology*, 12E. © 2009 Brooks/Cole, a part of Cengage Learning, Inc. Reproduced by permission. www.cengage.com/permissions

**A.**

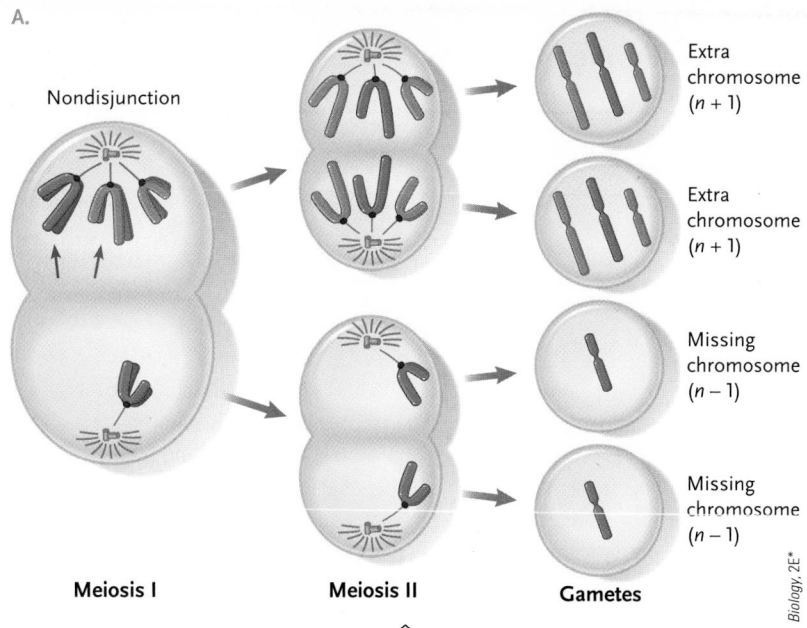

Nondisjunction during the first meiotic division causes both chromosomes of one pair to be delivered to the same pole of the spindle. The nondisjunction produces two gametes with an extra chromosome and two with a missing chromosome.

**B.**

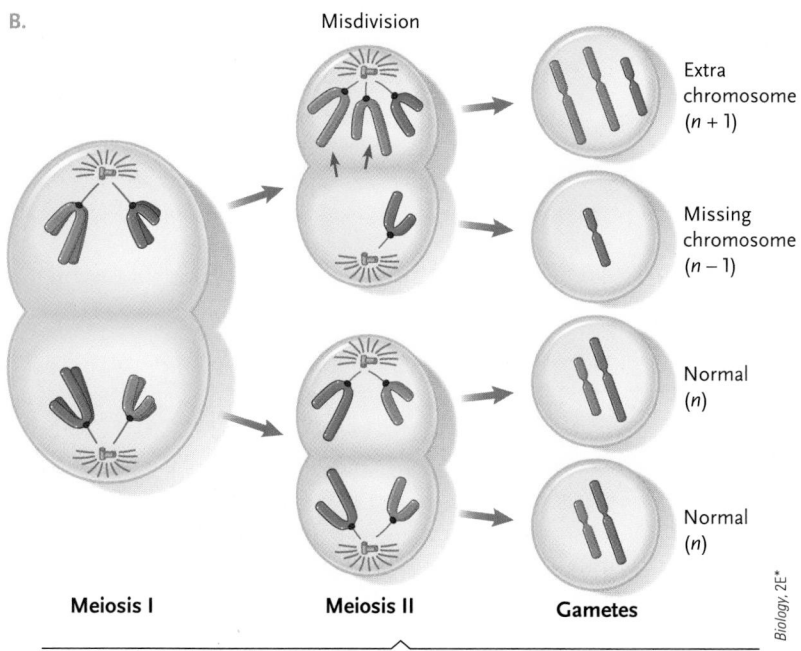

Misdivision during the second meiotic division produces two normal gametes; one gamete with an extra chromosome and one gamete with a missing chromosome.

**FIGURE 7.11 (a)** Nondisjunction during the first meiotic division and **(b)** misdivision during the second meiotic division.

chromosomes. Having 3 copies of chromosome 21 means having an extra copy of each of the genes found on this chromosome and, therefore, an abnormally higher expression of these gene products. As a result, individuals with Down syndrome suffer from some physical, mental, and social difficulties. However, new research is shedding light on how we may be able to silence the effects caused by the extra chromosome 21 by turning the entire chromosome off (read more in Box 7.2).

Nondisjunction can also occur with the sex chromosomes, X and Y, resulting in gametes having an abnormal number of these chromosomes. If these gametes participate in fertilization, these abnormalities will also be passed on to the new offspring **(Figure 7.12, p. 165)**. In some cases, an abnormal number of sex chromosomes results in death, such as the case of individuals with YO (missing an X chromosome). This is due to the loss of over 2,300 genes found on the X̄ chromosome. In other cases, the effects of abnormal chromosome numbers are not terribly significant. Individuals with an XXX or XYY sex chromosome combination do not exhibit any significant effects. In other cases, such as XXY or XO, these individuals exhibit abnormalities in sexual development, body stature, and possible impairment of learning or motor skills **(Table 7.1, p. 165)**.

## Polyploidy Can Drive New Species Formation

An abnormal number of chromosomes within a cell, as described in the last section, is called **aneuploidy.** In mammals, aneuploidy is often fatal. However, having a whole extra set of chromosomes in organisms such as plants and some insects and fish is beneficial. **Polyploidy** is the term used to describe those cells or organisms that contain more than two complete sets of chromosomes. These extra sets of chromosomes are also a result of errors during meiosis. More specifically, they are the result of the failure of the spindle to separate all homologous pairs of chromosomes during metaphase I of meiosis I. In flowering plants, such as wheat, potatoes, and cotton, polyploidy has increased genetic diversity and relative fitness among the organisms of these species.

Polyploidy can also result in new species formation if these gametes, which have an unusual number of chromosomes, fertilize to produce offspring that are viable and fertile. If the new offspring cannot successfully interbreed with the original parent species, this could

Down syndrome was first described in 1866; however, the cause of this condition remained a medical mystery until 1958, when Jérôme Lejeune, a French pediatrician and geneticist, discovered that individuals with Down syndrome contain an extra chromosome 21 (three copies instead of two) in their cells. The inherited extra chromosome 21, as observed in a karyotype, is a result of nondisjunction during meiosis in one of the parental gametes, and as such, the condition was named trisomy 21 **(Figure 1a)**. Since that time, scientists have tried to identify the risk factors that lead to Down syndrome (e.g., the mother's age; see **Figure 1b**) and improve detection mechanisms prior to birth to more accurately diagnose the condition as early as possible. More significantly, scientists are also investigating novel therapies to prevent the adverse effects caused by the presence of an extra chromosome 21.

A human cell contains 46 chromosomes, each carrying its own set of genes that collectively carry out normal function within the cell. An extra chromosome in the cell carries with it more genes, thus leading to cellular imbalance. In the case of Down syndrome,

the extra chromosome 21 leads to physical alterations in body stature and other physical features, mild to moderate cognitive impairment, and increased risk of various health conditions, such as heart disease. As such, scientists are investigating methods to overcome the effects of this extra chromosome and the extra genes it carries in an effort to restore cellular balance.

A group of scientists from the University of Massachusetts may have found a way to alleviate the effects of this extra chromosome 21 by introducing a silencing gene onto it. This gene, called **XIST** (the X inactivation gene), is not normally found on chromosome 21 but is instead found on the X chromosome. Activation of the *XIST* gene produces RNA molecules that blanket the chromosome and turn off all genes on this chromosome. In essence, activation of the *XIST* gene silences the entire chromosome. Since in mammals, females have two X chromosomes (XX), whereas males have only one (XY), silencing of one of the two X chromosomes in female cells is normal in an effort to balance the expression of X-linked genes (genes found on the X chromosome) between the genders. Scientists wondered if they could apply this

concept to the extra chromosome 21 found in people with Down syndrome. To test this concept, scientists have introduced the *XIST* gene to one of the three chromosomes 21 in human stem cells isolated from Down syndrome patients. Then they turned the gene on. Once activated, the *XIST* gene produced silencing RNA that covered the extra chromosome 21, changing its structure and ultimately shutting down the chromosome and deactivating its genes. As a result, the abnormal gene expression in these cells was reduced to more normal levels, causing some of the characteristics observed in cells from Down syndrome, such as loss of cell growth and defects in neuronal specialization, to be reversed.

Although these experiments were done with cells in a lab, this proof-of-principle study opens the possibility of one day treating Down syndrome patients with this method of "chromosome therapy" and restoring balance in the cell. These types of innovative therapeutic strategies, using a normal process found within female mammalian cells to treat a chromosomal abnormality, have the potential to positively change the lives of future Down syndrome patients.

**A.**

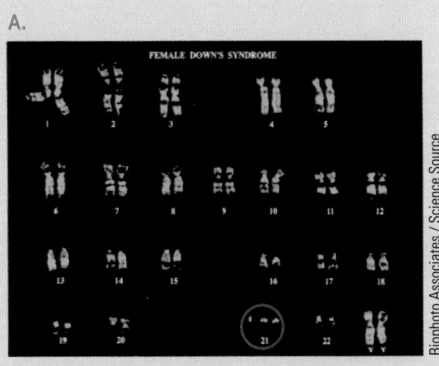

**B.**

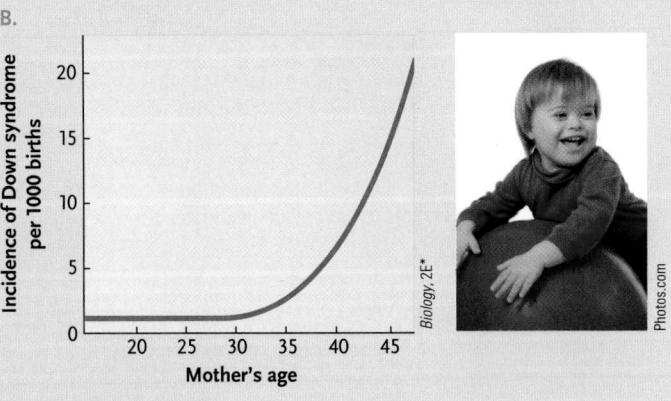

**FIGURE 1** Down syndrome. **(a)** A karyotype of a human individual with Down syndrome showing three copies of chromosome 21 (circled in red). **(b)** The incidence of Down syndrome increases with the age of the mother, as determined in a study conducted in Victoria, Australia, between 1942 and 1957.

potentially result in the formation of new species (speciation) **(Figure 7.13a)**. Although rarer in animals, in plants, polyploidy leading to new species formation is common. For example, the genus *Brassica* consists of many

polyploid plant species, including rapeseed (*Brassica napus*), Indian mustard (*Brassica juncea*), and Ethiopian mustard (*Brassica carinata*) **(Figure 7.13b)**. These polyploid species have an increased number of chromosomes

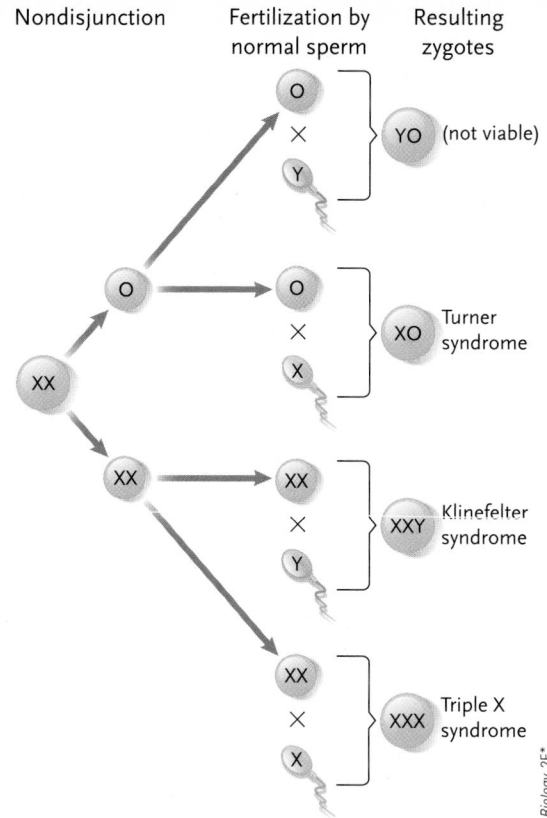

FIGURE 7.12 Some abnormal combinations of sex chromosomes resulting from disjunction of X chromosomes in females.

**TABLE 7.1** | **Effects of Unusual Combinations of Sex Chromosomes in Humans**

| Combinations of Sex Chromosomes | Approximate Frequency | Effects |
| --- | --- | --- |
| XO | 1 in 5000 births | Turner syndrome: females with underdeveloped ovaries; sterile; intelligence and external genitals are normal; typically, individuals are short in stature with underdeveloped breasts |
| XXY | 1 in 2000 births | Klinefelter syndrome: male external genitalia with very small and underdeveloped testes; sterile; intelligence usually normal; sparse body hair and some development of the breasts; similar characteristics in XXXY and XXXXY |
| XYY | 1 in 1000 births | XYY syndrome: apparently normal males but often taller than average |
| XXX | 1 in 1000 births | Triple X syndrome: apparently normal females with normal or slightly retarded mental function |

Source: *Biology*, 2E*

compared to their original diploid parent species and as such exhibit some differing characteristics. Although the molecular explanation for these variations is still not completely understood, scientists believe that duplicate genes in many polyploidy species may diverge and acquire new functions that will provide these species with long-term evolutionary advantage. You'll learn more about polyploidy and the formation of new species in Chapter 12.

## STUDY BREAK

1. Describe four ways in which a chromosome can be structurally altered.
2. How does nondisjunction lead to abnormal chromosome numbers?
3. How can alterations in chromosome numbers lead to the formation of new species?

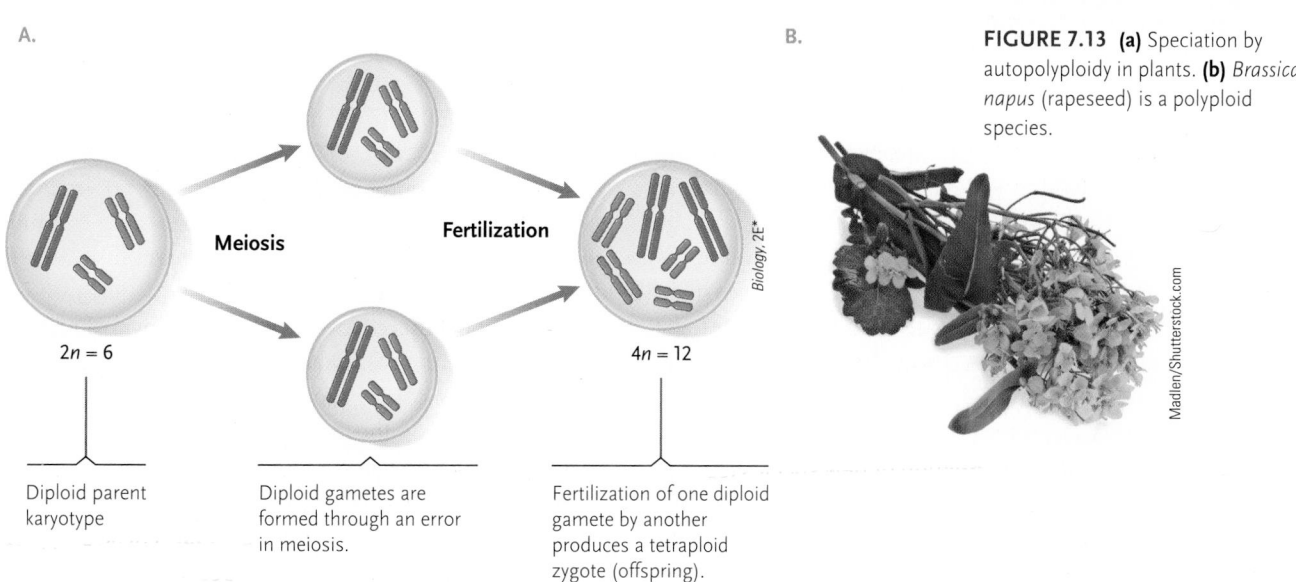

A.

B.

2n = 6     Meiosis     Fertilization     4n = 12

Diploid parent karyotype

Diploid gametes are formed through an error in meiosis.

Fertilization of one diploid gamete by another produces a tetraploid zygote (offspring).

FIGURE 7.13 **(a)** Speciation by autopolyploidy in plants. **(b)** *Brassica napus* (rapeseed) is a polyploid species.

Bdelloidea are a class of rotifers, microscopic freshwater animals that display a characteristic wheel-like structure at their mouth called a corona and a tail shaped like forceps **(Figure 1)** (see Chapter 19 for review). These animals are an important component of freshwater zooplankton as they serve as a major food source for fish and contribute to soil decomposition. But one of the most interesting features of

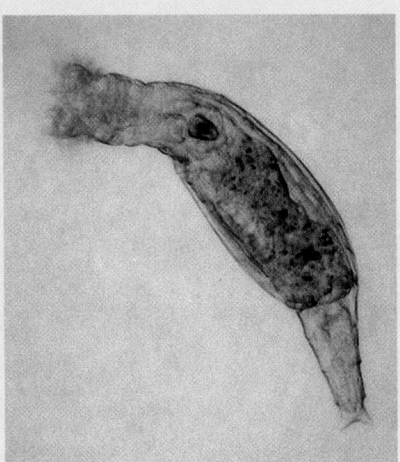

**FIGURE 1** *Habrotrocha rosa* is a member of the Bdelloidea rotifers.

SOURCE: Photo by Ryan D. Kitko, http://simple .wikipedia.org/wiki/File:Habrotrocha_rosa_1.jpg. This file is licensed under the Creative Commons Attribution-Share Alike 3.0 Unported license, http:// creativecommons.org/licenses/by-sa/3.0/deed.en

Bdelloidea is their lack of sex. For most animal species, the lack of sex would be an evolutionary death sentence. But Bdelloidea have adapted a mechanism to avoid species extinction in the absence of sex. Even more fascinating, males are also absent from the species. Female Bdelloidea are believed to have been reproducing in the absence of sex for millions of years via a mechanism called **parthenogenesis** (*partheno* = "without fertilization," *genesis* = "birth"). In parthenogenesis, unfertilized diploid eggs simply grow and divide by mitosis into individual female offspring. Other organisms that reproduce via parthenogenesis include aphids, nematodes, and even vertebrate species such as komodo dragons and hammerhead sharks. In the case of Bdelloidea, parthenogenesis is the exclusive method for reproduction.

Despite the lack of sexual reproduction, these animals have been able to evolutionarily diversify into over 300 different species. But how have these organisms been able to do this in the absence of meiosis and sexual reproduction? This has been achieved through two processes called horizontal gene transfer and gene conversion. Horizontal gene transfer describes non-traditional mechanisms in which an organism acquires DNA from another organism or from its environment. It is different from vertical gene transfer in which DNA is passed on from parent to offspring. Under conditions of stress, Bdelloidea desiccate (dry up) and enter a stage of dormancy. Once conditions become favourable, the organism rehydrates and restarts cellular activity. However, these harsh transition periods likely damage the double-stranded DNA and result in DNA fragmentation. Also, during this period of desiccation and rehydration, any damage to the cell membranes allows for entry of foreign DNA from the environment into the cell. Upon repair of the organism's damaged DNA, some of the foreign DNA taken up by the cell is incorporated into the repaired genome of the organism. This form of horizontal gene transfer along with DNA repair leads to gene conversion (replacing one segment of DNA with a homologous DNA sequence), which ultimately contributes to changes in the genetic makeup of the organism.

Hence, like prokaryotic organisms, Bdelloidea have evolved mechanisms to enhance genetic diversity within the species without engaging in meiosis or the energy-consuming steps required for successful sexual reproduction. As a result, these small microscopic organisms are now one of the most diverse groups of animals on the planet and as such are a testament to evolutionary success without sex.

## 7.4 Gaining Genetic Diversity in Prokaryotes

When we discuss reproduction in bacteria, we often refer to binary fission, a form of asexual reproduction leading to two genetically identical daughter cells. But what we often forget is that bacteria also have methods to exchange genetic information. In bacteria, however, reproduction does not include the formation and fertilization of gametes to form a zygote. Instead, it simply involves the transfer of bacterial DNA from one bacterial cell to another. And like sexual reproduction in other species, the objective is to promote genetic recombination and enhance genetic diversity among prokaryotic species. But why does DNA need to be transferred from one bacterial cell to another, and how is this accomplished? First, let's talk about the mechanism of DNA transfer, and then we will explore why this is critical to increase genetic diversity.

**Horizontal gene transfer** is a general term to describe the transfer of DNA from one existing cell or organism to another (vertical gene transfer is the transfer of DNA from a parent to a daughter cell). This process is not exclusive to prokaryotes as even some eukaryotes carry out horizontal gene transfer in an effort to maintain high genetic diversity in the absence of sexual reproduction (see Box 7.3 to read how this occurs in a unique group of animals called rotifers). In prokaryotes, it can occur through mechanisms such as conjugation, transformation, and transduction. In all of these cases, there will be a donor bacterium that donates its DNA and a recipient bacterium that will receive this DNA. In **bacterial conjugation**, donor bacterium forms a cytoplasmic bridge between itself and a neighbouring recipient bacterium **(Figure 7.14a)**. This

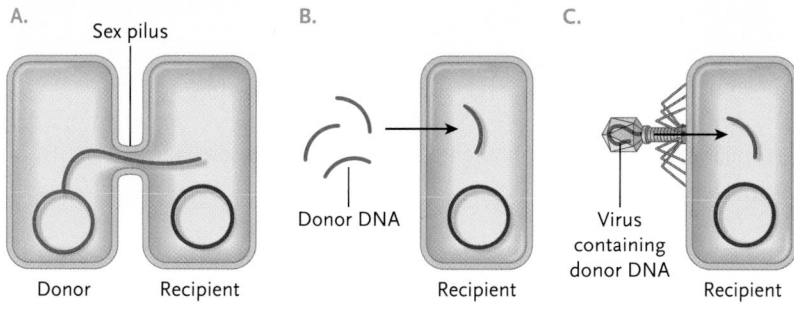

**FIGURE 7.14** Bacteria acquire homologous segments of DNA through **(a)** conjugation, **(b)** transformation, and **(c)** transduction.

temporary bridge, called the **sex pilus**, connects the cytoplasm of the two bacteria. The sex pilus is used by the donor bacterium to transfer a partial copy of its chromosome to the recipient bacterium. In **transformation**, a recipient bacterium has DNA binding proteins on its cell wall that can attach to and transport pieces of bacterial DNA found in its environment **(Figure 7.14b)** into its cytoplasm. The DNA found in the environment often originates from a dead donor bacterium that had ruptured and released its genetic material. In the case of **transduction**, a bacterial virus is involved in transferring parts of bacterial DNA from one host bacterium (the donor) to a subsequent host bacterium (the recipient) **(Figure 7.14c)**.

In all three cases, the transfer of DNA results in the recipient bacterium having two copies of a region of its genome (its own copy and the copy it acquired from the donor bacterium). In other words, the recipient bacterium went from being haploid before DNA transfer to now being a partial diploid following gene transfer (only a partial diploid because it often receives only a part of the donor DNA and not the entire genome). Recall that bacteria are haploid organisms and thus do not have homologous chromosomes. In addition, they typically have only one chromosome. These conditions therefore do not allow for genetic recombination to occur within a single organism as it occurs during meiosis in eukaryotes. Thus, when a recipient bacterium becomes a partial diploid through horizontal gene transfer, it now contains segments of its chromosome that are homologous to the transferred donor DNA. Homologous DNA is essential

for synapsis and crossing over to occur. Crossing over indeed occurs in these recipient bacterial cells between the homologous segments of DNA, resulting in genetic recombination **(Figure 7.15)**. Following crossing over, any remaining donor DNA is degraded by the recipient bacterium, rendering it haploid once again (this ensures an overall accurate chromosome number). Similar to what we discussed in eukaryotes, this genetic recombination alters the combination of alleles in the bacterial chromosomes. This new combination of alleles is then inherited by future daughter cells through binary fission (asexual reproduction). In turn, this augments the genetic diversity in these species, contributing to the evolutionary success of these organisms.

## STUDY BREAK

1. What is horizontal gene transfer?
2. Describe three ways in which horizontal gene transfer can occur in prokaryotes.

## 7.5 "Jumping Genes" Can Alter Genomes

The term "jumping genes" is used to describe segments of DNA that move or translocate to different parts of the genome either within the same chromosome or from one chromosome to another. The proper term for these DNA segments is **transposable elements.** Although it appears as if they are "jumping around" within the genome, transposable elements move using a method of recombination that involves non-homologous chromosomes (unlike in meiosis). As a result of this movement of DNA segments, the structure and arrangement of genes within the genome are altered. In many cases, this does not cause any significant effect to the cells or organisms as a whole. In fact, approximately 50% of the human genome consists of transposable elements. In some cases, however, the movement of these DNA elements can cause harmful mutations if they are inserted in the wrong location within chromosomes (i.e., in the middle of a fully functional normal gene). It other cases, it may be beneficial. For example, scientists recently discovered that certain transposable elements found in the genomes of fruit flies provide resistance to synthetic insecticide, thus giving these organisms an evolutionary advantage. Transposable elements are also found in prokaryotic cells and alter the genome of these organisms. In

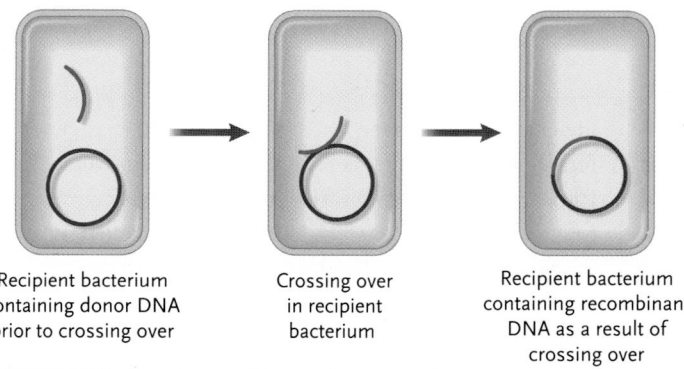

**FIGURE 7.15** Genetic recombination in recipient bacterium via crossing-over events between homologous segments of DNA.

Recipient bacterium containing donor DNA prior to crossing over

Crossing over in recipient bacterium

Recipient bacterium containing recombinant DNA as a result of crossing over

prokaryotes, some of these transposable elements carry antibiotic-resistant genes that allow the bacteria to survive in the presence of antibiotics. In this case, the movement of these DNA segments within the genome and to the genomes of other bacterial cells through horizontal gene transfer has also given these organisms an evolutionary advantage.

## STUDY BREAK

1. What are transposable elements?
2. How can transposable elements be evolutionarily advantageous? How can they be harmful?

## PUTTING IT IN PERSPECTIVE

The genetic diversity we see among members of our own species and how it has provided us with an evolutionary advantage may be obvious to us. Diversity, however, has also been the key driving force behind the success of the longest living group of organisms, bacteria. In many ways, they have been even more successful than us. For example, we have all experienced a bacterial infection in which we have been administered antibiotics as a treatment. Within a few days of taking the antibiotics, the infection begins to clear, and we begin to feel better. Sometimes, however, we don't feel better and require a second and different antibiotic treatment. In even more severe cases, the antibiotics available to us are useless.

Although antibiotics were often dubbed "miracle drugs" when they were initially discovered in the early part of the 20th century, the misuse and mismanagement of antibiotics over the last 70 years has us now facing a global public health threat, antibiotic-resistant bacteria. These strains of bacteria, also commonly known as "superbugs," have the ability to resist the effects of both natural and synthetic antibiotic drugs and, as such, are not affected by such treatments. These bacteria are resistant due to the fact that over time they have gained antibiotic-resistant genes that have allowed them to be better suited for the antibiotic-rich world. These genes have been acquired and incorporated into prokaryotic genomes via horizontal gene transfer followed by genetic recombination. More specifically, these antibiotic-resistant genes are often contained within prokaryotic transposable elements that can readily move around within a genome. These genes are advantageous to both the survival and reproductive success of these organisms. And without new strategies to combat these organisms, infections caused by these superbugs can result in very severe and potentially deadly outcomes. More concerning is the fact that the occurrence of these superbugs is becoming more and more prevalent within the community and not simply in hospitals and nursing homes.

But how can we stop these dangerously infectious superbugs? Scientists are trying to better understand how these antibiotic-resistant bacteria fend off the effects of these powerful drugs in an effort to develop novel and more effective treatments. In addition, they are also developing new biosensors that use bacterial viruses to detect these superbugs quicker so that treatment can begin sooner and in a more specialized and effective manner. Potentially, one day, we may also employ these viruses to kill these superbugs to prevent their spread. But until then, these superbugs, like all other organisms, will continue to shuffle their genes, come up with new combinations of alleles, and pass them along to the next generation. The goal is for future generations to have gained the "winning" genetic combination that will allow them to successfully combat our next new "miracle drug."

## KEY CONCEPTS REVIEW AND QUESTIONS

### 7.1 Alleles: The Variant Forms of a Gene

DNA is the hereditary material of all organisms. DNA makes up the chromosomes in cells and contains specific nucleotide sequences called genes. These genes encode for RNA and protein, which are required for cell structure and function. Different versions of a gene are called alleles. The distinct combination of alleles within cells makes each organism genetically unique and each group of species diverse.

1. What is the term used to describe the location of an allele on chromosomes?

### 7.2 Gaining Genetic Diversity in Eukaryotes

Meiosis is a two-staged form of cell division that generates four genetically diverse cells that mature into gametes. These gametes can fertilize via sexual reproduction to form a genetically unique offspring. Meiosis contributes to genetic diversity in species through crossing over events between homologous chromosomes. Crossing over results in the recombination (or shuffling) of alleles within a cell. In addition, independent assortment of homologous chromosomes during meiosis also contributes to increased genetic diversity in gametes.

Increased genetic diversity in species is evolutionarily advantageous.

2. What are homologous chromosomes?

3. Match the following description with the phases of meiosis listed in the box.

   a. Spindle microtubules begin to shorten, thereby pulling the chromosomes within homologous pairs toward the opposing spindle poles and away from the metaphase plate.

   b. The spindle moves and aligns the sister chromatids on either side of the metaphase plate in preparation for division.

   c. During this phase, the spindle disassembles and two new spindles form in preparation for meiosis II.

   d. Chromosomes condense and pair up with their homologue through a process called synapsis to form a four-DNA stranded structure called a tetrad.

   e. Spindle microtubules will direct the alignment of homologous chromosome pairs along the metaphase plate.

   ___ Prophase I

   ___ Prophase II

   ___ Metaphase I

   ___ Metaphase II

   ___ Anaphase I

   ___ Anaphase II

   ___ Telophase I

   ___ Telophase II

### 7.3 Errors in Meiosis Increase Genetic Diversity

Altering chromosomal structure or numbers can result in the gain or loss of genes. Changes in chromosome structure can occur by insertion, deletion, inversion, and translocation. Altering chromosome numbers can occur by nondisjunction. Moreover, an increase in entire chromosome sets can further drive new species formation.

4. True or False? Reciprocal translocation results in genes being moved and then returned to their original location on a chromosome.

5. The extra chromosome 21 found in the cells of a person with Down syndrome is likely the result of which of the following events?

   a. Failure to separate homologous chromosomes in the zygote after fertilization

   b. Failure to separate homologous chromosomes during meiosis I in a parent's cell that became a gamete

   c. Failure of homologous chromosomes to undergo synapsis during metaphase I

   d. Failure to separate an entire set of chromosomes from their homologues during anaphase II

6. Compare the number of chromosomes in a cell prior to meiosis I and in the daughter cells generated by meiosis II.

### 7.4 Gaining Genetic Diversity in Prokaryotes

Unlike eukaryotes, prokaryotes do not undergo meiosis and fertilization. However, recombination does occur in these organisms. Since prokaryotes are haploid organisms, horizontal gene transfer either through bacterial conjugation, transformation, or transduction brings foreign DNA into prokaryotic cells so that crossing over and genetic shuffling can occur between homologous segments of DNA.

7. True or False? The sex pilus is produced by the donor bacterium and used to transfer a copy of its DNA into the recipient bacterium.

8. What do conjugation, transformation, and transduction have in common?

   a. All occur only in eukaryotic organisms.

   b. All reduce the chances of gaining genetic diversity.

   c. All result in the transfer of foreign DNA into a prokaryotic recipient cell.

   d. All occur in the donor bacterium prior to genetic recombination.

9. Does horizontal gene transfer also occur in eukaryotic organisms?

### 7.5 "Jumping Genes" Can Alter Genomes

Transposable elements are segments of DNA that move between non-homologous chromosomes or within a chromosome itself. As a result, the arrangement of alleles is altered in these chromosomes, thus altering the genome as a whole.

10. Why are transposable elements called "jumping genes"?

    a. Because they can be translocated to new loci by a non-homologous recombination

    b. Because they move back and forth between homologous chromosomes

    c. Because they encode highly active protein

    d. Because they cause the DNA to move up and down

11. Why is genetic diversity important for the evolution of species?

# Genes and Patterns of Inheritance

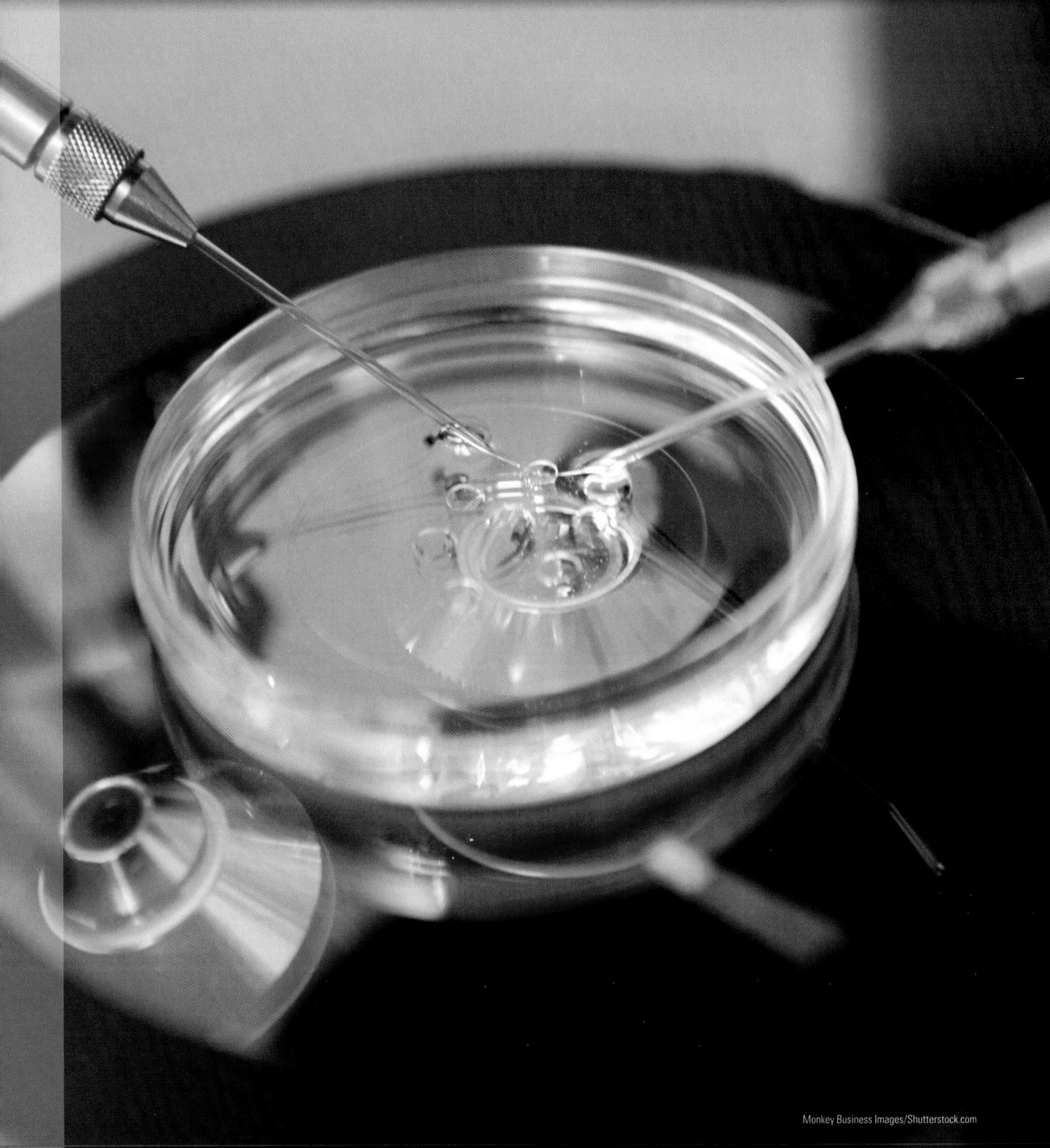

## WHY IT MATTERS

On July 25, 1978, Louise Brown became the first successful "test-tube" baby, born as a result of in vitro fertilization (IVF), a process in which an egg is fertilized by a sperm outside the body (**Figure 8.1**). At the time, this success story was considered both a scientific and a medical triumph, and many years later, in 2010, physiologist Robert G. Edwards was awarded the Nobel Prize in Physiology and Medicine for his development of IVF treatment. Today, IVF is one of the main treatments for infertility, commonly undertaken by couples who are unable to successfully conceive naturally.

With the advance of DNA technology, IVF treatment continues to be improved in conjunction with preimplantation genetic diagnosis (PGD). PGD, also known as embryo screening, is a procedure in which genetic testing is performed on embryos prior to implantation. PGD allows for the early detection of inherited genetic disorders (also known as Mendelian disorders). The advantage of screening for genetic disorders prior to implantation is that it avoids selective pregnancy termination (selecting to terminate the development of a fetus that is affected by a genetic disorder). In addition, it increases the odds that babies born from IVF will be free of certain genetic disorders since embryos testing positive for disease-related genetic mutations are not typically used in IVF. Although PGD is intended to screen for disease-related genes, theoretically, it can also be applied to the selection of non-health-related traits, such as gender, eye colour, or even intelligence. Although this type of genetic profiling is currently under strict governmental regulations, the idea that this technique could potentially be used in the creation of "designer babies" may not be too far off. This, of course, raises many social and ethical concerns regarding human rights and the overall effects on the human population (read more about genetic profiling and designer babies in the Box 8.1).

In this chapter, we will discuss various patterns of inheritance, what governs these patterns, and how this information can be applied to genetic screening and family planning. But first we will go back to the early scientific studies conducted on inheritance patterns by Gregor Mendel. We will describe his observations, explain his hypotheses, and illustrate how his laws of inheritance sparked a new and exciting field in biology called genetics.

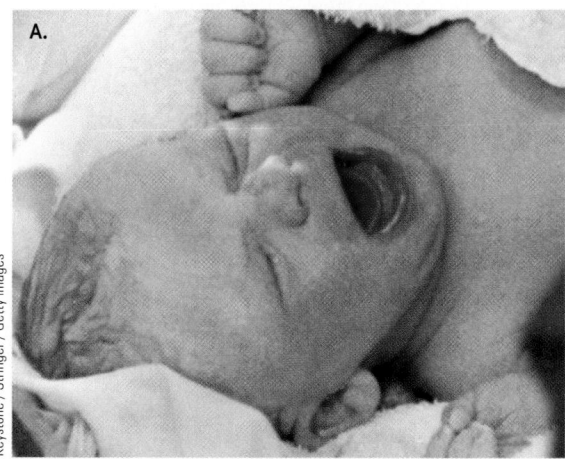
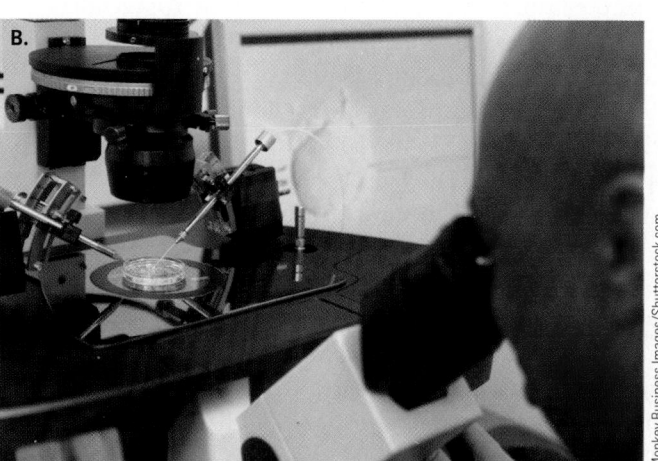

**FIGURE 8.1** In vitro fertilization. **(a)** Louise Brown is the first successful birth of a human by in vitro fertilization. **(b)** Image of the in vitro fertilization procedure.

The birth of the first test-tube baby through IVF sparked the idea that one day humans would be able to take the reins away from Mother Nature and be the drivers in the selection of genes for future generations. Today, with the advances made in DNA technology, this idea of "designer babies" appears closer to fruition than it did 30 years ago **(Figure 1)**. IVF treatment is commonly used in conjunction with preimplantation genetic diagnosis (PGD). Although PGD was originally implemented to detect mutated genes of inherited disorders such as Down syndrome or Huntington disease in embryos prior to IVF treatment, it is now being considered a mechanism to detect and select for non-disease-related traits, including gender, eye colour, and even intelligence. With this information, parents would be able to choose which embryo they prefer to have implanted, based on these non-disease-related traits.

In fact, in 2013, a personal genomics company in California named 23andMe was awarded a broad U.S. patent that could also theoretically be used to match

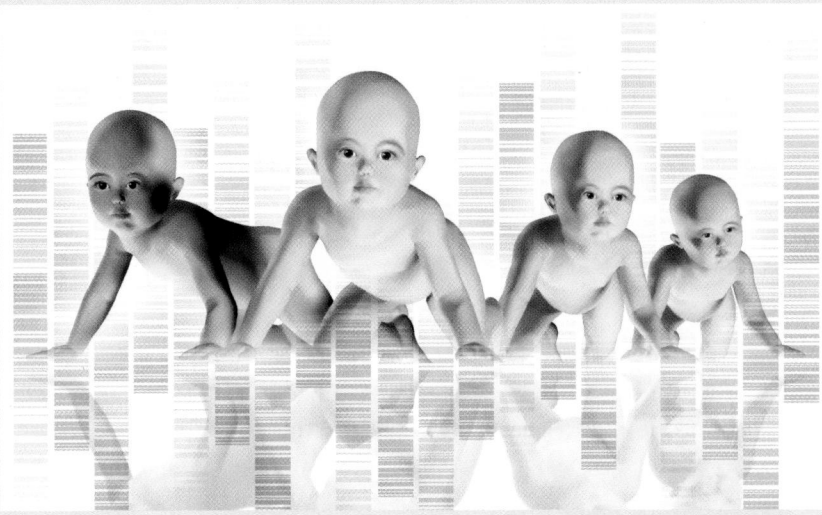

**FIGURE 1** A conceptual image of designer babies.

genetic profiles of would-be egg and sperm donors in an effort to select offspring with desirable traits. The company, which currently offers ancestry-related genetic reports and raw genetic data but does not provide health-related genetic reports, claims that it has no intention of linking the applications of the patent to fertility clinics for the genetic selection or bioengineering of children. It instead intends to use the technology in a "fun way" to simply calculate the probabilities of future children having certain desired or undesired traits based on the genetic

## 8.1 Mendel's Hypotheses Ignited the Field of Genetics

The story of Gregor Mendel's contribution to biology in some ways parallels those of many famous people in that the impact of their work was not fully appreciated until well after they were gone **(Figure 8.2)**. In Mendel's case, it would take almost 50 years after his original 1866 publication on the patterns of inheritance before the significance of his hypotheses was clearly understood and appreciated by the scientific community. As a result of his innovative studies, Mendel, who also was an Augustinian friar, was posthumously given the title of "father of modern genetics." His scientific work would shatter old theories about inheritance. In addition, it would be used to better elucidate and strengthen Charles Darwin's theory of evolution by means of natural selection, published in 1859. We will discuss Darwin's theory of evolution in Chapter 13.

**FIGURE 8.2** Gregor Mendel (1822–1884), the founder of genetics.

testing of two individuals. Bioethics argues that it is simply a stepping stone to future permission for selection or alteration of non-health-related traits. If allowed, individuals with the financial resources could pick their children based on desirable traits. This, of course, would mean that those in a higher socioeconomic position would have a "genetically competitive edge" over those who are less financially fortunate.

Moving one step forward, parents may also have the ability to change certain genes within the embryo or even in the parents' germ cells (egg and sperm) to match those desired traits. In other words, one could theoretically use germ-line gene therapy to design a baby from scratch based on the selection of desired traits. Germ-line gene therapy has already been established in many animal models, including mice, rats, and rabbits. For example, introduction of a rat growth hormone gene in a fertilized mouse egg prior to implantation results in a mouse offspring that is twice the size of its normal littermates. In many cancer research labs around the world, there are mice that contain human cancer genes introduced via germ-line gene therapy. The study of these transgenic mice (an organism containing genes of another organism) is critical in understanding the biology of the disease and thus the development of novel therapeutic strategies.

The application of these types of gene therapies in humans is currently prohibited. Indeed, countries such as Canada, Australia, and Germany, as well as others, have strict federal laws against the use of germ-line gene therapy in humans based on both safety and ethical concerns. These policies, however, are constantly being challenged. In 2013, the United Kingdom moved forward toward the introduction of human trials on mitochondrial replacement techniques. This would see the replacement of defective mitochondrial genes with normal ones and in turn reduce the risk of offspring developing mitochondrial diseases. In this event, a mother with a mitochondrial disease would have the nucleus in her egg transferred to the egg of an unaffected female, which could then be fertilized by the father's sperm. The offspring would then inherit the mitochondrial genes from the egg donor (recall that the inheritance of mitochondrial genes is uniparental). Supporters suggest that this technique does not quite fall under the regulations of germ-line gene therapies because mitochondrial genes make up an insignificant percentage of the human genome and do not determine identity. Critics, on the other hand, argue that any germ-line manipulation of genetic information (nuclear or non-nuclear) crosses both legal and ethical boundaries and could open the door to full germ-line genetic alteration permissions in the future. Indeed, the international community will be watching closely to see the outcome of the mitochondrial replacement therapy debates in British parliament as they will likely influence the potential outcome of designer babies in the future.

## Mendel's Observations and Hypotheses on Inheritance Patterns Lead to His Early Experiments

Until the 1900s, the blending theory of inheritance that suggested that the traits observed in offspring were a mere blend of those that they had inherited from both parents was the only working theory accepted by most people. The blending process was analogous to mixing red and white to achieve pink. But many realized that the theory was flawed as it could not explain how certain offspring expressed traits that were not a blend of their parents' traits. For example, how could two parents of short stature produce a tall offspring? In addition, the theory could not explain how certain traits persisted in the population even after they appeared to go missing. For example, how could a child inherit blue eyes when this trait was missing from certain generations within the family lineage?

Mendel's observations and experiments challenged the blending theory of inheritance and in time provided scientific evidence based on mathematical analysis that would falsify it. One of the most fascinating aspects of Mendel's hypotheses was that they were developed at a time in history (mid-1800s) when scientists were unaware of the major significance of genes, chromosomes, and the mechanisms of meiosis. However, the significance of Mendel's seminal work on genetics was not fully appreciated until the 1900s, as supported by the scientific efforts of many other scientists. This includes but is not limited to the works of Walter Sutton, which linked chromosomes to inheritance; Thomas Morgan, which linked genes to chromosomes and crossing over during meiosis; Alfred Hershey and Martha Chase, which confirmed DNA as the hereditary material; and James Watson and Francis Crick, which described both the molecular structure and replication of DNA.

For much of his studies on inheritance, Mendel used the garden pea (*Pisum sativum*), which proved to be an ideal model organism as it was simple and inexpensive to grow and could produce offspring rapidly and easily, and there were distinct varieties of the plant. This plant species could also self-fertilize because it produces both male gametes in pollen and female gametes in the carpel. Mendel initiated most of his experiments using true-breeding varieties of the plants. **True breeders** are organisms that when they self-fertilize only produce off-spring that exhibit the same **trait** for a particular **character** as the parent plant. For example, a true-breeding purple-flowered pea plant always produces offspring with purple flowers when it self-fertilizes. In this example, the flower colour is the character and the colour purple is the trait.

Mendel, however, was more interested in cross-fertilization of true-breeding plants that expressed a different trait for a particular character. An example is the cross-fertilization of a true-breeding purple-flowered pea plant with a true-breeding white-flowered pea plant. To better control these cross-fertilization experiments and prevent self-fertilization, Mendel would cut the anthers (contains the pollen) off one true breeder (e.g., the purple-flowered pea plant) and then brush its carpel (contains the eggs) with the pollen-covered anther of another true breeder that expressed a different trait for a particular character (e.g., the white-flowered pea plant) **(Figure 8.3)**. He then studied the offspring of this cross-fertilization and made observations about the patterns of inheritance for a variety of traits. From his extensive experimentation, he noted that the patterns of inheritance for the traits he observed were predictable. Moreover, he concluded that these traits, which are passed on from one generation to another, were inherited as discrete units. At the time, Mendel termed these units "hereditary factors." Today, we know them as genes. From the vast data Mendel collected and analyzed, he developed four hypotheses to explain the patterns of inheritance he observed. Here we first summarize Mendel's hypotheses as they were initially described (in italics) and then follow with a more modern-day explanation.

**Hypothesis 1:** *The traits for each character are governed by a pair of factors that are inherited one from each parent.* These hereditary factors are today termed genes. Remember from Chapter 7 that genes are specific nucleotide sequences found on a particular site (locus) on a chromosome. We inherit one full set of chromosomes, along with all of its genes, from each parent during fertilization.

**Hypothesis 2:** *If the hereditary factors in a pair are different versions of each other, then one will be dominant over the other, and the trait of the dominant version will be expressed in the organism.* The different versions of a gene are today termed alleles. Alleles can be dominant (often written as an upper-case letter, e.g., $A$) or recessive (often written as a lower-case letter, e.g., $a$). The trait for the dominant allele of a gene is expressed if at least one of the two alleles in a pair is dominant. Since the dominant allele masks the

**A.** This flower has been sectioned to show the location of its anthers and of the carpel with its attached stigma. Pollen grains form in the anthers. Egg cells develop, fertilization takes place, and seeds mature inside the carpel.

**B.** Pollen from one plant is brushed onto the stigma of a second plant. The anthers have been cut from the second plant so that it cannot self-fertilize.

**C.** The cross-fertilized plant produces seeds, which may be scored for seed traits, such as smooth or wrinkled shape, or may be grown into plants for scoring of adult traits, such as flower colour.

**D.** The adult pea plant ($F_1$ generation)

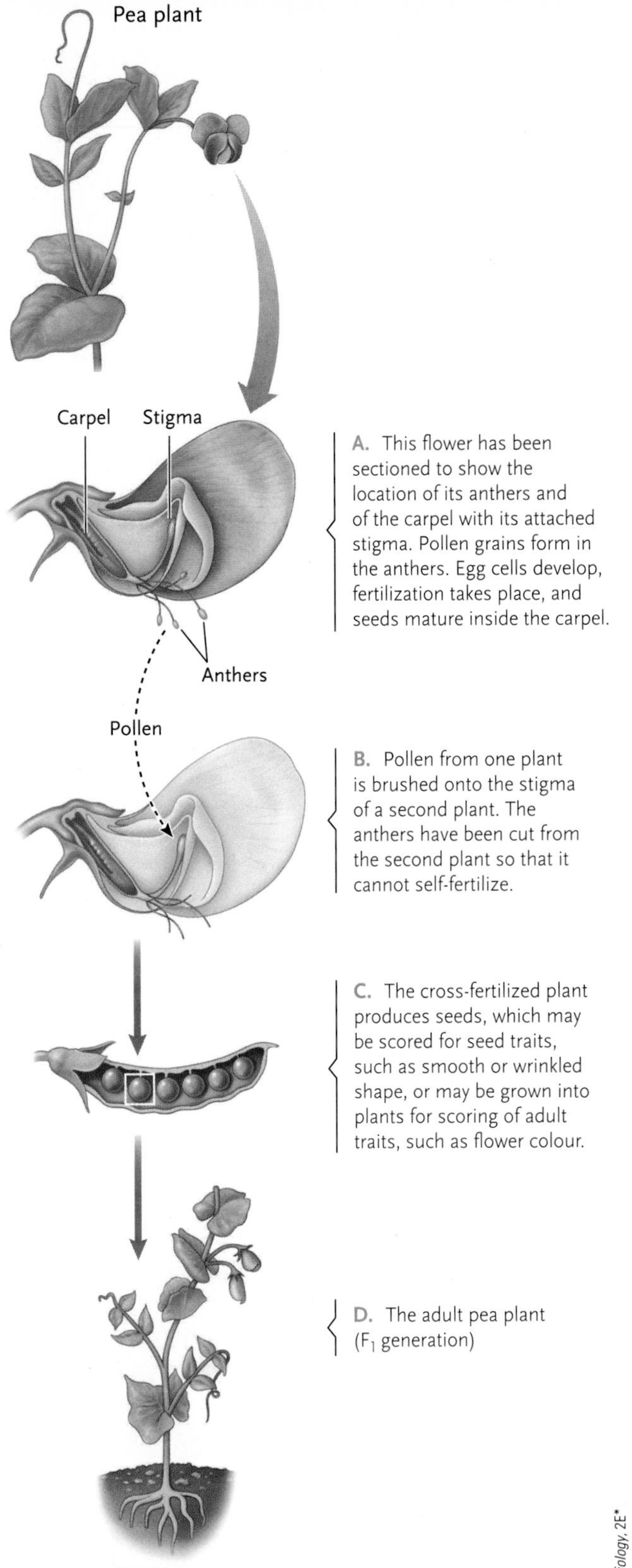

Biology, 2E*

**FIGURE 8.3** The garden pea (*Pisum sativum*), the focus of Mendel's experiments.

effects of the recessive allele, the recessive trait is expressed only if both alleles in the pair are recessive. When both alleles of a gene are identical, then the individual is considered homozygous for this gene. More specifically, the individual may be either **homozygous dominant** if both alleles are the dominant version (e.g., *AA*) or **homozygous recessive** if both alleles are the recessive version (e.g., *aa*). When the pair of alleles of a gene are different versions of each other, the individual is considered heterozygous (e.g., *Aa*) for this gene. The particular set of alleles that an individual carries is termed the **genotype**, and the observable trait governed by a particular genotype is termed the **phenotype**.

**Hypothesis 3:** *A pair of hereditary factors that govern the trait of a character will segregate (separate) from one another during gamete formation.* In other words, pairs of alleles separate during meiosis, resulting in half of the gametes containing one set of alleles and the other half of the gametes containing the other set of alleles (recall from Chapter 7 that meiosis results in cells that can mature into gametes). Sets of alleles come together as pairs once again when gametes fuse during fertilization. This hypothesis became the basis for Mendel's first law, known as the **law of segregation**. We will describe how Mendel developed this hypothesis in the next section.

**Hypothesis 4:** *Different pairs of hereditary factors that govern the traits of different characters segregate independently from each other during gamete formation.* This hypothesis indicates that how a pair of alleles for one gene separate during meiosis and go into gametes is independent of how another pair of alleles for a different gene separate during meiosis and go into gametes. It should be noted that this refers to different pairs of alleles that are found on different chromosomes. This hypothesis is more specifically known as Mendel's **law of independent assortment**. We will describe how Mendel developed this hypothesis later in the chapter.

All four of Mendel's hypotheses established the first scientifically supported set of rules on how traits are inherited from one generation to the next. Next we will go through the actual experiments that Mendel conducted and the data he acquired to support these hypotheses. Later in the chapter, we will discuss some of the exceptions to Mendel's laws of inheritance and under which conditions they apply.

## Mendel's Law of Segregation Describes the Separation of Allele Pairs during Meiosis

As mentioned, Mendel's model organism of choice to study inheritance patterns was the garden pea. He began his experiments by cross-fertilizing true breeders, which he named the **P generation** (P for parental). The parents had different traits for a particular character (**Figure 8.4, p. 176**). For instance, he would cross a true-breeding purple-flowered plant with a true-breeding white-flowered plant. Note that flower colour is the character and the purple and white colours are the different traits for this character. In his initial experiments, Mendel chose to follow

one individual trait at a time (e.g., flower colour). Hence, this type of cross-fertilization is termed a **monohybrid cross**. This approach differentiated his research from that of his contemporaries, who often followed multiple traits at the same time. This would prove to be key to Mendel's success in discovering the patterns of inheritance that would not have been evident if he followed the path of his colleagues.

Following cross-fertilization of the P generation, Mendel would count the number of new hybrid offspring, which he called the $F_1$ **generation** ($F_1$ for first filial, Latin for "son" or "daughter") (Figure 8.4). In particular, he would note the trait that each offspring expressed for the one character he was studying. In his experiments studying flower colour, he noted that all (100%) of the $F_1$ generation expressed the purple trait. Furthermore, the intensity of the purple colour in the $F_1$ generation was not reduced compared to that of the P generation, thus falsifying the blending theory. Mendel then questioned what had happened to the white colour trait in the $F_1$ generation and whether or not it was lost from the population. To investigate this, he crossed the hybrid $F_1$ generation offspring with each other and investigated this character in the $F_2$ **generation** (offspring of the $F_1$ generation cross). Interestingly, Mendel discovered that the white trait that appeared to have been lost in the $F_1$ generation reappeared in the $F_2$ generation at a ratio of 3:1 (purple:white). Mendel repeated these experiments many times and consistently observed this 3:1 ratio. In addition, he repeated these experiments investigating other characters in the plant, such as seed shape and seed colour, much to the same result (**Figure 8.5, p. 177**). This consistency then allowed Mendel to make predictions about how characters would be inherited.

From these observations, Mendel reasoned that the trait expressed for a character is determined by two hereditary factors (today known as the two alleles of a gene), each inherited from a parent. Moreover, if these two hereditary factors are different versions of each other, then one will be dominant over the other. In other words, the trait of the dominant hereditary factor will be expressed and thus mask the trait of the recessive one. He also proposed that these two hereditary factors will be separated from each other during gamete formation (today known to occur during meiosis) and will be distributed singly into these gametes. Mendel's reasoning essentially became the basis for his first three hypotheses (as summarized above).

Keeping Mendel's hypotheses in mind, let's take a closer look at the mechanisms involved in the patterns of inheritance that he observed using a **Punnett square**, a visual grid that illustrates the genotype and phenotype proportions for the progeny of a fertilization cross (Figure 8.4). We begin with the P generation of true breeders, each containing two alleles for their flower

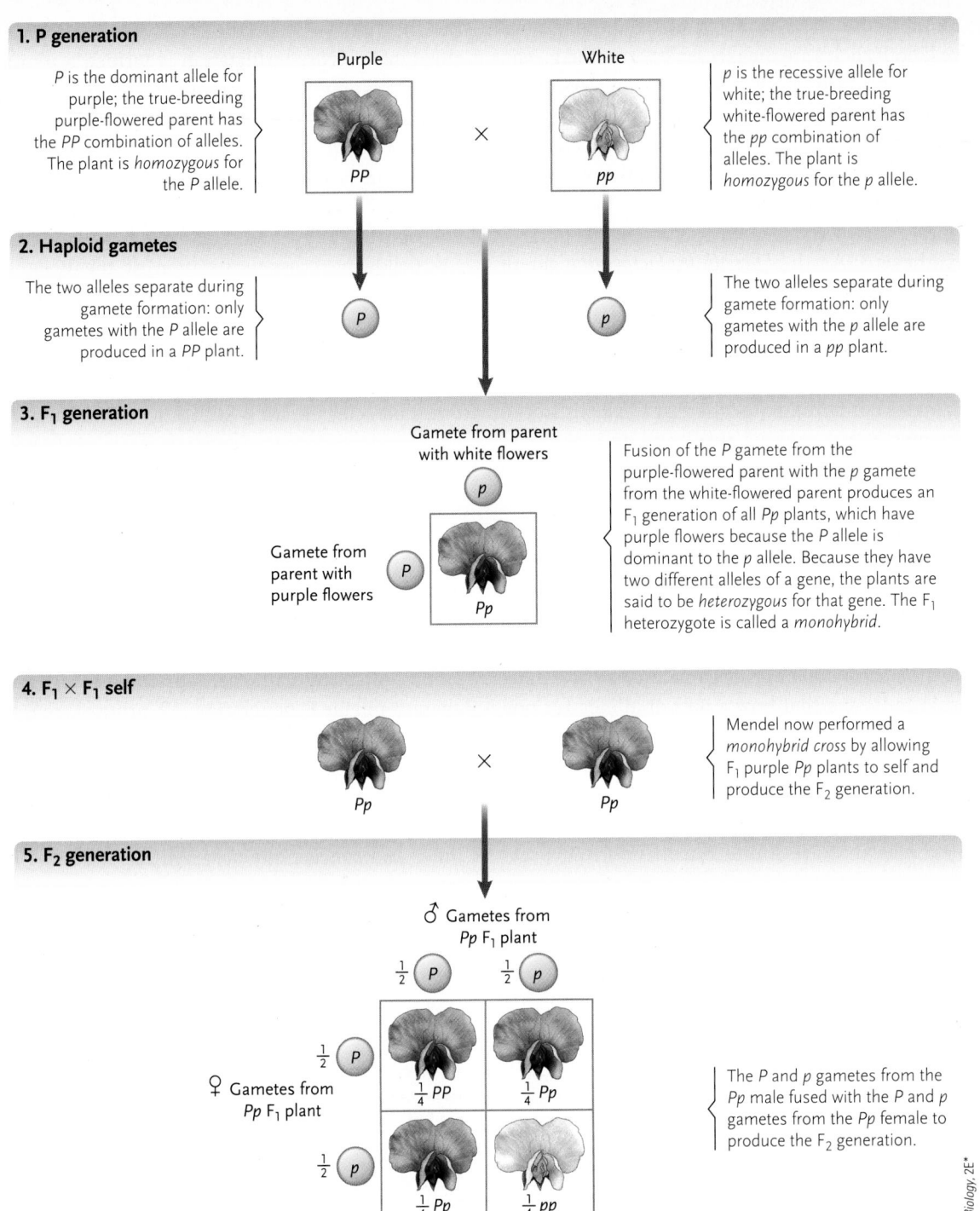

**1. P generation**

*P* is the dominant allele for purple; the true-breeding purple-flowered parent has the *PP* combination of alleles. The plant is *homozygous* for the *P* allele.

Purple

*PP*

×

White

*pp*

*p* is the recessive allele for white; the true-breeding white-flowered parent has the *pp* combination of alleles. The plant is *homozygous* for the *p* allele.

**2. Haploid gametes**

The two alleles separate during gamete formation: only gametes with the *P* allele are produced in a *PP* plant.

*P*

*p*

The two alleles separate during gamete formation: only gametes with the *p* allele are produced in a *pp* plant.

**3. F₁ generation**

Gamete from parent with white flowers

*p*

Gamete from parent with purple flowers

*P*

*Pp*

Fusion of the *P* gamete from the purple-flowered parent with the *p* gamete from the white-flowered parent produces an F₁ generation of all *Pp* plants, which have purple flowers because the *P* allele is dominant to the *p* allele. Because they have two different alleles of a gene, the plants are said to be *heterozygous* for that gene. The F₁ heterozygote is called a *monohybrid*.

**4. F₁ × F₁ self**

*Pp*

×

*Pp*

Mendel now performed a *monohybrid cross* by allowing F₁ purple *Pp* plants to self and produce the F₂ generation.

**5. F₂ generation**

♂ Gametes from *Pp* F₁ plant

$\frac{1}{2}$ *P*   $\frac{1}{2}$ *p*

♀ Gametes from *Pp* F₁ plant

$\frac{1}{2}$ *P*

$\frac{1}{2}$ *p*

$\frac{1}{4}$ *PP*   $\frac{1}{4}$ *Pp*

$\frac{1}{4}$ *Pp*   $\frac{1}{4}$ *pp*

The *P* and *p* gametes from the *Pp* male fused with the *P* and *p* gametes from the *Pp* female to produce the F₂ generation.

*Biology, 2E\**

**FIGURE 8.4** Mendel's experiment illustrating the principle of segregation for flower colour in peas.

colour character **(Figure 8.4, step 1)**. From Mendel's observations, purple colour is dominant over white. Thus, because it is a true breeder, the purple-flowered parent has two dominant alleles (*PP*). The white-flowered parent must have two recessive alleles (*pp*), by definition of the recessive nature of the allele. During meiosis, the allele pairs in each parent cell will be separated and distributed to gametes singly. As a result, all the gametes produced by the purple-flowered parent will receive a dominant allele (*P*), and all the gametes produced by the white-flowered parent will receive a recessive allele (*p*) **(Figure 8.4, step 2)**. When

these gametes fuse to form a zygote, all the offspring in the F₁ generation will be hybrids or heterozygous for this gene (*Pp*) **(Figure 8.4, step 3)**. Since the dominant allele masks the expression of the recessive one, all the F₁ generation offspring will have purple flowers.

Keeping with the same logic and our knowledge of meiosis (see Chapter 7 for review), when F₁ generation individuals produce gametes, half of their gametes will receive the *P* allele and the other half will receive the *p* allele. Thus, the probability of a gamete receiving a *P* allele is one-half or 50%, and, similarly, the probability of a gamete receiving

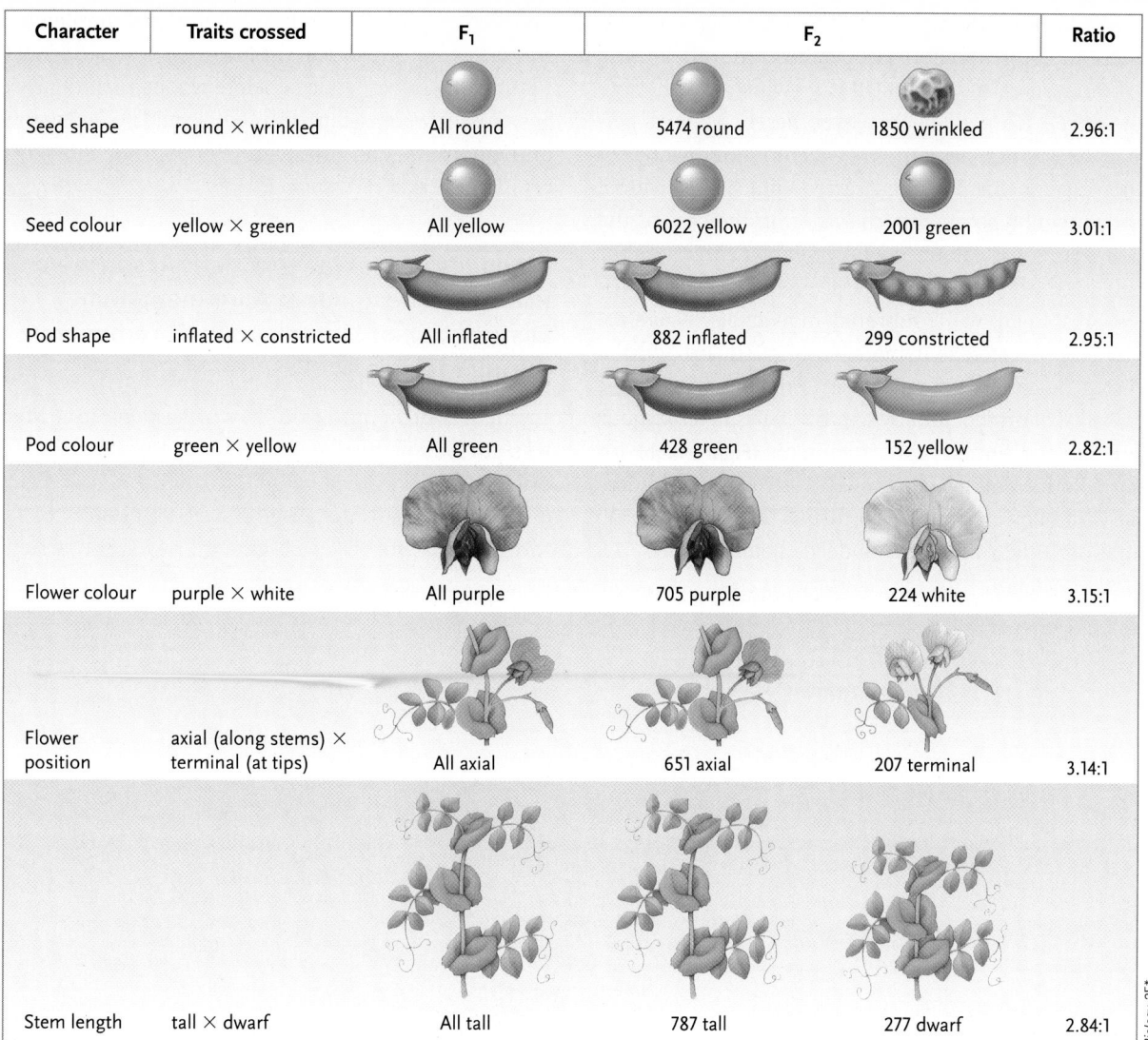

| Character | Traits crossed | F$_1$ | F$_2$ | | Ratio |
|---|---|---|---|---|---|
| Seed shape | round × wrinkled | All round | 5474 round | 1850 wrinkled | 2.96:1 |
| Seed colour | yellow × green | All yellow | 6022 yellow | 2001 green | 3.01:1 |
| Pod shape | inflated × constricted | All inflated | 882 inflated | 299 constricted | 2.95:1 |
| Pod colour | green × yellow | All green | 428 green | 152 yellow | 2.82:1 |
| Flower colour | purple × white | All purple | 705 purple | 224 white | 3.15:1 |
| Flower position | axial (along stems) × terminal (at tips) | All axial | 651 axial | 207 terminal | 3.14:1 |
| Stem length | tall × dwarf | All tall | 787 tall | 277 dwarf | 2.84:1 |

*Biology, 2E**

**FIGURE 8.5** Mendel's crosses with seven different characters in peas, including his results and the calculated ratios of offspring.

a *p* allele is also one-half, or 50%. Therefore, during an F$_1$ generation monohybrid cross **(Figure 8.4, steps 4** and **5)**, the probability of two gametes each containing dominant alleles (*P*) fertilizing each other is ½ × ½, or ¼ (you can also calculate this using percentages, where 50% × 50% = 25%). Using the same approach, we can determine that the probability of two gametes each containing recessive alleles (*p*) fertilizing each other is also one-quarter.

Determining the probability that the fertilized zygote will contain two different alleles (one *P* and one *p*) requires a modification of the calculation because there are two ways this can happen. The first case is if parent 1 supplies a *P* allele (probability of one-half) and parent 2 supplies a *p* allele (probability of one-half), rendering a total probability of this event occurring as one-quarter. However, we could also get a Pp combination if parent 1 supplies a *p* allele and parent 2 supplies a *P* allele. The probability that this occurs is also one-quarter. Because either of these events could occur, the total probability of a *Pp* combination is ¼ + ¼, or ½ (Figure 8.4, step 5). Therefore, the genotype ratio in the F$_2$ generation is ¼ *PP*:½ *Pp*:¼ *pp*. Since the heterozygotes

express the dominant trait similar to the homozygous dominant individuals, the phenotype ratio Mendel predicted and observed in the F$_2$ generation is 3 purple:1 white.

Mendel also tested these hypotheses using six other observable characters expressed by his pea plants. He consistently observed 3:1 phenotype ratios in the F$_2$ generation (Figure 8.5). These results supported his first three hypotheses and became the basis for Mendel's first law, the **law of segregation**. Today, we understand this law to describe the separation of alleles during meiosis. Recall from Chapter 7 that homologous pairs of chromosomes (chromosomes that have the same genes arranged in the same order) separate during anaphase I of meiosis I. As a result, the newly formed daughter cells, which after meiosis II will mature into gametes, each contain one set of chromosomes and, therefore, one allele for each gene.

The one drawback to Mendel's conclusions was the uncertainty of the genotypes of the purple-flowered individuals in both the F$_1$ and F$_2$ generations (remember that both homozygous dominant individuals and heterozygotes express the same phenotype). Thus, how could he be sure that the $F_1$ generation was indeed heterozygote ($Pp$) and which of the $F_2$ generation that expressed purple flowers were homozygous dominant ($PP$) and which were heterozygotes ($Pp$)? To validate his hypotheses, Mendel performed a **testcross**, a mating between one individual of unknown genotype for a character with an individual of known genotype for this character. In the case of the garden pea flower colour, the only genotype that was for certain was the homozygous recessive genotype ($pp$), which was expressed by white-flowered individuals. **Figure 8.6** illustrates the testcross using a Punnett square and the predicted outcomes using the same mathematical logic described above if the unknown individual is heterozygous **(Figure 8.6a)** or homozygous dominant **(Figure 8.6b)** for flower colour. Mendel performed testcross experiments using white-flowered plants to further verify that the $F_1$ generation offspring were indeed heterozygotes. As

predicted, half of the testcross offspring exhibited purple flowers and the other half white flowers, validating that the $F_1$ individuals were indeed heterozygous ($Pp$) (Figure 8.6). Testcrosses were also performed to validate the genotypes of the homozygous dominant ($PP$) and the heterozygous ($Pp$) $F_2$ generation offspring.

## Mendel's Law of Independent Assortment Predicted the Random Alignment and Distribution of Homologous Chromosomes during Meiosis

In further developing the law of segregation, Mendel was curious if the separation of one pair of alleles for one character during gamete formation had any effect on the separation of another pair of alleles for a different character. To investigate this, Mendel carried out

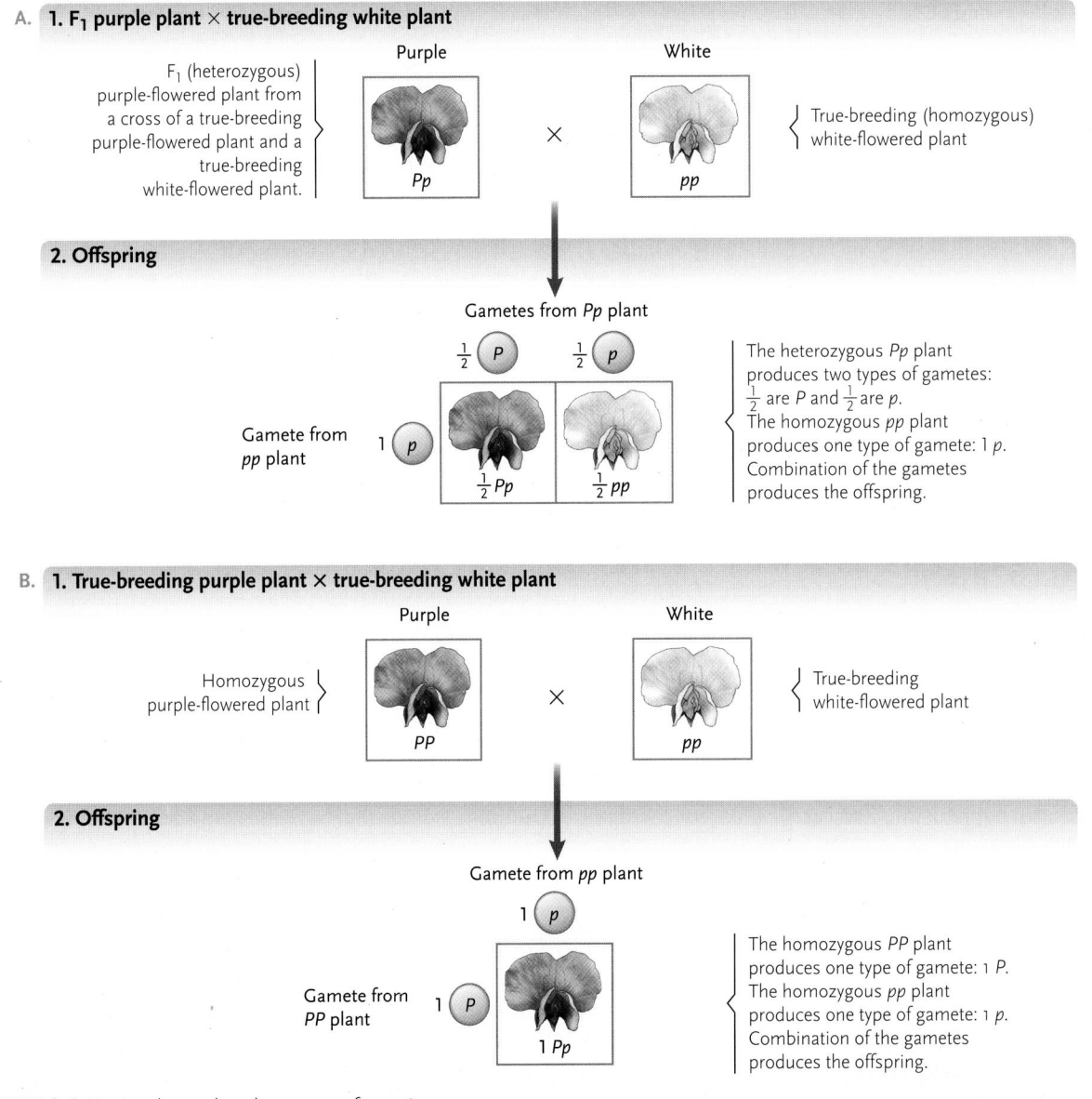

**FIGURE 8.6** Testing the predicted outcome of genetic crosses.

**dihybrid crosses** in which he cross-fertilized two true-breeding varieties in the P generation that differed in two characters. An example of two characters he investigated at the same time were seed shape [round is the dominant trait (*R*); wrinkled is the recessive trait (*r*)] and seed colour [yellow is the dominant trait (*Y*); green is the recessive trait (*y*)]. In the P generation cross

($RRYY \times rryy$), each true-breeding parent would produce one type of gamete (*RY* in the *RRYY* parent and *ry* in the *rryy* parent) **(Figure 8.7)**. As a result, all of the $F_1$ generation offspring of the dihybrid cross would be heterozygous for seed shape and colour (*RrYy*). As such, the $F_1$ generation expressed only the dominant traits for both characters (round and yellow seeds), despite

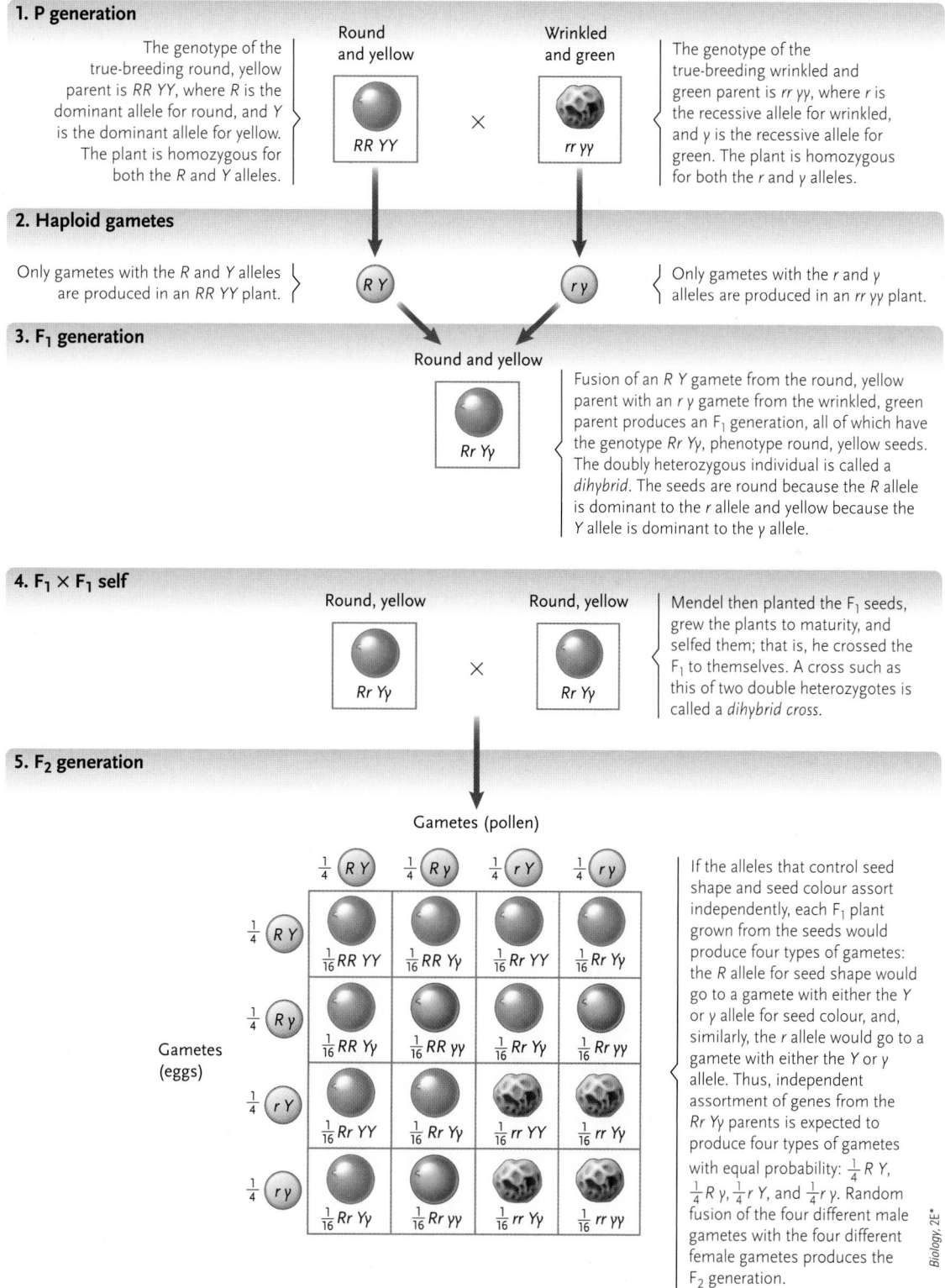

**FIGURE 8.7** Mendel's experiment illustrating the principle of independent assortment for seed shape and seed colour in peas.

having alleles for the recessive characters. In the $F_1$ generation dihybrid cross ($RrYy \times RrYy$), four combinations of gametes were generated by each individual ($RY$, $Ry$, $rY$, and $ry$). Because the chromosomes align randomly during metaphase I, each combination of alleles will be produced in equal proportions. Thus, the probability of any gamete having any one of these four particular alleles ($RY$, $Ry$, $rY$, or $ry$) would be one-quarter. Since fertilization is also random, the fusion of any two gametes containing any of the four possible combinations is $2/4 \times 2/4$, or $2/16$. This means that any fertilized zygote from two of these gametes could contain any one of 16 possible genetic combinations (Figure 8.7). Of these genetic combinations, there would be four

different possible combination phenotypes for seed shape and colour. Mendel observed all four of these phenotypes within the $F_2$ generation at the following proportions: $9/16$, round and yellow; $3/16$, round and green; $3/16$, wrinkled and yellow; and $2/16$, wrinkled and green. This can also be described more simply as a 9:3:3:1 ratio. Mendel consistently observed this 9:3:3:1 ratio in repeated experiments using combinations of other characters listed in Figure 8.5. Based on Mendel's predictable results, he hypothesized that the segregation of one pair of hereditary factors for one character is independent of the segregation of another pair of hereditary factors for a different character. This hypothesis was further validated in Mendel's dihybrid

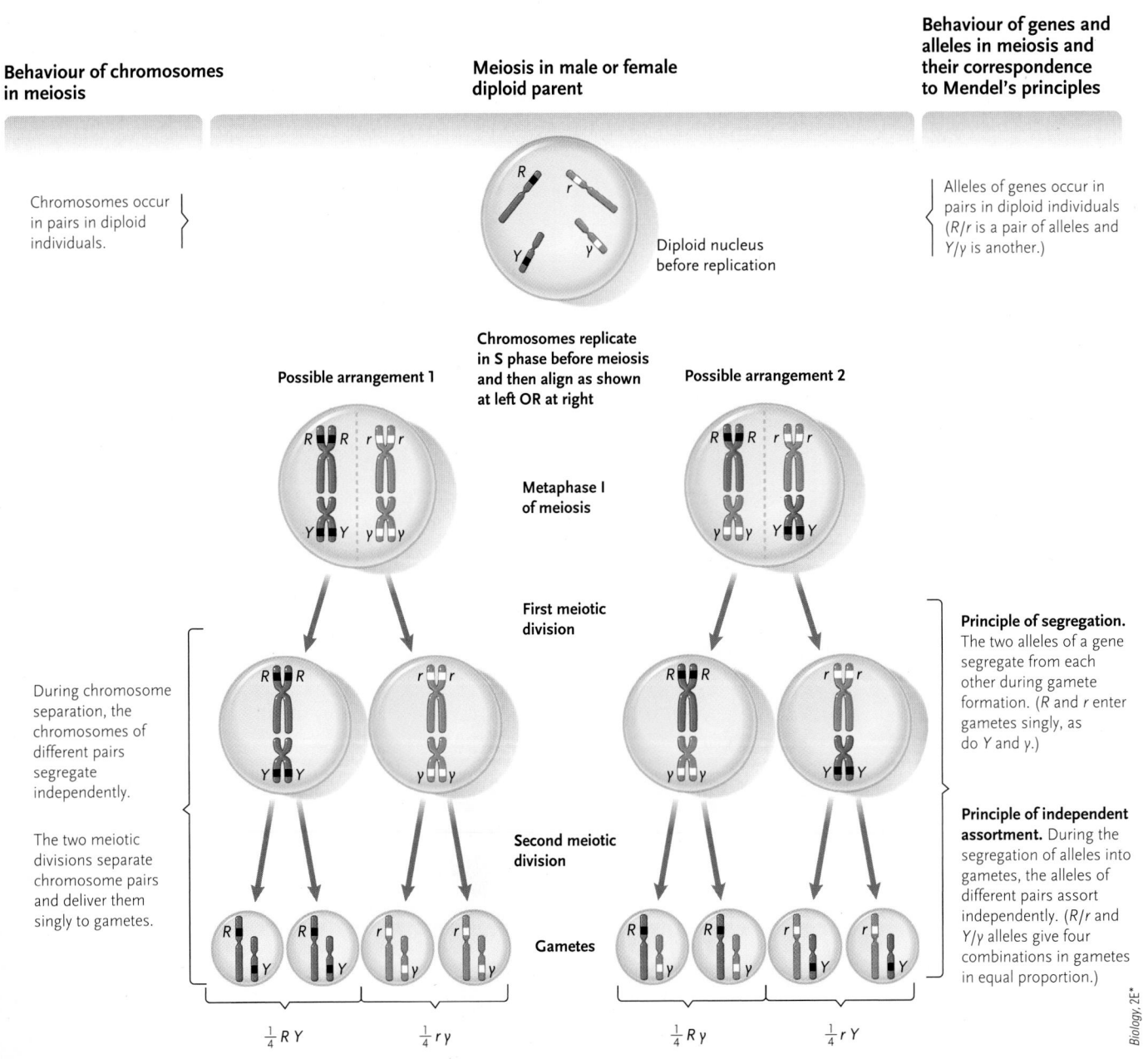

**FIGURE 8.8** The parallels between the behaviour of chromosomes and genes and alleles in meiosis. The gametes show four different combinations of alleles produced by independent segregation of chromosome pairs.

testcross, which verified the genotypes of both the $F_1$ and $F_2$ generations. In turn, Mendel's fourth hypothesis became the basis for Mendel's second law, the **law of independent assortment**.

Today, we understand the law of independent assortment to mean that during meiosis, the pair of alleles for one gene segregate from each other independently of the pairs of alleles for other genes. Since we learned in Chapter 7 that pairs of alleles are located on homologous chromosomes, the law also suggests that how one pair of homologous chromosomes align at the metaphase plate and then separate during meiosis I is independent of how other homologous pairs of chromosomes align and separate during this phase **(Figure 8.8)**.

## STUDY BREAK

1. Why is the garden pea a good model organism for genetic studies?
2. Describe Mendel's four hypotheses.
3. How does the law of segregation differ from the law of independent assortment?

## 8.2 The Modes of Inheritance Can Vary

Mendel's hypotheses and laws of inheritance were well supported by his extensive experimental results. It is thought that Mendel tested these hypotheses on over 25,000 plants. However, his described mechanisms for the patterns of inheritance that he published in 1866 were met with great criticism in the scientific community and were quickly dismissed. It wasn't until the 1900s (well after Mendel's death) that scientists began duplicating his work and testing his hypotheses in other model organisms. Their results would further support Mendel's hypotheses and provide more credibility and appreciation for his theories on inheritance, now known as Mendelian genetics (or Mendelian inheritance). As the field of genetics grew, however, some studies revealed inheritance patterns that varied from Mendel's original hypotheses. These varied patterns of inheritance were not as clear as Mendel had originally observed. Here we will discuss those patterns of inheritance that clearly follow Mendelian genetics, those that may not appear as clear, and those that defy it altogether.

### Autosomal Inheritance Patterns Include Dominant versus Recessive

Autosomal inheritance represents phenotypic patterns that are determined by the inheritance and expression of a single gene located on the **autosomes** (the non-

sex chromosomes). There are two described forms: **autosomal dominant inheritance** and **autosomal recessive inheritance.** Both of these patterns of heritance follow Mendelian genetics. The difference between the two forms is best reflected when discussing human disorders that are determined by a single gene. Abnormal traits that are representative of the disorder are expressed by either the dominant allele, as seen in autosomal dominant inheritance, or the recessive one, as seen in autosomal recessive inheritance. **Table 8.1** summarizes a list of human traits that represent these types of inheritance patterns. Here we highlight a few as examples.

Huntington disease is a neurodegenerative disease of the brain that affects the coordination of muscles and leads to the decline of cognitive function, psychiatric disorders, and, eventually, death. Onset of the disease usually begins between the ages of 35 and 44, and as such, many affected individuals are unaware of the disease until well into adulthood. The disease is

| TABLE 8.1 | Examples of Human Genetic Traits | |
|---|---|
| Trait | Adverse Health Effects |
| **Autosomal Recessive Inheritance** | |
| Albinism | Absence of pigmentation (melanin) |
| Attached earlobes | None |
| Cystic fibrosis | Excess mucus in lungs and digestive cavities |
| Sickle cell disease | Severe tissue and organ damage |
| Galactosemia | Brain, liver, and eye damage |
| Phenylketonuria | Mental retardation |
| Tay–Sachs disease | Mental retardation, death |
| **Autosomal Dominant Inheritance** | |
| Free earlobes | None |
| Achondroplasia | Defective cartilage formation that causes dwarfism |
| Early balding in males | None |
| Campodactyly | Rigid, bent small fingers |
| Curly hair | None |
| Huntington disease | Progressive, irreversible degeneration of nervous system |
| Syndactyly | Webbing between fingers |
| Polydactyly | Extra digits |
| Brachydactyly | Short digits |
| Progeria | Premature aging |
| **X-Linked Inheritance** | |
| Hemophilia A | Deficient blood clotting |
| Red–green colour-blindness | Inability to distinguish red from green |
| Testicular feminizing syndrome | Absence of male organs, sterility |

caused by a mutation in a single gene called **huntingtin** (*HD* or *HTT*). The gene encodes for a protein called huntingtin, which is highly expressed in the brain but whose exact function remains unknown. It is believed that the protein serves a role in cell signalling, protein transport, and protection against programmed cell death (apoptosis) in nerve cells. The mutated allele of the gene is dominant over the normal allele, and as such, the disease follows the autosomal dominant pattern of inheritance. Indeed, both homozygous dominant and heterozygote individuals are afflicted by the disease. Homozygous recessive individuals, however, express the normal phenotype and thus do not have Huntington disease. Since the disease usually presents itself later in adulthood, many affected individuals unknowingly pass on the mutated allele to their children prior to the onset of symptoms. Due to the fact that the mutated allele is dominant, children who have at least one parent with Huntington disease are at high risk (50% to 75% chance) for developing the disease themselves **(Figure 8.9a)**. The late onset of disease contributes to the persistence of the mutated allele within human populations. Currently, there is no cure for Huntington disease; however, genetic tests are available to individuals with a family history of the disease. These tests can be administered prior to the onset of symptoms, allowing treatments to begin earlier. However, there are some ethical concerns regarding testing in children and the management of confidentiality and disclosure. Even among adults, some individuals would rather not know that they are going to die, at a

relatively early age, from an incurable neurodegenerative disease. (Read Box 8.2 to learn more about recent research regarding how the structure and function of the huntingtin protein may aid patients with Huntington disease.)

Cystic fibrosis is an example of an autosomal recessive genetic disorder that affects the normal functioning of the lungs, pancreas, liver, and intestines. The most critical symptom in cystic fibrosis patients is the accumulation of mucus in the lungs, leading to shortness of breath, persistent coughing, and frequent respiratory infection. Recall from Chapter 7 that cystic fibrosis is caused by a mutation in the cystic fibrosis conductance regulator (*CFTR*) gene that encodes for the chloride channel protein CFTR. The most prevalent mutated allele has three nucleotide deletions that, when expressed, produce a malfunctioning version of the CFTR protein (Δ *F508*; see Figure 7.3a). Although the symptoms of cystic fibrosis usually present in early childhood, many affected individuals in North America are now living well into their late thirties and forties. Inheritance of the disease requires an individual to have two mutated or recessive versions of the gene. Heterozygotes carry one mutated allele, but the expression of this recessive allele is masked by the normal dominant one. Although these individuals are not affected by the disease, they are **carriers** and can unknowingly pass on the mutated recessive allele to their children **(Figure 8.9b)**. The risk of acquiring an autosomal recessive disorder, however, is lower than that of autosomal dominant disorders. Even if both

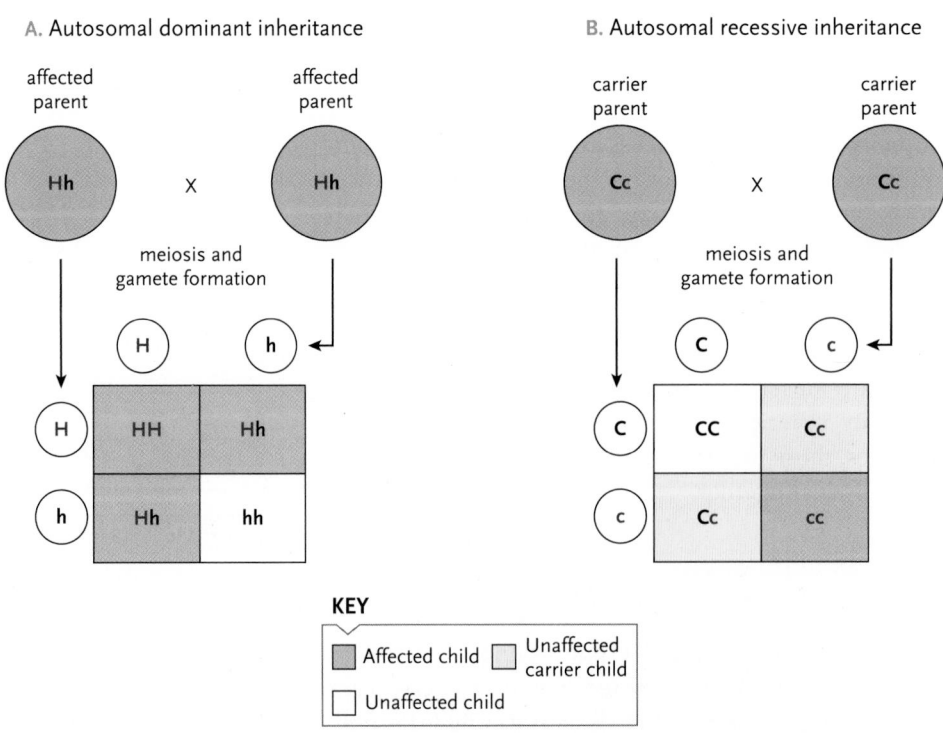

**FIGURE 8.9** Autosomal inheritance patterns. **(a)** Autosomal dominant inheritance in Huntington disease, in which the disorder-causing allele (*H*) is dominant. **(b)** Autosomal recessive inheritance, in which the disorder-causing allele (*C*) is recessive.

# THE MOLECULE BEHIND THE BIOLOGY 8.2
## Repetition Is Key in Huntington Disease

Huntington disease (HD) is an autosomal dominant inherited neurodegenerative disorder that affects muscle coordination, cognition, and psychological stability. The gene behind the disease, huntingtin (*HTT*), contains a three-nucleotide combination of CAG that is repeated at one end of the gene. The number of CAG repeats in the normal *HTT* allele ranges between 7 and 35. In people with HD, the number of repeats is well over 40. But what do these repeats mean? The CAG nucleotide combination encodes for the amino acid glutamine. Thus, repeats of CAG in the gene translate into glutamine repeats in the protein.

Although the exact function of these glutamine repeats in the huntingtin protein is still under investigation, a study recently published in the journal *Proceedings of the National Academy of Sciences* by Ron Truant and his research team from McMaster University in Hamilton, Ontario, may shed some clues. This study was the first to use microscopic imaging to show that the huntingtin protein derived from the living skin cells of HD patients changes shape in comparison with the normal version. It appears that the glutamine repeats (polyQ) act as a flexible arm connecting two other functional domains of the protein together. When the glutamine repeats of the protein are too long, as seen in HD patients, they lose their flexibility, thus failing to bring the two functional domains together **(Figure 1)**. This alteration in overall protein structure leads to protein malfunction.

Truant's team is now working to reverse the abnormal structure of the huntingtin protein back to its normal shape. Indeed, certain drugs can return the protein structure back to its normal configuration, thus restoring its proper function. Current work is under way to develop these drugs in a format that can easily penetrate into the brain. Methods used by Truant's lab are being scaled up to large robotic drug screening by a pharmaceutical company to test and identify these drugs more efficiently. In addition, this technology is being applied to other diseases that appear to have genetic defects similar to those of HD.

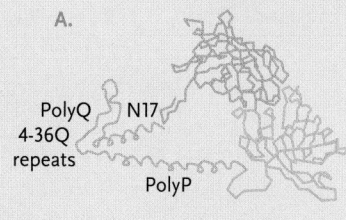
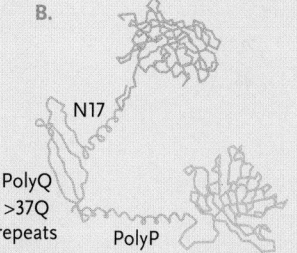

**FIGURE 1** Huntingtin protein. The glutamine repeats (polyQ) are shorter in the normal huntingtin protein **(a)** compared to the version found in Huntington disease **(b)**. Increased number of glutamine repeats changes the overall shape and function of the protein. N17 and PolyP represent the functional domains of the protein. To image the protein shape, blue and yellow fluorescent tags were placed on the protein.

SOURCE: Adapted from Nicholas Stephane Caron, Carly Robyn Desmond, Jianrun Xia, and Ray Truant, "Polyglutamine domain flexibility mediates the proximity between flanking sequences in huntingtin," *PNAS*, vol. 110 no. 36, 14610–14615.

---

parents are carriers, the probability of a child inheriting two recessive alleles and hence the autosomal recessive disease is 25% ($^2/_2 \times {}^2/_2 = {}^2/_4$). Nonetheless, because mutated recessive alleles are often masked and thus protected from natural selection within the heterozygotes that carry them, they continue to persist within populations.

## Modifications to Mendel's Pattern of Inheritance May Not Exhibit Predictive Ratios

Both forms of autosomal patterns of inheritance described in the previous section clearly follow Mendelian genetics. The dominant allele (whether it is normal or mutated) completely masks the recessive allele. Indeed, the 3:1 phenotypic ratios observed in Mendel's $F_1$ monohybrid cross experiments are also reflected in autosomal dominant and autosomal recessive patterns of inheritance. Below we will discuss other patterns of inheritance that follow Mendelian genetics but do not necessarily show the predicted phenotypic ratios.

In some cases, dominance is not always so absolute. Let's take, for example, the flower colour of snapdragon plants that are governed by two alleles, one dominant (*R*) and one recessive (*r*). Homozygous dominant individuals (*RR*) exhibit red flowers, and homozygous recessive (*rr*) individuals exhibit white flowers. Heterozygotes (*Rr*), however, do not exhibit the same flower colour of homozygous dominant individuals. Instead, their flowers are pink. At first glance, the pink phenotype appears to support the blending theory of inheritance. However, in subsequent crosses, the red and white phenotypes do reappear, thus falsifying the theory. The pink phenotype is instead a result of **incomplete dominance (Figure 8.10, p. 184)**. In other words, the dominant phenotype (red) does not completely mask the recessive one (white). In the case of

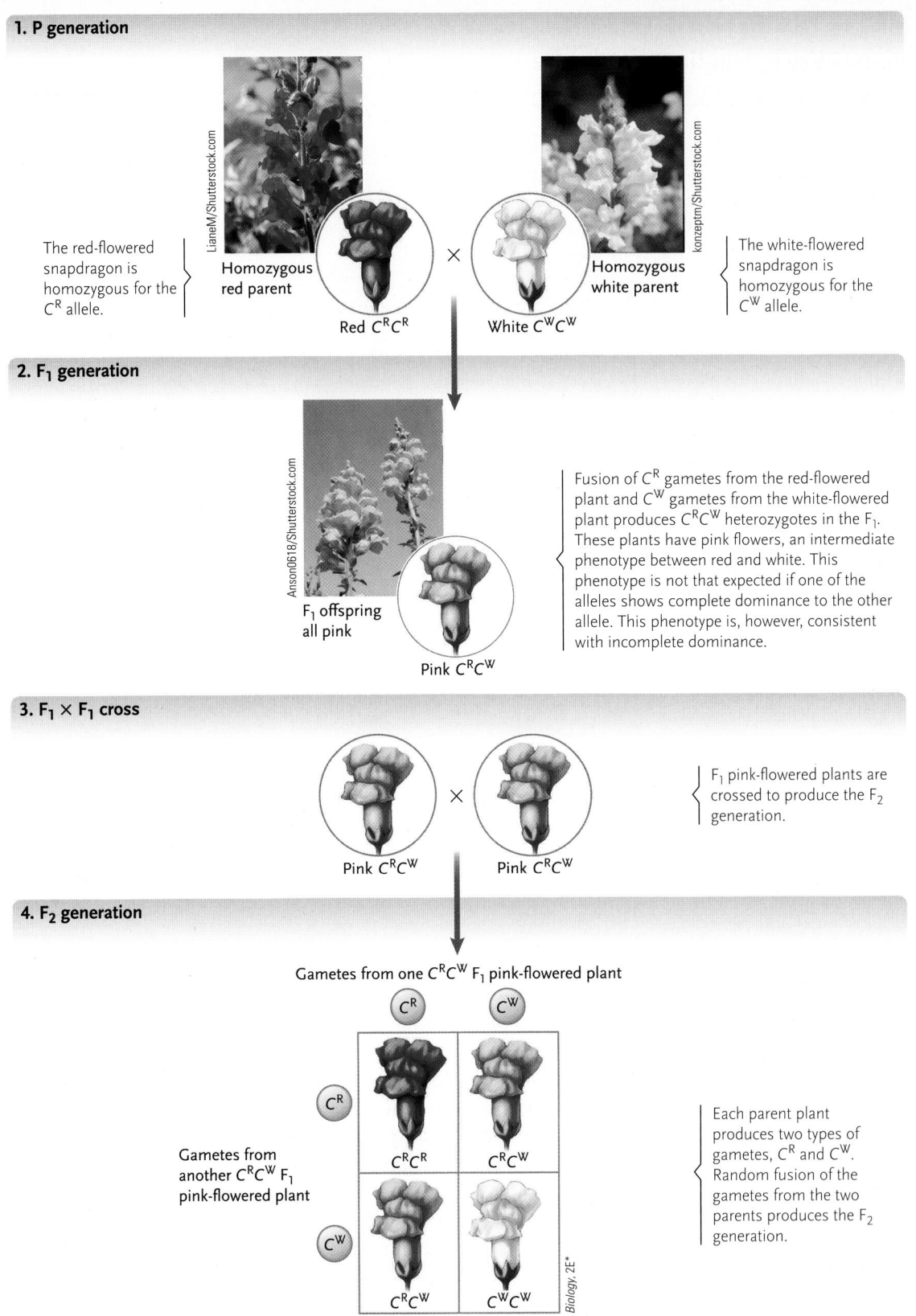

## 1. P generation

The red-flowered snapdragon is homozygous for the $C^R$ allele.

Homozygous red parent

Red $C^R C^R$

×

Homozygous white parent

White $C^W C^W$

The white-flowered snapdragon is homozygous for the $C^W$ allele.

## 2. F₁ generation

$F_1$ offspring all pink

Pink $C^R C^W$

Fusion of $C^R$ gametes from the red-flowered plant and $C^W$ gametes from the white-flowered plant produces $C^R C^W$ heterozygotes in the $F_1$. These plants have pink flowers, an intermediate phenotype between red and white. This phenotype is not that expected if one of the alleles shows complete dominance to the other allele. This phenotype is, however, consistent with incomplete dominance.

## 3. F₁ × F₁ cross

Pink $C^R C^W$

×

Pink $C^R C^W$

$F_1$ pink-flowered plants are crossed to produce the $F_2$ generation.

## 4. F₂ generation

Gametes from one $C^R C^W$ $F_1$ pink-flowered plant

$C^R$    $C^W$

Gametes from another $C^R C^W$ $F_1$ pink-flowered plant

$C^R$

$C^W$

$C^R C^R$    $C^R C^W$

$C^R C^W$    $C^W C^W$

Each parent plant produces two types of gametes, $C^R$ and $C^W$. Random fusion of the gametes from the two parents produces the $F_2$ generation.

**FIGURE 8.10** Experiment showing incomplete dominance in the inheritance of flower colour in snapdragons.

snapdragons, the red pigment is produced by an enzyme encoded by the dominant allele and the white (or lack of red pigment) trait is caused by a mutated version of this enzyme encoded by the recessive allele. Due to incomplete dominance, the phenotypic ratio of offspring from an $F_1$ monohybrid cross is 1 red:2 pink: 1 white instead of the typical 3:1 ratio. Taking incomplete dominance into account, the predicted ratio of 1:2:1 in the $F_2$ generation (Figure 8.10) does indeed support the Mendelian pattern of inheritance.

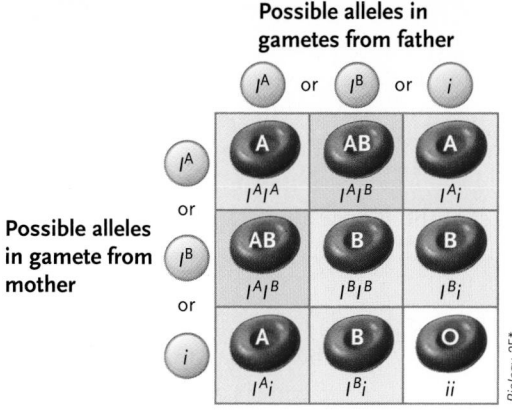

**Possible alleles in gametes from father**

**Possible alleles in gamete from mother**

*Biology, 2E\**

**FIGURE 8.11** Inheritance of the blood types of the human ABO blood group.

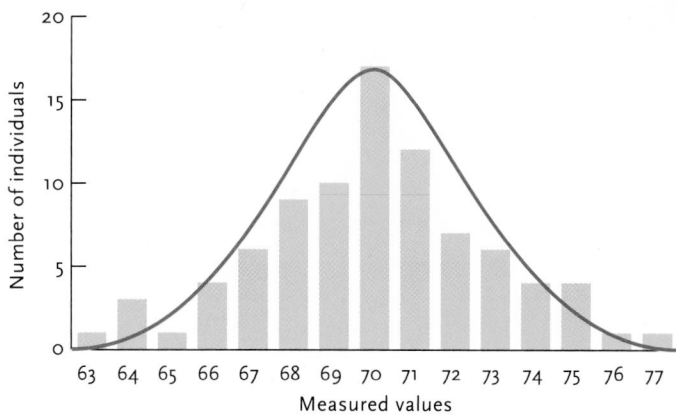

Height (inches)

**FIGURE 8.12** Continuous variation in height among male biology students at the University of Florida.

SOURCE: (Graph): From Starr. *Biology*, 8E. © 2011 Brooks/Cole, a part of Cengage Learning, Inc. Reproduced by permission. www.cengage.com/permissions; (Photo): Courtesy of Ray Carson, University of Florida News and Public Affairs

Another type of inheritance that results in a 1:2:1 ratio in the $F_2$ generation is **codominance**. In this case, both of the alleles for a character are fully expressed; thus, one does not mask the other. This is evident in human ABO blood typing, where the A and B antigens are encoded by the dominant $I^A$ and $I^B$ alleles, respectively **(Figure 8.11)**. These antigens are membrane proteins found on the surface of red blood cells. They are termed antigens because they will elicit an immunological response that results in the production of antibodies in individuals who do not normally express these proteins (see Chapter 26 for a review). Since both $I^A$ and $I^B$ are dominant versions of the gene, if both are present in an individual, then both will be fully expressed. Hence, heterozygotes ($I^A I^B$) express both A and B antigens on their red blood cell surface. In the case of human ABO blood typing, there is also a third allele, *i*. The *i* allele is recessive and is completely masked by either the dominant $I^A$ or $I^B$ allele. The recessive trait (no expression of A or B antigen on their red blood cells) is observed only in homozygous recessive individuals (*ii*). Having **multiple alleles** (more than two different alleles for a gene) within a population means more varying combinations of genotypes and potentially even more variations in phenotype. This is illustrated in Figure 8.11, where the three alleles for ABO blood typing can result in six different possible genotypes and four different possible phenotypes. Which of these genotypes and phenotypes we express is dependent on which two alleles we inherit from our parents.

Mendel's first hypothesis states that the trait for each character is determined by a pair of hereditary factors. This suggests that the expression of each character trait is dictated by one gene only. Some traits, however, are determined by more than one gene and thus follow **polygenic inheritance.** Phenotype variations for characters dictated by polygenic inheritance may appear continuous (also termed **quantitative characters**) or as multiple but distinct forms. Height, weight, and skin colour are all examples of continuous phenotypic variations as a result of polygenic inheritance controlled by multiple genes. In addition, these characters may also be influenced by environmental factors. For example, skin colour can be altered by exposure to sunlight and weight can be altered by dieting conditions. Furthermore, the more genes and/or environmental factors that control the phenotype, the more continuous it is in variation. In populations, the continuous phenotype distribution pattern typically follows a bell-shaped curve **(Figure 8.12)**, with most individuals expressing the median (central or medium) phenotype. For many of Mendel's contemporaries who were studing inheritance, the mistake they unwittingly made was to study traits that were controlled by polygenic inheritance. Observations of these complex traits led people to suggest the blending hypothesis. Often the blending hypothesis did fit their data. Mendel's most impressive methodological breakthrough was his focus on clearly different traits that he could score as a yes or a no.

In another case of polygenic inheritance called **epistasis**, one gene plays a direct role on the expression of another gene. Epistasis is evident in the coat pigmentation of Labrador retrievers **(Figure 8.13)**. Coat colour is reflected by the amount of melanin pigment deposited in the hair of these animals. There are three phenotypes for coat colour: black, brown, and yellow. Phenotype expression is dictated by two different genes: the *B* gene, which codes for an enzyme involved in melanin production, and the *E* gene, which controls the deposition of melanin. In other words, the *B* gene controls how much melanin is produced in the hair,

and the *E* gene controls whether or not melanin will be deposited in the first place. As such, if the genotype for the *E* gene is homozygous recessive (*ee*), no melanin pigment is deposited (the phenotype is yellow fur) regardless of the genotype for the *B* gene. If the genotype for the *E* gene is either *EE* or *Ee*, only then will the product of the *B* gene alter the phenotype. Under these conditions, *BB* and *Bb* individuals will have black fur and *bb* individuals will have brown fur. Since expression of the *B* gene is dependent on the expression of the *E* gene, then it is said that the *E* gene is epistatic to the *B* gene. As a result of epistasis, phenotypic ratios of the $F_2$ generation of an $F_1$ dihybrid cross are 9:3:4 instead of the expected 9:3:3:1 observed in Mendel's experiments (Figure 8.13).

Another modification to Mendelian genetics is **pleiotropy**, which is described as one gene influencing multiple traits. In the example of cystic fibrosis, we focused on the effect of the mutated *CFTR* gene on mucus accumulation in the lungs, leading to respiratory infection. However, the mutated *CFTR* gene also affects mucus accumulation in the gastrointestinal tract, leading to digestive problems. As well, cystic fibrosis patients often suffer from type 2 diabetes due to pancreatic damage, osteoporosis due to poor uptake of vitamin D, and infertility due to decreased sperm flow in thickened secretions. Other examples of disorders caused by pleiotropy are phenylketonuria (PKU) and sickle cell disease. Phenylketonuria is caused by a mutation in the gene that en-codes for an enzyme that breaks down the amino acid phenylalanine. Individuals with PKU suffer from mental retardation, hair loss, and a reduction in skin pigmentation. Sickle cell disease is caused by a mutation in the hemoglobin beta gene, resulting in a loss of oxygen to cells and tissues. As a result, individuals with sickle cell disease suffer from a multitude of symptoms, including fatigue, abdominal pain, heart failure, pneumonia, and paralysis.

A. **Black labrador**  B. **Chocolate brown labrador**  C. **Yellow labrador**

D. **Black × yellow labrador cross**

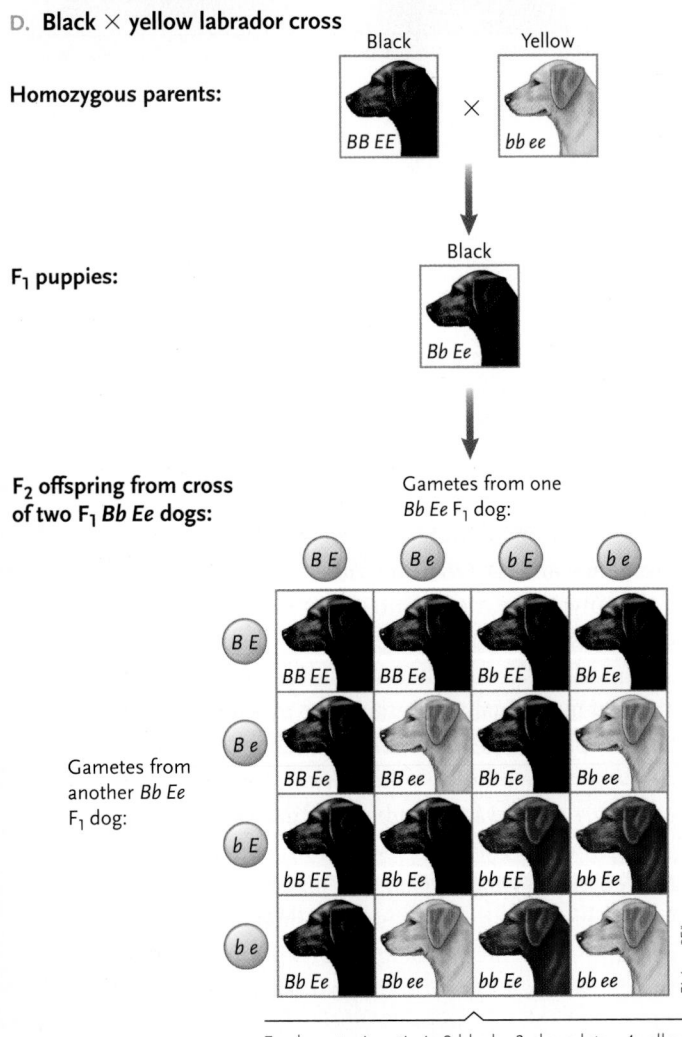

$F_2$ phenotypic ratio is 9 black : 3 chocolate : 4 yellow

**FIGURE 8.13** An example of epistasis: the inheritance of coat colour in Labrador retrievers.

## X-Linked Inheritance Pattern Is Associated with Gender

In mammals, the X and Y chromosomes are the two sex chromosomes that determine the gender or sex of the organism. However, these chromosomes also carry many genes that are not related to sexual traits. For example, the dystrophin gene, one of the longest human genes, is found on the X chromosome and is thus termed an **X-linked gene**. This gene encodes for the cytoplasmic protein dystrophin, which is part of a complex of proteins that connects the cytoskeleton of muscle fibres to the extracellular matrix across the plasma membrane of these cells. A deficiency in dystrophin is one of the leading causes of a group of muscle diseases called **muscular dystrophy**, a pathology that is characterized by a host of symptoms, including muscle fatigue, joint stiffness, and imbalance. Hence, muscular dystrophy is an example of pleiotropy. One of the most severe forms is Duchenne muscular dystrophy, which affects 1 in over 3000 people and has an early-onset age of less than 6 years old. By age 12, most affected individuals are wheelchair dependent, and the failure of cardiac muscle function is already evident. Indeed, many of these individuals will suffer an early death. Although the dystrophin gene itself does not encode for a sexual trait, its localization on the X chromosome makes muscular dystrophy, like other **X-linked recessive disorders**, more prevalent in males than in females. The reason is because in mammals, males have only one copy of the X chromosome (males also have one copy of the Y chromosome) and thus only one copy of the gene (most of the genes on the X chromosome are not present on the Y chromosome). As a result, only one copy of the recessive (mutated) allele is enough for the recessive (disease) trait to be expressed in males. Females, on the other hand, have two X chromosomes (and no Y chromosome), and as such, two recessive alleles are required to express the recessive trait. Heterozygotes do carry one copy of the recessive allele, but the recessive phenotype is masked by the dominant allele. Heterozygote females, therefore, are carriers of the recessive allele, although they do not express its phenotype.

Although the inheritance of X-linked genes follows Mendelian genetics, because males inherit only one X chromosome, the observed patterns of inheritance do not reflect those predicted by Mendel. Instead, inheritance patterns are sex dependent. Take, for example, red–green colour-blindness. This type of vision deficiency is the result of mutations in multiple genes found on the X chromosome. Individuals with red–green colour-blindness lack red and green retinal photoreceptors and therefore cannot distinguish between red and green hues. This vision deficiency is also more prevalent

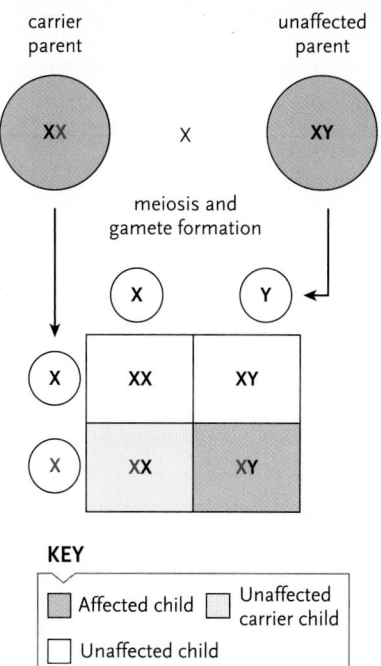

**FIGURE 8.14** X-linked recessive inheritance. Heterozygote females are carriers of the recessive alleles.

in males than in females. This X-linked recessive inheritance pattern is best illustrated in the Punnett square shown in **Figure 8.14**.

## Inheritance Pattern of Non-Nuclear Genes Is Not Traditional

Not all patterns of inheritance follow traditional Mendelian genetics. Indeed, non-nuclear genes, such as those found in mitochondria and chloroplasts, are primarily inherited from one parent (**uniparental inheritance**). During fertilization, the egg provides most of the cytoplasm, including organelles such as mitochondria and chloroplast, to the zygote (the sperm donates very little cytoplasm). Overall, offspring contain more maternal genes (total of nuclear plus non-nuclear) than paternal ones. Since these patterns of inheritance do not follow traditional Mendelian genetics, they are often classified as **non-Mendelian inheritance**.

Another form of inheritance that defies Mendelian genetics is **epigenetic inheritance**, where heritable changes in a gene's activity or function are not caused by alterations in actual DNA sequences. Instead, these heritable changes can result from DNA methylation of genes (the addition of a methyl group onto DNA nucleotides), modification of histone proteins that control chromosome structure, or even complete inactivation of the X chromosome in female mammals. In all cases, the actual nucleotide sequences of the genes are unaltered. Some epigenetic changes are initiated in response to environmental conditions. For example, some changes in the diet of mice can lead to epigenetic changes in the gene that affects fur colour, weight, and

## Epigenetics Is a Modern Twist to Traditional Genetics

If you've ever come across a calico cat **(Figure 1)**, you can almost be certain that it is a female and heterozygous for the O gene (*Oo*) that determines the trait for fur colour. The patches you see are some cells expressing the dominant allele

**FIGURE 1** A calico cat.

Sari ONeal/Shutterstock.com

(orange fur) and others expressing the recessive allele (black fur). The reason is due to the fact that in female mammals, one of the two X chromosomes within each cell is inactivated to compensate for males having only one X chromosome. Which of the two X chromosomes is inactivated is random in each cell, so if a female is heterozygous for a particular character, such as fur colour in cats, then a patchy appearance in phenotype will result. The X chromosome inactivation is due to epigenetic changes, a change in the activity of genes that is not caused by a change in the actual nucleotide sequence. The epigenetic changes include methylation of nucleotides on the X chromosomes and deacetylation of the histone proteins that control

chromosome structure. Both of these events cause the X chromosome to condense and render most of the X-linked genes inactive. These epigenetic changes occur during embryo development and are inherited by all cells generated from these embryonic cells. Typically, these epigenetic changes are cleared from the cells that produce gametes so that these changes are not inherited; however, if they are not removed then these changes will be inherited by the next generation. This is called epigenetic inheritance.

Epigenetic inheritance, a modern field of genetics, is growing in interest due to its association with many fields of biology, including developmental, evolutionary, and even cancer biology. Heritable changes to the genome without a change in

even the susceptibility of developing certain cancers. Theoretically, these epigenetic changes should be removed from the genome during the reprogramming stage of gamete formation. However, if these changes escape elimination, they can be passed on from parent to offspring, thus creating a non-traditional pattern of inheritance pattern (read more about the field of epigenetics in Box 8.3).

### STUDY BREAK

1. Explain how incomplete dominance does not support the blending theory of inheritance.
2. Explain how codominance and multiple alleles influence the inheritance pattern of ABO blood typing.
3. Explain the ratio 9:3:4 in the $F_2$ generation in the case of epistasis.
4. Why are X-linked inherited disorders more prevalent in males than in females?
5. Give two examples of non-traditional Mendelian inheritance patterns.

## 8.3 Genetic Linkage Challenges the Law of Independent Assortment

Mendel's fourth hypothesis and the results from his dihybrid crosses were the basis for his law of independent assortment. But remember that Mendel's studies

were conducted at a time when scientists were unaware of genes, DNA, and chromosomes. In fact, it wasn't until the early 1900s that a scientist named Walter Sutton discovered that the hereditary factors Mendel described in his studies behaved very similarly to chromosomes during meiosis and gamete formation. Today, we understand that Mendel's law of independent assortment applies to the independent separation of pairs homologous chromosomes during meiosis I (see Chapter 7 for a review). Because we inherit entire chromosomes and not just bits and pieces of them, genes that are arranged on the same chromosome are inherited together. Thus, genes on the same chromosome are not assorted independently of each other during gamete formation but instead are distributed together into the same gamete. In other words, they are genetically linked. Mendel was unable to observe **genetic linkage** in his garden pea experiments because the hereditary factors for the seven characters he studied were arranged on different chromosomes (with the exception of two genes) and therefore not genetically linked to one another. Genetic linkage was first described by British biologists, William Bateson and Reginald Punnett (for whom the Punnett square was named), in the early 1900s. They performed dihybrid crosses in sweet pea (*Lathyrus odoratus*), testing two separate characters, flower colour and pollen shape. In sweet pea, unlike the garden pea, the dominant flower colour is purple (expressed by the dominant allele *P*)

nucleotide sequences have been shown to regulate certain developmental mechanisms in organisms. And since they can be heritable, they may also influence the evolutionary process. In addition, these changes do not follow predicted Mendelian genetics. As such, many scientists are now curious as to which environmental conditions trigger these heritable changes and under which circumstances they are passed on to the next generation. Indeed, many geneticists are now becoming specialized epigeneticists.

This new and exciting field is even attracting many scholars outside the field of biology. Take, for example, Richard Tremblay, a University of Montreal psychologist. For the past 30 years, he has studied kindergarten children from impoverished neighbourhoods in the eastern parts of Montreal who display severe, aggressive behavioural problems. His research shows that with early intervention, these children's behaviour could be curtailed, thus limiting their susceptibility to an adult life of criminal activity. What makes his research novel is that he is linking these effects to molecular changes in gene expression through epigenetics. In collaboration with scientists at McGill University in Montreal and the U.S. National Institutes of Health, Tremblay is searching to uncover the epigenetic changes that occur early in development that may influence both health and behaviours in adults. The link between behaviour and biology has been investigated in other highly evolved organisms. The first primate study indeed found DNA methylation differences between nurtured monkeys versus those who were separated from their mothers. These epigenetic changes also appeared to remain stable for years, thus ruling them out as spontaneously random events. Tremblay and his colleagues also report methylation differences between aggressive individuals in their studies versus those who have had a normal development. However, the mechanisms and significance of epigenetic changes in human are far from simple. Nonetheless, this type of research may provide these children with the potential for a better adult life, generation after generation.

and the recessive is red (expressed by the recessive allele *p*), whereas the dominant pollen shape is long grains (expressed by the dominant allele *L*) and the recessive is short (expressed by the recessive allele *l*). The results of the dihybrid cross (*PpLl* × *PpLl*) **(Figure 8.15)**, however, did not follow Mendel's predicted 9:3:3:1 phenotype ratio for the F₂ generation (Figure 8.7). Instead, most of the F₂ generation (almost 75%) had phenotypes that were similar to the heterozygote parents, a purple flower and long-grain pollen. Only 14% of the F₂ generation exhibited the recessive phenotypes (a red flower and short-grain pollen), and even fewer percentages exhibited the other combinations (a red flower and long-grain pollen and a purple flower and short-grain pollen). These results did not support the law of independent assortment but instead indicated that these genes were linked to one another. It is now known that the genes that determine these two separate characters are indeed located on the same chromosome and thus are often inherited together.

## Recombination Frequencies Determine the Degree of Genetic Linkage

Can genes that are linked to one another on the same chromosome ever be separated? Recall in the example of the sweet pea that some individuals in the F₂ generation did have a phenotype combination not observed in the parent generations (a red flower and long-grain

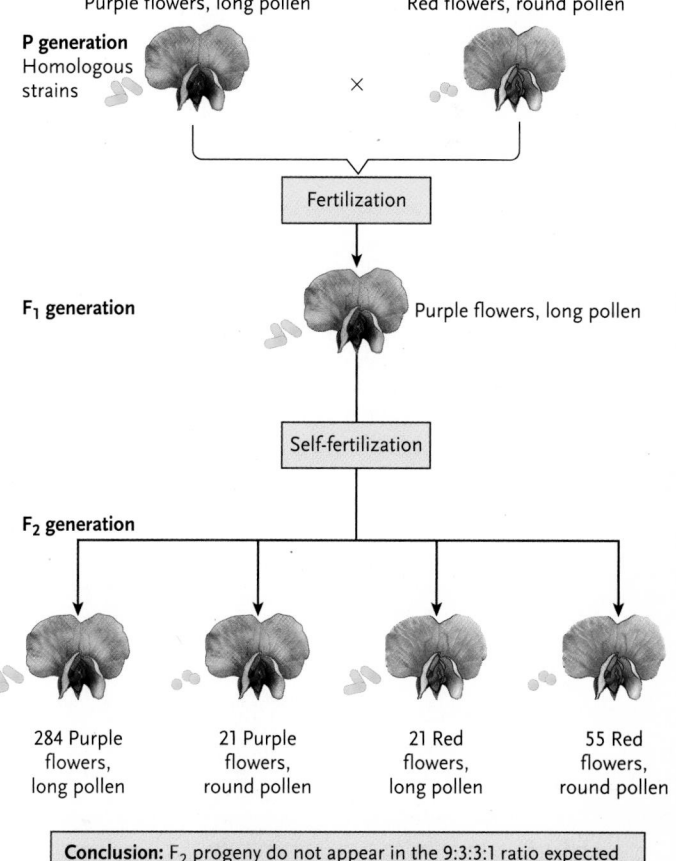

**FIGURE 8.15** Genetic linkage. Dihybrid crosses in sweet pea reveal ratios in the F₂ generation that do not follow Mendel's predicted 9:3:3:1.

pollen and a purple flower and short-grain pollen). These observed phenotype combinations would suggest that the two genes that determine the traits for these characters are not completely linked to one another. Indeed, there is a mechanism to break the linkage between two genes on the same chromosome. Remember from Chapter 7 that during prophase I of meiosis I, there are crossing-over events that occur between homologous chromosomes that may result in the rearrangement of alleles on the participating chromosomes. In the sweet pea example, the combination of *PL* on one chromosome and *pl* on the other homologous chromosome in the $F_1$ dihybrid cross can be switched to *Pl* and *pL* as a result of crossing over occurring. These new allele combinations can then be passed onto the gametes and reflected in the offspring following fertilization **(Figure 8.16)**. The **recombination frequency** or, in other words, the chance of a crossing-over event occurring between two different alleles on the same chromosome is dependent on how far apart they are located on the chromosome. The more physical distance between two alleles on a chromosome, the more likely

it is that crossing over will occur between them. Thus, the degree of genetic linkage between two genes on the same chromosome is inversely correlated to their physical distance. This will be reflected in the phenotypic ratios from the dihybrid crosses.

## STUDY BREAK

1. Explain why the $F_2$ dihybrid cross on the sweet pea example did not follow Mendel's law of independent assortment.
2. How can genetic linkage between two genes be unlinked?
3. How can one determine the degree of genetic linkage between two genes?

## 8.4 Genetic Screening and Counselling Can Be Used in Family Planning

Advances in DNA technology, including genetic testing, have allowed parents today to know more about their children, even prior to their birth, than ever before. These advances have even given some parents a sneak peek into the future of potential offspring. Consequently, individuals are able to make more informed decisions concerning family planning. At the same time, these advances have raised many ethical concerns regarding disclosure of personal information and genetic discrimination, issues that have many social implications.

The basis for genetic testing is dependent on the pattern of inheritance for any given character. To better understand human inheritance, researchers graph family phenotype and genotype data on standardized charts called **pedigrees**. These pedigrees illustrate genetic connections between family members and can be used to determine whether certain traits are dominant or recessive and/or autosomal or X-linked. This type of analysis can then be used to determine the probabilities of these traits showing up in future offspring and can also be applied to whole human populations. For example, a pedigree for hemophilia for the family of Queen Victoria of England is shown in **Figure 8.17**. Hemophilia is an X-linked disorder that causes affected individuals to bleed uncontrollably (hemorrhage) upon injury due to a defect in the blood-clotting proteins factor VIII (hemophilia A) and factor IX (hemophilia B). The genes for these proteins are located on the X chromosome. Thus, males need only one mutated (recessive) allele for either of these genes to exhibit the disease, whereas females need two mutated alleles. A pedigree is used to determine the pattern of inheritance of the mutated allele among family members. A pedigree also helps distinguish females who are

**A.** Here we focus on only two of the many genes on a chromosome. In this example, one gene has alleles *P* and *p*; the other has alleles *L* and *l*.

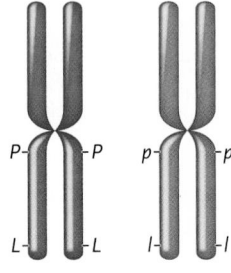

**B.** Close contact between homologous chromosomes promotes crossing over between nonsister chromatids. Paternal and maternal chromatids exchange corresponding pieces.

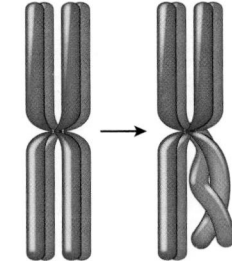

**C.** Crossing over mixes up paternal and maternal alleles on homologous chromosomes.

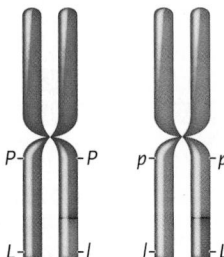

**FIGURE 8.16** Crossing over. Diagram illustrating how different alleles found on the same chromosome can become unlinked from each other by crossing over events between homologous pairs of chromosomes.

SOURCE: From Starr. *Biology*, 8E. © 2011 Brooks/Cole, a part of Cengage Learning, Inc. Reproduced by permission.www.cengage.com/permissions

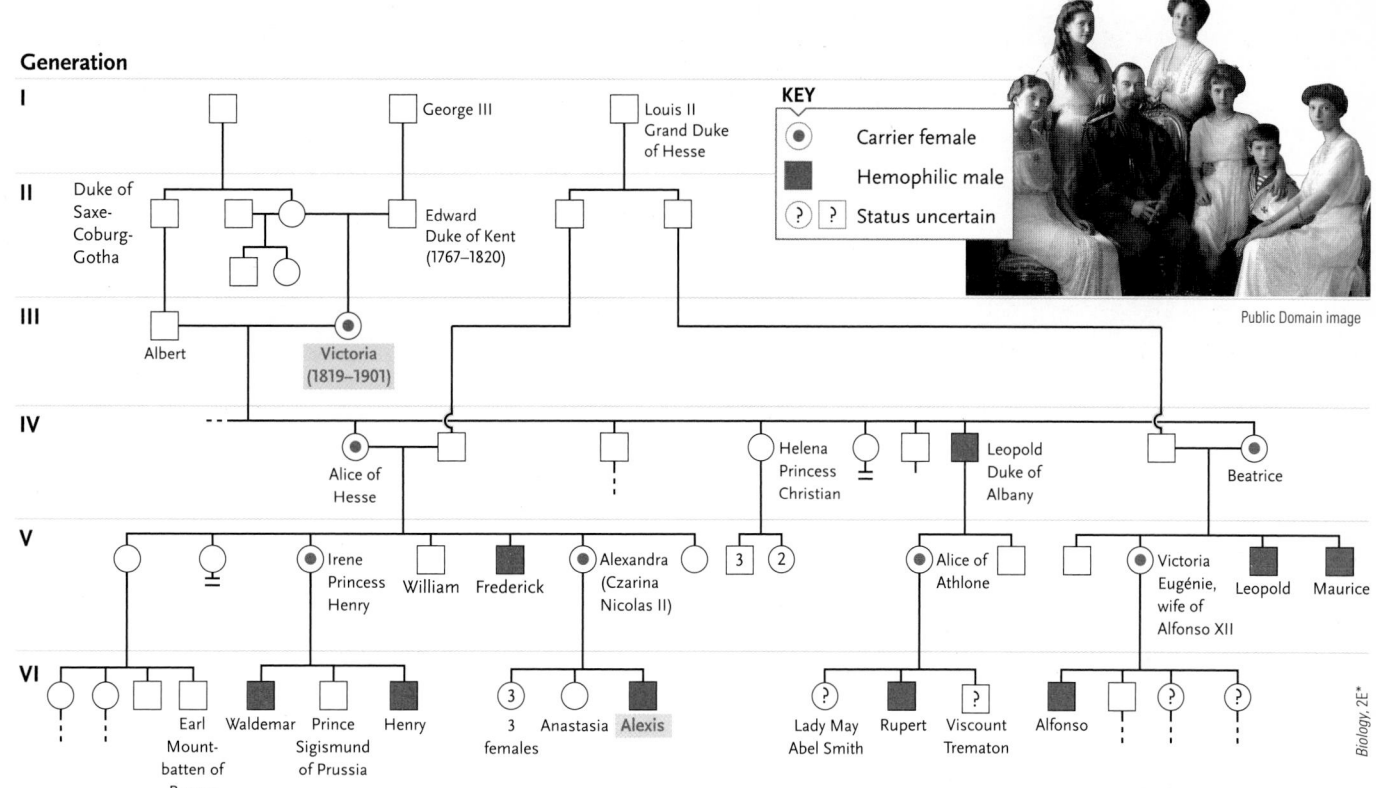

**FIGURE 8.17** A classic case of X-linked recessive inheritance: a partial pedigree of the descendants of Queen Victoria of England. At one time, the recessive X-linked allele that resulted in hemophilia was present in 18 of Victoria's 69 descendants, who sometimes intermarried. Of the Russian royal family members shown, the mother (Alexandra, Czarina Nicolas II) was a carrier.

homozygous dominant versus those who are carriers of the mutated allele.

Although Queen Victoria did not suffer from hemophilia, she was indeed a carrier (for the mutated gene that encodes for clotting factor IX). As such, she unknowingly passed the mutated allele on to three of her children, two daughters and a son. As a result, her son developed hemophilia and died at the age of 30, whereas her daughters were carriers (they received a dominant normal allele from their father). Further analysis of the family tree also suggests that the allele mutated spontaneously in Queen Victoria because there is no solid evidence of its presence in her ancestors.

Inheritance of the X-linked mutated allele, however, was prominently featured in European royalty in the 19th and 20th centuries, and as such, it is sometimes referred to as the "royal disease." Today, with advances in the treatment and management of hemophilia, the life expectancy is 50 to 60 years of age. In 2011, a team of British and American scientists reported that they had treated a group of patients with hemophilia B using a virus-based mechanism of gene therapy. In this treatment, a virus was used to replace the mutated allele for the gene that encodes factor IX with the normal allele. A follow-up in 2013 reported that treated individuals were still producing the normal factor IX clotting protein.

Without a family history of a particular disorder, most parents may simply rely on prenatal (before birth) testing during the course of the pregnancy. Testing can occur on the embryo (before 8 weeks following fertilization) **(Figure 8.18a, p. 192)** or the fetus (after 8 weeks following fertilization) **(Figure 8.18b)**. In the case of IVF, genetic testing will occur prior to implantation of the embryo into the uterus.

After implantation, prenatal genetic screening requires physicians to obtain cells of the embryo or fetus so that they can test for genetic mutations. But acquiring these cells is not a simple task, and as such, there are risks involved. One way to obtain cells is through a process called **amniocentesis (Figure 8.19, p. 192)**. This procedure involves drawing amniotic fluid from the amniotic sac where the fetus is enclosed within the uterus. This fluid contains cells that have shed off the fetus and thus can be used for genetic testing. Amniocentesis is not, however, without risk. The puncturing of the amniotic sac may result in leakage of the amniotic fluid, which is vital to the life of the fetus. Failure to repair this damage may result in a miscarriage.

An alternative method called **chorionic villus sampling** (CVS) is a process in which the cells of the chorion are obtained and used for genetic testing. The chorion is a membrane that surrounds the amniotic sac and will

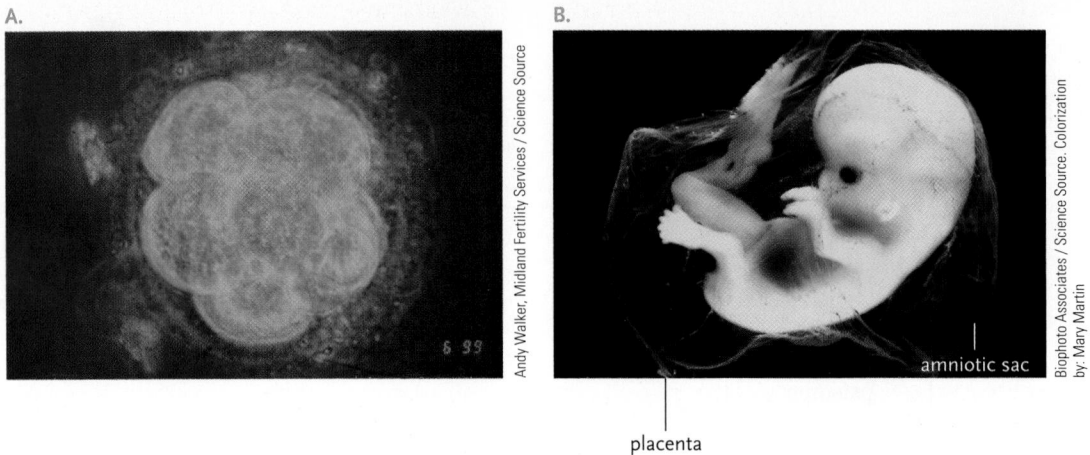

**FIGURE 8.18** **(a)** An embryo after three mitotic divisions. **(b)** An 8 week-old fetus. With amniocentesis, fetal cells shed into the fluid inside the amniotic sac are tested for genetic disorders.

help form the placenta, an organ that is developed during pregnancy and used to exchange nutrients, gases, and waste between mother and fetus. Since the cells of the chorion originate from the fetus itself, they are genetically identical to the fetus and therefore can be used in prenatal genetic screening. There is also risk associated with CVS. Damage to the chorion may lead to improper formation of the placenta, which in turn may lead to developmental abnormalities in the fetus.

Genetic counselling is also an important component of any genetic screen, whether it is performed on parents, their children, and/or close family relatives.

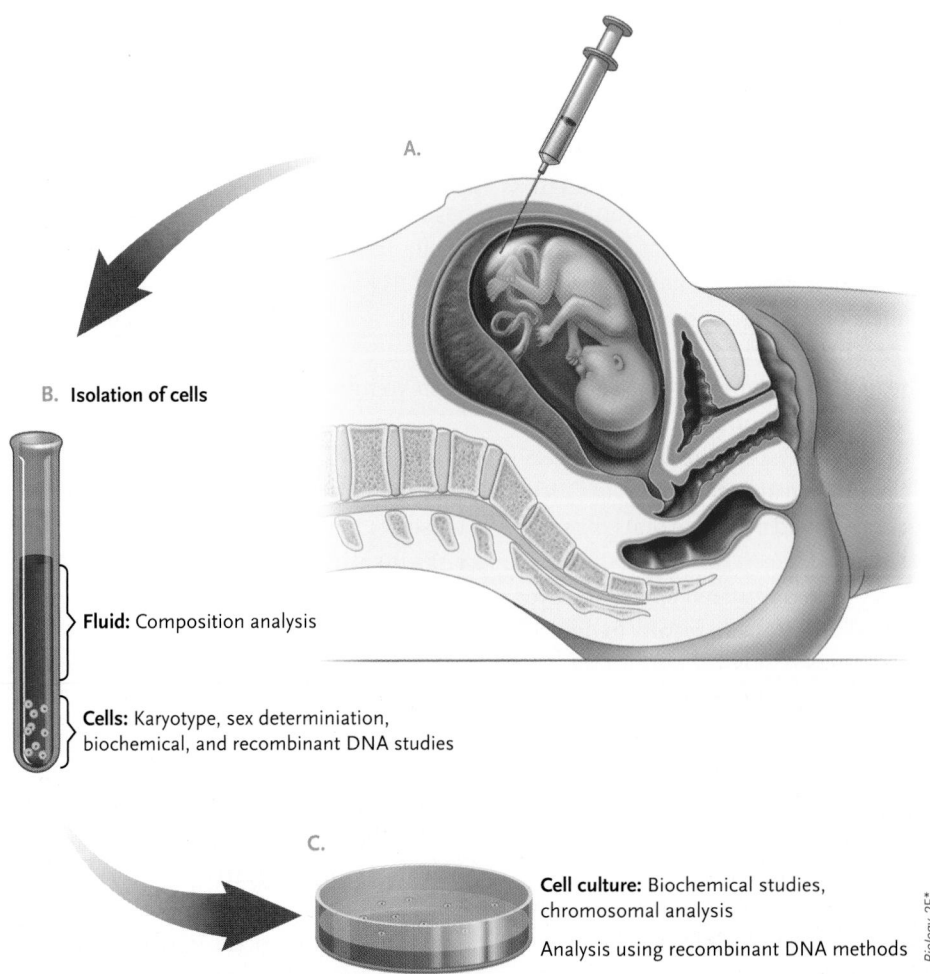

**FIGURE 8.19** Amniocentesis. This invasive procedure removes fetal cells from the amniotic fluid for genetic testing.

Genetic counsellors are trained individuals with a master of science degree in genetic counselling who have expertise in the analysis and interpretation of genetic testing and inherited disorders. These trained individuals may also provide psychosocial support to individuals and their families. Based on the genetic screens and family pedigrees, they can also make predictions of the probability of current and future offspring having certain genetic disorders and provide options for the management of family planning. This information is then used in collaboration with a physician's guidance so that individuals can make better informed decisions regarding their affected children and/or future pregnancies.

## STUDY BREAK

1. What types of information can pedigrees provide?
2. Explain the difference between amniocentesis and chorionic villus sampling.

## PUTTING IT IN PERSPECTIVE

We are all the result of a unique combination of heritable traits that we received from our parents. The process of this inheritance is both complex and fascinating. Any deviation or alteration in the transfer of this genetic material influences our identity and even our existence. Some changes turn out to be advantageous and favourable for continued inheritance, whereas others are undesirable and potentially lethal. The mixing and sharing of these heritable factors are also the lifeline for the continued existence our species. Using the garden pea, Gregor Mendel opened the door to the study of genetics, an ever-growing field of biology that has seen more twists and turns than DNA itself.

## KEY CONCEPTS REVIEW AND QUESTIONS

### 8.1 Mendel's Hypotheses Ignited the Field of Genetics

Gregor Mendel proposed four hypotheses that he used to make predictions about inheritance. He tested these hypotheses using the garden pea, and from his results, he developed the law of segregation and the law of independent assortment. Mendel's studies initiated the field of genetics and have been used to explain the patterns of inheritance.

1. The $F_1$ generation offspring of the cross BB × bb are _____.
   a. All BB
   b. All bb
   c. All Bb
   d. Half BB and half bb

2. An individual has sets of alleles *Dd* and *Ee* that assort independently. Which of the following are genotypes of gametes that will be produced by this individual?
   a. DE
   b. De
   c. dE
   d. de
   e. All of the above

3. What is the expected genotype ratio in the $F_2$ generation to support independent assortment between two genes?
   a. 1:0
   b. 3:1
   c. 9:3:3:1
   d. 1:1:1:1

### 8.2 The Modes of Inheritance Can Vary

There are many forms of inheritance that follow Mendelian genetics yet provide outcomes that differ from Mendel's predicted phenotype ratios. These include autosomal dominant and recessive inheritance, incomplete dominance, codominance, and X-linked inheritance. In addition, there are modes of inheritance that completely defy Mendelian genetic and thus exhibit unique inheritance patterns.

4. A gene that affects more than one trait is _____.
   a. Codominant
   b. Epistatic
   c. Recessive
   d. Pleiotropic
   e. Polygenic

5. A ratio of 9:3:4 in the $F_2$ generation of an $F_1$ dihybrid cross would likely indicate _____ between the two genes.
   a. Incomplete dominance
   b. Codominance
   c. Epistasis
   d. Pleiotropy
   e. Complete dominance

6. A phenotype ratio of 1:2:1 in the F$_2$ generation of an F$_1$ hybrid cross may indicate which of the following modes of inheritance?

   a. Codominance

   b. Incomplete dominance

   c. Epistasis

   d. Both codominance and incomplete dominance

   e. Both epistasis and codominance

7. Mitochondrial diseases are caused from mutations in mitochondrial genes. If an individual has a mutated mitochondrial gene, then he or she likely inherited this mutated gene from which family member?

   a. Mother

   b. Father

   c. Sister

   d. Brother

### 8.3 Genetic Linkage Challenges the Law of Independent Assortment

Since chromosomes are inherited as whole structures, all alleles on the same chromosome are genetically linked and therefore may not follow Mendel's law of independent assortment. The degree of linkage between two genes is inversely correlated to the distance between them on a chromosome. Genes are unlinked by crossing-over events during meiosis I.

8. The recombination frequency between genes *A* and *B* is 25%. This means that the chances of recombination (crossing over) occurring between these two genes during meiosis I is _____.

   a. 25%

   b. 50%

   c. 75%

   d. 100%

9. Genes *A*, *B*, and *C* are all located in this order on the same chromosome. The recombination frequency between *A* and *B* is 30%, whereas the recombination frequency between *B* and *C* is 10%. Is the *B* gene located closer to the *A* gene or the *C* gene? Explain.

### 8.4 Genetic Screening and Counselling Can Be Used in Family Planning

Pedigrees are used to show the inheritance pattern of certain genes within a family. They can also be used to predict the probabilities of inheritance of future offspring. Amniocentesis and CVS are procedures used to obtain fetal cells or cells of the chorion, which can be genetically tested.

10. According to the pedigree below, does the phenotype shown in black indicate a pattern of inheritance that is autosomal dominant, autosomal recessive, or X-linked? Circles are female and squares are males.

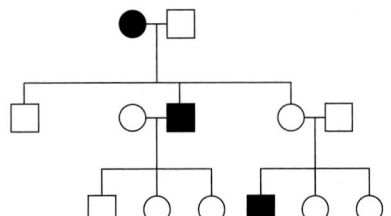

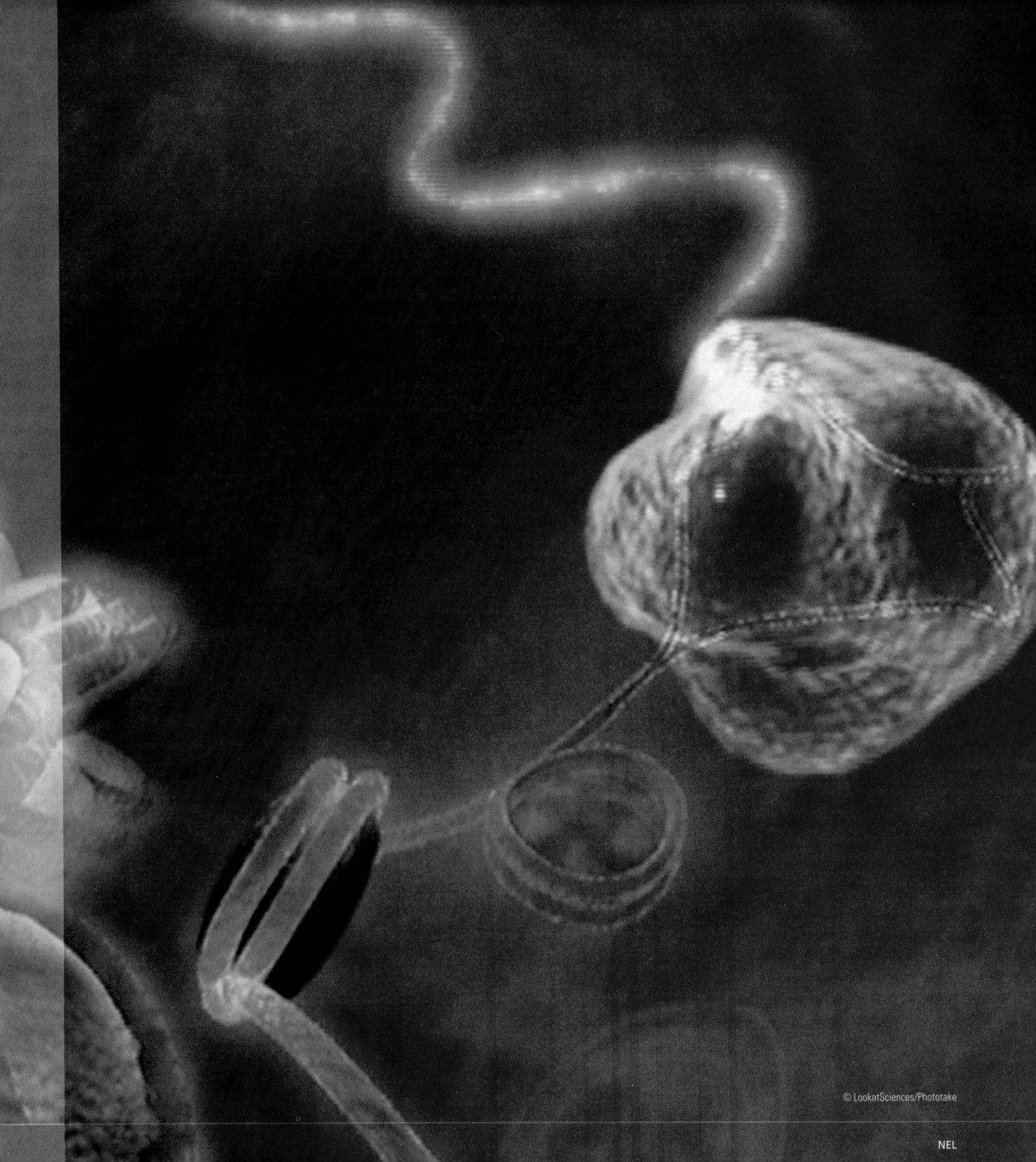

## WHY IT MATTERS

After a hot sunny day at the beach, you notice that your skin is a bit pink. It's a good thing you put on a lot of sunscreen or you would have a bad sunburn. The heat and inflammation caused by sunburn are the result of damage to the biomolecules in our skin cells.

As is true for any biological molecule or cellular component, DNA can be damaged by cellular metabolic processes or exposure to environmental factors. For example, exposure to sunlight is a frequent source of DNA damage. The nucleotide bases that compose the strands of DNA can absorb ultraviolet light from the Sun, leading to modification of the base, cross-linking between bases, and, in severe cases, breaks in the DNA strand. For DNA to be a stable source of information that can be passed on from generation to generation, such damage must be repairable. We see that organisms as simple and ancient as archaea and bacteria have complex systems for DNA repair. In fact, the organism that holds the record for being the most resistant to DNA damage is a bacterium called *Deinococcus radiodurans*. This small spherical organism can withstand a dose of radiation as high as 10,000 grays **(Figure 9.1)**. To put this in perspective, a common dental X-ray gives a dose of 0.005 grays, whereas a thoracic computed tomography (CT) scan will expose a patient to approximately 10 grays. A dose of over 30 grays is sufficient to kill humans in less than 48 hours. An incredibly tough organism, *D. radiodurans* was originally identified in 1956 after being cultured from canned meat that had been exposed to 4000 grays of radiation.

At the other extreme of DNA damage resistance are humans exhibiting the rare recessive genetic disorder xeroderma pigmentosum. These individuals lack one or more of the proteins needed to repair DNA damage caused by the ultraviolet component of sunlight, making them hypersensitive to sunburns. Because they are unable to repair damage to their DNA efficiently, xeroderma pigmentosum sufferers accumulate errors in the genes of their skin cells, and unless they take precautions to cover up and use sunscreens, they are highly prone to developing skin cancers. The average age at onset of non-melanoma skin cancers in xeroderma pigmentosum sufferers is 9 years. The average age at onset of non-melanoma skin cancers in the general Canadian population is 67 years. Studies on the effects and symptoms of xeroderma

**FIGURE 9.1** The extremes of sun sensitivity. On the right is a scanning electron micrograph of dividing *Deincoccus radiodurans* cells that are highly resistant to DNA damage. At the other extreme (left), a child who suffers from the rare genetic disorder xeroderma pigmentosum is extremely sensitive to sunburn. Researchers are trying to determine how this relatively simple bacterium can protect its genome from damage to help those affected by xeroderma pigmentosum lead more normal lives.

Yarruta/iStock/Thinkstock

Michael Daly

As we go through this chapter, we will examine a number of concepts about the DNA molecule, from the discovery by Griffith and Hershey and Chase that DNA can act as the inherited material, to Watson and Crick's deduction of its structure, to understanding that the critical importance of DNA to a cell's survival has led to the evolution of repair mechanisms. However, these findings only touch the surface of how DNA functions in a cell. When early biochemists were identifying and characterizing how important molecules function in organism physiology, they isolated chemicals such as hormones and then added them back to cells to see what happened. The next step was to chemically synthesize the hormone to double check that the response they were seeing was truly due to the hormone and not a secondary biological event. It was only when both sets of experiments were done together that the scientists felt confident in their knowledge of hormone biology.

Over the past decades, chemists and biochemists have developed chemical techniques to synthesize nucleotides and then strands of a DNA molecule. Today, it is a routine procedure to chemically synthesize a gene. One has simply to contact the appropriate molecular biology supply company; submit the sequence of A, T, C, and G's that you want; and then wait for the delivery of your DNA fragment. In 2010, a research team headed by Dr. Craig Venter, one of the key forces behind the Human Genome Project, used chemical and biochemical synthesis techniques to create the genome of a simple bacterium from its basic building blocks. Thus, these researchers created the blueprint of a living cell without the need for a cell. Just as the early biochemists studied hormone biology, Venter's group wanted to see if a bacterium could be created from the blueprint. Thus, in a chapter devoted to the structure, replication, and repair of DNA, it seems fitting to highlight a step humans have made toward creating life, using DNA as the starting point.

pigmentosum have been a key factor in our understanding of the relationship between sun exposure and skin cancer.

As research continues in the field of DNA damage and repair, a great question to ask is: what can we learn from the *D. radiodurans* bacteria to better understand the DNA repair system in human cells and thus reduce the rate of skin cancer? In the meantime, keep wearing your sunscreen.

## 9.1 DNA Structure

As we now pass the 60th anniversary of Francis Crick and James Watson's publication that first described the double helical structure of DNA, we take our knowledge and the research needed to characterize the structure and function of DNA for granted. In research labs around the world, students, technical specialists, and university professors isolate and manipulate DNA, seemingly at will. Taken to the extreme, in 2010, researchers working at the J. Craig Venter Institute synthesized the entire genome of a simple bacterium from scratch, beginning with only the basic nucleotide building blocks. (See Box 9.1 for a more detailed description of the Venter Institute's research.) It is also common for DNA to be used in criminal investigations where the identity of suspects may be in doubt or to legally determine paternity.

However, as with many areas of biology, it seems that just as we think we have figured things out, new experimental techniques and novel ways of thinking raise new questions. For example, although Watson and Crick's double helix model is 60 years old, researchers continue to discover new ways that the DNA molecule can fold inside cells. Small segments of DNA may have an extra level of structure, which we call a structural motif. For example, G-quadruplexes are a structural motif found in some guanine-rich regions DNA sequences. In these locations, a portion of the DNA molecule can fold back on itself to form four-stranded threads, which differs from the standard two-stranded double helix model of Watson and Crick. The G-quadruplexes may be required for cellular processes such as meiosis, chromosome stability, and perhaps even cell aging. We will begin this section by discussing the role of DNA as the hereditary material. Rather than a single "Ah ha!" moment, uncovering the role, structure, and function of DNA took many years and the work of a multitude of talented scientists. As we look at a few of the key moments and people, remember that it was the idea that DNA held the information to make us who we are that drove scientists such as Watson, Crick, and Linus Pauling to try to solve its structure.

### DNA Is the Hereditary Material

Given what we know now about DNA and heredity, it seems foreign to suggest that at one time DNA was not considered to be the hereditary material. In 1865, when

Gregor Mendel first presented his work on the laws of segregation and the particulate theory of genetics, no one knew how information was passed from generation to generation. As biology advanced through the end of the 19th century, Mendel's work was rediscovered and then duplicated by Hugo de Vries and Carl Correns. This led to heightened interest in the nature of the genetic particle postulated by Mendel. Initially, studies focused on the hypothesis that proteins formed the genetic material. Although this seems strange now, at the time, researchers thought that proteins were much more complex than DNA and would be able to store more information than nucleic acids. Some very elegant sets of experiments would change this outlook and demonstrate that DNA is the hereditary material.

In the 1920s, Frederick Griffith, a British medical officer working in the Pathology Laboratory at the Ministry of Health, was trying to develop a vaccine that could be used to protect people from exposure to *Streptococcus pneumoniae*, a bacterium that caused a particularly deadly form of pneumonia. Based on his medical experience, Griffith knew that inoculating animals with dead versions of bacteria could lead to the animals becoming immune to future exposures to those same bacteria (see Chapter 27 for a more detailed description of vaccines and the immune system). Griffith had been isolating bacteria from the mucus and lungs of pneumonia patients and comparing the various strains of bacteria. He found some strains to be more infectious and deadly than others. One thing he found in common among the strains of *S. pneumoniae* was that the ones that appear rough when grown on petri dishes were relatively benign and did not cause disease. These rough cells had no thick capsule surrounding the cell wall, making them more susceptible to the human immune system. The cells that appeared smooth when grown in a petri dish had a thick capsule and were much more deadly. Griffith used heat to kill the smooth cells and prepare a vaccine, mixed the dead smooth cells with a sample of live rough cells, and injected the mixture into mice. The mice died from a bacterial infection, and Griffith and his team were able to culture live smooth cells from the mouse's blood **(Figure 9.2)**. Griffith coined

**QUESTION:** What is the nature of the genetic material?

**EXPERIMENT:** Frederick Griffith studied the conversion of a nonvirulent (noninfective) *R* form of the bacterium *Streptococcus pneumoniae* to a virulent (infective) *S* form. The *S* form has a capsule surrounding the cell, giving colonies of it on a laboratory dish a smooth, shiny appearance. The *R* form has no capsule, so the colonies have a rough, nonshiny appearance. Griffith injected the bacteria into mice and determined how the mice were infected.

**1** Mice injected with live *S* cells (control to show effect of *S* cells)

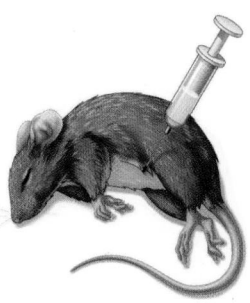

**RESULT:** Mice die. Live *S* cells in their blood; shows that *S* cells are virulent.

**2** Mice injected with live *R* cells (control to show effect of *R* cells)

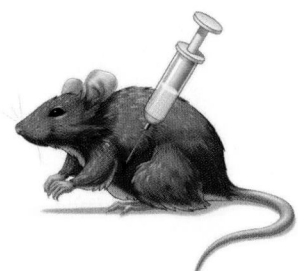

**RESULT:** Mice live. No live *R* cells in their blood; shows that *R* cells are nonvirulent. Evidently the capsule is responsible for virulence of the *S* strain.

**3** Mice injected with heat-killed *S* cells (control to show effect of dead *S* cells)

**RESULT:** Mice live. No live *S* cells in their blood; shows that live *S* cells are necessary to be virulent to mice.

**4** Mice injected with heat-killed *S* cells plus live *R* cells

Biology, 2E*

**RESULT:** Mice die. Live *S* cells in their blood; shows that living *R* cells can be converted to virulent *S* cells with some factor from dead *S* cells.

**CONCLUSION:** Griffith concluded that some molecules released when *S* cells were killed could change living nonvirulent *R* cells genetically to the virulent *S* form. He called the molecule the *transforming principle* and the process of genetic change *transformation*.

**FIGURE 9.2** In his search for a vaccine for *Streptococcus pneumoniae*, Frederick Griffith attempted to inoculate mice with a heat-killed strain of the bacteria. Although this type of vaccine is normally effective, he mixed a heat-killed strain that was particularly virulent with a live, non-infectious strain of *S. pneumoniae* and found that the non-infectious strain could be transformed into the deadly version of the bacterium.

the term *transformation* to describe this process. He suggested that genetic material from the dead smooth cells was taken up by the nonvirulent rough cells, turning the rough cells into a deadly form of the bacteria. Although Griffith's experiments did not identify the material that was transferred from one form of *S. pneumoniae* to the other, this work led to experiments that identified DNA as the hereditary material. The process of transformation and its role in horizontal gene transfer and the evolution of prokaryotes will be examined further in Chapter 15.

Scientific advances move forward in incremental steps. Illustrating this between 1933 and 1940, a team led by Oswald Avery, a Halifax, Nova Scotia–born researcher at the Rockefeller Institute for Medical Research, built on the results of Griffith's *S. pneumoniae* experiments. Avery's team initially questioned the interpretation of Griffith's data and set a goal to identify the component of the bacterial cell that was acting as the transforming principle in *S. pneumoniae*. Step by step, the Rockefeller researchers narrowed down the chemical responsible for transforming *S. pneumoniae*. First, it was narrowed down to a liquid solution isolated from the bacterial cells. Using this liquid as a starting material, Colin MacLeod and Maclyn McCarty worked for 7 years to carefully purify the transforming factor and then demonstrate that it was DNA and not protein.

Finally, in a truly elegant set of experiments, Alfred Hershey and Martha Chase, working at the Cold Spring Harbor Laboratory in New York in 1952, used several newly developing technologies to independently demonstrate that DNA is the heritable factor, not protein. Key among them was the use of radioactive isotopes. Following the Manhattan Project and the end of World War II, the production and use of radioactive isotopes greatly increased. Radioactive molecules were available from nuclear research centres. In Canada, the primary source of radioisotopes was the Chalk River National Laboratory located northwest of Ottawa. At its peak, Chalk River produced approximately one-third of the world's supply of the medical isotopes used in advanced imaging such as CT scans.

In their experiments, Hershey and Chase used sulphate that contained radioactive sulphur and phosphate that contained radioactive phosphorus to separately label protein (radioactive sulphur) and DNA (radioactive phosphorus). This gave the researchers a method that they could use to follow the transfer of protein and DNA from one location to another. Hershey and Chase used T2 phage, a bacterial virus, and the common lab bacteria *E. coli* as their model research organisms. T2 phage is composed of only protein and DNA. It infects *E. coli* by attaching to the bacterial cell membrane and injecting its hereditary material into the bacterium. Once the T2 phage's hereditary material is inside the cell, it is replicated by the bacterium, triggering production of new T2 phage inside the bacterium. When the bacterium fills beyond capacity, it bursts open and releases the phage into the growth medium. (Phage will be examined in more detail in Chapter 15.)

Hershey and Chase surmised that if the phage's hereditary material was composed of protein, phage labelled with radioactive sulphur would pass this radioactivity on to the bacteria and the next generation of phage. Alternatively, if the genetic material was composed of DNA, they expected to detect radioactive phosphorus in the bacteria and subsequent generations of phage. Finding that there was radioactive phosphorous in the *E. coli* and the next generation of T2 phage, Hershey and Chase concluded that the radioactive DNA was responsible for carrying the information needed for *E. coli* to produce new phage. Thus, DNA was the hereditary material. They clearly demonstrated that nucleic acids contain the information necessary to pass traits on from one generation to the next **(Figure 9.3)**.

## DNA Double Helix Model of DNA Structure

While the biological understanding of inheritance was progressing as described above, biochemists and physicists were advancing their understanding of the chemical nature of cells. Linus Pauling and his colleagues at the California Institute of Technology (Caltech) were attempting to determine the three-dimensional structure of proteins. In 1951, they determined the molecular structure of protein alpha-helices and beta-sheets and were the first to directly link a defective form of a protein (hemoglobin) with a human disease (sickle cell disease). Pauling was also in the race to determine the structure of DNA. As the race progressed in the early 1950s, scientists already knew that DNA was a polynucleotide chain composed of four different deoxyribose nucleotides. The individual subunits of DNA are constructed from a five-carbon sugar called deoxyribose **(Figure 9.4, p. 202)** and one of four different nitrogenous bases: adenine, cytosine, guanine, or **thymine**. (You can review the basic concepts of nucleic acids and nucleotide structure in the Purple Pages section.) When the two components are combined in the cell, they are called a nucleoside. To become part of a DNA molecule, the nucleosides must be phosphorylated, meaning that phosphorus must be added. Phosphorylated nucleosides are then called nucleotides. It is the nucleotide forms that are active in the cell and used to build DNA molecules.

In 1952, Erwin Chargaff, intrigued by Avery's findings, began studying the chemical makeup of DNA. He found that of the four different nucleotides that make up DNA, the amount of guanine was always equal to the amount of cytosine, and the amount of adenine was always equal to the amount of thymine. This finding, coined Chargaff's rule, was an essential piece of the puzzle that Watson and Crick needed to deduce the double helical structure of DNA. Watson and Crick knew that the purines (guanine and adenine) were larger than the pyrimidines (cytosine and thymine) (Figure 9.4). Chargaff's findings suggested to them that the guanines and cytosines would be found together and the adenosines and thymines would be found together. This concept

**QUESTION:** Is DNA or protein the genetic material?

**EXPERIMENT:** Hershey and Chase performed a definitive experiment to show whether DNA or protein is the genetic material. They used phage T2 for their experiment; it consists only of DNA and protein.

**1** They infected *E. coli* growing in the presence of radioactive $^{32}P$ or $^{35}S$ with phage T2. The progeny phages were either labelled in their protein with $^{35}S$ (top) or in their DNA with $^{32}P$ (bottom).

**2** Separate cultures of *E. coli* were infected with the radioactively labelled phages.

**3** After a short period of time to allow the genetic material to enter the bacterial cell, the bacteria were mixed in a blender. The blending sheared from the cell surface the phage coats that did not enter the bacteria. The components were analyzed for radioactivity.

**4** Progeny phages analyzed for radioactivity.

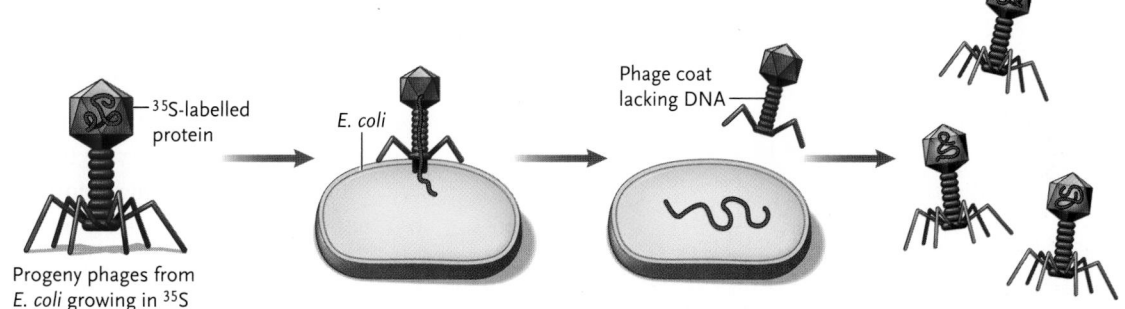

$^{35}S$-labelled protein

Progeny phages from *E. coli* growing in $^{35}S$

*E. coli*

Phage coat lacking DNA

**RESULT:** No radioactivity within cell; $^{35}S$ in phage coat.

**RESULT:** No radioactivity in progeny phages.

$^{32}P$-labelled DNA

Progeny phages from *E. coli* growing in $^{32}P$

*E. coli*

Phage coat lacking DNA

**RESULT:** $^{32}P$ within cell; not in phage coat.

**RESULT:** $^{32}P$ in progeny phages.

*Biology, 2E*

**CONCLUSION:** $^{32}P$, the isotope used to label DNA, was found within phage-infected cells and in progeny phages, indicating that DNA is the genetic material. $^{35}S$, the radioisotope used to label proteins, was found in phage coats after infection but was not found in the infected cell or in progeny phages, showing that protein is not the genetic material.

**FIGURE 9.3** Alfred Hershey and Martha Chase used what was known about proteins and DNA to determine which type of molecule was the hereditary factor. Because proteins contain very little phosphorus and DNA contains no sulphur, they could follow the movement of the phage components. It was an ingenious way to track and identify the heritable component of the phage.

was a key factor that Watson and Crick used to build and validate their model. Because a purine is always paired with a pyrimidine, the two strands of the DNA molecule are the same distance apart at every point in the molecule.

As we can see, Watson and Crick's double helix model of DNA structure built on the work of many other researchers. However, the most important piece of information that Watson and Crick had at their disposal, and Linus Pauling did not, came from the X-ray crystallography images of DNA taken by Dr. Rosalind Franklin, a biophysicist working at King's College London. Using partially purified DNA, Franklin and Maurice Wilkins, also a biophysicist, bombarded the sample with X-rays—a

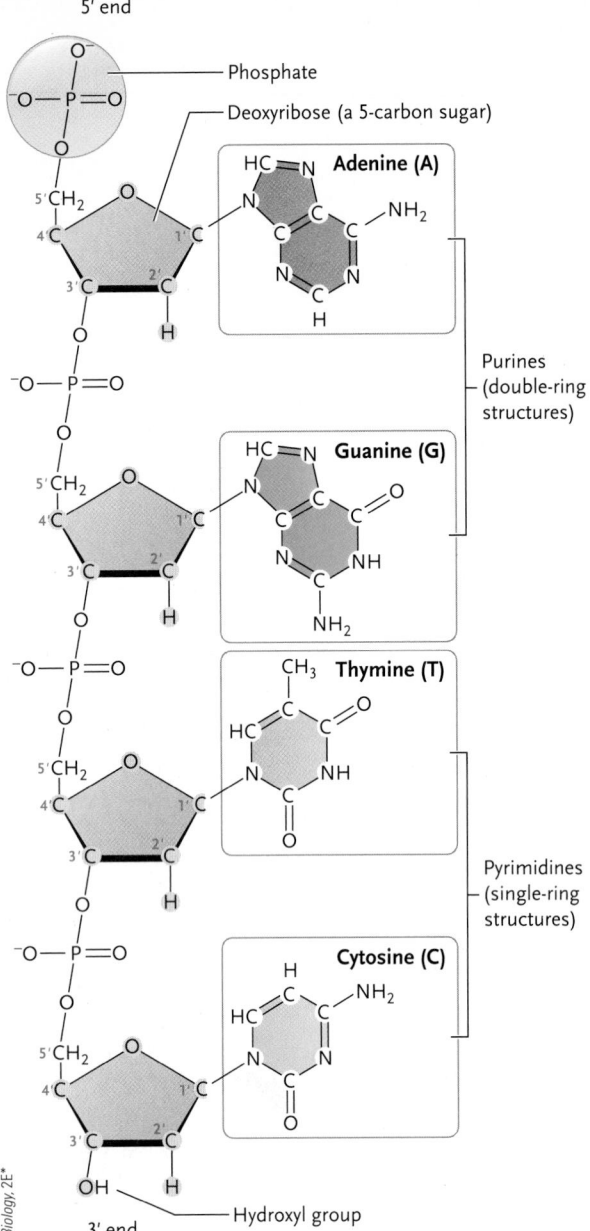

5' end

Phosphate

Deoxyribose (a 5-carbon sugar)

Adenine (A)

Guanine (G)

Thymine (T)

Cytosine (C)

Purines (double-ring structures)

Pyrimidines (single-ring structures)

Hydroxyl group

3' end

Biology, 2E*

**FIGURE 9.4** A single strand of DNA is composed of a repeating chain of individual nucleotides, joined together via their deoxyribose sugars through phosphate bonds. In a long DNA molecule, the ratios of the different nucleotides vary from section to section.

technique called **X-ray crystallography**. Molecules diffract X-rays in a pattern that depends on the molecule's atomic structure **(Figure 9.5)**. Although X-ray crystallography can now be used to determine the exact structure of biomolecules such as nucleic acids and proteins, the impure nature of the DNA sample used by Wilkins and Franklin and the limited computing power available at the time meant that they could only suggest that DNA had a helical structure. Based on her images, Franklin also deduced that the sugar–phosphate backbones were on the exterior of the DNA molecule.

The final breakthrough by Watson and Crick came from "playing around" with models of what they thought DNA should look like based on the initial X-ray crystallography data and the physics of chemical bonding. They spent over 2 years trying to arrange the atoms in their models into a structure that would fit the data as it was being discovered, incorporating both Chargaff's rule and Franklin's X-ray data.

## Finally, a Structure for the DNA Molecule

Watson and Crick's final model of the DNA molecule, published in 1953, shows that DNA is formed of two linear strands travelling in opposite directions, much like the opposing lanes of a highway. The two strands are held together by hydrogen bonds that form between the A-T and G-C pairings. This moves the sugar–phosphate backbone to the outsides of the structure, as was suggested by Franklin **(Figure 9.6, p. 204)**. Overall, the molecule is held in a rigid, repetitive structure, not only by the hydrogen bonds between the purines and pyrimidines in the opposing strands but also by hydrogen bonds between the phosphate molecules and the van der Waals forces— the stickiness between atoms—that exist between the stacks of relatively flat nucleotide bases.

Although Watson and Crick's model has held up to the test of time, it has been modified a little over the past 60 years. The structure deduced by Watson and Crick is now termed the B-form. Two other forms (A and Z) are also thought to be biologically relevant. Biophysical modelling tells us that many different structural models are possible for the DNA double helix; however, it is not clear under what circumstances each form may exist in a cell. Many of the structural refinements on Watson and Crick's model are due to the more complete understanding of the environment inside of a cell's nucleus. Remember that Watson and Crick's model was based in part on the X-ray crystallography images of Wilkins and Franklin, and those images were made of partially purified DNA.

James Watson, Francis Crick, and Maurice Wilkins shared the Nobel Prize for Physiology and Medicine in 1962 "for their discoveries concerning the molecular structure of nucleic acids and its significance for information transfer in living material." In a cruel twist of fate, Rosalind Franklin died of ovarian cancer in 1958 and was not eligible for a share of the Nobel Prize as it is not awarded posthumously. That being said, there was considerable controversy surrounding the recognition that Franklin received for her role in deducing the final structural model of DNA. Many people today feel that she should have received more formal recognition for her X-ray crystallography work.

Franklin's DNA diffraction pattern

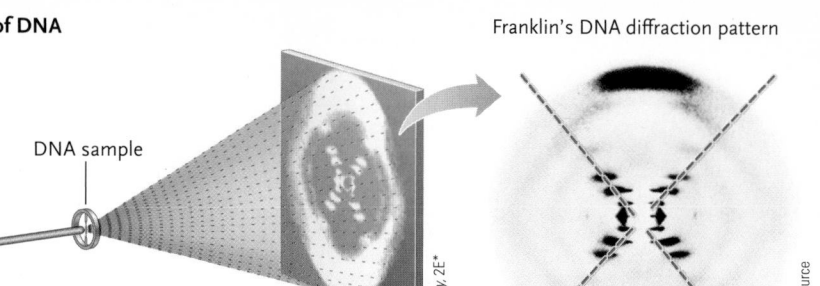

X-ray source

DNA sample

Beam of X-rays

Photographic plate

*Biology, 2E\**

Science Source

Science Source

**FIGURE 9.5** The X-ray crystallography images taken by Dr. Rosalind Franklin **(a)** became part of the scientific evidence that Watson and Crick used to construct their double helical model of the structure of DNA. When Franklin passed a beam of X-rays through a partially purified sample of DNA fibres and onto photographic film, she observed a distinctive X-shaped pattern of dots **(b)**. This pattern of dots strongly suggested a helical structure for the DNA molecule.

## The Structure of DNA inside a Cell

Figuring out the basic structure of the DNA molecule was complicated, in part because of how it is packaged in the cell. Inside the nucleus of a cell, the DNA strands are not naked and free floating. Instead, they are wound around proteins called histones and packaged into chromosomes.

### Prokaryotic Nucleoids

The difference in complexity between prokaryotes and eukaryotes can also be seen at the level at which they store their DNA. Prokaryotes generally have single circular chromosomes, ranging in size from 0.58 Mb (1 Mb is a megabase or 1 million nucleotides) in the bacterium *Mycoplasma genitalium* to 4.6 Mb in the common laboratory strain of *E. coli* to 10.2 Mb in *Amycolatopsis mediterranei*, an industrially important bacterium used to produce the antibiotic rifamycin. Based on Watson and Crick's model, a DNA strand with 4.6 million base pairs would be 1.5 mm in length. Of course, this is much larger than a typical prokaryotic cell, so a form of packaging or storage must have evolved to contain the DNA. Most prokaryotes have a single circular chromosome, which is twisted into a tight coil in the cell. This keeps the chromosome in the smallest package possible. However, because the prokaryotic chromosome is packaged this way, it does require some other specialized cellular machinery for replication, cell division, and reading the genes that are on the chromosome. We will examine how genes are read from chromosomes in the next chapter, when we explore the process of transcription.

### Eukaryotic Chromosomes

As we expect, eukaryotic chromosomes are much more complex than those of prokaryotes. They are longer—

often in the range of billions of nucleotides range—and linear. For example, the human genome is over 3 Gb (gigabases); stretched out like a string, it would be almost 10 cm long! Chromosome 1 alone is over 250 Mb (megabases, equivalent to 8.3 mm in length), and it is only one of 46 chromosomes found in the nucleus of a human cell. To fit these long chromosomes in the relatively small nucleus, eukaryotic cells use a set of proteins called histones. DNA is wound around histones in a fashion similar to winding thread on spools. The initial structures formed as DNA is wound onto histones are called nucleosomes. As we can see in **Figure 9.7** on p. 205, nucleosomes are large enough to be seen using electron microscopy. In fact, they have been described as "beads on a string," with individual nucleosomes connected by stretches of DNA called linkers. In the nucleosome, the DNA strand circles the histone core 1.67 times, and by doing this, it compacts the DNA strand. However, this is just the first step of the compaction process. The nucleosomes are then collected together to form a 30 nm diameter fibre called a solenoid. The solenoid has approximately six nucleosomes per turn. This compacts the strand even more, reducing its length even further (Figure 9.7).

Packaging of the DNA strand into a solenoid using histones not only compacts the DNA so that it can fit into the nucleus but also protects the DNA from physical and chemical damage. The DNA and proteins packed together in the physiological form found in the cell is called chromatin.

### Chromatin Packaging and Possible Roles in Gene Expression

Recent research has identified the packaging of DNA as an important factor in regulating how and when the information stored in the DNA as genes is used in the cell.

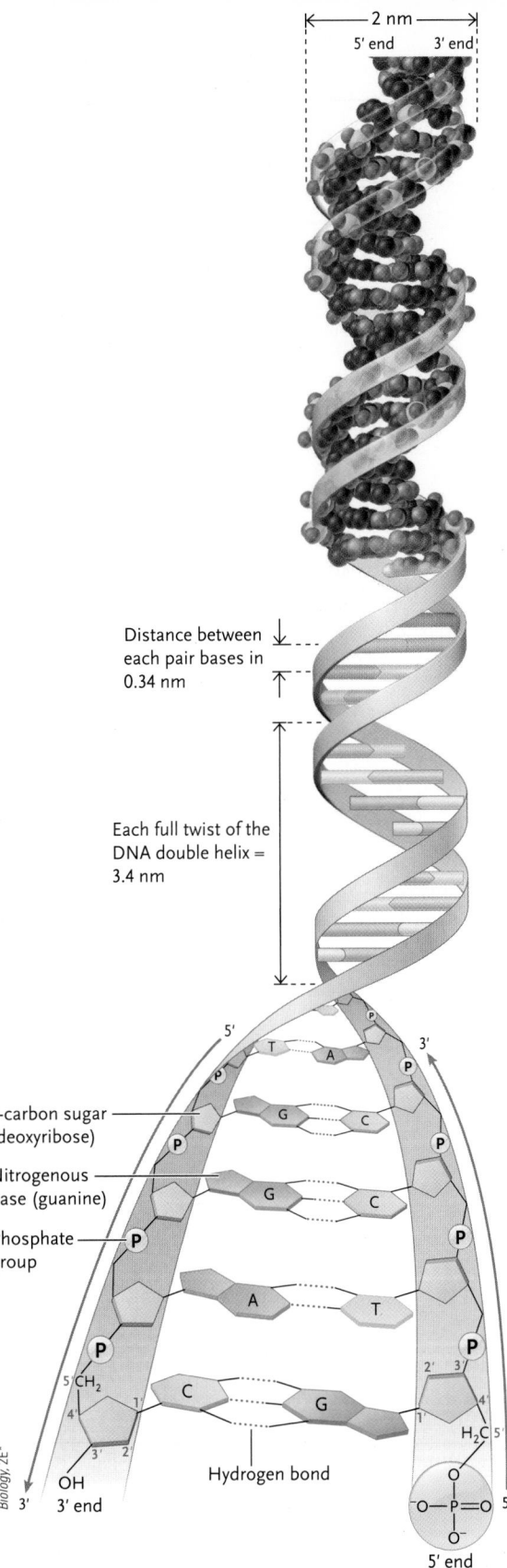

2 nm

5' end  3' end

Distance between each pair bases in 0.34 nm

Each full twist of the DNA double helix = 3.4 nm

5'

3'

T ⋯ A

5-carbon sugar (deoxyribose)

G ⋯⋯ C

Nitrogenous base (guanine)

Phosphate group

P

G ⋯⋯ C

P

A ⋯⋯ T

P

P

5 CH₂

C ⋯⋯ G

2' 3'

4' 1'

3' 2'

4' 1'

H₂C 5'

Biology, 2E*

OH

3' 3' end

Hydrogen bond

O—P=O 5'

O⁻

5' end

**FIGURE 9.6** In the photograph taken in 1952, James Watson looks on while Francis Crick points to a phosphodiester linkage in the deoxyribose chain of their model of a DNA molecule. We can represent the double helix in a number of different ways, as shown in the illustration on the right, but the chemistry and biophysics are the same. The sugar–phosphate chains twist in a right-handed coil around the outside of the strand, with the pyrimidine and purine bases held together in the centre of the strand by hydrogen bonds and van der Waals forces.

A. Barrington Brown / Science Source

Converting the genetically stored information into the pro-teins that do the work in the cell is a process called **gene expression**. Gene expression involves transcription, or copying, of DNA into a mobile form of the information called **RNA**. RNA is then translated by the ribosome (see Chapter 3 for a reminder of ribosomes) to yield proteins that become the functional product. In the next chapter, we will investigate the processes of transcription and translation and the need to control which genes are being expressed at any given time. The histone proteins that help package the DNA into chromatin have small physical extensions of specific amino acids that can interact to make the chromatin more or less dense. When histones are modified by the addition of methyl groups (—CH₃), it makes these extensions become more hydrophobic. Remember that hydrophobic compounds try to avoid water; thus, the methyl groups are attracted to each other and cause the chromatin to pack more densely. This form of chromatin is called heterochromatin. Genes in the heterochromatin region of the chromosome are generally not expressed because the tight packing blocks the enzyme complex needed for transcription from physically accessing the gene. Alternatively, the histones can be modified by adding acetyl groups, a process called **acetylation**. Acetylation makes the extensions more **hydrophilic.** The acetyl groups tend to take up more physical space, and because they are hydrophilic, they like to interact with water molecules. Together this causes the chromatin to be present in a less densely packed form called euchromatin. Genes in euchromatic regions of chromosomes tend to be more highly expressed. As we are now discovering, which regions of chromosomes are packed as

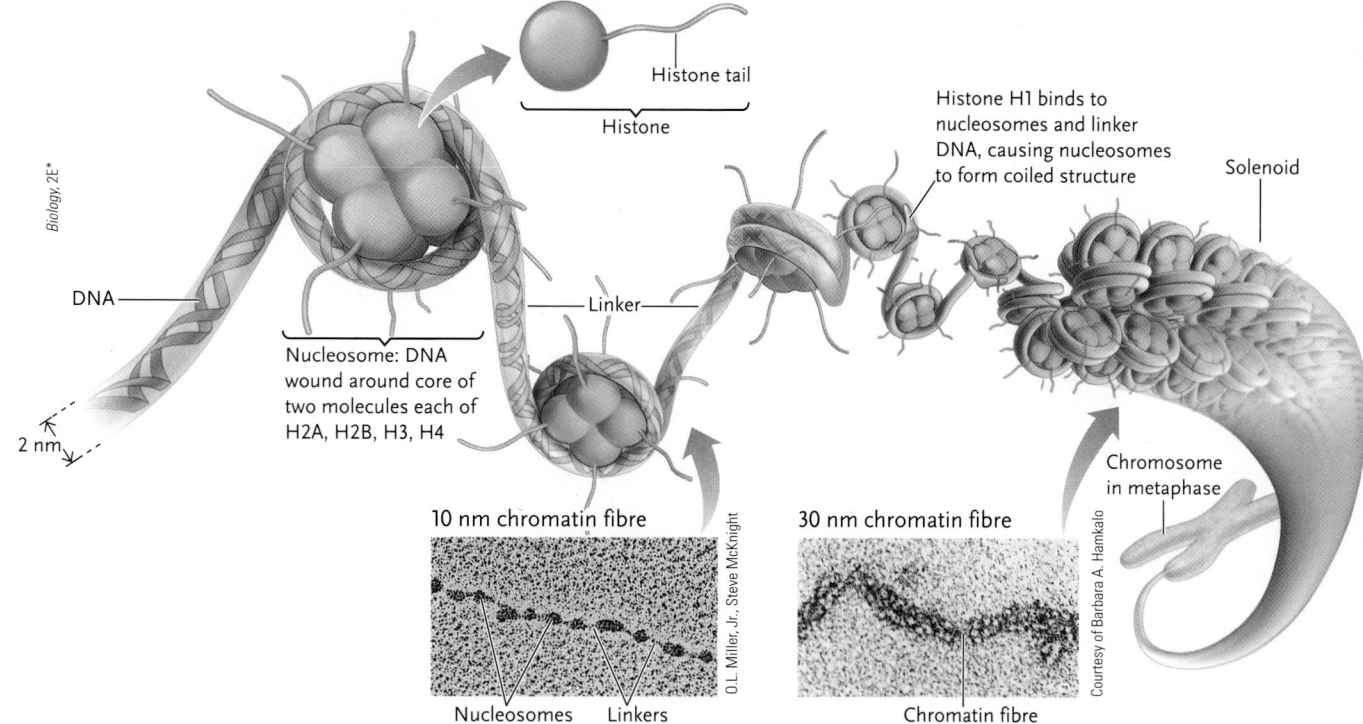

Biology, 2E*

Histone tail

Histone

DNA

Nucleosome: DNA
wound around core of
two molecules each of
H2A, H2B, H3, H4

Linker

2 nm

Histone H1 binds to
nucleosomes and linker
DNA, causing nucleosomes
to form coiled structure

Solenoid

Chromosome
in metaphase

10 nm chromatin fibre

O.L. Miller, Jr., Steve McKnight

Nucleosomes    Linkers

30 nm chromatin fibre

Courtesy of Barbara A. Hamkalo

Chromatin fibre

**FIGURE 9.7** In eukaryotes, the double-stranded DNA molecule that makes up nuclear chromosomes is packaged so that it can fit into the nucleus. In the first step of the packaging process, DNA is wound around a histone complex. The nucleosomes are further packaged into the solenoid to produce the much denser 30 nm chromatin fibre.

heterochromatin and which are packed as euchromatin are dynamic and can differ from tissue to tissue and even cell to cell within a given organism. Interestingly, it seems that the patterns of histone methylation and acetylation can be passed on from one generation to the next through a process called epigenetics. We will take a closer look at epigenetics in the next chapter.

## STUDY BREAK

1. How were Avery, MacLeod, and McCarty able to show that DNA was the transforming factor?
2. How did Chargaff's rules assist Watson and Crick to deduce the structure of DNA?
3. What advantage is there to a eukaryotic cell to have the DNA wound around histones to create nucleoids?

## 9.2 DNA Replication and Repair

In Chapter 6, we discussed the process of mitosis and found that for a cell to divide, it needs to copy its complement of DNA so that the new cells each contain the same information as the parent cell. DNA replication needs to be very accurate to maintain a constant source of

information. Watson and Crick suggested a possible mechanism in their initial publication, based on their model of the DNA molecule.

When we look at DNA replication, it is important to think about both the biochemical process itself—which will produce a second, identical copy of the genetic material—and about the biological need for replication. As with any complex topic, we need to ask ourselves a lot of questions: generally, how, why, and when does all of this happen?

### How Is DNA Copied?

In their initial publications of the structure of DNA, Watson and Crick comment that "the specific pairing" of nucleotides on opposing strands of a DNA molecule suggests a possible copying mechanism. Indeed, having two strands that are essentially mirror images of each other provides a template from which new strands could be produced.

Although Watson and Crick suggested the template mechanism **(Figure 9.8, p. 206)**, scientists still didn't know how the existing DNA strands were copied. A number of competing ideas were presented. The two main theories each had very high-profile backers in the scientific community. Watson and Crick suggested that the cellular machinery would split the two DNA strands and add new

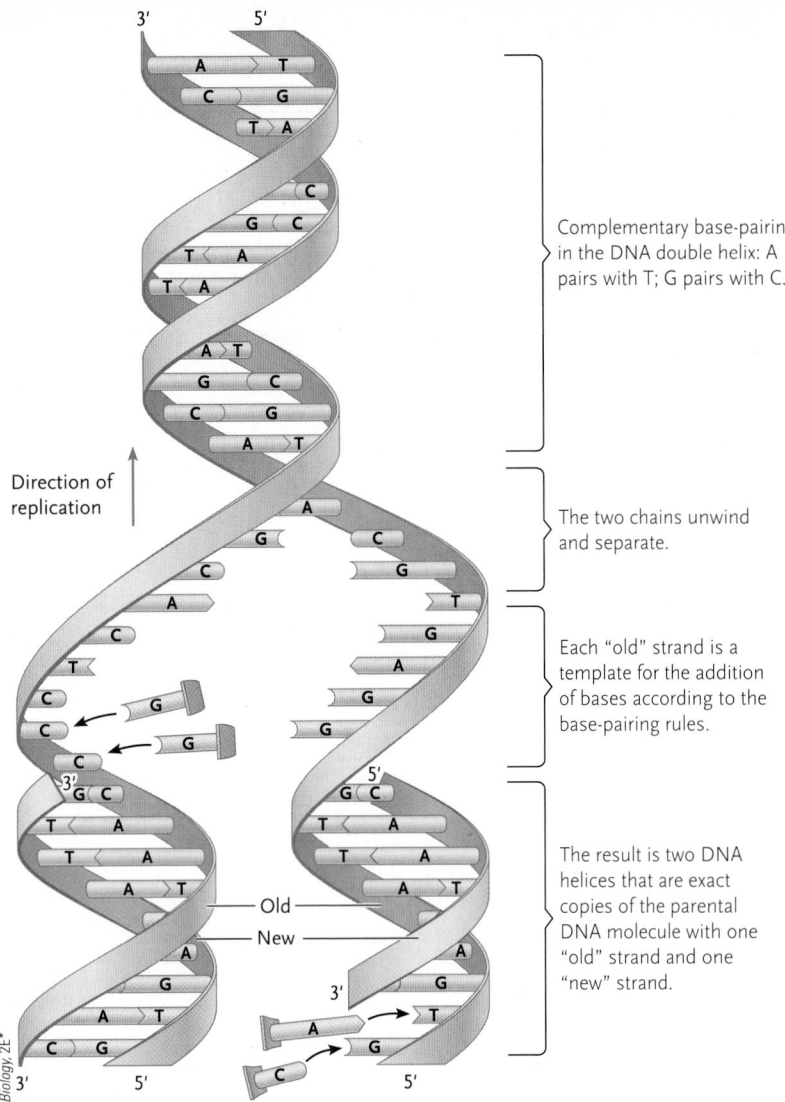

3′     5′

Complementary base-pairing in the DNA double helix: A pairs with T; G pairs with C.

Direction of replication

The two chains unwind and separate.

Each "old" strand is a template for the addition of bases according to the base-pairing rules.

Old
New

The result is two DNA helices that are exact copies of the parental DNA molecule with one "old" strand and one "new" strand.

Biology, 2E*

3′     5′       5′

**FIGURE 9.8** As originally suggested by Watson and Crick, the complementary base pairing of the purines and pyrimidines in a DNA molecule provides a template that can be used to copy the information. The hydrogen bonds holding the strands together are broken by helicases, and the strands are separated. New bases are then added sequentially to generate two copies of the DNA molecule.

nucleotides to form two new complete double-stranded DNA molecules. Their theory was called the **semi-conservative replication** mechanism because, when examining the new DNA molecules, they found each would have one strand carried over from the previous version and one brand new strand **(Figure 9.9)**. An alternative, the **conservative replication** mechanism, was postulated by the eminent biophysicist and "father of molecular biology" Max Delbrück. In the conservative replication mechanism, a completely new double-stranded molecule would be made (Figure 9.9). If conservative replication were correct, one new cell would have the old double-stranded DNA molecule and the second cell would have a newly synthesized DNA molecule.

It took a number of years of experimental research, but in 1958, Matthew Meselson and Franklin Stahl, from

Caltech, the home of Linus Pauling, demonstrated how DNA is replicated. Meselson and Stahl carefully designed a set of experiments to distinguish which of the theories was correct **(Figure 9.10, p. 208)**. In what has been called one of the most elegant experiments in modern biology, they clearly demonstrated that DNA is replicated in a semi-conservative fashion. The key to their experiment was to grow *E. coli* bacteria in the presence of a specific radioisotope of nitrogen, $^{15}N$ or "heavy" nitrogen. Heavy nitrogen contains one more neutron than the normal isotope, $^{14}N$, and this increases the molecular mass by 1 dalton (Da). Bacteria will incorporate nitrogen from their environment into the pyrimidine and purine nucleotides of their DNA when they replicate it. Meselson and Stahl's experiments compared the DNA of bacteria grown with $^{15}N$ to those grown with $^{14}N$. They demonstrated that they could use an ultracentrifuge to separate a mixture of heavy ($^{15}N$-containing) and light ($^{14}N$-containing) DNA. They hypothesized that if cells grown in the presence of $^{15}N$ were transferred to media containing $^{14}N$ shortly after dividing, when they copied their DNA to prepare for their next cell division, the researchers would be able to distinguish between the DNA products predicted by the conservative and the semi-conservative models. If the DNA was replicated by the conservative model, the two strands of heavy DNA would stay together and two new strands of light DNA would be produced (Figure 9.10). These two classes of DNA molecules would be easily separated using their ultracentrifuge technique. If the DNA was replicated by the semi-conservative model, where the two heavy strands were separated and each used as a template for a new, light strand, they would not expect to see either the heavy or the light DNA but something in between, a "hybrid" strand with both light and heavy DNA. Using this logical but simple approach, they were able to clearly demonstrate that DNA is replicated by the semi-conservative model (Figure 9.10).

Demonstrating semi-conservative DNA replication was just the beginning. It stimulated a whole new set of questions: How does the cellular machinery separate the two strands of a DNA molecule? How are the new nucleotides attached to one another? From Figure 9.8, DNA replication might appear relatively simple to you. However, copying a chromosome requires many proteins and

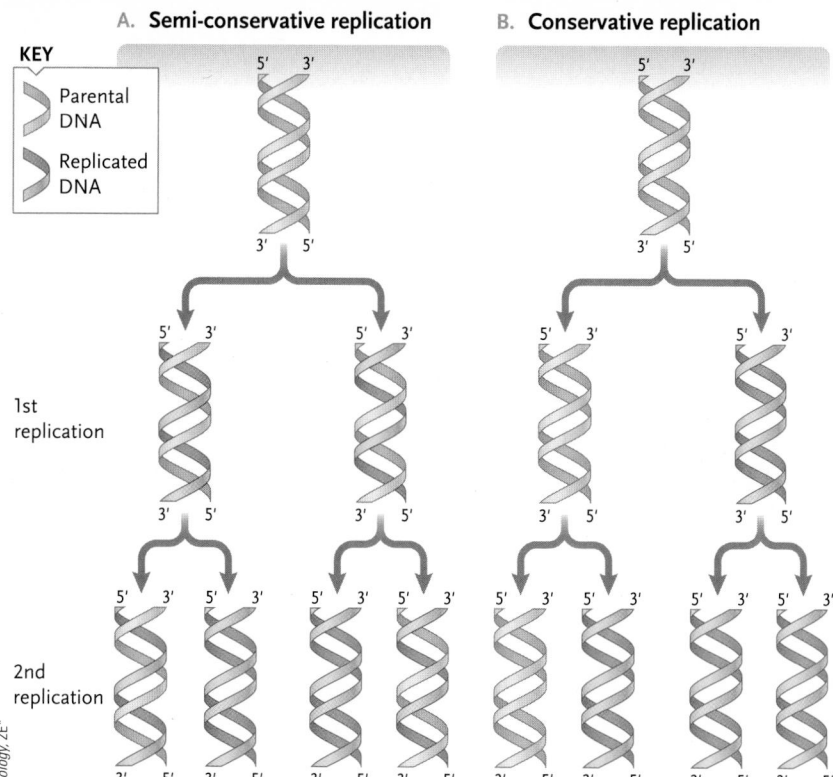

**A. Semi-conservative replication**

**KEY**

Parental DNA

Replicated DNA

1st replication

2nd replication

**B. Conservative replication**

Biology, 2E*

**FIGURE 9.9 (a)** With no knowledge of the mechanism of DNA replication, Watson and Crick suggested that the parent strand is opened up and new nucleotides are filled in to generate two new DNA molecules, each containing one parental strand and one replicated strand—the semi-conservative model of replication. **(b)** A competing hypothesis by Delbrück, called the conservative replication theory, suggested that DNA replication resulted in one molecule made of both original strands and one made of two newly replicated strands in the new DNA molecule.

is quite a complex process to complete, especially in eukaryotes with their linear chromosomes.

DNA strands are first unwound and separated by a set of enzymes called **helicases**. Once separated, a **replication bubble**—an open space between the two DNA strands—forms so that new matching nucleotides can be linked together using a set of **DNA polymerases (Figure 9.11, p. 209)**. Interestingly, each DNA strand is copied only in one direction due to a limitation of the activity of the DNA polymerases. Much like we read from left to right on a page of paper, the DNA polymerase reads the existing DNA strand from the 3′ end to the 5′ end, whereas the new strand is synthesized in the 5′ to 3′ direction. (DNA has a direction: one end is called 3′, and the other is called 5′. You can review this in the Purple Pages section of this book.) Of course, this raises even more questions: As the replication bubble opens, how are both strands synthesized equally? How are the ends of a linear eukaryotic chromosome copied? There always seems to be a lot of questions in biology to keep researchers busy.

Both strands of the DNA molecule are copied at the same time, but because the DNA polymerase can only work in one direction, the process proceeds differently on each strand. One is called the **leading strand**; it is made in a single continuous motion. The other is called the **lagging strand** because replication on this strand happens in small segments. The lagging strand is synthesized in small, discrete steps as the replication bubble opens **(Figure 9.12, p. 209)**. The small segments of copied

DNA that compose the lagging strand are then linked together by the work of a special DNA polymerase enzyme (DNA pol III) and another enzyme called a DNA ligase. The replication bubble will continue to expand as both the leading and lagging strands are copied (Figure 9.12). At some point, replication will be stopped—either when the replication bubble meets another replication bubble, as replication of eukaryotic chromosomes begins at many sites along the chromosome, or when it reaches the end of the chromosome. In bacteria, there is only a single replication bubble. Because the bacterial chromosome is circular, the replication bubble will grow until the two replication forks meet, and two complete copies of the chromosome are finished.

In eukaryotic cells, the DNA polymerase can copy the leading strand from the origin of replication right to the end of the chromosome. However, the lagging strand is a problem. To start and finish the lagging strand, a primer is required. A **primer** is a short segment of RNA bases that line up on the lagging strand as the replication bubble expands. The DNA polymerase uses these RNA bases to position itself on the lagging strand so that DNA copying can begin. As the replication bubble keeps exposing new template strand, the lagging strand copy is formed of a series of small RNA primers linked to longer DNA segments (Figures 9.11 and 9.12). These small RNA–DNA segments are called **Okazaki fragments**. Once the copying of the DNA molecule is complete, the RNA nucleotides in Okazaki fragments are replaced with DNA nucleotides

QUESTION: Does DNA replicate semi-conservatively?

EXPERIMENT: Matthew Meselson and Franklin Stahl proved that the semi-conservative model of DNA replication is correct and that the conservative model is incorrect.

**1** Bacteria grown in $^{15}N$ (heavy) medium. The heavy isotope is incorporated into the bases of DNA, resulting in all the DNA being heavy, that is, labelled with $^{15}N$.

**2** Bacteria transferred to $^{14}N$ (light) medium and allowed to grow and divide for several generations. All new DNA is light.

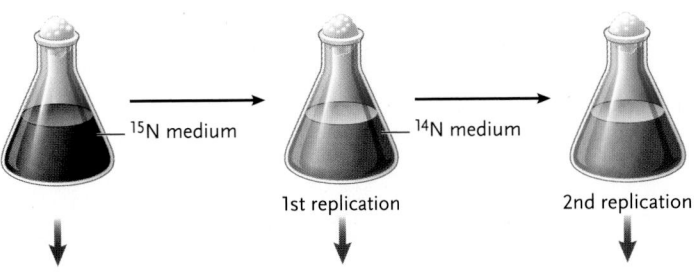

$^{15}N$ medium    $^{14}N$ medium

1st replication    2nd replication

**3** DNA extracted from bacteria cultured in $^{15}N$ medium and after each generation in $^{14}N$ medium.

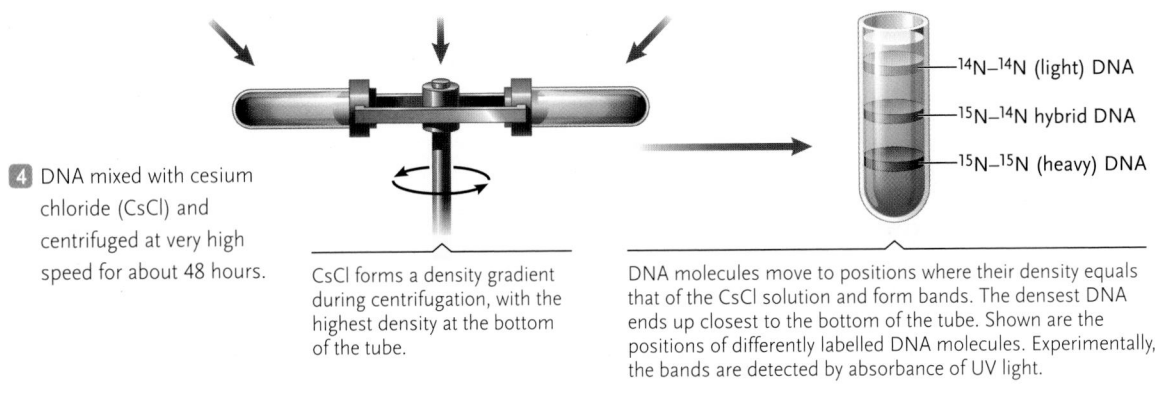

$^{14}N–^{14}N$ (light) DNA
$^{15}N–^{14}N$ hybrid DNA
$^{15}N–^{15}N$ (heavy) DNA

**4** DNA mixed with cesium chloride (CsCl) and centrifuged at very high speed for about 48 hours.

CsCl forms a density gradient during centrifugation, with the highest density at the bottom of the tube.

DNA molecules move to positions where their density equals that of the CsCl solution and form bands. The densest DNA ends up closest to the bottom of the tube. Shown are the positions of differently labelled DNA molecules. Experimentally, the bands are detected by absorbance of UV light.

RESULT: Meselson and Stahl obtained the following results:

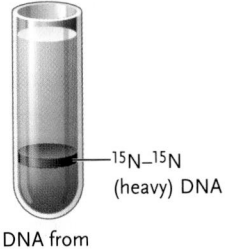

$^{15}N–^{15}N$ (heavy) DNA

DNA from $^{15}N$ medium

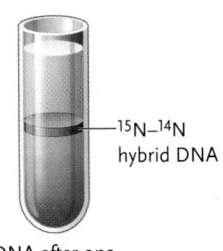

$^{15}N–^{14}N$ hybrid DNA

DNA after one replication in $^{14}N$

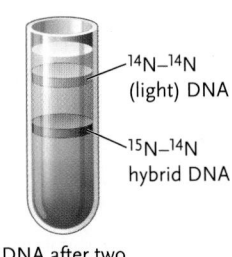

$^{14}N–^{14}N$ (light) DNA
$^{15}N–^{14}N$ hybrid DNA

DNA after two replications in $^{14}N$

Biology, 2E*

CONCLUSIONS: The predicted DNA banding patterns for the three DNA replication models were as follows:

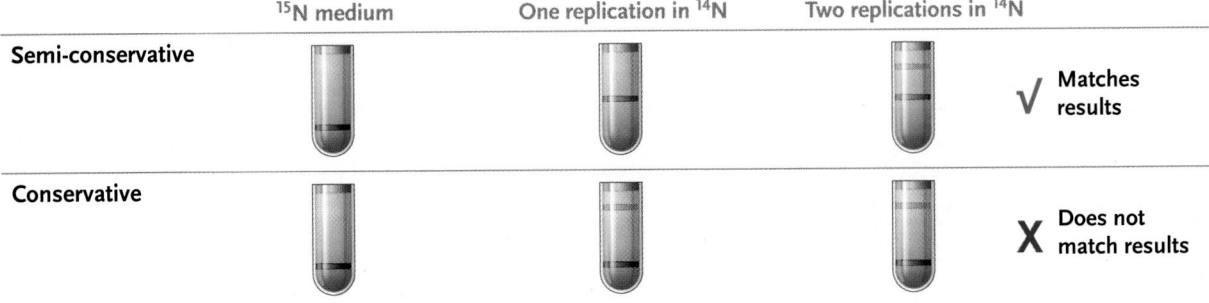

| | $^{15}N$ medium | One replication in $^{14}N$ | Two replications in $^{14}N$ | |
|---|---|---|---|---|
| **Semi-conservative** | | | | √ Matches results |
| **Conservative** | | | | X Does not match results |

The results support the semi-conservative model.

**FIGURE 9.10** Meselson and Stahl used radioactive $^{15}N$, which contains an extra neutron and is thus heavier, to label DNA made by *E. coli* cells. This allowed the researchers to separate heavy $^{15}N$-containing DNA from light $^{14}N$-containing DNA using ultracentrifugation. This technique allowed Meselson and Stahl to determine that DNA replication occurred by the semi-conservative model.

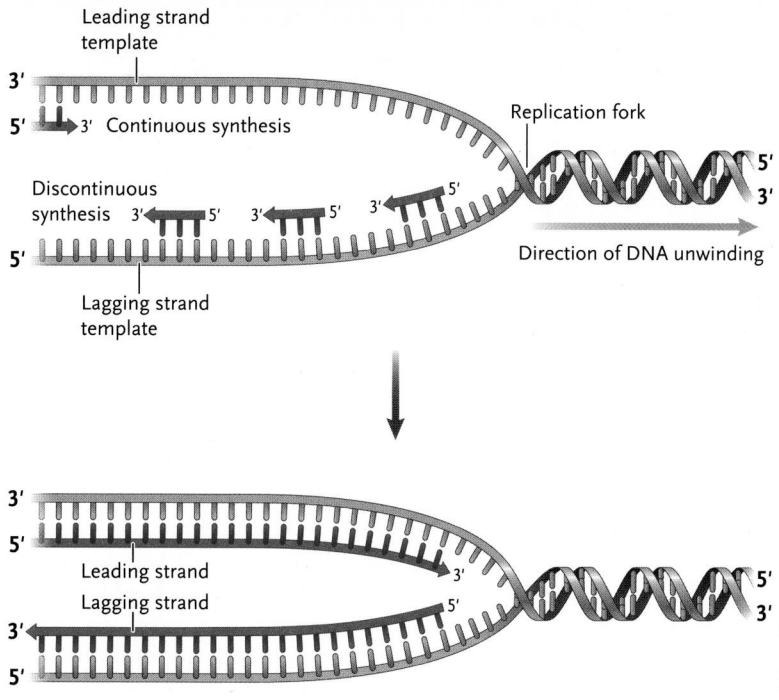

**FIGURE 9.11** The replication bubble forms once helicases open up the strands of a DNA molecule. The exposed nucleotide bases then act as a template to attract the matching nucleotide. The DNA polymerase links the nucleotides together to build a complete new copy of both strands.

and the pieces are connected together by an enzyme called DNA ligase.

Because copying the lagging strand requires a primer, copying the ends of linear chromosomes is a quite complex process. In the mid-1970s work by Elizabeth Blackburn at Yale University discovered that the DNA sequences at the ends of eukaryotic chromosomes are composed of simple repeat patterns. These repeat regions at the ends of the chromosomes are called telomeres. The telomere ends of our chromosomes are copied by an interesting enzyme called **telomerase**. You can imagine that the ends of your chromosomes are like the ends of your shoelaces. They are fragile and can unravel unless they are held together. Plastic or metal aglets keep the

ends of our shoelaces intact. Telomerase ensures that the tips of our linear chromosomes are copied and remain intact. However, researchers found that telomerase is not active in most cells. As a result, the telomere repeat regions of chromosomes in normal cells get shorter after each round of cell division. This has led to a number of theories about cell division and its effects on the longevity of cells. See Box 9.2 to discover more about telomerase and its role in cell aging.

## Why and When Is DNA Copied?

The question of why and when DNA is copied is more straightforward than how it is copied. For cells to divide and maintain the same amount of information stored in their chromosomes, each new cell must have an accurate copy of the original cell's DNA. Thus, DNA must be copied for an organism to grow, repair damaged tissue, or reproduce. As we saw in Chapter 6, the process of mitosis and the timing of cell division are highly controlled. The nuclear DNA is copied during the synthesis or S phase of the cell cycle. In fact, the cell cycle is so carefully controlled that there is a checkpoint quality-control system that ensures that DNA replication is complete before progressing past the S phase of the cycle. In this way, the cell cycle and DNA synthesis are controlled together.

## Why Must Damaged DNA Be Repaired to Maintain Cell Health?

As mentioned in the chapter opening, DNA is a sensitive molecule that can be damaged by environmental factors such as sunlight or chemical exposure. Light or chemical damage increases the possibility that a given

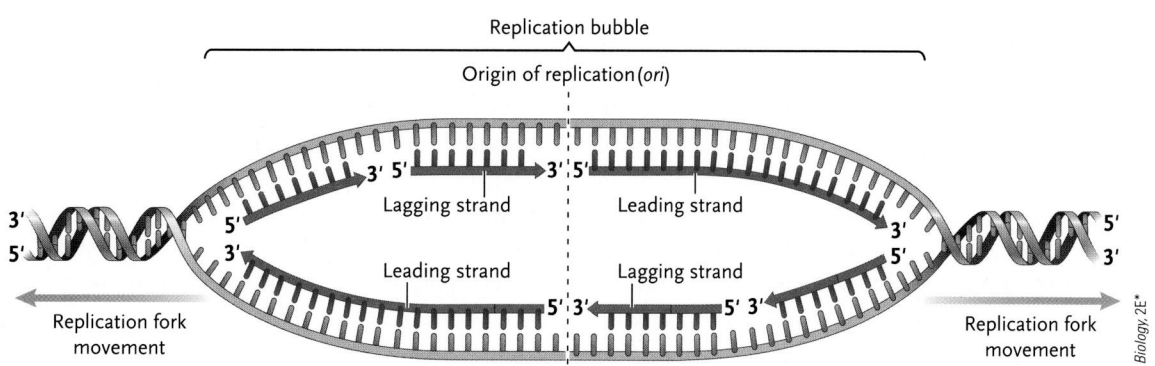

**FIGURE 9.12** The expanding replication bubble allows DNA replication to continue at both ends. It will keep expanding as replication progresses, until the end of the chromosome or another replication bubble is reached.

As we mentioned in our discussion of DNA replication, the ends of linear chromosomes pose a problem for the DNA copying system. The lagging strand requires a primer so that the DNA polymerase can bind to the DNA strand and link in the necessary DNA nucleotides. If this were the only system, the linear chromosome would get shorter each time the DNA was copied; in other words, each time the cell divided **(Figure 1)**. To protect the ends of chromosomes, eukaryotes have evolved special regions on the ends of the chromosomes called telomeres. The telomere is a region of repeated DNA sequence. In vertebrates, telomeres contain thousands of repeats of TTAGGG.

In the early 1960s, Leonard Hayflick discovered that there is a limit to how many times a human cell can divide. Once division stops, it will not restart. This finding puzzled many researchers, especially those studying aging. As organisms age, cell division is known to slow. But why? In the 1970s, researchers suggested that telomere length dictated when cells stop dividing. After a number of cell divisions, with their corresponding cycles of DNA replication, the telomeres became too short for the DNA to pass the required mitotic checkpoint. The results of many experiments in many research labs around the world led to the development of the **telomere theory of aging**.

Thus, cell "age" should be defined not by time, but by the number of divisions. But because the cell theory tells us that all cells come from other cells, wouldn't all organisms just run out of telomeres? This question led to the discovery of an enzyme complex called telomerase, which has the special job of lengthening telomeres. Researchers found that, in humans, telomerase is only active in reproductive cells. Thus, the tissues that produce our egg and sperm cells have long telomeres, but the rest of our cells slowly lose their telomeres. In a ground-breaking research project in 1998, researchers used biotechnological tools to express telomerase in cultured human fibroblast cells. (See Chapter 11 for more about biotechnology.) These human fibroblast cells were skin cells grown in a Petri dish. They were able to divide more times than cells that did not express telomerase, and they essentially become immortal. Although this seems like a great way to increase human life span and health, having cells that do not stop dividing can lead to cancer. In fact, a new theory is emerging that addresses the role of telomere length in the growth of cancerous tumours. Many types of cancerous cells seem to have long telomeres and active telomerase enzymes. Telomerase seems to epitomize the Goldilocks nature of human health. Both too much and too little of something is bad. We need just the right amount.

---

DNA sequence will be altered during DNA replication. The critical nature of the information that is stored in DNA has led to the evolution of repair mechanisms to mitigate damage. Just as we repair our cars to keep them running properly, cells maintain their DNA so that accurate copies can be transmitted to the next generation. We can see just how important DNA repair mechanisms are in several ways.

Scientists discovered that errors occasionally occur during the copying of DNA genomes. In prokaryotes, the error rate is approximately 1 out of every 10 to 100 million bases. This is incredibly accurate. Considering that the *E. coli* genome is 4.8 Mb, it is unlikely that a single mistake will be made when its genome is copied. Assuming a 1 in 50 million error rate, there would be a 9.6% chance of a single error occurring. Even if an error does occur, cellular proofreading mechanisms can repair mismatched bases in the genome after copying is complete. This is thought to lower the chance that an error would be passed on to the next generation of cells to between 1 and 0.1%. However, when growing a culture of *E. coli* in a research lab, a single flask could hold billions of cells that divide every 20 minutes. Therefore, the odds of a mistake happening in a population such as an *E. coli* culture become much more likely. This is one way that genetic variation can be introduced into a population, leading to evolution via natural selection.

Even the simplest bacteria that we have identified exhibit some form of DNA repair. This often involves a set of enzymes that will remove a damaged or mismatched nucleotide from the DNA strand and replace it with an undamaged version. *E. coli* uses several overlapping systems to repair DNA damage. Researchers have had a hard time studying what happens when the DNA repair fails to occur because they had trouble stopping all of the steps in the complicated repair system. There are often severe effects on cells and organisms that have defects in their DNA repair mechanisms. Scientists had to introduce multiple mutations into the

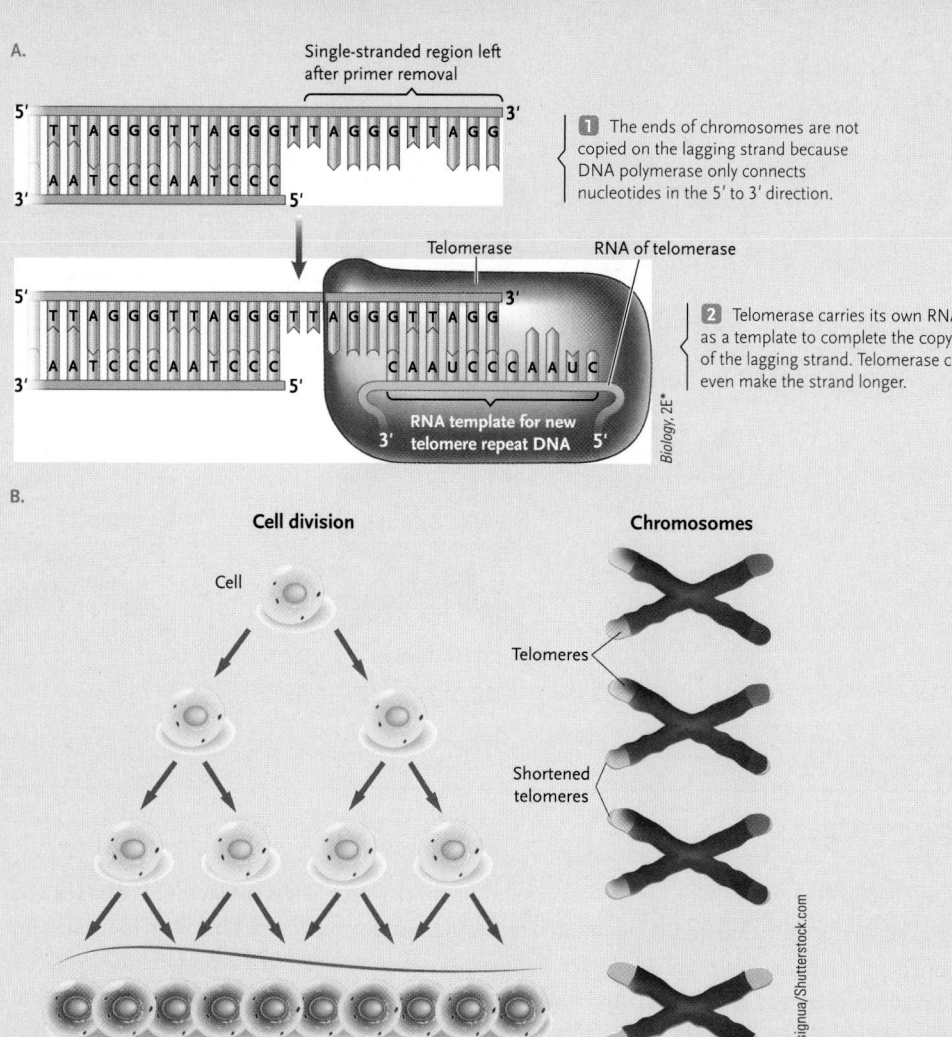

**A.**

Single-stranded region left after primer removal

5′ TTAGGGTTAGGGTTAGGGTTAGG 3′
3′ AATCCCAATCCC 5′

**1** The ends of chromosomes are not copied on the lagging strand because DNA polymerase only connects nucleotides in the 5′ to 3′ direction.

Telomerase      RNA of telomerase

5′ TTAGGGTTAGGGTTAGGGTTAGG 3′
3′ AATCCCAATCCC          CAAUCCCAAUC 5′

RNA template for new
3′ telomere repeat DNA 5′

*Biology, 2E\**

**2** Telomerase carries its own RNA as a template to complete the copying of the lagging strand. Telomerase can even make the strand longer.

**FIGURE 1** Telomerase **(a)** is an RNA–protein complex that binds to the ends of chromosomes to ensure that they are copied during DNA replication. As normal cells divide **(b),** the telomeres of their chromosomes get shorter until they reach a point where the chromosome can no longer be copied. Then cell division can no longer occur.

**B.**

**Cell division**          **Chromosomes**

Cell

Telomeres

Shortened telomeres

Senescent cells

Telomeres shorten, cell division stops

*Designua/Shutterstock.com*

---

*E. coli* genome to stop the repair system. Once they did this, the cells accumulated errors in their genome much more quickly. Over a number of generations, the errors reduced the fitness of the *E. coli* cells, thereby decreasing their growth rate, even under optimal conditions. In eukaryotes, the accumulation of DNA damage can lead to programmed cell death or apoptosis. However, the greater danger to humans, and other mammals, is when the DNA repair does not happen. Unrepaired DNA damage can lead to uncontrolled cell division, or cancerous tumours.

The need for sunlight exposure provides an interesting example of how natural selection balances traits during evolution. Vita-min D is a compound needed for our general health. We cannot make vitamin D directly, but when our skin is exposed to the high-energy ultraviolet rays from the sun, 7-dehydrocholesterol is photomodified into active vitamin D. If our skin is not exposed to enough ultraviolet light, we need to obtain vitamin D from our diet. Unfortunately, the exposure of skin cells to ultraviolet light also leads to DNA damage **(Figure 9.13, p. 212)**. Strong, covalent

bonds form between neighbouring T-T or C-T nucleotides, in effect fusing the neighbouring nucleotides into a single, less flexible unit. As a result, the normally stabilizing hydrogen bonds are disrupted, and the helical structure of the DNA molecule is altered in the region surrounding the damaged bases (Figure 9.13). The DNA replication system has problems copying the strand when it is damaged, increasing the chance of an error. If an error occurs in genes that control cell division, the result can be skin cancer. Like many aspects of our lives, there is a balance: too much sun exposure is bad, but so is too little.

## STUDY BREAK

1. Why do the ends of linear chromosomes, like those found in most eukaryotes, pose a problem for the process of DNA replication?
2. Why would natural selection favour the development of DNA repair systems in cells?

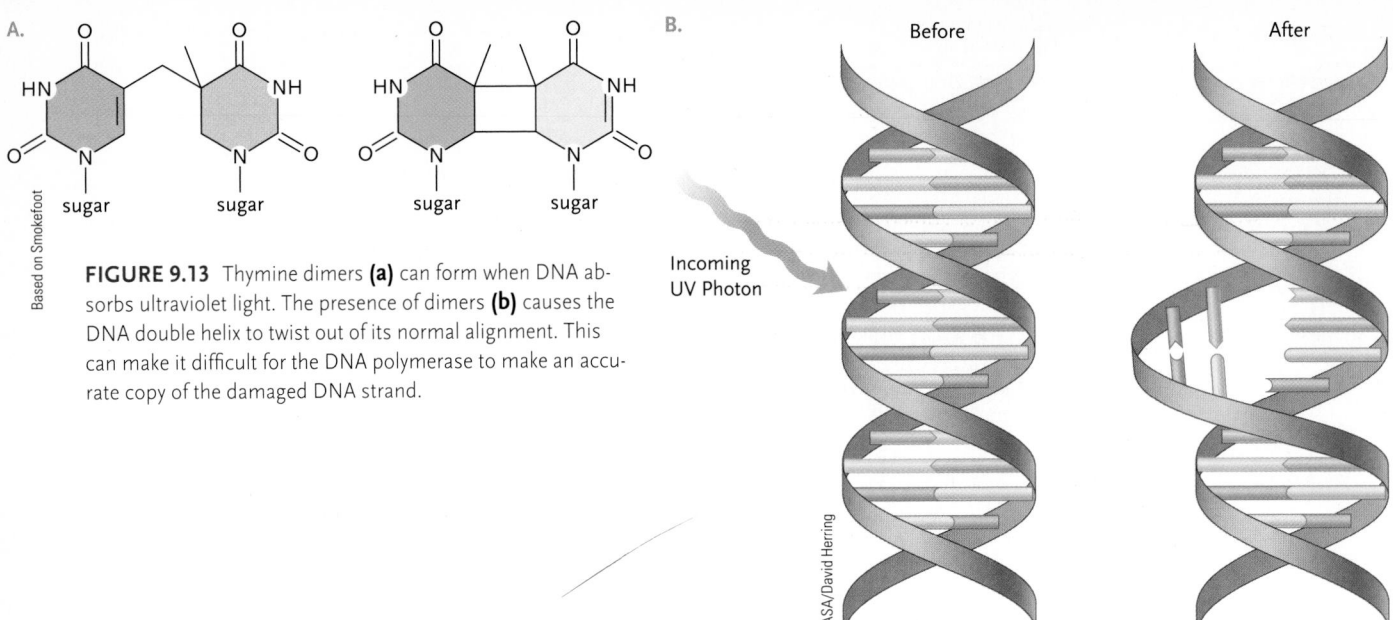

FIGURE 9.13 Thymine dimers **(a)** can form when DNA absorbs ultraviolet light. The presence of dimers **(b)** causes the DNA double helix to twist out of its normal alignment. This can make it difficult for the DNA polymerase to make an accurate copy of the damaged DNA strand.

Based on Smokefoot

NASA/David Herring

## PUTTING IT IN PERSPECTIVE

DNA contains the basic information needed to produce cells. Solving the structure of the DNA molecule not only changed our view of heredity but also opened up many avenues of research that we will look at more closely in Chapter 11. Similarly, replication of DNA by the cell is absolutely required for cell division. The control of this process underlies many current theories on aging and how we may prevent the growth and spread of cancerous tumours.

Natural selection led to the repair systems we see in cells. For example, UV light–induced damage can be repaired by an enzyme called **photolyase**. The enzyme binds to damaged nucleotides on a DNA molecule. It can restore damaged bases to their normal form. This is an ideal system for DNA repair because no changes are made to the DNA molecule. Another way to deal with UV damage is to ignore it. In eukaryotes, a specific member of the DNA–polymerase family (DNA polymerase-η or eta) can read through the dimer location and accurately replicate the DNA strands. In humans, when this gene is defective, the result is a specific form of the DNA repair disorder xeroderma pigmentosum, which we discussed earlier in the chapter, called variant XPV.

## KEY CONCEPTS REVIEW AND QUESTIONS

### 9.1 DNA Structure

Proving that DNA was the hereditary particle postulated by Mendel required years of research. The Griffith experiments demonstrated that one type of bacteria could be transformed by the presence of similar dead bacteria. The work of Avery, MacLeod, and McCarty demonstrated that DNA facilitated this process.

1. How could Hershey and Chase be sure that when radioactive phosphorus was taken up by *E. coli* cells, it was due to DNA and not proteins?

2. Why did initial hypotheses suggest that proteins are the hereditary material?

   a. Proteins are smaller and more mobile.

   b. Proteins are functional, whereas DNA is not.

   c. With 20 amino acids, proteins could encode more complexity than DNA.

   d. Proteins are much more stable than DNA.

DNA is a polymer composed of nucleotides. The adenosines and thymines are present in equal amounts, as are the guanines and cytosines. The complete DNA molecule is composed of two polymer strands aligned in opposite directions, held together by hydrogen bonds and van der Waals forces.

3. What does Chargaff's rule state about the relative amounts of pyrimidines and purines in a strand of DNA?

4. Describe how the nucleotides are arranged with respect to each other, both along the strand and between the two strands.

## 9.2 DNA Replication and Repair

DNA is copied in a semi-conservative fashion, in which the two strands are separated and then each is used as a template. DNA polymerases connect properly placed nucleotides in a 5′ to 3′ fashion. The leading strand is copied in a smooth, continuous manner, whereas the lagging strand is copied in small fragments, which are later linked together. Copying the ends of linear chromosomes requires a special mechanism using small repeat regions called telomeres.

5. What enzyme is used to separate the DNA template strands before replication?

6. Why do cells need to replicate their DNA?

DNA is an important compound that contains the genetic information that is passed on from generation to generation. As such, the DNA molecule must be maintained and protected from damage. DNA damage can occur because of copying errors, environmental exposure, or even cellular metabolism. Mechanisms to repair damaged nucleotides and DNA strands exist in even the most primitive organisms.

7. Why can accumulated DNA damage cause both a decrease in cell growth and uncontrolled cell growth (i.e., cancer)?

8. Why does the presence of a C-T or T-T dimer cause problems for DNA replication?

Now that you have read and reviewed this chapter, we encourage you to attempt to build a concept map incorporating these key concepts and indicate connections that exist between them. See Chapter 5 for some examples.

# Gene Expression and Regulation

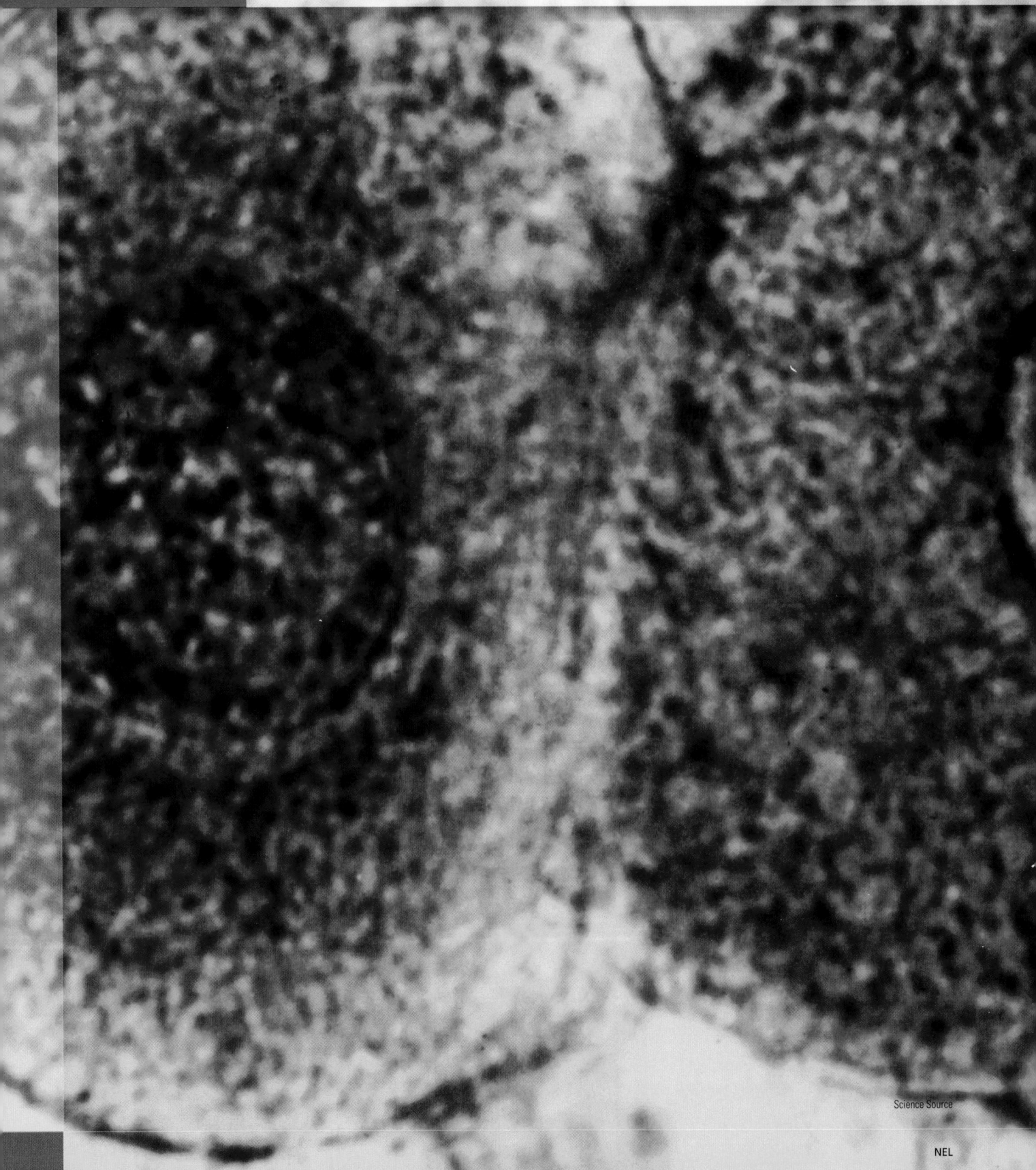

# CHAPTER OUTLINE

## WHY IT MATTERS

Walking through an apple orchard in the fall, it is easy to take for granted the abundance of delicious fruit (**Figure 10.1**). Looking back at the orchard over the year, we saw the snow melt and the first leaves and flowers burst forth in the spring. The flowers were pollinated by honeybees so that the seeds needed for the trees to reproduce were fertilized. The trees grew and photosynthesized over the summer, storing sugars in the fruit that protected the developing seeds. As the summer ended, the fruit ripened while the leaves turned colour and fell to the ground. The tree then went dormant for the winter in readiness for the next spring, so the cycle can continue. We can see this process as a romantic cycle of the seasons, or, from a biological view, we can look inside the cells of the trees and be equally amazed at the complex processes at work.

The regulation of gene expression is an intensely researched area in the field of biology. An amazing level of complexity is required for multicellular organisms to develop properly, and organisms must be able to respond to changes in their environment. Remember that every one of our cells contains the same genetic blueprint or **genome**. However, despite having the same genes, our cells can have very different structures and functions depending on which genes are turned on and which are turned off. When a gene is turned on, scientists say it is **expressed**. If it produces a lot of its particular protein, we say it is highly expressed.

We know that all of our cells have the same genes. Going further, if we compare the genes found in mice and humans, for example, we would find that they are very similar. Of the approximately 25,000 genes found in the mouse genome, approximately 99% of them have direct counterparts in humans. Thus, the basic building blocks of humans and mice are very similar, yet, as developed organisms, humans are vastly different from their rodent cousins. Again, we are so different because of when, where, and to what extent genes are expressed. Keep in mind that, for the most part, genes themselves are only a source of information; it is the production of functional proteins encoded by specific genes that controls how cells and organisms work.

Think about the apple tree again—perhaps one growing in the Annapolis Valley in Nova Scotia, Canada (Figure 10.1). In the spring, rising temperatures

**FIGURE 10.1** The changes we see in apple trees through the growing season are due to the regulation of specific genes.

accelerate enzymatic processes, causing the trees to break dormancy. New leaves begin to expand, and flower buds develop. All of these processes are controlled by the expression of specific genes. Later in the summer, as the days become shorter, a new set of genes are expressed that induce the formation of new leaf buds for the following year, halt the growth of the tree, and signal fruit development to begin the ripening phase. As autumn arrives, changing light levels and temperatures cause a different set of genes to facilitate the accumulation of carbohydrates in the living cells of the bark, the buds, and the roots. These carbohydrates will act as both an energy source for the tree in the following spring and antifreeze chemicals to reduce the risk of damage to living cells undergoing cycles of freezing and thawing during the winter months. The tree will ultimately change gene expression in the leaves to halt photosynthesis and transport nutrients out of the leaves for future use. The tree's leaves then **senesce** (die) and fall to the ground. The following year, the same general signals will be recognized by the apple tree, leading to a yearly cycle of gene expression that provides us with a dietary staple as the plants try to produce seeds for reproduction. Understanding which genes are turned on in response to specific signals from the environment allows horticultural scientists to select apple varieties that are better suited to the many types of growing locations in Canada. Understanding how genes in apple fruit are regulated allows us to slow ripening to reduce spoilage and provide a continuous supply of ripe apples to markets across the country, throughout the year. The ripening process is controlled by a plant hormone called **ethylene**. By placing ripening apples in storage containers that are both cold and have a high level of carbon dioxide, ripening can be slowed to an almost imperceptible level because the genes required for producing ethylene have their expression turned off by these environmental cues.

In this chapter, we will examine the processes leading from the gene to a protein. We will also examine how gene expression controls diverse aspects of biology, from aging and reproduction to disease and acclimation to environmental stimuli.

## 10.1 Gene Expression and the Central Dogma of Molecular Biology

The defining aspects of living organisms include their structural organization, capacity to perform metabolism, and ability to respond to their environment. Although we often refer to DNA as the "brains of the cell," remember from Chapter 9 that DNA is only the source of information. The proteins in cells build the cell structure, catalyze chemical reactions, and detect changes in the environment

surrounding the cell (if you need a reminder about proteins, see the Purple Pages). Therefore, we need to ask ourselves, how is the information stored in a DNA molecule used to make the proteins which do the work in the cell? In 1958, Francis Crick coined the term **central dogma of molecular biology** to describe the flow of information from the gene encoded on a strand of DNA to the production of an active protein (**Figure 10.2**). This process involved transcription of the gene to produce an RNA copy and subsequent translation of the RNA molecule by a ribosome (we introduced ribosomes in Chapter 3) to produce a protein. Over the years, research into each of these steps has provided us with immense detail about both how these processes function and how they are regulated.

### Genes Provide the Information for How and When to Make Proteins

A gene can be defined as a section of a DNA strand that contains information used by a cell to create a protein. Although there are other types of genes, they are not as common and have many of the same features, so for now we will focus on protein-encoding genes. However, the word "gene" has moved beyond this precise use by the scientific community, and genes are commonly discussed in the media and by the general public. We regularly hear about new genes that have been discovered for different diseases and how these genes can be targeted in future therapies. Elderly people in our communities brag about how their "good genes" have kept them healthy through old age. In Chapter 8, we talked about the gene and inheritance and learned about Gregor Mendel's theories of inheritance. Mendel had no idea of the molecular complexity of the cell, yet he was able to quite accurately describe and predict the inheritance of discrete traits from one generation to the next. In Chapter 9, we discussed how genetic information is encoded in DNA. However, major questions remained about how the information encoded in the DNA strand was converted to something functional. Perhaps an even more important question was what controlled when specific proteins were made? Thinking back to the apple trees, what regulates when the proteins for fruit ripening are produced? Too early and the seeds might not be mature; too late and frost might destroy the developing fruit before the seeds are ready.

With these questions in mind, the current state of genetics and molecular biology looks at genes in two ways: first, as the information to make a particular protein and, second, as controller of when, where, and how much of that protein is made by the cell. Shown graphically in **Figure 10.3**, a gene at its simplest is composed of three different segments: the promoter, the coding region, and the termination signal. Located at the beginning, or 5' end of the gene, the **promoter** binds the RNA

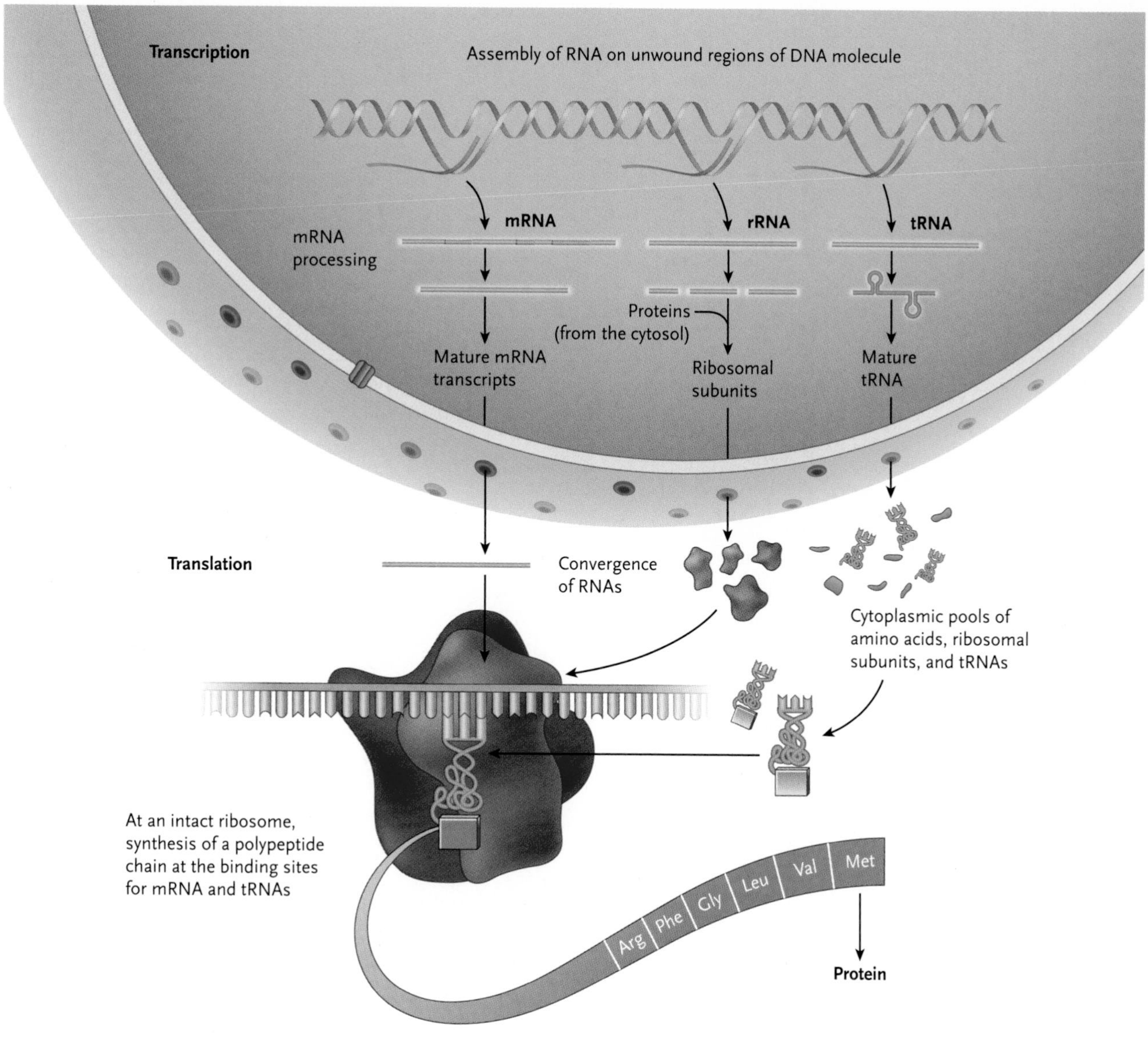

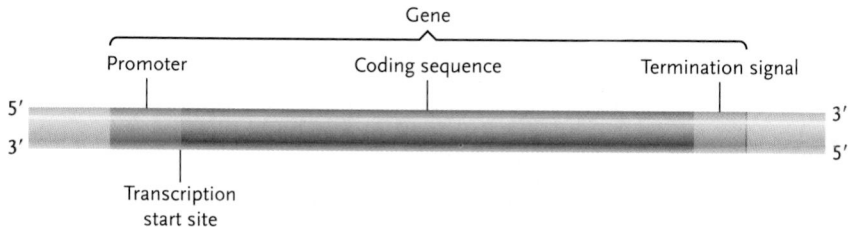

**Transcription**

Assembly of RNA on unwound regions of DNA molecule

mRNA processing

**mRNA**     **rRNA**     **tRNA**

Mature mRNA transcripts

Proteins (from the cytosol)

Ribosomal subunits

Mature tRNA

**Translation**

Convergence of RNAs

Cytoplasmic pools of amino acids, ribosomal subunits, and tRNAs

At an intact ribosome, synthesis of a polypeptide chain at the binding sites for mRNA and tRNAs

Arg Phe Gly Leu Val Met

**Protein**

**FIGURE 10.2** The central dogma of molecular biology describes the transfer of information from the gene to the protein.

SOURCE: From STARR/TAGGART/Evers/Starr. *Biology*, 12E. © 2009 Brooks/Cole, a part of Cengage Learning, Inc. Reproduced by permission. www.cengage.com/permissions

Gene

Promoter     Coding sequence     Termination signal

5′     3′
3′     5′

Transcription start site

**FIGURE 10.3** A typical bacterial gene contains information to make a protein: the promoter, the coding sequence, and the termination signal.

copying machine and tells it where to begin its work. This is the **transcription initiation site**, the point where the RNA polymerase begins making the RNA copy of the gene. The **coding region** of the gene contains the information needed to produce a protein translation of the genetic code. At the 3′ end of the gene, a **termination signal** tells the RNA copying machine where to stop. This is the bare minimum and what we normally find in bacteria and archaea cells. In eukaryotic nuclear genes, such as the one depicted in **Figure 10.4** on p. 218, we see a more complicated model. The promoter is accompanied by **enhancers**, which are short DNA sequences that provide extra control over when, where, and how frequently a gene is transcribed. However, unlike promoters,

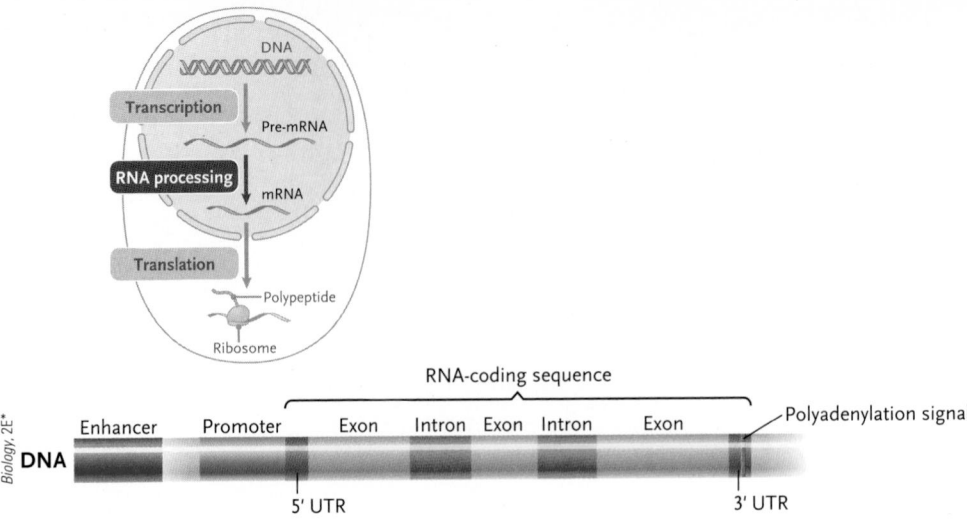

**FIGURE 10.4** The structure of a typical eukaryotic gene includes added control sequences and introns.

enhancers can be long distances away from the transcription initiation site. We also see that the coding region is interspersed with **introns**—segments of DNA that must be removed from the mRNA molecule after transcription. We will cover introns and other components of eukaryotic genes in a later section.

## Bacterial Genes Can Be Organized into Operons

An interesting observation in chromosomes of bacteria, chloroplasts, and mitochondria is that genes required for a similar purpose are often located together and transcribed in one long mRNA molecule that contains several coding sequences. This organization of genes as a unit is called an **operon**. By having a single promoter regulating transcription of a series of genes, it is thought that the bacterial cell can accurately control the accumulation of a series of proteins that rely on each other. For example, unlike mammals, bacteria are able to synthesize vitamin $B_{12}$ from the basic building blocks they have available. To do this, they require a series of 24 proteins that are encoded in the genome as individual genes. Much of the research into vitamin $B_{12}$ biosynthesis was completed using the model bacterium *Salmonella typhimurium*. It may seem strange to study vitamin metabolism using a bacterium that can cause gastroenteritis in humans; however, the more we know about disease-causing organisms, the better. In *S. typhimurium*, the genes required for vitamin $B_{12}$ biosynthesis are separated into two operons, one of which contains 20 genes. By transcribing the genes together, the amounts of the individual proteins produced will be relatively equal. This aids the flow of metabolites through the biosynthetic pathway and simplifies the regulation of gene expression. In eukaryotes, genes that encode proteins that function together are not found in operons and often not even on the same chromosomes; however, the promoters and enhancers are regulated in a similar manner and produce mRNA at the same time.

**STUDY BREAK**

1. What does the central dogma of molecular biology try to explain?
2. What is the function of the gene promoter?
3. What is an operon?

## 10.2 From Gene to Protein

Using our understanding of what constitutes a gene, let's follow the central dogma pathway and see how the information stored in a gene can be used to build a functional protein.

### Transcription of a Gene Produces an RNA Copy

Transcription is the process by which the genetic information stored as a gene in a DNA strand is copied into a mobile form. As mentioned in Chapter 3, the ribosomes located in the cytosol of the cell act as macromolecular machines that are able to translate the information stored in nucleotides (RNA) into the functional components of the cell—the proteins. Transcription of the DNA into RNA is required to allow the ribosome to access the nucleotide-based information.

Let us remind ourselves about the molecules we are discussing. In Chapter 9, we discussed the structure of DNA and RNA. DNA is a polymer of deoxyribonucleotides, and a stable DNA molecule is composed of two complementary strands running antiparallel to each other. In contrast, a molecule of RNA is a polymer of ribonucleotides and is composed of a single strand. We can think of the DNA as encoding a stable long-term source of information using a four-letter alphabet. It

# THE MOLECULE BEHIND THE BIOLOGY 10.1
## RNA

There are three main types of RNA molecules that we need to keep in mind as we discuss the basics of the central dogma of molecular biology. **Messenger RNA (mRNA)** is the mobile version of the gene. It encodes the information required to make a functional protein. Once it has been processed in the nucleus, it is exported to the cytoplasm, where a ribosome will attach to the mRNA molecule and begin translation. We will discuss mRNAs in more detail as the chapter progresses.

Ribosomal RNA (rRNA) has a very different function from mRNA molecules. The rRNA forms a structural part of the ribosome. In the nucleus of eukaryotic cells, it is transcribed as a large RNA molecule and is processed into three smaller pieces. The pieces are denoted by their size using units called Svedbergs (S). In typical eukaryotic cells, the rRNA molecules are denoted as 5.8S, 18S, and 28S. Following transcription, the rRNA molecules are not immediately exported from the nucleus; rather, they are processed into their mature sizes and move to the nucleolus, where a set of proteins binds to them to form the ribosomes, which are then exported to the cytosol, where they can begin translating mRNA molecules to produce proteins.

The third class of RNA that we will discuss is **transfer RNA (tRNA)**. The tRNAs are able to read the mRNA strand and translate the genetic code so that the correct protein can be made by the ribosome. tRNAs act as translational tools allowing the nucleotide sequence to supply the information to direct the proper sequence of amino acids needed to produce a protein. They translate three-base segments called **codons** into the amino acid alphabet of proteins.

The relatively small tRNAs fold into a quite specific shape, which fits into the assembled ribosome–mRNA complex **(Figure 1)**. At the one end, the tRNA contains a three-nucleotide segment that is called the **anticodon**. There are 64 different tRNAs, each with a different combination of three nucleotides at the anticodon position. Remember that there are four different nucleotides that could be in each of the three positions. Thus, to calculate the number of possible combinations, we multiply 4 × 4 × 4. In addition to those coding for amino acids, there are also codons that code for a start signal and a translational stop signal. At the other end of the tRNA,

the amino acid that is encoded by the anticodon is attached in preparation for translation. Thus, the tRNA can read the genetic code using the anticodon and provide the appropriate amino acid to build the protein that the genetic code prescribes.

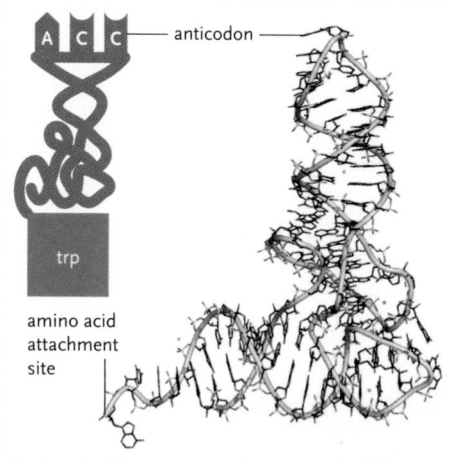

**FIGURE 1** tRNAs help the ribosome translate the genetic code. The anticodon reads the mRNA codon, and the tRNA delivers the correct amino acid to the growing protein during translation.

SOURCE: From STARR/TAGGART/Evers/Starr. *Biology*, 12E. © 2009 Brooks/Cole, a part of Cengage Learning, Inc. Reproduced by permission. www.cengage.com/permissions

---

encodes thousands of genes and can be millions, even billions, of nucleotides long. In eukaryotes, the DNA molecules are located in the nucleus of the cell. RNA molecules are more mobile and generally short-lived in the cell. Although they are made in the nucleus, they are translated in the cytoplasm, making them a portable source of information, Box 10.1 goes into more detail about different types of RNA molecules.

An RNA copy of the gene is made by a large enzyme complex called the **RNA polymerase**. This complex is composed of a number of different protein subunits. In bacteria, there are thought to be five proteins in the RNA polymerase; in eukaryotes, a minimum of 12 subunits is needed. To initiate transcription, proteins called transcription factors bind to the promoter region of the gene based on signals from the cell **(Figure 10.5, p. 220)**. The RNA polymerase binds to the transcription factors at the promoter region of the gene based on matching three-dimensional shapes, much like the interlocking pieces of a jigsaw puzzle. Once the right pieces are linked together—the RNA polymerase is bound to the promoter region—the DNA double helix is opened up to allow the RNA molecule to be made. The RNA polymerase links together the ribonucleotides that base-pair with the exposed DNA bases in the transcription region. Transcription continues down the DNA strand, generating an RNA copy of the gene, until the enzyme reaches the termination sequence (Figure 10.5). The polymerase complex will then separate from the DNA strand, and the RNA molecule is ready for the maturation process, which we will discuss in the next section.

## mRNAs Must Be Processed before They Can Be Translated

Once RNA molecules are made by the RNA polymerase, they need to go through a maturation process before they

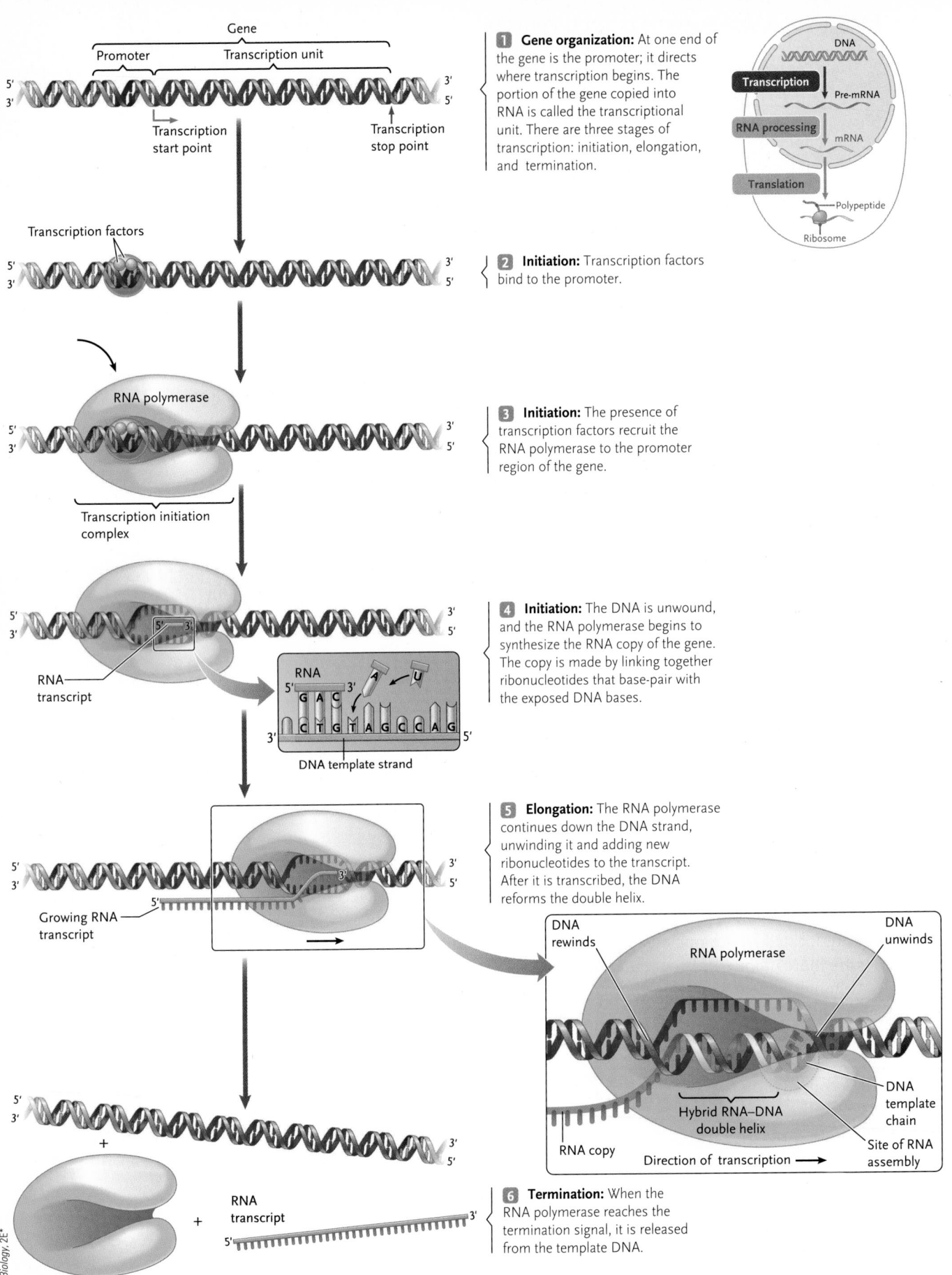

**1 Gene organization:** At one end of the gene is the promoter; it directs where transcription begins. The portion of the gene copied into RNA is called the transcriptional unit. There are three stages of transcription: initiation, elongation, and termination.

**2 Initiation:** Transcription factors bind to the promoter.

**3 Initiation:** The presence of transcription factors recruit the RNA polymerase to the promoter region of the gene.

**4 Initiation:** The DNA is unwound, and the RNA polymerase begins to synthesize the RNA copy of the gene. The copy is made by linking together ribonucleotides that base-pair with the exposed DNA bases.

**5 Elongation:** The RNA polymerase continues down the DNA strand, unwinding it and adding new ribonucleotides to the transcript. After it is transcribed, the DNA reforms the double helix.

**6 Termination:** When the RNA polymerase reaches the termination signal, it is released from the template DNA.

**FIGURE 10.5** Transcription progresses from initiation to elongation to termination after the RNA polymerase complex binds to the gene promoter region.

can be translated into proteins. The first step is a modification required for the ribosome to recognize the mRNA. It involves the addition of a 5′ cap to the RNA molecule (**Figure 10.6**). The 5′ cap is a methylated guanine ribonucleotide, which is added in a 5′ to 5′ linkage to the start of the mRNA molecule. This is an unusual connection as most nucleotides are linked by a 5′ to 3′ connection. The addition of this nucleotide in an unusual formation helps protect the mRNA molecule from digestion by exonucleases because the 5′ to 5′ linkage is much more resistant to cleavage.

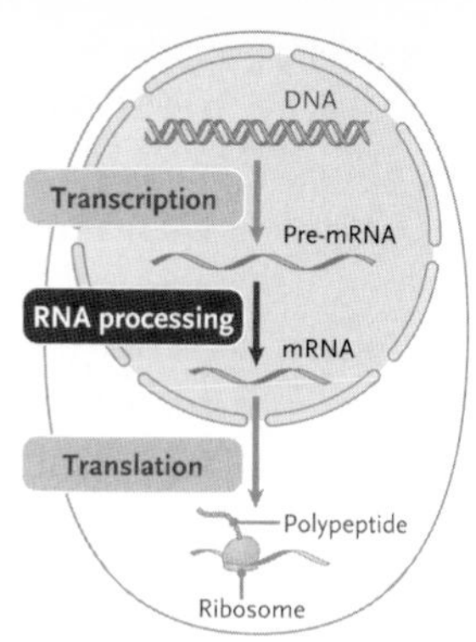

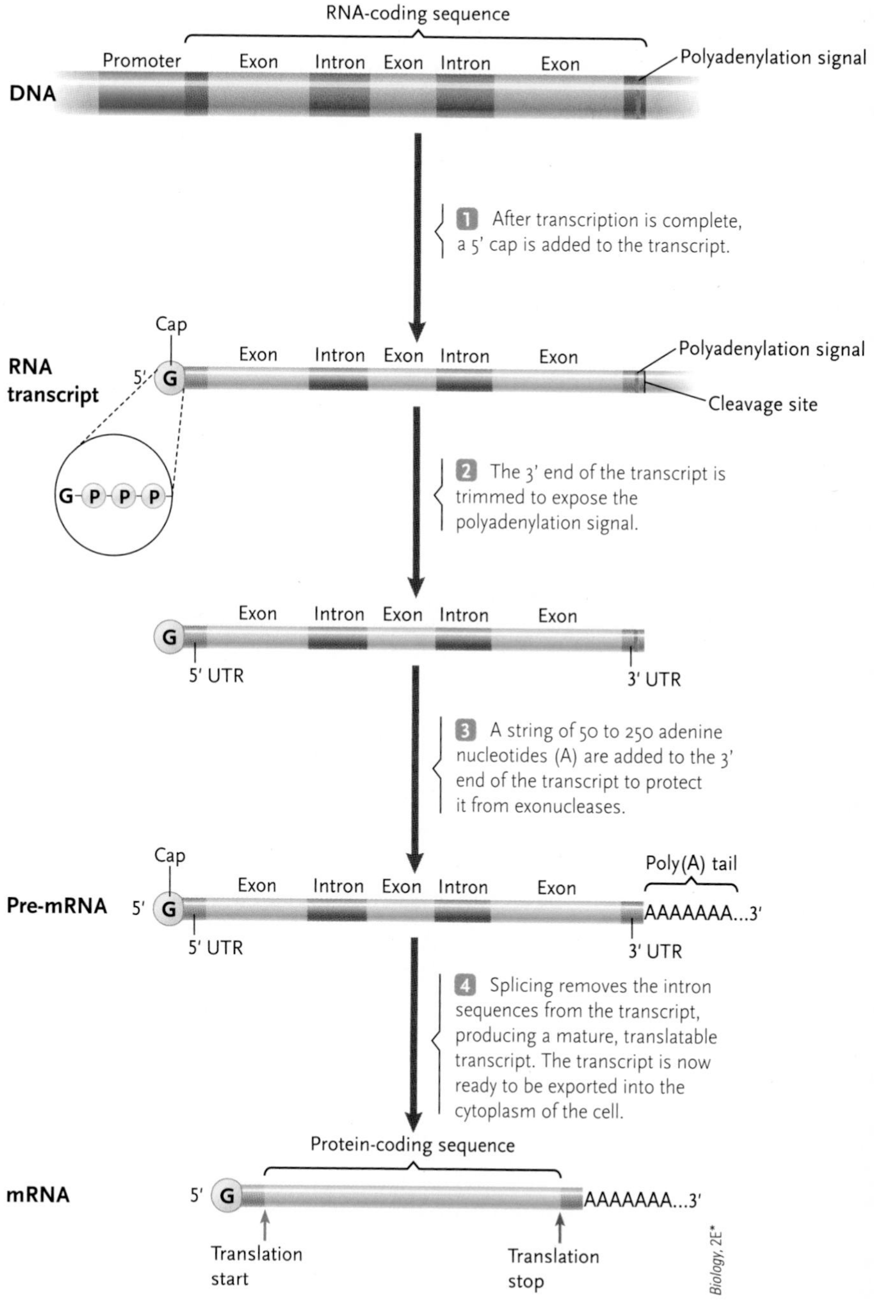

The second maturation step involves trimming the 3′ end of the transcript and adding a poly-A tail (Figure 10.6). A **poly-A tail** is simply a string of 50 to 250 adenine ribonucleotides that are not encoded by the gene on the DNA strand. The poly-A tail is important for the stability of the mRNA molecule. It helps protect the sensitive mRNA strand from digestion by **exonucleases**—RNA-digesting enzymes that begin work from one end of the RNA molecule and remove one base at a time. Thus, as an mRNA ages, the poly-A tail will shrink as bases are eaten away. If the poly-A tail is removed, not only is the mRNA sensitive to digestion, but it will also not be effectively translated as the ribosome looks for the poly-A tail before the start of translation.

As we mentioned, protein-encoding genes of eukaryotes normally contain introns that interrupt the protein-coding sequence of the exons. Therefore, in the final maturation step, the introns must be removed before the mRNA molecule can be translated into a functional protein. Immediately following transcription, the mRNA will still contain the extra information contained in the introns. They are removed by a complex process called **splicing**, which occurs in the nucleus of the cell. To simplify, one could compare it to editing a continuous-shot movie. There are portions of the movie, such as panning from one individual or object to another, that need to be removed from the film sequence to tell a more concise and accurate story. Before the advent of digital video recordings, this meant physically cutting the pieces of film and either gluing or taping the ends

**FIGURE 10.6** Following transcription, the mRNA molecule must go through a maturation process prior to export to the cytoplasm for translation.

together. Similarly, in the nucleus, the introns are spliced from the mRNA and the ends of the exons are linked together. This leaves just the protein-coding sequence. The removal of introns is performed by a complex of small RNA molecules and proteins called a **spliceosome**. For our level of inquiry, the exact process is not critically important; however, research has shown that not only is splicing required to remove the introns, but also the spliceosome helps export the mature mRNA molecule from the nucleus through the nuclear pores into the cytoplasm.

Thus, we can see how important it is to the cell that only accurately and completely transcribed mRNA molecules are made and sent to the next phase of the central dogma: translation. Once in the cytosol, it is equally important that proteins made from the mRNA molecules are correct translations of the gene. This explains why the level of quality control of the mRNA copies and the steps taken to ensure that they are protected from premature degradation are extreme. If they are not properly transcribed and processed, quality control machinery will rapidly degrade the mRNA in the nucleus so that it is not transported out to waiting ribosomes.

## Translation of the mRNA by Ribosomes Produces Proteins

Translation in molecular biology is very much like translation of words from one language to another, except in this case, we are translating nucleotides into amino acids. It is also a form of decryption, where three-letter nucleotide codes signify a single letter of the amino acid alphabet. In process, it is how the cell converts the information stored in a molecule of RNA into a protein. You will remember that genes are encoded as DNA for the stable transmission of information from generation to generation. As we discussed above, the gene's information is transcribed into a mobile RNA copy by an RNA polymerase. Both DNA and RNA information are in the form of polymers of nucleotides (remember the A, C, G, and T or U in the case of RNA from the Purple Pages). Although a good way to store information, the chemistry that nucleic acid polymers are capable of is rather limited. Although some RNA molecules have catalytic properties, speeding up chemical reactions in the cell, this is rare. The proteins in cells provide the fantastic array of functions and allow life to exist as we know it. Enzymes speed up chemical reactions, whereas other proteins form structural scaffolds that hold the cell together and allow communication to occur, not only inside the cell but also between neighbouring and distant cells. We rely on the process of translation to get from the information stage to the functional stage of the central dogma.

Once a mature mRNA molecule is properly spliced, processed, and exported from the nucleus, it will attract the pieces of an unassembled ribosome **(Figure 10.7)**. The small ribosome subunit will recognize the 5′ cap and move along the mRNA to the **translation start site**. The

start site for most mRNAs is the three-base sequence AUG—the **start codon**. It encodes the signal for a matching tRNA with its TAC anticodon, which is loaded with a methionine amino acid (Figure 10.7). The methionine will become the first amino acid of the protein. The presence of the small subunit of the ribosome and the first tRNA binding to the mRNA attracts the large ribosome subunit. The initiation phase of translation is completed when the two ribosome subunits are located at the start codon with a methionine tRNA base-paired to the start codon.

Once the initiation complex has formed, the elongation phase of translation can begin. The process of translation uses the ribosome for two critical steps. First, the ribosome frames the codon that needs to be translated so that the tRNA anticodon can base-pair with the mRNA strand. Only a tRNA with an anticodon that can base-pair with the exposed codon can remain in the exposed site. Once the second tRNA is in place, the ribosome then performs its second critical step **(Figure 10.8, p. 224)**. A peptide bond is formed between the amino acids, elongating the protein. After the peptide bond is formed, the first tRNA is released to be recycled, and the ribosome moves down the mRNA three bases. The ribosome pauses every three bases to allow a tRNA to base-pair with the three exposed codons of the mRNA. A tRNA that matches the newly exposed codon will now enter the ribosome, bringing the next amino acid for the growing protein chain, and the process is repeated.

Thus, the protein is made, one amino acid at a time, by reading the three-base code of the mRNA using a set of 64 possible tRNAs. The mRNA is completely translated when the ribosome reaches a **stop codon** (UGA, UAA, or UAG). The stop codon tRNA allows the newly synthesized protein to leave the ribosome. Once the protein leaves the ribosome, the large and small subunits disconnect from the mRNA molecule. These final steps complete the termination phase of translation.

Now that the protein is complete, it may need some additional processing and help folding into its functional three-dimensional shape before being packaged and sent to wherever it is needed within or outside the cell. To be active in the cell, many proteins need some further modification once translation is complete. These modifications are called post-translational processes.

## The Genetic Code Is Degenerate

Mathematically, scientists determined that at least three DNA bases would be required to separately encode the 20 different amino acids. For example, because there are four different DNA bases, a two-base code could only encode 16 amino acids: four choices

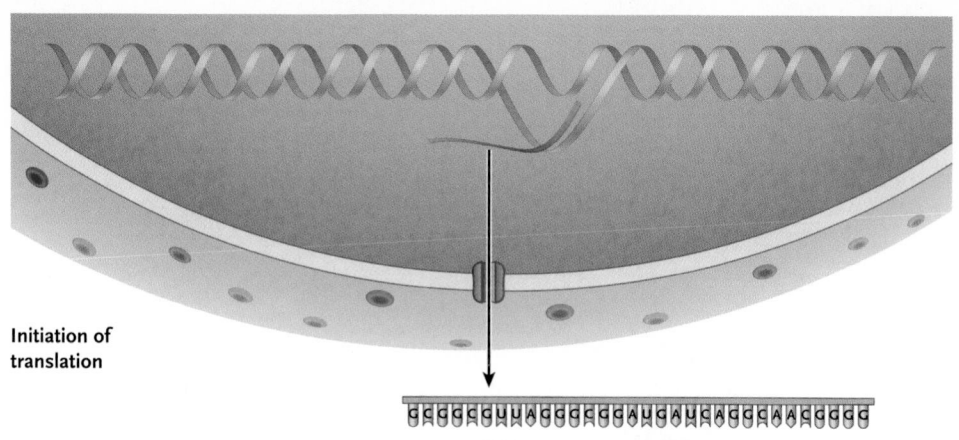

**FIGURE 10.7** The initiation phase of translation. The processed mRNA is exported from the nucleus, and the translation complex is assembled around the start codon.

**Initiation of translation**

**1** A mature mRNA leaves the nucleus and enters the cytoplasm, which has many free amino acids, tRNAs, and ribosomal subunits.

An initiator tRNA binds to a small ribosomal subunit and the mRNA.

mRNA

UAC
Met
Initiator tRNA

Small ribosomal subunit

AUGGUGUUAGGGCGCGA
UAC
Met

Large ribosomal subunit

**2** A large ribosomal subunit joins, and the cluster is now called an initiation complex.

AUGGUGUUAGGGCGCGA
UAC
Met

for the first base and four independent choices for the second base. (Mathematically, we can calculate the number of possibilities as 4 possibilities for the first base × 4 possibilities for the second base, or $4^2$). If the number of bases required to encode amino acids is expanded to three, the number of possibilities expands to 64 (4 possibilities for the first base × 4 possibilities for the second base × 4 possibilities for the third base, or $4^3$).

Scientists then began to try to break the code, to determine which series of nucleotide bases encoded which amino acids. Work by Marshall Nirenberg and Philip Leder at the National Institutes of Health in the United States and H. Gobind Khorana at the University of Wisconsin-Madison cracked this genetic code. They introduced chemically synthesized RNA molecules with a known order of nucleotides into an in vitro translation system and then observed what sequences of amino acids were connected together. For example, they chemically synthesized an RNA strand composed entirely of uracil molecules (U). This poly-U template made a peptide composed entirely of phenylalanine amino acids. Using brute force and systematic analysis, the labs of Nirenberg and Khorana determined each possible three-base code. It turns out that not all of the 64 possible combina-tions of three nucleotides code for an amino acid **(Figure 10.9, p. 225)**. AUG (which also codes for methionine) is the start signal, or start codon, that tells the ribosome where to start. There are also three possible combinations of three nucleotides that will tell the ribosome to stop translation; these are called stop codons. The other point that you may notice is if there

## Elongation

**3** An initiator tRNA carries the amino acid methionine, so the first amino acid of the new polypeptide chain will be methionine. A second tRNA binds the second codon of the mRNA (here, that codon is GUG, so the tRNA that binds carries the amino acid valine).

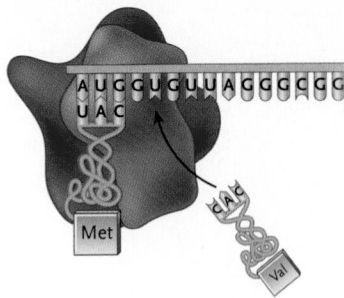

A peptide bond forms between the first two amino acids (here, methionine and valine).

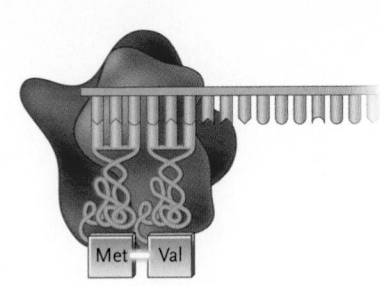

**4** The first tRNA is released, and the ribosome moves to the next codon in the mRNA. A third tRNA binds to the third codon of the mRNA (here, that codon is UUA, so the tRNA carries the amino acid leucine).

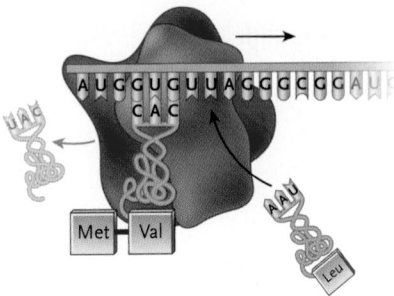

A peptide bond forms between the second and third amino acids (here, valine and leucine).

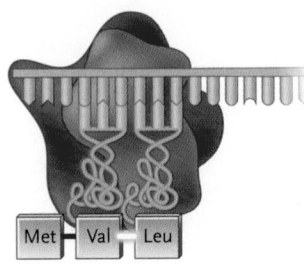

**5** The second tRNA is released, and the ribosome moves to the next codon. A fourth tRNA binds the fourth mRNA codon (here, that codon is GGG, so the tRNA carries the amino acid glycine).

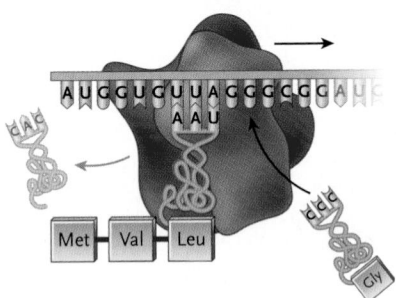

A peptide bond forms between the third and fourth amino acids (here, leucine and glycine).

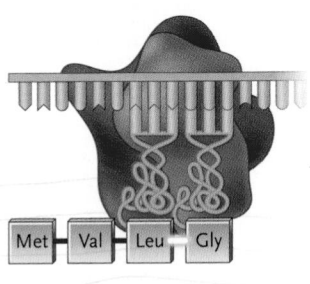

## Termination

**6** Steps 4 and 5 are repeated over and over until the ribosome encounters a stop codon in the mRNA. The mRNA transcript and the new polypeptide chain are released from the ribosome. The two ribosomal subunits separate from each other. Translation is now complete. Either the chain will join the pool of proteins in the cytoplasm or it will enter rough ER of the endomembrane system.

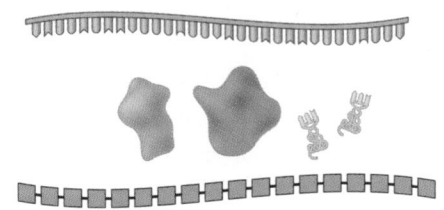

**FIGURE 10.8** Following translation initiation (see Figure 10.7), the ribosome moves down the mRNA in three-base steps, using tRNAs to translate the genetic code. When a stop codon is reached, the process ends and the components disassociate.

SOURCE: From STARR/TAGGART/Evers/Starr. *Biology*, 12E. © 2009 Brooks/Cole, a part of Cengage Learning, Inc. Reproduced by permission. www.cengage.com/permissions

are 64 possible nucleotide combinations for each codon, but only 20 amino acids, what are the other three-base codes signalling? It turns out that the genetic code has some redundancy. We mentioned above that there are three possible stop codons. Some amino acids are also encoded by more than one codon (Figure 10.9). Because of this redundancy, we say that the genetic code is degenerate. Based on this work, Nirenberg and Khorana shared the 1968 Nobel Prize in Physiology or Medicine with Robert Holley of Cornell University, who first isolated and characterized tRNAs, the crucial translator of the genetic code.

## In Bacterial Cells, We Can See the Central Dogma Frozen in Time

Section 10.2 provides an overview of the steps from gene to protein, as laid out in the central dogma of molecular biology. Although this process is complex and challenging to conceptualize because of the large numbers of steps and components involved, using electron microscopy, we can see the central dogma (**Figure 10.10**). Because bacterial cells perform transcription and translation in the same compartment, many transcripts can be made of a particular gene at the same time. Similarly, large numbers of ribosomes can attach to a single mRNA while

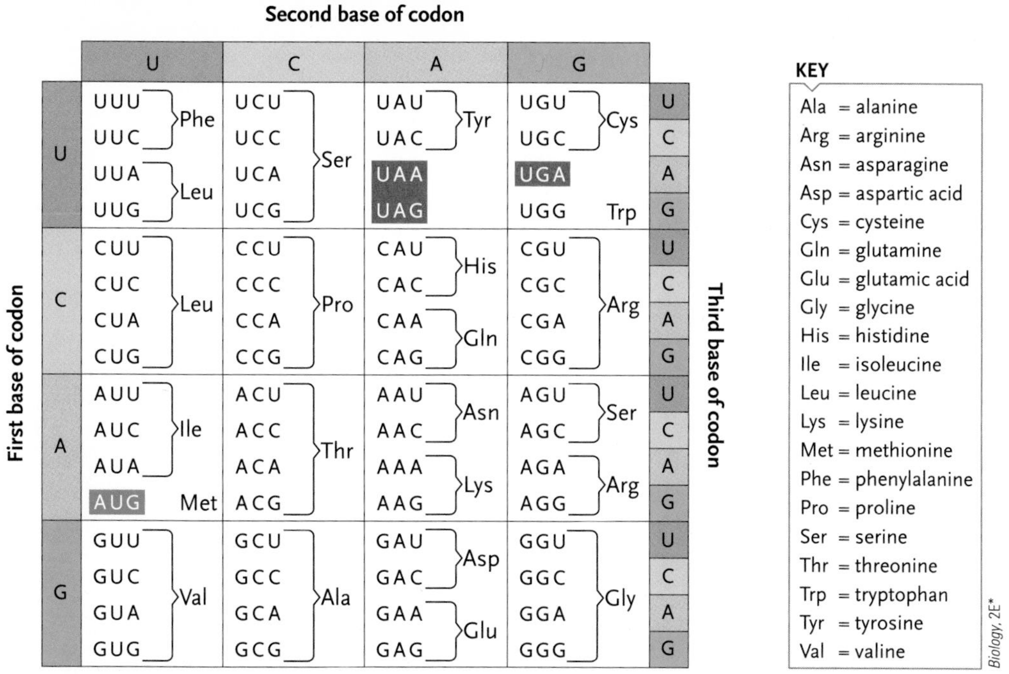

**Second base of codon**

| | U | C | A | G | |
|---|---|---|---|---|---|
| **U** | UUU ⎫ Phe<br>UUC ⎭<br>UUA ⎫ Leu<br>UUG ⎭ | UCU ⎫<br>UCC ⎪ Ser<br>UCA ⎪<br>UCG ⎭ | UAU ⎫ Tyr<br>UAC ⎭<br>UAA<br>UAG | UGU ⎫ Cys<br>UGC ⎭<br>UGA<br>UGG Trp | U<br>C<br>A<br>G |
| **C** | CUU ⎫<br>CUC ⎪ Leu<br>CUA ⎪<br>CUG ⎭ | CCU ⎫<br>CCC ⎪ Pro<br>CCA ⎪<br>CCG ⎭ | CAU ⎫ His<br>CAC ⎭<br>CAA ⎫ Gln<br>CAG ⎭ | CGU ⎫<br>CGC ⎪ Arg<br>CGA ⎪<br>CGG ⎭ | U<br>C<br>A<br>G |
| **A** | AUU ⎫<br>AUC ⎪ Ile<br>AUA ⎭<br>AUG Met | ACU ⎫<br>ACC ⎪ Thr<br>ACA ⎪<br>ACG ⎭ | AAU ⎫ Asn<br>AAC ⎭<br>AAA ⎫ Lys<br>AAG ⎭ | AGU ⎫ Ser<br>AGC ⎭<br>AGA ⎫ Arg<br>AGG ⎭ | U<br>C<br>A<br>G |
| **G** | GUU ⎫<br>GUC ⎪ Val<br>GUA ⎪<br>GUG ⎭ | GCU ⎫<br>GCC ⎪ Ala<br>GCA ⎪<br>GCG ⎭ | GAU ⎫ Asp<br>GAC ⎭<br>GAA ⎫ Glu<br>GAG ⎭ | GGU ⎫<br>GGC ⎪ Gly<br>GGA ⎪<br>GGG ⎭ | U<br>C<br>A<br>G |

First base of codon (left). Third base of codon (right).

**KEY**

Ala = alanine
Arg = arginine
Asn = asparagine
Asp = aspartic acid
Cys = cysteine
Gln = glutamine
Glu = glutamic acid
Gly = glycine
His = histidine
Ile = isoleucine
Leu = leucine
Lys = lysine
Met = methionine
Phe = phenylalanine
Pro = proline
Ser = serine
Thr = threonine
Trp = tryptophan
Tyr = tyrosine
Val = valine

*Biology, 2E\**

**FIGURE 10.9** The genetic code. The 64 possible codons allow some redundancy when encoding 20 amino acids and the stop signal (in red).

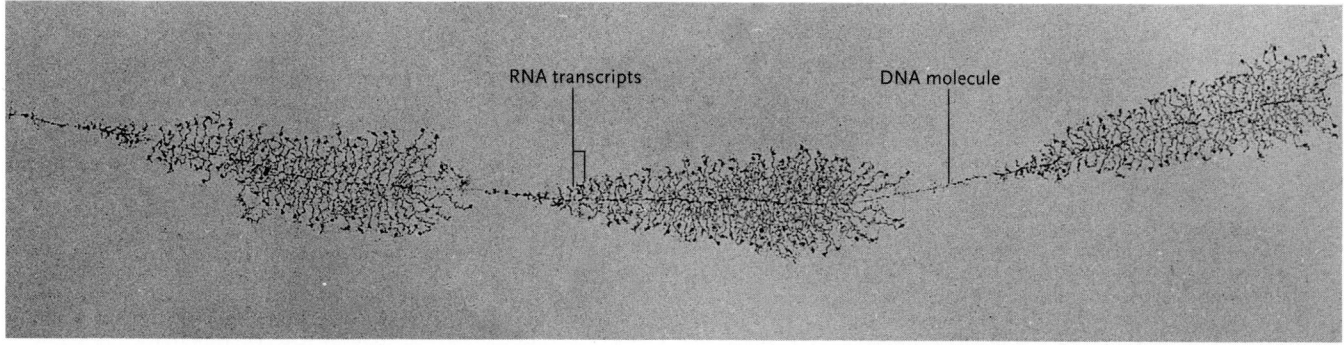

RNA transcripts

DNA molecule

**FIGURE 10.10** The central dogma of molecular biology in action. Individual genes are being transcribed by RNA polymerases to yield mRNA transcripts. Rapidly transcribed genes are transcribed by many RNA polymerases at the same time.

SOURCE: From STARR/TAGGART/Evers/Starr. *Biology*, 12E. © 2009 Brooks/Cole, a part of Cengage Learning, Inc. Reproduced by permission. www.cengage.com/permissions

it is still being transcribed. This allows bacteria to respond very quickly to produce the specific proteins they need. In the next section of this chapter, we will look at how cells control the steps from gene to protein so that specific proteins are made only when and where they are needed.

## Study Break

1. Why can we not see RNA polymerases and ribosomes in action on the same strand of RNA in eukaryotic cells?
2. What function do the 5′ cap and 3′ poly-A tail serve in eukaryotic mRNAs?
3. What is a codon? What is an anticodon? How are the two related?
4. Looking at Figure 10.10, can you determine in which direction the genes on the bacterial chromosome are being transcribed? Is it left to right or right to left on the page?

## 10.3 Regulation of Gene Expression

The steps required to produce a functional protein from a gene encoded on the DNA strand are only one part of the process of gene expression. The central dogma of molecular biology only describes flow of information from storage (DNA strand) to function (protein). It does not describe how the process of gene expression is controlled. If we think back to the apple trees again, only the cells on the surface of the apple fruit need the proteins capable of making the red pigments that indicate the fruit is ripe. Not all proteins are needed in each cell or at all times. The process of producing proteins must turn on and off in response to the needs of the organism—in other words, it must be possible to regulate gene expression. We see this process occurring during evolution as well. Looking at the genomes of related species, we often see genes that are present but not expressed. The unexpected expression can lead to unpredicted phenotypes, such as teeth in chickens. We explore this concept in greater detail in Box 10.2.

Professor Jack Horner is the curator of paleontology at the Museum of the Rockies in Bozeman, Montana, and one of the world's foremost experts in dinosaur behaviour and development. He is currently working on a project involving Dr. Hans Larsson, a Canadian Research Chair in Macro-evolution and Paleontology and curator of the Redpath Museum at McGill University in Montreal. Together they are attempting to turn back the evolutionary clock and produce a dinosaur-like organism by changing the expression of specific genes in the common chicken. The proposed organism has been nicknamed "chicken-o-saurus" **(Figure 1)**. According to Dr. Larsson, the project was inspired by a discussion of how evolution could be taught in schools.

In trying to develop exciting examples of evolution, they discussed the evolutionary links between dinosaurs and birds. How different are modern birds from dinosaurs? Is a chicken a small *T. rex*? Not exactly, but during the initial stages of development, chicken embryos have three-fingered hands much like those seen in fossils of ancient birdlike animals such as Archaeopteryx. As the chicken embryo matures, a gene or set of genes are expressed that cause the bones of the three-fingered hand to fuse into a single digit. This single digit is thought to have evolved to provide modern birds with the strength needed for flight. Thus, we can see how a change in gene expression in the "hand" of modern birds sets them apart from their ancestors, the dinosaurs. A similar trait that can be seen in the developing chicken embryo is the formation of a relatively long tail. However, as with the fusing of hand bones, a gene or set of genes is activated, during chicken embryo development, that causes the tail to be absorbed by the developing embryo; the chick that hatches has the small stubby tail we see in chickens. Once again, we can see that a change in the expression of specific genes changes the body shape of modern birds to make them more aerodynamic compared to their dinosaur ancestors.

Drs. Horner and Larsson propose that they can identify and alter the expression of the genes that control bone fusion in the hands of chicken embryos. Similarly, they suggest that they can alter gene expression in the embryo to limit tail absorption. These steps could result in chickens hatching with fingers and tails. Reversing millions of years of evolutionary processes, Horner and Larsson suggest that altering the expression of just a few genes at the right time could block the developmental cues that result in the chicken looking like a modern bird. Dr. Horner hopes that a "chicken-o-saurus" would attract more students to the study of evolution. One could imagine a flock of fluffy white chickens with fingers and tails, which result from altered gene expression. The appearance of phenotypic traits that were lost through the evolutionary process is called **atavism**. Infrequently, human children are born with tails, baby snakes hatch with crude legs, and, as we mentioned, chickens can grow teeth. Evolution does not always require new genes; sometimes it requires only a change in the pattern of gene expression. As the evolution of animal development has progressed as a subdiscipline of biology, it has clearly shown that it is not about what genes you have; it is about what genes you express and when you express them.

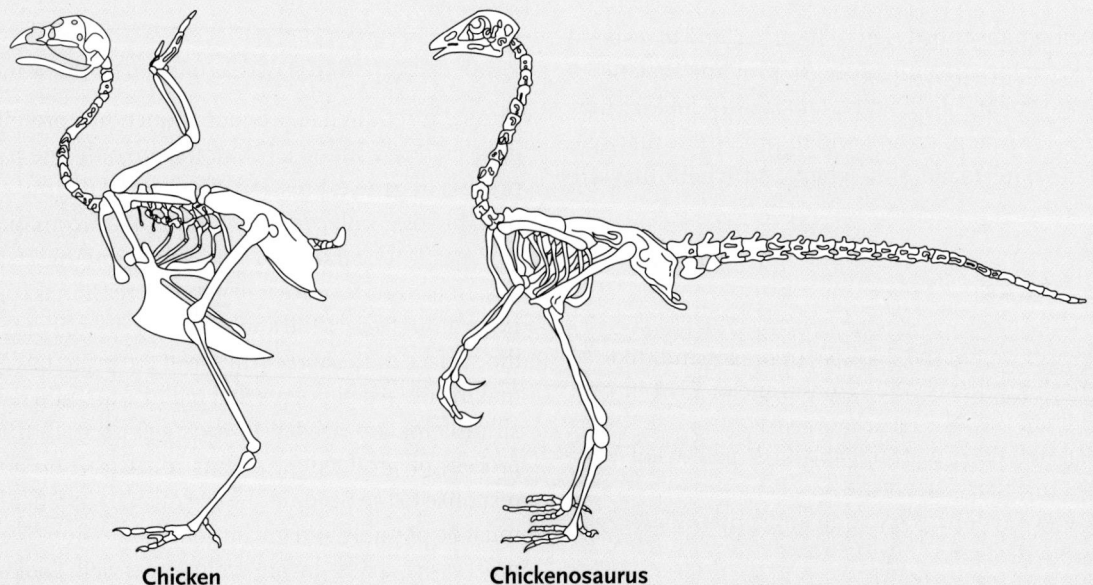

**Chicken**          **Chickenosaurus**

**FIGURE 1** Jack Horner proposes that altering the control of gene expression could lead to the "chicken-o-saurus."

SOURCE: Based on http://1.bp.blogspot.com/-WahDHnuEIG0/TviycdWdn7I/AAAAAAAADg/Q4T7oUUbKNU/s1600/Chicken_Chickenosaurus.png

The relatively simple model bacterium *Escherichia coli* (or *E. coli*) has approximately 4300 protein-encoding genes in its genome. The model plant *Arabidopsis thaliana* has 27,000; humans have 20,000. Only a fraction of the proteins encoded by these genes will be needed in a given cell at a particular moment. For example, a cell found in the root of an *Arabidopsis* plant will need different proteins to function properly than will a cell found in a flower petal or leaf. In fact, more specialized cells often require fewer different types of proteins to function. The cells that make up the eye of a fruit fly synthesize specific chemicals used to detect light. These would not be beneficial if they were made in cells that make up the insect's wing. To control which proteins are produced at a particular time, a complex process called **regulation of gene expression** is required. Gene expression as outlined by the central dogma of molecular biology is the production of an active protein, following transcription, translation, and processing. However, as we will see below, there are a number of ways that the expression of specific genes can be controlled or regulated **(Figure 10.11)**.

## Transcriptional Regulation Determines How Quickly mRNA Molecules Are Made

Often on receiving a signal from the environment, cells will change the level of expression of certain genes. One way this can be accomplished is through an increased rate of transcription. This will lead to the accumulation of more mRNA molecules and, correspondingly, a greater amount of the protein that it encodes. The opposite is also true, in response to specific cues; a signal is received in the nucleus to decrease the rate of transcription. This will lead to fewer mRNA copies and less of the encoded protein made (Figure 10.11, red box).

Transcriptional regulation of gene expression normally uses specialized proteins called **transcription factors**. These proteins are able to bind to DNA due to their specific tertiary structure. Their three-dimensional shape is so specific that it will bind only to certain sequences of DNA. Short sequences of nucleotides in the promoter and enhancer regions of the gene attract specific transcription factors. The binding or releasing of transcription factors from the promoter or enhancer

region of the gene can recruit or block the RNA polymerase complex, thus determining whether specific genes are transcribed. As we mentioned before, although eukaryotic cells do not have operons of genes needed for a specific purpose, their promoters and enhancers will bind the same transcription factors. This way, when the transcription factors are present, all of the genes needed for a purpose will be transcribed at a similar rate. When transcription factor binding is determined by the environmental conditions surrounding the cell, gene transcription is effectively controlled by these environmental cues.

The role of transcription factors in controlling gene expression has been well described by scientists. A classic example of how transcriptional control can regulate the amount of specific proteins in response to environmental signals uses the *lac* operon. The bacterium *E. coli* mostly uses glucose as a carbon source. As such, it has proteins in its plasma membrane that will

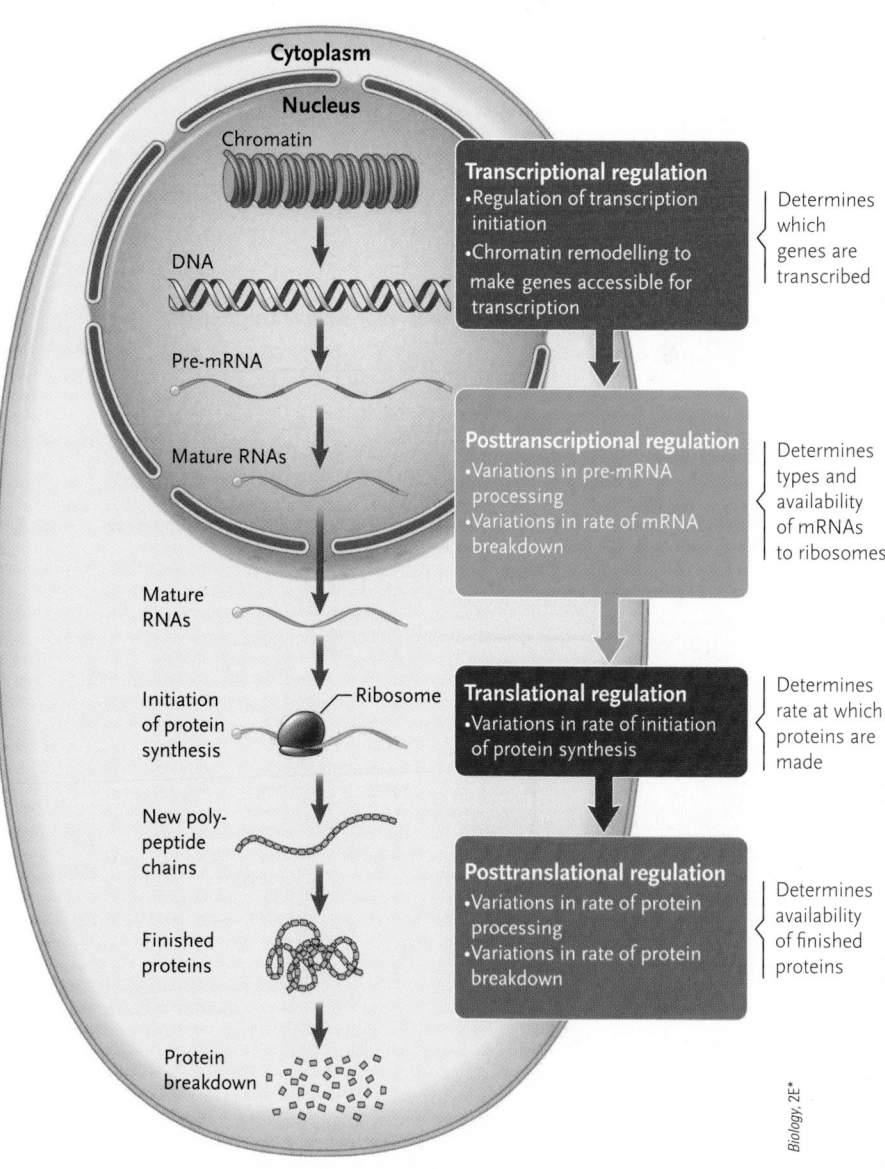

**FIGURE 10.11** Points where gene expression can be regulated in eukaryotic cells.

transport glucose into the cell. Once in the cell, it is ultimately broken down to provide energy for the cell. (See Chapter 5 for a review of cellular respiration.) However, because *E. coli* primarily lives in the intestinal tract of animals, it has little control over the type of carbohydrates it can access. As a result, it has evolved other systems to break down—or metabolize—more complex carbohydrates. When we drink milk, the *E. coli* in our intestine gets exposed to the sugar lactose. To use lactose as a source of energy, the *E. coli* cell must transport the sugar across the plasma membrane and metabolize it. If lactose is available for the *E. coli* cell, it can be taken

up slowly by the cell via a lactose transporter (remember that polar molecules cannot diffuse across the plasma membrane). Once inside the cell, lactose binds to a protein called the lactose repressor **(Figure 10.12)**. The lactose repressor is a protein that by default binds to the promoter of the *lac* operon and blocks transcription of the *lac* operon genes. Lactose changes the shape of the lactose repressor, breaking its attachment to the *lac* operon operator region (Figure 10.11). Now the promoter region of the *lac* operon is available to the RNA polymerase enzyme, the *lac* operon will be expressed, and the *E. coli* cell can get the energy it needs from

**A. Lactose absent from medium: structural genes expressed at very low levels**

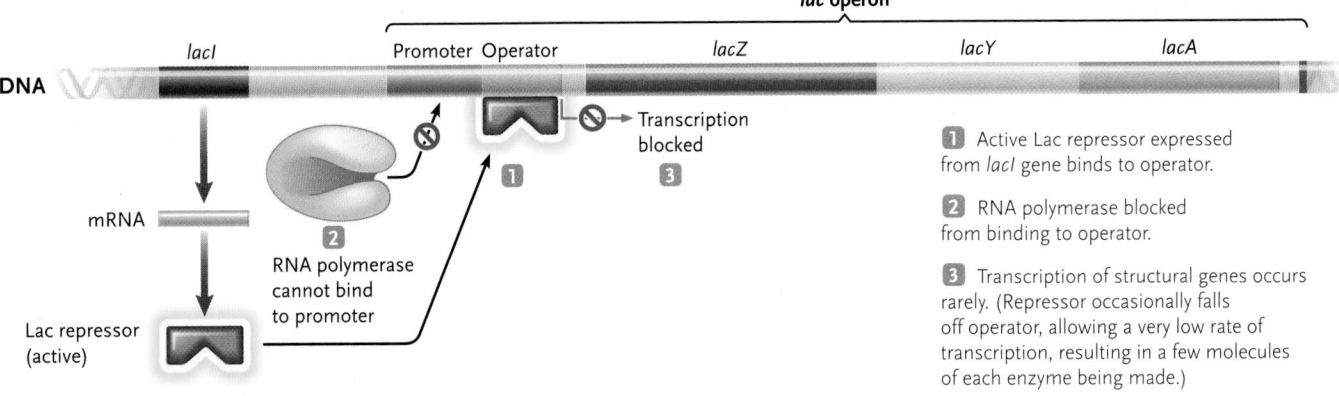

1. Active Lac repressor expressed from *lacI* gene binds to operator.

2. RNA polymerase blocked from binding to operator.

3. Transcription of structural genes occurs rarely. (Repressor occasionally falls off operator, allowing a very low rate of transcription, resulting in a few molecules of each enzyme being made.)

**B. Lactose present in medium: structural genes expressed at high levels**

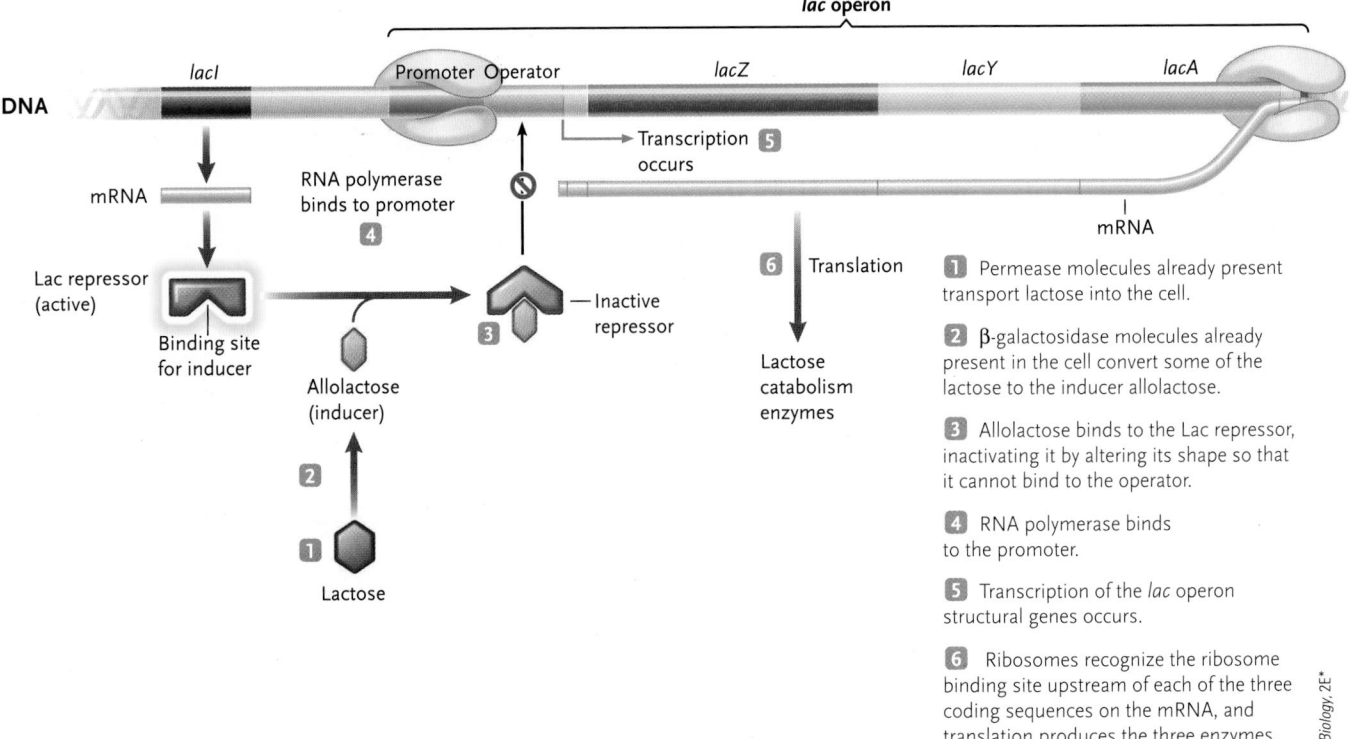

1. Permease molecules already present transport lactose into the cell.

2. β-galactosidase molecules already present in the cell convert some of the lactose to the inducer allolactose.

3. Allolactose binds to the Lac repressor, inactivating it by altering its shape so that it cannot bind to the operator.

4. RNA polymerase binds to the promoter.

5. Transcription of the *lac* operon structural genes occurs.

6. Ribosomes recognize the ribosome binding site upstream of each of the three coding sequences on the mRNA, and translation produces the three enzymes.

*Biology, 2E\**

**FIGURE 10.12** The *lac* operon is normally in a transcriptionally off position. The lactose repressor protein binds to the operator region of the *lac* operon, stopping the RNA polymerase from accessing the promoter **(a)**. When lactose is present, it binds to the lactose repressor, causing the repressor protein to let go of the *lac* operator region of the DNA strand and freeing the promoter to attract the RNA polymerase **(b)**.

lactose. We might ask ourselves why would the cell not express the *lac* operon all the time? Glucose is a smaller molecule and requires less energy and fewer resources to metabolize. If glucose is available, the cell would waste energy producing proteins to metabolize lactose when it is not needed.

There are many similar examples of transcriptional gene regulation in eukaryotic systems. In organisms that are more complex, signals are sent not just within cells but also between cells, sometimes from tissues that are quite far apart in the body. We will discuss how these signals work in Chapter 26, but for now let's use estrogen as an example. Estrogens are a group of steroid hormones produced in all vertebrates. They control the expression of genes that contribute to the onset of puberty, and in females, estrogens regulate the development of secondary sexual characteristics. At the cellular level, estrogens enter cells from the bloodstream by diffusing across the plasma membrane; they are lipophilic (fat soluble), so they do not need to be recognized by cell surface receptors **(Figure 10.13)**. Once inside the cell, the estrogen molecule can bind to a transcription factor found in the

**FIGURE 10.13** In eukaryotic cells, signalling from one cell or tissue can alter the expression of specific genes in other cells. Here we see how a steroid hormone can affect gene expression at the transcriptional level.

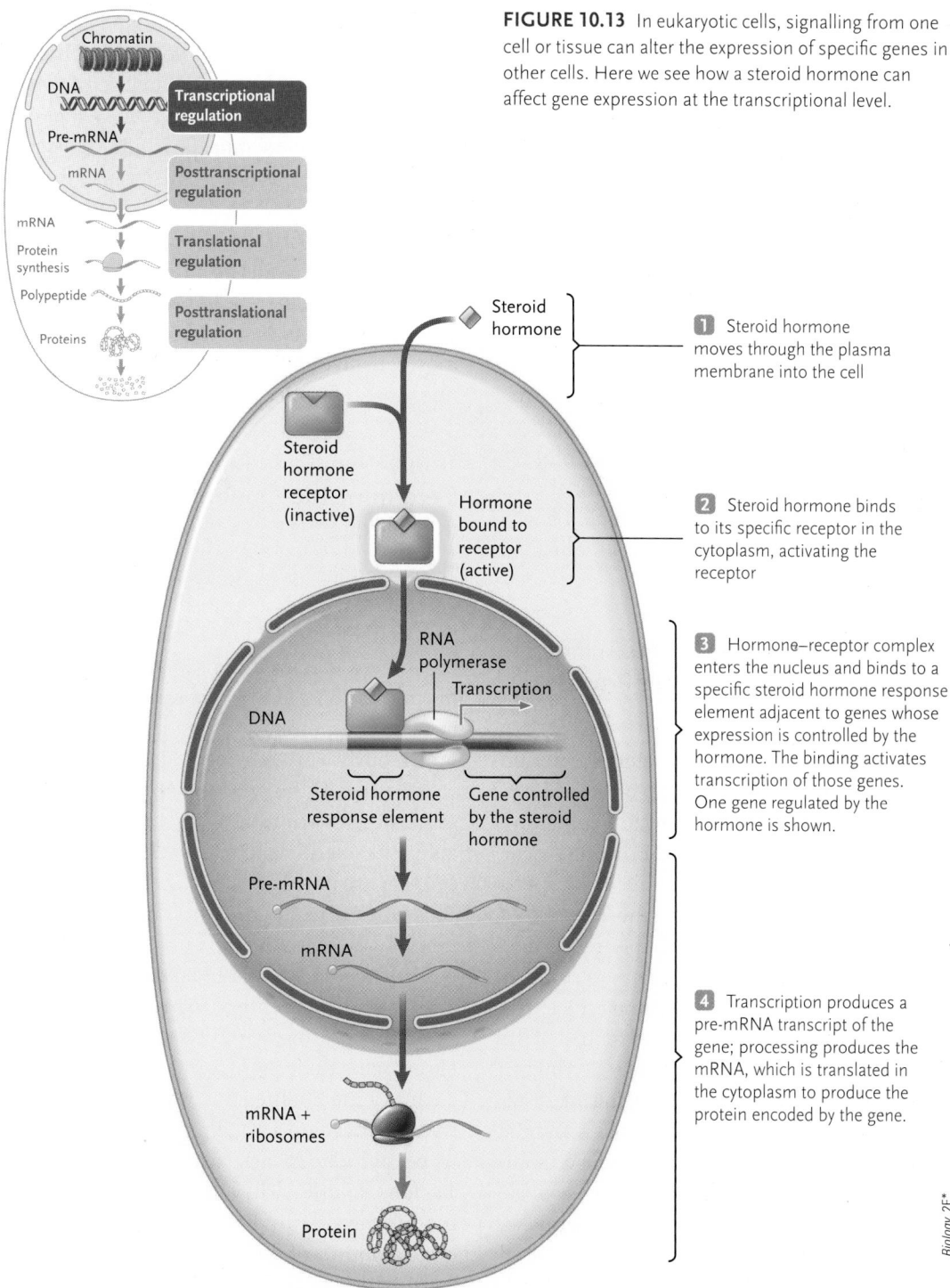

1 Steroid hormone moves through the plasma membrane into the cell

2 Steroid hormone binds to its specific receptor in the cytoplasm, activating the receptor

3 Hormone–receptor complex enters the nucleus and binds to a specific steroid hormone response element adjacent to genes whose expression is controlled by the hormone. The binding activates transcription of those genes. One gene regulated by the hormone is shown.

4 Transcription produces a pre-mRNA transcript of the gene; processing produces the mRNA, which is translated in the cytoplasm to produce the protein encoded by the gene.

*Biology, 2E\**

cytosol. The estrogen–transcription factor complex then migrates to the nucleus, where it binds to the steroid hormone enhancer region of specific genes. Of course, all of the genes that are more highly expressed in response to estrogen will have this particular enhancer. The result is increased expression of genes that respond to estrogens (Figure 10.13).

Relatively simple systems such as the steroid hormone signalling mechanism described above seem like an ideal process. When a hormone signal is present, a set of proteins are made, and the body changes as a result. However, we are discovering that foreign chemicals with a structure similar to that of estrogens can trigger developmental changes at the wrong times. A suite of compounds called **xenoestrogens** (*xeno* is a Greek prefix meaning alien; thus, xenoestrogens are alien or unnatural estrogens) are generated by both industrial and natural sources. One xenoestrogen that has received a lot of attention over the past few years is bisphenol A (BPA). BPA has been used since the 1950s to make certain types of plastics—in particular, the clear, hard plastics used in water bottles, food containers, sports equipment, and even DVDs. Very small amounts of BPA have been shown to leach out of the plastics. When ingested by animals, BPA can cause the same effects as ingestion of estrogen because it triggers the expression of the same genes. Hence, exposure to these types of alien estrogens may upset the balance of gene expression in cells, leading to structural and functional changes in tissues. This is only one example of why we need to monitor the quality and source of our food and water.

## Post-transcriptional Regulation Determines How Quickly mRNA Molecules Are Processed and Degraded

Transcriptional regulation of gene expression is common in bacteria; however, in eukaryotes, many other layers of regulation control how much of a given protein is produced at a specific time (Figure 10.12). Sometimes gene expression can be controlled by how much mRNA is available to be translated. Of course, the amount of mRNA is a reflection of the rate at which it is transcribed and the rate at which it is degraded. Cells have a complex suite of enzymes that can degrade mRNA molecules. The half-life of some mRNAs (the time required for half of the mRNA to be degraded) is only a few minutes. So you can imagine the amount of mRNA molecules being the result of equilibrium between the rate of transcription and the rate of degradation. Increasing the rate of transcription or decreasing the rate of degradation would have the same net effect of increasing the abundance of the mRNA and hence the amount of the specific protein that could be made in the cell.

A fantastic example of post-transcriptional regulation of gene expression occurs in cells of the yeast *Saccharomyces cerevisiae*. Being single cells and dependent on other organisms for food, yeast cells regularly face environmental stress. The cells can be affected by low or high temperature, a lack of nutrients, or a change in food source. To be prepared for stressful situations, yeast cells produce large amounts of mRNA for a gene called *UFO1*. It is thought that the UFO1 protein helps protect the genome of the yeast cell from damage caused by environmental stress. As you can imagine, this sounds like a pretty important protein. It turns out that yeast cells store UFO1 mRNA for tough times. As UFO1 is transcribed by the cell, some of the mature mRNAs are stored in packages called granules in the cytosol. Although packaged in granules, the mRNAs are not translated and not degraded; they are just waiting. When a stress event occurs, often cells are unable to quickly begin translation of new mRNAs. They would need to first transcribe new mRNAs, process them, export them, etc. However, in the case of UFO1, the mRNAs are in the cytosol, ready to go. So when a stress event does occur, the yeast cell unpacks its UFO1 mRNA, and translation can begin almost immediately. This is a great example of evolution protecting the most sensitive and important part of the cell, the genome. The yeast cell is like a Boy Scout: always prepared.

## Translational and Post-translational Regulation Determine the Amount of Each Protein in the Cell

Transcriptional and post-transcriptional regulation of gene expression determine the amount of a given mRNA that would be present in the cell. The final step to get to the protein is translation. Control of gene expression at the translational level is also critical for the accumulation of correct amounts of specific proteins (Figure 10.11, brown box).

We saw in the previous section how mRNA can be sequestered away from the ribosome and made unavailable. But scientists have also discovered mRNAs in the cell that are not translated unless the protein is needed. This type of "just in time" production is common in the manufacturing industry, but how can cells make these types of arrangements? In 2002, three different research groups independently discovered something called a **riboswitch**. A riboswitch is a segment of an mRNA that, based on its folded structure, can bind a small molecule such as a metabolite, ion, or vitamin. Researchers were trying to develop a system to produce vitamin B1 (thiamine pyrophosphate) using the model soil bacteria *Bacillus subtilis*. They hypothesized that they could modify the vitamin $B_1$ biosynthetic pathway to produce large amounts of the vitamin, which could then be used in nutritional aids. However, they found that as the

*B. subtilis* cells began to accumulate vitamin B$_1$, they stopped producing the enzyme proteins encoded by the thiamine operon. Looking into this further, they found that vitamin B$_1$, itself, was binding to the thiamine operon mRNA, which encodes the key biosynthetic enzymes. When vitamin B$_1$ binds to the operon mRNA, it alters the folded shape of the RNA molecule, blocking access to the AUG codon by the tRNA. This in turn stops ribosome assembly; hence, translation cannot occur. So, despite sufficient mRNA being present in the cell, because vitamin B$_1$ is not needed, translation does not occur. Riboswitches are an amazing trait that evolved to provide cells with an ability to detect the presence of molecules in the cytosol. Of course, they are just one example of how cells control rates of translation.

Much the way that a balance between transcription and mRNA degradation determines how much of a given mRNA will be present in the cell, the rate of translation is balanced with the rate of protein degradation. Some proteins remain in the cell for long periods of time,

whereas others are turned over very quickly. This level of control of gene expression is said to be post-translational (Figure 10.11, blue box). One other factor that is important to remember with respect to the accumulation of proteins in the cell is that they must be folded into their proper three-dimensional shape (you can review protein folding in the Purple Pages) and sent to the location where they are needed. Remember from Chapter 3 that many of the proteins required in the chloroplast for photosynthesis are translated in the cytosol and then imported into the chloroplast. Even when we think we understand gene expression, it seems that there are more complications. In the next two sections, we will look at how organismal development and epigenetics control gene expression.

## Developmental Regulation Coordinates Gene Expression at the Level of the Whole Organism

Of the many types of interactions that occur between different organisms, some of the most fascinating occur when one of the organisms takes over the gene expression system of the other. We see this quite often in viruses. Because viruses cannot replicate themselves, they take over the gene expression machinery of a host cell and trick it into making many, many copies of the virus genome and associated proteins. We will discuss the processes in more detail in Chapter 14. The types of relationships seen in larger, more diverse systems can be even more amazing. One example is the complex relationship that occurs between the gall-inducing fly *Eurosta solidaginis* and goldenrod plants (*Solidago* sp.) **(Figure 10.14)**. The female fly lays eggs by inserting her ovipositor into the terminal bud of a growing goldenrod plant. When the eggs hatch, the larvae begin eating the plant material in the stem, protected from potential predators by the very plant they are consuming. The fly larvae eat both structural parts of the stem, and the sugars dissolve in the phloem liquid that the plant transports from

**FIGURE 10.14** The gall that forms on the stem of a goldenrod plant (*Solidago sp.*) is caused by a plant hormone mimic released by the larvae living inside.

the leaves of the stem to the roots (see Chapter 17 for more details). While living inside the plant stem, the larvae release a chemical into the surrounding tissue that mimics the plant hormone **auxin**. Auxin controls many different aspects of plant development; however, in this case, it increases the expression of specific genes that result in the cells of the plant stem growing larger and dividing more times than they normally would. The result is a localized thickening of the plant stem in an area immediately surrounding the larva. The ball-shaped structure that results is called a gall, and its initial formation can be observed within just 3 weeks of the larvae hatching and will reach a final size by 7 weeks. This thickened area draws extra nutrients from the plant, providing a constant source of food for the larvae. In the winter, the gall provides added protection to help the larvae survive the drying effects of the cold weather. This example shows us how the expression of specific genes in the plant can be controlled by the behaviour of the larvae.

## Epigenetic Control of Gene Expression Occurs in Response to Chromatin Structure

In Chapter 9, we mentioned that eukaryotic chromosomes are wound around histones to form chromatin. We also mentioned that the chromatin structure can change between a tightly packed form called heterochromatin and a less tightly packed form called euchromatin. The packing of DNA in a chromosome can switch back and forth between the two forms. However, depending on the packing status of a particular region of a chromosome, genes located there may be more or less easily expressed. For example, tightly packaged heterochromatin tends to limit the access of RNA polymerases to gene promoters in that region. Thus, chromosome packaging can affect gene expression in a way that is not regulated by transcription factors or the promoter region of the gene. Because this level of regulation is thought to occur beyond the level of gene inheritance, it has been called epigenetics (literally "above the gene"). However, the definition has morphed over the years to include any change in inheritance that is not caused by permanent changes in the genetic sequence or code.

Epigenetics is a relatively new branch of biology that has started to explain a number of observations that could not be explained by Mendelian inheritance patterns. Although chromatin folding was one of the first explanations, scientists now realize that many other processes help determine chromatin structure. This includes the methylation of **histones**—proteins around which DNA is wound. At the most basic level, the methylation of histones, and even some DNA bases, leads to less actively transcribed regions of chromatin. One famous study examined the coat colour of mice. Mice with an "agouti" coat colour are generally a deep brown colour. However, research done in the lab of Dr. Michael Skinner at the University of Washington demonstrated that when pregnant mice were fed a diet that contained trace amounts of BPA (remember this compound from Section 10.2), the coat colours of their offspring tended to be lighter in colour, for their entire lives, even though the mice were genetically identical **(Figure 10.15)**. The

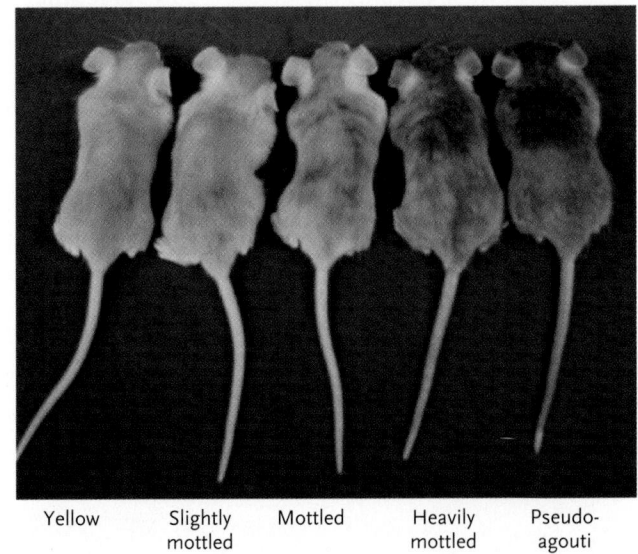

Yellow  Slightly mottled  Mottled  Heavily mottled  Pseudo-agouti

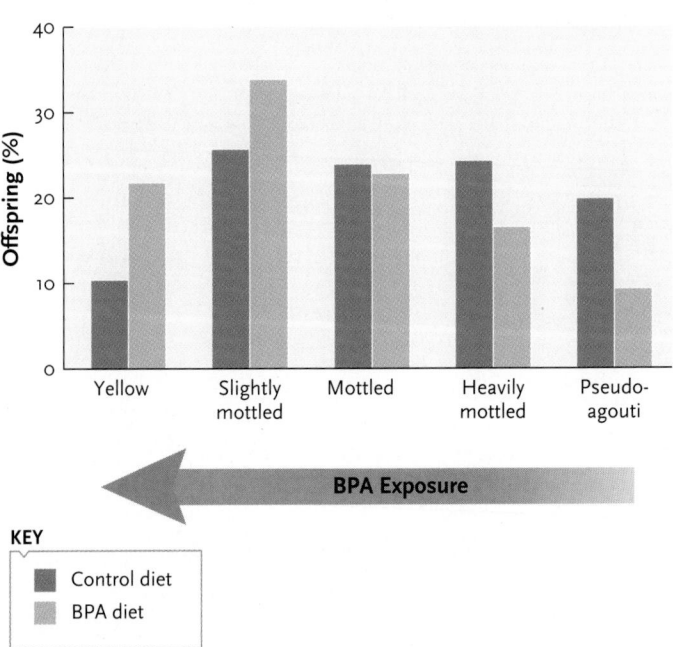

**FIGURE 10.15** Agouti-coloured mice lose colouration because their mothers were exposed to BPA.

SOURCE: Dana C Dolinoy, "The agouti mouse model: an epigenetic biosensor for nutritional and environmental alterations on the fetal epigenome," *Nutrition Reviews®* Vol. 66 (Suppl. 1):S7–S11. John Wiley and Sons. © 2008 International Life Sciences Institute.

researchers found that the histones and DNA surrounding the agouti gene were less methylated in mice with lighter coloured coats. Amazingly, when the diet of pregnant mice included BPA and folic acid—a compound that can donate methyl groups—methylation was partially restored, and the coat colour of the offspring tended to be darker. This is only one case of many in which scientists have shown that environmental effects can alter the long-term expression of genes.

## PUTTING IT IN PERSPECTIVE

Gene expression is such an important aspect of every living thing. Remember that we are 90% the same, at the genetic level, as mice. The similarity between humans and other primates is even greater, yet at some level, due to gene expression, we are vastly different. However, the similarities that we do have can lead to problems in how we share our resources. In Section 10.3, we discussed the effect that exposure to environmental contaminants can have on gene expression. Xenoestrogens and BPA interact with cellular communication proteins in our cells and the cells of other vertebrates and cause changes in gene expression, which can be passed from generation to generation. Vertebrates have been on Earth for nearly 500 million years. For that entire time, their cellular communication systems have evolved precisely to regulate the genes needed for their development. However, over the past 100+ years, humans have interfered with these finely tuned signals. By dumping chemical waste into rivers, lakes, and oceans and by spraying pesticides on our agricultural crops, we have inadvertently been providing external signals to animal cells.

One of the most interesting cases is the xenoestrogens. Members of this class of chemicals are also called endocrine disruptors. We will discuss the endocrine system in greater detail in Chapter 26, but for now let us remember that estrogens are responsible for female sexual characteristics and testosterone for male sexual characteristics. In the late 1990s, researchers began to report detecting relatively high numbers of wild fish with indeterminate sexual characteristics. A significant number of fish exhibited a combination of male and female characteristics. Careful examinations suggested that these changes were due to estrogens that could be detected in the river water that were traced back to sewage effluent. Although a complex mixture, one of the sources of estrogens in sewage water was shown to be from birth control pills.

Although certainly not working alone, it is amazing to think that unabsorbed pharmaceuticals can pass through our bodies, into the sewage treatment system, and then into our waterways. It shows that we need to take care of how we dispose of all of our unwanted or unused pharmaceuticals. The effects may not be limited to fish and other animals in the water; we often take our drinking water from these same rivers and lakes. We need to be much more careful in how we treat our waste water before releasing it back into the environment. Much more research is needed to look into both the effects of xenoestrogens on animal development and more effective ways of treating our waste. One thing is certain: we can change our waste treatment strategies much faster than animals can evolve new mechanisms to control gene expression.

## KEY CONCEPTS REVIEW AND QUESTIONS

### 10.1 Gene Expression and the Central Dogma of Molecular Biology

The central dogma of molecular biology describes the transfer of information in a cell, from the nucleotide code of the gene to the amino acid sequence of a protein. The gene includes not only the protein-coding sequence but also information that directs its expression.

1. Draw a model of a bacterial gene and a eukaryotic gene. Highlight their structural differences.

2. Which of the following roles is performed by the promoter sequence of a gene?

    a. The promoter directs the ribosome where to start transcription.

    b. The promoter marks the end of the gene.

    c. The promoter attracts the RNA polymerase complex to start transcription.

    d. The promoter increases the stability of the mRNA.

3. How does an operon structure help regulate gene expression?

## 10.2 From Gene to Protein

A key aspect of gene expression is getting the information stored as a gene in the DNA strand translated into a protein that will perform a function in the cell. To follow the central dogma, a gene is first transcribed by an RNA polymerase, to give an mRNA copy of the gene. This mRNA copy is then processed so that it can be recognized by the ribosome, and in the case of eukaryotes, the RNA molecule is exported from the nucleus to the cytoplasm. Once in the cytoplasm, the mRNA is translated by the ribosome using tRNA molecules to convert the information from three-base nucleotide codons into amino acids. To become functional, some proteins need to be modified. They are folded, and some are transported to specific places in the cell. The protein is then ready to perform the function for which it is needed.

4. Eukaryotes do not have operons in their nuclear chromosomes. How do they coordinate the expression of multiple genes?

5. List the steps involved in getting information from the gene to the protein.

6. What are the three main phases of translation?

## 10.3 Regulation of Gene Expression

As important as producing proteins to meet the needs of the cell is expressing them at the right time, in the correct place.

Gene expression is regulated to meet the needs of the cell, or organism as a whole. The expression of genes can be a complex process; we saw that eukaryotes can regulate gene expression at each stage outlined in the central dogma, from the use of transcription factors to modulate the amount of mRNAs transcribed to the use of riboswitches to regulate translation. There are many levels of fine control that dictate how much of a given protein accumulates in the cell. Finally, we saw that the overall control of gene expression can be dictated by developmental cues, such as the seasonal changes experienced by the apple trees in the Annapolis Valley. However, just to add another wrinkle, epigenetics can control the level of gene expression based on environmental exposure.

7. List the steps of the central dogma that can be regulated in eukaryotes to control gene expression.

8. Summarize how a cell from a plant's leaf and one from its root could have the same genome yet vastly different sets of proteins that allow them to perform their necessary functions for the plant.

9. Compare developmental regulation of gene expression with epigenetic control of gene expression.

# Biotechnology

## WHY IT MATTERS

In the spring of 1921, Dr. J.J.R. Macleod, director of the physiology lab at the University of Toronto, was approached by a young physician who thought he could cure diabetes. Imagine if Macleod, as many would have, had shut his door and told Frederick Banting to go home to his clinic. Despite the fact that Banting had almost no training in physiology, Macleod was convinced to give him a chance. Macleod was heading to his home in Scotland for the summer and let Banting use some of his lab space and one of his students. Charles Best won the coin toss to determine who would assist Banting for the summer **(Figure 11.1)**. The result was perhaps the greatest medical discovery in the history of Canada. However, the discovery of the role of **insulin** in diabetes by Banting and Best was only the beginning of treating this insidious disease. Banting and Macleod shared the Nobel Prize in Physiology and Medicine in 1923. At the age of 32,

Banting was the youngest individual to receive this award. His work was so important that he is routinely considered among the greatest Canadians, and the discovery of insulin is one of the most influential discoveries made by a Canadian scientist.

In the years immediately following the finding that diabetes is caused by a lack of insulin, producing insulin for medical treatments was incredibly challenging. Imagine knowing how to treat this devastating disease but being unable to produce the necessary drug. Insulin is a protein produced by specific cells in the pancreas, but it cannot be extracted from intact pancreatic tissue. The proteases (enzymes that degrade other proteins) produced in the pancreas to aid digestion destroy the insulin proteins. Initially, animals were surgically treated so that their pancreas would digest itself, destroying the protease-producing cells but leaving the insulin-producing cells intact. This was fatal to the animal but allowed the insulin-producing cells to be isolated. This technique allowed researchers to purify the insulin protein. However, the yield of insulin was incredibly low and the mixture obtained was not pure enough to administer to human patients.

With continued experimentation, insulin extraction improved, and soon the insulin protein was being produced on an industrial scale. However, the drug was still being produced using animals, usually pigs. Small differences between pig and human insulin caused some patients to develop allergic reactions to the drug they needed to survive. In the 1960s, scientists developed ways to synthesize proteins such as insulin in the lab. However, the cost was quite high. Despite scientific breakthroughs, cells are better at

**FIGURE 11.1** In 1921, University of Toronto scientists Dr. Frederick Banting (right) and medical student Charles Best made one of the greatest biological discoveries in Canadian history. They found that insulin could treat the symptoms of diabetes.

C. H. Best and F. G. Banting ca. 1924. Author: Unknown

making proteins. Today, the vast majority of insulin used to treat patients with diabetes is human insulin. There are fewer side effects and a much reduced chance of allergic reaction. Of course, human insulin is not produced from human pancreas extracts, nor is it synthesized in a lab. Instead, scientists clone the human insulin gene and express the protein in microbes such as *Escherichia coli or* the yeast *Saccharomyces cerevisiae* (**Figure 11.2**). Because the human insulin protein is produced in non-human cells, we call it **recombinant insulin**. This recombinant source of insulin is much cheaper, the drug is more effective, and obtaining it does not require the harming of animals. Human insulin production from a microbial culture is just one very successful example of biotechnology being used to improve human health at a lower cost and less environmental impact.

Biotechnology is a fascinating and powerful area of biological research known as much for the tools that it develops as for its contributions to medicine and agriculture. Many people are afraid of the changes that researchers in the field of biotechnology suggest are possible, but we must remember, biotechnology is just a set of tools, no different from those of a master woodworker. The difference is that rather than joining together select pieces of lumber to make a table, the biotechnologist can duplicate genes, make specific alterations, and sometimes even move genes from one organism to another to test a hypothesis or attempt to provide a product we need for our health or diet that is cheaper and with decreased impact on the environment.

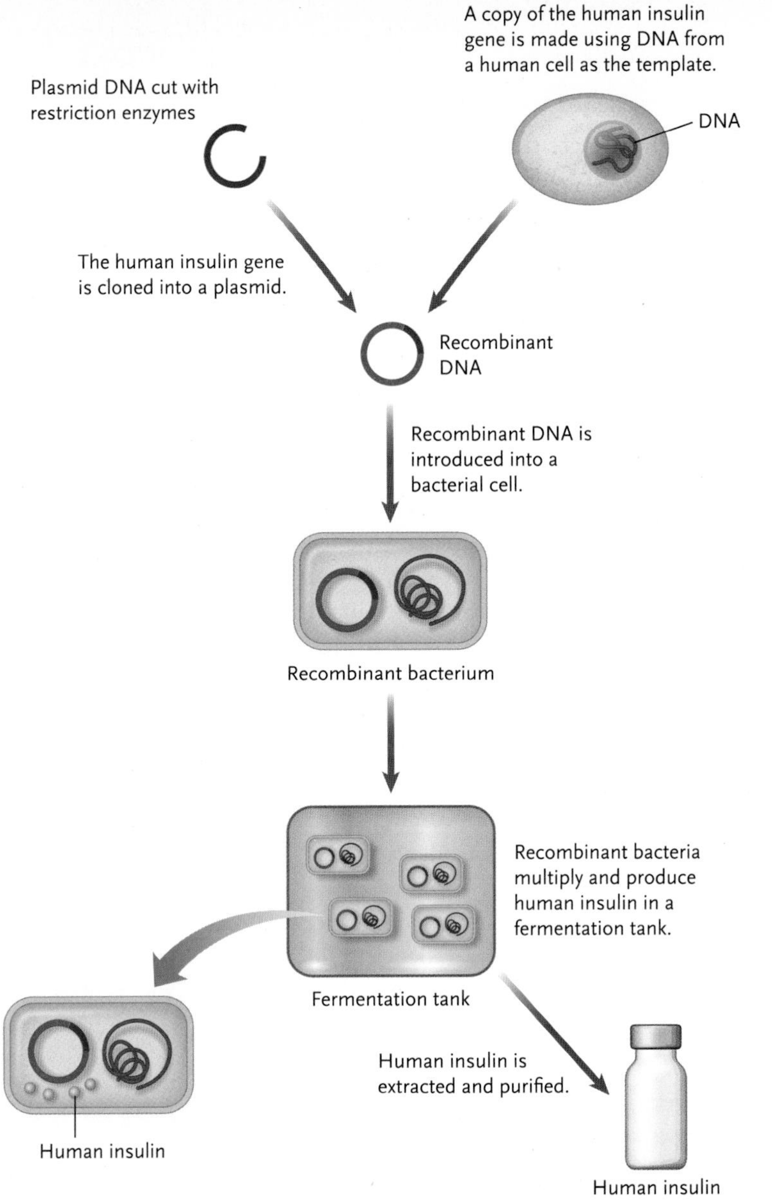

In this chapter, we will examine some common biotechnology tools and discuss how they can be used. Some possible uses are foods, medicines, and even the advancement of knowledge. We will also discuss some of the ethical questions that arise when we push the envelope of biotechnology.

**FIGURE 11.2** Recombinant human insulin is produced by cloning the human insulin gene and expressing it in bacteria. Large numbers of bacteria can be grown easily and cheaply. The human insulin protein is then recovered, purified, and used to treat diabetes.

## 11.1 What Is Biotechnology?

**Biotechnology** can be broadly defined as the use of biological organisms to produce useful products and processes. Thus, although some people lament the use of genetically modified organisms in agriculture and medicine, humans have long harnessed the metabolic processes of bacteria and yeasts to improve our food. We use yeast-based fermentation to produce breads, wines, and beers. We use bacterial cultures to make yogurt and sourdough. Even cheese is made through the concerted use of specialized combinations of bacterial and fungal cultures. Food preservation using biotechnological processes became very important as agricultural societies began to produce more food than they could immediately use. The traditional meals of many cultures involve food preserved by fermentation. Despite these traditional uses, there is a very understandable fear associated with the modern biotechnology industry. However, as we will discuss later in the chapter, much of this fear is due to very poor communication from industry, resulting in a lack of understanding by the general public. Throughout history, fear of changing industrial practices has been a common occurrence.

**Molecular biotechnology** is an area of biology that has seen enormous growth and development over the past 20 years. The development of molecular biology tools and the capability to harness bacteria to produce medicines such as insulin are examples. One of the strengths of biotechnology in laboratory settings is the ability of scientists to perform "biological reactions" outside living organisms. Such in vitro (Latin for "in glass"; we now use the term to describe any biological process studied outside a living organism) experiments allow biochemists to study the mechanisms of specific biological reactions without the "messiness" of the organism.

More recently, the ability to sequence the entire genomes of organisms has given scientists more insight into how cells work. Molecular tools initially developed for bacteria have been modified for use in eukaryotes such as yeast, higher plants, and human cells. Even viruses can now be used as a form of medical intervention. However, while we think of these high-tech modern biological marvels, we should consider them in the context of how humans have used other biological organisms as tools for thousands of years. In both modern biotechnology and traditional practices, a certain level of serendipity seems to be required.

Fermenting milk to produce yogurt and cheese was a fantastic technical advance. Early animal herders had no way to prolong the freshness of milk; they had to consume it quickly or it would spoil. Based on archaeological and anthropological evidence such as specifically designed clay pots and mural paintings, it is estimated that cheese making originated over 8000 years ago. Milk and other food materials were often collected and transported in holders constructed from animal stomachs and other internal organs. Ironically, one of the key enzymes needed in the production of cheese, rennin, is produced by cells lining the stomachs of ruminants such as cows and goats. A second process needed to produce cheese is the presence of bacteria that release lactic acid into the milk. The bacteria release the lactic acid as a by-product when they digest lactose to produce energy by fermentation (see Chapter 5 for a review of fermentation). The increasing acidity caused by the lactic acid (low pH) denatures the milk proteins. As the proteins change shape, they separate from the water and coagulate into clumps **(Figure 11.3a)**. The bacteria also add flavour to the developing cheese as their complex metabolism breaks down the milk fats into smaller molecules, such as amino acids and short-chain fatty acids. The bacteria present in different geographical areas give cheeses from those areas distinctive flavours and textures **(Figure 11.3b)**.

The International Dairy Foods Association estimates that there are over 2000 different varieties of cheese. Aged cheeses, which have the longest shelf life, are treated with secondary cultures of bacteria and fungi, which continue to break down large, complex molecules into smaller, simpler ones, resulting in even more varied flavours. Secondary treatment of aging cheeses with fungi leads to the characteristic colouring of blue cheese. The Romans were at the forefront of cheese aging as a way to feed their legionnaires while pushing their military might to the edges of their known world. It is quite an amazing idea that the accidental storage of fresh milk in an unprepared animal stomach may have led to such an important biotechnological advance in food preservation.

A.

B.

**FIGURE 11.3** **(a)** Protein coagulation occurs during cheese making. **(b)** Proprietary bacteria and fungi give mature cheeses their unique colours and flavours.

## 11.2 Technical Aspects of Molecular Biotechnology

Molecular biotechnology has its roots in the 1950s and 1960s. Researchers at that time began to unravel the mysteries of how proteins are made, the chemical structure of DNA, and how genetic information is passed from generation to generation at the molecular level. In 1951, Dr. Frederick Sanger, working at Cambridge University in the United Kingdom, became the first person to chemically determine the amino acid structure of a protein. Because of Banting and Best's work at the University of Toronto, insulin was widely available in a very pure form. Sanger purchased bovine insulin from the local pharmacy and used it in his sequencing studies. With this pure protein as a starting point, Sanger was able to determine the amino acids needed to make insulin and the order in which they are arranged. Sanger's results clearly demonstrated that proteins are composed of a distinct set of amino acids, linked together in a specific order. His conclusion that each protein would have a different amino acid sequence was critical to unraveling the genetic code that we discussed in Chapter 10. Based on this achievement, Sanger was awarded the Nobel Prize in Chemistry in 1958. It would be the first of two Nobel Prizes awarded to Sanger (to date, the only person to win two Nobel Prizes for Chemistry) for work that would set the stage for the molecular biology revolution to come.

### DNA Sequencing Tells Us the Order of Nucleotides in a DNA Molecule

Sanger's second Nobel Prize was awarded in 1980 for his contributions to the sequencing of DNA. We use DNA sequencing to determine the exact combination and order of nucleotides in a DNA molecule. The ability to cheaply and routinely sequence DNA has had a greater impact on modern biology than any other advance in the field of molecular biology. DNA sequencing has many applications, and new ones are in development. For example, access to accurate and complete DNA sequences allows us to identify mutations, characterize the evolutionary linkage of species, map disease genes to specific chromosomes, and study the regulation of gene expression.

The Sanger method of sequencing DNA uses a DNA polymerase and the same DNA replication process that is performed by cells in a living organism. Into a tube containing the DNA molecule to be sequenced are placed **DNA oligonucleotide** primers, some DNA polymerase enzymes, a mixture of deoxynucleotide triphosphates (dNTPs), magnesium-containing buffer, and a specific, labelled **dideoxynucleotide triphosphate (ddNTP)**. We will explain the role of each of these components as we go through the process, step by step.

The DNA oligonucleotide primer used is a short strand of DNA made synthetically and designed to base-pair with a segment of the template DNA that we want to sequence. Once the oligonucleotide primer has base-paired with the template, the DNA polymerase will use the mixture of deoxynucleotides (normal DNA building blocks) to extend the primer, one base at a time, exactly the way the DNA polymerase replicates DNA in living cells. However, the extremely clever trick that Sanger came up with is the addition of ddNTPs to the mixture. Although present at a lower concentration than the corresponding dNTP, DNA polymerase will periodically add ddNTPs to the growing DNA copy when it base-pairs with the corresponding nucleotide on the template strand. Because ddNTPs do not have a 3′-OH functional group **(Figure 11.4a)**, the DNA polymerase cannot add another base to the chain, and its elongation is terminated. This process happens over and over in the tube and at random times during elongation as the templates are being copied by the DNA polymerase **(Figure 11.4b)**. At the end of the reaction, we will have populations of newly synthesized DNA molecules of different lengths because of the random incorporation of the ddNTP. Although these DNA strands differ in length, at the end of each strand will be a labelled terminating ddNTP. To distinguish between the four groups of ddNTP that represent the four nucleotide bases (A, G, C, and T), each group has a different coloured label (Figure 11.4).

We next separate the copies based on their length. This is done by passing the mixture of labelled DNA fragments through an electrophoretic gel **(Figure 11.5, p. 242)**. The gel acts as a series of sieves. As you pour material into a sieve, the shortest DNA fragments will move through the holes most easily, and larger particles will move more slowly. Thus, fragments of DNA will emerge from the gel according to size and in order from smallest to largest. As the fragments emerge, a laser light is shone on the samples exiting the gel and the type of label attached to the DNA fragment is determined. Thus, we know if the fragment ends in an A, T, G, or C. As progressively longer fragments emerge, we keep track of the order of the labels detected and we will know the sequence of the original DNA template.

A skilled lab worker can produce accurate sequences for up to 1200 bases using Sanger sequencing. This was the method used to sequence the entire human genome, consisting of 3.2 gigabases. One can imagine the enormous undertaking required to produce a sequence of that size, 800 to 1200 bases at a time. Also consider

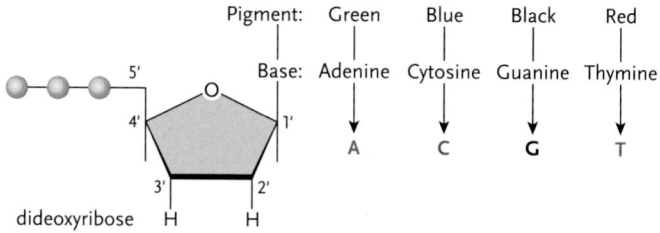

**A.**

Pigment: Green Blue Black Red

Base: Adenine Cytosine Guanine Thymine

A C G T

dideoxyribose

**FIGURE 11.4** Dideoxynucleotides are used in Sanger sequencing to terminate DNA extension. Notice that the 3′ carbon does not have an OH group **(a)**. Terminated fragments are then separated based on their size. The presence of specific dideoxynucleotides at the end of the fragments is detected to determine the DNA sequence **(b)**.

SOURCE: From STARR/TAGGART/Evers/Starr. *Biology*, 12E. © 2009 Brooks/Cole, a part of Cengage Learning, Inc. Reproduced by permission. www.cengage.com/permissions

**B.**

**1** The fragment of DNA to be sequenced is mixed with a primer, DNA polymerase, and nucleotides. The mixture also includes the four dideoxynucleotides labelled with four different coloured pigments.

5′ T C C A T G G A C C A
3′ A G G T A C C T G G T

T C C A T G G A C C A

T C C A T G G A C C

T C C A T G G A C

T C C A T G G A

T C C A T G G

T C C A T G

T C C A T

T C C A

T C C

T C

T

**2** The polymerase uses the DNA as a template to synthesize new strands again and again. Synthesis of each new strand stops when a dideoxynucleotide is added.

**3** At the end of the reaction, there are many truncated copies of the DNA template in the mixture.

that to get accurate sequences, we need to repeat the sequencing process. To achieve an estimated 99.9% accuracy, each base of the human genome was sequenced on average 10 to 15 times.

Newer sequencing methods employ more complex chemical and physical approaches to greatly speed up sequencing. Counterintuitively, these new techniques sequence smaller pieces each time. However, they can produce millions of bases of sequencing data in just a few hours. The major effort required to sequence genomes has thus shifted from the tedious technical work at the lab bench preparing and running Sanger sequencing reactions to the requirement of enormous amounts of computing power and skilled programmers who can put the millions of short sequences together into one long sequence. The most sought after employees in the biotechnology industry today are highly trained individuals who are comfortable working with truly massive amounts of data. The interface between biology and computer science and the relatively new field of **bioinformatics** are exploding with possibilities.

## PCR Is a Technique for Making Copies of DNA Sequences

The **polymerase chain reaction**, PCR for short, is a technique that can be used to make copies of segments of DNA. We call this process PCR-based DNA amplification. Just as the amplifier for a speaker system increases the amount of sound, PCR amplification increases the amount of DNA. Like Sanger sequencing, PCR uses short, chemically synthesized DNA oligonucleotides (typically 15 to 25 bases in length) to initiate the replication of a strand of DNA.

To perform this in vitro biochemical reaction, we place the DNA to be copied in a reaction tube along with a heat-stable DNA polymerase, deoxynucleotide triphosphates (dNTPs), and the DNA oligonucleotide primers **(Figure 11.6, p. 242)**. We then place the tube into a special machine called a **thermocycler**, which can rapidly heat and cool the mixture in the tube. The thermocycler is programmed to initially heat the sample to denature the DNA by breaking the hydrogen bonds that hold the two strands together in the double helix conformation. The thermocycler program will then cool the temperature of the

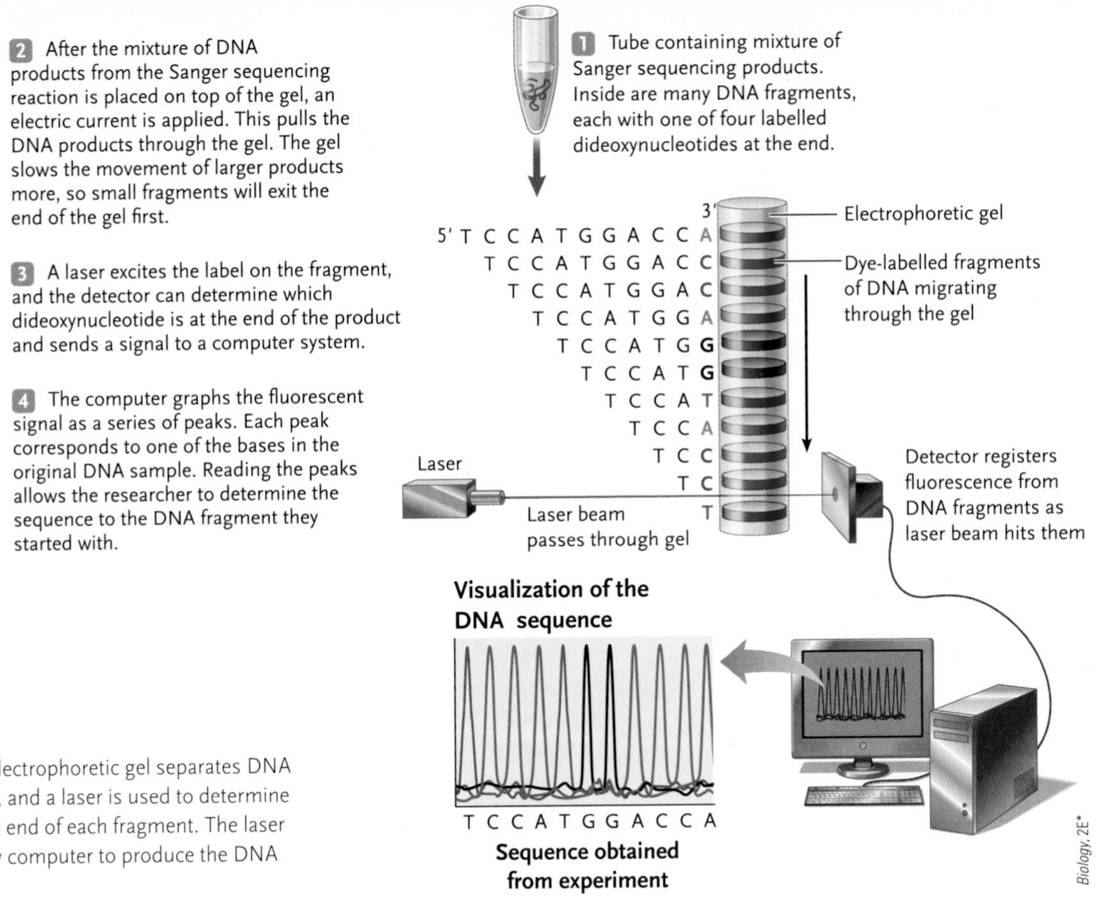

**2** After the mixture of DNA products from the Sanger sequencing reaction is placed on top of the gel, an electric current is applied. This pulls the DNA products through the gel. The gel slows the movement of larger products more, so small fragments will exit the end of the gel first.

**3** A laser excites the label on the fragment, and the detector can determine which dideoxynucleotide is at the end of the product and sends a signal to a computer system.

**4** The computer graphs the fluorescent signal as a series of peaks. Each peak corresponds to one of the bases in the original DNA sample. Reading the peaks allows the researcher to determine the sequence to the DNA fragment they started with.

**1** Tube containing mixture of Sanger sequencing products. Inside are many DNA fragments, each with one of four labelled dideoxynucleotides at the end.

5' T C C A T G G A C C A 3'
T C C A T G G A C C
T C C A T G G A C
T C C A T G G A
T C C A T G G
T C C A T G
T C C A T
T C C A
T C C
T C
T

Electrophoretic gel

Dye-labelled fragments of DNA migrating through the gel

Laser

Laser beam passes through gel

Detector registers fluorescence from DNA fragments as laser beam hits them

**Visualization of the DNA sequence**

T C C A T G G A C C A
**Sequence obtained from experiment**

**FIGURE 11.5** An electrophoretic gel separates DNA fragments by length, and a laser is used to determine which label is on the end of each fragment. The laser signal is recorded by computer to produce the DNA sequence.

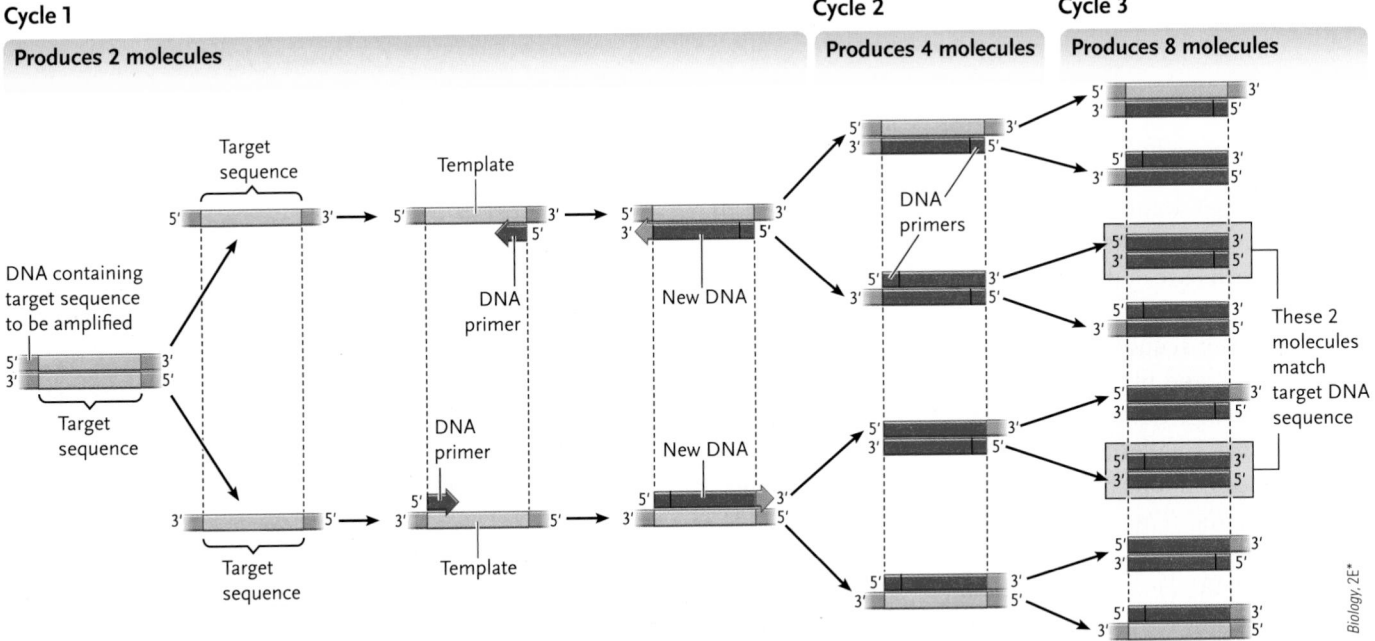

**Cycle 1**

**Produces 2 molecules**

Target sequence

Template

DNA containing target sequence to be amplified

Target sequence

Target sequence

DNA primer

DNA primer

Template

New DNA

New DNA

**Cycle 2**

**Produces 4 molecules**

DNA primers

**Cycle 3**

**Produces 8 molecules**

These 2 molecules match target DNA sequence

**1** Denaturation: Heat DNA containing target sequence to 95°C to denature it to single strands.

**2** Annealing: Cool the mixture to 55–65°C (depending on the primers) to allow the two primers to anneal their complementary sequences at the two ends of the target sequence.

**3** Extension: Heat to 72°C, the optimal temperature for DNA polymerase to extend the primers, using the four nucleoside triphosphate precursors to make complementary copies of the two template strands. This completes cycle 1 of PCR; the end result is two molecules.

**4** Repeat the same steps of denaturation, annealing of primers, and extension in cycle 2, producing a total of four molecules.

**5** Repeat the same steps in cycle 3, producing a total of eight molecules. Two of the eight match the exact length of the target DNA sequence (highlighted in yellow).

**FIGURE 11.6** PCR is a molecular biology technique used to amplify DNA in vitro. It uses heat-stable DNA polymerases and small oligonucleotide primers to get the process started. A sequence of 25 cycles can produce over 33 million copies of the target.

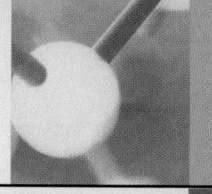

The high-temperature stable DNA polymerase isolated from the thermophilic bacterium *Thermus aquaticus* has undoubtedly had a greater impact on modern molecular biology than any other molecule. Called **Taq polymerase** for short, this enzyme has been a workhorse in molecular biology labs around the world since its use in the polymerase chain reaction was developed by researchers at Cetus Corporation.

*T. aquaticus* was first cultured and identified from a hydrothermal pool in Yellowstone National Park in Wyoming by microbiologist Dr. Thomas Brock in the 1960s. The amazing feature about this bacterium was its ability to thrive at temperatures up to 70°C. The finding of heat-loving bacteria raised the possibility that their enzymes must be able to function at equally high temperatures. Chemical engineers were interested in heat-stable enzymes that would allow them to design in vitro biological reactions that could be performed at high temperatures. Higher temperatures allow reactions to occur much faster. For chemical engineers, faster reactions mean more product and hence more profit. In 1976, the first report of the isolation of the *Taq* polymerase was published. Researchers from the University of Cincinnati discovered that not only could they isolate the enzyme in a very pure form, but it also retained DNA polymerase activity at up to 80°C.

In and of itself, *Taq* polymerase was an interesting example of a heat-stable enzyme but of little general use to biologists. However, in the early 1980s, American biochemist Kary Mullis, working at Cetus Corporation, came up with an idea to amplify small segments of DNA. His idea was to use small DNA fragments (called oligonucleotides) in the range of 15 to 25 nucleotides in length, which would bracket the fragment of interest. With one fragment on each strand of the DNA molecule, they would face each other as they were used to start a copy of the DNA molecule. Initially, this technique used a DNA polymerase isolated from *E. coli*. For the technique to work, the DNA strands needed to be separated from each other by heating them to approximately 95°C. This denatured the DNA molecule, separating the strands and oligonucleotides. However, heating the samples to 95°C also denatured and inactivated the *E. coli* DNA polymerase. Thus, to perform the number of cycles of the reaction needed to generate large amounts of the desired fragment, new *E. coli* DNA polymerase needed to be added after each cycle.

In 1986, one of Mullis's co-workers, Randall Saiki, came up with the idea to use the DNA polymerase from *T. aquaticus*. The *Taq* polymerase was shown to have a half-life of 40 minutes at 95°C; thus, the enzyme remains active for many cycles of the amplification reaction. The amplification reaction became known as the polymerase chain reaction, or PCR, and revolutionized the field of molecular biology. It is estimated that yearly sales of *Taq* polymerase exceed $500 million dollars. For his work in developing the PCR process, Kary Mullis shared the 1993 Nobel Prize in Chemistry with Canadian molecular biologist Michael Smith from the University of British Columbia, who developed a technique called site-directed mutagenesis, which became much easier to perform following the development of *Taq* polymerase-based PCR.

reaction mixture to allow the oligonucleotide primers to bind to their complementary portion of DNA. Once the primers are bound to the DNA template, the thermocycler program will increase the temperature in the tube to the optimal temperature for the heat-stable DNA polymerase (see Box 11.1 to learn more about heat-stable DNA polymerases). This begins the DNA replication process. At 72°C, *Taq* polymerase synthesizes a copy of the DNA template starting at the primers at a rate of about 1000 bases per minute. Thus, the length of time required to amplify the sample depends on its length. This represents one complete amplification cycle (Figure 11.6). Once the extension time is up, the thermocycler will increase the temperature of the mixture to denature the DNA strands. After one cycle, there will be twice as many copies of the desired fragment. After two cycles, there will be four copies of the fragment, and so on, with an exponential increase continuing until the reaction runs out of dNTPs. Typically, scientists will run a PCR through 25 to 35 cycles. This could amplify a single DNA fragment into between 33.6 million ($2^{25}$) and 34.3 billion ($2^{35}$) copies.

Recent advances in PCR technology have made the process simpler and more reliable. The original *Taq* polymerase (see Box 11.1) was known to make the occasional mistake while copying DNA. Its error rate is estimated to be approximately 1 in 8 million. Although this seems pretty good, remember that if you amplify a 1000-base fragment 50 million times (a typical PCR reaction), that is 6250 mistakes. Competing biotechnology companies are continually trying to reduce the error rate of their proprietary thermostable DNA polymerases. An important advance was identifying a DNA polymerase (called *Pfu*) from the hyperthermophilic archaean *Pyrococcus furiosus*, which is not only more heat stable than *Taq* polymerase but also possesses a proofreading ability. Thus, it can correct mismatched bases by detecting variations in the width between the DNA strands. This reduces its error rate but slows the copying rate. The latest generation of PCR polymerases has been biochemically engineered to reduce errors, work faster, and copy longer fragments. Ironically, biotechnology has improved the workhorse of the bio-technology industry.

# BIOLOGY IS EVERYWHERE 11.2
## Even Famous Scientists Struggle to Get Their Ideas Accepted

After Dr. Fredrick Banting, the next Canadian to be awarded a Nobel Prize in Chemistry was Dr. Michael Smith. Dr. Smith worked for the Medical Research Council of Canada within the Biochemistry Department of the University of British Columbia (UBC). Although originally from Blackpool, England, Dr. Smith immigrated to Canada in 1956 and became a Canadian citizen. Early in his career, Dr. Smith worked with some of the foremost researchers in the rapidly growing field of molecular biology. When he first arrived in Vancouver, he joined the lab of Dr. H.G. Khorana at UBC. You might remember Dr. Khorana from the work done to elucidate the genetic code (see Chapter 10). Smith was fascinated

by the role of nucleic acids in the central dogma of molecular biology. A key step in Smith's development as a world leader in molecular biology was a one-year visit to Dr. Frederick Sanger's lab at Cambridge University. When he returned, he asked the poignant question: Was it possible to design a specific mutation in a gene to change the encoded protein by a single amino acid? Using chemically synthesized DNA oligonucleotides, Smith's lab found that they could indeed alter a single codon and change the encoded protein. The process was called **site-directed mutagenesis**.

The research was published in 1978, and in 1993, Smith shared the Nobel Prize in Chemistry with Kary Mullis. Like

many scientists, Smith initially struggled to have his ground-breaking research appreciated by the scientific community. An initial submission of his manuscript describing site-directed mutagenesis was rejected by a leading research journal. The editor of the journal told Smith that the technique was an interesting gimmick but would never find widespread use. Perseverance like Smith's is a common trait in scientific researchers. The path to discovery is rarely an easy one. Often major findings are viewed with skepticism by the research community. This can be quite disheartening, but as Smith showed, belief and self-confidence can sometimes win the day.

DNA amplified using PCR is used for many different purposes, especially when combined with DNA sequencing: disease detection, species identification, detection of evolutionary change within species, solving crimes, and measuring levels of gene expression. PCR is an incredibly important tool. PCR is also used as a tool to study the relationship between protein structure and function. Using specially designed sets of DNA oligonucleotides, scientists can introduce mutations into the coding regions of genes in a highly controlled fashion. One such process is called **site-directed mutagenesis**. Site-directed mutagenesis is a technique used to change the primary sequence of a protein by changing a single codon in a gene. To learn more about using PCR as a tool to induce mutations, see Box 11.2.

## Plasmids Are Small DNA Molecules That Provide a Selective Advantage to a Cell

**Plasmids** are small extrachromosomal DNA molecules found in some bacteria, archaea, and fungi. Naturally occurring plasmids can range in size from 1000 base pairs to 200 kilobase pairs. They are normally circular double-stranded DNA molecules, just like a miniature bacterial chromosome. They can even be observed using electron microscopy (**Figure 11.7a**).

At their simplest, plasmids contain two specific types of DNA sequences. The first is an **origin of replication**, which tells the cell's DNA polymerase where to start copying. Without an origin of replication, the plasmid could not be copied and would be lost as the cell divides. The second set of sequences encodes one or

**FIGURE 11.7 (a)** Plasmids can be isolated from many types of microbes. **(b)** Engineered plasmids are designed for use in molecular biology labs. The map of the plasmid shown in (b) highlights the multiple cloning site on the right.

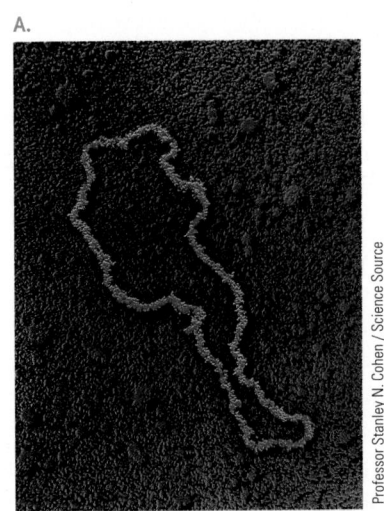

Professor Stanley N. Cohen / Science Source

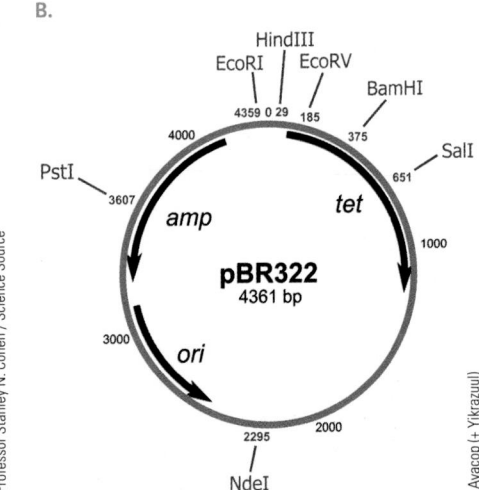

Ayacop (+ Yikrazuul)

more genes, which, when expressed, will provide the cell with a competitive advantage. A competitive advantage is required for the cell to keep replicating the plasmid because maintaining the plasmid costs the cell energy. When comparing cells with a plasmid to those without, under normal conditions, those carrying the plasmid will grow more slowly. A common example that we see of a competitive advantage provided by the protein encoded by a gene found on plasmids is resistance to an antibiotic.

Plasmids appear to be one of the common mechanisms for horizontal gene transfer between bacterial species (for a review, see Chapter 7). Many bacteria can take up foreign DNA from their environment. For example, if a bacterium dies and releases its DNA into its environment, small plasmids may be taken up by neighbouring bacteria. Although this occurs at a low frequency in nature, there are many bacteria, and the transfer of a trait such as antibiotic resistance would allow for survival under very strong selective pressure. The process of a bacterium taking up DNA from its environment and maintaining it in its own cell is called transformation. In molecular biology labs, we have developed very efficient protocols to transform bacteria with plasmid-containing genes we are interested in studying.

Most currently used plasmids were constructed by scientists in labs. Engineered plasmids are an important tool in molecular biology because they can be easily transformed into bacteria. Using our knowledge of molecular biology, we try to make smaller, more efficient plasmids. We want smaller plasmids because they place a smaller metabolic load on a cell when they are replicated. To maintain synthetic plasmids in cells, we add antibiotic resistance genes. Ideally, we would have a set of plasmids that contain different antibiotic resistance genes so that we could transform more than one type of plasmid into a bacterium if needed. Interestingly, in labs, we generally use genes that confer resistance to antibiotics, which are "old-fashioned" in medical terms. The most commonly used resistance gene is a beta-lactamase gene, which makes the bacteria resistant to penicillin-style antibiotics. This way, when we place the bacteria on agar plates or liquid media containing penicillin, only those containing the plasmid will be able to grow and reproduce. Scientists working with antibiotic-resistant bacteria are required to carefully sterilize all of their samples before disposing of them. The goal is to minimize the possibility of releasing drug-resistant plasmids into the environment.

When used in labs for molecular biology, plasmids are often called plasmid vectors. The name implies their use in transferring DNA from one host to another. As we will see in the next section, plasmid vectors are an essential part of the molecular cloning process. A key aspect of using plasmid vectors was engineering them to contain short DNA sequences that are recognized by enzymes called **restriction endonucleases**. Some bacteria naturally produce restriction endonucleases, enzymes that digest DNA at specific sequence motifs **(Figure 11.8)**. The sequences that are recognized are generally between four and eight bases in length. In the lab, we can use restriction endonucleases to specifically cut the plasmid vector in a predictable fashion, leaving overhanging unpaired DNA bases we call **sticky ends**, or **blunt ends** (Figure 11.8 and **Figure 11.9, p. 246**). Restriction endonucleases are often named after the species of bacterium from which they were obtained. A common restriction endonuclease is called EcoRI, which is named after *E. coli*. Similarly, the enzyme EcoRV, which is shown in Figure 11.8, was also isolated from *E. coli*. The EcoRV enzyme recognizes the DNA sequence CATATG, whereas the EcoRI enzyme cuts the DNA strand when it detects a GAATTC sequence (Figure 11.9). It is interesting to note that many restriction enzymes recognize what we call palindromic DNA sequences. A palindrome is a sequence that is the same forward as reverse. We can see this characteristic in both the EcoRI and the EcoRV target sequences.

If we mix fragments that have matching sticky ends with the plasmid vector, and an enzyme called a ligase is added, they can be connected into a single DNA strand (Figure 11.9). Modern engineered plasmids will have many different restriction endonuclease recognition sites

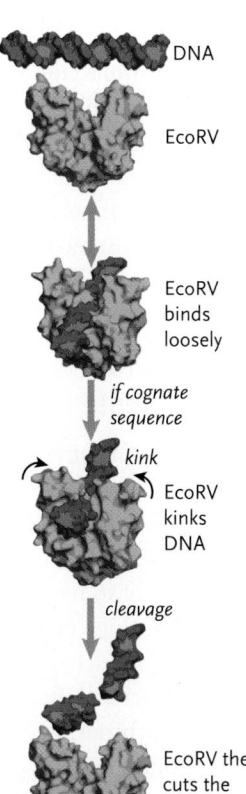

**FIGURE 11.8** The restriction enzyme EcoRV, cutting DNA. Restriction endonucleases recognize the three-dimensional shape of short DNA sequences and cut the sequence in a predictable way. Like all enzymes, they follow the lock-and-key mechanism with their substrate.

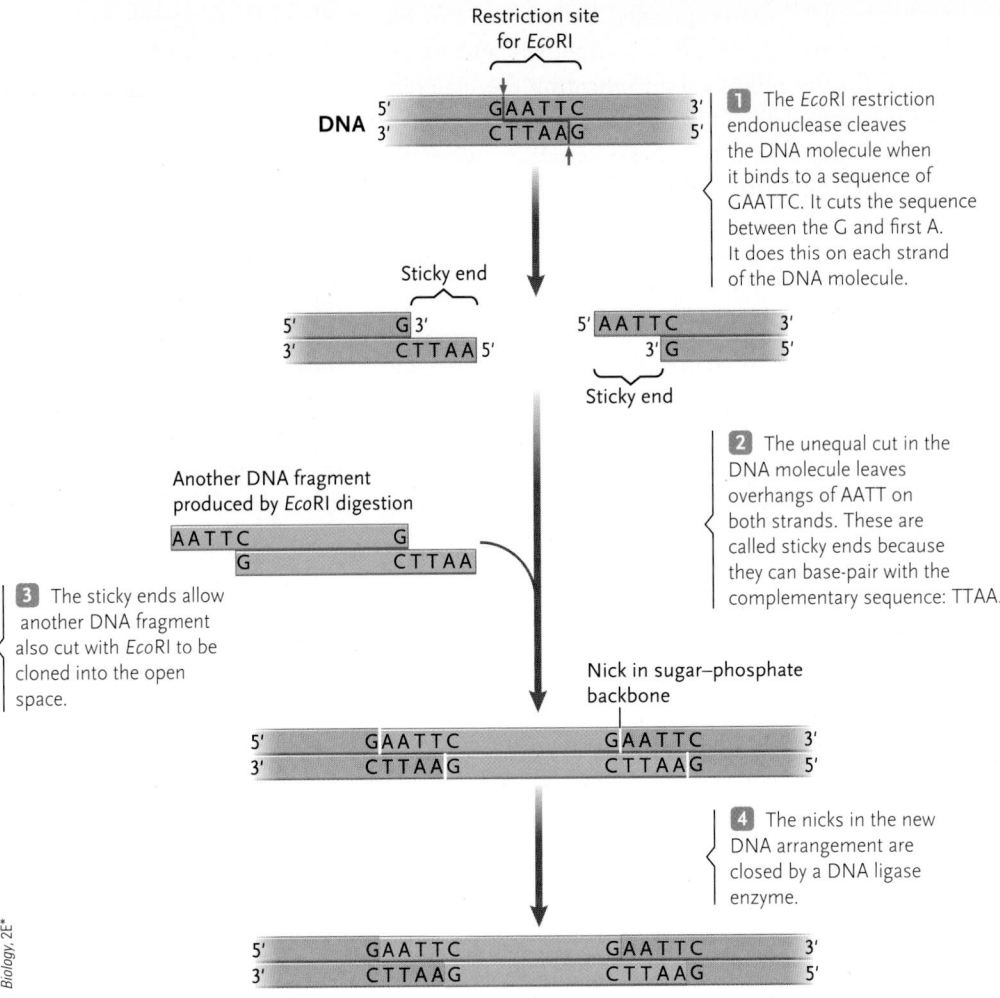

**FIGURE 11.9** Restriction endonucleases can be used to open one DNA molecule so that a second fragment can be cloned into the gap.

Restriction site for *Eco*RI

DNA
5' GAATTC 3'
3' CTTAAG 5'

**1** The *Eco*RI restriction endonuclease cleaves the DNA molecule when it binds to a sequence of GAATTC. It cuts the sequence between the G and first A. It does this on each strand of the DNA molecule.

Sticky end

5' G 3'
3' CTTAA 5'

5' AATTC 3'
3' G 5'

Sticky end

**2** The unequal cut in the DNA molecule leaves overhangs of AATT on both strands. These are called sticky ends because they can base-pair with the complementary sequence: TTAA.

Another DNA fragment produced by *Eco*RI digestion
AATTC G
G CTTAA

**3** The sticky ends allow another DNA fragment also cut with *Eco*RI to be cloned into the open space.

Nick in sugar–phosphate backbone

5' GAATTC GAATTC 3'
3' CTTAAG CTTAAG 5'

**4** The nicks in the new DNA arrangement are closed by a DNA ligase enzyme.

5' GAATTC GAATTC 3'
3' CTTAAG CTTAAG 5'

Recombinant DNA molecule

*Biology, 2E\**

clustered together in a region called the **multiple cloning site** (Figure 11.7b). This allows a molecular biologist to cut the plasmid and add a new DNA fragment to the plasmid. This addition is called **DNA cloning**. When the DNA fragments are later transformed into a different type of cell than the one it came from, we call them **recombinant DNA** fragments.

## Molecular Cloning Allows Scientists to Assemble Recombinant DNA Fragments

We introduced the concept of DNA cloning in the previous section, but it is important to understand that the term *clone* or *cloning* can have different meanings depending on what is being cloned and the field of biology. In general usage, we think of cloning as making a copy of something. We use our computers to clone DVDs. We clone our cell phones when we trade them in for a new model so that we do not lose any contacts or data. In science fiction movies, people are cloned by fantastic machines, generating an exact copy of the individual, often with tragic results. More benignly, we are also familiar with the cloning of the sheep Dolly; although this was done almost

20 years ago, it was a highly publicized success story. When we use vegetative cuttings to multiply plants, we are also cloning them. In fact, some plant species naturally reproduce almost exclusively by self-cloning. However, when we talk about cloning DNA, we mean making copies of DNA fragments that we can use for other purposes.

In the days before PCR amplification, obtaining enough of a specific piece of DNA to sequence could be a challenge. Often it was done by first cloning DNA fragments and creating a recombinant plasmid. For example, we could purify DNA from an organism or tissue and break it into random-length pieces by rapidly mixing it. The rapid mixing exerts extreme forces on the long DNA molecule, snapping it into many smaller pieces (you can get the idea by waving around a piece of dried spaghetti). Alternatively, we could digest the purified DNA using restriction endonucleases to produce smaller fragments. The smaller fragments could then be inserted into a plasmid using a ligase (Figure 11.9). The plasmid containing the new fragment could then be transformed into a bacterium. This process uses the bacteria's natural DNA replication system to amplify the plasmid. In the end, we will have amplified our selected piece of DNA many millions of times. DNA cloning using plasmids turned *E. coli* into the workhorse of the molecular biology lab. As PCR developed as a technique, it was also used to clone genes, and PCR copies of genes could be treated with endonucleases and ligated into plasmids for sequencing or for expression within a different host.

One of the most useful aspects of cloning is being able to manipulate the expression of specific genes and to link genes encoding different proteins together. Two proteins linked together in this way are said to be fused, and the resulting product is a **fusion protein**. A common way to refer to a gene that a scientist wants to study is to call it a "**gene of interest**." The coding sequence of a gene of interest can be cloned with a different promoter. This results in the gene being expressed in a different tissue or in response to a different stimulus. The gene of interest could also be attached to a **marker protein**, such as the green fluorescent protein. The **green fluorescent protein (GFP)** was first isolated from the jellyfish *Aequorea victoria* by Japanese biochemist Osamu

Shimomura. Using molecular cloning techniques, we can fuse our gene of interest with the gene from *A. victoria* that encodes the GFP to track when it is expressed, or where it is located in a cell, using fluorescence microscopy **(Figure 11.10)**.

A recombinant plasmid system can also be used to express a transgene. The term **transgene** describes the situation when the coding sequence of a gene from one organism is expressed in a different organism. In essence, the expression of GFP in a bacterium or green alga (Figure 11.10) is an example of transgene expression because the GFP gene originated in the *A. victoria* jellyfish. There are many examples of this technique, but GFP expression remains one of the most interesting and useful from a basic research point of view. Not only can it be visually stunning and allow for truly artistic microphotography, it can also provide critical information about the function of a poorly understood protein. GFP can now be expressed in nearly any living organism. GFP absorbs blue light and reemits light energy

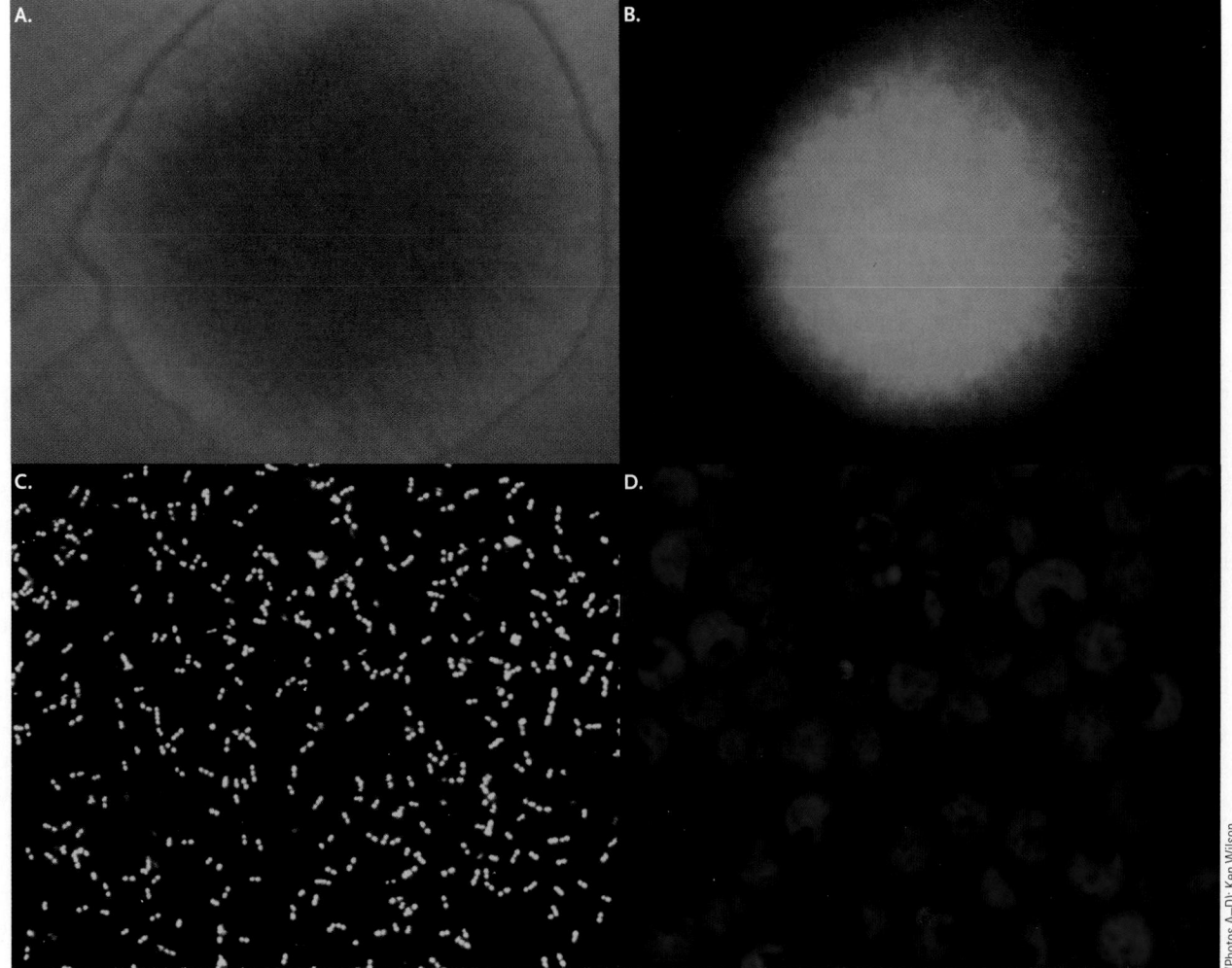

(Photos A–D): Ken Wilson

**FIGURE 11.10** The expression of green fluorescent protein (GFP) fusion proteins can be visualized in living cells using fluorescence microscopy. We can compare a bacterial colony growing on an agar plate using bright-field **(a)** or fluorescence microscopy **(b)**. We can also visualize a yellow fluorescent variant of GFP in individual bacteria **(c)** or determine where in a *Chlamydomonas reinhardtii* cell a GFP fusion protein is located **(d)**. In this case, it is in the nucleus (green). The chlorophyll fluoresces red, showing us the location of the chloroplast.

(fluoresces) back into the environment as green light. Thus, GFP can be used as an indicator. Its presence or absence can be used to test the activity of the promoter of a specific gene. It can also be used to determine where in a cell or organism a particular protein is produced. For example, one step we often use when trying to determine the function of an unknown protein is to find out where it is localized in a cell. The subcellular localization can allow us to make hypotheses about a protein's function. For example, if a protein is located in the chloroplast, there is a strong possibility it could be involved in photosynthesis, and equally likely, it is not part of the cellular respiration pathways.

Using promoters that only activate gene expression in certain tissues or during specific developmental stages allows us to use **transgenic organisms** to study where and when a gene is expressed. For example, if agricultural scientists wanted to make transgenic potato plants that are resistant to the Colorado potato beetle without affecting the edible tubers, they could use a leaf-specific promoter to drive the expression of the transgene. The transgenic organism is made by transforming some of its cells using a cloned DNA plasmid vector. Some organisms are easier to transform than others, but if germ-line cells can be transformed, the offspring of the transformed individual will inherit the transgene. Medical researchers often use this approach to study how proteins associated with diseases function. They can also learn how organs and tissues develop using transgenes fused to particular promoters **(Figure 11.11)**. Using simpler model organisms such as mice, zebrafish, and fruit flies, transgenic technology has rapidly advanced our understanding of how human tissues develop.

The techniques developed using molecular biology are very powerful and have allowed scientists to greatly improve our understanding of living cells. DNA sequencing and PCR are routinely used to detect diseases, identify new species, or solve crimes. Cloning and the production of transgenic organisms are similarly used in research. Knowing how proteins interact and where they are located in the cell helps us understand the molecular mechanisms of diseases and is the first step in developing new treatments.

## STUDY BREAK

1. How does the thermostability (ability to stay active at high temperature) of the *Taq* polymerase make PCR more convenient?
2. Why does the addition of dideoxynucleotide triphosphates to a Sanger DNA sequencing reaction cause many small fragments to be produced?
3. Define the term *transformation*.

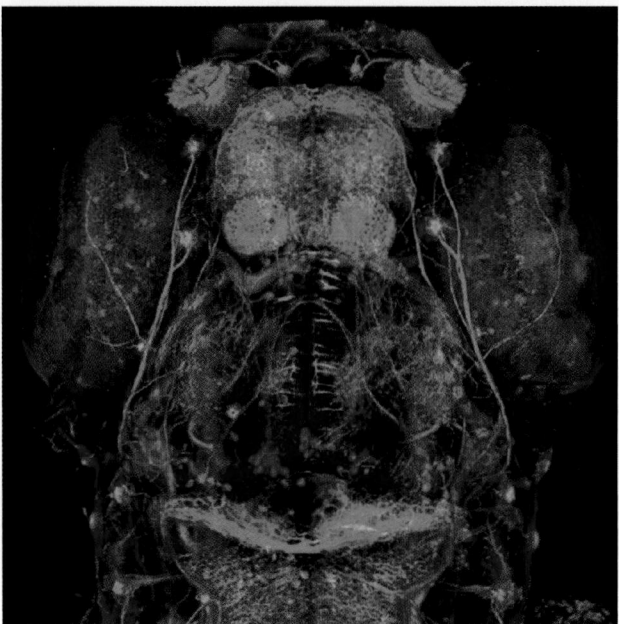

**FIGURE 11.11** The model organism *Danio rerio* (zebrafish) can be used to study retinal development. Here a zebrafish expressing multiple fluorescent proteins can be used to study neural connections between the eye and the brain.

SOURCE: Nikon Small World 2010 2nd Place. Dr. Hideo Otsuna, University of Utah Medical Center, Department of Neurobiology and Anatomy. Salt Lake City, Utah, USA. 5-day old zebrafish head (20x)

## 11.3 Bioinformatics

As mentioned above, one of the important emerging fields of biological analysis merges computer science and molecular biology. Bioinformatics involves the design of computer programs to compare and predict DNA or protein sequences. Bioinformatics approaches that meld biology, statistics, and computer science are improving our ability to work with extremely large sets of data, such as the 3.2 gigabases of DNA sequence found in a human cell. The National Institutes of Health in the United States started its National Center for Biotechnology Information (NCBI) in 1988. The NCBI stores a vast database of sequence data. It is the place where scientists store their sequence data when they are ready to share it with the public. As of February 2014, NCBI's genome database, called **Genbank**, contained over 700 trillion base pairs of DNA sequence data. As you could imagine, a big part of the NCBI's mandate is developing better and more useful computer analysis programs that allow scientists to find what they are looking for in this sea of information.

The people working at this interface between biology and computer science conduct research that helps them design programs to look for specific factors in genome sequences. For example, when initially assembling genomes, it is extremely helpful to identify which portions of the genome are genes that encode proteins. Not only does this help determine the number of genes, it also helps line up large, overlapping segments of the genome.

Using previously obtained knowledge about promoter sequences in the organism, and by performing **in silico** (computer-based) translation of the DNA sequences, computer analysis is very good at identifying possible genes and the introns that they contain. More support can be provided for the identity of genes by comparing the genome sequences of related organisms. If we were to compare the genomes of mice and humans, we would expect to see greater similarity in portions of the genome that encode proteins required for common processes.

The field of bioinformatics goes beyond simply comparing genomes. Clever individuals are using knowledge obtained from large genome data sets to make predictions about the proteins they encode. **Algorithms**—procedures for making calculations—are used to predict how proteins will fold, where they will be transported in the cell, and even what function they perform. These predictions are made by comparing what we do not know to what we do know. As we perform more research and figure out what more proteins do in cells and how different genes are expressed, our predictions about similar, yet unknown proteins get better.

Complete genome sequencing has provided new approaches to genetics. However, the ability to handle extremely large data sets is crucial. For example, the latest techniques in mapping genes do not involve crossing parents and examining large numbers of $F_1$ and $F_2$ offspring. Instead, comparisons are made using single nucleotide polymorphisms (SNPs), which are one-base alterations observed when comparing the genome of one individual to that of another. It is predicted that there is on average one SNP per thousand bases in the human genome—hence the idea that humans' genetic sequences are approximately 99.9% identical. These small differences are alleles that can be followed from generation to generation. If phenotypes such as a particular disease, eye colour, or male-pattern baldness are inherited with specific SNPs, then researchers can use the results to identify the location of the causative gene(s).

## 11.4 Genomics: Studying Gene Expression on a Large Scale

As the scale of research projects has gone from studying a single gene or protein at a time to examining changes in all of the genes or proteins at once, new terms have been introduced into the scientific dictionary. **Functional genomics** is a term used to describe large-scale studies that examine the response of all genes in a cell to a particular signal or during a specific developmental stage. Similarly, **proteomics** describes a study looking at thousands of proteins at a time. These types of studies are possible today as a result of the genome sequencing

projects, greatly improved automation in research labs, and the development of bioinformatics approaches to identifying changes in extremely large data sets.

### Genome Sequencing Projects Examine All of the DNA in an Organism

Genome sequencing projects aim to determine the absolute sequence of all of the chromosomes in a particular organism. Normally, this is done at the species level, but now with the decreasing cost and the speed at which sequencing can be done, personalized genome sequencing is becoming routine. The initial Human Genome Project used DNA from four randomized individuals (two males and two females); the individual genomes of a few other people were sequenced and assembled shortly thereafter. They include James Watson (co-discoverer of the structure of DNA) and individuals representing a variety of ethnic backgrounds. The Wellcome Trust in the United Kingdom sponsored a proposal, called the 1000 Genomes Project, to sequence the genomes of 1000 individuals to investigate the amount of variation in the human genome. A secondary goal was to develop better sequencing tools and make sequencing an individual's genome a routine procedure.

Proposed advantages of having your personal genome sequenced include a forewarning of possible genetic diseases. This may lead individuals to alter their lifestyles to decrease their chances of becoming ill later in life. Individual genetic knowledge could also allow treatments to be developed on an individual basis. For example, if your genetic makeup suggests that you might develop arthritis later in life, a specific treatment regimen may be developed for you to minimize your risk. Drugs that work on the exact type of arthritis you may develop could be selected. This approach would minimize the trial-and-error approach to treatment that is currently used. An interesting challenge may be in treating cancer through such an approach. Cancer often arises due to one or more mutations in a cell. It may require the sequencing of the cancerous cells in question to determine the exact cause of the disease and thus the appropriate course of treatment. Based on the results of sequencing projects, it is becoming clear that cancer is not one disease but is often a disease unique to each individual.

Of course, genome-scale DNA sequencing projects are not limited to humans. The genomes of many mammals, birds, reptiles, plants, fungi, bacteria, and viruses have been sequenced. This has been a treasure trove of information for evolutionary biologists. Rather than comparing similar organisms based on just their morphology, they can be compared using their DNA sequences, the blueprint on which their morphology is based. Although comparing the lineage and similarities of organisms using DNA sequences is not new, the scale over which the comparisons can be made is. What they have found has often been surprising.

## Genomics Is the Large-Scale Use of Genome Sequencing Data

Above, we mentioned the idea of using an SNP chip to map alleles on a genome. Chip technology got its start in an attempt to examine the expression level of every mRNA transcript in a cell, simultaneously. When performed on a global scale such as this, gene expression analysis is called **transcriptomics**. When discussing all of the transcripts present in a cell, we call it the **transcriptome**. Initially, transcriptomic experiments used a chip-based system to examine approximately hundreds of transcripts at a time. As technology advanced, more and more tests could fit on a single slide. What started off as a technology to study the expression of a few hundred genes at once advanced to one able to study the expression of tens of thousands of genes in one experiment. The results of chip-based transcriptomic experiments were revolutionary in that they allowed scientists to identify proteins that performed similar functions. For example, scientists studying fruit ripening performed transcriptomic studies on strawberry fruit as it progressed through the ripening process. They identified specific genes that encoded proteins needed for producing sweet, juicy, red strawberries that had never been identified before their study.

## Proteomics Examines All of the Proteins in a Cell or Tissue

Another type of functional genomics, proteomics, attempts to examine all of the proteins in a cell or tissue. Large-scale proteomics studies have proven more challenging than genome sequencing. This is true from both a technical and a biological perspective. On the technical side, proteins are not nearly as easy to sequence as fragments of DNA. Even with today's technology, it is both time-consuming and expensive to identify large numbers of unknown proteins. From the biological perspective, because the genome found in each cell in an organism is the same and relatively unchanging, a sequencing project can use any type of cell. On the other hand, different cell types in a multicellular organism do not all express the same suite of proteins. For example, our white blood cells do not express the same set of proteins as our liver cells. Thus, although our white blood cells and liver cells have identical genome sequences, their **proteomes**—the proteins found in the cell—would be quite different. Similarly, the proteome of a cell is not static and thus can change. The age of the cell, its reproductive stage, and the environmental conditions to which it is exposed all affect the proteins that are expressed. As an example, we can go

back to the model bacterium *E. coli* and the expression of the *lac* operon (see Chapter 10). Remember that when *E. coli*, an intestinal bacterium, is grown on glucose, it represses the expression of genes required for the metabolism of lactose. Following depletion of glucose in its medium, the cell may switch to lactose metabolism if lactose is present. Thus, we could use a "proteomics approach" to study the change in protein content in the cell during this environmental change. We could compare cells before and after glucose depletion. We would see an increase in the lactose metabolic enzymes, such as permease and beta-galactosidase, as the cells adapt to their new environmental conditions.

Despite the challenges associated with proteomics, it is a very important technique for understanding the physiological changes that cells undergo when their environment upsets their homeostasis. It is poised to become very important in assessing and treating disease. Proteomic results can tell the researcher about the functioning of a cell. Transcriptomic studies only tell the investigators how the levels of mRNA are changing with respect to the total mRNA pool. Using both transcriptomics and proteomics to study how organisms respond to their environment or how diseased cells are different from healthy cells allows us to investigate links between the steps of the central dogma of molecular biology (see Figure 10.2). For example, does a disease cause a change in gene transcription, or is the effect at the level of translation? Comparing transcript levels to protein levels would allow us to answer this question.

## STUDY BREAK

1. Why is the field of bioinformatics so important in modern molecular biology and biotechnology?
2. What is the difference between transcriptomics and proteomics?

## 11.5 Genetically Modified Organisms

Genetically modified organisms (GMOs) are a very contentious issue. Like many contentious issues, people debating the merits versus the risks of GMOs have valid points. Healthy debate is a good thing when there are truths on both sides. Scientists sometimes get distracted answering questions about what is possible. Corporations are duty bound to maximize profits. Activists sometimes do not want things to change and refuse to admit that some scientific advances have merit. All sides of the issue can go too far in their opinion making and discard scientific approaches and experimental data in their discussions.

Like most choices we make, the use of GMOs leads to trade-offs. They are merely tools used for specific purposes and not inherently bad. The production of GMOs and their use include producing the *E. coli* cells capable of making human insulin for the treatment of diabetes. Few people could argue against this case. It leads to the need for fewer animal deaths and produces a superior form of insulin. The bacteria are grown in carefully controlled incubators, with no release to the outside environment. At the other extreme, agrochemical companies develop crop plants that carry genes to make them resistant to herbicides. The most successful example in Western Canada is Roundup Ready canola. Roundup is a formulation of the herbicide glyphosate. This chemical blocks the formation of some amino acids in plants. Without these amino acids, the plant will grow poorly, and actively growing plants are killed. Glyphosate does not discriminate between plant types, so it is a very good option for killing all the plants in a field. Monsanto was originally awarded a patent for the use of glyphosate in 1970, which expired in 2000. At that time, any other company could produce and sell glyphosate for use as a herbicide.

To get a new patent, Monsanto needed a significant improvement in its bestselling herbicide. Instead of a better herbicide—glyphosate is already pretty good—imagine if you had a crop that was selectively resistant to glyphosate activity. You could spray your crop plants and only kill unwanted weeds. To achieve this goal, Monsanto scientists searched for and found a mutant version of the glyphosate target protein that is not inhibited by glyphosate. By cloning this mutant gene and expressing it in plants, they made genetically modified (GM) plants that were unaffected by glyphosate when used at normal levels. There were many advantages to this approach. For Monsanto, it provided a new patentable approach to weed control. They sold their GMO seed in conjunction with glyphosate herbicide. Some of the profits made from these sales were used to fund further research projects. For farmers, it meant a more efficient method of weed control. They could spray a herbicide on their crop plants that would kill every other plant in their field. In the long run, this saves farmers money because they only need one type of herbicide and it requires fewer applications. This reduces the cost of chemicals, employee salaries, and tractor fuel.

However, there have been some negative results as well. Some seed loss during harvesting means that glyphosate-resistant plants can sprout the following year. If the farmer has rotated his crop, for example, changed from canola to wheat, then the wheat crop may contain glyphosate-resistant canola plants. A second negative outcome was the emergence of the fear of possible outcomes caused by the use of GM plants in the field. Unlike GM bacteria, which were carefully contained in a production facility, the GM canola was released into the environment. Despite a lack of scientific evidence to support their claims, many environmental activists protested that GM plants were killing local insect and amphibian populations. Similarly, there were fears that GM plants would transfer their genes to native plant species and lead to the evolution of superweeds.

Although we cannot say that glyphosate herbicide, used in combination with glyphosate-resistant GM plants, has no negative effects, it may be safer and less damaging than the alternatives. However, both sides of the argument seem unable to clearly and scientifically make their arguments. Testing irregularities have tainted some of the agrochemical company research, and corporations often take defensive positions rather than clearly explaining the advantages of their products. Unfortunately, groups opposed to GM technology often use fear of the unknown to advance their arguments. As scientists, we want to use the scientific method to design controlled experiments that test and assess the evidence. In the end, compromises always need to be made between risks and rewards. The goal of everyone should be to maximize the rewards: greater crop yields, better quality food, less indiscriminate chemical use, and decreased use of fossil fuels by farm equipment. But we should also minimize the risks: environmental degradation, harm to native plant and animal species, and release of transgenes into the environment. These are not easy questions to answer, and they can only be addressed satisfactorily by using careful scientific assessment of thoughtful experiments conducted over the course of time.

## STUDY BREAK

1. Why do we need to be careful when growing GMO plants in farmers' fields?

## 11.6 Organismal Cloning

One of the most controversial and often misunderstood processes in the field of biotechnology is the cloning of organisms. This is especially true for the cloning of vertebrates. Media coverage of cloning ranges from fascination to fear mongering. Often in films and science fiction writing, clones and cloning are portrayed with negative undertones. Scientists who carry out the cloning are often portrayed as "mad scientists" in the stereotype of Victor Frankenstein. In this section, we will examine cloning first from a technical point of view and then from an ethical one.

The cloning of vertebrates is a challenging undertaking. A scientist removes the nucleus from a maturing egg cell and then replaces it with the nucleus from a different cell (**Figure 11.12, p. 252**). This is done using very fine needles and instruments. The egg cell is then allowed to divide in vitro until the early embryo stage. At this point, the developing clone is still undifferentiated but is composed of a few hundred cells. The embryo is then

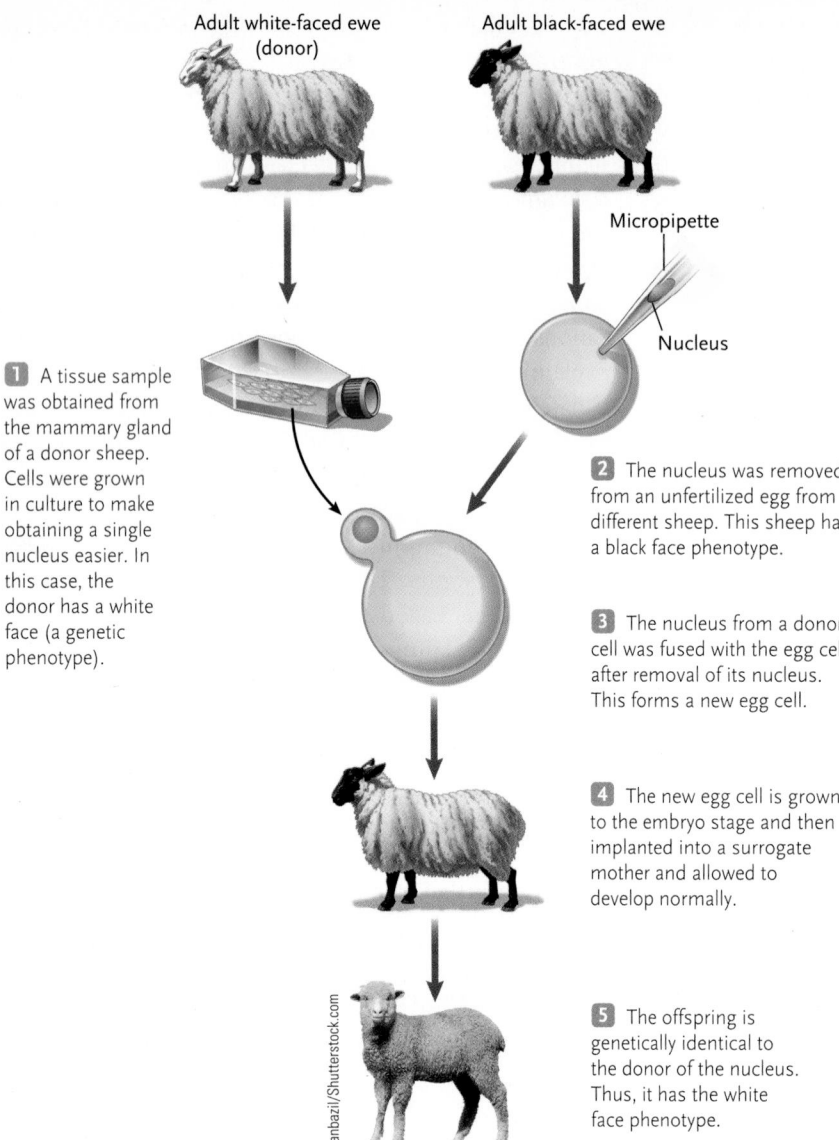

**1** A tissue sample was obtained from the mammary gland of a donor sheep. Cells were grown in culture to make obtaining a single nucleus easier. In this case, the donor has a white face (a genetic phenotype).

Adult white-faced ewe (donor)

Adult black-faced ewe

Micropipette

Nucleus

**2** The nucleus was removed from an unfertilized egg from a different sheep. This sheep has a black face phenotype.

**3** The nucleus from a donor cell was fused with the egg cell after removal of its nucleus. This forms a new egg cell.

**4** The new egg cell is grown to the embryo stage and then implanted into a surrogate mother and allowed to develop normally.

**5** The offspring is genetically identical to the donor of the nucleus. Thus, it has the white face phenotype.

*Biology, 2E\**

panbazil/Shutterstock.com

**FIGURE 11.12** Mammals are cloned by the insertion of a new nucleus into an egg cell. The rest of fetal development progresses as normal.

implanted into a surrogate mother, and if all goes according to plan, it will develop and be born just like any other offspring.

It is because the nuclei of the new offspring contain the identical DNA as the nucleus inserted into the egg that we call the new organism a clone. It will be genetically identical to the individual from whom the somatic cell nucleus was obtained. However, we are beginning to learn that epigenetics can play a fundamental role in how this new being develops. Our lack of understanding of how epigenetic changes are inherited during cloning, combined with the possibility that the donor cell may have acquired mutations in its genome prior to insertion, means that we have difficulty predicting the outcomes of cloning. As a society, we need to discuss and debate the benefits of cloning versus possible negative outcomes. However, to have these types of debate, we need to increase awareness of what is being done in labs and avoid falling prey to reactionary fear.

To ensure a fair debate, scientists need to explain how cloning can be beneficial. There are advantages in medical research for cloning. This does not involve cloning humans as a stock of organs for transplant purposes. Rather, medical scientists want to use genetically identical lab animals to study models of human diseases. It can be incredibly difficult to develop an animal model that responds to a disease in the same way as humans. Mouse models exist for different types of obesity, Parkinson's disease, and Alzheimer's disease. Similarly, mouse models exist for even more complex disorders for which we have no definitive cause, such as schizophrenia and autism. The breeding of such animals is so complex that cloning is the only way to produce enough of the animals to perform standardized drug trials, which can be replicated in multiple laboratories. Luckily, because of its technical challenges, cloning only needs to be done to generate an initial population; after that, standard breeding practices can resume.

One final aspect of cloning brought up recently in the media is the idea of bringing extinct species back to life. A number of people, scientists and theorizers, have begun debating the concept of de-extinction. Could we bring back an extinct species by cloning? A number of suggestions have been made for what the first species to be brought back from extinction should be. They include the passenger pigeon, woolly mammoths, and Tasmanian tigers **(Figure 11.13)**. Can these animals be brought back? The technical challenges are impressive. First, it would require that a complete copy of the genome of the animal be obtained. It would then need to be implanted into the egg cell of a surrogate to bring the embryo to term. In the case of the woolly mammoth, this would likely be an elephant. The important question to ask is: should we do this? The answer to this question is very complex. The presence of extinct animals could be incredibly useful to understanding evolutionary processes. But would they be anything more than a zoo attraction?

We have to remember that biotechnology is the use of biology tools to provide a product. In and of themselves, the tools are not harmful. However, as a society, we need to try to understand the tools at our disposal and how they can be used. An important question to ask is should they all be used? Maybe not. As we learn more about the molecular working of cells and complex animals, we will need to keep expanding our discussions about what should and should not be done in research labs. Research ethics boards are one safeguard that we have in place. Scientists working in government labs and universities are required to follow explicit ethical guidelines for the treatment of animals in their care. Canadian universities, like their international counterparts, have animal care committees composed of research staff, non-animal researchers, students, veterinarians, and members of the community. The animal care committee reviews research proposals that plan to use animals and must approve the experimental procedures before the research can take place. All experiments that use animals, even ones that simply observe behaviour, must be clearly planned and explained to the animal care committee. Research animals must be treated with the utmost care and respect. Any breach of ethics or animal care guidelines can result in the loss of research privileges and criminal charges. Working with research animals is truly a privilege.

## STUDY BREAK

1. Why does the clone have the same genetic phenotype as the donor of the nucleus and not the surrogate mother?

**FIGURE 11.13** Could an extinct species such as the woolly mammoth be brought to life through cloning? Should it be brought back? Could a modern elephant be a surrogate parent for a mammoth embryo?

## PUTTING IT IN PERSPECTIVE

At the heart of biotechnology is the goal of using other organisms to perform tasks for us that improve our lives. We can easily see this goal being met in some of the examples that we examined in this chapter. Modern biotechnological advances, such as the production of recombinant human insulin, the development of mouse models of complex diseases, and even sequencing projects that tell us more about the organisms with which we share Earth all seem like noble endeavours. The cloning of animals for non-scientific purposes and the idea of de-extinction seem more ethically dubious. Like any set of scientific tools, biotechnology's impact on society depends on its use or abuse. We will end this chapter with an example of how biotechnology can reduce our environmental impact on Earth.

We can all agree that the ever-increasing use of fossil fuels is having an effect on the biosphere. Increased levels of atmospheric carbon dioxide caused by human activities are warming the planet and increasing the likelihood of extreme weather events. A number of researchers across Canada and around the world are trying to develop biotechnological methods to reduce our need for fossil fuels. One focus has been on plants. Plants remove carbon dioxide when they photosynthesize, so if we grow plants and use them for fuel production, we should decrease the release of carbon dioxide. Interestingly, it seems that the types of plants we use are very important in this process. In the United States, the initial focus was on the production of "bioethanol" using corn. The process ferments corn grown by farmers to produce ethanol that is mixed with gasoline for use in cars. However, it turns out that growing corn uses more energy than the fermented ethanol can provide. Production of bioethanol from corn increased greenhouse gas emissions.

A more sustainable option that has been suggested is the growth of algae. Although often looked at as a nuisance in our lakes, aquariums, and swimming pools, these miniature plants also remove carbon dioxide from the atmosphere through photosynthesis. Unlike corn plants, algae can be grown in small ponds or engineered bioreactors **(Figure 11.14)**. A team from the National Research Council of Canada demonstrated an added benefit by growing algae for biofuel production using municipal waste water. In this situation, algae both help clean our water and provide us with energy. Even better, algae are quite amenable to genetic engineering (Figure 11.14), so the oils they produce can be modified to suit the industry needing the fuel. The United States Air Force is examining the use of algae for jet fuel production. A number of Canadian corporations are investigating and investing in algal biotechnology as a way to meet sustainability targets. Although this field of biotechnological research is still in its infancy, it does show promise for improving our interaction with the biosphere. Decreased carbon emissions and increased water quality are two targets that all Canadians should be working toward.

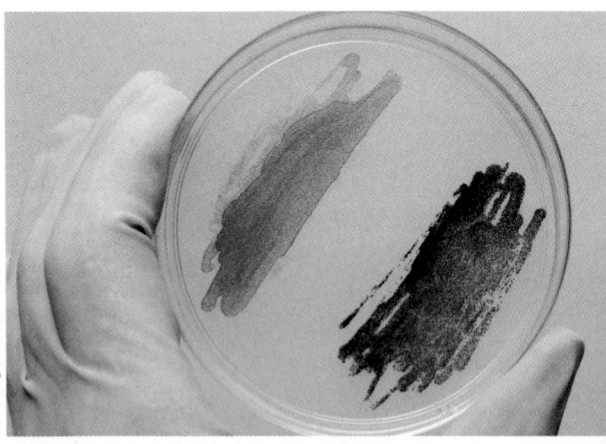

**FIGURE 11.14** Naturally growing or genetically engineered algae can be grown in large-scale ponds for the production of biofuels.

# KEY CONCEPTS AND REVIEW QUESTIONS

### 11.1 What Is Biotechnology?

Biotechnology can be defined as the use of biological organisms for human benefit. This can reflect any type of use, from the fermentation of grapes to make wine to the production of recombinant human insulin using the bacterium *E. coli*. Often modern views of biotechnology focus on the use of molecular biology tools to modify organisms.

1. Perform an Internet search to find a biologically produced drug used to treat a human disease.

2. Why are bacteria a good choice for generating biotechnological materials? What traits would make an organism a bad choice?

### 11.2 Technical Aspects of Molecular Biotechnology

The capacity to perform molecular biotechnology is driven by the technical advances of molecular biology. The advances made by Dr. Frederick Sanger drove molecular biology and subsequently biotechnology. The same was true of the development of the polymerase chain reaction. The ability to cheaply and routinely sequence DNA, combined with newly developing techniques, allows researchers to perform genome-wide sequencing and clone genes from different organisms into plasmid vectors.

3. What is the difference between blunt ends and sticky ends that are produced by restriction endonucleases?

4. How does the use of specific types of gene promoters allow scientists to control where in a transgenic organism a protein is expressed?

## 11.3 Bioinformatics

Bioinformatics is a new science developing at the interface of molecular biology and computer science. Dealing with the large amounts of data that are being produced by sequencing projects requires scientists to use new types of tools to examine their data. Another great advantage of bioinformatics is the tools that can make predictions about genes and proteins by comparing information from many different organisms.

5. Define the term *algorithm*.
6. How does the comparison of genome sequences help researchers identify protein coding genes?
7. Why are the nucleotide sequences that encode proteins more similar between species than other nucleotide sequences, such as introns?

## 11.4 Genomics: Studying Gene Expression on a Large Scale

Genome sequencing projects attempt to determine the order of all of the nucleotide bases in a given organism. Using bioinformatics tools, scientists put together all of the small sequences they generate into chromosome-length fragments. Once the entire sequence for an organism is known, new types of approaches, such as transcriptomics and proteomics, can be used to study gene expression patterns. Transcriptomics can examine the abundance of all of the mRNAs in a given sample at the same time, whereas proteomics attempts to quantify the amounts of all of the proteins. Together these techniques are providing scientists with unprecedented knowledge of the inner workings of the cell.

8. Using your knowledge of the central dogma of molecular biology from Chapter 10, if we performed a transcriptomic and proteomic experiment on the same samples, what could it tell us about which steps of gene expression are being regulated in eukaryotes?

## 11.5 Genetically Modified Organisms

The ability of scientists to insert new genes into organisms has opened up new avenues of research. The use of the green fluorescent protein to image the location of specific proteins inside living cells helps advance both medical and basic research. In areas of applied research such as medicine and agriculture, genetically modified organisms have allowed more rapid advances. The production of transgenic crop plants that are immune to herbicides, resistant to insect pests, or more tolerant of diseases has helped farmers produce more food while reducing the amount of work required and shrinking their carbon footprint.

## 11.6 Organismal Cloning

Perhaps the most ethically demanding area of modern biology, cloning organisms can provide significant scientific advances. The production of genetically identical mice allows new drugs to be tested in the most highly controlled system possible. With the idea of cloning extinct animals to bring back species that are no longer alive, we may be setting a bad precedent.

9. What extinct organism would you bring back to life? How would you argue your choice to a regulatory agency?

# Species: What Are They?

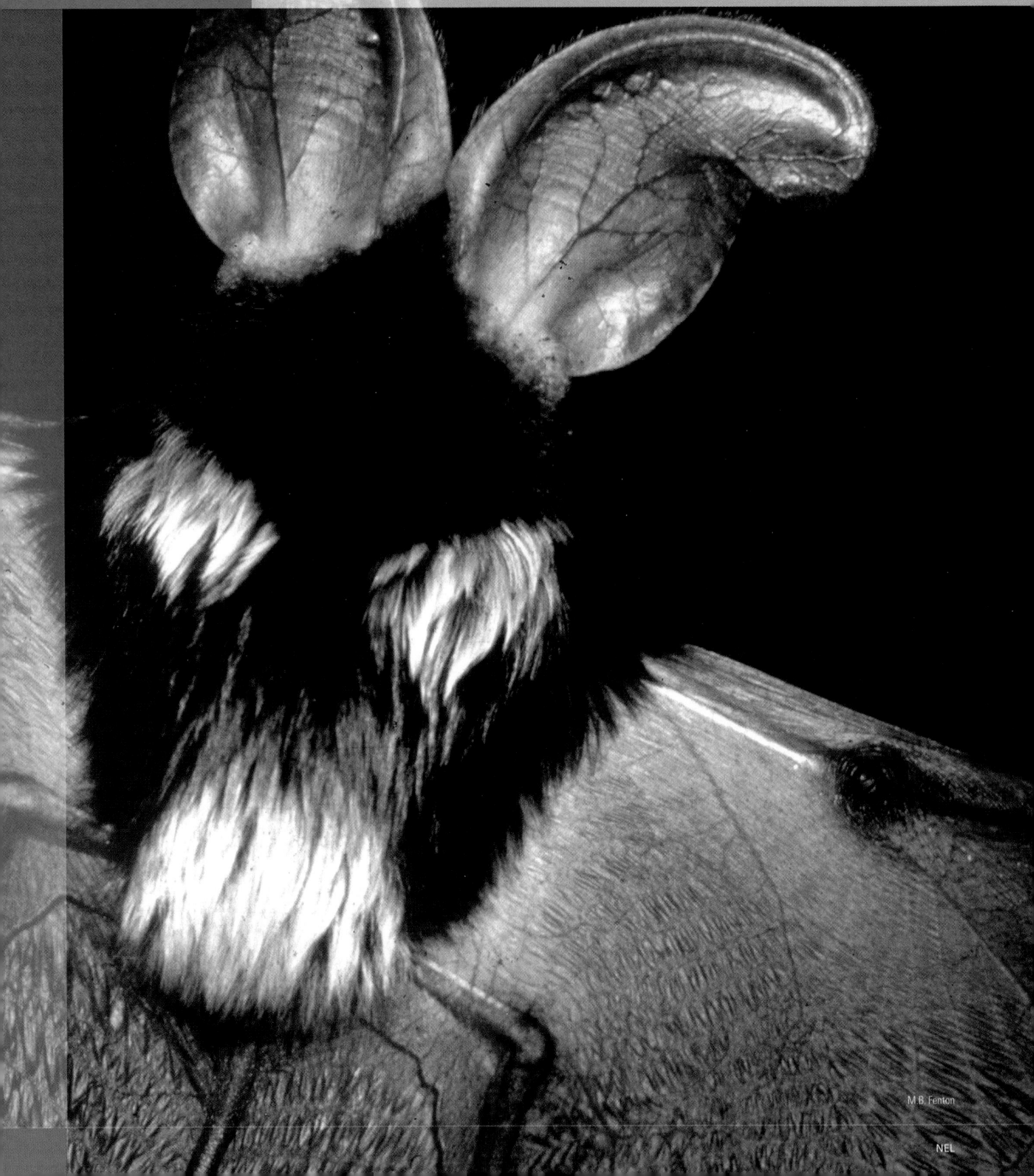

M.B. Fenton

## WHY IT MATTERS

Socrates, a famous Greek philosopher, was executed by being forced to drink a cup of tea made from poison hemlock. People who eat **poison** hemlock experience progressive paralysis that eventually stops the heart and lungs. Other names for poison hemlock are spotted parsley, poison snakeweed, and, in Scotland, dead man's oatmeal. The leaves of parsley are superficially similar to those of poison hemlock **(Figure 12.1)**, and both parsley and poison hemlock are species in the parsley family (Apiaceae). But distinguishing these two species is important because someone who did not know the difference could die by making the wrong choice. People regularly eat other plants in the Apiaceae, including anise, fennel, carrots, and celery. Knowing how to tell these species apart, in this case, could be a matter of life and death.

Biologists use **scientific names** to communicate precisely. But scientific names are a barrier to communication with non-biologists. The scientific names of the plants we have encountered to date in this chapter are *Petroselinum crispum* (parsley), *Conium maculatum* (poison hemlock), *Pimpinella anisum* (anise), *Foeniculum vulgare* (fennel), *Daucus carota* (carrot), and *Apium graveolens* (celery). Although they are more precise, none of these names would appeal to someone shopping in a market.

In this chapter, we will cover basic information about species, from how they are named to the role species play in biology. This will include how the mode of reproduction (sexual versus asexual) affects our definition of a species. It will quickly become obvious that species are units of convenience and that the definition used to identify one group of organisms as a species may be impractical for others. We will see how one can identify species and learn how important this can be from the standpoint of conserving biodiversity.

## 12.1 Naming Species

All **species** known to science have a technical or scientific name: a binomial (two-part name) that precisely identifies them. Some species, but not all, also have at least one common name. *Petroselinum crispum* is the scientific name for the plant with the common name parsley. Scientific names are always written in italics and consist of two words. The first word (the genus name) is capitalized, and the second word (the trivial name) is not. Genus and species names place the organism in a hierarchy of classification (see the Purple Pages for an overview of classification), in which organisms are grouped together in increasingly larger groups based on their evolutionary relationships (Box 12.1). The hierarchy of classification for a species allows us to put it in context, in the case of parsley to the plant family Apiaceae.

For those familiar with Latin and Greek, the scientific name can also provide information about the organism. *Conium* comes from the Greek *konas*, meaning "to whirl" (reflecting an effect of coniine on the sense of balance). But *maculatum* means "spotted," in this case describing the appearance of the poison hemlock leaves. *Euderma maculatum* is the scientific name for a spotted bat **(Figure 12.2, p. 259)**. Again, the trivial name *maculatum* means spotted, whereas *Euderma* means "good" (*eu*) skin (*derma*). Most of us are unfamiliar with Latin and Greek, so scientific names are intimidating. Listen to biologists using scientific names in conversation. The diversity of pronunciations reveals that even they are often not familiar with Latin and Greek.

**FIGURE 12.1** Parsley (*Petroselinum crispum*) **(a)**, poison hemlock (*Conium maculatum*) **(b)**, and **(c)** a molecule of coniine, the deadly ingredient.

BOX 12.1

# Classification and Names

Below are the names and classifications of a plant, a fungus, a bird, and a mammal to illustrate the relationship between scientific names and classification. Note that the scientific name consists of two words, starting with the name of the genus. Note that the classification places the organism in a kingdom, a phylum, a class, an order, and a family. Often there are additional subdivisions (e.g., suborder or subclass) that are not shown here.

| Common Names | | | |
|---|---|---|---|
| **Classification** | | | |
| **(a)** Morel (a type of mushroom) | **(b)** Poison hemlock | **(c)** Royal Flycatcher | **(d)** Mexican opossum |
| **Kingdom** | | | |
| Fungi | Plantae | Animalia | Animalia |
| **Phylum** | | | |
| Basidiomycota | Eudicota | Chordata | Chordata |
| **Class** | | | |
| Pezizomycetes | Magnoliopsida | Aves | Mammalia |
| **Order** | | | |
| Pezizales | Apiales | Passeriformes | Didelphimorphia |
| **Family** | | | |
| Morchellaceae | Apiaceae | Tyrannidae | Didelphidae |
| **Genus** | | | |
| Morchella | Conium | Onychorhynchus | Marmosa |
| **Species** | | | |
| *Morchella esculenta* | *Conium maculatum* | *Onychorhynchus coronatus* | *Marmosa mexicana* |

M.B. Fenton

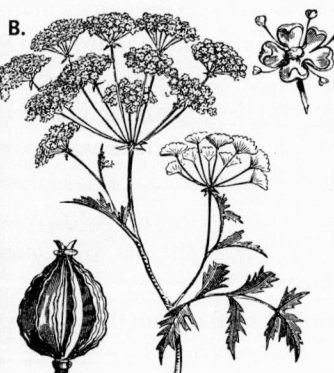

GJones Creative/Shutterstock.com

M.B. Fenton

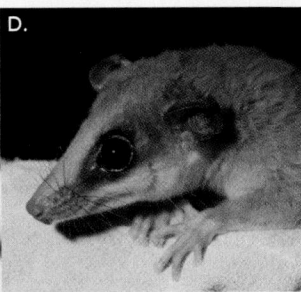

M.B. Fenton

In writing scientific names, the genus *Morchella* and the two names comprising the species *Morchella esculenta* are presented in italics. After the full name has been presented, it is acceptable to abbreviate the name thus: *M. esculenta*.

Scientific names can be presented with additional information. For example, the Canadian beaver can be referred to as *Castor canadensis* Kuhl, 1820, where Kuhl, 1820 indicates that it was originally described and named by Kuhl in 1820.

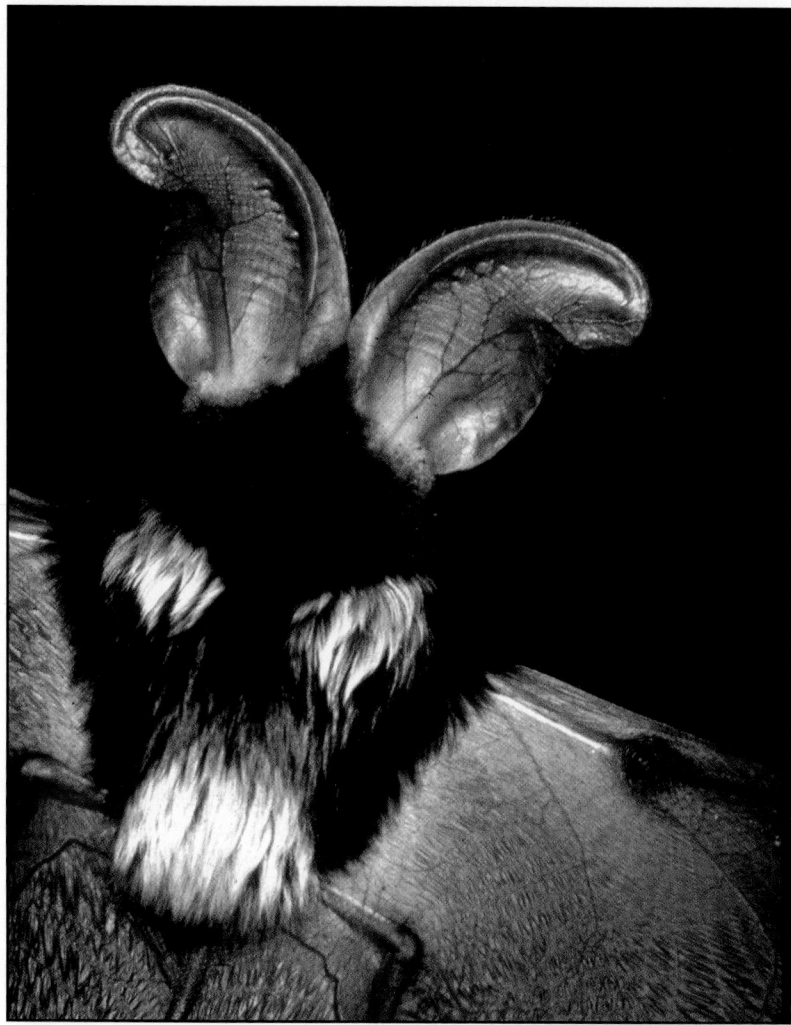

FIGURE 12.2 A spotted bat, *Euderma maculatum*, viewed from above.

the trunks of trees. When the same monkey gives a "leopard" alarm call, others within earshot look down and those on the ground climb trees. Many other prey species recognize that different predators pose different threats and signal accordingly.

The **common names** of birds in English are an exception; they are standardized, unlike those of most other species. The common names of birds are presented in capitals (Black-capped Chickadee – *Poecile atricapillus*, Peregrine Falcon – *Falco peregrinus*, Wandering Albatross – *Diomedea exulans*) because they are standardized. Our general familiarity with birds is probably the main reason we treat them differently from other animals. Bird watching is a very popular and common pastime—both for backyard enthusiasts and avid birders who travel the world to seek out new species—and standardized common names are helpful to both. Strong public interest in birds has helped drive important bird conservation efforts. Common name standardization was the result of an intensive initiative by the International Ornithological Congress in the 1990s to solve communication problems in bird conservation caused by confusion over names.

Scientific names allow us to talk about species very precisely. But since the Latin- and Greek-based names are difficult for most people to interpret, scientific names can be a barrier to communication. Most familiar organisms have a common name as well. Common names are just that—names commonly used to identify species. Many species have more than one common name. Take *Conium maculatum*, for example. The name "poison hemlock" provides a warning; its alternate name, "spotted parsley," gives no hint about the nature of the plant. It instead focuses on the plant's appearance. Sometimes more than one species has the same common name. There are many plants that some people would call "daisies," but they represent many different species. When there is a need to be precise, scientific names are essential.

Although humans are the only animals to classify other species and study their evolutionary origins, there are certainly other animals that find a way to name other species. Vervet monkeys **(Figure 12.3**—*Chlorocebus pygerythrus*) have different alarm signals for leopards and eagles. When a vervet monkey gives the "eagle" **alarm call**, its fellows look skyward and move closer to

## STUDY BREAK

1. What is the main advantage of scientific names for species?

FIGURE 12.3 A group of vervet monkeys.

## 12.2 Defining a Species

Asked to define a "species," a biologist would usually say "a population of organisms capable of interbreeding to produce fertile offspring." The same biologist might acknowledge that species is a cornerstone concept in biology. It is challenging to produce a tightly worded definition because life is diverse and complex, and evolution is an ongoing process.

Because of the extraordinary diversity of life on Earth, dozens of "species concepts" are in use as biologists (and paleontologists) work to document the diversity of life. A **species concept** is a way of defining a species: by the way it looks, its biology, its genetics, or its evolutionary relationships. Four of the more commonly used species are the biological, morphological, genetic, and phylogenetic species concepts. Paleontologists use another concept that defines fossil species by a combination of their location, physical features, and appearance over time.

In the **biological species concept**, a species is defined as the population of organisms that can interbreed to produce fertile offspring.

The **morphological species concept** implies that you can recognize a species by its morphological features—or its appearance. However, two individuals of the same species may not look exactly the same (e.g., Figure 12.9, a and b). We know that there are differences such as those between males and females or adults and young. Some features simply allow us to recognize individuals within a species, such as different hair colour, facial features, or body sizes in humans. These are known as **tokogenetic** features.

The **genetic species concept** is based on "genetically compatible, interbreeding, natural populations that are genetically isolated from other such groups," as defined by Robert Baker and Robert Bradley in their 2006 paper about speciation in mammals. This concept sometimes depends on modern tools of genetics to recognize and distinguish among species that are morphologically similar.

The **phylogenetic species concept** is based on recognizing species as organisms that share a common ancestor **(Figure 12.4)**. A phylogenetic species may include more than one variant (subspecies) (B, C, G, and H in Figure 12.4) or a single variant (A, D, and E in Figure 12.4). The red lines in Figure 12.4 represent the division between different species. How or where we draw these red lines will affect the numbers of species that we consider distinct. Because species are constantly changing and evolving, often it is not obvious where to draw the line between one species and another. This is because we are trying to apply an artificial concept (species) to a natural array of organisms.

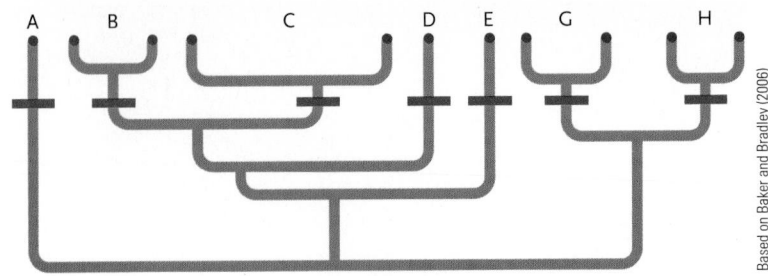

**FIGURE 12.4** The phylogenetic species concept uses an immediate common ancestry (denoted by red bars) to identify species. The phylogeny here shows the evolutionary relationships among seven species of bats based on an analysis of complete DNA sequences from the mitochondrial cytochrome *b* gene. B, C, D, E, F, G, and H represent difference species in the genus *Carollia*. A is a species in the same family but a different genus.

Variability in animals such as snails is relatively common and can be spectacular (e.g., **Figure 12.5**). A snail (*Acanthinucella spirata*) that occurs along the coast of California and adjacent Mexico illustrates how a single species varies over time and distance **(Figure 12.6)**. Examination of the shells of snails from 14 living populations revealed variation in shell morphology among northern (blue) and southern (red) populations. The shells of living northern snails differ from those of both living southern and fossil populations. This snail illustrates how a single species can vary morphologically over time and distance and that the differences that we can see are linked to underlying genetic variation.

**Chronospecies** is another species concept. This term is used by paleontologists to identify individuals by their position in time, usually within a geological sequence. This concept may not account for continuous change through time over which one species may evolve into another. These changes may not be obvious if the fossil record is incomplete. But a complete fossil record could make it impossible to draw boundaries among

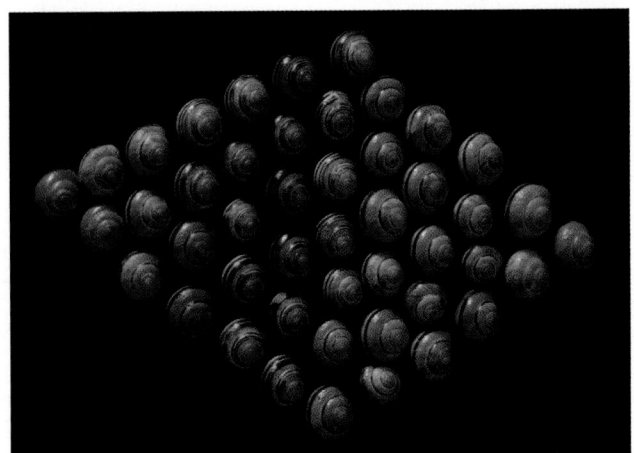

**FIGURE 12.5** Polymorphism in the colour and patterns of stripes on the shells of snails (*Cepaea nemoralis*), a common mollusc in gardens.

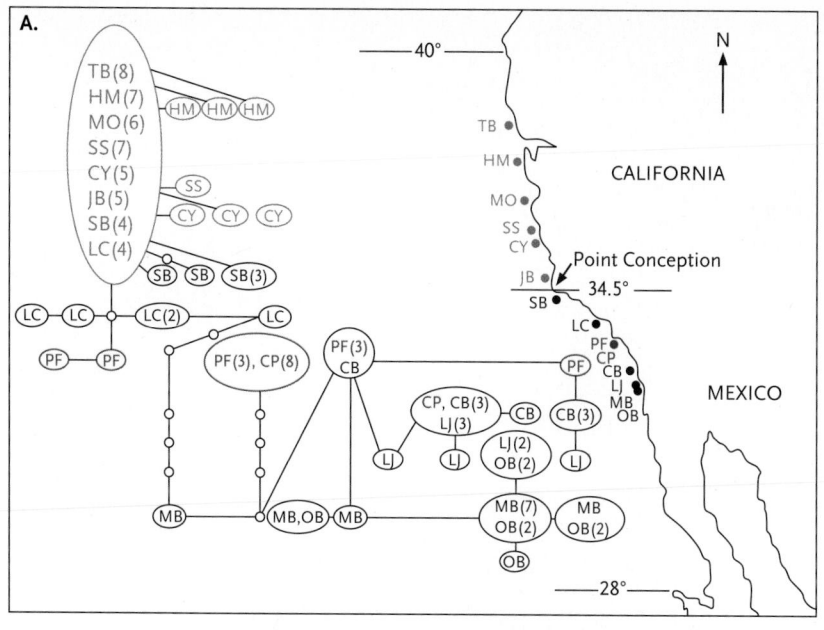

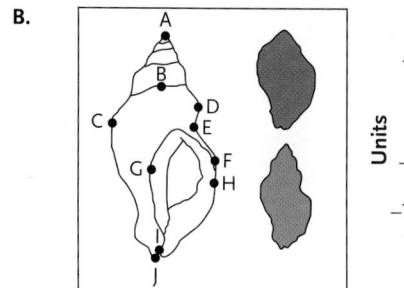

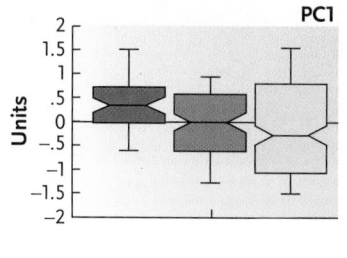

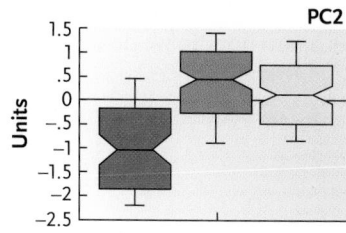

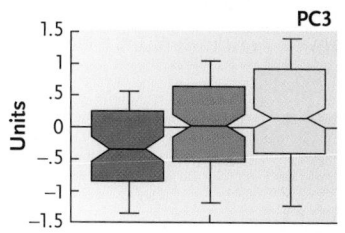

**FIGURE 12.6** Variations in shell morphology can be demonstrated by a series of measurements **(a)**, which indicate differences among northern (blue), southern (red), and fossil (grey) populations **(b)**.

SOURCE: From Michael E. Hellberg, Deborah P. Balch, Kaustuv Roy, "Climate-Driven Range Expansion and Morphological Evolution in a Marine Gastropod," *Science*, vol. 292, Jun 1, 2001, pp. 1707–1710. Reprinted with permission from AAAS.

species. How would we know where one species began and another ended?

## STUDY BREAK

1. What are the differences among the biological, phylogenetic, and genetic species concepts?
2. When is colour a useful character in identifying species? When is colour just confusing?

## 12.3 Recognizing Species

Perhaps as important as defining a species is recognizing distinct species. **Sexual dimorphism**—a phenomenon in which males and females of the same species look different—is one complicating factor **(Figure 12.7, p. 262)**.

Sexual dimorphism is commonly seen in many species, including in some birds **(Figure 12.7, a, b, c)** and mammals **(Figure 12.7d)**.

We can all tell the difference between a mushroom and an elephant or between an orange and an apple even if we do not have first-hand experience with these organisms. The diversity of programs about nature on television and the number of websites dedicated to this topic may mean that the mythical average person has a basic appreciation of the diversity of life. People who frequent zoos, botanic gardens, and museums may be even more familiar with the diversity of organisms.

When you look more closely at the range of organisms on Earth, you discover that there are many look-alikes. Many animals look like "worms" **(Figure 12.8, p. 262)**, but wormlike animals include both animals with and without backbones (vertebrates and invertebrates). The same

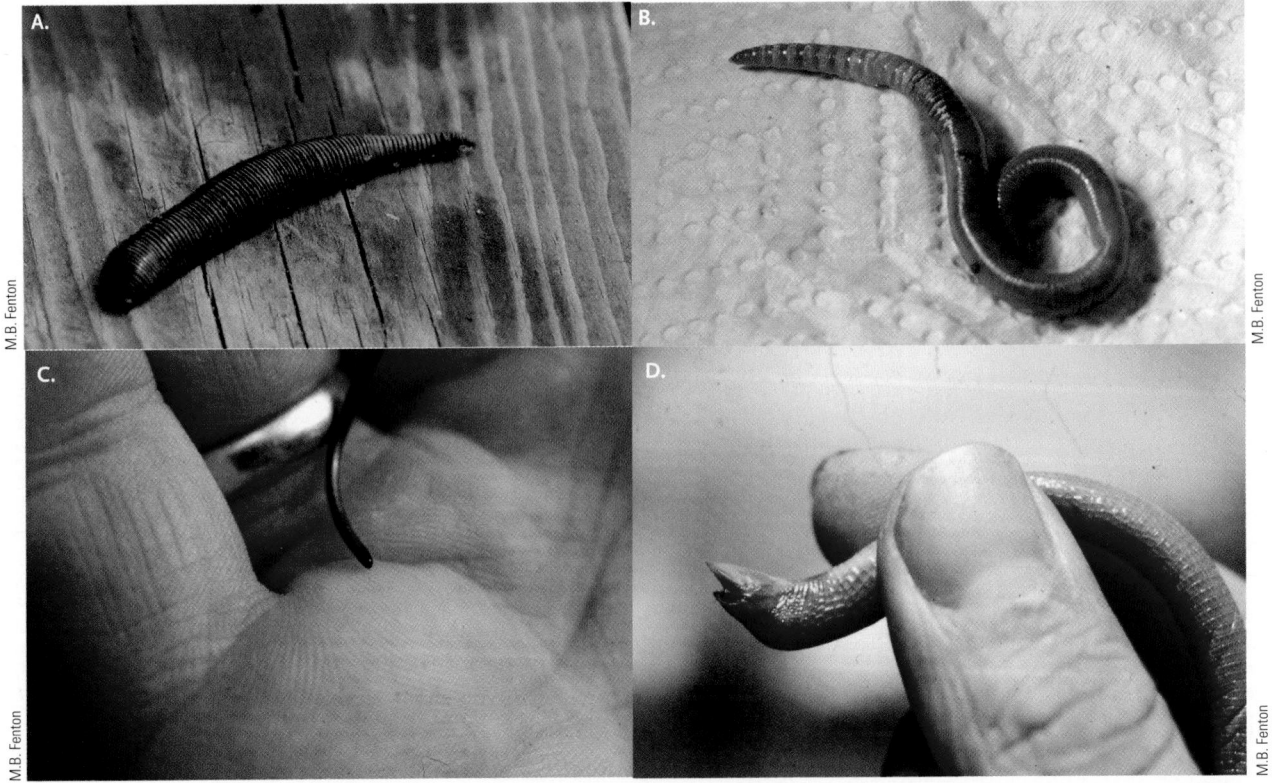

(Photos A–B) M.B. Fenton

**FIGURE 12.7** The animals shown in a, b, c, d, and e are males and females illustrating sexual dimorphism, which can complicate identification. Female and male Red Bishops **(a, b)** are distinct, unlike Grey Herons (*Ardea cinerea*) **(c)**. Egyptian Geese (*Alopochen aegyptiacus*) **(d)** appear dimorphic, as do male and female impalas (*Aepyceros melampus*) **(e)**.

applies to plants **(Figure 12.9)** and fungi. The cactuslike body form appears in at least two evolutionary lineages of plants. Some fungi look like flowers, and some orchids look like mushrooms. Ichthyosaurs, marine reptiles **(Figure 12.10)**, are superficially like whales, which are mammals. When first discovered, ichthyosaurs were thought to have been fossil whales. When physical appearance fails to give us enough clues to tell species apart, how do we do it?

**FIGURE 12.8** A freshwater leech **(a)**, an earthworm **(b)**, and two different burrowing snakes **(c** and **d)**.

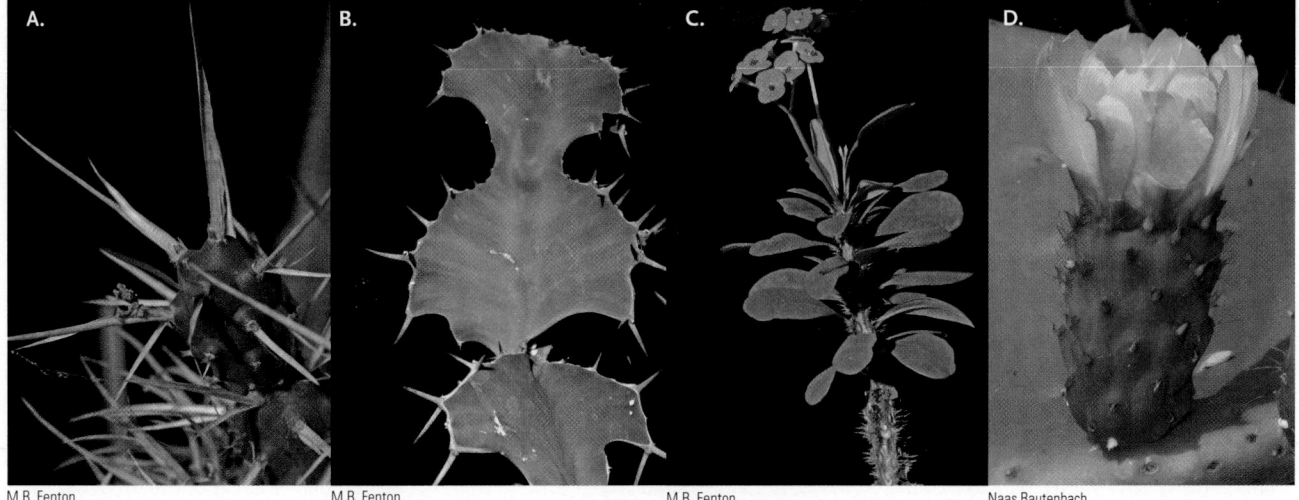

A. M.B. Fenton    B. M.B. Fenton    C. M.B. Fenton    D. Naas Rautenbach

**FIGURE 12.9** A cactus (*Opuntia turpinii*) **(a)** and a euphorb (*Euphorbia grandicornis*) **(b)**. The spines give these species a superficial similarity. The flowers of euphorbs, such as crown of thorns (*Euphorbia milii*) **(c)**, and those of cacti (*Opuntia* spp.) **(d)** are very different, reflecting their evolutionary history. Without the flowers, telling euphorbs from cacti can be very challenging.

For those of us who wish to try to recognize the organisms around us, field guides are important tools. Field guides are books that provide information about the organisms of an area (country, state, or province). The vast market for field guides reflects public interest in natural history. Guides to birds are excellent examples. Visit an online bookstore and assess the variety of available bird guides. Good guides to birds include coloured illustrations, maps showing distributions, and descriptions of the species. Finding a guide to the insects you might find in a local park, or the animals living in the soil, will present a different picture. Imagine the challenge of providing a complete inventory of the organisms (the biota) of an area (Box 12.2).

To experience the challenge of identifying a species, start with something relatively simple such as birds in a local park or the ones visiting a birdbath **(Figure 12.11, a, b, c, p. 265)** or feeder **(Figure 12.11, d, e, f)**. A bird guide will give you an idea of what to look for—perhaps behaviour, colour, and general appearance. Other details, such as the size and shape of the bill and/or colour of the eyes, may be important. Having a map showing the distribution of the possible candidates (a range map) also helps narrow the possibilities. This involves the same processes as learning to recognize different kinds of cars or bicycles by familiarizing yourself with key distinguishing features. The ubiquitous digital camera makes it much easier for someone to capture the image of a species and perhaps, from there, to identify it. Ultimately, to tell a lot of birds apart by sight will require you to use many different clues.

Variations in appearance (polymorphism, Figure 12.5) pose challenges to those trying to identify species. Sexual dimorphism (Figure 12.7) is one example. Often the males and females of the same species can look very different, such as the extravagant peacock and his much plainer peahen mate. Variations across life cycle are another because eggs, larvae, and adults may look quite different. Think of the life cycle of a butterfly: eggs, larvae (caterpillars), pupa, and adult. How do we know they all belong to the same species? Usually, the discovery of new specimens is key to resolving these problems.

For instance, little white-shouldered bats (*Ametrida centurio*) from South America were originally described as two species (*Ametrida centurio* and *Ametrida minor*). Examination of additional specimens revealed that the

M.B. Fenton

M.B. Fenton

**FIGURE 12.10** An ichthyosaur, a fish- or whalelike marine reptile. Inset shows details of eye size, flipper, ribs, and vertebrae.

In the 24 hours beginning at 15:00 h on June 15 and ending at 15:00 h on June 16, 2012, over 225 participants recorded over 1350 species in Rouge Park **(Figure 1)**, Toronto, Ontario. The blitz involved biologists familiar with a range of organisms, ecologists, and naturalists. Their goal was to obtain an indication of the diversity in part of the area that will become Rouge Valley National Park, the first partly urban national park in Canada. The list of species included 29 mammals, 76 birds, 6 reptiles, 6 amphibians, 19 fish, 474 insects, 96 spiders, 48 non-arthropod invertebrates, 520 plants, 90 fungi and slime moulds, 51 mosses, 7 algae, and 3 protists.

Who would have thought that the bioblitz team would find 6 species of bats, let alone 12 species of molluscs or almost 100 species of spiders? The list included over 500 species of plants and 51 species of mosses! All of this on the edge of an urban area with a population of more than 2 million people. Many of us might not have appreciated that creating a national park that protected 29 species of mammals and 76 species of birds could also protect the habitat used by another 1200+ species of organisms, including 5 species of mosquitoes and 3 species of deer flies.

Imagine the logistics involved with coordinating the activities of 225 participants, let alone the variety of sampling methods you would have to use to cover the range from protists to bats. Arguably, plants, fungi, and molluscs will be easier to sample than bats. If you started to do a bioblitz of your backyard, you would soon find that it is one thing to find and catch an organism and sometimes quite another to identify it. Yes, we can all recognize a spider, but few of us could identify the spider to species.

As soon as you move to organisms that have different body forms, the problem of identification can escalate dramatically. Think of a caterpillar or a leaf, a stem or a root. How can you be sure what leaf goes with what species of plant? What about eggs or seeds? What will that caterpillar be when it grows up?

How might the list be different if the bioblitz happened around the winter solstice? Just thinking of birds in this regard will remind us that many species migrate south for the winter, going from temperate to tropical areas. However, other birds may have come south to the Rouge Valley to avoid winter further north. Where would the bats that live in the area in the summer be in mid-December? What about chipmunks, jumping mice, or ground hogs? What about frogs, insects, and turtles?

One of the next steps in the bioblitz might be determining which of the species is native and which ones have been introduced, probably by human activity. Obvious candidates for introduction by people will be agriculturally important plants, as well as earthworms and other animals that live in soil. It is a relief not to find zebra mussels (*Dreissena polymorpha*) on the list as this species is now widespread in some of the Great Lakes. Unfortunately, this is surely a matter of a lack of suitable habitat as these invasive and damaging mussels spread quickly.

**FIGURE 1** *Cepaea nemoralis* **(a)** and *Limax maximus* **(b)**, two of the molluscs found during the bioblitz.

---

larger individuals (*Ametrida centurio*) were always females, and the smaller ones (*Ametrida minor*) were always males. With enough specimens to support this point, scientists identified them as one species: little white-shouldered bats.

Some marine fishes from depths of 1000 to 4000 m (**bathypelagic**) illustrate a more complicated situation. Biologists had described three species: whale fishes (family Cetomimidae), tapetails (Mirapinnidae), and bignose fishes (Megalomycteridae). Then a combination of new specimens and genetic data changed our view. Whale fishes, tapetails, and bignose fishes all belong to one family, Cetomimidae. The fish originally described as tapetails were larval forms, bignose fish were adult males, and whale fishes were adult females (**Figure 12.12**). The transformation from larva to adult involved changes in feeding reflected by changes in the head. Larvae use upturned mouths to feed on copepods. Adult females swallow larger prey whole, which explains their large mouths and gapes. Adult males do not feed at all, relying on the copepods they had consumed as larvae.

## Museum Specimens Can Help Identify Species

Museum collections often come to the rescue of the biologist challenged to confirm the identity of an organism

**FIGURE 12.11** Birds at a birdbath **(a, b, c)** and at at a feeder **(d, e, f)**: Purple Finch (*Carpodacus purpureus*), American Robin (*Turdus migratorius*), Common Grackle (*Quiscalus quiscula*), Northern Cardinal (*Cardinalis cardinalis*), Red-breasted Nuthatch (*Sitta canadensis*), and Black-capped Chickadee (*Poecile atricapillus*).

(Photos A–F): M.B. Fenton

**(Figure 12.13, p. 266)**. The specimens in zoological (animal), paleontological, (fossil), mycological (fungi), and botanical (plant) collections usually have a known identity that has been confirmed by appropriate authorities.

For each named species, there should be a **type specimen**, or the one on which the description and the name are based. Type specimens are kept in museums. Museum collections and their type specimens

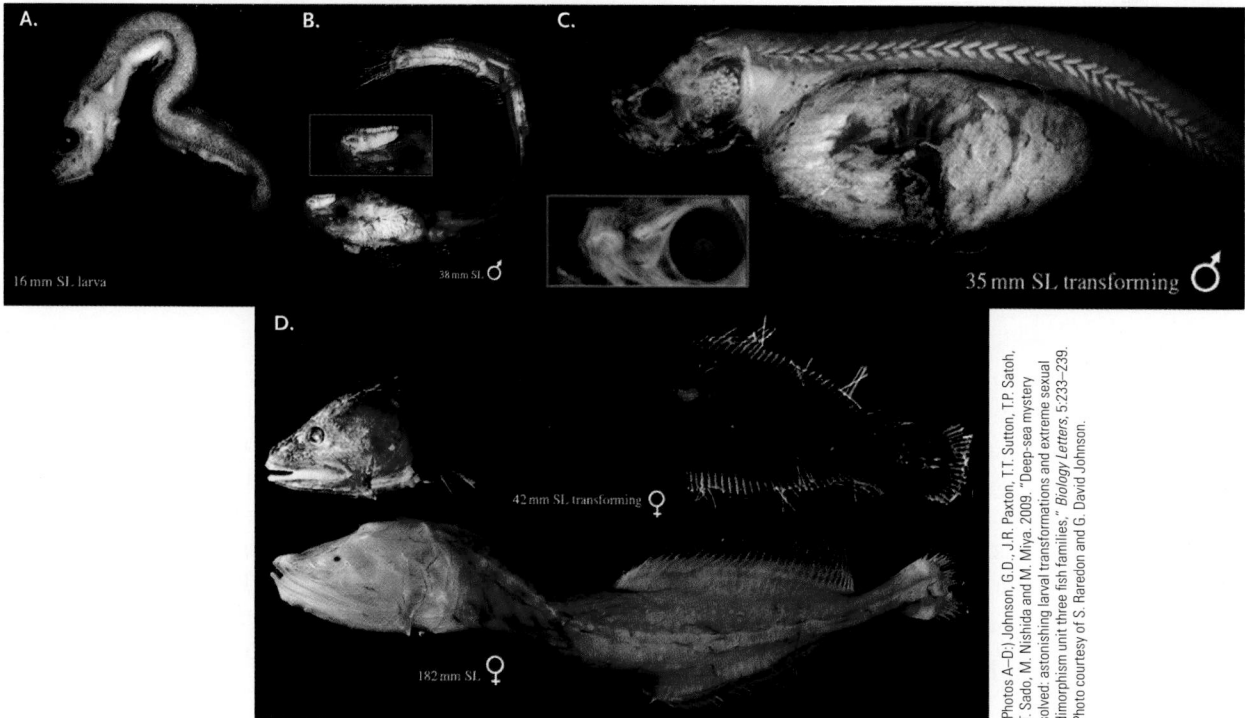

(Photos A–D): Johnson, G.D., J.R. Paxton, T.T. Sutton, T.P. Satoh, T. Sado, M. Nishida and M. Miya. 2009. "Deep-sea mystery solved: astonishing larval transformations and extreme sexual dimorphism unit three fish families," *Biology Letters*, 5:233–239. Photo courtesy of S. Raredon and G. David Johnson.

**FIGURE 12.12** A comparison of larvae **(a)**, larva transforming to adult male **(b)**, adult male **(c)**, and adult female **(d)** whalefish, now placed in the family Cetomimidae.

**A.**

**B.**

**HERBARIUM OF THE UNIVERSITY OF WESTERN ONTARIO (UWO) PLANTS OF ONTARIO**

**Name:** *Viburnum opulus* L.

**Locality and Notes:** University of Western Ontario.
At edge of sprots field beside Thames River.
UTM: 17T 47780 476104 NAD83

Weedy area at edge of naturalized river bank.
Branching shrub about 2 m high.
**Collector and Number:** Jane M. Bowles JB/2005.093
**Date:** 2 November 2005
**UWO Number:** 46717

Department of Biology
London, Ontario, N6A 5B7,
Canada

**FIGURE 12.13** Museum specimens, including a plant **(a)** preserved by pressing, drying, and mounting it on a herbarium sheet and bats **(b)** preserved as a study skin and skull (inset). The specimen on the herbarium sheet includes leaves and fruit and a detailed label (yellow arrows). The dried study skin with detailed label (attached) is typically housed in the same drawer (black arrow). Dried specimens are kept in airtight cabinets to minimize damage and discourage pests such as moths and beetles. Specimens are clearly and distinctly numbered.

(Figure 12.13) are indispensable because they allow newly obtained specimens to be compared to previously identified ones, perhaps confirming a species new to science or a previously described one. Detailed taxonomic studies include specific references (by collection and number) to the specimens that were used to help identify a specimen. This allows other researchers to go back and reexamine material should that be necessary.

## DNA Barcodes Are a New Way to Identify Species

The discovery that we can use part of the mitochondrial cytochrome *c* oxidase 1 (*CO1*) gene to distinguish among

species of animals has revolutionized the problem of identifying species of organisms. Every shopper is familiar with barcodes and the ability they give us to recognize products and determine prices. The **DNA barcode** makes it possible to identify a species with DNA extracted from a small fragment of tissue. A leaf, a piece of a caterpillar, the leg of an insect, a feather, or some fur all have the DNA and thus the genetic barcode. The Barcode of Life project, based at the University of Guelph (in Ontario, Canada), is the brainchild of Professor Paul D.N. Hebert.

Key to the effectiveness of the Barcode of Life project is the polymerase chain reaction (PCR), a tool that allows biologists to read the DNA code in 100 samples every 3 hours. This rate of operation improves with each new generation of equipment. Other advances in genomic technology make it possible to efficiently sequence DNA. When you combine this with an army of people collecting specimens (Box 12.2) and the precise location information provided by global positioning systems (**GPS**), we are able to quickly and accurately identify about 97% of animals sampled. The same appears to be true of plants and perhaps fungi.

An essential element in the Barcode of Life operation is the availability of barcodes from described species—a barcode library. Scientists need to create this library using as many species and specimens as possible and post the barcodes online for others to use. Fortunately, DNA samples needed to create the barcode library can be obtained from a fragment taken from preserved museum specimens, with little damage to the specimens. One fascinating early discovery to come from the Barcode of Life project was the revelation that what had been thought to be one species of butterfly, the two-barred flasher (*Astraptes fulgerator*), is actually 10 species.

Barcode information can also identify genetically distinct lineages of organisms (such as the two-barred flasher). In effect, these are examples of the phylogenetic species concept (Figure 12.3); they are species that are defined based on their phylogenetic relationships. In Pallas's long-tongued bat (*Glossophaga soricina*), barcode analysis suggests three phylogenetic lineages (**Figure 12.14**): one in Central America and two in South America. Our ability to identify an individual, however, can depend on the gene used for barcoding, and males can differ from females. In Pallas's long-tongued bats, the *Dby* gene on a region of the Y chromosome provides information about paternal inheritance and suggests some continued interbreeding between the two South American lineages; this represents a hybrid zone (see Section 12.4). Morphological analysis of features of the bats' skulls suggests that the Central American lineage is a new species, whereas hybridization continues between the other two lineages.

In other cases, genetic analysis has revealed that what had been treated as several species was really just one. For example, a large, armoured crustacean was first described in 1828. This mid-water, oceanic species is globally widespread. Then DNA barcoding revealed that it was in fact a larval form of another widespread species: an aristeid shrimp, *Plesiopenaeus armatus*. As in the whalefishes (above), genetic techniques and new specimens led to consolidation rather than expansion of biodiversity.

The barcode approach to identifying species has provided some unexpected benefits (**Figure 12.15**). Biologists studying the diets of bats wanted to know what kinds of insects the bats were eating. But they had to contend with finely chewed insect remains, which usually defy

A.

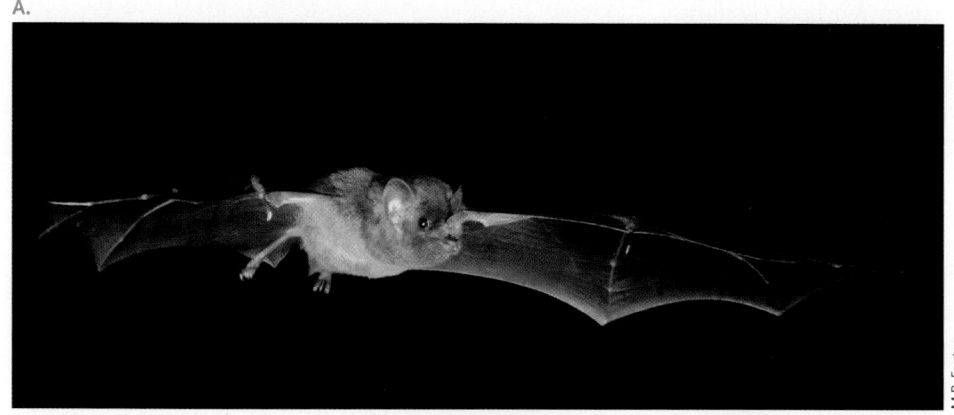

B.    C.    D.

COI

DBY 7th Intron

**FIGURE 12.14** Genetic analyses of populations of Pallas's long-tongued bat (*Glossophaga soricina*) **(a)** from Central and South America **(b)** suggest three independent phylogenetic lineages (1, 2, 3 by COI barcode) **(c)** and two independent lineages (2 versus 1 and 3), with partial separation between the two South American lineages **(d)**.

SOURCE: Clare EL (2011) "Cryptic Species? Patterns of Maternal and Paternal Gene Flow in Eight Neotropical Bats," *PLoS ONE* 6(7): e21460. doi:10.1371/journal. pone.0021460. © 2011 Elizabeth L. Clare.

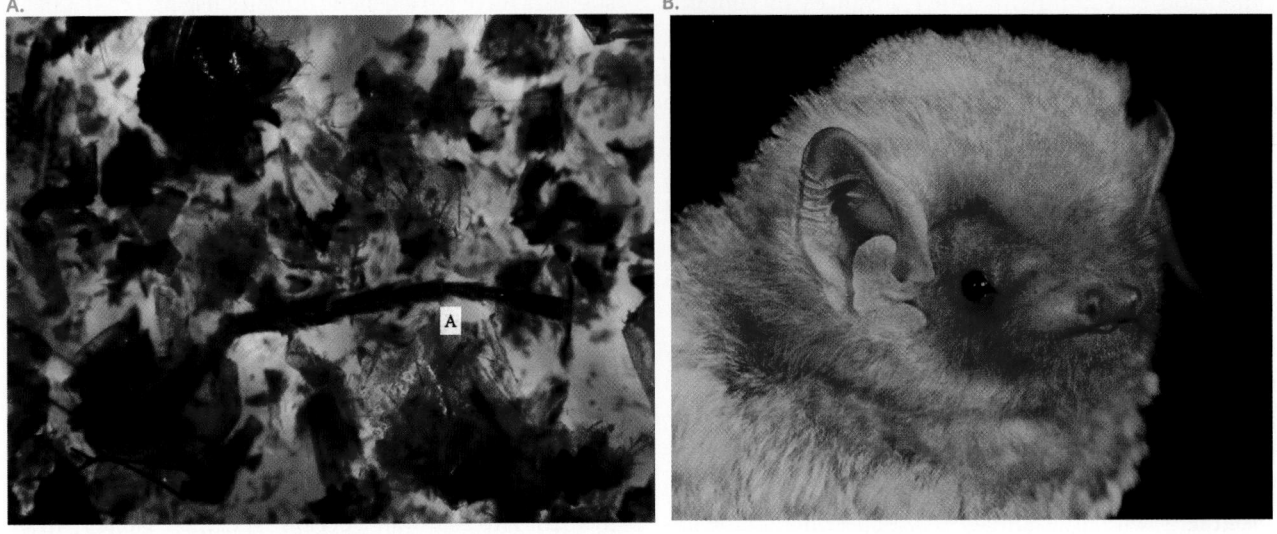

A.

B.

C.

0    320

321    571

FIGURE 12.15 Fragments of insects **(a)** in the feces of an eastern red bat (*Lasiurus borealis*) **(b)** and a DNA barcode **(c)** of an insect obtained from the feces.

SOURCE (Photo A): ELIZABETH L. CLARE, ERIN E. FRASER, HEATHER E. BRAID, M. BROCK FENTON, PAUL D. N. HEBERT, "Species on the menu of a generalist predator, the eastern red bat (Lasiurus borealis): using a molecular approach to detect arthropod prey," *Molecular Ecology*, Volume 18, Issue 11, pages 2532–2542, June 2009. John Wiley and Sons. © 2009 Blackwell Publishing Ltd.

identification beyond order or family. Using DNA barcoding, we can now say that eastern red bats (*Lasiurus borealis*) eat several species of moths that should have detected the echolocation calls of the bats and thus avoided them. DNA barcoding opens new avenues of research into the ecology and behaviour of all kinds of organisms, including bats and their insect prey (see Box 12.3).

### Identifying a New Species

Sometimes, when scientists use their tools to identify a species, they will reveal that they have discovered a new species. Whenever a new species is found, it must be identified. Until a species has been described and named, it does not "count" because it is not yet listed. Species that are not listed cannot be protected by **CITES**, the Convention on International Trade in Endangered Species (Chapter 31).

Identifying new species is a great feat. Even biologists lack the specific expertise to recognize a new species with any certainty when they see one, if at all. Within a group of biologists preparing a list of the species occurring in an area, lack of expertise can be a challenge. Many biologist have strong areas of expertise, but how many can accurately identify all species of mosses, spiders, and oak trees in an area and therefore know when they have found one that has not been described before? Extend the possibilities to fish, molluscs, birds, mammals, and earthworms and leeches, and the task becomes intractable to all but a full team of experts.

### STUDY BREAK

1. What is a museum specimen? Why is it important to recognizing a species?
2. What features can be used to recognize a species? To distinguish it from another?
3. How can DNA barcoding assist in identifying species?
4. How does sexual dimorphism affect our ability to recognize species?

## 12.4 Speciation

**Speciation**—the formation of a new species—typically happens when something interrupts genetic exchange (**gene flow**) among individuals in populations that had been interbreeding. When once connected populations become isolated, gene flow decreases or even stops altogether. In sexually reproducing species, barriers to interbreeding can occur before (**prezygotic**) or after (**postzygotic**) an egg is fertilized.

A prezygotic barrier to gene flow is one that prevents individuals from mating in the first place or one that prevents fertilization. An example of a prezygotic barrier is the failure of American Robins (*Turdus migratorius*) and European Robins (*Erithacus rubecula*) to interbreed.

A postzygotic barrier is when **hybrids**, or the offspring of two parents, each of a different species, are sterile and

BOX 12.3

# BOX 12.3
## Beth Clare: Person behind Biology

Beth Clare is a faculty member in the Department of Biology and Chemistry at Queen Mary College in London, England. She received her Ph.D. for work on the application of DNA barcoding to the diversity of bats in South and Central America (see Figure 12.14). This work demonstrated the genetically distinct species of relatively common bats originally recognized as one species. Parnell's moustached bat is of special note because it occurs widely in the West Indies as well as in Central and South America. Further work on these bats revealed morphological differences reflecting the genetic ones.

Beth also pioneered the use of DNA barcoding in the identification of insects eaten by bats (see Figure 12.15). This analysis has revealed that common species of bats in the United States and Canada (big brown bats – *Eptesicus fuscus* and little brown myotis – *Myotis lucifugus*) eat literally hundreds of species of insects. Specifically, big brown bats using one roost over several years ate at least 350 species, whereas little brown myotis from sites across Canada ate more than 600 species. The details identified similarities and differences in diet. Big brown bats are twice as big as little brown bats, yet they share quite a few species of insects in their diets. Knowledge of what species of insects had been consumed illustrated how the diets of bats could be used to assess the degree of contamination of waters over which the bats hunted.

Her career to date illustrates how learning to use and apply a new technique can provide many benefits. Using DNA barcoding to identify what bats eat is revealing all sorts of other details of their ecology and behaviour. Beth is also an accomplished photographer (see Figure 12.5).

---

unable to reproduce. Mules, the offspring of a male donkey (*Equus africanus asinus*) and a female horse (*Equus ferus caballus*), are sterile hybrids. When there is reproductive isolation (no more gene flow) between two populations, genetic differences between them will increase just because of random events (this is called **genetic drift**). Reproductive isolation is not always absolute; often there is still some gene flow, but it is reduced.

Speciation can occur when a barrier interrupts gene flow within a population. The examples that follow illustrate some of the documented ways in which species have formed. The diversity of details illustrates the challenge of coming up with one definition of a species. When two species occupy the same geographic range, they are **sympatric** (see Section 12.4), whereas species with non-overlapping ranges are **allopatric** (see Section 12.4). Speciation can occur in either situation.

## Sometimes Species Form When Populations Are Split Apart

In 2005, biologists used male–female pairs of lizards (brown anoles – *Anolis sagrei*) to study how populations can become reproductively isolated and the consequences of isolation **(Figure 12.16, p. 270)**. Researchers introduced one male and one female lizard from Iron Cay in the Bahamas, an island of more than 150,000 m², to seven small Bahamian islands (ranging from 35 to 75 m²). On the source island, brown anoles lived on larger plants with broad leaves. On the smaller islands, the plants were smaller, with narrower leaves. After the introduction, the founding populations were effectively cut off from the new, transplanted populations. Physical isolation like this is a prezygotic barrier to gene flow.

The scientists monitored the lizards' appearance, behaviour, and genetics and observed that newly established populations had less genetic variation than the source populations. This is an example of a **founder effect**—specifically, the effect of the limited gene pool of a small founding population.

So what happened in these new populations? Did anything change? Within a few generations, individuals that made up the introduced populations had adapted to the local conditions on the small islands. Populations on the newly occupied islands differed from one another and from the source population in both how they looked and genetically (Figure 12.13). Lizards on all seven island populations had shorter hindlimbs, reflecting a practical necessity for moving on narrow leaves. The differences between the populations on the seven small islands compared to the source island demonstrated how changes arise and persist when small populations are genetically isolated from one another and from the founding population, providing an example of genetic drift.

## Sometimes Species Can Form within a Population

There are a number of ways in which species can form in sympatric populations—or those with overlapping ranges. Sometimes it is sudden, perhaps due to genetic changes, and sometimes it happens slowly over time.

### Mutations

Sometimes one or more changes, or **mutations**, in the DNA sequence of one gene underlie the formation of a species. One species of fruit fly, *Drosophila pachea*, is

A.

B.

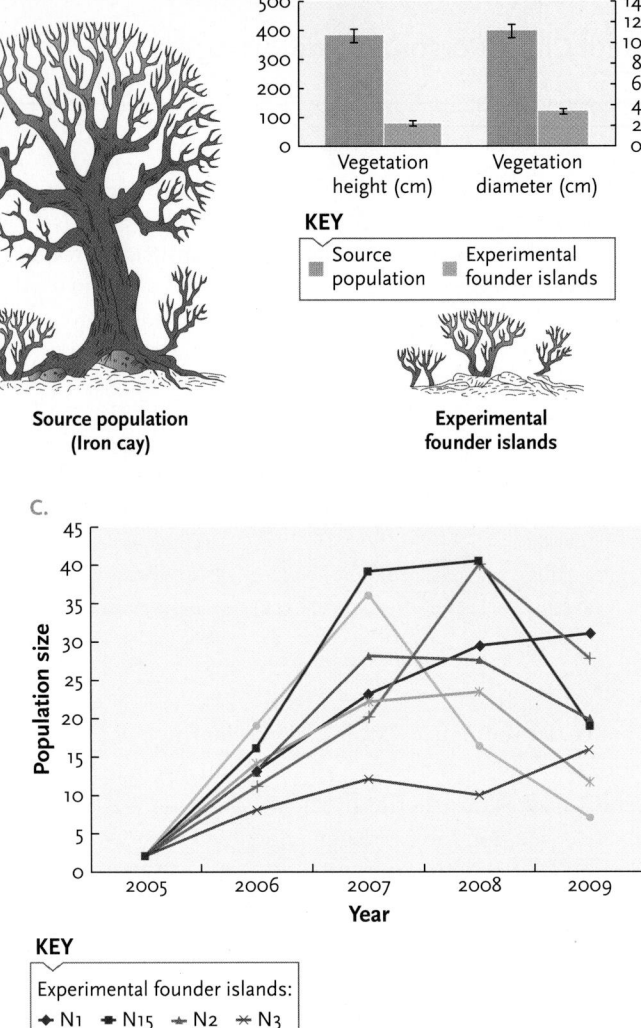

| Vegetation height (cm) | Vegetation diameter (cm) |

**KEY**
- Source population
- Experimental founder islands

Source population (Iron cay)

Experimental founder islands

C.

Population size vs Year (2005–2009)

**KEY**
Experimental founder islands:
- ◆ N1  ■ N15  ╉ N2  ✳ N3
- ✳ N4  ● X10  ✛ X3*

**FIGURE 12.16** **(a)** A brown anole (*Anolis sagrei*) shown with **(b)** a comparison of source and experimental islands and representative vegetation. **(c)** Estimated population sizes of brown anoles on the experimental islands.

SOURCE (Photos B–C): From Kolbe, J.J., M. Leal, T.W. Schoener, D.A. Spiller, and J.B. Losos, "Founder effects persist despite adaptive differentiation: a field experiment with lizards," *Science*, 335:1086–1089. Reprinted with permission from AAAS.

extremely specialized. It depends on a single host, the senita cactus (*Lophocereus schottii*), for the sterols it requires to produce steroid hormones. Changes to the *neverland* gene that codes for an enzyme that adds oxygen to other molecules (oxygenases) resulted in the ancestor of *D. pachea* being unable to transform cholesterol into 7-dehydrocholesterol. This change is fundamentally important to insects because it is the first reaction in the pathway responsible for biosynthesis of steroid hormones. When mutations resulting in specific environmental requirements are passed through generations, the population becomes more and more restricted in its distribution. This results in isolation from other species that lack the mutation and illustrates how a single mutation can give rise to a new species.

### Divergent Selection

Different populations can arise in one species when individuals in a large population that occurs over a large area diverge in their use of resources. This is **divergent selection**, and it can result in very different subpopulations.

Three groups of killer whales, *Orcinus orca*, occur in the waters off British Columbia and Alaska. Resident killer whales mainly eat fish, probably originally exploiting the abundance of salmon. Resident killer whales regularly hunt using echolocation. Transient killer whales mainly eat marine mammals, such as seals and other cetaceans, and tend to hunt silently. Open ocean killer whales mainly eat sharks and have been recognized because of the extensive wear on their teeth (reflecting the abrasive nature of shark skin). The three populations differ in behaviour and genetics. All three arose from a single, common ancestor. They provide a striking example of divergence.

### Disruptive Selection

Apple maggots (*Rhagoletis pomonella*) are an example of a species undergoing **disruptive selection**. This has occurred when there has been strong disruptive selection on a few genetic loci (sites on a chromosome) and gene flow results in an uneven pattern of genetic differentiation. Apple maggots are widespread, common, and native to North America. Studying overwintering populations of apple maggots revealed widespread divergence in the genome. Most loci showed variation, reflecting differences in hosts, latitude, and timing of the emergence of adults. This evidence suggested selection on different independent genomic regions, which resulted in disruptive selection rather than genetic drift across the genome of the population. Apple maggots show how speciation occurs without geographical isolation because specific genes can drive genetic isolation and speciation.

## Hybridization

Speciation is not always about divergence (like the situation in brown anoles and *D. pachea*). Sexual **hybridization** that unites genes and genomes provides another route to speciation. **Hybrid** offspring (where each parent is a different species) may become an entirely new species. Sometimes hybridization leads to changes in the number of chromosomes, but not always. Homoploid hybrid speciation involves the origin of a new hybrid lineage without any change in the number of chromosomes. Polyploid hybrid speciation **(Figure 12.17)** occurs when there is full duplication of the hybrid genome. Polyploid species have more than two full sets of chromosomes. There are two forms of polyploid species: **allopolyploid** and **autopolyploid**. Allopolyploid species have more than one set of chromosomes from two different species. Allopolyploid species do not involve a hybrid genome; they have multiple sets of chromosomes but all from the same original species. The initial hybrids of autopolyploids have reduced fertility, whereas allopolyploids do not, so allopolyploids are more common. Furthermore, duplication

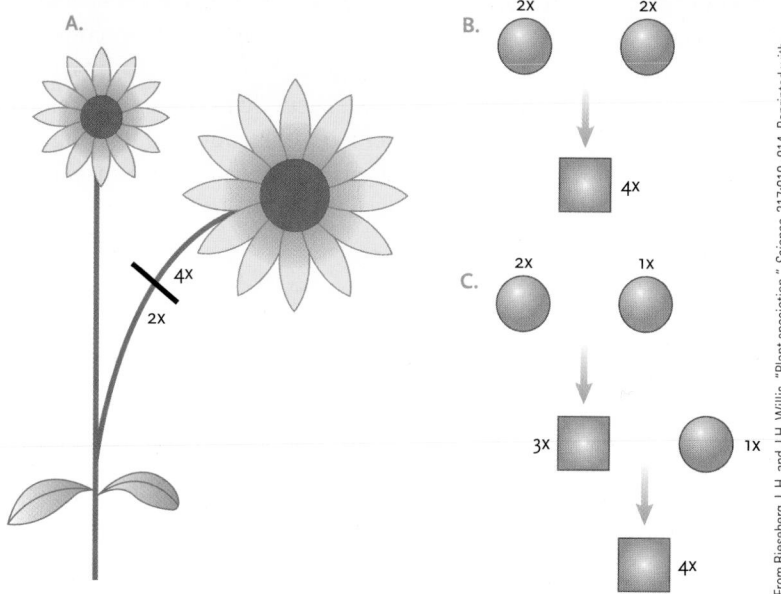

**FIGURE 12.17** Polyploids can arise when the chromosome number in vegetative tissue is doubled and gives rise to reproductive organs **(a)**. Polyploids also arise when unreduced gametes fuse **(b)** or through a triploid bridge **(c)**, where unreduced and reduced gametes fuse to form triploids. Further combinations of chromosome complement also occur (e.g., tetraploids).

From Rieseberg, L.H. and J.H. Willis, "Plant speciation," *Science*, 317:910–914. Reprinted with permission from AAAS.

of the genome protects the genetic integrity of initial hybrids, protection lacking in autopolyploids. Polyploid speciation appears to have been much more common in plants than in animals.

Homoploid and other types of hybrid origins of new species are documented less often than polyploid origins **(Figure 12.18)**. The discovery of Schwartz's fruit bat (*Artibeus schwartzi*)—a previously unknown species—is an example of a hybrid origin. Two known species contributed to both the nuclear and mitochondrial genomes of Schwartz's fruit bat. A third, unknown, species also contributed to the mitochondrial genome. This third species now appears to be extinct. None of these were **sister species**, or those most closely related to one another.

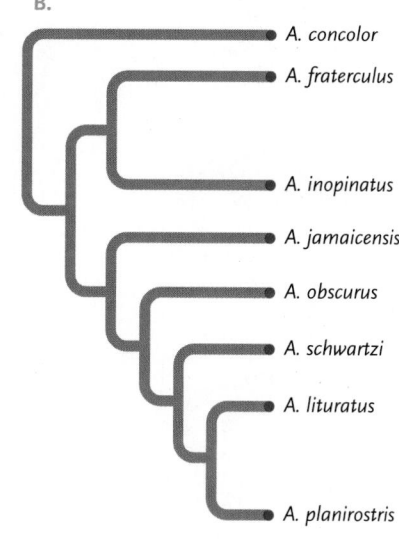

A. concolor
A. fraterculus
A. inopinatus
A. jamaicensis
A. obscurus
A. schwartzi
A. lituratus
A. planirostris

**FIGURE 12.18** Jamaican fruit bats, *Artibeus jamaicensis* **(a)**, *Artibeus planirostris*, and a third and as yet unknown species, have contributed to the nuclear genome of *Artibeus schwartzi*. The relationship among species of *Artibeus* **(b)** illustrates the relationship among the known species. Note that *A. planirostris* and *A. lituratus*, as well as *A. fraterculus* and *A. inopinatus*, are sister species.

SOURCE (Photo B): Larson, P.A., M.R. Marchan-Rivadeneira and R.J. Baker, "Natural hybridization generates mammalian lineage with species characteristics," *PNAS*, vol. 107 no. 25, 11447–11452.

Schwartz's fruit bat occurs on the islands of St. Lucia, St. Vincent, the Grenadines, and Grenada in the southern Lesser Antilles. The hybrid is most common on St. Vincent and somewhat less so on St. Lucia. Schwartz's fruit bat is morphologically distinct from the two non-sister members of the genus *Artibeus* (flat-nosed fruit bat – *Artibeus planirostris* and Jamaican fruit bat – *Artibeus jamaicensis*).

### Ring Species

Another example of sympatric evolution is **ring species (Figure 12.19)**. Ring species occur when an ancestral population expands its range around a geographic barrier such as a mountain range or river. Gene flow is limited because the increasing distance between the ancestral and expanding populations limits gene flow. Gene flow occurs among the populations that make up the ring, but typically the population at the end of the ring cannot interbreed with the ancestral population. Where terminal populations meet, there are higher mutation rates and larger dispersal distances, both of which appear to promote the formation of ring species.

Species such as the Sierra Nevada salamander (*Ensatina eschscholtzii*), from California, is an example of a ring species. Other examples come from birds such as Greenish Warblers (*Phylloscopus trochiloides*) from Asia,

which occur around the Tibetan Plateau. In these birds, courtship songs function in species recognition. Using playback presentations of courtship songs, biologists assessed the birds' view of the signals. The details of the songs and the birds' responses provided two measures of isolation.

## In Hybrid Zones, Species Can Overlap and Be Hard to Tell Apart

We have already seen examples of allopatric speciation, or when species form because two populations have been physically separated. We have also seen examples of sympatric speciation, or when species form even though their ranges overlap, at least to some degree. Sometimes lineages can be **parapatric**: they can occur side by side but show no overlap. Phylogenetic lineages can certainly be complicated **(Figure 12.20)**. When species overlap in distribution, the distinction between them can be difficult to resolve. Sometimes some individuals can successfully interbreed in the area of overlap; if so, this area is called a **hybrid zone**.

Hybrid zones will occur between lineages that have not achieved complete reproductive isolation. This is especially likely when closely related ("sister") species such as C and D in Figure 12.20 share an overlapping range. Hybrid zones are quite common between species in some groups of organisms, such as songbirds. Comparison of DNA sequences indicates how long sister

**FIGURE 12.19** Six of the seven subspecies of *Ensatina eschscholtzii* occur in a ring around the central valley of California. The two subspecies that nearly close the ring (arrow), *E. e. eschscholtzii* and *E. e. croceater*, rarely interbreed.

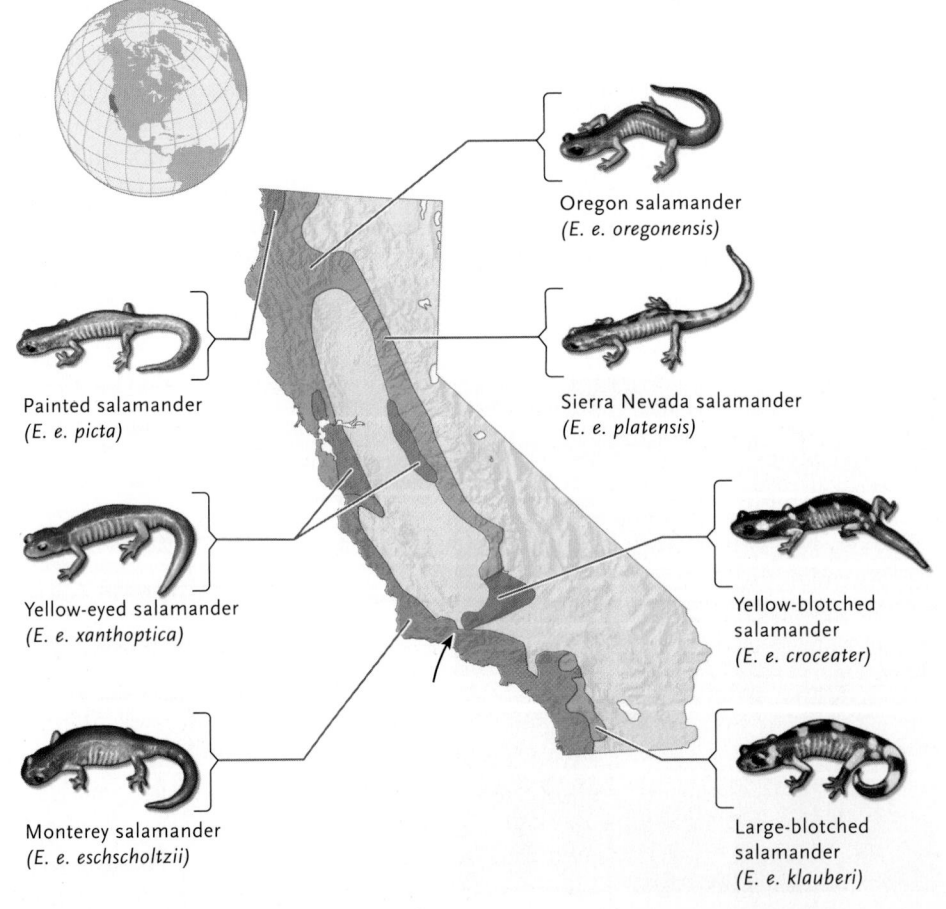

Oregon salamander
(*E. e. oregonensis*)

Painted salamander
(*E. e. picta*)

Sierra Nevada salamander
(*E. e. platensis*)

Yellow-eyed salamander
(*E. e. xanthoptica*)

Yellow-blotched salamander
(*E. e. croceater*)

Monterey salamander
(*E. e. eschscholtzii*)

Large-blotched salamander
(*E. e. klauberi*)

*Biology, 2E*

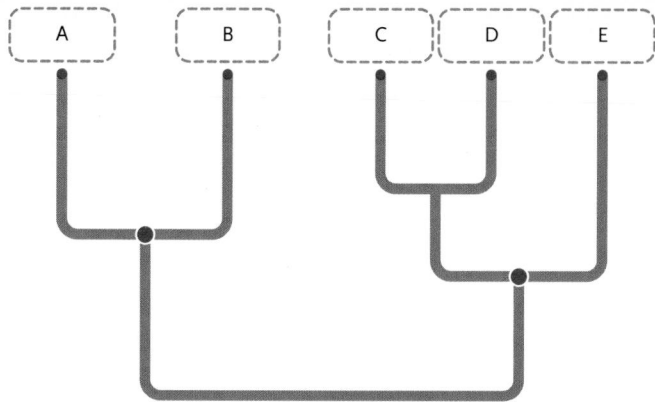

**FIGURE 12.20** The histories of five phylogenetic taxa (A, B, C, D, E) are shown, starting from two populations that were isolated. The delineated areas around each taxon identify areas where the taxa occur (their ranges). Two phylogenetic lineages arise, giving rise to one that, in turn, generates two others (A and B). The other gives rise to three lineages (C, D, E) that separate at different times. Two (C, D) have a zone of overlap, which could be a hybrid zone if they are able to interbreed and produce viable offspring. The range of the fifth (E) abuts another (D).

species have been isolated. Biologists can assess the degree of isolation by measuring the responses to play-back presentations of birds' territorial songs.

## STUDY BREAK

1. Name three means by which species arise.
2. What is the difference between prezygotic and postzygotic barriers?
3. What is a hybrid zone?

## 12.5 Problems without Sex

The species concepts presented in Section 12.2 all imply that a species is made up of organisms that reproduce sexually, meaning that there is exchange of genetic information among individuals. In sexually reproducing organisms, **recombination**—or the exchange of alleles—is achieved by the exchange of genetic material between chromosomes and is usually tied to reproduction. Recombination reduces the chances of selected mutations interfering with one another. How do these mutations affect organisms that reproduce asexually?

Individuals that reproduce asexually suffer more from excess accumulations of mutations than those that reproduce sexually. Some eukaryotic organisms deal with this by switching between sexual and asexual reproduction. Yeast, fungi, and many species of vascular plants reproduce sexually during times of stress and asexually at other times. How do we apply the species concept to organisms that do not reproduce sexually? None of the species concepts used for eukaryotes address the situation in prokaryotes: organisms in two

domains, Bacteria and Archaea. Prokaryotes lack membrane-bound organelles (e.g., nuclei, mitochondria, chloroplasts, Golgi apparatus, and endoplasmic reticulum; see Chapter 3.

How do organisms that reproduce asexually exchange alleles (recombination)? Although not recombination, l**ateral gene transfer**, also known as horizontal gene transfer, is a mechanism for achieving allelic exchange among prokaryotes **(Figure 12.21, p. 274)**. Although **vertical gene transfer** (lateral gene transfer among closely related taxa) is more common, lateral gene transfer occurs among distantly related organisms, especially when they live in similar environments. Lateral gene transfer also occurs among eukaryotes (although more rarely), where it has the same potential for effecting changes in the biology of the organisms involved.

In bacteria, recombination happens through occasional transfers of small DNA fragments among strains. Some genes associated with specific niches may be maintained in populations by freely recombining at different loci. This means that strains may be genetically isolated from one another for different chromosomal regions at different times because niche-specific genes may recombine less often. Scientists have tested and confirmed this proposal with two species of bacteria whose chromosomes have diverged over about 70 million years: *Escherichia coli* and *Salmonella enterica*.

In prokaryotes, as in sexually reproducing organisms, genetic distinctness is the key to distinguishing among species. Lateral and vertical gene transfer is a different approach to recombination and demonstrates the difficulty of applying species concepts to prokaryotes. The importance of differences among bacteria (e.g., *E. coli* and *S. enterica*) can be of critical practical importance, for example, in the context of disease and public health.

Species concepts do not necessarily apply to all eukaryotes either (organisms with membrane-bound organelles; see Chapter 3, partly because some eukaryotes use other ways to generate genetic exchange. If genetic exchange among individuals is central to a concept of species, then neither androdioecious nor gynogenetic species will be recognized.

In species with **androdioecy**, the population consists of males and hermaphrodites but no females. This approach to reproduction occurs not only in some plants and some invertebrate animals, but also in mangrove killifish (*Kryptolebias marmoratus*). In androdioecious species, males self-fertilize, and outbreeding (outcrossing) happens when males mate with hermaphrodites or hermaphrodites mate with one another.

In **gynogenetic** species, there are only females. In these females, mechanical stimulation of their eggs by sperm of another species stimulates development. In gynogenetic species, sperm does not contribute any genetic

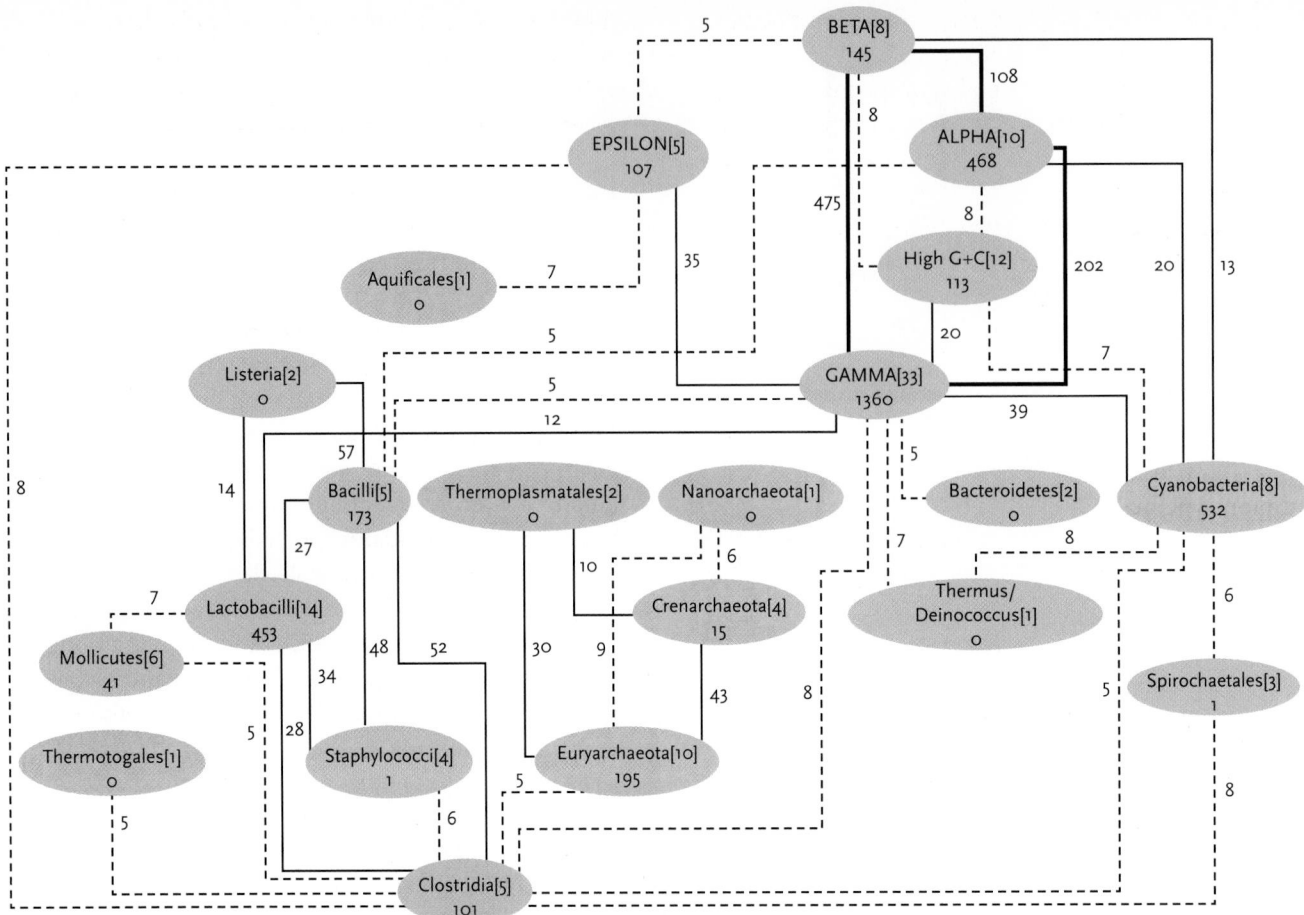

**FIGURE 12.21** Connections by lateral gene transfer among phyla and divisions of prokaryotes. Ovals represent prokaryotic groups and names, each showing numbers of taxa beside the name. Numbers below are inferred lateral gene transfers within the taxon, whereas numbers on links show inferred transfer among main groups. Dashed lines indicate 5 to 9 edits implied in the path, solid lines 10 to 99, and thick lines more than 100 edits.

SOURCE: Beiko, R.G., T.J. Harlow and M.A. Ragan, "Highways of gene sharing in prokaryotes," *PNAS*, vol. 102 no. 40, 14332–14337. Copyright (2005) National Academy of Sciences, U.S.A.

material to the offspring. The Amazon molly (*Poecilia formosa*) is gynogenetic and depends on sperm from two other species of molly (*Poecilia latipinna* or *Poecilia mexicana*). Originally, Amazon mollies appear to have been derived from a hybridization event between *P. latipinna* and *P. mexicana,* in which only females were viable hybrids.

## STUDY BREAK

1. Why is recombination central to speciation?
2. What is lateral gene transfer?
3. Name two approaches you could use to distinguish one species from another.

## 12.6 Species and Our Health

Earlier we discussed the results of a modelling exercise involving two species of bacteria, *S. enterica* and *E. coli*. Understanding the evolutionary relationships and biology of individual species in these examples is central to our health.

## Different Strains of *Salmonella enterica* Cause Different Types of Illness

There are several subspecies (smaller groups within species) of *S. enterica* that can affect human health. The list includes *Salmonella enterica enterica*, *S. e. salamae*, *S. e. arizonae*, *S. e. diarizonae*, *S. e. houtenae*, and *S. e. indica*. There are over 2600 variants (serotypes) of *S. e. enterica*. People infected with *Salmonella* poisoning can present four clinical conditions: gastroenteritis, bacteremia, enteric fever, and an asymptomatic carrier state. Gastroenteritis (also known as food poisoning) typically causes sudden nausea, vomiting, abdominal cramps, diarrhea, headache, chills, and fever. Some varieties cause more severe symptoms than others. Bacteremia is less common but has more severe effects, causing septic shock and endocarditis, particularly in people over 50. Enteric fever, also known as typhoid fever, is caused by two serotypes: *typhi* and *paratyphi*. This is characterized by fever, headache, slowing-down heart beat rate (brachycardia), and other symptoms.

Humans spread enteric fever when the bacteria are in their feces. Some people are "carriers" because they have active bacteria in their bodies but show no symptoms of them. Some carriers have been reported to be active for 5 years. The usual route of infection is through food contaminated with feces. This is not just a convincing argument for good hygiene, however. The dangers of *S. enterica* infection underscore our need to understand the species and to know which subspecies (and serotype) is involved when you are infected.

### Some Strains of *Escherichia coli* Are a Part of Our Healthy Gut Flora, whereas Others Cause Illness

Unlike *S. enterica*, *E. coli* is a natural part of the biota of our intestines. Along with many other symbionts, or organisms that live on or within a host organism without harming it, *E. coli* is vital to a healthy digestive system. But like *S. enterica*, there are many varieties of *E. coli*. One of these, *E. coli* O157:H7, has been associated with mild to severe gastrointestinal symptoms, such as abdominal cramping and diarrhea. Less fortunate patients suffer from a variety of complications that can be debilitating and/or lethal. Children under five are more vulnerable to hemolytic–uremic syndrome than adults. *E. coli* O157:H7 can be transmitted in food (uncooked or undercooked ground beef, contaminated sprouts, lettuce, salami, and unpasteurized milk), contact with contaminated water, or fecal–oral transmission from an infected person.

There were two recent noteworthy outbreaks of contamination and illness associated with *E. coli* O157:H7 in Canada. The first was in Walkerton, Ontario, in 2009, where contamination of the water supply was caused by agricultural runoff. About 50% of the 5000 residents of Walkerton became ill from *E. coli* O157:H7, and 7 of them died. Then, in late August 2012, the H7 *E. coli* was found in beef products from a meat processing plant in southern Alberta. This led to a recall of over 2000 products from the plant, and by mid-October 2012, over 2000 workers at the plant had been laid off.

Medical personnel can isolate bacteria from feces to distinguish between infections of different variants of *E. coli* (including O156:H7) or whether another organism altogether (such as *S. enterica*) is causing the illness. The tools for identifying species become important for the health of individuals and the health of our communities. But we rely on many, non-pathogenic forms of *E. coli*; they are the ones that are an integral part of the biota of our guts. So like so many things in life, we need to know the details about what forms or species are beneficial, whether the topic is plants in the family Apiaceae or strains of *E. coli*.

## STUDY BREAK

1. Look at the news and find two other species that are important to our health.
2. Can you find an example of a species, like *E. coli*, that can be either beneficial or harmful to our health?

## PUTTING IT IN PERSPECTIVE

"Species" is a fundamental unit in biology—the anchor for almost any biological undertaking. You must know what organisms you are working with or from which organisms you obtained the material you study, even if you never study the whole organisms but rather mitochondria, membranes, or any other component of living things. Names of species allow precise communication of information. The challenge of applying a species concept to an array of organisms reflects the fact that species are units of convenience that allow us to better understand and communicate about the natural world. The results of evolution often do not fit the categories that scientists have developed to describe the relationships between living things. Because evolution is an ongoing process, we can expect to find organisms that do not fit our categorizations.

## KEY CONCEPTS REVIEW AND QUESTIONS

### 12.1 Naming Species

Species have a unique, scientific binomial name based on Latin or Greek that clearly identifies them. The scientific name also provides information about the organism. There are also common names used to identify species, but sometimes different species may have the same common names. Other animals, in addition to humans, have names for other species.

1. Which is the correct presentation of a scientific name? *Eptesicus fuscus*, Eptesicus fuscus, eptesicus fuscus? What is *Eptesicus*? What is *fuscus*?

### 12.2 Defining a Species

Dozens of species concepts are used to document diversity of life. Species concepts define species by physical appearance, biology, genetics, or evolutionary relationships. Examples include the biological species concept, the morphological species concept, the genetic species concept, the phylogenetic species concept, and the chronospecies concepts.

2. Why are species so central to biology? How can a central element of biology be so open to interpretation and question?

3. Compare the biological species concept and the genetic species concept. How do they differ? How do they compare to the phylogenetic or morphological species concept? Which concept would you, as a bird watcher, for example, find most useful? What other animals have labels for different species? Why?

## 12.3 Recognizing Species

Variations in appearance, such as sexual dimorphism or across the life cycle, could make it difficult to tell that two organisms that appear to be different are the same species. Many species appear similar to other species. Field guides, museum specimens, and genetic barcodes can be helpful in identifying species. Sometimes new species are identified.

4. Why are field guides effectively documentations of biodiversity? What species concept(s) are field guides based on? What role do museum specimens play in advancing our knowledge of species and evolution?

5. How does DNA barcoding relate to species and species concepts? How could you use DNA barcoding to make yourself a more informed shopper? Can we use DNA barcoding to better enforce protection of endangered species? If so, how?

## 12.4 Speciation

Speciation could occur when gene flow is interrupted, such as when once connected populations become isolated. There are prezygotic or postzygotic barriers in sexually reproducing species. Speciation can occur when two species are sympatric or allopatric. Hybrid zones occur in areas where species overlap in distribution, and individuals can successfully interbreed.

6. Explain how gene flow and genetic drift relate to (are involved with) the origin of species. What role does or can mutation play in the origin of species? How do mutations spread through populations?

7. How can you account for three different types of killer whales living in the Pacific Ocean off the western coast of North America? What could account for the differences among these whales?

8. What is polyploidy? What variations are there in this phenomenon? How do polyploids arise?

9. What do ring species demonstrate to us about the origin of species?

## 12.5 Problems without Sex

Not all species reproduce sexually. Some organisms reproduce asexually. Prokaryotes can exchange alleles through lateral gene transfer. Recombination among bacteria occurs through occasional transfers of small DNA fragments. Other systems of genetic exchange occur in androdioecious and gynogenetic species.

10. How does the equivalent of genetic recombination occur in prokaryotes? How do organisms that reproduce asexually fit into our concepts of species? Do the ideas of gynogenetic and androdioecious species accommodate prokaryotes?

## 12.6 Species and Our Health

Understanding evolutionary relationships and biology of individual species is important to our health. Different subspecies of *S. enterica* can cause different illnesses. Many varieties of *E. coli* are vital to a healthy digestive system, whereas others cause illness.

# Selection and Evolution

# CHAPTER OUTLINE

## WHY IT MATTERS

Humans use chemicals (pesticides) to control weeds and other pests: herbicides for plants, insecticides for insects, and fungicides for fungi. The lethal effect of pesticides exerts strong selection (selective pressure) on pests. But all too often pesticides affect other organisms as well. Through mutations, individual organisms develop resistance to the effects of the pesticides designed to kill them. Resistance is an inheritable decrease in a population's susceptibility to a pesticide. The offspring of resistant individuals are also protected, as are their offspring.

Australian sheep blowflies are an example of evolution in response to a pesticide. They are 6 to 9 mm long flies that occur throughout Australia. They have spread widely through the world, including to Eastern Canada (**Figures 13.1** and **13.2**). They are considered pests when females deposit their eggs on livestock such as sheep (called "fly strikes"). Female Australian sheep blowflies deposit eggs in open wounds on live sheep. The eggs hatch into maggots that eat flesh and damage the wool. A single female can produce hundreds of eggs. These flies complete their life cycle—egg, larva, pupa, and adult—in about seven days. These flies have huge reproductive potential because of their egg production and short generation time.

Fly strikes by Australian sheep blowflies cost the wool industry over $A150 million a year. Tools for controlling the blowflies include bait traps and at least five kinds of chemical insecticides. Organophosphate insecticides have been particularly effective against Australian sheep blowflies because they affect the nervous system and rapidly kill both adult flies and maggots.

Some Australian sheep blowflies have a mutation that makes them resistant to organophosphate insecticides. This resistance is based on a single mutation that first appeared in just a few individuals of this species. Compared to susceptible flies, the DNA of resistant flies differs because a single amino acid is replaced in a single enzyme. This inheritable difference means that resistant flies can detoxify organophosphate insecticides by converting them to an enzyme. Consequently, if sprayed with the insecticide, resistant flies survive to reproduce, whereas the susceptible ones around them die. Obviously, many more resistant flies survive to reproduce and pass on the mutation to the next generation. The flies' short life cycle and high reproductive rate ensure rapid spread of the resistant mutation. Here the combination of a genetically based change and strong selective pressure (lethal

**FIGURE 13.2** Maggots of an Australian sheep blowfly.

SOURCE: Shuchi Arora, Carl Baptista and Chu Sing Lim, "Maggot metabolites and their combinatory effects with antibiotic on Staphylococcus aureus," *Annals of Clinical Microbiology and Antimicrobials* 2011, 10:6. © 2011 Arora et al; licensee BioMed Central Ltd. This is an Open Access article distributed under the terms of the Creative Commons Attribution License (http://creativecommons.org/licenses/by/2.0).

© Julian Money-Kyrle/Alamy

**FIGURE 13.1** An Australian sheep blowfly, *Lucilia cuprina*.

Lignin (**Figure 1**) is the main component of wood. This complex organic substance is rich in oxygen and is concentrated in the cell walls of woody plants. Lignin is a heterogeneous polymer that strengthens wood and makes it more rigid. Lignin also protects plant tissues from microbial attack. Animals, such as termites, that eat wood depend on symbionts to digest lignin, cellulose, and hemicellulose components. Most organisms that can digest lignin and other plant structural molecules (e.g., cellulose, hemicellulose) do so by fermentation achieved by symbionts. Termites and ruminant mammals are examples of animals that use fermentation to digest plant materials. Gribbles are wood-boring crustaceans, one of the few animals that can directly digest lignin. The ability to digest lignin and other structural molecules is important for the biofuel industry.

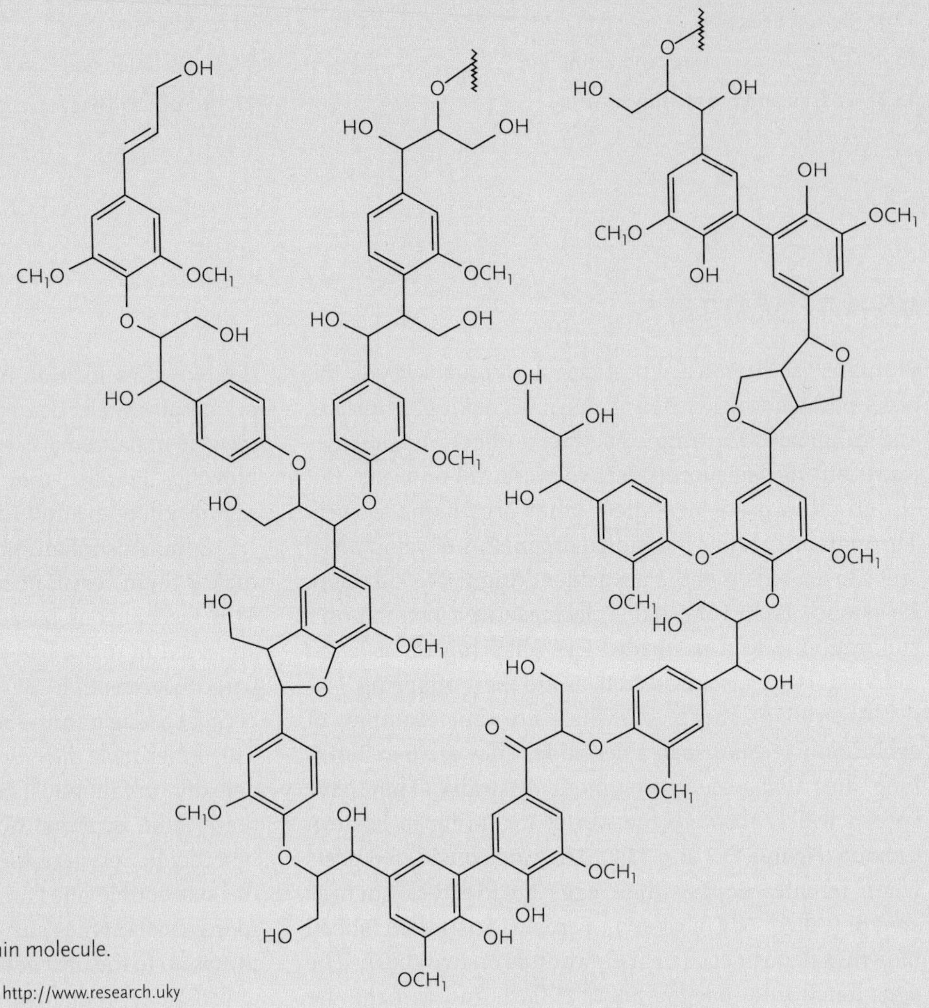

**FIGURE 1** Lignin molecule.

SOURCE: Based on http://www.research.uky.edu/odyssey/images/lignin.jpg

organophosphate insecticide) has altered the population of Australian sheep blowflies over time, reflecting the loss of individuals vulnerable to the pesticide. This is a clear example of evolution by natural selection. Since 1962, over 450 species of arthropods have developed resistance to at least one insecticide. Through mutations, insects can evolve the ability to detoxify insecticides, become less sensitive to them, or excrete them.

In this chapter, we begin by recognizing the contributions of Darwin and Wallace to our knowledge of evolution. We explore the combined impact of natural selection and evolution on modern biology. **Natural selection** is an environmental or other force that determines which individual organisms in a population survive to reproduce. **Evolution** is change in populations over time that results from selection. Fitness is measured by the transfer of genes to the next generation. Fundamental changes to the planet, such as those associated with the evolution of oxygenic photosynthesis and oxygenation of the biosphere, also affected the scope of life on Earth through the process of evolution.

Biologists have a long history of studying selection and change. Fossils and phylogeny show us organisms' evolutionary history. The distribution of organisms across the planet also influences the evolutionary opportunities for life, and organisms from different backgrounds often end up with comparable ways of exploiting available opportunities (Box 13.1). Changes in food and the movement onto land, into the air, or back to the water also illustrate the results of selection. Ongoing selection acts on our susceptibility to diseases such as malaria. It has affected the ability of plants to withstand heat and the diversification of birds. Furthermore, selection continues to act on humans. Nevertheless, some species remain virtually unchanged over millions and hundreds of millions of years.

## 13.1 Charles Robert Darwin and Alfred Russel Wallace

Charles Darwin's (1809–1882) name is synonymous with evolution. His 1859 book *On the Origin of Species* was one of the first compilations of information about how species form. In it, he inferred that evolution happened through natural selection. Natural selection explained how a species could split into one or more new species over successive generations. Much of his writings were based on information he collected during the 5-year-long voyage **(Figure 13.3)** he made on His Majesty's Ship (HMS) *Beagle*. He joined HMS *Beagle* as a dining companion for the captain and then became the ship's naturalist. In today's world, a 5-year voyage may be unimaginable. HMS *Beagle* was 27.5 m long with a 7.5 m beam, meaning that the crew of 74 lived in very close quarters. At such close quarters, five years must have seemed much, much longer.

Darwin's visit to the Galápagos Islands **(Figure 13.4)** was important because it gave him a chance to closely observe variations in the plants and animals from different islands. The similarity of the biota between the Galápagos Islands and neighbouring South America (972 km to the east) led Darwin to presume that the organisms of the islands had moved there from South America.

Darwin's background of living in the country made him very familiar with the importance of **artificial selection**, or humans' selective breeding of plants and animals for the traits they wanted. He had also been influenced by the

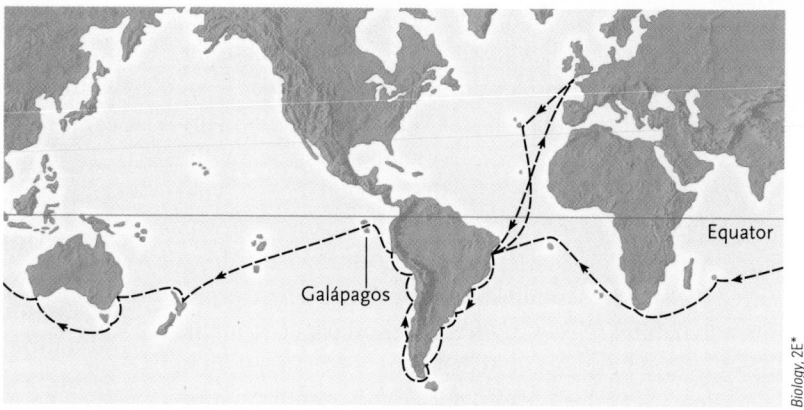

**FIGURE 13.3** Darwin's voyage: the route of HMS *Beagle*.

**FIGURE 13.4** The Galápagos Islands. Between 3 and 5 million years ago, volcanic eruptions created the Galápagos Islands **(a)** about 1000 km west of Ecuador. Many unique species have evolved there having arrived from South America. The islands were named for the giant tortoises **(b)** found there (in Spanish, *galdpa* means tortoise). This tortoise (*Geochelone elephantopus*) is native to Isla Santa Cruz. Marine iguanas (*Amblyrhynchus cristatus*) **(c)** dive into the Pacific Ocean to feed on algae. A male Blue-footed Booby (*Sula nebouxii*) **(d)** engages in courtship display.

writings of Thomas Malthus, particularly *An Essay on the Principle of Population*, which raised questions about the outcome of competition for limited supplies of food.

Alfred Russel Wallace (1823–1913) was a contemporary of Charles Darwin. He studied nature in the Amazon and then in the East Indies. He emerged with several ideas that paralleled those of Charles Darwin. Sometime in 1858, Charles Darwin received a paper from Alfred Wallace presenting Wallace's findings about evolution and natural selection. After his short paper about his theory of evolution was published in 1842, Darwin had been slow to put his ideas about evolution into a manuscript. The arrival of Wallace's paper spurred him to action. Wallace's paper and a brief contribution from Darwin were read at the same meeting of the Linnean Society in London, England. The two works were published together. Most people associate Darwin's name with the theory of evolution, but Wallace's contributions were equally important. It is important to remember that neither Darwin nor Wallace had any knowledge of genetics. To be specific, Darwin and Wallace described a mechanism (natural selection) for evolution that worked and could be seen to work.

Darwin and Wallace were not the first to write about the history of life. Aristotle (384–322 BCE) reflected on the fixed characteristics of living (animate) and non-living (inanimate) objects. He wrote about a "chain of being," or ladder of life. Others, such as George-Louis Leclerc (1707–1788), reflected on body parts that appeared to have no obvious function (e.g., pigs' toes that do not touch the ground). Leclerc suggested that some features were vestigial: useless today but functional in the past. George Cuvier (1769–1832) studied fossils. His theory of **catastrophism** was based on the idea that successive catastrophes (such as floods) eliminated some organisms.

Jean Baptiste de Lamarck (1744–1829) suggested that a perfecting principle caused organisms to become better suited to their surroundings. He suggested that characteristics acquired over an organism's life were passed on to the next generation, for example, explaining the change from short- to long-legged wading birds. Lamarck made four important comments about changes in organisms over time:

1. He proposed that species change over time.
2. He recognized that changes were passed from one generation to the next.
3. He acknowledged that organisms change in response to changes in the environment.
4. He hypothesized that specific mechanisms are responsible for change.

So although Lamarck was not right about the way in which it happens, he understood the general process of evolution. It is vital to bear in mind that Aristotle, Leclerc, Cuvier, Lamarck, Wallace, and Darwin had no knowledge of genetics as we know it.

The theory of evolution by natural selection profoundly influenced biology. Darwin's theory had four distinct components:

1. The theory provided a physical rather than spiritual explanation for the origins of biological diversity.
2. The theory recognized that evolutionary changes occurred in groups of organisms. Some members of a group survived and reproduced, whereas others did not.
3. Evolution was a multistage process, the result of natural selection acting on variations.
4. Some individuals performed better than others in some situations, and their descendants carried the advantageous traits.

Darwin's theory of evolution had a huge impact in Victorian England, and the repercussions of the theory continue today. In many parts of the world, evolution is still not widely accepted, and in some places, people who accept it and/or teach it are widely vilified.

## STUDY BREAK

1. Compare the contributions of Lamarck and Darwin to understanding evolution.
2. What were the four points of Darwin's theory?
3. Why was visiting the Galápagos Islands so important for Darwin?

## 13.2 Selection, Change, and Evolution

Darwin's theory of evolution by natural selection requires that there be heritable variation among individuals in a population. This population is subjected to selection that will favour variants that provide an organism with an advantage (think of Australian blowflies) and will impact subsequent populations. Evolutionary "success" such as this means that an individual's genes are represented in the next generation. As a result of natural selection, populations will change over time, possibly leading to the evolution of new species.

Note that not all change over time is evolution. We change as we age, a reality that confronts us every time we look at old pictures of ourselves, our friends, and family. In them, we see many changes in our appearance over time. These changes are not evolution; they are not heritable changes and will not be passed to the next generation.

Species are influenced by a wide range of **biotic factors** and **abiotic factors**. Biotic influences include interactions with others species and conditions associated with or arising from other species. Abiotic factors include those relating to rock and soil, climate, and weather and are not directly associated with other organisms.

## Selection Pressures Can Come from Abiotic Factors

The current warming of climate is one of the most pervasive environmental changes affecting life on Earth. One reflection of this is species extending their ranges northward, so that, in Canada, animals and plants now occur much farther north than they did even 10 years ago. Killer whales, once rare in the Arctic Ocean, are now becoming dominant predators in that ecosystem. In other cases, in spring, birds arrive back from migration much earlier than before. For Pied Flycatchers (*Ficedula hypoleuca*) in the Netherlands, this has reduced nesting success. The caterpillars the birds feed their young are now not available when the eggs hatch. The emergence of the insects is triggered by photoperiod rather than temperature because the insects the birds feed their young have not shifted their times of abundance.

In other cases, pesticides we apply to crops can put selective pressure on non-target species and can be agents of natural selection. As one of the most widely used pesticides, the herbicide 2,4-D provides a classic example. Grasshoppers such as *Romalea microptera* were not the targets of applications of 2,4-D, but they ingested this chemical with their food. These grasshoppers defend themselves against the attacks of ants by hissing and releasing an odoriferous froth from their spiracles (openings on the abdomen that lead to the respiratory system). The froth repels ants, and its active ingredient is 2,5-dichlorophenol, apparently derived from 2,4-D, which the grasshoppers ingested. Chlorinated compounds (*dichloro* = two atoms of chlorine) are rare natural products but could have been produced by the grasshopper from either 2,4-D or a derivative. This approach to repelling ants appeared within about 20 years of the first use of 2,4-D in areas where the grasshopper occurs. This example demonstrates the resiliency of nature and natural systems and illustrates how an artificial change has been converted to a natural one.

### *Impact of a Combination of Abiotic and Biotic Factors*

Some connections among species are less direct and reflect a combination of environmental (abiotic) and biotic factors. In North America and in Europe, loss of diversity of whitefish arose through changes in the communities of fish and changes in lake ecosystems. Sea lampreys (*Petromyzon marinus*) are parasites/predators of fish, and before 1829, they occurred in Lake Ontario, the Finger Lakes, and the St. Lawrence River. The 1829 completion of the Welland Canal allowed sea lampreys to get around Niagara Falls and into Lake Erie and the Upper Great Lakes. About 100 years later (1921), sea lampreys were reported in Lake Erie. From there they spread into Lake Michigan (1936), Lake Huron (1937), and Lake Superior (1946). Their populations exploded in these lakes and contributed to often catastrophic declines in populations of lake trout (*Salvelinus namaycush*) and

whitefish (*Coregonus* spp.). Before the arrival of sea lampreys, annual catches of lake trout were about 6.8 million tonnes, which dropped to 136,000 kg by the early 1960s.

After the arrival of sea lampreys and decimation of lake trout populations, the species composition of whitefish in lakes Huron, Michigan, and Superior changed. Specifically, larger, deep water, endemic species of whitefish (*C. nigripinnis, C. reighardi, C. kiyi, C. johannae,* and *C. alpenae*) disappeared. Whitefish that moved into the deep waters looked different from those that had occurred there before.

## Selection Pressures Can Come from Other Species

Species can influence one another, potentially resulting in the actions or presence of one species driving the evolution of another. Interactions can include competition for resources such as space and food and interactions between predators and prey, plants and pollinators, or host and parasite.

More generally, interactions among species result in large-scale speciation events. One excellent example is the diversification of life on the Hawaiian Islands as it existed before the arrival of people. After the islands formed about 28 million years ago, waves of plants and animals landed on the islands, setting the stage for the evolution of about 8500 endemic species, 2500 plants, and 6500 insects. The plants all evolved from about 275 ancestral species and the insects from about 250 original immigrants. The endemic (locally evolved) plants of Hawaii consist of many species classified in relatively few genera. This indicates that diversification occurred after the arrival of new immigrants. New arrivals generated new ecological opportunities for species already there, yet more species evolved to fill ever-expanding ecological niches. Again, the various situations that can produce new species (see Chapter 12) make it easy to appreciate the flora and fauna of the Hawaiian Islands. In this situation, new arrivals generated enriched conditions that spawned the diversification of plants and insects (for example). This diversity of endemic species reflects the age of the islands and the range of habitats in Hawaii, from drylands to rain forests to alpine situations.

### *Competition for Food, Space, or Other Resources Can Drive Evolution*

This can occur when a critical limiting resource is required by two sympatric species. Nest sites can be limiting for birds that nest in hollows, and competition may occur between species (**interspecific competition**) or among members of the same species (**intraspecific competition**). In general, larger individuals outcompete smaller ones in any confrontation.

In our own immediate ancestry, differences in morphology between species in the genera *Homo, Paranthropus,* and *Australopithecus* corresponded to differences in diet.

Among these genera, analysis of two isotopes of strontium in teeth revealed that *Australopithecus* had the most general diet, whereas *Paranthropus robustus* ate more plant materials than early species of *Homo*. In this situation, the range of food and ecological role differed between *Homo* and other hominids, so they could live in the same area and not compete for food. As we shall see in Chapter 30, different species that occur in the same area are expected to differ in some aspect of their lifestyle, such as diet.

## Predation and Prey Can Exert Strong Selective Pressures on One Another

Being able to effectively find food is an important aspect of an organism's fitness. Avoiding death by predation is about the most powerful pressure there is. Cardenolides are organic compounds that are toxic to mammalian herbivores because they interfere with the operation of sodium pumps crucial to muscle contraction.

Milkweeds and dogbanes (family Apocynaceae) produce cardenolides in the latex fluid **(Figure 13.5)** released at sites of injury (or attack by herbivores). Milkweeds and dogbanes produce cardenolides. Insects such as danaid butterflies and chrysomelid beetles eat these plants. They and many other insects in at least three orders have adaptations that allow them to process cardenolides. Cardenolides are important and effective for plant

**FIGURE 13.5** Latex sap containing cardenolides oozing from areas where a leaf of a spreading dogbane (*Apocyanum androsaemifolium*) was broken.

defence and put strong selective pressure on insects. The repeated, independent appearance of cardenolide-resistant insects is an example of parallel evolution, which we will discuss in Section 13.7. This example demonstrates that similar solutions to a problem can arise in different evolutionary lineages.

## Host–Parasite Interactions

Parasites are another, more macabre, example of how one species creates opportunities for others. The images in **Figure 13.6** show species whose survival depends on other species. This also raises the question of how to define

**FIGURE 13.6** Examples of organisms that depend on other species, including **(a)** *Viscum album* – mistletoe, **(b)** *Conopholis americana* – cancer root, **(c)** *Monotropa uniflora* – ghost plant, **(d)** a streblid fly in the tear duct (white arrow) of a bent-winged bat (*Miniopterus*), and **(e)** a mosquito whose abdomen is distended with blood.

*parasite*. A simple definition of a parasite is an individual (species) that lives on another species, the host. The parasite benefits, whereas the host does not. In Figure 13.6, there are three examples of higher plants that are parasites of other plants. Also shown is a bat with a streblid fly in its tear duct and a mosquito, which parasitizes mammals. In **Figure 13.6d**, the bat flies (Streblidae) are ectoparasites on the blood-feeding vampire bat. Is this bat also a parasite? If so, the bat fly is a parasite of a parasite. But are mosquitoes and bat flies really just specialized predators? There is no question about whether or not the nematode brainworms (*Parelaphostrongylus tenuis*) are parasites. These usually live in the brains of white-tailed deer (*Odocoileus virginianus*), but when they are transferred to moose (*Alces alces*), they are debilitating and even fatal. Climate warming has resulted in northward expansion of the range of white-tailed deer, so they more often overlap with moose, with possibly disastrous results for the moose.

### Plant–Pollinator Interactions

The examples that follow illustrate how natural selection simultaneously can drive change in both a plant and its pollinators. At one level, the shape of a flower's corolla (**Figure 13.7**) affects pollinator behaviour. Tobacco hornworm (*Manduca sexta*), a hawkmoth, prefers *Nicotiana* flowers that are specialized to be pollinated by hawkmoths. They will avoid other shapes, which rely more on hummingbirds or small moths for pollinations (Figure 13.7). In this situation, natural selection favours

pollinator characteristics that are most efficient at harvesting nectar (and pollen). At the same time, natural selection favours plant characteristics that maximize pollen transfer among flowers. When the traits of two organisms drive evolution in each other, this is called **coevolution**.

Movement of flowers often attracts pollinators, especially those with three-dimensional vision. But moving flowers may be more difficult to land on and to hang on to. Conical cells (**Figure 13.8, p. 286**) on the surface of petals give bees purchase. Tests with bumblebees (*Bombus terrestris*) and petunia flowers (*Petunia hybrida*) demonstrated the bee's preferences for flowers that provide better grip. Once again, natural selection favours both plant and pollinator, partly by giving bees something to hold on to.

POLYMORPHISM. Natural selection often reflects a combination of variations in morphology (polymorphism) and behaviour, particularly in a social context. Female Common Cuckoos (*Cuculus canorus*) are nest parasites (**Figure 13.9, p. 286**), laying their eggs in the nests of other birds. Host species, such as Reed Warblers (*Acrocephalus scirpaceus*), recognize and mob Common Cuckoos to reduce their chances of having their nests parasitized. But there are two morphs of Common Cuckoos. Grey morphs are hawklike in appearance and deter mobbing attacks. Rufous morphs are not hawklike and are more often mobbed. Reed Warblers can learn to recognize and mob the grey morph. Reed Warblers depend on neighbours to alert them to the presence of nest parasites and will learn to mob the more common cuckoo morph, regardless of its appearance.

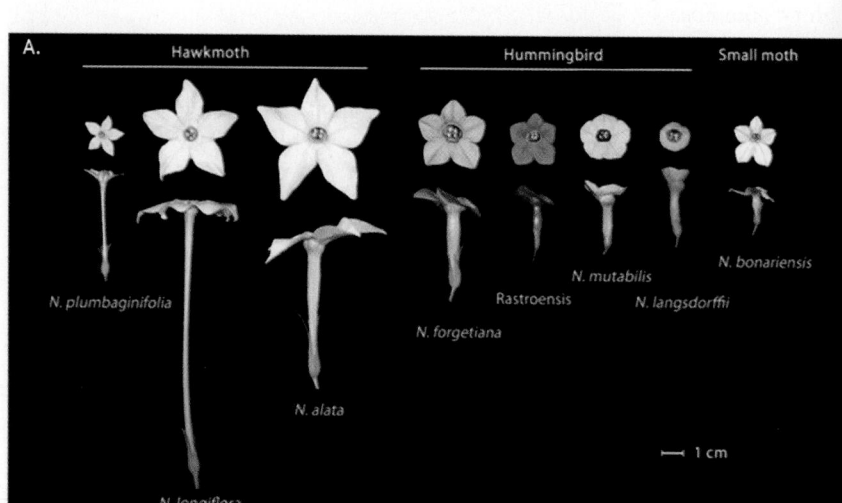

**FIGURE 13.7** Varieties of *Nicotiana* flowers **(a)** presented to tobacco hornworms **(b)**.

SOURCE: Kaczorwski, R.L., A.R. Seliger, A.C. Gaskett, S.K. Wigsten and R.A. Raguso. 2012. "Corolla shape vs size in flower choice by a nocturnal hawkmoth pollinator," *Functional Ecology*, 26:577–587. John Wiley and Sons. © 2012 The Authors. Functional Ecology © 2012 British Ecological Society.

**FIGURE 13.8** The petals of a sunflower (*Helianthus annus*) **(a)** are covered with conical cells **(b)**, as seen with a scanning electron microscope. Conical cells give bees a better grip on the flower, an advantage to bees and to sunflowers. Scale on SEM is 20 μm.

SOURCE: H.M. Whitney et al., "Why do so many petals have conical epidermal cells?," *Annals of Botany* (2011) doi: 10.1093/aob/mcr065, by permission of Oxford University Press.

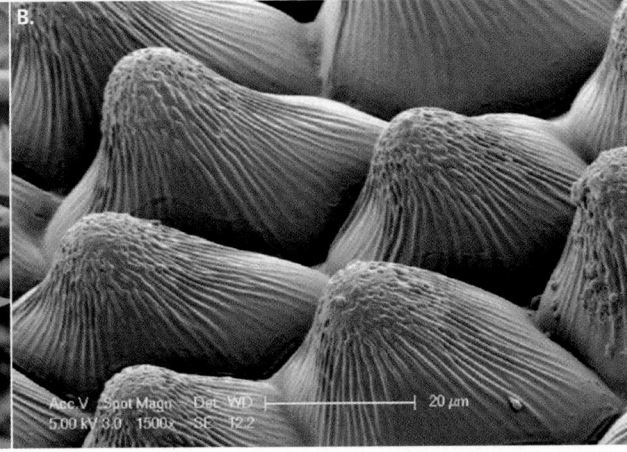

**FIGURE 13.9** A Hedge Sparrow (*Prunella modularis*) feeding a Common Cuckoo (*Cuculus canorus*) that it has raised in its nest.

## 13.3 Sexual Selection

Apart from differences in genitalia, males can look different from females (see Figure 12.7). Some of these differences serve as indicators of overall physical condition and are used in the choice of potential mates. This describes **sexual selection**, where mate choice influences the genetic composition of the population of a species. Sexual selection is responsible for some spectacular examples of diversity among animals (see Figure 12.7). Sexual selection may involve interactions among males competing for females **(Figure 13.11)** and/or reflect features used by females when selecting mates.

## Sometimes the Selective Advantage Is Not Clear

Flowers often contain yeasts that live in nectaries. In some cases, beetle larvae in morning glory (*Ipomoea* spp.) flowers eat growing yeast in the flowers. The details remain unclear. In winter-blooming hellebores **(Figure 13.10**, *Helleborus foetidus*), yeast-mediated fermentation in nectaries raises the temperature in the flowers. It remains to be determined just how insect pollinators might benefit from warmer flowers (see also Box 13.2).

## STUDY BREAK

1. How does 2,4-D relate to selection? To natural selection?
2. Give two examples of how flowers influence and are influenced by natural selection.
3. How can parasitism affect evolution?
4. How do you measure success?
5. How can competition influence evolution?
6. How could climate change affect evolution?

**FIGURE 13.10** A flower of a hellebore, *Helleborus foetidus*.

BOX 13.2

# Humans and Natural Selection

The question of whether natural selection continues to act on people is important to answer, if only to remind us that our roots are biological and that we are the products of natural selection and evolution. Two relatively recent studies have demonstrated that people continue to be affected by natural selection.

The first is evidence from a study of women in Framingham, Massachusetts, that began in 1948. Compared to the original group of women, their female descendants are shorter and stouter, with reduced levels of cholesterol and systolic blood pressure. Furthermore, the female descendants had their first children at younger ages and entered menopause later. In effect, selection has lengthened the reproductive period of the female descendants compared to their mothers, grandmothers, and great-grandmothers.

Similar results were obtained from a study of French Canadian women living in pre-industrial conditions on Ile aux Coudres, about 80 km northeast of Quebec City. In the female descendants, age at first reproduction was lower than it was in female ancestors. Over a period of 140 years, age at first reproduction declined from 26 to 22 years **(Figure 1)**. Age at first reproduction is a heritable trait, and the genetic trend among the women from Ile aux Coudres exceeded what would have been expected from genetic drift. Ile aux Coudres had been settled by 30 families between 1720 and 1773. The population was 1585 by the 1950s. The data about the women were obtained from church registers and provide clear pedigrees. The uniformity of the social setting (social class, education, and religion) is important to the credibility of the findings.

These studies of human demography provide evidence of selection for longer periods of reproductive activity, which have obvious implications for genetic fitness.

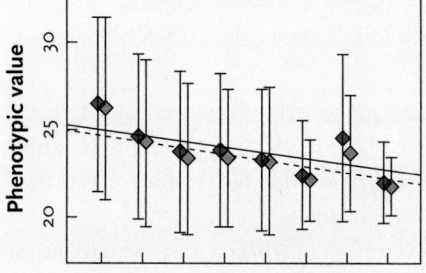

**Age at first reproduction**

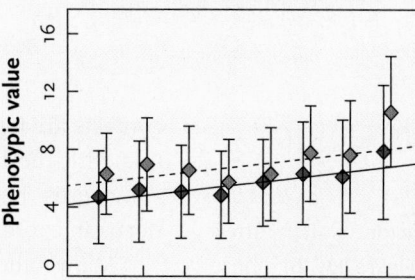

**Lifetime reproductive success**

**FIGURE 1** Changes in time in phenotypic value (age at first reproduction) and its impact on lifetime breeding success. The data are from women between 1800 and 1939 at Ile aux Coudres, Quebec. Values in years are for age at first reproduction. Lifetime reproductive success is numbers of children reaching age 15 years.

SOURCE: Emmanuel Milot, Francine M. Mayer, Daniel H. Nussey, Mireille Boisvert, Fanie Pelletier, and Denis Réale, "Evidence for evolution in response to natural selection in a contemporary human population," *PNAS*, vol. 108 no. 41, 11042–10108.

Changes in levels of hormones can influence the development of sexually dimorphic traits, or those traits that differ between genders. Research with Japanese rhinoceros beetles revealed that horn development was much more sensitive to larval nutrition than other parts of the body, such as wings, legs, and male genitalia. In these beetles, changes

**FIGURE 13.11** Armaments (in black) associated with male–male competition have evolved in multiple times. **(a)** A Chilean stag beetle (*Chiasognathus grantii*), **(b)** a whipscorpion (*Rowlandius longipalpus*), **(c)** a dinosaur (*Ankylosaurus magniventris*), **(d)** an amphipod (*Erictho-nius punctatus*), and **(e)** a giraffe weevil (*Lasiorhynchus barbicornis*).

SOURCE: Based on Emlen, D.J., "The evolution of animal weapons," *Annual Review of Ecology Evolution and Systematics* 39:387–413, 2008. From FENTON/DUMONT/OWEN. *Integrative Animal Biology*, 1E. © 2014 Nelson Education Ltd. Reproduced by permission. www.cengage.com/permissions

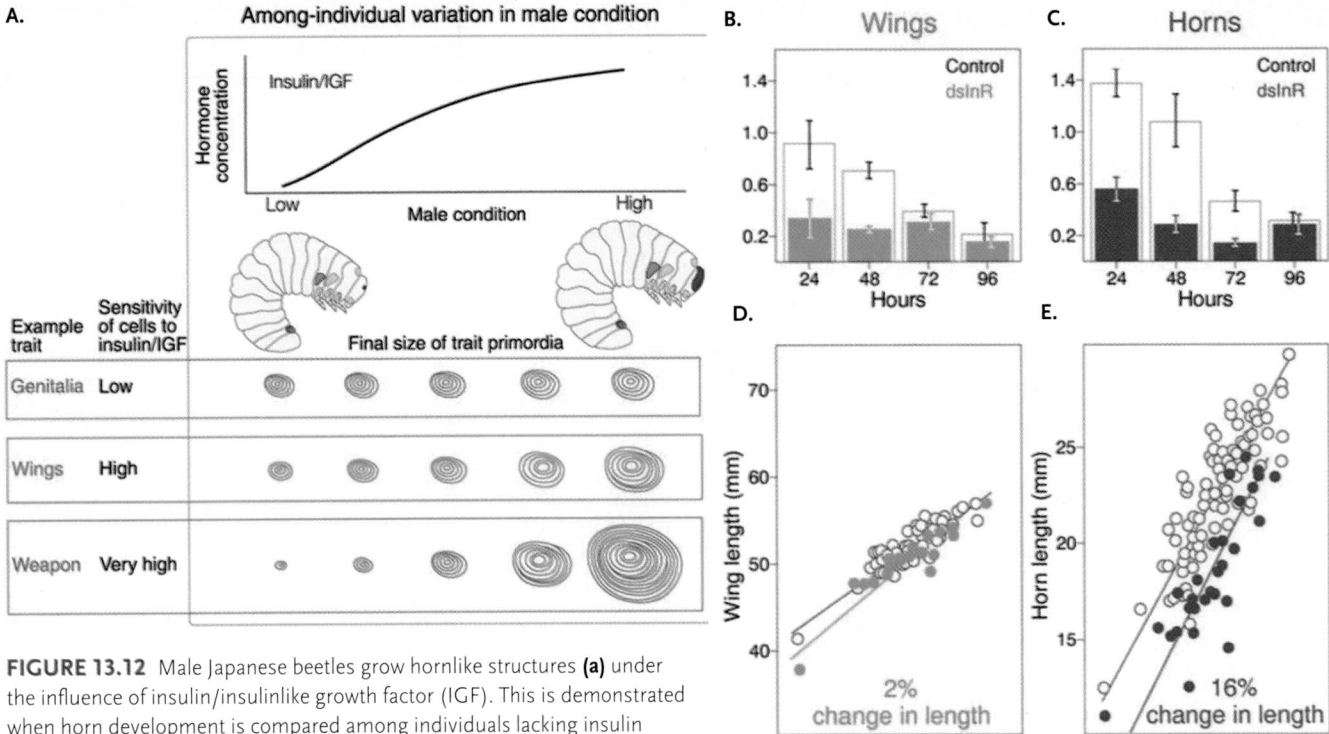

**FIGURE 13.12** Male Japanese beetles grow hornlike structures **(a)** under the influence of insulin/insulinlike growth factor (IGF). This is demonstrated when horn development is compared among individuals lacking insulin receptors and control individuals **(b, c)**. The differences in the lengths of wings and horns **(d, e)** are shown relative to overall body size.

SOURCE: From Douglas J. Emlen, Ian A. Warren, Annika Johns, Ian Dworkin, Laura Corley Lavine, "A Mechanism of Extreme Growth and Reliable Signaling in Sexually Selected Ornaments and Weapon," *Science* 17 August 2012: Vol. 337 no. 6096 pp. 860–864 Reprinted with permission from AAAS.

in levels of insulin/**insulinlike growth factor** result in differential growth of the horns of males **(Figure 13.12)**. These findings show how exaggerated body parts could reflect changes in growth mechanisms and may underlie many sexually selected traits across a wide range of animals.

Examples of the results of sexual selection are common among animals from many evolutionary backgrounds (Figure 13.11). Contests between male fiddler crabs (*Uca annulipes*) involve ritualized displays of large claws **(Figure 13.13)** that may escalate to grappling. Such

contests are typically settled when one male, usually the one with the larger claw, flips his opponent. Japanese rhinoceros beetles (*Trypoxylus dichotomus*) use their horns in contests with other males.

Many other examples of spectacular sexual dimorphism appear to have resulted from sexual selection. Among mammals, in many species of deer (family Cervidae), males (but not females) have antlers that are shed and regrown annually **(Figure 13.14)**. Bovids (species in the family Bovidae such as sheep, goats, antelope, bison, and domestic cattle) also show sexual dimorphism in **horns**, which, unlike antlers, are not regrown each year. The ornaments a male uses to thwart or defeat other males or to attract females also may

**FIGURE 13.13** Male fiddler crabs (*Uca annulipes*), but not females **(a)**, have an enlarged claw that is used in contests with other males **(b)**.

**FIGURE 13.14** Although male impala *(Aepyceros melampus)* have horns, females do not. Horns help males in interactions with other males, ultimately influencing which males mate with females.

be reliable indicators of his condition; they may allow a female to assess a potential mate's quality. More competitive males may also control more resources, such as food, nests, or an area of land.

But sexual selection may not apply in all situations. For example, a 10-year study of a population of pronghorn antelopes *(Antilocapra americana)* demonstrated that sexual selection occurred in some years (breeding seasons) but not in others. For male pronghorns, mating success or fitness only indicates male reproductive success in years with low predation on fawns by coyotes *(Canis latrans)*. If most of a male's offspring are lost to coyotes, the number of matings or fertilizations he achieved is not a reliable indication of success.

## STUDY BREAK

1. What is sexual selection?
2. What role can females play in sexual selection?
3. How can sexual selection generate changes in populations?
4. How do you measure fitness?

## 13.4 Time, Temperature, and Extinction

Evolution is fundamental to biology and to our understanding of how biological systems operate and change. This extends from what happens within a cell to the functioning of ecosystems, whether at a regional or global scale. Natural selection is a basic mechanism driving the process of evolution. It has played a pervasive role in generating the diversity of life throughout Earth's history. In this section, we consider the time over which evolution occurred, the impact of changes in Earth's temperature on evolution, and the role that extinctions play in evolution.

Current estimates place the age of Earth at 4.6 billion years, and life first appeared about 2 billion years later.

The Geological time scale (see the Purple Pages for an overview of the Geological time scale) presents the history of Earth in relative and absolute ages. Relative ages are determined by the positions of layers of rock, with younger layers usually overlying older ones. Fossils in layers of rock provide another indication of relative age and document the distribution of species of fossils in space.

### Absolute Dates Allow Biologists and Paleontologists to Establish Timelines

Radiometric or absolute ages are derived from analysis of **isotopes**. Radiometric dating is based on different isotopes, such as $^{14}$C (carbon 14) or $^{40}$K (potassium 40; other isotopes of K are $^{41}$K and $^{39}$K). Carbon 14 forms when atmospheric nitrogen—which has seven protons and seven neutrons—collides with free neutrons that have been created by the Sun's radiation. Carbon 14 has six protons and eight neutrons. It can combine with oxygen to form carbon dioxide, which is then taken up by plants through photosynthesis and moves up the food chain. When an organism dies, the carbon 14 begins to decay to carbon 12. At any given time in the atmosphere, the ratio of carbon 12 to carbon 14 is about a trillion to one. It takes 5730 years for half of these molecules to decay (the half-life). This relatively short half-life limits carbon 14 dating to no earlier than 50,000 years Before Present. The half-life of potassium 40 is 1250 million years, making it useful to date rocks from 100,000 years Before Present to 4 billion years. Radiometric dating is one source of evidence about the age of Earth.

When relative and absolute dating are combined with chronological analyses of DNA and protein sequences, biologists are able to estimate times of **divergences (Figure 13.15, p. 290)**, or when evolutionary lineages separated. This adds invaluable time dimensions to phylogenies and allows us to explore interactions that occurred over Earth's history of diversity of life and how environments have changed.

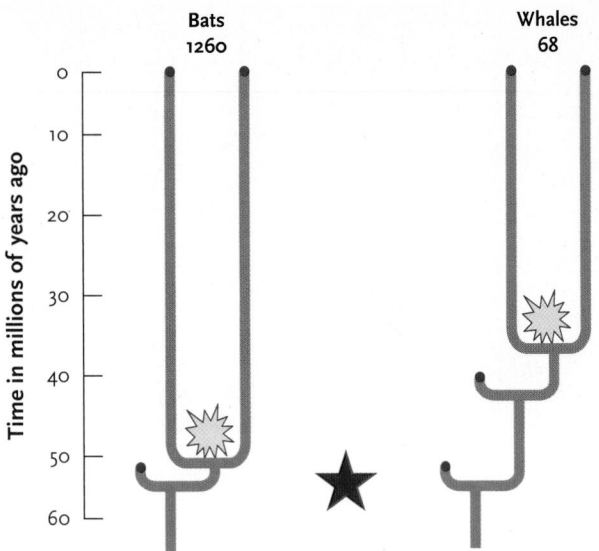

**FIGURE 13.15** A comparison of the timing and magnitude of diversification of bats (1260 living species; order Chiroptera) and whales (62 living species; order Cetacea). Although the timing of the origin of the two groups (star) is about the same, the time to diversification is different.

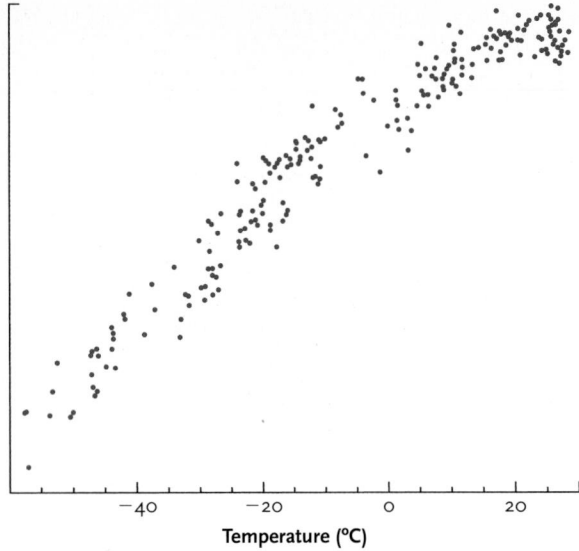

**FIGURE 13.16** Changes in global temperatures over time as indicated by the ratio of oxygen isotopes.

SOURCE: Adapted from Jouzel, et al. From *Paleclimatology: the Oxygen Balance*, NASA Earth Observatory

## Temperatures Have Changed over the History of Earth

Isotopic analysis can also provide data about how temperatures have changed through geologic time. The amounts of two isotopes of oxygen ($^{16}$O and $^{18}$O) in the atmosphere depend on temperature. $^{18}$O condenses more readily than $^{16}$O. The ratio of these two isotopes of oxygen in water trapped in ice (glaciers and ice sheets) preserves a record of change in temperature (climate) over time. This radiometric measure provides a clear picture about recent changes in global temperatures **(Figure 13.16)**.

Data about time and temperature allow us to put biotic changes in a chronological context, providing an idea of how changes over time are reflected in the fossil record (and the evolutionary history of organisms).

## Disappearances of Organisms Generate Opportunities for Others

**Extinction** is a fundamental component of the process of evolution. Extinctions occur repeatedly and may involve individual species (e.g., Passenger Pigeon – *Ectopistes migratorius* or Great Auk – *Pinguinus impennis*) or whole groups of species. One of the largest mass extinctions of organisms occurred about 250 million years ago, marking the end of the Permian and the beginning of the Triassic. This mass extinction coincided with rapid rises in temperatures, especially around the equator. Small-sized species of invertebrates dominated when temperatures were warmest. The fossil record indicates that plants and animals of the Early Triassic were driven out of the equatorial areas by heat that exceeded the maximum surface temperatures that we see in those areas today. The picture that

emerges is extinction of many types of organisms, followed by a widespread increase in diversity after cooling (e.g., conodonts, ammonites, and radiolarians in **Figure 13.17)**.

## STUDY BREAK

1. What is the difference between absolute and relative dates?
2. How do extinctions generate opportunities for evolution?

## 13.5 Fossils and the History of Life

The variety of fossils **(Figure 13.18)** reflects the astonishing diversity of life. **Fossils** are preserved evidence of prehistoric organisms. They can be anything from cells and their contents to bones, droppings, and footprints. Some fossils present unimaginable detail, whereas others present only a glimpse of earlier organisms. The fossil record gives us an indication of other organisms that have lived on Earth throughout geologic time, even though some of them defy the imagination. Most importantly, fossils allow us to put organisms, their predecessors, and their descendants in a historical perspective.

Some notable fossil deposits provide a clear picture of the organisms from past times. The Burgess Shale is a Cambrian deposit (545 to 525 million years ago) from Yoho National Park in British Columbia, Canada. The fine-grained shale preserves fine details of the fossils. The fauna included some animals we can identify to phylum, as indicated by a sampling of reconstructed animals **(Figure 13.19, p. 292)**. Included are arthropods **(Figure 13.19a)**,

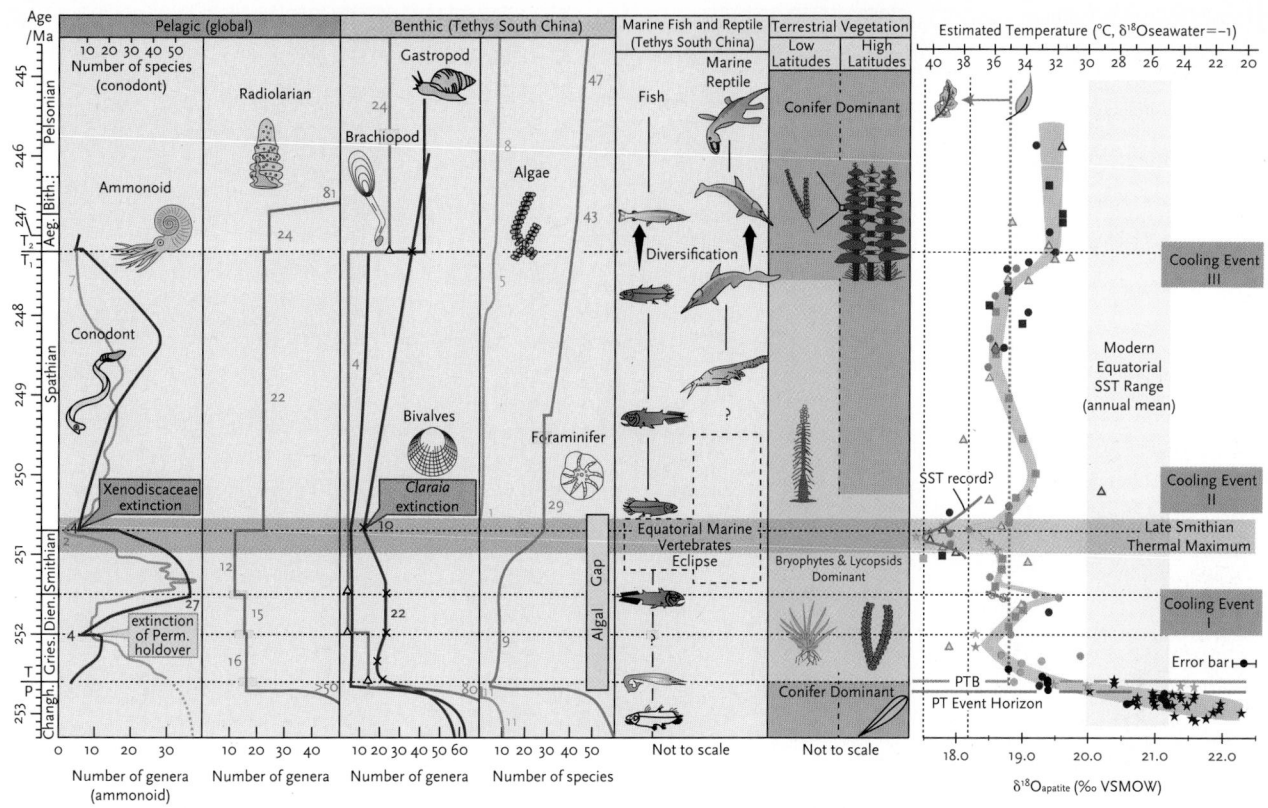

**FIGURE 13.17** The Early Triassic diversity of marine groups is shown along with terrestrial vegetation and trends in temperatures. Peak diversity of organisms at about 253 million years ago (before the Permian–Triassic boundary) coincides with cooler temperatures. Forests dominated by conifers disappeared during the hottest periods and reappeared only after temperatures cooled.

SOURCE: From Yadong Sun, Michael M. Joachimski, Paul B. Wignall, Chunbo Yan, Yanlong Chen, Haishui Jiang, Lina Wang, Xulong Lai, "Lethally Hot Temperatures During the Early Triassic Greenhouse," *Science* 19 October 2012: Vol. 338 no. 6105 pp. 366–370. Reprinted with permission from AAAS.

onychophorans **(Figure 13.19b)**, polychaete annelids **(Figure 13.19d)**, and a cephalochordate **(Figure 13.19e)**. Others, such as *Opabinia* (Figure 13.19b), are difficult to assign even to a phylum. To further complicate matters, as more fossils are discovered, our view of the animals they represent can change dramatically **(Figure 13.20, p. 292)**. Although

(Photos A–B): Labandeira, C.C. and T.L. Phillips. 1996. "A Carboniferous insect gall: insight into early ecologic history of the Holometabola." *PNAS*, 93:8470–8474. Copyright (1996) National Academy of Sciences, U.S.A.

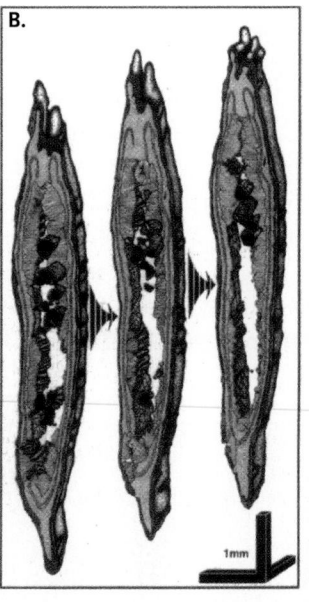
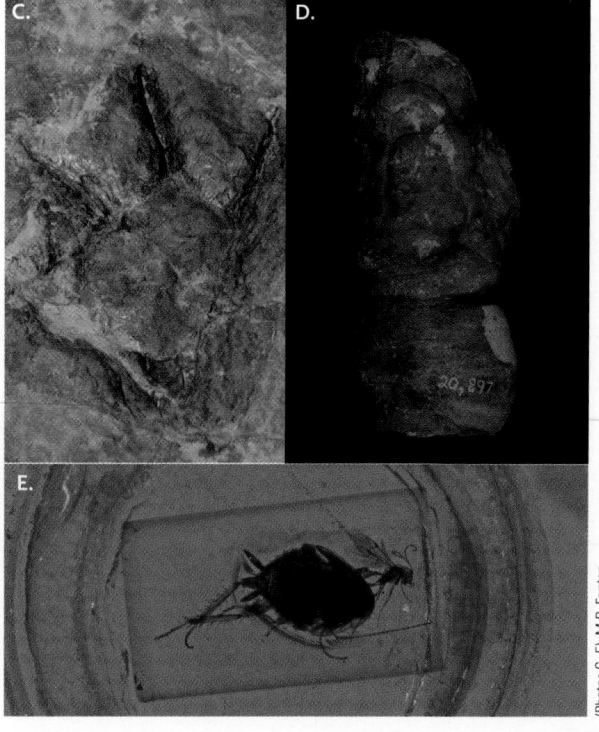

**FIGURE 13.18** A sampling of fossils, including **(a)** a 7 m tall tree fern (*Psaronius*) showing leaves and branches (inset) and **(b)** an insect gall in a leaf stem. Also shown are **(c)** a footprint of a dinosaur, **(d)** a fossilized alligator dropping (or coprolite), and **(e)** two insects preserved in amber. Scale bars in (b) are 1 mm.

(Photos C–E): M.B. Fenton

**FIGURE 13.19** Reconstructions of a sampling of five Cambrian animals from the Burgess Shale, from an exhibit at the Royal Tyrrell Museum. Included are an arthropod – *Marella* **(a)**, an animal of unknown phylum – *Opabinia* **(b)**, an onychophoran – *Aysheaia* **(c)**, a polychaete annelid – *Canadia* **(d)**, and a cephalochordate – *Pikaia* **(e)**.

*Nectocaris pteryx*, also from the Burgess Shale, was originally described as a chordate **(Figure 13.20a)**, analysis of recently discovered fossils indicates that it was, in fact, a cephalopod mollusc **(Figure 13.20b)**.

In other cases, fossil remains originally identified as different species turn out to be part of one species **(Figures 13.21** and **13.22)**. In Chapter 1, we saw how recent discoveries indicated that *Australopithecus afarensis* (Figure 1.4) was bipedal, adding to our knowledge of the history of our own species. Still other fossils are best known as black smears on black rock (Figure 13.22). The Australian fossil *Spriggina floundersi* is an example; it could represent either a polychaete annelid or a primitive arthropod.

Sometimes fossils are easy to identify, such as the 52.5 million-year-old bat seen in **Figure 13.23 (p. 294)**. In this case, there is enough detail to know from the shoulder girdles (shoulder blades, collar bones, and heads of the humeri) that the animal could fly. These bats had a claw on each finger, a feature not known from any living bats. Other fossil bats from the Eocene include enough details of stomach contents to indicate that the bats' last meal had been insects. Older fossils, such as those from the 520 million-year-old Chengjiang biota of China, include details of the nervous system. Specifically, the arthropod *Fuxianhuia protensa* has well-preserved optic lobes and three optic centres providing forward-viewing eyes. In structure, the eyes of *Fuxianhuia* are strikingly similar to those of modern insects and crustaceans.

From one perspective, the fragmentary nature of the fossil record is a blessing. If all or even many of the

**FIGURE 13.20** An early **(a)** and a more recent **(b)** reconstruction of *Nectocaris pteryx*. Structures originally identified as antennae (a – arrow) are now thought to be tentacles (b).

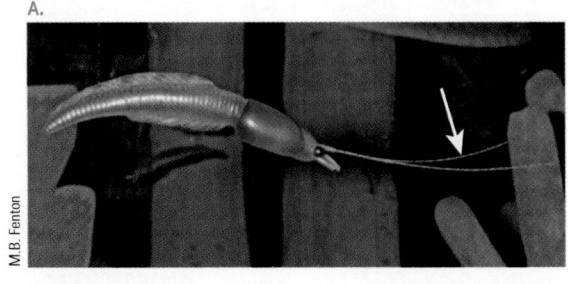

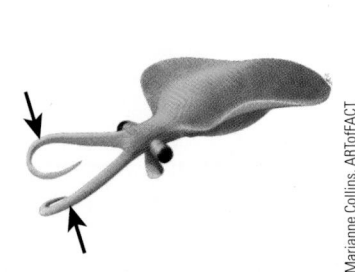

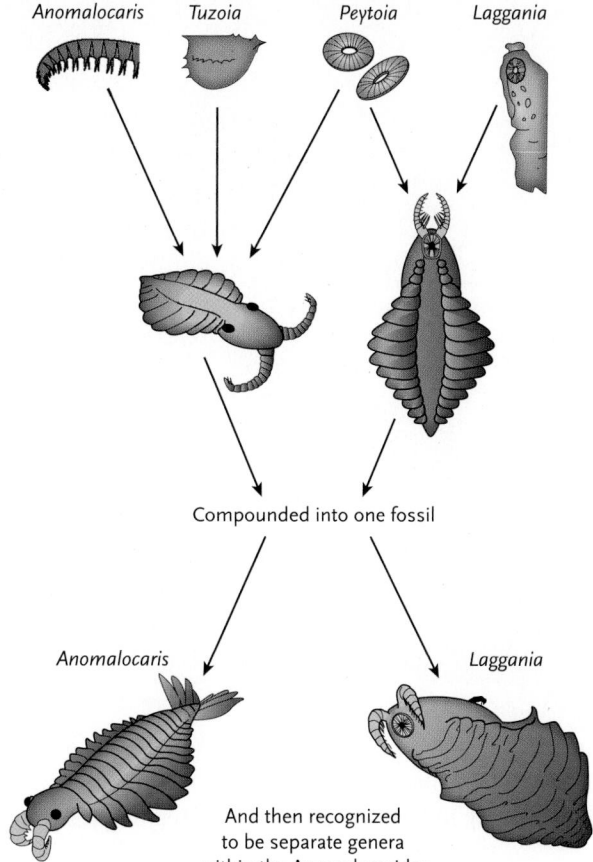

B.

*Anomalocaris*  *Tuzoia*  *Peytoia*  *Laggania*

Compounded into one fossil

*Anomalocaris*  *Laggania*

And then recognized
to be separate genera
within the Anomalocaridae

A.

M.B. Fenton

**FIGURE 13.21** This diagram illustrates how our knowledge of *Anomalocaris* **(a)** developed and emerged from the discovery of better fossils. In the end, *Anomalocaris* is a composite **(b)**, including parts originally described as a sea cucumber (*Laggania*), a type of medusa (*Peytoia*), a bivalve arthropod (*Tuzoia*), and another arthropod (*Anomalocaris*).

SOURCE: From FENTON/DUMONT/ OWEN. *Integrative Animal Biology*, 1E. © 2014 Nelson Education Ltd. Reproduced by permission. www.cengage.com/ permissions

organisms previously alive had been preserved, we would face a nightmare of details. How could we, for example, tell birds from dinosaurs? From another standpoint, the lack of fossils for many animals (e.g., bats) makes it impossible to identify their closest ancestors. With each passing year, the discovery of more fossils changes our view of the details of evolutionary history.

## Study Break

1. What is a fossil? What do fossils tell us about the history of life?
2. What do *Anomalocaris* and *Nectocaris* have in common?
3. How does the half-life affect radiometric dating?

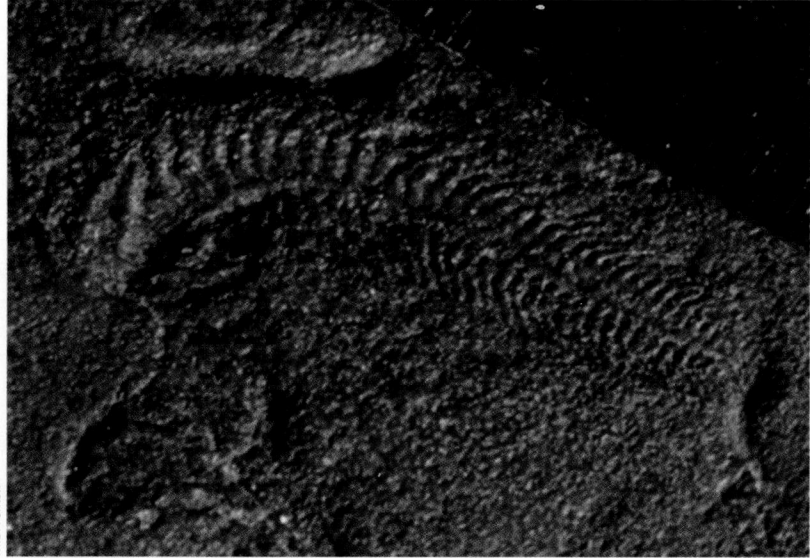

M.B. Fenton

**FIGURE 13.22** Fossil *Spriggina floundersi*, which was probably an errant polychaete or even a primitive arthropod from Australia.

## 13.6 Family Trees and Evolutionary Histories

The classification of organisms arranges like with like and provides a hierarchical arrangement of groups of species, from phylum down through class, order, family, and genus. The arrangement of groups of organisms on a family tree (**phylogeny**) is intended to provide a picture of evolutionary history. Originally, family trees were based primarily on morphological features combined with biologists' collective experience with the organisms in question. Today, phylogenies are constructed using larger data sets, including genetic sequence data.

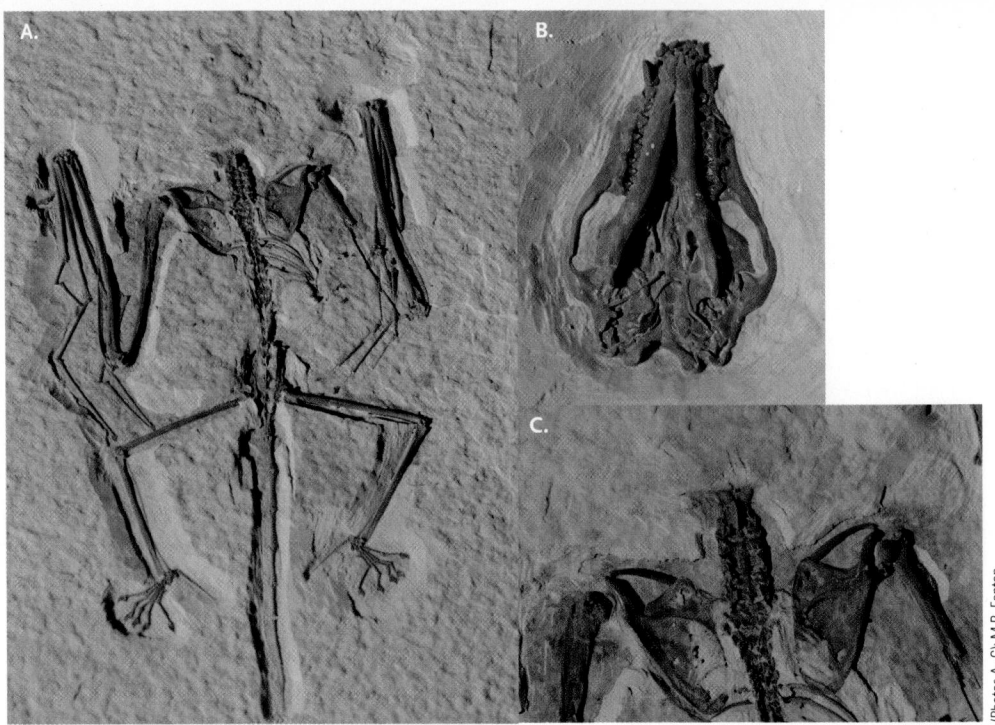

**FIGURE 13.23** The Eocene bat, *Onychonycteris finneyi*, from Wyoming. Shown are the skeleton of the body **(a)** and, by inset, the skull **(b)** and the details of the shoulder girdles **(c)**.

(Photos A–C): M.B. Fenton

A phylogeny is a picture of the evolutionary history of a group of organisms. In many cases, a phylogeny, such as the one for green algae **(Figure 13.24)**, reflects the detailed knowledge of its authors. It is supported by some mixture of qualitative and quantitative evidence. The phylogeny for green algae shows the degree of uncertainty depicted along

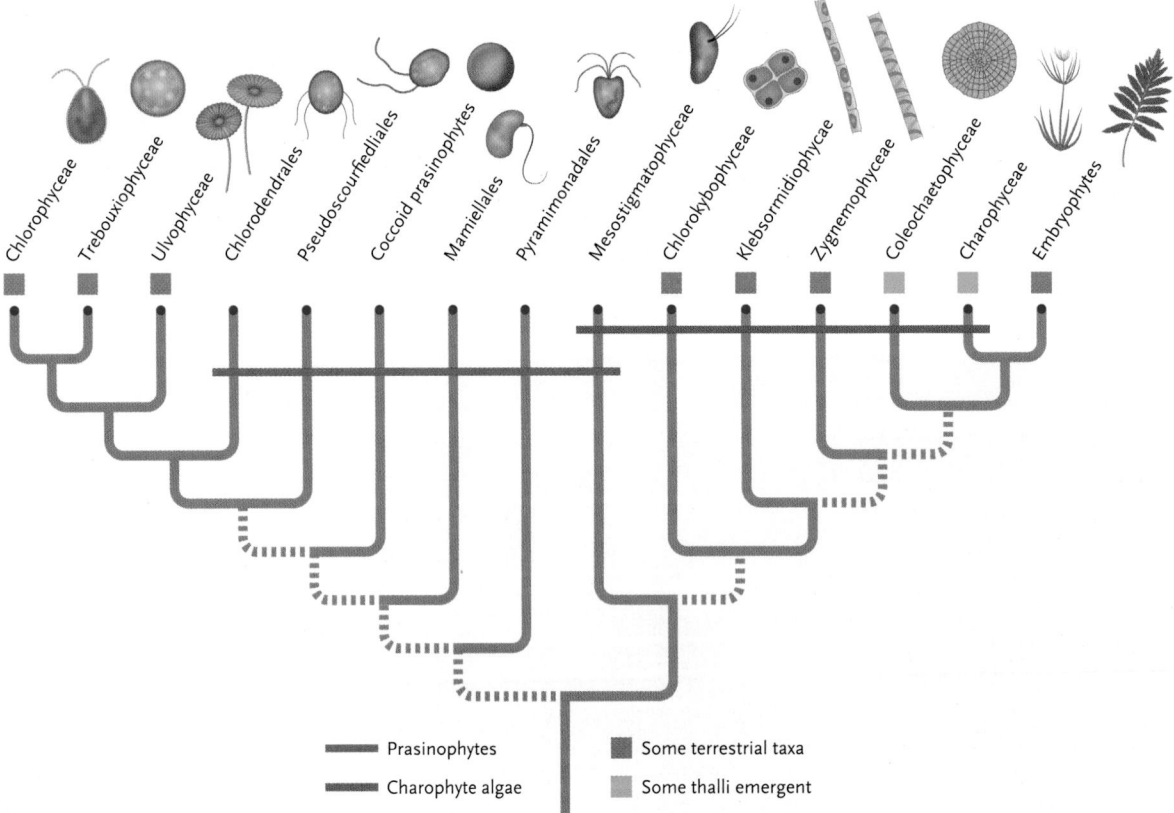

**FIGURE 13.24** DNA sequence data were used to illustrate phylogenetic relationships among major groups of green algae. Dotted lines indicate weak support from molecular data. Lineages with some terrestrial taxa are purple squares; yellow squares indicate groups with emergent undifferentiated plant bodies (known as thalli).

SOURCE: Louise A. Lewis and Richard M. McCourt, "Green algae and the origin of land plants," *American Journal of Botany* 91(10): 1535–1556. 2004. By permission of the Botanical Society of America.

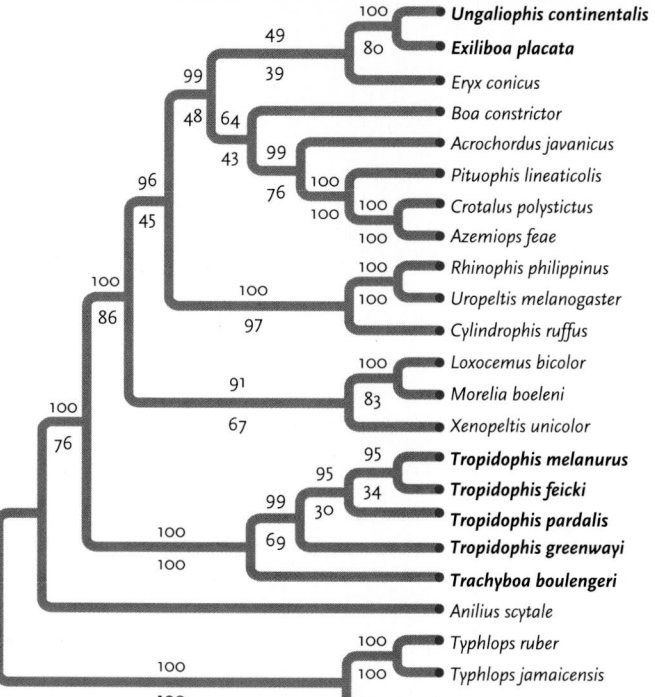

**FIGURE 13.25** Exploring the evolutionary relationship among some snakes (boas). This family tree is based on analysis of 1535 base pairs of mitochondrial DNA. Numbers above and below the lines are explained in the text. Species in bold were originally placed in the same subfamily (Tropidophiidae).

SOURCE: Reprinted from *Molecular Phylogenetics and Evolution*, Volume 25, Issue 2, Thomas P. Wilcox, Derrick J. Zwickl, Tracy A. Heath, David M. Hillis, "Phylogenetic relationships of the dwarf boas and a comparison of Bayesian and bootstrap measures of phylogenetic support," Pages 361–371, Copyright 2002, with permission from Elsevier.

with a possible evolutionary position on the family tree for a scaly green biflagellate alga (*Mesostigma*).

Other phylogenies present the results of a detailed statistical analysis of some combination of characters. In an analysis of the relationships among dwarf boas (snakes) from the New World **(Figure 13.25)**, the data came from mitochondrial DNA. The data did not support previous phylogenies that place some species in a subfamily (Tropidophiidae). Another example involves an examination of sundews—small carnivorous plants in the genus *Drosera* **(Figure 13.26)**. The phylogeny of sundews is based on analysis of a chloroplast gene (*RBCL*) and nuclear 18S ribosomal DNA sequences. Biologists depend on advanced statistical techniques to assess the credibility and reliability of phylogenies. In Figures 13.25 and 13.26, numerical values on the phylogeny report reliability (numbers above the lines) and frequency of appearance of a given branch (numbers below the lines).

In either phylogeny, one goal is to use **Occam's razor,** the simplest explanation for a phenomenon. In quantitative phylogenies, the most **parsimonious** trees are those that require the fewest changes from the ancestral to the derived conditions. This may be the most accurate reflection of the evolutionary

history of the group of organisms in question. Biologists currently use as much available data as possible when constructing phylogenies, such as evidence from morphology and behaviour to molecular genetics and physiology (see also Box 13.3).

Both types of phylogenies share one feature: they appear to be in a state of constant change. Changes in phylogenies reflect the discovery of new evidence, such as new fossils, genetic evidence, or changes of opinion. A phylogeny is really a hypothesis, presenting a view of the evolutionary relationships among organisms. Each phylogeny makes specific predictions about evolutionary relationships. These can be tested, verified, or falsified, confirming or rejecting previous views. In biology, some of the most heated discussions focus on phylogenetic representations of evolutionary history.

Phylogenies often allow identification of key selective pressures and associated key adaptations responsible for a diversification event (the emergence of new species in a group of organisms).

## STUDY BREAK

1. What features can biologists use to prepare a phylogeny?
2. What does a phylogeny tell us about the history of organisms such as sundews?
3. Why would phylogenies change?
4. What is Occam's razor, and how does it relate to phylogeny?

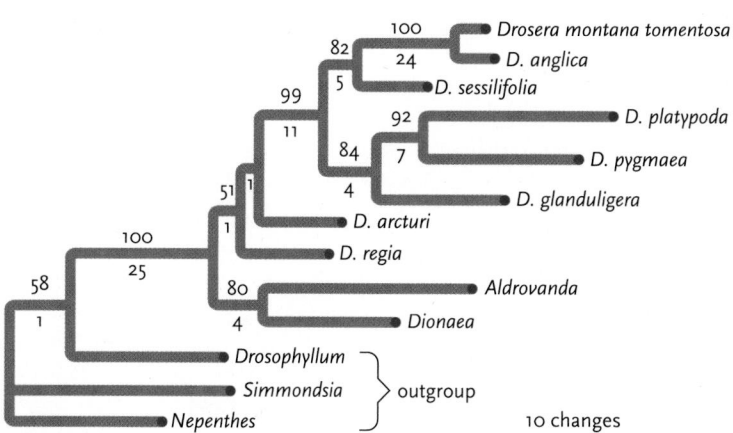

**FIGURE 13.26** Statistical analyses can be applied to many different data sets. Here an analysis of two different gene sequences shows the relationships among species of sundews (*Drosera*). The number of nucleotide substitutions is indicated by branch lengths.

SOURCE: Fernando Rivadavia, Katsuhiko Kondo, Masahiro Kato and Mitsuyasu Hasebe, "Phylogeny of the sundews, Drosera (Droseraceae), based on chloroplast rbcL and nuclear 18S ribosomal DNA Sequences," *American Journal of Botany* 90(1): 123–130. 2003. By permission of the Botanical Society of America.

BOX 13.3

# The Evolutionary History of Bats

The history of the classification and phylogeny of bats illustrates how opinions change and how additional information can generate new points of view. Two kinds of bats appear to be quite different **(Figure 1)**: the so-called flying foxes (family Pteropodidae) and the other bats (18 families).

The first fossil bats known to date (Figure 13.23) are from the Middle Eocene and are already bats. Bats are clearly mammals: they give birth to live young that are fed milk. Based on the eight species he examined, Linnaeus grouped bats among the Primates, the order that includes lemurs, monkeys, apes, and humans. By 1907, bats were generally considered to represent one order (Chiroptera) with two distinct suborders, Megachiroptera and Microchiroptera. The question of whether bats were **monophyletic** (evolved once) or **diphyletic** (evolved twice) was repeatedly considered. By 1998, the results of an analysis of a large number of morphological and genetic features convinced most biologists that bats (and therefore flight) evolved once in mammals. Bats were monophyletic, and their phylogeny **(Figure 2a)** was generally accepted. Still, not everyone agreed.

In 2004, the addition of more genetic evidence and a reconsideration of morphological data generated a new classification (Figure 2a). There were two suborders—Yinpterochiroptera and Yangochiroptera—but the bats included in them were not the same as had been in the previous suborders. Now some families of bats that had been Microchiroptera were grouped with the flying foxes (Pteropodidae) in the Yinpterochiroptera.

Although by 2012 the new classification and phylogeny of bats had been generally accepted by biologists who study bats, still not everyone agreed. The ability to fly sets bats apart from all other mammals. The extensive similarity in wing

**FIGURE 1** The flying foxes, family Pteropodidae, are quite different in facial appearance from other bats. Here a greater, short-nosed fruit bat (*Cynopterus sphinx*) **(a)** is a pteropodid, but the common big-eared bat (*Micronycteris microtis*) **(b)** is not.

(Photos A–B): M.B. Fenton

**FIGURE 13.27** Convergent and parallel evolution. Flight in chordates (birds, bats, pterosaurs) and in insects (Arthropoda) is an example of convergent evolution. Flight within chordates is an example of parallel evolution. In both phyla, the ancestors were wingless.

SOURCE: Re-drawn after Max Licht. From Fenton, M.B. 2001. *Bats*, revised edition. Facts On File, New York.

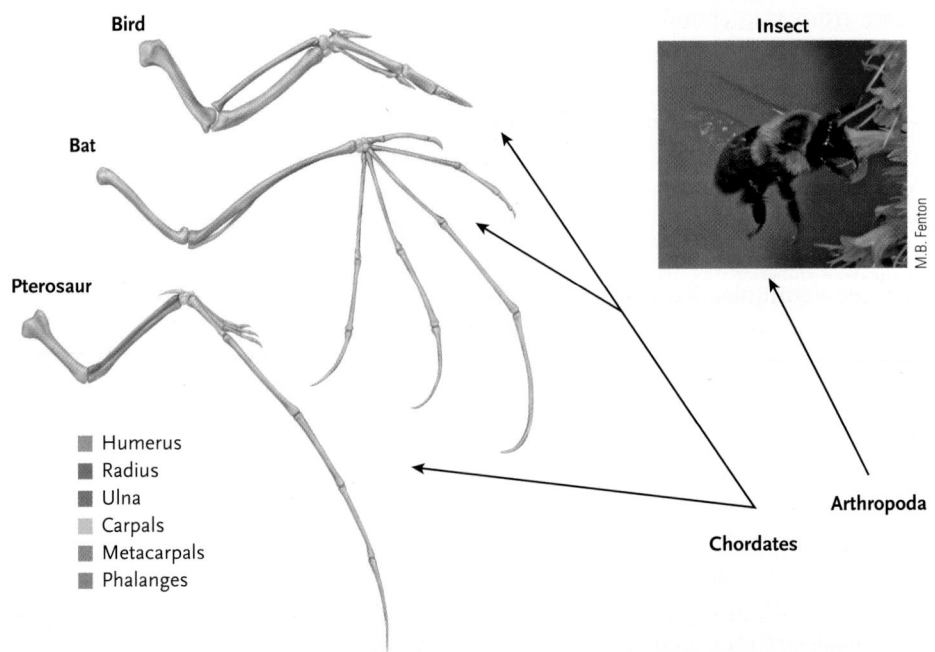

- Humerus
- Radius
- Ulna
- Carpals
- Metacarpals
- Phalanges

Bird
Bat
Pterosaur
Insect
Arthropoda
Chordates

M.B. Fenton

structures among the 1200+ living species and several fossil species of bats appears to suggest a common ancestor. The most parsimonious explanation of the evolution of bats is that flight evolved just once in this evolutionary lineage.

Echolocation, also known as biosonar, was first discovered in bats. But this behaviour is not characteristic of bats. Most pteropodids (flying foxes) do not echolocate, and there is considerable variation in echolocation behaviour and associated anatomy and physiology in the bats that do. To further complicate matters, the two dog-faced fruit bats (genus *Rousettus*) that echolocate use tongue clicks as echo-location signals. All echolocating bats produce their **echolocation** signals in their voice boxes (larynges); they are laryngeal echolocators.

The arrangement of bats in the suborders Megachiroptera and Microchiroptera recognized that these animals shared basic structures relating to flight. This classification also recognized that whereas the microchiropteran bats used laryngeal echolocation, none of the megachiropterans did. Placing bats in the suborders Yinpterochiroptera and Yangochiroptera retains the recognition of flight as a feature supporting a single evolution of bats. But echolocation is now a problem. All of the bats in the suborder Yangochiroptera are laryngeal echolocators, as are most of those placed in the Yinpterochiroptera. Among the Yinpterochiroptera, none of the pteropodids use laryngeal echolocation, but some echolocate with tongue clicks.

Did the ancestor of bats echolocate? Was echolocation lost in the lineage leading to the Pteropodidae but then regained in some *Rousettus*? Some biologists who study bats argue that having echolocation as an ancestral trait in bats means that it evolved once in this group and was lost in the pteropodids. They would view this as parsimonious, one origin for echolocation and one loss of this behaviour. Again, not everyone agrees.

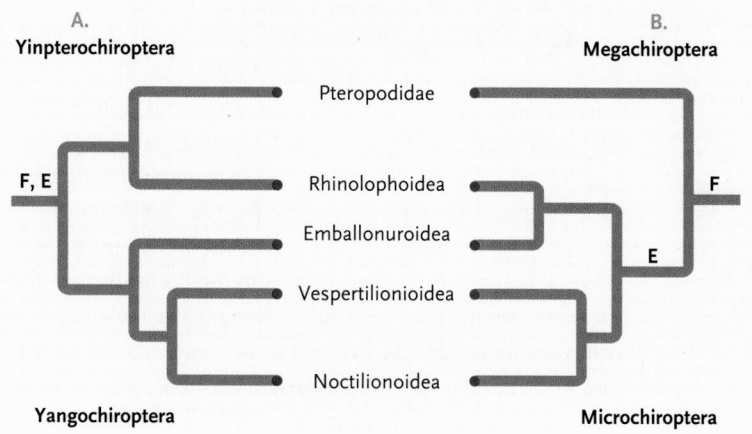

**FIGURE 2** The new **(a)** and old **(b)** classification of bats (order Chiroptera). The new suborders are Yinpterochiroptera and Yangochiroptera; the old ones were Megachiroptera and Microchiroptera. Family (Pteropodidae) and superfamilies (Rhinolophoidea, Emballonuroidea, Vespertilionoidea, Noctilionoidea) of bats are shown arrayed in new or old classification (and phylogeny). E denotes the appearance of laryngeal echolocation. F denotes the appearance of flight.

SOURCE: Based on Teeling 2009

## 13.7 Parallel and Convergent Evolution

We have seen that organisms can be very similar in appearance (e.g., Figure 12.8) and appreciate that this can challenge biologists trying to determine if resemblance reflects a close evolutionary relationship. Using animals that fly provides a revealing example. In **parallel evolution**, a feature (e.g., wings) appears independently in relatively closely related organisms (birds, bats, pterosaurs in **Figure 13.27**). In **convergent evolution**, a feature appears independently in two or more distantly related groups of organisms (insects in Figure 13.27). Phylogenetic analyses are extremely valuable for those trying to distinguish between parallel and convergent evolution. We should begin by realizing that distinguishing parallel from convergent evolution requires at least three different kinds of organisms because the determination rests partly on which organisms are more closely related. We need to consider at least three groups so that we have more than one relationship to compare. Bats, birds, and pterosaurs belong to the phylum Chordata, whereas insects belong to the phylum Arthropoda. Examples of parallel and convergent evolution can appear within any taxono-mic level—from phylum down to family or a genus (**Figure 13.28, p. 298**).

Parallel and convergent evolution have been recurring events throughout the history of life on Earth. Each instance reflects the selective forces acting in the environment at that time and the range of organisms that were present to respond to those forces.

### STUDY BREAK

1. How does parallel evolution differ from convergent evolution?
2. Why do you need at least three organisms to make the distinction?

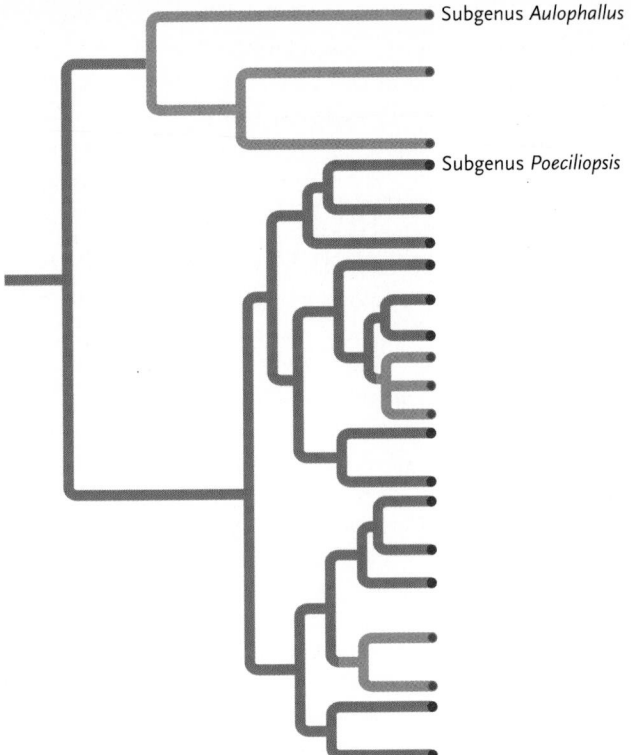

**FIGURE 13.28** Parallel and convergent evolution in fish reproduction. In this phylogenetic sketch of fish in the genus *Poeciliopsis*, red lines denote the development of placentalike structures associated with high levels of maternal investment in young. Green lines denote less maternal investment. Parallel evolution of high maternal investment occurs twice within the subgenus *Poeciliopsis*, which is convergent in this feature with species in the subgenus *Aulophallus*.

Subgenus *Aulophallus*

Subgenus *Poeciliopsis*

## 13.8 Biogeography

The biota (living organisms) differs among different parts of the world. Kangaroos are native to Australia and adjacent New Guinea but do not occur naturally elsewhere in the world. Cacti (Cactaceae) are plants that naturally occur in the New World (North, South, and Central America), whereas flowering plants called euphorbs (Euphorbiaceae) occur naturally in Africa, the New World, and Madagascar. The distribution of organisms has been complicated by human introductions (intentional and/or unintentional) from one area to another. Zebra mussels (*Dreissena polymorpha*) originally occurred in streams that drain into the Caspian and Black seas in southern Russia. Today, they can be found in many parts of the world.

In 1876, Alfred Russell Wallace created a map of **biogeographic realms**—a representation of the types of mammals, birds, plants, and other organisms that occur together in different places

on Earth **(Figure 13.29)**. Over the years, the addition of more information has changed some of the specific details, but the overall picture and pattern remain the same as the ones presented by Wallace. Each of Wallace's biogeographic realms (Figure 13.29) is characterized by a distinct biota. For terrestrial organisms, changes in the positions of land masses **(Figure 13.30)** that occurred between the Cambrian and the Middle Miocene influenced the biota of modern biogeographic realms.

Marsupials are pouched mammals (such as kangaroos, wallabies, and koalas) that we usually associate with Australia. Today, there are many species of marsupials in South America and in Australia and Papua New Guinea. This pattern of distribution is easier to understand when you know that South America and Australia were both once part of Gondwanaland, a supercontinent that included Antarctica. The discovery of an Eocene fossil marsupial (*Djarthia murgonensis*) in Antarctica was to be expected because of what we know about how the continents were once connected. In a phylogeny of marsupials, *Djarthia* is closely associated with Australian rather than South American genera.

**Wallace's line** in the East Indies is one of the sharpest biogeographic boundaries known to biologists. The line runs along the straits between Bali and Lombok, a distance of about 32 km. Wallace's line extends to the north and east, passing between Borneo and Sulawesi, and then south of the Philippines. On the Bali side of Wallace's line, the fauna is Asiatic, including tigers, elephants, rhinos, and orangutans. On the Lombok side, the fauna is Australian, including kangaroos, cuscus, and other marsupials. This dichotomy extends to plants and to animals other than mammals, including flying animals (bats, birds, and insects). Wallace surmised that New Guinea, Australia, and Lombok had been connected in the past **(Figure 13.31, p. 300)**, at a time when they were much more isolated from the Bali side than they are today.

Biogeographic data provide an indication of which organisms have filled what opportunities in different parts of the world. This perspective helps us better understand selective forces and their impact on organisms. An

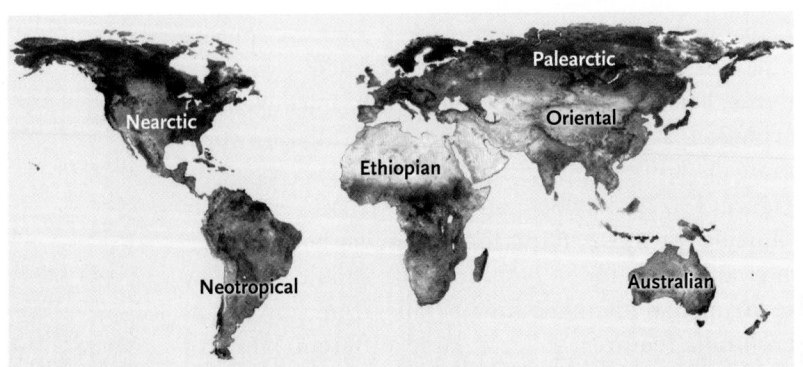

**FIGURE 13.29** Wallace's biogeographic realms.

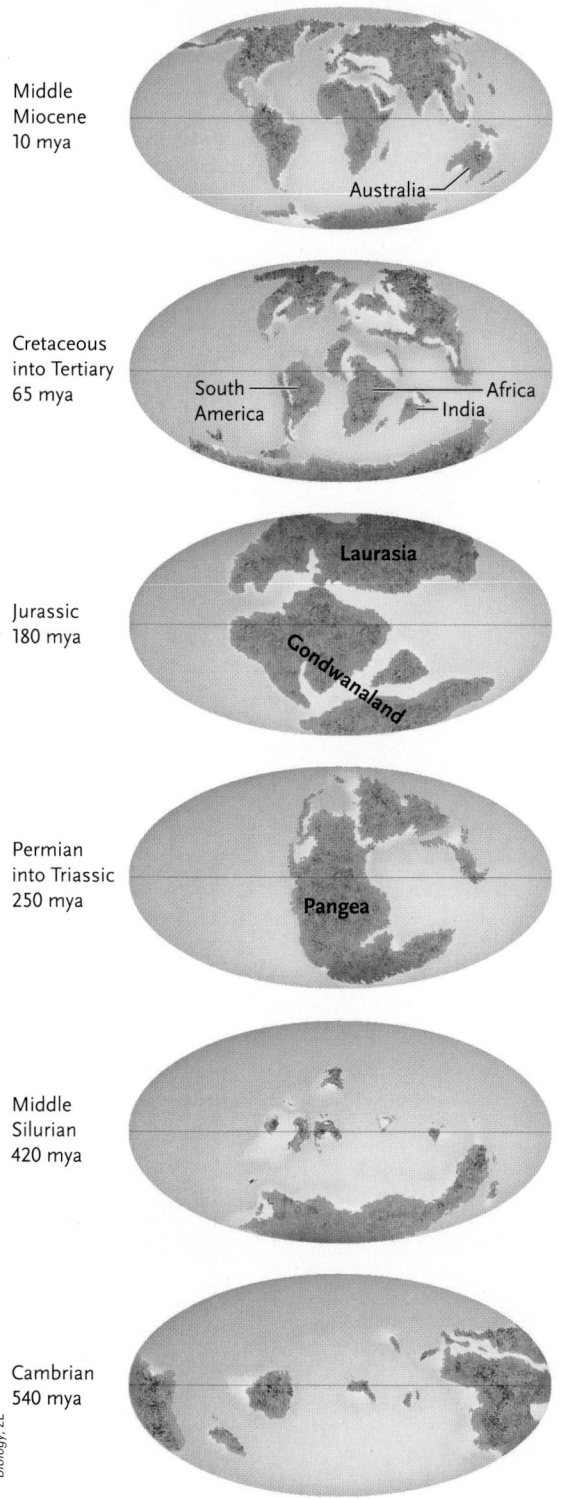

Middle
Miocene
10 mya

Australia

Cretaceous
into Tertiary
65 mya

South
America

Africa

India

Jurassic
180 mya

Laurasia

Gondwanaland

Permian
into Triassic
250 mya

Pangea

Middle
Silurian
420 mya

Cambrian
540 mya

*Biology, 2E*

**FIGURE 13.30** Long-term changes in the positions of continents from the Cambrian to the Middle Miocene. The supercontinent Pangaea formed in the Triassic and then separated into Gondwanaland and Laurasia. Africa and India separated from Gondwanaland, opening the South Atlantic and Indian oceans. About 55 million years ago, Australia separated from Antarctica. Movements of the continents changed the shapes and sizes of oceans.

excellent example is the similarities in appearances among different animals, from wormlike ones (see Figure 12.8) to molelike ones (**Figure 13.32, p. 300**). Why are they similar in appearance? Are they related, or do similar selective pressures consistently lead to similar evolutionary solutions? Using biogeographic and phylogenetic data, biologists can better inter-pret patterns of distribution and similarity among organisms.

Fundamental to parallel and convergent evolution is the reality that the organisms of an area adapt to and diversify in local conditions. So if the habitat is dry, plants from different evolutionary backgrounds adapt to it. If the lifestyle is that of fossorial mammals, molelike animals emerge, whether of marsupial, golden-mole, or mole stock.

## STUDY BREAK

1. Name Wallace's biogeographic regions.
2. Why would fossil marsupials be expected in Antarctica?

## 13.9  Evolution and Fundamental Changes

Evolutionary history was profoundly affected by fundamental changes in the defining characteristics of organisms' lives or their lifestyles. We consider access to energy (food and oxygen) to moving onto land, taking to the air, and reversals. These alterations changed the selection regimes in which organisms lived and operated. They were game changers that began as novelty radiations.

### Energy: Oxygen and Food

Conversion of solar to chemical energy by photosynthesis was an early fundamental change in lifestyle (**Figure 13.33, p. 301**). It changed the composition of the atmosphere and had many implications for the availability of food. At the first appearance of photosynthetic organisms in the early Proterozoic eon, the conditions were anoxic. There was no oxygen in the atmosphere. About 2.6 billion years ago, levels of oxygen in Earth's atmosphere approached 1%, well below the 20% that prevails today. This level first appeared between 750 and 635 million years ago, marking the appearance of "oxic" conditions. Chemicals such as molybdenum and vanadium react with oxygen, so levels of these elements in marine deposits indicate changes in the prevalence of oxic conditions over time.

The change from anoxic to oxic conditions was fundamental to the diversification of animals, especially metazoans. The early diversification of animal life coincided with adaptive radiations in other groups of organisms, such as plants and fungi. Early diversification also implies the importance of interactions among organisms that became increasingly complex as diversity expanded. In a sense, this is similar to the diversification of life on the Hawaiian Islands as more and more colonizing species arrived there after the islands first formed.

**FIGURE 13.31** Wallace's line.

SOURCE: "Map of Sunda and Sahul" by Maximilian Dörrbecker (Chumwa) - Self made, using this map for the background. Licensed under Creative Commons Attribution-Share Alike 3.0 via Wikimedia Commons - http://commons.wikimedia .org/wiki/File:Map_of_Sunda_and_Sahul .png#mediaviewer/File:Map_of_Sunda _and_Sahul.png

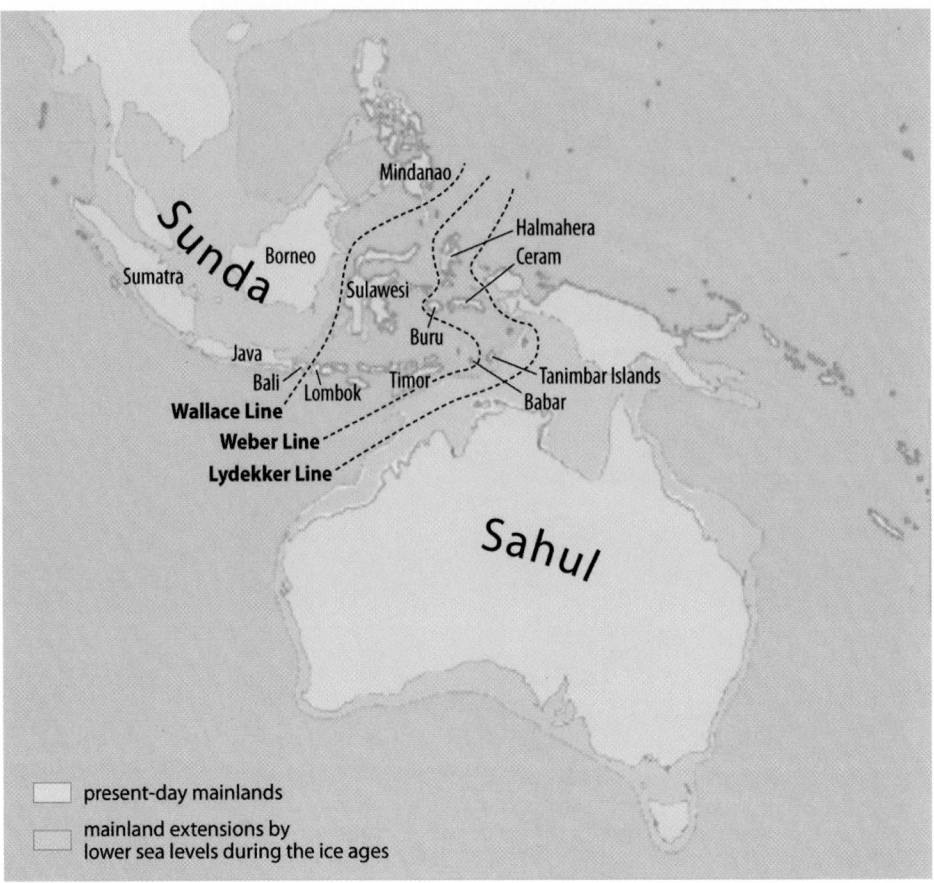

Photosynthesis appears to have originated in bacteria. Five modern lineages of bacteria have the capacity for photosynthesis: specifically, green non-sulphur bacteria, cyanobacteria, green sulphur bacteria, and purple bacteria **(Figure 13.34, p. 302)**. Remember from Chapter 5 that there are three photosynthetic pathways in land plants: $C_3$, $C_4$, and CAM. The $C_4$ and CAM pathways suppress photorespiratory activity in chloroplasts. Both are derived from the

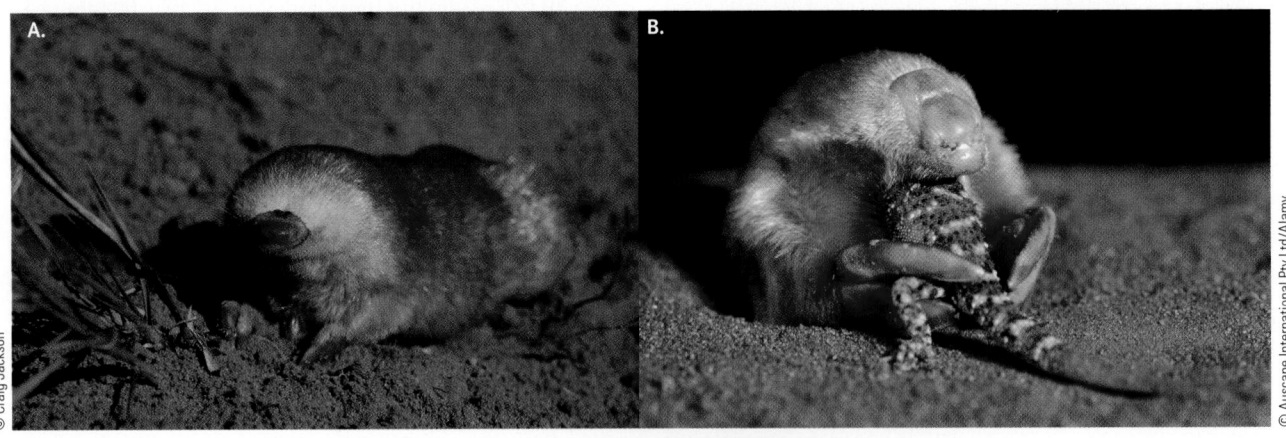

**FIGURE 13.32** Despite their similarities, Juliana's golden-mole *(Neamblysomus julianae)* **(a)** is a placental mammal in the order Afrosoricida, whereas the southern marsupial mole *(Notoryctes typhlops)* **(b)** is the sole member of the marsupial order Notoryctemorphia. A European mole *(Talpa europea* – order Insectivora) **(c)** represents a third evolutionary lineage of "moles."

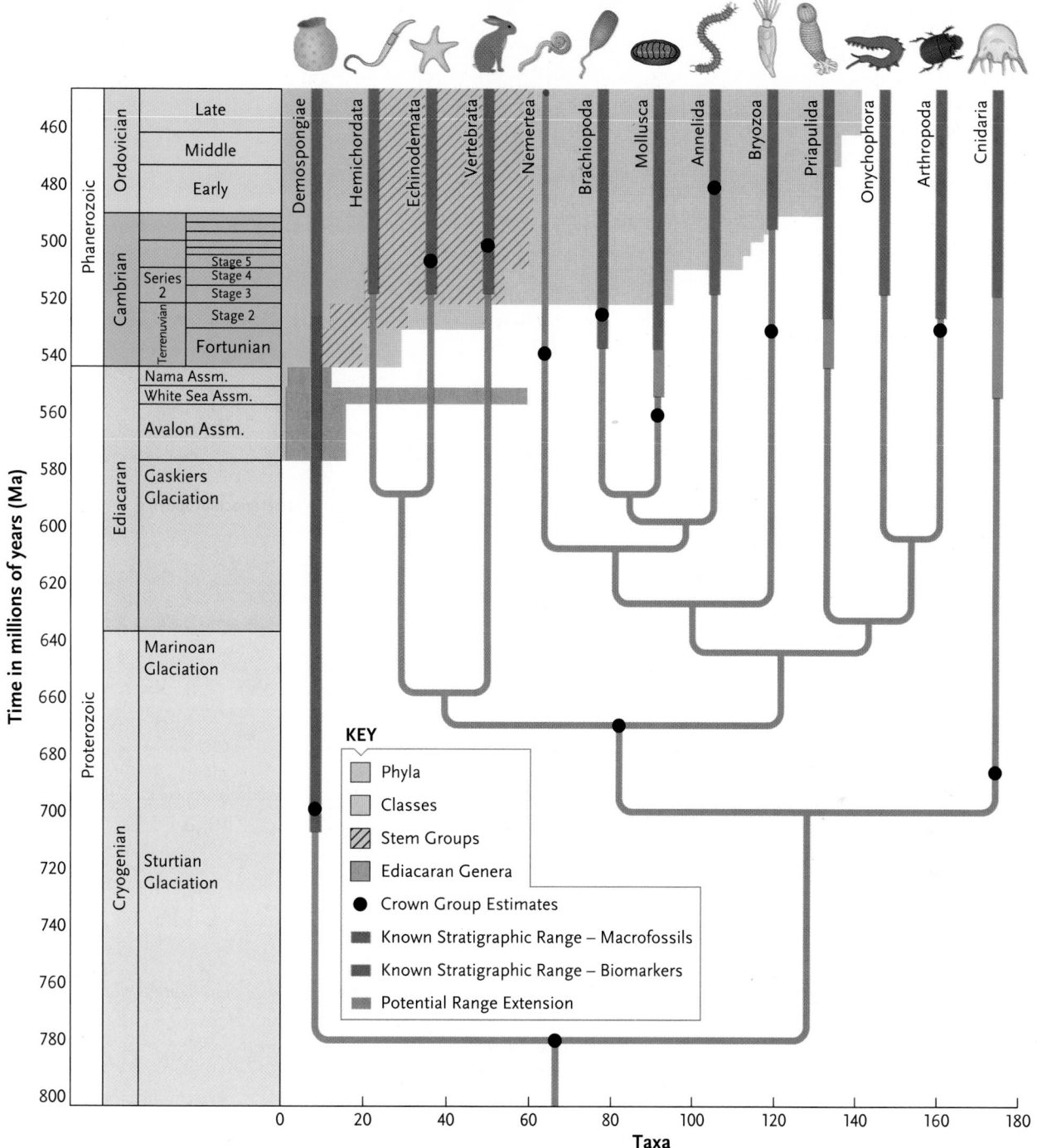

**FIGURE 13.33** Estimates of the diversification of 13 lineages of animals from the Proterozoic to the early Phanerozoic. Yellow and blue show the known fossil history of the animals shown; hatching identifies stem or ancestral lineages. Grey represents Ediacaran macroscopic fossils. Most lineages appear in the Cambrian, well after oxygen is thought to have reached modern levels.

SOURCE: From Erwin, D.H., M. Laflamme, S.M. Tweedt, E.A. Sperling, D. Pisani and K.J. Peterson. 2011. "The Cambrian conundrum: early divergence and later ecological success in the early history of animals," *Science* 334:1091–1097. Reprinted with permission from AAAS.

$C_3$ pathway. $C_4$ photosynthesis has arisen more than 45 times in 19 families of angiosperms (flowering plants). CAM photosynthesis has appeared in more than 30 families of angiosperms. When the same process arises multiple times, usually, existing pathways have been reorganized. There are few examples of new essential components to the process of photosynthesis.

In addition to available atmospheric oxygen, the appearance of photosynthesis provided opportunities for other organisms to exploit. Cyanobacteria were exploited as chloroplasts through endosymbiosis. This allowed eukaryotes to acquire the capacity for photosynthesis (see Chapter 4). Taking advantage of other organisms' abilities for photosynthesis appears in nudibranch molluscs such

**FIGURE 13.34** A phylogeny for gene sequences common to all lineages of photosynthetic lineages **(a)**. Left and right trees differ slightly. Also shown are four bacteriochlorophyll molecules **(b)**.

SOURCE: From Jin Xiong, William M. Fischer, Kazuhito Inoue, Masaaki Nakahara, Carl E. Bauer, "Molecular Evidence for the Early Evolution of Photosynthesis," *Science* 8 September 2000: Vol. 289 no. 5485 pp. 1724–1730. Reprinted with permission from AAAS.

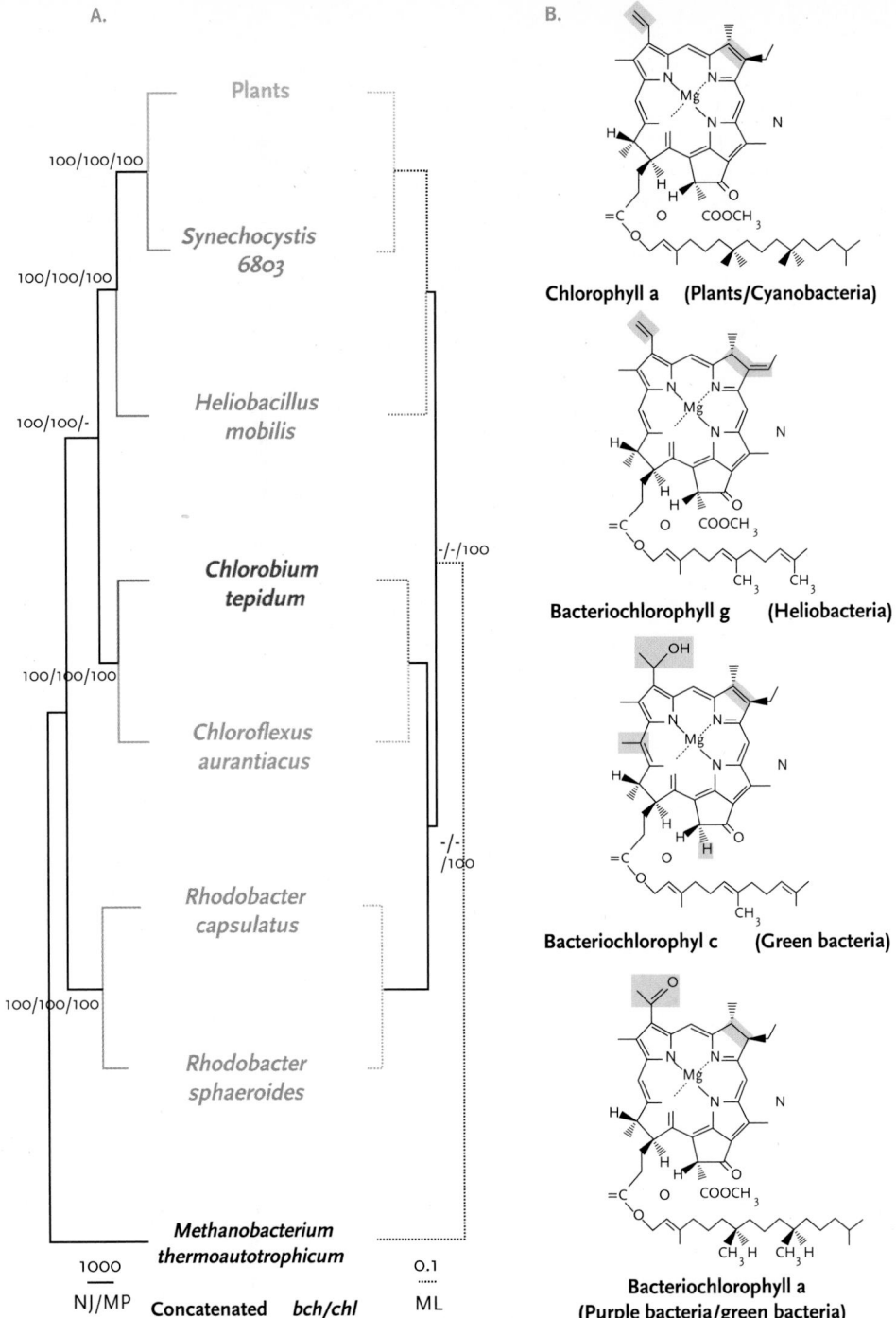

A.

Plants

100/100/100

Synechocystis 6803

100/100/100

Heliobacillus mobilis

100/100/-

Chlorobium tepidum

100/100/100

Chloroflexus aurantiacus

Rhodobacter capsulatus

100/100/100

Rhodobacter sphaeroides

Methanobacterium thermoautotrophicum

1000

NJ/MP    Concatenated    bch/chl

-/-/100

-/-/100

0.1

ML

B.

**Chlorophyll a** (Plants/Cyanobacteria)

**Bacteriochlorophyll g** (Heliobacteria)

**Bacteriochlorophyl c** (Green bacteria)

**Bacteriochlorophyll a** (Purple bacteria/green bacteria)

as sea slugs (*Elysia chlorotica*). These sea slugs remove chloroplasts from algae and use them to make solar panels that can provide fuel for several months. Of special importance is the fact that the sea slugs have the genes required to control the choloroplasts they take—yet another example of lateral gene transfer. More variations on this theme involve other nudibranch molluscs using symbiotic single-celled plants (zooxanthellae). Other instances involve some sponges (Porifera), corals (Cnidaria), flatworms (Acoelomorpha), and ascidians (Chordata) that exploit some variant of unicellular algae or cyanobacteria as independent photosynthetic operations.

Can animals be photosynthetic in other ways? In some cases, the answer is "yes." When raised at temperatures around 8°C, some green-coloured aphids (*Acyrthosiphon pisum*) capture light energy. In what may be an ancient variation of photosynthesis, green aphids use captured energy to transfer electrons into mitochondria, and there they can synthesize molecules of ATP. Carotenoid pigments are involved in this process. Genes that produce carotenoids are found in chloroplasts and in cyanobacteria, as well as in aphids. This appears to be yet another example of lateral gene transfer, presumably from bacteria.

In other cases, animals moved from eating mainly other animals to eating photosynthetic organisms, usually algae and plants. This move down the trophic food chain gave them access to larger volumes and diversity of food species. This change coincides with adaptive radiations or diversifications, as shown in herbivores from dinosaurs to mammals and arthropods to bony fish.

## Going Ashore

Atmospheric oxygen was an initial requirement for the appearance of eukaryote land organisms. This condition appears to have been met sometime between 750 and 635 million years ago. The earliest fossil land plants, eoembryophytes, date from about 476 million years ago, the Middle Ordovician. There is a discrepancy of about 50 million years between the appearance of spores assigned to land plants and the presence of the remains of other plant parts (e.g., stems and roots or megafossils). The earliest plant megafossils are known from the Middle Silurian and include some clubmosses Lycopodiaceae. By the Devonian, both ferns (Pteridophyta) and horsetails (Equisetopsida) also occur as fossils **(Figure 13.35)**.

The first apparently terrestrial animals were myriapods, millipedelike animals from the Silurian. Here "apparently" is appropriate because the fossils do not unequivocally indicate that the animals had been terrestrial. By the Devonian, some terrestrial insects appear as fossils, Fossilized footprints suggest that by the Middle Devonian, some early tetrapods (four-legged animals) were capable of considerable mobility on land. Some of these animals mark the transition from lobe-finned fish to amphibians (see Chapter 19).

Life on land presents several challenges relative to life in water. Water is about 1000 times denser than air and about 50 times more viscous. Although the partial pressures of oxygen are the same in air and in water (where it is dissolved), there is about 30 times more oxygen in air than there is dissolved in water. Carbon dioxide is about 35 times more soluble in water than is oxygen. Sound travels much faster in air (343 m.s$^{-1}$) than in water (1519 m.s$^{-1}$ in salt water, 1486 m.s$^2$ in fresh water). This and the greater numbers of aquatic organisms make water a much noisier place to live than land. Collectively, these differences mean that organisms living in water are well supported (higher density of water), experience higher costs of movement (higher viscosity in water), have less ready access to oxygen (more oxygen in the atmosphere than dissolved in water), and experience a quieter environment (because sound moves more slowly).

Organisms that move from living in water to living in air must solve several problems. They need ways to support their body weight, and they need to adopt different approaches to locomotion and gaseous exchange (breathing). They also have to minimize water loss, develop systems for internal transport of materials, and adopt different strategies for getting rid of metabolic end products (such as ammonia). Movement onto land also requires different approaches to reproduction. To take advantage of information conveyed by sound, organisms living on land require different ways to detect vibrations in air.

Some fossil lobe-finned fishes probably ventured onto land when the pools in which they were living dried up. Here movements onto land allowed the fishes to stay in the water. Other cases, for instance, modern eel catfish (*Channallabes apus*), go ashore to hunt and catch insect

**FIGURE 13.35 (a)** A modern clubmoss (*Dendrolycopodium*), **(b)** a horsetail (*Equisetum*), and **(c)** an ostrich fern (*Matteuccia struthiopteris*).

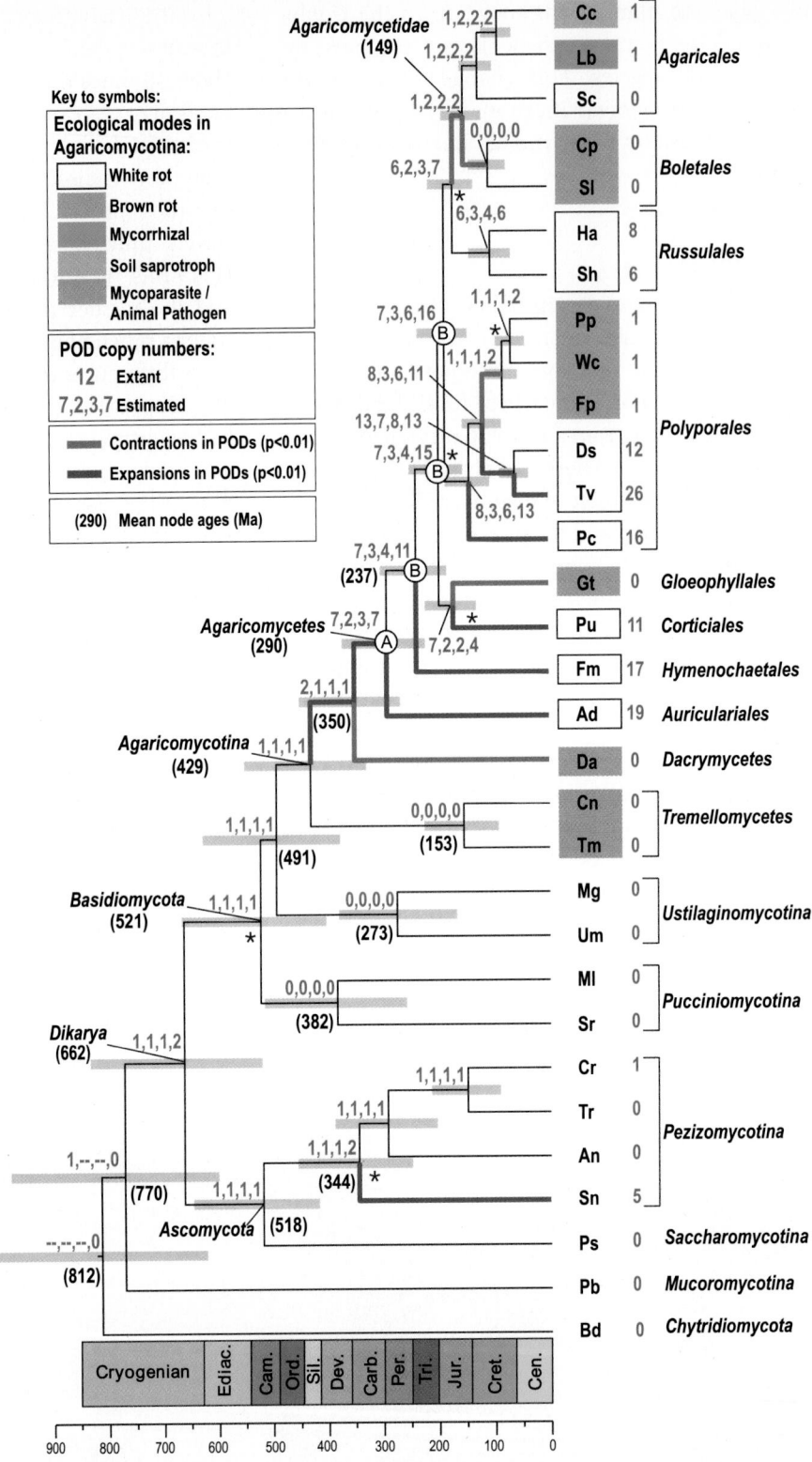

**FIGURE 13.36** This chronogram was reconstructed from a 26-gene data set in which light blue bars are 95% most likely node ages in millions of years Before Present. At red nodes, numbers separated by commas are fungal class II perodidazes (PODs) gene copies. Node A is an ancestor of Agaricomycetes, whereas node B identifies those retaining the white rot mechanism. Note recurring appearances of some ecological modes among Agaricomycotina.

SOURCE: From Dimitrios Floudas, Manfred Binder, Robert Riley, Kerrie Barry, Robert A. Blanchette, Bernard Henrissat, Angel T. Martínez, Robert Otillar, Joseph W. Spatafora, Jagjit S. Yadav, Andrea Aerts, Isabelle Benoit, Alex Boyd, Alexis Carlson, Alex Copeland, Pedro M. Coutinho, Ronald P. de Vries, Patricia Ferreira, Keisha Findley, Brian Foster, Jill Gaskell, Dylan Glotzer, Paweł Górecki, Joseph Heitman, Cedar Hesse, Chiaki Hori, Kiyohiko Igarashi, Joel A. Jurgens, Nathan Kallen, Phil Kersten, Annegret et al., "The Paleozoic Origin of Enzymatic Lignin Decomposition Reconstructed from 31 Fungal Genomes," *Science* 29 June 2012: Vol. 336 no. 6089 pp. 1715–1719. Reprinted with permission from AAAS.

prey. This amphibious existence may give eel catfish the benefits of living in both air and water. Other animals on the border between fish and tetrapods were more completely terrestrial, as suggested by their forelimbs and hindlimbs and feet, as well as their teeth and bites.

The appearance of woody plants and forests was a further enrichment of the movement onto land. This

fundamental change coincided with increased diversification, in part associated with lignin (Box 13.1 and **Figure 13.36**). The fossil record and analysis with molecular clocks suggest that fungi ancestral to the Agaricomycetes (a class of fungi) developed enzymes, peroxidases, for degrading lignin. The main lineage leads to fungi that cause "white rot," which degrades all components of plant cell walls. Brown rot—fungi that do not degrade lignin—also occur in the Agaricomycete lineage. In addition to providing multidimensional habitats for other species, the appearance of woody plants provided opportunities for decomposers.

## Into the Air

Plants have adapted to move through air. Some accomplish this with airborne spores, pollen, and seeds. The first fossil evidence of land plants is fossilized spores, which predate fossils of leaves, stems, and roots. The discrepancy in the timing of the appearance of plant spores versus megafossils (see above) reflects this situation. Many plants have structures that facilitate the wind-blown dispersal of seeds **(Figure 13.37)**.

**FIGURE 13.37** Seeds of dandelion *(Taraxicum officinale)* specialized for wind dispersal.

Another aspect of plants taking to the air is terrestrial plants that reach for the sun by climbing on surfaces, including other plants **(Figure 13.38)**. The climbing approach involves much less investment in support structures, and plants use different approaches to climbing. A climbing habit occurs in at least one genus of ferns (*Lygodium*), as well as in species in four families of monocotyledons. Furthermore, 23 families of dicotyledons are also climbers. This situation provides another array of examples of parallel and convergent evolution.

Charles Darwin is one of many biologists who has studied climbing plants—another example of the diversity of his curiosity. The selective advantage of gaining access to sunlight without investing heavily in structures such as trunks and stems is reflected clearly by climbing plants. A climbing lifestyle that involves vines and tendrils provides access to light and vertical spaces without investment in the infrastructure (stems, trunks, roosts) most terrestrial plants use to extend their vertical reach.

Flight (see Chapter 22) is another way to take to the air and has evolved in four evolutionary lineages of

**FIGURE 13.38** Although some plants climb by entwining their stems around the support **(a)**, others use tendrils **(b)** to reach out for support.

animals: insects (phylum Arthropoda), pterosaurs, birds, and bats (phylum Chordata; Figure 13.27). The diversity of species in these groups (known: insects, birds, and bats; suspected: pterosaurs) indicates that flight represents another novelty radiation. Flying animals tend to be small in size (body mass), although one group of pterosaurs was exceptional. Pterosaurs such as *Quetzalcoatlus northropi* (see Figure 21.46) had wing spans of ~12 m and body masses of ~85 kg, making them much larger than the largest known flying birds (3.4 m, 11 kg) or bats (2-m wingspan, 1.5 kg), let alone insects (0.8-m wing span of some fossil insects).

Flight allows more ready access to food sources compared to animals that do not fly. The range of foods used by bats, birds, and insects includes plants (leaves, stems, flowers, nectar, pollen) and animals across the spectrum from small to large. Flight gives animals relative immunity from some predators and access to nest or roosting sites not reachable by animals that do not fly **(Figure 13.39)**.

Many other animals, from insects to fish, amphibians, reptiles, and mammals, use gliding to move efficiently between locations and to evade predators. Some squid use water-propelled force to launch them into the air, in a manner reminiscent of flying fishes. The repeated appearance of gliding in different lineages of animals speaks to the advantages that it confers.

## Reversals

Life in the water offers many advantages to both plants and animals. Therefore, we should expect that organisms whose immediate ancestors were terrestrial would return to life in the water. Water lilies, whales, and penguins are three examples of aquatic organisms that evolved from terrestrial ancestors. Return to water has been a recurring theme in the diversification of life. The list of aquatic animals that evolved from terrestrial animals includes nemertine worms, myriapods and arachnids, molluscs, insects, and vertebrates. At least 25,000 species of living insects are aquatic for at least part of their life cycle. Usually, aquatic insects live in fresh water, but a few, perhaps hundreds of species, are marine. But some things do not typically reverse. As we will see in Chapter 23 for animals large enough to have gaseous exchange systems, breathing atmospheric oxygen is less expensive than extracting dissolved oxygen from water. Therefore, it is not surprising that animals that returned to the water from a terrestrial existence retained lungs and lunglike structures rather than returning to gills.

Loss of the ability to fly is another recurring theme among insects and birds (but not pterosaurs and bats). Flightlessness often evolves in birds and/or insects living on remote oceanic islands. In these situations, the loss of flight could be explained by the absence of predators—and therefore a need for flight as a defence mechanism—combined with strong prevailing winds that could present a risk that a flying animal would be blown away. Absence of predators also could explain loss of flight by birds such as penguins (Figure 13.39), which retain the ability to "fly" under water, which may or may not reduce their risk of predation.

Perhaps more interesting is the presence of large, flightless birds (both living and fossil) on the land masses that once formed Gondwanaland. South America, Africa, Madagascar, Australia, and New Zealand all have or had large flightless birds (emus, ostriches, elephant birds, cassowaries, rheas, and moas). Elephant birds are recently extinct, their disappearances probably coinciding with the arrival of humans on Madagascar and New Zealand.

Reversals suggest that the set of characteristics associated with one way of life—such as living on land—do not preclude exploiting another—such as living in water. Indeed, they may allow another variation on the theme of novelty radiations and are reflected by organisms such as marine mammals, marine reptiles, aquatic insects, and aquatic vascular plants (to pick just a few). Parasites may have simpler body plans than their

M.B. Fenton

**FIGURE 13.39** A penguin, an example of a flightless bird that uses its wings to fly under water.

free-living relatives. Compare tapeworms and planarians, for example (see Chapter 19).

## STUDY BREAK

1. Name three ways that access to food provides examples of parallel and convergent evolution.
2. How are plants and animals similar in their adaptations to land?
3. What advantages would flight confer on an animal?
4. How does natural selection work in "reverse" evolution?
5. How does photosynthesis vary among organisms?

## 13.10 Species That Have Not Changed

From the information presented so far in this chapter, it is easy to have the impression that Earth's biota is in a state of constant change and flux. Natural selection appears to inexorably lead species to change, and this may be a prevailing feature of life. But some organisms alive today are, as far as we can tell, virtually unchanged from millions of years ago.

Stromatolites **(Figure 13.40)** are one example. The first stromatolites appear in rocks that are about 3.5 billion years old. Stromatolites are layered rocks formed when cyanobacteria bind particles of sediment into thin sheets. Today, there are stromatolites along the shore in Shark Bay in Western Australia, and these 2000-year-old structures appear to be virtually identical to those from 3 billion years ago.

Today, clubmosses (Figure 13.35a) are small, sprawling plants with needlelike leaves and sporangia at the bases of the leaves. In the Devonian, forests of 40 m tall lycopsids (Figure 13.18a) were dominant features in the landscape, and much of our supplies of coal date come from the preserved carbon remains of these forests. In the Silurian, the clubmosses diverged from other early plants, the ferns and horsetails, as well as more modern vascular plants.

Ginkgoes (*Ginkgo biloba*; **Figure 13.41, p. 308)** are common ornamental trees in many temperate parts of the world. These deciduous trees can be large. They have diffuse branching and turn bright yellow in autumn. Male trees are preferred for decorative plantings because the female trees produce foul-smelling seeds. The earliest fossil ginkgoes (Ginkgoales) date from the Early Permian (~280 million years ago) and were widespread in the Cretaceous, with some being generally similar to the modern *G. biloba*—an example of a living fossil.

Horseshoe crabs (*Limulus* spp.; **Figure 13.42, p. 308)**, of the class Merostomata, belong to the arthropod subphylum Chelicerata. Although we call them crabs, they belong to their own, ancient class of arthropods, separate from other animals we know as crabs. Fossil horseshoe crabs from 350 million years ago look very much like the living species. Today, the eggs of horseshoe crabs in Delaware Bay are an important food source for Red Knots (*Calidris canutus*)—a migrating shore bird—and the survival of both species is in question.

These examples demonstrate how some species have endured over millions and hundreds of million years with little change. These examples suggest that some recipes for success are persistent and ensure survival.

## STUDY BREAK

1. Why do some organisms show little evidence of change?
2. What does this tell us about natural selection?

Inc/Shutterstock.com

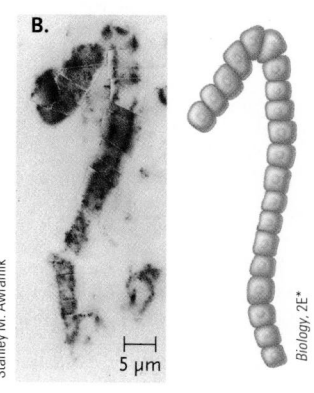

Stanley M. Awramik

5 μm

Biology, 2E*

**FIGURE 13.40** Stromatolites **(a)** exposed at low tide in Shark Bay in Western Australia. These mounds consist of mineral deposits made by photosynthetic cyanobacteria. These stromatolites are about 2000 years old and closely resemble fossil stromatolites from 3 billion years ago. Cyanobacteria form stromatolites, and fossil and living representatives are shown in **(b).** The fossil in (b) is from a 3.5 billion-year-old rock.

FIGURE 13.41 The typical leaves of a ginkgo tree.

FIGURE 13.42 A horseshoe crab, *Limulus polyphemus*.

## PUTTING IT IN PERSPECTIVE

Selection and evolution are the processes responsible for the diversity of life on Earth. The examples presented in this chapter are intended to provide a picture of the breadth of organisms, situations, and processes. The material provides examples of how selection operates on variation and the consequences for subsequent populations. The larger scale impact of evolutionary change is illustrated using a variety of examples in relation to family trees and phylogenies as well as the impact of specific changes relating to food and energy, moving onto land, or moving into the water.

## KEY CONCEPTS REVIEW AND QUESTIONS

### 13.1 Charles Robert Darwin and Alfred Russel Wallace

Charles Darwin's theory of evolution by natural selection profoundly influenced biology. Alfred Wallace's contributions to the theory of evolution were also important. Others, such as Aristotle, George-Louis Leclerc, and Jean Baptiste de Lamarck, also wrote about the history of life.

1. How do natural selection and variation relate to evolution? What is the importance of heritable variations? How does resistance to organophosphide insecticides in Australian sheep blowflies bring selection, variation, evolution, fitness, and success together?

2. What are the main features distinguishing the view of evolution presented by Darwin and Wallace from those of Lamarck and other early scholars of the natural world?

3. Why is aging of an individual not evolution?

### 13.2 Selection, Change, and Evolution

Natural selection will cause populations with heritable variations to change over time, which could lead to evolution of new species. Selection pressures could come from abiotic and biotic factors. Abiotic factors could include climate or pesticide application. Biotic factors could include interactions between predators and prey, plants and pollinator, host and parasite, or competition for resources.

4. What is 2,4-D? How do some grasshoppers use 2,4-D? How does this example illustrate natural selection and change in a population?

5. What is pollination? Why is pollination a good system in which biologists can explore natural selection, change, and evolution?

6. What is parasitism? What is a parasite? How could parasites and parasitism be used to illustrate variation and natural selection? Are Australian sheep blowflies relevant to this example?

## 13.3 Sexual Selection

Differences in physical appearance are used in choosing potential mates, and the mate choice affects the genetic composition of a population of species. Sexual selection occurs among animals from many evolutionary backgrounds. There are many examples of sexual dimorphism that appear to have resulted from sexual selection.

## 13.4 Time, Temperature, and Extinction

The history of Earth is presented in relative and absolute ages by the geological time scale. Relative and absolute dating are combined with chronological analyses of DNA to identify when evolutionary lines separated. Isotopic analysis supports how temperatures have also changed through geologic time. Extinctions have occurred repeatedly.

7. In the context of evolutionary history, what is the importance of using relative and absolute time in combination with time of divergence and fossils? How can this situation enrich our knowledge of evolutionary history?

## 13.5 Fossils and the History of Life

Differences in physical appearance are used in choosing potential mates, and the mate choice affects the genetic composition of a population of species. Sexual selection occurs among animals from many evolutionary backgrounds. There are many examples of sexual dimorphism that appear to have resulted from sexual selection.

## 13.6 Family Trees and Evolutionary Histories

Phylogenies provide a picture of evolutionary history in a group of organisms. They can be developed by using a mixture of qualitative and quantitative information and can provide insight into selective pressures and associated adaptations.

8. What is the difference between a family tree and a phylogeny? Why is it important for evolutionary biologists to use large databases and appropriate statistical analyses when developing phylogenies? How does the development of phylogenies relate to timing of divergences?

## 13.7 Parallel and Convergent Evolution

Organisms may possess similar features as a result of parallel or convergent evolution. Phylogenetic analyses are useful when trying to determine if the similar features are a result of parallel and convergent evolution.

9. What is the significance of parallel and convergent evolution? How do these topics relate to how an organism appears (looks)? How does this topic connect to biogeography?

## 13.8 Biogeography

Biogeographic realms are characterized by distinct biota. Biota in modern biogeographical realms have been influenced by the movement of land masses in prehistorical times. Biogreographic data help us better understand selection forces and impacts to organisms.

## 13.9 Evolution and Fundamental Changes

Fundamental changes in the characteristics of organisms' lives or lifestyles have strongly influenced evolutionary history. These changes include the occurrence of photosynthesis, which allowed solar energy to be converted into chemical energy, and the development of oxic conditions, which led to diversification of other organisms, trophic food chain changes, and other changes. Other fundamental changes include movement of organisms ashore or into the air or reversals such as returning to water or losing the ability to fly.

10. Why do fundamental changes affect evolutionary history? Consider this question from the standpoint of access to food and energy, to moving from aquatic to terrestrial environments, to moving into the air, or returning to the water (for example).

## 13.10 Species That Have Not Changed

Some modern organisms appear to be virtually unchanged from millions of years ago. Examples include ginkgo trees and horseshoe crabs.

11. Why would some organisms show no change over millions of years?

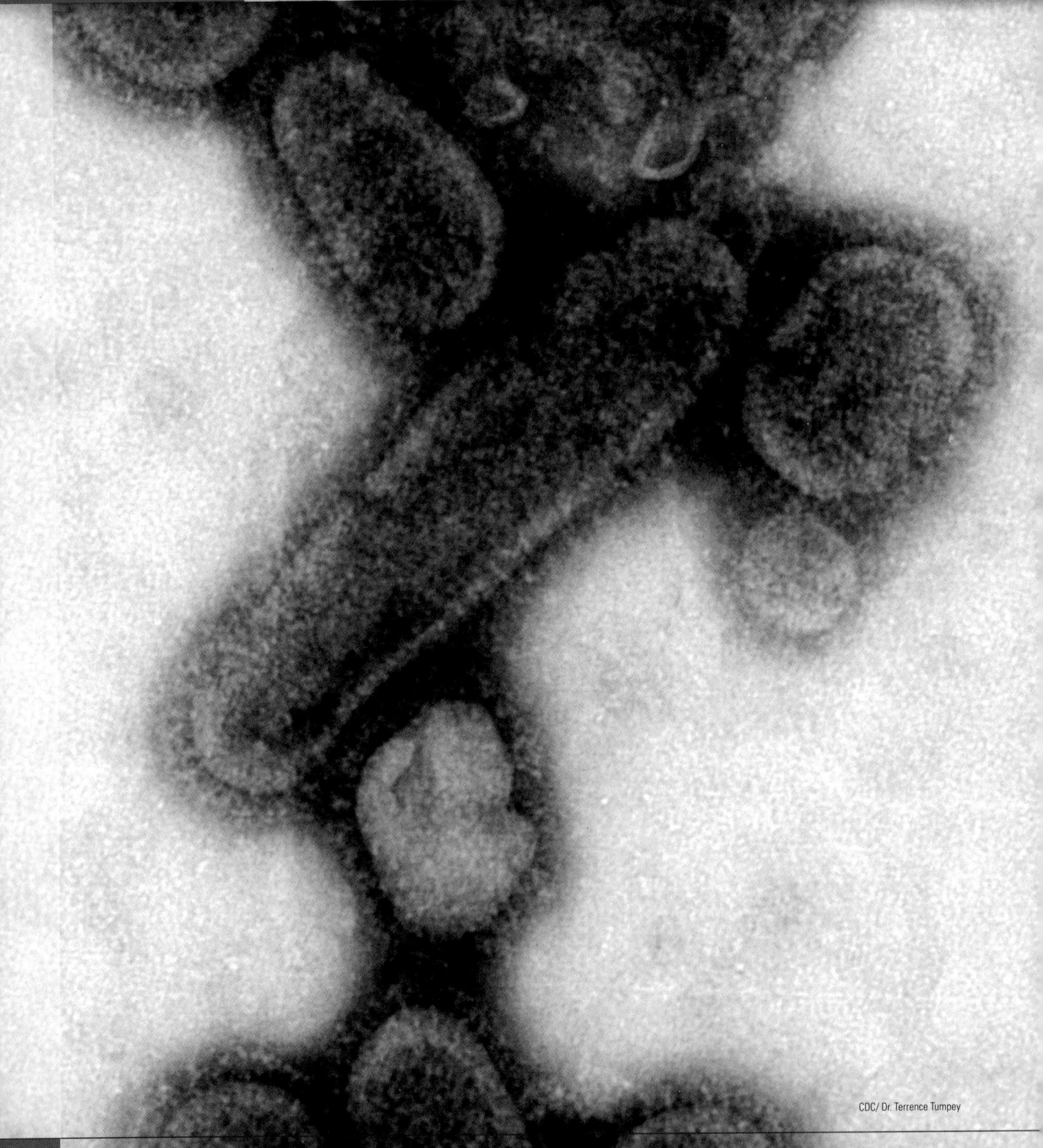

CDC/ Dr. Terrence Tumpey

# CHAPTER OUTLINE

## WHY IT MATTERS

In the spring of 1918, as World War I raged across France and Belgium, a more insidious battle was beginning. In January, what might have been the first cases of the 1918 viral influenza, or flu, pandemic were reported in the United States in rural Kansas. In March, over 500 American soldiers stationed at Fort Riley, Kansas, to prepare for overseas deployment were ill. The pandemic seemed to be slowing as the spring progressed, but in the summer of 1918, a second wave of the virus erupted in Europe. Thousands of soldiers were incapacitated by the flu. With the large numbers of soldiers travelling and interacting in training and staging zones, the virus spread rapidly. Worldwide, it is estimated that between 50 and 100 million people died during that influenza outbreak. In Canada, the number of deaths is estimated at 50,000. Indigenous peoples living in Canada were hit especially hard. The rate of infection among First Nations peoples was similar to that observed across the country, but they were more likely to perish from the infection. An interesting observation of the 1918 influenza was that it affected healthy young adults to a much greater extent than most influenza outbreaks do. A normal influenza outbreak has its greatest effect on children and the elderly—people with weaker immune systems. Scientists continue to find data extending the debate as to whether the 1918 influenza virus was special or whether health factors, such as previous influenza exposures, led to the high level of fatalities.

Viruses are perhaps the most effective parasites in the biosphere. Although not technically alive, they are able to take over the molecular machinery of their host cell and use it for reproduction. Once inside a cell, some viruses are even able to insert their genome into their host's chromosomes, allowing them to take up permanent molecular residence. With the development of medical antibiotics in the middle of the 20th century and a corresponding increase in our ability to fight bacterial diseases, viruses have taken the lead in causing serious illnesses. We do not need to look far to see the effect of viruses on modern society. The influenza virus seems to be launching a new attack on the human population each year. Part media hype, part fact, viruses that make up the broad influenza group undergo mutations at a very rapid rate. Mutations in the genetic makeup of influenza viruses cause changes to the three-dimensional structure of the proteins that coat the virus. Because the antibodies made by our immune system (see Chapter 26) use the three-dimensional shape of proteins to identify intruders, these new versions of the influenza virus are not immediately identified and can rapidly spread in our cells.

The high mutation rate of influenza makes it difficult for pharmaceutical companies to produce effective vaccines. Typically, the vaccines produced today are effective only for 1 to 2 years before the number of mutations renders the virus unrecognizable to our immune system.

Amazingly, influenza viruses can infect and reproduce in a number of different types of animal hosts. Some of the influenza strains that have proven most dangerous to humans seem to have originated in other animals. Starting in a different host can lead to different selective pressures during infection cycles. As you might imagine, some viral characteristics might help it when it infects ducks or pigs, whereas other characteristics make it a good parasite in humans. This makes it difficult for researchers to predict how dangerous specific influenza viruses will be. It can get even more unpredictable when single cells are infected by more than one subtype of the influenza virus. When this occurs, different virus genes may be combined, resulting in unusual new strains of the virus **(Figure 14.1a, p. 312)**. This increases the potential for a dangerous outbreak of influenza because when different viral characteristics become mixed together, our immune system may not recognize the virus. In terms of human health, a dangerous influenza virus would be highly transmissible, infect the lower respiratory track, and survive outside the body for longer than a less dangerous subtype.

Because we cannot easily stop the production of the influenza virus once someone begins to show symptoms, we need to take precautions to avoid getting the virus in the first place. The two most effective prophylactic measures are vaccination against seasonal influenza and improved sanitary protocols (e.g., increased hand washing, coughing and sneezing into tissues or the crook of your arm, isolating yourself from others when ill). With most viruses, the best offence is a good defence **(Figure 14.1b)**.

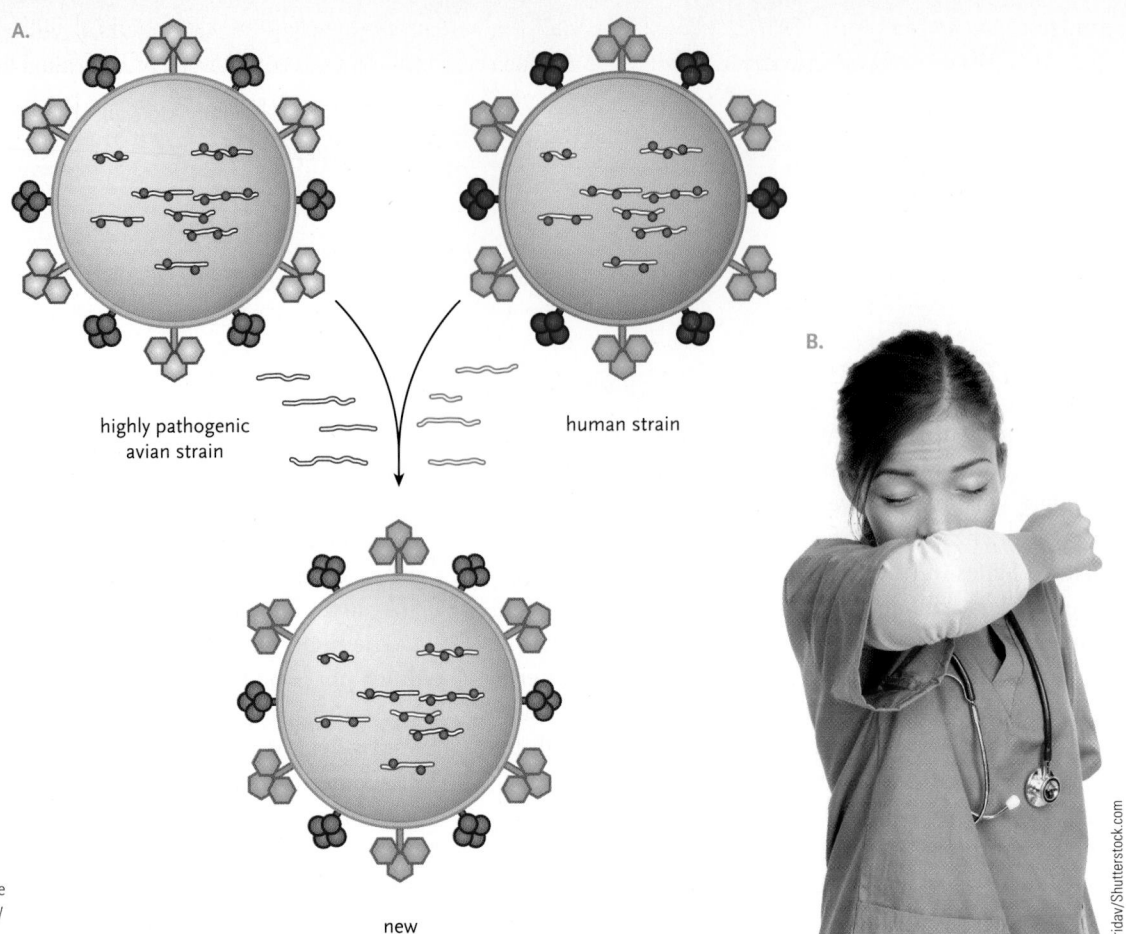

**FIGURE 14.1** The influenza virus mutates at a very fast rate **(a)**. To protect ourselves, we need to practise good hygiene **(b)** and get the flu vaccine yearly.

SOURCE: Jiver, http://en .wikipedia.org/wiki/ File:Influenza_geneticshift .svg. This file is licensed under the Creative Com- mons Attribution-Share Alike 3.0 Unported license, http:// creativecommons.org/ licenses/by-sa/3.0/deed.en

A.

highly pathogenic avian strain

human strain

B.

new highly pathogenic human strain

Maridav/Shutterstock.com

In this chapter, we will examine the structure, function, and replication of viruses. Looking at examples of viruses that infect bacteria, plants, and animals, we will see that they function and replicate in similar ways. Although we do not think of viruses as living organisms, it is fascinating that they can mutate and evolve over time. Because of this ability, some scientists suggest that viruses were a precursor to living cells, whereas other scientists think they evolved from bacteria that lost their ability to live independently. We will also investigate the structure of their genomes. Although they encode amino acid sequences in a fashion similar to that of the host cells, viral genomes can be made of DNA or RNA molecules. Finally, we will discuss ways in which we can protect ourselves, our pets, and even our crop plants from viral diseases.

## 14.1 What Are Viruses?

It is not easy to define viruses. The first question that comes up is: Are they alive? Instinctively, we answer no because they are not cells, and according to the cell theory, the cell is the basic unit of life. But if we look more closely at the list of requirements that are necessary for something to be defined as alive, viruses meet many of them.

One key factor used to decide whether something is alive is the ability to evolve over time. Viruses definitely have this capacity. Due to the nature of their genomes, viruses accumulate many mutations and thus evolve quickly. As mentioned in the opening of the chapter, the influenza virus changes so rapidly that vaccinations against the virus are normally useful only for a maximum of 2 years. Viruses are also composed of biomolecules and can reproduce. However, there are three key characteristics of life that they fail to meet: they do not perform metabolic reactions, they generally do not respond to their environment, and, although they can reproduce, they require the resources and machinery of another organism's living cells to do so. This leaves viruses somewhere between alive and inanimate. They are definitely more alive than a rock but somewhat less alive than a bacterium. Because viruses contain the genomic material needed to make copies of themselves, some scientists believe that viruses should be added to the tree of life.

Regardless of whether we classify viruses as living organisms, we have to appreciate their ability to be the most effective parasites in the biosphere. It is estimated that there are between 5 and 10 billion virus particles in a single litre of sea water (similar to the number of humans living on Earth). Such a huge number is hard to imagine, but it gets worse. When you catch a cold, the infected cells of your respiratory pathway can produce more than 100 trillion virus particles per day before you begin to feel better. Just imagine how many virus particles would be produced during a cold or influenza outbreak. You may feel like washing your hands now!

Where did viruses come from? Are viruses a primitive "pre-living" organism? If we look at the simple structure of viruses, they could be compared to the **protocells** or **protobionts** that are thought to have been an evolutionary stepping stone to the first cells on Earth. We think that in the step before being alive, protobionts possessed a form of genetic material surrounded by a coating of protein or lipid materials. Viruses certainly fit these criteria. Perhaps in our human-centric view, we are not looking at viruses in the appropriate time frame. Although many scientists agree that a protobiont origin of cells is possible, we also know that the time required for random replication of protobionts would be much longer than for living cells. Because these primitive versions of cells did not contain the enzymes needed to produce the molecules from which they were built, they had to wait for necessary molecules to be made by non-cellular mechanisms. This would have been a slow process when compared to cellular metabolism. Perhaps viruses were slowly self-replicating protobionts that began to be outcompeted by the first living cells. The viruses we have today could be those that evolved quickly enough to hitch a ride with the living cells.

There are also other theories about the origin of viruses. One theory suggests that mobile genetic elements such as **transposons** gained the ability not only to move around in the genome but also to leave the cell. One could imagine a piece of DNA containing a transposon leaving a cell by exocytosis (see Chapter 3) or when the cell died. The genetic material would remain in a vesicle that resembles the plasma membrane of the cell it just left. Fusing to a new cell, the vesicle could release the transposon into the new "host," where it could integrate into the genome. Viruses could have evolved from this simple system as they entered and exited cellular genomes and picked up extra genes along the way. This is called the **progressive theory** because it describes a process by which the present-day virus progressively emerged from a simpler structure.

The **regressive theory** suggests that viruses evolved from simple bacteria that lost the ability to survive on their own. When organisms go through this transition, we say they have become **obligate parasites**—they can only survive in their hosts. Such bacteria exist today. They must infect host cells to complete their life cycle. If a bacterium that was an obligate parasite lost more of its genome because it was not needed, perhaps it could ultimately end up as a modern virus.

None of these theories will completely answer the question of where viruses came from. Different viruses likely arose independently by different mechanisms. Perhaps all three of the above theories are correct, and each describes the origin of specific types of viruses. A true answer may never be possible, but we can develop hypotheses and test them experimentally to see if our assumptions are correct. We know that viruses are obligate parasites and that they can evolve over time. We also know that scientists can construct functional viruses in a lab. We can chemically synthesize a complete viral genome using deoxynucleotides. We can produce viral coat proteins using either an in vitro translation system or the bacteria *E. coli* (see Chapter 11). We can then mix the genome and coat proteins together in a test tube to get a functional, infectious virus. So far, this is the closest we have come to creating life from scratch. We have created a pseudo-living being: a functional replica of the tobacco mosaic virus **(Figure 14.2)**. Although not a hazard to humans, the tobacco mosaic virus infects a number of plant species, such as tobacco, tomatoes, bell peppers, and some ornamental flowers. Infected plants develop characteristic yellow patches on their leaves.

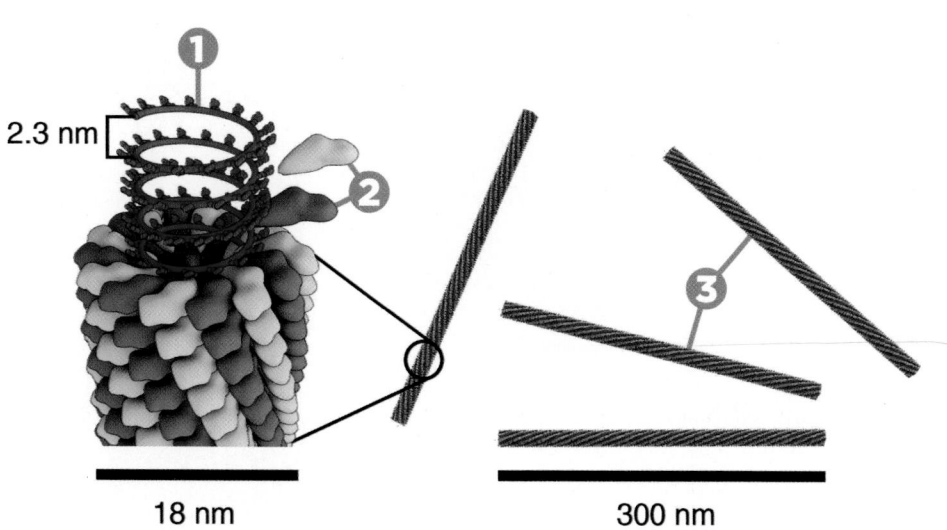

**FIGURE 14.2** Scientists are able to make copies of the tobacco mosaic virus by synthesizing its RNA genome and mixing it with coat proteins produced using *E. coli* and recombinant DNA technology. Once mixed together, the coat proteins (2) wrap around the RNA genome (1) and form a mature virus particle (3).

SOURCE: Thomas Splettstoesser, http://en.wikipedia.org/wiki/File:TMV_structure_full.png. This file is licensed under the Creative Commons Attribution-Share Alike 3.0 Unported license, http://creativecommons.org/licenses/by-sa/3.0/deed.en

2.3 nm

18 nm

300 nm

1. Define the term *obligate parasite*.
2. Why do viruses fit within the definition of an obligate parasite?

## 14.2 Structure and Function of Viruses

Despite being structurally simple, when compared to cells, different types of viruses have different shapes and structural components that help them infect their hosts and disperse to new individuals **(Figure 14.3)**. As we saw with basic cell structure, the genome of a virus is packaged inside a protective covering (Figure 14.3). This reduces the chance of the genetic material becoming damaged as the virus particle travels from one host cell to another. The outer shell of a virus is composed of protein and in some cases a layer of membranelike material that it picks up as it exits its host cell. Regardless of the structure of the virus, remember it is an obligate parasite and relies on the transcriptional and translational machinery of the host cell to make its protein coat. Even the viral genome must be synthesized by the host cell.

When considering the structure and function of cells, we often state that the information stored in the nucleus, or nucleoid in bacteria and archaea, directs the shape and structure of the cell because it contains the genetic blueprint. This statement is doubly true for viruses. Not only does the viral genome encode the proteins needed to make the shell or **capsid** that surrounds the genome, but the proteins of the capsid are also generally packed tightly around the genomic material. Thus, a larger genome dictates a larger virus. It is thought that natural selection would weed out mutations to the genome that affect its size if it negatively affected the virus's ability to infect host cells. Similarly, mutations affecting the shape of the capsid proteins may limit their effectiveness in packaging the genome and thus make the virus less successful.

Although not all viruses have membrane envelopes **(Figure 14.3c)**, those that do require them for the infection process. Envelopes are more common in animal viruses and may have evolved to help hide the virus from the animal immune system. Because the virus exits the host cell through the host–cell's plasma membrane, the viral envelope will be very similar to that of the host. Thus, antibody responses in the animal host may not detect the viral particle as being of foreign origin (see Chapter 26). However, viruses that have a membrane envelope are less tolerant to desiccation or drying out. This seems to have been an evolutionary trade-off, with membrane-enclosed viruses being more effective at eluding animal defences yet less resistant to environmental damage.

1. Draw and label a crude sketch of a typical virus and a membrane-bound virus.
2. What is the most important function of the capsid?

## 14.3 The Viral Hereditary Molecule: DNA or RNA?

Like the other forms of life that we recognize on Earth, the genetic information of viruses is stored using nucleotide polymers. They use the same genetic code we see in bacteria, archaea, and eukaryotes (Figure 10.10). Just like we see in our cells, their genes encode information that is translated into proteins using three base codons. However, although the three domains of life all store

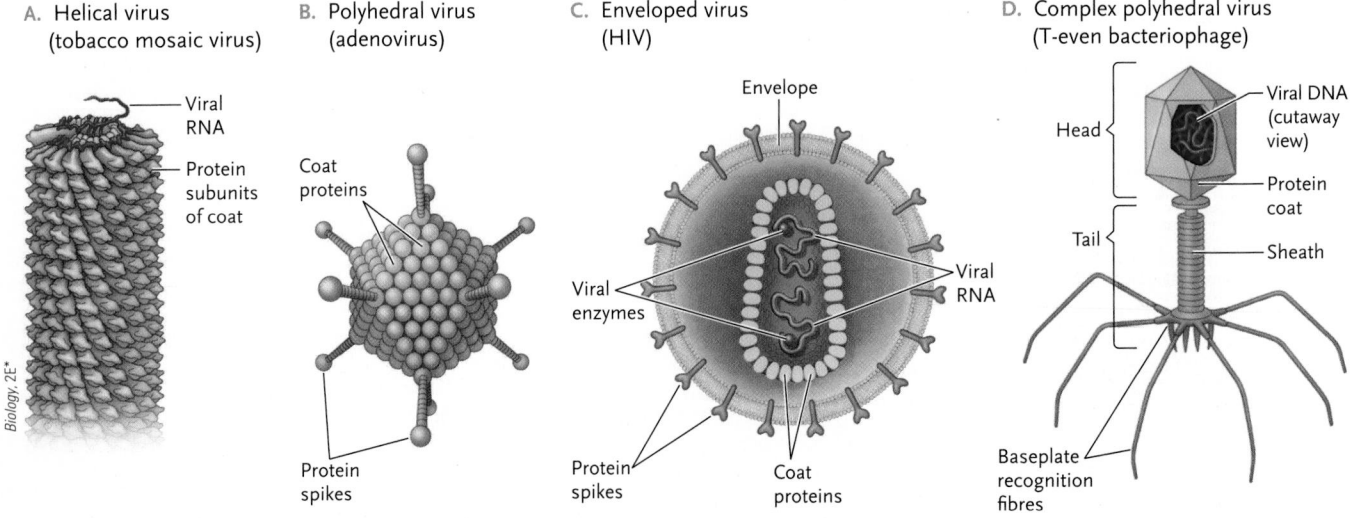

A. Helical virus
(tobacco mosaic virus)
— Viral RNA
— Protein subunits of coat

B. Polyhedral virus
(adenovirus)
Coat proteins
Protein spikes

C. Enveloped virus
(HIV)
Envelope
Viral enzymes
Viral RNA
Protein spikes
Coat proteins

D. Complex polyhedral virus
(T-even bacteriophage)
Head
— Viral DNA (cutaway view)
— Protein coat
Tail
— Sheath
Baseplate recognition fibres

*Biology, 2E\**

**FIGURE 14.3** Viral structures are species dependent. The strange structures have evolved to securely package the viral genome and aid the virus's attack on its host cell type.

their genetic material as DNA, the genomes of viruses can be in the form of either DNA or RNA (Figure 14.3). The type of genome varies depending on the type of virus but is always the same within a family of viruses. In fact, this is one of the key characters used to identify and classify viruses.

For example, the influenza virus and human immunodeficiency virus (HIV) have RNA genomes. They are both therefore classified as RNA viruses. Their genomes function slightly differently, however. When an influenza virus enters a cell, its coat opens up and the **viral RNA (vRNA)** is transported to the nucleus. Once in the nucleus, the vRNA is copied by a viral enzyme, made by the host cell, called an **RNA-dependent RNA polymerase**. As the name of this enzyme suggests, it uses RNA as a template to make RNA copies. Interestingly, the influenza virus genome is a "negative" RNA strand. This means that it does not directly encode the necessary proteins; instead, it needs to be copied to provide the positive strand. Thus, the negative strand acts as a template. Once the host generates the positive vRNA, the information is used to generate new viral proteins and new viral genomes.

On the other hand, the HIV is what we call a **retrovirus**. Its RNA genome is composed of two positive RNA strands. When it enters a host cell, a viral protein called **reverse transcriptase** becomes active. It "reverse transcribes" the positive RNA genome into a DNA molecule called a **complementary DNA (cDNA)**. As the copying occurs, the RNA strand is destroyed, leaving a single-stranded cDNA molecule. The reverse transcriptase then completes the copy of the genome by duplicating the cDNA to yield a double-stranded DNA molecule. This double-stranded cDNA is transported to the nucleus, where it can become fully incorporated into the DNA of a host cell chromosome. This is a fundamental difference from what we see in normal RNA viruses that only use the host cell machinery to replicate. The fact that the retrovirus inserts its genome into the host's means that it is there for the life of the cell and the life of its descendants. This makes curing people of retroviruses extremely challenging. From this point onward, the viral DNA is copied and transcribed along with the host chromosome.

Viruses that use DNA as their genomic material can be generally divided into two groups: group 1 viruses have a double-stranded DNA molecule as their genome. This is similar to what we see in bacteria, archaea, and eukaryotes, but generally the viral chromosomes are much smaller. **Bacteriophages**, viruses that infect bacteria, fall into this category. However, the group is very broad and contains many viruses that use many different bacterial species as hosts. It is often hard to believe that even marine cyanobacteria have specialized viral parasites.

Group 2 DNA viruses are a little different. Their genomes are made up of **single-stranded DNA (ssDNA)**. Their genomes can be linear or circular ssDNA molecules. Although it is beginning to sound redundant, the group 2 DNA viruses are also incredibly diverse. They seem to be found almost everywhere we look: in sea water, soil samples, and even extreme habitats such as glacial snow packs. The most amazing aspect of the group 2 viruses, and viruses in general, is how little we know about them.

## STUDY BREAK

1. Why is HIV called a retrovirus?
2. What is the difference between group 1 and group 2 DNA viruses?

## 14.4 Viral Reproduction

Like viruses themselves, viral reproduction is highly varied and depends largely on the type of genome used by the virus. However, all viruses have one common step: infection of a host cell. The virus cannot perform its own metabolism; thus, the replication of the genome and production of the protein coat must be done by the host cell after the virus takes over.

### Viruses Infect Host Cells by Binding to Their Surface and Then Moving Inside

Viruses use similar mechanisms to infect cells, whether they are bacterial, plant, or animal cells. However, some viruses are quite specific about the type of organism and even cell they are able to infect. We will look at specific examples below, but the general steps of infection are the same. Virus particles move through the environment due to random events. Having no metabolism, they are not self-propelled. Their movement can range from the simple movement of molecules, called Brownian motion, to the aerosol droplets forced into the air when a person coughs or sneezes. A virus particle detects a suitable host cell based on the proteins present on the cell's surface. In a positive interaction, the three-dimensional shape of proteins making up the virus coat interacts with matching proteins on the cell surface. As an example, we can look at how HIV infects a **T cell (Figure 14.4, p. 316)**. T cells are one of the types of white blood cells that play a role in our immune system (see Chapter 26). As with all cells, human T cells have specific proteins that emerge from the surface of the plasma membrane. These **protein epitopes** allow cell recognition and cell–cell interactions, a critical aspect of both the immune system and viral infection. One of HIV's coat proteins interacts with a T cell surface protein called CD4

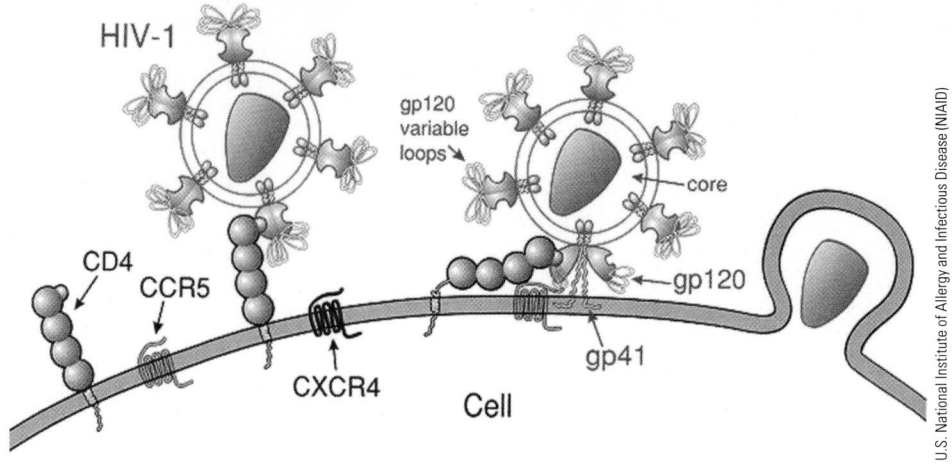

**FIGURE 14.4** An HIV particle approaches and then binds to cell surface proteins of a human T cell. Once bound to the surface, the virus can enter the cell and release its genome.

U.S. National Institute of Allergy and Infectious Disease (NIAID)

via a lock and key–like mechanism. When the CD4 protein binds to the HIV glycoprotein, it triggers a mechanism that allows the virus to merge with the T cell plasma membrane and release its RNA genome into the white blood cell (Figure 14.4). In a fascinating twist on evolution, some people have mutated versions of the CD4 protein on their T cells. As a result, they are immune to infection by the current versions of HIV.

This is a common theme. Viral coat proteins link up with protein epitopes on cell surfaces. The interaction attaches the virus to the cell. Either an opening in the plasma membrane can form, or the binding can trigger endocytosis (see Chapter 3). What happens next and its effect on the host cell or organism depend a lot on the type of virus and, more specifically, the type of viral genome.

## Bacterial Viruses Have a Well-Characterized Infection Cycle

Viruses that infect bacteria are often called bacteriophages. They have the strange lunar-lander shape that we commonly see used in the media to describe viruses **(Figures 14.3d** and **14.5)**. Bacteriophages have been incredibly useful tools in the fields of molecular biology and biotechnology. They can be used to clone DNA, storing extremely diverse libraries of genomic or cDNAs. Because they selectively infect bacteria, and often only certain

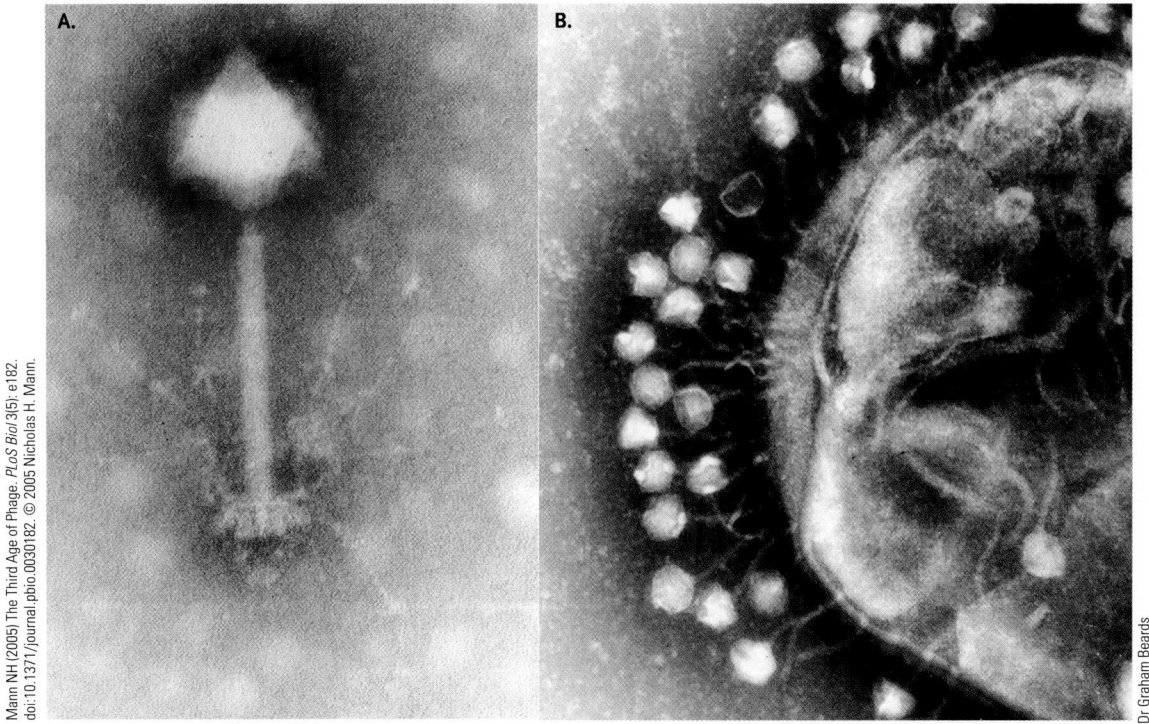

Mann NH (2005) The Third Age of Phage. *PLoS Biol* 3(5): e182. doi:10.1371/journal.pbio.0030182. © 2005 Nicholas H. Mann.

Dr Graham Beards

**FIGURE 14.5** Electron micrograph of an individual bacteriophage. Note the head and long tail fibres **(a)**. A swarm of bacteriophages is attempting to infect a single bacterium **(b)**.

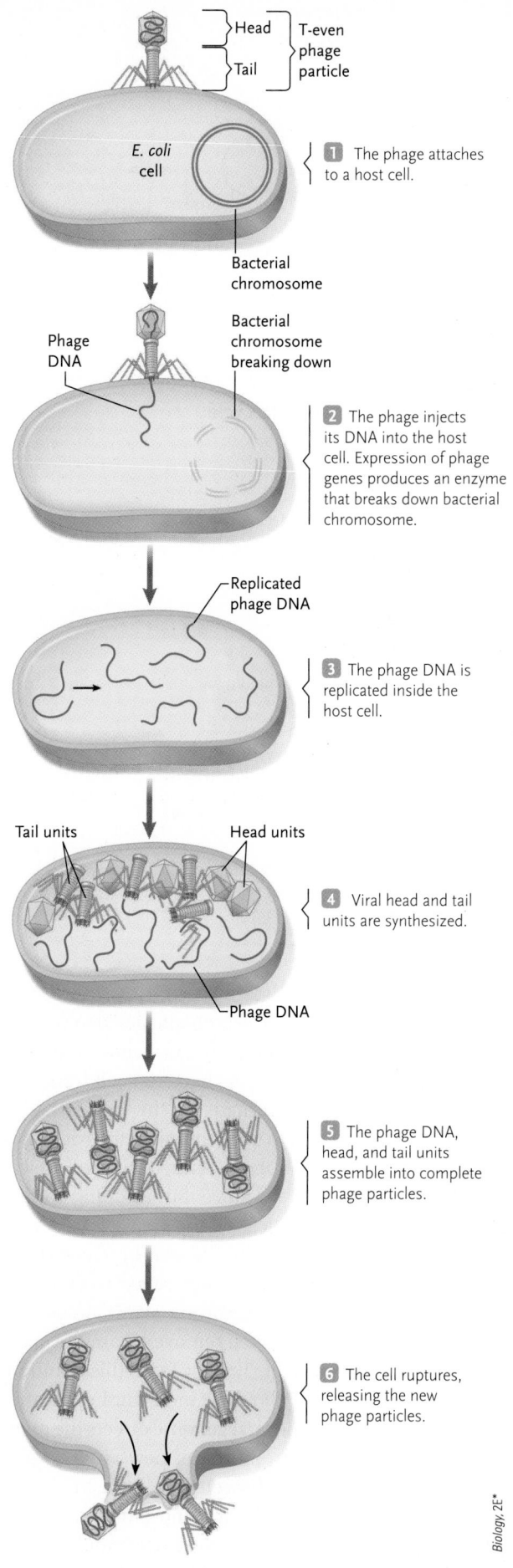

species of bacteria, some medical researchers suggest that they could be the next big advance in antibiotics.

The replication of phages can follow two pathways. Virulent phages, which rapidly lead to cell death, trigger their reproduction once they have introduced their genome into the host bacterial cell. This form of reproduction is called the **lytic cycle (Figure 14.6)**. Once the genome of a virulent phage is inside the bacterial cell, the phage DNA uses the bacterial transcription and translation machinery to produce a series of proteins. One protein in particular acts to digest and destroy the host cell chromosome. This diminishes the competition for transcription and translation resources in the cell and allows the phage to take complete control. The phage DNA is replicated in the host cell, and the proteins needed to form the coat of the phage are synthesized. At this point, even the bacterial protein folding machinery is taken over to properly fold and assemble the phage components into complete replicas of the original phage **(Figure 14.6, step 5)**. As individual phages are assembled, an enzyme encoded by the phage genome, called **lysozyme**, is produced that degrades the bacterial cell wall. When many phages are assembled, the amount of lysozyme produced is sufficient to structurally weaken the cell wall and allow the plasma membrane to rupture. This releases many new virus particles into the media. They can each then go on to infect new cells and repeat the reproductive process. This process of infection, replication, lysis, and reinfection is called the lytic cycle.

The virulent form of replication—the lytic cycle—is not used by all phages. Some employ a second system called the **lysogenic cycle** of replication. The lysogenic cycle involves a stage where the viral genome is inserted into the chromosome of the bacteria. Thus, as the bacteria replicate their chromosome and divide, more copies of the viral genome are made and dispersed, with little effect on the bacteria **(Figure 14.7, p. 318)**. However, do not feel too relieved for the bacterium. Eventually, a signal from the environment triggers a change, and the hijacked bacteria that contain the viral genome will begin to produce phages and the cell will enter the lytic cycle. Thus, we can consider the lysogenic cycle a slow amplification of viral genomes, whereas the subsequent lytic cycle rapidly produces many complete viral particles. In the end, once it is infected, the bacterium is going to be killed.

One particular type of bacteriophage that only infects *E. coli*, **enterobacteria phage lambda**, or lambda phage, is commonly used in molecular biology and for the study of viral biology. Like any other virus, lambda

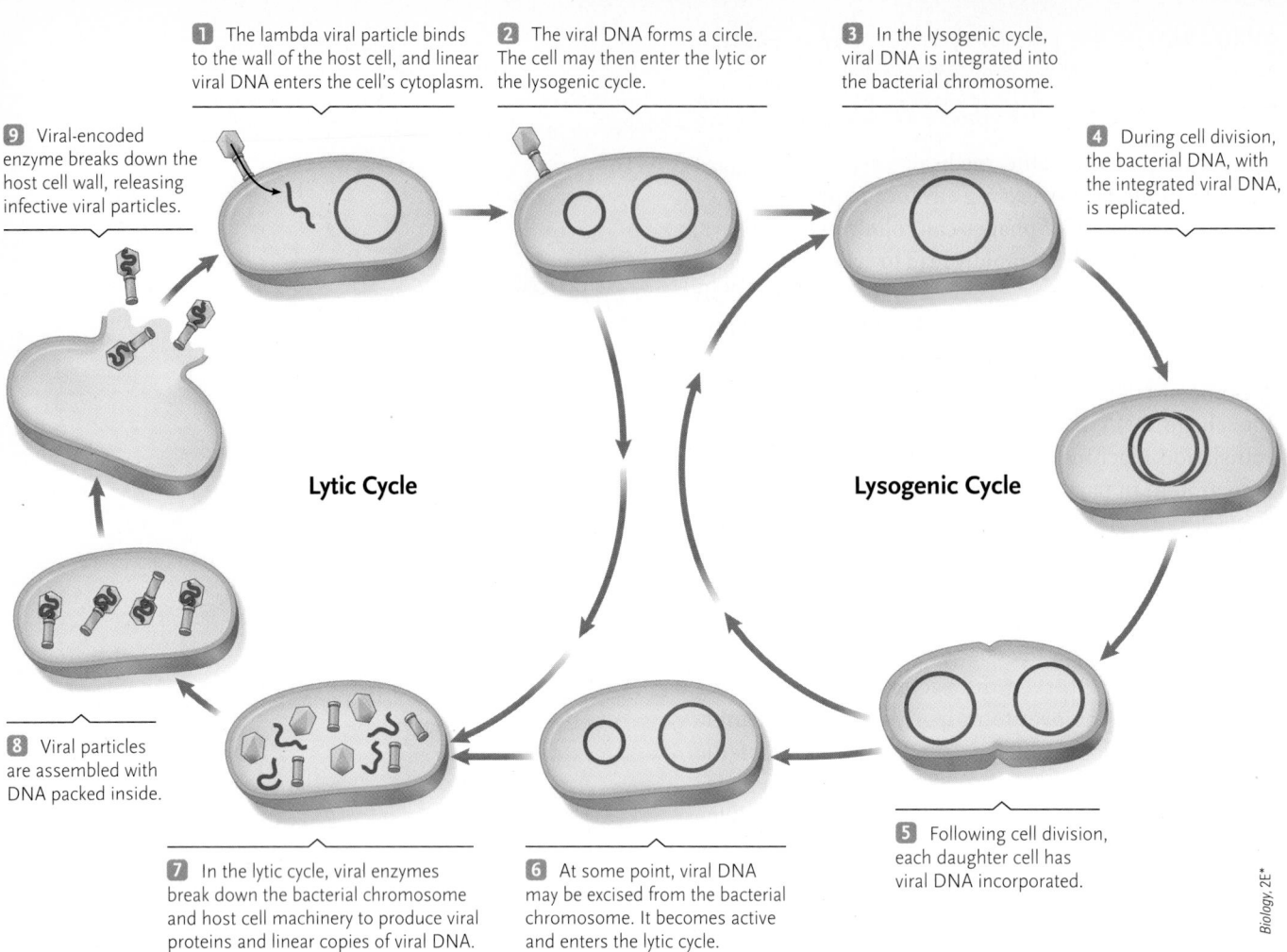

**1** The lambda viral particle binds to the wall of the host cell, and linear viral DNA enters the cell's cytoplasm.

**2** The viral DNA forms a circle. The cell may then enter the lytic or the lysogenic cycle.

**3** In the lysogenic cycle, viral DNA is integrated into the bacterial chromosome.

**9** Viral-encoded enzyme breaks down the host cell wall, releasing infective viral particles.

**4** During cell division, the bacterial DNA, with the integrated viral DNA, is replicated.

**Lytic Cycle**

**Lysogenic Cycle**

**8** Viral particles are assembled with DNA packed inside.

**5** Following cell division, each daughter cell has viral DNA incorporated.

**7** In the lytic cycle, viral enzymes break down the bacterial chromosome and host cell machinery to produce viral proteins and linear copies of viral DNA.

**6** At some point, viral DNA may be excised from the bacterial chromosome. It becomes active and enters the lytic cycle.

*Biology, 2E\**

**FIGURE 14.7** The reproduction of enterobacteria phage lambda occurs through a combination of the lysogenic and lytic cycles.

phage infects a cell by inserting its DNA genome into the cell. Once in the *E. coli* cell, the phage DNA forms a small circle. These small circles can behave like plasmids and be maintained in the bacterial cell from generation to generation. Alternatively, the viral DNA can become incorporated into the genome of the bacterium (Figure 14.7). In either of these cases, the bacterium can continue to grow and reproduce, but in doing so, it is inadvertently slowly replicating the virus. Many cycles of bacterial division during the lysogenic cycle only give rise to larger populations of the bacteria containing latent viral genomes. If the correct external cue happens, the viral genome can be removed from the bacterial genome, triggering the lytic cycle. At this point, the same events described above occur as viral replication enters the lytic cycle. The viral genome directs the digestion of the bacterial chromosome, new virus components are synthesized and assembled, and, finally, the cell is degraded from the inside and bursts, releasing the newly formed viral particles. Entire populations of *E. coli* cells can be destroyed in this way. When growing

*E. coli* cells infected with lambda phage on agar plates, we can see clear spots where all of the bacterial cells have been killed when the lytic cycle was triggered **(Figure 14.8)**. Because bacteriophages can be very specific about the species of bacteria they infect, scientists have suggested that they could be used as a form of antibiotic. For example, if we could find a bacteriophage that specifically targets *Streptococcus pneumoniae* bacteria, a person could be treated with the bacteriophage rather than traditional antibiotics. Although a controversial approach, it may become a more attractive alternative now that many species of bacteria are becoming resistant to antibiotics.

## Even Plants Can Be Infected by Viruses

As you may imagine, plant viruses are viruses that infect and replicate inside plant cells. Plant viruses fall into many of the virus groups discussed above. They can have RNA or DNA as their genomic material, although they normally do not have membranes. They are generally

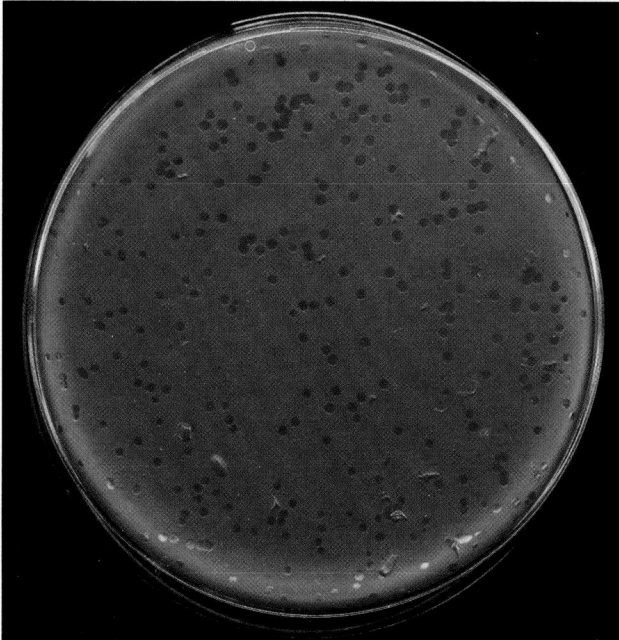

**FIGURE 14.8** A culture of *E. coli* inoculated with enterobacteria phage lambda can grow on an agar plate while the phages are in the lysogenic state. But when the lytic state is triggered, the *E. coli* cells die, leaving blank spots on the agar called plaques.

SOURCE: Madboy, http://en.wikipedia.org/wiki/File:LambdaPlaques.jpg. This file is licensed under the Creative Commons Attribution-Share Alike 3.0 Unported license, http://creativecommons.org/licenses/by-sa/3.0/deed.en

named after the type of plant they infect and the symptoms they elicit. For example, the tomato infectious chlorosis virus **(Figure 14.9a)** and the beet necrotic yellow vein virus have names that clearly reflect some of the symptoms they cause. At the early stages of infection, plant symptoms can vary from **chlorosis**, or yellowing, of the leaves to leaf curling. Later stages lead to the death of leaves and in extreme cases to the death of the plant.

Plant viruses have a more challenging task to get from plant to plant than the bacteriophages have finding a new host cell. Initial infections often come from outside sources or vectors. However, virus particles from one plant can be transferred to another by herbivores. Small, sucking insects are notorious for spreading plant viruses from one plant to another. Aphids will often drink virus particles in the sap of one plant and then move to another plant and transfer the virus particles when they insert their mouth parts to get more nourishment **(Figure 14.9b)**. Nematodes (small roundworms) in the soil can likewise transfer virus particles from one host to another when they eat root tissue. Nematodes can thus cause major problems of disease transfer in plants such as potato. Once the virus is inside the plant, it can move from tissue to tissue using the plant's vascular system and even the structures that connect the cytoplasm of neighbouring cells. In this way, plant viruses can even end up inside developing seeds and be passed on to the next generation of plants.

Plant viruses are a serious problem for agriculture both in the field and in the greenhouse. Contaminated tools and seed stocks can sometimes transfer the virus particles even more effectively than insect vectors. Viral infections in plants are extremely hard to get rid of once an infection begins. Because the viruses are not "alive," chemical pesticides do not work on them. Also, because they can be passed on to subsequent generations in the seed, great care must be taken when an infection occurs not to use seed generated from that crop.

## Zoonotic Viruses Specifically Infect Animals

Zoonotic viruses are those that infect animals. Some zoonotic viruses infect a single species, but others can be passed from species to species, including humans. Many

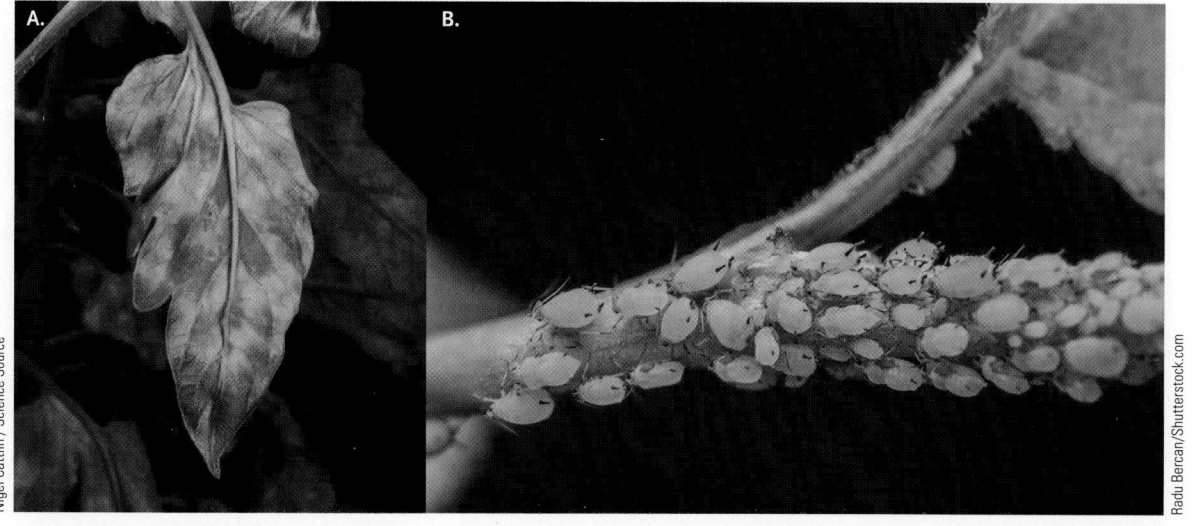

**FIGURE 14.9** Leaves of a tomato plant infected with the tomato infectious chlorosis virus **(a)**. In plants, viruses are often transmitted by small, sucking insects, such as aphids **(b)**.

of our devastating viral diseases can be categorized as zoonotic: Ebola virus, West Nile virus, and rabies, to name a few. One of the fascinating aspects of viral infections is that although the initial infection process is somewhat species dependent, once inside a cell, most cells work in a similar way. Remember that the key interaction is between the viral coat proteins and epitopes on the surface of cells. This can be both species and even cell specific. But the RNA polymerases and ribosomes of eukaryotic animals are all very similar. As a result, we frequently see viruses that can jump the species barrier. Initial infection rates may be low, but because of the high rate at which viruses can mutate, species specificity can quickly disappear.

We see this process occurring with the influenza virus, as mentioned in the introduction to this chapter. We also see it with other viruses, such as West Nile virus (WNV). The first cases of WNV in Canada occurred in the early 2000s. It was first discovered in birds, but there were soon human cases too. In North America, WNV is thought to have originated in New York City, but because birds are so mobile and many migrate twice yearly, the virus quickly spread, so that by 2007, it was found over most of North America. WNV can infect birds, humans, and other animals, such as horses. This particular virus seems to infect birds more readily. However, during the summer, as the mosquito population increases and bird populations disperse, humans become an alternative target for the mosquito. This inadvertently exposes humans and other animals to the WNV, and because the virus can infect human cells, we can become sick due to a "bird" virus.

The rabies virus (*Lyssavirus* sp.) is similarly infective in a broad range of species. The rabies virus is most commonly passed from animal to animal through saliva, generally as a result of being bitten by an infected animal.

Rabies infection can lead to a disease state in any warm-blooded animal and is almost always fatal. However, it seems that certain animals are more tolerant of the virus and live longer while infected. Thus, these animals can act as a reservoir for the disease in nature. These reservoir animals include raccoons, skunks, foxes, and some species of bats. In areas of southern Ontario, the Ontario Ministry of Natural Resources operates a rabies vaccination program for wildlife. Ministry research scientists drop small bait packages from helicopters that contain a rabies vaccine **(Figure 14.10)**. The targets for the bait are primarily foxes, skunks, and raccoons. The animals eat the bait package, and it protects them from future rabies exposures (we will talk more about vaccines in Chapter 26). This project has proven to be enormously successful in protecting provincial wildlife. Numbers of infected animals dropped from around 2000 cases per year in the 1980s, before the vaccination program started, to just 2 cases in 2011.

As we can see, zoonotic viral diseases can be a serious human health concern. However, they can also greatly impact farm production. As a result, the Canadian Food Inspection Agency and the Public Health Agency of Canada routinely monitor indicator animal species across Canada and rigorously investigate strange animal deaths. This is often done in collaboration with national research laboratories such as the National Microbiology Laboratory in Winnipeg, home to Canada's only Level 4 biosafety research facility (Box 14.1). You may have noticed from news reports that there are new animal diseases emerging in Canada all the time. Examples include eastern and western equine encephalitis virus (affects horses), porcine epidemic diarrhea virus (affects pigs), and lymphoproliferative disease virus (affects turkeys). Each is deadly to its particular host organism, and with farm animals

Ministry of Natural Resources and Forestry, on-line bulletin *Rabies Vaccine Bait Drop Protects Ontarians*. © Queen's Printer for Ontario, 2014. Reproduced with permission.

Leonid Dushin/Shutterstock.com

**FIGURE 14.10** A wildlife rabies vaccination program run by the Ontario Ministry of Natural Resources has proven very successful. No rabid raccoons have been found in the province since 2005.

# The National Microbiology Laboratory

Investigations into the strange deaths of animals are often done in collaboration between the Canadian Food Inspection Agency and national research laboratories such as the National Microbiology Laboratory in Winnipeg, home to Canada's only Level 4 biosafety research facilities **(Figure 1a)**. This special workspace is designed to ensure the safety of workers and the public while performing research on the world's deadliest viruses.

To enter a Level 4 lab, a person must be properly trained and wearing a full bio-safety suit equipped with an external air source **(Figure 1b)**. The lab rooms are under negative pressure so that if any spills occur and virus particles become airborne, the particles cannot leave the containment area. At the end of the time in the lab, the workers shower, remove their suits, and shower again. Nothing exposed to the air in the Level 4 lab is allowed outside unless it has been completely decontaminated.

Conducting research under such extreme and exacting conditions is tedious and uncomfortable, but it is the only way to ensure the safety of the research scientists as they go through their procedures. If viruses such as Ebola, smallpox, or deadly versions of influenza were released from containment, a large-scale epidemic could result. However, the only way we can learn more about these viruses and the diseases that they cause is by studying them. The extreme environment of the National Microbiology Laboratory Level 4 labs allows us to learn more about these deadly viruses while protecting both the researchers and the public.

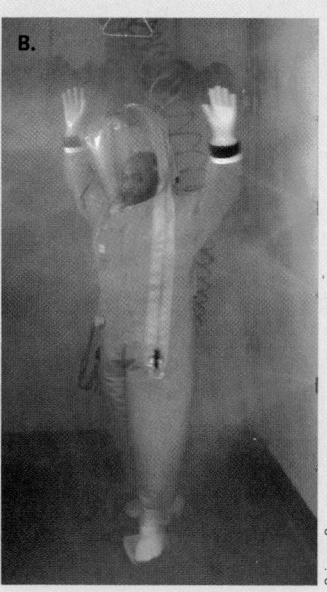

**FIGURE 1** **(a)** The National Microbiology Laboratory in Winnipeg is home to Canada's most deadly viruses. **(b)** Entering or exiting the most secure labs requires extensive preparation.

typically in close proximity to each other, the chance of virus transmission between individuals is very high. Often when one member of a herd or flock of animals becomes ill, the entire farm will be quarantined and, if necessary, the animals destroyed. The possible effects on agricultural livestock production are immense.

We are much more familiar with the zoonotic viruses that can infect humans. Two of the viruses most of us have the most experience with are the influenza virus and the virus that causes the common cold, the human **rhinovirus**. However, the list of diseases caused by viruses is long and includes some of the most dangerous afflictions that we know. Smallpox, Ebola, severe acute respiratory syndrome (SARS), HIV, and measles are all viral diseases. Once viral infections start, they are often difficult, if not impossible, to stop. Animal cells are infected in much the same way as bacteria or plant cells, although the presence of a membrane around the virus particle makes the entry and exit from the cell slightly different. The virus particle links up with the host cell surface receptor protein and merges with the host cell plasma membrane (Figure 14.4). In this way, the virus coat and genome enter the cell. As mentioned, the membrane surrounding the viral coat helps the virus evade animal immune systems (as described in Chapter 26).

An interesting aspect of some animal viral infections is their ability to go dormant. The varicella-zoster

AZT (azidothymidine) is a homologue of the deoxynucleotide thymidine, meaning that it is similar in shape and can be used by the DNA polymerase. It was the first drug shown to be effective in the treatment of HIV **(Figure 1)**. Shortly after scientists were able to demonstrate that HIV causes acquired immune deficiency syndrome (AIDS), research began to focus on ways to slow HIV replication. The magnitude of the problem HIV causes can be seen from the fact that following infection, an average person produces over 10 billion virus particles per day. This staggering number supported the position of many researchers that the way to control HIV is in slowing viral replication. If we think about how HIV infects cells and replicates (remember that it is a retrovirus), it has an RNA genome that is reverse transcribed into a DNA molecule that is later inserted into a host cell's chromosome. The key question was: How can this process be slowed down, or, even better, how can it be stopped? Because the reverse transcriptase plays such a central role in HIV replication, and human cells do not have a reverse transcriptase, this seemed like HIV's weak link. If reverse transcriptase could be slowed or stopped, it could halt viral replication with few side effects.

Scientists looked at the mechanism of the reverse transcriptase and decided to try blocking it using altered deoxynucleotide substrates. AZT was the first effective substrate that could slow or even stop the HIV reverse transcriptase. If the reverse transcriptase incorporates AZT into a growing DNA strand, it blocks further elongation (much like the dideoxynucleotides that are used in Sanger sequencing; see Chapter 11). As you might expect, AZT can also affect the function of normal DNA polymerases required by human cells. But when administered at the appropriate level, this side effect is not too severe. Interestingly, the DNA polymerase most affected by AZT is the one found in the mitochondrion.

AZT proved to be an initial success. When given to patients with AIDS, it helped restore their T cell counts (the first cells destroyed by HIV), improved their immune responses, and increased overall health. Side effects on muscle tissue, in particular heart muscle, due to the antimitochondrial effects of the drug could be monitored and dosages adjusted accordingly. However, problems began to arise. The reverse transcriptase of HIV is not a very good enzyme. It tends to be sloppy in its fidelity, meaning that it makes a lot of mistakes when it copies the RNA genome of HIV. As a result of errors introduced into the HIV genome by the reverse transcriptase, HIV mutants began to show up that were resistant to AZT.

Luckily, in the meantime, scientists continued to search for alternate drugs. To combat HIV's high mutation rate, pharmacologists developed cocktails composed of a mixture of different reverse transcriptase inhibitors. Using multiple inhibitors greatly reduces the chance of resistance. A single mutation that has an effect on the reverse transcriptase may be a rare event; three or even four simultaneous mutations all having a positive effect for the virus would be nearly impossible. These new formulations have vastly improved the lives of people with HIV infections. People infected with HIV can now have viral counts that are near zero and normal T cell counts and can lead much longer and higher quality lives.

**FIGURE 1** The chemical structure of AZT looks a lot like a deoxynucleotide **(a)**. It was the first antiretroviral drug used in the treatment of HIV. It is now used as one part of a drug cocktail **(b)** to reduce the possibility of resistance.

A.

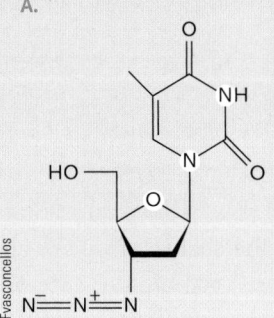

B.

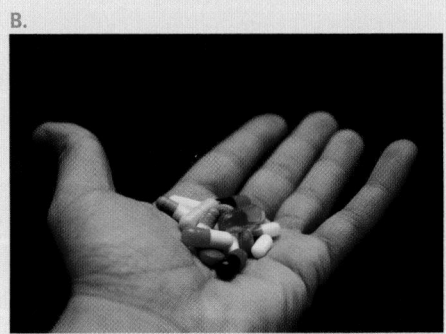

virus (VZV) causes the childhood disease chicken pox. Once the acute phase of chicken pox goes away, we normally think that our child has recovered and become immune to the disease. We normally do not develop chicken pox again later in life. However, VZV does not fully leave one's system. Rather, it enters into a dormant phase, and the VZV can be found in specific types of nerve cells. Sometimes, later in life, the dormant VZV can reactivate, causing shingles. Another example is the herpes simplex virus (HPV). One version of it (HPV-1), also called *Herpes labialis*, causes cold sores. These recurring blisters form on the lips and around the mouth of infected individuals. Normally, they will go away after 2 to 3 weeks, but as with VZV, the HPV-1 is only dormant. It localizes to nerve cells and will re-emerge anywhere from once to several times per year. In each of these cases, the production of new HPV-1 virus particles leads to inflammation and localized cell death. The blisters that form are a result of the virus replication, and the fluid they contain is teeming with new virus particles.

One factor that we can observe from both animal and human viral disease is the importance of avoiding infection. Because viruses reproduce using the host's cellular machinery, very few drugs can be used to control the virus. As we see with HIV (Box 14.2), viruses can rapidly become resistant to antiviral drugs. The most effective method for prevention of viral diseases such as influenza and measles is through large-scale vaccination. This has been an immensely successful approach. In Canada, diseases that used to kill thousands of individuals per year are now considered eradicated. Smallpox vaccination was so successful worldwide that the disease is almost completely gone. Canada was declared measles free in 2000; however,

because of the increasing amount of travel to areas where measles is still prevalent and a reduction in vaccination rates in Canada, measles outbreaks are increasing in frequency and severity. For example, in the winter of 2014, measles outbreaks occurred in Regina and Edmonton.

## STUDY BREAK

1. What cellular similarities allow zoonotic viruses to infect diverse hosts such as ducks, humans, and horses?
2. Compare the lysogenic cycle to the lytic cycle as a mechanism for bacteriophages to reproduce.
3. Because neither plants nor viruses can move from place to place, how are viruses often transmitted from plant to plant?

## PUTTING IT IN PERSPECTIVE

Despite the debate over whether viruses are living organisms, understanding their structure and how they interact with living cells is crucial to the health of our crops, our pets, and ourselves. The origin of the viruses likely meshes with the origin of life. Whether viruses evolved into living cells or from cells that became intracellular parasites, they are incredibly diverse.

Looking carefully, we find types of viruses that are capable of infecting every type of cell. There may never be another influenza pandemic as deadly as the 1918 flu, but being prepared will require medical researchers such as those at the Canadian National Microbiology Laboratory continuing their work, characterizing the strange and unusual viruses they identify.

## KEY CONCEPTS REVIEW AND QUESTIONS

### 14.1 What Are Viruses?

Viruses are obligate intracellular parasites. They are composed of the same biomolecules as are cells but do not perform metabolic reactions and cannot reproduce without infecting a host cell. Thus, they do not quite fit the definition of a living organism. Although we generally do not consider viruses to be living entities, it is not clear if they evolved from bacteria cells or if they are on an evolutionary trajectory toward becoming living cells.

1. Explain the progressive theory of virus evolution.
2. Scientists have constructed plant viruses from individual parts made in a lab. Should scientists be allowed to publish research on their progress toward constructing human viruses? Should scientists be allowed to construct new versions of the 1918 pandemic virus?

### 14.2 Structure and Function of Viruses

At their simplest, viruses are composed of a nucleotide genome surrounded by a protein capsid, or coat. Animal viruses often have one extra component, a membrane that surrounds the

coat proteins. It is thought that the membrane helps the virus evade detection by its host's immune system.

3. When considering animal viruses surrounded by a membrane, where does this membrane come from?

### 14.3 The Viral Hereditary Molecule: DNA or RNA?

Viruses can be partially classified based on the composition of their genome. Some viruses have RNA genomes, whereas others store their genetic material as DNA, like cells. We can subdivide the DNA viruses based on whether their genome is double stranded, like a cell, or single stranded. Viruses that use an RNA genome need also to supply an enzyme called reverse transcriptase to the host cell. This enzyme is needed to generate a DNA copy of the viral RNA. Only once the DNA copy has been made are the viral proteins translated and viral genomes copied so that new virus particles can be made.

4. The reverse transcriptase enzymes employed by RNA viruses have low fidelity, meaning that they make a lot of mistakes when reverse transcribing the

genome. What advantage could this provide the virus? Why has evolution not selected for a more high-fidelity reverse transcriptase?

5. Define what is meant by the term *retrovirus*.

## 14.4 Viral Reproduction

We have yet to find a type of living cell that cannot be affected by viruses. Despite the great diversity of cells, from bacteria and archaea to the eukaryotes, viruses attack them in essentially the same way. Proteins on the surface of the cell are detected by proteins on the surface of the virus. This allows the cell and virus to interact and the virus to insert its genomic material into the cell. Once inside the cell, the genome of the virus directs the cell to make copies of the virus. After sufficient copies are made, the cell dies, releasing the virus particles into the environment so that they can find new cells to infect.

6. Can you explain why *E. coli* cells infected with enterobacteria lambda phage would leave visible plaques (Figure 14.8) when plated on agar?

7. Compare the transfer of viruses from plant to plant by aphids to the transfer of West Nile virus between animals by mosquitos.

8. Thinking of how an HIV infects a cell, why are people infected by this virus never truly cured?

# Bacteria and Archaea

## WHY IT MATTERS

Imagine walking down a sandy path to the beach on a hot day at the end of the summer. After a few windy, rainy days, the weather has warmed up, and all you can think of is lying on the hot sand and taking a swim in the cool, refreshing water. You can feel the cool breeze on your face. Then, as the sandy path opens up onto the beach, it hits you. The water is covered in a green slime, and dead fish are washing up on the shore. The smell alone is enough to ruin your day at the beach.

Algal blooms are becoming more common around the world, from the west coast of Vancouver Island to the German Bight and the Gold Coast of Australia. Although many species of algae can lead to algal blooms, one of the more problematic groups are the cyanobacteria. Cyanobacteria as a group are the most abundant photosynthesizers on Earth. They are thought to generate approximately 30% of the yearly oxygen production. In addition, they convert carbon dioxide into sugars as primary producers, and some convert nitrogen from a gas into organic forms. Thus, although we should appreciate the importance of cyanobacteria in the biosphere, they can become an ecological problem when blooms of algae occur. Large blooms of cyanobacteria or other algae can lead to anoxic conditions in the water and to the release of toxins that further affect water quality.

Lake Erie is the smallest and shallowest of the Great Lakes. This leads to warmer water temperatures in the summer and a lower capacity to dilute nutrient inputs from human use. In the 1960s, large algal blooms were a regular occurrence in Lake Erie, with people joking that you could walk across the lake because there was so much algae floating on top of the water. Researchers found that the algal blooms were caused by large amounts of phosphorus entering the lake due to agricultural runoff and poorly treated municipal waste water. In 1972, the governments of Canada and the United States reached the *Great Lakes Water Quality Agreement*, aimed at reducing nutrient input into the Great Lakes. The agreement was very successful, with phosphorous inputs decreasing over 60% by 1980. Correspondingly, the number of algal blooms diminished in both number and severity. However, in recent years, the number of blooms has begun to increase. The blooms themselves are troubling. The large amount of decaying algal biomass exhausts the dissolved oxygen in the water, leading to fish kills and bad odours. Even more worrying is the presence of the cyanobacterium *Microcystis aeruginosa* in the blooms. This particular photosynthetic bacterium thrives when phosphate levels are high and had mostly disappeared from Lake Erie since the height of water quality problems in the 1960s. It is a concern because the cyanobacterium releases a toxin into the water called microcystin.

In 2011, there was a record-setting cyanobacterial bloom in Lake Erie **(Figure 15.1, p. 328)**. At first, scientists were at a loss to explain the bloom. It now appears, however, that a series of weather-related events combined with agricultural practices and decades of neglect were the causes. In the lead-up to the 2011 bloom, there was a period of hot, calm weather followed by a powerful storm. The weather led to warmer than normal surface water on the lake, allowing cyanobacteria to grow rapidly. When cyanobacteria exhausted the nutrients in the surface water, they stopped growing. Although, at first glance, this seems good, it actually encourages the growth of the toxin producing *M. aeruginosa*. The powerful storm caused a significant turnover of the surface water, mixing nutrient-rich sediments into the water column. This makes new nutrients available to the cyanobacteria. Decades of excess phosphorus previously stored in sediments were liberated by the high winds and rain, and the population of algae, previously limited only by phosphorus, exploded. Following this population explosion, the cyanobacteria again ran out of nutrients and began to die and produce more of the toxic microcystin. Many fish and birds then died as they ate smaller fish that had consumed the toxic cyanobacteria.

The point to remember is that although we thought we had solved the water quality problems in Lake Erie, the ecological problems that we cause do not go away quickly. In fact, the phosphorous concentrations in Lake Erie may never drop below the point where extreme weather events cannot lead to cyanobacterial blooms.

In this chapter, we will investigate two of the domains of life: the Bacteria and the Archaea. The species that

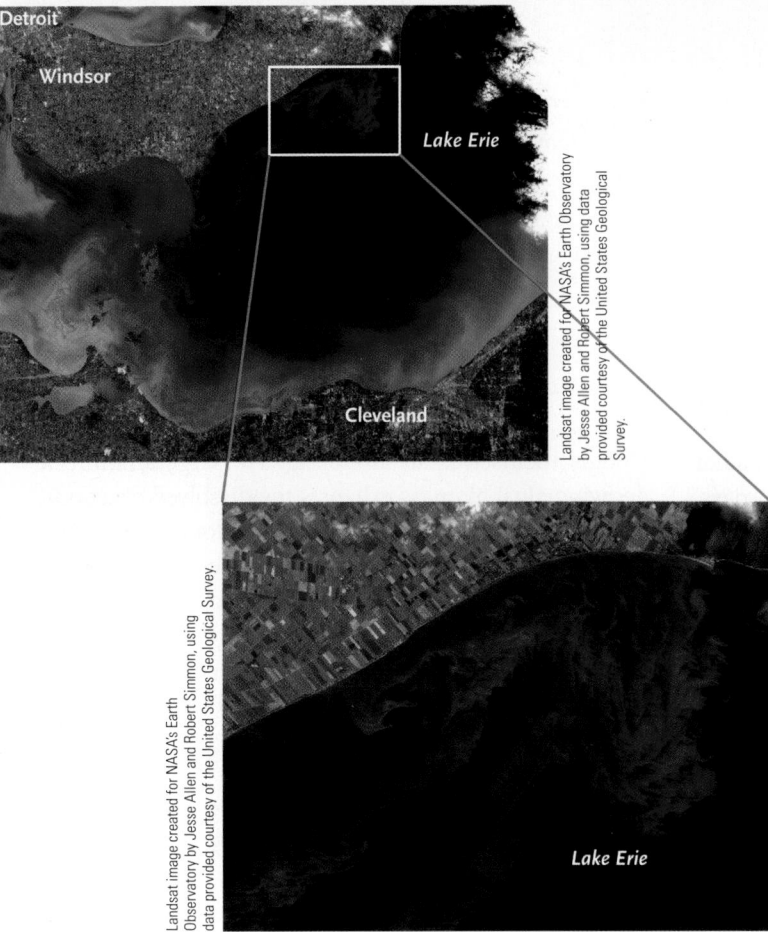

Landsat image created for NASA's Earth Observatory by Jesse Allen and Robert Simmon, using data provided courtesy of the United States Geological Survey.

Landsat image created for NASA's Earth Observatory by Jesse Allen and Robert Simmon, using data provided courtesy of the United States Geological Survey.

**FIGURE 15.1** Cyanobacterial blooms such as those in Lake Erie lead to fish and bird kills and can release harmful cyanotoxins into the water. It is quite amazing that bacteria can be numerous enough to be seen from space using satellite imaging.

make up these two domains play incredibly important roles in our daily lives, from the uses in biotechnology that we discussed in Chapter 11 to the diseases they cause. We will discuss the different ways we can describe bacterial cells and examine the different classes of organisms that make up this domain. This will lead to an examination of how horizontal gene transfer leads to the complex relationships that we see between bacterial and archaeal species, if indeed we can even define the term species in these organisms. We will then compare how the structures we find in bacteria and archaea allow them to survive and succeed in their environments. The specific structural characteristics of archaea allow them to survive in locations where scientists thought life could not exist.

## 15.1 Defining What It Means to Be a Bacterium or an Archaeon

Scientists often use the term **prokaryote** to define cells that do not contain membrane-bound organelles or a nucleus—in other words, any cell that is not a **eukaryote**.

In fact, if you go back through the chapters of this book, you will find that we use *prokaryote* quite frequently as a catch-all term for bacteria and archaea, the two types of cells that are not eukaryotes.

However, the use of the term *prokaryote* is somewhat controversial. In the past, the term was used as part of an organizational system in which all living organisms were divided into two domains. All organisms were either prokaryotic (no organelles or nucleus) or eukaryotic (containing organelles and a nucleus). As microbiologists discovered more about the bacteria and archaea, the two groups of organisms that were bunched together within the prokaryotes, they found that the two groups were quite different. The biochemical and physiological differences were reinforced by data obtained from comparing the DNA sequences of specific genes from species of bacteria to species of archaea. In recent years, this has expanded to comparing entire genome sequences. Genomic comparisons of bacteria and archaea suggest that archaea are more closely related to the eukaryotes than to the bacteria, despite their simple cellular plan. This has led to the archaea being placed closer to the eukaryotes in the tree of life **(Figure 15.2a)**.

However, we must remember that genetic information can be transferred between species (horizontal gene transfer) as well as from generation to generation in a population (vertical gene transfer). Remember from Chapter 9 that Griffith found that genetic information could be transferred from dead *Streptococcus pneumoniae* cells to living *S. pneumoniae* cells. That was an example of a process called transformation, where foreign genetic information can be taken up and used by bacterial cells. We will see later in the chapter that genetic information can also be moved from one species of bacteria to another by viruses, through a process called transduction. Both of these processes occur naturally and make delineating a tree of life for bacteria and archaea very challenging, if not impossible.

### Classification of the Bacteria and Archaea Makes for a Confusing Tree of Life

Scientists, like everyone else, can have problems changing their points of view. This is especially true when it comes to naming and classifying organisms. When Linnaeus began the binomial classification of life, he used two kingdoms: Plants and Animals. Bacteria

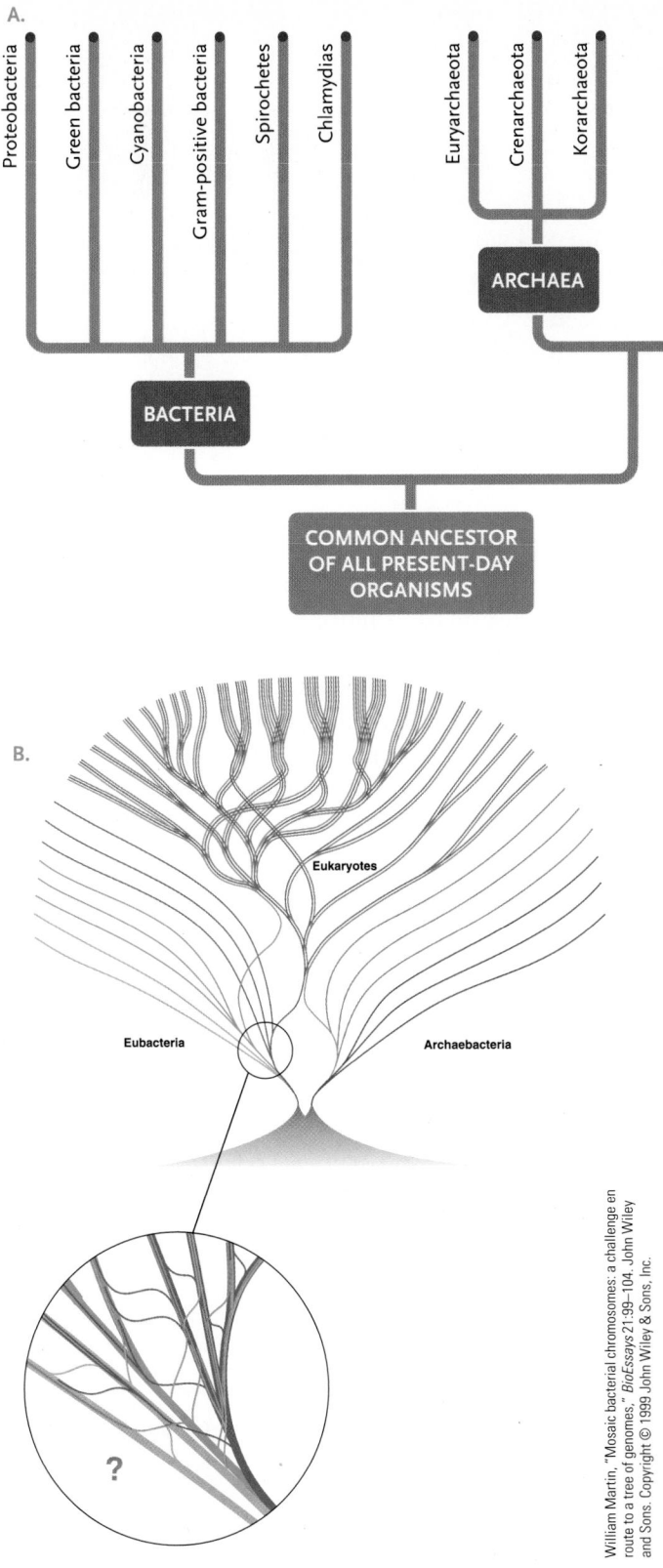

FIGURE 15.2 A linear **(a)** versus an interconnected **(b)** view of the tree of life.

William Martin, "Mosaic bacterial chromosomes: a challenge en route to a tree of genomes," *BioEssays* 21:99–104. John Wiley and Sons. Copyright © 1999 John Wiley & Sons, Inc.

this kingdom included bacteria and archaea. The refinements continued based on our increasing knowledge of the organisms. However, this seemed to complicate things even more. In the 1970s, based on DNA sequence data, Carl Woese (an expert on the archaea) suggested dividing organisms into three domains: the Bacteria, the Archaea, and the Eukaryotes (Figure 15.2).

As we obtain more and more data that can be used to compare the bacteria, archaea, and eukaryotes, the interconnections between the groups become more evident. Large-scale DNA sequencing projects of microbes in the ocean and soils and even those found inside the guts of other organisms that cannot be grown in research labs will greatly expand our understanding of how organisms are related to each other. No doubt, as scientists continue to discover new species of bacteria, archaea, and eukaryotes, refinements of the tree of life and how we classify organisms will continue.

## Horizontal Gene Transfer Moves Genes from Species to Species

When we discussed genetics in Chapter 8, we examined the inheritance of genes responsible for specific traits from one generation to the next. In Chapter 7, we saw that sexual reproduction and meiotic recombination events are important for increasing the variation in subsequent generations of individuals. Variation within a species provides a better chance that some members of the species will survive when stressful or challenging conditions occur. Because bacteria generally divide by simple binary fission, it is difficult to see how variation can be maintained in a population. One would expect that all of the bacteria within a population would be identical, excluding the random occurrence of mutations. However, the amount of diversity we can observe in bacterial genomes does not correlate with such a limited process.

and archaea fell in with the plants. Because of the confusion caused by some organisms that appeared to blur the line between plants and animals, the Protists were proposed by Ernst Haeckel in 1866 as a third kingdom. Because the Protists included all unicellular organisms,

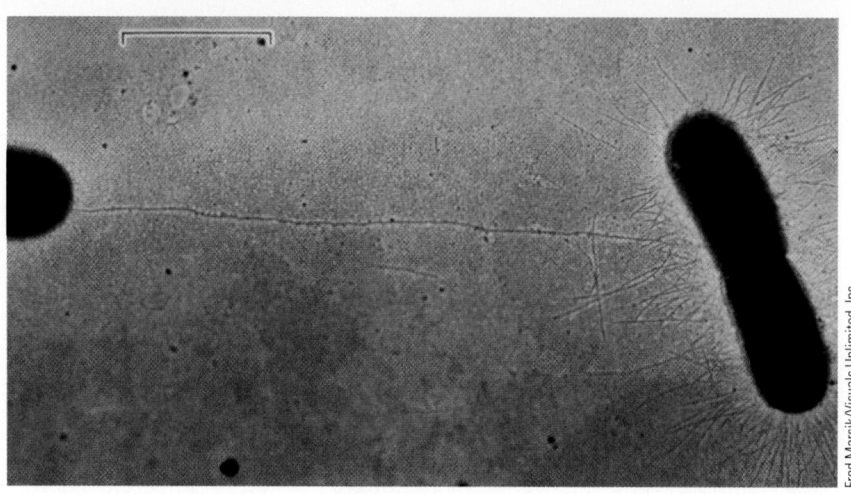

**FIGURE 15.3** A sex pilus connecting two bacteria facilitates horizontal gene transfer by allowing the movement of genetic material or plasmids between the two cells.

Griffith's experiments shed the first light on how bacteria could gain genetic traits without undergoing sexual recombination. In Chapter 9, we discussed how Griffith observed the transfer of a trait from dead bacterial cells to live bacterial cells, leading to increased virulence in a previously non-deadly *S. pneumoniae* strain. He called this process **transformation**. We now know that transformation is a common occurrence in bacteria, and it allows the transfer of plasmids or even segments of genomic DNA from a dead bacterium to a living cell. If the transfer conveys a selective advantage, it will be maintained in the new host. We generally consider the transfer of genes from one generation to the next during reproduction vertical gene transfer. Because transformation does not occur as part of reproduction, the movement of genetic information into the new cell is called horizontal gene transfer.

In addition to transformation, there are other mechanisms that lead to horizontal gene transfer. When a bacteriophage infects a host bacterium, it inserts its DNA. As the host cell begins replicating the viral DNA (see Figure 14.6), segments of the host DNA can be mixed in with the viral DNA. As the mature bacteriophages go on to infect other bacteria, they may take DNA from a previous host cell with them. This viral-mediated form of horizontal gene transfer is called **transduction**.

It seems that bacteria are even able to transfer genetic material directly from one cell to another. Some types of bacteria are able to produce a long, tubular structure called a sex pilus that attaches to a neighbouring bacterium, opening a tube between the two cells **(Figure 15.3)**. The sex pilus allows an exchange of materials such as DNA between the cells. Plasmids and even copies of the entire bacterial genome have been shown to transfer between the connected cells.

The key factor of horizontal gene transfer is the movement of helpful genes between unrelated species.

This is thought to be a considerable factor in the rapid development of antibiotic-resistant bacteria. These processes also make it much more complicated for us to delineate the tree of life to its root (Figure 15.2). Horizontal gene transfer between the domains occurred on a large scale during the endosymbiotic events that gave rise to mitochondria and plastids (Figure 15.2b). Only a small percentage of the genes originally present in the cyanobacterium that gave rise to the chloroplast and the mitochondria remain in those organelles. Most were transferred to the nucleus of the new host cell. Horizontal gene transfer between members of the three domains is still an ongoing process, leading to further confusion and adding fuel to the arguments about how to classify living organisms.

## STUDY BREAK

1. What is the difference between transduction and transformation?
2. Define the term *horizontal gene transfer*.
3. How does the process of horizontal gene transfer confuse the tree of life?

## 15.2 Bacterial Structure and Function

We discussed the basic parts of a bacterial cell and compared them to the parts of eukaryote cells in Chapter 3. In this section, we will examine some specific characteristics of bacterial cells and how they work.

### Cell Shape Can Be Used to Classify Bacterial Cells

Bacterial cell shape has been used as a taxonomic indicator since we have had microscopes powerful enough to see such small objects. Many common bacteria were named based on their shape and how the cells grew **(Figures 15.4** and **15.5, p. 332)**. *Streptococcus* species may have nothing more in common than the fact that they are round cells (*cocci*—plural of coccus—derived from the Greek word for berry) that grow in a linear strand (*strepto*, which is Greek for chain) (Figure 15.4). Cocci bacteria can be classified into several groups based on their growth form: diplococci (two cocci), streptococci, or staphylococci (shaped like a cluster of grapes) (Figure 15.4).

Other bacterial cells are rod shaped (*bacilli*—plural of bacillus—derived from the Latin word for wand or little staff). Just as we saw for cocci cells, compound names subdivide the bacilli into groups such as diplobacilli and streptobacilli (Figure 15.5). The third type of bacterial cell shape twists like a corkscrew; the formal term for these spiral-shaped cells is spirilla (plural of spirillum, which is Latin for coil) (Figure 15.5). Less common than the cocci or bacilli, all of the spirilla bacteria fall into the spirochete family. Interestingly, although the spirilla can have slightly different spiral shapes, they do not seem to form chains or clusters. Scientists hypothesize that they stay as single cells to aid in their movement.

## The Cell Wall and Capsule Form the Exterior of the Cell

We discussed the presence of the bacterial cell wall and capsule in Chapter 3. However, because of their importance in bacterial physiology and classification, we will look at them in a little more detail here. The bacterial cell wall is a complex mixture of carbohydrates and short, peptide sequences linked together by enzymes to form a strong, yet flexible, protective structure. It is fascinating that the complex shapes of bacterial cells are controlled by the genetic information contained in the chromosome and ultimately regulated by the construction of the cell wall.

In 1884, Hans Christian Gram was working with Carl Friedländer in the Berlin City Morgue. They were investigating the cause of pneumonia. It had been proposed in the 1870s that bacteria could be the causative agents of disease, but not all medical doctors believed this to be the case. Thus, in the 1880s, there was still much debate concerning the role of specific bacteria in causing pneumonia. Gram was trying to develop a microscopic staining technique to distinguish bacterial cells from human tissues. Most stains that were used for staining bacteria also stained the nuclei and connective tissues of lung samples, making it hard to see the

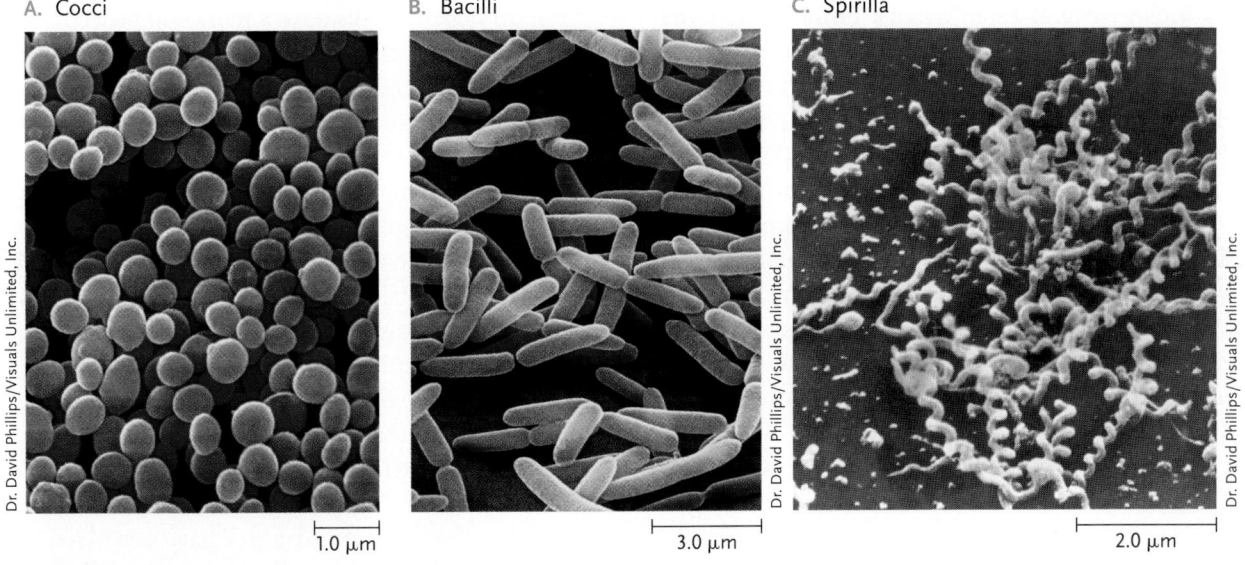

A. Cocci

Dr. David Phillips/Visuals Unlimited, Inc.

1.0 μm

B. Bacilli

Dr. David Phillips/Visuals Unlimited, Inc.

3.0 μm

C. Spirilla

Dr. David Phillips/Visuals Unlimited, Inc.

2.0 μm

D. Square cells

Courtesy of Mike Dyall-Smith

5 μm

**FIGURE 15.4** Bacteria were initially classified based on their shape.

**FIGURE 15.5** How bacterial cells grow together also contributed to their classification.

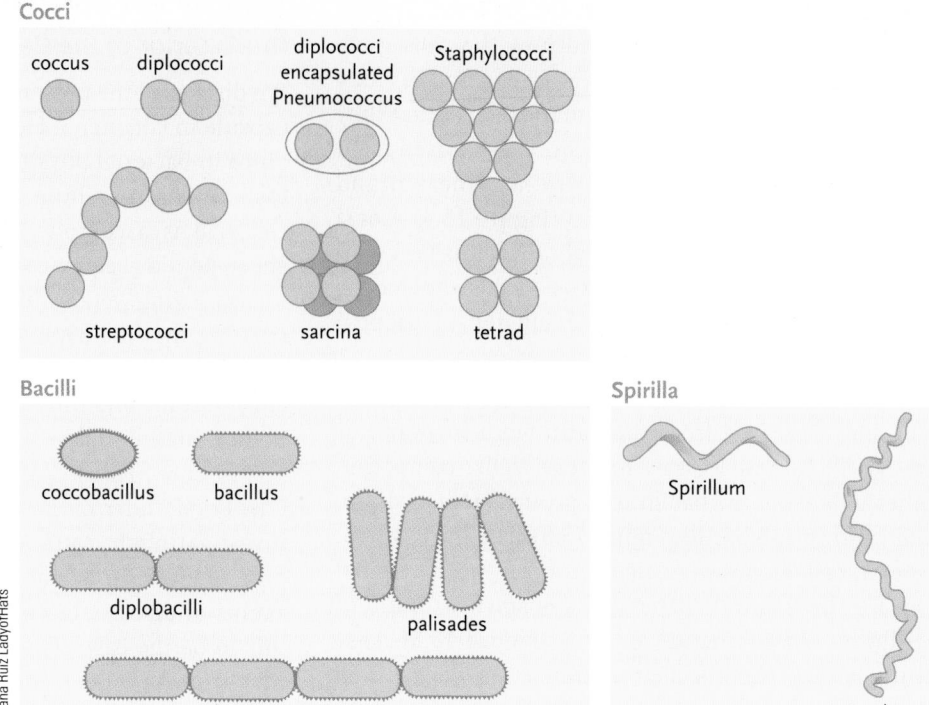

much smaller bacteria. Gram had a strong background from studies in botany and microscopy and was thus familiar with many of the stains that could be used to distinguish parts of cells. Gram's initial finding was that the stain crystal violet would permanently colour bacteria but could be washed away from human cells and tissues. Soon after, he discovered that crystal violet only permanently stained some bacterial cells dark blue. The dark blue-stained cells were termed **Gram positive**. Other cells did not retain the stain and were called **Gram negative (Figure 15.6a)**. Some modifications have been made to the technique over the years, the most important being a second staining step to allow Gram-negative cells to be more easily observed. Following the secondary stain, the Gram-negative cells are pink (Figure 15.6a).

Despite Gram's staining technique, it was not until much later that researchers discovered the physiological basis for the differential staining. We now know that Gram-positive and Gram-negative bacteria have different cell wall structures (Figure 15.6). Gram-positive cells produce a cell wall composed of a single, thick layer of **peptidoglycan**, a complex polymer composed of long chains of alternating carbohydrates that are cross-linked together by short chains of amino acids (for a review on carbohydrates and amino acids, see the Purple Pages). The peptidoglycan layer surrounds the exterior of the plasma membrane. It contains embedded proteins and is held to the plasma membrane by a group of lipid–carbohydrate polymers called **teichoic acid** and **lipoteichoic acid (Figure 15.6b)**. In terms of Gram staining, the thick peptidoglycan layer absorbs the crystal violet dye and retains it despite washing. This permanently colours the cells dark blue.

Gram-negative cells have a more complex covering. They have a much thinner layer of peptidoglycan to provide structural support, but it is surrounded by a second membrane layer called the outer membrane **(Figure 15.6c)**. Although the outer membrane is structurally different than the plasma membrane, it plays a similar role in limiting access of some molecules to the interior of the cell. It is the outer membrane of Gram-negative cells that excludes the crystal violet dye of the Gram stain. The outer membrane also blocks the uptake of some antibiotics, such as penicillin, which stops cell growth by disrupting peptidoglycan formation. These types of adaptations remind us that bacteria have been evolving mechanisms that protect them from a generally hostile environment for billions of years and trillions of generations. Their evolutionary advances have also aided their ability to extract the resources they need from their environment, whether it is soil, ocean water, or the stomach of a termite.

The bacterial capsule is a layer of polysaccharides surrounding the cell. It protects the cell and can greatly increase the cell's apparent size **(Figure 15.7)**. The polysaccharides tend to absorb and hold water, much like a sponge. This protects the bacterium from drying out when exposed to poor environmental conditions. The capsule can also help the bacterium adhere to surfaces such as your teeth, making it more difficult to remove them—hence the need for brushing. If we

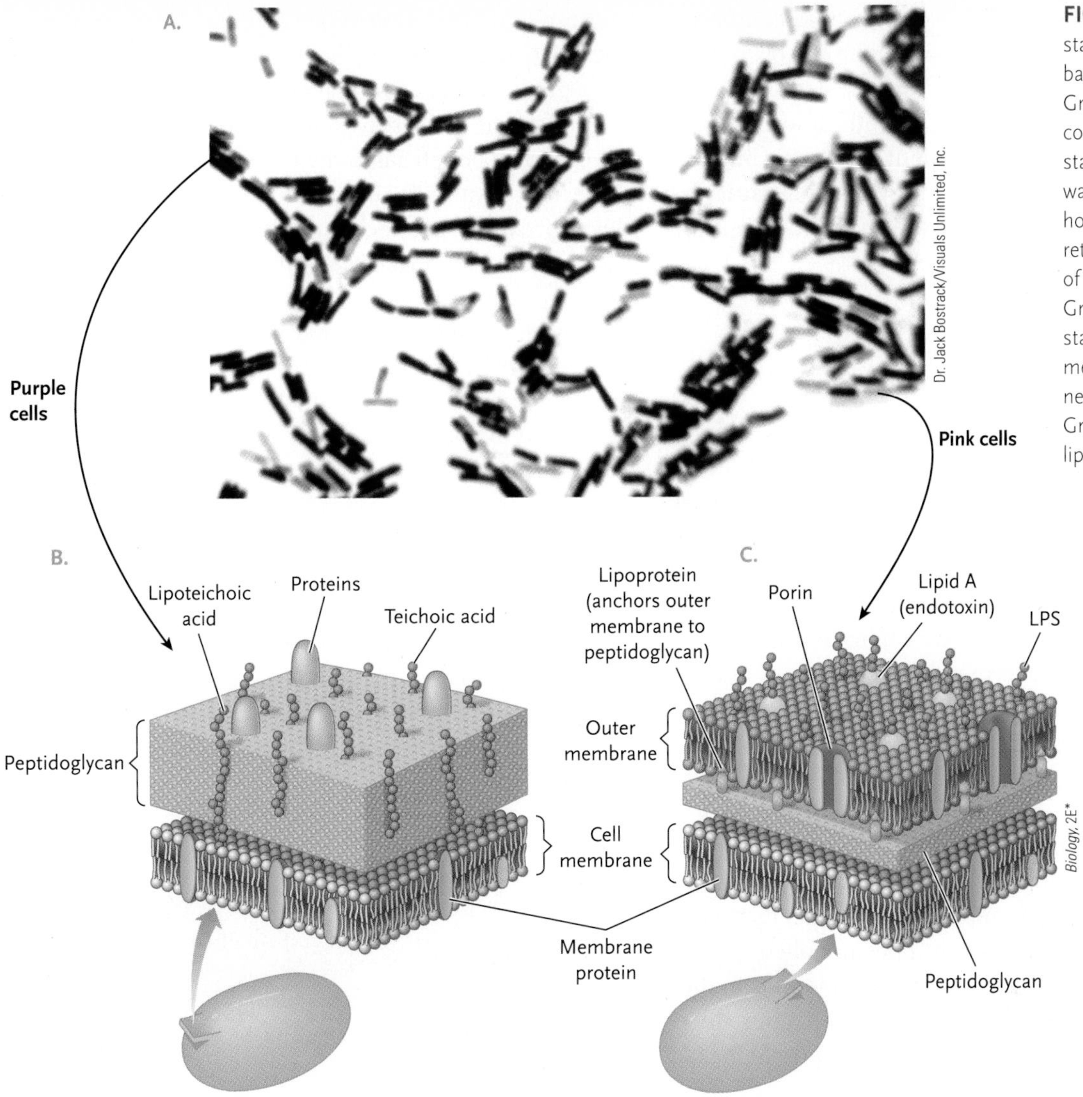

A.

Purple
cells

Pink cells

Dr. Jack Bostrack/Visuals Unlimited, Inc.

**FIGURE 15.6** The Gram stain turns Gram-positive bacteria dark blue, whereas Gram-negative bacteria are coloured pink by a secondary stain **(a)**. The bacterial cell wall structure determines how the Gram stain is retained. The outer layer of peptidoglycan of the Gram-positive cell holds the stain **(b)**, whereas the outer membrane of the Gram-negative cell excludes the Gram stain **(c)**. LPS = lipopolysaccharide.

B.

Lipoteichoic acid

Proteins

Teichoic acid

Peptidoglycan

C.

Lipoprotein (anchors outer membrane to peptidoglycan)

Porin

Lipid A (endotoxin)

LPS

Outer membrane

Cell membrane

Membrane protein

Peptidoglycan

*Biology, 2E\**

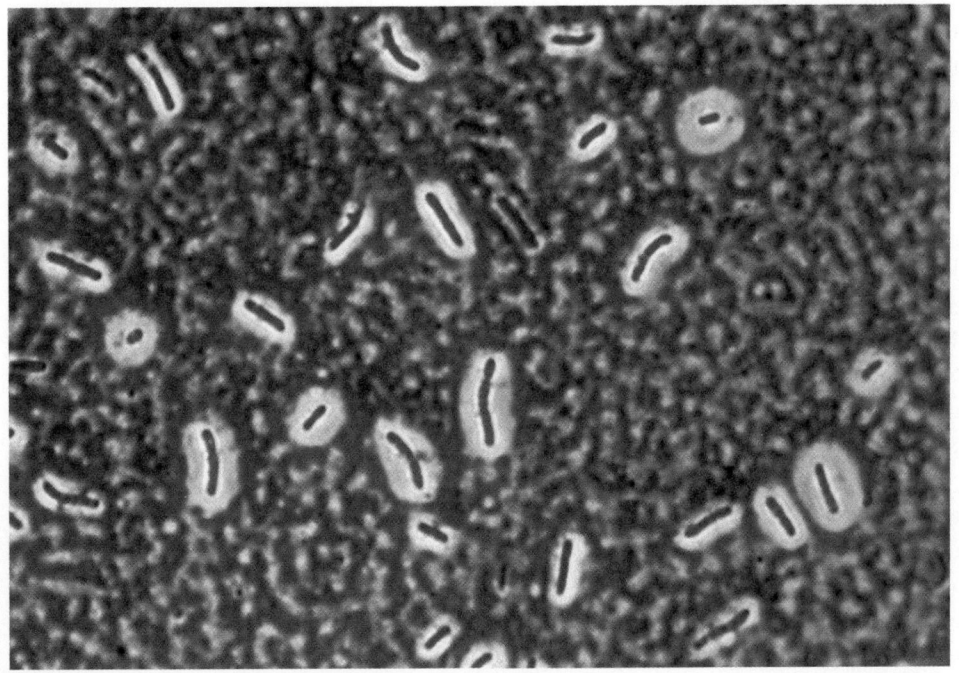

Michael Abbey / Science Source

**FIGURE 15.7** The bacterial capsule surrounds the cell and can make it appear much larger. This micrograph shows the darkly stained bacteria surrounded by the pale capsule.

remember back to Chapter 9, Griffith was comparing several strains of *Streptococcus* when he discovered that a transformative particle was responsible for the virulence of specific strains. The smooth strains that he examined not only had the virulent phenotype but were also more dangerous because they had a capsule that helped protect them from the patients' immune system.

## Bacteria Exhibit Amazing Levels of Metabolic Diversity

Metabolic diversity among the bacteria allows them to grow in many different environments. Some bacteria, such as the purple bacteria, green bacteria, and cyanobacteria, can meet their energy needs and fix carbon through different versions of photosynthesis. Organisms that can meet all of their energy needs without consuming organic carbon are called autotrophs. We can narrow the classification of photosynthetic members even more and call them photoautotrophs because they convert light energy into chemical energy that is used by the cell. Of these groups, only the cyanobacteria produce oxygen as a by-product. The purple and green bacteria only photosynthesize in the absence of oxygen and use different sources of electrons for generating high-energy reduced compounds. Often they use hydrogen sulphide ($H_2S$) rather than water.

Another class of autotrophs does not obtain energy from the Sun but rather from other compounds in their environment. Because they obtain energy from reduced compounds, they are called **chemoautotrophs**. Some fantastic organisms fall into this category. The archaea that live in hydrothermal vents (see Box 15.1) are an example. Iron-oxidizing bacteria are also considered chemoautotrophs. They are able to take electrons away from iron atoms and use them to power cellular metabolism. In essence, they use the energy from iron electrons to convert carbon dioxide into organic carbon so that the cells can grow. Because of their ability to get energy from strange places, chemoautotrophs are often the most important primary producers in otherwise barren locations.

At the other end of the metabolic spectrum are the heterotrophs. We can define **heterotrophs** as organisms that must consume organic carbon to survive. Most bacteria and archaea fall into this broad category. They obtain their energy and organic carbon from other organisms. They can digest and degrade materials from dead organisms or act as parasites and siphon off resources from living systems.

When we look at bacterial metabolism, we often forget that not only can bacteria use a wide range of molecules as food, but they also produce a wide range of molecules as waste. Sometimes their waste products are useful for us. The complex flavours of cheeses, for example, are the result of metabolic waste products from bacterial metabolism. Other times, bacterial metabolism can produce chemicals that are toxic. Depending on how the bacterial species lives, the production of toxins may prove to be beneficial to the bacteria and thus provide a selective advantage. Bacteria produce some very interesting toxins that affect humans and other animals. The bacterium *Vibrio cholerae* is the causative agent of the disease cholera. The symptoms of cholera include extensive vomiting and diarrhea, which can lead to extreme dehydration. The disease is caused by a toxin produced by *V. cholerae*, which tricks cells of the small intestine to release water—hence the cause of diarrhea. The selective advantage is that *V. cholerae* is transmitted from individual to individual through contaminated water supplies. So if a sick person pollutes the water supply, others could end up getting infected more easily. Another famous toxin is produced by the bacterium *Clostridium botulinum*. A strict anaerobe, *C. botulinum* produces a neurotoxin that can lead to paralysis. Of course, this bacterium is better known now as the source of botulinum toxin (Botox), and the toxin is commonly used in cosmetic procedures (see Box 15.2).

## STUDY BREAK

1. Which key structural feature of Gram-negative cells excludes the crystal violet stain, resulting in the cells not staining dark blue?
2. How might a capsule protect a bacterium from the immune system?
3. How can toxins produced by bacteria provide an advantage to the cells?

## 15.3 Domain Bacteria

When describing the relationships between bacteria, archaea, and eukaryotes in this chapter, we will follow the three-domain system. This separates the Bacteria from the Archaea and the Eukaryotes (Figure 15.2). This separation, and the further classification of organisms within the domain Bacteria, is based on both gene sequence data and morphological and biochemical traits. We should keep in mind, however, the connectedness of the Bacteria and the Archaea and remind ourselves that this linear branching classification does not take into account horizontal gene transfer. As we mentioned above, both transformation and transduction events are common in bacteria due to the existence of plasmids and the capacity for viruses to transfer genetic material between species (see Chapter 14). The limitations inherent in the linear branching classification have led some scientists, such as Dr. Ford Doolittle from

# LIFE ON THE EDGE 15.1
## Hyperthermophiles

In Chapter 11, we talked about *Thermus aquaticus*, the thermophilic (heat-loving) bacterium that Dr. Thomas Brock isolated from a hot spring in Yellowstone National Park in Wyoming and the use of its DNA polymerase in the process of PCR. However, despite *T. aquaticus*'s ability to grow at temperatures of up to 80°C, it is nowhere near the record holder in the "how hot can it get" challenge. Many researchers have searched for the most thermotolerant organism in an attempt to break the record. This search led to the term *hyperthermophiles*, or very hot-loving organisms. Over 70 new species of hyperthermophiles have been discovered since Brock isolated *T. aquaticus*, and the upper limit of survival has increased as well. The most extreme hyperthermophiles have been discovered living on the sides of hydrothermal vents in the deep ocean, where the pressure exerted by the water column keeps water in a liquid state well above 100°C.

In 2003, Kazem Kashefi and Derek Lovley from the University of Massachusetts were searching for hypothermophilic bacteria along a segment of the Juan de Fuca Ridge off the coast of Vancouver Island and Washington State. Near a black smoker called Finn **(Figure 1)**, with an estimated exhaust temperature of 300°C, and under 2200 m of water, they isolated a bacterium they wanted to study further. Once in the lab, they found that their isolate could not only grow at high temperatures, it could also grow in water above 100°C **(Figure 1c)**. When sterilizing lab equipment, researchers typically use a machine called an **autoclave**, which uses pressurized steam to heat the materials

to 121°C for between 10 to 30 minutes. Normally, this treatment will kill all the microbes in or on the equipment, leaving equipment sterile. However, in the case of Kashefi and Lovley's newly isolated archaea, it survived the autoclave treatment. In fact, not only did it survive the

sterilization procedure, it also continued to grow! This hyperthermophile doubled in numbers during a 24-hour exposure to 121°C. Kashefi and Lovely named their find Strain 121. Its official binomial name is *Geogemma barossii*, but Strain 121 seems to have a better ring to it.

**A.**

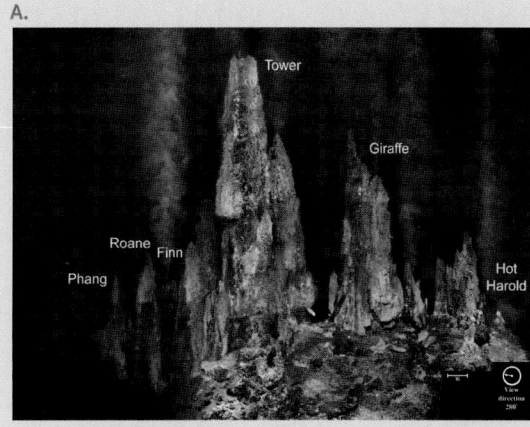

Kelley, D.S., J.R. Delaney, D.R. Yoerger (2001), "Geology and venting characteristics of the Mothra hydrothermal field, Endeavour segment, Juan de Fuca Ridge." *Geology*, 29:10, 959–962, 10.1130/0091 7613(2001)029<0959:GAVCOT>2.0.CO;2

**B.**

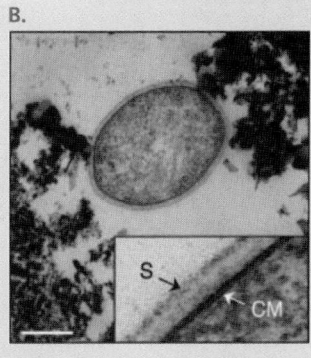

**C.**

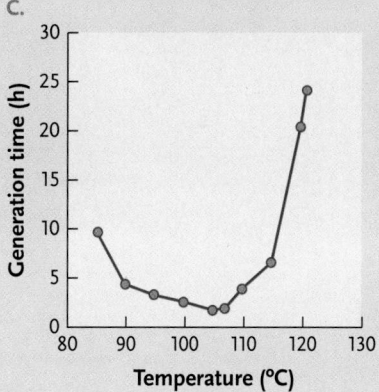

**FIGURE 1** Researchers examined active black smokers along the Juan de Fuca Ridge in a search for hyperthermophiles. Near Finn, third from the left above **(a)**, they found an archaea called Strain 121 **(b)**. Strain 121 grows the fastest (shorter generation time) at temperatures over 100°C **(c)**.

SOURCE: (B and C) From Kashefi, K. and Lovely, D.R., "Extending the upper temperature limit for life," *Science* 15 August 2003: Vol. 301 no. 5635 p. 934. Reprinted with permission from AAAS.

Dalhousie University in Halifax, to suggest that the branches of a tree of life should be shown as interwoven connections (Figure 15.2b). Some researchers are now even attempting to represent the tree of life in multiple dimensions to account for multiple horizontal gene transfer events over time.

To keep things simpler here, we will look at the six main groups within the domain Bacteria. Bacteria are placed into these six groups based on their similar structures and functions as well as their morphology and genomic sequences.

The six groups are the proteobacteria, green bacteria, cyanobacteria, gram-positive bacteria, spirochetes, and chlamydias (Figure 15.2a).

Proteobacteria are a highly diverse group of Gram-negative bacteria. They include purple photosynthetic bacteria that carry out a form of anaerobic photosynthesis with bacteriochlorophyll molecules that give the bacteria their characteristic purple colour. The purple bacteria develop internal membrane structures similar in function to that of the thylakoid membranes of

# THE MOLECULE BEHIND THE BIOLOGY 15.2
## Botulinum Toxin

The anaerobic bacterium *Clostridium botulinum* was long a greatly feared contaminant in improperly canned food. When food placed in cans is not properly processed, bacteria can survive in the product. The anaerobic environment inside a sealed can is the perfect environment for *C. botulinum*. This bacterium can grow and reproduce, leaving a swollen can as a calling card. The frightening part of *C. botulinum* contamination is not due to the spoiling of the food in the can but the deadly neurotoxin produced by this Gram-positive, rod-shaped bacterium **(Figure 1)**. Today, botulinum toxin is normally only a problem for individuals who can foods at home. However, botulism, the medical term for the disease caused by the botulinum toxin, can also be transmitted to infants who have an underdeveloped intestinal flora and to intravenous drug users who use dirty needles. The mortality rate of individuals affected by botulism has dropped from 70% in the early 1900s to almost zero today due to the introduction of antibiotics and accessibility of respirators to support the breathing of affected individuals.

Given the horrors of botulism, it is amazing to think that the botulinum toxin, in a formulation called Botox, is now used in non-surgical cosmetic procedures (Figure 1). Botox is a protein produced by the *C. botulinum* protein as it enters the spore stage. In animals, it blocks neuron-to-neuron communications through synapses. One effect is the relaxation of muscles. In cases of botulism, this can lead to muscle weakness, and in extreme cases, the muscles of the diaphragm are unable to function adequately for the individual to breathe. Botulism fatalities are normally due to suffocation. In cosmetic use, small doses of the toxin are injected into tissues to relax the muscles. This reduces wrinkles and is thought to provide an ageless look to older individuals. Although the importance of this use can be debated, the toxin does have other medical uses. Because of its effective neuron signal blocking ability, Botox can also be used to treat some migraine and headache disorders, as well as recurring muscle spasms. Thus, one of the most deadly biological agents known can have both significant positive medical impacts and perhaps keep us looking younger longer.

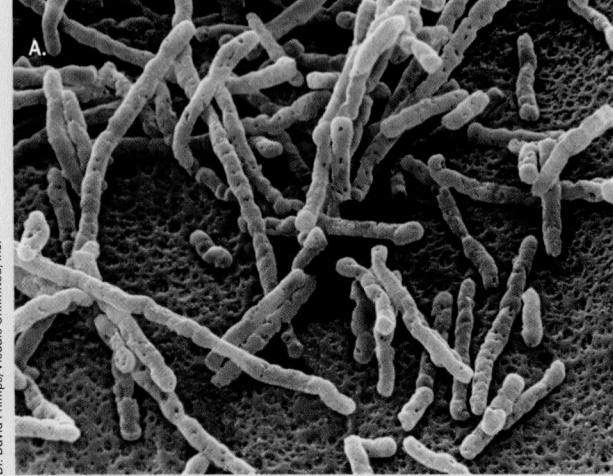

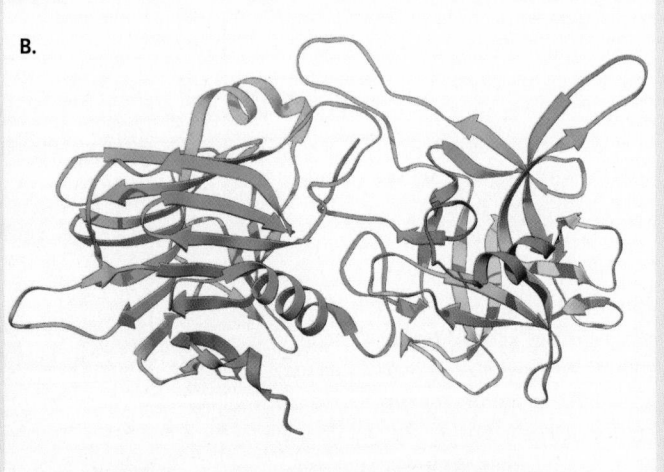

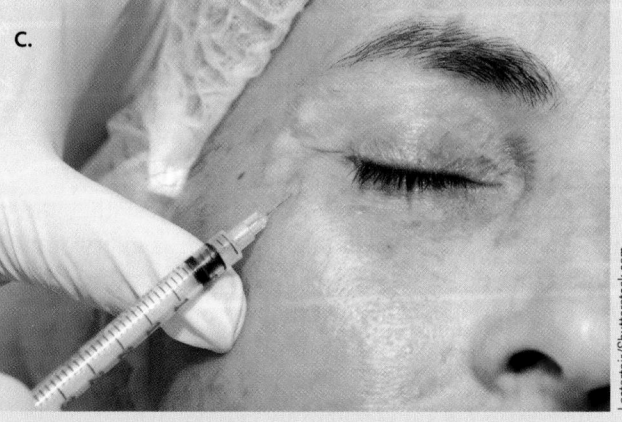

**FIGURE 1** The rod-shaped *Clostridium botulinum* bacteria **(a)** produces a protein toxin molecule **(b)** that affects nerve cell function. Botulinum toxin (Botox) injections **(c)** are now the most common form of cosmetic procedure.

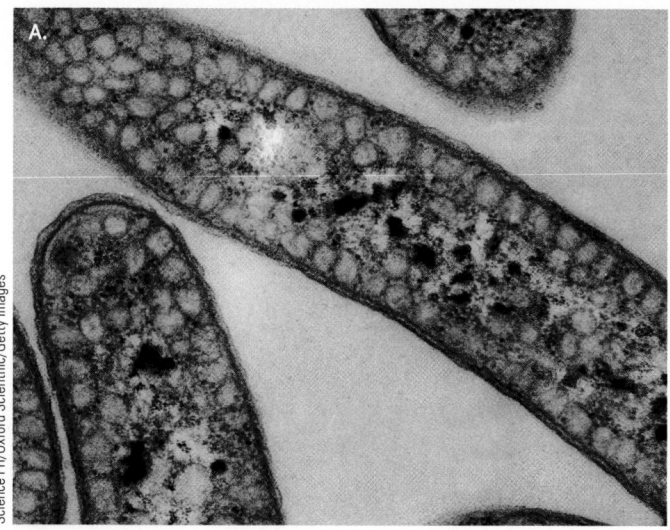

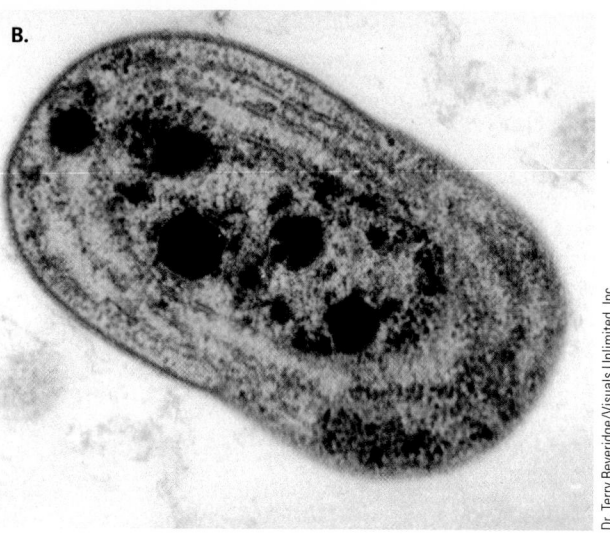

**FIGURE 15.8** Bacterial photosynthesis is also highly diverse. Purple bacteria such as *Rhodospirillum* sp. **(a)** perform anaerobic photosynthesis, whereas cyanobacteria such as *Synechococcus* sp. **(b)** perform oxygenic photosynthesis, much like higher plants.

chloroplasts **(Figure 15.8a)**. Many of the proteobacteria are thus self-sufficient photoautotrophs. They are able to obtain energy from non-living sources and turn inorganic carbon into organic compounds. However, not all members of the proteobacteria are autotrophs; many species must obtain the energy they need to grow and reproduce from the consumption of other materials. The gut microbe *E. coli*, which we have talked about in Chapter 11, falls into this group. It is therefore classified as a heterotroph.

Cyanobacteria are a less diverse group than the proteobacteria. They perform oxygenic photosynthesis using chlorophyll and thus are also autotrophs. They also produce specialized thylakoid membranes to perform photosynthesis. The thylakoid membranes give some cyanobacteria a fingerprint-like appearance **(Figure 15.8b)**. The bacterium that went through endosymbiosis to become a chloroplast is predicted to have been a cyanobacterium. These early photosynthesizers are also thought to have been primarily responsible for the oxygenation of Earth's

atmosphere that occurred approximately 2.5 billion years ago (see Box 2.3 in Chapter 2). As we will see with many types of bacteria, cyanobacteria exhibit very complex metabolic features. Unlike higher plants, some cyanobacteria are capable of using the chemical energy they convert from sunlight to convert atmospheric nitrogen gas into a form of nitrogen that cells can use for growth. This organic nitrogen is often a limiting nutrient that is needed for protein and nucleic acid biosynthesis. Making use of this trait, rice farmers have used *Anabaena* sp. (a genus of cyanobacteria) in their flooded fields as a source of nitrogen. In this case, the *Anabaena* cells form a symbiotic relationship with the water fern *Azolla* **(Figure 15.9)**. Because the oxygen produced by photosynthesis inhibits the function of the enzyme required to turn nitrogen gas into organic nitrogen, *Anabaena* forms specialized cells called **heterocysts** that do not photosynthesize **(Figure 15.9a)**. Heterocysts are nonphotosynthetic, meaning that they do not produce oxygen. In this way, *Anabaena* is able to spatially separate oxygenic production from nitrogen fixation.

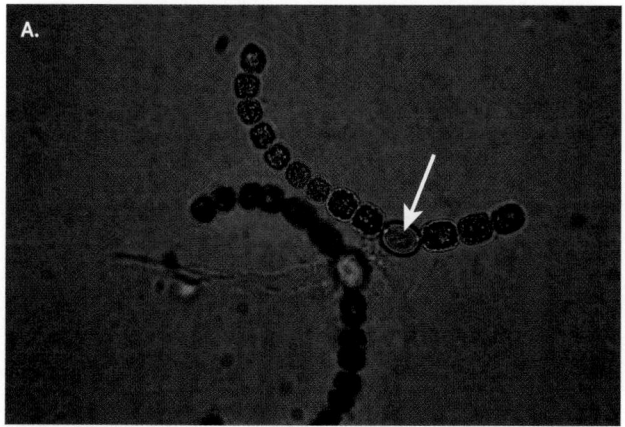

**FIGURE 15.9** The cyanobacteria *Anabaena* **(a)** forms a symbiotic relationship with the water fern *Azolla* **(b)**. The cyanobacteria fixes nitrogen using the specialized heterocyst (arrow).

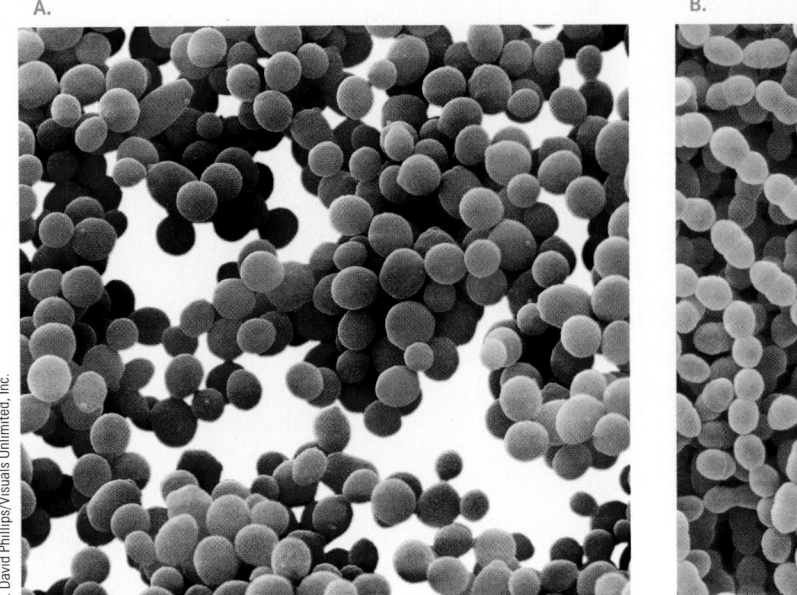

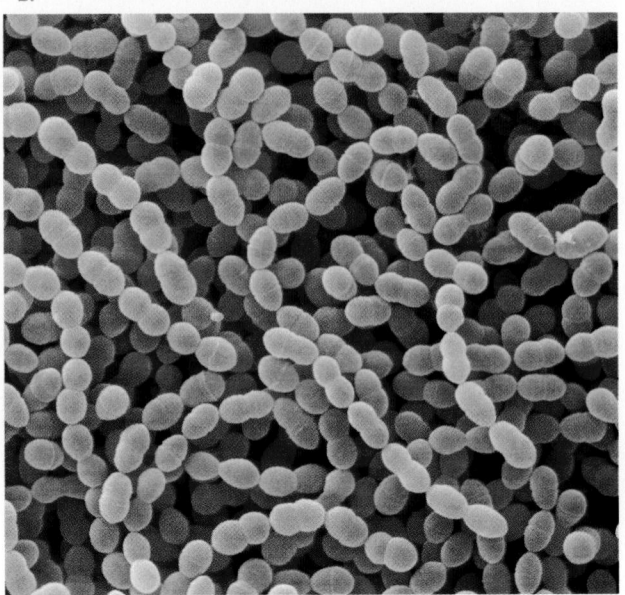

**FIGURE 15.10** Some members of the Gram-positive bacteria are pathogenic to humans. *Staphylococcus* sp. **(a)** and *Streptococcus* sp. **(b)** are common examples.

The green sulphur bacteria are another photosynthetic group of Gram-negative bacteria. They also contain chlorophyll and use it to absorb light energy for photosynthesis. Like purple bacteria, the green sulphur bacteria are anaerobic, and rather than taking electrons from water to produce oxygen, the way plants and cyanobacteria do, they take electrons from other compounds, such as sulphide and iron. This led to their being called green sulphur bacteria.

Remember from Section 15.2 that the Gram-positive bacteria are classified based on the composition of their cell wall. The Gram-positive bacteria are the single group; they are incredibly diverse in how they live and interact with other organisms in the biosphere. A number of Gram-positive bacteria cause diseases in humans and other animals. For example, *Staphylococcus* sp. **(Figure 15.10a)** can

cause septic shock, pneumonia, and even meningitis. *Streptococcus* sp. **(Figure 15.10b)** can cause strep throat, and as Griffith demonstrated, they can also cause pneumonia. Lucky for us, the Gram-positive cell wall is particularly sensitive to penicillin-class antibiotics, allowing us to more easily control the infections they cause. As part of the diversity we see in bacteria, this class of bacteria can also be used for food production, with *Lactobacillus* sp. being used in the production of yogurt and cheeses.

The spirochetes are classified based on their long, corkscrew shape. They have an unusual form of movement, facilitated by their long, filamentous shape **(Figure 15.11a)**. The cells appear to be wound around a central fibre and move by a flexing motion of the cell. This type of locomotion works best in thick, viscous solutions.

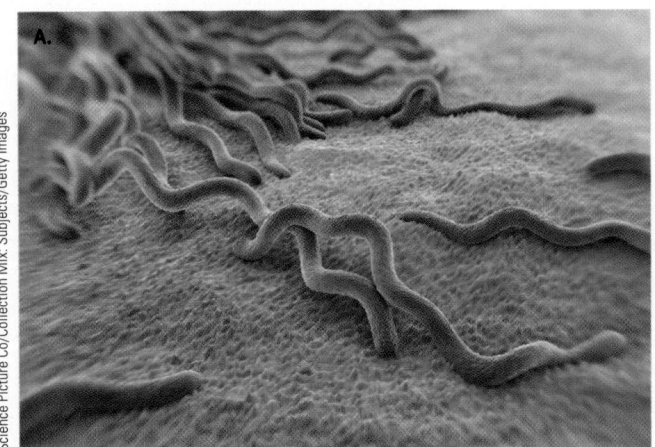

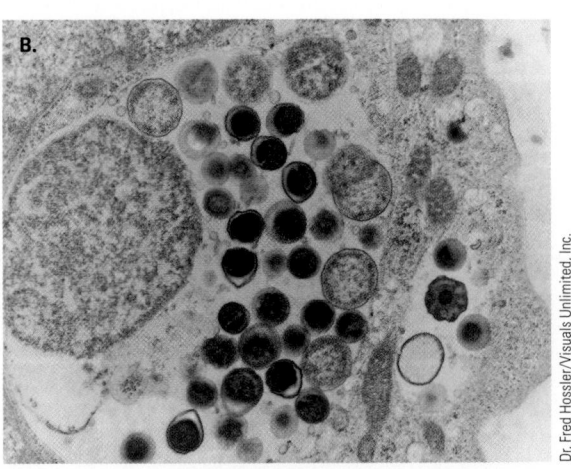

**FIGURE 15.11** Spirochetes have a long, corkscrew-shaped cell **(a)**. *Chlamydia* sp. are obligate intracellular parasites and must live inside other cells to reproduce **(b)**. In this artificially coloured TEM image, we can see the dark blue–coloured *Chlamydia* in the cytoplasm of a cell. The host nucleus is coloured purple, and other organelles are brown.

Spirochetes are often found in mud and even sewage. It is interesting that the spirochete form of motion is at its best in environments where flagella would be almost useless. Like most bacteria, the spirochetes include disease-causing organisms, such as *Treponema pallidum*, the bacterium that causes syphilis, and *Borrelia burgdorferi*, the cause of Lyme disease.

The last group of bacteria is the chlamydias. They are a strange group of bacteria. They are obligate intracellular parasites, meaning that they must live inside other cells to complete their life cycle **(Figure 15.11b)**. In a way, this makes them quite similar to viruses in their requirement for a host to reproduce. There are four species of chlamydia. One infects humans and is the most common sexually transmitted disease. The other three species infect other mammals, ranging from mice and hamsters to koalas and swine.

Even with this cursory overview, we can see that the diversity of bacteria is immense. In truth, we still do not know the extent of this diversity. We are most familiar with bacterial pathogens because we study them as a way to better understand the diseases that they cause. Of course, even in the study of pathogens, we are much more knowledgeable about bacteria that cause diseases in humans, our pets, and agriculturally important plants and animals. One of the greatest challenges facing researchers trying to estimate the number of different bacterial species is how to define what constitutes a different species. In fact, scientists are still debating what indicators and standards should be used to define a bacterial species. We used to examine bacteria by culturing them in a lab. This allowed us to determine their shape and size while also characterizing their metabolic properties. However, many bacterial species cannot be cultured under laboratory conditions. This problem has led scientists to make estimates of bacterial diversity using genome sequences. Scientists extract the DNA found in an environmental sample (such as a scoop of soil or the fecal matter of a grizzly bear) and then try to see how many different bacterial DNA sequences they uncover. However, even this technique misses rare individuals. It is also difficult to compare samples taken from different locations as **species richness** (the number of species present in one location) can vary greatly. It may never be possible to determine exactly how many species of bacteria exist on Earth. At the moment, many researchers are focused more on determining how many species of bacteria live in the human gut, and even that can be an ever-changing mixture that is hard to quantify.

## STUDY BREAK

1. Draw a table listing the six bacterial groups and fill in a defining characteristic for each group.

## 15.4 Domain Archaea

Looking at Figure 15.2, we can see three branches of archaea splitting off from the original ancestor of the archaeans. The three groups are called the euryarchaeota, the crenarchaeota, and the korarchaeota. However, the classification of the archaea is changing as we discover more species. Of course, as we mentioned for bacteria, a clear definition of what constitutes an archaea species is lacking. Thus, scientists are having problems grouping new archaea together with those we have already characterized. Members of the korarchaeota pose particular challenges as so far we have not been able to culture these cells under laboratory conditions. Thus, all of our knowledge comes from genome sequences from environmental samples, leaving us much to learn about the biology of these fascinating organisms.

### Archaea's Structure and Function Allow Them to Survive in Extreme Environments

Archaea have a number of structural differences common to both bacteria and eukaryotes that aid in their survival. As we will see in the next section, many archaea inhabit so-called **extreme environments**. These are environmental niches that pose significant barriers to the existence of life. Areas of very high or low temperatures, high salt content, or low oxygen are often thought of as uninhabitable; this is where we often find archaea. One interesting adaptation we find in some archaea is in the chemistry of their membrane lipids. We know that all cells are delimited from their external environment by their plasma membrane (Chapter 3). The selectively permeable plasma membrane is crucial for maintaining cellular homeostasis, and in bacteria, it is often also required for energy generation. To maintain its function under adverse conditions, the plasma membrane lipids of the archaea are a little bit different. They maintain the **amphipathic** nature required for the molecules, meaning that they have a polar end and a non-polar end (see the Purple Pages for a refresher). However, rather than having fatty acids with double bonds, the fatty acids found in archaea membrane lipids are branched. This is unlike the linear fatty acids seen in bacteria and eukaryotes **(Figure 15.12, p. 340)**. The branched fatty acids take up more space in the membrane, much like fatty acids that contain double bonds. The fatty acids of archaea have even been shown to form rings within the membrane. This produces structures similar to cholesterol, a membrane-stabilizing molecule not found in archaea or bacteria. Finally, when we look at some of the lipids in the plasma membranes of archaea, they span the lipid bilayer. In bacteria and eukaryotes, each side of the plasma membrane is separate, made up of different phospholipids. Only

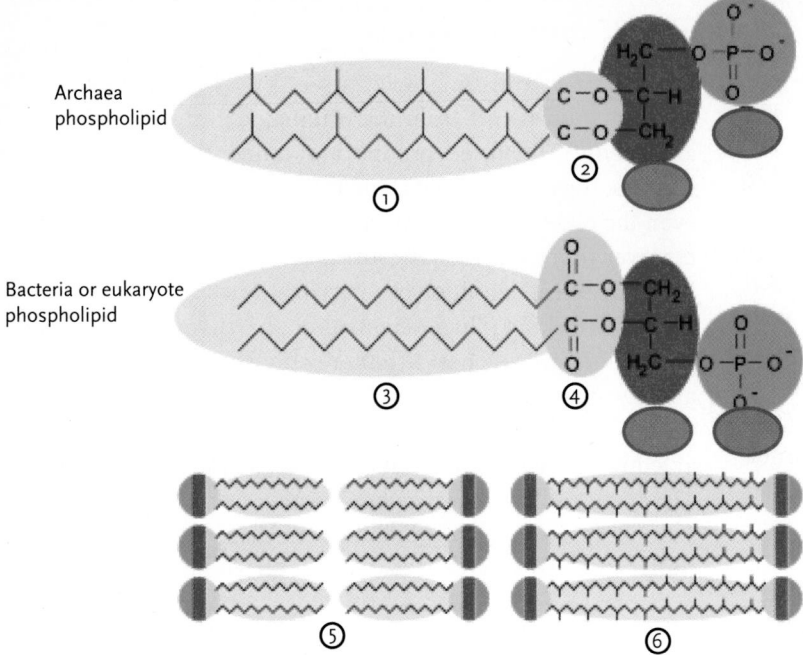

Archaea phospholipid

Bacteria or eukaryote phospholipid

**FIGURE 15.12** Archaea plasma membranes contain branched chain fatty acids (1) attached to the polar head group by ether linkages (2). In contrast, bacterial and eukaryotic phospholipids contain straight chain fatty acids (3) attached to the polar head group by ester linkages (4). While bacterial and eukaryotic membranes are composed of two leaflets (5), some archaea have membranes where long-chain fatty acids have polar groups at each end and form single transmembrane lipids (6).

SOURCE: "Archaea membrane" by Franciscosp2 - self-made (using xfig). Licensed under Public domain via Wikimedia Commons - http://commons.wikimedia.org/wiki/File:Archaea_membrane.svg#mediaviewer/File:Archaea_membrane.svg

proteins have been shown to cross the plasma membrane of bacteria and eukaryotes. In archaea cells, some fatty acids are linked together so that the ends of the fatty acid chains present in opposite sides of the plasma membrane are connected, creating a transmembrane lipid anchor that has a polar head group on each end.

The base of the tree of life (Figure 15.2) places the archaea closer to the eukaryotes due to similarities in genomic sequences. There are several characteristics shared by the two groups of organisms that help reinforce this organization. Only the archaea and eukaryotes wind their DNA around histone proteins, despite the archaea having a relatively simple, circular DNA molecule. This is another trait that is thought to protect the genome of the archaea cells. Histones keep the DNA sequence more compact and less exposed to chemical or UV stress. The archaea also have some eukaryote-like ribosomal proteins. Thus, we can observe a number of structural differences when comparing bacteria and archaea, many of which appear to be adaptations to life in harsher environments.

## We Find Archaea Inhabiting Extreme Environments

One of the reasons that the archaea were once thought to represent the first life on Earth is their ability to sur-

vive, grow, and thrive in harsh environments. Organisms that thrive in extreme environments such as salt lakes, hot springs, and glaciers are called **extremophiles** (see Box 15.1). The cells of extremophiles face extreme challenges. **Hyperthermophiles**, for example, featured in Box 15.2, live in environments above 60°C. To survive there, they need proteins that do not denature, membranes that are stable and able to perform their job of compartmentalizing the cell, and to protect their DNA from denaturation and copying mistakes. We saw some of the structural adaptations that archaea have for coping with these changes. The proteins of hyperthermophiles are more heat stable, their DNA is protected in part by histones, and some, such as *Pyrococcus furiosus*, have a DNA polymerase with a high degree of proofreading capacity. The fantastic colours associated with the hot springs of Yellowstone National Park are due to the presence of various species of hyperthermophilic archaea and, in the cooler regions, bacteria and even eukaryotic algae **(Figure 15.13a)**.

At the other end of the temperature spectrum, **psychrophiles** (the term comes from the Greek words *cryos*, meaning cold, and *phylein*, meaning love of) are cells that grow at very low temperatures. Typically, psychrophiles are defined by the inability to grow at temperatures above 16°C. Some psychrophiles grow in sea ice, where the temperature of liquid water can get as low as −15°C due to pockets of high salt content. Psychrophiles have a broader lineage than the hyperthermophiles as there are psychrophilic bacteria, archaea, and even some simple eukaryotes. Adaptations that allow these cells to survive again focus on the plasma membrane. It must be kept in a gel-like state to maintain cellular homeostasis. These cells also need enzymes that are adapted to functioning at low temperatures.

It seems that almost every extreme environment on Earth has some form of life associated with it. Salt ponds are often coloured by the archaea that live in the waters **(Figure 15.13b)**. Extremely salt-tolerant archaea are called **halophiles**. The fantastic colour of the Rio Tinto in Spain, translated as Red River, is due to the **acidophilic** archaea that are able to survive its highly acidic and metal-contaminated water (Figure 15.13b). The Rio Tinto drains an iron deposit, and the iron atoms in the water serve as a source of food for the chemoautotrophs. We often wonder how cells can survive in these incredibly harsh, stressful conditions. We find that they have equally incredible systems for coping with the stress. Although we may find that

**FIGURE 15.13** Extremophiles lend their colour to seemingly uninhabitable locations, such as the hyperthermophiles of Grand Prismatic Spring in Yellowstone National Park **(a)**, halophiles in salt evaporation ponds **(b)**, and red acidophiles of the Rio Tinto in Spain **(c)**.

extremophiles are slow-growing organisms, most extremophiles do not have much competition for resources. Thus, extremophiles may not have to have the highest growth rate or the best mechanisms for obtaining nutrients; they often just need to survive and slowly reproduce. When everything else dies, surviving is equal to winning. Understanding how archaea can survive under such harsh conditions may help researchers in their quest for knowledge about how life first evolved on Earth. Perhaps some of the extreme environments inhabited by the archaea supplied the "spark" needed to get life started.

## Study Break

1. Define the term *hyperthermophile*.
2. What adaptations are necessary for archaea to survive in extreme hot and extreme cold?

## PUTTING IT IN PERSPECTIVE

If nothing else, when we think of bacteria and archaea, we should think of the level of diversity that they represent. Living in almost every place on Earth, they are vital components of our biosphere. Consider that there are more bacterial cells in our bodies than there are human cells. What a creepy concept. Although we use many types of bacteria in biotechnological processes and we know of many bacteria that cause disease, there are many times more that remain undiscovered. Understanding how bacteria function is thus important not only in how we treat some diseases but also because they represent the most primitive living organisms on Earth. They are descended from our oldest ancestors. Bacteria are likely to give us our closest look at what the first living organisms on Earth were like. Archaea provide us with an insight into where it is possible for life to exist and to what lengths evolution can go to survive in extreme habitats. At the border between science and science fiction, some scientists suggest that archaea may be the first organisms we use to colonize other planets. It has been suggested that we take psychrophiles with us to Mars in an attempt to colonize the red planet.

# KEY CONCEPTS REVIEW AND QUESTIONS

## 15.1 Defining What It Means to Be a Bacterium or Archaeon

We can define the bacteria and archaea based on their location in the tree of life. As two of the three main branches, along with eukaryotes, they are fundamentally different types of organisms. Perhaps the easiest way to define the bacteria and archaea is that they do not have the characteristics of eukaryotes. They do not have membrane-bound organelles, nor do they have a nucleus in their cells.

1. How does the process of horizontal gene transfer make delineating the first branches of the tree of life more challenging?

2. Make a table comparing the traits of bacteria, archaea, and eukaryotes.

## 15.2 Bacterial Structure and Function

The structure of bacterial cells is species dependent and is often used as a taxonomic indicator. In the early days of microscopy, bacteria were characterized by their cell shape into the broad categories of cocci, bacilli, and spirilla. Secondary characteristics related to their growth form were used to further delineate the cells to at least the genus level—hence *Streptococcus* sp. The development of the Gram stain technique allowed the further description of bacterial cells based on their cell wall structure. Gram-negative cells, which are often more difficult to control using antibiotics, exclude the crystal violet stain because of their outer membrane. Bacteria can also be characterized by their metabolic characteristics. Autotrophs are able to obtain energy from light or inorganic compounds, whereas heterotrophs require an organic source of energy.

3. What aspect of the Gram-negative cell wall structure makes the cells more resistant to antibiotics?

4. Define the terms *autotroph*, *photoautotroph*, and *heterotroph*.

5. How does a sex pilus allow bacteria to exchange genetic information?

## 15.3 Domain Bacteria

The domain Bacteria is made up of six groups of organisms as we move up the tree of life. Their subclassification is made based on taxonomic characteristics such as whether they have a Gram-positive or a Gram-negative cell wall, whether they are an autotroph, their ability to perform oxygenic photosynthesis, or whether they are an intracellular parasite. It is incredibly difficult to estimate just how many different types of bacterial species exist because it is hard to tell them apart.

6. Why do scientists place all of the Gram-negative bacteria into one subgroup?

## 15.4 Domain Archaea

Much less is known about the archaea. This is due in part to them being difficult to culture under laboratory conditions. In addition, because they are generally non-pathogenic, there has been less interest in studying the archaea. However, we are now finding out just how interesting they are. The capacity to survive under extreme environmental conditions may help scientists better understand how life evolved on Earth. We can see how particular traits found in the archaea allow them to survive where other organisms cannot.

7. What advantage does the presence of branched-chain fatty acids provide archaea cells?

8. In what way do high temperatures, low temperatures, high salt content, and an acidic environment all pose a similar problem to living organisms?

# Protists

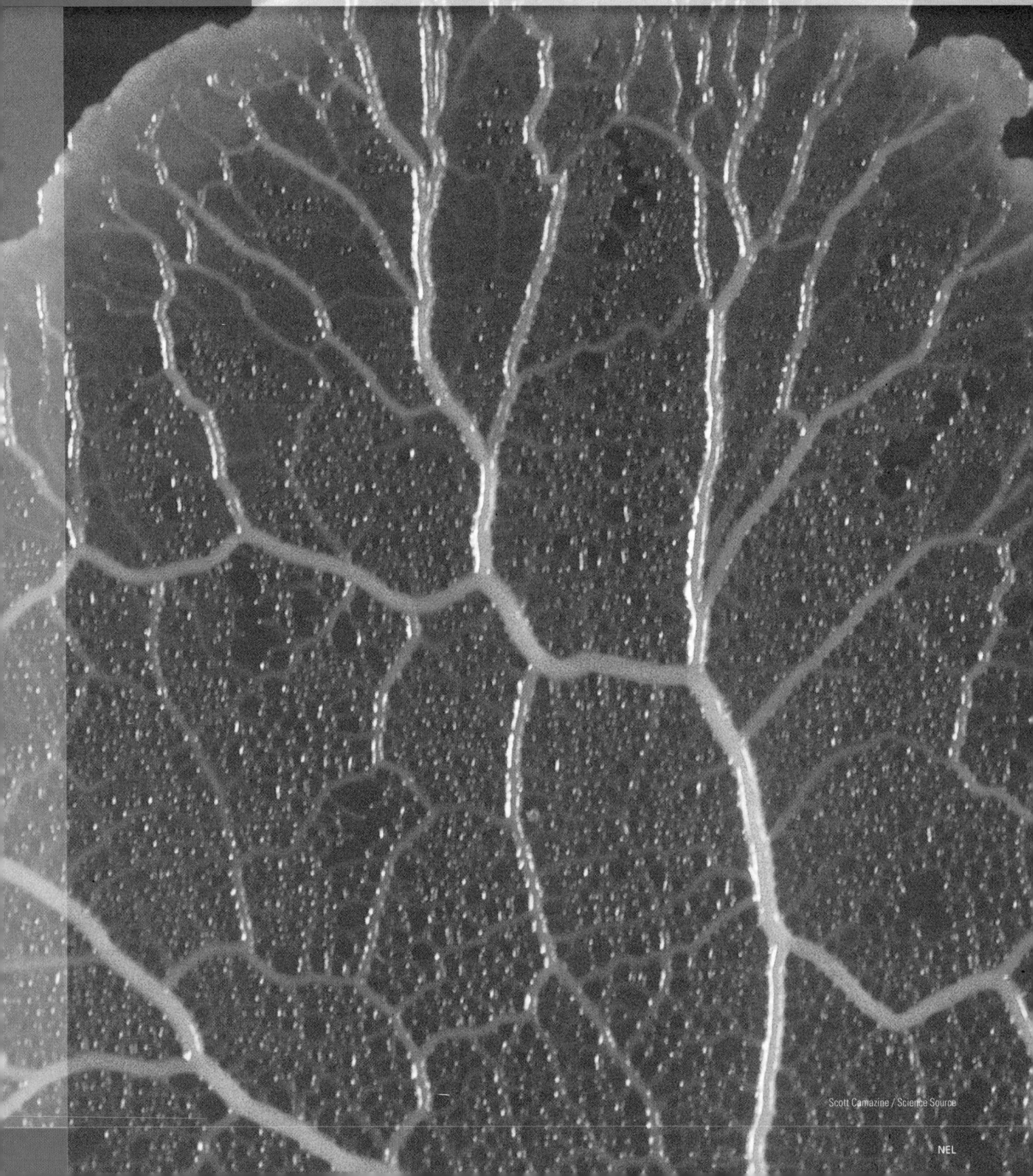

## WHY IT MATTERS

When asked to imagine a cat and mouse, we typically think of the hunter and the hunted. The cat is a powerful, skilled predator. The mouse normally hides and takes evasive measures when it senses the presence of a cat. We would not consider it normal for a mouse to walk up to a cat and sniff its paws. However, mice infected with a common, microscopic parasite lose their fear of cats. Indeed, mice infected with *Toxoplasma gondii* are attracted to the scent of cat urine. A unicellular eukaryote, *T. gondii* is classified as a member of the kingdom Protista. Cats are the primary host of the *T. gondii* parasite. Although this protist can infect most warm-blooded animals, to reproduce sexually, the parasite must be present in the intestinal tract of a member of the cat family (Felidae). Infection with *T. gondii* causes a disease called toxoplasmosis. In mice suffering from toxoplasmosis, a loss of their fear of cats is observed as a strange behavioural change **(Figure 16.1)**. This is thought to provide an evolutionary advantage for *T. gondii*. If the mice are less afraid of the smell of cats, they are more likely to be eaten, allowing the population of *T. gondii* cells present in the mouse to enter the digestive system of the cat. Within the feline digestive system, these parasites can sexually reproduce, and their offspring can be passed on in the fecal material, ready to infect other hosts. What an amazing adaptation in such a simple organism!

Researchers have now discovered that the change in the perception of cats by mice infected by *T. gondii* is permanent. Behavioural scientists infected mice with *T. gondii* and observed the expected loss of fear of cat odours. They then gave the mice drugs to kill the *T. gondii* cells, curing them of toxoplasmosis. Even months after being cured, the mice still had reduced levels of fear in response to cats and cat odours. A similar study demonstrated that rats infected with *T. gondii* demonstrated not only an increase in their attraction to cats but also a decrease in their attraction to non-predatory animals. Thus, it has been suggested that toxoplasmosis leads to an overall increase in risk-taking behaviour in rodents.

The parasitic effects of *T. gondii* are not limited to rodents. It is estimated that over 60 million North Americans are infected with *T. gondii* at a given time.

Tsekhmister/Shutterstock.com

**FIGURE 16.1** Mice infected with the protist *Toxoplasma gondii* permanently lose their fear of cats and are attracted to the smell of cat urine.

In healthy humans, there are few, if any, symptoms, although pregnant women and immunocompromised individuals may be affected to a greater degree. Typical symptoms are similar to those of the flu: fever, fatigue, and body aches. In more severe cases, the infection can lead to seizures, confusion, and a loss of coordination. Toxoplasmosis in humans has also been suggested to alter behaviour. In fact, a number of elaborate theories have suggested that toxoplasmosis can alter risk-taking behaviour, lead to schizophrenic traits, and, on a global scale, influence the rise and fall of nations. However, these hypotheses have not been empirically tested. Anecdotal evidence and correlations may be observed, but it has not been clearly demonstrated that toxoplasmosis causes these changes. Be sure to read the section in the Purple Pages that discusses the scientific method and difference between correlation and causation.

## 16.1 What Are Protists?

Protists are a challenging group of organisms to study. Protists are the closest organisms, evolutionarily, to the first eukaryotes. They were formed by the process of endosymbiosis, during which an engulfed bacterium established a permanent partnership with its host. Rather than being digested, the engulfed bacterium provided a selective advantage to the host. Over time, the engulfed bacterium became what we call the mitochondrion (see Chapter 3 for more details on endosymbiosis). As the relationship between the mitochondrion and the host cell developed, the host cell took on many of the functions previously performed by the endosymbiont. Genes encoding most of the proteins needed by the mitochondria are found in the nucleus, for example. A subsequent endosymbiotic event, in which a cyanobacterium was engulfed, led to the development of the chloroplast. Once again, we see that most of the proteins required by the chloroplast are encoded by genes found in the nucleus.

Protists are the most immediate descendants of these two endosymbiotic events. They are single-celled eukaryotes containing mitochondria and, in some cases, chloroplasts. As a result, the protists are at the base of eukaryote evolutionary trees. The origin of protists as products of one or two endosymbiotic events explains their relationship with both plant and animal lineages. Similar to bacteria, protists often have short generation times, allowing them to adapt to suit their environment quite quickly. As a result, protists are present in almost all environments on the planet that contain sufficient amounts of liquid water.

### Protists Are Related to Plants and Animals

One of the challenges faced by scientists is deciding how to characterize protists. Because they are eukaryotes, it is relatively simple to separate protists from the bacteria and archaea. However, after that separation, things get challenging, and if you are a **protistologist**, they get pretty fun. In Linnaeus's early phylogenetic classifications, some protists were placed in the plant kingdom and others in the animal kingdom. This characterization worked for many species of protists. Algae, which represent any photoautotrophic protist, contain chloroplasts and perform oxygenic photosynthesis; thus, they were placed in the plant kingdom. In fact, some researchers use algae as model organisms for the study of plant metabolic processes. Many of the basic steps of photosynthesis were elucidated using green algal species such as *Chlamydomonas reinhardtii* **(Figure 16.2a)** and *Chlorella vulgaris*. Similarly, protists such as *Amoeba proteus* and *Trypanosoma gambiense* have many of the characteristics of simple animal cells **(Figure 16.2, b** and **c)**. They are mobile heterotrophs and contain the same organelles commonly found in the cells of more complex animals.

However, many protists seem to blur the line between plants and animals. It became a challenge to place them into either the plant or the animal kingdom. A classic example that led to many arguments in terms of placement in the two-kingdom system is *Euglena gracilis* **(Figure 16.2 d)**. The Euglenozoa are a group characterized by the presence of chloroplasts, similar to those of plants, and the ability to move using flagella. These organisms can photosynthesize and live as autotrophs, but they can also capture and consume food particles using phagocytosis, a characteristic of heterotrophs. Because of this flexibility in how Euglenozoa obtain the energy they need for growth and reproduction, they are said to be **mixotrophic**: they use both autotroph and heterotroph lifestyles. It was the continued discovery of mixotrophic protists such as *Euglena* that led to the proposal of a third kingdom of life: **Protista**. More modern classification systems have further divided the eukaryote domain into several supergroups based primarily on DNA sequence data. Although many scientists favour different versions of the classification system, the protists fall into all of the major groupings. In **Figure 16.3**, we present one hypothesis about how the different groups of eukaryotes are related to each other. The tree represents theoretical groupings made by comparing a combination of DNA sequences and structural morphology. We see that all of the supergroups contain species of protists. Through the rest of Section 16.1, we will examine the characteristics of species found in each of the groups illustrated in Figure 16.3, from left to right.

### The Excavates Lack True Mitochondria

The excavates are a supergroup of eukaryotes consisting of only protist species that lack a true mitochondria. If you recall, mitochondria are one of the main distinguishing features found in all eukaryotes and help distinguish them from prokaryotes. The lack of true mitochondria in the excavates led biologists to suggest that these organisms may be a link between the bacteria and archaea and the

A.
B.
C.
D.
Wim van Egmond/Visuals Unlimited, Inc.
Wim van Egmond/Visuals Unlimited, Inc.
Michael Abbey / Science Source
Eric V. Grave / Science Source

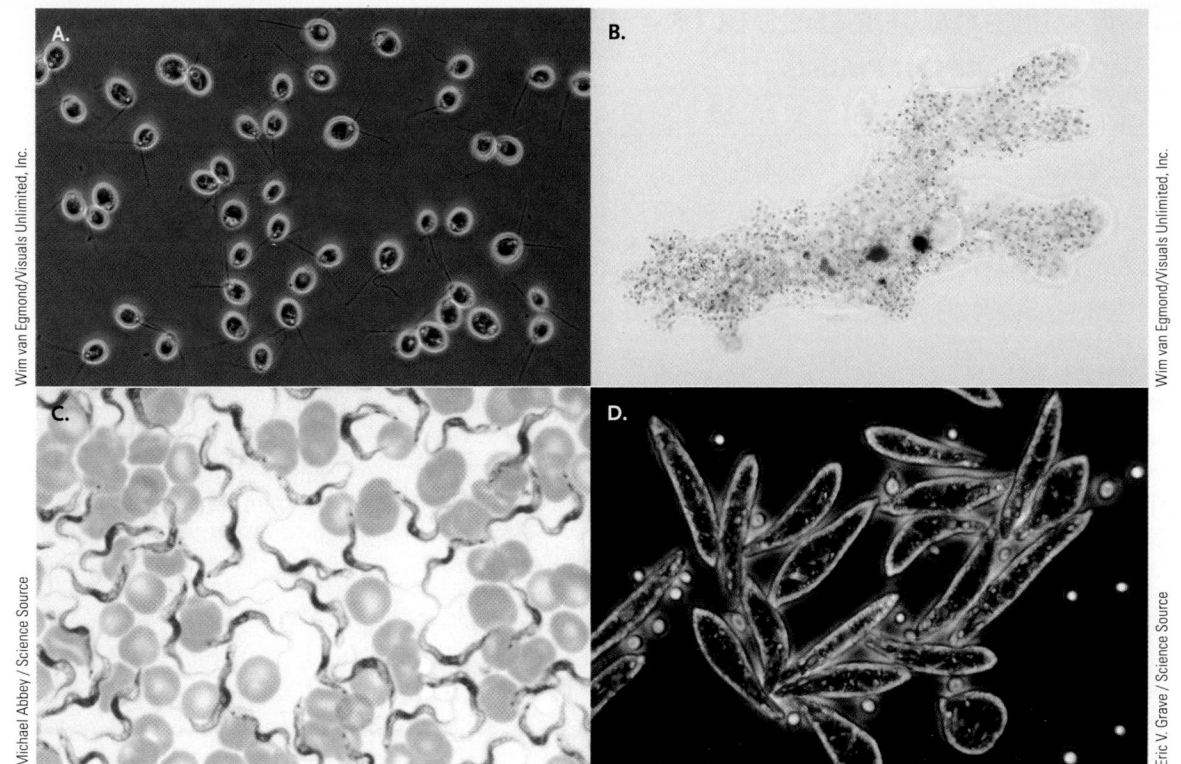

**FIGURE 16.2** Protists can fall into the plant (**(a)** *Chlamydomonas eugametos*) or animal (**(b)** *Amoeba proteus*; **(c)** *Trypanosoma gambiense*) categories, whereas some fall in between (**(d)** *Euglena gracilis*).

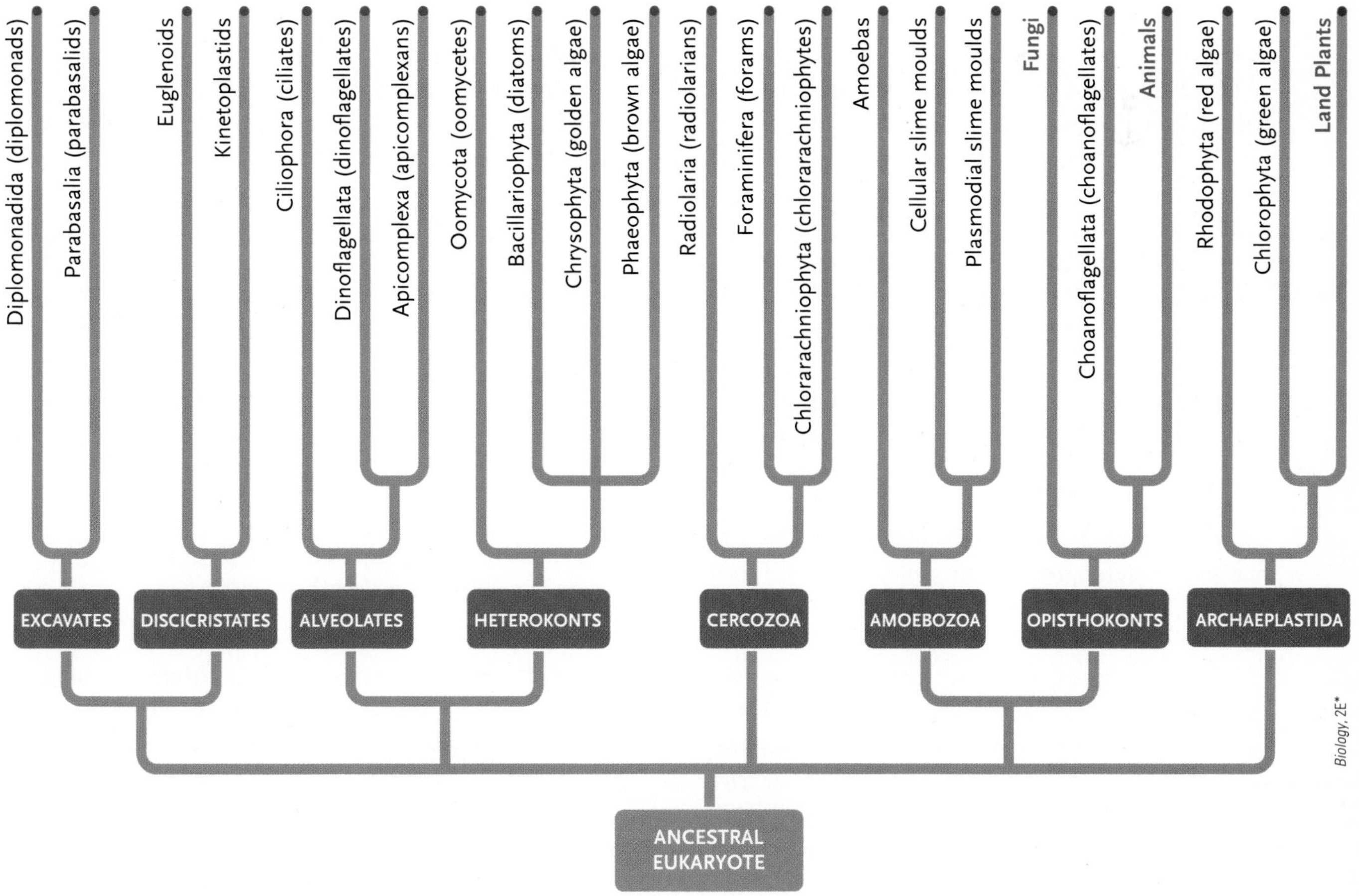

Diplomonadida (diplomonads)
Parabasalia (parabasalids)
Euglenoids
Kinetoplastids
Ciliophora (ciliates)
Dinoflagellata (dinoflagellates)
Apicomplexa (apicomplexans)
Oomycota (oomycetes)
Bacillariophyta (diatoms)
Chrysophyta (golden algae)
Phaeophyta (brown algae)
Radiolaria (radiolarians)
Foraminifera (forams)
Chlorarachniophyta (chlorarachniophytes)
Amoebas
Cellular slime moulds
Plasmodial slime moulds
Fungi
Choanoflagellata (choanoflagellates)
Animals
Rhodophyta (red algae)
Chlorophyta (green algae)
Land Plants
EXCAVATES
DISCICRISTATES
ALVEOLATES
HETEROKONTS
CERCOZOA
AMOEBOZOA
OPISTHOKONTS
ARCHAEPLASTIDA
ANCESTRAL EUKARYOTE
Biology, 2E*

**FIGURE 16.3** A phylogeny of the eukaryotes.

## LIFE ON THE EDGE 16.1
### Termite Gut Protists

It may seem like an odd place to look for new life forms that could help us better describe the tree of life, or even help us in our quest for more ecofriendly fuels, but the gut of termites has been a gold mine over the past few years. Researchers from the Department of Botany at the University of British Columbia recently discovered two new protists in the gut of the Cuban subterranean termite (*Prorhinotermes simplex*) **(Figure 1a)**. These two new protists were named *Cthulhu macrofasciculumque* (Figure 1a) and *Cthylla microfasciculumque* after the hideous, godlike creature described by the science fiction writer H.P. Lovecraft **(Figure 1c)**. Apparently, the numerous long flagella of *C. macrofasciculumque* reminded the discoverers of Lovecraft's description of the legendary Cthulhu.

Considering the lifestyle of these two organisms, to the termite, they are more of a help than a monster. Termites, like many multicellular organisms that live strictly on plant material, are generally unable to digest lignin and cellulose, the complex organic polymers found in plant cell walls (see the Purple Pages for an overview of cellulose and lignin). Thus, to extract the energy of the chemical bonds of cellulose and lignin, the termite relies on an ecosystem of bacteria and protists that live in their gut. Much like the bacteria that aid us in digestion, the symbionts that live in the gut of the termite provide an advantage, while getting a service in return. The termite symbionts *C. macrofasciculumque* and *C. microfasciculumque* possess enzymes capable of catalyzing the breakdown of cellulose and lignin into glucose and simple amino acids. This provides the termite with a usable source of nutrition. Researchers have demonstrated that termites are absolutely dependent on the presence of these symbionts within their digestive system. Without them, the termites would starve to death, regardless of how much plant material they ate.

The protists, on the other hand, benefit from obtaining a protective home. Living in the hindgut of the termite would be a strange environment for us. It would contain almost no oxygen, which suits the members of the parabasala because they do not perform aerobic respiration. The protists also receive a steady source of food within the gut of the termite. Unlike free-living protists, their food comes to them.

Biotechnologists studying ways to extract energy from cellulose are interested in these types of protists because of their ability to digest cellulose and lignin at low temperatures. One approach to the production of biofuels is the fermentation of corn, wood chips, and grass cuttings into ethanol, which can then be

---

eukaryotes. However, further study suggests that members of the excavates have some form of mitochondrial remnant, which no longer produces ATP by oxidative phosphorylation. Instead, these organisms generate ATP using glycolysis (check back to Chapter 5 for a review of how cells make ATP). Interestingly, most excavates are parasites that live within an animal host, including *Giardia lamblia* (the causative agent behind giardiasis, also known as beaver fever). It has been hypothesized that the loss of fully functioning mitochondria is an evolutionary adaptation to living inside another animal, where oxygen would be a limiting factor for growth. According to this hypothesis, the energetic cost of constructing and maintaining mitochondria in the cell was greater than the benefit they provided. The excavates are also characterized by the presence of a groove in the surface of the cell. This groove is often a feeding structure that the organism uses to collect food particles as it swims with the aid of its flagella.

The excavates can be further broken down into two subgroups, the Diplomonadida and the Parabasalia. The Diplomonadida (meaning "double cell") often look as if they are composed of two cells—hence their name. They have two nuclei and multiple flagella. *Giardia* falls into this subgroup, and light micrographs of these cells often make them appear to have two eyes and a mouth **(Figure 16.4a)**. A "grinning *Giardia*" makes for a creepy Halloween costume. The Parabasalia also include a number of human pathogens, including *Trichomonas vaginalis*, a commonly occurring sexually transmitted disease. As we often see with relatively simple, single-cell organisms, the parabasalids are highly adapted to their living environment. Rather than have multiple flagella arranged around the cell, as we see in the diplomonads, the parabasalids have a structural adaptation that appears as a type of "fin" (also known as an undulating membrane) **(Figure 16.4b)**. Flagella located inside this finlike structure allow the organisms to move better in highly viscous environments such as the human reproductive tract. As an example of the strange places we find protists in general, and more specifically parabasalids, see Box 16.1, which presents a protist found in the gut of a termite.

## The Discicristates Have Mitochondria with Disc-Shaped Cristae

The next group of protists is the discicristates. They are a group of over 1800 species that range from euglenoids to trypanosomes (Figure 16.2, c and d). In general, they are highly mobile and named after the shape of their mitochondria. The cristae of their mitochondria tend to be disc-like in shape, although this is very difficult to observe without advanced electron microscopy. This is the first grouping in which we see protists containing chloroplasts. The euglenoids contain chloroplasts that are quite similar to those of the green algae and higher plants. They use

combined with gasoline to power cars and trucks. Cellulose- and lignin-degrading enzymes, such as those produced by *C. macrofasciculumque*, may greatly increase the ability of biofuel producers to maximize ethanol production from plant material. Thus, from a very unlikely location, the hindgut of a termite, we not only learn more about the evolution of protists but may also find a better way to fuel our energy needs. It seems strange that a positive spin could be placed on an organism named after a mythical monster whose very name evokes fear of the unknown.

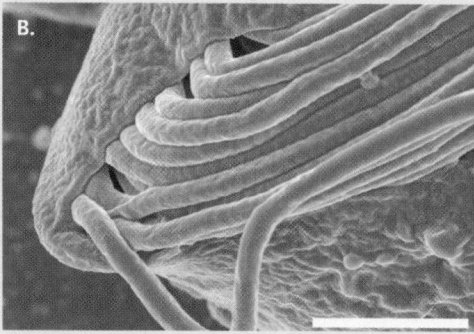
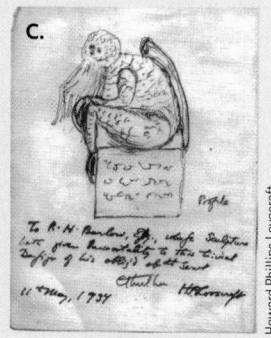

**FIGURE 1** The Cuban subterranean termite (*Prorhinotermes simplex*) **(a)** consumes wood particles but relies on a complex group of gut protists and bacteria to digest the cellulose and lignin. The parabasalid protist *Cthulhu macrofasciculumque* **(b)** is only known to exist in the gut of this particular termite species. The protist genus was named after the mythical monster Cthulhu created by H.P. Lovecraft **(c)** because of its many flagella, which appear to originate from a "mouth."

SOURCE (Photo B): James ER, Okamoto N, Burki F, Scheffrahn RH, Keeling PJ (2013) Cthulhu Macrofasciculumque n. g., n. sp. and Cthylla Microfasciculumque n. g., n. sp., a Newly Identified Lineage of Parabasalian Termite Symbionts. *PLoS ONE* 8(3): e58509. doi:10.1371/journal.pone.0058509. © 2013 James et al.

chlorophyll a and b to collect light energy. However, they have three membranes surrounding the chloroplast instead of the usual two. As we will see later in the chapter (Section 16.2), the number of membranes surrounding the chloroplast is used to explain the evolutionary pathway leading to the current protist family tree (for a review of chloroplasts, see Chapters 3 and 5). Euglenoids are a challenging group to classify because they not only

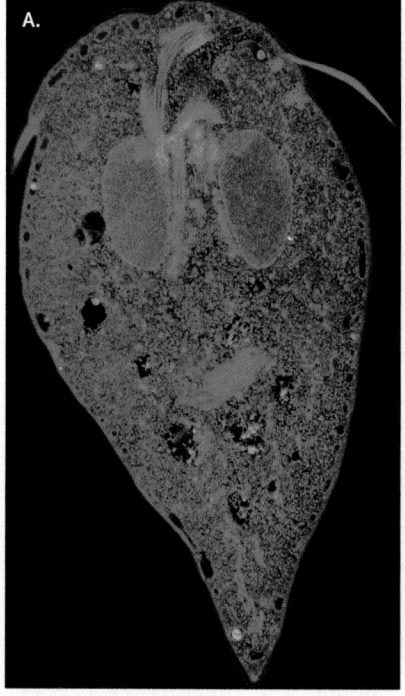
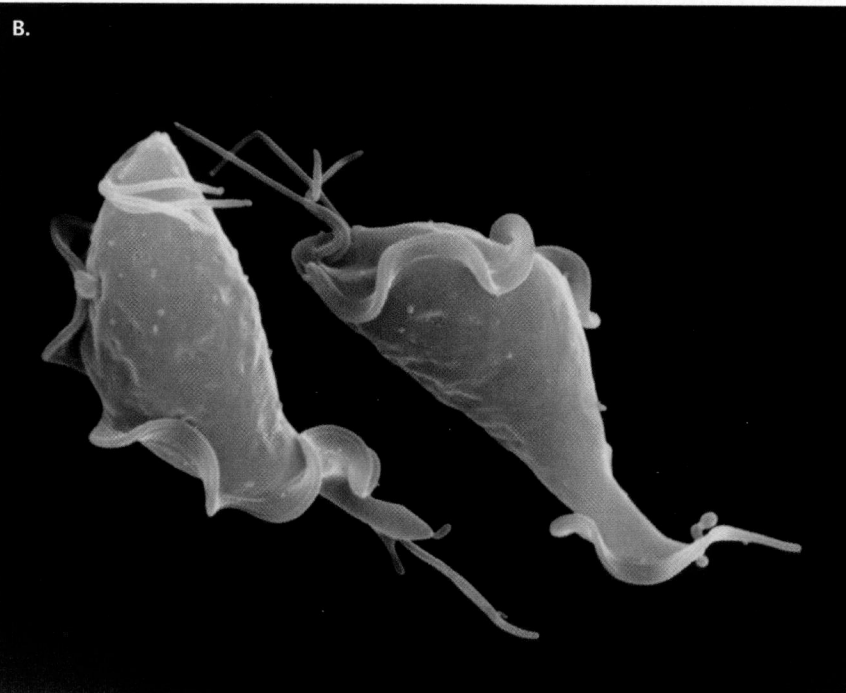

**FIGURE 16.4** Examples of excavates. **(a)** Light micrograph of *Giardia* highlighting the double nucleus and **(b)** a colourized SEM image of *Trichomonas vaginalis* showing its undulating, enclosed flagella.

photosynthesize but also consume food particles from their environment, such as bacteria or other debris.

The kinetoplastids are predominantly animal parasites. They live as heterotrophs, consuming the energy supplied by their host organisms. They are characterized by the presence of a single large mitochondrion and get their name from a large DNA deposit located in the mitochondria called a kinetoplast. Most kinetoplastids have two flagella: one in a leading orientation and one in a trailing orientation. In some species, one of the flagella is attached to the plasma membrane, resulting in a finlike structure called an undulating membrane similar to what we saw in the parabasalids. Kinetoplastids are also adapted to swimming in viscous fluids such as blood, and the undulating membrane allows them to move more effectively than loose flagella.

A number of these organisms are human pathogens and the cause of some very debilitating diseases. For example, *Trypanosoma brucei*, the protist that causes African sleeping sickness, is transmitted by the tsetse fly to humans and other animals. Sleeping sickness, also called trypanosomiasis, initially causes fever, joint pain, and fatigue. However, if left untreated, the protist can begin infecting cells of the central nervous system. This leads to confusion, tremors, and general weakness. As the disease progresses, individuals' sleeping patterns are disrupted. They often sleep during the day and remain awake at night. This is the symptom that gave the disease its name. If left untreated, the infection can be fatal, with about 9000 people dying from the disease each year in sub-Saharan Africa.

## The Alveolates Are Named after the Small Vesicles Located Inside Their Plasma Membrane

The alveolates are a group of protists that are characterized by the multiple small membrane-bound vesicles, called alveoli, located along the inside of their plasma membrane. These alveoli are thought to provide support and protection to the plasma membrane, and in some alveolates, they can lead to the formation of hard, armourlike plates. Within the alveolates group, we find three subgroups: the ciliophora, the dinoflagellata, and the apicomplexa. As we investigate these three groups, we again see the difficulty in arranging protists into nice, neat groups. Some members of the alveolates appear quite different from each other and share similarities with protists of other supergroups.

Dinoflagellates are photosynthetic, move using flagella, and are considered algae. They have two flagella of different lengths, a characteristic they share with another supergroup called the heterokonts. One of the dinoflagellates' flagella extends from the cell, whereas the shorter flagella is often wrapped tightly around the middle of the cell and does not aid in locomotion. Like the euglenoids, dinoflagellates also have chloroplasts that are surrounded by three membranes (we will explore the origin of their

three membranes in Section 16.2). However, rather than using chlorophyll a and b as euglenoids, they have chlorophyll a and c. This difference in pigmentation is used to help classify dinoflagellates. Despite having chloroplasts, many dinoflagellates are mixotrophic, meaning that they both photosynthesize and consume other food as heterotrophs.

The ciliates of the alveolates are heterotrophic and covered in **cilia** (short flagella that move in an oarlike fashion), whereas the apicomplexa are non-motile parasites of animals (see Box 16.2 for more information about these parasites and their impact on human health). Despite their apparent differences, their genome sequences support them being grouped together. Interestingly, it is believed that the ancestor to all alveolates was a photosynthetic organism. This means that the loss of photosynthetic ability in the ciliates and apicomplexans is an adaptation to a new lifestyle, where photosynthesis did not provide an advantage. Some species of this group still have remnants of a chloroplast that can be seen in electron micrographs. Evolutionary changes, such as the loss of a functional chloroplast, highlight the amazing adaptability of the protists. Of course, this adaptability also makes them much more difficult to classify and is one of the confounding factors when building phylogenetic trees, especially before we developed the ability to sequence DNA.

## The Heterokonts Have Two Unequal Flagella

Defined by their flagellar structure, the heterokonts have a larger "hairy" flagellum and a shorter smooth flagellum **(Figure 16.5a)**. The heterokonts are divided into three subgroups of algae, the diatoms (Bacillariophyta), the golden algae (Chrysophyta), and the brown algae (Phaeophyta), and one additional subgroup, the Oomycota, which were once classified as fungi. It almost seems redundant to consider how the Oomycota could be grouped with three classes of algae. The diversity of the heterokonts is amazing. From the fruit-destroying downy mildews **(Figure 16.5b)** to the diatoms with their crystalline shells **(Figure 16.5c)**, to the enormous giant kelps **(Figure 16.5d)**, these organisms are incredibly diverse at the structural level. The importance of each group to their ecosystem and, indirectly, to humans is immense.

The Oomycota are common plant and animal pathogens. The blight that led to the Irish potato famine in the 1840s and 1850s was caused by *Phytophthora infestans*, a member of the Oomycota (see Chapter 26 for a more detailed outline of *P. infestans*). This plant pathogen continues to be problematic for potato and tomato growers in Canada. It grows and reproduces especially well when the weather is cool and wet. Water moulds are also members of the Oomycota. They are similar to fungi in their filamentous growth habit. They form non-motile hyphae and aid in decomposition. Thus, although water moulds look like and act like fungi, their genome sequences are much more

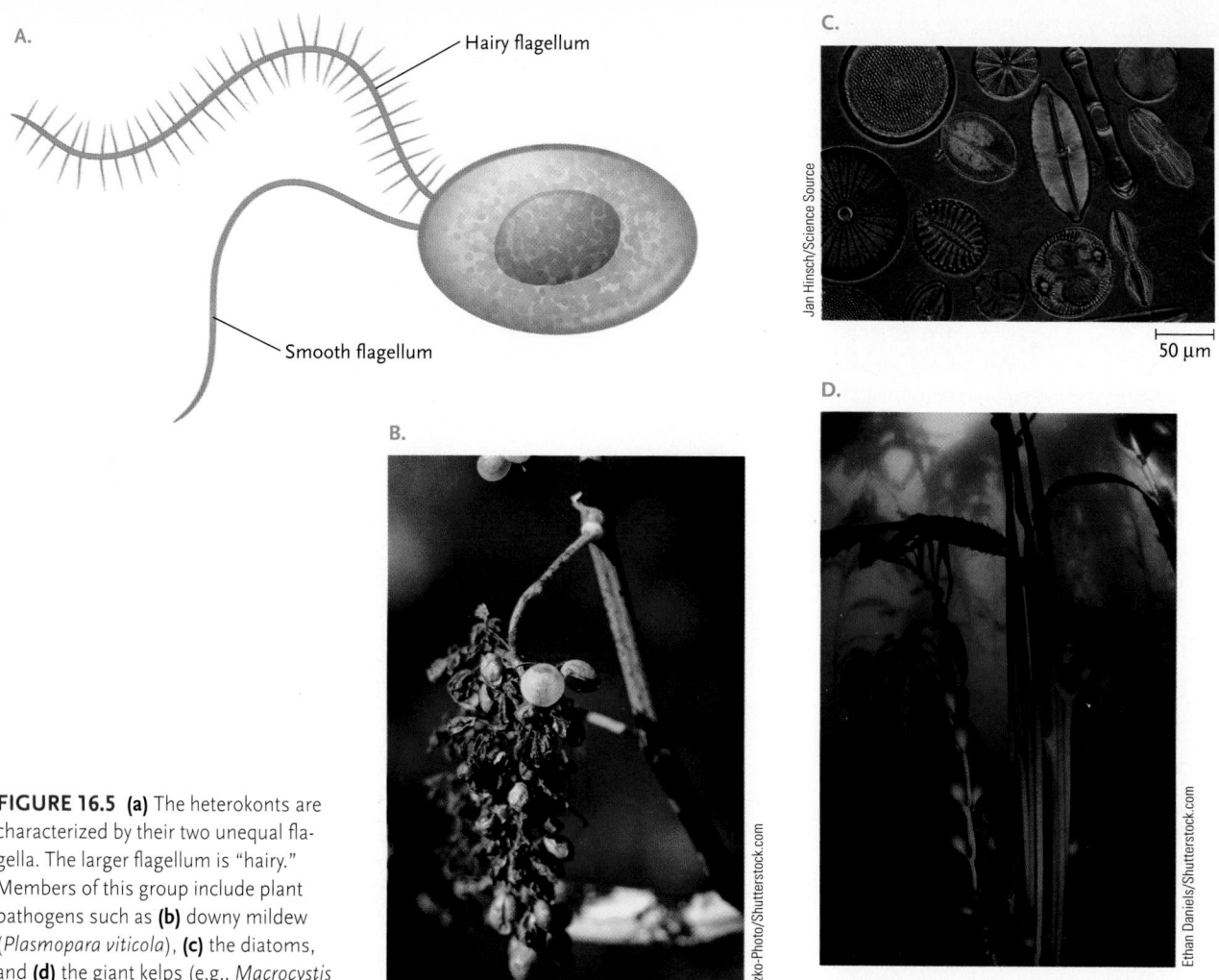

**A.**

Hairy flagellum

Smooth flagellum

**B.**

Gyuszko-Photo/Shutterstock.com

**C.**

Jan Hinsch/Science Source

50 µm

**D.**

Ethan Daniels/Shutterstock.com

**FIGURE 16.5 (a)** The heterokonts are characterized by their two unequal flagella. The larger flagellum is "hairy." Members of this group include plant pathogens such as **(b)** downy mildew (*Plasmopara viticola*), **(c)** the diatoms, and **(d)** the giant kelps (e.g., *Macrocystis pyrifera*).

similar to the other heterokonts, and, as a result, they have been reclassified as protists in recent years.

The diatoms, chrysophytes, and phaeophytes all play critical roles as primary producers in their ecosystems. Each of these types of heterokonts possesses chloroplasts and performs photosynthesis, but their chloroplasts have four membranes surrounding them rather than the two membranes seen in higher plants or the three membranes observed in dinoflagellates and euglenoids. Also similar to the dinoflagellates, their chloroplasts use chlorophylls a and c to absorb light energy for photosynthesis.

Diatoms are found in both fresh water and marine environments. They are characterized by the elaborate silica shell that they form around their plasma membrane (Figure 16.5c). Each species of diatom produces a differently patterned shell, allowing them to be distinguished from each other using light or electron microscopy. Because the shells of diatoms are made from silica, they survive long after the diatom itself dies. This allows researchers to study how bodies of water have changed over periods of thousands of years. Much like tree rings allow biologists to examine how tree growth has changed over the life of a tree, by taking sediment cores from lakes

or ponds, it is possible to see how the populations of diatoms have changed over time. We can study changes in both the number and types of cells. Similarly, because certain species of diatoms are found only in specific locations, their presence in biological samples can be used to track movement. Forensic scientists can use diatom populations to determine where a person drowned by examining diatoms in the water in the individual's lungs. Industrially, the shells of diatoms are used as an abrasive powder. A product called diatomaceous earth is a soft white powder that contains the fossilized remains of diatoms. We use diatomaceous earth in filtration processes and in the cleaning up of toxic spills. We even use it to help purify DNA from biological samples. Because of the grittiness of diatomaceous earth and the fact that it is inert, it is used as the polishing material in toothpaste.

Chrysophytes (commonly known as golden algae) are generally less common than diatoms but tend to become more prevalent in the spring and fall in freshwater lakes. They are named after their colour, which is due to the accumulation of yellow carotenoid pigments. Interestingly, chrysophtes are often colonial organisms, where a number of identical cells form characteristic aggregates, the shape

When we examined the different lineages and examples of protists in Section 16.1, a number of parasitic and disease-causing organisms were highlighted. Although we discussed the incredible diversity of living organisms that fall under the umbrella of the protists, we did not examine the incredibly complex life cycles that some of them use to reproduce. It is the combination of their diversity, complex life cycles, and the fact that they use many of the same cellular processes as human cells that makes protist infections a challenge to treat for doctors and pharmaceutical researchers.

In the chapter opening section, we discussed *Toxoplasma gondii*, a protist that can infect and parasitize any warm-blooded animal but can sexually reproduce only in the gut of the cat. Another strange and complicated organism is *Plasmodium falciparum*, the causative agent of malaria. *P. falciparum* infects humans and lives in our blood cells **(Figure 1)**. Just as an aside, to highlight some of the confusion in the naming of the protists, remember that *P. falciparum* is not found in the *Plasmodium* slime mould group but rather in the apicomplexa group; thus, it is more closely related to the dinoflagellates than the true amoebas. If an infected person is bitten by the right species of mosquito (*Anopheles gambiae*), the mosquito will consume blood containing *P. falciparum* cells. Once in the gut of the mosquito, the *P. falciparum* cells can reproduce, increasing in number (Figure 1). If the female mosquito then bites another person, she can transmit the protists to the new host as she inserts her mouth parts into their skin and injects an anti-coagulation cocktail into the host to allow their blood to flow more easily. Immature *P. falciparum* cells accumulate in the liver of the human host. As they mature, they move into the blood and inhabit red blood cells. When they reproduce in the red blood cells, they can cause the cell membrane to rupture, releasing new *P. falciparum* cells. Malaria tends to cause periodic symptoms of fever, chills, anemia, and exhaustion because many red blood cells tend to rupture at the same time. A weakened individual is more likely to be bitten by mosquitos; hence, the cycle can continue.

Treating malaria is a challenge because the protists are eukaryotes and use many of the same biochemical pathways as our cells. Also, because the disease is often dormant in terms of symptoms, it is sometimes difficult to determine if the person has been cured. Because of our biochemical similarities, anti-malarial drugs have many severe side effects. To make matters worse, the continued improper use of the drugs in Africa has led to many strains of *P. falciparum* becoming resistant to the anti-malarial drugs. Unfortunately, this has often occurred because of poor medical treatment practices by Western medical clinics. The anti-malarial drugs are normally in short supply and expensive. Therefore, patients stop taking the drugs once they start to feel better, but before the infection has completely cleared from their system. This allows them to share their drugs with family members who are sick, in an attempt to help as many people as possible with the resources they have. This allows the strongest and most resistant *P. falciparum* cells to survive and reproduce. This is a form of artificial selection, leading to the evolution of drug resistance. To help prevent the development of drug-resistant *P. falciparum*, doctors now use anti-malarial drug cocktails to reduce the chances of selecting for drug-resistant strains of the protists. This approach was very successful in the treatment of HIV (see Chapter 14), so researchers are hopeful that new drugs will be useful for a longer period of time.

Malaria remains a significant human health problem. This disease claims the lives of over 500,000 people every year, primarily in Africa. This would be the equivalent of eliminating all of the people in a city the size of Winnipeg from the planet every year. The fight against malaria has been plagued by a lack of leadership and from a pharmaceutical point of view: a low reward to risk ratio. Pharmaceutical companies must recover costs to remain viable. Supplying drugs to cure a disease that mainly afflicts the poorest people in the world is not a route to riches.

Recognizing this problem, the Bill & Melinda Gates Foundation has become one of the largest contributors to the development of malaria reduction

---

of which is genetically determined and can be used to identify the genus and species of the organism. In this way, they are somewhat of a link between the unicellular diatoms and the multicellular phaeophytes.

There are over 1800 species of phaeophytes (commonly known as brown algae), ranging from the giant kelps such as *Macrocystis pyrifera*, which can grow to lengths of 50 m and form dense underwater forests (Figure 16.5d), to the tiny tuftlike structures formed by some species that are only millimetres in length. All of the phaeophytes identified to date are autotrophic. Although it is easy to wonder why these large, plantlike organisms are classified as protists, they do not have a vascular system, as we see in higher plants. Similarly, their holdfasts are a modified rootlike structure that attaches one end of the algal structure to a solid object. The holdfast keeps the giant kelps in place despite wave and tidal action that attempts to dislodge them. It is also easy to question where we would find the flagella that classify the brown algae as heterokonts. Vegetative cells of the algae, the ones that make up the majority of the structure, do not have flagella. However, these organisms reproduce sexually. As the reproductive tissues undergo meiosis, they produce haploid spores that have the long hairy flagellum and short flagellum characteristic of the heterokonts.

## The Cercozoa Have Filamentous Pseudopods

The phylum Cercozoa contains three subgroups: Radiolaria, Foraminifera, and Chlorarachniophyta. They are

programs. They recognized that past eradication programs were very successful in eliminating malaria from developed countries in Europe and North America. Thus, they fund research into the development of new drugs, as well as research targeting transmission of the parasite by mosquitos. They support proactive programs to reduce malaria transmission. The best way to protect people is to help them avoid getting malaria in the first place. To this end, the Gates Foundation supports the purchase and distribution of mosquito netting and the development of insecticides that are safe for indoor use. Targeting the mosquitos responsible for transmitting the malaria-causing protists from host to host may prove the most effective way of ridding the world of this debilitating and deadly disease.

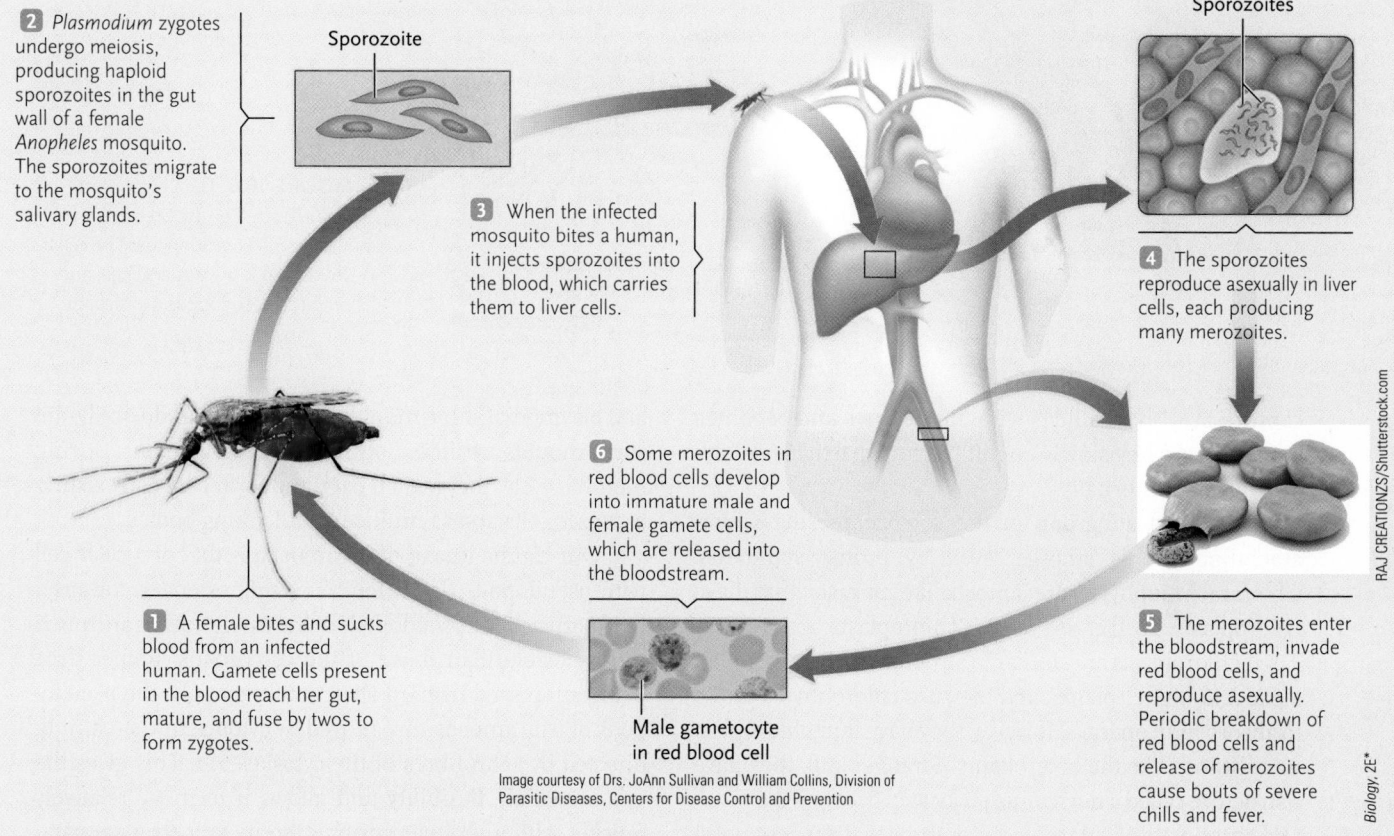

**2** *Plasmodium* zygotes undergo meiosis, producing haploid sporozoites in the gut wall of a female *Anopheles* mosquito. The sporozoites migrate to the mosquito's salivary glands.

Sporozoite

**3** When the infected mosquito bites a human, it injects sporozoites into the blood, which carries them to liver cells.

Sporozoites

**4** The sporozoites reproduce asexually in liver cells, each producing many merozoites.

**6** Some merozoites in red blood cells develop into immature male and female gamete cells, which are released into the bloodstream.

**1** A female bites and sucks blood from an infected human. Gamete cells present in the blood reach her gut, mature, and fuse by twos to form zygotes.

**5** The merozoites enter the bloodstream, invade red blood cells, and reproduce asexually. Periodic breakdown of red blood cells and release of merozoites cause bouts of severe chills and fever.

Male gametocyte in red blood cell

Image courtesy of Drs. JoAnn Sullivan and William Collins, Division of Parasitic Diseases, Centers for Disease Control and Prevention

RAJ CREATIONZS/Shutterstock.com

*Biology, 2E*

**FIGURE 1** The life cycle of *Plasmodium falciparum* makes the control of malaria extremely challenging.

grouped together based on their use of filamentous pseudopods for catching and consuming their prey **(Figure 16.6, p. 354)**. Once again, the current division of protists into the subgroups of the cercozoans is based mostly on their genome sequences as their morphological structures are quite diverse. The radiolarians produce a glasslike shell, similar to that of the diatoms. Their name comes from their pseudopods, which radiate outward like rays of light **(Figure 16.6b)**. The structure of the radiolarians is quite interesting. Their cells are divided into two compartments: an internal compartment where the nucleus, mitochondria, and Golgi are located, and an ectoplasm compartment that surrounds the shell. This area also contains many small, bubblelike vesicles that are thought to help the radiolarians float in the water column. The cell's pseudopods extend from the ectoplasm compartment and surround the spinelike extensions of the shell. Thus, in a way, the cell has an internal shell.

The forams have even more complex external shells than the radiolarians **(Figure 16.6, c and d)**. Rather than a glasslike complex, their shells are made of calcium carbonate mixed with organic materials such as proteins and carbohydrates. The initial shell has many small holes in it, which gives this subgroup its name (*foramen* is Latin for window). Through the small holes, long, thin strands of cytoplasm stick out **(Figure 16.6e)**. These long strands are reinforced on the inside by needlelike extensions of calcium carbonate. Both the radiolarians and forams

**A. Radiolarian**

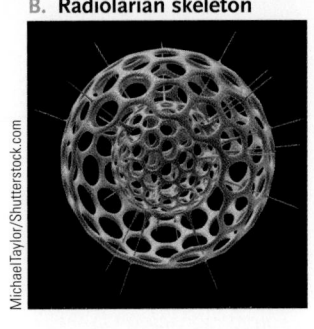

*Oxford Scientific / Getty Images*

**B. Radiolarian skeleton**

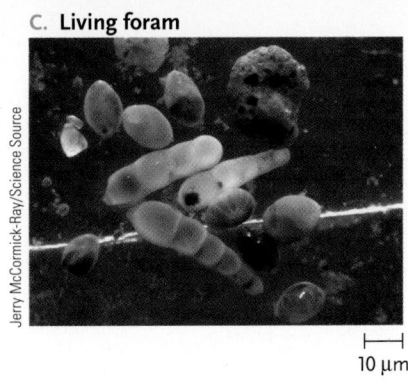

*MichaelTaylor/Shutterstock.com*

10 μm

**C. Living foram**

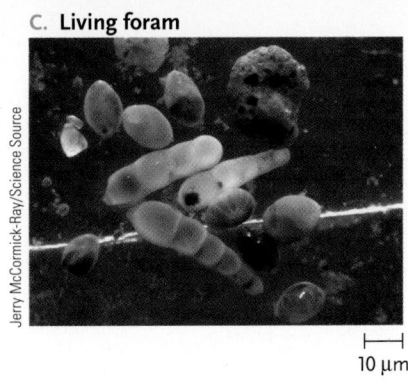

*Jerry McCormick-Ray/Science Source*

10 μm

**D. Foram shells**

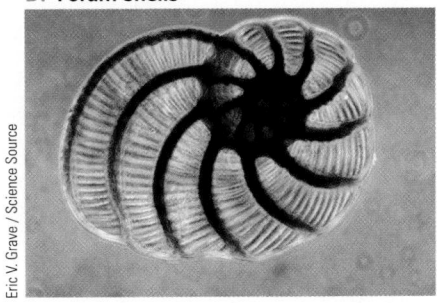

*Eric V. Grave / Science Source*

**E. Foram body plan**

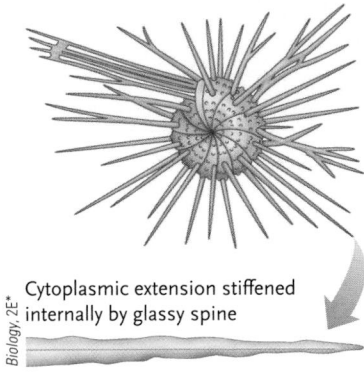

Cytoplasmic extension stiffened internally by glassy spine

*Biology, 2E\**

**FIGURE 16.6** The Cercozoa are characterized by the presence of filamentous pseudopods. The cells are coated in a glasslike shell, and even the pseudopods are structurally reinforced.

capture prey that collides with their spines and becomes stuck there. They slowly engulf the food particles, which are digested internally.

The third subgroup of the cercozoans, the Chlorarachniophyta, is strange, even by protist standards. Chlorarachniophytes are amoebalike protists that have chloroplasts. In fact, even their chloroplasts are strange. Their chloroplasts are similar in structure to those of green algae and higher plants, and they use chlorophyll a and b to absorb light energy. However, they have four chloroplast membranes like the heterokonts. Stranger still, they have a structure called a **nucleomorph** located between the inner and outer pairs of chloroplast membranes (between membranes 2 and 3). The nucleomorph is thought to represent a remnant nucleus. It contains a very small genome. The nucleomorph of the chlorarachniophytes contains three chromosomes housing only about 500 genes. Despite their chloroplast, the chlorarachniophytes fall in the phylum Cercozoa based on their filamentous pseudopods and can supplement their photosynthetic energy supply by eating food particles they capture with them. Again, during the classification of these organisms, scientists were challenged and questioned whether these organisms are animals that photosynthesize or plants that move.

## The Amoebozoa Are Characterized by Their Flowing Pseudopods

The Amoebozoa includes some fascinating organisms. In addition to species in the genus *Amoeba* such as *A. proteus* (Figure 16.2b), this group includes the cellular slime moulds

and plasmodial slime moulds. Somewhat paradoxically, the slime moulds are incredibly interesting organisms. During their life cycle, they switch back and forth between existing as single cells and as multicellular fruiting bodies.

Our classic image of an amoeba is that of a clear cell with pseudopods (Latin for false feet), extended toward a food particle. The pseudopods of the true amoebas are much more flexible than those of the cercozoans. Rather than being supported by hard structural materials, the pseudopods of true amoebas are moved by cytoplasmic streaming directed by actin fibres of the cytoskeleton. This gives the cell incredible flexibility and allows it to move relatively quickly. Although heterotrophic, some amoebas are parasites. There are a number that can cause a disease in humans called amoebic dysentery. The cells of *Entamoeba histolytica* can be ingested in contaminated water. This is often a problem in areas where sewage treatment is inadequate. The ingested amoeba will reproduce in the host digestive system and disrupt the chemical balance in the intestine. This leads to diarrhea, which can lead to debilitating dehydration and even death. As we saw previously with *Toxoplasma* and trypanosomes, the symptoms caused by an *E. histolytica* infection help it spread to other hosts.

Cellular slime moulds live most of their lives as single-celled organisms that move in much the same way as a true amoeba. Unlike the true amoebas, which reproduce strictly by binary fission, the slime moulds can also reproduce sexually. Two haploid cells can fuse to form a zygote, which then undergoes meiosis to form four haploid daughters. They will continue to grow and reproduce in this way

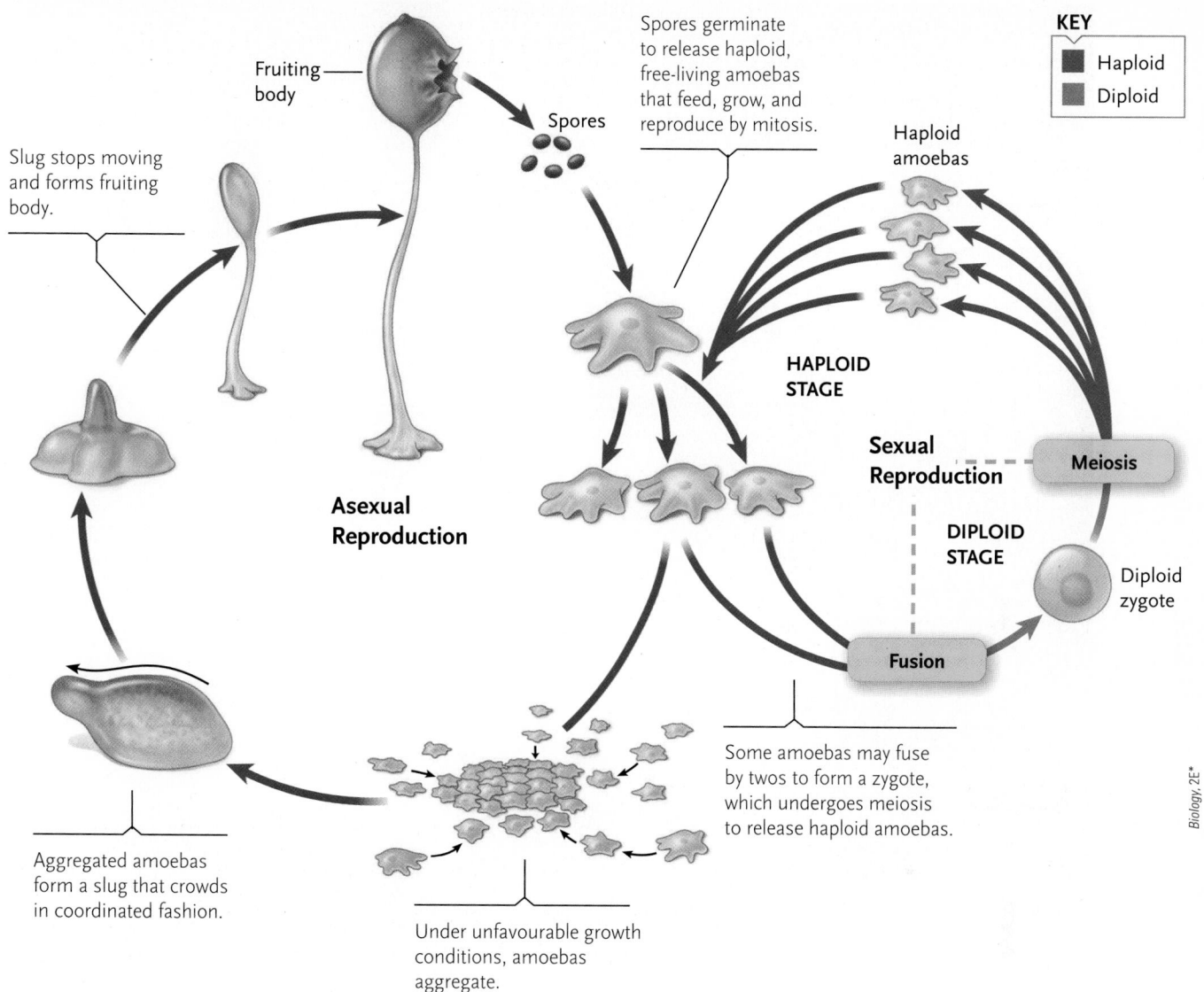

**KEY**
■ Haploid
■ Diploid

Fruiting body

Spores

Spores germinate to release haploid, free-living amoebas that feed, grow, and reproduce by mitosis.

Haploid amoebas

Slug stops moving and forms fruiting body.

**HAPLOID STAGE**

**Sexual Reproduction**

Meiosis

**Asexual Reproduction**

**DIPLOID STAGE**

Fusion

Diploid zygote

Aggregated amoebas form a slug that crowds in coordinated fashion.

Under unfavourable growth conditions, amoebas aggregate.

Some amoebas may fuse by twos to form a zygote, which undergoes meiosis to release haploid amoebas.

*Biology, 2E\**

**FIGURE 16.7** The life cycle of a cellular slime mould. The haploid cells can reproduce sexually through fusion and meiosis, but when a lack of nutrients begins to limit growth, the cells release a chemical signal that attracts them together to form the larger multicellular fruiting body, which, interestingly enough, is an asexual form of reproduction.

unless they encounter unfavourable growth conditions. At this time, some of the cells begin to release a chemical signal, which attracts the cells together. As the cells come together, they join into a mass called a slug **(Figure 16.7)**. The slug cells become differentiated into pre-stalk and pre-spore cells. The slug will move to a suitable location and begin the transformation into a fruiting body. The first stage is called the "Mexican hat" as it resembles a sombrero (Figure 16.7). The stalk will then elongate, lifting the fruiting body containing the spore higher into the air. This process takes 8 to 10 hours, but once complete, spores are released. The spores can fall or be blown by the wind. As long as a spore lands in a moist environment, it will germinate into a new amoebalike cell, allowing the slime mould offspring to start over in a new and potentially more favourable growth environment. The slime moulds can produce quite fascinating and intricate fruiting bodies **(Figure 16.8,**

**p. 356)**. Fruiting body structures and colours are species dependent, allowing them to be distinguished by eye.

Plasmoidal slime moulds also exist as amoebalike cells. However, rather than having a single nucleus, they can have hundreds, if not thousands, of diploid nuclei inside a single cell. This strange occurrence can lead to cells that are a few centimetres to over a metre in diameter. The large plasmodium can move much like an amoeba by extending pseudopods and flowing from one location to another. Just like the cellular slime moulds, when nutrients run out where they are located, they will become more spongelike, with spore-producing fruiting bodies forming on the tips. The scrambled-egg or dog vomit slime mould (*Fuligo septica*) is an elegantly named example of a plasmoidal slime mould (Figure 16.8). As an aside, it is important to know that plasmoidal slime moulds are not the same as the *Plasmodium* species of the alveolates that

Matt Meadows/Getty Images

Larry West/Science Source

Matt Meadows/Getty Images

**FIGURE 16.8** Slime moulds often have common names reflecting the structure and colour of their fruiting bodies. **(a)** Chocolate tube slime mould (*Stemonitis splendens*) is a cellular slime mould, whereas **(b)** red raspberry slime mould (*Tubifera ferruginosa*) and **(c)** scrambled-egg slime mould or dog vomit slime mould (*Fuligo septica*) are plasmodial slime moulds.

cause malaria. There are many times in biology when names seem to get reused in inconvenient ways.

### The Opisthokonts Include the Closest Protist Relative of the Animals

An incredibly diverse group of organisms, two subgroups of the opisthokonts are the fungi and the animals. Yes, this is our group, and the first supergroup discussed thus far in this chapter that is not composed solely of protists. Of course, even this group of organisms contains a few species of protists. They belong to the third subgroup, the Choano-flagellata. These organisms are named after the collarlike structure that surrounds its flagellum **(Figure 16.9)**. The collar is suggested to aid in food capture. As the cell is pulled through the water using the flagella, the collar acts

as a basket, scooping up any bacteria that float past. Their placement in the tree of life based on DNA sequencing and morphology makes the choanoflagellates a close relative to the sponges. Thus, they are an ancient relative of the animals, with both groups sharing a more recent common ancestor than any of the other protists.

### The Archaeplastida Include the Protists Most Closely Related to Plants

The Archaeplastida are the final group of eukaryotes. There are two subgroups that contain protists: the Rhodophyta, or red algae, and the Chlorophyta, or green algae. There is also a third subgroup, the Viridaeplanta, which is made up of all the plants. All three of these groups contain chloroplasts with two membranes.

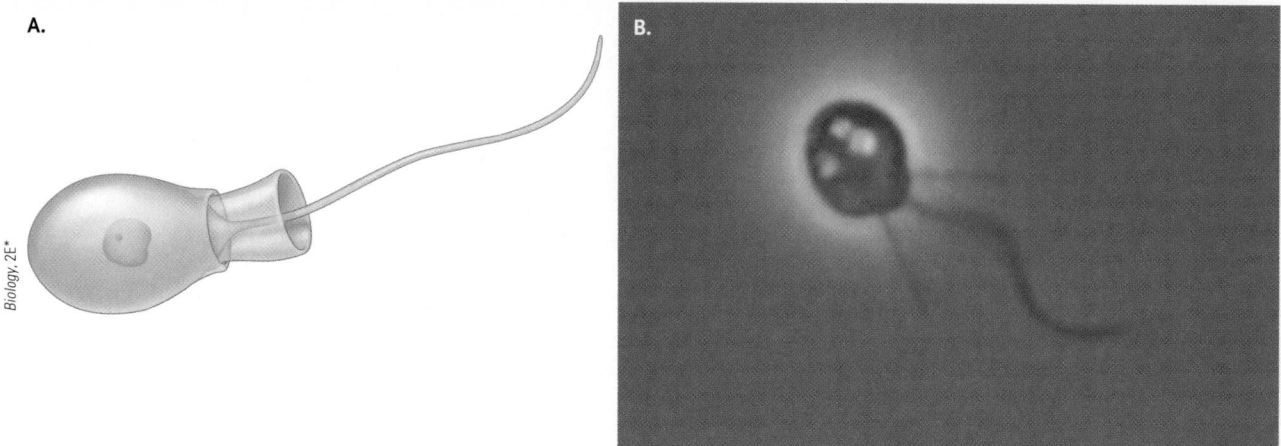

A.

*Biology, 2E\**

B.

**FIGURE 16.9** The stylized structure of a unicellular choanoflagellate **(a)**. Light micrographs of choanoflagellates clearly highlight the collar and flagellum **(b)**.

The red algae are thought to be the oldest of the three subgroups. Their chloroplasts maintain a number of biochemical holdovers from the cyanobacteria. The most obvious one is the presence of phycobilisomes. These are pigment–protein complexes that function in light gathering, but instead of using chlorophyll b, like green algae or higher plants, they use pigments called phycocyanin or phycoerythrin similar to the cyanobacteria. The phycobilisomes perform the same function as light-harvesting proteins and their chlorophyll molecules (you can review photosynthesis in Chapter 5). However, the phycobilisomes give red algae their colour because they reflect red light, masking the green light reflected by chlorophyll. The red algae are normally multicellular and form elaborate branching patterns **(Figure 16.10)**. Although they may appear to have stems, like higher plants, these are simply larger cells; they do not have a differentiated vascular system.

Interestingly, we commonly use red algae for both food and industrial production. When we eat sushi rolls, the thin, dark material wrapped around the fish and rice is nori, a red alga of the genus *Porphyra*. Nori is the Japanese name for edible red algae. The polysaccharides found in the cell walls of some red algae are extracted and

A.

*Andrew J. Martinez / Science Source*

B.

**C.** Filamentous red alga

*Wim van Egmond/Visuals Unlimited, Inc.*

*PASIEKA/Getty Images*

**FIGURE 16.10** Red algae such as *Chondrus crispus* **(a)** form intricate fanlike structures. However, as shown in the images of **(b)** *Plumaria elegans* and **(c)** *Antithamnion plumula*, the cells are not differentiated.

## THE MOLECULE BEHIND THE BIOLOGY 16.3
### Carrageenan

Carrageenan is a polysaccharide produced by red algae. It is the main structural component of the cell wall of these protists and is constructed from alternating glucose and galactose monomers (see the Purple Pages for an overview of sugar monomers). Many of these monomers have sulphate attached. This complex construction makes them relatively indigestible by mammals, much like the cellulose that makes up the cell walls of plants. Thus, carrageenan is essentially a water-soluble form of fibre when eaten.

Since the 1st century BCE, Chinese coastal communities have harvested red algae and extracted carrageenan for use in food preparation. Similarly, records show that people in Ireland have used carrageenan since at least 400 CE. In Western cultures, *Chondrus crispus*, the most common species of red algae harvested to extract carrageenan, is called Irish moss, although it is common across the shores of the north Atlantic. The name carrageenan is thought to have come from an Irish fishing village called Carragheen.

To this day, people living in coastal areas around the world harvest red algae for the extraction and production of carrageenan **(Figure 1)**. In Prince Edward Island alone, the harvesting of *C. crispus* is estimated to be worth over $1 million annually. In 2011, the worldwide production of carrageenan was worth an estimated $650 million. Because of its hydrophilic nature and capacity to absorb large amounts of water, it is used in the manufacture of fire extinguisher foams. This ability to absorb and hold water in its complex chemical structure is the key to its industrial and dietary use. It provides the "mouth feel" in chocolate milk, salad dressings, and many types of

vegetarian milk substitutes. In traditional Canadian Maritime cooking, sea moss pudding is a dessert made from milk, Irish moss, sugar, and vanilla. The carrageenan from the red algal cell walls thickens the mixture into a semi-solid gel.

The process of collecting red algae on Prince Edward Island is famous enough to inspire "The Song of the Irish Moss," by Stompin' Tom Connors (you can find the lyrics and a performance of the song on YouTube).

**FIGURE 1** The people of Prince Edward Island harvest red algae **(a)** for industrial uses. After harvesting, the *Chondrus crispus* is dried and ground into flakes **(b)** for easier transport and processing.

used for food production. Carrageenan (see Box 16.3) is used as a thickening agent in many dairy products, such as ice cream and low-fat cream. Funnily enough, it is also used to thicken paint. People around the world have been collecting red algae for use in soups and different foods for thousands of years.

The green algae can range from single cells to larger, more complex, partially differentiated organisms **(Figures 16.2a** and **16.11)**. An example of this process of added structural complexity can be seen within the Volvocales **(Figure 16.12)**. This green algal lineage passes from the relatively simple, single-celled *Chlamydomonas* species,

FIGURE 16.11 Green algae can also form intricate multicellular structures. In some species, such as **(a)** *Volvox aureus* cells differentiate to perform specific roles. Some cellular specialization can also be seen in **(b)** *Acetabularia acetabulum* and **(c)** *Chara* species.

through colonial species with undifferentiated cells such as *Gonium* and *Pandorina*, to larger colonial species such as *Volvox*, which have specialized vegetative and reproductive cells within the colony (Figure 16.12). The green algal lineage most closely related to the primitive land plants is the Charophyta (Figure 16.11c). Species of *Chara* exhibit

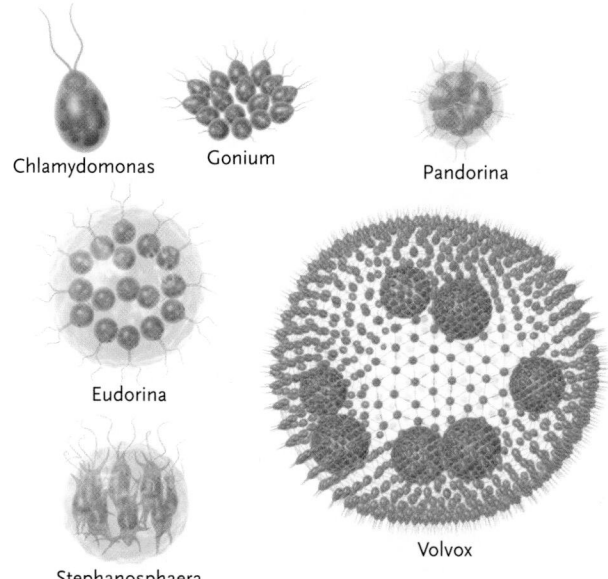

FIGURE 16.12 The Volvocales family of green algae highlights the usefulness of protists in deducing evolutionary patterns. We can see the increasing complexity from the unicellular *Chlamydomonas* species to the colonial, multicellular, and partially diferentiated *Volvox* species.

stem- and leaflike structures and in many ways resemble an aquatic plant. However, they do not have differentiated internal tissues, such as a vascular system, that are present in higher plants. Interestingly, aquatic plants did not evolve directly from algae but rather from terrestrial plants that later adapted to life under water.

## STUDY BREAK

1. Make a table listing each group of protists and their major defining characteristics.
2. How did endosymbiosis give rise to the protists?

## 16.2 Endosymbiosis Caught in the Act

Because of their incredible level of diversity, protists can tell us a lot about adaptation of living organisms to specific environments and often can illustrate the result of evolutionary processes. Even more incredible, at times, some groups of protists seem to have stopped evolving in the middle of a process. Apparently, the partial adaptation was enough for them to succeed in particular environments. We can see this when comparing the evolution of algae within the numerous eukaryotic groupings above. It is thought that the chloroplast evolved as the result of a single endosymbiotic event (review the theory of endosymbiosis in Chapter 3). If this is the case, how can we reconcile the presence of photosynthetic protists, such as dinoflagellates, euglenoids, diatoms, red algae, and green algae, in five of the eight eukaryotic supergroups? Following a simple tree of life organization, one would expect a monophyletic (single ancestor) origin for chloroplasts. You might come up with a couple of possible explanations to explain this conundrum.

One is to hypothesize that the currently arranged groupings are wrong and that all of the chloroplast-containing protists should be located in a single branch of the tree. This was once the way these organisms were arranged. However, an incredible array of morphological, biochemical, and genetic data gathered over many years supports the current groupings.

A second hypothesis may follow on the process of endosymbiosis itself. If it happened once, why could it not happen a second time? The singular event leading to the formation of the chloroplast seems pretty firm; however, what if a unicellular green alga was incorporated into the body of another non-photosynthetic eukaryotic cell? What types of structures might we see if we searched for data to support this hypothesis? The evidence of a primary chloroplast endosymbiosis includes a double membrane around the chloroplast, a bacterial chromosome–like DNA molecule in the chloroplast, and the presence of bacteria-sized ribosomes in the chloroplast. Evidence in support of a **secondary endosymbiotic theory** includes the presence of three or even four membranes around the chloroplasts found in some protist groups and the presence of a nucleomorph in some groups **(Figure 16.13)**. Recall from above that a nucleomorph is a small remnant of what is thought to have been the nucleus of the secondary endosymbiont. It has limited functions and is located between the inner and outer pairs of chloroplast membranes. In theory, this would place it between the endosymbiont chloroplast membranes and the plasma membrane of the endosymbiont (Figure 16.13). Based on the order in which researchers think the chloroplast

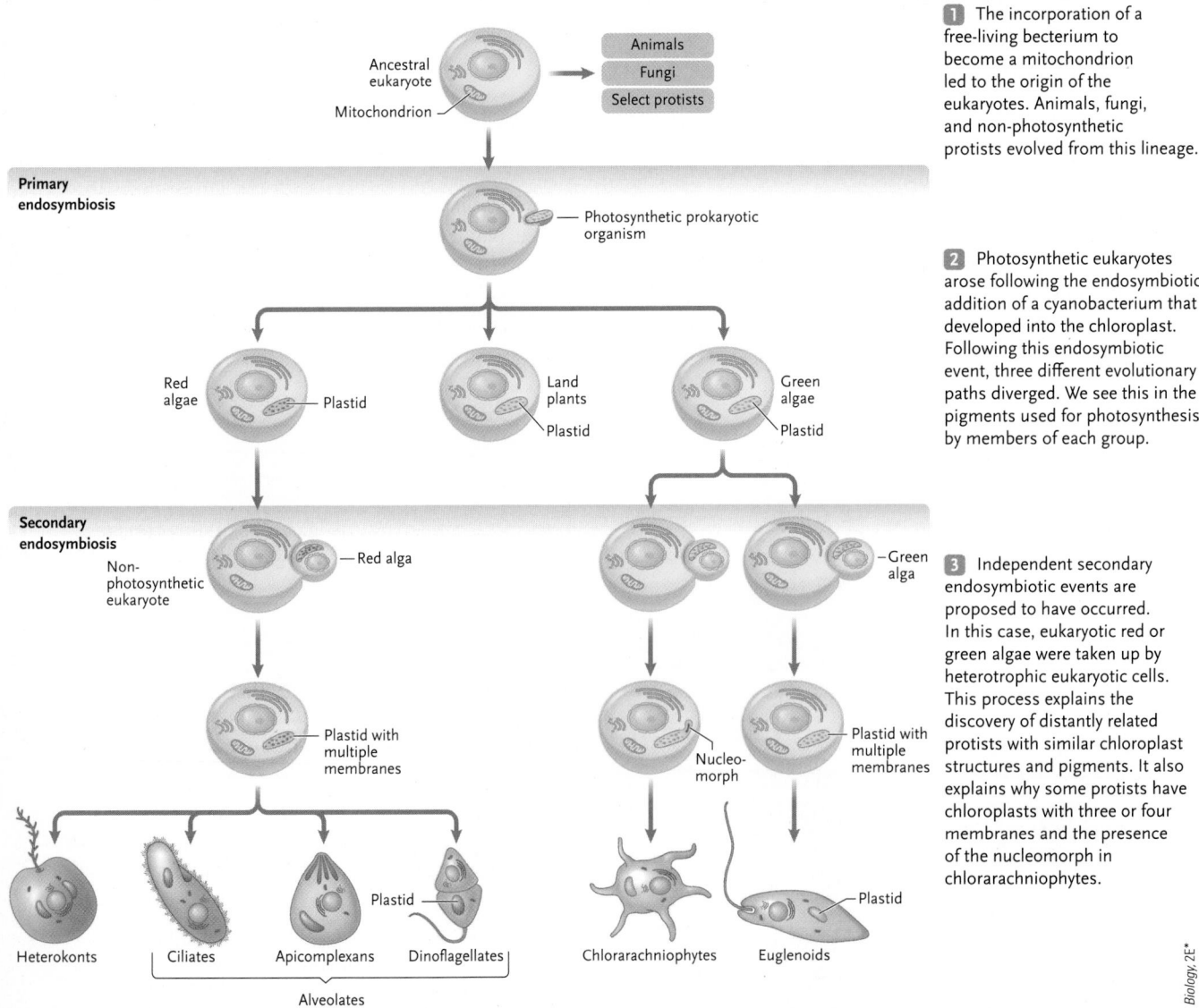

**1** The incorporation of a free-living becterium to become a mitochondrion led to the origin of the eukaryotes. Animals, fungi, and non-photosynthetic protists evolved from this lineage.

**2** Photosynthetic eukaryotes arose following the endosymbiotic addition of a cyanobacterium that developed into the chloroplast. Following this endosymbiotic event, three different evolutionary paths diverged. We see this in the pigments used for photosynthesis by members of each group.

**3** Independent secondary endosymbiotic events are proposed to have occurred. In this case, eukaryotic red or green algae were taken up by heterotrophic eukaryotic cells. This process explains the discovery of distantly related protists with similar chloroplast structures and pigments. It also explains why some protists have chloroplasts with three or four membranes and the presence of the nucleomorph in chlorarachniophytes.

**FIGURE 16.13** Secondary endosymbiotic events led to the complex lineages of chloroplast-containing protists.

-containing protists evolved, secondary endosymbiotic events may have occurred more than once.

The endosymbiotic events also seem to have progressed to different degrees. These separate events gave rise to the different groups of photosynthetic algae and help explain both the level of diversity found and the lineages in which molecular sequencing data place the organisms. For example, euglenoids have three plastid membranes and pigments similar to those of the green algae, whereas the heterokonts and dinoflagellates have three membranes but pigments more similar to the red algae. Thus, one would predict that the euglenoids arose from a secondary endosymbiotic event that occurred between an ancient chlorophyte and an ancient member of the discicristates. The heterokonts and dinoflagellates, on the other hand, would have arisen following an endosymbiotic event that occurred between an ancient red algal cell and an ancient protist that later gave rise to the alveolates and heterokonts (Figure 16.13). To make it more complicated, we see the nucleomorph remnants in the chlorarachniophytes, which have chloroplasts that seem to be descendants of green algae. The apicomplexans, which are closely related to the dinoflagellates but parasitic rather than photosynthetic, still have non-functional remnants of chloroplasts (Figure 16.13). It is thought that as they moved to a parasitic lifestyle, maintaining a functional chloroplast was not needed. However, the remnant chloroplast must serve some purpose in the cell.

Thus, we can explain more of the apparent complexity of the protists as we start to understand their evolutionary origins. The theory of secondary endosymbiosis provides a clear hypothesis explaining how photo-synthetic protists can be present in so many different branches of the phylogenetic tree.

## STUDY BREAK

1. How is secondary endosymbiosis different from primary endosymbiosis?

## PUTTING IT IN PERSPECTIVE

Although easy to overlook in the natural world, the protists play important roles as primary producers, degraders of organic materials, and infectious agents. At a basic level, understanding how these strange and diverse organisms live and grow helps us figure out our place in the tree of life. However, protists have much more information to offer us. Protists such as the cellulose- and lignin-degrading *C. macrofasciculumque* can be used to improve biotechnological processes. The carrageenan extracted from the red alga *Chondrus crispus* is found in a diverse array of food and cosmetic supplies. Protists, like viruses, also pose significant health challenges. Because protists are eukaryotes and share many of the same biochemical pathways as our cells, selectively killing them when they are inside our bodies is a much greater challenge than treating bacterial infections.

## KEY CONCEPTS REVIEW AND QUESTIONS

### 16.1 What Are Protists?

Formed from a combination of primary and secondary endosymbiotic events, the protists represent the first eukaryotic cells. They are challenging to study and classify into related groups because not only are they highly adaptable, they also can evolve quickly due to their relatively simple genomes and short life cycles. The complexity of structure and function observed in organisms such as euglenoids led to the expansion of our definition of what animals and plants are. Each of the eight subgroups of eukaryotes contains species of protists. They are placed there based on DNA sequence and morphological comparisons. Each subgroup has specific characteristics that are used to place them in that location of the tree of life. ●

1. What morphological characteristics of euglenoids led to the proposal to expand the classification system of living things beyond the two-kingdom model?

2. Why did members of the excavates lose the function of their mitochondria through natural selection?

   a. They have chloroplasts and therefore do not need mitochondria.

   b. They are parasites and obtain all of their energy from glycolysis.

   c. They are parasites and obtain ATP directly from the host tissues.

   d. They exist in a symbiotic relationship with cyanobacteria.

3. The parabasalids and some spirilla bacteria have flagella enclosed in a finlike structure that allows them to move more effectively through thick, viscous liquids. This is an example of _____ evolution.

4. Why can protists such as diatoms, radiolarians, and forams be used to help us understand how lakes have responded to climate change?

5. What important trait differentiates between green algae such as *Chara* and higher plants?

## 16.2 Endosymbiosis Caught in the Act

The first eukaryotes evolved from the endosymbiotic addition of a bacterium that over time became the mitochondrion. An additional step that gave rise to the first plants involved the similar addition of a cyanobacterium that led to the modern chloroplast. However, although there is no evidence to suggest that these primary endosymbiotic events occurred more than once, we see many different types of chloroplasts in the protists. To address this discrepancy, researchers developed the secondary endosymbiotic theory, in which eukaryotic algal cells were incorporated into existing eukaryotic cells. This process is used to explain the presence of chloroplasts with multiple membranes in different protist subgroups. It also helps explain the presence of nucleomorphs.

6. Which of the following characteristics of apicomplexans supports the secondary endosymbiotic theory?
   a. They have six chloroplast membranes.
   b. They have two chloroplast membranes.
   c. They collect light energy using phycobilisomes.
   d. They contain a nucleomorph.

7. Because red algae have only two chloroplast membranes and use phycobilisomes to collect light energy, which is the most likely origin of its chloroplast?

## WHY IT MATTERS

Canadians produce the majority of the world's maple syrup. In fact, in 2009, Québec alone produced more than 80% of global supplies. Maple syrup is made by boiling the sap of the sugar maple (*Acer saccharum*) until it is thick and sweet **(Figure 17.1)**. The sugar maple is the most common species of maple used to produce syrup because its sap has an average sugar content of 2%, higher than any other. Other maple species, such as red maple (*Acer rubrum*), silver maple (*Acer saccharinum*), or Manitoba maple (*Acer negundo*), can also be used, although up to twice as much sap must be used to produce the syrup.

The native peoples and settlers of Canada have been making maple syrup and maple sugar for centuries. But what is the biology behind the tree's sap production and our harvesting it? To understand where maple syrup comes from, we need to understand what sap is and how it is moved through a plant, in this case, a tree.

Trees all have specialized tissue through which they move water, minerals, sugars, and hormones from the roots to the branches and from the leaves to other parts of the tree. This is called vascular tissue. Two types of vascular tissue make this possible: **xylem** and **phloem**. The xylem is responsible for moving water and minerals from the roots to other plant organs, whereas the phloem takes the carbohydrates that are created in the leaves to other parts of the plants where they are needed. Interestingly, though the phloem is the main conduit of plant sugars, it is the xylem which is tapped to harvest maple sap. In the stem of a tree such as the sugar maple, the xylem is located close to the centre of the stem and, the phloem surrounds it, closer to the bark. For the trunk of a tree to grow wide and sturdy, the trunk must grow both upward (called **primary growth**; see the section on stems below) and outward (called **secondary growth**). As this happens, the xylem and phloem nearer to the centre of the stem are replaced by new xylem and phloem cells that grow along the outside perimeter of the existing cells. This increases the width of the trunk (leading to the growth rings in trees that allow us to count how many years trees have been growing). Over time, the inner layers of xylem become inactive. These layers, made from non-living cells, form the innermost wood of the tree and are collectively called the **heartwood (Figure 17.2, p. 366)**. Surrounding the heartwood is the **sapwood**. The sapwood is made up of the layers of active xylem, and this part of the trunk is tapped during syrup production. Outside the sapwood is a region called the **vascular cambium**. This is where the secondary growth takes place. On the inside of this region, facing the heartwood, new xylem cells are laid down. On the outside of this region, facing the outside of the tree, new phloem cells (**secondary phloem**) are laid down. Outside the secondary phloem are the outer layers of the tree, collectively called the bark (Figure 17.2).

During the summer months, **transpiration** takes place. Transpiration is the process in which water is drawn from the soil through the tree's roots and all the way up into the leaves of the canopy. The water can then be used by the leaves or returned

GoodMood Photo/Shutterstock.com

**FIGURE 17.1** A tap inserted into a sugar maple (*Acer saccharum*) drips sap into a collecting bucket. The sap, plant water collected from xylem, will be boiled down to create maple syrup.

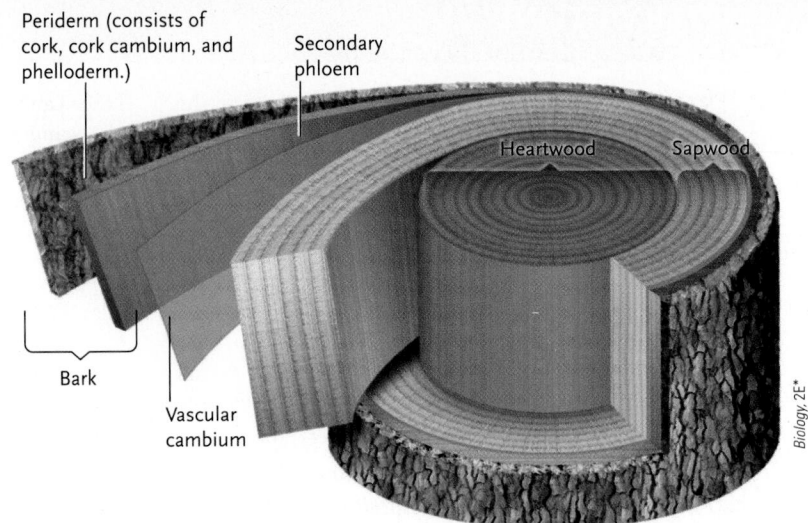

**FIGURE 17.2** Structure of a woody stem showing extensive secondary growth. Heartwood, the mature tree's core, has no living cells. Sapwood, the cylindrical zone of xylem between the heartwood and the vascular cambium, contains some living cells. Everything outside the vascular cambium is bark. Everything inside it is wood.

Periderm (consists of cork, cork cambium, and phelloderm.)

Secondary phloem

Heartwood

Sapwood

Bark

Vascular cambium

*Biology, 2E*

to the atmosphere through openings in the leaves called stomata. The sugars produced through photosynthesis in the leaves are also transported to a tree's trunk, where they are stored as starch for later use. This process of transpiration stops when the leaves fall from the trees in the late fall and early winter. The tree remains dormant until the late winter or early spring. In the spring, sugar-rich sap must move up the trunk toward the branches to nourish the new shoots, buds, and leaves.

When the season begins to warm, with temperatures above freezing during the day and below freezing at night, sap once again begins to move. This time, however, it is not through the process of transpiration. In fact, perhaps surprisingly, the exact mechanisms that drive sap up through the tree trunks and into our syrup taps and buckets are still the matter of some controversy. The main question is whether the movement is driven strictly by abiotic forces (i.e., non-living forces such as gravity or pressure) or some combination of abiotic forces and biological activity within cells that forces the sugary sap up through the trunk. In 2013, a model built by mathematicians attempted to shed light on this question. Their model showed that pressure from the carbon dioxide gas bubbles coming from cellular respiration within the tree would be sufficient to force sap upward. Carbon dioxide is more easily dissolved in sap at colder temperatures and so is incorporated into the sap in the fall. Then, as the sap freezes and expands, the increase in pressure keeps the carbon dioxide from forming bubbles, much like soda water in a sealed bottle. When the temperature warms and the sap begins to melt, the carbon dioxide gas bubbles expand, much like when you open a sealed bottle of soda water. The bubbles push the sap upward and outward through the xylem and into the taps. Other researchers think there is more to the story. This matter has yet to be resolved.

Sap is collected beginning in mid-February to early March and is collected for 4 to 6 weeks. After this time, the buds on the trees begin to swell and the sugar content

of the sap drops. As previously mentioned, the sap that is collected from the tree at the height of this harvest period contains approximately 2% sugar. To be called maple syrup, however, the final product must contain 66% sugar. This means that a lot of boiling and evaporation of excess water is necessary; it takes approximately 40 L of sap to produce 1 L of syrup!

Plants are found all over the globe. They fill our yards, farm fields, and forests, providing us with shade, oxygen, food, fibre, and even some of our fuel. In addition, many of the medicines in use today were derived from plants (see Box 17.1). This chapter will introduce you to the structure and function of the plant body and to the evolutionary history that has led plants to be such successful organisms. As you will see many plant characteristics evolved as adaptations to living on land. In contrast to life in the sea, for example, plants on land require a way to get water from one end of the plant to the other, the structural ability to hold themselves up and expose the right tissues to light to fuel photosynthesis, and the ability to prevent desiccation. Plants have also evolved a number of ways to deal with the challenge of reproduction on land rather than in the water. This chapter will introduce you to a number of plant adaptations that are important to overcoming all of these challenges.

## 17.1 Plant Structure and Function

### What Do Plants Do?

Plants are eukaryotic, multicellular organisms that are unique from other eukaryotic organisms in a number of ways. Land plants, unlike any terrestrial animals, are **sessile**: that is, they grow in place. Plants must obtain energy and nutrients, grow, and reproduce, all without the ability to move their bodies. Plants have evolved amazing ways to overcome these challenges. For example, as you will see, though plant bodies are sessile, the reproductive

# Acetylsalicylic Acid

For millennia, people have exploited plants for medicinal purposes. One such medicine is Aspirin, now a ubiquitous medicine used to treat pain, fever, and inflammation, and to reduce the risk of heart disease. The active ingredient in Aspirin is acetylsalicylic acid, a synthetic derivative of salicylic acid (**Figure 1**). Salicylic acid is an organic acid produced by many plants. The bark of willow trees (*Salix alba*) in particular has long been exploited for its salicylic acid content (**Figure 2**). Interestingly, people across the globe discovered the pain-relieving properties of willow independent of one another. As early as 4 BCE in ancient Greece, women chewed on willow leaves during childbirth. And the native peoples of North America, long before the arrival of European colonists, used compresses of soaked and ground willow bark to relieve pain and reduce fevers. By 1991, Aspirin and Aspirin-related medicines were the most commonly used painkillers and fever reducers in the world. People use salicylates (derivatives of salicylic acid) in a variety of ways, some far from its common uses. Salicylic acid is used to treat acne, dandruff, and other skin conditions, for example. Botanists even use it to induce flowering in some plants!

Although the bark of willows has a long history in folk medicine, it wasn't until the 19th century that chemists and pharmacists attempted to extract and isolate the active molecules from it. Early extraction processes were inefficient and required large amounts of willow bark, making the final products expensive. In the 1860s, German scientists discovered how to synthesize salicylates and built a large-scale factory to produce them by the mid-1870s. As a result of those advances, the price of salicylates dropped and they became more and more common.

The product we currently know as Aspirin was first synthesized at the beginning of the 20th century. Felix Hoffmann, a German, had a father who suffered from rheumatoid arthritis and was not able to tolerate the salicylates in production at the time (early salicylates were quite acidic and hard on the stomach). Hoffmann created a slightly less acidic alternative, acetylsalicylic acid, and it was named Aspirin (the name took the "a" came from acetyl and altered the German word for salicylate, *Spirsäure*).

In plants, salicylates perform a variety of functions, not all of which are currently understood. Salicylic acid plays a role in inducing flowering, protecting plants against disease, discouraging the growth of neighbouring plants, and even generating heat (cycads and some angiosperms generate heat in cones or flowers, perhaps as part of their interaction with pollinators). Salicylic acid is important to fighting infection in plants, and its role in disease prevention is of particular interest to scientists today. It is possible that these properties could be exploited for applications in agriculture or other industries. For example, crop plants might be genetically modified to increase the levels of salicylic acid produced, which might increase their resistance to a number of different pathogens.

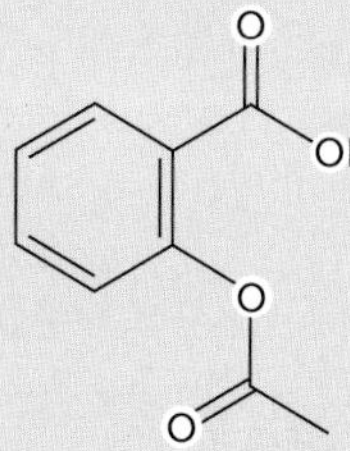

**FIGURE 1** The molecule acetylsalicylic acid. This molecule is the active ingredient in Aspirin and is a derivative of salicylic acid, a compound produced by plants.

SOURCE: cacycle, http://commons.wikimedia.org/wiki/File:Acetyl_salicylic_acid_chemical_structure.png. This file is licensed under the Creative Commons Attribution-Share Alike 3.0 Unported license, http://creativecommons.org/licenses/by-sa/3.0/deed.en

Hellen Sergeyeva/Shutterstock.com

**FIGURE 2** A large willow tree (*Salix alba*).

structures of many plants can and do move (e.g., motile sperm, pollen transferred by insects, dispersal of seeds, and other means discussed later in this chapter).

Plants are the primary producers of the terrestrial biosphere. Plants use energy from the Sun, carbon dioxide from the atmosphere, and water to build energy-rich sugar compounds. These sugars can be broken down by the plants themselves and are used, directly or indirectly, to fuel almost all other organisms. They thus make up the bottom level of the trophic pyramid, and, as the source of energy for most terrestrial organisms, they are essential to life on land (see Chapter 2 and Chapter 30 for more information about trophic levels and Chapter 5 for an overview of photosynthesis).

## What Do Plants Look Like?

Most land plants are green (there are exceptions; see Figure 18.18. The green colour comes from chlorophyll, the molecule that absorbs light from the Sun in the process of photosynthesis. Chlorophyll is green because of the way it interacts with incoming light. Most plants have **leaves**, organs where photosynthesis takes place, and **stems** that hold the plants up. Plants come in a wide variety of shapes and sizes **(Figure 17.3)**:

- Trees have thick, woody stems and can grow extraordinarily tall. Bushes and shrubs also have woody stems but are shorter and wider. Bushes and shrubs do not have the large, central wooden trunk that trees have.
- Vines can be woody or **herbaceous** (lacking woody tissues), but all of them climb. Vines depend on objects such as trees or the ground for support.
- Grasses have a narrow stem from which a few slender leaves extend on each stalk.
- Succulent plants, such as cacti, store water in their tissues and have fleshier or more swollen plant organs than other plants. This water storage ability allows succulent plants to survive in dry environments such as deserts. The unusual appearance of succulents, and perhaps their limited water requirements, has made them very popular as ornamental plants and houseplants (think of aloe [Aloe vera] or jade [*Crassula ovata*]).
- There are also plants with modified leaves and stems that defy the above categories. For example, Venus flytrap (*Dionaea muscipula*) leaves are modified to trap insects and other invertebrates. The leaves of cacti are the protective spines that extend from the succulent stems. In addition, some of the plant parts we consume, such as the onion (*Allium cepa*) or the potato (*Solanum tuberosum*), are modified leaves and stems.

In addition to having a wide variety of growth forms, plants also come in many sizes. Species of the *Wolffia* genus **(Figure 17.4a)** are typically considered the world's smallest flowering plants. *Wolffia* plants are members of the duckweed family that live on the surface of flat, fresh water. The body of these plants is about the size of the head of a pin (about 1 mm). In a thick layer of duckweed on a stagnant pond, there can be 1 or 2 million individual plants! On the other end of the size spectrum is the world's tallest tree, the redwood (*Sequoiadendron sempervirens*), with individual trees alive today that are over 100 m tall **(Figure 17.4b)**. The current record holder for the tallest living tree is named Hyperion and is located in northern California. Hyperion, at 115.6 m, is more than 20 m taller than the Statue of Liberty.

## Plant Cells Have Cell Walls and Organelles That Make Them Unique

Plant cells are different from animal cells in a few fundamental ways **(Figure 17.5)**.

Notably, plant cells contain a cell wall (see Chapters 3 and 22 for additional information on cell structure, support, and movement). The cell walls of plants surround the flexible plasma membranes that differentiate cells from one another. Cell walls make plant cells more rigid than animal cells (fungi and some bacteria also contain cell walls; see Chapters 15 and 18). The cell walls are built from a number of polysaccharides (compounds built from long chains of sugar molecules), but the main component is **cellulose**, a strong polysaccharide that maintains its shape even as water pressure from inside the cells, called turgor pressure, pushes outward. This combination of rigid cell walls and turgor pressure gives

Adrian T Jones/Shutterstock.com

Petr Baumann/Shutterstock.com

ARSimonds/Shutterstock.com

JoMo333/Shutterstock.com

a9photo/Shutterstock.com

**FIGURE 17.3** Some of the variety of plant growth forms, including **(a)** a tree; **(b)** a vine using a tree for support; **(c)** pasture grasses; **(d)** a cactus; and **(e)** the modified leaves of a Venus flytrap.

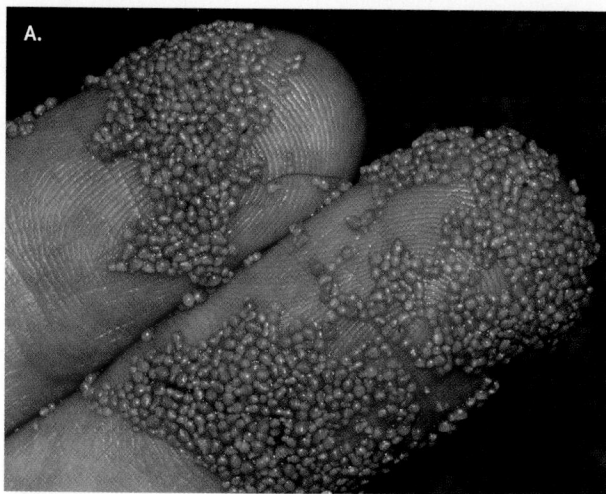

**FIGURE 17.4** **(a)** Plants from the genus *Wolffia* on a person's fingers. Each disc is an individual plant. **(b)** A giant redwood (*Sequoiadendron sempervirens*) towers above the forest canopy.

urosr/Shutterstock.com

plant cells their structure and rigidity. Cellulose is synthesized at the plasma membrane and deposited on the extracellular matrix. You could imagine the cell walls as scaffolding around the jellylike plant cell. As long as there is enough water, the cells swell to push out against the scaffolding and hold a rigid shape. If there's not enough water, the cells contract, and the scaffolding can no longer support the weight of the cells around it. That is why a plant wilts when you forget to water it but stands up tall when you do.

A primary cell wall is the first layer of cellulose and other polysaccharides deposited outside the cellular

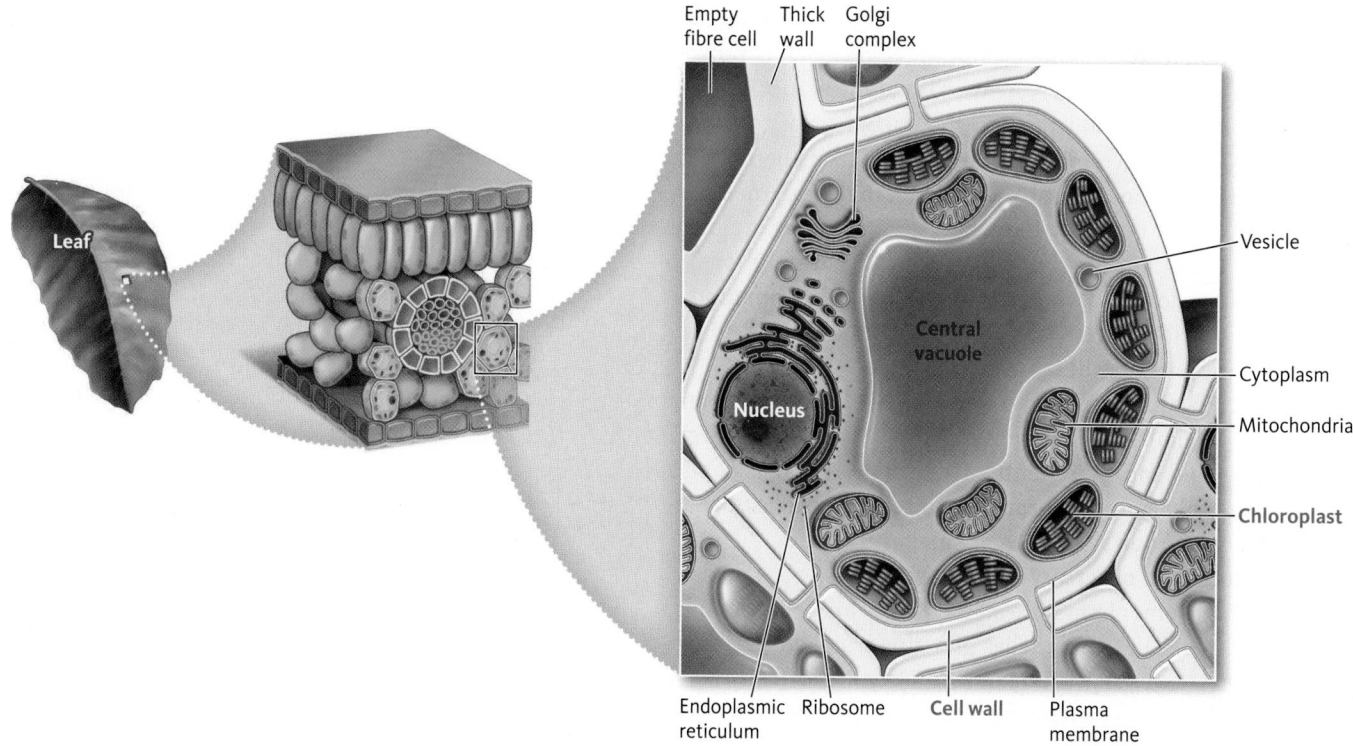

**FIGURE 17.5** A look at a plant cell shows many of the same features and organelles of all eukaryotic cells. Other features differentiate plant cells from other cells, specifically animal cells. These features are highlighted in red. Some of these features, such as the cell wall, are found in other organisms, such as fungi, but not in animals.

membrane during growth. The primary cell walls of plants are less permeable than the plasma membranes of animal cell walls. However, they are not impermeable and the thickness and rigidity of the cell wall can vary. In fact, movement of material across cell walls is important for chemical signalling. Water and ions move freely across the primary cell wall, although some large proteins and other materials cannot. The tightly knit fibres of the primary cell walls can be loosened to facilitate plant growth. In some plants, there are also secondary cell walls added to the primary cell walls of cellulose. Secondary cell walls contain **lignin**, a complex compound that provides additional structure and strength. Lignin is the most abundant component of wood. Secondary cell walls are not as permeable to the movement of materials as are primary cell walls, nor can they be loosened to facilitate growth. Some plant cells with secondary cell walls are connected to other cells by holes that make it easier to transfer materials.

Plants have two other organelles that are not found in animal cells: central vacuoles and plastids (Figure 17.5). **Central vacuoles** play an important role in storage, cell structure, and protection. The central vacuole is filled mostly with water and is the main source of turgor pressure. However, the central vacuole also stores a variety of substances important to plant defence. For example, the central vacuole of the coffee plant stores the caffeine you may be ingesting right now, a substance produced by the plant to discourage herbivory. In some plants, molecules are stored in the central vacuole that interact with molecules in the cytoplasm when a cell is broken, such as when a herbivore tries to eat the plant. The molecules inside and outside the vacuole work together when they encounter each other, a bit like a bomb and a match. When the molecular match in the cell meets the molecular bomb in the central vacuole, the explosion (reaction) creates a chemical that is distasteful or poisonous to browsing herbivores. This phenomenon is responsible for the pungent taste of garlic and is why your eyes tear when you cut an onion.

Plastids hold many of the pigments that give plants their colours and also store sugars (central vacuoles can also hold some pigments). There are three types of plastids: **chloroplasts**, **chromoplasts**, and **leucoplasts**.

Chloroplasts are the organelles that store the green chlorophyll necessary for photosynthesis.

Chromoplasts store pigments that are yellow, orange, and red. These organelles give ripe fruits such as mangoes (genus *Mangifera*) and tomatoes (*Solanum lycopersicum*) their characteristic colours and produce the brilliant colours of leaves in the fall. During leaf senescence in the fall, the chlorophyll is lost from leaves. The pigments of the chromoplasts in the leaf become the dominant colour. In contrast, when a green fruit ripens into a yellow, orange, or red fruit such as a banana (genus *Musa*) or a red bell pepper (*Capsicum annuum*), chloroplasts become chromoplasts.

Leucoplasts are slightly different. They do not contain pigments like chloroplasts or chromoplasts and so are colorless (*leuco-* means "white"). They can serve a variety of functions in a cell but most often serve as a storage site for sugars (see Chapter 3 for more information on cells and organelles).

## Most Plant Bodies Are Composed of Roots and Shoots

Over 90% of land plants are vascular plants. Vascular plants have specialized tissues that transport water and nutrients to and from various plant organs. The maple tree that transports sap is a vascular plant. We will focus on the structure of vascular plants in the following sections that describe plant structure and function, although we will discuss non-vascular plants later in this chapter. In vascular plants, plant bodies consist of two systems: the **shoots** and the **roots (Figure 17.6)**. The shoot system is typically above ground and contains the stems and leaves of green plants that we are familiar with. The shoots provide the structure of the plant and usually contain the photosynthetic tissue that plants use to build sugars. The root system is most often located below ground. The roots secure the plant in the ground and allow the plant to obtain water and nutrients from the soil or other medium in which the plant is growing.

## Plant Growth Is Continuous and Takes Place in the Meristems

The shoots and roots of plants elongate from specific tissues, called **meristems**. Meristems are most often located at the tip of a stem, branch, or root. This may be counterintuitive: plants do not grow from the bottom and get pushed up. The cells of the meristem are undifferentiated; they do not yet have a specific structure and function within the plant body (they are stem cells, which you may be familiar with in animals).

The **apical meristem**, the meristem at the apex or tip of a shoot or root, contains continuously dividing cells **(Figure 17.7a)**. In shoot apical meristems, some of these cells move to the periphery of the meristem and become part of developing plant organs (Figure 17.7a). These cells become leaves or flowers depending on their position and the growth stage of the plant. Root apical meristems are found near the tip of the root and are protected by the **root cap**, a layer of cells that surround the root tip (Figure 17.7a). In some plants, the apical meristem of one shoot or root dominates, inhibiting lateral growth. This is called **apical dominance**. If the apical meristem is clipped off, lateral growth will

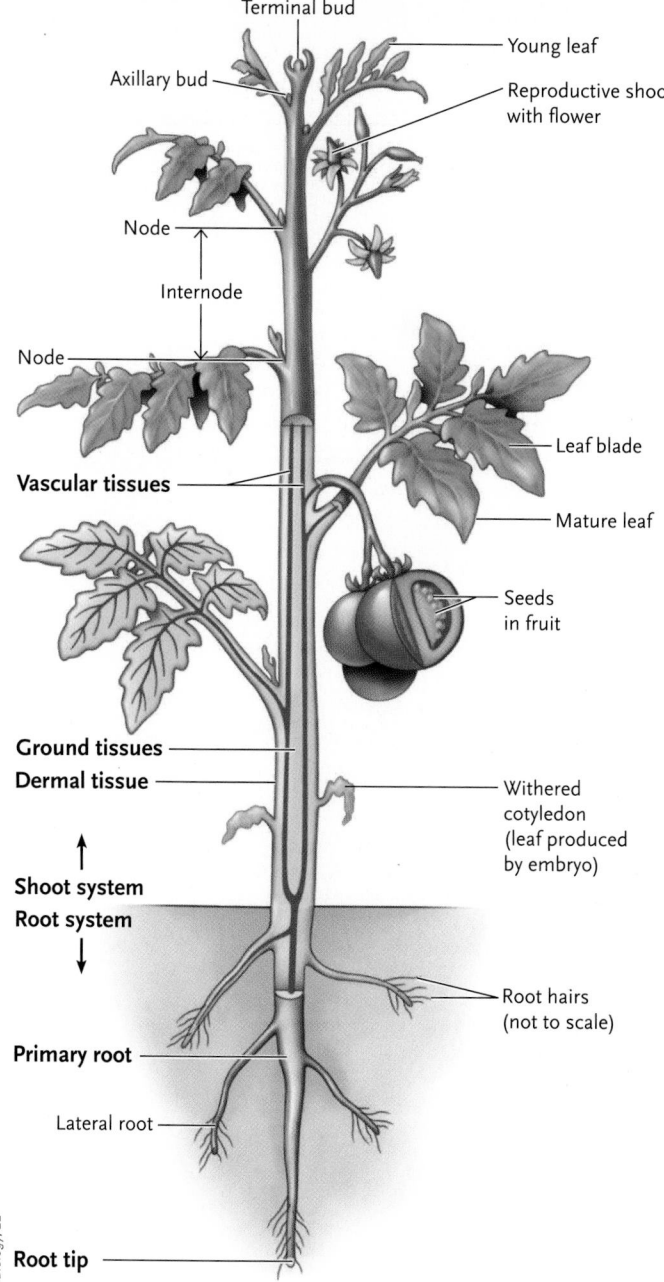

Terminal bud
Young leaf
Axillary bud
Reproductive shoot with flower
Node
Internode
Node
Leaf blade
**Vascular tissues**
Mature leaf
Seeds in fruit
**Ground tissues**
**Dermal tissue**
Withered cotyledon (leaf produced by embryo)
**Shoot system**
**Root system**
Root hairs (not to scale)
**Primary root**
Lateral root
**Root tip**

Biology. 2E*

**FIGURE 17.6** Basic body plan for the tomato plant *Solanum lycopersicum*, a typical vascular plant. Vascular tissues (purple) conduct water, dissolved minerals, and organic substances. They thread through ground tissues, which make up most of the plant body. Dermal tissues cover the surface of the root and shoot systems.

**A. Plants increase in length by cell divisions in apical meristems and by elongation of the daughter cells derived from the apical meristems.**

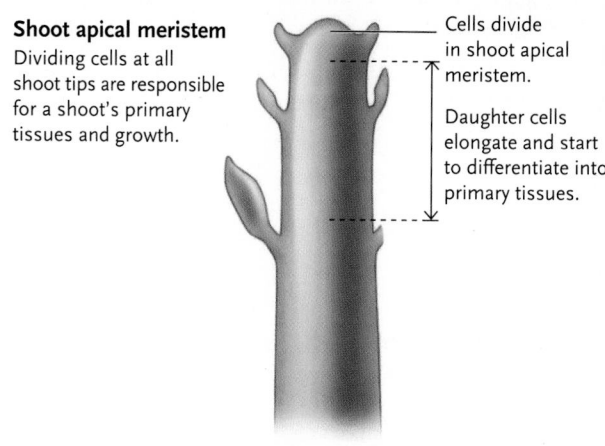

**Shoot apical meristem**
Dividing cells at all shoot tips are responsible for a shoot's primary tissues and growth.

Cells divide in shoot apical meristem.

Daughter cells elongate and start to differentiate into primary tissues.

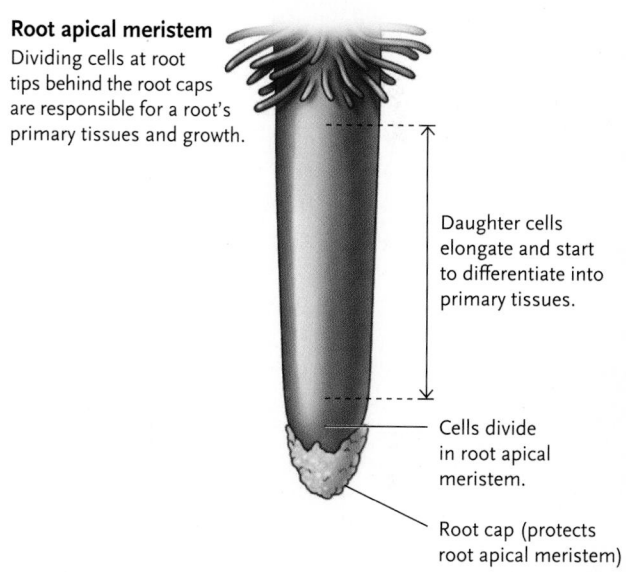

**Root apical meristem**
Dividing cells at root tips behind the root caps are responsible for a root's primary tissues and growth.

Daughter cells elongate and start to differentiate into primary tissues.

Cells divide in root apical meristem.

Root cap (protects root apical meristem)

**B. The stems of some plants increase in girth by way of cell divisions in lateral meristems: the vascular cambium and cork cambium.**

Vascular cambium
Cork cambium

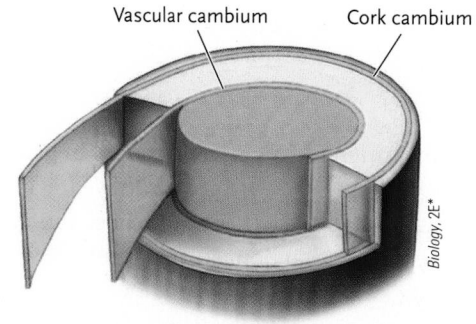

Biology. 2E*

**FIGURE 17.7** Approximate locations of types of meristems that are responsible for increases in the length and diameter of the shoots and roots of a vascular plant.

take place. Gardeners often clip apical meristems, for example, to make fuller, bushier plants (see Box 17.2).

**Primary growth** of plant bodies occurs as plants elongate (typically when they grow vertically), as from dominant apical meristems. Lateral growth is called **secondary growth**. This growth originates in regions called **lateral meristems (Figure 17.7b)**. This is what happens in woody stems and tree trunks, for example (Figure 17.2).

In contrast to organisms such as humans that reach an adult size and stop growing, plants continue to grow throughout their lives. This is known as **indeterminate growth**. It allows plants to respond to changes in the

Throughout history, people have created amazing works of living art using plants. A variety of art forms manipulate plants into sculptures, including topiary, bonsai, and mosaïculture. These art forms require knowledge of plant biology, especially of apical meristems and apical dominance. In many cases, the removal of meristematic tissue through pruning or pinching maintains the plant's shape or encourages lateral growth to create new shapes.

Both bonsai and topiary have long histories. The art of bonsai, for example, in which miniature trees are cultivated in small pots, has existed in some form for thousands of years. Trees are kept small by continually removing buds and meristems while limiting water and nutrients. Although most people associate bonsai with Japan, the art form is thought to have begun in China more than 2000 years ago. In China, the art form is called *Penjing*. Images of miniature trees have been found in Chinese tombs dating back to the Tang dynasty (618–907 CE), although references to cultivating small plants in pots predate this image.

Topiary involves cultivating perennial plants, often conifers, and manipulating them to form particular shapes. Topiary also has a long history, with its roots (no pun intended) in Greece, from where it was adopted by the Romans. Pliny the Younger includes a description of topiaries at his Roman villa in the first century CE. Including topiary in gardens and landscapes has come in and out of style and is still practised in many places today. Topiary involves trimming, pruning, and carefully shaping plants into sculptural shapes. Modern topiary also sometimes involves building the outline of a sculpture out of wire or a similar material and allowing plants to grow into the shape.

In more recent times, a new art form called mosaïculture has been developed that expands on the idea of building sculptures from plants. The centre of mosaïculture is in Montréal, the home of Mosaïcultures Internationales de Montréal (MIM). MIM, founded in 1998, has sponsored an international mosaïculture competition every 3 years since 2000. In mosaïculture, unlike topiary, artists do not use many perennial plants, as is common in bonsai or topiary. Instead, artists combine carefully crafted sculpture with plants, often focusing on the broad colour palette of annual flowering plants **(Figure 1)**.

**FIGURE 1** An example of mosaïculture from the 2013 international competition in Montréal.

environment despite being rooted in place. Plants may not always grow taller, but they are always capable of building new roots or branches. You may have seen, for example, that houseplants often grow new branches on the side closest to a window. This is an example of indeterminate growth allowing the houseplant to maximize its light-gathering abilities despite its inability to take steps.

### The Root System

There are two types of root systems: **fibrous roots** and **taproots (Figure 17.8)**. Root systems with a taproot have a long central root that is the largest root, in terms of both root diameter and length. A series of shorter and thinner roots extend laterally from the taproot. A fibrous root system lacks this large central root and instead contains a network of branching roots of similar size and thickness. Although roots typically grow as a branching network, always elongating and growing from existing root tissue, this is not always the case. **Adventitious roots** grow from other plant tissues such as stems, branches, or leaves. These roots can increase plant stability and uptake of water and nutrients. They can be found on plants with both types of rooting systems (Figure 17.8).

*Biology, 2E\**

Pathompong Chai-onnom/Shutterstock.com

**FIGURE 17.8** Types of roots. **(a)** Taproot system of a California poppy (*Eschscholzia californica*). **(b)** Fibrous root system of a grass plant. **(c)** Example of adventitious roots, the numerous prop roots of mangrove trees (genus *Rhizophora*).

Some soils can hold on to a lot of water and are rich in nutrients, so plants can get as much as they need relatively easily. In other places, however, one or all of the resources essential to plant growth can be scarce, and a number of plant adaptations help plants exploit as much of the soil as possible. One is the production of root hairs. Tiny hairs on the surface of roots increase the surface area of the root in contact with soil and through which material can be passed into the plant. Many plants also exude enzymes from their roots that help break the chemical bonds that hold nutrients within the soil matrix.

Symbiotic relationships between plants and other organisms, fungi and bacteria, also increase the ability of the root system to obtain nutrients (see Chapter 2 for additional information about symbioses). **Mycorrhizal fungi** form associations with plant roots, growing either around the outside of the roots or inside and between the plant's own cells (*myco-* means "fungus" and *rhiza* means "root"). This association, like root hairs, increases the surface area of the plant's root system. The fungi can pass water and nutrients to the plant, and, in exchange, the plant provides carbohydrates (energy) to the fungi. In the case of bacteria, some plant roots house bacterial species that can "fix" nitrogen, an important nutrient that is frequently in short supply. These bacteria, rhizobia, can remove nitrogen from the atmosphere and convert it into forms that plants can use. The rhizobia live in nodules that grow on the end of plant roots and, like mycorrhizal fungi, receive carbohydrates from the plant in exchange for their work (for more information on nitrogen fixation, see Chapter 30).

## The Shoot System

The stems of plants can be woody or herbaceous. Woody stems are thicker and sturdier—the stems of trees or bushes. Woody stems contain lignin. Herbaceous stems can be of different strengths and have different amounts of cellulose. Herbaceous plants typically die after a single growing season, although this does not mean that the plant cannot regrow the following season. Herbaceous plants can be annual, biennial, or perennial **(Figure 17.9, p. 374)**. **Annual** plants live for only one growing season, for one year. **Perennial** plants grow year after year. **Biennial** plants live for 2 years. In the first growing season, biennial plants produce stems and leaves but only flower and produce **seeds** in the second year. Although there are herbaceous plants with all three life history strategies, woody plants are always perennial.

Buds are the embryonic shoots that develop at meristematic tissue along a stem and that become the leaves. **Axillary buds** are those that develop laterally along the stem and grow as branches from the main

**FIGURE 17.9** Plants have a diversity of life history strategies. There are **(a)** annual, herbaceous plants such as the lady slippers (*genus Cypripedium*), **(b)** biennial plants such as carrots (*Daucus carota*) that have 2-year life cycles, and **(c)** perennial plants such as chicory (*Cichorium intybus*) that grow year after year.

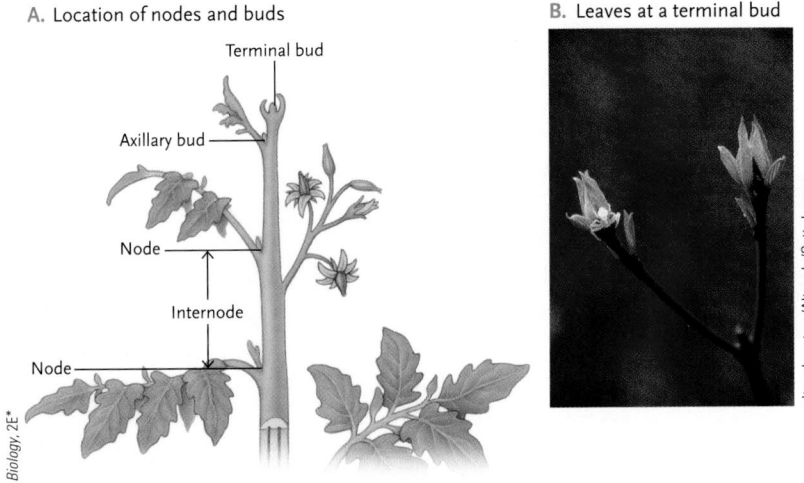

A. Location of nodes and buds

B. Leaves at a terminal bud

**FIGURE 17.10** Modular structure of a stem. **(a)** The arrangement of nodes and buds on a plant stem. **(b)** Formation of leaves at a terminal bud of a dogwood (genus *Cornus*).

stem. The **terminal bud** is one that develops at the tip of a vertical shoot. The locations of the buds on the stems are called **nodes**, and the spaces between the nodes are called **internodes (Figure 17.10)**.

Leaves are plant organs that in many plants are the centre of photosynthesis and gas exchange **(Figure 17.11)**.

The main body of the leaf is called the **blade**. The leaf blade typically contains a high concentration of chloroplasts (see Chapters 3 and 5 for additional information). To photosynthesize, plants need light, carbon dioxide, and water. Most leaves have adaptations to facilitate all of these needs. Leaves are often wide and flat, a geometry that maximizes the surface area that can absorb light. Most leaves have pores, or **stomata** (singular = **stoma**), through which the plant takes up carbon dioxide and releases oxygen and water vapour. Leaves also contain vascular tissue (discussed in more detail below) that brings water from the roots into and through the leaves. The bundles of vascular tissue make up the veins in leaves that we can see.

There are a number of examples of modified stems and leaves that are of particular interest to humans

**FIGURE 17.11** The anatomy of a leaf. Photosynthesis typically takes place in the cells of the mesophyll, made up mostly of parenchyma cells. The stomata control gas exchange between the environment and the leaf.

SOURCE: From Noyd/Krueger/Hill. *Biology*, 1E. © 2014 Brooks/Cole, a part of Cengage Learning, Inc. Reproduced by permission. www.cengage.com/permissions

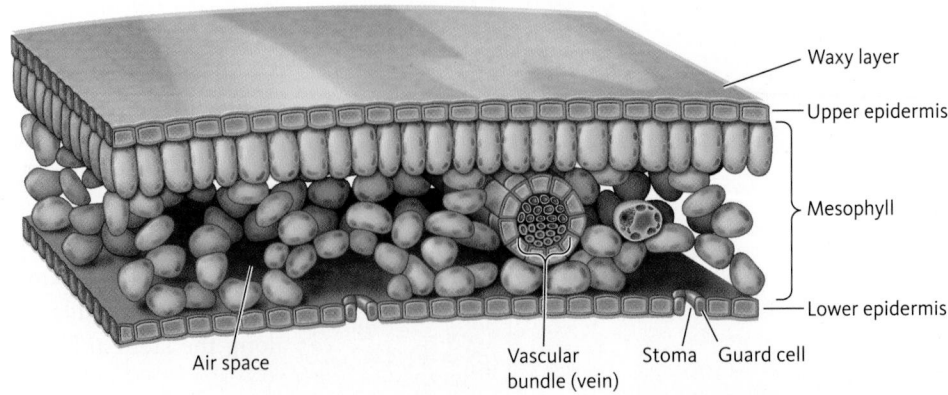

Waxy layer

Upper epidermis

Mesophyll

Lower epidermis

Air space

Vascular bundle (vein)

Stoma

Guard cell

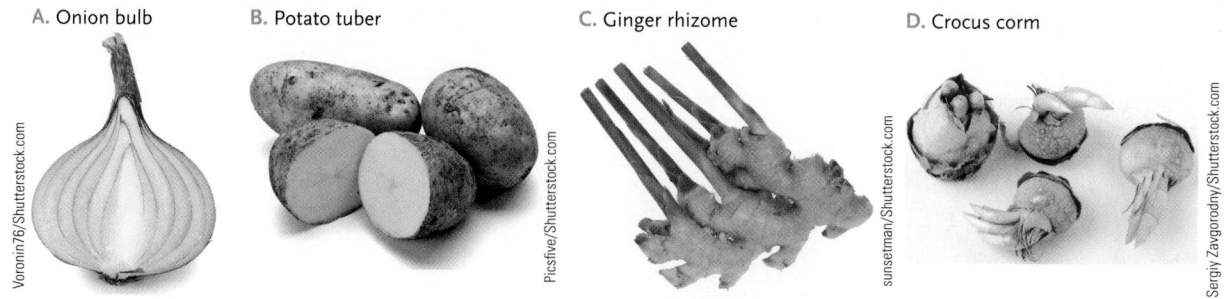

**A. Onion bulb**     **B. Potato tuber**     **C. Ginger rhizome**     **D. Crocus corm**

Voronin76/Shutterstock.com    Picsfive/Shutterstock.com    sunsetman/Shutterstock.com    Sergiy Zavgorodny/Shutterstock.com

**FIGURE 17.12** A selection of modified shoots. **(a)** The fleshy bulbs of onions (*Allium cepa*) are modified leaves in which the plant stores starch. **(b)** A potato (*Solanum tuberosum*), a tuber, another starch storage organ on an underground stem or root. **(c)** Ginger "root," the pungent, starchy underground stem (rhizome) of the ginger plant (*Zingiber officinale*). **(d)** Crocus plants (genus *Crocus*) typically grow from a corm, another swollen underground stem.

**(Figure 17.12)**. Onions, for example, and other bulbs, such as garlic (*Allium sativum*) or tulips (genus *Tulipa*), are shoots underground; what we eat of an onion or garlic is mostly fleshy leaves and some stem. Tubers, such as potatoes, are also underground stems that are enlarged for nutrient storage. In fact, the eyes of potatoes are buds. Potatoes have nodes and internodes just like other stems.

## STUDY BREAK

1. What are three features of plant cells that distinguish them from animal cells?
2. What is an apical meristem? What is produced there?
3. Why are stomata an important adaptation for life on land?

## 17.2 Plant Tissue Systems

There are three types of tissue systems in vascular plants **(Figure 17.13)**: the **ground tissue** system, the **dermal tissue** system, and the **vascular tissue** system. Each type of tissue has specific functions within the plant body, and each is composed of specialized cells.

### The Ground Tissue System Makes Up the Most Plant Mass and Is the Site of Most Photosynthesis

The tissue system that makes up the majority of the mass of a plant is the ground tissue system. Most photosynthesis takes place in ground tissue. It is also where sugars are stored. There are three types of cells that make up ground tissue: parenchyma, collenchyma, and sclerenchyma.

**Parenchyma** cells are found not only in ground tissue but in all three tissue systems. Parenchyma cells can divide and are the main cells found in the meristems. Compared to other types of plant cells, they have thin primary cell walls. Parenchyma cells are the cells in leaves where photosynthesis takes place (called the mesophyll; Figure 17.11) and make up most of the fleshy body of fruits.

**Collenchyma** cells are living cells like parenchyma cells. These cells, however, have thicker cell walls, typically thickened primary cell walls, and are often longer than parenchyma cells. They are used in maintaining plant structure, especially in elongated organs such as stems and roots. Collenchyma cells provide flexible support to plants. For example, the strings you find on celery stalks (*Apium graveolens* var. *dulce*) are made of collenchyma cells.

**Sclerenchyma** cells are also important to plant structure. Like collenchyma cells, these cells also have thickened cell walls, but the cell walls of sclerenchyma cells are mostly lignified secondary cell walls. Sclerenchyma cells are also dead on maturity when they are functional. They no longer have plasma membranes or active organelles. Instead, they can provide rigid structure and can also function as elongated tubes or conduits through parts of the plant. The pits of fruits, the hard exterior of nut shells, and even the cells that contribute the gritty texture to pears (genus *Pyrus*) are made of sclerenchyma cells.

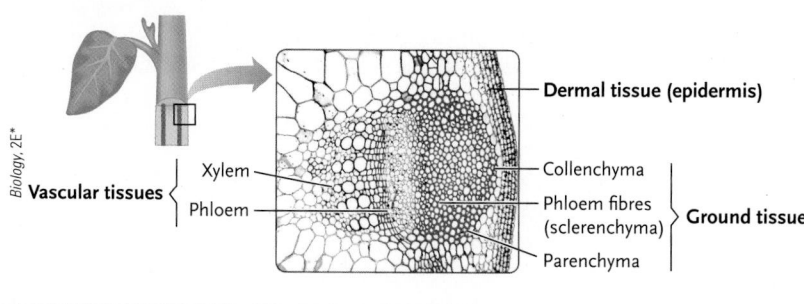

Biology, 2E*

Vascular tissues — Xylem / Phloem

Dermal tissue (epidermis)

Collenchyma

Phloem fibres (sclerenchyma)

Parenchyma

Ground tissues

© E. C. Yeung

**FIGURE 17.13** Locations of ground, vascular, and dermal tissues in one kind of plant stem. Ground tissues are simple tissues, whereas vascular and dermal tissues are complex, containing various types of specialized cells.

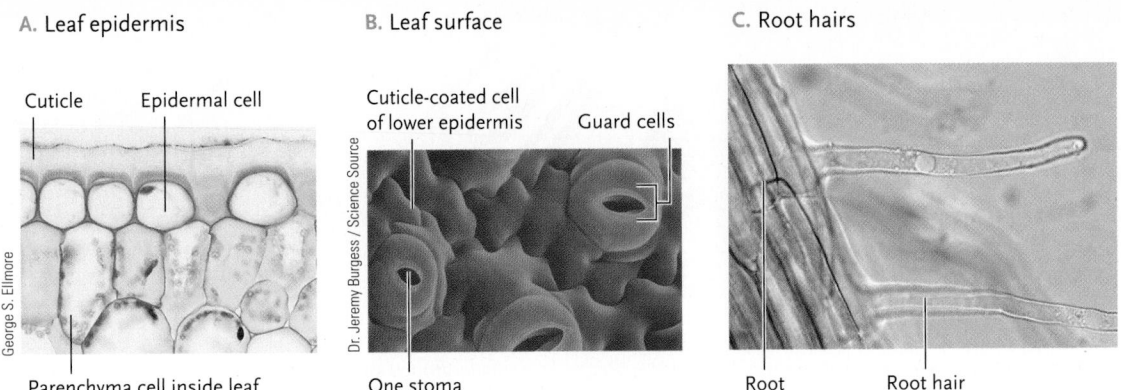

A. Leaf epidermis

Cuticle Epidermal cell

Parenchyma cell inside leaf

B. Leaf surface

Cuticle-coated cell of lower epidermis Guard cells

One stoma

C. Root hairs

Root Root hair

**FIGURE 17.14** Structure and examples of epidermal tissue. **(a)** Cross section of leaf epidermis from a bush lily (*Clivia miniata*). **(b)** Scanning electron micrograph of a leaf surface showing cuticle-covered epidermal cells and stomata. **(c)** Root hairs, an epidermal specialization.

SOURCE: (Photo C): Photographer: Michael Clayton. University of Wisconsin Plant Teaching Collection, http://botit.botany.wisc.edu

## The Dermal Tissue System Provides the Plant with Protection and Structure

The dermal tissue makes up the outermost layer of cells (or, in some cases, multiple layers of cells) on a plant **(Figure 17.14)**. These cells, with the exception of dermal cells along portions of the roots that absorb water and nutrients, excrete a layer of waxes called a **cuticle** along the outside edge of the cell. The cuticle serves as protection, particularly against drying out. Dermal cells can also produce hairs, called **trichomes**. The root hairs, so essential to increasing the absorptive abilities of roots, are a type of trichome. This layer of cells also controls the exchange of gases and water with the atmosphere. **Guard cells**, specialized dermal cells on either side of each stoma, control the timing and extent of the opening of stomata to the environment. Dermal tissue protects the plant from the environment, much like your skin protects you. It can protect the plant against threats such as infection by pathogens or herbivory.

## The Vascular Tissue System Transports Water, Minerals, and Food

You have already been introduced to the two types of vascular tissue: xylem and phloem (see Why It Matters). This tissue transports water, nutrients, and carbohydrates through the plant. Vascular tissue is a key adaptation to life on land. It allows plants to both obtain and move the material essential to life through all of the plant body. Xylem and phloem tissues are typically bundled together in the interior of plant stems, although the arrangement of these bundles can vary **(Figure 17.15**; also see the section on monocots and eudicots). The cells in xylem are dead on maturity and have lignified secondary cell walls. These cells have pores either laterally between adjacent cells or a series of pores or a wide opening between vertical cells that facilitate the flow of water and nutrients. Thus, because the xylem cells are dead and do not contain any membranes, they form a continuous open path from the roots to the leaves. Phloem cells that transport food are not always dead when they are mature, although many die over time in perennial plants. Many phloem cells do, however, have a reduced layer of cytoplasm with fewer and smaller organelles along the lining of the cell wall. Phloem tissue also often contains **companion cells**, specialized parenchyma cells that help move sugars in and out of phloem and sugar storage

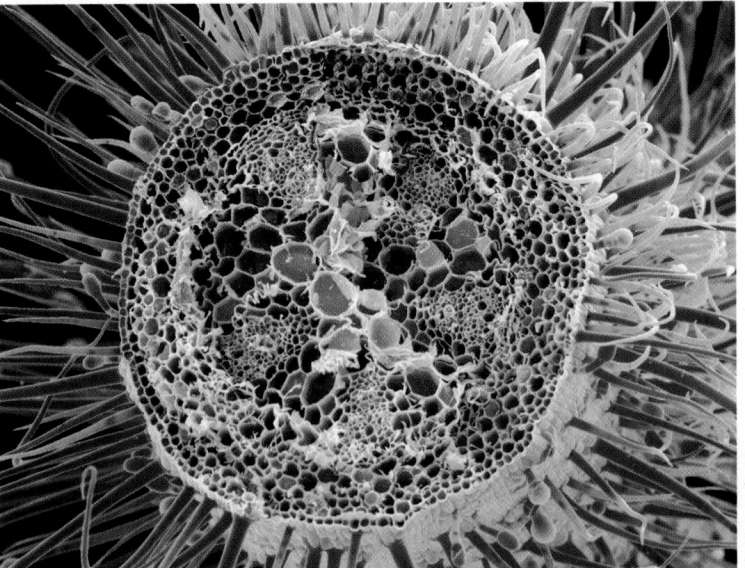

**FIGURE 17.15** Cross section of the stem of geranium (genus *Pelargonium*). This false-colour image shows large-diameter xylem vessels, which carry water and minerals, as whitish cells in the centre and radiating out from the centre. Phloem cells, which transport sugars and other organic molecules, are shown in pale green and are located between the "arms" of xylem. Layers of parenchyma cells (pink) surround the vascular tissue; epidermal cells form the outermost layer.

(see Chapters 24 and 25 for more information on transport in plants).

## STUDY BREAK

1. What are the three types of cells found in ground tissue? What distinguishes them from one another?
2. What are two ways that dermal cells protect a plant?
3. Why would the height of a plant be limited by a lack of vascular tissue?

## 17.3 Land Plant Diversity, Evolution, and Success

So far this chapter has focused on the structure and function of the most common type of plant, the vascular plant. However, there are other kinds of land plants with unique body plans and structures. The rest of the chapter describes the evolution of land plants, what makes them unique, the different groups of plants, and some of the ways in which plants have been successful organisms.

Plants are a monophyletic group. That means that all land plants originated from one common ancestor, likely an aquatic alga **(Figure 17.16)**.

Land plants have profoundly shaped both biotic (living) and abiotic (non-living) environments on Earth. The oxygen released by plants as a by-product of photosynthesis is largely responsible for our oxygenated atmosphere (see the discussion of the Great Oxygenation Event in Chapter 2). In addition, the physical and chemical activities of plant roots are responsible for much weathering of rock and contribute to the formation of soils.

The oldest fossilized plant body comes from around 418 million years ago **(Figure 17.17)**.

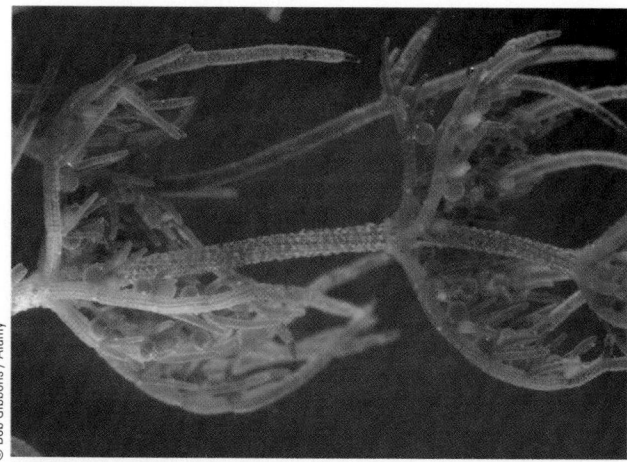

**FIGURE 17.16** A stonewort in the genus *Chara*. This representative of the charophyte lineage is known commonly as a stonewort due to the calcium carbonate that accumulates on its surface.

*Baragwanathia longifolia*

© The Natural History Museum / Alamy

**FIGURE 17.17** One of the oldest known land plant fossils, *Baragwanathia*. This fossil was found in southeastern Australia and is from the Early Devonian, between 420 and 390 million years ago.

However, this underestimates the age of the oldest plants. We know this from the analysis of fossilized **spores** and **pollen**. Pollen (the male gametophyte of a seed plant) and spores (a haploid reproductive structure, usually a single cell, that can develop into a new individual without fusing with another cell) can be preserved in layers of sediment and can tell us what kinds of plants were reproducing with these structures over geological time. The analysis of spores and pollen shows us that more than 430 million years ago, the kinds of spores produced by plants such as those alive today were already circulating. Also, spores (called cryptospores) that are different from spores produced by extant (currently living) plants but that are now commonly agreed to be associated with early land plants have been found in deposits from up to 470 million years ago. Plants are thought to have established on land somewhere between 425 and 490 million years ago. The first land plants were likely liverworts, a type of non-vascular plant called a bryophyte.

Although there are many lineages of plants with unique features, there is one feature of plants that is common across extant plants and plays an important role in plant reproduction: the **alternation of generations** between plant bodies with one set of chromosomes and plants with two sets of chromosomes (for more detailed information on plant reproduction and development, see Chapter 26).

## Alternation of Generations Is Common to All Land Plants

All types of **embryophytes** (land plants) share an important life history trait, one that makes them unique among organisms. In Chapters 3 and 6, you learned about chromosomes and how they are divided among cells. You will recall that in the cells that make up the human body, for example, there are two sets of chromosomes. These cells are diploid. In our reproductive cells (sperm and egg), or gametes, there is one set of chromosomes. Cells with one set of chromosomes are haploid. The gametes of humans are single celled. In contrast, plants have multicellular stages with both haploid and diploid cells. The multicellular diploid stage of a plant is called the **sporophyte**. The sporophyte has specialized structures that produce spores through meiosis (see Chapter 6 for details about meiosis). Spores are haploid and produce multicellular but haploid bodies, gametophytes. The **gametophyte** then produces gametes, which fuse to form a diploid zygote that grows into a sporophyte. This cycling between diploid and haploid life stages is called the alternation of generations (**Figure 17.18**).

In vascular plants, the roots and shoots are the diploid sporophyte. The gametophyte has been reduced to the nutritive coat surrounding the seed. However, this is not true of all embryophytes. Some groups of plants have longer and larger gametophytes as part of their life cycles (see Chapter 26 for more information on plant reproduction and development).

## Bryophytes Are the Oldest Type of Land Plant

Bryophytes are the oldest type of land plant. They are non-vascular plants and as a group include three types of plants: the mosses, liverworts, and hornworts. You are

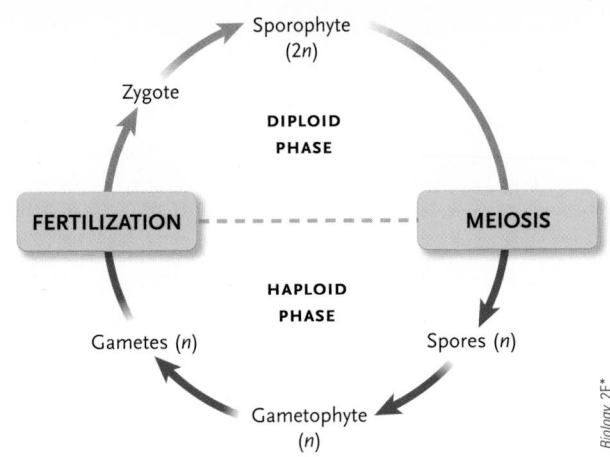

**FIGURE 17.18** Overview of the alternation of generations, the basic pattern of the plant life cycle. The relative dominance of haploid and diploid phases is different for different plant groups.

likely familiar with mosses but perhaps are less familiar with liverworts and hornworts. All three of these groups of plants are diverse. There are approximately 10,000 species of mosses (**Figure 17.19**), 6000 to 8000 species of liverworts (**Figure 17.20**), and 100 to 150 species of the more enigmatic hornworts (**Figure 17.21**).

**FIGURE 17.19** Arctic moss grows along a stream.

**A.** Thallus of *Calypogeia muelleriana*

**B.** Thallus of *Marchantia*

**C.** Male plant — Male gametophyte

**D.** Female plant — Female gametophyte

**E.** Asexual reproduction — Gemmae

**FIGURE 17.20** A variety of liverworts. Some liverworts have a body shape known as a thallus **(a, b)**. A thallus is plant tissue that is not differentiated into organs. Many liverworts have both male and female gametophytes **(c, d)**. Liverworts can also produce asexually and do so with gemmae. Gemmae are small discs of vegetative tissue that grow in small, cuplike structures. On disturbance (e.g., from falling rain), the gemmae are ejected from the cup and are able to grow into a new plant. Other plants, such as some mosses, are also capable of asexual reproduction with gemmae **(e)**.

SOURCE: (Photos A-E): Image Copyright © Malcolm Storey, 2000, www.bioimages.org.uk; © Clive/hiddenforest.co.nz; Martin Hutten/National Park Service; Paul Stehr-Green/National Park Service; Wayne P. Armstrong, Professor of Biology and Botany, Palomar College, San Francisco, CA

**FIGURE 17.21** A hornwort. The "horns" growing up from the plant body are the sporophyte generation, whereas the vegetative tissue on the ground surface is the gametophyte generation.

These three groups of plants are different from each other and are not monophyletic (they do not all share one common ancestor). Scientists still don't know which branch of the bryophytes is most closely related to the vascular plants; some data suggest that it is the liverworts, whereas other data suggest that it is the hornworts. However, there are many features that are unique to all the plants in this group and that highlight how land plants have solved the challenges of living on land in a number of different ways.

Bryophytes are not vascular plants and therefore do not have xylem or phloem. Bryophytes also lack roots. They instead are held in soil by thin filaments called **rhizoids**. In large part because they do not have a mechanism to transport water and nutrients, all of these plants are relatively low-lying, often acting as a covering over bare soil or rock. The water content in a bryophyte matches that of the surrounding environment. This is called **poikilohydry**. Bryophytes are also able to withstand desiccation. They are able to survive even when they are dry at the cellular level. However, although they can survive being dried out, bryophytes require water to reproduce sexually. Bryophytes, unlike other plants, have swimming sperm and thus require water for sperm to reach an egg (see Chapter 26 for more on plant reproduction). These features make bryophytes vulnerable to their physical environments. They are often used as indicators of climate, pollution, and other changes in the abiotic environment. Bryophytes also play an important role in shaping the abiotic environment. They prevent erosion, for example, and contribute to soil development. In many rocky, dry, wind-blown environments, bryophytes such as mosses might be the only plants able to survive.

Additionally unique to bryophytes, the main body of the plant is the gametophyte. The part of sphagnum moss, for example, that is leafy and soft is made up of haploid cells. The gametophyte photosynthesizes and provides food for the rest of the plant. The diploid cells of bryophytes are limited to the **sporangia** (singular = sporangium), stalklike structures in which gametes are produced. The gametes are produced in organs called **gametangia** (singular = gametangium). Sperm form in a gametangium called an **antheridium**, whereas eggs form in a gametangium called an **archegonium (Figure 17.22)**. All bryophytes can also reproduce asexually (see Chapter 27 for more details).

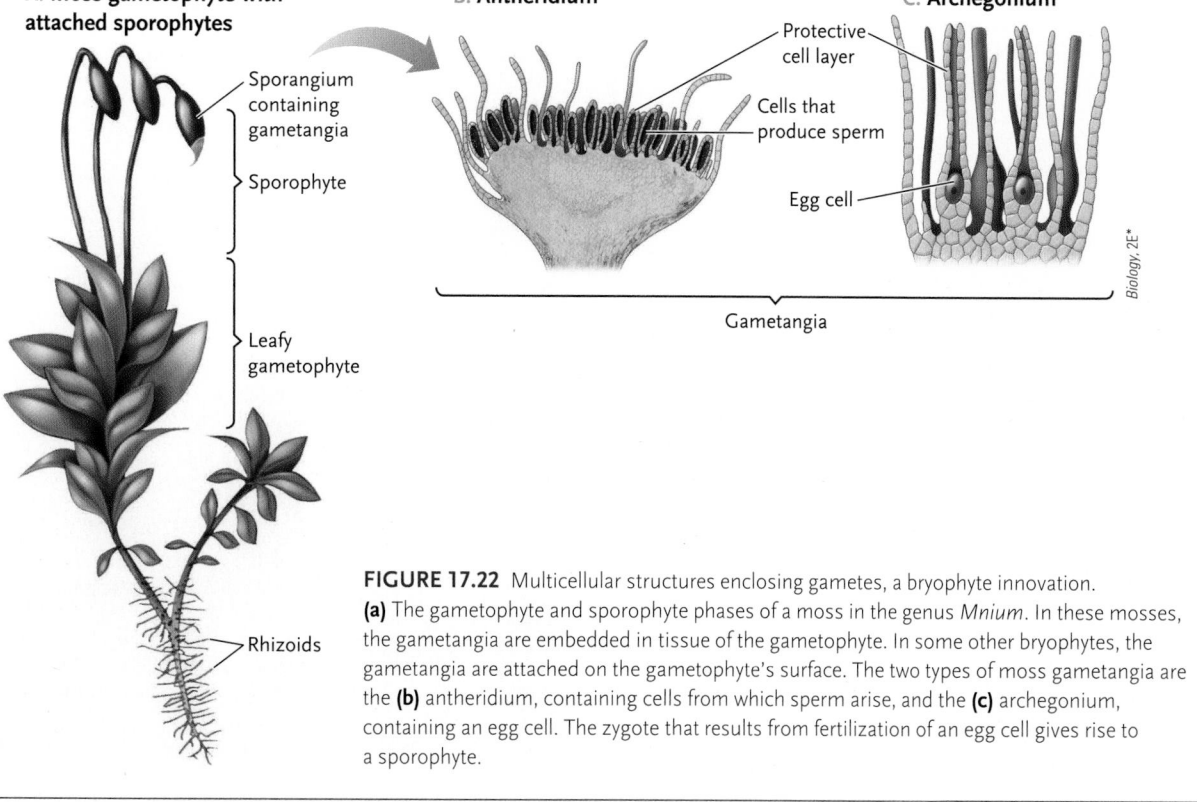

**FIGURE 17.22** Multicellular structures enclosing gametes, a bryophyte innovation. **(a)** The gametophyte and sporophyte phases of a moss in the genus *Mnium*. In these mosses, the gametangia are embedded in tissue of the gametophyte. In some other bryophytes, the gametangia are attached on the gametophyte's surface. The two types of moss gametangia are the **(b)** antheridium, containing cells from which sperm arise, and the **(c)** archegonium, containing an egg cell. The zygote that results from fertilization of an egg cell gives rise to a sporophyte.

Bryophytes spend a longer portion of their life cycle as haploid organisms than any other group of land plant.

## STUDY BREAK

1. What is meant by the phrase "alternation of generations"?
2. What is a sporophyte?
3. How do bryophytes deal with water stress in the absence of vascular tissue?

## The First Vascular Plants Were the Seedless Vascular Plants

The first vascular plants to evolve were seedless. Although they have vascular tissue (xylem and phloem), they still produce spores and have flagellated sperm. Several lineages of seedless vascular plants exist in the fossil record that no longer exist today, but four lineages remain. The largest group, and the most well known, is the ferns. If you look at a fern, you'll notice that it has no seeds but instead has spores on the undersides of its leaves **(Figure 17.23)**. There are about 12,000 fern species. The smallest group of seedless vascular plants is the whisk ferns, which includes only two genera and only a few species in each **(Figure 17.24)**. There are two other groups of seedless vascular plants, the horsetails **(Figure 17.25)** and the clubmosses **(Figure 17.26)**.

A key difference between seedless vascular plants and the bryophytes is the role of the diploid sporophyte generation. The sporophyte generation of seedless vascular plants is much larger in size than the sporophyte generation of bryophytes. This is facilitated by vascular tissue allowing the largest of seedless vascular plants, the tree ferns, to grow leaves (fronds) up to 3 m across. With the exception of some horsetails, the gametophyte generation (not only for

**FIGURE 17.23** An example of a fern, a seedless vascular plant. In this photo, you can see sori (singular = sorus) on the undersides of the fern fronds. Sori are clusters of sporangia where spores are produced.

**FIGURE 17.24** A whisk fern in the genus *Psilotum*. The sporangia are located on the yellow growths at the end of various shoots.

**FIGURE 17.25** A horsetail (*Equisetum telmateia*). The horsetail has two types of stems; one holds the strobili (singular = strobilus), where spores are produced **(a)**. The other type of stem, which is green, is the site of the plant's photosynthetic activity **(b)**.

**A. Sporangia**

**B. Sporophyte stem**

Strobilus, an aggregation of sporangia and sporophylls at the tip of the horsetail sporophyte

**FIGURE 17.26** A clubmoss (*Lycopodium clavatum*). Note the cones where sporangia are located.

SOURCE: Jason Hollinger, https://www.flickr.com/photos/7147684@N03/1289194411. This file is licensed under the Creative Commons Attribution 2.0 Generic license, http://creativecommons.org/licenses/by/2.0/deed.en

seedless vascular plants but also for all plants) does not contain vascular tissue. Both the gametophyte and sporophyte generations of seedless vascular plants are capable of photosynthesis. In the case of ferns, the gametophyte generation is a small, heart-shaped plant that is very small, about 1 mm across. It is a free-living, independent plant, however, that is different from the gametophyte of any seed plant, which is always contained within the larger body of the sporophyte generation.

## Gymnosperms Produce Seeds but Not Flowers or Fruits

Seeds represent a major innovation in plant evolution. Seeds are the structures that form when an ovule matures after a pollen grain reaches it and a sperm fertilizes the egg (see Chapter 26 for more on plant reproduction). The first seed plants evolved during the Permian, around 270 million years ago. These first seed plants were gymnosperms. The gymnosperms, in fact, dominated the world of land plants in the ancient world of the non-bird dinosaurs through most of the Mesozoic era. Many fewer species of gymnosperms are alive today, between 850 and 1000, and they belong to one of four groups: the cycads, the ginkgoes, the gnetophytes, and the conifers **(Figure 17.27)**. These groups

**FIGURE 17.27** Species from the four groups of extant gymnosperms. **(a)** Conifers (bristlecone pine, *Pinus longaeva*), **(b)** cycads (*Zamia*), **(c)** ginkgo (*Ginkgo biloba*), and **(d)** gnetophytes (*Welwitschia mirabilis*).

contain some familiar species that are also economically important, such as pine and spruce trees. The majority of extant gymnosperm species are conifers. The gymnosperms, however, also contain some other amazing plants with which you may be less familiar. The gymnosperms are often called "living fossils," with several species retaining their physiologies and life histories over many millions of years, such as the ginkgo (*Ginkgo biloba*). Recent work, however, has shown that there has been recent evolution within the gymnosperms even in these ancient species.

The word **gymnosperm** means "naked seed," and the name denotes one of the key differences between these first seed plants and the seed plants that now dominate the plant kingdom, the **angiosperms** (angio = receptacle or vessel and sperm = seed, so angiosperms have enclosed seeds). Gymnosperm seeds are not contained in fruits or flowers, although some have a fleshy layer of tissue around the seed, such as *Ginkgo biloba*. Many gymnosperm species have both male and female cones. In male cones, the haploid male gametophyte is produced, whereas in female cones, the haploid female gametophyte grows. Two groups of gymnosperms, the cycads and the ginkgoes, have motile sperm like the bryophytes and seedless vascular plants, although these sperm move inside rather than outside the plant. In the gnetophytes and conifers, however, sperm cells are not flagellated and are not motile. The male gametophyte of all gymnosperms is packaged as pollen grains and must be transported to the female gametophyte by way of pollination. Ginkgoes and conifers are wind pollinated, but cycads and gnetophytes are insect pollinated.

The ginkgoes contain only one extant species, the tree species *Ginkgo biloba*. This tree is often planted as an ornamental in gardens and urban areas, so you may have noticed it before with its distinctive fan-shaped leaves. A species with plants of different sex are known as **dioecious**, and plants that have both male and female gametophytes on a single plant are known as **monoecious**. Ginkgoes are dioecious. Male *Ginkgo* plants produce cones, whereas female *Ginkgo* plants produce ovules that develop into fleshy seeds. Any *Ginkgo* plants that you see are likely males. The female seeds produce particularly foul-smelling chemicals, making them pretty unpleasant neighbours and unlikely to be planted on city streets or in gardens.

The gnetophytes contain three unique genera. One of these, the *Welwitschia mirabilis*, is a strange giant restricted to the Namib Desert in western Africa. This plant, like the ginkgo, is dioecious, and both male and female plants have cones. There are only two leaves per plant, but they are enormous and split with age into what looks like several leaves, extending across the desert ground. These plants also have a large taproot. For many years, researchers hypothesized that *Welwitschia* obtained much of its water from the fog that rolls into the Namib

in the mornings and on which other desert organisms depend, but recent research has shown that *Welwitschia* uses groundwater, obtained, no doubt, through this large taproot.

The cycads contain about 300 extant species. The cycads live mostly in tropical or subtropical environments, and many are rare or endangered. The cycads have fern- or palmlike leaves and often have beautiful colourful cones. Cycads contain a number of poisons and toxins that make them generally unpalatable. Despite this, people in many places use cycad tubers for food, leaching the toxins from the plant tissue before grinding the starch into a kind of flour.

There are about 600 species of conifers. They occupy mostly cool and dry ecosystems of high latitudes or altitudes. Conifers dominate many Canadian forests. Conifers have several adaptations that make them particularly suited to these environments. The needles of trees such as pines, spruce, and cedars are modified leaves that minimize water loss and can tolerate freezing temperatures. Most conifers are also evergreen: they do not lose their leaves during the winter months of temperate ecosystems. Because the needles minimize water loss and can tolerate freezing, the energetic costs for conifers of survival in cold, dry, and otherwise inclement climates are lower.

## Angiosperms Have Become the Most Diverse Group of Plants

Angiosperms are the flowering plants. The angiosperms include the plants with which you are most familiar, including many of the plants that humans exploit for food and fibre. There are over 10 times more species of angiosperm plants than any other group of extant plants. Recent counts estimate that there are approximately 250,000 species of angiosperms.

Because the angiosperms have diversified into so many more species than other plant lineages, evolutionary biologists often call them a "successful group." So what has made the angiosperms so much more successful than the other plants? A number of characteristics have been proposed as facilitating the dominance and diversity of flowering plants on the planet today, and it is likely that a combination of many or all of these has contributed to the rise of angiosperms. Five of these characteristics include the following:

1. Movement of water and nutrients through the plant body is more efficient in angiosperms. Angiosperms have alterations to both xylem and phloem cells that allow them to be more efficient at transporting water, nutrients, and sugars through the plant compared to other plant groups.
2. Evolution of broad leaves facilitated higher levels of photosynthetic activity.

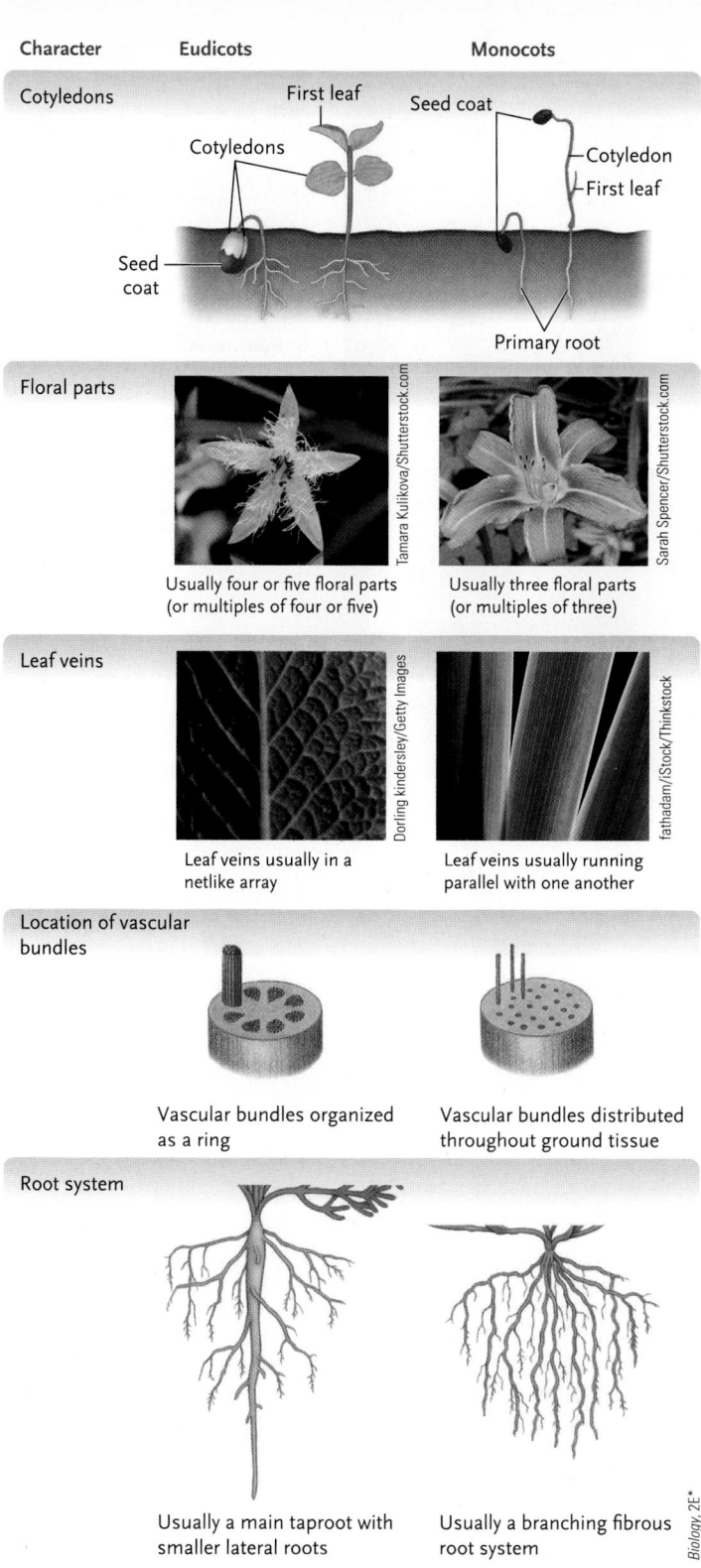

| Character | Eudicots | Monocots |
| --- | --- | --- |

Cotyledons

Usually four or five floral parts (or multiples of four or five)

Usually three floral parts (or multiples of three)

Leaf veins usually in a netlike array

Leaf veins usually running parallel with one another

Vascular bundles organized as a ring

Vascular bundles distributed throughout ground tissue

Usually a main taproot with smaller lateral roots

Usually a branching fibrous root system

**FIGURE 17.28** Eudicots and monocots compared.

3. Angiosperm seeds are protected in flowers and fruits. Before fertilization, the female gametophyte of an angiosperm is protected from predation or climatic variability. Following fertilization, the ovary of a flower becomes a fruit. This both protects seeds and serves as a dispersal mechanism as it attracts animal consumers that eat and carry the seeds across the landscape.

4. The evolution of animal and plant partnerships for dispersal and for pollination (see Pollination and Coevolution below) has also likely played a substantial role in the diversification and success of angiosperms.

5. Generally faster reproductive strategies may give angiosperms advantages over other plant lineages. Even in other seed plants, such as conifers, reproduction can take a long time. It can take years to go from pollen grains and ovules to germinating gymnosperm seeds. The angiosperms, in contrast, can reproduce multiple times in a single growing season (a summer in a temperate climate such as Canada's).

## There Are Two Main Groups of Angiosperms: Monocots and Eudicots

Almost all the angiosperms can be separated into two major groups, the **monocots** and the **eudicots**. These two groups of plants are named for the number of leaves that first grow from a germinating seed. These structures are not considered true leaves and are called **cotyledons**. In a monocot, one cotyledon grows on germination. In a eudicot, there are two. There are a number of other differences between these two types of flowering plants, including differences in flower structure, leaf venation (you'll recall that the veins of leaves are bundles of vascular tissues), the location of vascular tissue in the stems, and the shape of the root systems **(Figure 17.28)**. The monocots include grasses and other plants, such as corn, orchids, lilies, bananas, and palm trees **(Figure 17.29a, p. 384)**. The eudicots include plants such as beans and peas, sunflowers, roses, and fruit and nut trees **(Figure 17.29b)**.

### STUDY BREAK

1. What are dioecious and monoecious plants?
2. Describe one of the qualities of angiosperms that is unique among plants and what it is about this quality that gives angiosperms an advantage.
3. What are three differences between monocots and eudicots?

### Pollination and Coevolution

It is probably a familiar concept to all of us that insects such as bees and butterflies pollinate flowers. By feeding on nectar, a sugar-rich liquid produced by flowers, and pollen, insects end up covered in pollen. Some insects,

## A. Representative monocots

Wheat (*Triticum*)

Trillium (*Trillium*)

Western wood lily
(*Lilium philadelphicum*)

## B. Representative eudicots

Wild rose (*Rosa acicularis*)

Twinflower (*Linnaea borealis*)

Claret cup cactus
(*Echinocereus triglochidiatus*)

**FIGURE 17.29** Examples of monocots and eudicots, the major groups of angiosperms. **(a)** Representative monocots: wheat (genus *Triticum*), trillium (genus *Trillium*), and Western wood lily (*Lilium philadelphicum*). **(b)** Representative eudicots: wild rose (*Rosa acicularis*), twinflower (*Linnaea borealis*), and a hedgehog cactus (*Echinocereus triglochidiatus*).

such as bees, have specialized pollen-carrying body parts. The pollen is transferred to other flowers as the animals continue to forage. Pollen contains the male gametes, which can reach the ovules of the flowers. The male and female gametes fuse, and a zygote, in most cases a seed, forms. Many other types of organisms act as pollinators, including other insects, such as beetles and flies, as well as mammals, such as bats, and birds.

The adaptations that have coevolved between some plants and their pollinators are astounding. **Coevolution** occurs when two interacting species evolve adaptations, either behavioural or morphological changes that are important to both species—in other words, that are reciprocal. Snapdragons, for example, open only if a heavy pollinator, such as a bumblebee, lands on a flower. The flower will remain closed to smaller pollinators such as honeybees. In other relationships, coevolution has led to increased proboscis length of pollinators and increased floral length. These traits are favoured because pollinators will reach into a flower only as far as required to reach their food reward, and increased contact between proboscis and flower leads to increased pollen transfer. There are also more than 20 genera worldwide of so-called "sexually deceptive" orchids that mimic female insects in both smell and appearance. Males are attracted to the flowers and attempt to mate, thereby becoming covered

in pollen. When they move to the next flower that looks like another mate, they transfer the pollen.

In addition to, and likely long before, interactions like these that evolved between angiosperms and pollinators, there were interactions between insect pollinators and gymnosperms, some of which still exist today. Although many gymnosperms are wind pollinated, a number of groups are pollinated by insects. Fossil thrips, small winged insects, have recently been discovered preserved in amber (amber is fossilized tree sap from gymnosperms, usually from conifers) holding gymnosperm pollen grains on specialized pollen-collecting body parts. The thrips show that the insects interacted with gymnosperm pollen and had specialized pollen-collecting body parts more than 100 million years ago. This may represent an intermediate step between wind-pollinated plant species and the specialized coevolution between flowering plants and pollinators observed in many angiosperm plant species.

The modern interaction between thrips and cycads, all of which are dioecious, is also interesting. Experiments on an obligatory mutualism between one cycad species (*Macrozamia lucida*) and thrips of the genus *Cycadothrips* show a "push-pull" interaction between the cycad and its pollinators. Male cones typically serve as a habitat for the thrips as they provide a pollen food source. Each day, the cones experience changes in temperature and release varying amounts of volatile compounds. In the early morning, the cones are cool, and a low level of volatile compounds serves to attract the thrips. Between 11 a.m. and 2 p.m., however, the cones heat up, sometimes increasing in temperature by 12°C, and volatile emissions increase more than a million-fold. The combination of heat and potentially toxic volatile concentrations drives an exodus of thrips from the cones. Female cones likewise experience changes in temperature and volatile emissions, although the increase in emissions at midday is many times less than that of the male cones. Later in the day, the temperature and volatile emissions again decrease, and thrips are once again attracted to the cones. Because the female and male cones emit the same attractive low-level emissions of volatile compounds, some thrips enter female cones, thereby transferring pollen and facilitating sexual reproduction.

### Human Domestication of Plants

Throughout the world, dozens of times, humans have domesticated wild plants and have established agricultural societies. Scientists estimate that about 2500 species of wild plants have been domesticated for use in human agriculture (less than 1% of the total plant species).

However, only a subset of these species has become economically and nutritionally important crops. In fact, based on data from 1990, 103 plant species provide over 90% of the calories eaten by humans. Fifteen species of domesticated plants are used to provide fibre.

Monocots from the grass family (Poaceae) have been domesticated most often. Cereal grains are in this category, and three provide a majority of human calories consumed: rice, wheat, and maize. Plants in the legume family (Fabaceae) are next, with over 300 domesticated species. Many plant species have been selected for different qualities and now produce a number of surprisingly different crop plants. For example, broccoli, Brussels sprouts, cabbage, calabrese, cauliflower, kale, and kohlrabi are all the same eudicot species, *Brassica oleracea*.

Human dependence on a small number of agricultural species, however, does not mean that we do not depend on many other plant species. We have used thousands of species in medicine, for example, and are continually learning more about the qualities and abilities of different plants across the world. Plants also provide myriad services to both ecosystems and humans. Plants along stream channels, for example, serve to both filter water and slow erosion (see Chapter 30 for more on ecosystem services).

## PUTTING IT IN PERSPECTIVE

In this chapter, you have been introduced to the complex and charismatic plants. The plants are an incredibly diverse group of organisms that make up the bottom of the food pyramid on which most other organisms on land, including humans, depend. Plants have evolved a wide variety of ways to obtain food and water, reproduce, and grow while rooted in place. Plants provide most of the energy that you use to fuel your everyday life. You eat many plants directly or eat animals that were fuelled by plants. Even your electricity and the gas in your car come from plants. So-called "fossil fuels" are the fossilized remains of plants. Just as our bodies break carbon compounds to fuel metabolism, we break the carbon compounds of fossilized plants through combustion to fuel our lives.

## KEY CONCEPTS REVIEW AND QUESTIONS

### 17.1 Plant Structure and Function

Plants obtain energy, water, and minerals without the ability to move their bodies. All vascular plant bodies contain roots and shoots. The roots hold the plant in place and allow the plant to obtain resources from the soil. In the shoots, sunlight is converted to chemical energy by photosynthesis and gases are exchanged with the atmosphere. Plant cells have unique structures and functions. Plant cells are all surrounded by a cell wall. This wall is made of cellulose and often lignin, both of which increase the strength and rigidity of plant cells. Plant cells also contain a number of organelles that are unique, including plastids and a large central vacuole.

1. Describe two of the ways plant roots increase their ability to obtain nutrients and water from soils.

2. What are stomata, and what function do they serve?

3. Citrus fruits store organic acids in their cells, which give them their distinctive flavours. Where might these organic acids be stored? Why?

4. If you are eating a plate of crudités, which vegetables contain chloroplasts? Chromoplasts? Leucoplasts?

### 17.2 Plant Tissue Systems

There are three main tissue systems in vascular plants: the ground tissue system, the dermal tissue system, and the vascular tissue system. Each system contains unique cell types and supports the plant in different ways. The ground tissue system makes up the majority of the mass of a plant and is the site of the majority of photosynthetic activity. The dermal tissue system is the outermost layers of plant cells and is important for protection and structure. The vascular tissue system contains the tissues that transport food and water throughout the roots and shoots of the plant, transporting soil resources and the products of photosynthesis to different parts of the plant.

5. Animals also made the evolutionary transition from water to land. What are two systems in animals that are analogous in form and function to the tissue systems of plants?

6. What are the three types of cells that make up ground tissue?

## 17.3 Land Plant Diversity, Evolution, and Success

All plants have life cycles that contain haploid and diploid plant bodies. This life cycle is called the alternation of generations. Haploid plant bodies are gametophytes, whereas diploid plant bodies are sporophytes. The size and dominance of these plant bodies vary among the different groups of plants. In bryophytes, the gametophyte generation is larger than the sporophyte generation. In vascular plants, however, the gametophyte generation is smaller in size than the sporophyte generation, with its main role being to nourish new plant embryos. Angiosperms are the most diverse group of plants. Angiosperms are the flowering plants. They can be separated into two main groups, the monocots and the eudicots.

7. The gametophyte generation has the ability to photosynthesize in which groups of plants?

8. Are the cells of tree trunks haploid or diploid? What about the cells of moss?

9. Match the following descriptions with either monocots or dicots.
   a. Parallel bundles of vascular tissue in leaves
   b. Has a large taproot
   c. Has two cotyledons
   d. Floral parts in multiples of three
   e. Vascular bundles in stem arranged in a ring

10. What is coevolution? What role has it played in angiosperm evolution?

Now that you have read and reviewed this chapter, we encourage you to attempt to build a concept map using these key concepts and indicate the connections between them. See Chapter 5 for some examples.

## The Scientific Method

Since the nineteenth century, researchers have used the scientific method to study all disciplines of science. The scientific method is an investigative approach to acquiring knowledge in which scientists make observations about the natural world, develop working explanations about these observations, and then test those explanations by collecting more information.

Application of the scientific method requires both curiosity and skepticism: successful scientists question the current state of our knowledge and challenge old concepts with new ideas and observations. Explanations of natural phenomena must be backed up by objective evidence rooted in observation and measurement. Most importantly, scientists share their ideas and results by publishing their work.

### Testing a Hypothesis Is Central to the Scientific Method

A hypothesis can be defined as a tentative explanation for an observation, phenomenon, or scientific problem that can be tested by further investigation. Scientific hypotheses have two fundamental elements. First, a hypothesis must be testable—that is, there must be some set of observations or experiments that can be undertaken to support the hypothesis. For example, if you are studying a gene in yeast that you find is activated when cells are placed under conditions of heat stress, then you may hypothesize that the protein encoded by this gene is essential for the yeast to survive short-term exposure to high temperature. You can test this hypothesis by inactivating the gene, using molecular techniques, in a population of yeast cells and observing if there is a change in heat tolerance. Today, this hypothesis is easily testable. A scientist may have had a similar idea 30 years ago, but given the lack of molecular techniques at that time, the hypothesis would not have been testable.

The second key to a scientific hypothesis is that it must be falsifiable—that is, through observation or experimentation, you must be able to show that the original hypothesis is false if, in fact, it is not correct. In the yeast example, it is very possible that through analysis you would find that inactivation of the gene does not change the ability of yeast cells to survive high temperatures. In this case, the hypothesis is falsified.

Scientists test the predictions that come from hypotheses with experimental or observational tests that generate relevant data. And if data from just one study refute a scientific hypothesis (i.e., demonstrate that its predictions are incorrect), the scientist must modify the hypothesis and test it again or abandon it altogether. Keep in mind, however, that no amount of data can prove beyond a doubt that a hypothesis is correct; there may always be contradictory evidence that has not yet been uncovered, and it is impossible to test every imaginable possibility. That is why scientists say that positive results are "consistent with" or "support" a hypothesis.

## Elements of the Scientific Method

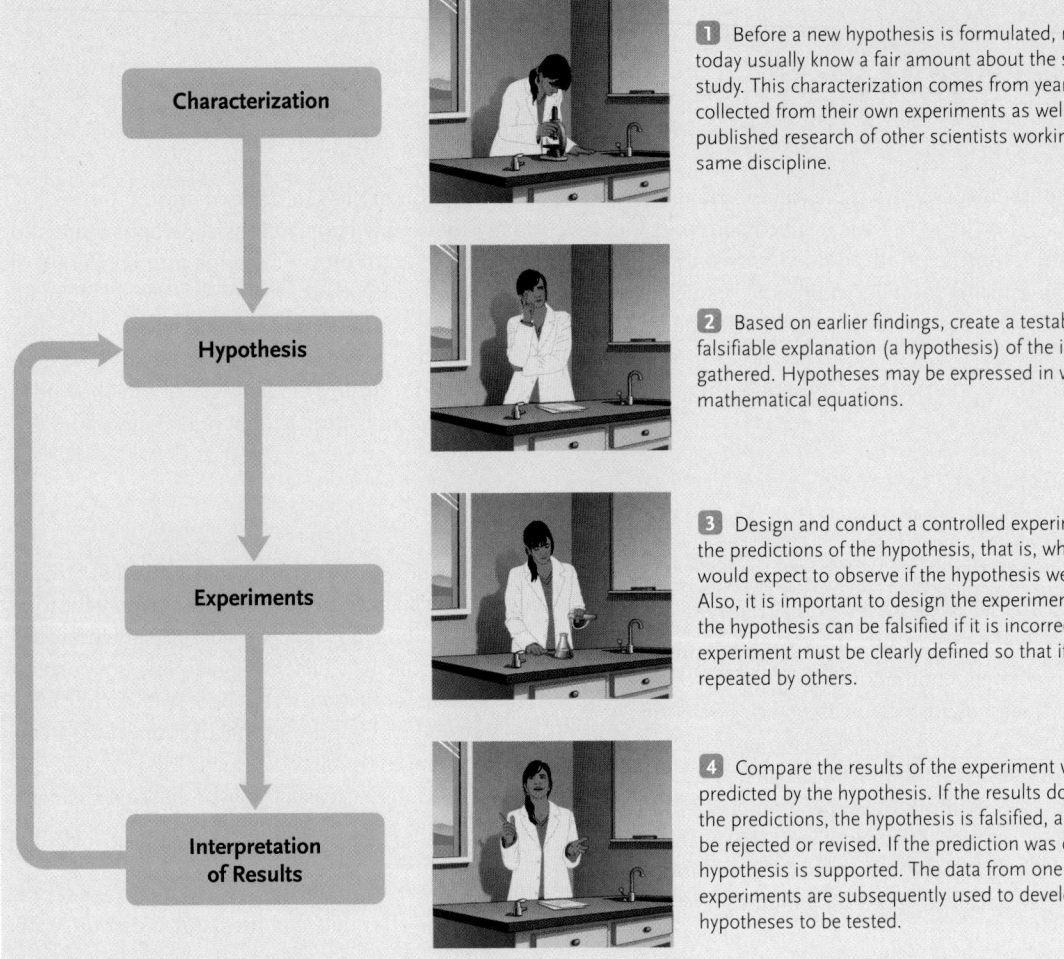

**Characterization**

1 Before a new hypothesis is formulated, researchers today usually know a fair amount about the subject under study. This characterization comes from years of data collected from their own experiments as well as the published research of other scientists working in the same discipline.

**Hypothesis**

2 Based on earlier findings, create a testable and falsifiable explanation (a hypothesis) of the information gathered. Hypotheses may be expressed in words or in mathematical equations.

**Experiments**

3 Design and conduct a controlled experiment to test the predictions of the hypothesis, that is, what you would expect to observe if the hypothesis were correct. Also, it is important to design the experiment so that the hypothesis can be falsified if it is incorrect. The experiment must be clearly defined so that it can be repeated by others.

**Interpretation of Results**

4 Compare the results of the experiment with those predicted by the hypothesis. If the results do not match the predictions, the hypothesis is falsified, and it must be rejected or revised. If the prediction was correct, the hypothesis is supported. The data from one set of experiments are subsequently used to develop additional hypotheses to be tested.

## An Example of Hypothesis Development and Testing

Consider this simple example of hypothesis development and testing.

**Observation:** A friend gives you a plant that she grew on her windowsill. Under her care, the plant always flowered. You place the plant on your windowsill and water it regularly, but the plant never blooms. You know that your friend always gave fertilizer to the plant, but you have not.

**Question:** Will giving the plant fertilizer induce it to flower?

**Hypothesis:** This type of plant will flower if it receives fertilizer. This is a good hypothesis because it is testable and falsifiable.

**Experiment:** Establish six replicates of an experimental treatment (identical plants grown with fertilizer) and six replicates of a control treatment (identical plants grown without fertilizer). With all experiments, it is important to include a control—a set of individuals that will not be subject to the treatment. The presence or absence of fertilizer is the experimental variable. With the exception of the experimental variable, everything else—the flower pots, the soil, the amount of water, and exposure to sunlight—is kept the same between the treated and control individuals. This control experiment ensures that any differences in flowering pattern observed between plants that receive the experimental treatment (fertilizer) and those that receive the control treatment (no fertilizer) can be attributed to the experimental variable.

Nearly all experiments in biology include replicates, multiple subjects that receive either the same experimental treatment or the same control treatment. Scientists use replicates in experiments because individuals typically vary in genetic makeup, size, health,

**Question:** Your friend fertilizes a plant that she grows on her windowsill, and it flowers. After she gives you the plant, you put it on your windowsill, but you do not give it any fertilizer, and it does not flower. Will giving the plant fertilizer induce it to flower?

Friend added fertilizer.

You did not add fertilizer.

**Experiment:** Establish six replicates of an experimental treatment (identical plants grown with fertilizer) and six replicates of a control treatment (identical plants grown without fertilizer).

### Experimental Treatment

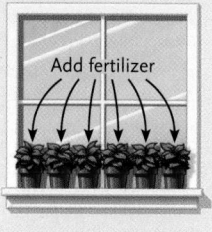

Add fertilizer

### Control Treatment

No fertilizer

**Possible Result 1:** Neither experimental nor control plants flower.

### Experimentals

### Controls

**Possible Result 2:** Plants in the experimental group flower, but plants in the control group do not.

### Experimentals

### Controls

**Conclusion:** Fertilizer alone does not cause the plants to flower. Consider alternative hypotheses and conduct additional experiments, each testing a different experimental treatment, such as the amount of water or sunlight the plant receives or the temperature to which it is exposed.

**Conclusion:** The application of fertilizer induces flowering in this type of plant, confirming your original hypothesis. Pat yourself on the back and apply to graduate school in plant biology.

or other characteristics—and because accidents may disrupt a few replicates. By exposing multiple subjects to both treatments, we can use a statistical test to compare the average result of the experimental treatment with the average result of the control treatment, giving us more confidence in the overall findings. Please read below about scientific uncertainty and statistical significance.

**Possible Result 1:** There is no difference in the flowering pattern between the experimental and control plants.

**Possible Conclusion 1:** Fertilizer alone does not cause the plants to flower. Consider alternative hypotheses and conduct additional experiments, each testing a different experimental treatment, such as the amount of water or sunlight the plant receives or the temperature to which it is exposed.

**Possible Result 2:** Plants in the experimental group flower, but plants in the control group do not.

**Possible Conclusion 2:** The application of fertilizer induces flowering in this type of plant, supporting your original hypothesis.

## Scientific Uncertainty and Statistical Significance

In any scientific study, there is an inherent level of uncertainty—scientific uncertainty—that arises because of natural variability or because there is a limit to how accurate and precise scientific measurements can be. The uncertainty in accuracy (degree of closeness of a measurement to the true value) and precision (degree of reproducibility of a measurement) stems primarily from the physical limitations of measurement tools, such as thermometers, clocks, balances, etc. For example, a typical biology lab will have analytical balances that can measure mass to one hundredth of a milligram (0.01 mg). To minimize inaccuracies, these balances also have a draft shield that prevents air current and dust from interfering with measurement. This will ensure that the measurement is accurate or is very close to the true mass of the object. However, if a sample weighs less than 0.01 mg, it will be difficult to measure it accurately using these types of balances, thus increasing the level of scientific uncertainty. To avoid this uncertainty, scientists will need to use the right tools—in this case, microbalances that can measure smaller masses more accurately. However, even the most sophisticated balances have their limitation, and as such, even a low level of uncertainty will always exist. To further reduce the level of uncertainty, scientists will also seek precision in measurement by using tools that provide a high degree of reproducibility. In the case of balances, if you weigh the same object multiple times under the same conditions, the measurements should be close to one another. This degree of closeness (or reproducibility) between measurements determines the level of precision. Note that precision is independent of accuracy. Just because a measurement is precise (high degree of reproducibility) doesn't necessarily mean it's accurate.

Natural variability also contributes to scientific uncertainty, especially in studies of biological or natural systems. Often natural parameters are dynamic; there are rarely absolutes. For example, the optimal pH needed for a biological enzyme to function is often not an exact number but instead is a range that could also be influenced by several other factors, including temperature, electrical charges in the environment, and natural inhibitors. Thus, the degree of uncertainty in many biological studies is often impacted by the surrounding natural variability. This is even more evident in ecological studies that involve complex interactions among species and their environment.

Scientific uncertainty can be measured using statistical analysis. To do this, experiments must be repeated several times to acquire multiple data sets. These data are then used to determine statistical significance—a probability that the outcome of the experiment is not due to chance alone. In essence, it provides scientists with a degree of certainty that their hypothesis is supported by the results. Statistical significance does not mean that a result or conclusion is important. Instead, it means that the result obtained is not likely due to chance alone. In other words, there is value or certainty in data that is supporting the hypothesis. Often in science, statistical significance is depicted as a $p$ value, a level of uncertainty that will be accepted as significant. For example, if statistical analysis of the experiment determined the $p$ value to be less than 0.05, then this means that the odds that the results acquired are due to chance alone (or the degree of uncertainty) is less than 5%. Thus, the results are considered statistically significant, and there is a high level of confidence in the results. If the $p$ value was less than 0.01, the degree of uncertainty is even less (1%) and the level of confidence is even higher. If, however, the $p$ value is greater than what is predetermined to be statistically significant, this would indicate that there is a higher degree of uncertainty in the results and therefore a lower level of confidence. In this case, scientists may have to accept the null hypothesis—the hypothesis that states that there is no relationship between the two phenomena being investigated. As such, a scientist will then either modify the working hypothesis or test an alternative one.

## Causation versus Correlation

There is an expression used in science: "correlation does not imply causation." It means that a correlation between two variables does not imply that one causes the other. We see correlations presented in the media all the time. For example, recent media coverage suggests that obesity rates are rising with sugar consumption. From this media coverage, can one infer that obesity is caused by sugar consumption? Or could people be eating more sugar because they are obese, not the other way around? Could something else be causing both to rise at the same time? How do we know?

Here's a hypothetical example of a correlation: the national homicide rate increases whenever bread prices rise. This statement implies that the cost of bread is directly linked to the homicide rate. Perhaps it causes changes in behaviour that make humans more violent. Intuitively, we know that this is a false statement, and, of course, there are no scientific data to support this claim. Thus, we must be very careful not to imply causation between these two correlated facts.

Here's a less obvious but real example. In the 1980s to 1990s, observational studies reported that hormone replacement therapy (HRT) to treat the symptoms of menopause might reduce coronary heart disease (CHD) in women. Although these studies did not directly investigate the role of HRT in CHD, the correlation between the two events in this study implied causation. These studies, however, were later contradicted by large-scale randomized controlled trials that did directly examine the correlation between HRT and CHD. The results revealed a small but statistically significant negative relationship between two events. Indeed, these studies not only refuted the earlier observational studies but showed that women on HRT were at a slightly greater risk of, not protection from, CHD. Reanalysis of the earlier observational studies revealed that differences in socioeconomics, which were not originally taken into consideration, likely played a role in their observed results. Women undertaking HRT often have a higher socioeconomic status and as such have access to a better diet, exercise, and care. Therefore, these women are already generally at a lower risk of developing CHD. Thus, the initial finding of a correlation between HRT and CHD was simply a coincidence and not a cause-and-effect relationship, as originally inferred.

The example of HRT and CHD is just one of many that speak to the fact that scientists must be critical when reviewing and analyzing data. However, this is not only limited to scientists. Science writers who present science stories in the media also need to be objective. Although these writers often have science backgrounds and a clear understanding of the scientific method and statistical significance, sometimes the sensationalism of the story outshines the scientific evidence. And even with the best and most honest intentions, some coincidences mistakenly appear to be "real" connections. And, finally, we as readers need to remain objective and critical of the results that are being reported so that we also don't fall into the trap of believing that a correlation implies causation. As a reader, ask yourself about whether the study included proper experimental controls, what the level of scientific uncertainty and statistical significance is, and whether or not the data truly support the hypothesis.

## The Scientific Theory

When a hypothesis stands up to repeated experimental tests, it is gradually accepted as an accurate explanation of natural events. This acceptance often takes many years, and it usually involves repeated experimental confirmations. When many different tests have consistently supported a hypothesis that addresses many broad questions, it may become regarded as a scientific theory—a scientifically acceptable, well-substantiated explanation of some aspect of the natural world. Most scientific theories are supported by exhaustive experimentation; thus, scientists usually regard them as established truths that are unlikely to be contradicted by future research.

In common usage, the word *theory* most often labels an idea as either speculative or downright suspect, as in the expression, "It's only a theory." But when scientists talk about theories, they refer to concepts that have withstood the test of many experiments. Because of the difference between the scientific and common usage of the word *theory*, many people fail to appreciate the extensive evidence that supports scientific theories. For example, scientists accept the theory of evolution as a fully supported scientific truth: all species change with time, new species are formed, and older species may eventually die off. Although evolutionary biologists debate the details of how evolutionary processes bring about these changes, very few scientists doubt the theory. Moreover, no scientist who has tried to cast doubt on the theory of evolution has ever devised or conducted a study that disproves any part of it. Unfortunately, the confusion between the scientific and common usage of the word *theory* has led, in part, to endless public debate about supposed faults and inadequacies in the theory of evolution.

## Experimental versus Observational Science

In some scientific disciplines, the system under study may be too large or too complex to establish controlled experiments. In astronomy, for example, one cannot manipulate stars and galaxies as if they were potted plants. Astronomy is considered an observational science, as are research themes in ecology and evolutionary biology. Observational science relies on sophisticated statistical techniques to analyze detailed observational data to test hypotheses. The statistical tools provide a method for researchers to infer pattern and underlying cause from the collected data.

Many scientific disciplines rely on a combination of observational and experimental science. For example, ecology researchers studying global climate change often set up experiments that take place in the field or environment. These enable a certain level of control of variables under far more realistic conditions than would be possible in a laboratory. These so-called field experiments complement the analysis of observational data that may reflect changes to our climate that occurred hundreds of years ago.

# Measurement and Scale

## The SI System of Measurement

The International System of Units is the most widely used system of measurement in the world. Its abbreviation, SI, is from the French Système International d'Unités. The SI system uses seven base units, each of which measures or describes a different kind of physical quantity. Each unit is strictly defined, although the definitions have been modified (and made more accurate) over time. As an example, the metre was originally defined by the French Academy of Sciences as the length between two marks on a platinum–iridium bar that was designed to represent 1/10,000,000 of the distance from the equator to the North Pole through Paris. This definition was changed in 1983 by the International Bureau of Weights and Measures as the distance travelled by light in absolute vacuum in 1/299,792,458 of a second.

### The Seven Base Units of the SI System

| Name | Symbol | Quantity |
|------|--------|----------|
| metre | m | length |
| kilogram | kg | mass |
| second | s | time |
| ampere | A | electric current |
| kelvin | K | temperature |
| mole | mol | amount of substance |
| candela | cd | luminous intensity |

The SI system also uses a series of prefix names and prefix symbols to form the names and symbols of the decimal multiples of the base SI units and range from yotta, at $10^{24}$ (one septillion), to yocto, at $10^{-24}$ (one septillionth).

| Factor | Prefix | Symbol | Factor | Prefix | Symbol |
|--------|--------|--------|--------|--------|--------|
| $10^{24}$ | yotta | Y | $10^{-1}$ | deci | d |
| $10^{21}$ | zetta | Z | $10^{-2}$ | centi | c |
| $10^{18}$ | exa | E | $10^{-3}$ | milli | m |
| $10^{15}$ | peta | P | $10^{-6}$ | micro | m |
| $10^{12}$ | tera | T | $10^{-9}$ | nano | n |
| $10^{9}$ | giga | G | $10^{-12}$ | pico | p |
| $10^{6}$ | mega | M | $10^{-15}$ | femto | f |
| $10^{3}$ | kilo | k | $10^{-18}$ | atto | a |
| $10^{2}$ | hecto | h | $10^{-21}$ | zepto | z |
| $10^{1}$ | deca | da | $10^{-24}$ | yocto | y |

## Derived SI Units

Several other units have been derived from combinations of the seven base units of measure. Three of the more common concern units of force (newton), pressure (pascal), and energy or heat (joule). The measurement of temperature in degrees Celsius is also considered a derived. However, 0°C = 273.16 K (note that no degree symbol is used when expressing temperature in kelvins).

| Name | Symbol | Quantity | Expression |
|------|--------|----------|------------|
| newton | N | force | $m \cdot kg \cdot s^{-2}$ |
| pascal | Pa | pressure | $N \cdot m^{-2}$ |
| joule | J | energy and work | $N \cdot m$ |

## Non-SI Units in Common Usage

A number of units not derived from the base SI units are accepted for use with SI units.

| Name | Symbol | Value in SI Units |
|---|---|---|
| minute | min | 60 s |
| hour | h | 3600 s |
| day | d | 86,400 s |
| litre | L | $1 \text{ dm}^3 = 10^{-3} \text{ m}^3$ |
| angstrom | Å | $10^{-10}$ m |
| calorie, a measure of food energy* | cal | 4.184 J |
| unified atomic mass unit or dalton** | u or Da | $\sim 1.66054 \times 10^{-24}$ kg |

*One food calorie = 1 Cal = 1000 cal.

**Value determined experimentally to be 1/12 the mass of an unbound atom of carbon-12.

## Why Everyone Should Use SI Units

In December 1998, NASA launched the Mars Climate Orbiter on a mission to study the Martian weather and climate. As it approached Mars, the spacecraft received instructions from flight control on Earth to fire thruster engines to enter into a proper orbit about 140 to 150 km above the Martian surface. However, as it approached the planet, a navigation error caused the spacecraft to descend into an orbit of only 57 km above the surface. The spacecraft was soon destroyed by the heat caused by atmospheric friction.

The review of the incident found that the root cause was a mix-up between the use of SI units and an older system of measure, imperial units (e.g., inches, feet, and pounds). More specifically, the software that was used to control the thruster engines of the spacecraft from the ground was written using the imperial unit of force, the pound-force, whereas onboard the spacecraft, information was interpreted in terms of newtons, the metric unit of force. Since 1 pound-force equals about 4.45 N, instructions from the ground were thus multiplied by 4.45.

The total cost of the mission was approximately $327 million.

## Scale in Biology

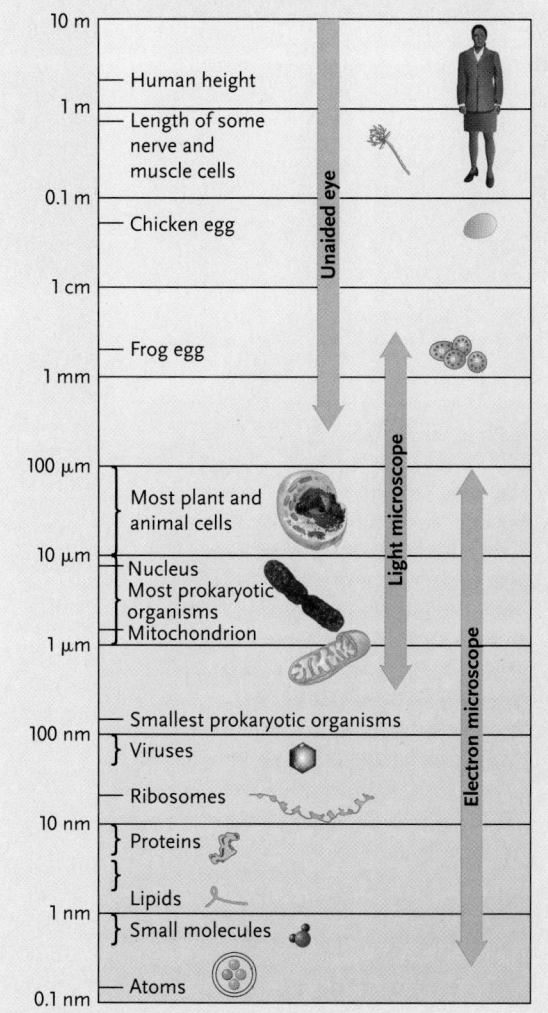

| | |
|---|---|
| 10 m | |
| 1 m | Human height |
| | Length of some nerve and muscle cells |
| 0.1 m | Chicken egg |
| 1 cm | |
| 1 mm | Frog egg |
| 100 μm | Most plant and animal cells |
| 10 μm | Nucleus / Most prokaryotic organisms / Mitochondrion |
| 1 μm | |
| 100 nm | Smallest prokaryotic organisms / Viruses |
| | Ribosomes |
| 10 nm | Proteins |
| 1 nm | Lipids / Small molecules |
| 0.1 nm | Atoms |

Unaided eye — Light microscope — Electron microscope

# The Organization of Matter

Any substance in the universe that has mass and occupies space is defined as matter. The fundamental scientific concepts that explain how matter is organized in biological systems are no different from those for non-living forms of matter. Living organisms are built from the same chemical building blocks as non-living systems and abide by the same fundamental laws of chemistry and physics. Because of this, a basic understanding of how all matter is organized is important for a complete picture of the structure and function of organisms.

## Elements and Compounds

All matter is composed of elements. An element is a pure substance composed of only one type of atom. Ninety-two different elements occur naturally on Earth. Living organisms are composed of about 25 elements, with only four elements—carbon, hydrogen, oxygen, and nitrogen—accounting for more than 96% of the mass of an organism. Seven other elements—calcium, phosphorus, potassium, sulphur, sodium, chlorine, and magnesium—contribute most of the remaining 4%. The proportions by mass of different elements differ markedly in sea water, the human body, a fruit, and Earth's crust, as shown below.

A compound is a substance that contains two or more elements. For example, hydrogen and oxygen are the elements that make up the compound water ($H_2O$). The chemical and physical properties of compounds are typically distinct from those of their atoms or elements.

| Sea water | | Human | | Pumpkin | | Earth's crust | |
|---|---|---|---|---|---|---|---|
| Oxygen | 88.3 | Oxygen | 65.0 | Oxygen | 85.0 | Oxygen | 46.6 |
| Hydrogen | 11.0 | Carbon | 18.5 | Hydrogen | 10.7 | Silicon | 27.7 |
| Chlorine | 1.9 | Hydrogen | 9.5 | Carbon | 3.3 | Aluminum | 8.1 |
| Sodium | 1.1 | Nitrogen | 3.3 | Potassium | 0.34 | Iron | 5.0 |
| Magnesium | 0.1 | Calcium | 2.0 | Nitrogen | 0.16 | Calcium | 3.6 |
| Sulphur | 0.09 | Phosphorus | 1.1 | Phosphorus | 0.05 | Sodium | 2.8 |
| Potassium | 0.04 | Potassium | 0.35 | Calcium | 0.02 | Potassium | 2.6 |
| Calcium | 0.04 | Sulphur | 0.25 | Magnesium | 0.01 | Magnesium | 2.1 |
| Carbon | 0.003 | Sodium | 0.15 | Iron | 0.008 | Other elements | 1.5 |
| Silicon | 0.0029 | Chlorine | 0.15 | Sodium | 0.001 | | |
| Nitrogen | 0.0015 | Magnesium | 0.05 | Zinc | 0.0002 | | |
| Strontium | 0.0008 | Iron | 0.004 | Copper | 0.0001 | | |
| | | Iodine | 0.0004 | | | | |

Andriano/Shutterstock.com

©iStock.com/Hon Lau

## The Atom

Elements are composed of atoms—the smallest units that retain the chemical and physical properties of an element. Any given element has only one type of atom identified by a standard one- or two-letter symbol. The element carbon is identified by the single letter C, which stands for both the carbon atom and the element.

Each atom consists of an atomic nucleus surrounded by one or more smaller, fast-moving particles called electrons. All atomic nuclei contain one or more positively charged particles called protons. The number of protons in the nucleus of each kind of atom is referred to as the atomic number. This number does not vary and thus specifically identifies the atom. The smallest atom, hydrogen, has a single proton in its nucleus, so its atomic number is 1. Carbon with six protons, nitrogen with seven protons, and oxygen with eight protons have atomic numbers of 6, 7, and 8, respectively.

With one exception, the nuclei of all atoms also contain uncharged particles called neutrons, which occur in variable numbers approximately equal to the number of protons. The single exception is the most common form of hydrogen, which has a nucleus that contains only a single proton. Atoms are assigned a mass number based on the total number of protons and neutrons in the atomic nucleus. Electrons are ignored in determinations of atomic mass because the mass of an electron is negligibly small.

| Atomic Number and Mass Number of the Most Common Elements in Living Organisms | | | |
|---|---|---|---|
| Element | Symbol | Atomic Number | Mass Number of the Most Common Form |
| Hydrogen | H | 1 | 1 |
| Carbon | C | 6 | 12 |
| Nitrogen | N | 7 | 14 |
| Oxygen | O | 8 | 16 |
| Sodium | Na | 11 | 23 |
| Magnesium | Mg | 12 | 24 |
| Phosphorus | P | 15 | 31 |
| Sulphfur | S | 16 | 32 |
| Chlorine | Cl | 17 | 35 |
| Potassium | K | 19 | 39 |
| Calcium | Ca | 20 | 40 |
| Iron | Fe | 26 | 56 |
| Iodine | I | 53 | 127 |

**Hydrogen**

Nucleus
(1 proton)

1 electron

**Carbon**

6 protons
6 neutrons

2 electrons

4 electrons

## Isotopes

All atoms of a specific element have the same number of protons, but they may differ in the number of neutrons. These distinct forms of an element, where atoms have the same atomic number but different atomic masses, are called isotopes. The nuclei of some isotopes are unstable and break down, or decay, giving off particles of matter and energy that can be detected as radioactivity. The decay transforms the unstable, radioactive isotope—called a radioisotope—into an atom of another element. For example, the carbon isotope $^{14}C$ is unstable and undergoes radioactive decay in which one of its neutrons splits into a proton and an electron. The electron is ejected from the nucleus, but the proton is retained, giving a new total of seven protons and seven neutrons, which is characteristic of the most common form of nitrogen. Thus, the decay transforms the carbon atom into an atom of nitrogen.

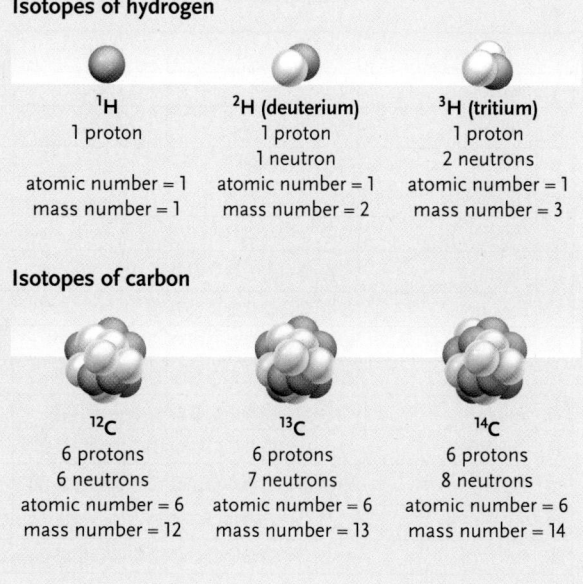

**Isotopes of hydrogen**

$^{1}H$
1 proton

atomic number = 1
mass number = 1

$^{2}H$ (deuterium)
1 proton
1 neutron
atomic number = 1
mass number = 2

$^{3}H$ (tritium)
1 proton
2 neutrons
atomic number = 1
mass number = 3

**Isotopes of carbon**

$^{12}C$
6 protons
6 neutrons
atomic number = 6
mass number = 12

$^{13}C$
6 protons
7 neutrons
atomic number = 6
mass number = 13

$^{14}C$
6 protons
8 neutrons
atomic number = 6
mass number = 14

## Use of Radioisotopes

Radioactive decay occurs at a steady, clocklike rate. The length of time it takes for one-half of a sample of a radioisotope to decay is termed its half-life. Each type of radioisotope has a characteristic half-life. For example, the radioisotope $^{14}C$ decays with a fixed half-life of 5730 years, whereas the uranium radioisotope $^{238}U$ has a half-life of 4.5 billion years. Because unstable isotopes decay at a fixed rate that is not affected by chemical reactions or environmental conditions such as temperature or pressure, they are used to estimate the age of organic material, rocks, and fossils. These radiometric techniques have been vital in dating animal remains and tracing evolutionary lineages. A number of radioisotopes that have short half-lives, including the iodine radioisotope $^{123}I$ and the thulium radioisotope $^{201}Tm$, are used in medical imaging and in the treatment of diseases.

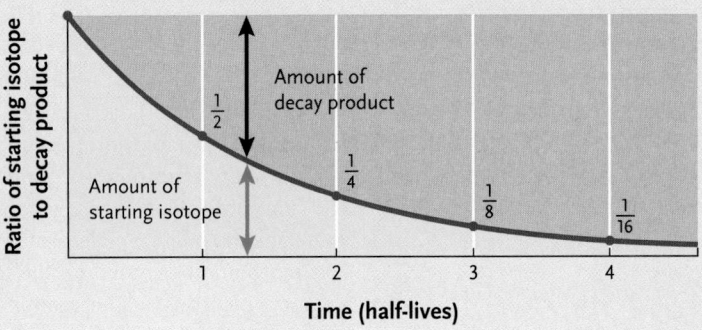

## Electrons and Electron Shells

In an atom, the number of electrons is equal to the number of protons in the nucleus. Because electrons carry a negative charge and protons are positively charged, the total structure of an atom is electrically neutral.

Electrons move around the atomic nucleus in orbitals, which are grouped into electron shells. As shown below, the first shell (I) may be occupied by a maximum of two electrons. The second (II) and third (III) shells can hold a maximum of eight electrons each. The fourth shell can hold 18 electrons (not all shown). Atoms with more than four electron shells are very rare in biological molecules.

The chemical behaviour of an atom depends primarily on the number of electrons in its outermost shell. This is referred to as the valence shell, which holds valence electrons. Atoms in which the valence shell is not completely filled with electrons tend to be chemically reactive; those with a completely filled valence shell are nonreactive, or inert.

For example, as shown on the left, hydrogen has a single, unpaired electron in its outermost and only electron shell and is highly reactive; helium has two valence electrons filling its single orbital and is unreactive (stable), or inert. Along with helium, neon and argon are also referred to as inert gases because their outer electron shell is full, which renders them chemically unreactive.

Because an unfilled electron shell is less stable than a filled one, atoms with an incomplete outer shell have a strong tendency to interact with other atoms in a way that causes them to either gain or lose enough electrons to achieve a completed outermost shell. All elements commonly found in living organisms have unfilled outermost shells (purple balls in the accompanying figure table above) and can thus participate in chemical reactions with other atoms. Because they are unreactive, helium, neon, and argon are not found in living systems.

**Atomic number**

| Element | I | II | III | IV |
|---|---|---|---|---|
| 1 Hydrogen | 1 | | | |
| 2 Helium | 2 | | | |
| 6 Carbon | 2 | 4 | | |
| 7 Nitrogen | 2 | 5 | | |
| 8 Oxygen | 2 | 6 | | |
| 10 Neon | 2 | 8 | | |
| 11 Sodium | 2 | 8 | 1 | |
| 12 Magnesium | 2 | 8 | 2 | |
| 15 Phosphorus | 2 | 8 | 5 | |
| 16 Sulphur | 2 | 8 | 6 | |
| 17 Chlorine | 2 | 8 | 7 | |
| 18 Argon | 2 | 8 | 8 | |
| 19 Potassium | 2 | 8 | 8 | 1 |
| 20 Calcium | 2 | 8 | 8 | 2 |

# Chemical Bonds

An atom with an incomplete valence shell has a strong tendency to interact with other atoms so that they have a completely filled valence shell. These interactions, called chemical bonds, are caused by closely associated atoms sharing or transferring electrons to complete the valence shell. Four types of chemical bonds are important in biological molecules: ionic bonds, covalent bonds, hydrogen bonds, and van der Waals forces. Because of their importance in hydrogen bonding, polar molecules are also discussed in this section.

## Ionic Bonds

Ionic bonds form between atoms that gain or lose valence electrons completely. A sodium atom (Na) readily loses a single electron to achieve a full valence shell, and chlorine (Cl) readily gains an electron to do the same. After the transfer, the sodium atom, now with 11 protons and 10 electrons, carries a single positive charge. The chlorine atom, now with 17 protons and 18 electrons, carries a single negative charge. In this charged condition, the atoms are called ions: sodium with a positive charge is a cation, whereas chloride with a negative charge is an anion.

Ionic bonds are common among the forces that hold ions, atoms, and molecules together in living organisms because these bonds have three key features:

- They exert an attractive force over greater distances than any other chemical bond.
- Their attractive force extends in all directions.
- They vary in strength depending on the presence of other charged substances.

**Ionic bond formation between sodium and chlorine**

**Crystals of sodium chloride (NaCl)**

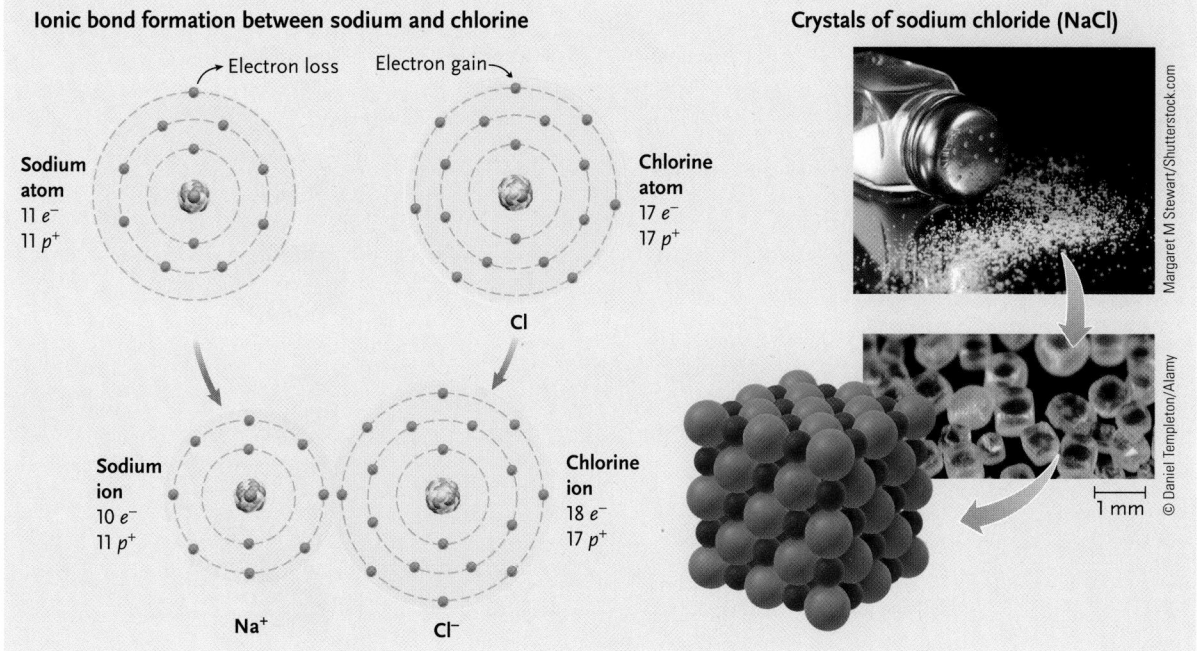

Electron loss

Electron gain

Sodium
atom
11 $e^-$
11 $p^+$

Chlorine
atom
17 $e^-$
17 $p^+$

Cl

Sodium
ion
10 $e^-$
11 $p^+$

Chlorine
ion
18 $e^-$
17 $p^+$

Na$^+$

Cl$^-$

1 mm

Margaret M Stewart/Shutterstock.com

© Daniel Templeton/Alamy

## Covalent Bonds

Covalent bonds form between two atoms when they share valence electrons. This is distinct from ionic bonds, where electrons are gained or lost from atoms. The term *molecule* refers to two or more atoms held together by covalent bonds. The formation of molecular hydrogen, $H_2$, by two hydrogen atoms is the simplest example of a covalent bond. If two hydrogen atoms collide, the single electron of each atom may join in a new, combined two-electron orbital that surrounds both nuclei and stably links the two hydrogen atoms. The linkage formed by the shared orbital is a covalent bond.

A structural formula represents a covalent bond of a pair of shared electrons as a single line. For example, in $H_2$, the covalent bond that holds the molecule together is represented as H:H or H—H. Generally speaking, the covalent bonding capacity of an atom is equal to the number of valence shell electrons necessary to fill the shell: hydrogen, 1; oxygen, 2; nitrogen, 3; and carbon, 4.

As shown below, a single oxygen atom has six valence shell electrons, and two oxygen atoms form a single molecule.

Carbon, with four unpaired outer electrons, typically forms four covalent bonds to complete its outermost energy level. An example is methane, $CH_4$, the main component of natural gas.

Unlike ionic bonds, which extend their attractive force in all directions, the shared orbitals that form covalent bonds extend between atoms at discrete angles and directions, giving covalently bound molecules distinct, three-dimensional forms. For biological molecules such as proteins, which are held together primarily by covalent bonds, the three-dimensional form imparted by these bonds is critical to their functions.

The four covalent bonds formed by the carbon atom are fixed at an angle of 109.5° from each other, forming a tetrahedron. The tetrahedral arrangement of the bonds allows carbon atoms to link extensively to each other in chains and rings in both branched and unbranched forms. Such structures form the backbones of an almost unlimited variety of molecules. Carbon can also form double bonds, in which atoms share two pairs of electrons, and triple bonds, in which atoms share three pairs of electrons.

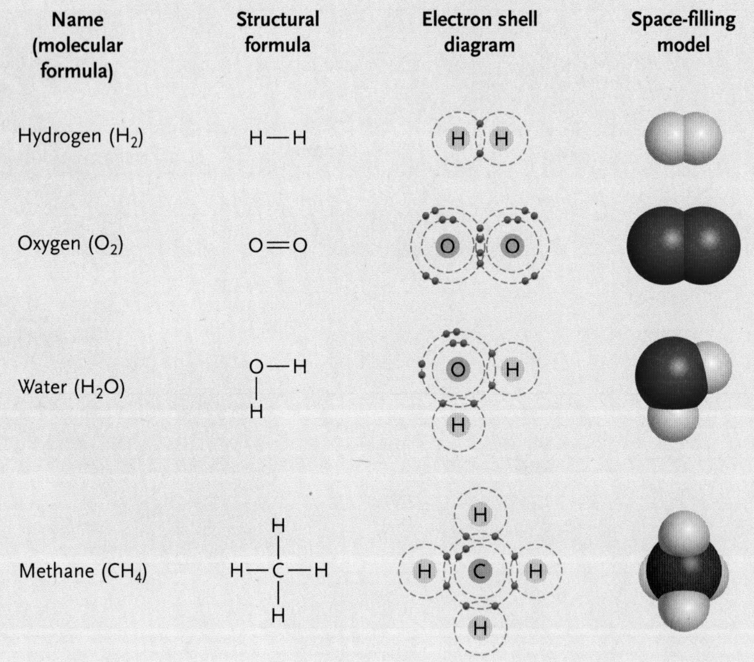

| Name (molecular formula) | Structural formula | Electron shell diagram | Space-filling model |
| --- | --- | --- | --- |
| Hydrogen ($H_2$) | H—H | | |
| Oxygen ($O_2$) | O=O | | |
| Water ($H_2O$) | O—H \| H | | |
| Methane ($CH_4$) | H—C—H (with H above and H below) | | |

## Polarity and Hydrogen Bonding

Although all covalent bonds involve the sharing of valence electrons, they differ widely in the degree of sharing. Electronegativity is the measure of an atom's attraction for the electrons it shares in a chemical bond with another atom. The more electronegative an atom is, the more strongly it attracts shared electrons. Among atoms, electronegativity increases as the number of protons in the nucleus increases and as the distance of electrons from the nucleus increases. The unequal sharing of electrons between two atoms that differ in their electronegativity results in a polar covalent bond.

The atom that attracts the electrons more strongly carries a partial negative charge, and the atom deprived of electrons carries a partial positive charge. The atoms carrying partial charges (denoted by $\delta^-$ or $\delta^+$) may give the whole molecule partially positive and negative ends; this is referred to as polarity, and the molecule is termed polar.

Polar molecules attract and align themselves with other polar molecules and with charged ions and molecules and tend to exclude non-polar molecules. Polar molecules that associate readily with water because it is strongly polar are identified as hydrophilic (*hydro* = water; *philic* = preferring). Non-polar substances that are excluded by water and other polar molecules are identified as hydrophobic (*phobic* = avoiding).

When hydrogen atoms are made partially positive by sharing electrons unequally with oxygen, nitrogen, or sulphur, they may be attracted to nearby oxygen, nitrogen, or sulphur atoms made partially negative by unequal electron sharing in a different covalent bond. This attractive force is the hydrogen bond, illustrated by a dotted line in structural diagrams of molecules. Hydrogen bonds may form between atoms in the same or different molecules.

Individual hydrogen bonds are about 1/20 the strength of a covalent bond. However, large biological molecules may offer many opportunities for hydrogen bonding, both within and between molecules. When numerous, hydrogen bonds are collectively strong and lend stability to the three-dimensional structure of molecules such as proteins. Hydrogen bonds between water molecules are responsible for many of the properties that make water uniquely important to life.

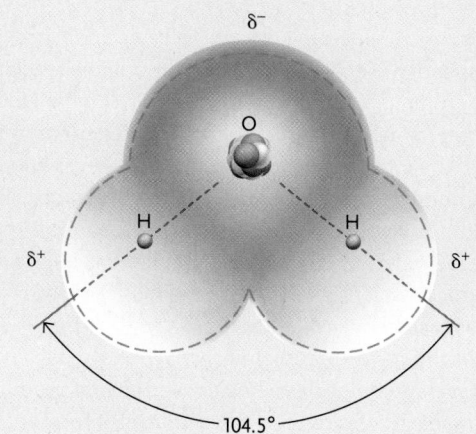

| Hydrogen bond donor | | Hydrogen bond acceptor |
|---|---|---|
| $\delta^-$  $\delta^+$ | | $\delta^-$ |
| —N—H | ····················· Hydrogen bond | N— |
| —N—H | ····················· | O— |
| —O—H | ····················· | N— |
| —O—H | ····················· | O— |

## Van der Waals Forces

Van der Waals forces are even weaker than hydrogen bonds. These forces develop between non-polar molecules or regions of molecules when, through their constant motion, electrons accumulate by chance in one part of a molecule or another. This process leads to zones of positive and negative charge, making the molecule polar. If they are oriented in the right way, the polar parts of the molecules are attracted electrically to one another and cause the molecules to stick together briefly. Although an individual bond formed with van der Waals forces is weak and transient, the formation of many bonds of this type can stabilize the shape of a large molecule, such as a protein.

A striking example of the collective power of van der Waals forces concerns the ability of geckoes to cling to and walk up vertical smooth surfaces. The toes of the lizard are covered in millions of pads, each one forming a weak interaction using van der Waals forces—with the molecules on the smooth surface.

Nathalie Speliers Ufermann/Shutterstock.com

## Chemical Reactions

Chemical reactions occur when atoms or molecules interact to form new chemical bonds or break old ones. As a result of bond formation or breakage, atoms are added to or removed from molecules, or the linkages of atoms in molecules are rearranged. When any of these alterations occur, molecules change from one type to another, usually with different chemical and physical properties. In biological systems, chemical reactions are accelerated by *enzymes*, which are discussed in Chapter 4.

The atoms or molecules entering a chemical reaction are called the reactants, and those leaving a reaction are the products. A chemical reaction is written with an arrow showing the direction of the reaction; reactants are placed to the left of the arrow, and products are placed to the right. Both reactants and products are usually written in chemical shorthand as formulas.

For example, the overall reaction of photosynthesis, in which carbon dioxide and water are combined to produce sugars and oxygen (see Chapter 5), is written as follows:

$$6CO_2 + 6H_2O \rightarrow C_6H_{12}O_6 + 6O_2$$

Carbon dioxide · Water · A sugar · Molecular oxygen

The number in front of each formula indicates the number of molecules of that type among the reactants and products (the number 1 is not written). Notice that there are as many atoms of each element to the left of the arrow as there are to the right, even though the products are different from the reactants. This balance reflects the fact that in such reactions, atoms may be rearranged but not created or destroyed. Chemical reactions written in balanced form are known as chemical equations.

Although some chemical reactions result in all the reactant molecules being converted into products, many reactions are reversible; that is, the products of the forward reaction can become the reactants of the reverse reaction. That a reaction is reversible is illustrated by using opposite-headed arrows. As an example, hydrogen and molecular nitrogen can react to produce ammonia, but ammonia can also break down to produce hydrogen and nitrogen:

$$3H_2 + N_2 \rightleftarrows 2NH_3.$$

# Water

All living organisms contain water. On average, cells contain about 70% water by weight, although the amount can vary from 50% to more than 95%. Many kinds of organisms live directly immersed in water. Water is so important that organisms living in dry environments have evolved complex systems to obtain and conserve the water they need. The water inside organisms is crucial for life: it is required for many important biochemical reactions and plays major roles in maintaining the shape and organization of cells and tissues.

## Hydrogen Bonds and the Properties of Water

The properties of water molecules that make them so important to life depend to a great extent on their polar structure and their ability to link to each other by hydrogen bonds (see Chemical Bonds, above).

Hydrogen bonds form readily between water molecules, linking the relatively positive H atoms with the relatively negative O atoms. These bonds are relatively weak when compared to other chemical bonds, but they give water a loose structure. Hydrogen bonds also give water its viscosity—a thickness not found in other liquids. In liquid water, hydrogen bonds constantly break and reform. The amount of energy present in the moving water molecules is enough to break the relatively weak bonds. If the temperature of the water is increased, the rate of bond breakage increases. Similarly, as water is cooled, the process of breaking hydrogen bonds decreases. When water freezes, the hydrogen bonds become fixed and the water molecules form the characteristic rigid, crystalline structure we know as ice. Interestingly, the crystal structure of ice spaces the water molecules farther apart than the water lattice. Because of this greater spacing, water has the unusual property of being about 10% less dense when solid than when liquid. Imagine what Earth would be like if ice sank to the bottom, as most solids do.

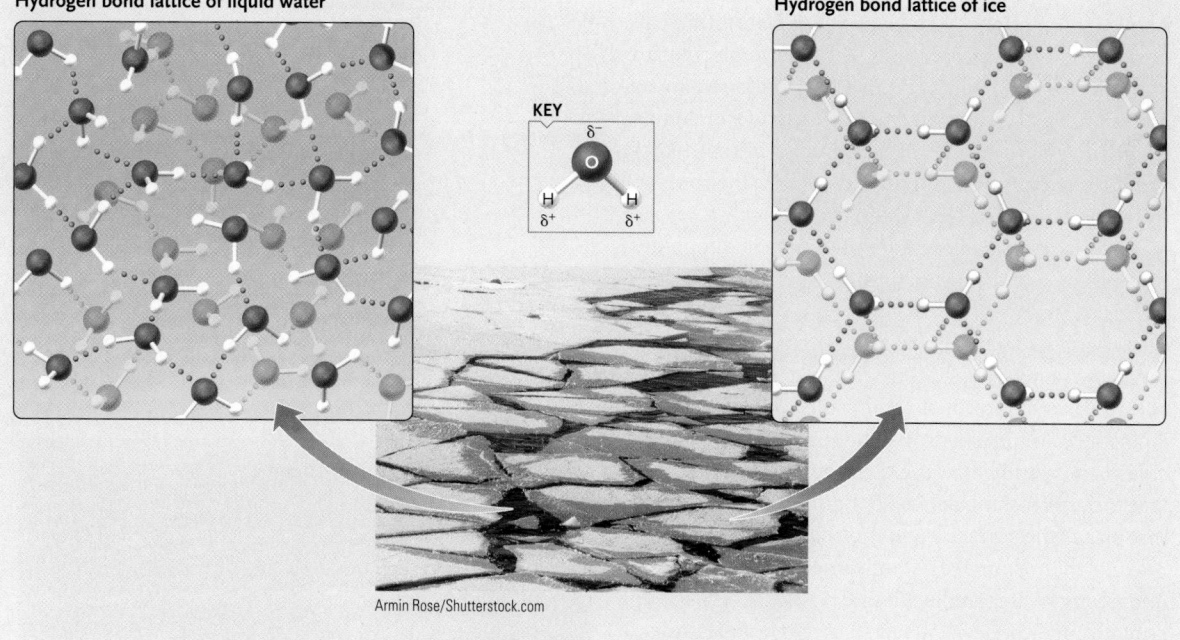

Hydrogen bond lattice of liquid water

KEY

Hydrogen bond lattice of ice

Armin Rose/Shutterstock.com

THE BUILDING BLOCKS OF BIOLOGY

## Specific Heat and Heat of Vaporization

Because of the continuous formation and breakage of hydrogen bonds, as the water is heated, a portion of the heat is used to break hydrogen bonds rather than speed up the movement of water molecules. As a result, the temperature of water, reflected in the average motion of its molecules, increases relatively slowly as heat is added when compared to other liquids. This results in water having a high specific heat, defined as the amount of energy required to increase the temperature of a given quantity of water. For example, relatively high temperatures and the addition of considerable heat are required to break enough hydrogen bonds to make water boil. The high boiling point maintains water as a liquid over the wide temperature range of 0 to 100°C. Importantly, the opposite is also true. Once heated, water holds a large amount of energy and releases it slowly to its environment. Taken together, the high specific heat of water helps reduce the rate of temperature fluctuation in living organisms. On a larger scale, it also helps reduce the rate of temperature fluctuations in our environment. This is especially evident if we compare the climate of coastal and mid-continental locations. In desert areas, the temperature can fluctuate tens of degrees Celsius between daytime and nighttime. This is largely due to the lack of water as a sink for heat energy during the day and a slow release of heat energy during the night.

To convert water to a gas, a large amount of energy, 586 cal/g, must be added to allow water molecules to evaporate. This required energy, known as the heat of vaporization, allows humans and many other organisms to cool off when hot. In humans, water is released onto the surface of the skin by more than 2.5 million sweat glands. The energy absorbed by the water in sweat as the sweat evaporates cools the skin and the underlying blood vessels. The heat loss helps keep body temperature from increasing when exertion levels or environmental temperatures are high. Plants use a similar cooling mechanism as water evaporates from their leaves.

## Surface Tension

Above we mentioned the viscosity of water; this can also be thought of as the ability of water molecules to stay together, a phenomenon that is referred to as cohesion. For example, in land plants, cohesion holds water molecules in unbroken columns in the microscopic conducting tubes that extend from the roots to the highest leaves. As water evaporates from the leaves, water molecules in the columns, held together by cohesion, move upward through the tubes to replace the lost water.

Related to cohesion is surface tension, which is a measure of how difficult it is to stretch or break the surface of a liquid. The water molecules at surfaces facing air can form hydrogen bonds with water molecules beside and below them but not on the sides that face the air. This unbalanced bonding produces a force that places the surface water molecules under tension, making them more resistant to separation than the underlying water molecules. This force is strong enough to allow small insects such as water striders to walk on water.

**Creation of surface tension by unbalanced hydrogen bonding**

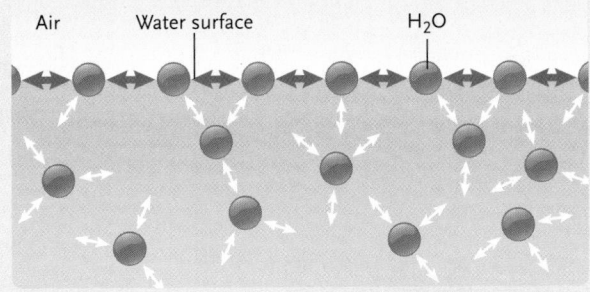

Air    Water surface    $H_2O$

**Spider supported by water's surface tension**

©iStock.com/Alasdair Thomson

## Aqueous Solutions

In biological systems, many chemicals are dissolved in water. We call this an aqueous solution. When defining an aqueous solution, water is called the *solvent*, and the molecules of a substance dissolved in water are called the *solute*. Because water molecules are small and strongly polar, they readily surround other polar and charged molecules and ions. In a solution, the water molecules will form a coat surrounding the other molecule or ion, called a hydration shell. The hydration shell reduces the attraction between the molecules or ions and promotes their separation and entry into a solution. Once dissolved, they are surrounded by water molecules with the hydration shell, preventing the solutes from reassociating.

Sodium chloride (table salt) dissolves in water because water molecules quickly form hydration layers around the $Na^+$ and $Cl^-$ ions in the salt crystals, reducing the attraction between the ions so much that they separate from the crystal and enter the surrounding water lattice as individual ions. In much the same way, hydration shells surround macromolecules such as nucleic acids and proteins, reducing their electrostatic interaction with other molecules and allowing them to dissolve in the aqueous solution of the cell.

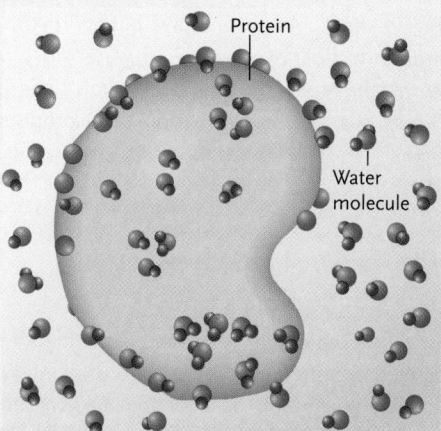

## Solubility in Water

Because water is the essential, universal solvent in cells, we talk about whether other atoms and molecules are "water soluble." We can discuss water-soluble chemicals such as table salt (NaCl) or sugar (sucrose – $C_{12}H_{22}O_{11}$); we say they are hydrophilic. Based on the Greek, *hydrophilic* means water loving. Hydrophilic compounds will dissolve readily in water. In general, when we look at the chemical structure of hydrophilic compounds, they are polar, meaning that they are charged or have unequally shared electrons. This polarity allows hydrogen bonds to form with water molecules and a hydration shell to develop. The opposite of hydrophilic compounds are hydrophobic compounds. Also from the Greek, *hydrophobic* means water fearing. As you may guess, hydrophobic compounds do not dissolve in water. In biological systems, the most common hydrophobic compounds are lipids, oils, and waxes. Hydrophobic compounds are generally not polar. This means that the atoms making up hydrophobic compounds share their electrons equally and are thus unable to form hydrogen bonds with water or other polar molecules. One last class of molecules we need to consider is fatty acids, which have a polar portion (the acid part of the fatty acid) and a non-polar portion. We call these types of molecules amphipathic. The amphipathic nature of membrane lipids allows them to form bilayers in aqueous solutions.

The differences in polarity are crucial for cells. The hydrophobic nature of lipids allows membranes to form and limit the movement of polar molecules into and out of the cell. A classic example of how polar and non-polar molecules interact is a vinaigrette salad dressing. If you mix olive oil (hydrophobic) and vinegar (95% water and 5% hydrophilic acetic acid), the two liquids will not mix. No matter how much you shake them, the fats will separate from the water.

## Calculating Solute Concentrations

In the cell, chemical reactions depend on solutes dissolved in aqueous solutions. To understand these reactions, you need to know the number of atoms and molecules involved. Concentration is the number of molecules or ions of a substance in a unit volume of space, such as 1 mL or 1 L. The number of molecules or ions in a unit volume cannot be counted directly, but it can be calculated indirectly by using the mass number of atoms as the starting point.

The mass number of an atom is equivalent to the number of protons and neutrons in its nucleus. From the mass number, and the fact that neutrons and protons have approximately the same mass (i.e., $1.66 \times 10^{-24}$ g), you can calculate the mass of an atom of any substance. For an atom of the most common form of carbon, with six protons and six neutrons in its nucleus, the total mass is

$$12 \times (1.66 \times 10^{-24} \text{ g}) = 1.992 \times 10^{-23} \text{ g.}$$

For an oxygen atom, with eight protons and eight neutrons in its nucleus, the total mass is

$$16 \times (1.66 \times 10^{-24} \text{ g}) = 2.656 \times 10^{-23} \text{ g.}$$

Dividing the total mass of a sample of an element by the mass of a single atom gives the number of atoms in the sample. Suppose you have a carbon sample with a mass of 12 g—a mass in grams equal to the atom's mass number. (A mass in grams equal to the mass number is known as the atomic weight of an element.) Dividing 12 g by the mass of one carbon atom gives

$$\frac{12}{(10.992 \times 10^{-23} \text{ g})} = 6.02 \times 10^{23} \text{ atoms.}$$

If you divide the atomic weight of oxygen (16 g) by the mass of one oxygen atom, you get the same result:

$$\frac{16}{(2.656 \times 10^{-23} \text{ g})} = 6.02 \times 10^{23} \text{ atoms.}$$

In fact, dividing the atomic weight of any element by the mass of an atom of that element always produces the same number: $6.02 \times 10^{23}$. This number is called Avogadro's number, after Amedeo Avogadro, the nineteenth-century Italian chemist who first discovered the relationship.

The same relationship holds for molecules. The molecular weight of any molecule is the mass in grams equal to the total mass number of its atoms. For NaCl, the total mass number is $23 + 35 = 58$ (a sodium atom has 11 protons and 12 neutrons, and a chlorine atom has 17 protons and 18 neutrons). The mass of an NaCl molecule is therefore

$$58 \times (1.66 \times 10^{-24} \text{ g}) = 9.628 \times 10^{-23} \text{ g.}$$

Dividing the molecular weight of NaCl (58 g) by the mass of a single NaCl molecule gives

$$\frac{58}{(9.628 \times 10^{-23} \text{ g})} = 6.02 \times 10^{23} \text{ atoms.}$$

When concentrations are described, the atomic weight of an element or the molecular weight of a compound—the amount that contains $6.02 \times 10^{23}$ atoms or molecules—is known as a mole (abbreviated mol). The number of moles of a substance dissolved in 1 L of solution is known as the molarity (abbreviated M) of the solution. This relationship is highly useful in chemistry and biology because we know that two solutions with the same volume and molarity but composed of different substances will contain the same number of molecules of the substances.

## Dissociation of Water and pH

A second property of water that is critical for life is its ability to separate or dissociate. This occurs when a hydrogen atom that is involved in a hydrogen bond between two water molecules moves from one molecule to the other. What leaves is an $H^+$ ion or proton. The electron associated with the H atom is left behind. This proton switch results in the formation of a hydroxide ion ($OH^-$) and a hydronium ion ($H_3O^+$).

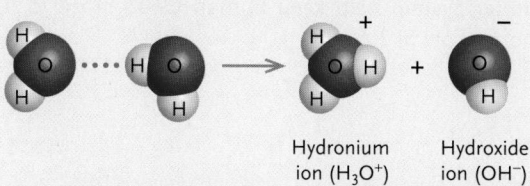

Hydronium ion ($H_3O^+$)    Hydroxide ion ($OH^-$)

It is convention to simply use $H^+$ (the hydrogen ion) to denote the hydronium ion. The proportion of water molecules that dissociate to release hydrogen and hydroxide ions is small. However, because of the dissociation, water always contains some $H^+$ and $OH^-$ ions.

In pure water, the concentrations of $H^+$ and $OH^-$ ions are equal. However, adding other substances may alter the relative concentrations of $H^+$ and $OH^-$, making them unequal. Some substances, called acids, are proton donors, which release hydrogen ions (and anions) when they are dissolved in water, effectively increasing the $H^+$ concentration. For example, hydrochloric acid (HCl) dissociates into $H^+$ and $Cl^-$ when dissolved in water:

$$HCl \rightarrow H^+ + Cl^-.$$

Other substances, called bases, are proton acceptors, which reduce the $H^+$ concentration of a solution. Most bases dissociate in water into hydroxide ions ($OH^-$) and cations. The hydroxide ion can act as a base by accepting a proton to produce water. For example,

sodium hydroxide (NaOH) separates into $Na^+$ and $OH^-$ ions when dissolved in water:

$$NaOH \rightarrow Na^+ + OH^-.$$

The excess $OH^-$ coming from NaOH combines with $H^+$ ions already in solution to produce water,

$$OH^- + H^+ \rightarrow H_2O,$$

thereby reducing the $H^+$ concentration. Basic solutions are also called *alkaline* solutions.

Other bases do not dissociate to produce hydroxide ions directly. For example, ammonia ($NH_3$), a poisonous gas, acts as a base when dissolved in water, directly accepting a proton from water, producing an ammonium ion, and releasing a hydroxide ion:

$$NH_3 + H_2O \rightarrow NH_4^+ + OH^-.$$

The concentration of $H^+$ is measured on a numerical scale from 0 to 14, called the pH scale. Because the number of $H^+$ ions in solution increases exponentially as the acidity increases, the scale is based on logarithms of this number to make the values manageable:

$$pH = -\log_{10} [H^+].$$

In this formula, the brackets indicate concentration in moles per litre. The negative of the logarithm is used to give a positive number for the pH value. For example, in a water solution that is *neutral*—neither acidic nor basic—the concentration of *both* $H^+$ and $OH^-$ ions is $1 \times 10^{-7}$ M (0.000 000 1 M). The base 10 logarithm of $1 \times 10^{-7}$ is −7. The negative of the logarithm −7 is 7. Acidic solutions have pH values less than 7, whereas basic solutions have pH values greater than 7. Each whole number on the pH scale represents a value 10 times or one-tenth the next number.

| | | | | | | | | | | | | | | |
|---|---|---|---|---|---|---|---|---|---|---|---|---|---|---|
| Hydrochloric acid (HCl) | Lemon juice, cola drinks, some acid rain | | Black coffee | | | $[H^+] = [OH^-]$ | | | Phosphate detergents, bleach, antacids | Household ammonia (10.5–11.9) | | | Oven cleaner | |
| | | | | | Urine (5.0–7.0) | Pure water | Egg white (8.0) | | | | | | | |
| | | | Tomatoes | Bread | | | | | | | | | | |
| **0** | **1** | **2** | **3** | **4** | **5** | **6** | **7** | **8** | **9** | **10** | **11** | **12** | **13** | **14** |
| | Gastric fluid (1.0–3.0) | Vinegar, wine, beer, oranges | | Bananas | | Typical rainwater | Milk (6.6) | Blood (7.3–7.5) | Sea water (7.8–8.3) | Soapy solutions | | Hair remover | | Sodium hydroxide (NaOH) |

**pH**

## Buffers Keep pH within Limits

Acidity is important to cells because even small changes, on the order of 0.1 or even 0.01 pH unit, can drastically affect biological reactions. In large part, a small change in pH can cause structural changes in proteins that can damage or destroy the proteins' function. Consequently, all living organisms have elaborate systems that control their internal acidity by regulating $H^+$ concentration near the neutral value of pH 7.

Living organisms control the internal pH of their cells with *buffers*—substances that compensate for pH changes by absorbing or releasing hydrogen ions. When hydrogen ions are released in excess by biological reactions, buffers combine with them and remove them from the solution; if the concentration of hydrogen ions decreases, buffers release $H^1$ to restore the balance. Most buffers are weak acids, weak bases, or combinations of these substances that dissociate reversibly in water solutions to release or absorb $H^+$ or $OH^-$. (Weak acids, such as acetic acid, or weak bases, such as ammonia, release relatively few $H^+$ or $OH^-$ ions in an aqueous solution, whereas strong acids or bases dissociate extensively. HCl is a strong acid; NaOH is a strong base.)

The buffering mechanism that maintains blood pH near neutral values is a good example. In humans and many other animals, blood pH is buffered by a chemical system based on carbonic acid ($H_2CO_3$), a weak acid. In water solutions, carbonic acid dissociates readily into bicarbonate ions ($HCO_3^-$) and $H^+$:

$$H_2CO_3 \rightarrow HCO_3^- + H^+.$$

The reaction is reversible. If hydrogen ions are present in excess, the reaction is pushed to the left—the excess $H^+$ ions combine with bicarbonate ions to form $H_2CO_3$. If the $H^+$ concentration declines below normal levels, the reaction is pushed to the right—$H_2CO_3$ dissociates into $HCO_3^-$ and $H^+$, restoring the $H^+$ concentration. The back-and-forth adjustments of the buffer system help keep human blood close to its normal pH of 7.4.

## Concentration and Charge across Membranes

A very important characteristic of cellular membranes is their ability to limit the movement of some chemicals. For example, the polar nature of a glucose molecule or a $Ca^{2+}$ ion does not allow them to freely cross a biological membrane. Movement of both of these compounds will require a transport protein or channel. As a result, we sometimes see a situation arise where more of a polar chemical will be present on one side of the membrane than the other. During cellular respiration and photosynthesis, the movement of electrons through their respective electron transport chains is coupled to the movement of $H^+$ ions across a membrane. This leads to the buildup of an $H^+$ gradient (more $H^+$ ions on one side of the membrane than the other). This results in the storage of potential energy because, due to random movement, the $H^+$ ions repel each other. The $H^+$ ions repel each other to an even greater degree because of their charge. The buildup of positive charge is also a form of potential energy. We can call this an electrochemical gradient. During cellular respiration and photosynthesis, the electrochemical gradient associated with $H^+$ ions is used to generate ATP.

Electrochemical gradients are also important for cellular communication. Nerve impulses are electrical waves generated as $K^+$ and $Na^+$ electrochemical gradients present across the plasma membrane of a neuron are relaxed. $Ca^{2+}$ gradients can also change in response to different stimuli, resulting in changes to cellular gene expression.

# Carbon Compounds

## Carbon Bonding

Compounds that contain carbon form the structures of living organisms and take part in all biological reactions as well as serving as energy sources. Collectively, molecules based on carbon are known as organic molecules. All other substances, that is, those without carbon atoms in their structures, are inorganic molecules. A few of the smallest carbon-containing molecules that occur in the environment as minerals or atmospheric gases, such as $CaCO_3$ and $CO_2$, are also considered inorganic molecules.

Carbon's central role in life's molecules arises from its bonding properties: it can assemble into an astounding variety of chain and ring structures that form the backbones of all biological molecules. The reason for this is that carbon has four unpaired outer electrons that it readily shares to complete its outermost energy level, forming four covalent bonds. With different combinations of single, double, and even triple bonds, an almost limitless array of molecules is possible. Carbon atoms bond covalently to each other and to other atoms, chiefly hydrogen, oxygen, nitrogen, and sulphur, in molecular structures that range in size from a few to thousands or even millions of atoms. Molecules consisting of carbon linked only to hydrogen atoms are called hydrocarbons (*hydro-* refers to hydrogen, not water). The simplest hydrocarbon, $CH_4$ (methane), consists of a single carbon atom bonded to four hydrogen atoms. Removing one hydrogen atom from methane leaves a methyl group, which occurs in many biological molecules:

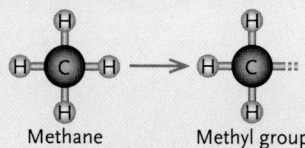

Methane          Methyl group

Now imagine bonding two methyl groups together. Removing a hydrogen atom from the maximum of four bonds, the number of hydrogen atoms in a molecule decreases as the resulting structure, ethane, produces an ethyl group:

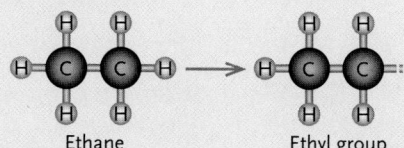

Ethane          Ethyl group

Repeating this process builds a linear hydrocarbon chain:

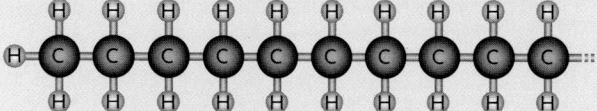

Branches can be added to produce a branched hydrocarbon chain:

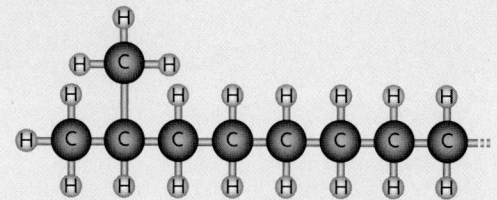

A chain can loop back on itself to form a ring. For example, cyclohexane, $C_6H_{12}$, has single covalent bonds between each pair of carbon atoms and two hydrogen atoms attached to each carbon atom:

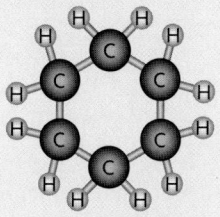

$C_6H_{12}$, cyclohexane

Hydrocarbons gain added complexity when neighbouring carbon atoms form double or triple bonds. Because each carbon atom can form a maximum of four bonds, the number of hydrogen atoms in a molecule decreases as the number of bonds between any two carbon atoms increases:

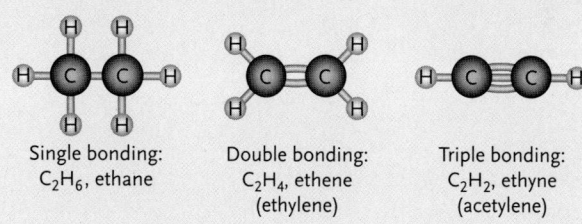

Single bonding: $C_2H_6$, ethane

Double bonding: $C_2H_4$, ethene (ethylene)

Triple bonding: $C_2H_2$, ethyne (acetylene)

Double bonds between carbon atoms are also found in carbon rings:

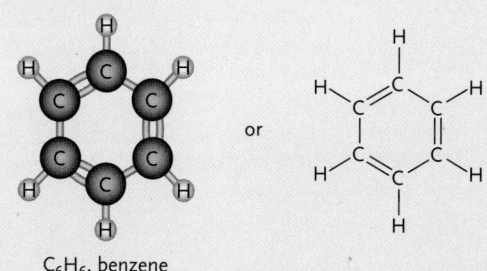

$C_6H_6$, benzene

or

We will also use this depiction of a carbon ring in figures:

Many carbon rings can join together to produce larger molecules, as in the string of sugar molecules that makes up a polysaccharide chain:

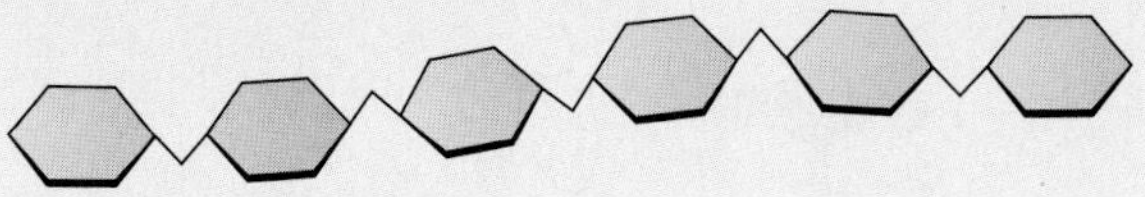

There is almost no limit to the number of different hydrocarbon structures that carbon and hydrogen can form. However, the molecules of living systems typically contain other elements in addition to carbon and hydrogen. These other elements confer functional properties on organic molecules, producing the four major classes of organic molecules: *carbohydrates*, *lipids*, *proteins*, and *nucleic acids*.

## Functional Groups

Carbohydrates, lipids, proteins, and nucleic acids are synthesized and degraded in living organisms through interactions between small, reactive groups of atoms attached to the organic molecules. The atoms in these reactive groups, called functional groups, occur in positions in which their covalent bonds are more readily broken or rearranged than the bonds in other parts of the molecules.

The functional groups that enter most frequently into biological reactions are the hydroxyl, carbonyl, carboxyl, amino, phosphate, and sulfhydryl groups. The unconnected covalent bonds written to the left of each structure link these functional groups to other atoms in biological molecules, usually carbon atoms. The symbol R is used to represent a chain of carbon atoms. One additional aspect of the presence of functional groups in biological molecules is the fact that they tend to increase the molecule's polarity and hence solubility in water. The carboxylic acid group on the end of a fatty acid plays a large role in making these otherwise non-polar molecules amphipathic.

### Common Functional Groups of Organic Molecules

| Functional Group | Major Classes of Molecules | Example |
|---|---|---|
| Hydroxyl<br><br>R —OH | Alcohols | 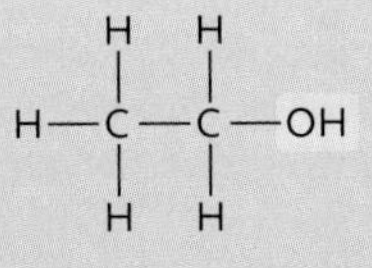 <br>Ethyl alcohol (in alcoholic beverages) |

A hydroxyl group (—OH) consists of an oxygen atom linked to a hydrogen atom. Hydroxyl groups are polar and confer polarity on the parts of the molecules that contain them. The presence of the hydroxyl group enables an alcohol to form linkages to other organic molecules through dehydration synthesis reactions.

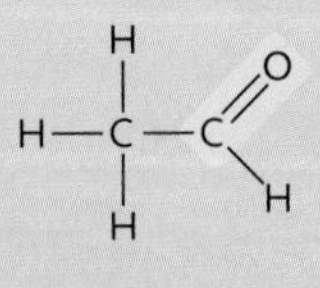

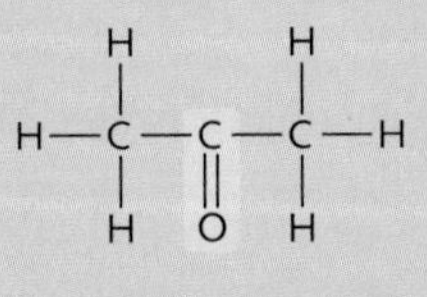

| | | |
|---|---|---|
| Carbonyl<br><br>R—C=O<br>  \|<br>  H | Aldehydes | <br>Acetaldehyde |
| R—C=O<br>  \|<br>  C<br>  \| | Ketones | <br>Acetone (a solvent) |

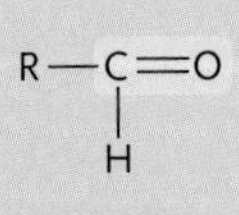

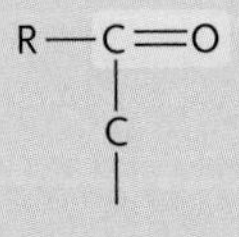

A carbonyl group (C=O) consists of an oxygen atom linked to a carbon atom by a double bond. Carbonyl groups are the reactive parts of aldehydes and ketones, molecules that act as major building blocks of carbohydrates and also take part in the reactions supplying energy for cellular activities. In an aldehyde,

the carbonyl group is linked—along with a hydrogen atom—to a carbon atom at the end of a carbon chain, along with a hydrogen atom, as in acetaldehyde. In a ketone, the carbonyl group is linked to a carbon atom in the interior of a carbon chain, as in acetone.

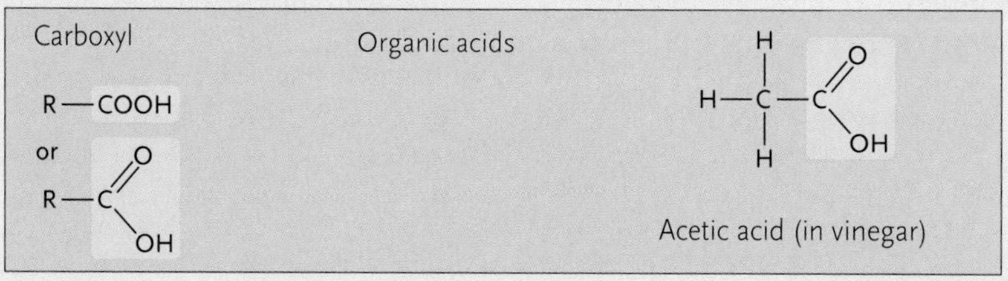

Carboxyl — Organic acids

$R-COOH$

or

$R-C$ with $=O$ and $-OH$

Acetic acid (in vinegar)

A carboxyl group (—COOH) is formed by the combination of a carbonyl group and a hydroxyl group. The carboxyl group is the characteristic functional group of organic acids (also called carboxylic acids). The

carboxyl group gives organic molecules acidic properties because its —OH group readily releases the hydrogen as a proton ($H^+$) in solution.

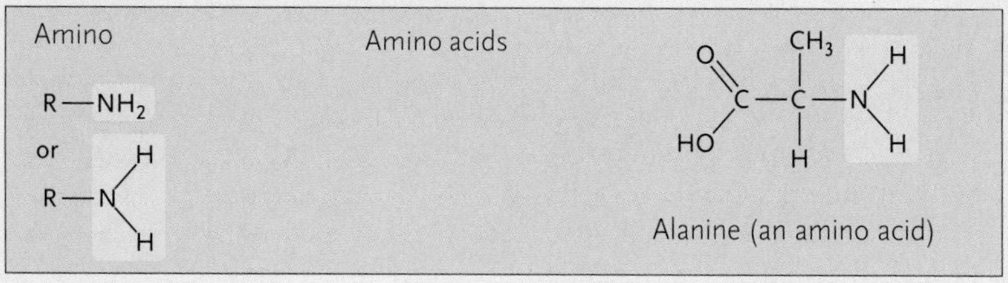

Amino — Amino acids

$R-NH_2$

or

$R-N$ with two H

Alanine (an amino acid)

The amino group (—NH$_2$) consists of a nitrogen atom bonded on one side to two hydrogen atoms; in a

molecule, it is linked to an R group on the other side, as in the amino acid alanine and all other amino acids.

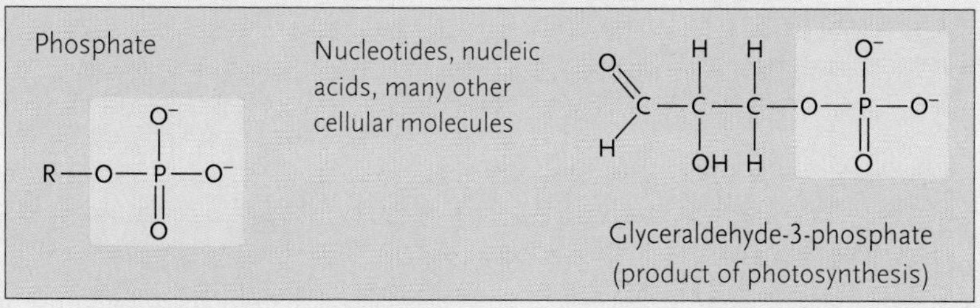

Phosphate — Nucleotides, nucleic acids, many other cellular molecules

$R-O-P-O^-$ with $O^-$ and $O$

Glyceraldehyde-3-phosphate (product of photosynthesis)

The phosphate group (—OPO$_3^{2-}$) consists of a central phosphorus atom bonded to four oxygen atoms, as shown at the left. Among the large biological molecules linked by phosphate groups is the nucleic acid DNA. Phosphate groups are added to or removed

from biological molecules as part of reactions that conserve or release energy. In addition, they control biological activity—the activity of many proteins is turned on or off by the addition or removal of phosphate groups.

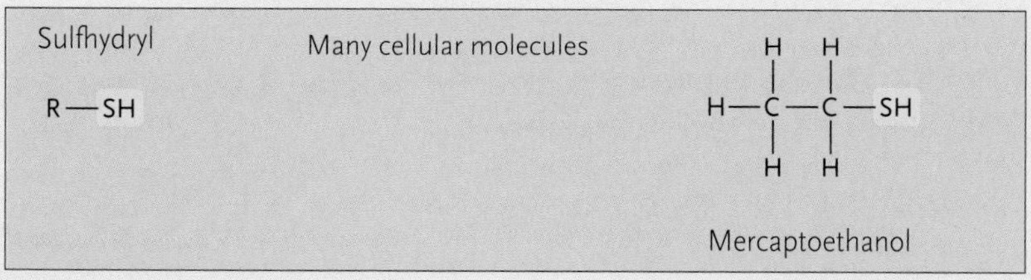

Sulfhydryl — Many cellular molecules

$R-SH$

Mercaptoethanol

In the sulfhydryl group (—SH), a sulphur atom is linked on one side to a hydrogen atom; in a molecule, the other side is linked to an R group. The sulfhydryl group is easily converted into a covalent linkage in which it loses

its hydrogen atom as it binds. In many of these linking reactions, two sulfhydryl groups interact to form a disulfide linkage (—S—S—). In proteins, the disulfide bond contributes to tertiary structure.

# Carbohydrates

Carbohydrates, the most abundant biological molecules, serve many functions. Together with fats, they act as the major fuel substances providing chemical energy for cellular activities. Chains of carbohydrate subunits also form structural molecules such as cellulose, one of the primary constituents of plant cell walls. Carbohydrates get their name because they contain carbon, hydrogen, and oxygen atoms, with the approximate ratio of the atoms being 1 carbon: 2 hydrogens:1 oxygen ($CH_2O$). Carbohydrates occur either as monosaccharides or as chains of monosaccharide units linked together.

## Monosaccharides

Monosaccharides are the simplest sugars. They are soluble in water, and most have a distinctly sweet taste. The term *saccharide* is Greek for sugar. Of the monosaccharides, those that contain three carbons (*trioses*), five carbons (*pentoses*), and six carbons (*hexoses*) are most common in living organisms.

All monosaccharides can occur in the linear form, where each carbon atom in the chain except one has both an —H and an —OH group attached to it. Monosaccharides with five or more carbons can fold back on themselves to assume a ring form. Folding into a ring occurs through a reaction between two functional groups in the same monosaccharide, as occurs in glucose. The ring form of most five- and six-carbon sugars is much more common in cells than the linear form.

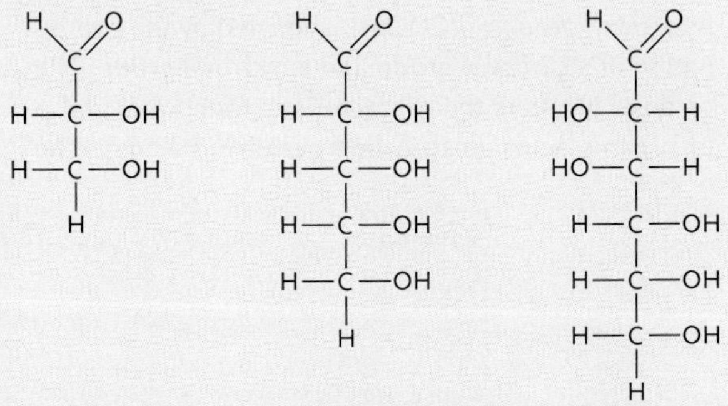

Glyceraldehyde
(3 carbons;
a triose)

Ribose
(5 carbons;
a pentose)

Mannose
(6 carbons;
a hexose)

## Disaccharides

Disaccharides are typically assembled from two (*di-* is a chemical prefix meaning two) monosaccharides linked by a dehydration synthesis reaction. For example, the disaccharide maltose is formed by the linkage of two glucose molecules with oxygen as a bridge between the number 1 carbon of the first glucose unit and the number 4 carbon of the second glucose unit. Bonds of this type, which commonly link monosaccharides into chains, are known as glycosidic bonds. A glycosidic bond between a 1 carbon and a 4 carbon is written in chemical shorthand as a $1 \rightarrow 4$ linkage. Linkages such as $1 \rightarrow 2$, $1 \rightarrow 3$, and $1 \rightarrow 6$ are also common in carbohydrate chains. Maltose, sucrose, and lactose are common disaccharides.

**Formation of maltose**

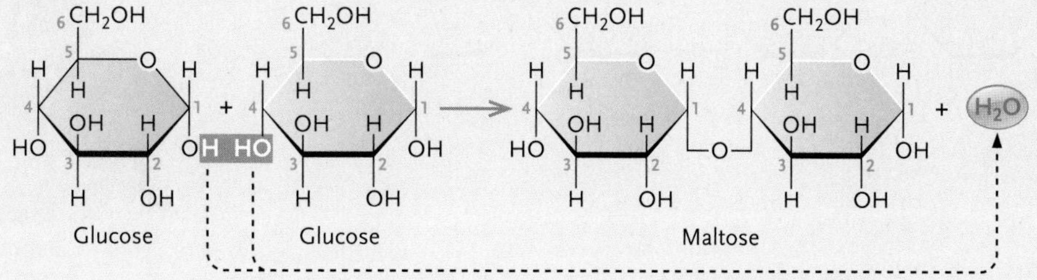

Glucose + Glucose → Maltose + $H_2O$

**Sucrose**

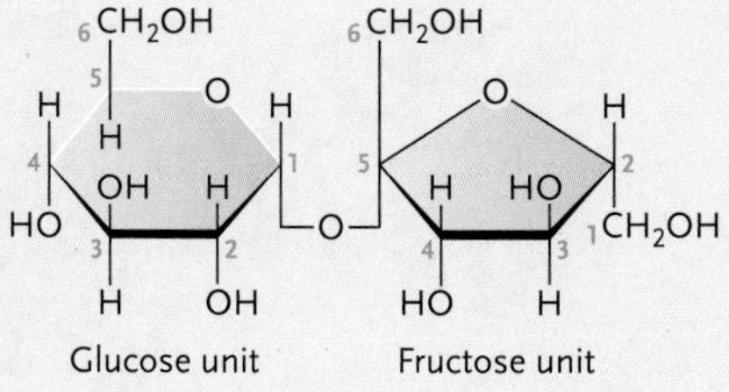

Glucose unit     Fructose unit

**Lactose**

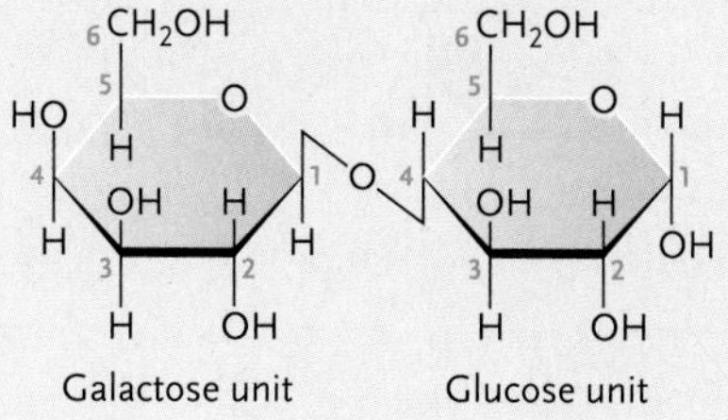

Galactose unit     Glucose unit

## Polysaccharides

Polysaccharides are longer chains formed by the end-to-end linking of many (poly- is a chemical prefix meaning many) monosaccharides through dehydration synthesis reactions. Also known as complex carbohydrates, polysaccharides are classed as a type of macromolecule, which is a very large molecule assembled by the covalent linkage of smaller subunit molecules. The subunit for a polysaccharide is the monosaccharide.

The dehydration synthesis reactions that assemble polysaccharides from monosaccharides are examples of polymerization, in which identical or nearly identical subunits, called the monomers of the reaction, join like links in a chain to form a larger molecule called a polymer. Linkage of a relatively small number of non-identical subunits can create highly diverse and varied biological molecules. Many kinds of polymers are found in cells, not just polysaccharides. DNA is a primary example of a highly diverse polymer assembled from various sequences of only four different types of monomers.

The most common polysaccharides—the plant starches glycogen and cellulose—are all assembled from hundreds or thousands of glucose units. Other polysaccharides are built up from a variety of different sugar units. Polysaccharides may be linear, unbranched molecules or may contain one or more branches in which side chains of sugar units are attached to a main chain.

Amylose, formed from α-glucose units joined end to end in α(1→4) linkages. The coiled structures are induced by the bond angles in the α-linkages.

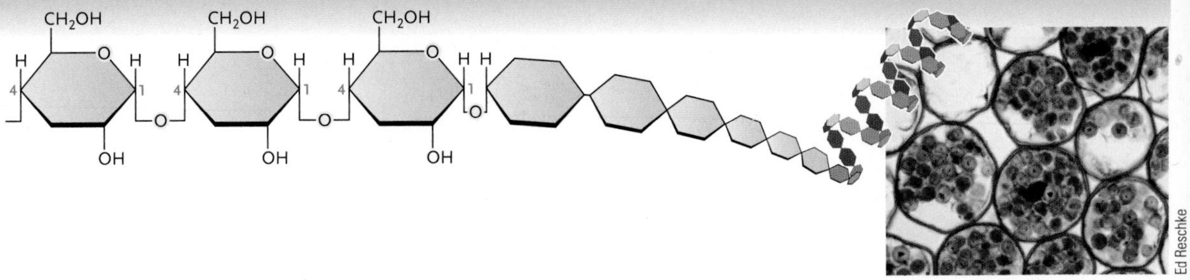

Amylose grains (purple) in plant root tissue

Glycogen, formed from glucose units joined in chains by α(1→4) linkages; side branches are linked to the chains by α(1→6) linkages (boxed in blue).

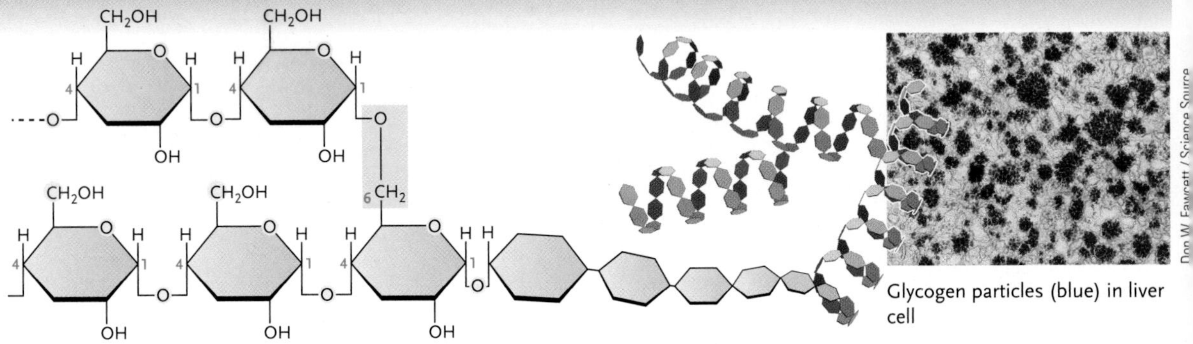

Glycogen particles (blue) in liver cell

Cellulose, formed from glucose units joined end to end by β(1→4) linkages. Hundreds to thousands of cellulose chains line up side by side, in an arrangement reinforced by hydrogen bonds between the chains, to form cellulose microfibrils in plant cells.

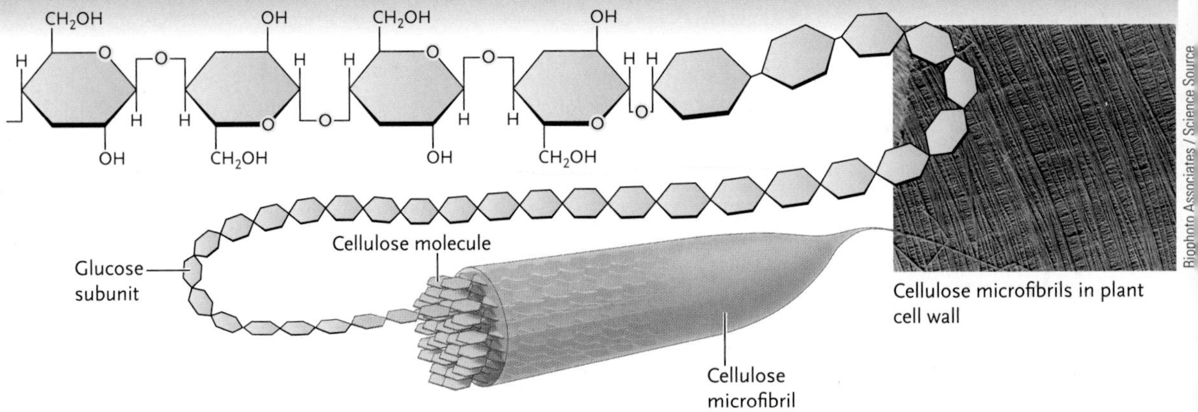

Glucose subunit

Cellulose molecule

Cellulose microfibril

Cellulose microfibrils in plant cell wall

Chitin, formed from β-linkages joining glucose units modified by the addition of nitrogen-containing groups. The external body armor of the tick is reinforced by chitin fibres.

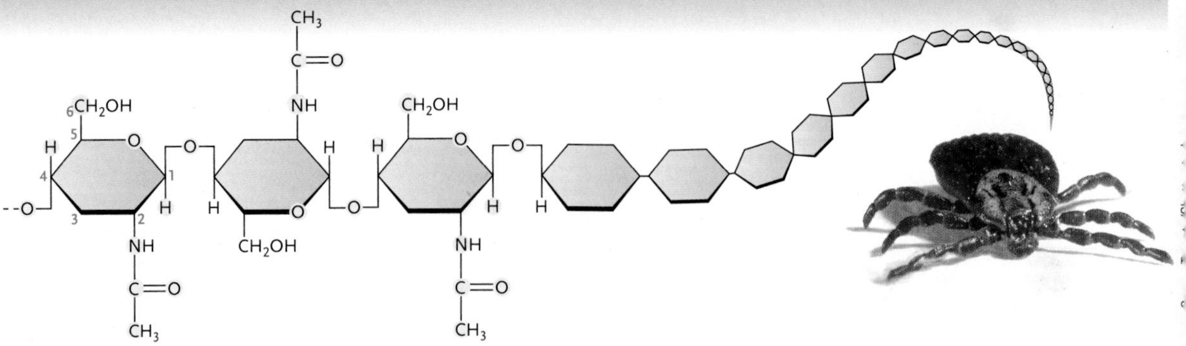

Ed Reschke
Don W. Fawcett / Science Source
Biophoto Associates / Science Source

# Proteins

Proteins, which are polymers of amino acids, are the most diverse group of biological macromolecules. Proteins vary hugely in terms of both their chemical composition and their function. Even the simplest prokaryotic cell contains thousands of proteins, each with a defined composition and specific function within the cell. The major protein functions are listed below.

| Protein Type | Function | Examples |
|---|---|---|
| Structural proteins | Support | Cytoskeleton proteins form supporting fibres inside cells; collagen and other proteins surround and support animal cells; cell wall proteins support plant cells. |
| Enzymatic proteins | Increase the rate of biological reactions | Among thousands of examples, DNA polymerase increases the rate of duplication of DNA molecules; RuBP (ribulose 1,5-bisphosphate) carboxylase/oxygenase increases the rates of the first synthetic reactions of photosynthesis; the digestive enzymes lipases and proteases increase the rate of breakdown of fats and proteins, respectively. |
| Membrane transport proteins | Speed up movement of substances across biological membranes | Ion transporters move ions such as $Na^+$, $K^+$, and $Ca^{2+}$ across membranes; glucose transporters move glucose into cells; aquaporins allow water molecules to move across membranes. |
| Motile proteins | Produce cellular movements | Myosin acts on microfilaments (called thin filaments in muscle) to produce muscle movements; dynein acts on microtubules to produce the whipping movements of sperm tails, flagella, and cilia (the last two are whiplike appendages on the surfaces of many eukaryotic cells). |
| Regulatory proteins | Promote or inhibit the activity of other cellular molecules | Nuclear regulatory proteins turn genes on or off to control the activity of DNA. |
| Receptor proteins | Bind molecules at cell surface or within cell; some trigger internal cellular responses | Hormone receptors bind hormones at the cell surface or within cells and trigger cellular responses; cellular adhesion molecules help hold cells together by binding molecules on other cells; LDL receptors bind cholesterol-containing particles to cell surfaces. |
| Hormones | Carry regulatory signals between cells | Insulin regulates sugar levels in the bloodstream; growth hormone regulates cellular growth and division. |
| Antibodies | Defend against invading molecules and organisms | Antibodies recognize, bind, and help eliminate infecting bacteria and viruses and many other types of molecules, both natural and artificial. |
| Storage proteins | Hold amino acids and other substances in stored form | Ovalbumin is a storage protein of eggs; apolipoproteins hold cholesterol in stored form for transport through the bloodstream. |
| Venoms and toxins | Interfere with competing organisms | Ricin is a castor bean protein that stops protein synthesis; bungarotoxin is a snake venom that causes muscle paralysis. |

## Amino Acids

All proteins are polymers of amino acids. The generalized structure of an amino acid has a central carbon atom attached to an amino group ($-NH_2$), a carboxyl group ($-COOH$), and a hydrogen atom:

$$H_2N-\underset{\underset{H}{|}}{\overset{\overset{R}{|}}{C}}-COOH$$

The remaining bond of the central carbon is to 1 of 20 different side groups represented by the R. The R group, also called the side chain, ranges from a single hydrogen atom in the amino acid glycine to complex carbon chains or rings in some others. Differences in the side groups give the amino acids their individual properties. When discussing protein structure, amino acids are commonly referred to as amino acid residues or simply residues.

Proteins are synthesized from 20 different amino acids. These 20 are most commonly grouped according to the properties of their side chains. Here the amino acids are shown in the ionic form common at the pH typical of a cell, 7.2.

*continued on next page*

## Non-polar amino acids

Alanine
Ala
A

Valine
Val
V

Leucine
Leu
L

Isoleucine
Ile
I

Glycine
Gly
G

Cysteine
Cys
C

Phenylalanine
Phe
F

Tryptophan
Trp
W

Methionine
Met
M

Proline
Pro
P

## Uncharged polar amino acids

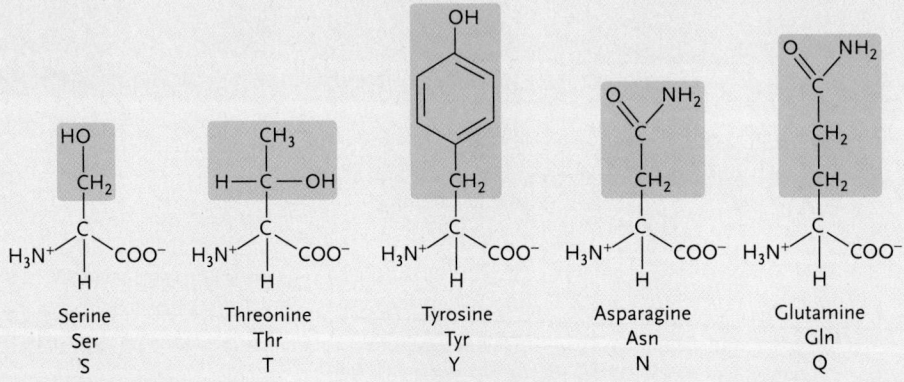

Serine
Ser
S

Threonine
Thr
T

Tyrosine
Tyr
Y

Asparagine
Asn
N

Glutamine
Gln
Q

## Negatively charged (acidic) polar amino acids

## Positively charged (basic) polar amino acids

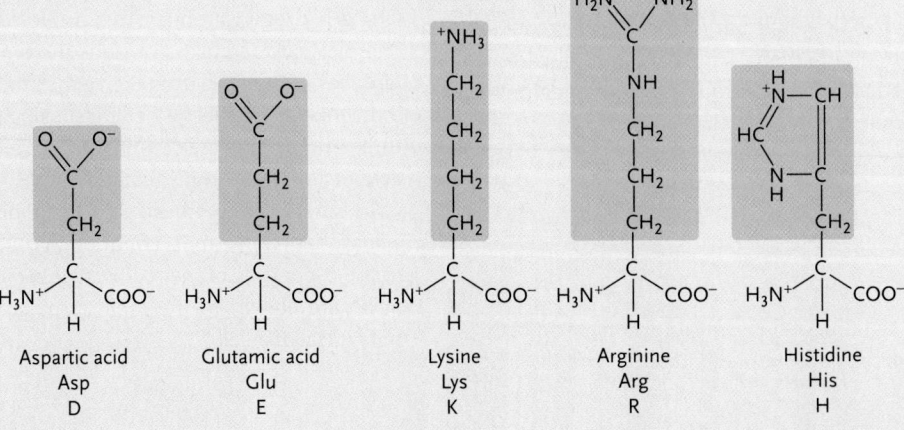

Aspartic acid
Asp
D

Glutamic acid
Glu
E

Lysine
Lys
K

Arginine
Arg
R

Histidine
His
H

## Polypeptides

Covalent bonds link amino acids into chains called polypeptides. The link between each pair of amino acids in a polypeptide, a peptide bond, is formed by a dehydration synthesis reaction between the —$NH_2$ group of one amino acid and the —COOH group of a second. An amino acid chain always has an —$NH_2$ group at one end, called the N-terminal end, and a —COOH group at the other end, called the C-terminal end. In cells, amino acids are added only to the —COOH end of the growing peptide strand.

The distinction between a polypeptide and a protein is that a polypeptide is simply a string of amino acids. A protein is a polypeptide that has folded into the specific three-dimensional shape that is required for most proteins to be functional. The following figure shows the formation of a peptide bond.

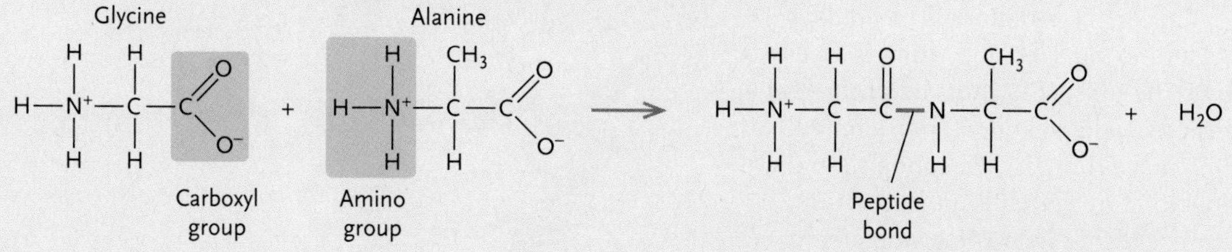

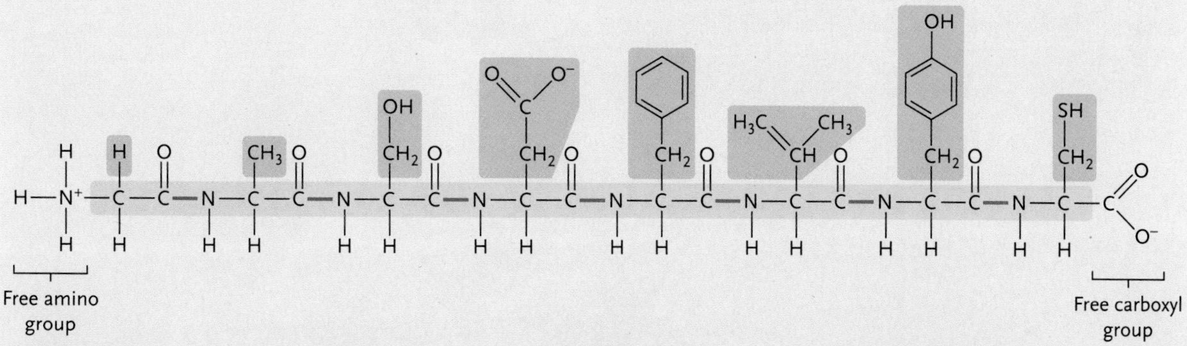

**A polypeptide—a linear chain of amino acids.**

The backbone of the polypeptide is highlighted in the bottom figure above. The amino end of the polypeptide is called the N-terminus, while the carboxyl end is called the C-terminus.

## The Four Levels of Protein Structure

Proteins have potentially four levels of structure, with each level imparting different characteristics and degrees of structural complexity to the molecule. Primary structure is the particular and unique sequence of amino acids forming a polypeptide; secondary structure is produced by the twists and turns of the amino acid chain. Tertiary structure is the folding of the amino acid chain, with its secondary structures, into the overall three-dimensional shape of a protein. All proteins have primary, secondary, and tertiary structures. Quaternary structure, when present, refers to the arrangement of polypeptide chains in a protein that is formed from more than one chain. Each structural level depends on the level before it.

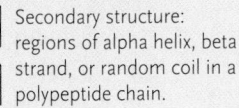

--- | Ser | Glu | Gly | Asp | Trp | Gln | Leu | His | ---

Primary structure: the sequence of amino acids in a protein.

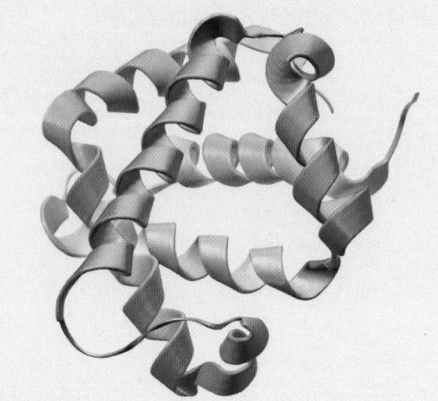

Secondary structure: regions of alpha helix, beta strand, or random coil in a polypeptide chain.

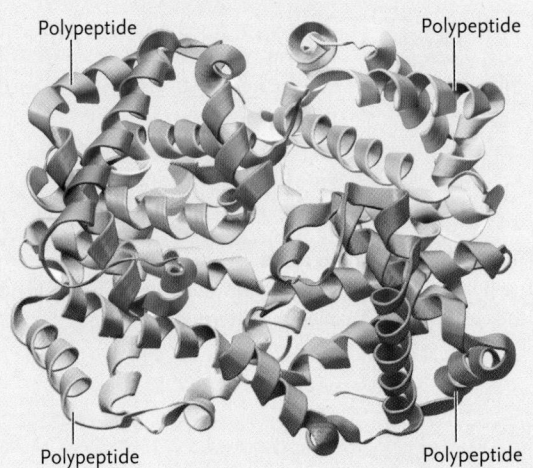

Tertiary structure: overall three-dimensional folding of a polypeptide chain.

Polypeptide     Polypeptide

Quaternary structure: the arrangement of polypeptide chains in a protein that contains more than one chain.

Polypeptide     Polypeptide

## Primary Structure

The primary structure of a protein is simply its complete amino acid sequence. The primary sequence is determined by the nucleotide sequence of the coding region of the protein's corresponding gene.

$H_3N^+$ — | Phe | Val | Asn | Gln | His | Leu | Cys | Gly | Ser | His | Leu | Val | Glu | Ala | Leu | Tyr | Leu | Val | Cys | Gly | Glu | Arg | Gly | Phe | Phe | Tyr | Thr | Pro | Lys | Ala | — COO⁻

## Secondary Structure

The amino acid chain of a protein, rather than being stretched out in linear form, is folded into arrangements that form the protein's secondary structure. Secondary structure is based on hydrogen bonds between atoms of the backbone. More precisely, the hydrogen bonds form between the hydrogen atom attached to the nitrogen of the backbone and the oxygen attached to one of the carbon atoms of the backbone. Two highly regular secondary structures are the α helix and the β sheet. A third, less regular arrangement, the random coil or loop, imparts flexibility to certain regions of the protein. Most proteins have segments of all three arrangements.

### The α helix

A model of the α helix (left), a coil shape formed when hydrogen bonds form between every N—H group of the backbone and the C=O group of the amino acid four residues earlier. In protein diagrams (right), the α helix is depicted as a cylinder or barrel.

### The β sheet

A β sheet is formed by side-by-side alignment of β strands (picture shows two strands). The sheet is formed by hydrogen bonds between atoms of each strand. In protein diagrams, the β strands are depicted by ribbons with arrowheads pointing toward the C-terminal.

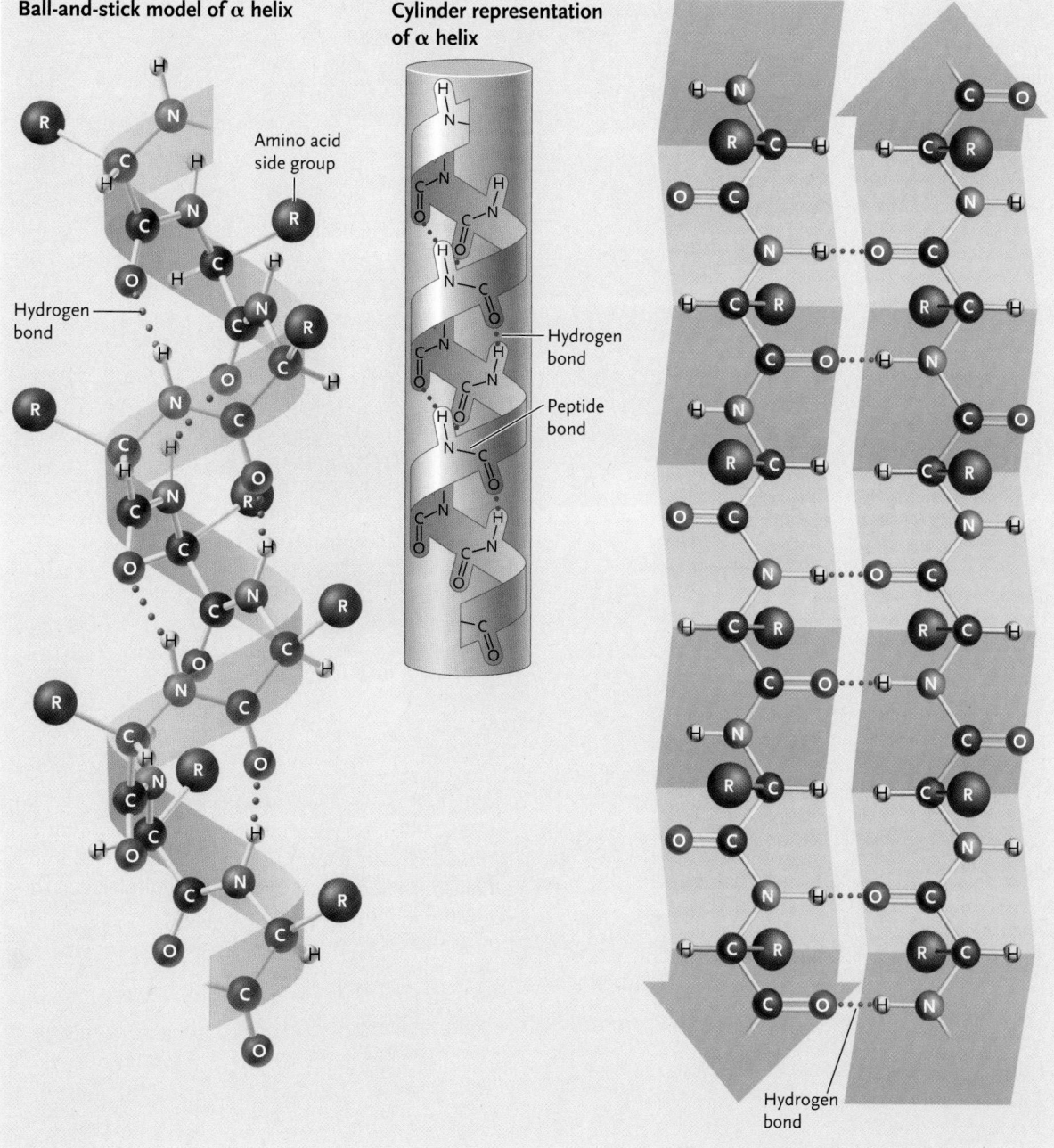

**Ball-and-stick model of α helix**

Amino acid side group

Hydrogen bond

**Cylinder representation of α helix**

Hydrogen bond

Peptide bond

Hydrogen bond

## Tertiary Structure

The four major interactions between R groups that contribute to tertiary structure are shown below: (1) ionic bonds, (2) hydrogen bonds, (3) hydrophobic interactions, and (4) disulfide bridges. The tertiary structure of most proteins is flexible, allowing them to undergo limited alterations in three-dimensional shape known as conformational changes. These changes contribute to the function of many proteins, particularly enzymes, as well as other proteins involved in cellular movements or in the transport of substances across cell membranes.

Below are two representations of the three-dimensional structure of the enzyme lysozyme. In a ribbon diagram, α helices are shown as a cylinder, β strands are depicted as flat arrows, and random coils are shown as thin ropes. In a space-filling model, spheres represent different atoms. The sizes of the spheres and the intersphere distances are proportional to the actual dimensions. Atoms of different elements are represented by different colours. Disulfide bonds are shown in yellow.

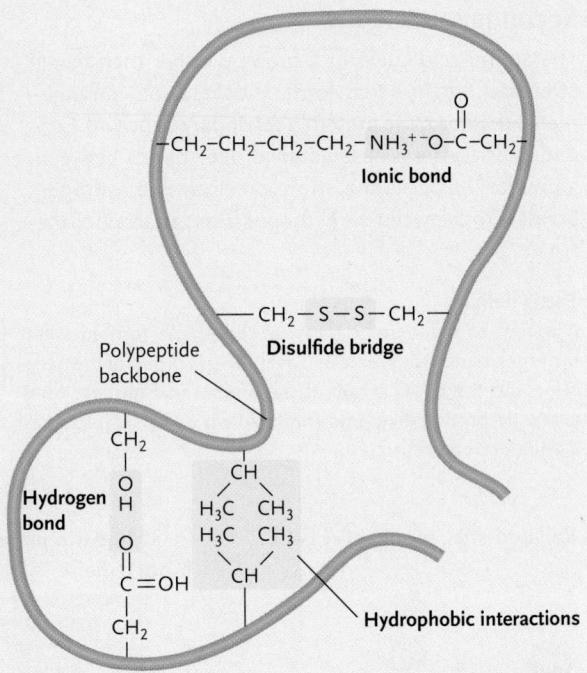

**Lysozyme**

**Space-filling model of lysozyme**

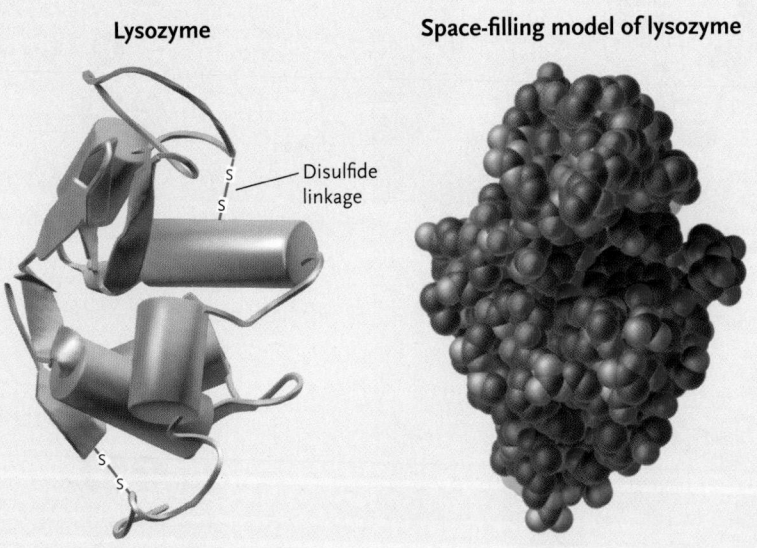

Disulfide linkage

## Quaternary Structure

Some proteins consist of two or more polypeptides that come together to form a functional protein. An example of a protein that exhibits quaternary structure is collagen. The collagen molecule consists of three helical polypeptides that aggregate to form a triple helix structure. Collagen is a major component of the connective tissue, is found exclusively in animals, and is the most abundant protein in mammals.

## Cofactors/Prosthetic Groups

A cofactor (also called a prosthetic group) is a non-protein chemical compound that is bound to a protein and is required for the protein to function. Many enzymes require cofactors, which can be either organic or inorganic molecules. Many vitamins are essential to life because they act as key cofactors. A good example of a prosthetic group is the molecule heme, which is a key component of the oxygen-carrying protein hemoglobin. Each molecule of hemoglobin contains four heme molecules—one attached to each globin protein. Each heme contains a central iron atom that is responsible for binding molecules of oxygen.

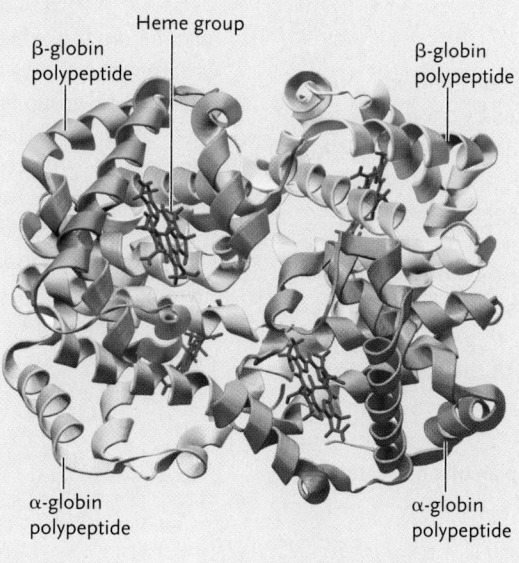

β-globin polypeptide

Heme group

β-globin polypeptide

α-globin polypeptide

α-globin polypeptide

# Nucleic Acids

Two types of nucleic acids exist: DNA and RNA. Deoxyribonucleic acid (DNA) stores the hereditary information in all eukaryotes, bacteria, and archaea. In all organisms, ribonucleic acid (RNA) carries out a diversity of functions.

RNA carries the instructions for assembling proteins from DNA to the site of protein synthesis, the ribosome, which is itself composed partially of RNA. Another type of RNA serves to bring amino acids to the ribosome for their assembly into proteins.

## Nucleotides

All nucleic acids are polymers of nucleotides. A nucleotide consists of three parts linked by covalent bonds: (1) a nitrogenous base formed from rings of carbon and nitrogen atoms; (2) a five-carbon, ring-shaped sugar; and (3) one to three phosphate groups.

In nucleotides, the nitrogenous bases link covalently to a five-carbon sugar, either deoxyribose or ribose. The carbons of the two sugars are numbered with a prime symbol—$1'$, $2'$, $3'$, $4'$, and $5'$. The prime symbols are added to distinguish the carbons in the sugars from those in the nitrogenous bases, which are written without primes. The two sugars differ only in the chemical group bound to the $2'$ carbon: ribose has an —OH group, whereas deoxyribose has an —H at this position—hence the term *deoxy* (without oxygen).

The two types of nitrogenous bases are pyrimidines, with one carbon–nitrogen ring, and purines, with two rings. Three pyrimidine bases—uracil (U), thymine (T), and cytosine (C)—and two purine bases—adenine (A) and guanine (G)—form parts of nucleic acids in cells.

**Overall structural plan of a nucleotide**

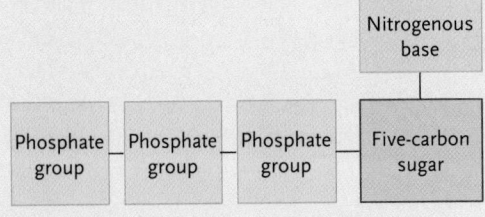

**Chemical structures of nucleotides**

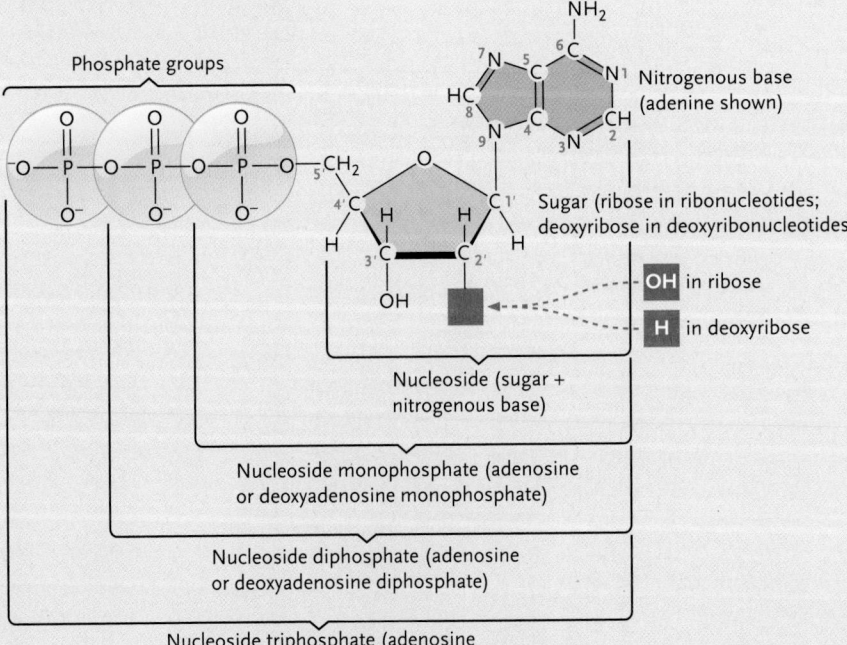

## Pyrimidine and Purine Bases of Nucleic Acids

The three single-ring pyrimidines and two double-ring purines are the nitrogenous bases of nucleotides. The red arrows indicate where the bases link to ribose or deoxyribose sugars to form nucleotides.

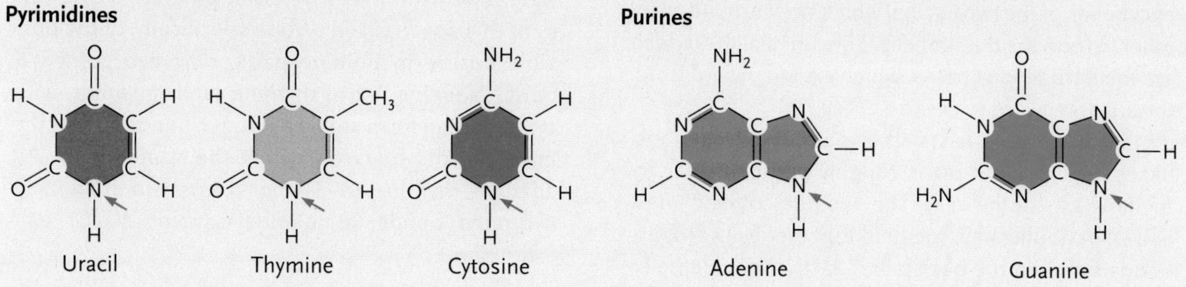

**Pyrimidines**

Uracil          Thymine          Cytosine

**Purines**

Adenine          Guanine

## DNA and RNA Structure

Nucleotides in DNA and RNA are linked together by a bridging phosphate group between the 5′ carbon of one sugar and the 3′ carbon of the next sugar in line. This linkage is called a phosphodiester bond. This arrangement of alternating sugar and phosphate groups forms the backbone of a nucleic acid. The nitrogenous bases of the nucleotides project from this backbone. Note that the nucleotide thymine (T) is only found in DNA. It is replaced by uracil (U) in RNA.

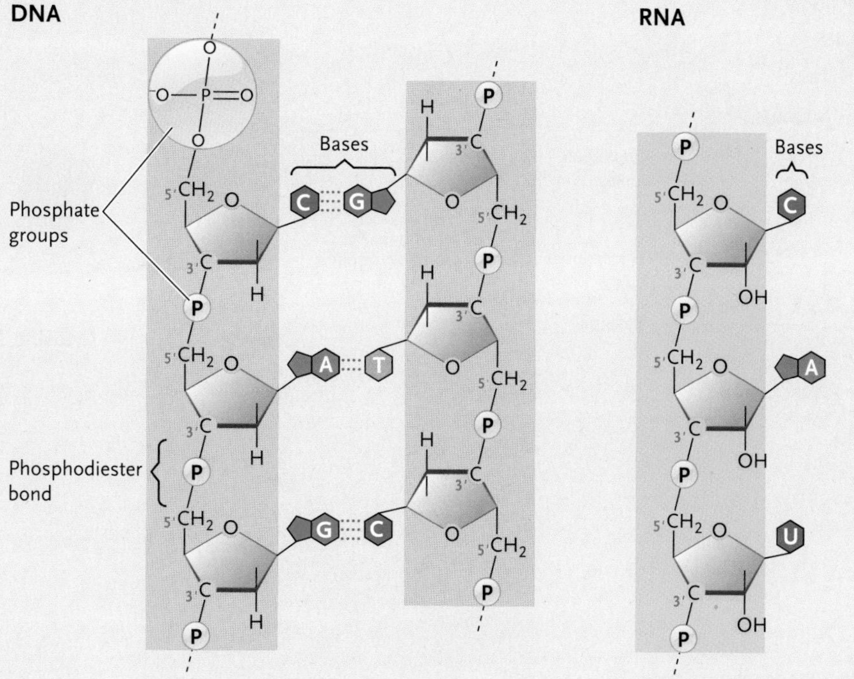

DNA

RNA

## DNA Double Helix

In cells, DNA takes the form of a double helix: two nucleotide chains wrapped around each other in a spiral that resembles a twisted ladder. As shown below, the sides of the ladder are the sugar–phosphate backbones of the two chains, which twist around each other to form the double helix. The rungs of the ladder are the nitrogenous bases, which extend inward from the sugars toward the centre of the helix.

Each rung consists of a pair of nitrogenous bases held in a flat plane roughly perpendicular to the long axis of the helix. The two nucleotide chains of a DNA double helix are held together by hydrogen bonds between the base pairs. A DNA double helix molecule is also referred to as double-stranded DNA. The space separating the sugar–phosphate backbones of a DNA double helix is just wide enough to accommodate a base pair that consists of one purine and one pyrimidine. Purine–purine base pairs are too wide and pyrimidine–pyrimidine pairs are too narrow to fit this space exactly. More specifically, of the possible purine–pyrimidine pairs, only two combinations, adenine with thymine and guanine with cytosine, can form stable hydrogen bonds so that the base pair fits precisely within the double helix. An adenine–thymine (A–T) pair forms two stabilizing hydrogen bonds; a guanine–cytosine (G–C) pair forms three.

**DNA double helix, showing arrangement of sugars, phosphate groups, and bases**

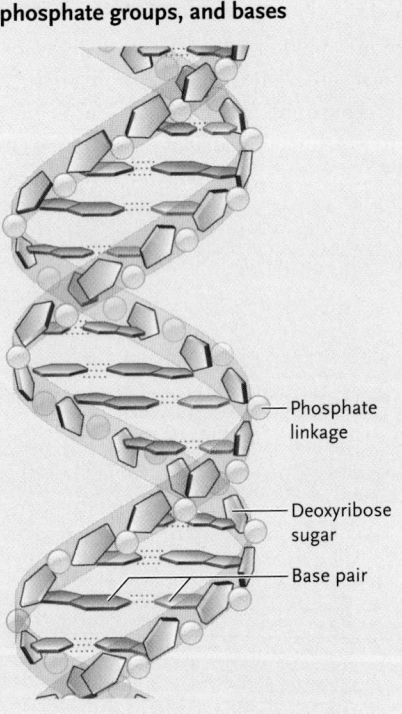

Phosphate linkage

Deoxyribose sugar

Base pair

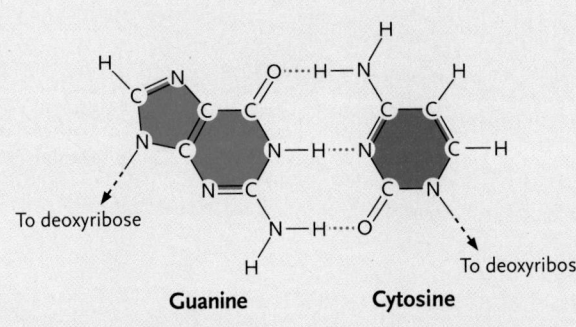

Adenine     Thymine

Guanine     Cytosine

# Lipids

Lipids are a diverse group of water-insoluble, primarily non-polar biological molecules composed mostly of hydrogen and carbon (hydrocarbons). The term *lipid* is a catch-all word for a range of non-polar molecules. They are not large enough to be considered true macromolecules and, unlike nucleic acids and proteins, are not considered polymers of defined monomeric subunits. As a result of their non-polar character, lipids typically dissolve much more readily in non-polar solvents, such as acetone and chloroform, than in water. In other words, they are hydrophobic. Their insolubility in water underlies their ability to form cell membranes. In addition, some lipids are stored and used in cells as an energy source. Other lipids serve as hormones that regulate cellular activities. Lipids in living organisms can be grouped into one of three categories—fats, phospholipids, and steroids.

## Fatty Acids

A fatty acid consists of a single hydrocarbon chain with a carboxyl group (—COOH) linked at one end. The carboxyl group gives the fatty acid its acidic properties. The fatty acids in living organisms contain four or more carbons in their hydrocarbon chain, with the most common forms having even-numbered chains of 14 to 22 carbons. As their chain length increases, fatty acids become progressively less water soluble and more solid at room temperature.

If the hydrocarbon chain of a fatty acid binds the maximum possible number of hydrogen atoms so that only single bonds link the carbon atoms, the fatty acid is said to be saturated with hydrogen atoms. If one or more double bonds link the carbons, reducing the number of bound hydrogen atoms, the fatty acid is unsaturated. Fatty acids with one double bond are monounsaturated; those with more than one double bond are polyunsaturated. Unlike saturated fatty acids, the presence of double bonds imparts a "kink" in the molecule.

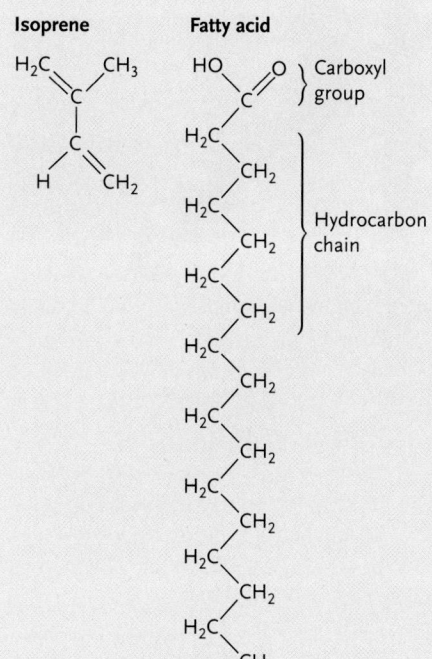

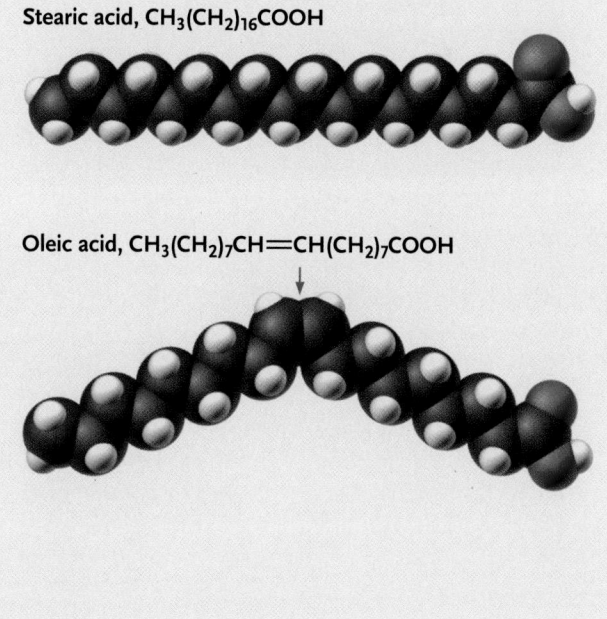

Stearic acid, $CH_3(CH_2)_{16}COOH$

Oleic acid, $CH_3(CH_2)_7CH{=}CH(CH_2)_7COOH$

# Phospholipids

Phosphate-containing lipids, or phospholipids, are the primary lipids of cell membranes. In the most common phospholipids, glycerol forms the backbone for the molecule. Glycerol can form ester bonds with three other molecules. In phospholipids, two of the glycerol binding sites are linked to fatty acids. The third site is linked to a polar phosphate group, which can then bind to another polar unit. Thus, a phospholipid contains two hydrophobic fatty acids at one end, attached to a hydrophilic polar group, often called the head group. As mentioned in our discussion of polarity, molecules that contain both hydrophobic and hydrophilic regions are called amphipathic molecules.

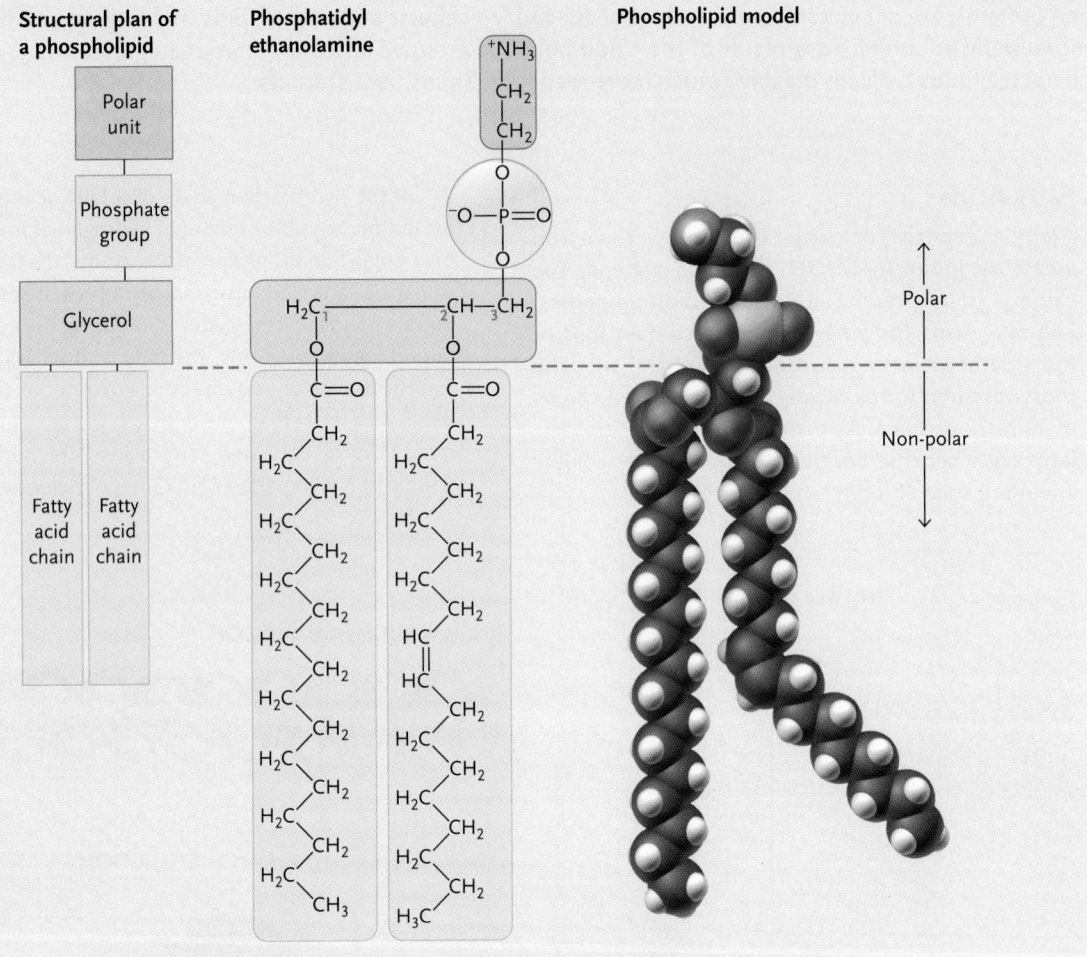

**Structural plan of a phospholipid**

Polar unit

Phosphate group

Glycerol

Fatty acid chain | Fatty acid chain

**Phosphatidyl ethanolamine**

**Phospholipid model**

Polar

Non-polar

## Fats

A fat consists of three fatty acid chains linked to a single molecule of glycerol. Because of this, fats are also often referred to as triacylglycerols or triglycerides. Triglycerides are used widely as stored energy in animals. Gram for gram, they yield more than twice as much energy as carbohydrates. Therefore, fats are an excellent source of energy in the diet.

Storing the equivalent amount of energy as carbohydrates rather than fats would add more than 45 kg to the mass of an average man or woman. A layer of fatty tissue just under the skin also serves as an insulating blanket in humans, other mammals, and birds. Triglycerides secreted from special glands in waterfowl and other birds help make feathers water repellent.

**Formation of a triglyceride**

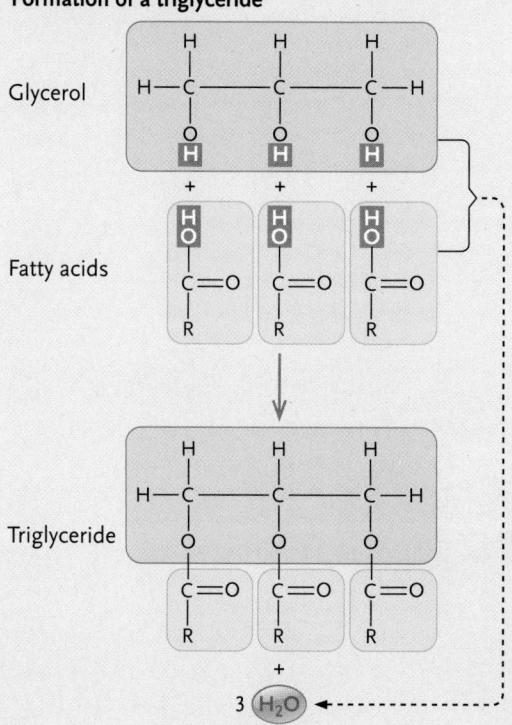

**Glyceryl palmitate**

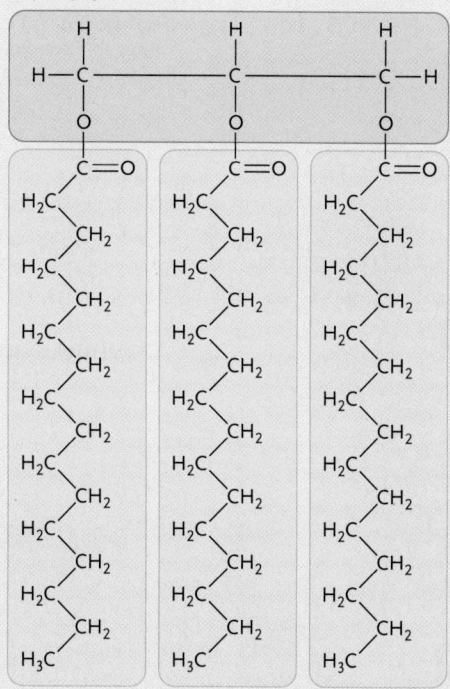

**Triglyceride model**

## Steroids

Steroids are a group of lipids with structures based on a framework of four carbon rings that are derived from isoprene units. Small differences in the side groups attached to the rings distinguish one steroid from another. The most abundant steroids, the sterols, have a single polar —OH group linked to one end of the ring framework and a complex, non-polar hydrocarbon chain at the other end. Although sterols are almost completely hydrophobic, the single hydroxyl group gives one end of the molecules a slightly polar, hydrophilic character. As a result, sterols also have dual solubility properties and, like phospholipids, tend to assume positions that satisfy these properties.

Cholesterol is an important component of the plasma membrane surrounding animal cells; similar sterols, called phytosterols, occur in plant cell membranes.

**Arrangement of carbon rings in a steroid**

**Cholesterol, a sterol**

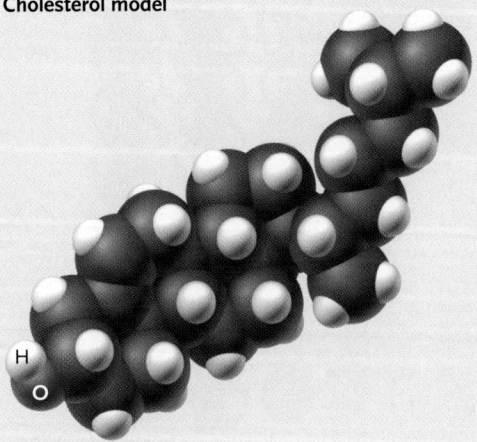

**Cholesterol model**

# The Biosphere

The biosphere is the area occupied by life on Earth, from the depths of the ocean to the sky above. The various physical environments of Earth and their different abiotic factors, such as sunlight, temperature, humidity, wind speed, cloud cover, and rainfall, influence the evolution and diversity of organisms. These abiotic factors contribute to a region's climate, the weather conditions prevailing over an extended period of time. Climates vary on global, regional, and local scales and undergo seasonal changes almost everywhere.

## Solar Radiation: Energy from the Sun

The global pattern of environmental diversity results from latitudinal variation in incoming solar radiation, Earth's rotation on its axis, and its orbit around the Sun. Earth's spherical shape causes the intensity of incoming solar radiation to vary from the equator to the poles. Solar radiation is more concentrated near the equator than it is at the poles, causing latitudinal variation in Earth's temperature.

**Solar radiation**

Near the poles, solar radiation travels a long distance through the atmosphere and strikes a large surface area.

Near the equator, solar radiation travels a short distance through the atmosphere and strikes a small surface area.

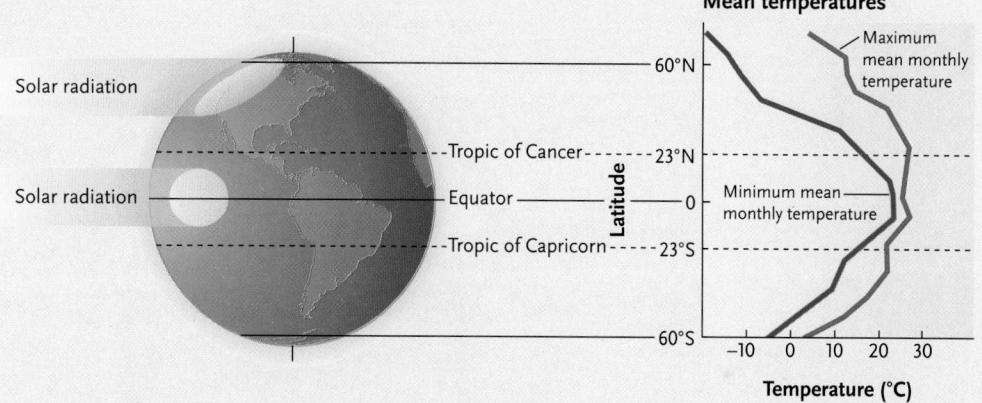

## Seasonality: Weather throughout the Year

Earth is tilted on its axis by 23.5°. This tilt produces seasonal variation in the intensity of incoming solar radiation. The northern hemisphere receives its maximum illumination, and the southern hemisphere its minimum, on the June solstice (around June 21), when the Sun shines directly over the Tropic of Cancer (23.5° N latitude). The reverse is true on the December solstice (around December 21), when the Sun shines directly over the Tropic of Capricorn (23.5° S latitude). Twice each year, on the vernal and autumnal equinoxes (around March 21 and September 21, respectively), the Sun shines directly over the equator. Only the Tropics, the latitudes between the tropics of Cancer and Capricorn, ever receive intense solar radiation from directly overhead. Moreover, the tropics experience only small seasonal changes in temperature and day length, with high temperatures and day length of approximately 12 hours throughout the year.

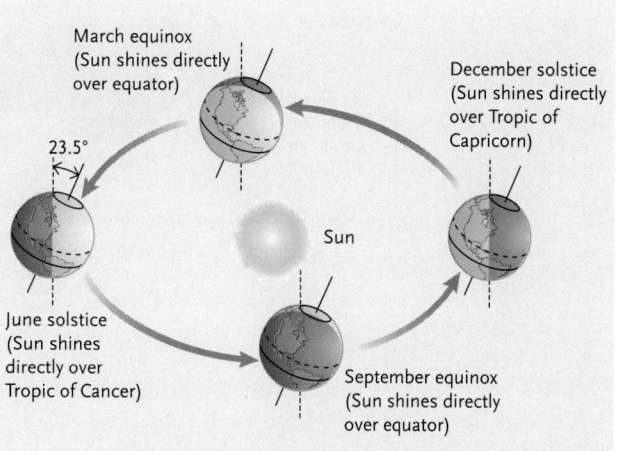

Seasonal variation in temperature and day length increases steadily toward the poles. Polar winters are long and cold, with periods of continuous darkness, and polar summers are short, with periods of continuous light.

## Air Circulation: Wind Patterns

Sunlight warms air masses, causing them to expand, lose pressure, and rise in the atmosphere. The unequal heating of air at different latitudes initiates global air movements, producing three circulation cells in each hemisphere. Warm equatorial air masses rise to high altitude before spreading north and south. They eventually sink back to Earth at about 30° N and S latitude. At low altitude, some air masses flow back toward the equator, completing low-latitude circulation cells. Others flow toward the poles, rise at 60° latitude, and divide at high altitude. Some of this air flows toward the equator, completing the pair of middle-latitude circulation cells. The rest moves toward the poles, where it descends and flows toward the equator, forming the polar circulation cells.

The flow of air masses at low altitude creates winds near the planet's surface. But the planet's surface rotates beneath the atmosphere, moving rapidly near the equator, where Earth's diameter is greatest, and more slowly near the poles. Latitudinal variation in the speed of Earth's rotation deflects the movement of the rising and sinking air masses from a strictly north–south path into belts of easterly and westerly winds; this deflection is called the Coriolis effect. Winds near the equator are called the trade winds; those farther from the equator are the temperate westerlies and easterlies, named for their direction of flow.

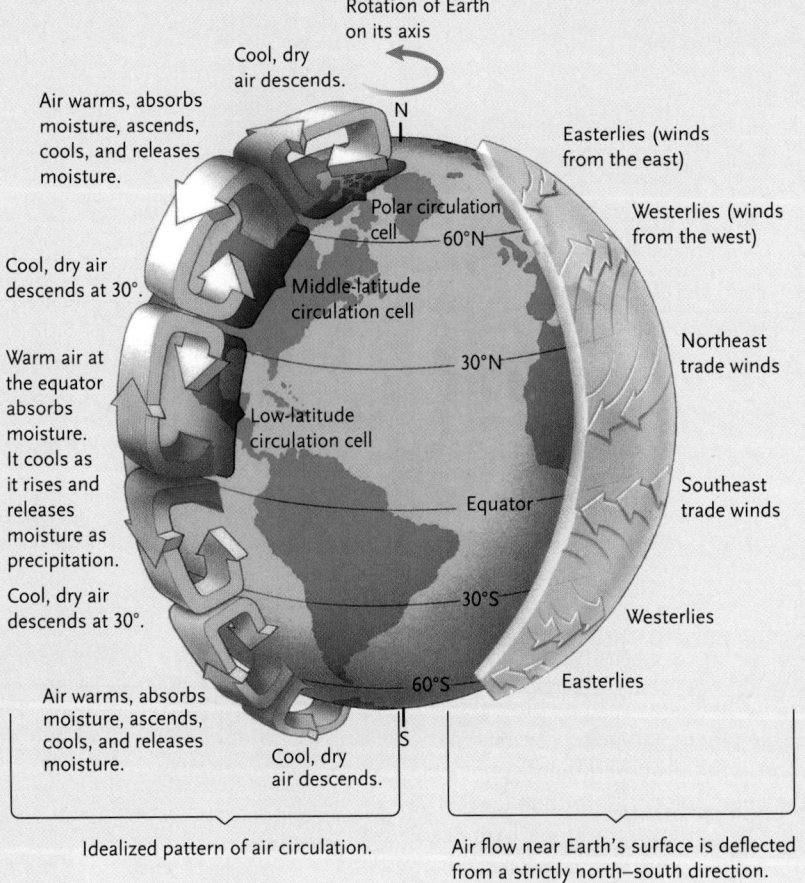

Rotation of Earth on its axis

Cool, dry air descends.

Air warms, absorbs moisture, ascends, cools, and releases moisture.

Cool, dry air descends at 30°.

Warm air at the equator absorbs moisture. It cools as it rises and releases moisture as precipitation.

Cool, dry air descends at 30°.

Air warms, absorbs moisture, ascends, cools, and releases moisture.

Cool, dry air descends.

N

Polar circulation cell

60°N

Middle-latitude circulation cell

30°N

Low-latitude circulation cell

Equator

30°S

60°S

S

Easterlies (winds from the east)

Westerlies (winds from the west)

Northeast trade winds

Southeast trade winds

Westerlies

Easterlies

Idealized pattern of air circulation.

Air flow near Earth's surface is deflected from a strictly north–south direction.

## Precipitation

Differences in solar radiation and global air circulation create latitudinal variations in rainfall. Warm air holds more water vapour than cool air does. As air near the equator heats up, it absorbs water, primarily from the oceans. However, the warm air masses expand as they rise, and their heat energy is distributed over a larger volume, causing their temperature to drop. A decrease in temperature without the loss of heat energy is called adiabatic cooling. After cooling adiabatically, the rising air masses release moisture as rain. Torrential rainfall is characteristic of warm equatorial regions, where rising, moisture-laden air masses cool as they reach high altitude.

As cool, dry air masses descend at 30° latitude, increased air pressure at low altitude compresses them, concentrating their heat energy, raising their temperature, and increasing their capacity to hold moisture. Descending air masses absorb water at these latitudes, which are typically dry. Some air masses continue moving poleward in the lower atmosphere. When they rise at 60° latitude, they cool adiabatically and release precipitation, creating moist habitats in the northern and southern temperate zones.

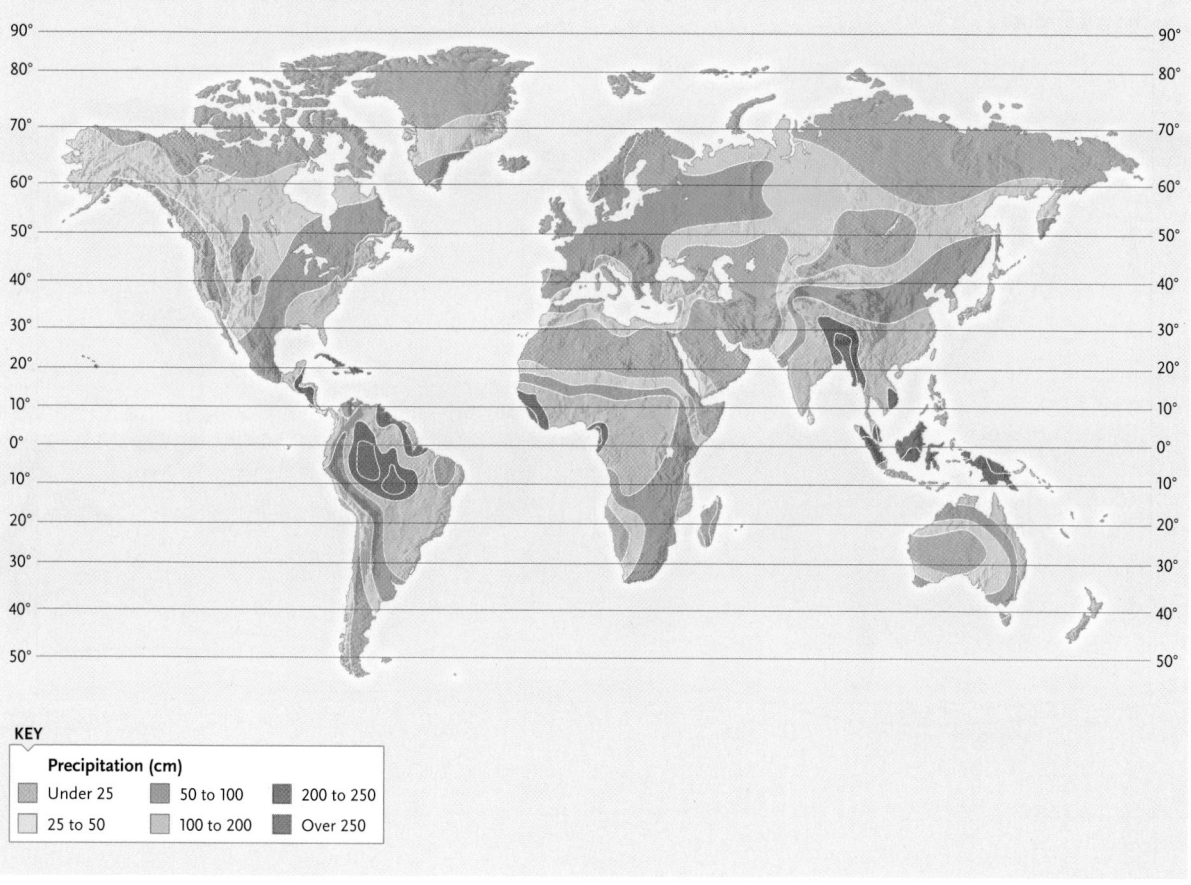

**KEY**

**Precipitation (cm)**

- Under 25
- 25 to 50
- 50 to 100
- 100 to 200
- 200 to 250
- Over 250

## Ocean Currents

Latitudinal variations in solar radiation also warm the oceans' surface water unevenly. Because the volume of water increases as it warms (= decrease in density), sea level is about 8 cm higher at the equator than at the poles. The volume of water associated with this "slope" is enough to cause surface water to move in response to gravity. The trade winds and temperate westerlies also contribute to the mass flow of water at the ocean surface. Thus, surface water flows in the direction of prevailing winds, forming major currents. Earth's rotation, the positions of landmasses, and the shapes of ocean basins also influence the movements of these currents.

Oceanic circulation is generally clockwise in the northern hemisphere and counterclockwise in the southern hemisphere (see figure below). The trade winds push surface water toward the equator and westward until it contacts the eastern edge of a continent. Swift, narrow, and deep currents of warm, nutrient-poor water run toward the poles, parallel to the east coasts of continents. For example, the Gulf Stream flows northward along the east coast of North America, carrying warm water toward northwestern Europe. Cold water returns from the poles toward the equator in slow, broad, and shallow currents, such as the California Current, that parallel the west coasts of continents.

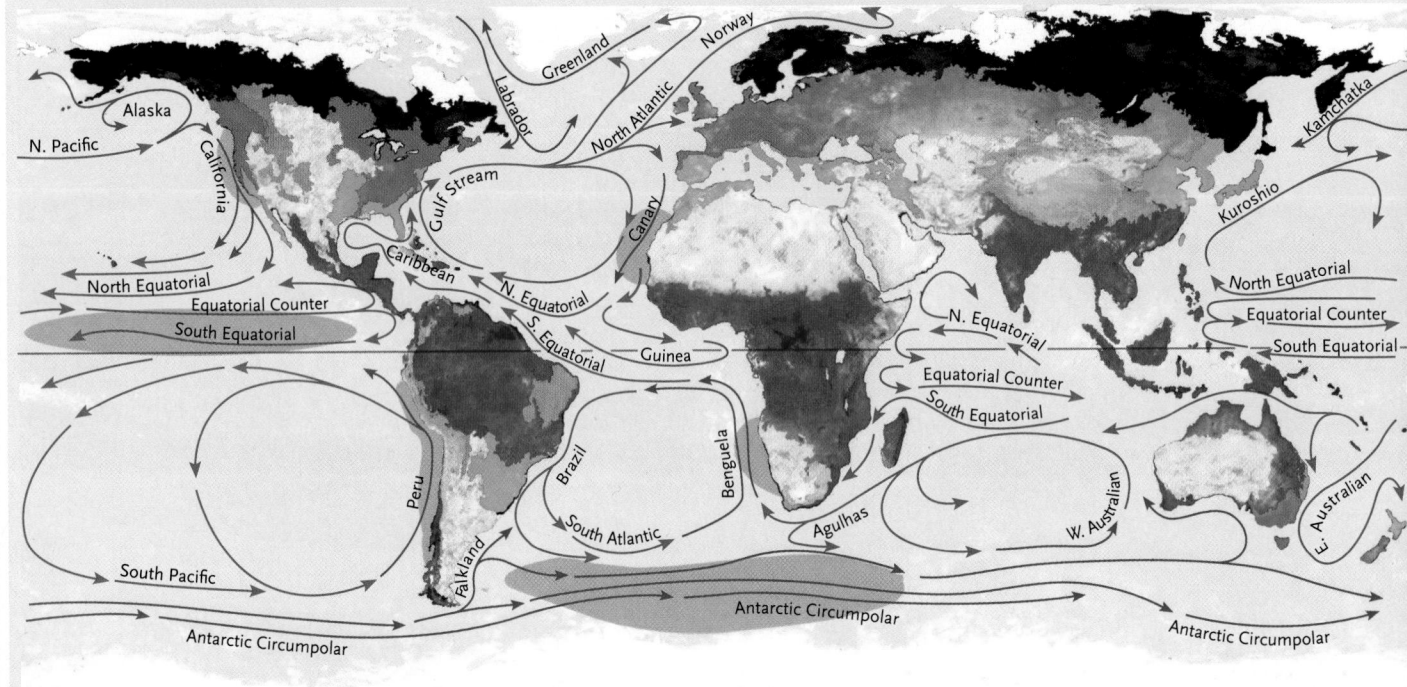

KEY
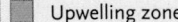 Upwelling zone
→ Warm surface current
→ Cold surface current

## Regional and Local Effects

Although global and seasonal patterns determine an area's climate, regional and local effects also influence abiotic conditions. Currents running along sea coasts exchange heat with air masses flowing above them, moderating the temperature over the nearby land. Breezes often blow from the sea toward the land during the day and in the opposite direction at night (see figure right). These local effects sometimes override latitudinal variations in temperature. For example, the climate in London, England, is much milder than that in Winnipeg, even though Winnipeg is slightly farther south. London has a maritime climate, tempered by winds that cross the nearby North Atlantic Current, but Winnipeg's climate is continental, not moderated by the distant ocean.

Ocean currents also affect moisture conditions in coastal habitats. For example, the region off the southeast coast of Newfoundland known as the Grand Banks is one of the foggiest places on Earth. Here, as the warm Gulf Stream current meets the cold Labrador current, the air above the water cools and its water vapour condenses into heavy fog and rain.

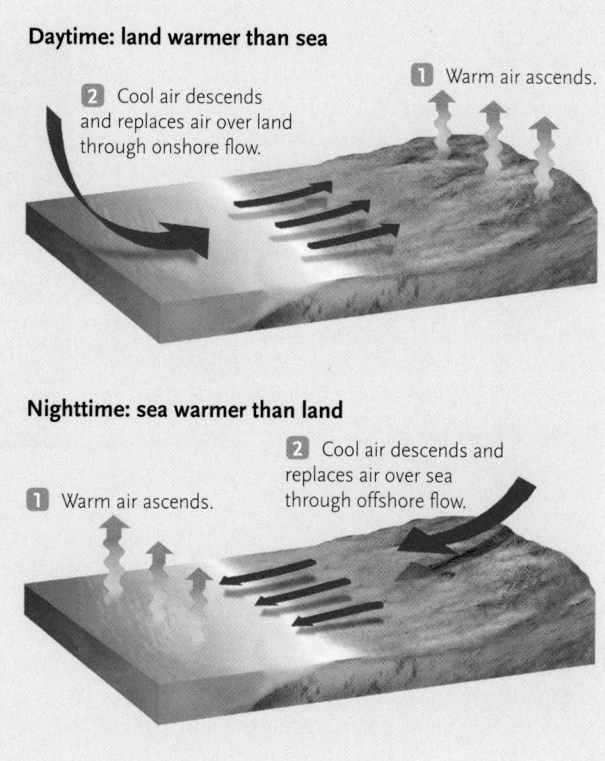

**Daytime: land warmer than sea**

2 Cool air descends and replaces air over land through onshore flow.

1 Warm air ascends.

**Nighttime: sea warmer than land**

2 Cool air descends and replaces air over sea through offshore flow.

1 Warm air ascends.

## The Effects of Topography

Mountains, valleys, and other topographic features are a major influence on regional climates. In the northern hemisphere, south-facing slopes are warmer and drier than north-facing slopes because they receive more solar radiation. In addition, adiabatic cooling causes air temperature to decline 3 to 6°C for every 1000 m increase in elevation. Mountains also establish regional and local rainfall patterns. For example, warm air masses pick up moisture from the Pacific Ocean and then move inland toward the Rocky Mountains. As air rises to cross the mountains, it cools adiabatically and loses moisture, releasing heavy rainfall on the windward side (see below). After the now-dry air crosses the peaks, it descends and warms, absorbing moisture and forming a rain shadow. Habitats on the leeward side of mountains, such as the eastern slopes of the Rocky Mountains in Alberta, are typically drier than those on the windward side.

1 Winds carry moisture inland from Pacific Ocean.

2 Clouds form and rain falls on windward side of mountain range.

3 Rain shadow forms on leeward side of mountain range.

Moist habitats

4000/75
3000/85
1800/125
1000/85
15/25
2000/50
1300/30

## Microclimate

Although climate influences the overall distributions of organisms, the abiotic conditions that immediately surround them, the microclimate, have the greatest effect on survival and reproduction. For example, a fallen log on the forest floor creates a microclimate in the underlying soil that is shadier, cooler, and moister than the surrounding soil, which is exposed to sun and wind. Many animals, including some insects, worms, salamanders, and snakes, occupy these sheltered sites and avoid the effects of prolonged exposure to the elements.

Aleksander Bolbot/Shutterstock.com

## Biomes

Various climatic factors interact to create and regulate biomes—groups of ecosystems that share distinctive combinations of soils, vegetation, and animals. Fourteen different biomes have recently been defined (see below). Why is climate so important in defining biomes? Climatic factors, particularly temperature regimes and water availability, control the rate of photosynthesis by plants, which produce the organic molecules that provide the energy and carbon required by all other organisms in a biome.

In addition, climate influences the type of plants that make up the dominant vegetation of a biome through the selection pressures it creates: certain climatic regions favour certain adaptations and strategies. For example, in arid regions, the dominant plants that have adaptations for storing water or reducing water loss by evaporation, or are metabolically active only in the wettest season, have an advantage over other plants. Biomes are often classified climatically (e.g., desert) or on the basis of the dominant vegetation (e.g., grassland, tropical rainforest).

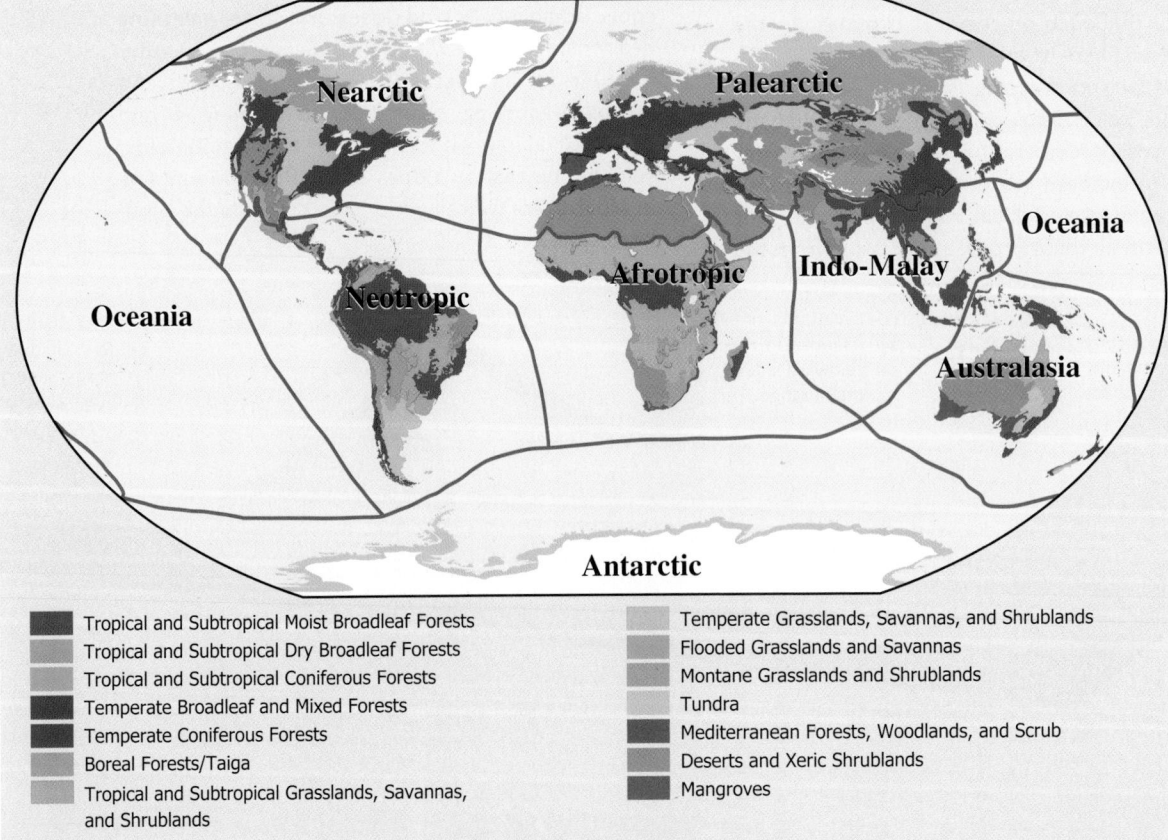

Tropical and Subtropical Moist Broadleaf Forests
Tropical and Subtropical Dry Broadleaf Forests
Tropical and Subtropical Coniferous Forests
Temperate Broadleaf and Mixed Forests
Temperate Coniferous Forests
Boreal Forests/Taiga
Tropical and Subtropical Grasslands, Savannas, and Shrublands

Temperate Grasslands, Savannas, and Shrublands
Flooded Grasslands and Savannas
Montane Grasslands and Shrublands
Tundra
Mediterranean Forests, Woodlands, and Scrub
Deserts and Xeric Shrublands
Mangroves

SOURCE: Olson, D.M. et al, "Terrestrial Ecoregions of the World: A New Map of Life on Earth," *BioScience*, 2001, Vol. 51, No. 11, pp. 933–938, by permission of Oxford University Press.

Shelby Riskin

## WHY IT MATTERS

Just like any group of organisms, fungi can do tremendous harm to other organisms as well as tremendous good. Fungi serve as the primary decomposers of dead organic material in many ecosystems and are a source of food and nutrition to many animals. In contrast, aside from humans, fungi might pose some of the most critical threats to biodiversity on our planet. In the last few decades, we have seen fungal pathogens threaten the survival of whole species of plants and animals. Understanding the biology of these fungi and their life histories has become critically important. Two examples highlight some of the challenges we face in the fight to save species in a rapidly changing global environment.

The first involves infection of bats by a fungus, *Pseudogymnoascus destructans* (formerly *Geomyces destructans*). This fungus has been known to Europe for many years. The European strain of the fungus does not appear to negatively affect European bats. In North America, however, the introduction of the European strain of the fungus has wrought almost inconceivable damage. It has killed almost 6 million bats of multiple species and is very likely to extirpate (cause the local extinction of) what was one of the most common bat species (the little brown bat, *Myotis lucifugus*) in the United States and Canada by 2020. The fungus is cold loving and infects bats during hibernation in caves or mines when their body temperatures are low. The infection caused by *P. destructans* is known as white-nose syndrome. The fungus infects the skin tissue on and around the nose, ears, and wings of the bats **(Figure 18.1)**.

During hibernation, bats lower their metabolic rate to reduce their energy use and survive using stored body fat. Although all bats wake up during hibernation, the number of times infected bats wake up is three to four times higher than for uninfected bats. Each time one of these bats wakes up, it uses the same amount of energy it would use to fuel 60 days of hibernation. If an infected bat wakes up too many times, it will not have enough energy to survive the winter. Most infected bats, which must feed on insects, are not able to eat during winter to restock their fat supplies. Without enough calories to make it through the winter, many infected bats starve to death. It is still not known why infection increases the frequency with which bats awaken throughout the winter. Currently, the most well-supported hypothesis is that the fungus causes dehydration by increasing evaporative water loss.

The disease was first observed in North America in three caves near Albany, New York, in March 2006. The fungus appears to have been brought from Europe, where it had been previously observed. In Europe, however, the fungus has not been observed to cause any bat deaths, although it has been observed to occasionally cause skin

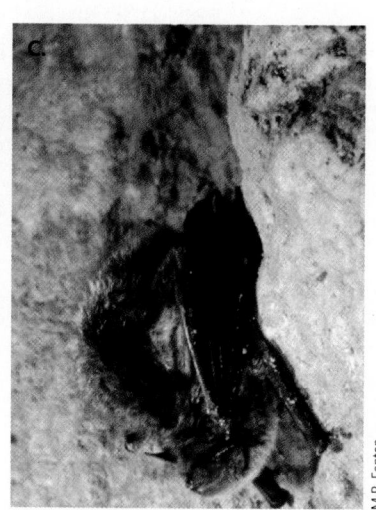

**FIGURE 18.1** **(a)** A little brown bat (*Myotis lucifugus*) with white-nose syndrome. Note the visible white fungus on the skin of the nose, ears, and wings. Little brown bats **(b)** hibernate and **(c)** mate in caves, where they are both exposed to the fungus and in close contact with one another.

Marvin Moriarty/USFWS

M.B. Fenton

M.B. Fenton

lesions. It appears most likely that people, perhaps people who recreate or work in caves or mines, transferred the fungus from Europe to North America. Each year, the fungus spreads further across North America, reaching new caves and killing almost every bat in each infected cave.

In amphibians, infection by another pathogenic fungi, *Batrachochytrium dendrobatidis*, has caused large population declines such that amphibians are the most threatened group of vertebrates. Of about 7000 species of amphibians worldwide, the fungus affects at least 350 species, contributing to population declines in more than 200. Infection by *B. dendrobatidis* has caused the extinction in the wild of at least three species: the Panamanian golden frog (*Atelopus zeteki*), the sharp-snouted day frog (*Taudactylus acutirostris*), and the Australian gastric brooding frogs (species in the genus *Rheobatrachus*).

An aquatic fungus, *B. dendrobatidis* is also a cold-loving fungus, like the fungus responsible for white-nose syndrome. This is a chytrid fungus, a type of fungus that is flagellated and thus can move in water during part of its life cycle. Chytridiomycosis is caused by *B. dendrobatidis* and again, like white-nose syndrome, is an infection of the skin **(Figure 18.2)**. Amphibians depend on their skin for essential body regulation, including gas exchange and moisture control. Chytridiomycosis causes serious electrolyte imbalances in amphibians, disrupting their ability to regulate body functions, often resulting in death by cardiac arrest. In 1997, *B. dendrobatidis* was identified as an agent of disease and was named in 1999. The fungus has been found on all continents except Antarctica, and global trade in amphibians for pets and other uses is believed to have caused its spread. Furthermore, global trade facilitated the evolution of a hypervirulent strain. The African clawed frog

(*Xenopus laevis*), once used in pregnancy tests, is an example of a species that carries the fungus.

Both pathogens described above have several interesting commonalities. First, it is likely that in both cases, the pathogenic fungus was introduced to new populations because of humans. This suggests that more carefully managing the exchange of organisms across geographic regions may prevent the spread of future fungal pathogens. Second, both species of fungi are host–generalists and can survive and reproduce without a host. This means that they can affect many species and perhaps even more distantly related groups of organisms. For example, reptiles have been identified as carriers of *B. dendrobatidis*, although they do not exhibit symptoms of chytridiomycosis. Both fungi grow on non-living substrates and decompose dead organic matter as well. These qualities, the ability to infect many groups of organisms and to survive without a host organism, mean that the fungi can persist for a long time in many places even if the originally infected organisms leave or are killed. Third, both amphibians and bats have life histories that make them especially vulnerable to disease. Most spend at least part of their lives in high densities or where there is a lot of contact among individuals, increasing the spread of disease. In the case of bats, for example, mating occurs in underground caves where bats are exposed to the fungus and to a lot of bat-to-bat contact (Figure 18.1). And during **metamorphosis** in amphibians and hibernation in bats, their immune systems are suppressed, further facilitating infection.

We have much to learn about the biology and ecology of both of these pathogens. Some of what we learn might aid in slowing or stopping the spread of these diseases. Currently, scientists are looking at how temperature, pH, moisture levels, and various chemical compounds affect the growth and reproduction of the fungi in the hope that they might find ways to inhibit its growth. Scientists are also studying the genetic relationships among different strains of the fungi to better understand their spread and the role humans played in their introduction to new geographic areas.

These pathogenic fungi highlight how destructive these organisms can be and how much we have to learn about the biology of these organisms to prevent widespread infection. As you will see in this chapter, however, not all fungi are dangerous pathogens. Fungi are amazing organisms with unique lives. Fungi provide irreplaceable services to the function of ecosystems worldwide.

Fungi play a more pervasive role in our lives than you might imagine. We do not interact with fungi only when we go the forest to pick mushrooms or order a pizza. In this chapter, you will be introduced to some of the biology of the fungi. Perhaps because of their role in decomposition, the dark habitats in which they often thrive, and the ability of some to poison us, fungi have been feared and associated with death and even the supernatural through much of

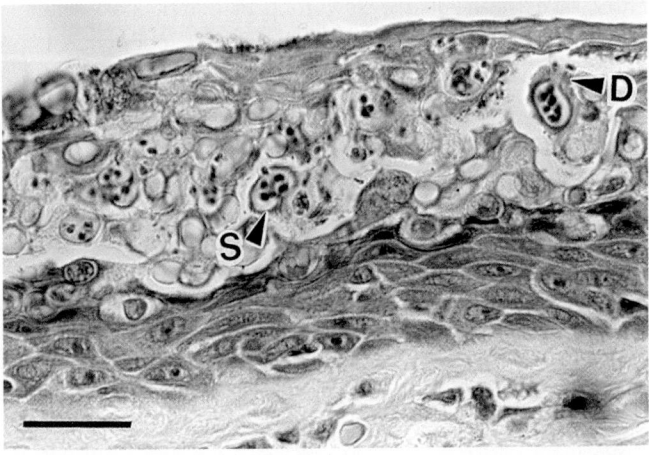

**FIGURE 18.2** Skin from an Australian green tree frog (*Litoria caerulea*) from Queensland, Australia, severely infected by chytridiomycosis. In this image, you can see the structures where spores are developing (S = sporangia) and the tube through which spores are released (D). The spores of chytrid fungi are called zoospores and are flagellated.

SOURCE: Lee Berger et al., "Chytridiomycosis causes amphibian mortality associated with population declines in the rain forests of Australia and Central America," *PNAS* vol. 95 no. 15, pp. 9031–9036. Copyright (1998) National Academy of Sciences, U.S.A.

human history. Fungi, however, play very important roles in the biological world, with both positive and negative effects on other organisms. For example, although fungi cause the majority of plant diseases, fungi also facilitate the success of most plants by extending their root systems and increasing their access to nutrients and water. For humans, fungi are also important and even fatal drivers of disease, but we also derive penicillin and other antibiotics from them. We consume fungi and their products virtually every day. Besides the mushrooms we eat directly, we can thank fungi for bread, alcoholic drinks, and anything else made with yeast.

## 18.1 Fungal Diversity and Characteristics

Most fungi spend most of their lives invisible to the human eye. The mushrooms in our yards and the mould on the cheese in our refrigerators are by far the exception to the rule. This makes fungal species difficult to identify and count. About 99,000 species of fungus have been identified worldwide. But scientists estimate that this is just the tip of the iceberg. An estimate of fungal diversity in 1991 suggested that there are at least 1.5 million species of fungi, but even this is likely too conservative. Estimates in the last 10 years vary between 700,000 and 5.1 million fungal species worldwide. In fact, one recent paper estimated that it will take us well over 1000 years to identify all of the fungal species on Earth.

### Fungi Are Unique among Organisms

Fungi share characteristics with other groups of organisms. Because they share many characteristics with plants, they were once considered part of the plant kingdom. They are, in fact, more closely related to animals than plants and now are considered to be a kingdom of their own. All fungi, whether big or small, made up of one or billions of cells, share five features in common. (1) They are all **eukaryotic**, with cells containing a nucleus and organelles.

One striking characteristic unique to fungi, as you will see, is that some fungal cells can contain two dissimilar nuclei for much of their life cycle. Also, (2) all fungi have cell walls. (3) Fungi are sessile rather than motile. They can, however, extend rapidly and in multiple directions to continue accessing needed water and nutrients. (4) Fungi are heterotrophs. That is, none of them make their own food. They obtain the energy they need feeding on other organisms, either living or dead. (5) Fungi absorb their food. In filamentous fungi, fungal filaments are able to penetrate a nutrient-rich substrate (e.g., soil or a decaying log or animal). The fungi excrete digestive enzymes that liberate minerals and nutrients from organic matter and the soil by breaking large molecules into smaller ones. The fungi then absorb these materials. In other words, fungi digest their food first and then eat it.

## 18.2 Fungal Structure

Fungal bodies range in size from single cells that measure micrometres (μm) across to networks of fungal filaments that extend across hundreds of hectares. You are likely familiar with some single-celled fungi, such as the yeasts used to make bread or beer. Baker's yeast, *Saccharomyces cerevisiae*, has been used for thousands of years in baking and the fermentation of alcoholic drinks. Baker's yeast cells are ovoid, measuring about 5 to 10 micrometres on one axis and 1 to 7 μm on the other **(Figure 18.3a)**.

The very large fungi that cover many square kilometres are sometimes called the largest organisms on Earth. The most recent and the largest of these giant fungi to be described was found in the Blue Mountains of Oregon in 1998. The fungus, *Armillaria ostoyae*, a species of honey mushroom, extends across 965 hectares, or 10 km² **(Figure 18.3b)**. That's an area equivalent to more than 1230 Canadian football fields.

The fungus is thought to be thousands of years old. The mushrooms of the fungus are edible (they are

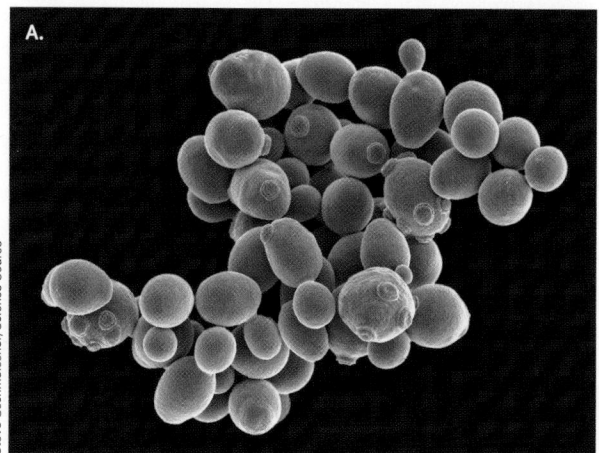

**FIGURE 18.3** **(a)** Baker's yeast cells (*Saccharomyces cerevisiae*), a unicellular fungus, and the fruiting bodies **(b)** of honey mushrooms (species in the genus *Armillaria*). The underground fungal bodies of honey mushrooms have been called the largest organisms on Earth.

# THE MOLECULE BEHIND THE BIOLOGY 18.1
## Luciferase

A luciferase is a type of enzyme. Named after Lucifer, the fallen angel of the Bible whose name means light bringing or light bearing, luciferases catalyze reactions in living organisms that result in the emission of light. There are many types of organisms that emit light, or bioluminesce, following reactions controlled by luciferase. These include insects, bacteria, and, yes, fungi.

Bioluminescent fungi have been described for thousands of years (**Figure 1**). Aristotle (384–322 BCE) mentions the glow emitted from rotting wood, and glowing fungi with medicinal properties were described by Pliny the Elder (23–29 CE). Later, Europeans described bioluminescent fungi being used by native peoples in Indonesia and Micronesia. A Dutch physician in the 18th century described people in Indonesia carrying bioluminescent fungi to light their way. Observations from the 19th century describe Micro-nesians using glowing fungi on their faces to frighten their enemies and as decorations during dances and rituals.

More than 60 species of bioluminescent fungal species have been described. All of these are basidiomycetes (see Section 18.4 for more information on basidiomycetes). Some produce bioluminescent mycelia, some produce bioluminescent mushrooms, and some produce both.

The light emitted by glowing fungi is greenish, and no one knows exactly what it's for. Many hypotheses have been proposed. For example, the light may attract invertebrates that could aid in the dispersal of spores. There is some evidence that this is true, but it does not explain glowing mycelia. It has also been suggested that the light might attract animals that would prey on fungiphores (animals that eat fungi), or that some fungiphores might be repelled by the light, or that the light could be some kind of warning to potential fungiphores. It has even been proposed that there is no ecological purpose for the bioluminescence, that it is simply a by-product of chemical reactions that occur for other reasons, especially the decomposition of lignin. All species that are bioluminescent break down wood.

Luciferase has applications in medicine and biotechnology. Researchers have used the luciferase and bioluminescence reactions of fireflies and copepods (small marine invertebrates) to track the spread of disease in vivo and in real time. Although fungal luciferase has not been exploited in this way, this technique has been used to track fungal pathogens. Luciferase from copepods has been used to track fungal infections in small animals, suggesting that this technique could be used in the examination and treatment of humans as well. By causing the fungi to glow, doctors can more precisely assess and treat fungal infections.

**FIGURE 1** A photo of bioluminescent fungi (*Filoboletus manipularis*) found in Malaysia taken in the light **(a)** and in the dark **(b)**.

described as having a sweet flavour—hence the name honey mushroom), but it is also a pathogen, infecting the roots of conifers.

Fungal physiology is also unique, as you will see. Many fungi have some amazing properties—some even glow in the dark (see Box 18.1).

## Many Fungi Use Hyphae to Search for and Obtain Water and Nutrients

Many fungi are unicellular, or have unicellular growth forms. Most fungi, however, are multicellular, and most of their biomass is made up of very thin filaments called hyphae (singular = hypha; **Figure 18.4**). Hyphae extend through the soil, across the surface of your rotting peach, or perhaps across the growth medium of your petri dish to access water and nutrients. Each hypha is very thin, typically between 1 and 30 micrometres in diameter. This diameter stays relatively constant along the length of a hyphal filament. These very thin filaments grow together, forming thick mats called mycelia (singular = mycelium; Figure 18.4). You have probably seen mycelia. If you have ever peeled back bark on a fallen tree, for example, you may have seen white mats or extensions of fungal mycelia. You can even often see mycelia in a handful of soil.

A.

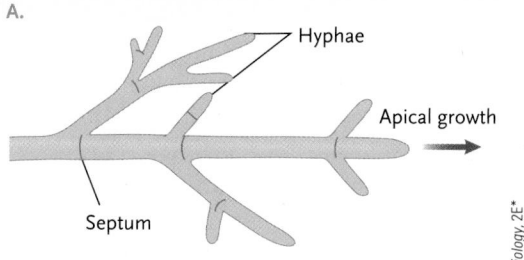

Hyphae

Apical growth

Septum

*Biology, 2E\**

B. Mycelium on leaf litter

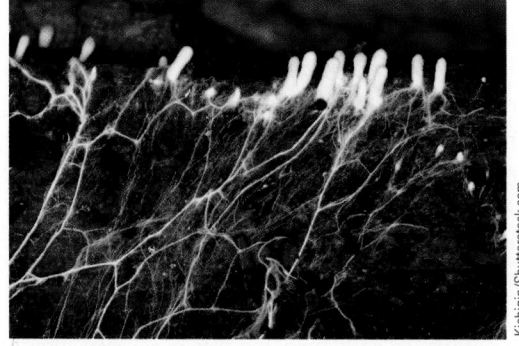

Kichigin/Shutterstock.com

**FIGURE 18.4 (a)** Fungal hyphae are the filaments that form a fungus's body. In some fungi, septa divide each hypha into separate compartments. **(b)** Grouped together, hyphae form mycelium.

Hyphae grow from the tip, or apex. As the hyphae elongate, separations, or **septa**, often form behind the apex at regular intervals, forming cell-like compartments (Figure 18.4). The septa contain pores through which water, nutrients, and even cellular organelles can flow. This makes it difficult to define individual cells in hyphae. It is possible, for example, to regularly find 50 nuclei in a single hyphal compartment! The apexes of hyphae are also important in nutrient acquisition. By excreting digestive enzymes, nutrients are liberated from the soil and then are absorbed by the fungus. Nutrients and water can be moved through the hyphal compartments to where they are most needed.

When a filamentous fungus grows in an environment with consistent resources available in all directions, hyphae extend in all directions, at once forming a circular body of mycelia. This is clear looking at a petri dish in the lab, for example, when a fungus radiates in a circle from a central inoculation point. This phenomenon can also be observed in nature. Ringworm, the human infection, is not caused by worms but by a fungus. This skin infection is characterized by red rings that grow from the site of the infection. Fairy rings are circles of mushrooms that often form in the same area year after year **(Figure 18.5)**. These rings have inspired many supernatural stories. They are sometimes called witches' rings or elves' rings and are often described as the sites of these creatures' dances and rituals.

## Yeasts Are Unicellular Fungi That Reproduce Asexually

Most unicellular fungi are yeasts, such as the baker's yeast described above (Figure 18.3a). Other yeasts, such as *Cryptococcus neoformans* and *Candida albicans*, are human pathogens. *C. neoformans* causes cryptococcosis, an infection, most often of the lungs, that can be fatal, particularly to AIDS or otherwise immunocompromised patients. *C. albicans* causes what we typically call a yeast infection or thrush. Although all of these fungal species are called yeasts, they are not particularly closely related. The word *yeast* refers to the growth form of the fungus as unicellular and that reproduces asexually by budding or fission. Many yeast species, in fact, have both a yeast growth form and a multicellular growth form and can switch between the two depending on environmental conditions. Interestingly, *C. albicans*, the yeast responsible for vaginal yeast infections and thrush, is not harmful in its single-celled yeast form. It becomes problematic when an environmental trigger causes it to become filamentous.

Many yeasts are pigmented. Baker's yeast, for example, has a cream colour. One yeast, *Xanthophyllomyces dendrorhous*, is red. This yeast is sometimes used as a dietary supplement in aquaculture for salmon and some crustaceans.

A.

NajaShots/iStock/Thinkstock

B.

**FIGURE 18.5 (a)** A so-called fairy ring grows in someone's lawn. Although now they are often considered distasteful and are eradicated, much folklore has surrounded them, as illustrated in the painting **(b)**.

SOURCE (Photo B): "Plucked from the Fairy Circle" by T. H. Thomas - Google Books version of Sikes, Wirt (1880). *British Goblins: Welsh Folk-lore, Fairy Mythology, Legends and Traditions*. London: Sampson Low, Marston, Searle, & Rivington. Licensed under Public domain via Wikimedia Commons - http://commons.wikimedia.org/wiki/File:Plucked_from_the_Fairy_Circle.png

Those fish, although known for their red and pink hues, do not produce the pigments that create these colours themselves. They get those pigments from their food, so fish in farms receive red fungal food supplements to produce the colours to which we are all accustomed.

## Fungal Cells Contain Cell Walls

Just like plants, some bacteria, algae, and other single-celled organisms, all fungi contain cell walls. Cell walls across the biological world usually contain polysaccharides (big carbohydrate molecules made up of long chains of small carbon molecules), which lend them strength and some rigidity. Although plant cell walls contain cellulose as the main structural protein, fungal cell walls contain the polysaccharide **chitin**. Chitin is a type of carbohydrate molecule that contains nitrogen. It is found throughout the biological world. Although chitin is not found in the cell walls of other organisms, it is found in the exoskeletons of arthropods (insects and crustaceans such as lobsters and crabs) and in the internal shells of cephalopods such as octopus and squid.

The cell walls of fungi play a number of important roles, including structural support and the regulation of water and metabolism. These cell walls add rigidity to fungal bodies. The cell walls also regulate water movement across cell membranes. By preventing water from rushing in or out, the cell is able to maintain structural integrity. Fungal cell walls also play a role in communication. As you will see, some aspects of fungal reproduction and growth involve the release of chemicals underground that fungi use to find each other and fuse. Much of this process is mediated by activity in the cell wall.

### STUDY BREAK

1. What is the difference between hyphae and mycelia?
2. What are yeasts?
3. What distinguishes fungal cell walls from plant cell walls?

## 18.3 Fungal Reproduction

Many details about fungal reproduction are covered in Chapter 28. However, because of the importance of fungal sexual structures and life cycles to the classification and phylogeny of fungi, we will discuss the basic features of fungal reproduction in this chapter as well. This information allows us to distinguish between two groups of multicellular, sexually reproducing fungi, sometimes called the true fungi, the ascomycetes and basidiomycetes (see Section 18.4).

Even today, a lot of how we identify fungal species is based on the type of fruiting body a fungus produces. The most familiar type of fungal fruiting body is the **mushroom (Figure 18.6)**, but there are other types of fruiting bodies as well. Fruiting bodies are the reproductive structures where fungal spores are produced and from where they are released. Fruiting bodies are almost entirely haploid—each cell contains only one set of chromosomes.

Fungal spores are also haploid. In contrast to the haploid sperm and eggs of animals, haploid fungal spores do not need to combine with other cells to grow into multicellular organisms. Instead, under the correct environmental conditions, haploid hyphae can grow from haploid spores that have been released into the environment. If the hyphae of two compatible fungi find each other as they extend through the soil (or other substrate), they can then fuse. The fusion of cells is called **plasmogamy** (*plasmo-* means plasma or cytoplasm, and *-gamy* means marriage or union).

After fungal cells fuse, the nuclei remain separate for some period of time. **Karyogamy** is the process of nuclear fusion between cells (*karyon* means nut). Karyogamy eventually occurs in fungi following plasmogamy, but the time between the fusion of the cells and the fusion of the nucleus varies among fungal groups. After plasmogamy and before karyogamy, each cell contains

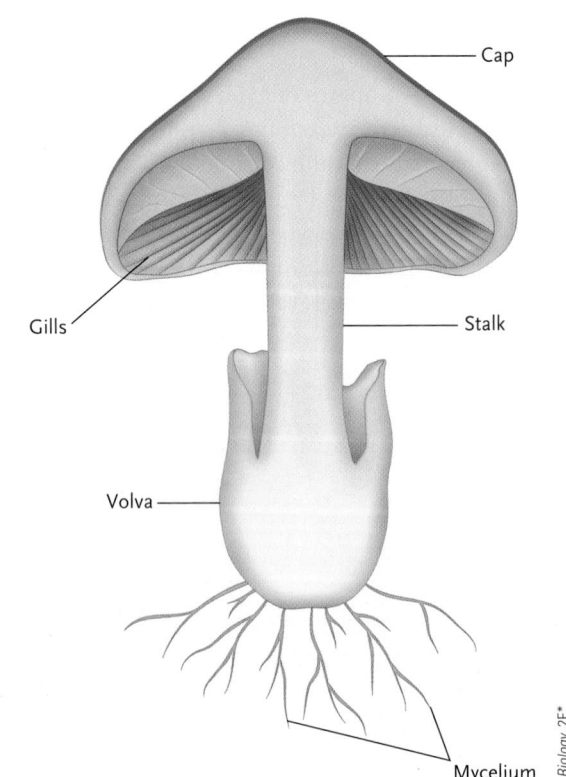

**FIGURE 18.6** The fruiting body and mycelium for a mushroom-forming fungus. The first step in identifying mushrooms includes an examination of the parts of the mushroom, including the cap, gills, stalk, and volva.

two distinct nuclei. Fungi in this phase, with two nuclei per cell, are called **dikaryon**, whereas fungi with one nucleus per cell are **monokaryon**. In dikaryons, both nuclei divide during growth (mitosis), maintaining two separate haploid nuclei in all cells.

Eventually, the dikaryotic fungus produces a fruiting body that produces new spores. Here, in the spore-producing cells, housed within the fruiting body, the haploid nuclei finally fuse, and karyogamy occurs. Just as in animal reproduction, genetic recombination between the two individuals takes place. The nuclei in the spore-producing cells are then diploid. Afterward, meiosis occurs, resulting in new and unique haploid spores (see Chapter 3 for more information on meiosis). These spores are released into the environment, and the process continues.

## STUDY BREAK

1. What are three characteristics shared by all fungi?
2. What is plasmogamy?
3. What is karyogamy?
4. What is a dikaryon?

## 18.4 Fungal Classification

Fungi were once considered part of the plant kingdom. We now know that they are more closely related to animals than to plants. Traditionally, within the group of organisms we know as fungi, groups were classified mainly by their reproductive structures and by their morphological characteristics. In the last decade, however, scientists have used molecular techniques to improve our understanding of how different groups of fungi are related. The results have been interesting and surprising and have led to more questions than answers about how different groups of fungi evolved. In this chapter, we will focus in detail on two fungal phyla: the Ascomycota and Basidiomycota, the two groups of fungi that produce mushrooms. It is important to note that many other groups exist, but we will not focus on them here (but see Chapter 30 for details about another group of fungi known as chytrid fungi). Instead of a taxonomic survey, we will focus on the ecological roles that different groups of fungi play in their environments.

The differences between ascomycetes and basidiomycetes are found in their life cycles and the structures on which spores are produced. Under particular environmental conditions (usually "cool but not cold" and "damp but not wet"), hyphae will grow into knots, which eventually develop into mushrooms (Figure 18.6).

### Ascomycota Includes Many Fungi with Which We Often Interact

The Ascomycota includes a diverse assemblage of fungi **(Figure 18.7)**. This phylum includes bread moulds, baker's yeast, *C. albicans* (the species that causes thrush in humans), the fungus that causes athlete's foot and

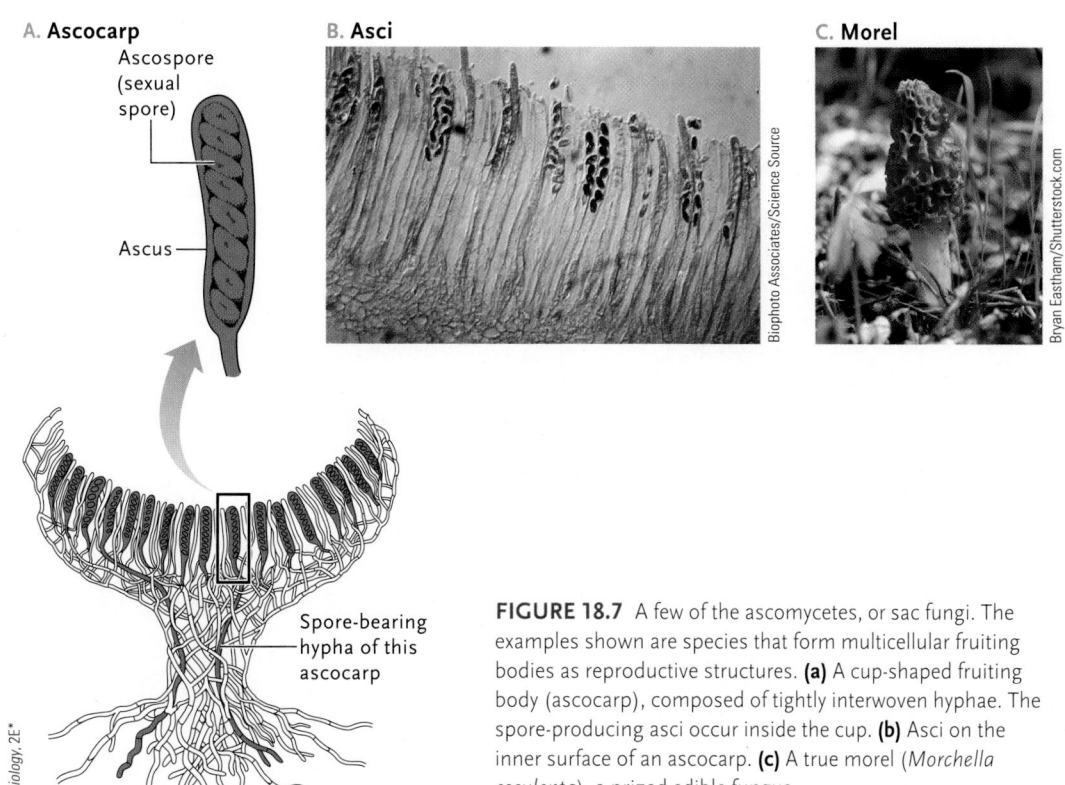

**A. Ascocarp**

Ascospore (sexual spore)

Ascus

Spore-bearing hypha of this ascocarp

*Biology, 2E\**

**B. Asci**

*Biophoto Associates/Science Source*

**C. Morel**

*Bryan Eastham/Shutterstock.com*

**FIGURE 18.7** A few of the ascomycetes, or sac fungi. The examples shown are species that form multicellular fruiting bodies as reproductive structures. **(a)** A cup-shaped fruiting body (ascocarp), composed of tightly interwoven hyphae. The spore-producing asci occur inside the cup. **(b)** Asci on the inner surface of an ascocarp. **(c)** A true morel (*Morchella esculenta*), a prized edible fungus.

ringworm, the prized truffle (*Tuber melanosporum*), and even the morel (*Morchella esculenta*), the fungal delicacy prized across much of North America. The fungus that is responsible for white-nose syndrome in bats (*P. destructans*) described earlier is also an ascomycete. Currently, about 64,000 species of ascomycetes have been identified.

As described above, the sexual life cycle of filamentous fungi, including ascomycetes, involves plasmogamy, or the fusion of hyphae from compatible strains **(Figure 18.8)**. In ascomycetes, these strains are commonly referred to as + or − rather than male or female. Following plasmogamy, the cells of the ascomycete are dikaryons, containing two haploid nuclei. The tips of the dikaryotic hyphae develop into sacs, called **asci** (singular = ascus). It is in the asci that karyogamy, the fusion of the two haploid nuclei into one diploid nucleus, takes place. Meiosis then takes place, and this diploid nucleus becomes four haploid spores. In ascomycetes, mitosis then takes place, resulting in two copies of each spore, for a total of eight haploid spores, called

**ascospores**. The asci grow within a larger structure called an **ascocarp**, which begins to develop soon after the asci initially form. The ascospores can then be released from the ascocarp, and if they reach an appropriate substrate and environmental conditions are right, they can begin to grow into a new mycelium.

Ascomycetes can also reproduce asexually. Yeast growth forms reproduce by budding or fission. But even filamentous growth forms can produce asexual spores. This can happen during mycelial growth. The ends of modified hyphae can produce haploid spores, called **conidia**, which are then released to the environment. These spores are genetically identical to the parent mycelium.

## Basidiomycota Includes Toadstools and Many Mushrooms

The Basidiomycota includes most of the organisms you imagine when you think of mushrooms or toadstools

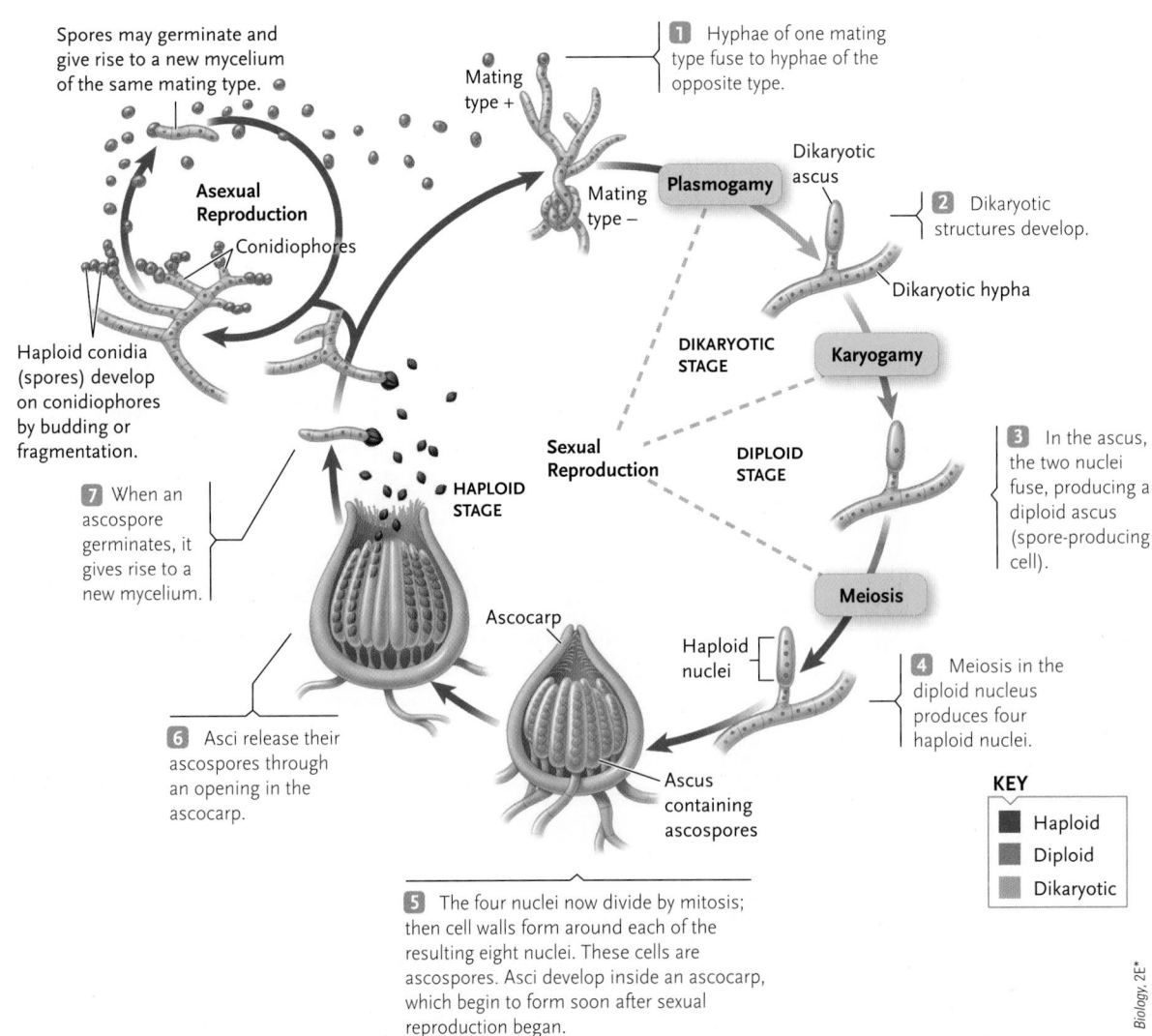

**FIGURE 18.8** Life cycle of the ascomycete *Neurospora crassa*.

**FIGURE 18.9** Examples of basidiomycetes. **(a)** An earthstar mushroom in the family Geastrales. The "star" peels away from the spore-containing puffball at maturity. **(b)** The fly agaric mushroom (*Amanita muscaria*), popular in design and fairy tales. **(c)** An edible shelf fungus, chicken-of-the-woods (a species in the genus *Laetiporus*). **(d)** A coral fungus.

(Figure 18.9). This group includes the button mushrooms you put on your pizza and most of the other mushrooms available from a grocery store. In fact, white button mushrooms, cremini mushrooms, and portobellos are all the same species, *Agaricus bisporus*. The word "button" refers to the growth stage of the mushroom. A mushroom is a button when it has a differentiated stalk and cap but has not yet opened its cap. Portobello mushrooms are simply button mushrooms that have been allowed to grow past the button stage.

Some basidiomycetes have yeast growth forms, but most are filamentous. Like ascomycetes, many can produce asexual spores, or conidia. During sexual reproduction, the dikaryotic phase following plasmogamy and before karyogamy lasts much longer in basidiomycetes than in ascomycetes (**Figure 18.10, p. 398**).

The mycelia of many basidiomycetes are dikaryotic (the cells contain two dissimilar nuclei) for most of their life. Karyogamy will not take place until a fruiting body, called a **basidiocarp**, forms. A toadstool, a puffball, and a shelf fungus growing on the trunk of a tree are all examples of basidiocarps (Figure 18.9). The spores of basidiomycetes are produced on external structures called **basidia** (singular = basidium), which are often found on gills, as you might see on the underside of a mushroom cap. The basidia are club shaped, and inside these basidia, karyogamy finally takes place, producing a single diploid nucleus. Meiosis then occurs, producing four haploid spores, which form on the end of the basidium. The spores are then ready to be released and can then establish as new mycelial bodies.

Using two basidiomycetes as models, the shiitake mushroom (*Lentinula edodes*) and the oyster mushroom (*Pleurotus ostreatus*), recent research has shown that mushrooms can do more than just release their spores. Mushrooms manipulate the air around them by altering the water vapour content and actively cooling the area below the mushroom cap. This essentially creates a wind, which aids in the dispersal of their spores and facilitates longer-range transport.

## STUDY BREAK

1. What is a mushroom?
2. What are asci? What are basidia?
3. What are conidia?

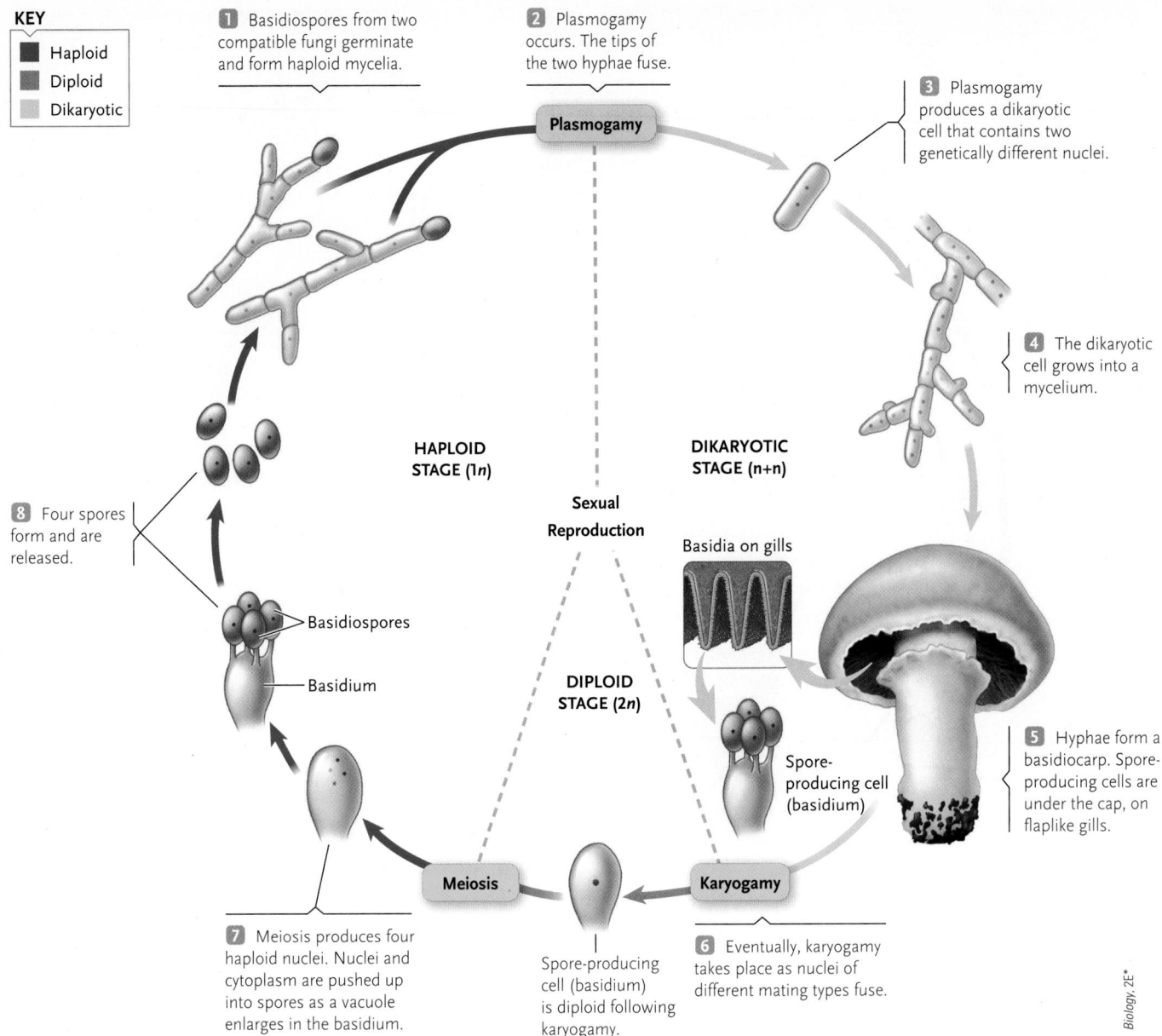

KEY
- ■ Haploid
- ■ Diploid
- ■ Dikaryotic

**1** Basidiospores from two compatible fungi germinate and form haploid mycelia.

**2** Plasmogamy occurs. The tips of the two hyphae fuse.

Plasmogamy

**3** Plasmogamy produces a dikaryotic cell that contains two genetically different nuclei.

**4** The dikaryotic cell grows into a mycelium.

HAPLOID STAGE (1n)

DIKARYOTIC STAGE (n+n)

Sexual Reproduction

Basidia on gills

**8** Four spores form and are released.

Basidiospores

Basidium

DIPLOID STAGE (2n)

Spore-producing cell (basidium)

**5** Hyphae form a basidiocarp. Spore-producing cells are under the cap, on flaplike gills.

Meiosis

Karyogamy

**7** Meiosis produces four haploid nuclei. Nuclei and cytoplasm are pushed up into spores as a vacuole enlarges in the basidium.

Spore-producing cell (basidium) is diploid following karyogamy.

**6** Eventually, karyogamy takes place as nuclei of different mating types fuse.

Biology, 2E*

**FIGURE 18.10** Life cycle of the basidiomycete *Agaricus bisporus*, a species commonly known as the button mushroom.

## 18.5 Fungal Lifestyles

Most fungi can be characterized as having one of three fundamental lifestyles. Some are **saprotrophic**, which means that they obtain energy from decomposing organic matter. Some are parasitic, obtaining energy from other living organisms called hosts, which pay a cost. And, finally, some fungi are mutualists. These fungi are in close symbiotic relationships that generally benefit both partners. Most fungal mutualists are either mycorrhizal fungi (see Figure 18.17) or lichens (fungi in a close symbiotic relationship with species of algae; see Figure 18.19).

There is also a fraction of fungal species (less than 0.5%) that, despite being unable to locomote, are carnivorous. More than 100 species of fungus have been identified that are able to trap and digest animals, particularly nematodes, much like carnivorous plants. Some are saprotrophs that are able to supplement their diets with some amount of carnivory. It is hypothesized that because wood is high in carbon but low in other nutrients, such as nitrogen, fungi obtain additional nutrients from animal sources. Many ascomycetes have specialized structures to trap prey. Some have small lassoes they use to actively trap nematodes, for example, whereas others have adhesive extensions that look like knobs or even nets **(Figure 18.11)**. Even the oyster mushroom (*Pleurotus ostreatus*), a common and commonly consumed mushroom found in North American forests, can digest nematodes.

### Saprotrophs Absorb Their Food from Dead and Decaying Organic Matter

Saprotrophs (from Greek, with *sapro-* meaning rotten and *-troph* referring to food) use dead organic material as their

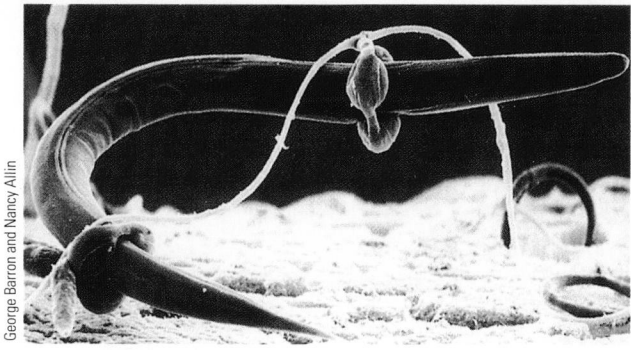

**FIGURE 18.11** A nematode-trapping fungus. Hyphae of this ascomycete (a species from the genus *Arthrobotrys*) form nooselike rings. When a prey organism enters the loop, rapid changes in the concentration of charged particles draw water into the loop by osmosis. The increased pressure inside the loop causes the noose to tighten, trapping its prey. Enzymes produced by the fungus then break down the nematode's tissues.

main source of energy. Fungal saprotrophs are essential to food webs and material recycling in many ecosystems, and most fungal species are decomposers, returning nutrients to the soil so that they can be taken up by plants that grow there. Fungi, with their fast-growing hyphae and extracellular digestive enzymes, are very good at breaking down materials that are difficult for animals or plants to break apart and break down, such as leaf litter, tree trunks, and animal carcasses.

Dung is another important and common substrate for saprotrophic fungi. One group of fungi, in the genus *Pilobolus*, contains species that are common decomposers of dung, specifically the dung of herbivores. Fungi of this genus are found worldwide and have been observed on the dung of wallabies in Australia and of caribou in Alaska. The mycelia of these fungi grow throughout the dung. The asexual spore structures of these fungi often require exposure to light to grow. Following this (or another) environmental cue, small fluid-filled stalks form on the surface of the dung **(Figure 18.12)**.

These stalks elongate and eventually swell at the growing end, creating a bulb that is under pressure from the fluid within the stalk. At the tip of the bulb is a cluster of spores. The pressure of the fluid causes the stalk to dramatically rupture, and the spores, along with some of the fluid from the stalk, are launched into the environment at somewhat remarkable speeds and distances. The spores can be dispersed up to 3 m from the original fungus. The spores can accelerate at 210,000 m per second squared. This is all especially impressive considering that the height of the stalk is generally less than 10 mm. A 2008 Aston Martin's top acceleration is about 6.5 m per second squared.

If the spores encounter grass or plant material after being shot out of their cannon, they can stick. And in this way, the grazing herbivores, whose dung is home, are likely to eat the spores. The spores pass through the gut of the herbivore unharmed and begin to grow when they are deposited in dung. The fungi are also phototropic; the stalks grow toward light and release their spores toward light very accurately. This is not because the fungi get energy from the Sun. Instead, phototropy increases the likelihood that released spores will land in sunny areas full of plants that are appealing to herbivores. The aerial skills (and even the phototropism) of *Pilobolus* spores even inspired the modern dance group of the same name (see Box 18.2).

## Parasitic Fungi Are Important Pathogens of Plants, Animals, and Even Other Fungi

Parasitic fungi get their food from another living organism **(Figure 18.13)**. Well, at least the organism is alive when the fungus initially inoculates it. There are many thousands of species of parasitic fungi, but all can be categorized as either **necrotrophs** or **biotrophs**. Necrotrophs kill part (or all) of their host and feed off the dead tissue. Most necrotrophs do this by secreting toxins to kill tissue, followed by the digestive enzymes to break it down. Biotrophs are not necessarily fatal to their hosts or their host's tissues and instead of killing tissue first, these fungi continuously take some of the host's resources while leaving enough for the host to survive.

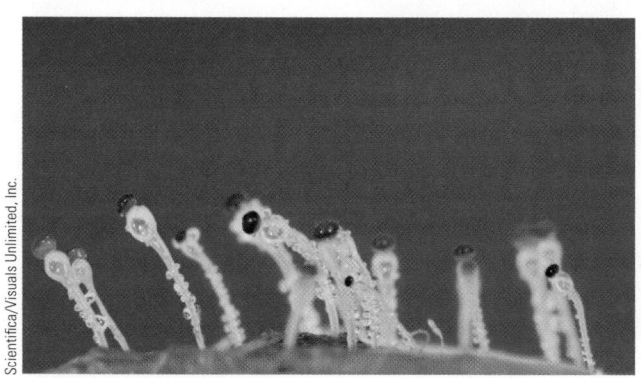

**FIGURE 18.12** The spore-producing cells (sporangia) and stalks of fungi in the genus *Pilobolus*.

**FIGURE 18.13** One fungus living off another.

Pilobolus, in addition to being the genus of a number of remarkable species of fungus, is also an innovative modern dance company. One of the dance company's founders, Jonathan Wolken, had a biophysicist for a father. He discovered the fungus *Pilobolus* working in his father's lab as a teenager. He describes the fungus, growing toward the light until it is ready to explode, as a metaphor for the dance company, which is known for its energetic, athletic, quirky style, which often involves weight sharing and astounding lifts and shapes **(Figure 1)**.

The group was founded in 1971 at Dartmouth College in New Hampshire. Throughout its history, the company has fostered an interest in science, education, and biology, collaborating with the MIT Distributed Robotics Laboratory, Radiolab, and others. They performed a duet, "Symbiosis," as a TED Talk in 2005.

Pilobolus has gained international attention for its unique approach to dance, having performed at the Academy Awards and on a number of television shows. But it is not the only example of combining the art of modern dance with science. There is even an annual contest called Dance Your PhD, where scientists and dancers perform works based on real research projects.

Photo of Pilobolus Dance Theater by John Kane/Silver Sun Studio

**FIGURE 1** Performers from the dance group Pilobolus.

Parasitic fungi have also long been of interest in agriculture. Fungi are, in fact, the agents responsible for most plant diseases, and these parasites can cause crop losses pre- and post-harvest. Fungal parasites that are plant pathogens include many diseases that you may have heard of—rusts and smuts, for example **(Figure 18.14)**. Rusts and smuts have been responsible for large crop losses in agriculture. In the Middle Ages, many wheat crops were lost when plants were infected with what is now known to be stinking smut (fungi in the genus *Tilletia*). In the 1950s, stem rust (*Puccinia graminis tritici*) greatly reduced many wheat harvests

Damian Herde/Shutterstock.com

Nataliia Melnychuk/Shutterstock.com

**FIGURE 18.14** Rusts and smuts. **(a)** An example of a rust, with the powdery, orange-coloured spores visible. **(b)** Corn smut (*Ustilago maydis*), a delicacy in Mexico.

across the Canadian prairies, causing losses of many millions of bushels.

Rusts and smuts are both biotrophic parasites that attack growing plants and so are responsible for pre-harvest losses. There are thousands of species of both smuts and rusts. Rusts are named for the yellow or orange spores that many release. Corn smut (*Ustilago maydis*) is a smut species that has been a pest for North American corn crops (Figure 18.14). However, whereas farmers in Canada and the United States work hard to eradicate it, Mexican growers are often able to sell infected crops for more money than crops without infection. *Huitlacoche*, as the fungus is called in Mexico, is a prized delicacy that is incorporated into cooking and can even be found canned in supermarkets.

Fungi are also important animal parasites. You saw this with chytridiomycosis in amphibians and white-nose syndrome in bats at the beginning of this chapter. Many parasitic fungal species also infect terrestrial invertebrates, such as ants or larvae, eventually killing their hosts and rupturing their hosts' bodies by extending fruiting bodies through them, with which they can disperse spores. A number of species from the genus *Ophiocordyceps* are known to infect ants **(Figure 18.15)**.

As the ants progress in their infection, the parasite is able to manipulate its behaviour, leading the fungus to be called a zombie or brain-manipulating fungus. The ants die only after climbing to some exposed surface—a leaf of a shrub, for example, or a tall grass—and biting onto the substrate. This allows for better spore dispersal by the fungus, perhaps even improving the rate of infection of other ants.

## Mycorrhizal Fungi Are Essential to the Survival and Success of Many Plants

Like parasitic fungi, mycorrhizal (*myco-* means fungus and *-rhiza* means roots) fungi obtain energy from other organisms. In this case, however, the relationship forms between the fungus and plant roots and is beneficial to

**FIGURE 18.15** An ant infected by a brain-controlling fungus of the genus *Ophiocordyceps* in Malaysia.

**FIGURE 18.16** Effect of mycorrhizal fungi on plant growth. The 6-month-old juniper seedlings on the left were grown in sterilized low-phosphorus soil inoculated without a mycorrhizal fungus. The seedlings on the right were grown under the same conditions but with the fungus.

both organisms. This type of symbiosis benefits both the host and the symbiont and is known as a mutualism (see Chapter 2 for additional details about mutualisms and mycorrhizae). The fungus obtains carbon compounds from the roots, and the plant is able to get additional water and mineral nutrients from the fungus. These fungi effectively increase the surface area through which water and nutrients can be taken up from the soil **(Figure 18.16)**.

Fungi are also good at quickly reaching and exploring hot spots of nutrients in soils. Shallow soils full of organic matter, for example, are also often full of the hyphae of mycorrhizal fungi. At least 80% of plant species are thought to have mycorrhizal partners, and these associations are ancient. Fossil evidence of mycorrhizal fungi and plant roots has been found from more than 400 million years ago.

Most mycorrhizal fungi fall into one of two groups. In one group, the fungal hyphae wrap themselves around the cells inside plant roots but do not penetrate the cells. This type of mycorrhizal fungi is called **ectomycorrhizae** (*ecto-* means outside). Most ectomycorrhizal fungi are basidiomycetes, and there are also some ascomycetes in this group. In the other group, the hyphae do penetrate the roots directly. This type of mycorrhizal fungi is called **endomycorrhizae** (*endo-* means inside). Endomycorrhizae are more common than ectomycorrhizae, and most are not basidiomycetes or ascomycetes. Most endomycorrhizae are **arbuscular mycorrhizae**. Arbuscular mycorrhizae are named for the structures, arbuscles, that grow inside the cell walls of plant root cells. Arbuscles are branching and bushy structures and are the interface where nutrients and carbon compounds are exchanged between the fungus and the plant **(Figure 18.17, p. 402)**.

Some plants are so dependent on fungal partners that they have lost their chlorophyll and photosynthetic

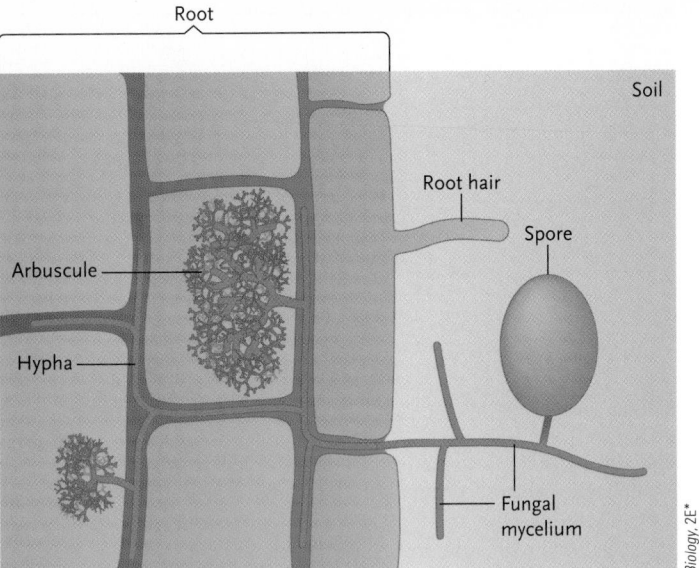

FIGURE 18.17 A fungus forming a mycorrhiza. Notice the arbuscules that have formed as fungal hyphae branch after entering the root.

capacity **(Figure 18.18)**. These plants depend on mycorrhizae not just for water and nutrients but for carbon as well, changing the relationship between these organisms to one that is costly to the fungus and therefore a parasitism. Orchids, a diverse plant group making up almost 10% of plant species, also have a unique and dependent relationship with fungal symbionts. Most orchid seedlings lack chlorophyll and the ability to photosynthesize. During this early life stage, the orchids are completely dependent on fungal partners. This relationship becomes less important and is sometimes abandoned in later

FIGURE 18.18 A parasitic plant, Indian pipe (*Monotropa uniflora*), that has lost its ability to photosynthesize and instead depends on mycorrhizal fungi for energy.

growth stages of the orchid but seems a clear example of parasitism by the orchid seedlings. All of the identified fungi in these symbioses can survive without the orchid partner, whereas the orchid partner cannot.

## Lichens Play Important Roles in Harsh Environments

Lichens are composite organisms made of usually two and sometimes three partners (symbionts). A fungus is one of the symbionts, and the other is algae or cyanobacteria. Because the algae or cyanobacteria can photosynthesize, they provide the lichen with energy, whereas the fungus provides structure, protection, and a way to attach to a substrate. In some instances, a fungal partner can be found with both algae and cyanobacteria. The large majority of lichens are ascomycetes (approximately 98%). Lichens are found worldwide and often occupy habitats that other organisms cannot colonize. You have probably seen lichens on bare rock, for example, or on tree bark, bare soil, or bones, to name only a few.

In large part because of their ability to colonize what are often harsh or inhospitable habitats, lichens play an important role in many ecosystems. They can prevent soil erosion, for example. Also, because cyanobacteria can take atmospheric nitrogen and convert it into forms that are available to organisms, they can contribute to the nutrient pool of an ecosystem, helping increase productivity.

A lichen body is usually made up of three layers **(Figure 18.19)**. The first, the outer layer, is called the **cortex**. This layer is fungal tissue and is strong and tough, giving the lichen structure and protecting it from harsh environmental conditions. The photosynthetic partner is found in the second layer. The third layer in many lichens is a layer of hyphae that attaches the lichen to its substrate. In some lichens, however, there is a second cortex adding protection for lichen bodies that are not flush against their substrate.

Lichen reproduction, like reproduction in many fungi, can be asexual or sexual. In some lichens, the fungal partner produces sexual spores similar to the process in other fungi. The problem with this strategy, however is that the partnership is not propagated with the spores. The fungi are capable of finding new partners in some cases, but many spores do not and are not successful. Some lichens have specialized structures for asexual reproduction. **Isidia** are structures that contain both the fungal and the photosynthetic partner and that extend from the **thallus**. These isidia can easily break off and can thus serve to propagate the lichen. **Soredia**, similarly, are propagules that contain both the fungal and the photosynthetic partner. The soredia are powdery and can also be dispersed from the lichen to establish a new lichen. Some lichens are propagated simply by chance when pieces of the lichen are broken off and re-establish elsewhere.

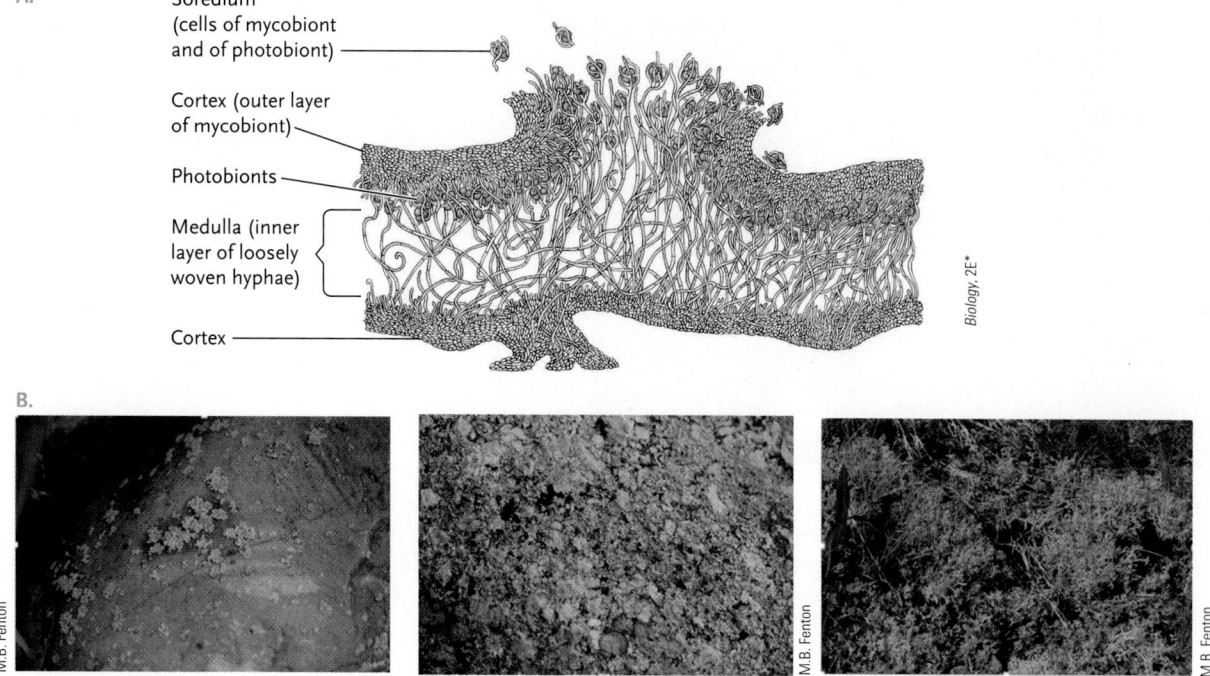

**A.**

Soredium
(cells of mycobiont
and of photobiont)

Cortex (outer layer
of mycobiont)

Photobionts

Medulla (inner
layer of loosely
woven hyphae)

Cortex

*Biology, 2E\**

**B.**

M.B. Fenton

M.B. Fenton

M.B. Fenton

**FIGURE 18.19 (a)** Diagram of a cross section through a lichen, *Lobaria verrucosa*. **(b)** Lichens come in many shapes, ranging from crustose, flush against a substrate, to more leaflike, or foliose.

Many animals use lichen as a food source, as a material to build nests, and as camouflage. In Canada, lichens are an important food source for caribou, particularly during winter. During winter, lichens often make up more than 50% and sometimes more than 80% of a caribou's diet.

The native people of North America have also traditionally used lichens, most often as a dye and, in some cases, medicinally. Along the northern Pacific coast of British Columbia, wolf lichens were used as the brown dye to create the well-known Chilkat dancing blankets created by the Tlingit and other groups. Lichens are also used as folk remedies, with the first written record of the use of lichens in medicine from 1673. A number of substances produced by lichens have antimicrobial properties and have been used as an antibiotic for wound and burn dressing.

Today, lichens are rarely used in these traditional ways; instead, they are used as indicators of air quality. Lichens can absorb particulates from the atmosphere. Because lichens do not have roots and do not take up material from soils or other substrates, any contamination with heavy metals, for example, or other chemicals can be attributed to the atmosphere.

## STUDY BREAK

1. What are two types of symbioses between a fungus and another organism?
2. Why do fungal parasites matter to agriculture?
3. What is a lichen?

## 18.6 Humans and Fungi

### Foraging for and Eating Mushrooms Is Rewarding, but Be Careful

Eating mushrooms has been a pastime of people likely as long as there have been people. Throughout the world, people use both cultivated and wild mushrooms in a variety of ways. As was mentioned earlier, the large majority of mushrooms available from grocery stores, particularly in North America, are the species *Agaricus bisporus*. Wild mushrooms such as morels (*Morchella esculenta*) have been becoming increasingly popular and increasingly valuable **(Figure 18.20)**.

Daniel K. Riskin

**FIGURE 18.20** Foraging for wild mushrooms. This fungus is the giant puffball (*Calvatia gigantea*).

A.

B.

Phototribe/Shutterstock.com

Richard Peterson/Shutterstock.com

**FIGURE 18.21** Several species of *Amanita* mushrooms, known as the destroying angels or **(a)** the death cap (*Amanita phalloides*), have a cap, stalk, and volva (the white casing around the base of the stalk) similar to those of the **(b)** paddy straw mushrooms (*Volvariella volvacea*), an edible mushroom from Southeast Asia. The two mushrooms do have distinguishing features, including their spore colour. Spore prints can be made by placing a mushroom cap on a white piece of paper. The colour of spores is often used in mushroom identification.

Foraging for wild mushrooms still has a caché as a bit of a wild and risky pastime. There are many mushrooms that you should not eat or even touch because they are deadly poisonous. Good examples are certain species in the genus *Amanita*. In 2007, in Minnesota, the United States, seven people were taken ill, and one, a 10-year old girl, died after ingesting mushroom soup made with *Amanita bisporigera*, sometimes known as the destroying angel. The group was a Hmong family from Southeast Asia that mistook the mushroom for common, edible, Asian mushrooms called paddy straw mushrooms **(Figure 18.21)**.

However, only five or six identified mushroom species in North America are lethally poisonous. Many are edible, with no side effects; many others will make you very sick or very sleepy; and the effect of others lies somewhere in between.

In many cases, identification of edible mushrooms involves not only accurately assessing the macroscopic features of the mushrooms (the shape of the cap and stalk, for example, or the presence of a volva; Figure 18.6) but also the identification of microscopic features. Some mushrooms must be distinguished by the colour of their spores. This is true for what are often called the little brown mushrooms, which include that fabled fungus, the "magic mushroom." These little brown mushrooms are common and are mostly saprotrophs. They are well known for growing on dung, for example. Many species of little brown mushrooms are capable of inducing serious illness, and it is difficult to distinguish the species from one another. The mushrooms that cause hallucinations are in the genus *Psilocybe*, and the compound psilocybin is responsible for those psychedelic effects.

## Mildew and Mould Are Household Hazards

Mould and mildew occur on a variety of surfaces inside and out **(Figure 18.22)**. In your home, you have likely smelled mildew on damp towels and have probably encountered food covered with mould in the back of your refrigerator. Both mould and mildew are fungi. Mildews are mould fungi that have not developed visible spores or mycelium. There are a number of species in a number of fungal phyla that can be found as mildew or mould in your home. To grow these fungi requires what any fungi require: temperatures that are not too hot or too cold, the right amount of humidity, and nutrients. The surfaces of many objects in your homes have enough nutrients to feed a fungus, and it is difficult to make the temperature of your home inhospitable to fungi, so you can best prevent mould and mildew by controlling the humidity in your home. Most mould that you find can be removed easily with soap and water or a bleach solution.

U.S. Environmental Protection Agency

**FIGURE 18.22** Mould growth following flooding.

Mildew and mould can decrease your indoor air quality and can affect your health. There will always be fungal spores in the air around you. Moulds and their spores, however, have been shown to trigger respiratory ailments, particularly in people who have, or are genetically predisposed to develop, asthma. Respiratory infections caused by moulds are especially risky for immunocompromised people.

Even moulds are not all bad, however. You may be familiar with the story of Alexander Fleming, a medical doctor and bacteriologist from Scotland in the early 20th century. In 1928, Fleming returned to his lab after some time away and observed a blue-green mould in a petri dish containing a pathogenic bacteria. The mould made a ring around the bacteria and, most interestingly, surrounding the fungus was an area void of bacteria. Fleming had serendipitously discovered the antimicrobial properties of fungus in the genus *Penicillium* from which penicillin is derived. Even in our homes today, fungi in the genus *Penicillium* are common causes of mildew and mould. Fleming's discovery is considered one of the most important milestones in microbiology and in the treatment of disease, and he was awarded the Nobel Prize in 1945.

## PUTTING IT IN PERSPECTIVE

Fungi are unique, and we have much to learn about their diversity and biology. These organisms spend much of their lives invisible to humans, yet they are critical components of nearly all ecosystems and affect our crops, our food, and even our health. Understanding how they work and the roles that they play has even helped us clean up polluted soils. Fungi can be used to remediate former industrial sites or the sites of pollutant spills. Because fungi absorb nutrients from their substrates, they are capable of taking up heavy metals and other compounds from soils. These fungi can then be harvested, removing these compounds permanently. In this chapter, you have been introduced to the sometimes surprising biology of fungi. In the next chapter, you will be introduced to the biology of fungi's closest relatives, the animals.

## KEY CONCEPTS REVIEW AND QUESTIONS

### 18.1 Fungal Diversity and Characteristics

Fungi are diverse and unique organisms. Fungi are found in all shapes and sizes and range from unicellular individuals to individuals that cover many square kilometres in area. Fungi have many characteristics that they share with both plants and animals, as well as characteristics that are unique. Much remains unknown about fungal diversity.

1. List three characteristics shared among all fungi.
2. What is a yeast?
3. Are fungi autotrophs or heterotrophs?

### 18.2 Fungal Structure

The majority of fungal biomass for multicellular fungi is found underground or within another growth substrate. Fungal bodies are made up of the filaments called hyphae that extend through the substrate. These filaments make dense networks of fungi called mycelium. The mushrooms with which we are familiar are the above-ground reproductive structures of fungal mycelium.

4. Draw a diagram of filamentous fungi, including what is underground and a fruiting body.
5. What is chitin?
6. How does a fungus obtain water and nutrients?

### 18.3 Fungal Reproduction

Sexual reproduction in filamentous, multicellular fungi includes the fusion of fungal hyphae, fusion of the cellular nuclei, spore production, spore dispersal, and the establishment of new fungal mycelia.

7. Match the term with the definition.
   a. Plasmogamy        ___ The fusion of nuclei
   b. Karyogamy         ___ Containing one set of chromosomes
   c. Dikaryon cell     ___ A fungus with two dissimilar nuclei
   d. Haploid           ___ The fusion of hyphae

8. What are two differences between fungal and animal reproduction?

### 18.4 Fungal Classification

It has been difficult to identify and classify species of fungi. For many years, scientists depended on the macroscopic features of fungi, particularly the fruiting bodies and reproductive structures, for identification. Many species, however, do not produce such structures or cannot be cultured in laboratories to produce them. In recent years, molecular techniques have allowed for an explosion of fungal identification and classification that has made the phylogeny of fungal diversity even more interesting as well as more mysterious. However, two groups of fungi represent many of the species with which we are most familiar: the mushroom-producing fungi. These two groups, the Ascomycota and the Basidiomycota, are differentiated by their life cycles and reproductive structures.

9. What is the difference between basidia and asci?

10. Does karyogamy occur earlier in ascomycetes or basidiomycetes?

## 18.5 Fungal Lifestyles

Fungi play a number of essential roles in ecosystems. Fungi are the primary decomposers in most ecosystems. These saprotrophs are able to break down dead organic matter, including wood, leaf litter, animal carcasses, and many other materials. Many fungi are also involved in close interactions with other organisms called symbioses. These relationships can be beneficial to both organisms involved, or there can be a cost to one of the symbiotic partners. Two types of fungal symbioses, mycorrhizal associations between fungi and plants and lichens, are themselves essential to many ecosystems.

11. What is the difference between ectomycorrhizal fungi and endomycorrhizal fungi?

12. Describe two fungal parasites of humans.

13. What are three ecosystem services provided by lichens?

## 18.6 Humans and Fungi

Humans interact with different types of fungi every day. We eat mushrooms and other food products made with fungi, such as bread, beer, and wine. We also deal with fungi in our homes, trying to get rid of mildew from our towels and throwing away mouldy food. Just like in ecosystems, fungi are both beneficial and detrimental to our lives.

14. Name three ways humans exploit three different types of fungi for their benefit.

15. Name three ways three different types of fungi are detrimental to humans.

Now that you have read and reviewed this chapter, we encourage you to attempt to build a concept map using these key concepts and indicate the connections between them. See Chapter 5 for some examples.

# Animals

## WHY IT MATTERS

How do we know an animal is an animal? Many animals, even fossilized ones such as the *Tyrannosaurus rex*, we recognize as animals. Their features are familiar to us. But what defines an animal? The T. Rex is relatively easy; it had an internal skeleton, like we do. The only organisms with internal skeletons are animals; we call them vertebrate animals. But, certainly, not all animals have this kind of skeleton. Insects do not. Worms do not. Nor do sponges. What do we and all of these other animals have in common?

Animals are multicellular organisms. All are mobile, or can move, at least at some stage of their life cycle. All are heterotrophs, meaning that they must consume food for energy, unlike plants, which are autotrophs and can gain energy from the Sun (see Chapter 6 for an overview of plant and animal cells). Like plants and fungi, animal cells are eukaryotic (contain a membrane-bound nucleus and organelles), but unlike plants and fungi, animal cells do not have a rigid cell wall. A huge range of organisms with very diverse body plans—or basic body shapes—fit into this definition of animals.

We classify animals into groups called phyla (plural of phylum; see Chapter 12 for a review of classification). As we will see below, animals can be classified based on a number of features of their body plans.

Usually, we have to look beyond the immediate appearance of an animal to decide to which phylum it belongs. If you were to see an animal shaped like a "worm" **(Figure 19.1)**, you could place it in one of several phyla, unless you knew more about its size, internal structure, life stage, and perhaps even its DNA.

In this chapter, we will see that the diversity of animals is astonishing. We will introduce you to animals and provide you with some background about how they are organized and how they work. We progress from an overview of body plans and tissue and organ types to an overview of several different animal phyla, including some details on what features are shared by the members of each phyla and an example of at least one animal from each phyla. We finish by showing how the fossil record helps us understand the history of animals and their evolutionary relationships. To facilitate appreciating the

**A. *Dermophis mexicanus***

**B. *Contia tenuis***

Suzanne L. Collins/Science Source

**FIGURE 19.1** Animals with wormlike bodies. Included are an amphibian (giant land caecilian, *Dermophis mexicana*) **(a)**, and a reptile, a sharp-tailed snake (*Contia tenuis*) **(b)**.

diversity of animals, use the information presented below to highlight the similarities and differences among animals. Consider how these reflect lifestyle.

## 19.1   The Animal Organ Systems

Every cell in a body must receive the nutrients it needs for survival and must eliminate its wastes. For many small invertebrates, each cell is close enough to the surface of the animal that these transactions can occur by simple diffusion between the cells and their environment. For large complex organisms such as vertebrates, however, 12 specialized organ systems work in a cooperative fashion to meet all of an animal's needs. Although each system has a primary function, most serve more than one role, and all work together in an integrated fashion. Here we provide a brief description of the role of each of the 12 organ systems found in vertebrate animals. Versions of some of these systems are found in other animals as well.

1. The **integumentary system** protects the body against mechanical damage and infection. It also has other roles, including protection from UV light and cryptic/warning or camouflage colouration. In certain animals, it plays a role in osmotic regulation (water balance), excretion, gas and ion exchange, and heat exchange. It is a versatile organ system. In humans, the skin makes up our integumentary system.

2. The **skeletal system** provides support for the body. It also functions as the levers that muscles attach to, to produce movement. In addition, it protects certain vital organs, such as the brain, heart, and lungs.

3. The **muscular system** produces movement. This includes both movement of the limbs (skeletal muscle) and movement of food through the digestive system (smooth muscle) and blood throughout the body (cardiac and smooth muscle). Muscles also maintain posture and can produce heat.

4. The **digestive system** ingests food, breaks it down and absorbs nutrients, and eliminates undigested material.

5. The **urinary system** or excretory system eliminates the waste products of nitrogen metabolism and plays a key role in regulating pH and water and ion balance.

6. The **reproductive system** produces eggs and sperm in females and males, respectively. It also produces key hormones that play roles in the development of secondary sexual characteristics as well as regulate pregnancy and birth.

7. The **respiratory system** is involved in gas exchange, ensuring that adequate oxygen is taken up from the environment to produce ATP and that the carbon dioxide formed from metabolism is eliminated.

8. The **circulatory system** distributes compounds between the specialized exchange surfaces and all the cells of the body. For instance, it delivers oxygen from the lungs to the cells and carries waste products from the cells to the excretory sites. It moves hormones from their sites of secretion to their sites of action and moves nutrients either to storage sites or to metabolically active cells as required.

9. The **lymphatic system** ensures that all excess fluids are removed from the tissues and returned to the circulatory system. It plays a key role in the immune system.

10. The **immune system** protects the body against bacteria, viruses, and other infectious agents.

11. The **endocrine system** secretes chemical messengers called hormones that regulate various body functions, such as metabolism, growth, and reproduction. It is one of two control systems in the body. In general, it regulates processes that are slow and long acting and involves many parts of the body.

12. The **nervous system** is the other control system. It is fast acting and regulates very specific activities, such as movement. It is involved in sensing the environment, integrating information, and producing coordinated responses to change.

Each system is composed of several organs that work together to perform each function (**Figure 19.2**). For instance, the digestive system is a complex system that requires the integrated action of several organs, including the mouth, esophagus, stomach, and intestines working together with the liver, gallbladder, and pancreas. The circulatory system requires the integrated action of the heart, along with the regulation of blood flow through the arteries, capillary beds, and veins in each organ of the body.

## STUDY BREAK

1. List the major organ systems of animals.
2. Which is the most important system?

---

## 19.2 Animal Tissues

Despite the large number of organs and organ systems found in animals, all are composed of various combinations of only four types of tissue: epithelial tissue, connective tissue, muscle tissue, and nervous tissue. The primary differences in the structure and function of each tissue reflect differences in the structure and organization of the cytoskeleton within the cells, the type and organization of the extracellular matrix surrounding the cell (a variety of proteins and glycoproteins secreted by the cells), and the junctions holding the cells together (see Chapter 3 for a review). The extracellular matrix provides support and shape for tissues and organs.

Animals, like plants, are covered by an outer protective epidermal layer of **epithelial tissue (Figure 19.3, p. 412)** that acts as a defence against physical damage and infectious agents. This tissue also covers the sur-

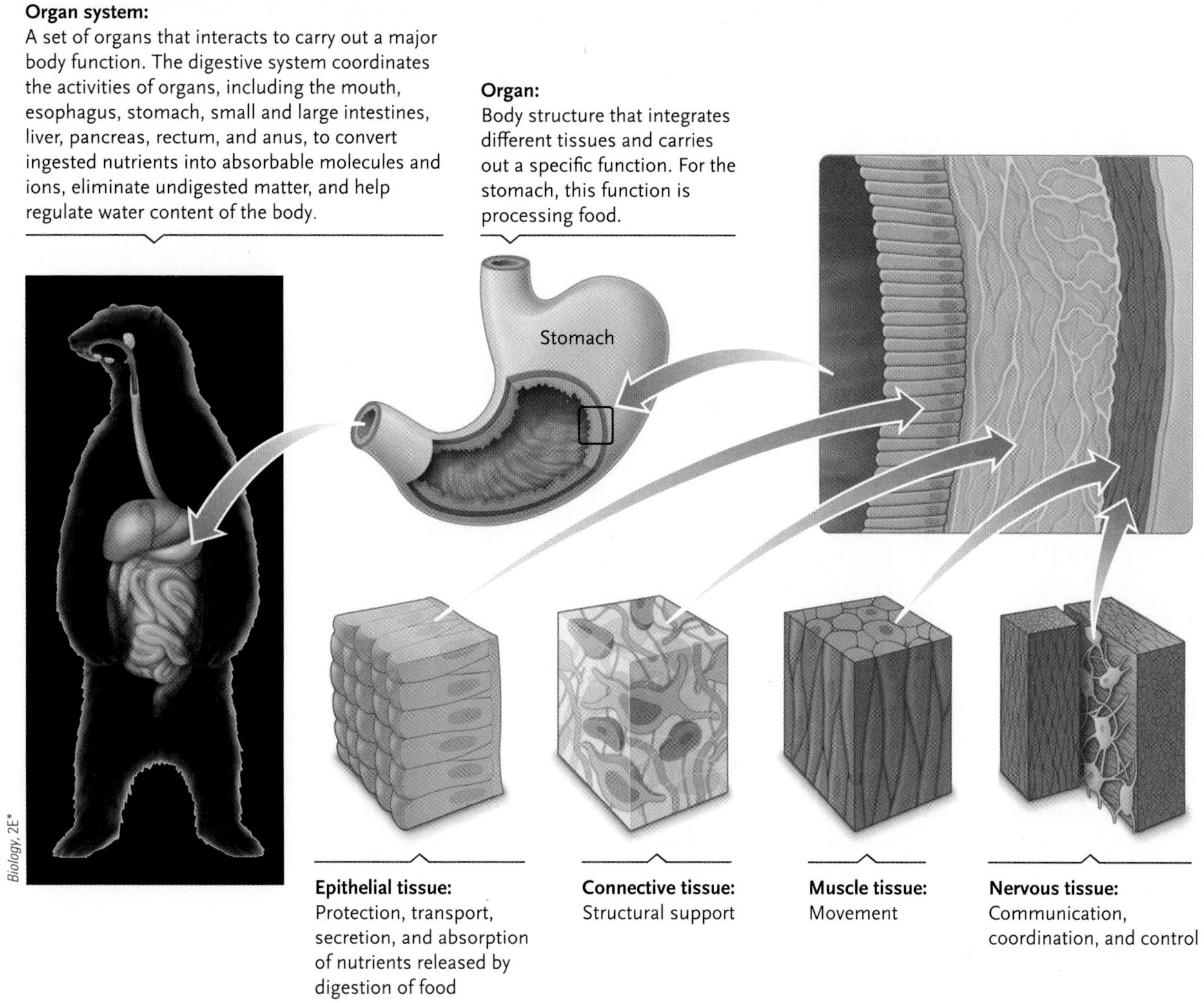

**Organ system:**
A set of organs that interacts to carry out a major body function. The digestive system coordinates the activities of organs, including the mouth, esophagus, stomach, small and large intestines, liver, pancreas, rectum, and anus, to convert ingested nutrients into absorbable molecules and ions, eliminate undigested matter, and help regulate water content of the body.

**Organ:**
Body structure that integrates different tissues and carries out a specific function. For the stomach, this function is processing food.

Stomach

*Biology, 2E\**

**Epithelial tissue:**
Protection, transport, secretion, and absorption of nutrients released by digestion of food

**Connective tissue:**
Structural support

**Muscle tissue:**
Movement

**Nervous tissue:**
Communication, coordination, and control

**FIGURE 19.2** The organization of animal cells into tissues, organs, and organ systems as illustrated by the digestive system. This also demonstrates the different general types of tissues.

faces of internal organs and lines the cavities and ducts within the bodies of animals. The structure of the epidermis depends on its function. It can be a thin, mucus-covered layer of live cells that allow exchange of substances with the environment. Or it can be a thick, protein-reinforced (keratinized) layer of dead cells that serves for protection, with limited ability for exchange (Figure 19.3). The lining of the intestine and the skin of amphibians are examples of thin epithelium that is composed of living cells that must divide constantly to replace worn and dying cells. These epithelia typically contain secretory cells or glands that produce things such as mucus, digestive enzymes, or hormones. The outer epithelial surface in internal cavities and ducts is often covered with cilia—small hairs that generate fluid currents—or with villi or microvilli—folds that increase the area available for secretion or absorption. The scales of fish and reptiles, the feathers of birds, and the hair, claws, hooves, horns, and fingernails of mammals are examples of thick epithelium that is a tough

layer of dead cells reinforced with fibrous proteins (Figure 19.3).

**Connective tissue** consists of cells that form networks or layers in and around body structures, to provide support **(Figure 19.4, p. 412)**. Vertebrates have six major types of connective tissue: loose connective tissue, fibrous connective tissue, cartilage, bone, adipose tissue (fat), and blood. The structure of each type of connective tissue correlates with its function. For example, connective tissue with a lot of elastin fibres will be more elastic, allowing it to retain its shape. Elastin in the connective tissues in our lungs helps them return to their original shape after they deflate. On the other hand, connective tissue with a lot of collagen is very strong. Collagen provides strength to tendons, allowing them to transfer the force of muscle contraction to bones during movement.

Nervous tissue contains cells with ion channels that allow them to generate and transmit electrical signals. The primary cell type is called a **neuron** or nerve cell,

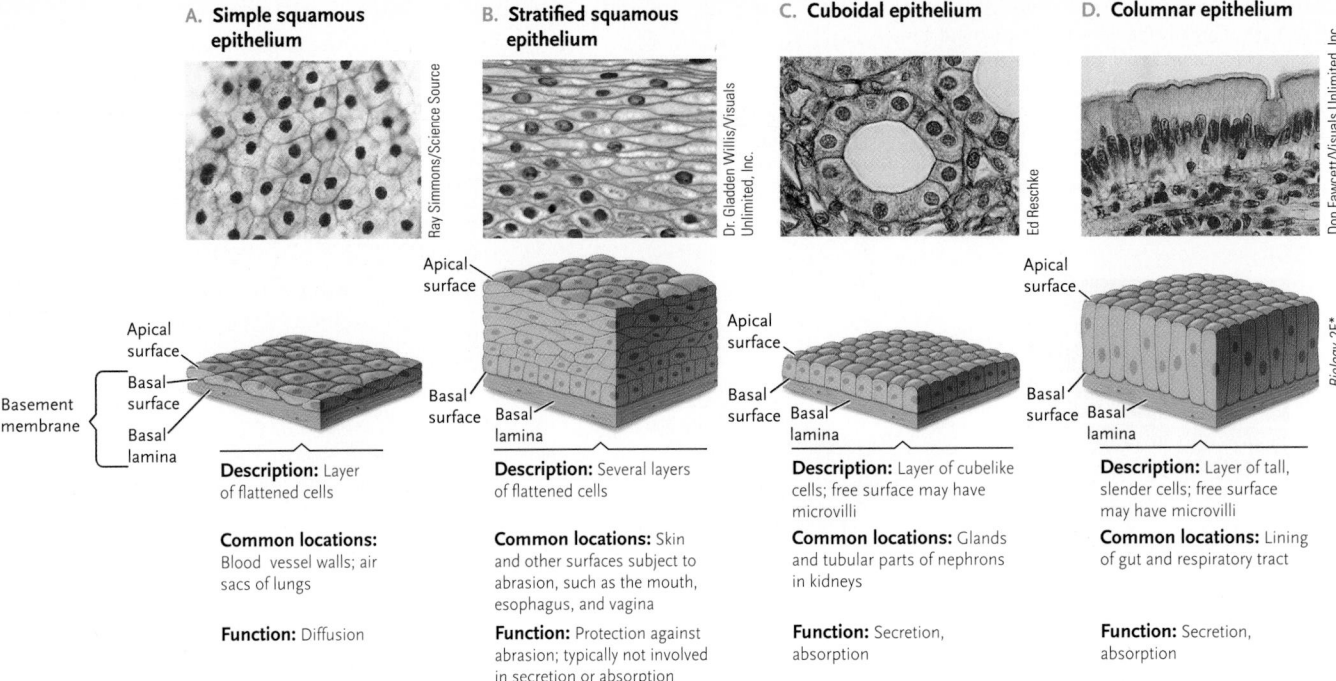

**A. Simple squamous epithelium**

Ray Simmons/Science Source

**B. Stratified squamous epithelium**

Dr. Gladden Willis/Visuals Unlimited, Inc.

**C. Cuboidal epithelium**

Ed Reschke

**D. Columnar epithelium**

Don Fawcett/Visuals Unlimited, Inc.

Biology, 2E*

Basement membrane { Apical surface / Basal surface / Basal lamina

**Description:** Layer of flattened cells

**Common locations:** Blood vessel walls; air sacs of lungs

**Function:** Diffusion

Apical surface / Basal surface / Basal lamina

**Description:** Several layers of flattened cells

**Common locations:** Skin and other surfaces subject to abrasion, such as the mouth, esophagus, and vagina

**Function:** Protection against abrasion; typically not involved in secretion or absorption

Apical surface / Basal surface / Basal lamina

**Description:** Layer of cubelike cells; free surface may have microvilli

**Common locations:** Glands and tubular parts of nephrons in kidneys

**Function:** Secretion, absorption

Apical surface / Basal surface / Basal lamina

**Description:** Layer of tall, slender cells; free surface may have microvilli

**Common locations:** Lining of gut and respiratory tract

**Function:** Secretion, absorption

**FIGURE 19.3** Principal types of epithelia.

which comes in many shapes and sizes. Many are extremely thin and long, allowing them to serve as lines of communication and control between body parts. Neurons may extend from a few micrometres to more than a metre. Neurons that connect limbs to the spinal cord in vertebrates such as elephants and giraffes can be extremely long.

**Muscle tissue** contains two proteins, **actin** and **myosin**, that allow the cells to shorten (contract). They also have membrane channels that make them excitable, or capable of transmitting electrical signals. Muscles are used to move body limbs and other structures, pump the blood, and produce a squeezing pressure in organs such as the intestine and uterus. There are

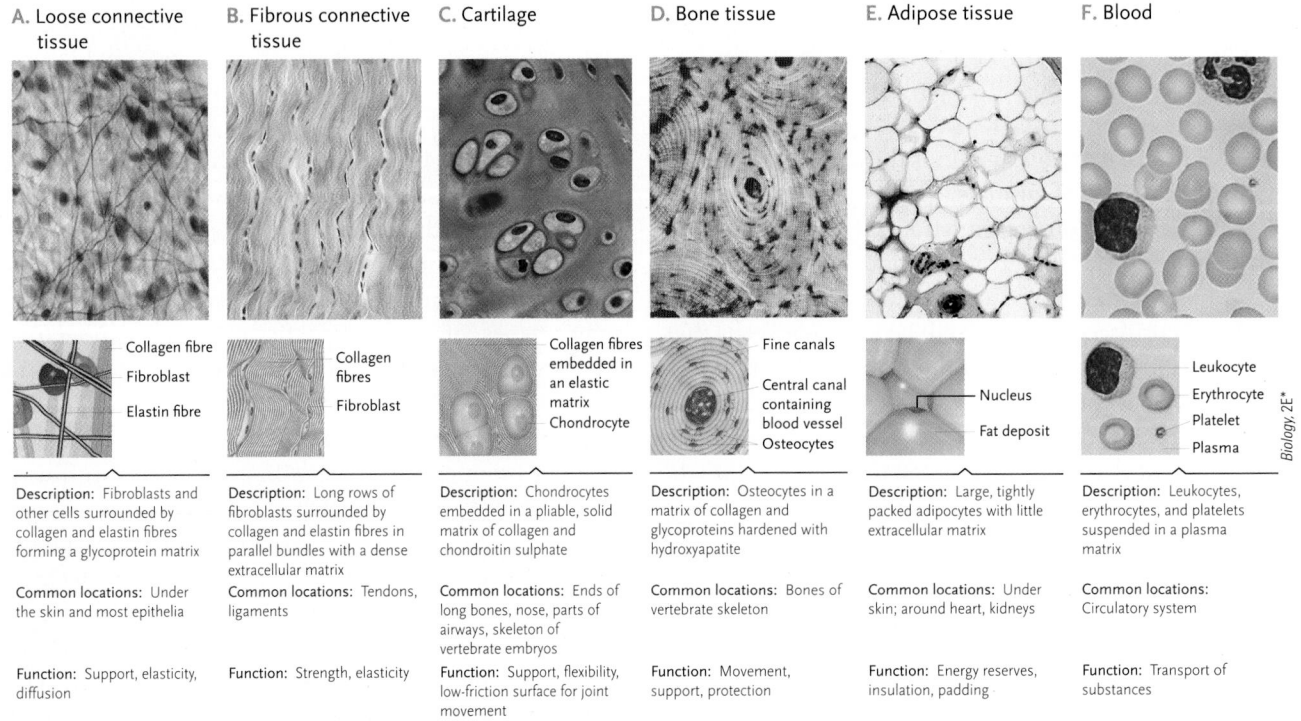

**A. Loose connective tissue**

Collagen fibre / Fibroblast / Elastin fibre

**Description:** Fibroblasts and other cells surrounded by collagen and elastin fibres forming a glycoprotein matrix

**Common locations:** Under the skin and most epithelia

**Function:** Support, elasticity, diffusion

**B. Fibrous connective tissue**

Collagen fibres / Fibroblast

**Description:** Long rows of fibroblasts surrounded by collagen and elastin fibres in parallel bundles with a dense extracellular matrix

**Common locations:** Tendons, ligaments

**Function:** Strength, elasticity

**C. Cartilage**

Collagen fibres embedded in an elastic matrix / Chondrocyte

**Description:** Chondrocytes embedded in a pliable, solid matrix of collagen and chondroitin sulphate

**Common locations:** Ends of long bones, nose, parts of airways, skeleton of vertebrate embryos

**Function:** Support, flexibility, low-friction surface for joint movement

**D. Bone tissue**

Fine canals / Central canal containing blood vessel / Osteocytes

**Description:** Osteocytes in a matrix of collagen and glycoproteins hardened with hydroxyapatite

**Common locations:** Bones of vertebrate skeleton

**Function:** Movement, support, protection

**E. Adipose tissue**

Nucleus / Fat deposit

**Description:** Large, tightly packed adipocytes with little extracellular matrix

**Common locations:** Under skin; around heart, kidneys

**Function:** Energy reserves, insulation, padding

**F. Blood**

Leukocyte / Erythrocyte / Platelet / Plasma

Biology, 2E*

**Description:** Leukocytes, erythrocytes, and platelets suspended in a plasma matrix

**Common locations:** Circulatory system

**Function:** Transport of substances

**FIGURE 19.4** The six major types of connective tissues in vertebrates.

SOURCE: (Photos A,B,D–F): Ed Reschke; (C): Ed Reschke/Photolibrary/Getty Images

three types of muscle tissue—skeletal, cardiac, and smooth—each with a slightly different structure and function.

All four major tissue types—epithelial, connective, nervous, and muscle—combine to form the organs and organ systems of animals, described in Section 19.1.

## STUDY BREAK

1. What are the major tissues of animals?
2. What are the main categories of tissues?
3. Prepare a table comparing the form and function of the major tissues of animals.

## 19.3 Animal Body Plans

The emergence of multicellular organisms was a fundamental early step in the evolution of animals. The earliest multicellular animals could have begun as a colony of protists in which dividing cells remained together. This is true of some modern protists, whose daughter cells do not disperse to become independent organisms. With multicellularity frequently came larger individual sizes, a support (skeletal) system, and increased mobility compared to unicellular animal-like protists. From these basic changes came other important developments in different animal groups, including the through gut (gastrovascular cavity) with both a mouth and an anus, bilateral symmetry, more complex nervous systems, additional body cavities, and cephalization through concentration of neural tissues in the anterior end. The developments that appear in a given organism define its **body plan.**

Just as organs and organ systems can be "packaged" differently in herbaceous and woody plants, so too can the organs and organ systems of animals be assembled in different ways into a body plan **(Figure 19.5, p. 414)**. Fundamental differences in body plan could include the following:

1. How many layers of tissues form the adult organism
2. Whether there is a coelom (body cavity)
3. Whether there is a digestive tract and, if so, whether it has one or two openings
4. Whether there is a **nerve** cord and, if so, whether it is solid or hollow
5. Whether there are limbs and, if so, what kind
6. Whether the animal is symmetrical and, if so, what kind of symmetry
7. What pattern of embryonic development the animal follows

Despite the tremendous diversity within the animal kingdom, there are only a few different types of body plan. Many different animals descend from a single common ancestor, and the common ancestry determines much of the basic similarity in body organization (see Section 19.1). In each case, the final organization represents a unique way of producing a group of highly adapted animals with distinct lifestyles and habitats. There are departures from each plan (parasites for instance), raising questions about why and how these deviations have occurred. Some of the diversity of body plans is illustrated by digestive and vascular cavities (Figure 19.5).

There are several aspects to an animal's body plan, including variation in the presence of cavities within the body (Figure 19.5). A **gastrovascular cavity** is a body cavity that combines the functions of digestion with the transport of nutrients and other particles. They are found in most animals. In animals such as most Platyhelminthes (flatworms; **Figure 19.5b**), there is no cavity between the lining of the gastrovascular cavity and the body wall. These animals are **acoelomate** (no coelom). In animals with a coelom **(Figure 19.5d)**, or **coelomate** animals, this cavity is separated from the body wall. In **pseudocoelomate** animals, or animals with a body cavity that has only some of the features of a true coelom **(Figure 19.5c)**, the cavity (pseudocoelom) forms between the gut and the body wall.

There is also variation in the numbers of layers of cells that form the tissues and organ systems in all animals. The tissues of humans and most other animals are all derived from three layers of cells: **endoderm**, **mesoderm**, and **ectoderm**. We call these animals triploblastic. The tissues of some animals, however, like the cnidarians **(Figure 19.5a)**, are derived from only two layers of tissues: endoderm and ectoderm. These animals are **diploblastic**.

Other features of different body plans include whether they are symmetrical, the number of openings to the gastrovascular cavity (one or two), and the presence of an obvious "head" ("cephalization"). To appreciate these differences, we need to know how we are looking at an animal. Biologists use terms such as "dorsal" (back), "ventral" (belly), "anterior" (head end), "posterior" (rear end), and "lateral" (sides) **(Figure 19.6, p. 415)** to describe places on the animal, or our views of it. Modifiers such as "proximal" (toward the animal's centre line) and "distal" (away from the centre line) are also useful.

There is great diversity in animal appendages. For example, among chordates, the Agnatha (hagfishes and lamprey eels) have no appendages (paired fins), nor did their known common ancestors. Other chordates, such as caecilians (a type of amphibian), snakes, and some lizards, also lack appendages (legs and arms), but their ancestors did have them, indicating that natural selection drove the loss of appendages over evolutionary time.

## A.

**Cnidarian body plans**

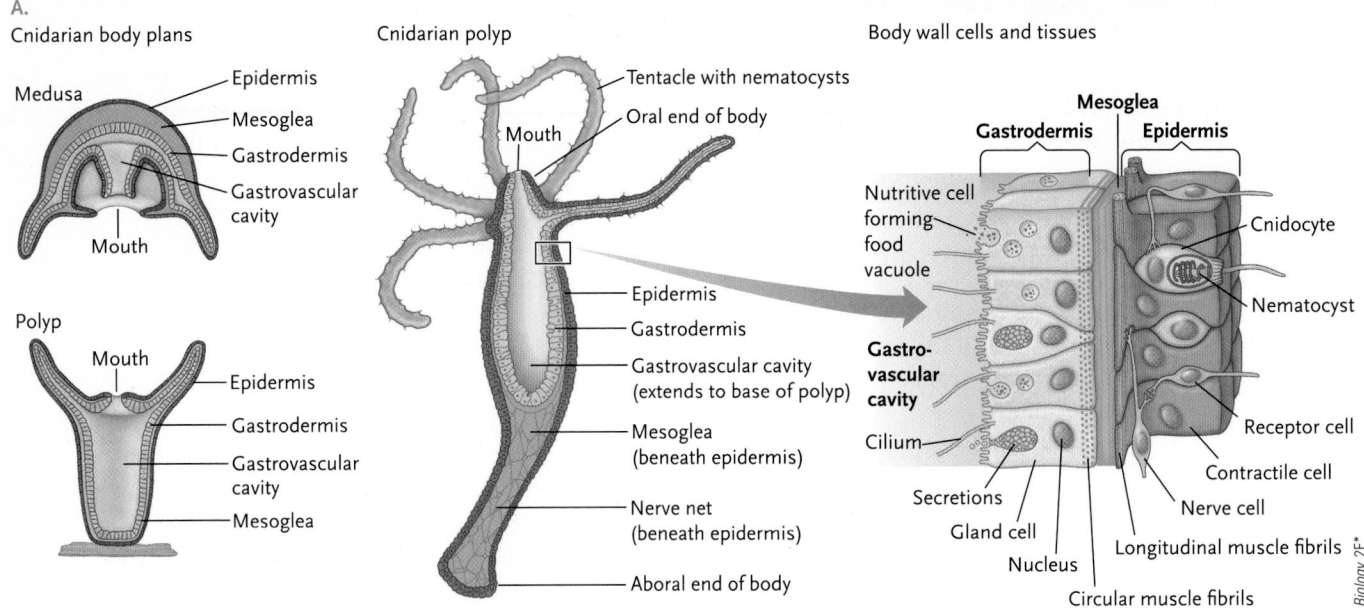

Medusa
- Epidermis
- Mesoglea
- Gastrodermis
- Gastrovascular cavity
- Mouth

Polyp
- Mouth
- Epidermis
- Gastrodermis
- Gastrovascular cavity
- Mesoglea

**Cnidarian polyp**
- Tentacle with nematocysts
- Oral end of body
- Mouth
- Epidermis
- Gastrodermis
- Gastrovascular cavity (extends to base of polyp)
- Mesoglea (beneath epidermis)
- Nerve net (beneath epidermis)
- Aboral end of body

**Body wall cells and tissues**

Mesoglea
Gastrodermis — Epidermis
- Nutritive cell forming food vacuole
- Cnidocyte
- Nematocyst
- Gastrovascular cavity
- Receptor cell
- Cilium
- Contractile cell
- Secretions
- Nerve cell
- Gland cell
- Longitudinal muscle fibrils
- Nucleus
- Circular muscle fibrils

*Biology, 2E*

**B.** In acoelomate animals, no body cavity separates the gut and body wall.

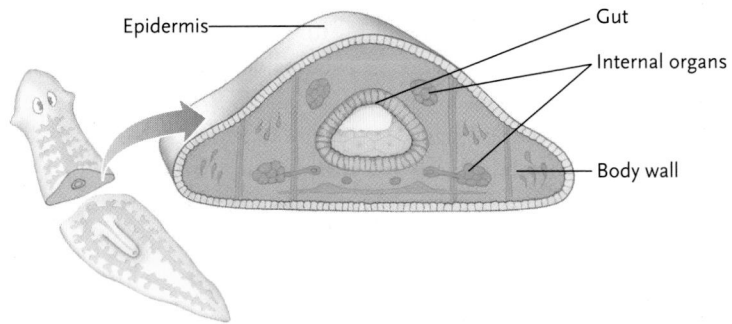

- Epidermis
- Gut
- Internal organs
- Body wall

**C.** In pseudocoelomate animals, the pseudocoelom forms between the gut (a derivative of endoderm) and the body wall (a derivative of mesoderm).

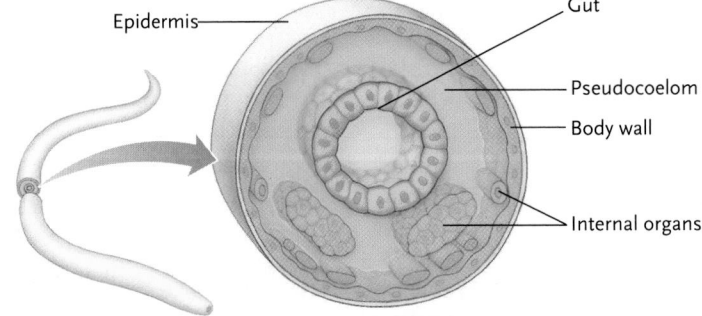

- Epidermis
- Gut
- Pseudocoelom
- Body wall
- Internal organs

**FIGURE 19.5** Combined digestive and vascular cavities (gastrovascular) and coelomic body cavities in a sample of animals: a cnidarian **(a)**, a flatworm (platyhelminth) **(b)**, a pseudocoelomate **(c)**, and an annelid **(d)**. The cnidarian and the platyhelminth are solid and have a gastrovascular cavity, whereas the pseudocoelomate and annelid have a coelom in addition to the gastrovascular cavity.

**D.** In coelomate animals, the coelom is completely lined by peritoneum (a derivative of mesoderm).

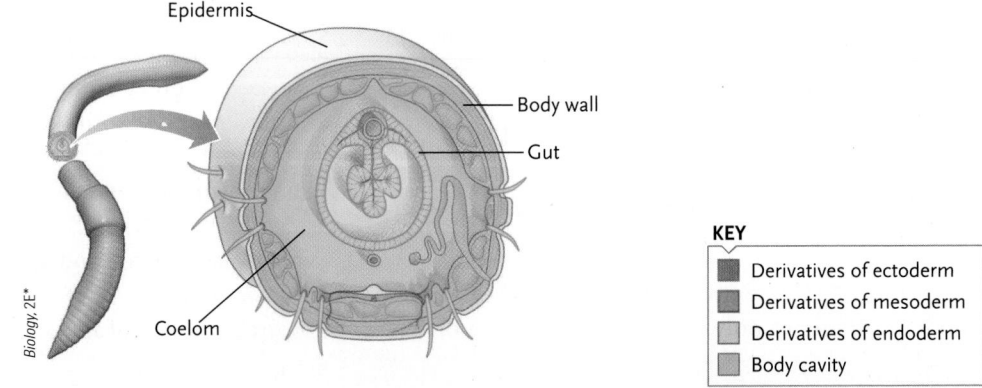

- Epidermis
- Body wall
- Gut
- Coelom

*Biology, 2E*

**KEY**
- Derivatives of ectoderm
- Derivatives of mesoderm
- Derivatives of endoderm
- Body cavity

The joint-legged appendages are characteristic of Arthropods. Centipedes, millipedes, and some crustaceans have many pairs of appendages, spiders and scorpions have four pairs, and insects typically have three pairs.

A few animals are **asymmetrical**, meaning that there is no obvious front or back, top or bottom **(Figure 19.6c)**. Most animals, however, are symmetrical, meaning that they can be divided into two or more matching parts. Some animals are **radially symmetrical (Figure 19.6a)**, like a sea star, with several matching parts that radiate out from a central point. Phyla of radially symmetrical animals are grouped together as the radiata. Most animals are **bilaterally symmetrical**, like humans, with two halves mirroring one another **(Figure 19.6b)**. Phyla of bilaterally symmetrical animals are grouped together as bilateria.

There are two main patterns of development among the bilateria: **protostome** and **deuterostome** development. We will discuss these two patterns of development further in Chapter 28. The primary difference between them is in the way the coelom develops.

Some animals have only one opening to their internal gastrovascular cavity through which food enters and waste leaves, such as in sea anemones and flatworms. The gastrovascular cavity of many animals has two openings, one through which food enters (by definition, the **mouth**) and one through which waste is expelled (by definition, the **anus**). Many, if not most, animals have a skeleton, which may be external (**exoskeleton**) or internal (**endoskeleton**) or a combination of both.

In any particular species, secondary modifications may have changed or even eliminated some features. For example, both tapeworms (phylum Platyhelminthes) and some species of marine bivalves (genus *Solemya*, phylum Mollusca) lack digestive tracts, although their ancestors did have digestive tracts. Natural selection favoured more and more reductions in their digestive systems over time because these animals live in a rich medium of food that they can absorb across the surfaces of their bodies.

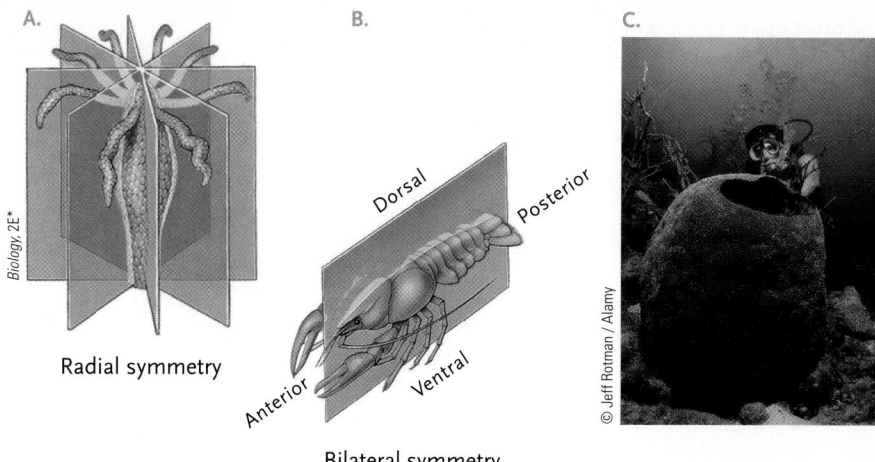

**FIGURE 19.6** Orientation and symmetry in animals, including **(a)** a radially symmetrical cnidarian, **(b)** a bilaterally symmetrical arthropod, and **(c)** an asymmetrical stinker vase sponge (*Ircinia campana*). Also shown in (b) are dorsal, ventral, anterior, and posterior orientations.

## 19.4 The Major Groups of Animals

Biologists now recognize about 30 phyla of animals **(Table 19.1, p. 416)**. Some are familiar to us, such as the ones that include birds, snakes or fish (phylum Chordata), or insects (phylum Arthropoda). Others are less familiar, such as beard worms (phylum Pogonophora) or penis worms (phylum Priapulida). Species classified in the same phylum share diagnostic features, even if these features are not immediately obvious. For example, three features of animals in the phylum Chordata—the phylum to which humans belong—are that at least at some point during development they all have gill slits, a notochord, and a dorsal hollow nerve chord. Although we are chordates, our gill slits or our notochord can only be seen at an early stage in embryonic development. Our dorsal hollow nerve chord persists through to adulthood as the brain at the front end and the spinal cord running along our backs.

Although phyla such as Arthropoda include literally millions of species, others are much smaller. The phylum Xenoturbellida, for example, has only one known species. The mysterious phylum Placozoa has never even been observed in the wild. It is only known from specimens found on aquaria glass. We will now look at the charac-teristics of several of the most commonly known animal phyla.

### Phylum Porifera (the Sponges) Consists of Loosely Organized Animals with Skeletons Composed of Spicules

The phylum Porifera includes animals that we know as sponges. They show little evidence of features we associate with other animals. They do not have any true tissues—just loosely grouped cells. As such, they are not included in the group we refer to as eumetazoans, or true animals.

| TABLE 19.1 | Animal Phyla |
| --- | --- |
| **Phylum Name** | **Common Name** |
| Placozoa | Placozoans |
| Porifera | Sponges |
| Radiata Cnidaria | Jellyfish, corals, anemones, Portuguese men-of-war |
| Ctenophora | Comb jellies |
| Acoela | Organized, unsegmented worms? |
| Platyhelminthes | Flatworms, flukes, and tapeworms |
| Gastrotricha | Gastrotrichs |
| Cycliophora | Ciliates |
| Entoprocta | Goblet worms |
| Bryozoa | Moss animals, including micrognathozoans |
| Gnathostomulida | Jaw worms |
| Syndermata | Rotifers and acanthozoans |
| Protostomia Annelida | Segmented worms (clam worms, earthworms, leeches) |
| Mollusca | Molluscs (clams, squid, octopus, snails, slugs) |
| Nemertea | Ribbon worms |
| Brachiopoda | Lamp shells |
| Phoronida | Tube worms |
| Chaetognatha | Arrow worms |
| Nematoda | Roundworms |
| Nematomorpha | Horsehair worms |
| Priapulida | Penis worms |
| Kinorhyncha | Kinkorhynchs |
| Loricifera | Loriciferans |
| Tardigrada | Tardigrades |
| Onychophora | Velvet worms |
| Arthropoda | Joint-legged animals (crustaceans, insects, scorpions, spiders) |
| Phoronida | Horsehair worms |
| Brachiopoda | Lampshells |
| Deuterostomia Xenoturbellida | Xenoturbellid worms |
| Hemichordata | Acorn worms |
| Echinodermata | Echinoderms (sea cucumbers, sea lilies, starfish, urchins) |
| Chordata | Chordates (sea squirts, amphioxus, vertebrates) |

They also have no specialized nerve or muscle cells or organs. Most are not symmetrical. Few adult sponges move; they are sessile. The larva, however, do move. Sponges, like other animals, consume food for energy. Their cells are animal-like eukaryotic cells with no rigid cell wall.

Sponges are among the earliest multicellular organisms known from the fossil record and likely represent the earliest animal lineage. Sponges contain different cells that perform different functions, such as feeding, reproduction, or producing compounds that provide the sponge with skeletal structure. Some of these cells closely resemble single-celled organisms, providing supporting evidence for the idea that these early multicellular animals first evolved from associations between single-celled organisms.

There are over 5000 known species of sponges. Sponges are grouped in three classes, defined primarily by the composition of their skeletons. They get their structure from networks of **spicules**, which are needle-like structures made up of either calcite or silica. The skeletal structures of some are soft and spongy, whereas others are extremely hard and rigid. Most species, such as the azure vase sponge (*Callyspongia plicifera*; **Figure 19.7a**), are filter-feeders, which capture particles through the water as it is pushed through their hollow bodies, mostly trapping food with special collared cells called **choanocytes**. A few sponges, such as *Chondrocladia lyra*, are carnivorous. They trap and digest multicellular animals such as small crustaceans, which they capture on vanelike structures **(Figure 19.7b)**. These sponges live in deep waters of the North Pacific Ocean and were first described from near Monterey Bay in California.

## STUDY BREAK

1. What are three salient features of Porifera (sponges)?

## Phylum Cnidaria Includes Radially Symmetrical Animals with Two Distinct Body Forms

There are over 10,000 species of cnidarians, including many you may be familiar with, such as corals, jellyfish, and the Portuguese man-of-war (*Physalia physalis*) **(Figure 19.8)**. Jellyfish are not restricted to the tropics, and many species, including some that sting, also occur in Canadian waters. Cnidarians are composed of two layers of cells (they are diploblastic) and one opening to their gastrovascular cavity. Although cnidarians may seem simplistic compared to animals with more complex body plans, their body form is well matched to its required function. The rates of food consumption and digestion and rates of oxygen uptake and consumption in some jellyfish are as high as those in bony fish.

Cnidarians have one of two body plans. They are either **medusas** or polyps, sometimes in the same animal at different life phases. Polyps, like the sea anemone, look like flowers with tentaclelike petals and are sessile **(Figure 19.8c)**. Medusas, like jellyfish, are mobile. Many

Dennis Sabo/Shutterstock.com

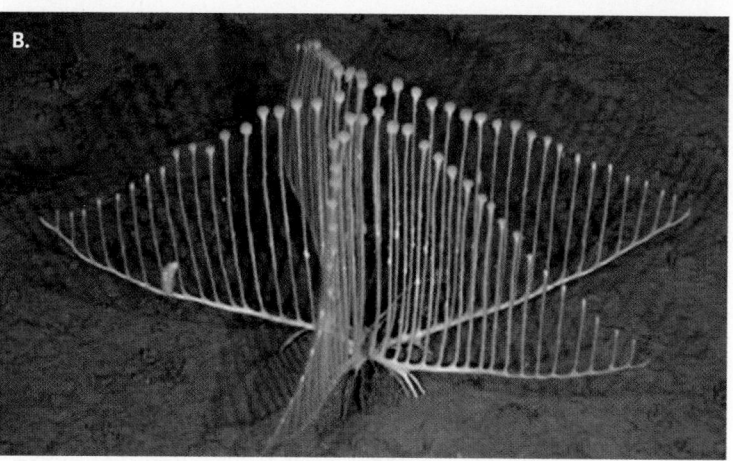

**FIGURE 19.7** **(a)** An azure vase sponge (*Callyspongia plicifera*) and **(b)** a carnivorous sponge (*Chondrocladia lyra*).

SOURCE: (Photo B): Welton L. Lee, Henry M. Reiswig, William C. Austin, Lonny Lundsten, "An extraordinary new carnivorous sponge, Chondrocladia lyra, in the new subgenus Symmetrocladia (Demospongiae, Cladorhizidae), from off of northern California, USA," *Invertebrate Biology*, Volume 131, Issue 4, pages 259–284. John Wiley and Sons. © 2012, The American Microscopical Society, Inc.

medusas almost look like clear or opaque floating umbrellas that open and close as the animal moves through the water (see **Figure 19.8b**). Medusas generally have long rows of tentacles that trail behind them. All cnidarians have specialized stinging cells called **nematocysts** that contain a toxin that they can use to paralyze their prey (see Box 19.1).

## STUDY BREAK

1. What are the main body forms/plans of cnidarians?
2. What are nematocysts?

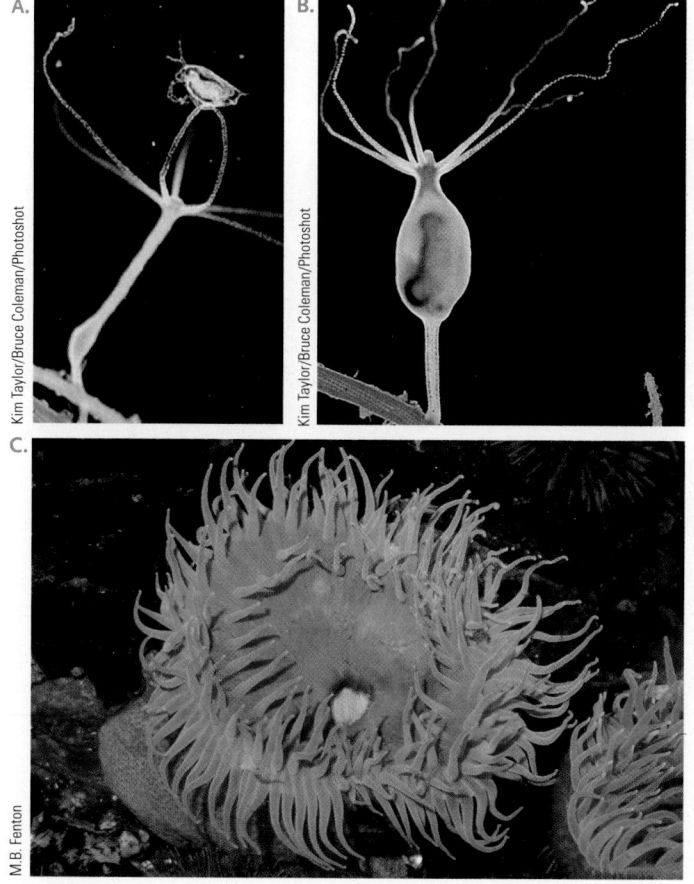

Kim Taylor/Bruce Coleman/Photoshot

M.B. Fenton

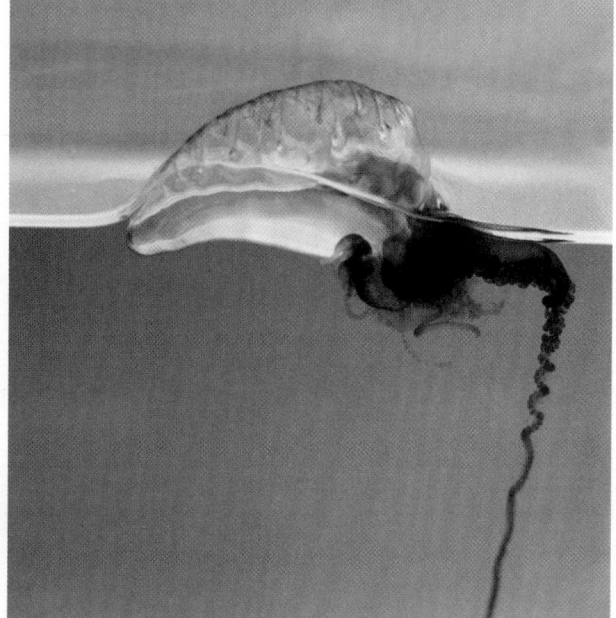

© Natural Visions/Alamy

**FIGURE 19.8** Cnidarians including a hydra catching and eating a small crustacean **(a, b)**, a sea anemone **(c)**, and a Portuguese man-of-war **(d)**.

In 1987 in Florida, stings from special defensive cells called nematocysts in the tentacles of a Portuguese man-of-war were fatal for a human swimmer. On the beach, the victim suffered respiratory arrest followed by cardiac collapse. Phospholipase A is the toxin in nematocysts (see below) that is used to immobilize prey such as small fish. In Venezuela in 2006 and 2007, 59 patients were treated for stings of the nematocysts of a Portuguese man-of-war. The symptoms, including intense burning pain and inflammation, were treated with topical drugs such as antihistamines. None of the incidents were fatal.

Inflatable bladders, the "sails" (see **Figure 19.8d**) of Portuguese men-of-war make them visible, and when lifeguards on duty at beaches where these animals may occur see the sails, they ask people to leave the water. The sail allows the animal to trawl with its tentacles, increasing the rates at which it encounters prey.

## Phylum Platyhelminthes Includes Flat, Wormlike Animals That Can Absorb Nutrients through Their Body Surface

Platyhelminths are flat, wormlike, bilaterally symmetrical animals with solid bodies and two cell layers. There are about 20,000 species of flatworms **(Figure 19.9)**. Most have gastrovascular cavities with one opening. This is the first phylum of animals we have looked at that have a true coelom, and the development of their coelom follows a protostome pattern. Some flatworms are free-living, whereas others are parasitic (they extract resources from a host to survive). We call free-living flatworms planarians. Planarians can regenerate entire individuals from small, isolated pieces of tissue. This process involves neoblasts, which are a kind of stem cell that can develop into many other kinds of cells. Neoblasts form neuronal, intestinal, and other cell types distributed throughout the flatworm's body.

Although most planarians are aquatic, detritus feeders, some are terrestrial and predatory. In some parts of Africa, the terrestrial *Microplana termitophaga* **(Figure 19.9b)** is a planarian that hunts and eats termites. They can catch and eat a termite every six minutes.

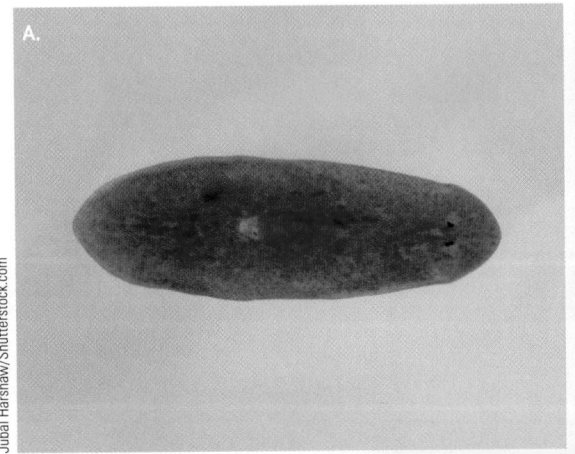

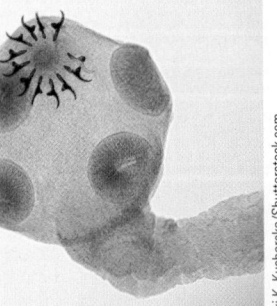

**FIGURE 19.9** Planaria: a free-living flatworm **(a)**, a termite-eating flatworm (*Microplana termitophaga*) **(b)**, and a tapeworm, whole body **(c)** and head or scolex **(d)**.

One kind of parasitic flatworm that many of us have heard of before is the tapeworm. Tapeworms have no digestive tracts **(Figure 19.9c)**, and they absorb nutrients through their body surfaces. Humans can serve as hosts for adult pork tapeworms (*Taenia solium*). Pigs (*Sus scrofa*) are the intermediate hosts because they house the larval stages of these tapeworms. Humans with adult pork tapeworms pass the eggs in their feces. When the eggs are on food eaten by pigs, they hatch into minute larvae. These larvae penetrate the lining of the pig's intestinal wall, enter a blood vessel, and travel to other locations within the pig, where it forms a cysts. When humans eat pork with these cysts, the head of a future tapeworm emerges and attaches itself to the lining of the human's intestinal wall. Living in a pool of digested food, the adult tapeworm grows up to 6 m long, robbing its human host of much-needed nutrients.

## STUDY BREAK

1. What are the three main groups of platyhelminths?
2. Which platyhelminths are parasitic?

## Phylum Syndermata Includes Tiny Invertebrates Called Rotifers That Can Survive Extreme Conditions

There are approximately 2000 species of rotifers (wheel animals) in the phylum Syndermata. They are tiny invertebrates that are common in aquatic habitats **(Figure 19.10)**. Their digestive, reproductive, and nervous systems are well developed. Their development followed a protostome pattern. Some species of rotifers can reproduce both sexually and asexually (see Chapter 28). These animals can endure extreme conditions—such as desiccation and ionizing radiation—that are common in the transient freshwater environments in which many of them live. Rotifers are important components of aquatic systems and play a vital role in trophic interactions.

## STUDY BREAK

1. How do rotifers reproduce?
2. What role do rotifers play in lateral gene transfer?

## Phylum Annelida Includes Worms That Have Repeated Body Segments

There are more than 22,000 species in the phylum Annelida, including earthworms, the often dramatically decorated marine polychaete worms **(Figure 19.11, p. 420)**, and leeches. Annelids have a coelom, developed from three layers of body tissues (they are triploblastic) via a protostome pattern of development, and are bilaterally symmetrical. They all have bodies made up of repeated segments, and many of these segments have repeated sets of internal structures. This is why you can cut an earthworm in half and both halves can continue to live as separate worms; each half still has all of the machinery necessary for life. Annelids have well-developed digestive, circulatory, reproductive, and nervous systems. Their digestive system is complete, with both a mouth and an anus. Many, but not all, annelids are hermaphroditic,

**A. Rotifer body plan**

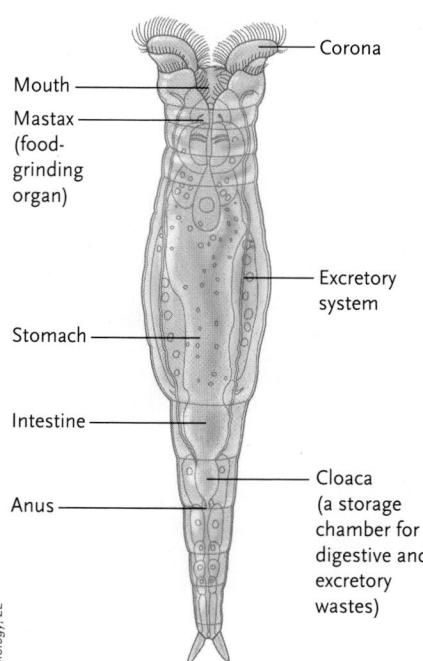

**B. Rotifer laying eggs**

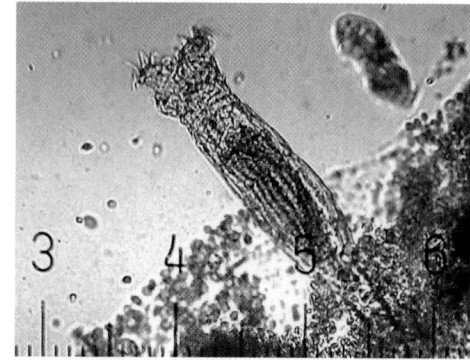

Bob Blaylock at English Wikipedia. This file is licensed under the Creative Commons Attribution-Share Alike 3.0 Unported license, http://creativecommons.org/licenses/by-sa/3.0/deed.en.

**FIGURE 19.10** The tiny rotifers, such as *Philodina roseola* **(a)**, have well-developed body systems. **(b)** Another species in the genus *Philodina* laying eggs.

A.

Michael Aw

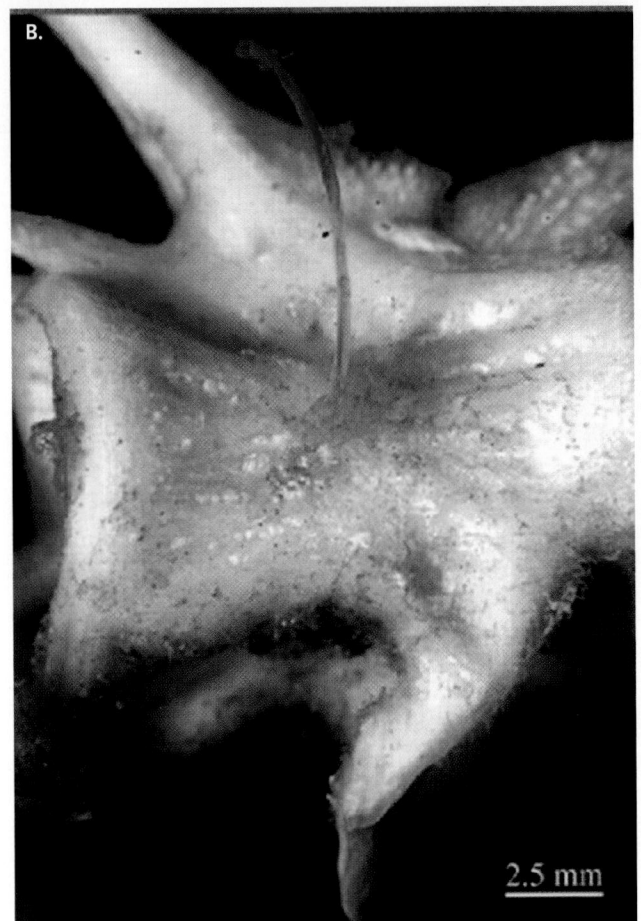

B.

2.5 mm

Greg W. Rouse, Shana K. Goffredi, Shannon B. Johnson and Robert C. Vrijenhoek, "Not whale-fall specialists, Osedax worms also consume fishbones," *Proceedings A*, The Royal Society, 15 April 2011, by permission of the Royal Society.

**FIGURE 19.11** Two annelids: **(a)** a newly described pelagic polychaete (*Teuthidodrilus samae*) and **(b)** a whaleworm (*Osedax samae*) in the vertebra of a large bony fish.

meaning that each individual has both male and female reproductive organs.

The squid worm *Teuthidodrilus samae* **(Figure 19.11a)** is a deep-water polychaete found in the Celebes Sea in the Southwest Pacific Ocean and was described in 2010. These 9 cm long animals have 10 anterior appendages that are longer than their bodies. Squid worms were discovered using a remotely operated camera. They are pelagic, swimming in the open water by propelling themselves with broad paddles, and appear to be filter-feeders.

## Study Break

1. What are the three main groups of annelids?
2. In what main habitats do they occur?

## Phylum Mollusca Is a Diverse Group of Animals That Often Have Shells

There are about 85,000 living species of molluscs **(Figure 19.12)** and many more known only as fossils. Among the most familiar living molluscs are bivalves, clams, mussels, scallops, snails and slugs, octopus, and squid,

as well as nudibranchs (also known as "sea slugs"). Molluscs are bilaterally symmetrical and have a coelom that develops following a protostome pattern. They have well-developed respiratory, digestive, and reproductive systems. They have an **open circulatory system**—or one in which the blood or similar fluid is not enclosed in special vessels. The bodies of many molluscs, such as

M.B. Fenton

**FIGURE 19.12** In part, the diversity of Mollusca is reflected by the variety of shells in which they live.

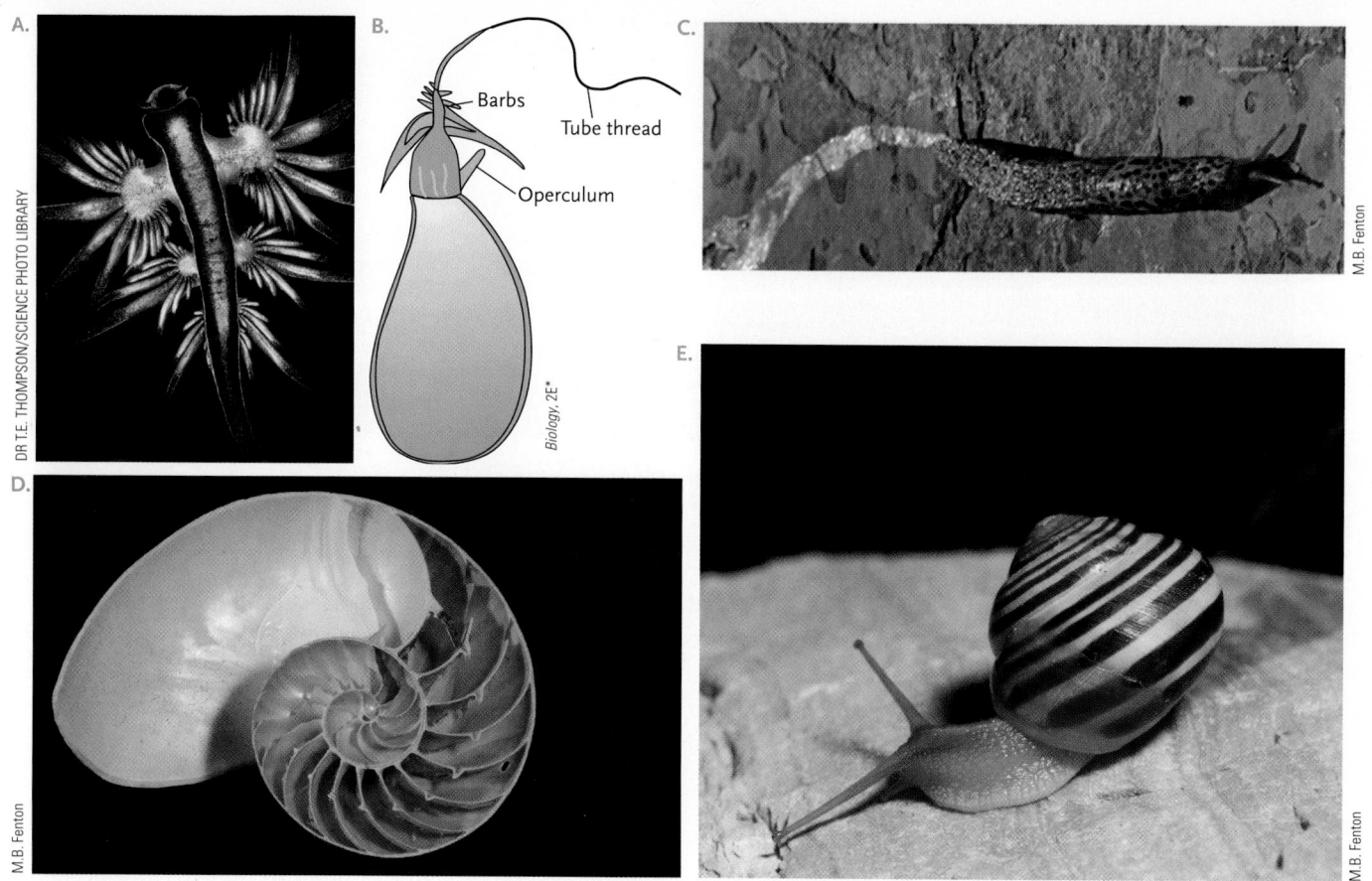

**FIGURE 19.13** A sampling of the diversity of molluscs, including sea slugs (*Glaucus atlanticus*) **(a)** shown with an unexploded nematocyst **(b)**, a leopard slug (*Limax maximus*) **(c)**, half a shell of a chambered nautilus **(d)**, and garden snail (*Cepia nemoralis*) **(e)**.

clams or snails, are enclosed in shells. But many others, such as slugs and squid, are not. Molluscs generally have a visceral mass and a mantle. The visceral mass is the main part of the body and contains the main body organs needs for digestion, excretion, circulation, and reproduction. The mantle is a fold in the body wall that contains the respiratory structures. In shelled molluscs, the mantle also secretes the shell. Many molluscs also have a head region, where sensory structures are concentrated, a foot region that is used for locomotion, and a radula, or a toothed structure that can be used to scrape food off surfaces or bore into the shells of prey organisms.

Among the nudibranchs, or sea slugs, there are some astonishing specializations for feeding. Sea swallows (**Figure 19.13a**; *Glaucus atlanticus*) and blue sea slugs (*Glaucilla marginata*) are renowned for their ability to feed on cnidarians. This is quite a feat—recall that cnidarians all have stinging, toxin-containing nematocysts. Astonishingly, sea slugs can move the nematocysts to their own tentacles and use them in self-defence. This was discovered at beaches in northern Australia, when swimmers showed the symptoms of having been stung by a Portuguese man-of-war when none had been seen near the beach.

Cephalopods, notably squids, are among the largest molluscs. With their long tentacles, colossal squid (*Mesonychoteuthis hamiltoni*) and giant squid (*Architeuthis dux*) can be 12 m long. Especially impressive are their eyes, which are the size of soccer balls—much larger than the eyes of blue whales, which are far bigger animals. At depths of over 600 m, the eyes of colossal and giant squid may allow them to spot hunting sperm whales and thus avoid them.

## STUDY BREAK

1. Do all molluscs have shells?
2. Are all molluscs aquatic?

## Phylum Arthropoda Is a Massive Phylum That Includes Segmented Animals with External Skeletons

There are well over 1 million species of insects, making them perhaps the most familiar of the arthropods. Phylum Arthropoda is a massive groups of animals—the largest on Earth—that includes scorpions, insects, ticks, spiders, and crabs and other crustaceans. Arthropods

**FIGURE 19.14** Two species of insects: a tree hopper with its dramatic "helmet" **(a)** and honeybees **(b)**. The queen bee is in the middle; note that she is larger than the worker bees around her.

have segmented bodies and hard external skeletons called exoskeletons. They are bilaterally symmetrical and have highly developed muscle, nervous, digestive, respiratory, and reproductive systems. Their development follows a protostome pattern. Like molluscs, they have an open circulatory system. The structures in each arthropod segment are different and specialized for different things, unlike in annelids.

Tree hoppers (family Membracidae; **Figure 19.14**) are among the most bizarre-looking arthropods, whereas bees may be the most familiar (Figure 19.14). The helmet of tree hoppers represents an innovation on the body plan of insects. In these insects, the helmet expands over the animal's back. Helmets show a wide range of forms, colours, and textures superficially resembling plant parts (thorns or seeds), animal droppings, or even ants. The helmet arises developmentally through a change in genetic control.

Gribbles **(Figure 19.15)** are a kind of marine isopod, sometimes known as shipworms. There are about 60 species, and they are economically important because of the damage they do to wooden structures submerged in salt water. Unlike other animals that eat wood, gribbles do not rely on other (symbiotic) organisms to digest plant structural materials such as cellulose and lignin. Genetic analysis revealed that at least one gribble species (*Limnoria quadripunctata*) can produce the enzymes needed to digest cellulose.

## STUDY BREAK

1. What does the name Arthropoda mean?
2. Which arthropods have wings and can fly?
3. Are arthropods deuterostomes or protostomes? Why?

**FIGURE 19.15** The gribble (*Limnoria quadripunctata*) **(a)** has evolved the ability to digest wood without the help of symbiotic organisms. The stomatopod shrimp (*Odontodactylus scyllarus*) **(b)** is known for the speed at which it moves its clublike appendages.

## Phylum Echinodermata Includes Radially Symmetrical Animals with Hard Skeletons

The approximately 7000 living species of echinoderms **(Figure 19.16)** are the living remnants of a group with a history extending back more than 600 million years to the Cambrian. Phylum Echinodermata includes sea stars, brittle stars, and sea urchins. They are all radially symmetrical, although the symmetry is more obvious in some, such as asteroids **(Figure 19.16d)** and sea urchins **(Figure 19.16f)**, than in others, such as sea cucumbers **(Figure 19.16e)**. Development in echinoderms follows a deuterostome pattern. They share a more recent common ancestor with chordates (the phylum that includes vertebrate animals) than do the other phyla we have discussed so far. Adult echinoderms are either slow moving or sessile and all are bottom-dwelling marine animals. Echinoderm means "spiny skin," referring to the spiny surface of animals such as sea stars or sea urchins. Underneath that skin in many echinoderms lies a hard, protective skeleton called the **stereom**. Echinoderms all have a unique system called a water vascular system that they use for locomotion, to move food and waste and to exchange gases. Many echinoderms have characteristic sets of tube feet as part of the water vascular system that allow them to use suction to grasp objects and to move (Figure 19.16d).

We know some types of echinoderms only as fossils. In 1963, the Helicoplacoidea **(Figure 19.16a)** were described as a new class of echinoderms, based on fossils from the Lower Cambrian. These spirally coiled, free-living echinoderms had 10 arms, which they apparently used in filter-feeding. Others, like the sea lilies, are known through the fossil record, but there are several species still living on Earth today. Sea lilies are flowerlike echinoderms that are attached to the ocean bottom by a stalk. The earliest sea lilies and their relatives (crinoids) are known from fossil records beginning at least 450 million years ago. It is rare to have such an extensive fossil records for a group of organisms, so scientists are studying these fossils, and living crinoids, carefully as they may tell us a lot about how natural selection led to evolutionary change in these organisms. And if we understand how it happened in a group such as the sea lilies and their relatives, it may help us understand how evolution happens in other groups too.

## STUDY BREAK

1. What are the major groups of echinoderms?
2. Are echinoderms deuterostomes or protostomes? Why?

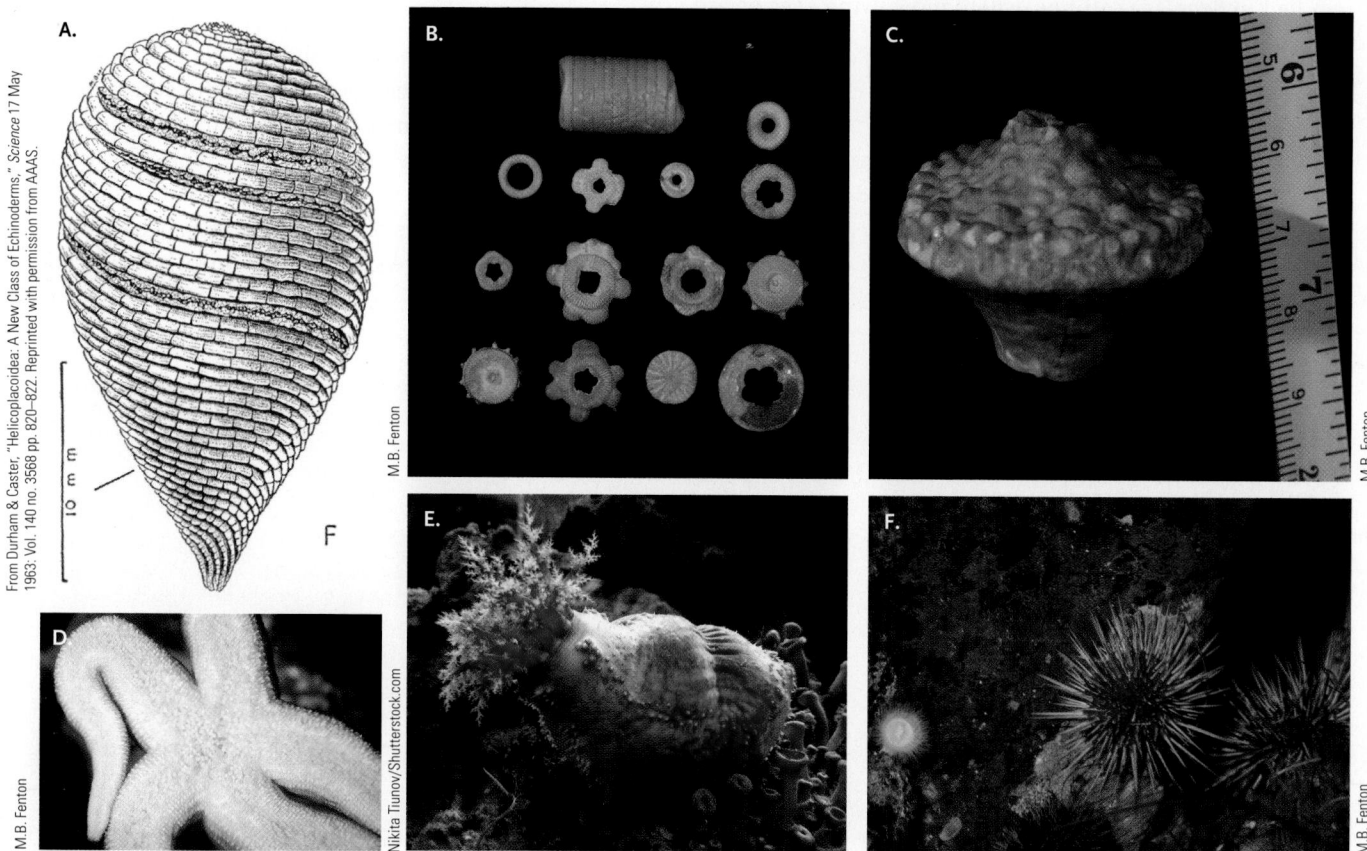

**FIGURE 19.16** Echinoderms include fossil **(a, b, c)** and living forms **(d, e, f)**. The fossils include helicoplacus (a), and sea lilies (crinoids; stems (b), head (c). Living echinoderms include a starfish (d) in ventral view showing tube feet, a sea cucumber with feeding tentacles extruded (*Cucumaria miniata*) (e), and a purple sea urchin (*Strongylocentrotus purpuratus*) (f). There are living species of sea lilies.

## Phylum Hemichordata Is a Small Phylum of Wormlike Marine Animals That Appear to Be the Closest Relatives of Chordates

Hemichordates are a small but interesting phylum of about 80 species of marine wormlike animals **(Figure 19.17)**. They share some of the characteristics of chordates. They, like echinoderms and chordates, are deuterostomes. They have gill slits, a dorsal nerve chord, and a structure called a stomochord that looks much like the notochord of chordates. Hemichordates are the closest known relative of chordates. Thus, understanding the evolution of hemichordates can help scientists better understand the origin of the phylum Chordata and our earliest animal ancestors.

Hemichordates live in the deep ocean, making them difficult to study. Scientists have used remotely operated vehicles to explore deep-sea habitats in the Atlantic, Pacific, and South Pacific oceans and have revealed important details about hemichordates and discovered many new species. We now know that hemichordates can move on currents between feeding sites by changing their body postures. They also appear to use food material in the gut as ballast, altering their body weight in the proportions needed to move and maintain balance. Phylogenetic evidence suggests that these animals originated in shallow waters but then moved to and diversified in deep-sea settings, where most living species are now found.

### STUDY BREAK

1. What are hemichordates? Are they deuterostomes or protostomes?

## Phylum Chordata Includes All Vertebrate Animals

The approximately 60,000 species of chordates include some of the animals most familiar to us, from humans to fish, dinosaurs to birds, frogs to snakes. The chordate fossil record extends back to the Cambrian. Arguably, some of the most spectacular chordates (see the photograph at the beginning of this chapter) are known only as fossils. Chordates, along with echinoderms and hemichordates, are deuterostomes. Most chordates are vertebrates, or animals with backbones. They all share the characteristics we discussed earlier: all have gill slits, a notochord, and a dorsal hollow nerve chord at least at some point in their development. The earliest known fossil chordate is called Pikaia. It was discovered in the Burgess Shale, a massive deposit of fossils from the Cambrian period, about 500 million years ago. Pikaia looked much like modern lancelets do today. A lancelet is a small, eel-like marine animal and is one of the few chordates alive today that does not have vertebrae made of bone or cartilage protecting its dorsal nerve chord. In the remainder of this section, we will look at some of the diversity in vertebrates, which include fish, amphibians, reptiles, birds, and mammals.

### Fish

Fishes, broadly defined, are the most diverse group of vertebrates. Included are those with cartilaginous skeletons (the Chondrichthyes: sharks, skates, rays) and the bony fishes (Osteichthyes: most of the other fishes). Bony fishes show an astonishing variation in body shape **(Figure 19.18)**, which has implications for swimming **(Figure 19.18, a, b, c, e)** or movement onto land **(Figure 19.18d)**. Analysis of over 600 extinct species of fish revealed that the large-scale extinction of species that

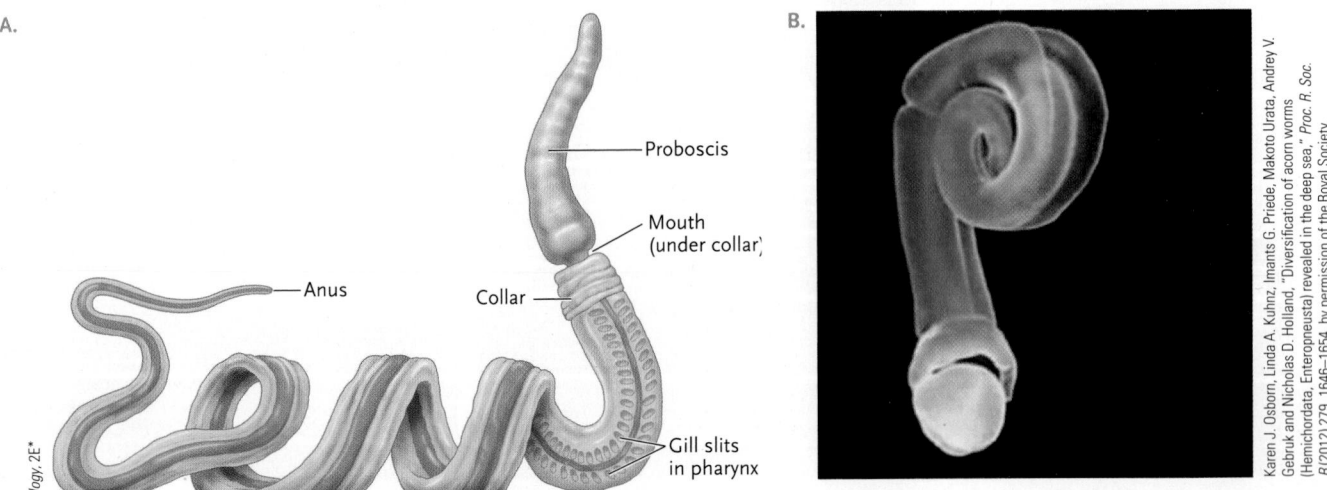

**FIGURE 19.17** A diagram of a typical hemichordate **(a)**. A high-resolution image of an as yet undescribed species recorded 20 m above the ocean floor **(b)**.

**FIGURE 19.18** Variation in the body shapes of bony fishes, including a sea horse (*Hippocampus erectus*) **(a)**, a discus fish (*Symphysodon* spp.) **(b)**, a pirhana (*Serrasalmus niger*) **(c)**, a mudskipper (*Periophthalmus barbarus*) **(d)**, and a fossil (*Syngnathus acer*) **(e)**.

occurred at the end of the Cretaceous (Chapter 2) opened up many new **ecological niches**, which allowed for the subsequent mass diversification of spiny-finned fishes (Acanthomorpha), mainly the perchlike fishes. The array of modern spiny-finned fishes includes over 15,000 species.

## Amphibians

In general, the approximately 7000 living species of amphibians **(Figure 19.19)** are **tetrapod** (four-limbed) animals that depend on access to standing water to complete their life cycles. Most can exchange gases and other

**FIGURE 19.19** A sampling of living amphibians, including a tiger salamander (*Ambystoma tigrinum*) **(a)**, a red-eyed tree frog (*Agalychnis callidryas*) **(b)**, a cane toad (*Bufo marinus*) **(c)**, an axolotl (*Ambystoma mexicanum*) **(d)**, and **(e)** a caecilian.

FIGURE 19.20 The grey foam-nest tree frog (*Chiromantis xerampelina*) **(a)** and the waxy monkey tree frog (*Phyllomedusa sauvagii*) **(b)** use a waxlike secretion to waterproof their skin.

A.

B.

M.B. Fenton

M.B. Fenton

substances through their skin. Over time, some amphibian species have evolved adaptations that veer quite a bit from this general body plan. The caecilians (Apoda) are tropical, wormlike, limbless amphibians with very reduced eyes. They burrow underground, and their body form is adapted to that function. Many others have reproductive cycles that do not require standing water. Some amphibians are fully terrestrial, and the adults are as resistant to desiccation as some reptiles.

In southern Africa and South America, species in two genera of tree frogs use a waxy coating on their skins to protect them from drying out (desiccation) **(Figure 19.20)**. Scientists have conducted experiments to compare the ability of grey foam-nest tree frogs (*Chiromantis xerampelina*) from southern Africa to withstand desiccation to that of

other species of amphibians and reptiles. They found that the grey foam-nest tree frogs were as good at withstanding desiccation as were as chameleons.

### Reptiles

The approximately 9700 living species of reptiles **(Figure 19.21)** include an incredibly diverse array of body plans and lifestyles in animals such as turtles, crocodiles, lizards, snakes, and tuataras. The evolution of **amniotic eggs**, which can be laid away from water, was the most significant evolutionary for reptiles. They also have skin that protects them from drying out, so they are not required to be near water to survive and reproduce.

Although we think of reptiles as being egg-layers (are oviparous), many give birth to live young (are viviparous).

(Photos A–D): M.B. Fenton

**FIGURE 19.21** A sampling of living reptiles, including a stinkpot (*Sternotherus odoratus*) **(a)**, a chameleon (*Chamaeleo*) **(b)**, a massasauga rattlesnake (*Sistrurus catenatus*) **(c)**, and a Nile crocodile (*Crocodylus niloticus*) **(d)**.

FIGURE 19.22 This sampling of birds includes a Red Bishop (*Euplectes orix*) **(a)**, a Swallow-tailed Bee Eater (*Merops hirundineus*) **(b)**, a Black Egret (*Egretta ardesiaca*) **(c)**, a Crowned Crane (*Balearica regulorum*) **(d)**, a flamingo (*Phoenicopterus* spp.) **(e)**, a Pygmy Falcon (*Polihierax semitorquatus*) **(f)**, and a guinea fowl **(g)**.

Some of those that give birth to live young also have a close connection between mother and young during development, as most mammals do. Bearing live young comes at a surprisingly high cost to the mother. In Australia, female viviparous skinks (*Tiliqua rugosa*) give birth to live young, but as the developing young increase in size, they limit their mother's lung capacity. During pregnancy, female skinks breathe more often but suffer a 30% reduction in their ability to inflate their lungs. Non-pregnant female skinks spend about 20% of their energy budget on breathing, whereas pregnant skinks spend about 62%.

## Birds

There are about 10,000 living species of birds **(Figure 19.22)** that occupy a wide range of habitats around the world. Often colourful and melodious, birds can be conspicuous in their habitats and are generally familiar to many people. It is now clear that birds evolved in the same lineage as theropod dinosaurs. The presence of feathers and flight appear to characterize birds, but we now know that many other theropods also had feathers, and some birds do not fly (although they emerged from ancestors that did). Feathers serve birds in flight, in communicative displays, and in providing insulation, either by reflecting heat or holding it in the body. Birds, like mammals, are able to self-regulate their internal body temperature; they are **homeothermic**.

Although the wing is a defining feature of birds, over evolutionary time, many species have lost the ability to fly.

We are familiar with some of these: the ostrich that relies instead on incredible running speed or penguins that use their wings to "fly" under water with incredible adeptness. Fossil history reveals other interesting adaptations of flightless birds. A structure resembling the stomatopod club (above) appeared in a species of flightless birds known only from fossils found in Jamaica. These flightless ibises (*Xenicibis xympithecus*) had wings that differed from other ibises that fly. One bone, the metacarpus, is long and enlarged. The walls of this bone are thick, the finger bones are short and blocklike, and one of the arm bones is much wider at one end **(Figure 19.23)**. We do not know how these extinct flightless ibises behaved, and the

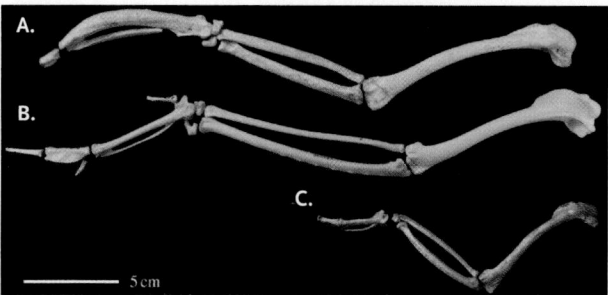

FIGURE 19.23 A comparison of the wing bones of a Jamaican Flightless Ibis (*Xenicibis xympithecus*) **(a)**, a White Ibis (*Eudocimus albus*) **(b)**, and a Moloka'i Ibis (*Apteribis glenos*) **(c)**.

SOURCE: Nicholas R. Longrich, Storrs L. Olson, "The bizarre wing of the Jamaican flightless ibis Xenicibis xympithecus: a unique vertebrate adaptation," *Proceedings B*, published 5 January 2011, by permission of the Royal Society.

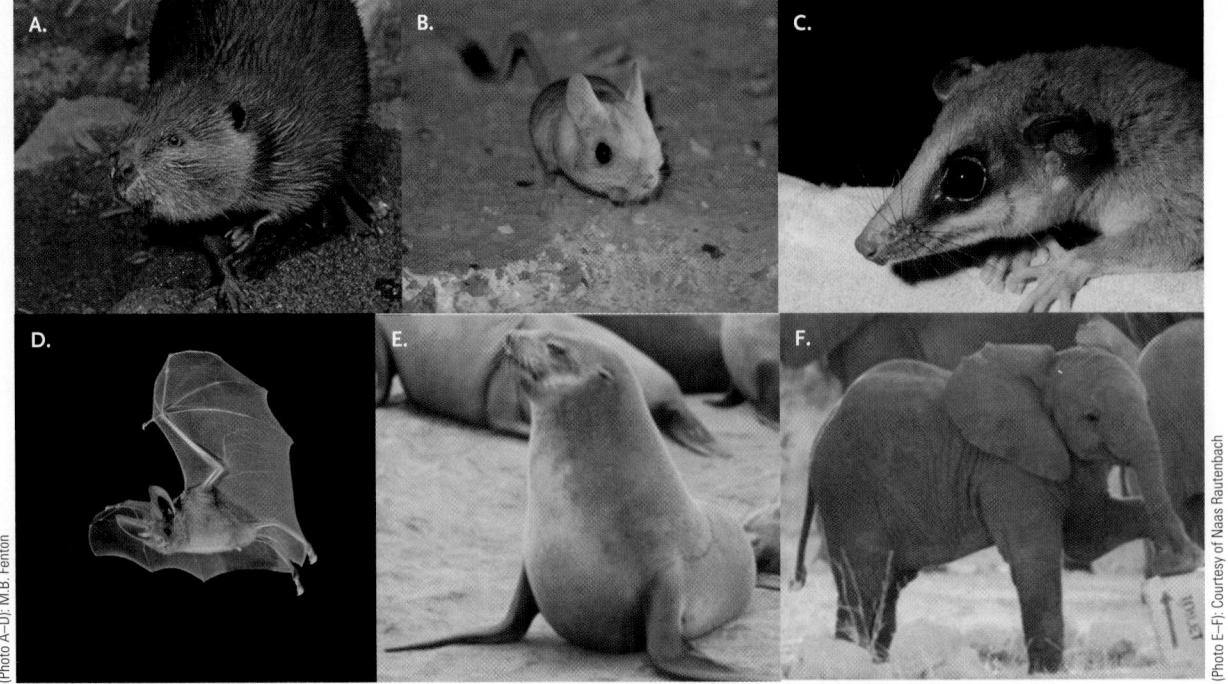

**FIGURE 19.24** A sampling of mammals including some rodents such as **(a)** the beaver (*Castor canadensis*) and **(b)** the lesser Egyptian jerboa (*Jaculus jaculus*), **(c)** a marsupial, the Mexican mouse opossum (*Marmosa mexicana*), **(d)** Waterhouse's leaf-nosed bat (*Macrotus waterhousii*), **(e)** a Cape fur seal (*Arctocephalus pusillus*), and **(f)** an African bush elephant (*Loxodonta africana*).

purpose of the club remains a mystery. Perhaps it was used in defence during conflicts between individuals. The only other known flightless species of ibis is from Hawaii (Moloka'i Ibis – *Apteribis glenos*), and it did not have a clublike structure on its wing.

### Mammals

The approximately 5700 species of mammals **(Figure 19.24)** on Earth today occur in habitats from tropical rainforests to Arctic and Antarctic waters. The distinct features of mammals include the presence of fur and the ability to produce milk to feed their young (lactation). Like birds, mammals are homeothermic. They exhibit a wide range of adaptations to their habitats.

In the mountains of Borneo, mountain tree shrews (*Tupaia montana*) interact with pitcher plants (*Nepenthes lowii*), demonstrating just one of the incredibly diverse ecological niches that mammals occupy. Nectaries around specialized pitchers attract mountain tree shrews, which sit over the pitcher as they drink nectar. The pitchers allow the plants to collect the urine and feces deposited by feeding tree shrews. Male mountain tree shrews protect these pitchers within their home range, providing them access to a rich energy supply and attracting females that want to share in those resources in the process. Although squirrel-like in appearance, tree shrews are placed in a separate order more closely related to Primates (the order that includes humans) than Rodentia (the order that includes rats, mice, squirrels, and their relatives).

Mammals show great diversity in behaviours as well. Bearded capuchin monkeys (*Sapajus libidinosus*) of Brazil have long been known to use tools to crack nuts. The details of the behaviour are intriguing. These monkeys may weigh only 1.5 kg, but they use stone hammers weighing about 1 km to crack palm nuts they have placed on a hard surface such as a flat stone or root. Experienced bearded capuchins place the nut in a position where it is unlikely to roll and drop the hammer on it **(Figure 19.25)**. Tool using involves selecting a hammer and a surface and correctly placing the nut. Originally, tool using had been thought of as a human trait, but it is now clear that many animals use tools to their advantage.

### STUDY BREAK

1. Why do many people consider the Chordata to be the main phylum of animals?
2. What are the diagnostic features of Chordata?
3. Which of the chordates are vertebrates?

## 19.5 The Fossil Record

We often use tools that analyze or compare genetic or developmental information to deduce patterns of evolutionary history in animals. But for animals that existed thousands, hundreds of thousands, or even millions of years ago, our only way to see structures and connect

© 2013 Fragaszy et al. Fragaszy DM, Liu Q, Wright BW, Allen A, Brown CW, et al. (2013) Wild Bearded Capuchin Monkeys (*Sapajus libidinosus*) Strategically Place Nuts in a Stable Position during Nut-Cracking. *PLoS ONE* 8(2): e56182. doi:10.1371/journal.pone.0056182.

**FIGURE 19.25** This wild male bearded capuchin monkey is about to drop a hammer onto a nut he has placed on a hard surface, in this case, a root. The black line on the nut shows the position when it stopped rolling.

them to their habitats is through the fossil record. Although they provide far from a complete record, fossils are an excellent source of information about evolutionary changes in animals over time. Some fossil deposits (fossil beds) contain a rich diversity of flora and fauna, whereas others are more fragmentary. New fossil discoveries continue to cause us to change our views of living organisms and their ancestors.

Fossil beds in two parts of the world (Canada – Burgess Shale, China – Chengjiang) provide a showcase of the animals that thrived in the Cambrian, about 600 million years ago. These assemblages included penis worms (as noted above) and representatives of many of the phyla that are still around (Mollusca, Chordata, Arthropoda). But other Cambrian fossils are of animals astonishingly different from anything we know today.

*Opabinia regalis* **(Figure 19.26a)** is a good example of a Cambrian animal that is nothing like what we see today. Apparently, *Opabinia* was an arthropod, but quite unlike any modern one. These 5 cm long, five-eyed creatures had a long flexible proboscis with grasping spines at the tip.

*Anomalocaris* **(Figure 19.26b)** had large compound eyes, like those of insects, suggesting that it was a predator that depended on being able to see its potential prey. These animals were up to a metre in length and were likely apex predators of their time (see Chapter 30 for an overview of apex predators). Each eye consisted of at least 16,000 lenses, making them as structurally complex as those of modern insects. Furthermore, the eyes of *Anomalocaris* should have provided at least as many details of images as those of modern insects. Trilobites, a huge group of fossil arthropods that are also represented in the Burgess Shale, had similarly complex compound eyes **(Figure 19.27, p. 430)**.

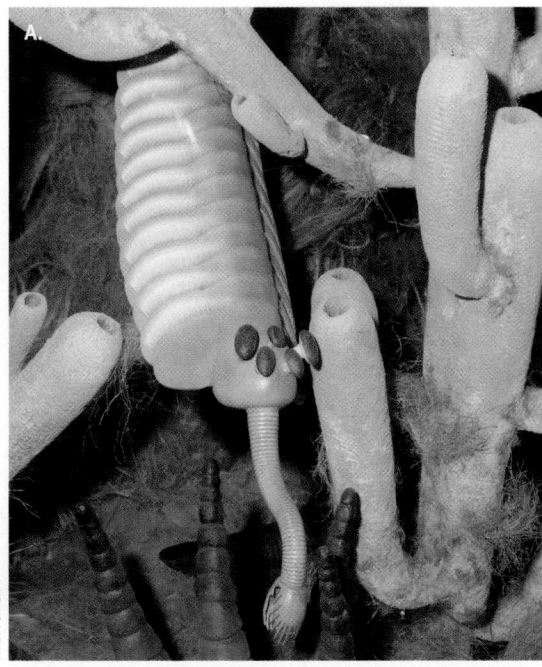

**FIGURE 19.26** Artists' interpretations of two arthropod-like creatures from the Burgess Shale, *Opabinia* **(a)** and *Anomalocaris* **(b)**, which are unlike any species living today.

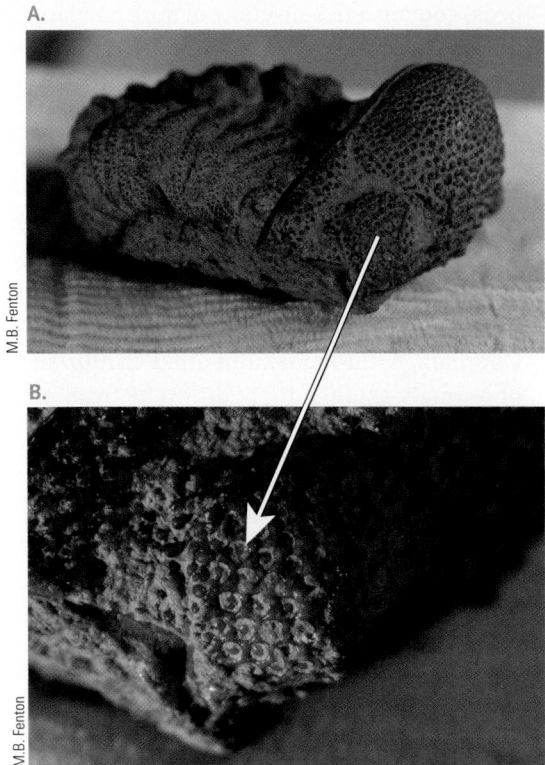

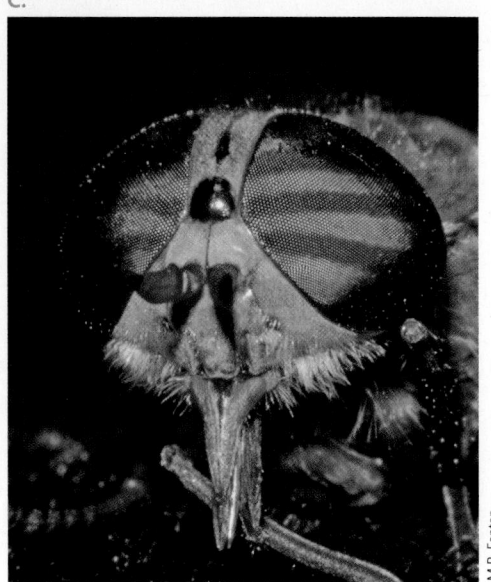

**FIGURE 19.27** Trilobites, other extinct arthropods, also had impressive compound eyes. In this case, *Phacops iowensis* **(a)** and a close-up of the compound eye **(b)**. Also shown for comparison is a close-up of the compound eyes of a tabanid fly **(c)**.

We continue to examine fossils (Box 19.2) to learn more about the biology of organisms that are long extinct, and new technologies allow us to solve more mysteries. Ammonites are cephalopod molluscs with external shells, much like modern chambered nautiluses. Ammonites are well represented in the fossil record over 340 million years, from the Early Devonian to the Late Cretaceous. In spite of their importance in the fossil record, until recently, there was little evidence of their mode of feeding. An advanced kind of X-ray reconstruction of the mouth area of some ammonites from the Mesozoic has provided details of feeding structures and of their food. The data demonstrate that at least some ammonites ate small planktonic animals that would have been present in the open water, unlike the living chambered nautilus that appears to be a scavenger feeder near the ocean floor.

Sometimes newly discovered specimens change our views of organisms originally described from fossils. For example, an animal known as *Nectocaris* **(Figure 19.28)** was originally described as an early chordate. Then, with more details from more specimens, it was reclassified as a cephalopod mollusc (compare a and b in Figure 19.28).

Formally describing the species a fossil represents and placing this in an evolutionary context can be a challenge for paleontologists—the scientists who study fossils. For example, cervical ribs **(Figure 19.29)**—or ribs that extend from the bones in the neck—were

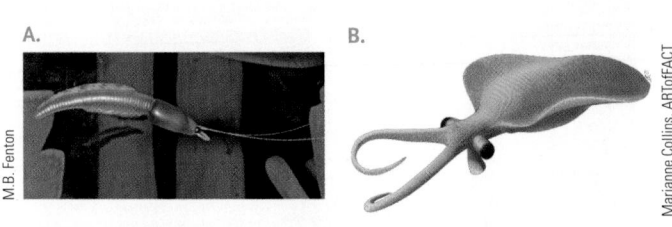

**FIGURE 19.28** An early **(a)** and more recent **(b)** reconstruction of *Nectocaris pteryx*. In (a), the fossil was thought to have been a chordate, but the presentation in (b) presents the animal as a cephalopod mollusc based on additional fossils.

**FIGURE 19.29** A mounted skeleton of *Saurornitholestes langstoni* showing short cervical ribs. These are not as well developed as those of some other dinosaurs.

# BIOLOGY IS EVERYWHERE 19.2
## Everyday Fossil Hunters

It is clear that the discovery of new fossils can change our view of evolutionary history. We expect professional palaeontologists to be the ones to find new fossils, and often this is true. But anyone can find fossils and perhaps change scientific perspectives. At age 4 years, Daisy Morris found and collected a fossil on the Isle of Wight. The small pterosaur was new to science, and in 2013, *Vectidraco daisymorrisae* was described. Its name reflects the Greek for Isle of Wight (*Vectis*), the Greek for dragon (*draco*), and recognition of the person who found the fossil (*daisymorrisae*). There was enough detail in the pieces Daisy found—the pelvic girdle and associated vertebrae **(Figure 1)**—to assign the fossil to a family and place it in a phylogenetic context.

A.

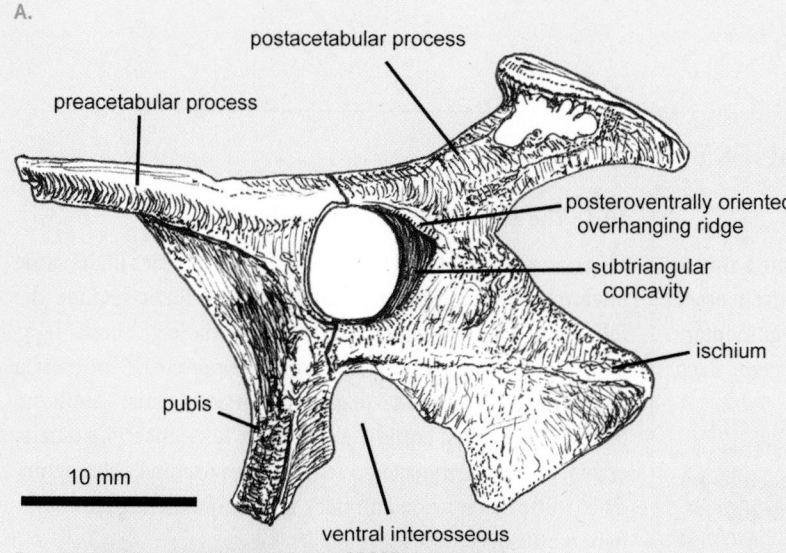

preacetabular process

postacetabular process

posteroventrally oriented overhanging ridge

subtriangular concavity

ischium

pubis

10 mm

ventral interosseous space

**FIGURE 1** The pelvis (drawing **(a)** and photograph **(b)**) of *Vectidraco daisymorrisae*, a newly described pterosaur. **(c)** A complete fossil pterosaur, *Pterodactylus elegans*.

SOURCE: (Photos A–B): © 2013 Naish et al. Naish D, Simpson M, Dyke G (2013) A New Small-Bodied Azhdarchoid Pterosaur from the Lower Cretaceous of England and Its Implications for Pterosaur Anatomy, Diversity and Phylogeny. *PLoS ONE* 8(3): e58451. doi:10.1371/journal.pone.0058451

B.

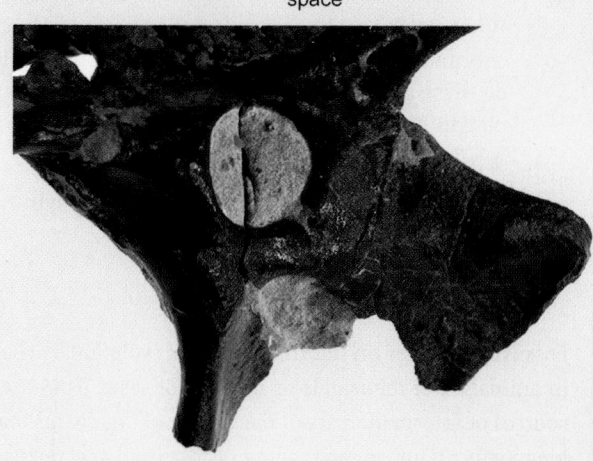

C.

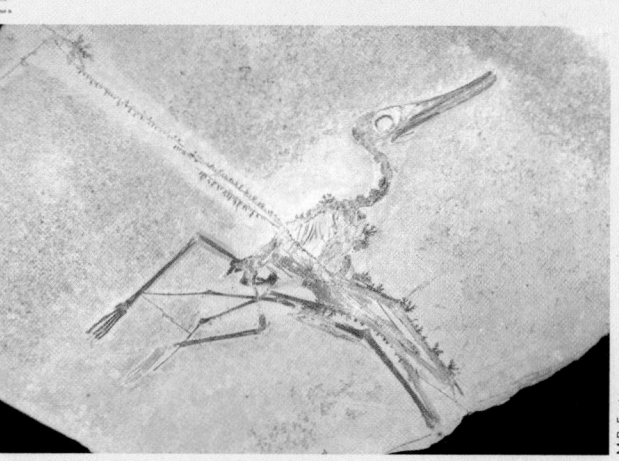

M.B. Fenton

common in sauropod dinosaurs, but their function is not particularly clear. They were thought to have served as ventral braces for the neck. But a histological examination of cervical ribs has indicated that they consisted mainly of mineralized collagen fibres. Indeed, cervical ribs look more like ossified (bonelike) tendons. This discovery suggests that overlapping cervical ribs that were ossified tendons would have made the long necks of sauropods more flexible and much lighter.

Smaller dinosaurs sometimes had shorter cervical ribs (Figure 19.29).

## STUDY BREAK

1. What does the fossil record tell us about animals?
2. Why did the classification of *Nectocaris* change?
3. What is the Burgess Shale?

# PUTTING IT IN PERSPECTIVE

Animals are a huge part of our lives. They can have a major negative impact on humans, either directly by causing disease or indirectly by affecting our food crops. But they can also have positive impacts, as pets or things in nature to admire and appreciate. Some animals are important because they illustrate fundamental evolutionary change. From the time the first animals appeared on Earth, more than a billion years ago, they have both diversified and gone through mass extinctions, only to diversify again, bringing about the dramatic adaptations of the animal body plans that we see today.

The animals on Earth now represent those millions of years of evolutionary history. Scientists continue to discover new animals all the time. And animals are disappearing all the time. Some extinctions probably just reflect a species whose evolutionary time is up. Others are most certainly being driven to extinction by human activities. We will explore the impact of human activities on other living things in later chapters. We hope that in this chapter, we have generated an appreciation of the diversity of animal life on Earth today and throughout history.

# KEY CONCEPTS REVIEW AND QUESTIONS

## 19.1  The Animal Organ Systems

Twelve organ systems work cooperatively in vertebrate animals to meet their needs. Versions of these systems also exist in other animals. Examples of organ systems include integumentary system, the skeletal system, and the muscular system. Each system may be composed of several organs.

1. Compare the circulatory and respiratory systems of animals in three phyla (note that you will need to get information from another chapter to answer this question).

## 19.2  Animal Tissues

There are four major types of tissues in animals: epithelial, connective, muscle, and nervous. There are different kinds of each of these tissue types. These tissue types combine to form organs and organs systems.

## 19.3  Animal Body Plans

Body plans are defined by presence of certain developments, such as a gut with a mouth and anus, symmetry, more complex nervous systems, etc. Organs and organ systems can be packaged in different ways according to the organism's body plan. There are only a few different types of body plan. There many different kinds and numbers of appendages. Secondary modifications have changed or eliminated some features.

2. Name four phyla of animals in which many species have limbs. Have species in any of these phyla lost limbs?

## 19.4  The Major Groups of Animals

There are about 30 known phyla of animals. Species in the same phylum share similar diagnostic features. Phyla include the following: Porifera (e.g., sponges), Cnidaria (e.g., corals, jellyfish), Platyhelminthes (e.g., flatwormlike animals), Syndermata (e.g., rotifers), Annelida (e.g., segmented worms), Mollusca (e.g., clams, slugs, squid), Arthropoda (e.g., insects, spiders, crabs), Echinodermata (e.g., sea stars, sea urchins), Hemichordata (wormlike marine animals), and Chordata (e.g., humans, fish, reptiles).

3. What are the main organ systems of animals such as chordates, annelids, arthropods, and molluscs? How do these animals differ from cnidarians and platyhelminths?

4. Why are sponges considered to be animals?

5. Which phyla have species that are radially symmetrical? Bilaterally symmetrical?

## 19.5  The Fossil Record

Fossils are sources on information about evolutionary changes in animals over thousands or millions of years. They are also sources of information about the biology of organisms that are long extinct. Our understanding of fossilized specimens may change as new specimens are discovered. Placing a fossilized species into the correct evolutionary context can be challenging for paleontologists.

6. When did the first fossil animals appear?

# Organized to Survive and Prosper

## WHY IT MATTERS

The diversity of plants and animals alive on Earth today is astounding. More astounding are the number of species that have existed but gone extinct. The diversity of these species in their shape or form reflects the demands of environment (both external and internal) on the functioning of each organism. For example, both cacti and coniferous trees are plants **(Figure 20.1)**, but their structures are dramatically different, reflecting the extent to which members of different phyla within the same kingdom (Plantae) can diverge as they adapt to different environmental challenges. On the other hand, praying mantis, and mantis shrimp (Figure 20.1) are also members of different phyla within the same kingdom (Animalia) but have converged on a common anatomy that is highly specialized but extremely efficient in allowing them to exploit similar lifestyles. The streamlined forms

**FIGURE 20.1** **(a)** Saguaro cactus (*Carnegiea gigantea*), **(b)** coniferous tree (*Pinus sp.*), **(c)** praying mantis (*Mantis religiosa*), and **(d)** mantis shrimp (*Odontodactylus scyllarus*).

of sharks, dolphins, and marine turtles are another example of convergent evolution, whereas differences in the forelimbs of a mole, a bat, and a cheetah or the leaves of a maple, a palm tree, and a pine tree are examples of divergent evolution (see Chapter 13 for more discussion on convergence and divergence). In all cases, these similarities and differences in form reflect the constraints (or trade-offs) of serving specific functions in different environments. A dusky-chested flycatcher (*Myiozetetes granadensis*) is shown sitting on a cactus leaf in the opening photograph to this chapter. Both cactus and flycatcher are adapted to live in hot dry environments. The form of a part or of a whole organism reveals much about its function or lifestyle, whereas the function of a part dictates much about its form.

In this chapter, we will explore the relationship between form and function in plants and animals. Plants and animals are faced with similar challenges, and the way in which they deal with them may or may not be similar. Not surprisingly, the similarities and differences in the way plants and animals face challenges most often arise from corresponding similarities and differences in

the way in which they are built. We will review the fundamental body parts (**anatomy**) of plants and animals that were described in detail in Chapters 17 and 19, to prepare ourselves to explore the functions (**physiology**) of the different structures described in subsequent chapters. We will explore the common elements that plants and animals share despite their differences in appearance and provide some insight into what differences in form indicate about the environmental stresses they face.

## 20.1 Structure–Function Relationships

Single-celled organisms exchange everything with their environment across their cell membranes. Cells in multicellular organisms, on the other hand, divide labour. Specialized organs and organ systems have evolved to handle specific chores, such as nutrient uptake and digestion, gas exchange, and internal transport. The design of these systems reflects the specific demands that are placed on them. Thus, the digestive systems of an herbivorous and a carnivorous mammal are distinctly different (**Figure 20.2**), reflecting differences in diet. The root systems

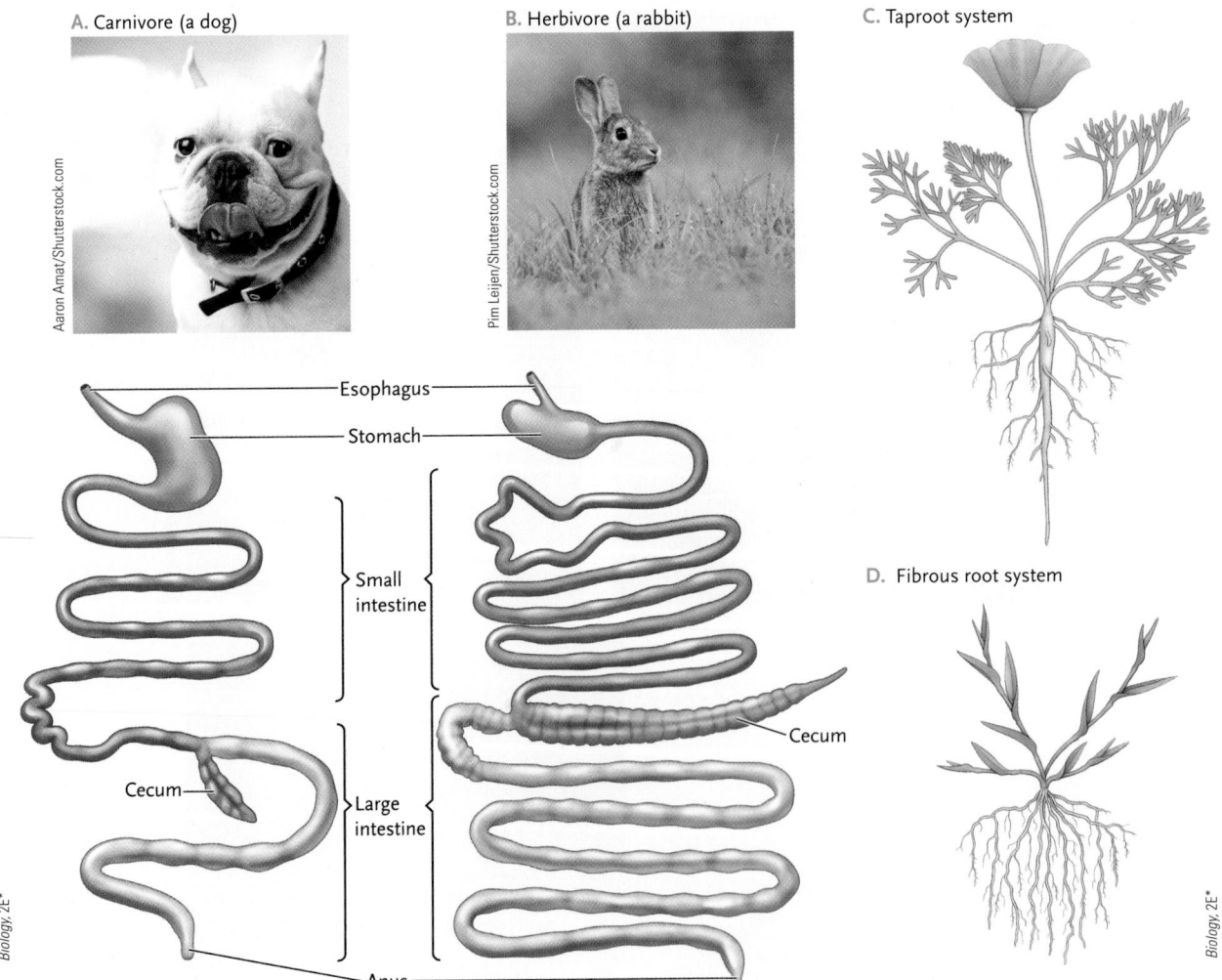

A. Carnivore (a dog)

B. Herbivore (a rabbit)

C. Taproot system

D. Fibrous root system

**FIGURE 20.2 (a)** Digestive tract of a carnivore (dog) and **(b)** a herbivore (rabbit). **(c)** Tap root of a California poppy and **(d)** fibrous root of a grass plant.

of different plants are distinctly different (Figure 20.2), reflecting differences in the soils in which they live. Form evolves to suit function, leading to organisms that have the right tool for each job.

By the same token, function is also constrained, or limited, by form. The ultimate form of any structure is constrained by the physical characteristics of the raw material from which it is built. The structural adaptations available to a jellyfish differ from those available to a turtle; those available to a woody plant differ from those available to an herbaceous plant.

Physical laws also influence form in other ways. For example, the maximum size an organism can achieve is restricted by its need for support. Although there are magnificent examples of tall trees on all continents, there are limits to how large they can grow and still be supported above ground. Fungi that are supported by soil (rather than by themselves) have reached sizes in terms of biomass that far exceed the biomass (the mass of living cells) of even the most enormous towering trees. For animals, maximum size is not only limited by the need for support; they also need to be mobile. For terrestrial animals, the need for support interferes with the ability to move as animals get larger. The bigger you are, the harder it is to move. This compromise is not a problem for aquatic animals, which benefit from the support provided by water. The largest mammal on Earth is the blue whale (*Balaenoptera musculus*) (average 110 tonnes), which reaches 20 to 25 times the biomass of the largest terrestrial mammal, the African elephant (*Loxodonta exoptata*) (average 5 tonnes).

Finally, we must remember that many structures serve multiple functions; thus, the final design of that structure will reflect a balance (or trade-off) of the forces placed on the structure for each of the different functions. Specialized adaptations for one function come at the expense of their ability to perform other functions. The forelimb of a mammal is a multifunctional appendage, but adaptations for running, flight, or burrowing restrict its use primarily for that one function **(Figure 20.3)**.

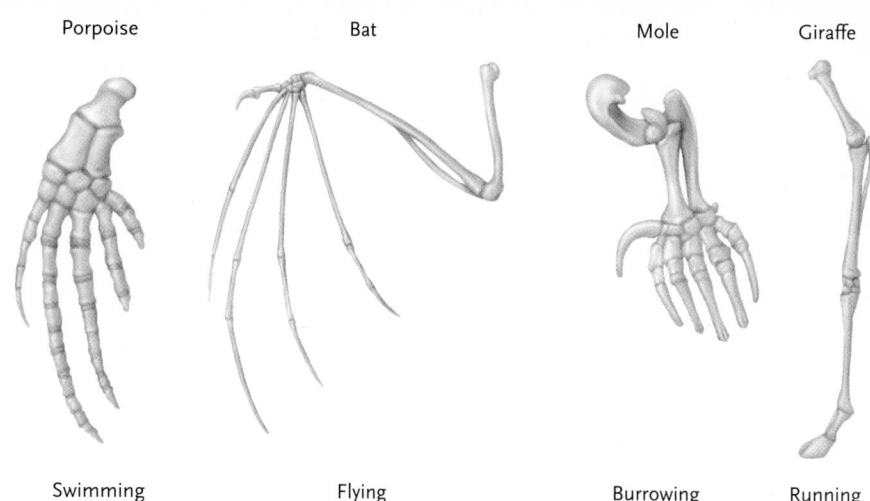

**FIGURE 20.3** Mammalian forelimbs from a swimmer, a flyer, a digger and a runner.

## 20.2 Tissues, Organs, and Systems

There is a fundamental hierarchy of organization in all multicellular organisms. The basic unit of life is the cell. Although all cells within an organism have the same genetic makeup, during the development of the organism, cells differentiate in ways that allow them to take on different functions (see Chapter 28). As described in Chapters 17, 18, and 19, groups of plant, fungal, and animal cells with a common structure and function are organized into **tissues**. Different tissues are assembled in various ways to produce different organs, and these organs are assembled in distinct ways to form systems or **organ systems**. Finally, organ systems are assembled in distinct ways (body plans) in different organisms. We need to remember that at each level of this biological hierarchy, new properties emerge. For instance, tissues can perform functions that isolated cells cannot, whereas organs can perform functions that their individual tissues cannot.

We have already seen the fundamental structures of plant and animal cells in Chapter 3. Differences in the characteristics of each cell type limit or allow the different forms that distinguish plants from animals. Plant and animal cells share many common features that reflect their early ancestry. Multicellularity appears to have evolved independently in each of these groups, however. The specific ancestor of plants was distinct in possessing a photosynthetic endosymbiont, a cyanobacterium, which is present in modern plants as the chloroplast (see Chapter 3 for a review of the theory of endosymbiosis). As a result, most plants are photosynthetic and only require water, some minerals, carbon dioxide, and sunlight for survival. For most plants, this means that they need to be rooted in soil to obtain water and nutrients, but they project into air for exposure to sunlight and carbon dioxide. In association with this, plant cells have also evolved rigid cellulose cell walls for support and vacuoles to store energy as sugars. Plants must obtain energy and nutrients, grow, and reproduce, all without the ability to move.

Animals, on the other hand, must obtain energy and carbon from the food they eat. Although many animals (such as clams, mussels, and barnacles) are sessile (do not move) as adults, most adult animals and all larvae are mobile. This requires that they be flexible and that they store energy compactly as fat. Clearly, some plants and animals have body plans that allow them to meet their needs without the requirement for highly specialized structures or organs (hydra, parasites, tapeworm, parasitic plants, algae), but the more complex the organism, the greater the need for specialized structures (refer to Chapters 17 and 19). The fundamental differences between plants and animals, however, have required each to find very different solutions to environmental challenges.

## STUDY BREAK

1. How are form and function related to one another?
2. Discuss how the need to serve multiple roles can constrain the evolution of structures.
3. Describe the structural hierarchy from cells to whole organisms.

## 20.3 Basic Organs and Systems of Plants

As you saw at the beginning of Chapter 17, the angiosperms, the group of flowering terrestrial plants that have dominated land for over 100 million years, can be classified by the way they look—whether they are trees, shrubs, vines, grasses, or succulent plants (see **Figure 17.3**). They can also be classified by the way they grow—whether they are a **woody plant** or a **herbaceous plant**. Woody plants grow in width each year by producing layers of woody tissues to the stems and roots. This category includes trees and shrubs and also cactuses, which produce woody tissues for support. Herbaceous plants do not produce woody tissues. This group includes ferns, grasses, and wildflowers, as well as most food crops. Vines can be either woody or herbaceous.

Despite the diversity of forms and ways of classifying terrestrial plants, all terrestrial plants require water and minerals that they obtain from the soil and $CO_2$ and light that they obtain from air (**Figure 20.4**). As a result, all terrestrial plants are composed of two basic systems: a **subterranean root system** and an **aerial shoot system**, neither of which can survive without the other. The three basic organs that compose these two systems are the roots, which belong to the root system, and the stems and leaves, which belong to the shoot system. These are described in detail in Chapter 17.

### Roots and Shoots: The Organ Systems

Each of the two basic systems in plants serves multiple functions. The roots of plants serve to anchor the plant in the soil and to absorb water and minerals from that soil. In most plants, they are also sites for food storage.

The shoot consists of the stems and leaves, as well as reproductive adaptations such as flowers and fruits. The stems support the leaves and flowers and link them with the roots.

These plant organs and systems come in many shapes and sizes that represent adaptations for different functions in different environments. Remember that each organ and system performs more than one function, and the primary function of each varies in different plants. Roots and stems are commonly modified for food storage. Common examples where roots are used for storage are beets,

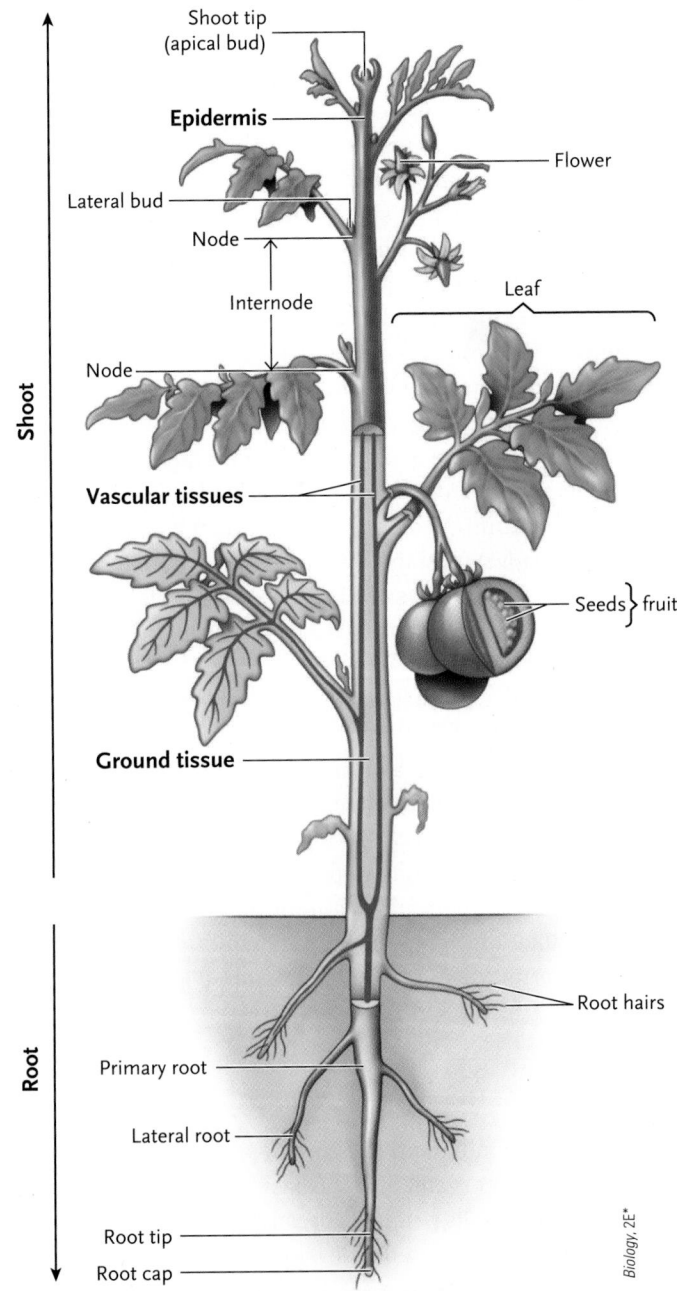

**FIGURE 20.4** Basic body plan for a typical angiosperm plant.

**FIGURE 20.5** Adaptations of stems: **(a)** a carrot (*Daucus carota*), **(b)** a potato (*Solanum tuberosum*), **(c)** an onion (*Allium cepa*), and **(d)** a cactus (*Opuntia aciculata*).

sweet potatoes, and carrots **(Figure 20.5a)**, whereas examples where shoots are used for food storage are potatoes, the bulbs of many common garden flowers (which are also swollen underground shoots) **(Figure 20.5, b and c)**, and cacti **(Figure 20.5d)**. Plant leaves are perhaps the most common and obvious example of diversity in shape and size. The massive leaves of many jungle plants, the blades of grasses, the needles of a pine tree, the spines of a cactus, and the tendrils of many climbing plants are all examples of modified leaves **(Figure 20.6)**.

**FIGURE 20.6** Adaptations of leaves: **(a)** broad leaves (*Victoria amazonica*), **(b)** pine needles (*Pinus* sp.), **(c)** Venus flytrap (*Dionaea muscipula*), and **(d)** tendrils.

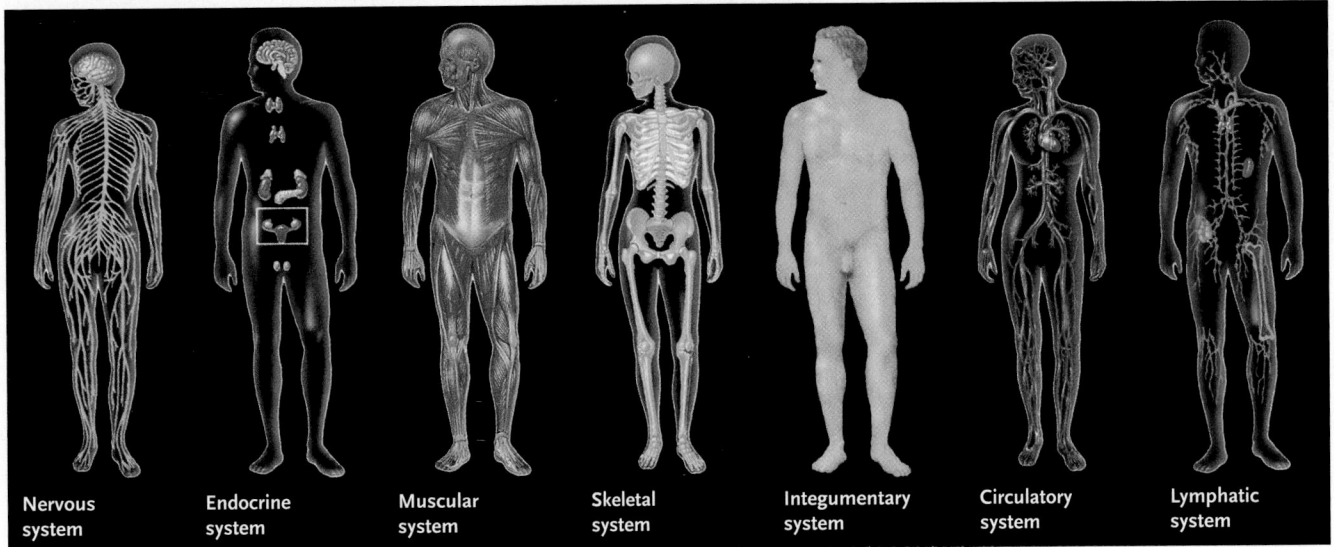

| Nervous system | Endocrine system | Muscular system | Skeletal system | Integumentary system | Circulatory system | Lymphatic system |
|---|---|---|---|---|---|---|
| **Main organs:** Brain, spinal cord, peripheral nerves, sensory organs | **Main organs:** Pituitary, thyroid, adrenal, pancreas, and other hormone-secreting glands | **Main organs:** Skeletal, cardiac, and smooth muscle | **Main organs:** Bones, tendons, ligaments, cartilage | **Main organs:** Skin, sweat glands, hair, nails | **Main organs:** Heart, blood vessels, blood | **Main organs:** Lymph nodes, lymph ducts, spleen, thymus |
| **Main functions:** Principal regulatory system; monitors changes in internal and external environments and formulates compensatory responses; coordinates body activities. Nervous systems are present in all metazoans except sponges. | **Main functions:** Regulates and coordinates body activities through secretion of hormones. Endocrine systems are also present in most metazoans. | **Main functions:** Moves body parts; helps run bodily functions; generates heat. Specialized muscle cells do not appear in evolution until triploblastic animals. | **Main functions:** Supports and protects body parts; provides leverage for body movements. An internal skeleton composed of bone and/or cartilage occurs only in the vertebrates. Similar functions in invertebrates are carried out by an external skeleton or by internal hydrostatic pressure. | **Main functions:** Covers external body surfaces and protects against injury and infection; helps regulate water content and body temperature. All Metazoa except sponges have an integument of some sort. | **Main functions:** Distributes water, nutrients, oxygen, hormones, and other substances throughout body and carries away carbon dioxide and other metabolic wastes; helps stabilize internal temperature and pH. Specialized circulatory systems occur in all vertebrates and in the annelids, molluscs, and arthropods. | **Main functions:** Returns excess fluid to the blood; defends body against invading viruses, bacteria, fungi, and other pathogens as part of immune system. Invertebrates do not have a specialized lymphatic system. |

## STUDY BREAK

1. Name the systems and organs found in plants.
2. What are the functions of each system?
3. Describe ways in which roots and leaves have been modified in plants living in different environments.

## 20.4 Basic Organs and Systems of Animals

Like plants, animals come in a wide variety of shapes and sizes. And like plants, they can be classified in various ways. For instance, they can be classified by the environment in which they live: as **aquatic**, **terrestrial**, or **aerial**. There are many differences, however, that separate animals beyond these categories. For example, birds, bats, and butterflies are all aerial, but they are distinctly different in many other ways. Birds and bats

are both vertebrates (have a vertebral column for support) with a dorsal hollow nerve cord, but birds have feathers and lay eggs, whereas bats have fur and give birth to live young. Butterflies have an external skeleton and a ventral solid nerve cord. Although they also lay eggs, these eggs develop in a very different way from those of vertebrates.

Unlike plants, animals are not photosynthetic. As a result, animals must eat and drink to obtain energy, nutrients, and water. For most adult animals, this requires that they be able to move around to find food. These demands require complex tissues and organ systems; thus, in the vertebrates, the group of animals of which we are a part, we find 12 distinct organ systems **(Figure 20.7)**, as opposed to the two that are found in plants. These 12 systems are described in detail in Chapter 19.

Animal organs and systems also come in many shapes and sizes, representing adaptations for different functions in different environments. For instance, although the epidermis or skin primarily protects animals

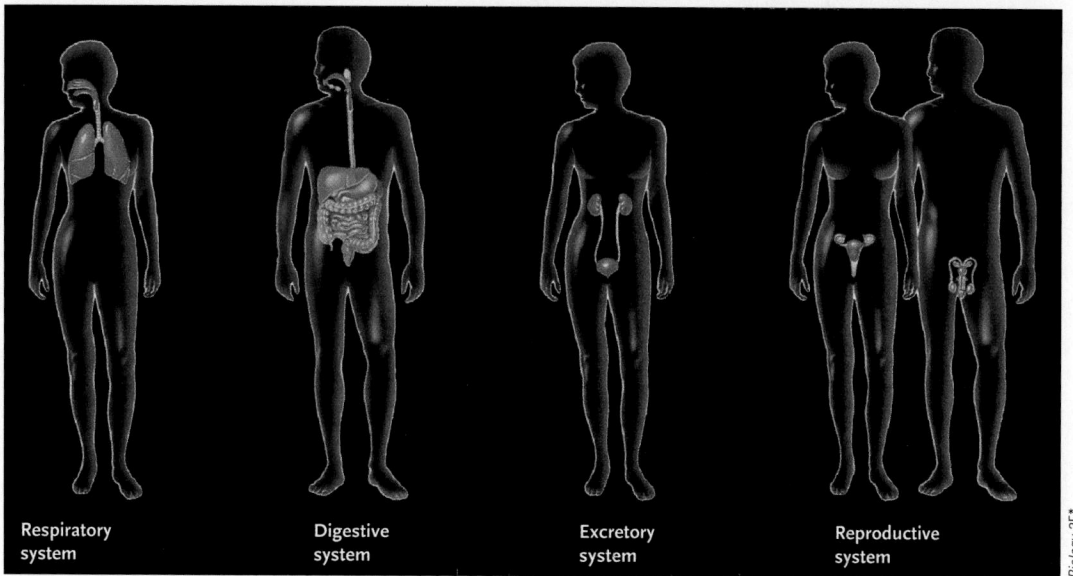

**FIGURE 20.7** Organ systems of the human body. The immune system, which is primarily a cellular system, is not shown. The functions performed by these organ systems are performed by all animals.

**Respiratory system**

**Main organs:**
Lungs, diaphragm, trachea, and other airways

**Main functions:**
Exchanges gases with the environment, including uptake of oxygen and release of carbon dioxide. Fish have a respiratory system that involves gills. Some form of specialized respiratory system occurs in most invertebrates.

**Digestive system**

**Main organs:**
Pharynx, esophagus, stomach, intestines, liver, pancreas, rectum, anus

**Main functions:**
Converts ingested matter into molecules and ions that can be absorbed into body; eliminates undigested matter; helps regulate water content. Most metazoans, with the exception of some parasitic forms, have a digestive system.

**Excretory system**

**Main organs:**
Kidneys, bladder, ureter, urethra

**Main functions:**
Removes and eliminates excess water, ions, and metabolic wastes from body; helps regulate internal osmotic balance and pH. All animals perform these functions. All vertebrates have kidneys, and most invertebrates have specialized excretory organs and systems.

**Reproductive system**

**Main organs:**
*Female:* ovaries, oviducts, uterus, vagina, mammary glands
*Male:* testes, sperm ducts, accessory glands, penis

**Main functions:**
Maintains the sexual characteristics and passes on genes to the next generation. Most triploblastic animals have specialized reproductive organs and systems.

against injury and infection, it can also be involved in gas exchange or used to attract mates or avoid predators **(Figure 20.8, p. 442)**. Animal skeletons are perhaps the most common and obvious example of diversity in shape and size, from the massive support structures seen in rhinos, hippos, and elephants to the lightweight wings of birds and the armoured shells of crabs, lobsters, and turtles.

## STUDY BREAK

1. Name the systems and organs found in animals.
2. What are the functions of each system?

## 20.5 Integrated Body Systems

Body systems work together to respond to environmental change. The environments in which all organisms live are subject to change—change in temperature and in the availability of the nutrients and gases (oxygen and carbon

dioxide) essential for life. Unicellular and simple multicellular organisms are largely unable to control for the effects of these changes and frequently exhibit adaptations that allow them to simply withstand change. For example, adaptations that allow them to withstand freezing in the winter or dehydration during periods of drought (for an extreme example, see Box 20.2). More complex organisms, however, exhibit adaptations that act to keep their internal environment stable in the face of changes in their external environment. This is the principle of homeostasis, the maintenance of a stable or steady internal environment (see Chapter 3).

The extent to which organisms use homeostasis and the manner in which they do so vary tremendously. Most multicellular plants and animals can control salt and water balance very accurately, although the ability to tolerate large changes in water availability in the external environment varies tremendously; cacti can survive long periods without rain, whereas most food crops perish quickly when conditions are dry. Vertebrates such as fish,

# THE MOLECULE BEHIND THE BIOLOGY 20.1
## Lignin and Keratin in Plants and Animals

In both plants and animals, dead cells serve important specific functions. In all of these cells, polymers (long chains of molecules), made up of either aromatic alcohols (alcohols that form in a ring configuration) (lignin) or proteins (**keratin**), are laid down in the cells before they die to give them their special properties.

Lignin is an integral part of the secondary cell wall in plant cells **(Figure 1)**. The special cells of the internal transport system that move water up the plant (xylem; see Chapter 17) are dead and hollow and act as conducting vessels. Their lateral walls, however, contain lignin, which makes the cell walls relatively impermeable to water and improves the efficiency with which they conduct water. The tissue that provides support to most plants (**sclerenchyma**, a type of ground tissue; see Chapter 17) also must die before these cells can take on their role in support. The cell walls remain, however, and the lignin in the walls provides the strength required to support the plant. The lignin makes up from a quarter to a third of the dry mass of wood.

In terrestrial vertebrates, the epidermis often forms an outer **keratinized** cell layer. These cells, in the process of self-destruction, accumulate a class of proteins, keratin, that serve to reduce water loss and/or prevent mechanical damage.

Keratin in animals is a fibrous protein that is assembled into bundles to form a strong, unmineralized tissue (Figure 1). It is found in the epidermis and its derivatives are found in reptiles, birds, amphibians, and mammals forming scales, feathers, hair, nails, claws, hooves, and horns.

**FIGURE 1** Lignin provides the strength in wood, whereas keratin provides resistance to mechanical damage in the skin of reptiles.

**FIGURE 20.8** The integument of animals can be highly adapted for **(a)** protection in tortoises (*Gopherus agassizii*), **(b)** gas exchange in frogs (*Deandrobates reticolatus*), **(c)** mate attraction in toucans (*Ramphastos sulfuratus*), or **(d)** predator avoidance in moths (*Artace cribrarius*).

# LIFE ON THE EDGE 20.2
## *Lithops aucampiae*, the Living Stone

Research has shown that several species of plants live their lives primarily or entirely underground. One such species is *Lithops aucampiae*, a plant referred to as a "living stone." These plants display extreme morphological and physiological adaptations that enable them to grow in very hot, dry (xeric) desert environments. Although their underground existence minimizes water loss by transpiration from their leaves, it raises serious problems for photosynthesis.

Researchers have shown that there are "windows" on the upper surfaces of the plant's leaves that break the surface of the soil **(Figure 1)**. The epidermal cells of these windows are large and flat, allowing light to penetrate deep into the leaves below ground. These cells also contain non-photosynthetic pigments (flavonoids), which are known to filter incoming solar radiation and screen out harmful UV radiation. This pigmentation may also provide camouflage to the plant, protecting it from being eaten by small mammals. Finally, an increased concentration of chlorophyll *a* in the above-ground regions of leaves enables maximum photosynthetic use of incoming light.

In the below-ground regions of the leaves, the epidermal cells are thick and conical and believed to contain microcrystalline deposits of calcium oxalate. These deposits are thought to minimize loss of light and to maximize below-ground internal reflectance of incoming light from the leaf windows to the less illuminated below-ground photosynthetic tissues. The below-ground tissues also have an increased concentration of chlorophyll *b*. Chlorophyll *b* absorbs light of wider wavelengths than chlorophyll *a* and transfers the "extra" captured photons to chlorophyll *a* for use in photosynthesis. This maximizes the absorption and use of low light levels within the below-ground region of the leaf.

Thus, this plant simultaneously exhibits intense-light (above-ground) and shade-tolerant (below-ground) features found in other plants, but in this case, in the same structure! This unique combination of traits allows the leaves of *Lithops aucampiae* to maximize photosynthesis and be protected against oxidative, UV damage while reducing rates of water loss.

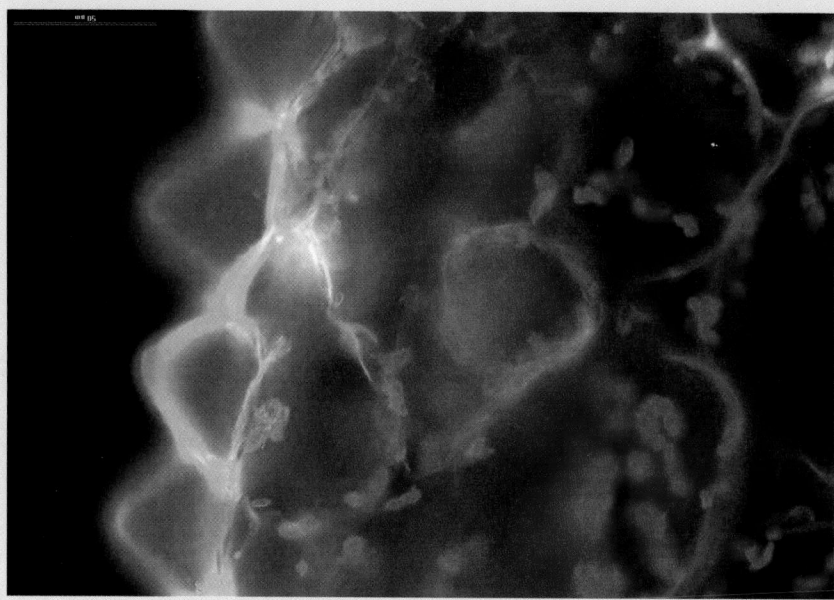

**FIGURE 1** This is a longitudinal image of the epidermal cells on the above-ground surface of a leaf of *Lithops aucampiae* under UV light.

SOURCE: Courtesy of Matthew P. Davey and Rachel M. George, from Field KJ, George R, Fearn B, Quick WP, Davey MP (2013) Best of Both Worlds: Simultaneous High-Light and Shade-Tolerance Adaptations within Individual Leaves of the Living Stone Lithops aucampiae. PLoS ONE 8(10): e75671. doi:10.1371/journal.pone.0075671

---

amphibians, and reptiles can only control body temperature by behavioural means, perhaps by lying in the sun or taking shelter. Birds and mammals can accurately control body temperature physiologically over wide ranges of environmental temperature. Such homeostatic control invariably requires that multiple organ systems work in a highly integrated and interdependent fashion.

## Control Systems Regulate Exchange and Continuously Adjust Internal Conditions

For organs and organ systems to work together in an integrated fashion requires communication. This is the role of the endocrine system in both plants and animals as well as of the nervous system in animals. Communication is used to control these systems, most often through a process referred to as **negative feedback control**. This is the process by which changes in the levels of key compounds in the bodies of plants and animals activate physiological mechanisms that reverse these changes. Let's explore two examples, one present in animals and one in plants.

The most common example of negative feedback control in vertebrate animals is body temperature regulation in birds and mammals. This control consists of three parts: receptors, integrators, and effectors. First, the body must be able to sense its own temperature. This requires sensors of some sort. Second, this information must be

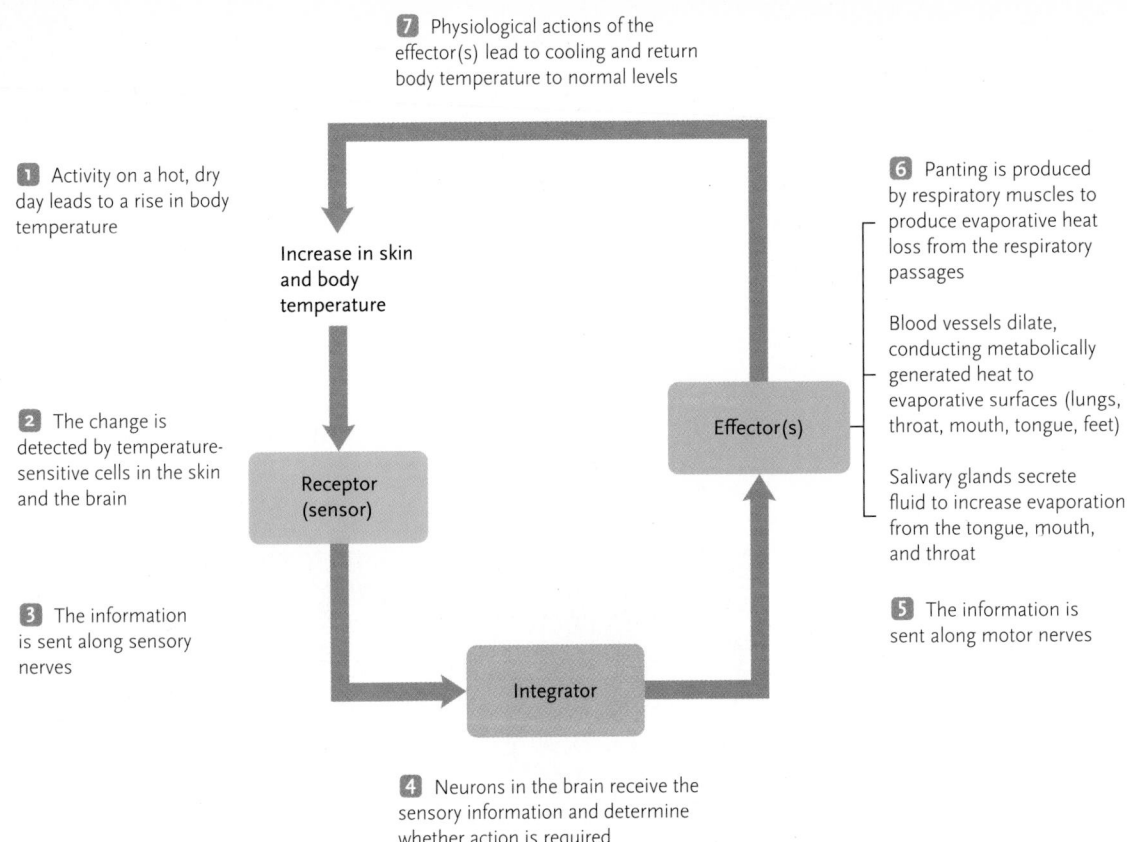

**7** Physiological actions of the effector(s) lead to cooling and return body temperature to normal levels

**1** Activity on a hot, dry day leads to a rise in body temperature

**2** The change is detected by temperature-sensitive cells in the skin and the brain

**3** The information is sent along sensory nerves

**4** Neurons in the brain receive the sensory information and determine whether action is required

Increase in skin and body temperature

Receptor (sensor)

Integrator

Effector(s)

**6** Panting is produced by respiratory muscles to produce evaporative heat loss from the respiratory passages

Blood vessels dilate, conducting metabolically generated heat to evaporative surfaces (lungs, throat, mouth, tongue, feet)

Salivary glands secrete fluid to increase evaporation from the tongue, mouth, and throat

**5** The information is sent along motor nerves

**FIGURE 20.9** Homeostatic mechanisms maintaining the body temperature of a bird or mammal when body temperature rises.

integrated to determine whether it is too high, too low, or just right. Third, this information must lead to physiological changes (effects) that return the body temperature to the desired level. In the example in **Figure 20.9**, we can trace this path for a mammal exercising on a hot, dry day. This activity (1) leads to an increase in skin (from the Sun) and body temperature (heat from muscle activity). This change is detected (2) by temperature receptors present in the skin as well as in the brain and spinal cord. This information is sent to a special area of the brain (3) (the **hypothalamus**), where the body temperature is determined to be rising (4). This leads to the neural activation (5) of a variety of processes (6) designed to return the body temperature to normal (7). Effectors are the organs or systems that bring about the desired effect, in this case, panting, sweating (and other forms of evaporative heat loss), and salivation.

Plants also use negative feedback control systems to regulate normal functions. In the example illustrated in **Figure 20.10**, insects feeding on the leaves (1) of a plant cause the release of the hormone systemin from the site of the wound. This hormone travels throughout the plant in the phloem (2) and binds to receptors on the plasma membrane of many cells (3). Through a series of steps, this leads to the production of a second plant hormone, jasmonate (4), which in turn leads to

the expression of genes coding for a proteinase (enzymes that digest proteins) inhibitor (5). This occurs not only around the wound site but also in cells throughout the plant. Now when insects feed on these cells, they ingest the proteinase inhibitor (6), which disrupts protein digestion and seriously disrupts the ability of the insects to grow and survive. This in turn reduces the risk of further predation on the plant by the insects (7).

Positive feedback systems also exist in plants and animals. These are systems that are self-exciting and explosive. This is the process by which changes in the levels of key compounds in the bodies of plants and animals activate physiological mechanisms that lead to further and further increases. These are much less common. Classic examples are the nerve action potential (see Chapter 26) and the process of birth (see Chapter 28).

## STUDY BREAK

1. Define homeostasis and list examples of variables that are homeostatically controlled in a plant, an invertebrate animal, and yourself.
2. Describe in detail one example of a negative feedback control system, pointing out the three key processes.

# BIOLOGY IS EVERYWHERE 20.3
## Biological Engineering

Scientists have long marvelled at the wonders of nature, at the ways in which evolution has produced anatomical adaptations of the most amazing kind—feathers in birds, spider silks, tall trees, and fire-resistant seeds. Not surprisingly, they have also turned to biology for insight and inspiration in the design of manufactured structures. This has blossomed into the field of biological engineering, the application of biological concepts and methods to the design of synthetic devices and the solution of engineering problems. Negative feedback control systems such as those involved in body temperature regulation and blood pressure regulation are employed in the design of home heating systems and the complex stabilization of aircraft in flight. Biomaterials, either natural or synthetic, are used in such medical applications as heart valve and hip replacements, dental surgery, and drug delivery systems and most recently for the design of nanocomposites.

For example, researchers from around the world have been seeking to find ways to artificially manufacture an equivalent to spider silk **(Figure 1)**. This material is stronger than steel, tougher than Kevlar, and lighter than carbon fibre. Not only that, it can also be stretched by as much as 40% without breaking. Potential uses for the product include the production of artificial ligaments and blood vessels, protective clothing, and car bumpers capable of absorbing heavy impacts. The genome for spider silk is now known, and several companies are looking at ways to produce large quantities of this protein using either genetically modified bacteria or genetically modified goats that produce milk containing spider silk.

These endeavours are producing job opportunities on a variety of fronts. CNNMoney ranks biomedical engineering as #10 in the top 100 best jobs in America.

**FIGURE 1** The silk of a spider's web has both strength and elasticity, allowing it to withstand the impact forces of flying insects.

Matthijs Wetterauw/Shutterstock.com

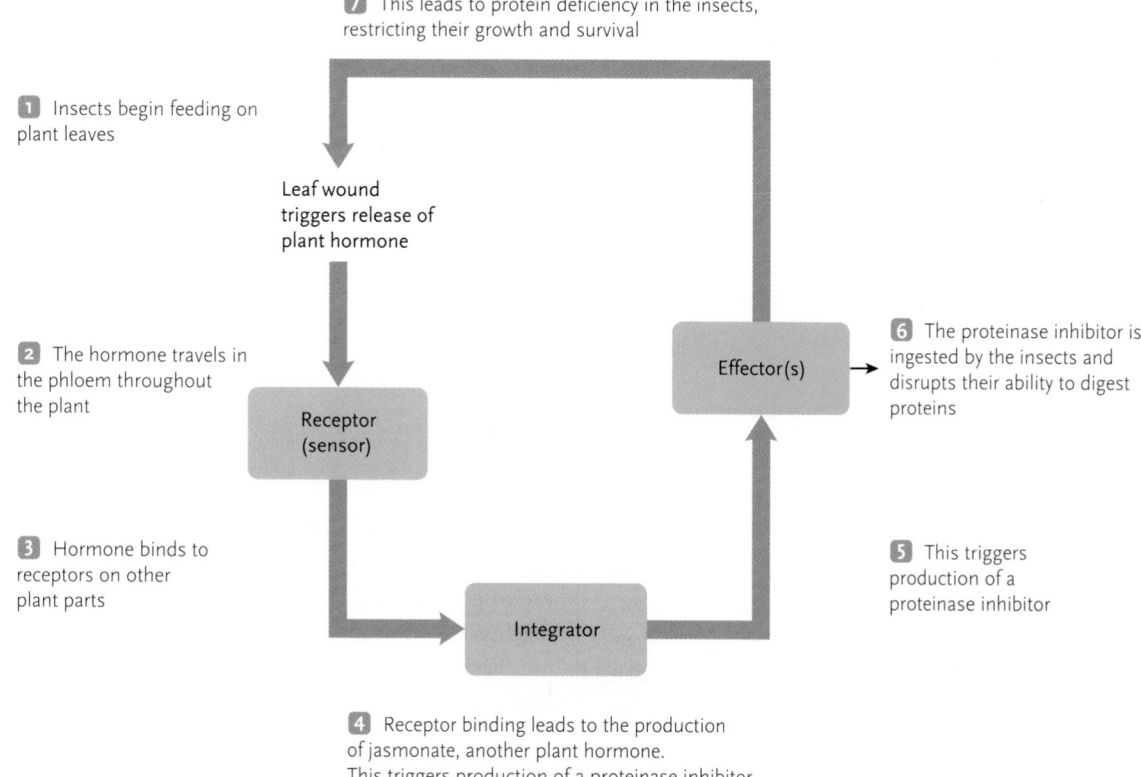

**7** This leads to protein deficiency in the insects, restricting their growth and survival

**1** Insects begin feeding on plant leaves

Leaf wound triggers release of plant hormone

**2** The hormone travels in the phloem throughout the plant

Receptor (sensor)

**3** Hormone binds to receptors on other plant parts

Integrator

**4** Receptor binding leads to the production of jasmonate, another plant hormone. This triggers production of a proteinase inhibitor

Effector(s)

**6** The proteinase inhibitor is ingested by the insects and disrupts their ability to digest proteins

**5** This triggers production of a proteinase inhibitor

**FIGURE 20.10** Homeostatic mechanism restricting further damage to a plant following leaf wound damage due to insect feeding.

## PUTTING IT IN PERSPECTIVE

In the chapters to follow, we will explore the basis of how plants and animals work. As emphasized throughout this chapter, function relies heavily on form. Our understanding of form with regard to plants and animals not only allows us to understand how they function but has also provided both the inspiration and the insight for the construction of buildings, machinery, and even prosthetic limbs and other medical devices (see Box 20.3). The Mother Nature Network lists seven "amazing examples of biomimicry" where research into plant and animal form has inspired engineers and designers. These range from the sharkskin-inspired swimsuits seen in the 2008 Summer Olympics to termite nest-inspired buildings, whale fin-inspired wind turbines, and lotus flower-inspired dust-repellent paint.

## KEY CONCEPTS REVIEW AND QUESTIONS

(*Note:* Some of the questions posed here require you to integrate information from Chapters 17 and 19 with the information presented in this chapter.)

### 20.1/2   Structure–Function Relationships/Tissues, Organs, and Systems

There is a strong correlation between structure and function in both plants and animals. Each influences the other. Function is influenced by form, whereas form adapts to suit function.

Both plants and animals are composed of different types of cells that arise by differentiation from a single cell. Tissues are groups of cells with a common function, whereas systems are composed of organs made up of several tissue types. There are emergent properties at each level of organization.

1. Match the terms on the left with the descriptions of levels of organization on the right. Each term may apply to more than one description.

   a. Cell _____ A group of cells with a common function

   b. Tissue _____ Stomach, leaves, hearts, and stems are at this level

   c. Organ _____ The highest functional level of organization

   d. Organ system _____ Fundamental unit of structure and function

2. True or False? Animal and plant tissues are composed only of living cells. Explain your answer.

### 20.3   Basic Organs and Systems of Plants

The root system anchors the plant in place and serves for the uptake of water and minerals from the soil. It also supports the shoot system composed of the stem, leaves, flowers, and fruit. The stem supports the leaves and reproductive organs and serves for transport between the leaves and the roots. It often also serves a storage function. The leaves are the main photosynthetic organs of the plant, producing sugars from sunlight and $CO_2$.

Each organ system in the plant is composed of the three tissue types: dermal, vascular (xylem and phloem), and ground (parenchyma, sclerenchyma, and collenchma) tissue.

3. In the leaves of a maple tree, which tissue type (a) produces sugars, (b) transports the sugars to the roots, (c) transports water to the leaves, and (d) protects the leaves from desiccation?

4. Match the terms on the left with the descriptions on the right. Each term may apply to more than one description.

   a. Epidermis _____ Site of photosynthesis

   b. Xylem _____ Regulate gas exchange and water loss

   c. Phloem _____ Transports sugars

   d. Parenchyma _____ Protects against infestation and water loss

   e. Sclerenchyma _____ Transports minerals and water

   f. Guard cells _____ Largely consists of dead cells that form fibres for support

5. Which plant organ (root, stem, or leaf) is associated with each of the following functions?

   a. Obtaining water

   b. Providing access to sunlight

   c. Performing photosynthesis

   d. Storing sugars

   e. Obtaining minerals

### 20.4   Basic Organs and Systems of Animals

Animals possess 12 different organ systems. These perform specialized functions, such as defence, support, movement, gas exchange, acquiring food, and eliminating wastes. They work together in an integrated fashion.

Each organ/system is composed of two or more of the four major tissue types: epithelial, connective, muscle, and nervous tissue.

6. You watch a young kitten licking a plate after eating its dinner. Which tissue type in this organ (a) moves

the tongue back and forth, (b) protects the tongue from abrasion, and (c) tastes the food left on the plate?

7. For the following examples, indicate whether the epithelial cell layer will be thin or thick and whether or not it will be keratinized.
   a. Skin of a lizard
   b. Lining of the lungs where gas exchange takes place
   c. Lining of the small intestine where digested food is absorbed
   d. Soles of the feet of a bird

8. Which 2 of the 12 organ systems in animals are essential for the regulation of the activities of all the other systems?

## 20.5 Integrated Body Systems

All organisms can control their internal environment to some extent—some more than others. In complex organisms, the endocrine system (and in animals the nervous system) monitors and responds to changes in the internal environment, producing behavioural or physiological changes that act to stabilize the internal environment. This is usually in the form of negative feedback control.

9. Which of the following best illustrates homeostasis?
   a. Leaves and lungs tend to have large surface areas.
   b. All adult members of a species are about the same size.
   c. When blood pressure rises, heart rate and blood vessel tone are altered to return it to normal levels.
   d. When there is no sunshine, the rate of photosynthesis decreases.
   e. Plants and animals do not thrive at altitudes where oxygen is limiting.

10. What are the three components of a negative feedback loop? Give an example of a feedback loop describing each of the three components.

# Obtaining Nutrients and Energy

## WHY IT MATTERS

Major disruptive events such as volcanic eruptions, tsunamis, and typhoons can completely obliterate all life in an area, plant and animal. Slowly over time, however, life returns through the process of succession, which is described fully in Chapter 13. The first organisms to colonize such areas must settle, grow, and reproduce. Initially, very few organisms can achieve this, but over time, the diversity of organisms living in these areas increases. There are many factors that underlie this phenomenon, but an important one is nutrition. The nutrients that are available in an area and the nutritional requirements of different organisms determine who the colonizers will be and the direction subsequent events will take. The eruption of Krakatoa in the South Pacific in 1883 was so massive that the explosion was heard almost 5,000 km away and is considered to have been the loudest sound ever heard in modern history. The only living thing found by the first researchers to inspect the island after the eruption was a spider. By 1884, grasses were growing on the island, and today it hosts shrubs and trees and over 60 species of vertebrates **(Figure 21.1)**.

The island was visited by Captain George Vancouver aboard HMS *Discovery* prior to the eruption, and the flora was described as typical of that of the tropical forests of the region. The area is still subject to volcanic activity that disrupts the normal chain of succession. The vegetation on the island has primarily arisen from seeds washed up from the sea or transferred in the droppings of birds, and the chain of succession reflects the ability of the first colonizers to turn pumice and volcanic ash into soil and to extract nutrients from it.

A thorough understanding of what the nutritional requirements are for different organisms, and what nutrients are available in different habitats, allows biologists to fully understand the biodiversity that exists in any region and how it is likely to change over time, particularly if the climate or the carbon footprint in the area is changing over time.

In this chapter, we will discuss the nutritional requirements of both plants and animals and explore the ways in which they obtain them. Some nutrients are essential to all living cells, whereas others are specific to different groups. The methods of obtaining nutrients

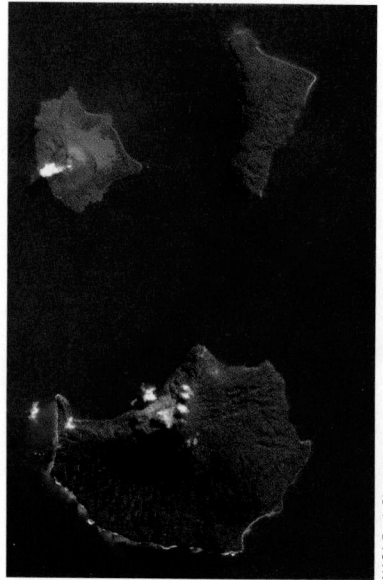

**FIGURE 21.1** This picture, taken from the NASA Earth Observatory (July 7, 2009), shows Anak Krakatoa (Child of Krakatoa, a new island formed in 1927, upper left), which is still very active and hosts little vegetation, and Rakata (remnant of the old Krakatoa, bottom), which now exhibits significant recolonization.

reflect lifestyle, and many unique adaptations have arisen in both plants and animals for this purpose.

## 21.1 Nutrient Requirements for Growth, Development, and Survival

What are nutrients, and why are they required? All living organisms need both organic and inorganic molecules for two main purposes. Remember that organisms are built of organ systems composed of tissues made from different types of cells (see Chapter 20). Some organic and inorganic molecules are required to build these structures—to build cell membranes, cell walls, organelles, etc. These are required to allow organisms to grow and develop. Furthermore, building and maintaining these structures require energy, which is obtained from carefully breaking chemical bonds and ultimately harnessing that energy as ATP, adenosine triphosphate. The primary sources of the fuel for this energy are organic compounds. The organic and inorganic molecules required for these two purposes are referred to as nutrients, and they are essential for life.

Many of these nutrients are required in large amounts and are referred to as macronutrients. Others are required only in very small quantities or trace amounts and are referred to as micronutrients (*macro-* and *micro-* refer to the quantity needed and not the size of the molecule). These divisions are relative, and some nutrients may fall between these two categories. If they must be obtained from the environment in plants or from eaten food in animals, they are referred to as essential nutrients. Nutrients that can be obtained by converting other compounds by the plant or animal are not essential.

With this in mind, let's take a look at the specific needs of plants and animals.

## There Are Essential Macro- and Micronutrients Required by Plants

Plants grow, develop, and survive exclusively on inorganic compounds. Although this may seem surprising at first, remember that most plants make all of the organic compounds essential for their lives themselves; hence, plants are referred to as autotrophs. These organic compounds are principally sugars and starches that are constructed from atmospheric $CO_2$ and water through the process of photosynthesis (see Chapter 5). Plant cells use the sugars made through photosynthesis to construct all other organic materials they need for growth (e.g., the cellulose in cell walls) and as a stored source of energy (starches and sugars used for glycolysis by mitochondria to make ATP) (see Chapter 4).

The inorganic material, or minerals that plants require, on the other hand, are taken up from the soil. Advances in our understanding of these requirements have been greatly aided by the use of hydroponics, a method of growing plants in mineral solutions without soil **(Figure 21.2)**. This method was pioneered in the late 1800s and was the basis of the field of plant nutrition.

Three of the key minerals that plants require are nitrogen, phosphorus, and potassium. Nitrogen is a key component in all amino acids (hence all proteins) and nucleic acids (all genetic material) and in chlorophyll and is also an essential component of ATP, many plant enzymes, and plant hormones. Phosphorus is an essential component of nucleic acids, ATP, and the phospholipids that make up cell membranes. Potassium is a main solute in intra- and extracellular fluids and is also a key component in many enzymes. These compounds are needed in sufficient quantities to be considered macronutrients. Lack of available nitrogen in the soil often limits plant growth in early successional communities (glaciated regions or volcanic areas such as Krakatoa) because little nitrogen is found in uninhabited soil and most nitrogen is made available from decomposing organic matter. Phosphorus, on the other hand, is available but replaced slowly. Thus, conversely, phosphorus is often readily available in early successional communities but limited in old weathered soils (such as in the tropics).

**PURPOSE:** In studies of plant nutritional requirements, using hydroponic culture allows a researcher to manipulate and precisely define the types and amounts of specific nutrients that are available to test plants.

**PROTOCOL:** In a typical hydroponic apparatus, many plants are grown in a single solution containing pure water and a defined mix of mineral nutrients. The solution is replaced or refreshed as needed and is aerated with a bubbling system.

A. **Basic components of a hydroponic apparatus**

Plant support

Nutrient solution

Air pumped into bubbling system

B. **Procedure for identifying elements essential for proper plant nutrition**

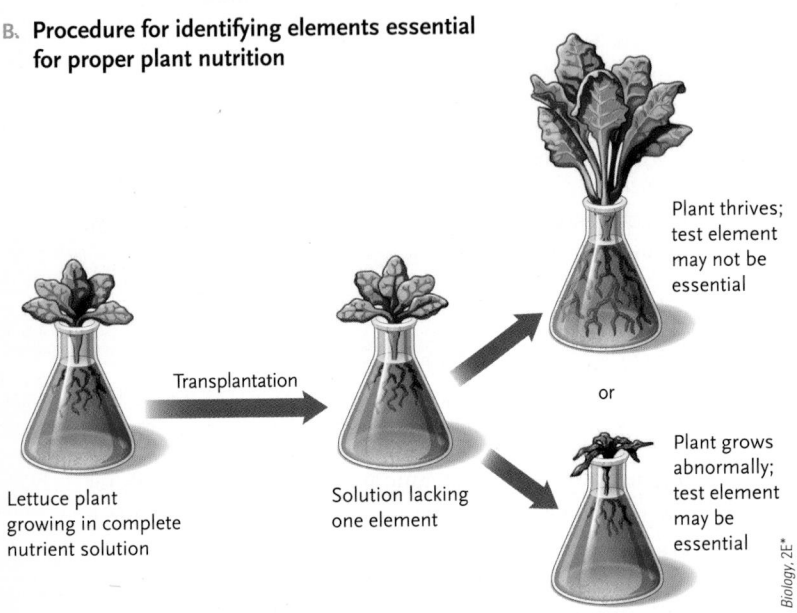

Lettuce plant growing in complete nutrient solution

Transplantation

Solution lacking one element

or

Plant thrives; test element may not be essential

Plant grows abnormally; test element may be essential

*Biology, 2E*

A complete solution contains all the known and suspected essential plant nutrients. An incomplete solution contains all but one of the same nutrients, in the same amounts. For experiments, researcher first grow plants in a complete solution and then transplant some of the plants to an incomplete solution.

**INTERPRETING THE RESULTS:** Normal growth of test plants suggests that the missing nutrient is not essential, whereas abnormal growth is evidence that the missing nutrient may be essential.

**FIGURE 21.2** Growing plants hydroponically.

Three other minerals considered macronutrients are calcium, magnesium, and sulphur. Calcium is found in cell membranes, cell walls, and the matrix that holds cells together in tissues. Magnesium is an essential component of chlorophyll, and sulphur is important for forming the chemical bridges that give many proteins their three-dimensional structure.

These six minerals along with the carbon, oxygen, and hydrogen obtained from $CO_2$, $O_2$, and water constitute the nine macronutrients needed by plants.

There are also eight known micronutrients required in small amounts by plants. These are chlorine, iron, manganese, boron, zinc, copper, nickel, and molybdenum. These minerals act primarily as cofactors in enzymes: they take the place of an amino acid and give an enzyme the unique shape and binding properties that allow it to catalyze specific chemical reactions (see Chapter 4). Since enzymes and their cofactors are not consumed in the reactions they catalyze but are used over and over again, the cofactors need only be replaced infrequently as enzymes age and degrade. As a result, these cofactors are needed only in very small amounts.

Although these 17 nutrients just described are essential to all plants, there are other micronutrients that are essential only to certain specific species, such as sodium to plants adapted to hot, dry conditions and silicon in horsetails and grasses such as wheat. Plants also take up minerals that are not required as nutrients. These molecules diffuse into plants from the soil in solution in water and are then stored by the plants. Among these minerals are gold, lead, arsenic, and uranium. This characteristic of some plants is now being used as a means to clean up polluted soil and ground water through a process called phytoremediation. Many plants readily take up heavy metals, and some can concentrate these at levels that would be toxic to other plants. Sunflowers are a classic example of a plant used for this purpose. Mature plants can concentrate large quantities of these toxic substances and can then be harvested and taken to hazardous-waste landfills, providing an inexpensive way to detoxify an area without having to completely disrupt (dig up) the landscape.

## There Are Essential Macro- and Micronutrients Required by Animals

Unlike plants, which can produce the organic materials they need through photosynthesis, animals must obtain both the organic and the inorganic nutrients required to build complex biological structures and to burn as fuel. Many animals obtain all the nutrients they need as herbivores, eating only plants. Carnivores eat an exclusively meat diet, whereas omnivores obtain nutrients from a mixed diet of both plants and animals.

Any of the three major groups of macronutrients, carbohydrates, fats, and proteins can be used as fuel. In all cases, their chemical bonds are enzymatically broken down, releasing energy that is ultimately used to produce the ATP required to drive biological processes. Carbohydrates are often the preferred source of energy as they can be broken down rapidly. Fats, on the other hand, yield more than twice the energy per gram of tissue than carbohydrates or proteins but are harder to process. Plants are rich sources of carbohydrates, whereas meat, eggs, nuts, and seeds are rich sources of protein and fats.

Both plants and animals store excess energy—plants for use when energy is needed in greater supply than can be provided by photosynthesis, and animals for use between meals. Plants convert sugars into starch for this purpose, whereas animals convert excess energy, no matter what form it comes in (carbohydrate, protein, or fat), into fat. Starch is a storage form that can be quickly mobilized to release stored energy, but as it contains only half the stored energy per gram of tissue as fat, it is bulky. This is not a probem for a stationary plant. For mobile animals, however, bulk can be a problem, and animals store their energy in the compact, energy-rich form of fat. This is critically important for the many species of birds that make long migration flights as well as species of small mammals that may more than double their weight in summer as they store sufficient fat to see them through a long winter of hibernation.

Animals can synthesize many of the compounds that they need as building blocks for cell structure from whatever food they obtain in their diets by converting compounds back and forth between one form and another. There are many compounds, however, that they cannot build, and it is therefore essential that they obtain these in their diet. These include certain amino acids, fatty acids, minerals, and vitamins (see Box 21.1). The list of these varies from species to species. As with plants, what is essential to one species may not be to another, and quantities required by some may be toxic to others. Again, some of these nutrients are macronutrients, required in large quantities, and some are micronutrients, required in small amounts.

Using humans as an example, we require eight essential amino acids in our diet for manufacturing proteins (nine in infants and young children). Although we cannot make these ourselves, they are readily available in proteins obtained from sources such as meat (including fish), egg whites, and milk products (including cheese) but are rarely all present in proteins obtained from individual plants. Thus, the diets of vegetarians must contain a mix of plant species to ensure that they contain all essential amino acids. The remaining 12 amino acids required for protein synthesis

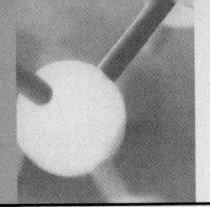

# THE MOLECULE BEHIND THE BIOLOGY 21.1
## Vitamins

Vitamins are organic molecules that are required for proper body function in all animals. Many vitamins function as coenzymes (see Chapter 4). These are non-protein molecules that are inserted in place of amino acids in building enzymes. They contribute to the unique shape and binding properties of enzymes that allow them to catalyze specific chemical reactions. This gave rise to their initial name of "vital amines," which has subsequently been shortened to vitamins. Other vitamins are used for the synthesis and maintenance of structural elements. Cofactors are inorganic substances that act in similar ways.

Humans require 13 known vitamins, and these are listed in **Table 1** along with their common sources, main functions, and deficiencies that arise if they are chronically absent from our diets. Depending on whether or not the molecules are charged determines whether they are soluble in fat (uncharged or non-polar) or in water (charged or polar). The fat-soluble vitamins can be stored in the body when they are available in excess of our needs. The water-soluble vitamins cannot; excess vitamins in our blood are filtered out by the kidneys and eliminated in our urine.

As a result, there is a need to acquire water-soluble vitamins from our diet on a continual basis.

Individual species differ in the vitamins they require in their diets. Most mammals can synthesize vitamin C, but humans, other mammalian primates, guinea pigs, and fruit bats cannot. Although humans cannot make vitamin K, we obtain it from bacteria living in our guts. Ruminants such as cattle and deer also obtain the B vitamins in similar fashion, from microorganisms living in their digestive tracts.

| TABLE 1 | Vitamins: Sources, Functions, and Effects of Deficiencies in Humans | | |
|---|---|---|---|
| **Vitamin** | **Common Sources** | **Main Functions** | **Effects of Chronic Deficiency** |
| **Fat-Soluble Vitamins** | | | |
| A (retinol) | Yellow fruits, yellow or green leafy vegetables; also in fortified milk, egg yolk, fish liver | Used in synthesis of visual pigments, bone, teeth; maintains epithelial tissues | Dry, scaly skin; lowered resistance to infections; night blindness |
| D (calciferol) | Fish liver oils, egg yolk, fortified milk; manufactured when body exposed to sunshine | Promotes bone growth and mineralization; enhances calcium absorption from gut | Bone deformities (rickets) in children; bone softening in adults |
| E (tocopherol) | Whole grains, leafy green vegetables, vegetable oils | Antioxidant; helps maintain cell membrane and red blood cells | Lysis of red blood cells; nerve damage |
| K (naphthoquinone) | Intestinal bacteria; also in green leafy vegetables, cabbage | Promotes synthesis of blood-clotting protein by liver | Abnormal blood clotting, severe bleeding (hemorrhaging) |

Biology, 2E*

(Continued)

we can make by conversion from other sources. Likewise, we require two essential fatty acids for the synthesis of the phospholipids in cell membranes as well as the manufacture of some hormones. These are readily available in most diets. We also require inorganic elements such as calcium, iron, and magnesium in our diets, along with 13 known vitamins. The latter are needed in small quantities primarily for incorporation into proteins as coenzymes (see Box 21.1).

## Nutrient Deficiencies Have Severe Consequences

Deficiencies in any given nutrient have deleterious effects for any plant or animal, particularly if the deficiency is for an essential nutrient. Other than as use as energy sources, all nutrients are needed in their appropriate amounts, and a deficiency of one nutrient cannot be compensated by the abundance of another. The amount of each essential nutrient that a given plant requires is very species specific. In fact, the amount essential for one species may be toxic to another. This reflects differences in metabolic processes in each species and is why the nutrient content of soils is so important in determining which plants will and will not grow in a given area. It explains why certain plants can settle as pioneering species in one area following a catastrophic event, such as the volcanic eruption on Krakatoa, whereas other species cannot. In the presence of nutritional deficiencies, plants develop characteristic abnormalities, such as stunted growth, yellow-green colouration, or dead spots on leaves reflecting which

| TABLE 1 | Vitamins: Sources, Functions, and Effects of Deficiencies in Humans (Continued) | | |
|---|---|---|---|
| Vitamin | Common Sources | Main Functions | Effects of Chronic Deficiency |
| **Water-Soluble Vitamins** | | | |
| B₁ (thiamine) | Whole grains, green leafy vegetables, legumes, lean meats, eggs, nuts | Connective tissue formation; folate use; coenzyme forming part of enzyme in oxidative reactions | Beriberi; water retention in tissues; tingling sensations; heart changes; poor coordination |
| B₂ (riboflavin) | Whole grains, poultry, fish, egg white, milk, lean meat | Coenzyme | Skin lesions |
| Niacin | Green leafy vegetables, potatoes, peanuts, poultry, fish, pork, beef | Coenzyme of oxidative phosphorylation | Sensitivity to light; contributes to pellagra (damage to skin, gut, nervous system, etc.) |
| B₆ (pyridoxine) | Spinach, whole grains, tomatoes, potatoes, meats | Coenzyme in amino acid and fatty acid metabolism | Skin, muscle, and nerve damage |
| Pantothenic acid | In many foods (meats, yeast, egg yolk especially) | Coenzyme in carbohydrate and fat oxidation; fatty acid and steroid synthesis | Fatigue; tingling in hands; headaches; nausea |
| Folic acid | Dark green vegetables, whole grains, yeast, lean meats; intestinal bacteria produce some folate | Coenzyme in nucleic acid and amino acid metabolism; promotes red blood cell formation | Anemia; inflamed tongue; diarrhea; impaired growth; mental disorders; neural tube defects and low birth weight in newborns |
| B₁₂ (cobalamin) | Poultry, fish, eggs, red meat, dairy foods (not butter) | Coenzyme in nucleic acid metabolism; necessary for red blood cell formation | Pernicious anemia; impaired nerve function |
| Biotin | Legumes, egg yolk; colon bacteria produce some | Coenzyme in fat and glycogen formation and amino acid metabolism | Scaly skin (dermatitis); sore tongue; brittle hair; depression; weakness |
| C (ascorbic acid) | Fruits and vegetables, especially citrus, berries, cantaloupe, cabbage, broccoli, green pepper | Vital for collagen synthesis; antioxidant | Scurvy; delayed wound healing; impaired immunity |

nutrient is deficient and which metabolic process is hindered by the missing element **(Figure 21.3, p. 454)**. Because macronutrients are required in larger quantities, deficiencies in nitrogen, phosphorus, and potassium are particularly common and are the most common ingredients in fertilizers used commercially and by home gardeners (usually listed as the N-P-K ratio) to enrich soils. Keep in mind, however, that although many micronutrients are needed only in trace amounts, deficiencies in these minerals can be equally devastating.

This is also true of animals. Essential macronutrients and micronutrients must be obtained from their diets. As with plants, the amount of each essential nutrient that a given animal requires is very species specific and explains the unique dietary needs of different animals (eucalyptus leaves for koala bears [*Phascolarctos cinereus*], for instance).

Absence of essential amino acids will lead to protein deficiency and will hinder normal growth and development. Since amino acids cannot be stored as such, a deficiency of a single amino acid impairs all protein synthesis. Absence of essential fatty acids in some low-fat diets will make individuals prone to coronary heart disease. This may at first seem counterintuitive given the association between heart attacks and high-fat diets, but remember that the cell membranes of all cells are composed of a phospholipid bilayer and that some fats, especially the essential fatty acids, are needed for their construction (see Section 21.1). Mineral and vitamin deficiencies have also been well characterized, and chronic deficiencies lead to a host of debilitating conditions (Figure 21.3). In humans, these deficiencies are particularly prevalent in southern Asia and sub-Saharan Africa.

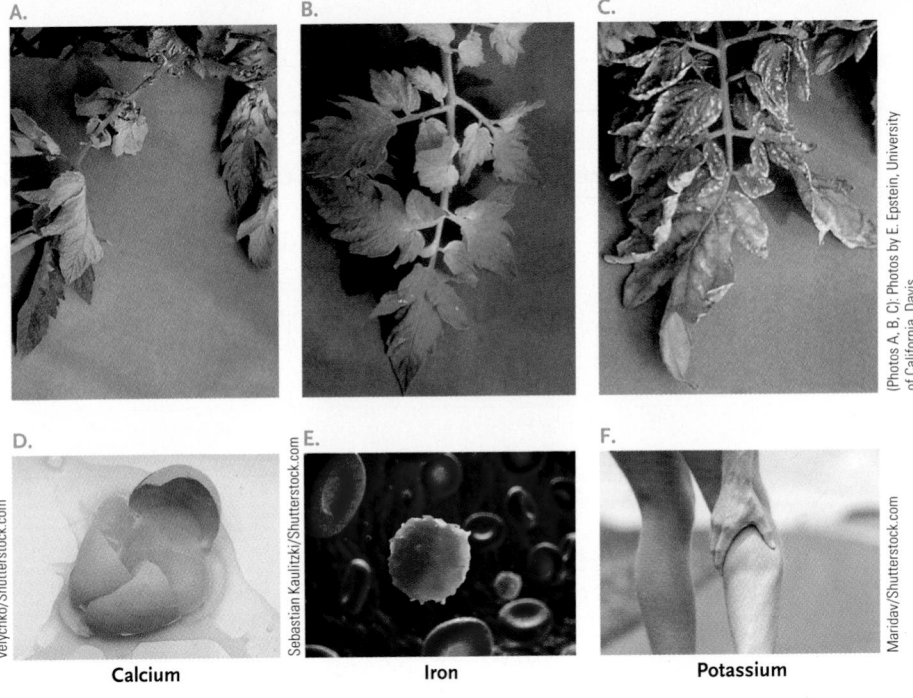

**FIGURE 21.3** Results of mineral deficiencies in plants and animals. Calcium deficiencies lead to deformed leaves in plants **(a)**, osteoporosis in humans, and thin eggshells in birds **(d)**. Iron deficiency leads to chlorosis (yellowing leaves) in plants **(b)** and anemia (low hemoglobin) in animals **(e)**. Potassium deficiency leads to curled, mottled, and spotted leaves in plants **(c)** and muscular weakness and cramping in animals **(f)**.

A.

B.

C.

D.

E.

F.

**Calcium**

**Iron**

**Potassium**

Worldwide, more than 20 million infants are born every year with low birth weights, and almost 4 million die during the neonatal period. These deaths result from undernutrition, and micronutrient deficiencies resulting from inadequate amounts of meat, fruits, and vegetables in the diet are common. The World Health Organization (WHO) is working strenuously to remedy this situation by the use of micronutrient supplements to both pregnant women and young infants.

Nutritional deficiencies in animals, however, come not only in the form of inadequate supplies of inorganic molecules for building cells but also in the form of inadequate fuel for providing energy. Malnutrition refers to either an inadequate supply of organic fuel or inadequate assimilation of these fuels, as well as an excessive intake of specific nutrients. Although it is easy to understand how an inadequate supply of food will lead to undernourishment, our understanding of the causes of uncontrolled weight gain is incomplete. For many animals in nature, weight gain is tightly genetically controlled. As mentioned earlier, many species of birds that make long migration flights lay down fat in preparation for the journey. At other times of the year, they do not. Species of small mammals that hibernate lay down fat through the summer in preparation for the harsh winter ahead. For many, body weight dictates when they enter hibernation. Furthermore, it has been shown in some species that if individuals are maintained in the laboratory under favourable conditions all winter, they eat less and lose weight at the same rate as animals living off their fat in hibernation. Thus, both hibernating and non-hibernating animals reach the same sleek body conditon in the spring.

The genetic factors that regulate body weight remain an intense area of research, an area becoming increasingly important with the growing incidence of obesity in the human population.

## STUDY BREAK

1. What are nutrients, and why are they necessary?
2. What nutrients must plants obtain from soils?
3. If $O_2$ is so abundant in air, why must roots obtain it from the soil? In what kind of soils is this difficult to achieve?
4. Why do animals need to obtain organic molecules as nutrients, whereas plants do not?
5. Which vitamins can animals store, and which ones must be obtained on a regular basis and why?

## 21.2 Obtaining Nutrients

All plants obtain nutrients across their roots and their leaves from the environments in which they grow. This requires that all substances be in solution, that is, dissolved in water. Although this is also true of some simple aquatic animals, for many animals, nutrients are ingested in more complex forms and broken down into soluble forms internally by the process of digestion. In all cases, nutrients must ultimately be in a form that can be transported actively or passively across cell membranes. They cannot enter the body between cells; they must enter by passing through cells and once inside the body must be taken up and used by cells.

## Plants Obtain Nutrients from the Air Above and the Soil Below

Large trees have been found on all continents of the world except Antarctica. Several species of trees have been recorded growing to roughly 90 to 115 m in height (280 to 380 ft), including the coast redwoods (*Sequoiadendron giganteum*) in California, the Douglas fir (*Pseudotsuga menziesii*) in the Pacific northwest (including British Columbia), various species of eucalyptus tree (*Eucalyptus* sp.) in Tasmania, and the yellow meranti (*Shorea acuminatissima*) in Borneo. Equally impressive are some of the stoutest trees measuring from over 5 to 10 m in diameter (roughly 15 to 40 ft). These include the Montezuma cypress from Mexico, the baobab trees (*Adansonia* sp.) from South Africa, and the kauri trees (*Agathis australis*) from New Zealand. What is most impressive is that trees of this mass acquire most of their bulk from the carbon in $CO_2$ in air and the H in $H_2O$ taken up from the soil! Air, water, and some minerals from the soil are the basis of plant growth **(Figure 21.4)**.

### Acquiring Nutrients from the Air

Although 90% of a plant's total mass is water, approximately 96% to 98% of the remaining dry mass is organic (carbon containing) material built from atmospheric $CO_2$ (Figure 21.4). The significance of this is lost on many of us until we realize that we can grow plants from seeds to large mature plants in a pot of soil by only adding water as needed. Almost the entire mass of the mature plant arose out of thin air!

Interestingly, plants also exchange $O_2$ with the air surrounding them. In Chapter 5, you saw that $O_2$ is a waste product resulting from the splitting of water molecules during photosynthesis in the leaves. However, as with all living cells, plant cells also require $O_2$ as the electron acceptor in cellular respiration when the sugars produced by photosynthesis are broken down aerobically to make ATP (see Chapter 5). Although, in general, plants are net producers of $O_2$, consumption can exceed production at certain times, such as at night and during certain seasons (particularly during periods of rapid growth by aquatic plants and phytoplankton). This is why grandmothers are reported to recommend that plants be removed from the rooms of persons who are ill at night and why many fish die in small shallow ponds (kill-off) in the spring when aquatic plants bloom.

### Acquiring Nutrients from the Soil

For terrestrial plants, the major source of water is the soil. This water is the main constituent of intra- and extracellular fluids, just as it is in animals. In plants, it is also required as the source of electrons for carbon fixation in photosynthesis. The minerals enter the root passively

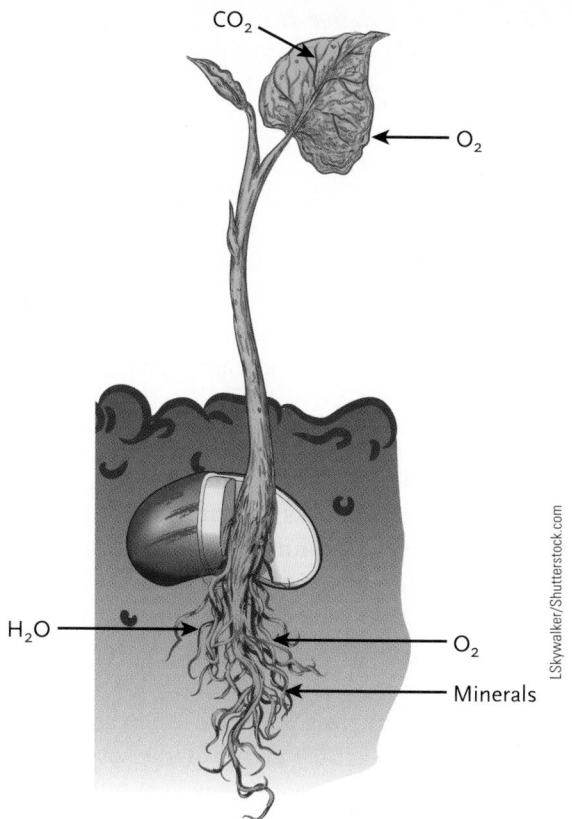

**FIGURE 21.4** Sources of nutrients required for plant growth.

dissolved as solutes in the water. The water and solutes can move between cells in the extracellular fluid but ultimately must cross the plasma membranes of cells to enter their cytoplasm. As ions are charged particles, they cannot penetrate the phospholipid bilayer of the membrane and must be carried across by ion-specific transport proteins (see Chapter 3). Although some of the water and minerals are retained for use by the roots, much will be distributed to the rest of the plant, as described in Chapter 24. The cells of the plant sequester the minerals in vacuoles and in the cell cytoplasm, where they are used for metabolic processes.

$O_2$ is also taken up from the soil for cellular respiration by the roots themselves. The source of this $O_2$ ultimately is the atmosphere, but penetration into the soil to provide $O_2$ for the roots is essential. Providing $O_2$ to the roots of plants living in shallow water or flooded soils is more difficult because $O_2$ diffuses so much more slowly in water than in air. Most plants adapted to living under these conditions (such as bullrushes) have stems and roots containing air chambers, which allow $O_2$ to diffuse from the air above water to the tissues below.

Although plants are not able to move about seeking new or better soils, their root systems do grow and explore surrounding areas. In areas where water or nutrients are scarce, the root systems of plants can grow to occupy over 50% of the mass of the plant. The plant must produce roots with sufficient surface area to absorb all the water and nutrients required for proper growth and mainte-nance. The fine root hairs of the individual epidermal cells contribute extensively to this process. In long-lived perennial plants, the root systems continue to grow and become very extensive.

Since many minerals are essential nutrients, plants are also protective of them. In the fall, before deciduous trees shed their leaves, many of the minerals are with-drawn from the leaves and stored in the twigs and branches, and in many perennial grasses, they are with-drawn and stored in the roots and stems.

### Soil Characteristics Affect Nutrient Uptake

We tend to think of soil as simply dirt, but it is in fact a complex mixture of rocks and minerals, water, air, living organisms (microbes, fungi, plants, and animals), and organic matter (the decayed remains of the living organisms) **(Figure 21.5)**. During soil formation, following an eruption such as Krakatoa, for example, or the scraping of a landscape by glaciers, rocks break down into particles of three different sizes: sand, silt, and clay. Sandy soils contain as much as 50% air by volume. As a result, they provide much $O_2$ for root metabolism but retain water poorly. Clay soils, on the other hand, are compact, contain little $O_2$, and retain water. Mixed in among the soil par-ticles is the organic matter, the decomposing parts of plants, animals, and animal droppings. This organic matter, or humus, is spongelike, adding air spaces and increasing the ability of the soil to absorb water. It also serves as food for decomposers, whose metabolic activi-ties release many minerals essential for plant growth.

Because the minerals in the soil are charged particles (ions), they tend to adhere to the soil particles, making them less available to enter solution and be taken up by the roots. This is particularly true of the cations (posi-tively charged ions) such as potassium, calcium, and magnesium because most soil particles are negatively charged. However, the production of $CO_2$ by respiring roots (remember that roots do not photosynthesize but do respire, thus producing $CO_2$) and the breakdown of organic acids by the roots lead to the production of hydrogen ions ($H^+$). This cation displaces the other cations on soil particles, making them available to the plant. Not surprisingly, the natural pH of soils greatly influences the availability of minerals to plants.

Anions (negatively charged ions), on the other hand, are not as tightly bound to soil particles and are more available for plant uptake. There is a drawback to this, however, as these ions are also more easily leached or washed away in heavy rains. Nitrate ($NO_3^-$) is an anion that is easily leached out of soils, rendering them nitrogen deficient (and rendering the run off in nitrate-fertilized regions that are potentially nutrient rich, contributing to nutrient pollution).

For plants to thrive for long periods, the minerals they remove from the soil must be replaced. The sources of this are the breakdown or weathering of rocks and the decomposition of organic matter (see the following sec-tion). The commercial use of fertilizers adds many minerals back to the soil but without the humus, which is why compost, decayed organic matter, is a preferable solution for enriching poor soils as long as the nutrient balance in compost is a good match to the nutrient requirements of plants or crops.

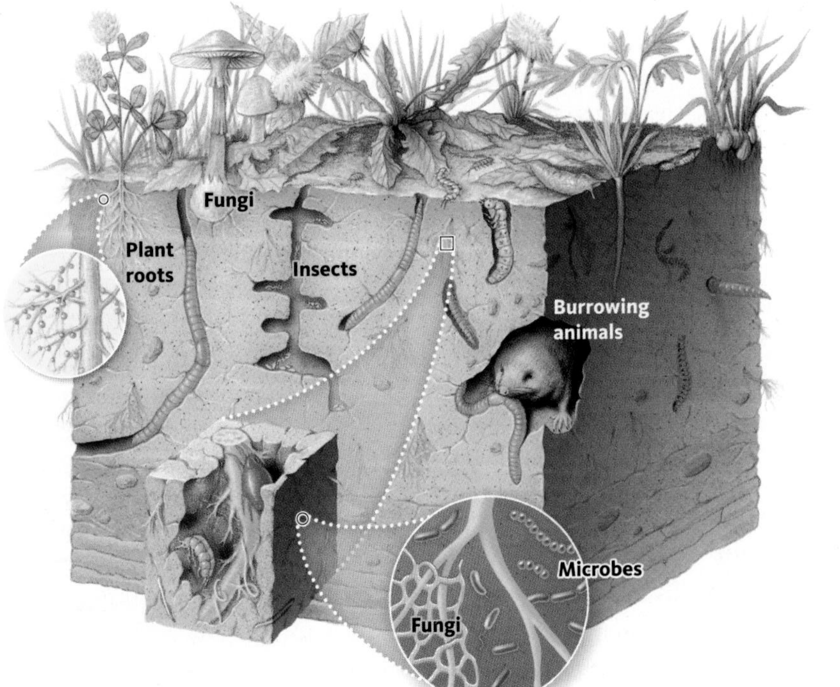

### Sources of Available Nitrogen in Soil

Although the atmosphere contains more nitrogen than any other compound (it is roughly 79% $N_2$), $N_2$ in this form is not avail-able to plants. To be usable by plants, it must first be converted from a gas to ionic form as either ammonium ($NH_4^+$) or nitrate ($NO_3^-$). Although these ions are obtained from the soil, they do not arise from the weathering of rock. They are produced from atmospheric $N_2$ or from organic material by soil bacteria (Figure 21.5) through a process referred to as nitrogen fixation. Atmo-spheric $N_2$ is converted to $NH_3$ by nitrogen-fixing bacteria, which is then converted to $NH_4^+$ by reacting with water. A second group of soil bacteria produce $NH_4^+$ directly

**FIGURE 21.5 Recycling of soil nutrients.** Communities of microbes, fungi, and animals modify the soil by creating air spaces and recycling nutrients.

Perhaps no one knows the essentials of plant nutrition and the palates of humans better than farmers, and among the most specialized and in demand these days are vintners, the makers of the quality wines consumed worldwide **(Figure 1)**. The success of any vineyard depends on a complex of factors, including soil type, site conditions and aspect (sun facing or shaded), local microclimate, plant nutritional requirements, and irrigation. Grapes in general do not have high nutritional requirements, and, ironically, this is a case where too much nitrogen in the soil can be a bad thing. When nitrogen levels are high, canopy growth is promoted over fruit production and reduces the yield of grapes that can be harvested. Furthermore, the canopy shades the fruit, delaying ripening. A challenge facing the growers of wine grapes is to maintain soil nitrogen at levels that maximize the yield without compromising the quality.

One example of a Canadian success story is that of the Mission Hill winery in British Columbia. The first chardonnay it produced in 1992 won the award for "Best Chardonnay in the World" at the International Wine & Spirit Competition in London in 1994. This past year, the Mission Hill Family Estate took on the best in the world again and won top honours as "World's Best Pinot Noir" in the under £15 category at the Decanter World Wine Awards in London, England. Mission Hill's proprietor, Anthony von Mandl, and chief vintner, John Simes, have been instrumental in putting the Okanagan Valley wines on the map.

**FIGURE 1** Balancing nutritional needs is essentail in the production of quality wines.

by the ammonification of organic matter. Although plants can absorb this ammonium directly, the soil is also teeming with nitrifying bacteria that rapidly convert the $NH_4^+$ to $NO_3^-$. As a result, $NO_3^-$ is far more abundant in most soils, but once absorbed by the roots, it must be converted back into $NH_4^+$, which is then used to synthesize amino acids and other organic materials needed by the plants.

Many plants, especially those of the legume family (peanuts, beans, clover, alfalfa), have formed mutualistic associations with nitrogen-fixing bacteria. The roots of these plants provide the bacteria with carbohydrates and other organic compounds that the bacteria need for cellular respiration, and in return, the bacteria provide the plant roots with $NH_4^+$. The bacteria are housed in root nodules, swellings on the roots where the bacteria live in cytoplasmic vacuoles within root cells. Because these plants are so good at **fixing nitrogen**, farmers often plant them in rotation with other plants. Once mature, the legume plants are plowed under the soil, where they decompose, adding nitrogen to the soil that can be used by other crops the following year.

There is another mutualistic relationship that exists between some plants and certain fungi that help these plants improve nutrient uptake. In this relationship, the plants and the fungi produce a mutual structure called a mycorrhiza that enwraps the roots and root hairs. The fungi of mycorrhizae are more efficient at absorbing minerals and make them available to the plant roots, again in return for a supply of sugars from the plant. Plants that pioneer nutrient-poor soils such as the lava extruded by volcanoes such as Krakatoa usually have mutualistic associations with fungi, and it has been hypothesized that such relationships may have been one of the evolutionary adaptations that allowed plants to colonize land.

Too much nitrogen can also be a bad thing, as explained for growing grapes in Box 21.2.

1. Why is it so difficult for roots to obtain cations from the soil?
2. Where does most of the bulk of a tree come from: soil or air?
3. How are the roots of plants in nutrient-poor soil likely to differ from those in nutrient-rich soil?

## Animals Obtain Nutrients by Feeding but Must Digest Them

In animals, converting food into nutrients for use by the cells of the body generally involves three key processes: eating or ingesting food; physically and chemically digesting the food, breaking it down into small molecules; and absorbing those small molecules across epithelial cells and distributing them throughout the body. A fourth process, the defecation or elimination of undigested materials, is also generally required.

In most invertebrates and all vertebrates, digestion takes place in a gastrointestinal tract (gut or GI tract), a tubelike digestive system with a mouth where food is ingested and an anus where undigested waste is eliminated. Along the way are a variety of chambers, the number and function of each reflecting the diets of the animals. The chambers where digestion takes place usually come before those where absorption occurs and must be designed to withstand being digested themselves. In many cases, there are chambers where ingested food can be stored before being processed, allowing animals to accumulate larger quantities of food than can be processed immediately.

A summary of these processes as they occur in humans is depicted in **Figure 21.6**, and in the following sections, we examine these processes in detail. We will discuss food acquisition first followed by digestion and, finally, absorption. Note, however, that the processes of both digestion and absorption can take place along several segments of the gastrointestinal tract with varying degrees of overlap.

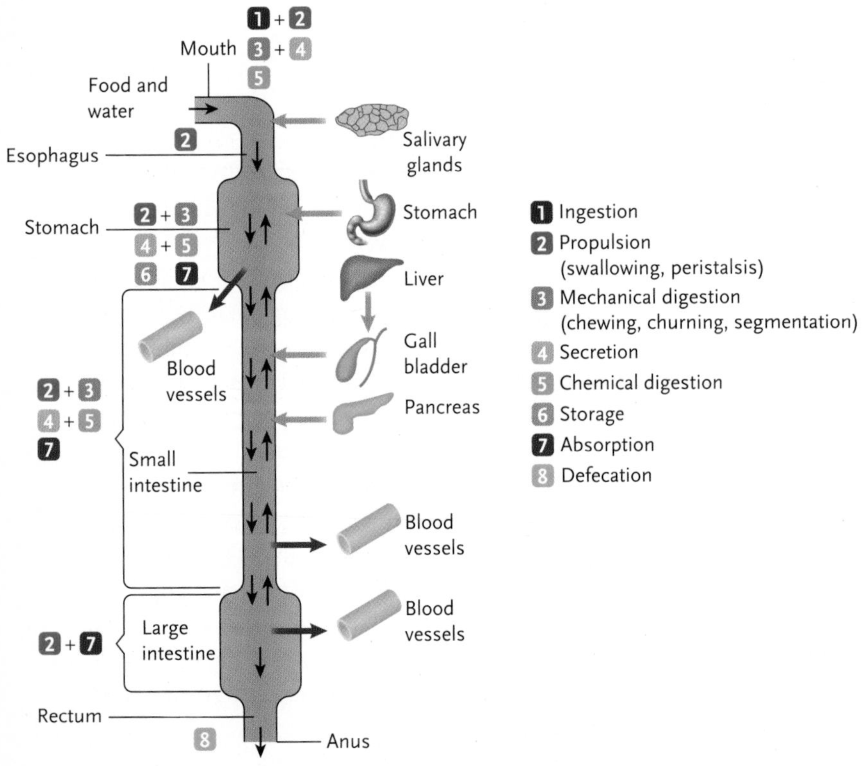

### Acquiring (Ingesting) Nutrients

Food comes in many forms, and animals are highly adapted to acquire it from many sources **(Figure 21.7)**.

Decaying organic matter is a rich source of nutrients, and many animals are adapted to take advantage of this. Some **deposit feeders** or detritivores simply eat the soil and the decaying organic matter they live in or on, absorbing nutrients and eliminating undigested waste. Others selectively extract the organic matter from the substrate. Included in this group are many invertebrates, such as earthworms, sea stars, sea cucumbers, fiddler crabs, dung flies, and dung beetles **(Figure 21.7a)**, and vertebrates, such as some vultures.

**Fluid feeders** obtain nutrients by ingesting liquids. These nutrient-rich fluids come in many forms. Many insects, butterflies, hummingbirds, and bats feed on the nutrient-rich nectars produced by flowering plants as a lure to aid them in pollination **(Figure 21.7b)**. Other species, such as mosquitoes, bedbugs, leeches, and vampire bats, feed on the body fluids of other animals, using piercing mouthparts to penetrate their bodies. Most produce anticoagulants in their saliva to keep ingested blood from clotting. Aphids use penetrating mouthparts to obtain vascular fluids from plants in a similar way. Leeches and eels use rasping mouthparts to disrupt the skin and obtain body fluids. Spiders trap their prey and then secrete enzymes to liquefy their tissues, providing a nutrient-rich broth that they then ingest.

In aquatic environments, **filter feeders** or **suspension feeders** use specialized structures (bristles, hairs, gills, or fringes of horny fibres) to filter small organisms such as phytoplankton, zooplankton, and small crustaceans from the water column. The food is usually filtered from the water and trapped in mucus, which can be funnelled into the gastrointestinal tract. Although the food is small, the organisms that employ this technique range in size from aquatic invertebrates such as barnacles, clams, and mussels to large baleen whales **(Figure 21.7c)**.

**FIGURE 21.6** Processes involved in nutrient acquisition in mammals.

Mouth ❶+❷ ❸+❹ ❺
Food and water
Esophagus
❷
Salivary glands
Stomach ❷+❸ ❹+❺ ❻❼
Stomach
Liver
Gall bladder
Blood vessels
❷+❸ ❹+❺ ❼
Pancreas
Small intestine
Blood vessels
Blood vessels
Large intestine ❷+❼
Rectum
❽
Anus

❶ Ingestion
❷ Propulsion (swallowing, peristalsis)
❸ Mechanical digestion (chewing, churning, segmentation)
❹ Secretion
❺ Chemical digestion
❻ Storage
❼ Absorption
❽ Defecation

**A. Deposit feeder**

Stacey Ann Alberts/Shutterstock.com

**B. Fluid feeder**

Sari ONeal/Shutterstock.com

**C. Filter feeder**

John Turney/Shutterstock.com

**D. Bulk feeder**

chris2766/Shutterstock.com

**FIGURE 21.7** Different types of feeding in animals. Deposit feeding by dung beetles **(a)**, fluid (nectar) feeding by hummingbirds **(b)**, filter feeding by baleen whales **(c)**, and bulk feeding of a baby bird by an owl **(d)**.

**Bulk feeders** eat large objects, either whole or in large pieces. This group includes some invertebrates and most of the vertebrate animals. Most fish, adult amphibians, reptiles, birds, and mammals fall into this category **(Figure 21.7d)**. With the exception of the mammals, all either swallow their food whole or in large pieces. This group includes herbivores, carnivores, and omnivores. Mammals are the only group capable of chewing their food before swallowing. Humans, for the most part, indulge in bulk feeding.

### Digesting Nutrients

Digestion is the process of physically and chemically breaking down food into molecules small enough that they can be taken up by epithelial cells and thus enter the bodies of animals. Physical digestion results from the tearing, chewing, and grinding of food into smaller particles, making it easier for food to move through the digestive system and increasing the surface area on which chemical digestion can act. Chemical digestion involves the secretion of enzymes and acids that break the chemical bonds of large macromolecules, reducing them to their molecular

subunits. Carbohydrates are broken down into mono- and disaccharides, proteins are broken down into amino acids, and fats are broken down into glycerol and fatty acids. The enzymes that accomplish this are carbohydrases, proteases, and lipases, respectively.

In some invertebrates, such as the sea anemone, digestion occurs in a simple sac, a gastrovascular cavity, with a single opening **(Figure 21.8, p. 460)**. In the case of the anemone, food is entrapped by mucus on its tentacles and moved into the gastrovascular cavity. Glands in the cavity wall secrete enzymes into the cavity that digest the food. Small molecules are absorbed directly by the cells lining the wall, whereas larger molecules are taken up by endocytosis (see Chapter 4) and digested further inside the cells. Undigested food and metabolic wastes secreted into the cavity are periodically eliminated through the single opening by compression of the cavity by retractor muscles.

As mentioned above, in most invertebrates and all vertebrates, digestion takes place in a gastrointestinal tract, a tubelike digestive system with a mouth where food is ingested; a series of chambers for storage, digestion, and absorption; and an anus where undigested waste is

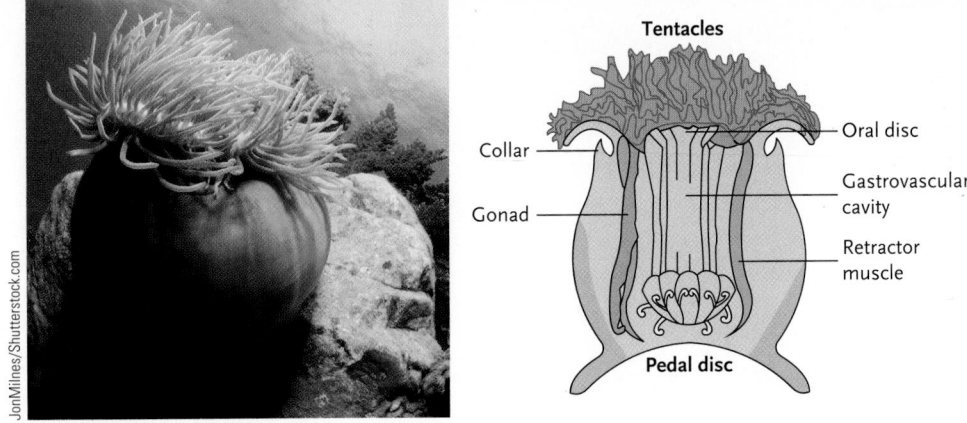

**FIGURE 21.8** The gastrovascular cavity of a sea anemone.

SOURCE: (Photo B): From FENTON/ DUMONT/OWEN. *Integrative Animal Biology*, 1E. © 2014 Nelson Education Ltd. Reproduced by permission. www .cengage.com/permissions

Tentacles

Collar

Gonad

Oral disc

Gastrovascular cavity

Retractor muscle

Pedal disc

JonMilnes/Shutterstock.com

eliminated. Note that although food may enter and pass through the tract, unless it is digested and absorbed, it will not have passed across any cell membranes, and although it will have passed through the animal, it will not have entered the animal. The lumen of the gastrointestinal tract is continuous with the environment, and digestion within the tract is still extracellular.

Food is moved through the system by a variety of muscular actions, including swallowing and peristalsis (rhythmic movements of the walls of the tract), and this movement is assisted by secretions of mucus and emulsifiers. Fats are not water soluble (they will separate, like the oil in salad dressing), and emulsifiers combine with fat molecules to make them water soluble and easy to transport.

The size and shape of the various chambers that comprise the gastrointestinal tract (gut) reflect the diets and lifestyles of the animals. Let's take a look at four different examples of gastrointestinal tracts to illustrate this point **(Figure 21.9)**.

The earthworm is a detritivore; it ingests soil as it digs its burrow. The soil enters the mouth and passes through the esophagus into a storage chamber called the crop, where it is stored. It is mixed with mucus here and then passes into a muscular gizzard, where the organic content is ground into fine particles, assisted by the abrasive action of sand and other soil particles. It then enters the intestine, where chemical digestion by enzymes takes place, breaking down macromolecules into molecules that can be absorbed.

The grasshopper is an herbivore that tears leaves and other plant parts into small pieces with its mandibles and external mouthparts (it is a bulk feeder). This food is then ingested through the mouth into the pharynx, where it is moistened by saliva. It then passes into the crop, where food is stored before being ground into finer particles in the gizzard. It then passes into the stomach, where much of the chemical digestion takes place. Gastric ceca are outpockets of the stomach that secrete the digestive enzymes and provide a large surface area for absorption of the digested nutrients. The remaining material then passes into the intestine, where further processing (digestion and absorption) takes place.

Pigeons are seed eaters. As the seeds pass through the mouth and esophagus, they are moistened and then stored in the crop. In the proventriculus, the glandular portion of the stomach, enzymes and acids are added to begin chemical digestion. The food then passes into the gizzard, where further mechanical digestion takes place due to grinding, assisted commonly by bits of sand and rock that the birds deliberately ingest. Once ground to fine particles, the food enters the intestine, where enzymes and emulsifiers secreted from the liver and pancreas finish the chemical digestion of the food, making it ready for absorption.

Humans are omnivores—different populations eating just about anything. As with other mammals capable of chewing their food, physical digestion begins in the mouth and is assisted by chemical digestion by salivary amylase, an enzyme that begins the digestion of sugars and starches, making certain foods taste sweet. The food then passes to the stomach, where acid and a protease (a protein-digesting enzyme), pepsin, are added. This enzyme works well at the low pH produced by the acid in the stomach. The combination of mechanical churning and chemical digestion by both the acid and the pepsin reduces the food to a liquid called chyme. Heavy secretions of alkaline mucus protect the stomach lining from the pepsin and the acid. When sufficiently broken, the chyme is slowly released into the small intestine, where it is neutralized by bicarbonate, stopping the action of the pepsin and preventing the acid from damaging the intestine. Now carbohydrases, lipases, other proteases, and nucleases are secreted from the liver, the pancreas, and the epithelial cells lining the intestine itself to finish the act of chemical digestion. Bile produced by the gallbladder contains cholesterol and bile salts that aid in fat digestion by emulsifying fats and dispersing them into fine droplets that the pancreatic lipases can act on.

One of the more difficult substances to digest is the cellulose in plant cell walls. Most animals lack the enzyme cellulase, which is required to break cellulose down into

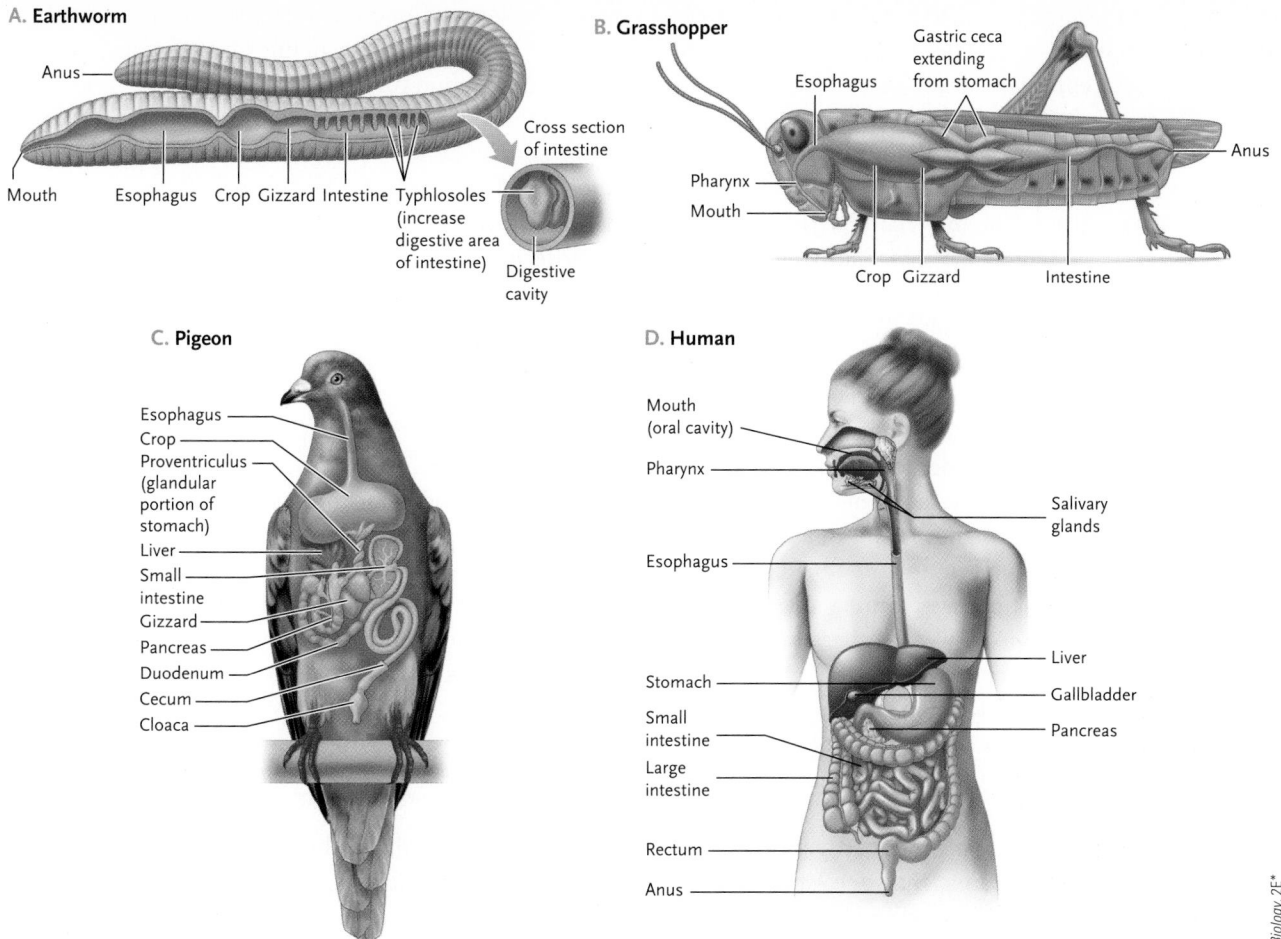

**FIGURE 21.9** The digestive systems of **(a)** an annelid (earthworm), **(b)** an insect (grasshopper), **(c)** a bird (pigeon), and **(d)** a mammal (human).

glucose. Many herbivorous animals that depend on plant material for their nutrients form mutualistic relationships with microorganisms (bacteria, protists, and fungi) that can break the cellulose down for them by fermentation. The herbivores provide specialized structures along the gastrointestinal tract to house the symbionts. In foregut fermenters, these chambers are part of the esophagus or stomach; hence, the cellulose digestion takes place before the food enters the stomach and intestine. Ruminants such as cows, horses, and deer are foregut fermenters. Other species, such as rabbits, are hindgut fermenters and house the cellulose-digesting microorganisms in their cecum, a blind-ending pouch between the small and large intestines (Figures 19.2 and 21.10) (the vermiform appendix in humans is derived from this). In these species, the plant material is broken down by passage through the digestive tract rather than by regurgitation and chewing, as it is in ruminants. Because the cellulose digestion takes place beyond the small intestine, however, these species must first eliminate the digested material in their feces (usually at night) and then re-eat it (coprophagia) to attain the nutrients. These are absorbed on the second pass through the gut, and the feces now produced (during daytime) are dry, hard, and devoid of nutrients.

## Absorbing Nutrients and Eliminating Waste

Once broken down sufficiently, the molecular subunits of food substances (mono- and disaccharides, amino acids, glycerol and fatty acids, nucleic acids) can be taken up by specialized epithelial cells, either passively (passive diffusion, facilitated diffusion) or by active transport. They can then be distributed throughout the body to be used either as fuel for making ATP or as building blocks to make cellular structures. Equally importantly, water must also be taken up. In the process of digestion, much fluid is secreted into the gastrointestinal tract with the saliva, mucus, and gastric and intestinal juices, the fluids carrying the secreted enzymes and other compounds, along with water that is ingested by drinking. Humans secrete about 7 L of fluid per day into the GI tract, of which roughly 90% is reabsorbed. Cows chewing on grass can produce over 60 L of saliva a day! Once the nutrients and water have been absorbed, what remains is waste and is then evacuated.

Again, let's consider how this is achieved in our four examples.

In the earthworm, chemical digestion and nutrient absorption both take place in the intestine. Folds in the wall of the intestine called typhlosoles aid in the process by increasing the surface area available for nutrient and water uptake to take place. Material that is too large to be absorbed is then eliminated through the anus.

In the grasshopper, the gastric ceca not only serve as chambers for digestion; these long, fine, blind-ending tubes also provide tremendous surface area, across which absorption takes place. The material that is too large to enter the ceca passes into the intestine, where further digestion takes place, and nutrients released here are also absorbed by the walls of the intestine. Water too is absorbed, particularly from the hind end of the intestine, to produce frass, semi-solid feces with almost no water content.

In the pigeon, nutrients are absorbed across the intestine along with water. Undigested food is excreted through the anus into a cloaca, a common chamber that also receives the openings of the urinary and reproductive systems. Cloacae are found in all amphibians, reptiles, and birds, as well as monotreme mammals. The name is derived from the Latin for sewer because this chamber receives the products from all of the body's plumbing.

In humans, most absorption begins in the small intestine. Some substances are highly soluble and can be absorbed across the lining of the stomach, and these include water, caffeine, aspirin, and alcohol, explaining why all of these substances can produce rapid effects once ingested. The lining of the small intestine is highly folded into ridges, which are covered with microscopic finger-like extensions called villi, of which each epithelial cell produces its own fingerlike extensions, called microvilli, giving the lining of the small intestine the appearance of a fine brush (often referred to as the brush border). The large intestine is also a site of absorption, primarily for water and a few ions (notably $Na^+$ and $Cl^-$). The large intestine of humans also hosts a population of bacteria that thrive on the sugars and other nutrients remaining in the feces. Many of these sugars are ones that we cannot digest but that the bacteria can. The bacteria produce fatty acids as well as folic acid and biotin (vitamins K and B, respectively), which are absorbed across the intestinal wall. They also produce $CO_2$, methane, and hydrogen sulphide, the gases that create flatulence, the composition and quantity of which varies with the food consumed. Although not widely acknowledged, $CO_2$ and methane production from the guts of cows, pigs, and sheep can produce as much or more greenhouse gas as all the automobiles on the road in some countries.

An extreme example of the rates at which food can be absorbed and turned into body tissue is described in Box 21.3

## Control of Digestive Processes

Digestion in animals is a highly regulated process. The movement of food along the gastrointestinal tract is monitored by receptors and controlled by hormones and nerves. **Figure 21.10** briefly outlines a few of the receptors

**FIGURE 21.10** Control of digestion by receptors and hormones in the digestive system.

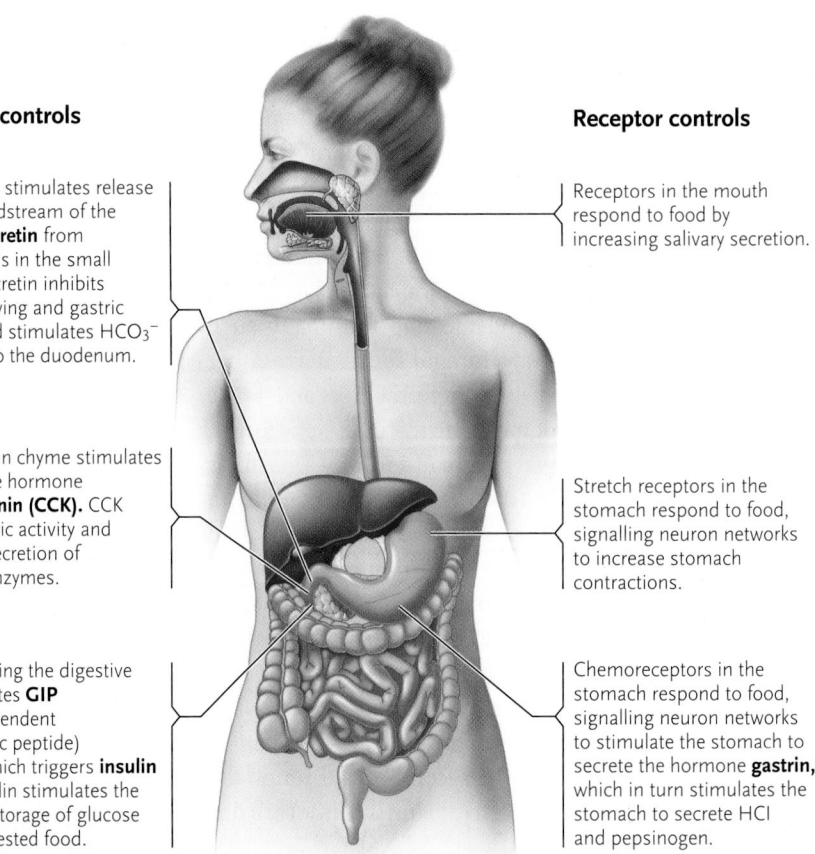

**Hormonal controls**

Acidic chyme stimulates release into the bloodstream of the hormone **secretin** from glandular cells in the small intestine. Secretin inhibits gastric emptying and gastric secretion and stimulates $HCO_3^-$ secretion into the duodenum.

Fat (mostly) in chyme stimulates release of the hormone **cholecystokinin (CCK).** CCK inhibits gastric activity and stimulates secretion of pancreatic enzymes.

A meal entering the digestive tract stimulates **GIP** (glucose-dependent insulinotropic peptide) secretion, which triggers **insulin** release. Insulin stimulates the uptake and storage of glucose from the digested food.

**Receptor controls**

Receptors in the mouth respond to food by increasing salivary secretion.

Stretch receptors in the stomach respond to food, signalling neuron networks to increase stomach contractions.

Chemoreceptors in the stomach respond to food, signalling neuron networks to stimulate the stomach to secrete the hormone **gastrin,** which in turn stimulates the stomach to secrete HCl and pepsinogen.

*Biology, 2E\**

and hormones involved in the control of digestion in humans. The nerves controlling gastrointestinal function (the enteric nervous system) are largely autonomous; that is, they work independently of input from the central nervous system (from the brain and spinal cord). This system is often referred to as a second brain or the stomach's brain because it can work independently and is capable not only of producing reflexes; it can also integrate the information arising from the chemoreceptors and mechanoreceptors lining the gastrointestinal tract to control peristalsis and stomach churning as a function of the bulk and nutrient content of the food. Among the inputs they do receive from the central nervous system are those associated with appetite that match food ingestion with metabolic needs.

## STUDY BREAK

1. What is digestion? How does physical digestion differ from chemical digestion?
2. Why do some animals store food internally before digesting it?
3. Why do the chambers of the GI tract, where digestion takes place, usually come before those where absorption occurs?
4. What is the source of flatulence, and why is this not such a bad thing?

## 21.3 Variations for Obtaining Nutrients

This chapter has focused on the most common means of acquiring nutrients by plants and animals. There are many variations on this theme, however. This should not be surprising given the necessity of obtaining nutrients for survival. The variations range from gutless animals that function more like plants to carnivorous plants that function more like animals.

### Plants

There are thousands of species of flowering plants that are parasitic. Some, such as the dodder (*Cuscuta* sp.), cannot photosynthesize and obtain organic molecules, water, and minerals from other plant species using specialized roots that penetrate into the vascular tissues of the host plant **(Figure 21.11b)**. Plants such as the snow plant (*Sarcodes sanguinea*) also cannot photosynthesize but obtain their nutrients from other plants through shared mycorrhizal fungi **(Figure 21.11c)**. Other plants, such as the mistletoe, are photosynthetic but obtain minerals and water from their hosts and supplement their own sugar production from the sap of their hosts.

There are many species of epiphytic plants (mosses, lichens, orchids, staghorn ferns) that simply grow on other plants, using them for support but obtaining nutrients (water and minerals) largely from rain **(Figure 21.11d)**.

**A. Bladderwort**   **B. Dodder**   **C. Snow plant**   **D. Lady-of-the-night orchid**   **E. Pitcher plant**

**FIGURE 21.11  (a)** A bladderwort has bladders that serve as insect traps. **(b)** Dodders have slender stems that twine around host plants before producing specialized invasive roots that absorb nutrients and water from the host's xylem and phloem. **(c)** The roots of snow plants intertwine with the hyphae of soil fungi. **(d)** The lady of the night is an epiphytic orchid. **(e)** The pitcher plant traps insects.

SOURCE: (Photos A–E): Perennou Nuridsany / Science Source; Dr. Morley Read/Shutterstock.com; Jeffrey T. Kreulen/Shutterstock.com; A.Ryser/Shutterstock.com; Photogrape/Shutterstock.com

Then there are the carnivorous plants. These plants usually live in open, sunny environments but in nutrient-poor soils. They obtain many of their nutrients by luring in and killing insects. Many are photosynthetic but rely on insects for their nitrogen. Classic examples are the sundew plant and the pitcher plant **(Figure 21.11e)**. Less well known is the bladderwort (*Utricularia* sp.), an underwater plant named for the bladderlike organs that it uses to suck in small aquatic insects **(Figure 21.11a)**. These plants secrete digestive enzymes into their various traps that decompose the insect prey to small molecules that they can then absorb. Note that although they depend on their prey for their nitrogen, they also obtain many other nutrients in this way as part of the process.

## Animals

Variation abounds in the ways of acquiring nutrients by animals as well, both in the ways of ingesting food and of digesting food. Here are a few of the many examples that exist **(Figure 21.12)**.-

As with plants, there are many forms of parasitic animals that obtain their nutrients across a permeable body wall simply living in a host at a site where nutrients are readily available. Different species are adapted to live in the GI tract, the blood, or the body tissues of their hosts **(Figure 21.12a)**.

Some herbivorous nudibranchs (sea slugs) have evolved branches of their gut that extend out into their body wall. These animals feed on algae, from which they extract the plastids responsible for photosynthesis and store them in these chambers (called cerata) **(Figure 21.12b)**. They keep the plastids alive and use the cerata as solar panels, exposing them to sunlight and harvesting the products of photosynthesis directly. Other sea slugs are carnivorous, eating prey that has formed symbiotic relationships with single-celled plants. They eat the host and nurture the plant symbionts, keeping them alive in their bodies and thus obtaining nutrients from both sources.

Suction feeding has evolved as a means for ingesting food in numerous species across the vertebrate clade. Anglerfish living in the depths of the ocean where light does not penetrate have evolved a "lure" from the spine of the dorsal fin that dangles above their mouth. These fish have established a symbiotic relationship with bioluminescent bacteria that live within the lure and that cause it to glow, attracting other fish **(Figure 21.12c)**. As the prey approaches, the anglerfish rapidly expands its buccal

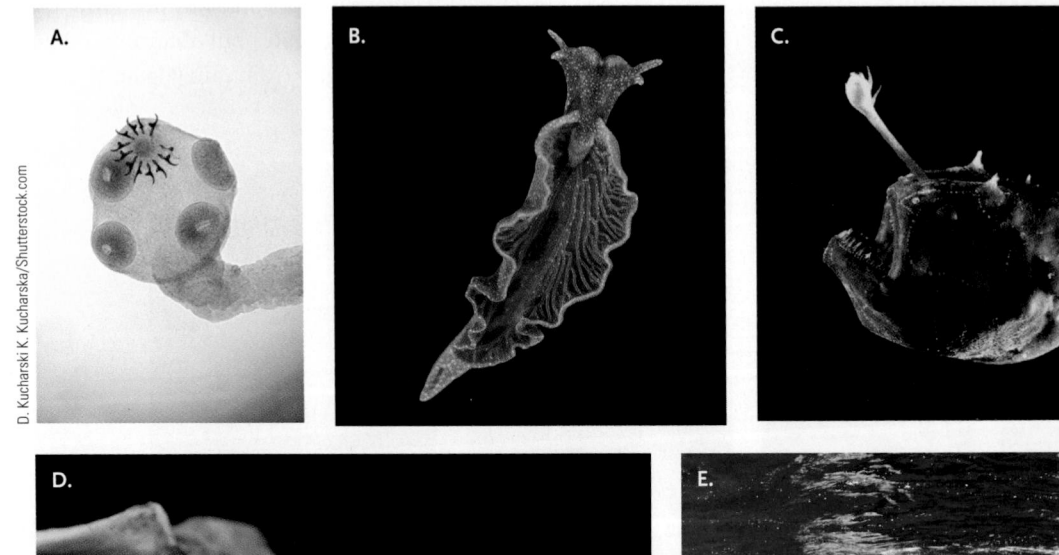

**FIGURE 21.12** Alternate forms of feeding in animals: **(a)** tapeworm (*Taenia solium*), **(b)** sea slug (*Elysia chlorotica*), **(c)** anglerfish (*Lophiiformes* sp.), **(d)** matamata (*Chelus fimbriata*), and **(e)** humpback whale (*Megaptera novaeanglia*) (see text for details).

SOURCE: (Photo B): Dr. Mary Tyler & Dr. Mary Rumpho, University of Maine, (2008). "Horizontal gene transfer of the algal nuclear gene psbO to the photosynthetic sea slug *Elysia chlorotica,*" *PNAS*, 105 (46), 17868, Copyright 2008 National Academy of Sciences, U.S.A.

# LIFE ON THE EDGE 21.3
## Nutrient Uptake in Newborn Hooded Seals

Hooded seals *(Cystophora cristata)* live in deep waters of the North Atlantic and Arctic Oceans **(Figure 1)**. They haul out onto drifting pack ice to give birth to their young. This is an unstable environment, and the young must grow quickly and become independent and capable of venturing into the water and foraging for their own food. The pups weigh around 25 kg at birth when they begin to suckle and take milk from their mothers (Figure 1). Although the milk of terrestrial mammals is relatively low in fat (roughly 3% to 4% for cows and humans, for instance), the milk

of the hooded seal is up to 65% fat. The seal pups suckle for only 3 to 5 days, the shortest known time of any mammal. During this time, they consume roughly 7.5 kg of milk each day (on average, a total of 30 kg during the suckling period). Of the fat in the milk they drink, over 80% is digested, absorbed, and deposited as fat (blubber) in the pups. That is, the mothers are converting stored fat into milk fat, whereas the pups are converting milk fat into energy stores at an amazing rate. Within these 4 days, the pups may double in body weight. This provides the pups with

a significant energy store that they can use as they learn to swim and dive and begin to feed on their own. The pups initially feed primarily on crustaceans, but as adults, they feed on mussels, starfish, fish, and squid.

The hooded seal receives its name because of the elastic "hood" that adult males can inflate and extend from the front of their face to the top of their head (Figure 1). Sexually mature males also have a red, elastic nasal septum, which they inflate to attract females and warn other males to stay away.

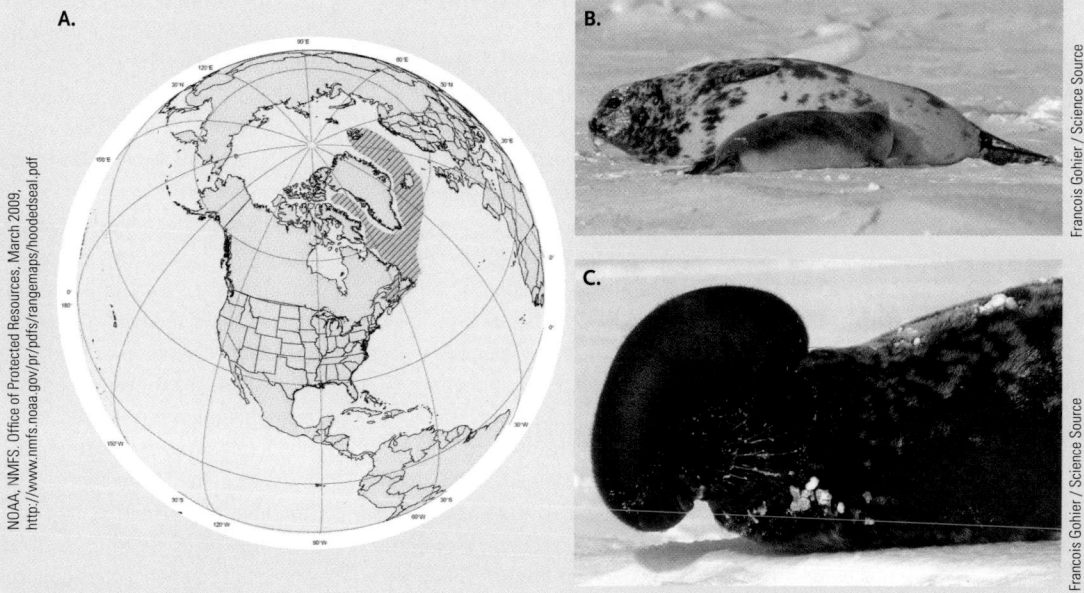

A.

NOAA, NMFS, Office of Protected Resources, March 2009,
http://www.nmfs.noaa.gov/pr/pdfs/rangemaps/hoodedseal.pdf

B.

Francois Gohier / Science Source

C.

Francois Gohier / Science Source

**FIGURE 1** **(a)** The distribution of hooded seals in the North Atlantic and Arctic Oceans is shown by the grey diagonal lines. **(b)** A hooded seal mother and her pup. **(c)** A male hooded seal attempting to attract females with his inflated nasal septum.

(mouth) cavity, sucking the prey in. Many other species simply use disguise to blend in with their surroundings and suck in prey that chances along. Moray eels and the matamata, a freshwater turtle of the Amazon **(Figure 21.12d)**, use this technique.

The opposite of suction feeding is the lunge feeding seen in birds such as pelicans and in many species of whales. The largest of the lunge feeders are the rorqual whales, a group that includes the humpback whale and the blue whale. Lunge feeding is a dynamic process in which the whale accelerates to high speed and lunges toward its prey, in this case, schools of fish, opening its mouth wide and engulfing the prey along with

tremendous amounts of water **(Figure 21.12e)**. As you can imagine, the drag this causes is huge (similar to opening a parachute) and energetically expensive and puts tremendous force on the hinge of the jaw itself. Adaptations that facilitate this process in the rorqual whales are jaws that are only loosely articulated with the skull and that separate at the front, very expandable pleats in the blubber of the throat. These allow the throat to open wide. Recently, scientists discovered that a special sensory organ is present within the loose symphysis where the jaws are unfused at the front derived from vascular and nervous tissue that has arisen from the first tooth socket. This organ appears to sense the rotation of the jaws and

BOX 21.4
## Diets versus Genetics?

If you type "diet" into your Internet browser and sit back, you will receive over 100 million hits in under one minute! Why is there so much literature on the topic and so much disagreement? In general, all diets are designed to achieve two things: to provide individuals with all the essential nutrients they need for normal function and to balance energy intake with energy expenditure. Failure to achieve the first leads to the nutrient deficiencies discussed earlier in the chapter. Failure to achieve the second leads to weight gain or weight loss. The literature on weight control through dieting is overwhelming, and much is written in an authoritative manner that can be compelling. Simplistically, we all know that if the calories taken in over the course of a day do not match the calories expended, we will either gain or lose weight. So why is it so easy for some people to match these two and so difficult for others? Not surprisingly, the answer is complex.

Most diets that are designed to promote weight loss regulate either the size of a meal or the content of the meal and thereby restrict caloric intake. And although there is no doubt that restricting caloric intake will lead to weight loss, history shows that most such diets fail. Throughout the chapters on form and function, the emphasis has been on the homeostatic control of body processes. It should not be surprising that something as vital as body energy stores is homeostatically controlled. Excessive weight loss or weight gain is an indication that something is amiss with this control system, and knowledge of the neurobiological basis of eating will lead to the rational treatment of disorders of energy homeostasis such as obesity.

How does any animal know what its energy stores are? Over the years, various metabolites (such as glucose levels) were hypothesized to signal energy state. The observation that body weight and fat com-position can be maintained over long periods despite daily fluctuations in food intake led to the hypothesis that the key metabolic signal must come from the fat itself. This led to the discovery that fat releases a hormone called leptin and that the brain contains receptors for this hormone in areas of the hypothalamus and brain stem associated with feeding and energy expenditure. Scientists currently think that we evolved to store some excess energy when food was available for use during periods when it was scarce. As body fat stores build up, leptin levels increase, suppressing appetite. If fat stores fall too low, leptin levels decrease, stimulating feeding. This discovery led to the hope that obesity could be controlled by regulating blood leptin levels.

It now appears that leptin, insulin, and other metabolic hormones related to fat stores (such as thyroid-releasing hormone and corticotropin-releasing hormone [see Chapter 26]) regulate body weight under the control of multiple genes. The causes of obesity in the human population can arise from problems associated with hormone production, hormone transport, and/or the sensitivity of brain receptors to each hormone. A reduced sensitivity of the brain to leptin, for instance, would be perceived as a reduction in body energy stores and lead to weight gain. Although many of these problems may be genetically based, some may be diet induced.

More recently, scientists discovered orexin/hypocretin. This hormone was discovered simultaneously by two groups and given two names. To date, there is no consensus on which name to use. This hormone stimulates food intake, energy expenditure, and wakefulness. It is part of a control system that integrates information about metabolic, circadian, and sleep debt states to determine whether an animal should be awake and active or asleep and inactive. It is likely to play a major role in regulating weight gain associated with preparation for hibernation or dormancy in many species.

To add to this complex story, it now also appears that the microbes living in our guts have a mind of their own and also play a role in this process. Using the latest genome techniques, scientists have discovered that the diversity of microbial species inhabiting our guts varies among individuals. It is not clear whether obesity influences the makeup of the gut microbiome (the diversity of species of microbes in the gut) or whether the gut microbiome contributes to obesity. Scientists have shown, however, that thin mice became obese after receiving microbes from an obese mouse.

Finally, we all know that we don't just eat to obtain energy. Eating many foods can be very enjoyable and serves more than just meeting metabolic needs. The sight, smell, and taste of food can stimulate eating even when we are full. Balancing these effects with those related specifically to energy balance requires mental discipline.

Insights into how metabolic signals from the gut, our fat stores, and our emotional system interact within the brain must be gained from animal studies and non-invasive brain imaging studies in humans. Using the latest techniques (molecular, genetic, physiological, and behavioural), we should slowly gain a better understanding into the basis of energy homeostasis, such as obesity and ways to treat it.

When reading about dieting in the popular media, keep these things in mind: a good diet must meet nutritional needs (for both organic and inorganic substances), calories in must meet calories out, averaged over time to keep weight constant, and, importantly, your body is designed to accomplish this through homeostatic mechanisms that we are slowly beginning to understand.

the expansion of the ventral groove blubber and acts to coordinate the initiation, modulation, and termination of engulfment. The researchers speculate that it was the evolution of this organ, allowing these animals to engulf food in this way, that facilitated the evolution of such massive animals.

## PUTTING IT IN PERSPECTIVE

Proper nutrition is important to every living thing. Whether growing fruit, root crops, wheat, or corn or raising dairy cattle, beef cattle, sheep, or pigs, getting the balance of nutrients right is the key to success. Animal food companies now make special diets for everything from cats and dogs to horses, cows and pigs, deer and elk, and chickens and ducks to special foods for fish, amphibians, and reptiles. Fertilizer companies make organic and inorganic fertilizers with a wide variety of ingredients, each specially designed with specific plants in mind. And the popular media boasts an overwhelming number of special diets designed to keep human health in balance. Weight loss products and services are now a multibillion dollar business in North America. Although feed and fertilizer companies have in general produced healthy animals and enriched soils, the enormous amount of money being spent on combating human obesity has yet to produce sustained advances in achieving healthier, thinner bodies. Although many weight-loss diets have produced success for some individuals, for most they offer only short-lived benefits (see Box 21.4). Although there is no doubt that genetic makeup plays a role in determining why some people gain weight more easily than others, staying healthy comes down to balancing calories in with calories out in combination with a diet that provides all the essential nutrents.

## KEY CONCEPTS REVIEW AND QUESTIONS

### 21.1 Nutrient Requirements for Growth, Development, and Survival

Nutrients are the organic and inorganic molecules that plants and animals need for growth, development, and survival. They provide fuel for energy to drive biological processes and the building blocks required to construct cells. Some are required in large quantities (macronutrients) and some in only very small quantities (micronutrients), usually to serve as cofactors in enzymes. Nutrient deficiencies materialize, hampering the growth and health of an individual when essential nutrients, those molecules an individual cannot make from other existing compounds in the body, are unavailable.

1. What are micronutrients, and why do plants and animals only need them in such small quantities?
2. What makes a nutrient an essential nutrient?
3. Would a lack of sunlight for a plant be considered a nutritional deficiency?
4. Which of the following is not a source of nitrogen for plants?
   a. Nitrogen in the atmosphere
   b. Nitrogen-fixing bacteria
   c. Nitrifying bacteria
   d. Ammonifying bacteria
   e. Fungal mycorrhiza
5. Pair the macromolecule on the left with its molecular subunit on the right.
   a. Carbohydrates      ___ Glycerol
   b. Proteins           ___ Nucleic acids
   c. Fats               ___ Monosaccharides
   d. DNA                ___ Amino acids
                         ___ Fatty acids

### 21.2 Obtaining Nutrients

Plants only require inorganic nutrients because they can manufacture all the organic compounds they need from water and $CO_2$ in the presence of sunlight. Their roots seek out the inorganic nutrients they need from the soils in which they grow. The needs of individual species vary tremendously, as do the characteristics of different soils, explaining why certain plants thrive in areas where others cannot become established.

6. Which of the following are common components of soil?
   a. Rocks
   b. Minerals
   c. Water
   d. Air
   e. Living organisms
   f. All of the above
7. Pair the minerals on the left with cellular structures on the right for which they are required (some structures may require more than one mineral).
   a. Nitrogen       ___ Membrane phospholipids
   b. Phosphorus     ___ Amino acids
   c. Potassium      ___ Osmolyte
   d. Calcium        ___ Plant intracellular matrix
                     ___ Chlorophyll
                     ___ ATP
                     ___ Nucleic acids
8. What determines which plants are likely to be pioneering plants that first settle in a disrupted area?

Animals require both organic molecules in their diet to fuel energy production and inorganic molecules to build the new molecules required for producing new cells and tissues. They obtain these nutrients from eating either plants or other animals, either whole or in parts, or their fluids or decomposing remains. This food is ingested and then undergoes the process of physical and chemical digestion, rendering large complex molecules into their molecular subunits that can be absorbed across the membranes of the cells lining their digestive cavities. Water is also absorbed, and undigested matter is subsequently eliminated.

9. An animal that eats other animals could be which of the following? (*Note*: There may be more than one correct answer.)
   a. Carnivore
   b. Omnivore
   c. Herbivore
   d. Autotroph
   e. Detritivore

10. What contains the most calories per gram?
    a. Protein
    b. Carbohydrates
    c. Nucleic acids
    d. Fat
    e. Cellulose

11. Compare digestion in a sea anemone versus a mammal. Are both forms of digestion extracellular?

## 21.3 Variations for Obtaining Nutrients

Both plants and animals are extremely opportunistic and have evolved a wide range of adaptations for acquiring necessary nutrients.

12. We have described the various chambers of the GI tract of vertebrate animals, and **Figure 21.13** compares the GI tracts of a carnivore and an herbivore. How many differences can you identify, and can you explain them based on your understanding of the diets of the animals and the functions of the different segments of the GI tract?

Carnivore (a dog)

Herbivore (a rabbit)

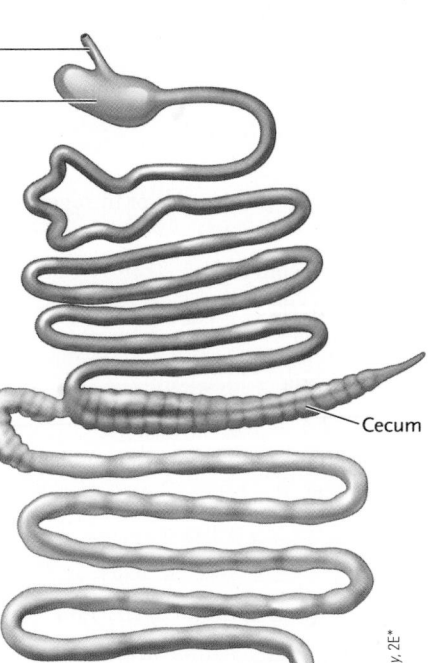

**FIGURE 21.13** Comparison of the lengths of the digestive systems of a carnivore (dog) and an herbivore (rabbit).

# 22 Support and Movement

M.B. Fenton

## WHY IT MATTERS

In Chapter 1, we saw how differences in the structure of the bones in our feet can influence our potential as sprinters. Running on the balls of our feet allows us to move faster than running flat-footed because we have lengthened our stride. Mammals that walk and run use a range of patterns of footfall, from plantigrade (landing flat-footed on the soles of the feet where heel to toe touches the ground), to digitigrade (landing on your toes), to subunguligrade (walking on the tips of the toes), to unguligrade (walking on your toenails).

Modern elephants walk on the tips of their toes (subunguligrade), in part because of specialized bones (sesamoids) that anchor tendons in the pads of their fore- and hind-feet **(Figure 22.1)**. Fossils of more ancient elephants that were smaller as adults indicate that they used plantigrade locomotion and lacked specializations for subunguligrade gaits. These findings indicate that in elephants and their ancestors, increasing body size coincided with a change in gait.

Sesamoid bones are common to tetrapod (four-limbed) animals, but the ancestral form has been modified for many different functions. Examples include the "false thumbs" of pandas and moles **(Figure 22.2, p. 472)**, as well as the front and hindlimbs of some frogs. In modern elephants, sesamoid bones contribute to gait; in pandas, they are associated with food handling; and in moles, they expand the digging surface of the forefeet.

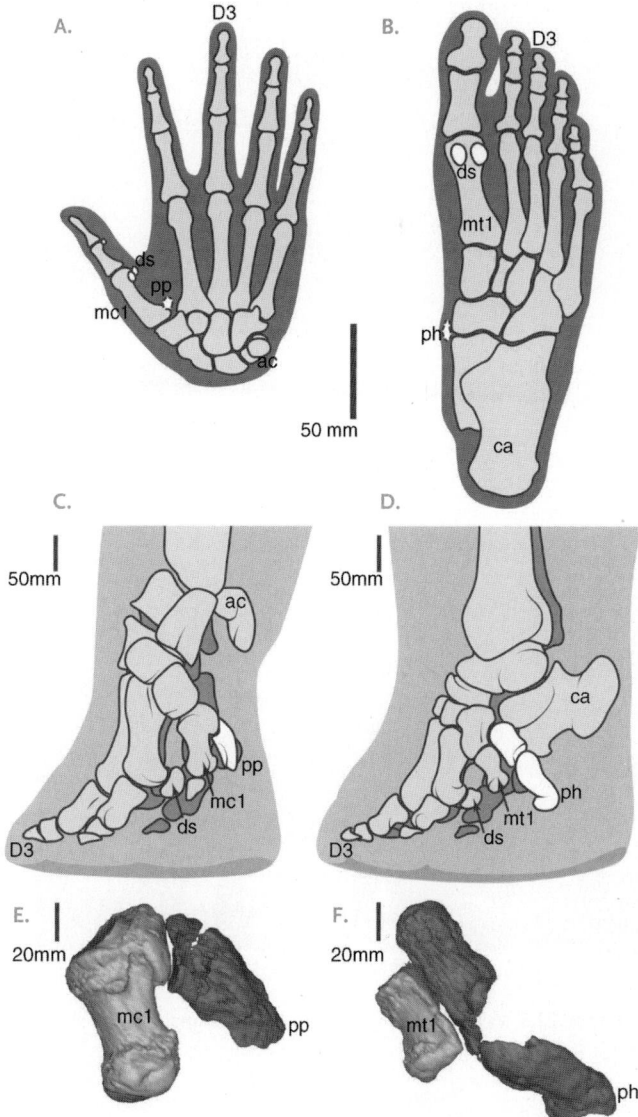

Courtesy of Naas Rautenbach

**FIGURE 22.1** Elephant feet (photograph) are large and impressive. Sesamoid bones are shown in white in this comparison of the fore- **(a, c)** and hind- **(b, d)** feet of a human (a, b) and an elephant (c, d). Also shown are reconstructions from CT scans of the elephant fore- **(e)** and hind **(f)** feet. ac = accesorium (pisiform); ca = calcaneus; D3 = third digit; ds = digital sesamoids; mc1 = metacarpal 1; mt1 = metatarsal 1; ph = prehallux; pp = prepollex.

SOURCE: (Photos A–F): From John R. Hutchinson, Cyrille Delmer, Charlotte E. Miller, Thomas Hildebrandt, Andrew A. Pitsillides, Alan Boyde, "From Flat Foot to Fat Foot: Structure, Ontogeny, Function, and Evolution of Elephant "Sixth Toes"," *Science* 23 December 2011: Vol. 334 no. 6063 pp. 1699–1703. Reprinted with permission from AAAS.

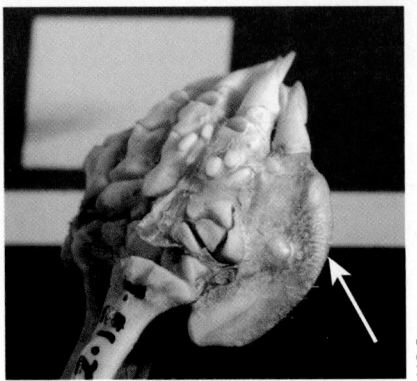

**FIGURE 22.2** Sesamoid bone (arrow) in the forelimb of a European mole (*Talpa europaea*).

M.B. Fenton

In this chapter, we review a sampling of structural elements in organisms and how they function. We also examine the means organisms use to move, from passive movement on currents to active movements of limbs in feeding, to movements of whole organisms. Structures involved in support, such as skeletons and cell walls, provide integrity of shape for organisms and, as fossils,

document their history. Movements often directly reflect underlying structural elements working together with contractile cells such as muscles. We also consider the impact of environment on the business of support and movement. As you progress through the chapter, note solutions to common problems to emphasize the diversity of animals and their structures.

## 22.1 Support Holds Things Up

### Size and Density Both Reflect and Affect the Support System

The structure of an organism is fundamentally linked to its size and the density of the medium in which it lives. Consider the differences among the animals **(Figure 22.3)**. Which ones have skeletons? Which ones lack them? How do the environments in which they live differ? What happens when you make a similar comparison among lichens, clubmosses, sunflowers, and trees **(Figure 22.4)**?

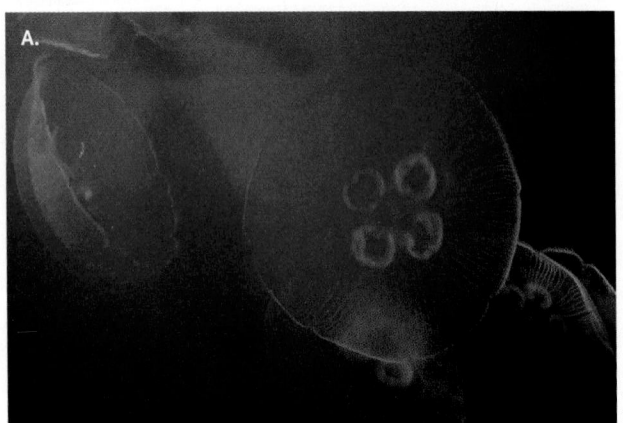

A.

M.B. Fenton

B.

M.B. Fenton

D.

M.B. Fenton

C.

M.B. Fenton

**FIGURE 22.3** Variations in the appearances of animals. A jellyfish **(a)**, a slug **(b)**, an elephant **(c)**, and a beluga **(d)**.

**FIGURE 22.4** A variety of plants, including a lichen **(a)**, a clubmoss **(b)**, sunflowers **(c)**, and harvested timber **(d)**.

The very largest known living organism is the honey fungus (*Armillaria ostoyae*). One honey fungus covers 965 hectares of soil in Oregon, the equivalent of 10 sq km. Based on its growth rate, this fungus is at least 2400 years old. Even larger specimens of *A. ostoyae* have been reported from other locations in the United States. Most of a honey fungus lives underground in soil. Soil is a dense medium that can support the organism's mass with minimal other structural supports. The mushrooms or fruiting bodies of honey fungus that we see above the ground are much smaller than the entire fungus itself **(Figure 22.5a, p. 474)**. These fungi cause **armillaria**, a disease of roots of coniferous trees, and, as such, are economically and ecologically important where they occur.

You may already know that the largest animal ever to have lived is the blue whale. No terrestrial animal has come close. This is because on land, an animal must have structure sufficient to support its weight. Air is not very dense and offers little support. Water, on the other hand, is much denser and provides a great deal of support. The density of water explains why most of the world's largest animals (living or fossil) have been aquatic **(Figure 22.5)**. Whether we think of a blue whale (*Balaenoptera musculus*), a giant Japanese spider crab (*Macrocheira kaempferi*), or a

Devonian fossil sea scorpion (the eurypterid *Jaekelopterus rhenaniae*), the support provided by water makes being large much more feasible than it is on land. More specifically, the mass of aquatic animals is offset by the similarity in density between water and the bodies of aquatic animals.

The comparisons above demonstrate connections between an organism and its environment. In addition to support and mobility, there are many other connections that link an organism's form and function with its environment, including the need for water conservation, circulation, disposal of wastes, reproduction, and protection from UV radiation and infection. In this chapter, we focus on structures involved in support, from tubes to shells and bones, as well as movement, of bodies and body parts. You will see that most features of organisms can and do serve more than one function. We will begin with the materials involved in structures associated with support.

## Biomineralization Is a Key Factor in Support Systems

Materials in structures that many organisms use for support show an interesting blend of strength, rigidity,

A.

B.

(1)    (2)    (3)

(4)

Martin Fowler/Shutterstock.com

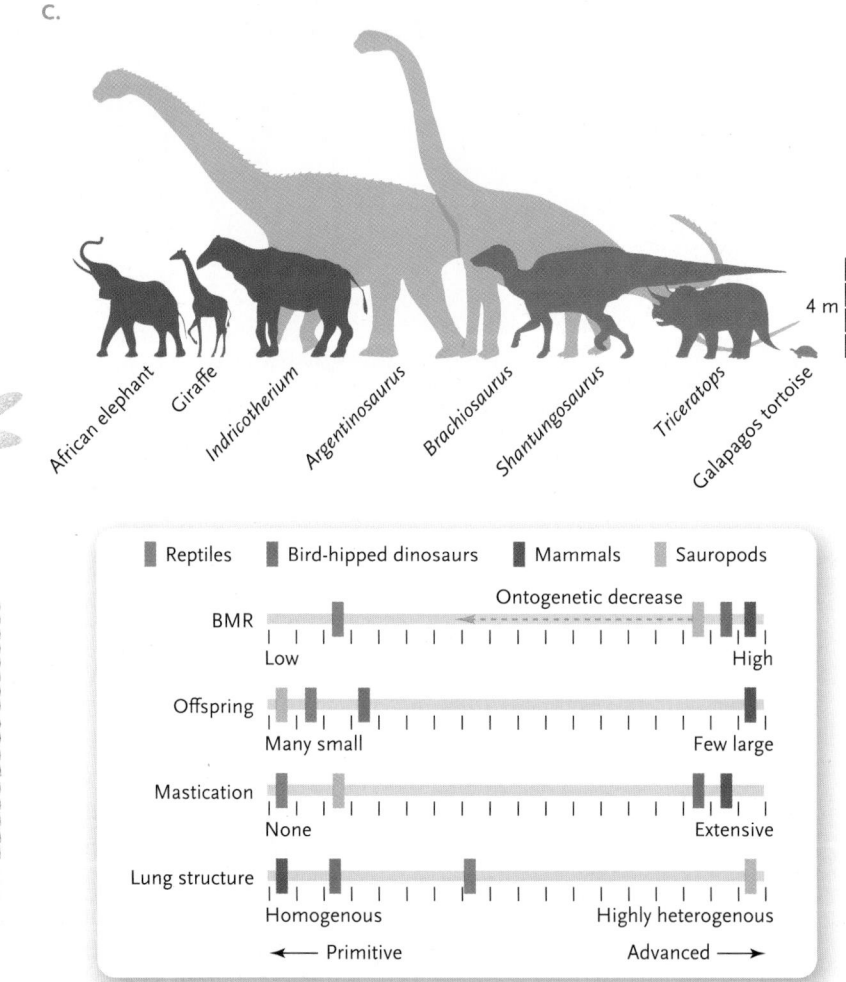

**FIGURE 22.5** A sampling of some of the world's largest organisms. The honey fungus (*Armillaria ostoyae*) **(a)** is the largest. In part **(b)**, some of the larger invertebrates known as fossils are compared to a human: a sea scorpion – *Jaekelopterus rhenaniae* (1); a trilobite – *Isotelus rex* (2); a dragonfly – *Meganeura monyi* (3); and a millipede – *Arthropleura armata* (4). In part **(c)**, some of the largest terrestrial dinosaurs are compared to mammals and a giant tortoise.

SOURCE: (Photo B): Simon J Braddy, Markus Poschmann, O. Erik Tetlie, "Giant claw reveals the largest ever arthropod," *Proceedings A*, published 23 February 2008, by permission of the Royal Society.; (Photo C): From Sander, P.M. and M. Clauss, "Sauropod gigantism," *Science* 322, 2008:201–202. Reprinted with permission from AAAS.

C.

African elephant   Giraffe   *Indricotherium*   *Argentinosaurus*   *Brachiosaurus*   *Shantungosaurus*   *Triceratops*   Galapagos tortoise

4 m

■ Reptiles   ■ Bird-hipped dinosaurs   ■ Mammals   ■ Sauropods

BMR        Ontogenetic decrease
           Low                          High

Offspring  Many small                   Few large

Mastication  None                       Extensive

Lung structure  Homogenous             Highly heterogenous

← Primitive              Advanced →

stiffness, and toughness (Box 22.1). Some supporting tissues are more flexible than others. Flexible materials occur in the cell walls of plants and fungi **(Figure 22.6)**, the cuticles of many arthropods, and bones and other features, such as the feathers, horns, or beaks of vertebrates. The shells of molluscs or brachiopods and the skeleton (stereom) of echinoderms are strong but less flexible.

In large measure, flexibility is a function of structures (known as **Bouligand structures**) that have well-defined levels of hierarchical organization. Specifically, 180° rotations alternate between layers **(Figure 22.7, p. 476)**.

Biological composites result from **biomineralization**, which involves inorganic and organic materials **(Table 22.1, p. 476)**. Biomineralization refers to the addition of minerals to organic material, usually proteins. They usually form layers separated by minerals. Biomineralized materials are strong, tough, and flexible. In humans and other mammals, the addition of calcium phosphate to the extracellular matrix is another example of biomineralization.

The exoskeletons of crabs (Arthropoda, Crustacea) illustrate how biomineralization enhances flexibility. In these crabs, biomineralization involves calcium carbonate deposited within a matrix of fibrils (long-chain

BOX 22.1

# Size, Strength, Surface Area: Volume, Stiffness, Toughness

Typically, support structures in organisms are stiff when under load. They also tend to be tough, meaning that they can absorb energy without fracturing. The ability of supporting structures to bend (flex) is vital, and Bouligand structures are often central to this feature.

Some basic mathematical relationships govern the size and shape of an organism. The volume of an organism varies with its length, but strength varies with cross-sectional area. When an organism doubles in size, its weight increases by a factor of 8, but its strength increases only by a factor of 4. The rigidity of a cylinder is denoted by I, which can be calculated using the formula

$$I = (\pi/4) * (R^4 - r^4),$$

where R is external radius and r is internal radius, providing an indication of the thickness of the walls. If the cross-sectional area of the walls remains the same, the larger cylinders will have thinner walls. I/R is the strength of the cylinder's walls. There is a clear relationship between strength, radius, and rigidity, reflecting how increasing one does not automatically increase the others "enough." Furthermore, strength, stiffness, and toughness are relative terms:

|  | Relative values | | | |
|---|---|---|---|---|
| External radius (R) | 1 | 2 | 4 | 10 |
| Rigidity (I) | 1 | 7 | 31 | 199 |
| Strength (I/R) | 1 | 3.5 | 7.8 | 19 |

Surface area and volume are two other important features. A 1 mm diameter sphere has a surface area of 12.6 mm² and a volume of 4.2 mm³. This means that its surface area–volume ratio is 3:1. A 10 mm diameter sphere has a surface area–volume ratio of 0.3:1 (its surface area is 1257 mm², its volume is 4189 mm³). Larger spheres have smaller surface areas. These examples are spheres, and other factors also influence the relationship. Your arm has a higher surface area–volume ratio than your torso.

But how does this apply to a tree bending in the wind? What about grasses or flowers on long stems? What are the underlying structures and challenges? Why is freezing rain particularly dangerous to trees (and power lines)? Think of how these challenges also would apply to building a chair, from the material to be used to the means of joining the parts together.

---

polysaccharides). Proteins wrap around the fibrils, forming fibres that are assembled in bundles and arranged in parallel layers (Figure 22.7). In plant cell walls, the microfibrils of the Bouligand structures are made of cellulose.

Three other examples of biomineralization come from sponges and molluscs. The skeletons of sponges (made of spicules; see below) consist primarily of silica or calcite with added proteins on which the silica and calcite can condense. By mass, the shells of molluscs are more

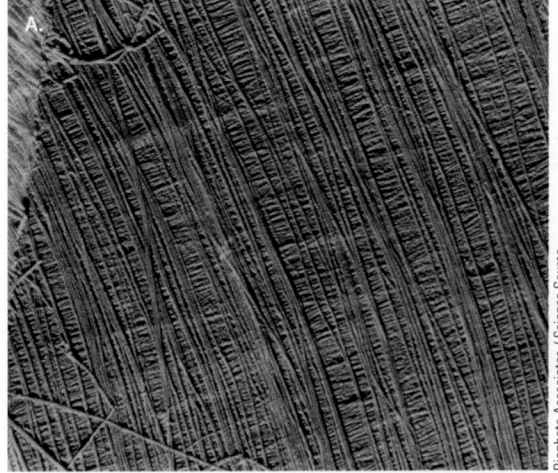
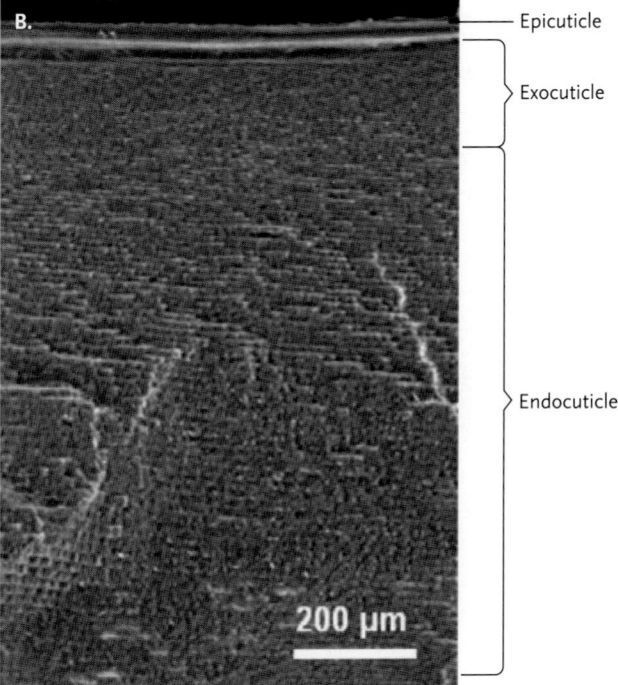

**FIGURE 22.6** Cellulose microfibrils in a plant cell wall **(a)** and a cross section through the cuticle of a sheep crab (*Loxorhynchus grandis*) **(b)**.

SOURCE: (Photo B): Reprinted from *Acta Biomaterialia*, Volume 4, Issue 3, Po-Yu Chen, Albert Yu-Min Lin, Joanna McKittrick, Marc André Meyers "Structure and mechanical properties of crab exoskeletons," Pages 587–596, Copyright 2008, with permission from Elsevier.

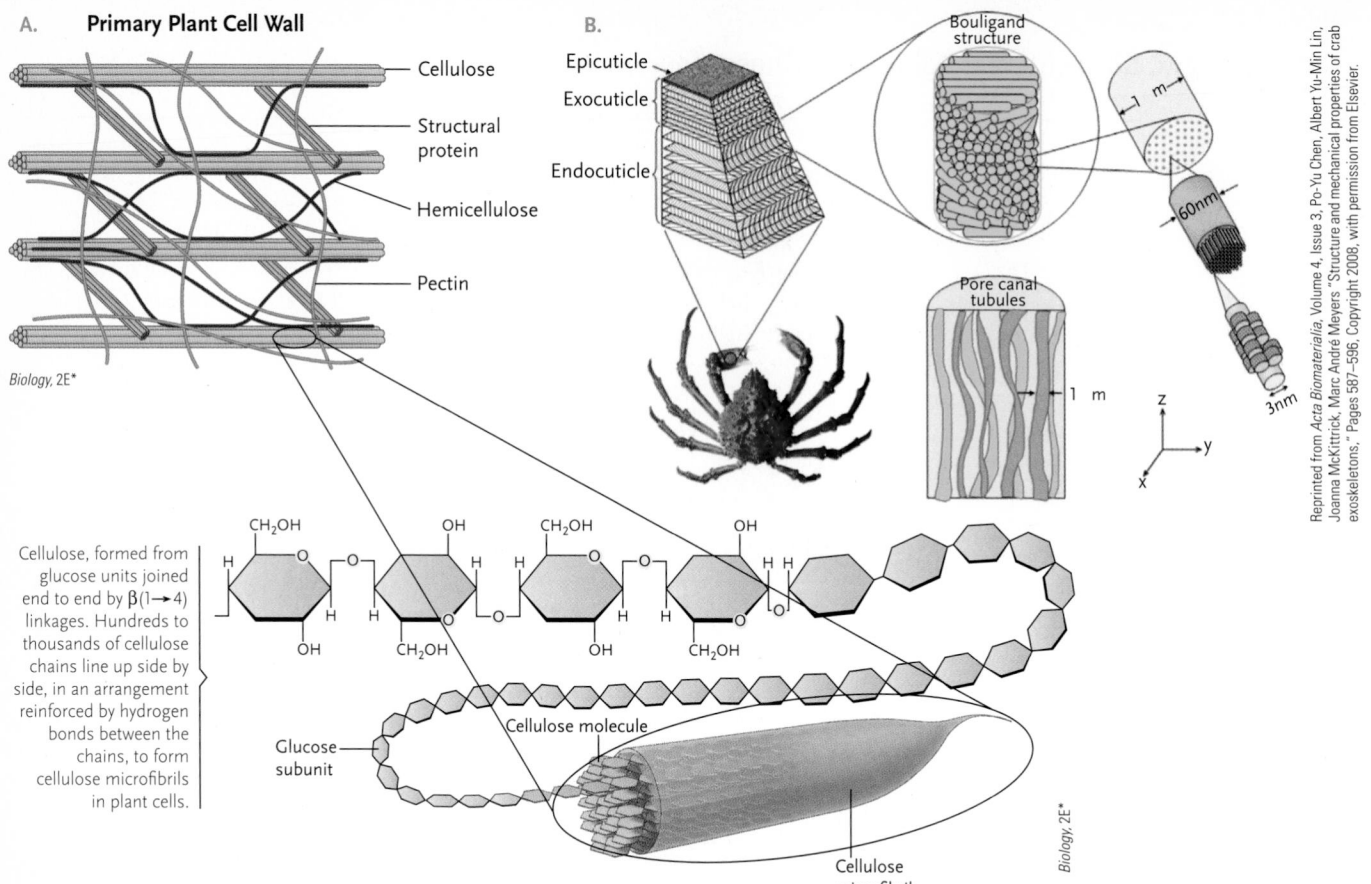

**A. Primary Plant Cell Wall**

Cellulose

Structural protein

Hemicellulose

Pectin

*Biology, 2E\**

**B.**

Epicuticle
Exocuticle
Endocuticle

Bouligand structure

1 m

60 nm

3 nm

Pore canal tubules

1 m

Reprinted from *Acta Biomaterialia*, Volume 4, Issue 3, Po-Yu Chen, Albert Yu-Min Lin, Joanna McKittrick, Marc André Meyers "Structure and mechanical properties of crab exoskeletons," Pages 587–596, Copyright 2008, with permission from Elsevier.

Cellulose, formed from glucose units joined end to end by β(1→4) linkages. Hundreds to thousands of cellulose chains line up side by side, in an arrangement reinforced by hydrogen bonds between the chains, to form cellulose microfibrils in plant cells.

$CH_2OH$   OH   $CH_2OH$   OH

OH   $CH_2OH$   OH   $CH_2OH$

Glucose subunit

Cellulose molecule

Cellulose microfibril

*Biology, 2E\**

**FIGURE 22.7** A comparison of the arrangements of microfibrils of cellulose in plant cell walls **(a)** and those from the cuticle of a sheep crab **(b)**. In both, the diagrammatic views illustrate finer and finer detail of the fibres and fibrils. The Bouligand structure is identified in (b). Ribbonlike tubules run through pore canals that run in the same direction in the crab cuticle.

than 96% mineral, with the rest organic content. Typically, layers of some form of calcium carbonate (calcite or aragonite) are separated by organic layers, often involving a protein. The shells of conchs (*Strombus gigas*) are 99% mineral by volume and are two to three orders of magnitude tougher than single crystals of the pure mineral.

## STUDY BREAK

1. How does the density of the medium in which an organism lives relate to support?
2. What is the relationship between flexibility and Bouligard structures?

**TABLE 22.1** | **Principle Components of Common Structural Biological Composites**

|  | CaCO$_3$ | Ca | Silica | Hydroxyapatite | Keratin | Collagen | Chitin | Cellulose | Other |
|---|---|---|---|---|---|---|---|---|---|
| Shells | + |  |  |  |  |  |  |  | + |
| Horns |  | + |  |  | + | + |  |  |  |
| Bones |  |  |  | + |  |  |  |  |  |
| Teeth |  |  |  | + |  |  |  |  | + |
| Bird Beaks |  | + |  |  | + |  |  |  |  |
| Crustacean Exoskeleton | + |  |  |  |  |  | + |  | + |
| Spicules |  |  | + |  |  |  |  |  | + |
| Insect Cuticle |  |  |  |  |  |  | + |  | + |
| Fungi |  |  |  |  |  |  |  | + |  |
| Wood |  |  |  |  |  |  |  | + |  |

Modified from Meyers et al. JOM 2006 page 35.

SOURCE: Marc A. Meyers, Albert Y. M. Lin, Yasuaki Seki, Po-Yu Chen, Bimal K. Kad, Sara Bodde, "Structural biological composites: An overview," *JOM*, July 2006, Volume 58, Issue 7, pp 35–41, Copyright © 2006, Minerals, Metals & Materials Society. With kind permission from Springer Science and Business Media.

## 22.2 Supporting Structures

Supporting structures may be located within the organism (endoskeleton), on the exterior (exoskeleton) of the organism, or some combination of the two. You are an example of an animal with an endoskeleton. Endoskeletons grow with the organism. A scallop, a kind of bivalve mollusc, has an exoskeleton. Turtles and armadillos are animals with both endo- and exoskeletons. An exoskeleton is a suit of armour. It sometimes grows with the organism and sometimes does not. Growth occurs in sporadic bursts when the exoskeleton is moulted and before it reforms. The exoskeletons of scallops, turtles, and armadillos grow slowly. Those of lobsters, cockroaches, and many other animals grow in sporadic bursts; then they shed or **moult** their exoskeleton and grow another one.

### Cell Walls Keep Things in Their Place

Cell walls are the main supporting structures in plants (Figure 22.7a) and fungi. In plants, there is considerable diversity in the details of the structures and the composition of the cell walls. The variety of polymers used in cell walls is considerable, and there is variation within and between species. In essence, plant cell walls are complex fibre composites that form a load-bearing network infiltrated with other polymers to form a matrix. In primary cell walls, there is a matrix of proteins and complex sugars that cross-links with cellulose microfibrils together in a matrix of glycoproteins and polysaccharides. A kind of lignin is the embedding material for secondary cell walls in woody plants.

Many genes work together to produce cell walls. In many species, several additional genes are involved in biosynthesis of the components of cell walls before they are put together. We do not yet know if green algae (Coleochaetales), the closest relatives of today's land plants, have layered cell walls typical of land plants. In vascular plants, the water potential of vacuoles generates turgor pressure, affecting rigidity. These vacuoles contribute significantly to the support systems (see Chapter 17 for more on vacuoles).

Coal is an economically important product derived from plant cells. Some extensive coal deposits are remnants of forests of the Devonian and Carboniferous periods (see the Purple Pages for an overview of geologic time). Some of the forests were composed of treelike clubmosses that were 40 m tall. Today, the biofuel industry depends on being able to digest the structural components of plant cell walls to produce ethanol for use as fuel. This is an important alternative to burning coal, gas, and oil.

The main component of fungal cell walls is polysaccharides (Figure 22.7). Chitin is also a key component, along with proteins, including some enzymes. In essence, the fungal cell wall is a three-dimensional network based on polysaccharides. The traditional view that the cell wall was an inert exoskeleton has given way to recognition that it is a living, dynamic structure. The cell wall is strong enough to accommodate changes in osmotic pressure while being plastic enough to permit growth. As in plants, the cell wall also mediates adhesion of cells to one another and serves as a signalling centre that activates pathways for signal transduction (see Chapter 15). Fungi vary considerably in their texture, in part because of their cell walls and the substrate on which they grow (**Figure 22.8**).

### Spicules Are Part of a Support System

Spicules (**Figure 22.9, p. 478**) are important structural elements in invertebrates such as corals but are more commonly associated with sponges. Spicules made of silica or calcite are brittle, whereas the protein in those formed by biomineralization is flexible. Silica and calcite condense

**FIGURE 22.8** Diversity of fungi ranges from bracket fungi that are woody in texture **(a)** to a sampling of less robust forms **(b)** that are common in grocery stores.

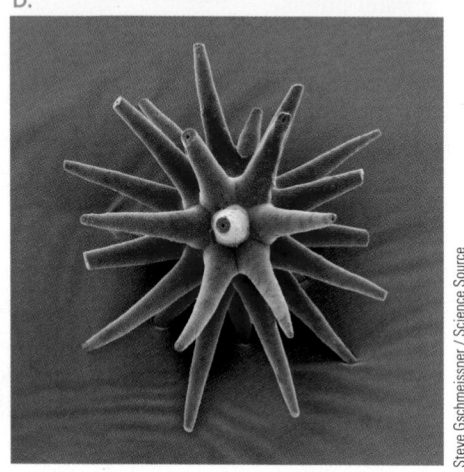

**FIGURE 22.9** A sampling of silica spicules from sponges. Two light microscope images of an assortment of spicules **(a, b)** and two scanning electron micrographs of two others **(c, d)**. Spicule shapes are under genetic control.

appear to have been an ancestral condition—or one that appeared early in evolutionary history—in both phyla. But several groups of species of molluscs lack shells, including octopuses, many squid, slugs, and nudibranchs, which are sea slugs. The shells grow by adding layers. You can sometimes tell the age of a mollusc by counting the number of layers in its shell, much like you can age a tree by its rings. The layers allow cracks to travel easily in the direction that separates the layers but not in other directions.

Mother-of-pearl (Figure 22.11c; nacre) is another form of mollusc shell. Mother-of-pearl is commonly used in jewellery and artwork. Here flat sheets of aragonite or calcite, about 0.5 micrometres thick, are separated by layers mainly of lustrine (Figure 22.11a), a protein. The organic layer gives nacre considerable strength and accounts for its healing capacity, an important feature of a shell.

## Stereoms Are the Skeletons of Echinoderms

The stereom, or skeleton, of echinoderms presents an interesting puzzle. It is initially deposited as amorphous (shapeless) calcium carbonate. Through biomineralization, it converts to calcite in a crystalline structure with very little organic material. The stereom looks as though it is one crystal with interconnecting cavities **(Figure 22.12)**. Scientists initially thought that this structure acted to prevent cracks, but that idea has been disproven. Many details of the structure and function of the stereom are still not well understood. There is a striking resemblance between the stereom and spongy or **cancellous** bone in vertebrate animals (see below). Cancellous bone, however, is always covered by compact bone, and there is no continuous shell over the stereom (Box 22.3).

## Bones Are the Building Blocks of Vertebrates

Vertebrate animals are structurally supported by bone. The mineral content of bone is the main determinant of its mechanical properties **(Figure 22.13, p. 480)**. Biomineralization of bone involves calcium phosphate (hydroxyapatite) crystallizing in a mixture of organic material—mainly collagen. The bending strength of bone is directly related to the degree of mineralization (Young's modulus;

on filaments of protein in concentric layers. The results of condensation provide the structure of spicules.

## Tubes Provide Protection and Support

Many animals live in tubes secreted and/or constructed from a variety of materials **(Figure 22.10)**. Tubes appeared early in the fossil record, providing both support and protection. Animals that live in the substrate represent several phyla and, apparently, independently evolved tubes. Tubes of many annelids are made from chitin, although some spiders line their burrows with silk. Caddisflies construct cases from materials available in the environment, such as plant fibres and pebbles, which they weave together with silk. In many cases, the main function of dwelling tubes is protection rather than support.

## Shells Are Armour

Many brachiopods and molluscs live in shells **(Figure 22.11)**, structures that provide support and protection and that

FIGURE 22.10 **(a)** Giant tube worms (*Riftia pachyptila*) shown with mollusc and white crabs near a deep sea vent in the Pacific Ocean. **(b)** A larval caddisfly in its tube constructed from sand grains and small pebbles held together by silk woven by the larva.

FIGURE 22.11 This sample of mollusc shells includes a chambered nautilus **(a)**, a cephalopod, and two bivalves (**b** and **c**). The pearl oyster (*Pinctada radiate*) clearly shows mother-of-pearl (nacre), although it is also evident on the inner surface of the nautilus shell.

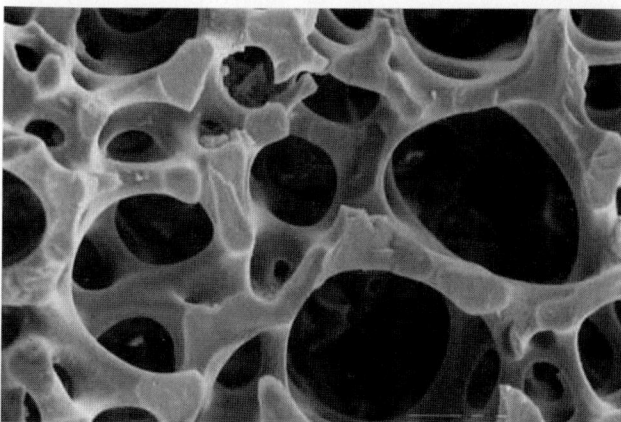

FIGURE 22.12 Stereom of a sea urchin, *Heterocentrotus lividus*.

SOURCE: Currey, "The design of mineralised hard tissues for their mechanical functions," *JEB* 1999 Dec;202(Pt 23):3285–94. *Journal of Experimental Biology* by Company of Biologists Reproduced with permission of COMPANY OF BIOLO-GISTS LTD. in the format Republish in a book via Copyright Clearance Center.

Figure 22.13). There is considerable variation in the relative amounts of mineral, water, and organic materials in bones (Figure 22.13). Highly mineralized bones fracture easily, whereas those with a lot of organic material are more flexible and less breakable. Overmineralization, such as overcalcification, can make bones more brittle. Osteoporosis is an example of a condition arising from overmineralization.

Bone is living tissue with a clear hierarchical structure. Bone lamellae (layers) are about 4 micrometres thick with mineral crystals and collagen fibrils that line up in parallel. Variation in bone structure and composition is associated with specific environmental or life history demands. The bones surrounding the ear (auditory bullae) of whales are more mineralized. The density of the bullae isolates the inner ear from sounds other than those produced directly or indirectly (echoes) by the whale. The thigh bones of

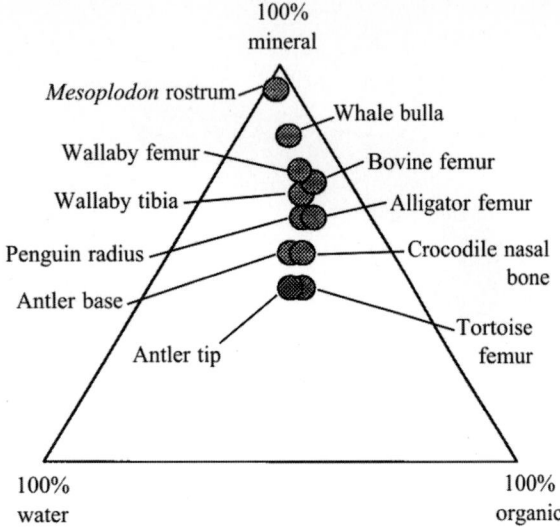

**FIGURE 22.13** This figure illustrates the relationship between water content, mineral content, and organic content of different bones. Data are shown on a per mass basis. The mineral content of bone can be very high, for example, in the whale (*Mesoplodon*) rostrum.

SOURCE: Currey, "The design of mineralised hard tissues for their mechanical functions," *JEB* 1999 Dec;202(Pt 23):3285–94. *Journal of Experimental Biology* by Company of Biologists Reproduced with permission of COMPANY OF BIOLOGISTS LTD. in the format Republish in a book via Copyright Clearance Center.

tortoises or the tip of an antler are less mineralized and therefore much more resistant to breaking under the weight of a heavy animal (tortoise) or during a battle over mates (antler) **(Figure 22.14)**. Changes in bones can reflect environmental conditions and cyclical growth. This is

obvious as annual rings in thigh bones of living mammals and dinosaurs; in years with better conditions, the rings are thicker than those produced in leaner years. In other cases, calcium from bones is mobilized during times of stress, such as hibernation and lactation in temperate bats.

As the name implies, species of cartilaginous fishes (Chondrichthyes)—the sharks, rays, and ratfishes—have skeletons made mainly of cartilage, not bone **(Figure 22.15)**. In some sharks (tiger – *Galeocerdo cuvier*; and great white – *Carcharodon carcharias*), the jaws of small individuals are cartilaginous, whereas those of larger animals are calcified with layers of minerals. These age differences are related to bite strength and stiffness of jaws, but age is not the only factor. Smaller species in the genera *Galeocerdo* and *Carcharodon* also have calcified lower jaws. Rays (Figure 22.15), such as the cow-nosed ray (*Rhinoptera bonasus*), crush hard-shelled prey such as bivalves, and their jaws and tooth plates are layered. They also have mineralized hollow cylinders or bars (trabeculae) that provide support, rather like those found in cancellous or porous bone. The trabeculae in the jaws of rays are hollow, unlike the solid trabeculae of cancellous bones.

**Tendons** usually connect muscles to a bone, and most are not ossified (mineralized), although some tendons are in some animals. For instance, the so-called cervical ribs of some dinosaurs were ossified tendons that had great strength and flexibility in one direction. In very large sauropod dinosaurs **(Figure 22.16)**, these ossified tendons would have reduced the mass of the neck while

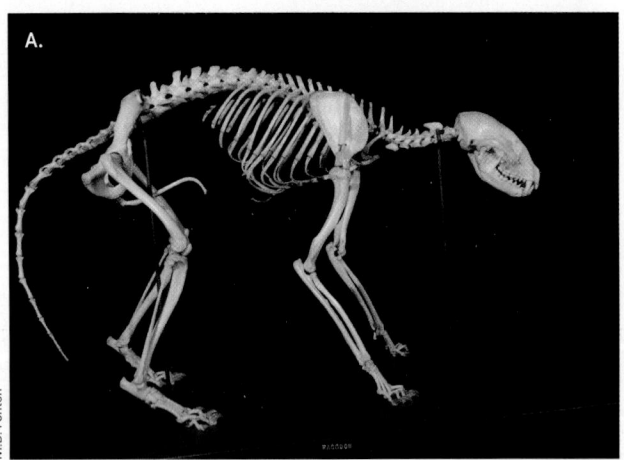

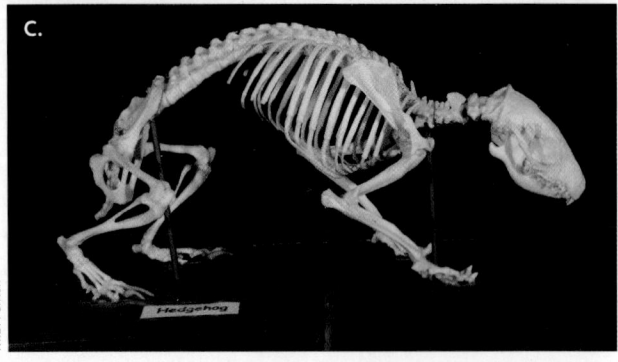

**FIGURE 22.14** Skeletons of three mammals illustrate both the general similarity among them and the diversity of the group. Included are a raccoon **(a)**, a flying lemur **(b)**, and a hedgehog **(c)**, representing the orders Carnivora, Dermoptera, and Eulipotyphla, respectively.

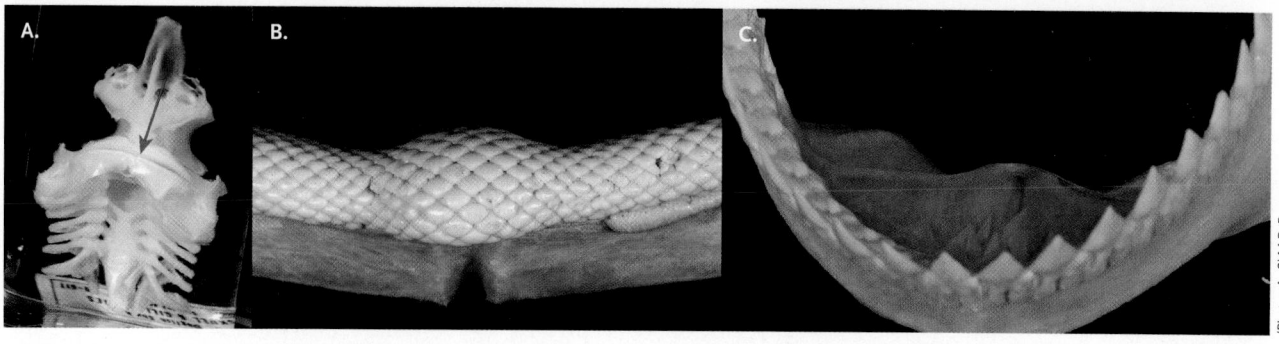

**FIGURE 22.15** Cartilaginous skeleton of a dogfish **(a)** where an arrow points to the mouth, compared to the ossified lower jaws of a shell-crushing ray (*Rhynchobatus* spp.) **(b)** and of a cutting cookiecutter (*Isistius plutodus*) shark **(c)**.

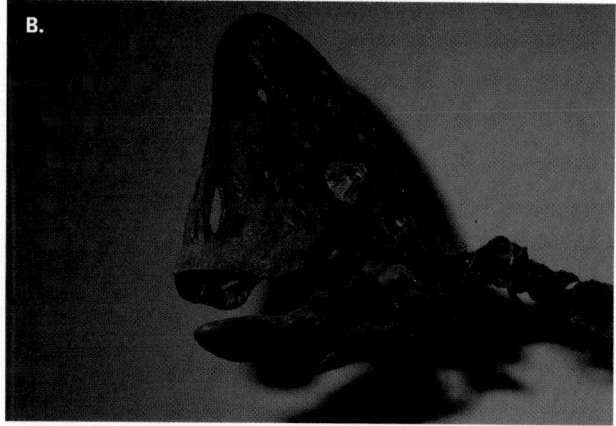

**FIGURE 22.16** Three pairs of cervical ribs **(a)** and the skull **(b)** of an ornithomimid theropod dinosaur.

providing strength and flexibility. Ossified tendons will be familiar to those who eat drumsticks from birds such as chickens and turkeys.

## STUDY BREAK

1. What role do silica and calcium phosphate have in supporting structures?
2. What are the basic components of mollusc shells?
3. What are the basic components of bones?

## 22.3 Movement

Whereas some organisms and/or some of their component parts move, others are virtually immobile. We tend to think of plants and fungi as immobile species and associate animals with the capacity for locomotion. Some animals are sessile, however, living their adult lives attached to a substrate. And some plants (or their seeds or pollen) are quite mobile, often specialized to move on currents of wind or water. Tumbleweeds (Russian thistles – *Echinops exaltatus*) move with the wind. A clearer distinction between mobility in animals and that of plants and fungi is the extent to which each moves under its own power. So leaves, flowers, or stems of a plant moving in

the breeze involve the wind and generally do not move under their own power. But there are exceptions: remember the traps of Venus flytraps (page 484; see Figure 22.20) or the tendency of plants to move in response to light or other stimuli (see Box 26.1, Plant Tropisms).

## STUDY BREAK

1. What does sessile mean? Give an example of a sessile animal.

## 22.4 Plants and Fungi

Plants and fungi are able to **disperse**, or move to a new location. If they could not, we would not see the wide geographic range of many species. Dispersal patterns often reflect prevailing wind patterns as so many plants disperse by wind. One classic example is the distribution of plants around the Svalbard archipelago in the North Atlantic **(Figure 22.17, p. 482)**. Data from DNA fingerprinting were used to demonstrate that post-glaciation colonization of the archipelago by plants involved arrivals from adjacent regions. Dispersals of plants in this situation appear to have occurred by wind-blown seeds and plants across expanses of sea ice.

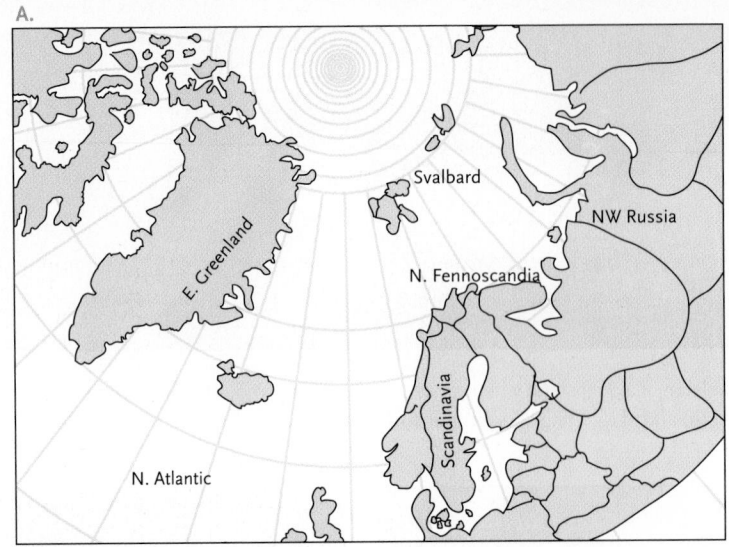

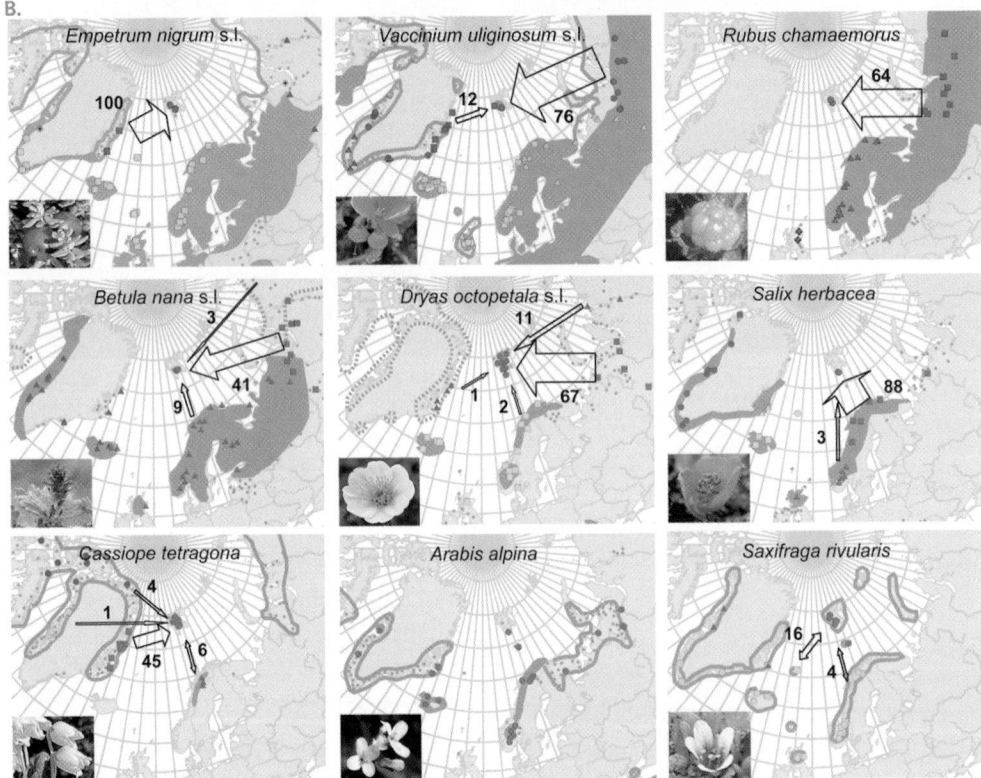

**FIGURE 22.17** Some plants that occur on the Svalberg archipelago (general location, **a**), come from surrounding areas **(b)**. The distribution data for nine species of plants are shown in (b).

SOURCE: From Inger Greve Alsos, Pernille Bronken Eidesen, Dorothee Ehrich, Inger Skrede, Kristine Westergaard, Gro Hilde Jacobsen, Jon Y. Landvik, Pierre Taberlet, Christian Brochmann, "Frequent Long-Distance Plant Colonization in the Changing Arctic," *Science* 15 June 2007: Vol. 316 no. 5831 pp. 1606–1609. Reprinted with permission from AAAS.

In other cases, pollen and/or seeds are specialized for dispersal by wind **(Figure 22.18)**.

Other specializations also enhance wind dispersion. Winged seeds called samaras, like those on maple trees, spin during descent, autorotating about their centre of mass **(Figure 22.19)**. Autorotation helps seeds move away from the parent plant.

Some of the most impressive plant behaviours involve the movements in trapping insects. When an insect touches trigger hairs on modified leaves **(Figure 22.20, p. 484)**, it sends a signal to the plant to close the trap. There are three stages in the process: (1) the plant perceives a stimulus; (2) the signal is transmitted; and (3) a response is induced. Triggered snap traps in carnivorous plants appear to have evolved only once. They are also found in waterwheel plants (*Aldrovanda vesiculosa*) and bladderworts (*Utricularia* spp.).

## STUDY BREAK

1. How do plants hitchhike?
2. What role does wind play in the movement of plants?
3. How does a carnivorous plant move to trap insects?

A.

David M. Phillips / The Population Council / Science
Source: Colorization by: Meredith Carlson

B.

Elena Elisseeva/Shutterstock.com

**FIGURE 22.18** The pollen **(a)** of ragweed (*Ambrosia acanthicarpa*) **(b)** is wind dispersed, making it a potent allergen. The seeds **(c)** of dandelions (*Taraxacum officinale*) are wind dispersed. The seed head (c) is covered with many individual seeds **(d)**.

C.

D.

M.B. Fenton

M.B. Fenton

## 22.5 Movement by Animals

We do not usually think of snails as having an exceptzional capacity for long-distance travel. How then does a terrestrial snail (*Balea perversa*) achieve a distribution from Tristan da Cunha in the South Atlantic, north along the coast of Europe to Iceland in the North Atlantic **(Figure 22.21, p. 484)**? The answer lies in its ability to hitchhike on migrating birds. Many other species of animals that are sessile as adults achieve widespread distribution by hitchhiking, whereas others are more mobile as larvae than as adults.

### Costs of Movement Must Be Covered

Moving can be expensive **(Figure 22.22, p. 484)**. If heartbeat rate reflects cost, we can measure the impact of locomotion by comparing our heartbeat rates when we are lying down, sitting, walking, or running. We can extend this com-

parison by measuring heartbeat rate when we are carrying a load while walking (or running). The faster we move, and the more load we carry, the faster our hearts beat—and the more energetically costly our movement is. This is immediately apparent when we look at data on energy consumption by Sherpas **(Figure 22.23, p. 484)**. Mind you, we still do not know the details of how Sherpas achieve their astonishing capacity for carrying large loads over long distances.

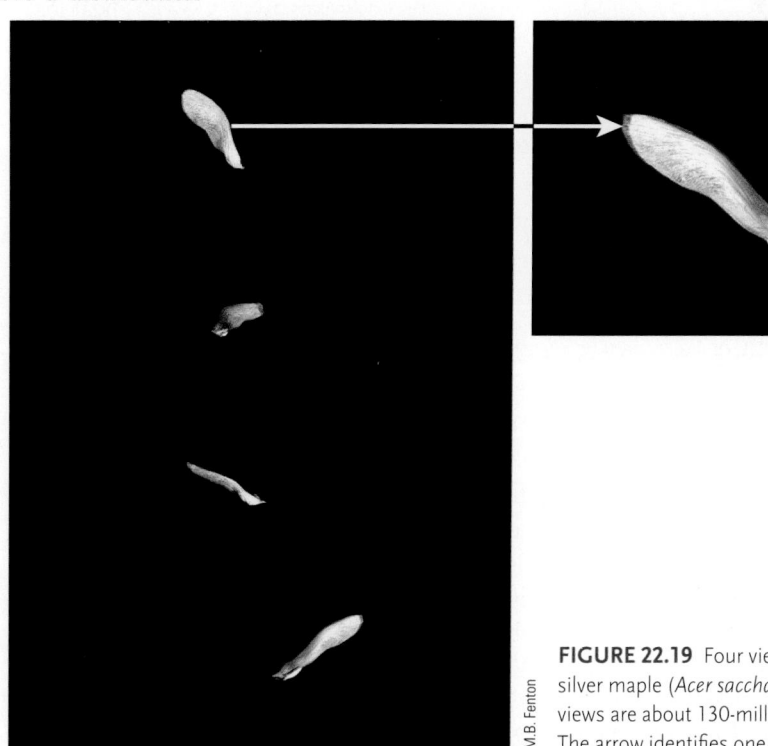

M.B. Fenton

**FIGURE 22.19** Four views of a spiralling silver maple (*Acer saccharinum*) key. The views are about 130-millisecond intervals. The arrow identifies one enlarged view.

**FIGURE 22.20** Trigger hairs, obvious on the left modified leaf of a Venus flytrap (*Dionaea muscipula*), are instrumental in insect capture by these carnivorous plants.

M.B. Fenton

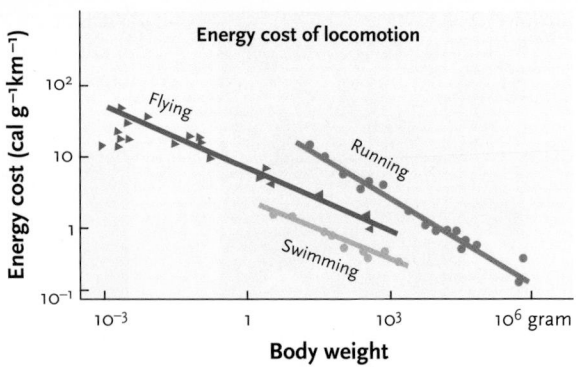

**FIGURE 22.22** A comparison of the energy cost of flying, running, and swimming across a range of body sizes.

SOURCE: From Schmidt-Nielsen, K., "Locomotion: energy cost of swimming, flying and running," *Science* 21 July 1972: Vol. 177 no. 4045 pp. 222–228. Reprinted with permission from AAAS.

**A.**

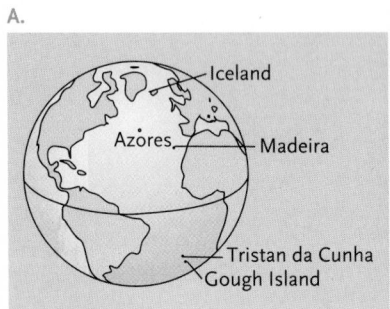

**B.**

Courtesy of Jiří Novák

**C.**

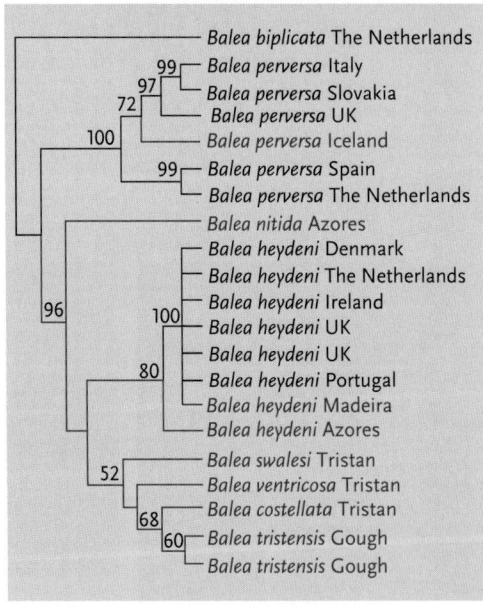

**FIGURE 22.21** The geographic range **(a)** of a snail (*Balea perversa*) **(b)**. Genetic analysis of its populations **(c)** revealed that one continuous population is made possible because the snails hitchhike on migrating birds.

SOURCE: Reprinted by permission from Macmillan Publishers Ltd: *NATURE*, "Biogeography: Molecular trails from hitch-hiking snails," by Edmund Gittenberger, Dick S. J. Groenenberg, Bas Kokshoorn and Richard C. Preece, vol. 439, p. 409, copyright 2006.

reflects, in part, the animal's muscle mass. In many animals, most of the musculoskeletal system is composed of hard tissues (skeleton) rather than contractile tissues (muscles). Birds are an interesting exception because of their specialized lightweight bones.

Heat is an important by-product of locomotion. Heat is produced when our muscles contract. This is why your skin flushes and you start to sweat while exercising. Your body is trying to dissipate the heat you have generated. When exercising in the sun at air temperatures from 8° to 35°, female Asian elephants (*Elephas maximus*) accumulate 56% to 100% of heat produced in core body tissues **(Figure 22.24)**. Even though sparse body hairs on elephants appear to effectively increase convective heat loss, especially when there is any wind, heat still accumulates. These data suggest why very large terrestrial animals are active at night as a way

Another crucial element for human speed is our ability to see ahead of us as we move. We need to be able to see details of the ground ahead from about two step lengths. An analysis of eye size and maximum running speed in 50 species of mammals (representing 10 orders) supports the proposal that eye size in vertebrates is related to ground speed—vertebrates with larger eyes can run faster.

Size strongly affects the metabolic cost of locomotion in animals (Figure 22.22), partly because size

**FIGURE 22.23** A laden Sherpa.

Zvet/Shutterstock.com

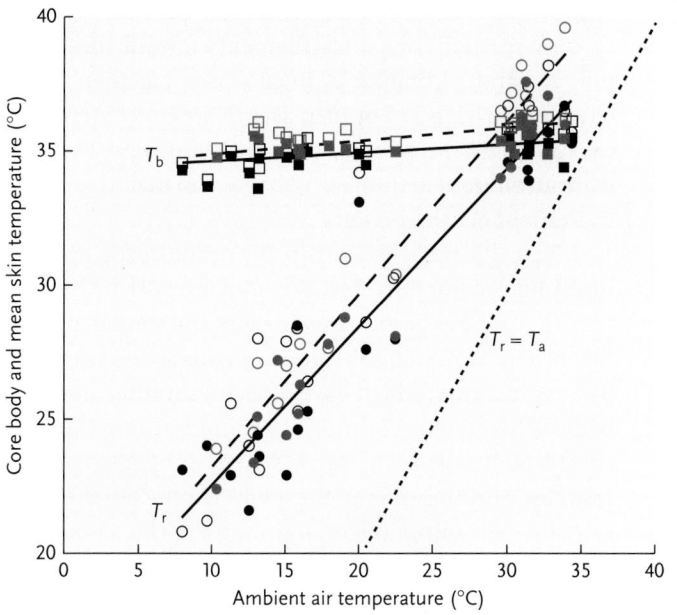

**FIGURE 22.24** In two Asian elephants, core body temperatures and skin temperatures differ between pre-exercise (solid symbols and solid lines) and post-exercise (open symbols and lines with long dashes). Linear relationships describe pre- and post-exercise increases in body temperature. The line with short dashes represents the situation where $T_r$, skin temperature = $T_a$ is ambient temperature. $T_B$ = core temperature. Photo of African elephants (*Loxodonta africana*) illustrates the importance of shade.

SOURCE: M. F. Rowe, G. S. Bakken, J. J. Ratliff and V. A. Langman, "Heat storage in Asian elephants during submaximal exercise: behavioral regulation of thermoregulatory constraints on activity in endothermic gigantotherms," *JEB* 216, 1774–1785. *Journal of Experimental Biology* by Company of Biologists Reproduced with permission of COMPANY OF BIOLOGISTS LTD. in the format Republish in a book via Copyright Clearance Center.

of avoiding some heat loading. The same may have applied to other huge terrestrial animals, such as some dinosaurs. Some dinosaurs may have evolved complex structures to dissipate heat; scientists now think that the plates on a stegosaurus may have served this function. Restrictions caused by overheating may apply less to aquatic animals depending on the difference in temperature between water and body core. For more information about cooling, see page 553 (Chapter 25).

Features such as the mode of locomotion, the distance covered, and the speed at which the animal moves all influence the cost of movement. These variables are used to calculate the **Reynolds number (Re)**, which, in turn, is used to predict patterns of flow around a moving animal. Smaller animals are more vulnerable to viscous forces (how viscous the medium is), whereas larger animals are more subject to the forces of inertia. In flying animals, Re range from 100 to 100,000, corresponding to body weights from 1 microgram to 75 kg (smallest insect to largest flying bird, respectively). In 2014, a fossil bird (*Pelagornis sandersi*) with a 6.4-m wing span and weighing 21 to 40 kg was still much smaller than the largest known flying animal. *Quetzalcoatlus northropi* weighed an estimated 85 kg and had a wing span of approximately 12 m).

For those designing and building drones (unmanned aerial or submersible vehicles), making something very small will reduce its conspicuousness but can result in a lower Re, making it more subject to viscous forces.

Thinking about how we travel by automobile can put the cost of locomotion in perspective. If the car has a tank that holds 60 L of fuel and at 100 km per hour uses 6 L of fuel per 100 km, there is enough fuel to drive 1000 km. But if the car uses twice as much fuel (12 L of fuel per 100 km at 100 km per hour), the distance travelled drops by half (to 500 km). The range (distance travelled) is determined by the amount of fuel and the rate at which it is used. Speed affects fuel consumption too. For example, at 120 km per hour, a car will be able to travel 142.9 km per litre; at 100 km per hour, it can travel 166.7 km per litre; and at 80 km per hour, it can travel 200 km per litre.

If minimizing cost is the main goal, then travelling at 80 km per hour is the best alternative. When minimizing time is the main goal, travelling at 120 km per hour is the best choice. If maximizing the distance travelled on a tank of fuel (maximum range speed) is the objective, then 80 km per hour also is the best choice (1200 km). The cost of fuel and the available budget are other important factors—both to us and to animals. However, to animals, the cost is their available energy rather than money. Travelling faster (consuming more fuel) or more slowly (taking more time) is not always a viable option.

Shorebirds such as Bar-tailed Godwits (*Limosa lapponica*) fly 11,000 km non-stop from Alaska to New Zealand. These long-legged shorebirds feed along the shore and cannot land on and take off from the water's surface. Birds caught in Alaska before migration weighed

455 to 515 g, with fat composing almost 505 g of their body weight. Marked animals took 5.3 to 8.2 days to cover 7240 to 12,928 km, representing flight speeds of about 55 to 68 km per hour. The fuel consumed during this flight represents all of their body fat (~200 grams) and about half of their pectoral (flight) muscles (40 grams). Migrating Bar-tailed Godwits use maximum-range speed.

## STUDY BREAK

1. What currency(ies) is(are) used to measure the cost of locomotion?
2. What is the Reynolds number (Re)?
3. What is maximum-range speed?

### Muscles Work by Contracting

Contraction (shortening) of muscles is the basis for movement and other bodily processes in animals. Muscle cells occur in animals ranging from cnidarians to chordates. In their ability to contract, the specialized ectodermal cells of cnidarians resemble the muscle cells of other animals. Muscles in vertebrates consist of elongated (10 to 100 micrometres long) fibres running the length of the muscle. Myofibrils are cylindrical bundles of contractile proteins (about 1 micrometre in diameter) that run lengthwise in the cell and consist of thick and thin filaments arranged in alternating layers.

**Sarcomeres** are the basic units of contraction within a myofibril. The sarcomeres attach at either end to a **Z line**, which is a point of contraction. Two filaments made up mostly of two different types of proteins—actin (the thin filament) and myosin (the thick filament)—in the sarcomere slide across one another to contract muscles. This is called the **sliding filament theory** of muscle contraction.

Muscles contract when thin filaments on each side of a sarcomere slide over thick filaments toward the center (the A band), bringing Z lines closer together. These changes are triggered by increases in the concentration of calcium ions. Muscle contraction is initiated by input from an efferent neuron (see Chapter 26) that triggers the movement of calcium ions.

Typically, muscles are directly or indirectly involved in animal locomotion. Because muscles work by contraction, they tend to be arranged in pairs and work in opposition **(Figure 22.25)**. This is true of animals such as annelids like earthworms, which have muscles running along the body. When one set of muscles running along the body contracts, the body thickens. When an opposing set of muscles running along the body contracts, the body extends, becoming longer and thinner. The same principle applies to limbs. Some muscles draw the limb toward the body (flexors), whereas others move it away (extensors).

Typically, the **origin of a muscle** is the part that does not move when the muscle contracts. In contrast, the **insertion of a muscle** moves when the muscle contracts. When it contracts, the muscle that originates on the front surface of your upper arm bone (the humerus) and inserts on the forearm moves the forearm toward the humerus. Contraction of the opposing muscle that originates on the back surface of the humerus extends the forearm away from the body. Simultaneous, controlled contraction of both muscles operating in opposition permits precise, controlled movements of the forearm.

## STUDY BREAK

1. What is the difference between a flexor muscle and an extensor muscle?

**FIGURE 22.25** Skeletal muscles are often arranged in antagonistic pairs. In **(a)**, when the biceps muscle contracts and raises the forearm, its antagonistic partner, the triceps muscle, relaxes. In **(b)**, when the triceps muscle contracts, extending the forearm, the biceps muscle relaxes.

A.

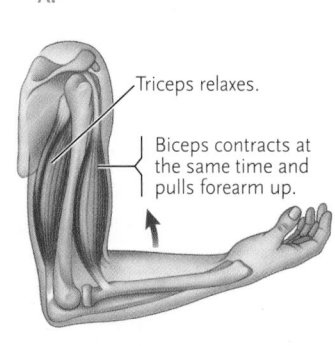

Triceps relaxes.

Biceps contracts at the same time and pulls forearm up.

B.

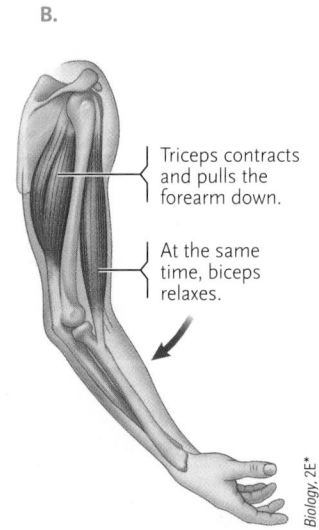

Triceps contracts and pulls the forearm down.

At the same time, biceps relaxes.

*Biology, 2E\**

## Joints Contribute to Flexibility

The cell walls of plants and fungi are flexible—much more so than the biomineralized skeletal parts of animals. Skeletons are composed of many component parts, and flexibility often involves movements at joints between elements of a skeleton **(Figure 22.26)**. Some joints operate in one plane (e.g., hinge joints such as your knee or your elbow), whereas others allow movement in more than one plane (e.g., the ball and sockets of your hip or shoulder). Although we may know most about joints in our bodies and those of other vertebrates, the same range of joints also occurs in other skeletons, from those in the exoskeletons of arthropods to the components of Aristotle's lantern, a feeding structure in sea urchins (Echinodermata).

The joints of vertebrates typically do not involve bone-to-bone contact (Figure 22.26). Where two bones meet at a synovial joint, fluid-filled capsules of connective tissue cover the ends of the bones. The human shoulder is one of many synovial joints in the human body. Within the joint, layers of cartilage are lubricated by synovial fluid that allows smooth movement of one bone on the other. Ligaments outside the joint capsule join the two bones (Figure 22.26). As many athletes learn to their dismay, damaged joints can be much less flexible and show reduced weight-bearing capacity.

Cartilaginous joints occur between individual vertebrae or between ribs and vertebrae. These joints involve bone, cartilage, and fibrous connective tissue. They allow some motion, for example, movement associated with breathing and flexing of the backbone.

Fibrous joints consist of stiff fibres of connective tissue that join bones (for example, to teeth) and allow little movement.

Hero shrews (*Scutisorex somereni*) have complex lumbar vertebrae with direct bone-to-bone contact. The functional significance of these joints is not well known. These relatively large (60 grams) shrews from Africa live in rock piles and have a distinct posture. They are renowned for their ability to survive the effect of a 70–kilogram person standing on them.

## STUDY BREAK

1. What are the differences between a hinge and a ball-and-socket joint?

A.

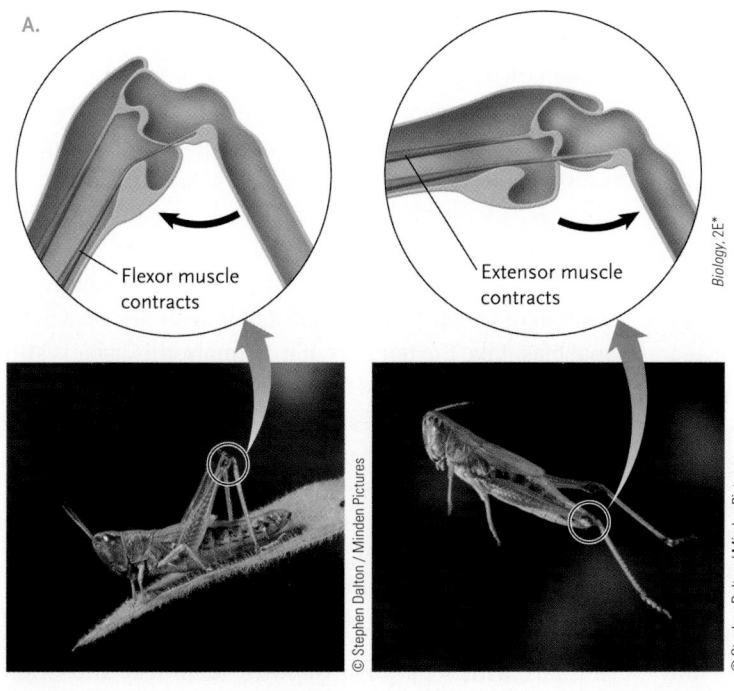

Flexor muscle contracts

Extensor muscle contracts

© Stephen Dalton / Minden Pictures

B. **Synovial joint cross section**

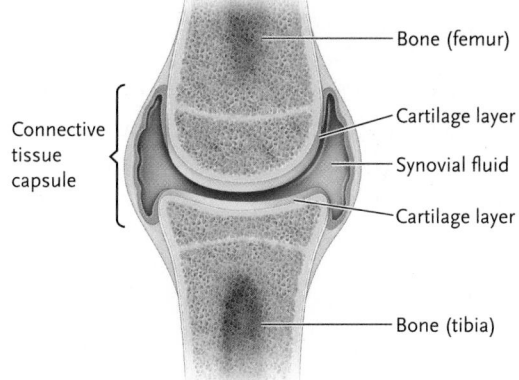

Connective tissue capsule

Bone (femur)
Cartilage layer
Synovial fluid
Cartilage layer

Bone (tibia)

**Knee joint ligaments**

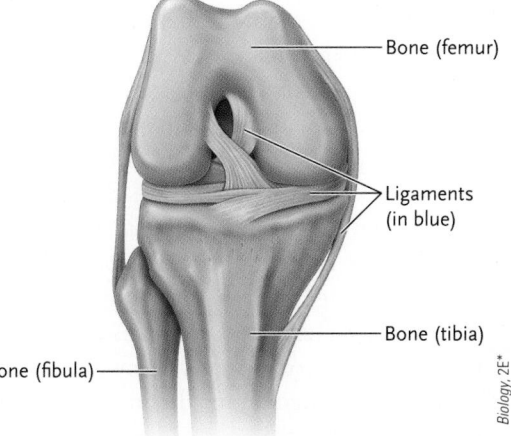

Bone (femur)

Ligaments (in blue)

Bone (tibia)

Bone (fibula)

Biology, 2E*

**FIGURE 22.26** In arthropods **(a)** such as a grasshopper, muscles attach to the inside surfaces of the exoskeleton. In vertebrates **(b)**, the details of the synovial joint (see text) are quite different.

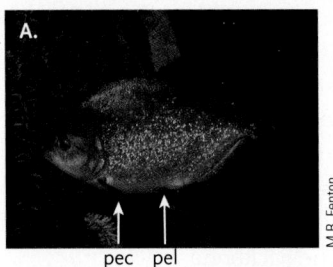 

pec  pel          pec  pel

**FIGURE 22.27** A comparison of a piranha (*Serrasalmus* spp.) **(a)** and a clownfish (*Amphiprion ocellaris*) **(b)** shows differences in the arrangement of pectoral and pelvic fins. In the piranha, pectoral (pec) and pelvic (pel) fins are located ventrally, whereas in the clownfish, the pectoral fins are lateral and enlarged, and the pelvic fins are ventral and more anterior. Both species power swimming by lateral movements of the tail (caudal) fin, but although clownfish use their pectoral fins for precise manoeuvring (stopping, turning), these fins in piranhas function more as stabilizers.

### Control Makes It Possible for Organisms to Determine Their Directions

In some movements, animals maximize power to get started and change position. In others, they maximize control and stability. A comparison of two fishes, a piranha and a clownfish **(Figure 22.27)**, emphasizes the difference. The piranha uses its tail (caudal) fin for propulsion, maximizing power output and using its pectoral and pelvic fins (both located along the animal's underside) for stabilization. The clownfish uses pectoral fins located on the sides of the body to maximize control. The clownfish operates much like someone rowing a boat moves forward by pulling simultaneously on both oars. But by pulling on the left oar and pushing on the right, the boat can be turned quickly.

Many buildings have cockroach infestations (*Periplaneta americana*). One way to tell is to leave some food on the floor, turn out the light, and wait. Then enter the room and turn on the light—and watch as cockroaches run from the food and then take shelter. Their initial response (around 54 milliseconds) is to run because moving is their best first line of defence. Their second, more directed, response is to run to shelter. Here coordination of locomotion is combined with direction from the central nervous system that is informed by the animal's position and goal.

For effective control over locomotion, animals require feedback about the positions of their bodies and component parts. In ray-finned fishes (such as the piranha or clownfish), rays in the fins provide sensory feedback about the position and relative movement of the fin. In animals with limbs, this feedback is derived from sensors associated with the position and relative movement, including tension on muscles associated with the limb. In bats, sensory hairs on the wing surface provide this kind of information in addition to airspeed and airflow across the wing.

**STUDY BREAK**

1. How is stability important in locomotion?
2. What are pectoral fins? How do they work?
3. What role does feedback play in locomotion?

## 22.6 Locomotion in Animals

Now we know how animals move, but how do they coordinate that movement to get from one place to another? This distinguishes movement from **locomotion**. Locomotion in animals involves pushing against something: the ground, water, or air. In some cases, flagellae or cilia are used as pushers, but other body parts (feet, wings, flippers, tails, etc.) are also commonly used in different kinds of animals.

Pushers are often specialized to increase surface area and gain purchase, allowing effective propulsion. The skeletons of animals are often involved, acting to transmit force generated by contractions of muscles into movement. This may involve the movement of a limb or some part of the body, for example, of the tail of a shark. The clownfish achieves the same effect by pulling on the left pectoral fin and pushing with the right one.

Studies of captive lemon sharks (*Negaprion brevirostris*) reveal how changes in internal pressures vary during locomotion. At rest, the internal pressure is 14 Newtons per square metre. But it ranges from 20 to 35 Newtons per square metre when swimming and up to 200 Newtons per square metre when swimming rapidly. Higher internal pressures provide a more resistant anchorage for muscles, increasing their efficiency of operation. The variation in pressure reflects changes in area and compression relative to surface area. The white inner layer of shark skin consists of collagen and is arranged on a diagonal bias. Like the tendons of mammals, this layer is stiff when under tension but flexible when not under tension. Changes in internal pressure alter transfers of energy. In swimming, lemon sharks' higher internal pressure means more efficient transfer of energy from muscle contraction to movements of the tail.

### Feet Keep Animals in Touch with the Substrate

Animals with legs push off with their feet and often depend on friction between foot and substrate to convert muscle contractions to forward motion. Specializations of limbs and feet correspond to different modes of locomotion and to different substrates **(Figure 22.28)**. The gait animals use (see also page 471) depends on the number of limbs (feet), the patterns of footfall, and the situations in which animals are operating. Animals such as millipedes have two pairs of legs per segment (centipedes have one pair) and move by coordinating

**FIGURE 22.28** Animals show a considerable range of specializations in their feet. In millipedes **(a)**, there are two pairs of legs per body segment with little specialization along the length of the animal. In scorpions **(b)**, three pairs of legs are specialized for walking and one pair for grabbing. The feet of a tiger salamander are generalized **(c)**, whereas those of birds such as a White-bellied Sunbird effectively grasp a perch **(d)**. The forefoot of a sabre-toothed tiger **(e)** has retractile claws, whereas a wildebeeste **(f)** has hooves. A red squirrel (*Tamiasciurus hudsonicus*) **(g)** at a bird feeder shows how feet can do different jobs (hang on and hold food) at the same time.

their legs in a pattern that looks like a wave. Tetrapods—animals with four legs—tend to use all four legs in locomotion, although the actual pattern of footfall will depend on whether the animal is walking or running.

When walking or running **(Figure 22.29)**, birds are bipedal (two-footed), as are some mammals, such as humans. Other animals, such as anurans and mammals from kangaroos to kangaroo rats, hop using both

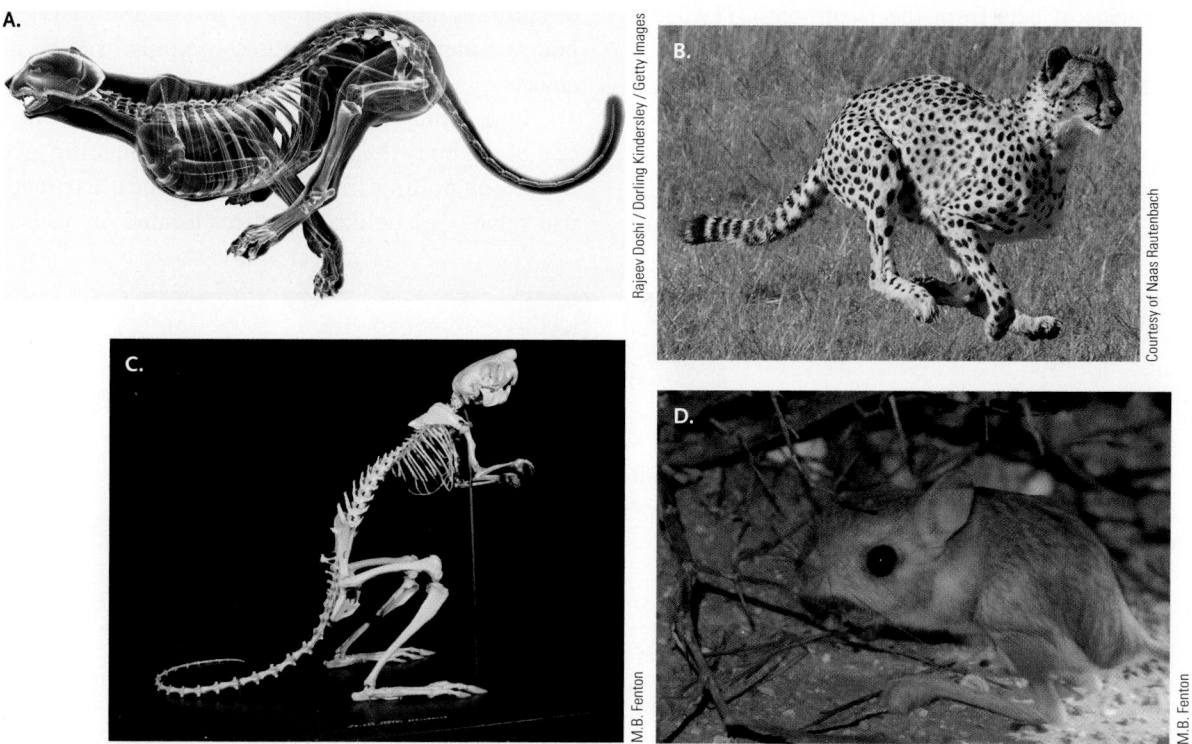

**FIGURE 22.29** Whereas some tetrapods, such as the cheetah (*Acinonyx jubatus*) **(a** and **b)**, run, others, such as springhares (*Pedetes capensis*) or jerboa (*Jaculus jaculus*), use richochetal locomotion **(c** and **d)**.

hindlimbs in unison. Also known as **ricochetal** or saltatory locomotion, animals that use it tend to have marked differences between fore- and hindlimbs (Figure 22.29). In rodents such as springhares and jerboas, the forelimbs are reduced, the neck is shortened, and the number of vertebrae attaching the pelvic girdle to the backbone (sacral vertebrae) has increased (Figure 22.29).

Almost everyone is familiar with the sight of an insect moving around on a flower. Through the flowers, plants provide nectar and pollen, while the insect moves pollen from one plant to another, which is fundamental to cross-pollination (see Chapter 13). There can be more to this than meets the eye. Like many other flowers, there are conical cells on the petals of flowers such as sunflowers (Figure 22.30). The conical cells provide bees and other insects with something to grip as they move around on the flower. A good grip is important because flowers blow in the wind, motion that attracts pollinators but also makes the flowers more difficult to grasp. Conical cells are an effective way for the plant to give would-be pollinators a grip on a moving surface.

In the absence of conical cells, some plant surfaces, such as the upper surfaces of leaves of *Heliconia* plants, are slippery. Insects and some bats use suction or adhesion to stick to such surfaces (Figure 22.31). Many other animals are also specialized to adhere to smooth surfaces. Two species of bats with adhesive discs occur in Madagascar (*Myzopoda* spp.) and use wet adhesion to stick to smooth surfaces (Figure 22.32, a and b). Three other species of bats from the Neotropics (*Thyroptera* spp.) use suction discs to adhere to smooth surfaces (Figure 22.32, c to e). Geckoes and many lizards obtain purchase on smooth surfaces via specialized setae on their feet.

There are other ways that animals can deal with moving on smooth surfaces. In 2011, it was clearly demonstrated that a large species of tarantula (*Aphonopelma seemanni*) secreted silk directly from nozzles (spigots) on their tarsi (feet). Specifically, Chilean rose (*Grammostola rosea*), Indian ornamental (*Poecilotheria regalis*), and Mexican flame knee (*Brachypelma auratum*) tarantulas secrete silk from their tarsi. These species are distantly related, suggesting that the phenomenon is widespread in the family (Theraphosidae). The results of earlier work had questioned this ability in tarantulas. The structure of the abdominal spinnerets in these tarantulas resembles that of the earliest spiders from the Devonian. These tarantulas produced tarsal silk when the animal slipped on a smooth surface.

## STUDY BREAK

1. How do animal gaits differ?
2. How do animals gain traction during locomotion?
3. What role can silk play in locomotion?

## Undulations Are One Way to Move

Undulation of the body (Figure 22.33, p. 492) is one way to move, whether the animal is in water, on the ground, or in the soil. This pattern of movement is common in fish with eel-like bodies but also occurs in annelids and in limbless tetrapods (e.g., caecilian amphibians, snakes, and legless lizards). For pushing against water, eel-like fishes use their tail fin, whereas snakes rely on specialized scales to gain traction when moving on the ground or climbing in trees. Leeches swim by undulating their bodies. **Lateral undulation** is commonly used by many snakes.

**Concertina locomotion** involves anchoring one end of the body (head or tail) and then pushing against it (tail) or pulling from it (anterior end). Earthworms use **setae**—bristlelike structures located on each body

**FIGURE 22.30** The petals of sunflowers **(a)** have microscopic grips **(b)** Scale in (b) is 20 μm.

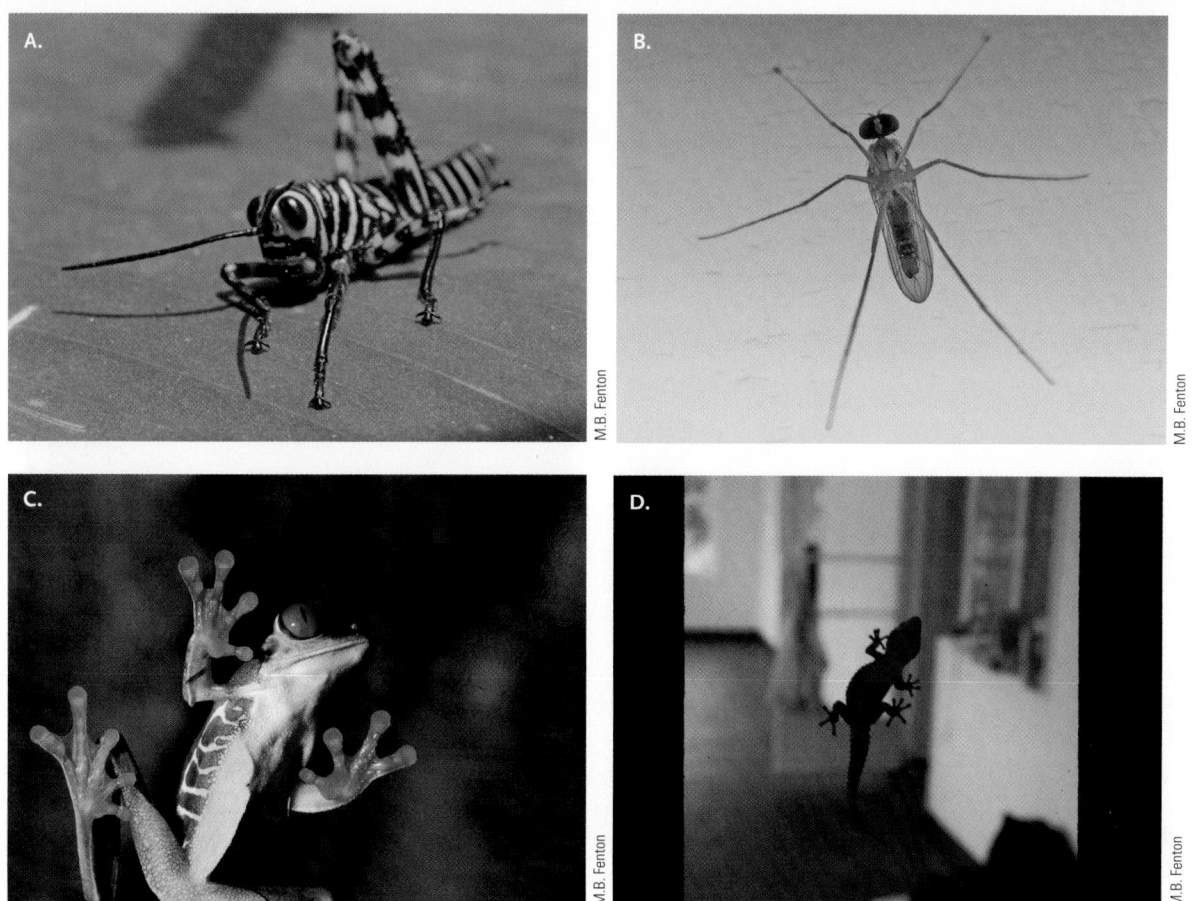

**FIGURE 22.31** Leaf surfaces such as those of *Heliconia* species are very smooth. The nymphal acridid grasshopper **(a)** has no trouble adhering to the surface of the *Heliconia* leaf. Glass also is a smooth surface, and a variety of animals, from flies **(b)** to frogs **(c)** and geckoes **(d)**, readily walk on glass.

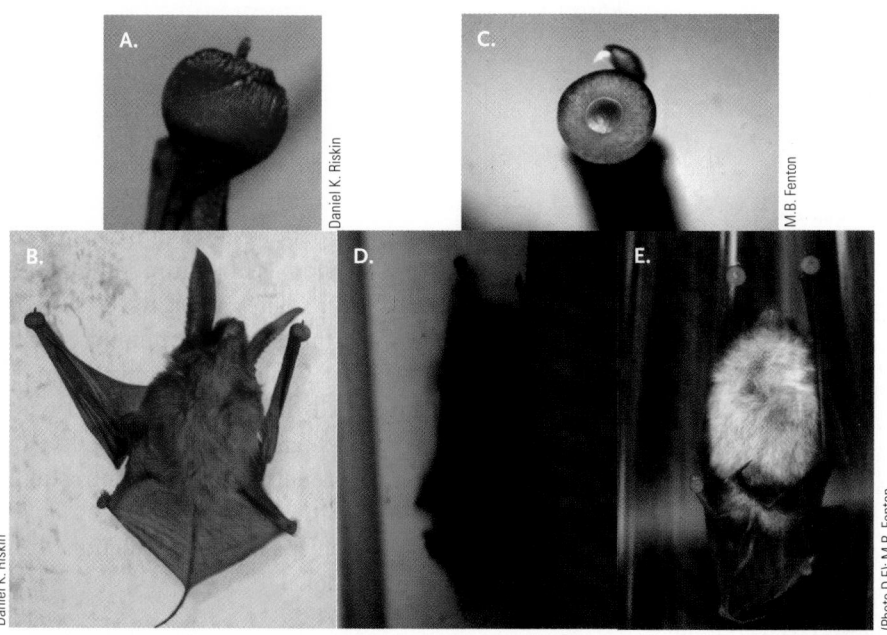

**FIGURE 22.32** Species of bats in two families have discs on their wrists **(a, b)** and ankles. The myzopodid bats from Madagascar **(a, c)** use wet adhesion to stick to slippery leaves on which they roost. The thyropterid bats from the Neotropics use suction **(b, d, e)** to adhere to the surfaces of unfurled leaves **(d)** or an empty drinking glass **(e)**.

segment—to anchor parts of the body and gain purchase. Leeches attach a posterior sucker and extend their proboscis, which they anchor, release the sucker, and contract, bringing the posterior forward. Snakes gain purchase with specialized scales. If you watch a snake trying to move on a slippery surface, you will realize the importance of friction between its scales and the substrate it is moving on. Without friction between its scales and the surface, the snake will struggle to move.

Other snakes, such as the burrowing *Rhinophis drummondhayi* from India, use concertina locomotion.

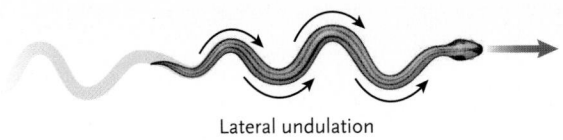

Lateral undulation

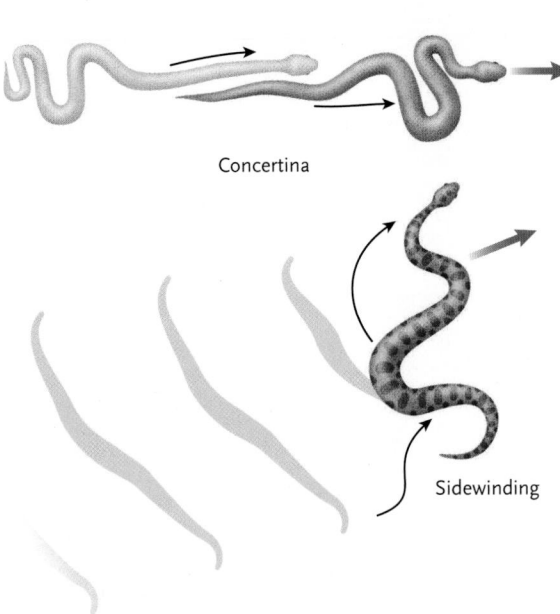

Concertina

Sidewinding

**FIGURE 22.33** A comparison of lateral undulatory, concertina, and sidewinding locomotion in snakes. Large horizontal arrows identify the overall direction of movement.

SOURCE: From FENTON/DUMONT/OWEN. *Integrative Animal Biology*, 1E. © 2014 Nelson Education Ltd. Reproduced by permission. www.cengage.com/permissions

These snakes anchor their posterior end and burrow by driving the head forward. The snake then anchors the anterior end, draws the posterior end forward, and repeats the process. This has been referred to as the "freight train" approach to burrowing because the front end does all the work.

Many of the organisms that move in an undulating manner have evolved from ancestors that had limbs. They lost the limbs over evolutionary time. What is the advantage of losing limbs? Perhaps being limbless means less cost of locomotion because of the energy required to move individual limbs. By measuring the amount of energy used (oxygen consumed), biologists demonstrated that locomotion costs snakes using lateral undulation the same as it costs lizards of the same size to walk or run. But when snakes use concertina locomotion, the costs are much higher. So energy cost is not the reason why the evolution of snakes involved loss of limbs.

Did the ancestors of snakes lose their limbs in an aquatic or a terrestrial habitat? A fossil snake, *Coniophis precedens*, from the Cretaceous may provide an answer to this question. The deposits in which the fossils occurred suggest a terrestrial rather than an aquatic habitat. This

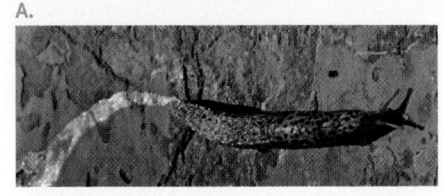

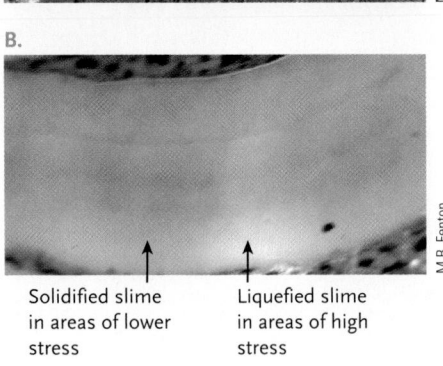

Solidified slime in areas of lower stress    Liquefied slime in areas of high stress

**FIGURE 22.34** **(a)** A garden slug (*Limax maximus*) leaving an obvious mucus trail as it moves. **(b)** A ventral view of the foot showing regions of liquid and gel mucus.

species had reduced neural spines that suggest that it was adapted to digging and living underground—it was **fossorial**. Loss of limbs is a recurring feature in many fossorial animals, from earthworms to lizards and snakes. Loss of limbs reduces the cost of locomotion in fossorial animals because animals without limbs can move more readily through narrow tunnels.

## Mucus Can Provide a Slippery Substrate

Snails and slugs provide another variation on locomotion. Terrestrial species slide over a layer of mucus, which leaves a distinct trail **(Figure 22.34)**. In this setting, mucus minimizes friction, reducing the cost of locomotion resulting from contractions of muscles. Here a sequence of waves in the foot of the slug (or snail) correspond to areas where the foot is lifted from the surface on which the slug is moving. The mucus itself is interesting because depending on its water content, it can act as either a lubricant or a glue. This reflects a change from gel to fluid associated with the strain associated with locomotion. In snails and slugs, the cost of mucus production exceeds the cost of fuelling muscle contraction. Other snails, such as the moon snail (*Polinices duplicatus*), move by combining muscular contraction with the action of cilia on the foot.

## STUDY BREAK

1. What is the difference between lateral undulation and concertina locomotion?
2. What role does mucus play in locomotion by molluscs?

*Scalopus aquaticus*

*Geomys* spp.

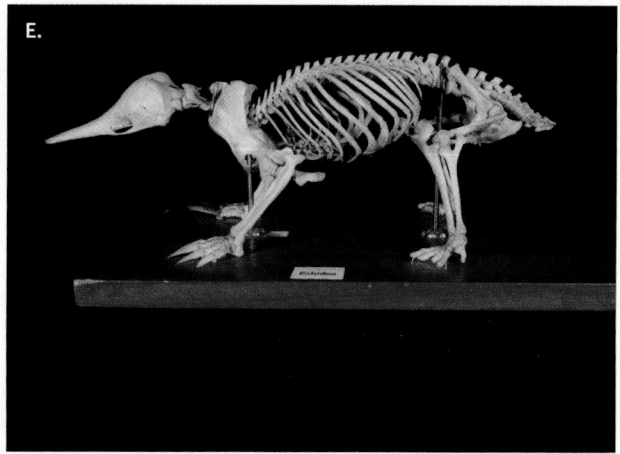

**FIGURE 22.35** Mammals that burrow, including a marsupial mole **(a)**, a golden mole **(b)**, a "true" mole **(c)**, a pocket gopher **(d)**, and an echidna **(e)**.

## Burrowing Is a Way of Life

Burrowing mammals such as marsupial moles, golden moles, moles, and gophers have specialized limbs for digging. Marsupial moles, true moles, and golden moles are small and fossorial (live underground) **(Figure 22.35)**. Echidnas, spiny anteaters, are larger diggers, also with strong forelimbs. There are fossorial species in at least eight evolutionary lineages of rodents. These "gophers" tend to use enlarged incisor teeth for burrowing and do not have enlarged forelimbs.

## STUDY BREAK

1. What is a fossorial lifestyle?
2. What are three different adaptations that allow fossorial animals to move underground?

## Swimming Is Movement in Water

Swimming involves moving by pushing against the water. Swimmers push with limbs (paddles or flippers) or by undulating the body. Controlled movement during swimming may involve maximizing power or manoeuvrability **(Figure 22.36, p. 494)**. Both swimming by undulations of the body and swimming with flippers (Figure 22.36) are widespread in the animal kingdom, among invertebrates and vertebrates **(Figure 22.37, p. 494)**. The many different modes of swimming provide many examples of parallel and convergent evolution (see Chapter 13).

Animals that dive also need to maintain their supply of oxygen. Taking air underwater raises issues of buoyancy and the cost of swimming. In some aquatic vertebrates, bones, and often ribs, are very dense. Manatee bones lack marrow cavities. These specialized bones appear to be involved in maintaining buoyancy.

## STUDY BREAK

1. How does the swimming behaviour differ between sharks and rays?
2. How do animals use flippers?

(Photos A,B,C) M.B. Fenton

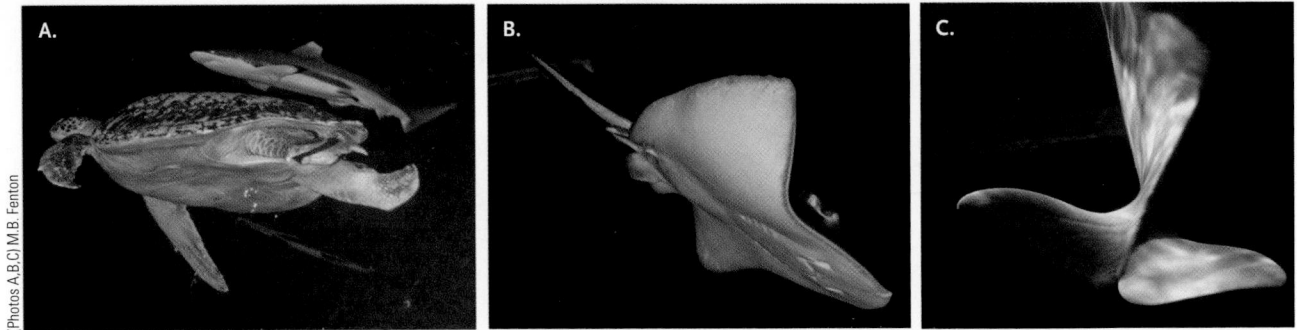

**FIGURE 22.36** Various modes of propulsion by swimming animals. In **(a)**, propulsion by the tail (caudal) fin is typical of a black tip reef shark (*Carcharhinus melanopterus*), which uses its pectoral and pelvic fins as stabilizers. The green turtle (*Chelonia mydas*) powers its swimming with its pectoral flippers and uses its pelvic flippers for stabilization. **(b)** A sting ray (*Dasyatis* spp.) powers swimming with enlarged pectoral "wings," and **(c)** a beluga whale (*Delphinapterus leucas*) does so with its tail fluke.

M.B. Fenton

M.B. Fenton

M.B. Fenton

M.B. Fenton

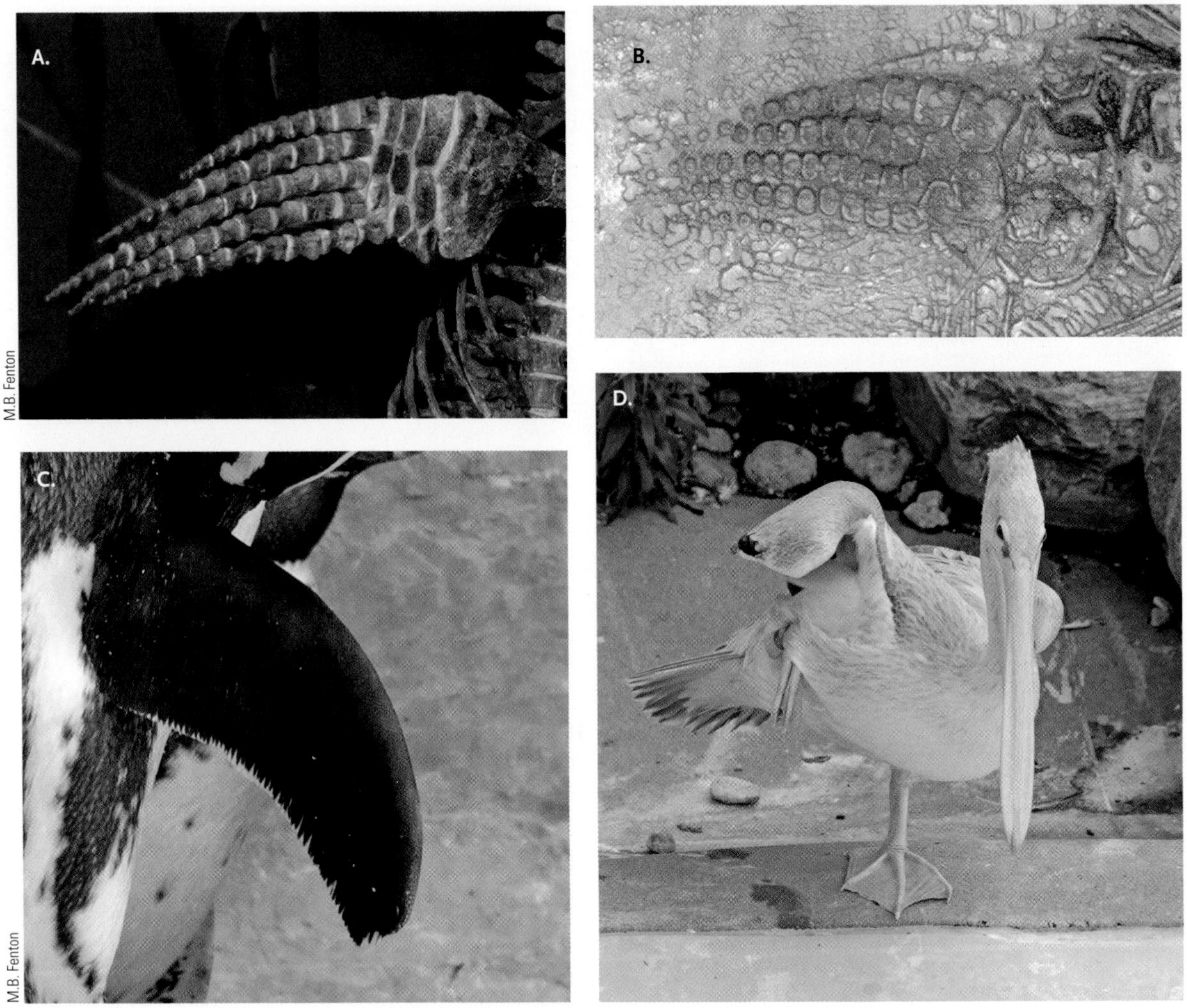

**FIGURE 22.37** Foreflippers of a plesiosaur **(a)**, an ichthyosaur **(b)**, and a penguin **(c)**. In each case, marine species have evolved from terrestrial ancestors. The fore- (pectoral) flippers are used to generate power during swimming. Many other tetrapods have webbed feet **(d)**, which are used to power swimming.

## Taking to the Air Can Involve Different Approaches

We are accustomed to the idea of animals gliding, parachuting, and flying. We may appreciate that taking to the air is a recurring theme among animals (including humans). Yet, in 2010, the observation that many species (and genera) of ants can glide was unexpected. Specifically, some arboreal (tree-living) ants of Central and South America control their descent when they fall from a tree. Although they initially tumble, apparently out of control, they then right themselves and glide, backside first, to the

FIGURE 22.38 The flying squirrel (*Glaucomys sabrinus*) can achieve a gliding equilibrium of descent ($\theta < 45°$). Its posture during gliding illustrates the positioning of the fore- and hindlimbs. The specific position of the wrist and attitude of the forelimb affect gliding performance.

ground or to a lower part of a tree. This behaviour was not expected from animals that lack any apparent specialization for gliding or parachuting.

The angle of descent is a useful way to distinguish between gliders and parachuters. Good gliders **(Figure 22.38)** descend at angles of less than 45°, whereas animal parachuters descend at angles of more than 45°. In addition to the ants noted above, gliding and parachuting have evolved independently in bony fishes, frogs in the families Rhacophoridae and Hylidae, and reptiles (lizards, geckoes, and snakes). At least two species of fossil reptiles also were gliders, *Sharovipteryx mirabilis* and *Microraptor gui*. Among mammals, gliding species occur in marsupials (pouched mammals) and placental mammals as well as in the extinct docodonts. Gliding has evolved more than once in rodents and in flying lemurs (Cynocephalidae). Gliding and parachuting can be advantageous because they confer some protection against predators. Both forms of locomotion provide a rapid and inexpensive means of descent, perhaps in the context of escape or during foraging where the animal works a tree from the bottom up.

Flapping (powered) flight **(Figure 22.39)**, by definition involving the generation of lift and propulsion, has evolved independently in insects (phylum Arthropoda) and three times in Chordates, specifically Pterosauria (pterosaurs), Aves (birds), and Chiroptera (bats). The wing structures of insects differ from those of the flying chordates. Although the wings of pterosaurs, birds, and bats all involve modified forelimbs, the details are different. In addition to providing a means of escape, flapping flight also allows access to otherwise unreachable resources, such as food or shelter. Active flight allows

A.

B.

FIGURE 22.39 Three pictures of flying animals, including **(a)** a male gypsy moth (*Lymantria dispar*), **(b)** a Waterhouse's leaf-nosed bat, and **(c)** a ruby-throated kummingbird (*Archilochus colubris*).

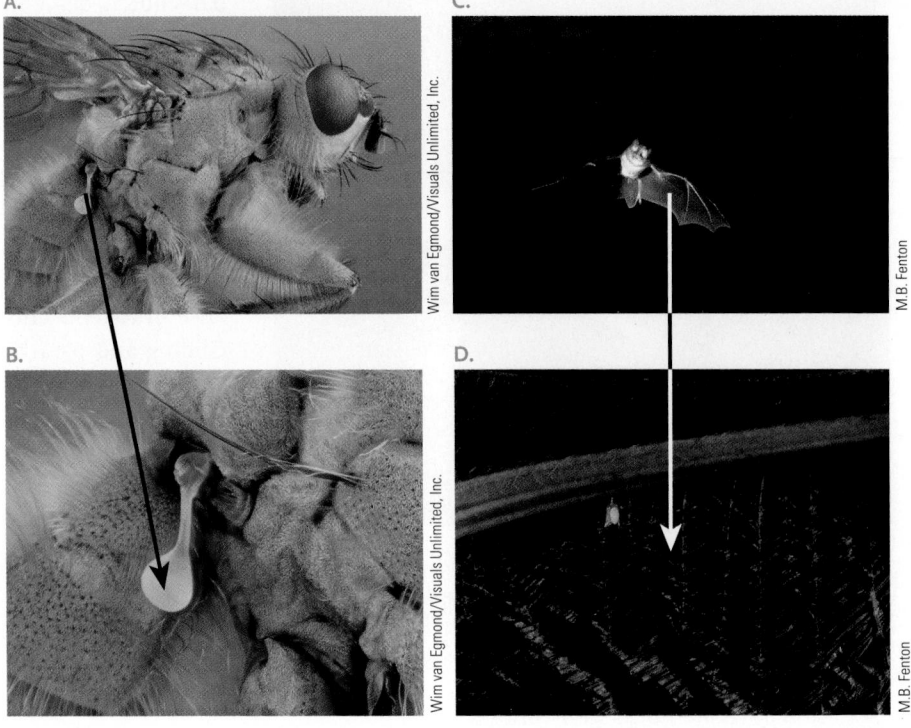

**FIGURE 22.40** Halteres, vestigial wings on a fly shown in position **(a)** and close up **(b)**. The ventral surfaces of the wings of Parnell's moustached bat (*Pteronotus parnellii*) **(c)** have rows of sensory hairs **(d)** that transduce air movements. Also obvious in (d) are elastin fibres in the bat's wing.

birds, bats, and insects to exploit widely distributed food supplies.

Unlike most flying insects that have four wings, flies have two. Flies use small club-shaped vestigial wings **(Figure 22.40)** known as **halteres** to sense (transduce) information about body orientation during flight. For example, halteres monitor pitch (tendency of the body to move the nose down or up), roll (rotation along the long axis), and yaw (move the nose to the left or right). Some flying bats (Figure 22.40) have sensory hairs on the ventral surface of the wing. These transduce information about patterns of airflow and speed across the surface of the wing. Using a depilatory cream to remove the sensory hairs deprived bats of their deft and manoeuvrable flight. When the hairs grew back, the bats regained their agility in flight.

Loss of flight is also a recurring theme among insects and birds, although there is no evidence of it in bats and pterosaurs. Flightlessness occurs in some populations of birds or insects living on remote oceanic islands. Here taking off into prevailing winds could blow a bird or insect away from its home range. Remote oceanic islands (e.g., New Zealand, Easter Island, Hawaii, Mauritius) may lack terrestrial predators and therefore the need to fly, an expensive mode of transport. In these situations, the arrival of humans, along with cats and rats, can and has repeatedly led to the extinction of flightless species of birds and insects. Other flightless birds, such as ostriches, emus, rheas, and cassowaries, persist in the presence of predators. Among birds and insects, flightlessness can arise relatively quickly, for example, the extinct flightless ibis from Hawaii (Box 22.2).

## STUDY BREAK

1. How does gliding differ from powered flight?
2. Among pterosaurs, why was *Quetzalcoatlus* so impressive?
3. Use the evolution of powered flight to illustrate the difference between parallel and convergent evolution.

## Jet Propulsion Is an Aquatic Thing

Recent documentation shows that at least four species of squid (*Sthenoteuthis pteropus*, *Dosidicus gigas*, *Illex illecebrosus*, and *Loligo opalescens*) use forceful expulsion of water from the mantle cavity to launch from the water's surface and fly. Moving in air, *S. pteropus* **(Figure 22.41)** travelled three times faster than in water, 265 versus 79 body lengths per square second. This difference reflects the difference in density between air and water and the drag associated with moving through water. Jet propulsion, by expelling water, allowed the squid to cover 1 to 2 m in the air.

The use of fluid under pressure (hydraulics) is a recurring theme among animals. Bats that visit flowers to obtain nectar and pollen have long faces and even longer tongues **(Figure 1)**. An erection of the penis of a male mammal also reflects local movement of blood, providing another example of a hydraulic operation. In some arthropods, limbs are extended by direct muscle contraction but pumped back into the starting position by hydraulics, in this case, pressure acting on hemolymph.

Soft-bodied animals such as caterpillars use gut propulsion as another means of locomotion, commonly seen in soft-bodied animals such as caterpillars. The body of a tobacco hornworm (*Manduca sexta*) is flexible and fluid filled with two separate hydrostatic components, the gut and the body. The gut is anchored at the mouth and at the anus but slides freely within the animal's body. Again, anchoring the posterior, pushing the head forward and anchoring it, and bringing the hind end up is the operational mode.

The water-propelled movements of cephalopod molluscs are another variation on a hydraulic theme, whether the mollusc is operating in water or in air.

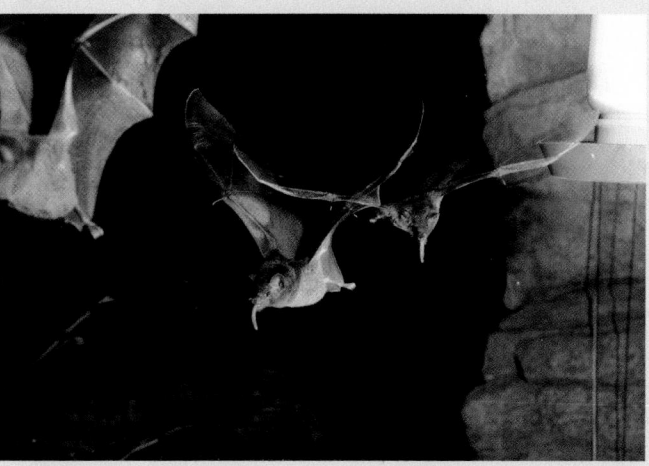

**FIGURE 1** At the Biodome in Montréal, three nectar-feeding bats (*Glossophaga soricina*) leave a feeder filled with sugar water. In the wild, these bats visit flowers to get nectar and pollen but readily learn to substitute a hummingbird feeder for a flower. To extend their tongues, the bats pump them full of blood. This also affects the papillae on the tip of the tongue, acting as a sponge to soak up nectar. We presume that the distended tongues of these bats reflects the fact that they were just feeding and had not had time to withdraw the blood from the tongue.

**FIGURE 22.41** These squid (*Sthenoteuthis pteropus*) use jet propulsion to move in water and, even, in air.

Squid and other cephalopod molluscs are renowned for their use of jet propulsion while moving through water. Again, forceful expulsion of water from the mantle cavity is key to this approach to locomotion. The cost of jet-propelled swimming in water (13 joules per kilogram per metre) is higher than that for a salmon (*Oncorhynchus nerka*) (2 joules per kilogram per metre).

Several genera of scallops (bivalve molluscs) also swim by jet propulsion (forceful expulsion of water from the mantle cavity). The muscle associated with forcefully drawing the shell parts together is the part of the animal prized by many people as food. The larvae of some dragonflies also use jet-propelled swimming, expelling water from the gill chamber. Some jellyfish also use jet propulsion. This form of locomotion also occurs in salps, which are urochordates. Jet propulsion is more uniform in salps, translating into less expensive movement.

Collagen is a fibrous protein (**Figure 1**) that is a major component of extracellular matrix (ECM; see page 71) in animals. Collagen is widespread throughout the animal kingdom. Individual molecules of collagen consist of three polypeptide chains wrapped around one another in a helix. There are at least 16 different forms of collagen, some with high tensile strength, others forming a basal lamina. Collagen is rich in the amino acids glycine and proline and contains some unique amino acids.

Keratin, which forms the feathers and beaks of birds, is one example of collagen. In mammals, the horns, hairs, toenails, and fingernails are also made of keratin, which is rich in the amino acid cysteine. The "horns" of rhinos are made from fused hairs and have no value as aphrodisiacs or fever suppressants —a belief that accounts for the market for rhino horn.

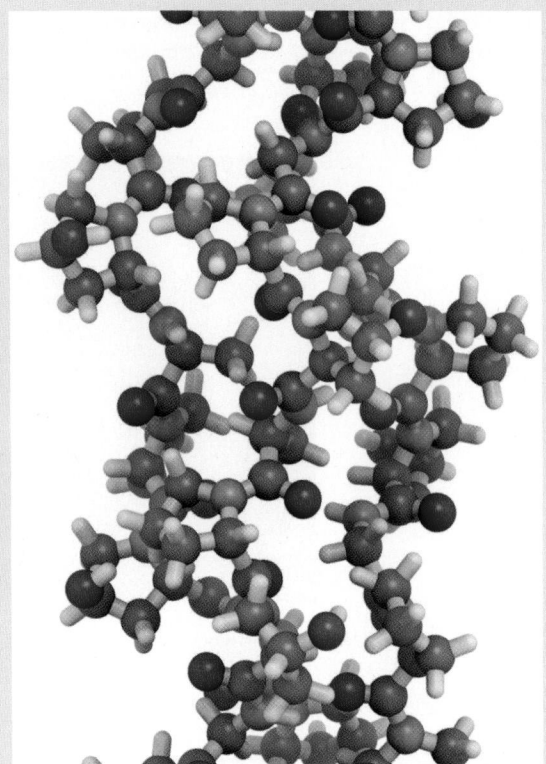

**FIGURE 1** A collagen molecule showing the triple helix structure.

molekuul.be/Shutterstock.com

## PUTTING IT IN PERSPECTIVE

One recurring theme in the topic of support and movement is the examples of parallel and convergent evolution. The evolution of powered flight has occurred at least four times in animals (in insects, birds, pterosaurs, and bats). Here the modification of forelimbs as wings in bats, birds, and pterosaurs is an example of parallel evolution. Flight in insects is convergent with flight in chordates. The discovery of jet-propelled flying squid demonstrates that organisms use what they have to survive and prosper. The information in the chapter provides many other examples of animals coming up with different (or similar) solutions to the same challenges.

## KEY CONCEPTS REVIEW AND QUESTIONS

### 22.1 Support Holds Things Up

An organism's structure is linked to its size and the density of the medium in which it lives. Water is denser than air and provides support, explaining why most of the world's largest animals have been aquatic. There are many other connections linking an animal's form and function with its environment. Materials in support structures may have a blend of strength, rigidity, stiffness, and toughness. Some may be more flexible than others.

1. What are the largest known organisms in the world? Why is this reality not surprising?

2. What is biomineralization? Give at least three examples and explain why biomineralization is an important element in systems that support organisms.

3. Explain the difference(s) between strength, stiffness, and toughness.

### 22.2 Supporting Structures

Supporting structures include endoskeletons and exoskeletons. The main supporting structures in plants and fungi are cell walls. Spicules are structural elements in invertebrates such as sponges and corals. Tubes secreted or constructed from various materials by some animals provide support and protection. Shells are found in many brachiopods and molluscs. The stereom is the skeleton of echinoderms. Bones provide the structural support to vertebrates. The skeletons of Chondrichthyes are mainly made from cartilage. Tendons usually connect muscles to bones.

4. How do the support systems of fungi and plants differ from those of animals? What are the consequences of these differences?

5. What do bones and shells have in common?

## 22.3 Movement

There is a difference between animals and plants in terms of how each category moves under its own power. There are exceptions such as those animals that are sessile during their adult lives and the traps of Venus flytraps.

6. Compare the capacity for movement of plants and animals. How does this comparison relate to the supporting systems in these organisms?

## 22.4 Plants and Fungi

Plants and fungi can disperse to new locations. Wind is an important dispersal mechanism. Triggered snap traps in carnivorous plants are other examples of plant movement.

## 22.5 Movement by Animals

Animals can move by hitchhiking on other animals. Others may have mobile larvae even though adults are sessile. Movement costs energy and generated heat. Organisms that move faster require better eyesight to see the details of terrain as they move.

The metabolic energy cost associated with moving can be affected by the size and mass of the organism, mode of locomotion, distance covered, and speed. Muscle contraction is the basis of movement in animals. Joints allow for flexibility between elements of a skeleton. Animals require feedback about the portions of their bodies and component parts to control their locomotion.

7. Explain how muscle contraction underlies much of the capacity of animals to move. What are the differences between direct and indirect effects of muscle contraction?

## 22.6 Locomotion in Animals

Animals move from one location to another by pushing against something else with specialized pushers. There is a great diversity in how animals conduct locomotion. Locomotion could involve walking on feet, undulations, use of mucous excretions, burying using specialized limbs, swimming (including jet propulsion) through water, and travel through the air.

8. What influence does the pattern of footfall have on a running animal? Why?

9. What are the main costs of locomotion? How do animals cover these costs?

10. What role does friction play in the locomotion of animals?

11. Which animals move by undulation? How does that work?

12. In what sense are flippers water-wings? How do wings and flippers differ?

# Gas Exchange

## WHY IT MATTERS

Why do we breathe? What is the purpose? Most humans cannot survive more than a few minutes without breathing, and we only began to understand why with the discovery of oxygen in the late 1700s. It then quickly became clear that we need to breathe to extract oxygen ($O_2$) from the air around us and excrete carbon dioxide ($CO_2$) back into it. The mitochondria in our cells need a constant supply of $O_2$ from the environment to produce ATP during cellular respiration (see Chapter 5). In addition, the metabolic processes that ultimately produce the ATP also produce $CO_2$. $CO_2$ needs to be rapidly removed from cells. In animals, too much $CO_2$ in cells is a narcotic poison that damages nerve function. Too much $CO_2$ in cells also produces changes in the cell's pH, which in turn alters the activity levels of all functional proteins (enzymes, receptors, transport proteins, etc.) (see Chapter 4). Many animals have become adapted to prolong the time between breaths, but very few animals can produce adequate ATP without breathing. This explains, for instance, why marine mammals must routinely return to the surface of the ocean to breathe **(Figure 23.1)**.

There are exceptions to the rule, however. Two of the most remarkable vertebrates are the crucian carp (*Carassius carassius*) and the freshwater turtle (*Trachemys scripta*) (Figure 23.1). These species can routinely survive over long winters in frozen lakes where oxygen levels fall to extremely low levels and there is no access to the surface. They recruit alternate anaerobic metabolic pathways that do not require oxygen but that also

**FIGURE 23.1** **(a)** Killer whales (*Orcinus orca*) breathing at the surface of the water. **(b)** A frozen lake. **(c)** A crucian carp. **(d)** The freshwater red-eared slider.

produce much less ATP and reduce their metabolic rates so that they need much less ATP.

Plants are no exception. Their mitochondria also need oxygen, and they also produce $CO_2$. Ironically, at the same time, the chloroplasts of plant cells need $CO_2$ for photosynthesis, and in the light, these chloroplasts release $O_2$ as a waste product (see Chapter 5). The net balance between these two processes—respiration and photosynthesis—will determine which prevails at any given time. As a rule, photosynthesis dominates in the daytime, leading to a net production of $O_2$ and consumption of $CO_2$. Respiration prevails at night, leading to net $O_2$ consumption and $CO_2$ production.

In this chapter, we discuss the physical basis of gas exchange and how evolution has produced a range of adaptations that maximize the rate of gas exchange both into and out of the tissues of plants and animals living in different environments. These adaptations allow organisms to perform metabolically challenging activities in different habitats. For single-celled organisms, exchange is simply across the plasma membrane. For large, multicellular organisms, however, many cells are far from the external environment and gas exchange generally involves a series of steps known as the gas transport cascade. These steps transport oxygen and carbon dioxide between the environment and chloroplasts or mitochondria **(Figure 23.2)**.

## 23.1 General Principles of Gas Exchange

Air normally contains about 78% nitrogen ($N_2$), 21% oxygen ($O_2$), and very small amounts of carbon dioxide ($CO_2$) and other gases **(Table 23.1)**. This percentage composition of air remains constant from sea level up into the atmosphere. Given this, how do we explain the fact that at high altitude in the mountains it gets harder to take in enough oxygen? To answer this, we need to appreciate that air has weight. The more air above us, the greater the pressure due to this weight pushing down, and the more compressed (thicker) the air is. At higher altitudes, there is less pressure pushing down, so the air expands and gets thinner. As the air gets thinner, there are fewer molecules of all of the gases that compose the atmosphere, even though the fractional composition—or the proportion of each type of gas—remains the same.

The density (thickness or thinness) of the air in the atmosphere is measured as the atmospheric pressure. Atmospheric pressure is greater the closer you are to sea level and falls with increasing altitude (see Box 23.1). The unit of measurement is often millibars, or pounds per square inch, although in the biomedical world, it is usually expressed as millimetres of mercury (mm Hg). At sea level,

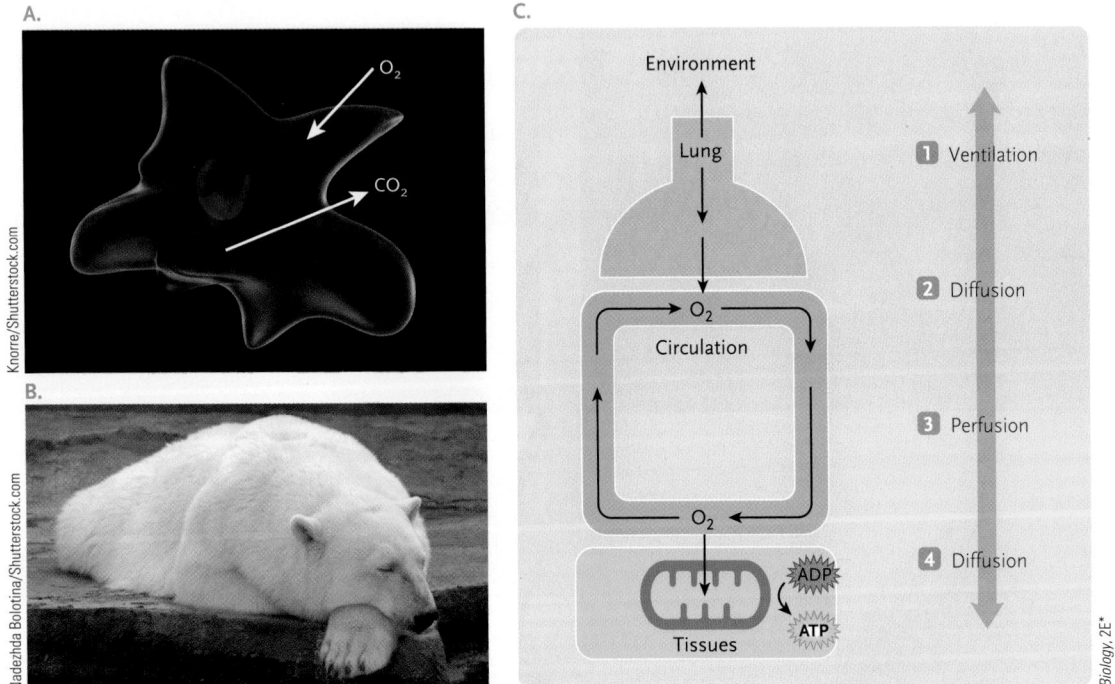

**FIGURE 23.2 (a)** In single-celled organisms, oxygen and carbon dioxide are exchanged with the external environment directly across the cell membrane. **(b)** For large multicellular organisms (polar bear – *Ursus maritimus*), this is not possible because most cells have no contact with the external environment. For these organisms, gas exchange involves multiple steps. **(c)** The steps in the cascade for the transport of oxygen between the environment and the mitochondria in an air-breathing vertebrate are shown here. There are four steps: (1) ventilation to move gas into and out of the lungs; (2) diffusion of oxygen into the blood; (3) perfusion or transport of blood by the heart to the tissues; and (4) diffusion of oxygen from the blood in the capillaries in the tissues into the mitochondria in the cells. The steps for the transport of $CO_2$ from the cells to the environment are the reverse of this.

TABLE 23.1

**The Gas Composition of the Atmosphere at two Different Elevations and in an Underground Burrow**

The composition of each gas is given both as a percentage of the total and, in brackets, as a partial pressure of the total atmospheric pressure.

| Gas | Sea Level Atmosphere | Top of Mount Everest Atmosphere | Burrow Atmosphere |
|---|---|---|---|
| Nitrogen ($N_2$) | 78.09 (593) | 78.09 (196) | 78.09 (593) |
| Oxygen ($O_2$) | 20.95 (159) | 20.95 (53) | 12–18 (91–137) |
| Carbon Dioxide ($CO_2$) | 0.03 (0.25) | 0.03 (0.08) | 3–9 (23–68) |
| Other Gases | 0.93 (7.75) | 0.93 (1.82) | 0.93 (1.82) |
| Total | 100 (760) | 100 (251) | 100 (760) |

Julie Lubick/Shutterstock.com

Mike Charles/Shutterstock.com

Vadim Petrakov/Shutterstock.com

the atmospheric pressure is 760 mm Hg: that is, the weight of a column of air descending from outer space to the surface of Earth is sufficient to support a vertical column of mercury 760 mm high. This pressure is the sum of the pressures due to the weights of all of the gases in the atmosphere. The individual pressure exerted by each gas within a mixture of gases such as air is defined as its **partial pressure**. For any one gas, the partial pressure is the percentage of the total pressure that is due to the presence of that gas. Thus, for oxygen, the partial pressure is 21% of 760 mm Hg, or 160 mm Hg in air at sea level (Table 23.1). As we will see shortly, the partial pressures of $O_2$ and $CO_2$ are important for gas transport, not their concentrations.

As you can see from Table 23.1, whereas the fractional composition of air at the top of Mount Everest is the same as that at sea level, the partial pressures of each major gas in air are reduced to roughly one-third of those at sea level. The atmospheric pressure in a burrow, on the other hand, is the same as that of the air outside. If animals are living in the burrow, however, the composition will vary due to the slow exchange of gases between the burrow and the environment; the oxygen will be lower and the carbon dioxide higher (Table 23.1).

## The Sources of Oxygen and Carbon Dioxide in the Environment

Where does oxygen in the environment come from? The answer is photosynthesis. Oxygen was first produced by cyanobacteria almost 3 billion years ago, when it began to accumulate slowly. Over the last 600 million years, levels in the environment have fluctuated between lows of approximately 15% of the atmosphere to highs of almost 35% during the late Paleozoic (300 to 500 million years ago). This was a time of giant insects and spontaneous fires, both a result of the oxygen-enriched atmosphere.

The carbon dioxide in the atmosphere originally came from volcanic outgassing. It now comes primarily from respiration by plants and animals and other aerobic organisms and from burning organic matter. The biggest human source of atmospheric $CO_2$ comes from burning fossil fuels. The biggest overall contributor of carbon dioxide to the environment, however, is natural and not human made. It is through plant and animal decay as microorganisms break down dead material, releasing carbon dioxide into the air as part of the process. The amount of $CO_2$ in the atmosphere at any one time is a balance between that produced by all of these means and the rate at which plants convert carbon dioxide to carbohydrates during photosynthesis. This is why deforestation also contributes to increasing levels of $CO_2$ in the atmosphere. Indeed, the contribution of humans to global climate change comes as much indirectly from changing the speed of natural processes such as soil decomposition and deforestation as it does directly from the addition of $CO_2$ to the atmosphere. Like oxygen, atmospheric $CO_2$ levels have also fluctuated over time, reaching a high of roughly 3% of the atmosphere in the early Paleozoic. They declined to present-day levels (0.03%) in the late Paleozoic before rising again to high levels of

# BIOLOGY IS EVERYWHERE 23.1
## Evangelista Torricelli and Igor Gamow

Evangelista Torricelli **(Figure 1a)** was a mathematician and physicist. In 1644, he wrote a letter to his friend, Michelangelo Ricci, who was a mathematician and a cardinal in Rome. In the letter, he stated, "we live submerged at the bottom of an ocean of the element air, which by unquestioned experiments is known to have weight." It is this weight of the sea of air above us bearing down on the surface of Earth that is responsible for the atmospheric pressure. Torricelli was the first person to appreciate this. He went on to invent the mercury barometer. He also realized that barometric pressure decreases with altitude and that the weight of air was "greatest in low places where men

and animals live, but that at the tops of mountains, begins to be distinctly rare and of much less weight." As humans ascend to high altitudes in the mountains, many begin to struggle with the thin air, succumbing to acute mountain sickness or, worse yet, pulmonary or cerebral edema (fluid leaking from the blood into the lungs and brain). These latter two conditions can be fatal if not treated rapidly, usually by descent to lower altitudes.

In circumstances where rapid descent is not possible, a Gamow bag is often used to provide temporary relief. This is an inflatable bag, large enough to place a person inside, that can be inflated by a foot pump, increasing pressure and effectively lowering

the altitude by between 1000 and 3000 m (3281 to 9743 ft). The Gamow bag was named after its inventor, Dr. Igor Gamow **(Figure 1b)**, son of the celebrated cosmologist and physicist George Gamow and ballet dancer Rho Gamow. Igor's parents defected from Russia to America, and Igor grew up in Colorado. He joined the National Ballet Company himself after graduating from high school and held jobs breaking horses and teaching karate before becoming a microbiology professor at the University of Colorado. He patented the Gamow bag in 1990 and was congratulated on his invention by Sir Edmund Hillary, the first expedition leader to summit Mount Everest.

**A. Evangelista Torricelli**

**B. Igor Gamow**

**FIGURE 1** **(a)** Evangelista Torricelli invented the barometer, a device for measuring air pressure, in the late 1600s. **(b)** Igor Gamow invented the Gamow bag to treat altitude sickness.

almost 2% in the late Mesozoic period. Atmospheric $CO_2$ levels have been quite low for the last 20 million years but are on the rise again (see Chapters 29 and 30).

## The Movement of Gases Is Due to Several Factors

Gases move by diffusion because of differences in partial pressure, not differences in concentration. If this comes as a surprise, remember that all movement is because of differences in energy levels, and many things affect the energy level of molecules. Gases are not equally soluble

in different fluids or in the same fluid at different temperatures. For instance, oxygen is far more soluble in air or in lipids than it is in water. It is more soluble in cold fluids than in warm ones. Thus, when oxygen is in equilibrium between two solutions with different solubilities, the concentrations in each may be very different. However, their partial pressures will be the same. Just as a solute will move by simple diffusion from an area of high concentration to an area of low concentration (all other things being equal), a gas will move down a partial pressure gradient, from a region of high partial pressure to one of low partial pressure (all other things being equal).

Although gases diffuse between two sites because of differences in partial pressure, the rate (amount per unit time) at which a gas will diffuse depends on a set of factors. Only one of these factors is the difference in partial pressure between the two regions. The other factors include the area of the surface across which diffusion occurs, the thickness of the surface across which it occurs, and the temperature. Anything that increases the area of the exchange surface, enhances the partial pressure gradient, or reduces the diffusion path will speed the rate of diffusion. We will discuss some of these factors briefly next.

## The Concentrations of Oxygen and Carbon Dioxide Are Very Different in Air and in Water

There are two important physical principles that we need to remember when considering gas exchange: (1) the rate of diffusion of any gas is slower in water than in air and (2) the solubility of any gas may be dramatically different in air than in water. For $O_2$ at 20°C, the rate of diffusion in air is 10,000 times faster than in water. In addition, for the same volume, there is approximately 30 times more $O_2$ in air than in water for the same partial pressure. These two factors require animals that breathe water to breathe much more to get the same volume of $O_2$ as animals breathing air. Moreover, the density of water is about 1000 times that of air, and its viscosity (its resistance to flow) is about 50 times that of air. Therefore, it takes significantly more energy to breathe water than air.

In addition, as either the temperature or the amount of solute in water increases, the amount of gas that can dissolve in water decreases. Therefore, when it comes to obtaining $O_2$, aquatic animals that live in warm water are at a disadvantage compared to those that live in cold water. And because solutes (such as sodium chloride) are higher in seawater than in fresh water, animals living in a marine environment are at a disadvantage compared to those living in a freshwater environment.

There are advantages to breathing water, however. Since $CO_2$ is roughly 20 times more soluble in water than $O_2$, $CO_2$ is easily excreted. Because aquatic animals must breathe so much to obtain oxygen, the $CO_2$ is rapidly lost to the water flowing over the gills. Thus, aquatic animals face challenges in obtaining $O_2$ from water compared to terrestrial animals but have a much easier time eliminating $CO_2$.

For air-breathing organisms, the relatively high $O_2$ content, low density, and low viscosity of air greatly reduce the energy required to ventilate the **respiratory surface** to get $O_2$. There are disadvantages to breathing air, however. In addition to the challenge of eliminating $CO_2$, breathing air constantly evaporates water from the

respiratory surface. Gases must go into aqueous solution before they can cross a cell membrane to enter the organism (they cannot enter as gas bubbles), so respiratory surfaces must always be moist in air-breathing organisms. Therefore, except in an environment with 100% humidity, air-breathing animals lose water by evaporation during breathing and must replace the water to keep the respiratory surface from drying. We lose roughly 1 L per day of water just due to breathing at rest and significantly more when we breathe hard during exercise or at altitude. This is also why we get thirsty when we talk a lot or exercise, especially in the heat.

## STUDY BREAK

1. If the air at the top of Mount Everest still contains 21% oxygen, why is it so difficult to breathe?
2. How do you explain the fact that when water and air are in equilibrium, there is 30 times as much oxygen in each millilitre of air as there is in each millilitre of water? Why doesn't oxygen keep diffusing into the water?
3. What are the advantages and disadvantages of air versus water as a respiratory medium?
4. Redraw Figure 23.2c for a fish.

## Adaptations Increase the Surface Available for Gas Exchange

In all plants and animals, gas must enter the body across a respiratory surface. The respiratory surface may consist of the outer membrane of each cell of the organism, the general external surface of the organism, or highly specialized exchange surfaces restricted to specialized areas of the body (**Figure 23.3, p. 506**). The first two strategies work well for small organisms, where all cells of the body are close to the body surface (**Figure 23.3a**). Larger and more complex organisms, however, require either larger specialized respiratory surfaces and/or some means of transporting gases to and from the surfaces to other cells deeper within the organism. In aquatic organisms, these specialized surfaces usually take the form of **gills** as outward extensions of the body surface (**Figure 23.3b**). In terrestrial organisms, they take the form of inward projecting surfaces that can be protected and kept moist, such as **lungs (Figure 23.3c)**. The specialized respiratory surfaces are often very large. The total surface area of the alveoli in the lungs in humans is about 100 m squared (roughly the size of a tennis court). In addition, the cells that make up the specialized respiratory surface are usually very thin, reducing the distance the gases have to diffuse.

**A. Extended body surface: flatworm**

**B. External gills: axolotl**

**C. Lungs: human**

**FIGURE 23.3** Adaptations increasing the area of the respiratory surface. **(a)** The flattened and elongated body surface of a flatworm (Platyhelminthes). **(b)** The highly branched, feathery structure of the external gills in an amphibian, the axolotl. **(c)** The many branches and pockets expand the respiratory surface in the human lung.

respiratory surface (Figure 23.2). The rate at which blood or other fluids is replaced on the internal side of the respiratory surface also helps maintain a high partial pressure difference. The evolution of muscular pumps to ventilate specialized gas exchange surfaces (the chest wall in birds and the **diaphragm** in mammals) and muscular pumps (hearts) to transport gases between the environment and the tissues throughout the bodies of animals was essential for the evolution of large multicellular organisms.

## STUDY BREAK

1. Gas exchange surfaces are generally large, thin, and moist. What are the advantages of each of these factors?
2. How do muscular hearts and respiratory pumps contribute to gas exchange?

## Gas Exchange Surfaces Must Be Moist

For the gases to pass across an epithelium and enter the cells of plants and animals, they must be dissolved and in solution. For aquatic and marine organisms that breathe water, that is already the case. For terrestrial organisms, which breathe air, the respiratory epithelium must be covered by a thin film of fluid. In animals, the most highly evolved respiratory exchange surfaces are correspondingly large, thin, moist, and delicate and are usually highly protected to prevent damage and desiccation (Figure 23.3c).

## Ventilation and Perfusion Increase Gas Exchange across Respiratory Surfaces

Gas exchange across all respiratory surfaces occurs by diffusion. Remember that the primary factor driving diffusion is the difference in partial pressure of each gas across the membrane. Two adaptations help most animals maintain a large partial pressure difference between gases outside and inside the respiratory surface, increasing the rate of diffusion. Both required the evolution of pumps. The first adaptation is **ventilation,** the flow of the air or water (depending on the animal) over the respiratory surface. As they respire, organisms remove $O_2$ from the air or water and replace it with $CO_2$. Without ventilation, the concentration of $O_2$ would fall in the air or water close to the respiratory surface, and the concentration of $CO_2$ would rise. This would gradually reduce the partial pressure difference for both gases and reduce the rate of diffusion. The second adaptation is **perfusion,** the flow of blood or other body fluids on the internal side of the

## 23.2 Adaptations for Gas Exchange

### Small Organisms Exchange Gas by Simple Diffusion across the Body Surface

Only organisms with a large surface area–volume ratio can rely on diffusion across the body surface alone for gas exchange. This generally limits both the size and, to some degree, the shape of the organism. Unicellular organisms such as bacteria and protists can clearly rely on diffusion alone for gas exchange because their body surface is large with respect to their volume and the distance that the gases must diffuse is relatively small. Among multicellular organisms, gas exchange by diffusion alone across the body surface can usually occur only if the organisms are thin and flat.

Flatworms (Figure 23.3a) are an example of a multicellular organism that relies on simple diffusion for gas exchange. Most free-living flatworms are small, but they can range up to 10 cm or more in length, and parasitic forms such as tapeworms can grow to more than 3 m (see Chapter 19).

### Most Aquatic Animals Have Either External or Internal Gills

Gills are respiratory surfaces that are branched and folded outward extensions of the body. They increase the area over which diffusion can take place. **External gills (Figure 23.4a)** extend out from the body and do not have protective coverings. They occur in some molluscs, some annelids, the larvae of some aquatic insects, the

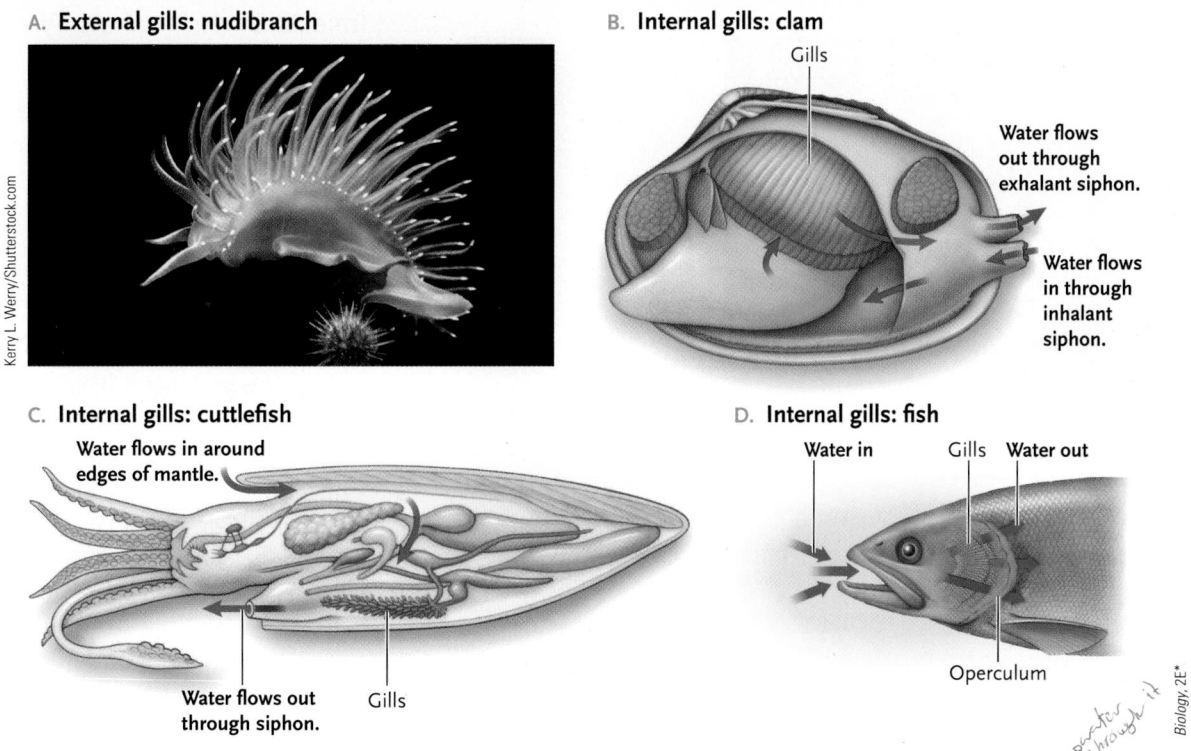

**A. External gills: nudibranch**

Kerry L. Werry/Shutterstock.com

**B. Internal gills: clam**

Gills

Water flows out through exhalant siphon.

Water flows in through inhalant siphon.

**C. Internal gills: cuttlefish**

Water flows in around edges of mantle.

Water flows out through siphon.

Gills

**D. Internal gills: fish**

Water in    Gills    Water out

Operculum

Biology, 2E*

**FIGURE 23.4** External and internal gills. **(a)** The external gills of a nudibranch (*Flabellina iodinea*). **(b)** The internal gills in a clam. **(c)** The internal gills of a cuttlefish. **(d)** The internal gills of a bony fish. Water enters through the mouth and passes over the filaments of the gills before exiting through an opening at the edges of the flaplike protective covering, the operculum.

larvae of some fishes, and the larvae of amphibians. These gills are ventilated by either general body movement or slow waving of the gills themselves. **Internal gills (Figure 23.4, b, c, d)** are located within chambers of the body. Most crustaceans, molluscs, sharks, and bony fishes have internal gills. This not only provides protection for delicate structures but also allows water to be pumped over the gills (ventilation). Some invertebrates, such as clams and oysters, use beating cilia to circulate water over their internal gills (Figure 23.4b). Others, such as the cuttlefish, use contractions of the muscular mantle to pump water over their gills (Figure 23.4c). In adult bony fishes, the gills extend into a chamber that is covered by a flap called an **operculum** (plural = operculae), meaning a little lid, on either side of the head. Muscles in the wall of the mouth cavity and the chamber housing the gills pump water over the gills (Figure 23.4d).

## Plants Exchange Gases Primarily through the Leaf

Remember that plants require $CO_2$ for photosynthesis but also produce it during respiration. They require $O_2$ for respiration but produce it during photosynthesis. The balance between photosynthesis and respiration at any one time will determine which direction each gas moves in.

Like flatworms, a plant leaf has a large surface area over which gas exchange can take place. However, unlike the flatworm, the external surface of a leaf is not available for gas exchange: leaves are covered by a waxy cuticle that is impermeable to gases. Gases gain access to the interior of the leaf through pores called stomata (see Chapter 5). Inside the leaf, there is space where gases can diffuse rapidly and the diffusion distance between the external environment (the air *within* the leaf) and the inside of individual cells is very short **(Figure 23.5, p. 508)**. Moreover, the total area of the cell walls inside the leaf is large. These two factors maximize the rate of diffusion of gases between the cells and the environment. This is the primary route for the uptake of $CO_2$ and the release of $O_2$ produced by photosynthesis to the environment.

The need to exchange gas across a moist membrane is a serious problem for plants in hot, dry regions. Scientists have recently proposed that $C_4$ photosynthesis (described in Chapter 5) has evolved more than 60 times as a carbon-concentrating mechanism. This process transports $CO_2$ across the outer surface of the plant leaf, augmenting the ancestral $C_3$ photosynthetic pathway while conserving water by decreasing evaporation through open stomata.

There are living cells in the trunk and branches of trees as well, and these cells also need to exchange gases with the environment. **Lenticels**, scattered throughout the bark of woody stems and roots of many flowering

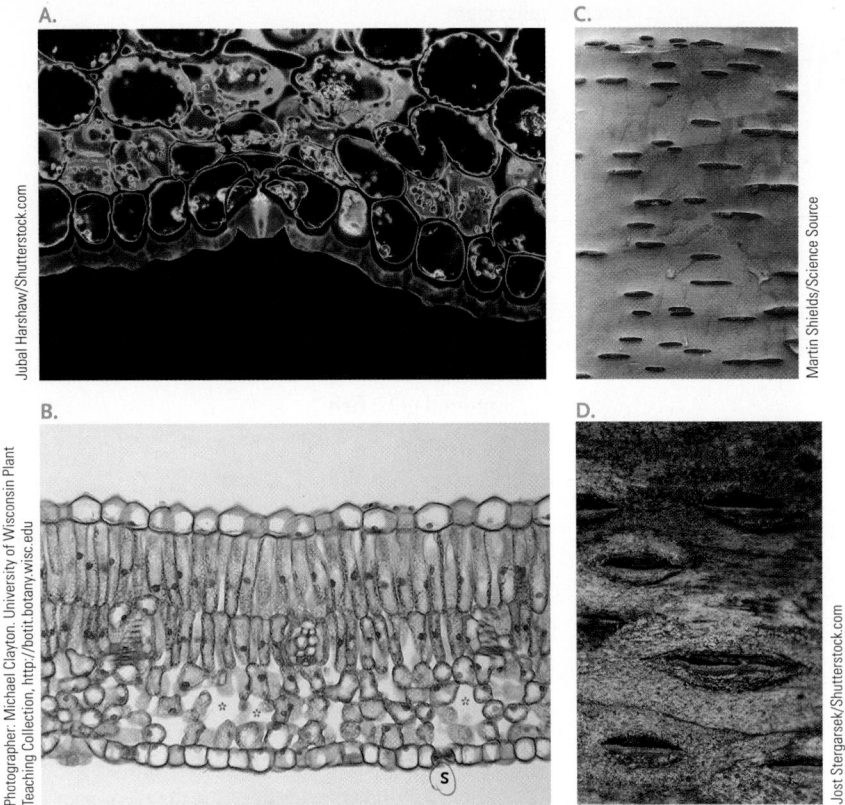

A.

B.

C.

D.

**FIGURE 23.5 (a)** The scanning electron micrograph of leaf stomata. **(b)** A cross section of a leaf of a lilac bush. The network of interconnecting spaces, marked by an asterisk, brings most cells in direct contact with gases. There are two stomata, through which gases gain access to the spaces inside the leaf, on the lower surface. One of the stomata is labelled S. Photos of the trunk of a cherry tree (*Prunus avium*) **(c)** and a poplar tree (*Populus* sp.) **(d)** illustrating the external appearance of lenticels.

plants, are porous tissues consisting of cells with large intercellular spaces. They function just like stomata, allowing gases to pass freely between the internal tissues and atmosphere through the bark.

Young roots exchange gases by diffusion across the membranes of root hairs and other epidermal cells. These root hairs provide an enormous surface area for gas exchange. As roots grow and mature, the epidermis is often replaced by bark. Lenticels are present in such roots to allow gases to exchange with the interior tissues. Uptake of $O_2$ by this route is extremely important. The roots do not photosynthesize but can have high rates of respiration and therefore high $O_2$ requirements.

The same is true for most fungi. There are many different types of fungi growing in a wide variety of environments. Most of the bodies of many fungi grow underground. These fungi exchange gas much like the roots of other types of plants. They produce a large number of threadlike roots called hyphae that make up most of the fungus body. These hyphae exchange oxygen and carbon dioxide with air pockets in the soil just like plant rootlets. When a fungus produces fruiting bodies such as mushrooms or other growths, they exchange gas with the atmosphere just as plants do.

## Insects Use a Tracheal System for Gas Exchange

Insects breathe air by a unique respiratory system consisting of air-conducting tubes called **tracheae** (trachea = windpipe) **(Figure 23.6)**. The tracheae are invaginations (pockets) of the insect's outer surface. They lead from the body surface and branch repeatedly, with each branch getting smaller, ultimately ending as **tracheoles** at the level of the individual cells throughout the body of the animal. Each tracheole is less than 1 micrometre in diameter. Every cell in an insect's body makes contact with at least one tracheole. Air diffuses along the tracheal system to the blind endings where gas exchange occurs with the body cells. At places within the body, the tracheae may expand into internal air sacs that act as reservoirs to increase the volume of air in the system. In some cases, muscles actively pump these sacs to enhance gas exchange.

Air enters and leaves the **tracheal system** at openings in the insect's exoskeleton called **spiracles** (*spiraculum* = airhole). The spiracles are located in a row on either side of the thorax and abdomen, typically one pair per body segment (Figure 23.6). Each spiracle includes a muscle that allows the spiracles to open and close. In periods of greater activity, as in flight, this mechanism is replaced by one in which alternating compression and expansion of the thorax by the flight muscles also pump air through the tracheal system. The spiracles open and close in synchrony with this rhythm. Recent research suggests that there may be other reasons that insects regulate the opening and closing of spiracles. Closing the spiracles is a strategy to reduce water loss in insects that live in dry climates. It may also help maintain lower oxygen levels in the tissues when there is a risk of generating reactive forms of oxygen that can damage tissues.

## Most Air-Breathing Vertebrates Exchange Gases Using Lungs

Like the trachea of insects, lungs are internal invaginations that allow air to enter protected spaces. Lungs are subdivided to provide large, thin, highly vascular, moist surfaces where gas exchange can take place. Many scientists believe that air-breathing organs first evolved as invaginations of the upper digestive tract in the bony fish. In many fish, the lung lost its connection to the digestive

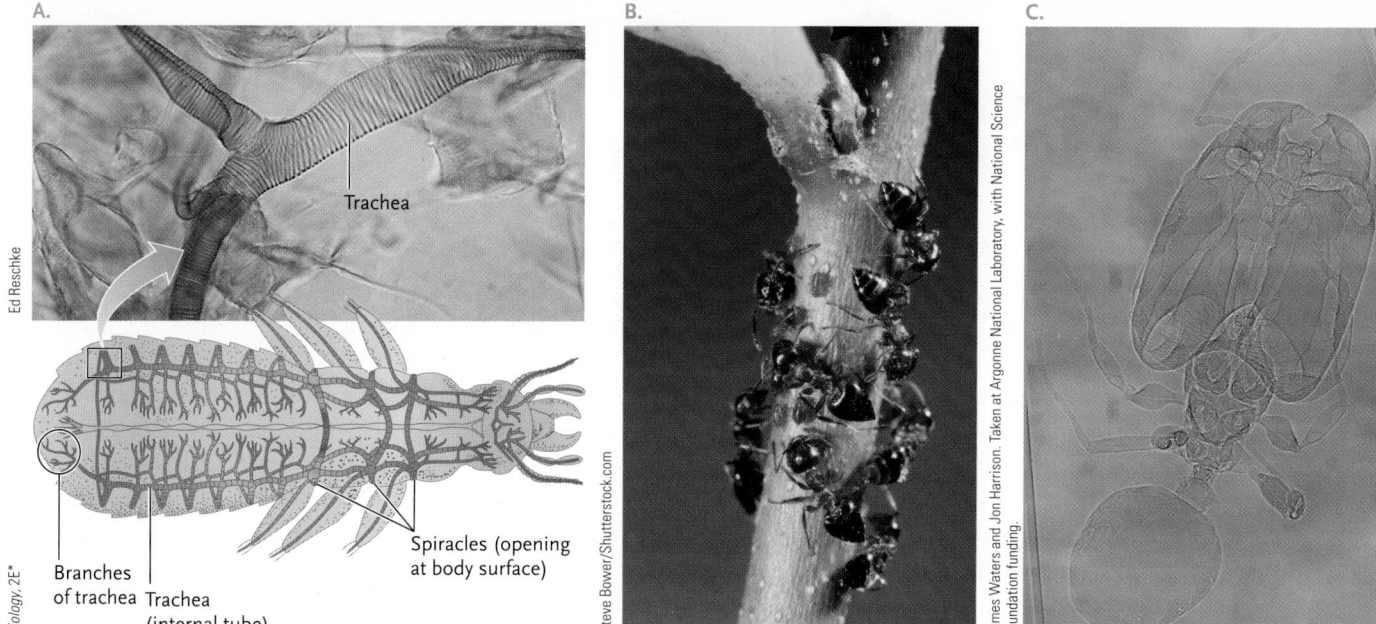

**FIGURE 23.6** **(a)** The tracheal system of insects. The photograph shows the chitinous rings that reinforce the tracheae, keeping them from collapsing. The tracheal system terminates in many tracheolar end cells that have branches with a diameter of less than 1 μm. **(b)** A photograph of the ant, Pheidole tepicana. **(c)** An x-ray synchrotron image of the ant. If you look carefully you can see the trachea running throughout the body delivering oxygen directly from the atmosphere to the tissues.

system and became the swim bladder, an organ that controls buoyancy in the modern bony fishes. The few living species of lungfishes have retained the connection, and their air-breathing organ coevolved along with cardiovascular adaptations, giving rise to a true lung. This line gave rise to the terrestrial vertebrates.

The extent of the subdivision of the lungs reflects the metabolic demands of the animal. The lungs of air-breathing fishes and amphibians such as frogs and salamanders are thin-walled sacs with relatively little folding or pocketing **(Figure 23.7, a to e)**. In reptiles, the lungs become more folded, with many pockets, increasing the surface for gas exchange. In birds and mammals, the lungs reach their highest degree of complexity. Mammalian lungs consist of millions of tiny, blind-ending air pockets, the **alveoli** (singular = alveolus), each surrounded by dense capillary networks **(Figure 23.7f)**. The lungs of birds consist of millions of **parabronchial tubes** that are not blind ending but that form one-way passages, allowing air to flow through the lungs. Small, blind-ending air capillaries branch off the parabronchi, where they are surrounded by blood capillaries, where gas exchange takes place **(Figure 23.7g)**.

Since the lungs are internal and protected, vertebrates require pumps to move the air in and out of these highly

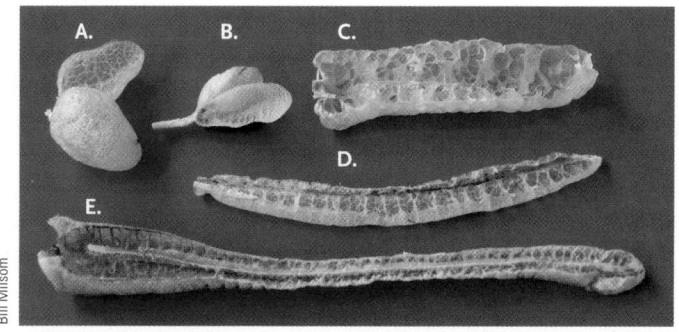

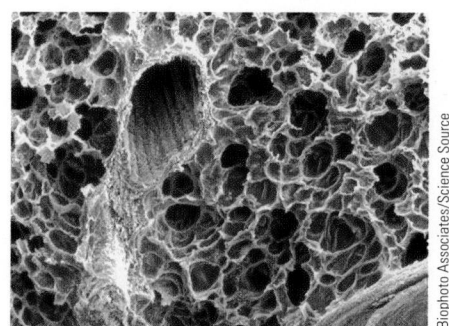

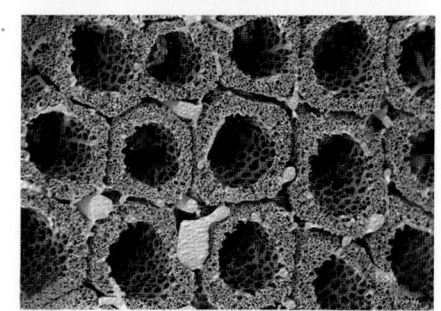

**FIGURE 23.7** Photographs of the lungs of **(a)** a bullfrog (*Lithobates catesbeianus*), **(b)** a tegu lizard (*Tupinambis merianae*), **(c)** the bowfin (*Amia calva*, an air-breathing fish), **(d)** a gar (*Lepisosteus osseus*, another air-breathing fish), and **(e)** the African lungfish (*Protopterus aethiopicus*). Also shown are scanning electron micrographs of **(f)** the alveoli in a mammalian lung and **(g)** the parabronchial blood vessels in a bird lung.

SOURCE(Photo G): A. N. Makanya, V. Djonov. 2009. "Parabronchial angioarchitecture in developing and adult chickens." *J Appl Physiol* 106:1959–1969. Copyright © 2009, The American Physiological Society.

**FIGURE 23.8** Positive pressure breathing in an amphibian (frog).

*Biology, 2E\**

**1** The frog lowers the floor of the mouth and inhales through its nostrils.

**2** Air in the lungs is exhaled when the glottis opens due to elastic recoil of the lungs and body wall.

**3** The frog closes its nostrils and elevates the floor of the mouth, forcing air into the lungs.

**4** Rhythmic movements flush the mouth cavity with fresh air for the next cycle.

specialized areas. In air-breathing fish and amphibians, the lungs are inflated by gulping or swallowing, a motion that forces air into the lungs using the same muscular pump fish use for water breathing. In most adult amphibians, for instance **(Figure 23.8)**, a breathing cycle begins with expansion of the mouth (buccal) cavity with the nostrils open and the entrance into the lungs constricted by the opening to the trachea (**glottis**). This draws fresh air into the mouth. Next, the glottis opens and gas from the lungs enters the **buccal cavity**, where it mixes with the fresh air to varying degrees as it exits via the mouth and nares, which remain open. The nares and mouth then close, and buccal compression forces buccal gas into the lungs. The glottis then closes, and any excess gas left in the buccal cavity is expelled through the nares or mouth at the end of the buccal compression phase. Rhythmic motions of the floor of the mouth with the nostrils open ensure that the buccal cavity contains fresh air for the beginning of the next cycle.

Reptiles, birds, and mammals, on the other hand, fill their lungs by suction. Muscular contractions expand the chest and lungs, lowering the pressure of the air in the lungs and causing air to be pulled inward. The muscles involved in doing this are largely those of the rib cage, but they can be assisted by other muscles. In crocodilians, for example, contraction of a muscle connecting the liver to the pelvis pulls the liver back, causing the lungs to expand, whereas compression of the abdomen pushes the liver forward, forcing gases out of the lungs. In mammals, a muscle in the chest cavity plays an important role in creating suction. The lungs are located in the rib cage above the diaphragm, a dome-shaped sheet of skeletal muscle that separates the chest cavity from the abdominal cavity **(Figure 23.9)**. As an inhalation begins, the diaphragm contracts and flattens, and one set of muscles between the ribs, the external intercostal muscles, contracts, pulling the ribs upward and outward **(Figure 23.10)**. These movements expand the chest cavity and lungs, lowering the air pressure in the lungs below that of the atmosphere. As a result, air is drawn into the lungs, expanding and filling them.

The expansion of the lungs is much like filling two rubber balloons. Like balloons, the lungs are elastic and resist stretching as they are filled. And also like balloons, the stretching stores energy that will cause the lungs to deflate when the inspiratory muscles relax. When physical activity increases the body's demand for $O_2$, contractions of other muscles help expel the air by forcefully reducing the volume of the chest cavity. That is, abdominal wall muscles contract, which increases abdominal pressure. That pressure exerts an upward-directed force on the diaphragm, which is pushed upward. In addition, internal intercostal muscles contract, pulling the chest wall inward and downward, causing it to flatten. As a result, the chest cavity becomes smaller.

In addition to paired lungs, birds have up to nine pairs of air sacs that branch off the respiratory tract **(Figure 23.11, p. 512)**. The air sacs, which collectively contain several times as much air as the lungs, do not exchange gases. Unlike other vertebrate lungs, bird lungs are rigid and do not expand or contract. The air sacs do, however, and they set up a pathway that allows air to flow in one direction through the lungs rather than in and out, as in other vertebrates. As illustrated in Figure 23.11, two cycles of inhalation and exhalation are needed to move a specific volume of air through the bird respiratory system. Within the lungs, air always flows from back to front through an array of fine, parallel tubes that are surrounded by a capillary network (Figure 23.7g), setting up a cross-current exchange system (described below in Section 23.3).

## STUDY BREAK

1. Compare gas flow through the stomata and air spaces of plants and the spiracles and trachea of insects.
2. How did the high levels of $O_2$ in the environment during the Paleozoic lead to giant insects and spontaneous fires?
3. What is the primary factor determining the extent to which lungs are subdivided?
4. What is the difference between positive pressure breathing and negative pressure breathing?

## Ventilation Is Initiated and Controlled by Centres in the Central Nervous System

The pumps that move water or gas over the respiratory surfaces are controlled by centres in the central nervous system of all animals. Nerve signals travelling from these

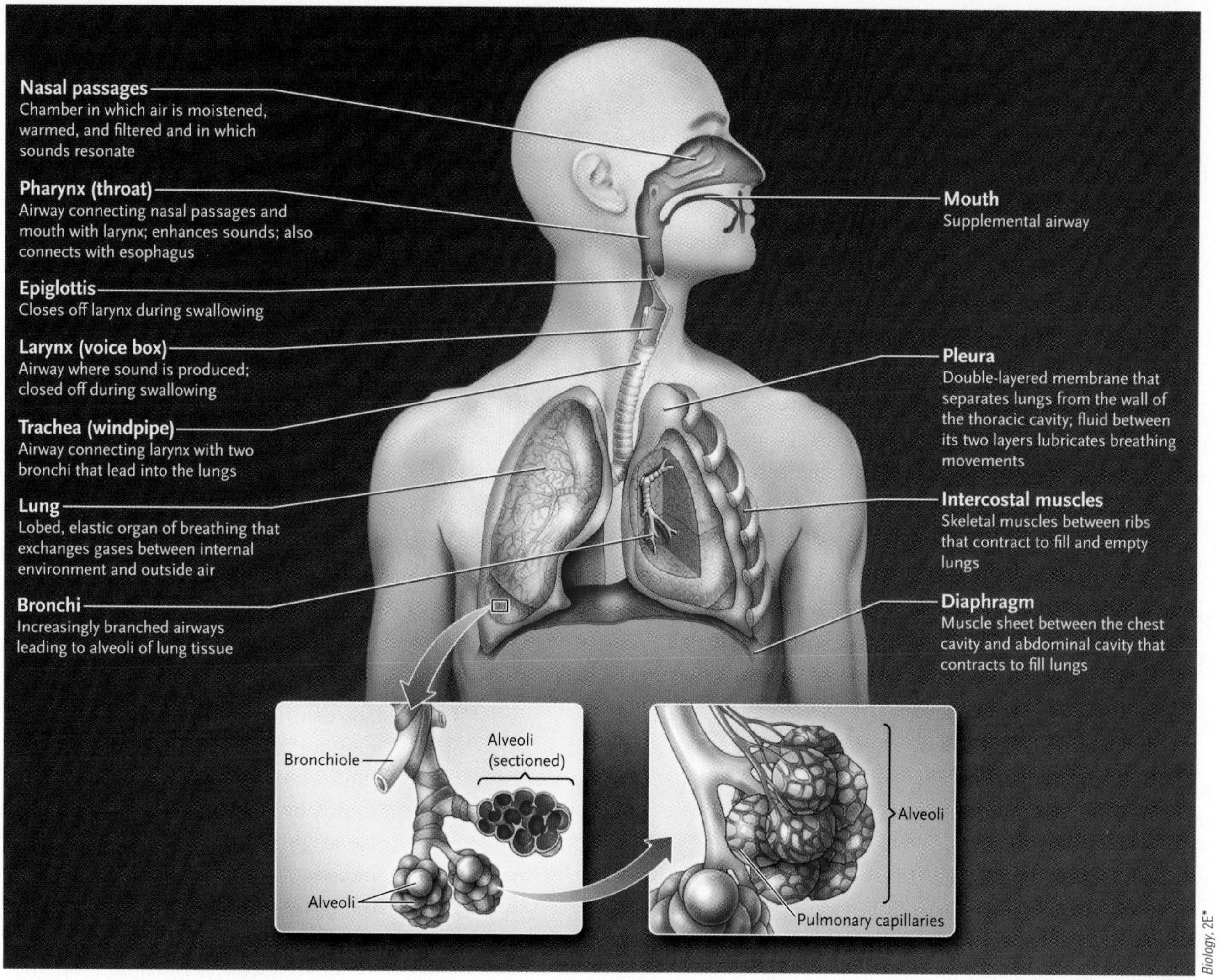

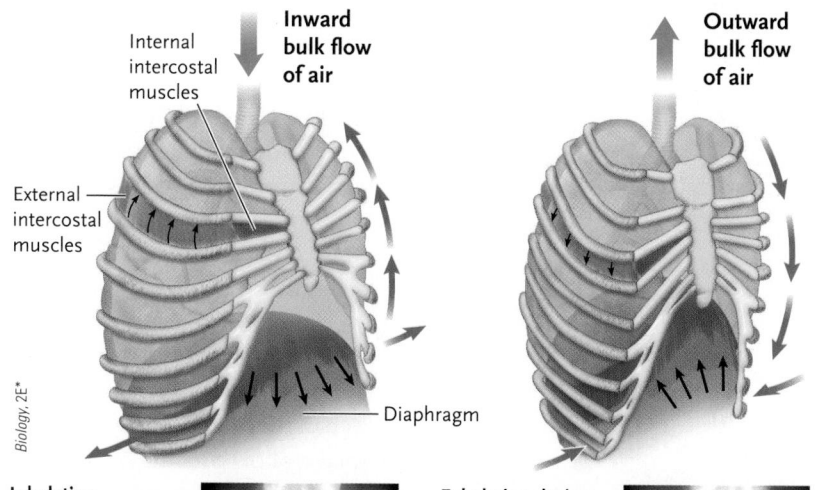

**Nasal passages** — Chamber in which air is moistened, warmed, and filtered and in which sounds resonate

**Pharynx (throat)** — Airway connecting nasal passages and mouth with larynx; enhances sounds; also connects with esophagus

**Epiglottis** — Closes off larynx during swallowing

**Larynx (voice box)** — Airway where sound is produced; closed off during swallowing

**Trachea (windpipe)** — Airway connecting larynx with two bronchi that lead into the lungs

**Lung** — Lobed, elastic organ of breathing that exchanges gases between internal environment and outside air

**Bronchi** — Increasingly branched airways leading to alveoli of lung tissue

**Mouth** — Supplemental airway

**Pleura** — Double-layered membrane that separates lungs from the wall of the thoracic cavity; fluid between its two layers lubricates breathing movements

**Intercostal muscles** — Skeletal muscles between ribs that contract to fill and empty lungs

**Diaphragm** — Muscle sheet between the chest cavity and abdominal cavity that contracts to fill lungs

Bronchiole

Alveoli (sectioned)

Alveoli

Alveoli

Pulmonary capillaries

*Biology, 2E*

**FIGURE 23.9** The human respiratory system, which is typical for a terrestrial mammal.

Internal intercostal muscles

External intercostal muscles

*Biology, 2E*

**Inward bulk flow of air**

Diaphragm

**Outward bulk flow of air**

**FIGURE 23.10** The respiratory movements of humans during breathing at rest. The movements of the rib cage and diaphragm fill and empty the lungs. Inhalation is powered by contractions of the external intercostal muscles and diaphragm, and exhalation is passive. During exercise or other activities characterized by deeper and more rapid breathing, contractions of the internal intercostal muscles and the abdominal muscles add force to exhalation. The X-ray images show how the volume of the lungs increases during inhalation and exhalation.

**Inhalation.** Diaphragm contracts and moves down. The external intercostal muscles contract and lift rib cage upward and outward. The lung volume expands.

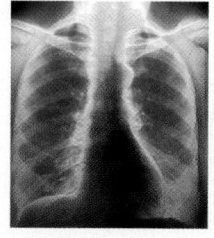

ZEPHYR/SCIENCE PHOTO LIBRARY

**Exhalation during breathing or rest.** Diaphragm and external intercostal muscles return to the resting positions. Rib cage moves down. Lungs recoil passively.

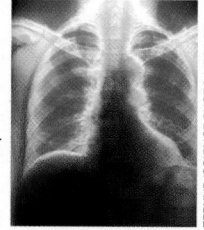

ZEPHYR/SCIENCE PHOTO LIBRARY

## A. Lungs and air sacs of a bird

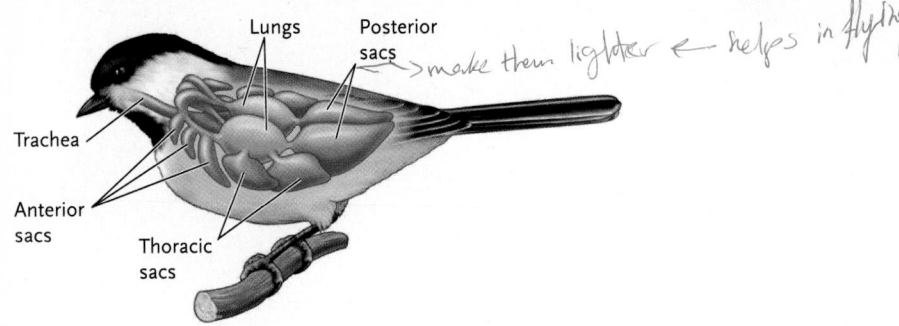

Lungs
Posterior sacs
→ make them lighter ← helps in flying
Trachea
Anterior sacs
Thoracic sacs

## B. Cross-current exchange

### Cycle 1

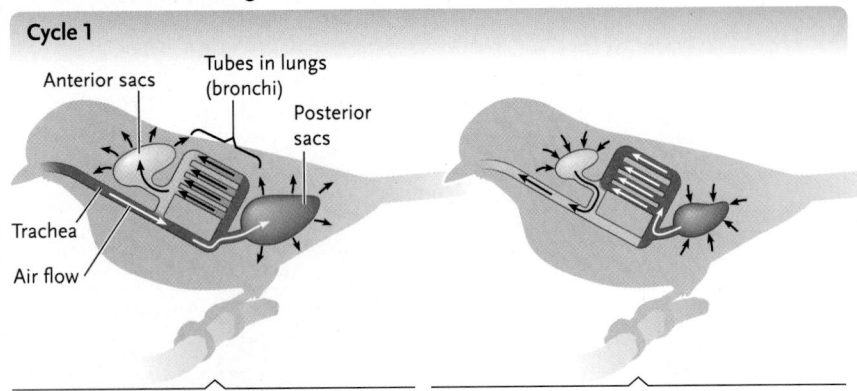

Anterior sacs
Tubes in lungs (bronchi)
Posterior sacs
Trachea
Air flow

**1** During the first inhalation, most of the oxygen flows directly to the posterior air sacs. The anterior air sacs also expand but do not receive any of the newly inhaled oxygen.

**2** During the following exhalation, both anterior and posterior air sacs contract. Oxygen from the posterior sacs flows into the gas-exchanging tubes (bronchi) of the lungs.

### Cycle 2

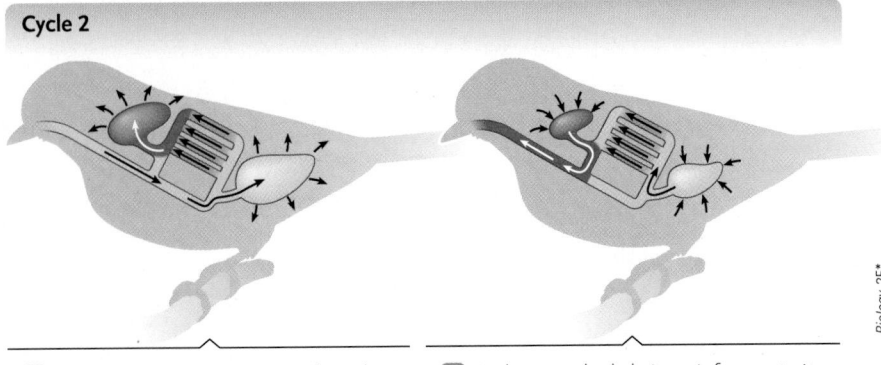

**1** During the next inhalation, air from the lung (now deoxygenated) moves into the anterior air sacs.

**2** In the second exhalation, air from anterior sacs is expelled to the outside through the trachea.

**FIGURE 23.11** Cross-current exchange in bird lungs. **(a)** Unlike mammalian lungs, bird lungs do not expand and contract. Changes in pressure in the expandable air sacs move air in and out. **(b)** Air flows in one direction through the tubes of the lungs; blood flows across this direction in the surrounding capillary network. Two cycles of inhalation and exhalation are needed to move a specific volume of air through the bird respiratory system.

*Biology, 2E\**

has been a focus of intensive research, and recent studies indicate that a primary rhythm generator produces the basic respiratory rhythm and a second rhythm generator is recruited to produce active expiration. Both rhythm generators may be instrumental in producing normal breathing in fish, amphibians, and reptiles where both inspiration and expiration are normally active. Nerve signals travelling from these centres to the muscles involved in breathing can vary the intake of air from as little as 5 to 6 L per minute to as much as 150 L per minute (for very brief periods) in humans. These centres integrate information about $O_2$ and $CO_2$ in the blood from $O_2$ and $CO_2$ receptors located in special sense organs—the **carotid body**—in the carotid arteries that supply the brain. The medulla integrates this information with information coming from its own receptors that monitor the pH of the **cerebrospinal fluid**. The pH of this fluid is determined mostly by the $CO_2$ concentration in the blood (pH decreases as $CO_2$ levels increase). In air-breathing vertebrates, the system is most sensitive to changes in $CO_2$; $O_2$ receptors act as a backup system that comes into play only when blood $O_2$ concentration falls to critically low levels. This reflects the fact that air-breathing vertebrates have far more trouble eliminating $CO_2$ than obtaining $O_2$ under normal conditions, along with the fact that small changes in pH due to changes in the levels of $CO_2$ throughout the body profoundly affect the activity of all functional proteins, such as enzymes.

## 23.3 Exchange of Gas with Blood

Ventilation moves water or air over the gas exchange surface. The next step in the uptake of oxygen and elimination of $CO_2$ is to exchange these gases between the water or air and the blood (oxygen in, $CO_2$ out). Although this takes place by diffusion, the manner in which the water or air and the blood meet determines the efficiency of this exchange. This occurs in one of three ways: by counter-current flow, cross-current flow, or **uniform (mixed pool) flow**. Let's take a look at each.

centres to the muscles involved in breathing can alter the frequency or the size of each breath. This in turn is largely determined by the need to breathe: the need to take up $O_2$ and eliminate $CO_2$ from the body.

In mammals, including humans, breathing is controlled by centres in the medulla and pons, part of the brain stem (see Chapter 26). The source of the breathing rhythm

Sharks, fishes, and some crustacea take advantage of one-way flow of water over the gills to maximize the amounts of $O_2$ and $CO_2$ exchanged with water. In this mechanism, called **countercurrent exchange**, the water flowing over the gills moves in a direction opposite to the flow of blood under the respiratory surface. **Figure 23.12** illustrates the uptake of $O_2$ by countercurrent exchange. At the point where fully oxygenated water first passes over a gill filament in countercurrent flow, the blood flowing beneath it in the opposite direction is also almost fully oxygenated. However, the water still contains $O_2$ at a higher concentration than the blood, and the gas diffuses from the water into the blood, raising the concentration of $O_2$ in the blood almost to the level of the fully oxygenated water. At the opposite end of the filament, much of the $O_2$ has been removed from the water, but the blood flowing under the filament has just arrived from body tissues and is fully deoxygenated, containing even less $O_2$. As a result, $O_2$ also diffuses from the water to the blood at this end of the filament. The same relationship exists along the entire length of the gill filament so that, at any point, the water is more highly oxygenated than the blood and $O_2$ diffuses at a high rate from the water into the blood across the respiratory surface. The overall effect of countercurrent exchange is the removal of 80% to 90% of the $O_2$ content of water as it flows over the gills.

In comparison, by breathing in and out and constantly reversing the direction of airflow (uniform or mixed pool flow), mammals, including humans, manage to remove only about 25% of the $O_2$ content of air (Figure 23.12). In birds, the blood flows in a direction across that of the airflow, setting up a **cross-current exchange**. The cross-current exchange allows bird lungs to extract more of the $O_2$ from the air compared to the lungs of mammals but less than with the countercurrent exchange system seen in fish (Figure 23.12). This increased efficiency of gas exchange helps support the high metabolic rates required for flight in birds.

## 23.4 Mechanisms of Gas Transport

Oxygen taken up at the lungs must be transported to the tissues that need it, whereas the carbon dioxide produced in the tissues must be transported to the respiratory exchange surfaces.

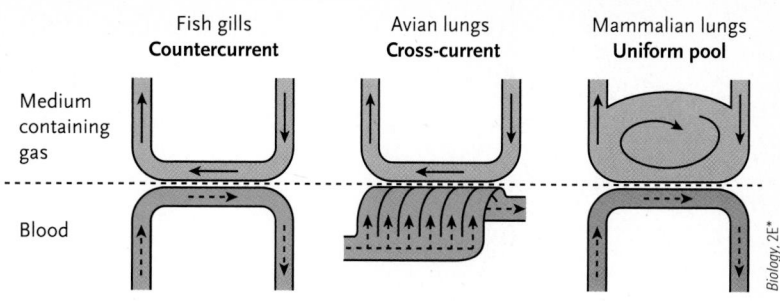

**FIGURE 23.12** The three patterns of gas transfer encountered in vertebrate gas exchange organs are countercurrent, cross-current, and uniform (mixed) pool.

## Oxygen Is Primarily Transported Bound to Special Pigments

Recall that $O_2$ is not very soluble in fluids. Transport within the body is aided in most animals by pigment molecules that can bind and transport large quantities of $O_2$. **Hemocyanin** and **hemoglobin** are the two respiratory pigments most commonly found in the blood of animals (see Box 23.2).

At both the respiratory exchange surface and body tissues, gas exchange occurs when the gas diffuses from an area of higher partial pressure to an area of lower partial pressure. At the sites of gas exchange with the environment, the partial pressure of $O_2$ in the environment is higher than the partial pressure of $O_2$ in deoxygenated blood entering the network of capillaries in the gills or lungs **(Figure 23.13)**. As a result, $O_2$ readily diffuses into the plasma solution in the capillaries.

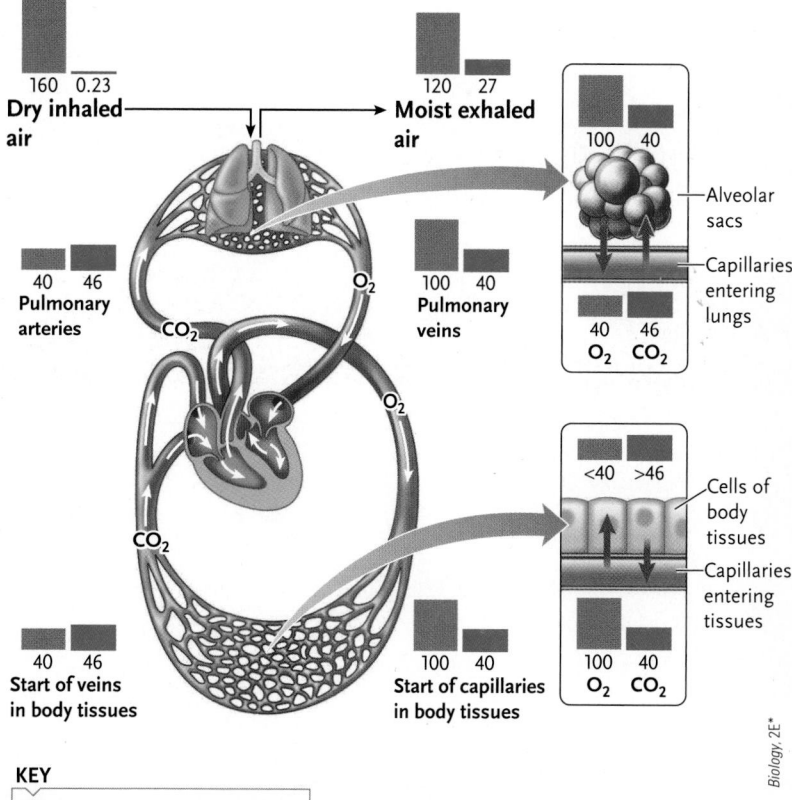

**KEY**

Partial pressure of $O_2$ ($P_{O_2}$)
Partial pressure of $CO_2$ ($P_{CO_2}$)

**FIGURE 23.13** The partial pressures of $O_2$ (pink) and $CO_2$ (blue) in various locations in the body.

# Hemocyanin and Hemoglobin: Transporting Gases To and From the Cells

Hemocyanin and hemoglobin are the two respiratory pigments most commonly found in the blood and/or tissues of animals. They are made up of subunits (proteins called globins) that have been found in almost all living animals. The reversible binding of $O_2$ to these pigments is related to the amount of oxygen available in a pattern described by the *hemoglobin–$O_2$ equilibrium curve* in **Figure 1**. (The curve is generated by measuring the amount of hemoglobin saturated [binding all four $O_2$ molecules] at a given partial pressure of oxygen [$Po_2$]). In air-breathing vertebrates, the curve is not linear but is S shaped, with a plateau region. As the amount of oxygen in the plasma increases, hemoglobin binds to the $O_2$ until every hemoglobin molecule is bound to four molecules of $O_2$. Once the hemoglobin is fully saturated—meaning that it cannot bind any

more $O_2$—further increases in $Po_2$ lead to only a small extra amount of $O_2$ going into solution. The hemoglobin can hold no more. Note that over the steep part of the curve between 0 and 60 mm Hg (the range found in the capillaries throughout the bodies of most vertebrates), small changes in $Po_2$ result in large changes in the amount of $O_2$ bound to hemoglobin.

Several factors contribute to the release of $O_2$ from hemoglobin, including increased acidity (lower pH) in active tissues. The acidity increases because oxidative reactions release $CO_2$, which combines with water to form carbonic acid ($H_2CO_3$). Carbonic acid in turn dissociates to form bicarbonate ($HCO_3^-$) and $H^+$. This lowers pH and reduces the affinity of hemoglobin for $O_2$, which is released and used in cellular respiration.

Carbon monoxide (CO) is a gas that binds even more readily with hemoglobin. It competes with oxygen for the binding sites on hemoglobin, displacing the oxygen and reducing the oxygen content of the blood. Interestingly, the body produces small amounts of CO, and it acts as a **neurotransmitter** at some sites in the body. In higher concentrations, however, such as how much might be produced by open flames, space heaters, water heaters, and internal combustion engines, CO is toxic. The gas is colourless, odourless, and tasteless, making it hard for us to detect and giving it the name "the silent killer." CO detectors with built-in alarm systems are now commercially available, however, and are recommended to be placed in every home.

Hemocyanin has many of the same characteristics as hemoglobin. It is found in molluscs and arthropods.

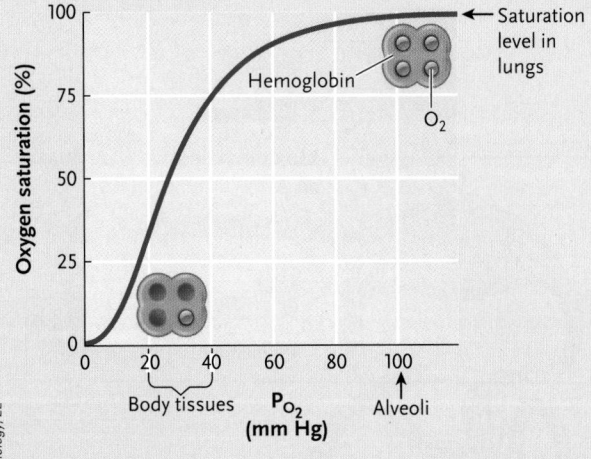

**A.** **Hemoglobin saturation level in lungs**

In the alveoli, in which the $Po_2$ is about 100 mm Hg and the pH is 7.4, most hemoglobin molecules are 100% saturated, meaning that almost all have bound four $O_2$ molecules.

**FIGURE 1** Hemoglobin–$O_2$ equilibrium curves, which show the degree to which hemoglobin is saturated with $O_2$ at increasing $Po_2$. **(a)** Hemoglobin saturation level in lungs. **(b)** Hemoglobin saturation range in body tissues.

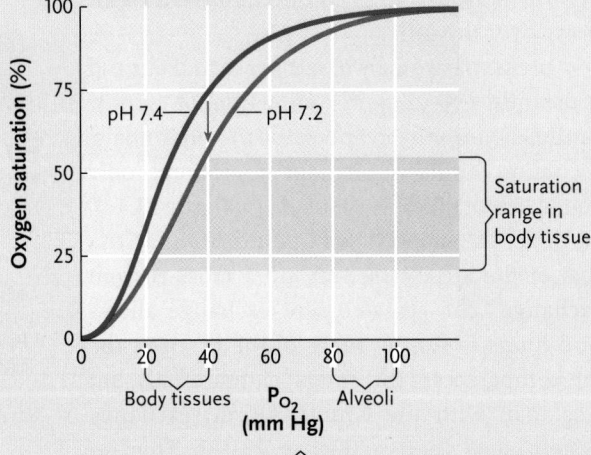

**B.** **Hemoglobin saturation range in body tissues**

In the capillaries of body tissues, where the $Po_2$ varies between about 20 and 40 mm Hg depending on the level of metabolic activity and the pH is about 7.2, hemoglobin can hold less $O_2$. As a result, most hemoglobin molecules release two or three of their $O_2$ molecules to become between 25% and 50% saturated. Note that the drop in pH to 7.2 (red line) in active body tissues reduces the amount of $O_2$ hemoglobin can hold as compared with pH 7.4. The reduction in binding affinity at lower pH increases the amount of $O_2$ released in active tissues.

In vertebrates, after entering the plasma, $O_2$ diffuses into red blood cells (erythrocytes), where it combines with hemoglobin. Hemoglobin molecules have four heme groups, each containing an iron atom that can

combine reversibly with an $O_2$ molecule. A hemoglobin molecule can therefore potentially bind a total of four molecules of $O_2$. There are many hemoglobin molecules in every red blood cell (roughly 250 million). Thus, the combination of $O_2$ with hemoglobin allows blood to carry about 60 times more $O_2$ (about 200 mL per litre) than it could if the $O_2$ simply dissolved in the plasma (about 3 mL per litre). About 98.5% of the $O_2$ in blood is carried by hemoglobin, and about 1.5% is carried in solution in the blood plasma.

Most of the hemoglobin molecules in the blood leaving the gills or lungs are fully saturated, meaning that most of the hemoglobin molecules have bound four $O_2$ molecules. This blood will also change colour, reflecting the bright red colour of oxygenated hemoglobin compared to the darker red colour of deoxygenated hemoglobin. From the gills or lungs, the oxygen is transported in the blood to the tissues.

As the oxygenated blood enters the capillary networks of body tissues, it encounters regions in which the partial pressure of $O_2$ in the interstitial fluid and body cells is lower than that in the blood because the mitochondria in these cells have been consuming oxygen. As a result, $O_2$ diffuses from the blood into body cells.

The net diffusion of $O_2$ from blood to body cells continues until by the time the blood leaves the capillary networks in the body tissues, roughly 30% of the $O_2$ has been removed from hemoglobin. The blood now returns in veins to the heart, which pumps it to the gills or lungs for oxygenation. Note that blood returning to the gas exchange surface still contains much oxygen that is a reserve. The organism can be drawn on this reserved oxygen when metabolic demands increase, such as during exercise.

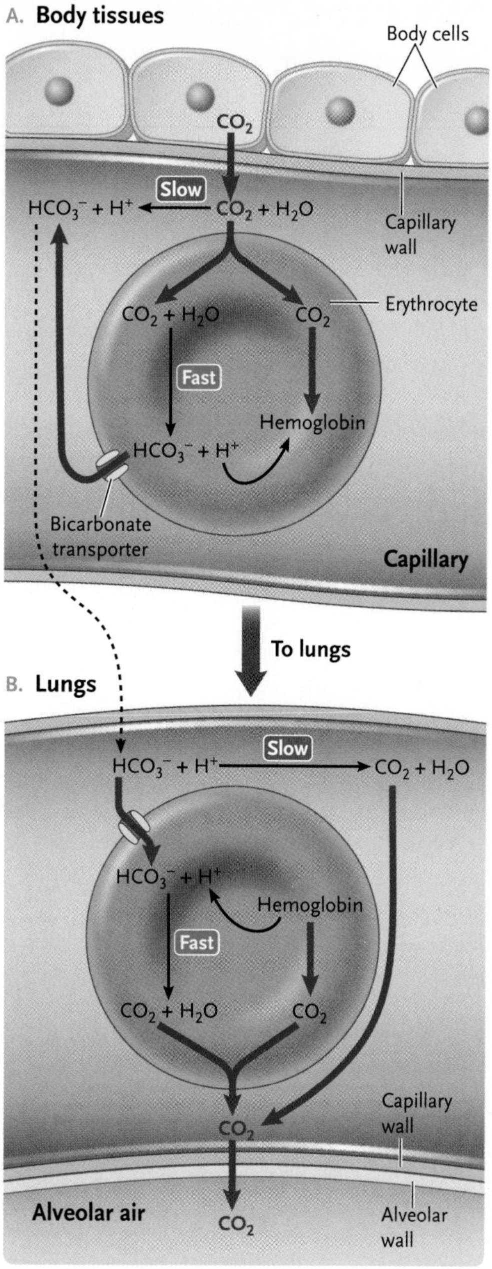

In body tissues, some of the $CO_2$ released into the blood combines with water in the blood plasma to form $HCO_3^-$ and $H^+$. However, most of the $CO_2$ diffuses into erythrocytes, where some combines directly with hemoglobin and some combines with water to form $HCO_3^-$ and $H^+$. The $H^+$ formed by this reaction combines with hemoglobin; the $HCO_3^-$ is transported out of erythrocytes to add to the $HCO_3^-$ in the blood plasma.

In the lungs, the reactions are reversed. Some of the $HCO_3^-$ in the blood plasma combines with $H^+$ to form $CO_2$ and water. However, most of the $HCO_3^-$ is transported into erythrocytes, where it combines with $H^+$ released from hemoglobin to form $CO_2$ and water. $CO_2$ is released from hemoglobin. The $CO_2$ diffuses from the erythrocytes and, with the $CO_2$ in the blood plasma, diffuses from the blood into the alveolar air.

**FIGURE 23.14** The reactions occurring during the transfer of $CO_2$ from body tissues to alveolar air: **(a)** body tissues; **(b)** lungs.

## Carbon Dioxide Is Primarily Transported in the Blood as Bicarbonate in the Plasma

The $CO_2$ produced by cellular oxidation diffuses from active cells into the interstitial fluid. The $CO_2$ then diffuses from the interstitial fluid into the blood plasma **(Figure 23.14a)**.

Some of the $CO_2$ remains in solution as a gas in the plasma. In many organisms, however, significant amounts combine with water to produce carbonic acid ($H_2CO_3$), which dissociates into bicarbonate ($HCO_3^-$) and $H^+$ ions. In the erythrocyte, the enzyme carbonic anhydrase accelerates the reaction. This reaction maintains a maximal concentration gradient of $CO_2$ between the cells and the blood and is a means of storing the gas

in a harmless form temporarily while it is transported to the respiratory surface of the animal for release once more as a gas.

Most of the $H^+$ ions produced by the dissociation of carbonic acid combine with hemoglobin or with proteins in the plasma so that the pH is maintained. Note, however, that if $CO_2$ levels are high, pH will fall, resulting in changes in breathing. $CO_2$ dissolving in the plasma, conversion to bicarbonate, and combining with hemoglobin together maximize the rate of diffusion from the interstitial fluid into the blood.

The blood leaving the capillary networks of body tissues is returned to the heart, which pumps it through

With increasing altitude, atmospheric pressure decreases, and with it the air gets thinner and the partial pressure of $O_2$ decreases. At an elevation of 5000 m, the atmospheric pressure is about half that at sea level; thus, there is only half as much oxygen in each millilitre of air. This reduces the partial pressure gradient between the alveolar air and the blood, and, in turn, the supply of $O_2$ to the tissues is reduced. Humans who normally live at or near sea level and travel to higher elevations above about 2500 m experience fatigue, dizziness, and nausea until their systems produce additional red blood cells (erythrocytes), a physiological response to the stress of reduced $O_2$. Even with acclimation (adjustment to altitude), there is a maximum elevation at which humans can live for extended periods. Individuals have lived for as long as 2 years at an altitude of 5950 m, and there was a miners' barracks at 5500 m in northern Chile at Aucanquilcha. The highest permanently inhabited town in the world today appears to be the mining town of La Rinconada, in southern Peru, at an altitude of 5100 m.

However, there are animals that live at high altitudes **(Figure 1)**. The Bar-Headed Goose (*Anser indicus*) migrates over the Himalaya mountains at elevations in excess of 6000 m using one of the most energetically challenging forms of locomotion. The llama (*Lama glama*), Andean goose (*Chloephaga melanoptera*), and crested duck (*Anas specularioides*), among other species from the Andes, live at elevations up to 5000 m. Llamas, as placental mammals, produce fetuses that will experience even lower levels of oxygen than their parents. To live and perform at altitude requires that there be adaptations in every step of the path connecting the air in the atmosphere to the processes in the mitochondria (Figure 23.2c). One of the best-studied factors that permits these animals to exploit what is a marginal environment for other animals is a genetic difference in the hemoglobin molecule that makes it easier for hemoglobin to bind $O_2$.

Hemoglobin is particularly polymorphic: the gene has a number of alleles, and the alleles present in the animals that can live at very high altitudes produce the appropriate forms of hemoglobin. This is well illustrated by the deer mouse *Peromyscus maniculatus*, which occupies an extreme range of altitudes from below sea level in Death Valley to above 4300 m in the Sierra Nevada mountains. Recent studies show that the populations of deer mice at higher altitudes have alleles of the hemoglobin genes with higher affinities for $O_2$ (bind $O_2$ more easily) than the alleles of mice at low altitudes. Recently, scientists have found, using experiments involving protein engineering, that this beneficial adaptation arose from interactions between single amino acid mutations at distant sites within one of the hemoglobin protein chains.

A.

B.

C.

D.

**FIGURE 1** **(a)** Mount Everest. The amount of oxygen at the top of the mountain is roughly one-third that found at sea level. Species that are adapted for life at altitudes include **(b)** the Bar-Headed Goose, **(c)** the llama, and **(d)** the common deer mouse (*Peromyscus* sp.).

the gills or lungs. As the blood enters the capillary networks in the gills or lungs, the entire process of $CO_2$ uptake is reversed **(Figure 23.14b)**. As a result, $CO_2$ diffuses from the blood and into the water or air. As $CO_2$ diffuses away, bicarbonate ions in the blood combine with $H^+$ ions, forming carbonic acid molecules that break down into water and additional $CO_2$. This $CO_2$ adds to that diffusing from the blood into the water or air.

## STUDY BREAK

1. Why is hemoglobin so important for $O_2$ transport in the blood?
2. Why is the pH of the blood different in the tissues and in the lungs? What is the effect of the change in pH between these two sites for $O_2$ binding to hemoglobin?

# PUTTING IT IN PERSPECTIVE

Most plants and animals need a continuous supply of oxygen to sustain life. Some organisms are more sensitive to oxygen availability than others (Box 23.3). Even within a single organism, some tissues are more sensitive than others. In humans, the heart and brain are particularly sensitive, explaining why even temporary disruption of oxygen delivery to these tissues, such as occurs with cerebrovascular accident (CVA or stroke) or with myocardial infarction (MI or heart attack), can be so damaging. Providing supplemental oxygen is the first priority in treating these patients. A thorough understanding of our own respiratory system along with the study of the adaptations seen in animals for enhancing gas exchange has led to new therapeutic treatments for respiratory diseases and an understanding of the challenges and solutions associated with living in extreme environments. This helps us understand how some species can survive exposure to low oxygen or high carbon dioxide in burrows, at altitude, and in the depths of the oceans as examples.

# KEY CONCEPTS REVIEW AND QUESTIONS

## 23.1  General Principles of Gas Exchange

Air has weight and as a result is more compressed and exerts more pressure at sea level than at higher altitudes. Each gas in air contributes to this pressure in proportion to its concentration in air. The major gas in air is $N_2$ (78%) followed by $O_2$ (21%). Air contains very little $CO_2$ (0.03%). The $O_2$ is produced by photosynthetic organisms, and the $CO_2$ now largely comes from the breakdown of dead plant and animal matter by microorganisms. The amount of oxygen in any given habitat will be a balance between the rate at which it is produced (photosynthesis), the rate at which it is consumed, the ease with which it can diffuse in from elsewhere, and the barometric pressure. Environments where oxygen may be limiting include soil, burrows, stagnant bodies of water, and high altitude.

1. Which of the following statements are true?
   a. The % $O_2$ in each millilitre of air is lower at altitude.
   b. Animals breathe more $O_2$ in less volume at sea level.
   c. $O_2$ is less available at altitude due to lower barometric pressure.
   d. The partial pressure of $CO_2$ is greater at sea level than at altitude.

2. Which of the following statements are true?
   a. Historically, the greatest source of atmospheric $CO_2$ came from volcanoes.
   b. Pork and beef production in Canada produces more $CO_2$ each year than driving cars.
   c. Plants play very little role in determining atmospheric levels of $CO_2$.
   d. $CO_2$ levels in the atmosphere are at an all-time high.

3. Design an experiment to demonstrate that air does have weight.

The rate at which gases are exchanged between organisms and their environment depends on the surface area available, the distance the gas has to diffuse, the time available for exchange to take place, and the difference in partial pressure. The solubility of gases in air and in water is very different. $CO_2$ is very soluble in water, whereas $O_2$ is not. Because of this, when air and water (or plasma or other body fluids) are in equilibrium, they will have the same partial pressure for each gas but can have very different concentrations. The surfaces across which gases diffuse must be moist as gases must be dissolved and in solution to cross cell membranes. Gas exchange by simple diffusion alone is limited to small or flattened organisms. In larger animals, respiratory surfaces are increased, and the difference in partial pressures across a membrane is optimized by ventilation and perfusion. Water and air, as respiratory media, have different advantages and challenges.

4. Which of the following statements are true?
   a. The larger the partial pressure gradient, the lower the rate of diffusion
   b. The greater the surface area for exchange, the greater the rate of diffusion
   c. The thinner the barrier, the higher the rate of diffusion
   d. The lower the temperature, the higher the rate of diffusion

5. Fill in the blanks to indicate which of the following statements applies to air or water:
   a. Oxygen is more soluble in _____.
   b. It is easier to excrete $CO_2$ in _____.
   c. It is energetically more demanding to ventilate with _____.
   d. Breathing _____ can rapidly lead to dehydration.
   e. Animals breathing _____ must ventilate more to obtain the same amount of oxygen.

## 23.2  Adaptations for Gas Exchange

Gases are exchanged across moist surfaces. In very small organisms, this can be directly across the body surface. In plants, most exchange takes place in the leaves but also occurs to some extent in the stems and roots. In larger animals, specialized surfaces have evolved in the form of tracheal systems in insects and gills and lungs in vertebrate animals. Most of these exchange surfaces are thin and delicate, so that blood comes into close contact with the environment, and hence are situated in protected places. This gives rise to the need for ventilation: muscular pumping that renews the medium at the exchange surface. Perfusion with blood also enhances the diffusion gradient for gas exchange. Both ventilation and perfusion in these systems are under neural control.

6. Match each of the following respiratory organs with a description or example. Each term on the left may match more than one description on the right. Each description on the right may apply to more than one respiratory organ.

   a. Skin          ___ Gases diffuse directly from the atmosphere to individual cells

   b. Tracheal systems   ___ Gases diffuse into blood moving in the opposite direction

   c. Leaves        ___ Requires muscular pumps for adequate gas exchange

   d. Internal gills    ___ Gas exchange is enhanced by blood perfusion

   e. Lungs         ___ Produces the most effective gas exchange mechanism

7. Which of the following statements are correct?

   a. Birds use a one-way flow of air through their lungs for gas exchange.

   b. The primary drives to breathe in mammals is to excrete $CO_2$.

   c. A disadvantage of breathing air is the need to keep the lung surface moist.

   d. Gas exchange in plants is always the opposite of that in animals ($CO_2$ in and $O_2$ out).

   e. Tidal ventilation, such as occurs in mammals, including humans, is the most efficient type of gas exchange.

8. The control of the spiracular opening in insects is assumed to be important in avoiding water loss during gas exchange. Suggest an experiment to test this hypothesis.

## 23.3 Exchange of Gas with Blood

At the gas exchange surface, oxygen and $CO_2$ are exchanged between the water or air and the blood (oxygen in, $CO_2$ out). Although this takes place by diffusion, the manner in which the water or air and the blood meet determines the efficiency of this exchange. This occurs in one of three ways. In fish, the water flowing over the gills moves in a direction opposite to

the flow of blood through the gills (countercurrent flow). This is the most efficient form of gas exchange. The system seen in mammals, including humans, in which air flows in and out of the lungs (uniform or mixed pool flow) is much less efficient. Birds use air sacs as bellows to move air through their lungs in a constant direction, producing an exchange system (cross-current flow) that is almost as efficient as that seen in fish.

9. Match each of the following types of gas exchange on the left with the proper description on the right.

   a. Countercurrent exchange        ___ Helps support the high metabolic rates required for flight in birds

   b. Cross-current exchange         ___ Produces exchange of 80% to 90% of the available oxygen

   c. Uniform (mixed pool) exchange  ___ Is associated with tidal, back and forth, movement of air

## 23.4 Mechanisms of Gas Transport

Because $O_2$ is not very soluble in fluid, in most animals, it is transported by special pigments that have an ability to easily and reversibly bind to oxygen. These pigments (hemocyanin and hemoglobin) are usually contained within the red blood cells (this is what makes them red). $CO_2$, on the other hand, leaves the tissues, dissolves in the plasma, and enters the erythrocytes, where most of it is converted into $H^+$ and $HCO_3^-$ and released back into the plasma. The remaining $CO_2$ combines with hemoglobin. At the alveolar surface, the $HCO_3^-$ is converted back to $CO_2$, which flows down its partial pressure gradient and is excreted to the environment.

10. The majority of $CO_2$ in the blood is

    a. Bound to hemoglobin

    b. Transported as $HCO_3^-$

    c. Dissolved as $CO_2$ in the plasma

    d. Dissolved as $CO_2$ in the red blood cells

11. You and your pet dog live at sea level. The atmospheric $P_{O_2}$ = 150 mm Hg. Your dog's arterial $P_{O_2}$ = 100 mm Hg, and his tissue $P_{O_2}$ = 10 mm Hg. You expect your dog to

    a. Die

    b. Accumulate $CO_2$

    c. Have a serious but non-lethal $O_2$ deficit

    d. Become dizzy from too much $O_2$

    e. Function normally

12. The ability to live at high elevations appears to have genetic components beyond the properties of the blood in many animals. What experiments can you devise to explore this possibility? (Hint: some animals have high and low elevation populations.)

# Transport

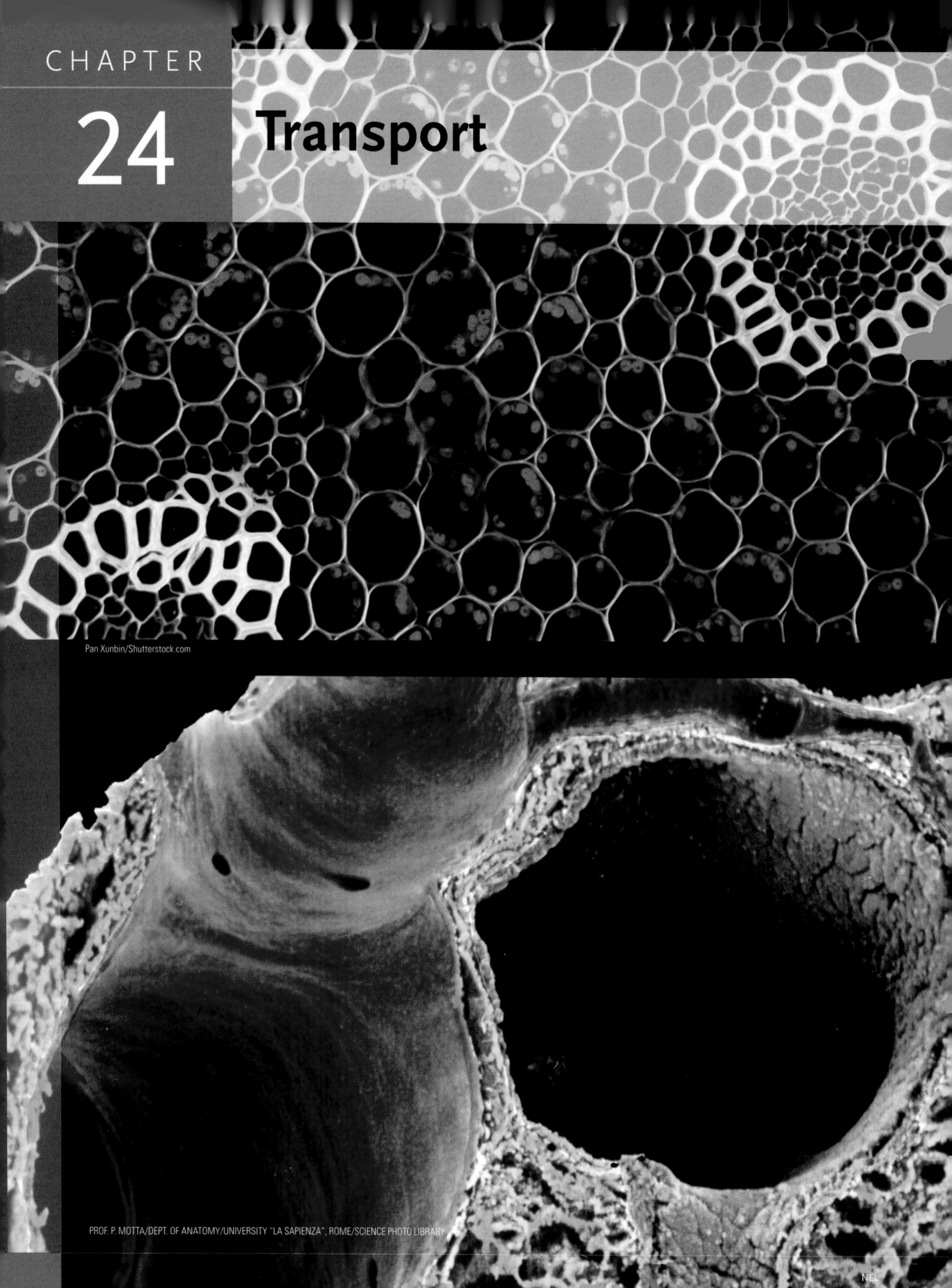

## WHY IT MATTERS

The giraffe is currently the tallest animal on earth. These creatures stand roughly 6 m tall. The circulatory or transport system in these animals has the task of delivering oxygen and other nutrients to all tissues throughout the body and of picking up and disposing of wastes. Their hearts, therefore, have the task of pumping blood not only all the way to the feet but also, more impressively, all the way to the brain against the forces of gravity. To push blood over these distances and against such forces requires a heart that can generate blood pressures that are roughly twice those of other mammals. They achieve this by having a more muscular heart. This increased muscle thickness, however, reduces the size of the heart cavity and hence reduces the amount of blood that can be pumped with each beat. This suggests that the ability of giraffes to generate high blood flow, such as during exercise, may be limited. This may be one of the factors that limit the maximum height that terrestrial animals can achieve. The trees that the giraffes feed on, however, are taller yet **(Figure 24.1)**. Indeed, the tallest trees on Earth reach over 100 m in height. All plants too require a transport system to move nutrients from areas of uptake to areas of need. Astoundingly, plants do this without muscles, without a pump, and without the expenditure of energy. They meet their needs through the movement of solutes and water driven by osmosis, cohesion, and evaporation (described in this chapter). In this chapter, we will explore the different ways in which plants and animals have solved the problem of transporting fluids and dissolved materials over large distances in a manner that satisfies the individual needs of all the cells of their bodies. They face similar problems but have solved them in very different ways. The opening photographs to this chapter demonstrate one example of both similarities and differences between plants and animals. These photomicrographs show the capillary vessels in a mammalian lung and the xylem vessels in a plant. Can you tell which is which?

**FIGURE 24.1** Although transporting blood to the head of a giraffe (*Giraffa camelopardalis*) is an impressive feat, transporting water to the top of tall trees is even more impressive.

## 24.1 Transport Systems

Transport systems facilitate exchange between all body tissues. As noted earlier in the book, for single-celled organisms, all exchange with the environment takes place across the cell membrane. For multicellular organisms, on the other hand, a division of labour exists, and specialized organs and organ systems have evolved to handle specific chores, such as nutrient uptake and gas exchange.

In plants, water and organic ions and minerals are taken up by the roots, whereas $CO_2$ is converted to sugar in the leaves by photosynthesis. The photosynthesis in the leaves requires the water taken up by the roots, whereas the cells in the roots require the sugars produced in the leaves for energy. Plants must be able to move water, dissolved minerals and ions, and sugars throughout the body from areas of uptake and storage to sites where they are needed. This is achieved by the vascular tissue described in Chapters 17 and 20. This tissue is made up of specialized plant cells called xylem and phloem. Although phloem cells are generally living, xylem cells are dead, with lignified secondary cell walls. The details of the functioning of the vascular tissues in plants are described in the next section.

In animals, organ systems are even more specialized. Most animals possess a circulatory system consisting of a pump (the heart) and vascular tissue (blood vessels) that distribute compounds between the specialized exchange surfaces and all the cells of the body. In this case, the vessels are composed of smooth muscle and the pump of cardiac muscle. Both are living and contractile. The details of the functioning of the pumps and vascular tissues in animals are described in the section that follows.

Although the ways in which plants and animals have solved the problem of internal transport are very different, the fundamental components of each transport system are the same; there are vessels through which fluids and dissolved substances are moved, a means of generating the pressures required to move them, and ways in which to ensure that all cells are able to match supply and demand. Let's take a look at the very different ways in which this is achieved.

## 24.2 Transport in Plants

### Uptake and Transport of Water and Solutes by Roots

As discussed in Chapter 22, most plants obtain the water and minerals they need for growth and maintenance from the soil. Some of the water and minerals will be used by cells within the roots themselves, although much will be transported throughout the body of the plant. In this section, we will consider the uptake and short-distance transport of water and solutes within the root itself. For this and subsequent discussion of water, solute, and sugar transport, it is important to recall two key features of the structure of plants. The first feature to remember is that the living cells of plants are interconnected by plasmodesmata (see Chapters 17 and 20). That is, the cytoplasm in adjoining cells is connected, and once substances have entered one cell, they can move freely between cells. The second feature to remember is that each cell is surrounded by a cell wall that is porous and that there is a continuous network of cell walls and spaces between cells that is non-living.

Water, therefore, can enter the root in one of two ways (**Figure 24.2**). Some diffuses across the plasma membrane of epidermal cells on the outside of the root and is then free to move between cells through the plasmodesmata. Most water, however, flows through the cell walls, moving through these non-living intercellular spaces without crossing a plasma membrane. These pathways are not exclusive, however, and water can enter cells within the root cortex from the intercellular spaces at any point, and vice versa; it can leave cells and enter the intercellular space. This raises the question, "What determines the rate and direction of movement of the water?"

There are two principal forces causing water to move: pressure and osmosis. In the case of movement through the roots, the root cells contain more dissolved solutes than the soil water. Because the cells actively transport minerals into their cytoplasm (see Chapter 21), this creates a concentration gradient that draws water by osmosis into the cells. This will cause the cells to swell, increasing the pressure within the cells. The cell walls prevent the cells from expanding to the point where they burst, and the pressure builds within the cells until the outward pressure due to swelling is offset by the osmotic pressure, drawing water into the cells.

If the soil surrounding terrestrial plants dries out, the flow of water may reverse. As the soil dries, the solute content of the remaining soil water can increase until it

In the **extracellular pathway** (red), water moves through non-living regions—the continuous network of adjoining cell walls and tissue air spaces. However, when it reaches the endodermis, it must pass through the cytoplasm of endodermal cells.

In the **intracellular pathway** (black), water passes into and through living cells. After being taken up into root hairs, water diffuses through the cytoplasm and passes from one living cell to the next through plasmodesmata.

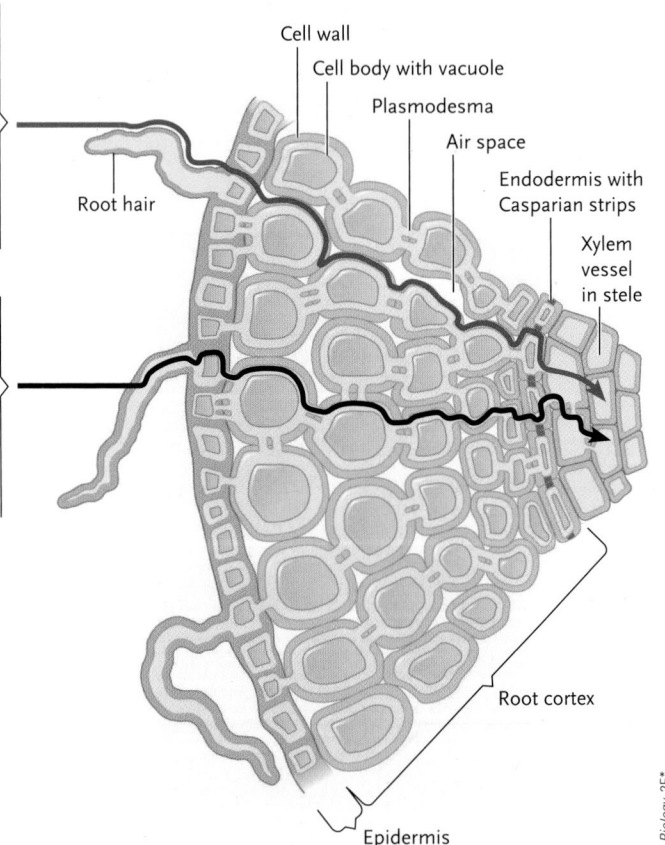

*Biology, 2E**

**FIGURE 24.2** Pathways for the movement of water in roots. Ions also enter roots via these two pathways but must be actively transported into cells.

is greater than that in the cytoplasm, and water will leave the cells, reducing the internal pressure and resulting in wilting of the plant.

The mineral ions dissolved in soil water can also enter the plant by both routes. Because most ions important for plant nutrition are in higher concentration inside the root cells than in the soil water, they cannot move passively into the cell as the concentration gradient is in the opposite direction. As ions are charged particles, they cannot penetrate the phospholipid bilayer of the membrane and must be actively transported across by ion-specific transport proteins (see Chapter 3). The cells sequester the minerals in vacuoles as well as in the cell cytoplasm, where they are used for metabolic processes.

## Movement of Water and Solutes from the Root Cortex into Xylem Vessels

Although some water and some minerals are retained for use by the roots, much of the water and the mineral ions taken up by the roots will be distributed to the rest of the plant. To achieve this, they must first be transported into the xylem vessels in the **stele** in the centre of the root. To do this, they must first cross the **endodermis**, the innermost layer of the root cortex. This layer of cells is densely packed, and the cell walls between neighbouring endodermal cells are impregnated with

a waxy substance that is impermeable to water and dissolved solutes. This is the **Casparian strip (Figure 24.3)**. To penetrate the endodermis, water and dissolved solutes must enter the endodermal cells themselves and be passed via their plasmodesmata into the outermost cell layers of the stele. The movement of the water will again be driven by osmosis and the ions by active transport processes. This process controls the movement of water into the plant cells. Up to this point in the root, water can travel extracellularly. The Casparian strip and cell membrane function to limit access of unwanted materials to the interior of the plant. The Casparian strip also prevents the leakage of minerals and water back out of the stele.

Inside the stele, both the water and the ions will now enter the xylem vessels. Recall from Chapters 17 and 20 that these are composed of two types of conducting cells, **tracheids** and **vessel elements**, both of which, when mature, consist of the cell walls of dead cells in the form of very thin tubes connected end to end. These run all the way from the roots to the tips of all shoots and branches of the plant.

Whether the ions leave the live cells to enter the dead vessels by passive diffusion or are extruded by active outward transport is still not clear. The water moves out due to two processes, osmosis and transpiration, as will be described in the next section.

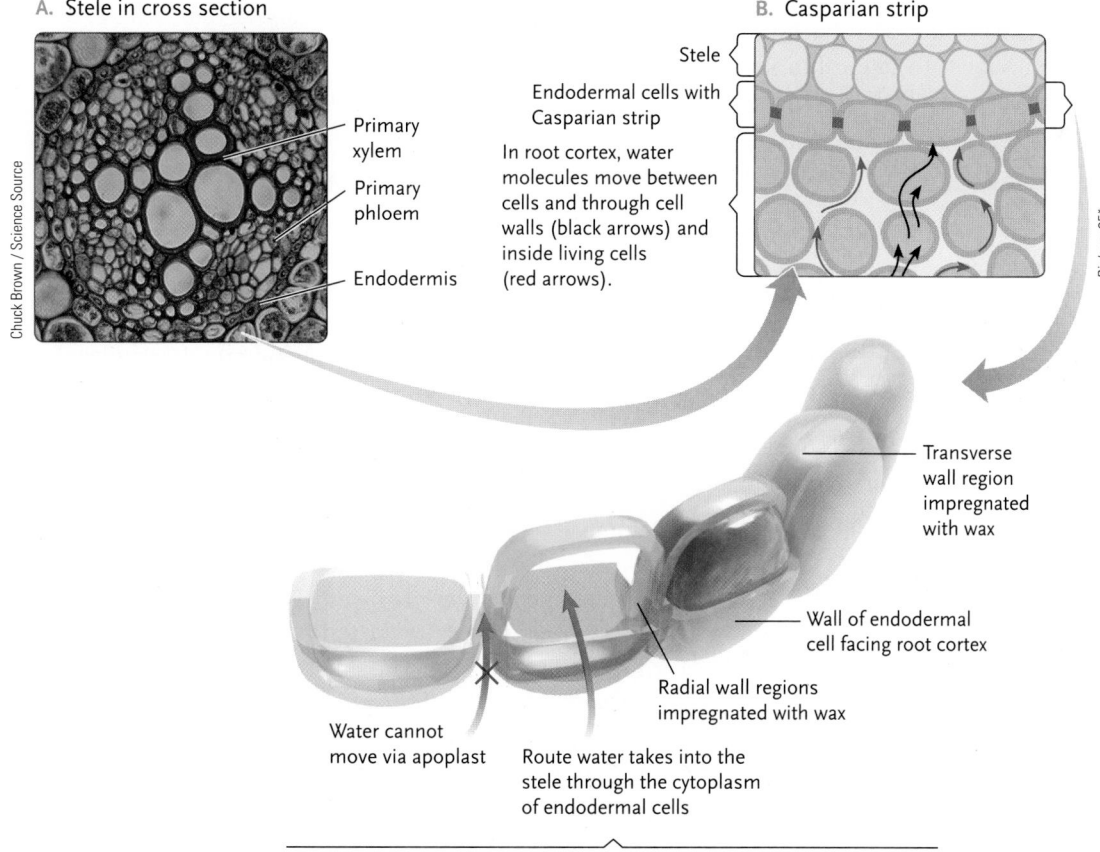

**A. Stele in cross section**

Chuck Brown / Science Source

- Primary xylem
- Primary phloem
- Endodermis

**B. Casparian strip**

Stele

Endodermal cells with Casparian strip

In root cortex, water molecules move between cells and through cell walls (black arrows) and inside living cells (red arrows).

Biology, 2E*

**FIGURE 24.3** Location and function of the Casparian strip in roots.

Transverse wall region impregnated with wax

Wall of endodermal cell facing root cortex

Radial wall regions impregnated with wax

Water cannot move via apoplast

Route water takes into the stele through the cytoplasm of endodermal cells

Waxy, water-impervious Casparian strip (gold) in abutting walls of endodermal cells that control water and nutrient uptake.

## Transport of Water and Solutes in the Xylem

### Root Pressure Can Push Water Up Xylem Vessels

Whatever the means by which solutes enter the xylem vessels, the net effect will be to draw water with them. As ions accumulate in the xylem, unable to re-enter the root through the Casparian strip, water will enter by osmosis. This will produce a positive pressure in the vessels, called root pressure, which will push the water and solutes in the xylem vessels, now referred to as xylem sap, up the vessels. The water must move upwards since the strong, lignified walls of the xylem cells prevent them from expanding outwards. Although this pressure is not sufficient to move xylem sap to the top of tall trees, it is sufficient to move fluids in shorter, non-woody plants (such as grasses) and contributes to fluid movement when transpiration is reduced (in high humidity or at night).

### Transpiration Pulls Water Up Xylem Vessels

So how are water and dissolved solutes transported to the tops of tall trees? The answer is that they are pulled up by the leaves through the process of transpiration.

Two biologically important properties of water are that water is both cohesive and adhesive. Water molecules tend to form hydrogen bonds with one another (**cohesion**) as well as with other substances (**adhesion**), notably the carbohydrates in the cell walls of the xylem vessels. As a result, the water in the xylem vessels is in essence a long chain of molecules both held together and attached to the vessel walls by hydrogen bonds. In long, thin vessels, these forces are strong enough to hold the water together as a column.

As described in Chapter 23, the mesophyll cells in the leaves of plants are always moist, a condition that is essential for gas transport. Since the air surrounding the leaves is usually drier than the space between the mesophyll cells within the leaves, water is always evaporating from the mesophyll cell surface. Since as much as two-thirds of a leaf's volume may be air space, a large surface area is available for evaporation to occur. As water evaporates, the water film on the surface of the mesophyll cells becomes thinner, increasing the tension between the water molecules, This pulls water out from the mesophyll cells, and this in turn pulls water into the mesophyll cells from the xylem sap in the xylem vessels in the leaf veins (**Figure 24.4**).

The column of water is continuous even across cell membranes. Because of cohesion between water molecules, this tension is transmitted all the way down through the xylem vessels to the roots, drawing water in across the root endodermis. Thus, transpiration, the evaporation of water from the leaves and other aerial parts of terrestrial plants, acts through a cohesion–tension mechanism to move large volumes of water from the

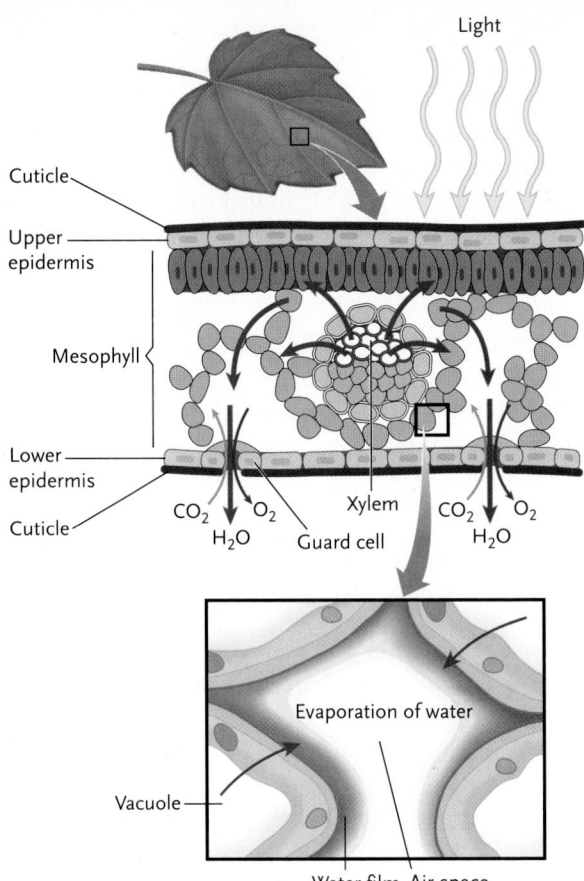

FIGURE 24.4 Water evaporating from a leaf causes increasing tension on the remaining water inside the leaf, eventually pulling water up out of the xylem. As water evaporates from the water-lined spaces in a leaf, the film of water on the mesophyll cells around the air space becomes thinner and thinner. The water molecules in this film are under increasing tension, which pulls water out of the mesophyll cells and ultimately out of the xylem.

roots to the tips of the shoots of even the tallest plants (**Figure 24.5**). Most impressive is that this does not require the expenditure of any energy on the part of the plant but results solely from the physical properties of water. Researchers estimate that the maximum tension that can be sustained before the bonds between water molecules in a column of water in xylem will break could support water transport by this mechanism in trees up to roughly 120 to 130 m, suggesting that the tallest living trees have reached the physical limit for the upward transport of water.

The dissolved solutes are transported along with the water. Once in the xylem vessels, water and solutes can move either upward in the vessels or laterally to and from the tissues they pass. The solutes will be taken up by cells as needed by active transport and the water by osmosis.

### Guard Cells Control Transpiration

The use of transpiration to move water from the roots to the shoots in plants is a mixed blessing. It means that internal transport of water and solutes is dependent on

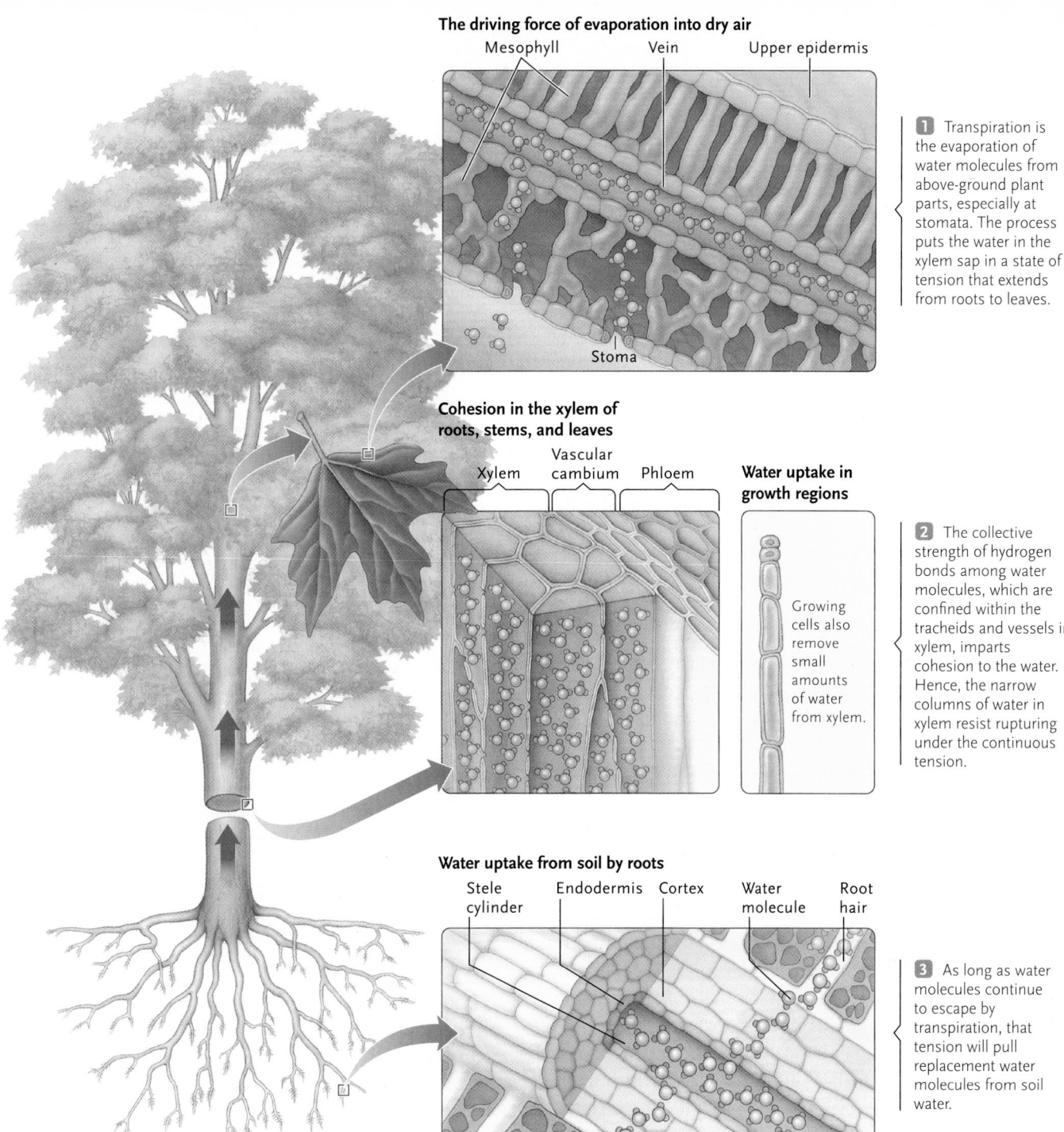

**The driving force of evaporation into dry air**

Mesophyll    Vein    Upper epidermis

Stoma

**1** Transpiration is the evaporation of water molecules from above-ground plant parts, especially at stomata. The process puts the water in the xylem sap in a state of tension that extends from roots to leaves.

**Cohesion in the xylem of roots, stems, and leaves**

Xylem    Vascular cambium    Phloem

**Water uptake in growth regions**

Growing cells also remove small amounts of water from xylem.

**2** The collective strength of hydrogen bonds among water molecules, which are confined within the tracheids and vessels in xylem, imparts cohesion to the water. Hence, the narrow columns of water in xylem resist rupturing under the continuous tension.

**Water uptake from soil by roots**

Stele cylinder    Endodermis    Cortex    Water molecule    Root hair

**3** As long as water molecules continue to escape by transpiration, that tension will pull replacement water molecules from soil water.

**FIGURE 24.5** Cohesion–tension mechanism of water transport. Transpiration, the evaporation of water from shoot parts, creates tension on the water in xylem sap. This tension, which extends from roots to leaves, pulls upward on columns of water molecules that are bonded to one another by hydrogen bonds.

the evaporation and loss of water and hence is also dependent on the constant uptake of water by the roots. To put things in perspective, roughly 90% of the water taken up by a plant is lost again through transpiration. Only a small percentage of the water (roughly 2%) is used in the chloroplasts for photosynthesis. On a hot, dry, windy day, some plants will replace all of the water in their leaves every hour! Not surprisingly, mechanisms have evolved to allow plants to regulate the loss of water

by transpiration, and the most important is by the regulation of the opening and closing of the stomata on the lower leaf surface. These openings are the major communication route between the atmosphere surrounding the leaves and the air spaces between the mesophyll cells within the leaves.

Each stoma is surrounded by two guard cells. These cells control the opening of the stoma by changing shape. Their inner walls are thicker and less elastic than

FIGURE 24.6 Control of stomatal opening. **(a)** Increasing solute concentration in the cytoplasm of the guard cells causes water influx and cell swelling opening the stoma. **(b)** Lowering solute concentration inside the cells causes water to flow out of the cell, reducing swelling and closing the stoma. Solute influx is regulated by such factors as light, low levels of $CO_2$, biological rhythms and the hormone abscisic acid (ABA).

**A.** **Stoma is open; water and solutes have moved in.**

Solutes  Water

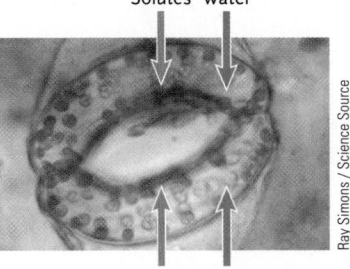

Ray Simons / Science Source

**B.** **Stoma is closed; water and solutes have moved out.**

ABA signal  Solutes  Water

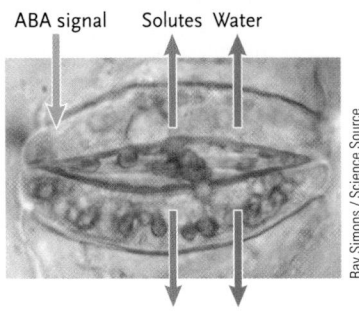

Ray Simons / Science Source

their outer walls such that when these cells swell due to water uptake, they bow outwards, pulling apart and increasing the size of the stoma **(Figure 24.6)**. The uptake of water that leads to guard cell swelling is the result, primarily, of the uptake of $K^+$ as a result of the creation of an electrochemical gradient by an ATP-driven process. The water then follows by osmosis. Closing of the stoma is due to a reverse process. The active pumps ultimately responsible for the movement of the $K^+$ are regulated by a variety of mechanisms, including light, $CO_2$, **abscisic acid** (released by leaf mesophyll cells under conditions of water stress), and an intrinsic biological clock. These mechanisms are integrated to increase stomatal opening to enhance gas exchange and photosynthesis during the day but to balance this with the need to regulate water loss—the photosynthesis–transpiration compromise.

## STUDY BREAK

1. What are the two pathways by which water can penetrate plant roots?
2. What is the Casparian strip, and what does it do?
3. What are the similarities and differences between adhesion and cohesion?
4. What is the cohesion–tension mechanism that creates water transport in plants?
5. How is the opening and closing of the stomata in the leaves regulated?

## Transport of Sugars and Organic Substances in the Phloem

Although the movement of water and solutes in the xylem (xylem sap) is in one direction, from roots to shoot tips, driven primarily by transpiration, plants must be able to move sugars (primarily sucrose), fatty acids, amino acids, and hormones in different directions at different times. They must be able to move sugars from the sites of synthesis (a sugar source) to any part of the plant that requires sugar either to consume for energy or to store for later use (a sugar sink). The sources of sugar are either the photosynthesizing cells (primarily in the mature leaves) or the sites where sugars are stored as starch (usually in the roots or stems; see Chapter 21). The sinks vary daily and seasonally. A storage organ such as a root or bulb will be a sink, accumulating starch, during the summer but will be a source in the spring, when sugar is required faster than it can be produced to fuel new growth. Accordingly, the leaves will be a source in the summer, but new, growing leaves will be a sink in the spring. Growing roots and fruits are also sugar sinks **(Figure 24.7)** (Box 24.1).

This movement is achieved by directional flow (translocation) in the living sieve tube member cells of the phloem vessels. The sieve tube member cells are connected end to end to form sieve tubes. Their top and bottom walls contain abundant pores (the sieve plate) through which the plasmodesma of adjoining cells communicate freely. This allows **phloem sap** to move easily

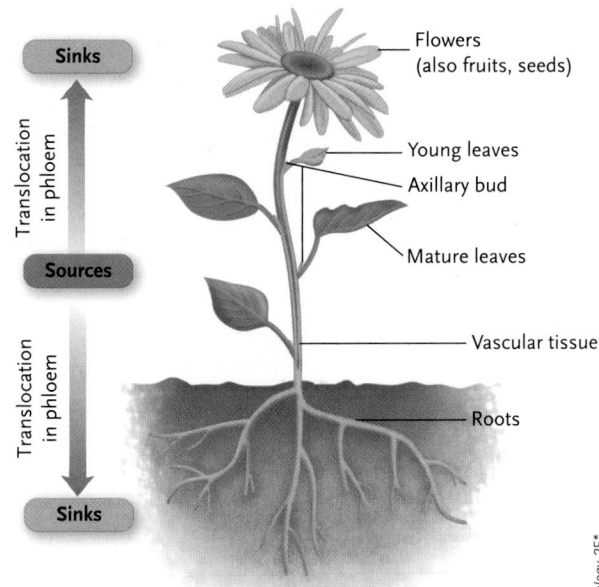

Biology, 2E*

**FIGURE 24.7** Sources and sinks in a plant. Mature leaves of this plant are producing sugars (sugar source), whereas young leaves, flowers, and fruits require sugars (sugar sink) for growth and the roots accumulate sugars (another sugar sink) to store for use the following spring (at which time, they will become a sugar source).

from cell to cell through the sieve tube. Companion cells associated with the sieve member cells assist with both the loading and unloading of sugars in the phloem sap.

Movement of phloem sap is the result of pressure flow due to the establishment of concentration gradients. At the source end of each sieve tube, macromolecules (primarily sugar) are actively transported into the phloem, whereas at the sink end, they are transported out of the phloem and into cells for storage or consumption. The loading of sugar at the source end raises the solute concentration, and this in turn draws water into the sieve tubes by osmosis, raising the hydrostatic pressure of the phloem sap. At the sink end, where the sugars are being unloaded, water will follow by osmosis, reducing the hydrostatic pressure in the tube. These two activities (sugar loading and unloading) thus create a pressure gradient that results in the bulk flow of phloem sap from source to sink—wherever that sink may be.

As the water flows through the sieve tubes, it carries the sugars and other macromolecules with it. At the sink, the unloading of macromolecules is largely through the plasmodesmata into the receiving cells. Most of the water re-enters the xylem to be transported back to the source (Figure 24.8).

## STUDY BREAK

1. Define *translocation* and *transpiration* and describe where they occur and why they are important.
2. Describe how sugars stored in a plant root are moved in the sieve tubes in the phloem to growing shoots in the spring.

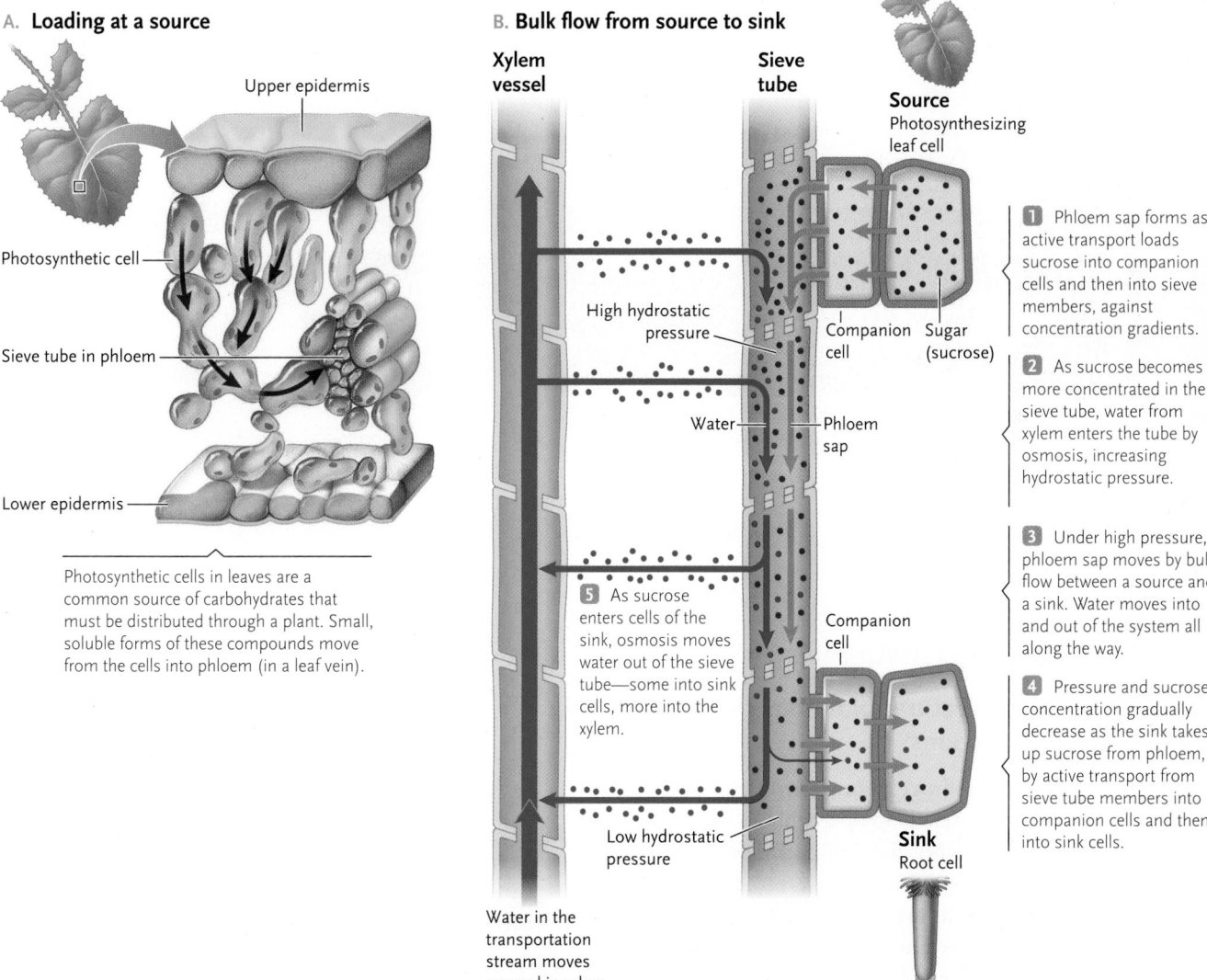

**A. Loading at a source**

Upper epidermis

Photosynthetic cell

Sieve tube in phloem

Lower epidermis

Photosynthetic cells in leaves are a common source of carbohydrates that must be distributed through a plant. Small, soluble forms of these compounds move from the cells into phloem (in a leaf vein).

**B. Bulk flow from source to sink**

Xylem vessel

Sieve tube

**Source**
Photosynthesizing leaf cell

High hydrostatic pressure

Companion cell    Sugar (sucrose)

Water

Phloem sap

**5** As sucrose enters cells of the sink, osmosis moves water out of the sieve tube—some into sink cells, more into the xylem.

Companion cell

Low hydrostatic pressure

**Sink**
Root cell

Water in the transportation stream moves upward in xylem

**1** Phloem sap forms as active transport loads sucrose into companion cells and then into sieve members, against concentration gradients.

**2** As sucrose becomes more concentrated in the sieve tube, water from xylem enters the tube by osmosis, increasing hydrostatic pressure.

**3** Under high pressure, phloem sap moves by bulk flow between a source and a sink. Water moves into and out of the system all along the way.

**4** Pressure and sucrose concentration gradually decrease as the sink takes up sucrose from phloem, by active transport from sieve tube members into companion cells and then into sink cells.

*Biology, 2E*

**FIGURE 24.8** Summary of the pressure flow mechanism responsible for the movement of phloem in sieve tubes. Organic solutes are loaded into sieve tubes at a source, such as a leaf **(a)**, and move by bulk flow toward a sink, such as roots or rapidly growing plant parts **(b)**.

Few people understand and appreciate the movement of sugar in plants between sites of storage and sites of use more than the maple sugar producers of Eastern Canada. Sugar produced by red or black maple trees (*Acer nigrum*) throughout the summer is stored in the roots and trunks for the winter. This stored sugar becomes a source of energy for growth in the spring. Although much of the sugar is transported in the phloem, in the spring, sugar is drawn out of storage sites and into the xylem as well. When small holes are bored into the trunks of the trees, penetrating into the xylem vessels, a process called tapping, the sap can be collected and used to produce syrup.

The source of the pressure that drives the xylem sap upwards at this time of year (and out of the taps into the buckets of the syrup producers) has only recently been described. The movement of the xylem does not involve the cohesion–tension mechanism just described in the text as the trees do not yet have leaves and there is no transpiration. It is also not due to root pressure. It is due to the production of $CO_2$ during respiration by the living parenchymal cells. This gas enters the xylem and expands as temperatures rise during the day, forcing the xylem sap upwards. At night, the gas contracts and the flow of sap stops and may even reverse.

Sap tapping takes place over four to eight weeks in the spring, and each adult tree will produce about 50 L of sap. This is about 5% to 7% of the total sap of the tree. The sap is largely water and must be boiled down to produce syrup **(Figure 1)**. It takes 40 to 50 L of sap to produce 1 L of maple syrup. The province of Québec produces almost 25 million litres of maple syrup each year, roughly 75% of all the maple syrup produced in the world. The provinces of Ontario, New Brunswick, Nova Scotia, and Prince Edward Island produce another 10%, and the United States produces the remaining 15%.

It is not known who first made the discovery that the xylem sap of the maple tree could be distilled into such a sweet delicacy, but Aboriginal rituals centred around sugar making existed long before Europeans arrived in North America. Recently, it has been shown that the sugars and other organic compounds found in xylem sap have antioxidant and antimutagenic (cancer preventing) properties as well, making it more than just a sweet delight.

A.

B.

C.

**FIGURE 1** Xylem sap is collected by tapping maple trees **(a)** and is then boiled down **(b)** to concentrate the sugars and produce maple syrup **(c)**.

## 24.3 Transport in Animals

### Fundamental Features of Animal Circulatory Systems

In larger, multicellular animals, most cells lie deep enough within the body to be unable to exchange substances directly with the environment. Specialized organs and organ systems have evolved for this, each specializing in a different function (see Chapter 20). Circulatory systems have evolved in conjunction with the need to connect these specialized regions where substances are exchanged with the environment to all other cells in the body. Animals are generally mobile and not rooted. Unlike plants that rely on a one-way flow of water from roots to shoots for internal transport (a flow-through system), animals must conserve water and rely on a system that recirculates fluids to transport materials between the different sites in the body (a recirculation system). Although there are some differences in the design of these systems in different animals, all share certain fundamental features: they use a muscular pump to transport vascular fluids through tubular vessels.

### Vascular Fluids

The primary role of the **vascular fluids** in most animals is to transport nutrients and oxygen to cells and to carry wastes and carbon dioxide to sites of disposal. It is also involved in regulating the internal pH and body temperature of animals as well as in transport of hormones, protection against foreign bodies, and healing of wounds.

All vascular fluids are complex and are considered to be a form of connective tissue. The fluid, or non-living, portion is a form of extracellular matrix containing a variety of proteins and glycoproteins. This fluid is referred to as the **plasma**, and in all vertebrates and many invertebrates, blood cells are suspended in it.

The plasma is about 90% water. Besides nutrients and metabolic wastes, a variety of important ions and proteins are also dissolved in it. The ions, or electrolytes, are carefully regulated to maintain the pH of the vascular fluid at appropriate levels for enzyme function and appropriate levels of ions ($Na^+$, $K^+$, $Ca^{2+}$, $Cl^-$, and $HCO_3^-$) to allow normal nervous system and muscle function (see Chapters 22 and 26). The proteins act as buffers helping to maintain pH and assist in the transport of other molecules. For instance, proteins such as albumin are important for transporting hormones, whereas globulins help transport lipids and fat-soluble vitamins. Yet other proteins play key roles in body defence (immunoglobulins, as part of the immune system) and in blood clotting (fibrinogen).

There is huge variation in the presence of cells suspended in the plasma, such that in nematodes, there are few or no suspended cells, whereas in arthropods, there are up to 275,000 cells (hemocytes) per microlitre, and in humans, roughly 5,000,000 erythrocytes (red blood cells) per microlitre (cubic millimetre).

The **erythrocytes** of vertebrates contain hemoglobin, a protein that binds to oxygen and tremendously increases the ability of the blood to transport oxygen (see Chapter 23). In invertebrates, the oxygen-transporting proteins (there are several different ones, including hemoglobin) may be present within the cells or, in some cases, (such as in annelids) free in the plasma. All contain a nucleus and are capable of normal cellular functions except the mammalian red blood cell, which lacks a nucleus once mature. This is believed to allow these cells to carry more hemoglobin while remaining small enough to squeeze through narrow capillaries. The lack of a nucleus reduces their life span.

Vertebrates also have **leukocytes** (white blood cells) that protect against foreign bodies (such as parasites, bacteria, and viruses). You will learn more about the role of these cells in Chapter 27. Vertebrate blood also contains **platelets** that play a key role in wound healing by forming blood clots. Platelets are fragments of cells that remain enclosed in their own plasma membrane. When blood vessels are injured, circulating platelets come into

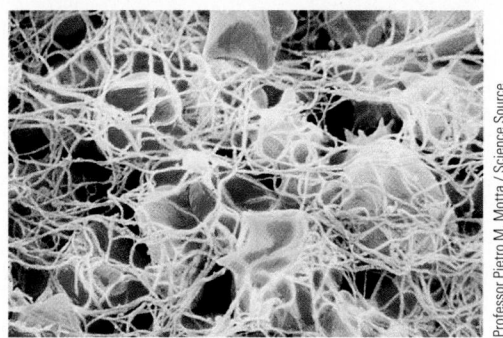

**FIGURE 24.9** Red blood cells caught in a meshlike network of fibrin threads during formation of a blood clot.

contact with collagen fibres from the extracellular matrix of the vessel wall. They are normally not exposed to them, but when they are, they stick to them. The platelets then release chemicals that cause other platelets to stick to them, forming a plug. The platelets also release chemicals, called **clotting factors** (in humans, there are more than a dozen clotting factors), that activate an enzyme that converts the **fibrinogen** dissolved in the plasma into long threads of an insoluble protein called **fibrin**. These long threads form cross-links with one another, forming a mesh that holds red blood cells and platelets tightly **(Figure 24.9)** together, forming a blood clot that effectively seals the wound. Blood cells in insects also play roles in protection against foreign bodies and wound healing.

The average composition of human blood and the relative roles of the different components are given in **Table 24.1, p. 530.**

### Open versus Closed Tubular Systems

The tubular systems through which the vascular fluid flows can be of one of two types in animals: an open circulatory system or a **closed circulatory system**. With an open circulatory system, fluid is pumped by the heart into vessels that open directly into the body cavities surrounding the various organs. This fluid, called **hemolymph**, circulates freely through the cavities and re-enters the heart through valves in the wall of the heart. These valves open inwards and are forced closed each time the heart contravvcts, establishing a one-way flow **(Figure 24.10a, p. 531)**. Each time the heart relaxes and expands, the valves open, drawing hemolymph in, and each time the heart contracts, the valves close, and the hemolymph is pushed out through the vessels. In these systems, there is no distinction between interstitial fluid and hemolymph, and exchange is direct between the cells of the body and the hemolymph. Arthropods and most molluscs have open circulatory systems, as do the urochordates and the cephalochordates, the ancestors of the vertebrates **(Figure 24.10c)**.

## TABLE 24.1 The Composition of Human Blood

The sketch of the test tube shows what happens when you centrifuge a blood sample. The blood separates into three layers: a thick layer of straw-coloured plasma on top, a thin layer containing leukocytes and platelets, and a thick layer of erythrocytes. The table shows the relative amounts and functions of the various components of blood.

| Components | Relative Amounts | Functions |
|---|---|---|
| **Plasma Portion (55%–58% of total volume)** | | |
| 1. Water | 91%–92% of plasma volume | Solvent |
| 2. Plasma proteins (albumin, globulins, fibrinogen, etc.) | 7%–8% | Defence, clotting, lipid transport, roles in ECF volume, and so on |
| 3. Ions, sugars, lipids, amino acids, hormones, vitamins, dissolved gases, urea and uric acid (metabolic wastes) | 1%–2% | Roles in ECF volume, pH, eliminating waste products, and so on |
| **Cellular Portion (42%–45% of total volume)** | | |
| 1. Erythrocytes (red blood cells) | 4,800,000–5,400,000 per microlitre | Transport oxygen, carbon dioxide |
| 2. Leukocytes (white blood cells) | | |
| Neutrophils | 3000–6750 | Phagocytosis during inflammation |
| Lymphocytes | 1000–2700 | Immune response |
| Monocytes/macrophages | 150–720 | Phagocytosis in all defence responses |
| Eosinophils | 100–360 | Defend against parasitic worms |
| Basophils | 25–90 | Secrete substances for inflammatory response and for fat removal from blood |
| 3. Platelets | 250,000–300,000 | Roles in clotting |

*Biology, 2E\**

Plasma

Leukocytes and platelets

Packed cell volume, or hematocrit

Erythrocytes

With a closed circulatory system, the blood circulates throughout the body, confined to the blood vessels (Figure 24.10b). Blood is pumped by the heart into arteries that branch repeatedly, delivering blood throughout the body into progressively smaller and more numerous vessels, ultimately ending up in microscopic, thin-walled vessels called capillaries. Here nutrients and wastes are exchanged between cells and blood via the interstitial fluid. The blood is then collected in veins that carry blood back to the heart. Annelids, cephalopod molluscs (squids and octopuses), and all vertebrates have closed circulatory systems. An advantage of these systems is that they enable higher rates of blood flow and allow blood flow to be independently regulated to each capillary bed within the body. A disadvantage is that they impose a greater resistance to blood flow that requires hearts to generate higher pressures.

### Muscular Pumps

The pumps that push the vascular fluids through the system are built of special muscle, cardiac muscle (see Chapter 20). They can be single or numerous. For instance, most insects have accessory hearts associated with the wings and with each leg. This is not uncommon in open circulatory systems (Figure 24.11b, p. 532). In earthworms,

there is one heart in each segment. The hearts of invertebrates are also **neurogenic**; that is, the heart itself has no intrinsic rhythm but is stimulated to contract by nervous input, which can be modulated by the action of hormones.

All vertebrate hearts, on the other hand, are **myogenic**. That is, the muscle of the heart has its own intrinsic rhythm (which will be described shortly). This rhythm can also be modulated by hormones and neural input, but the muscle is capable of generating a rhythm in isolation. The size of the heart and the thickness of the muscular walls reflect the amount of pressure the heart has to produce, and this in turn reflects the resistance to the flow of blood in the tubes through which the blood is pushed; that is, it reflects the anatomy of the vascular beds. The greater the number of blood vessels in the circuit and the smaller the diameter of the vessels (as described in Section 24.3), the more resistance there is to flow and the greater the pressure the heart must produce.

When we examine the hearts of the different vertebrate groups, from fish to birds and mammals, however, the most notable difference we see is in the number of chambers each heart possesses. If we examine the cardiovascular system in fish first, we can see the general features of a circulatory system. The veins returning

**A.** Open circulatory system: no distinction between hemolymph and interstitial fluid

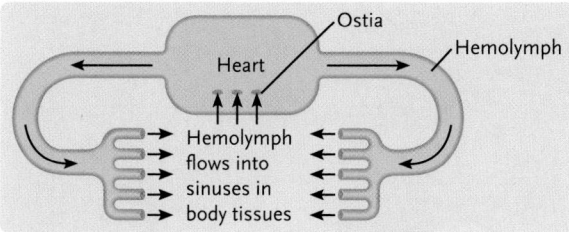

**B.** Closed circulatory system: blood separated from interstitial fluid

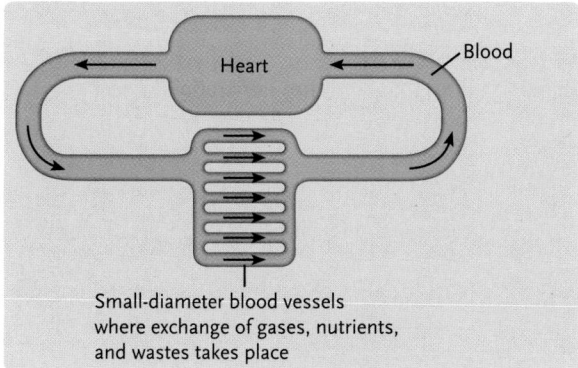

Small-diameter blood vessels where exchange of gases, nutrients, and wastes takes place

blood from the body merge, ultimately into a single large venous sinus, the sinus venosus. From here, the deoxygenated blood returning from the body is pumped into the atrium, which pumps blood into the muscular ventricle. The ventricle is the chamber that must pump the blood with sufficient pressure to propel it throughout the body and back to the heart and is thus the most muscular chamber **(Figure 24.12a, p. 533)**. Valves between the sinus venosus and atrium, between the atrium and ventricle, and between the ventricle and ventral aorta prevent the backflow of blood and ensure that blood is pumped in only one direction.

After leaving the heart, the blood must first flow through the ventral aorta, then through the capillaries in the gills, and from there through the arteries that distribute the blood to the capillary beds that service all the tissues of the body **(Figures 24.11c and 24.12a)**. In this circuit, all blood passes through at least two capillary beds, one in the gills and the other in the tissues of the body.

**C.** Evolutionary trends in animal circulatory systems

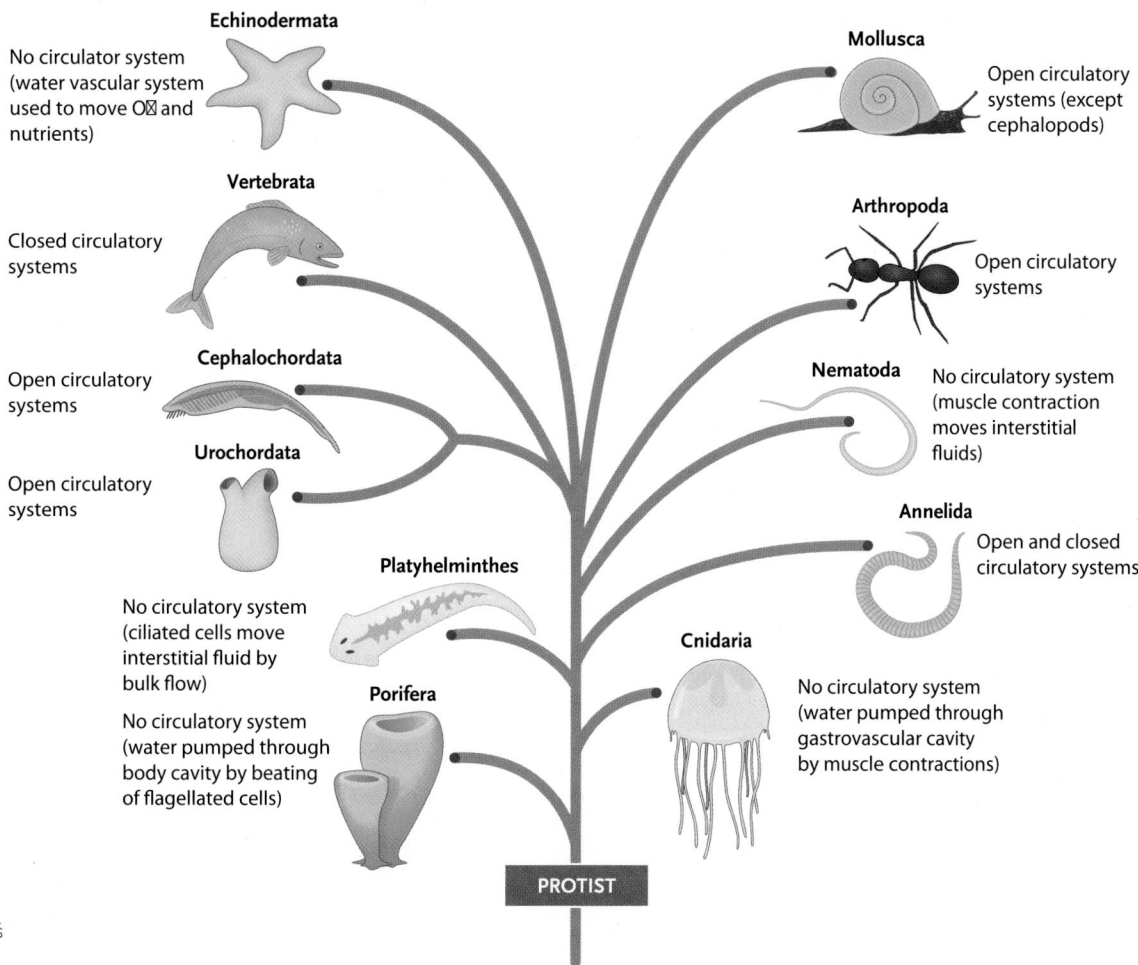

**Echinodermata**
No circulator system (water vascular system used to move O☐ and nutrients)

**Vertebrata**
Closed circulatory systems

**Cephalochordata**
Open circulatory systems

**Urochordata**
Open circulatory systems

**Platyhelminthes**
No circulatory system (ciliated cells move interstitial fluid by bulk flow)

**Porifera**
No circulatory system (water pumped through body cavity by beating of flagellated cells)

**Mollusca**
Open circulatory systems (except cephalopods)

**Arthropoda**
Open circulatory systems

**Nematoda**
No circulatory system (muscle contraction moves interstitial fluids)

**Annelida**
Open and closed circulatory systems

**Cnidaria**
No circulatory system (water pumped through gastrovascular cavity by muscle contractions)

PROTIST

*Biology, 2E*

**FIGURE 24.10 (a)** Open circulatory system: hemolymph bathes the organs and body tissues. **(b)** Closed circulatory system: blood is confined to vessels that pass through the organs and the tissues. **(c)** Evolutionary trends in the distribution of open and closed circulatory systems.

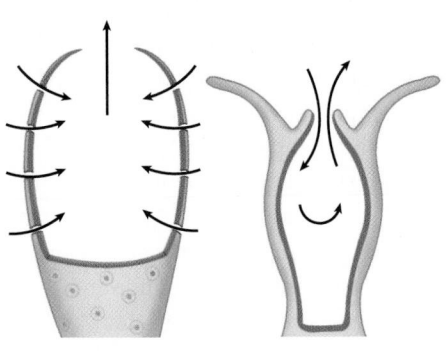

**Sponge**      **Cnidarian**

A. Circulation of external fluid through an open body cavity

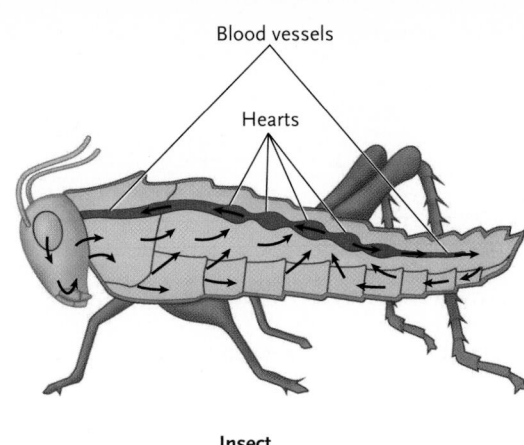

Blood vessels

Hearts

**Insect**

B. Circulation of internal fluid through an open circulatory system

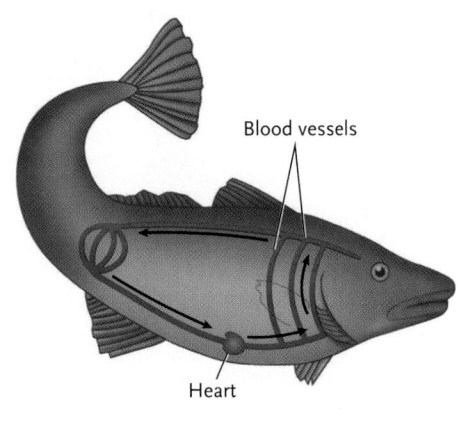

Blood vessels

Heart

**Fish**

C. Circulation of internal fluid through a closed circulatory system

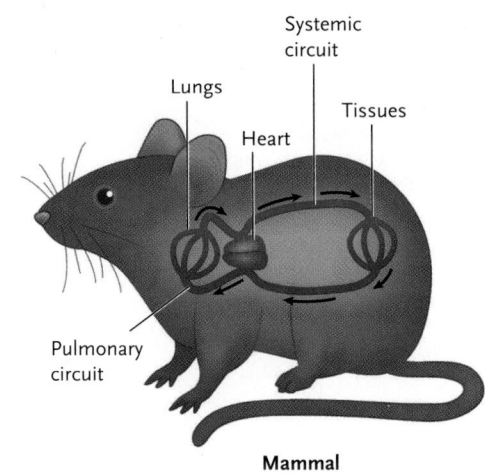

Systemic circuit

Lungs

Tissues

Heart

Pulmonary circuit

**Mammal**

D. Circulation of internal fluid through a closed circulatory system with a double circuit

*Biology, 2E*

**FIGURE 24.11** The general plan of the circulatory system in different animals. **(a)** Multicellular organisms such as sponges and cnidarians use the external medium to transport molecules between cells, often through an open body (gastrovascular) cavity. **(b)** Most invertebrates circulate hemolymph through an open circulatory system. **(c)** Some invertebrates and all vertebrates move blood through a closed circulatory system in which blood is separated from the interstitial fluid. **(d)** In birds and mammals, two separate circuits serve the lungs and all other body tissues.

If we now examine the system in crocodiles, birds, and mammals, what we see is a dual system with what is in essence two pumps and two separate circuits, a pulmonary and a systemic circuit. Here deoxygenated blood returning from the body enters the right atrium through the vena cava (the superior vena cava receives blood from the head and forelimbs, whereas the inferior vena cava receives blood from the trunk and hindlimbs). The right atrium pumps blood into the right ventricle, which pumps it through the pulmonary arteries that deliver blood to the capillary beds in the lungs. Again, one-way valves serve to prevent backflow and ensure efficient movement of blood in one direction. This is the pulmonary circuit. The oxygenated blood returning from the lungs in the pulmonary veins enters the left atrium that pumps blood to the left ventricle, which then pumps the blood through the aorta

into arteries that branch to feed all of the capillary beds throughout the body **(Figures 24.11d** and **24.12c)**. This is the systemic circuit. In humans, the first two of these branches coming off the aorta are the coronary arteries that provide blood to the capillaries of the cardiac muscle of the heart itself. When coronary arteries become blocked, the cardiac muscle cells that rely on it for nutrient and oxygen supply become compromised and that region of the heart begins to fail, leading to a heart attack.

From an evolutionary perspective, we see a transition from the single atrium and ventricle in fish to a system with two atria but only a single ventricle in amphibians **(Figure 24.12b)**, to a system with two atria and a ventricle that is partially divided in two in the non-crocodilian reptiles, and finally to the dual system just described in crocodilians, birds, and mammals. In

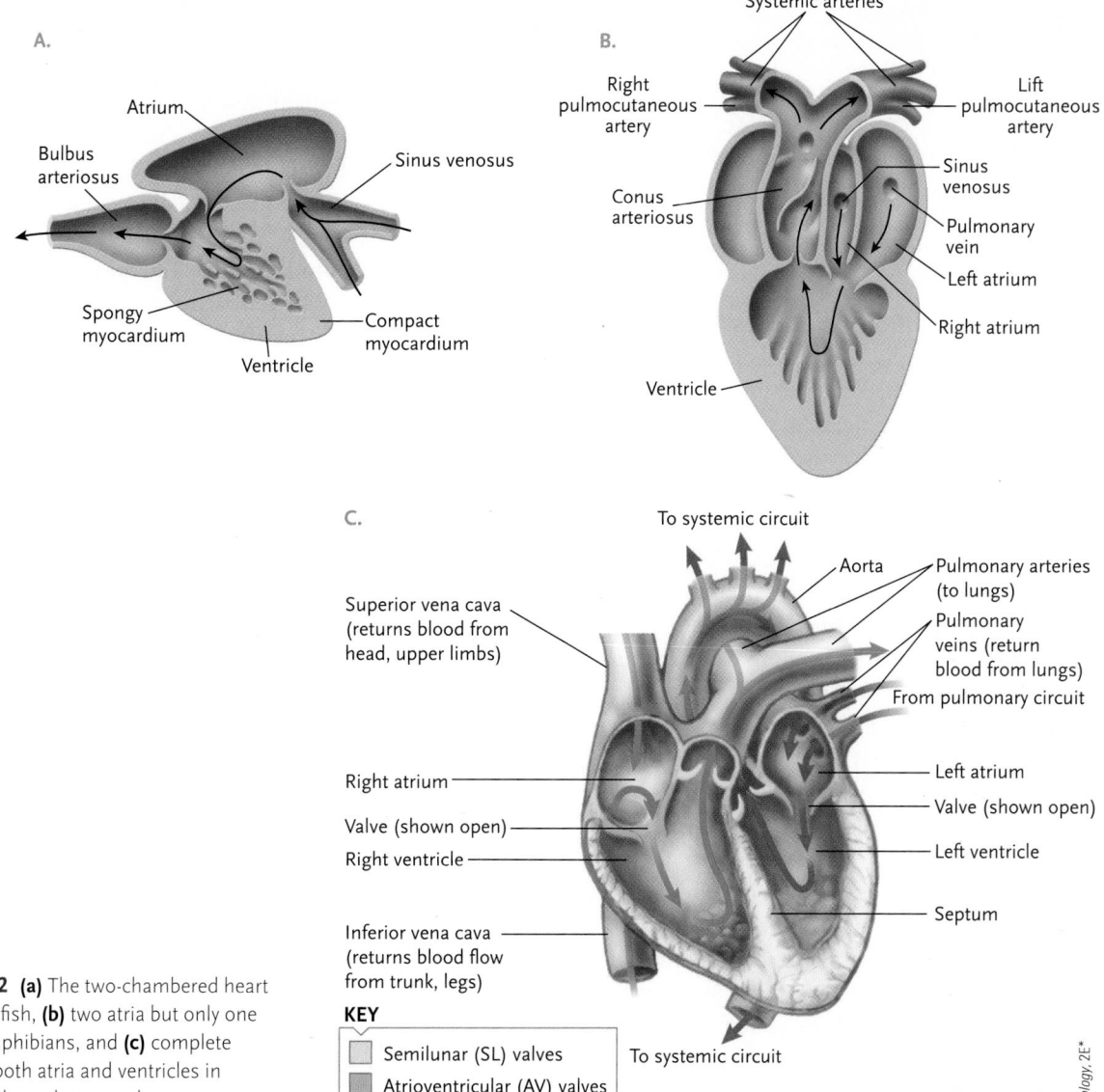

**FIGURE 24.12** **(a)** The two-chambered heart in a shark or a fish, **(b)** two atria but only one ventricle in amphibians, and **(c)** complete separation of both atria and ventricles in crocodiles, birds, and mammals.

A.

Atrium
Bulbus arteriosus
Sinus venosus
Spongy myocardium
Compact myocardium
Ventricle

B.

Systemic arteries
Right pulmocutaneous artery
Lift pulmocutaneous artery
Conus arteriosus
Sinus venosus
Pulmonary vein
Left atrium
Right atrium
Ventricle

C.

To systemic circuit
Superior vena cava (returns blood from head, upper limbs)
Aorta
Pulmonary arteries (to lungs)
Pulmonary veins (return blood from lungs)
From pulmonary circuit
Right atrium
Left atrium
Valve (shown open)
Valve (shown open)
Right ventricle
Left ventricle
Septum
Inferior vena cava (returns blood flow from trunk, legs)
To systemic circuit

**KEY**

|  | Semilunar (SL) valves |
|  | Atrioventricular (AV) valves |

To systemic circuit

*Biology, 2E\**

parallel with this transition is the transition from water breathing to air breathing and to animals with much higher metabolic rates. For animals of equal body weight, birds and mammals have roughly a 10 times higher metabolic rate than fish and amphibians. As a result, they need to deliver more nutrients and $O_2$ to their tissues each minute and to remove more wastes and $CO_2$. They achieve this by having more capillaries through which they push blood at higher flow rates. This requires far more pressure, and through this transition, we see blood returning to the heart after being pushed through the pulmonary capillaries to be pumped back up to high pressures before being distributed to the capillary beds in the rest of the body. In the dual circuit, most blood passes through only one capillary bed before returning to the heart. Interestingly, a dual circuit has evolved independently in the lines leading to mammals and to crocodilians and birds (which are closely related), another example of convergent evolution.

Thus, the number of chambers in the heart and the arrangement of the major blood vessels leaving the heart reflect evolutionary changes primarily associated with the transition from fish with low metabolic rates living in water and breathing through gills to endothermic birds and mammals with high metabolic rates living on land and breathing with lungs.

## STUDY BREAK

1. What is plasma, and what are the roles of the ions and proteins found in it?
2. What types of cells are found in the plasma of vertebrates?
3. What is the difference between an open and a closed circulatory system?
4. What evolutionary trends do we see in vertebrate hearts, and what evolutionary forces may have produced these changes?

## The Source and Nature of the Rhythmic Heartbeat

As mentioned earlier, many invertebrates, such as crustaceans, such as crabs and lobsters, have a neurogenic heart. Their hearts are controlled by their nervous system. Each contraction is initiated by a signal, usually from a neural ganglion that sits on the heart and receives input from the central nervous system and from hormones of the endocrine system.

The hearts of all vertebrates, as well as those of insects, are myogenic. Every cell of their hearts is capable of initiating a cardiac contraction; that is, all cells have the ability to pace the heart; they have **pacemaker** properties. Recall that cardiac muscle cells, like all muscle cells, are excitable; they are capable of generating action potentials if their membranes depolarize and reach threshold (see Chapters 22 and 26). Cardiac myocytes (single cardiac muscle cells) have leaky membranes that slowly allow ions to cross, leading to a cycle of depolarization, generation of an action potential, and repolarization. The rate at which the membranes leak determines the period between each action potential and hence each heartbeat. Nerves, hormones, and drugs all act on ion channels in cardiac myocytes to alter the rate at which ions leak across the membrane and hence modulate the rhythm of the heart.

Although all cardiac myocytes are capable of initiating contraction, their activities are coordinated by the region of the heart with the fastest intrinsic rhythm. Since cardiac myocytes are connected by gap junctions, once one myocyte becomes excited, it excites its neighbour, and the excitation passes as a wave throughout the heart. As the cells repolarize, the first cell to reach threshold again will initiate the next wave of excitation. In fish, the region with the fastest intrinsic rhythm is the **sinus venosus**, and hence the wave of contraction spreads from the sinus venosus to the atrium and finally to the ventricle. In mammals, the region with the fastest rhythm is the **sinoatrial (SA) node**—a small node of specialized cardiac myocytes that is evolutionarily derived from the sinus venosus and that sits where the systemic veins enter the right atrium. In many humans suffering cardiac arrhythmias, small, electronic, artificial pacemakers are implanted under the skin of the chest with electrodes that impart a steady rhythm to this region of the heart.

## The Cardiac Cycle

Before each heartbeat, while the heart is relaxed, the atria passively fill with blood returning from the veins (1 in **Figure 24.13**). This phase of the cardiac cycle is referred to as **diastole**. As blood fills the atria, it pushes the atrioventricular valves between the atrium, and the ventricles open and begin to fill the ventricles. The valves between the ventricles and their major arteries (the semilunar valves) remain closed.

When cells in the SA node become excited, a wave of excitation begins that spreads over both atria (2 in Figure 24.13). This pushes the blood that has filled the atria into the ventricles, completely filling them (3 in Figure 24.13).

Note from Figure 24.12c that the major blood vessels leaving the ventricles of a bird or mammal are at the top of the heart, very close to where the atria open into the ventricles. If the wave of contraction were to spread directly from the atria to the ventricles, it would produce a wave of excitation and contraction that would push blood toward the blind-ending tips of the ventricles—very much like squeezing a tube of toothpaste from the top. Instead, there is a band of fatty connective tissue that separates the atria from the ventricles and acts as a layer of electrical insulation, preventing action potentials from spreading directly onto the ventricles (4 in Figure 24.13). A second specialized node of muscle cells that behave more like neurons in the nervous system than like muscle cells have their cell bodies in this node located between the right atrium and the right ventricle. This is the **atrioventricular (AV) node**. These cells give rise to the Purkinje fibres, which transmit the action potentials to the tips of the ventricles (5 in Figure 24.13), where they initiate a wave of contraction that now spreads upwards from cell to cell (6 in Figure 24.13). This wave of contraction is very efficient and generates high pressures, forcing the semilunar valves to open and pushing the blood into the pulmonary arteries and the aorta (7 in Figure 24.13). This pressure also closes the atrioventricular valves to prevent backflow of blood into the atria. This phase of the cardiac cycle is referred to as **systole**.

At the end of the ventricular contraction, as the ventricle relaxes, the pressure in the aorta and pulmonary artery is at its highest (the **systolic pressure**) and pushes the semilunar valves closed and prevents blood from flowing back into the ventricles. At this point, both the atria and ventricles are relaxed in diastole. The pressure in the arteries slowly begins to fall as the blood flows out into the system. It will fall to its lowest (the **diastolic pressure**) just as the ventricles contract again, pushing the next wave of blood out and increasing the pressure in the arterial system back to systolic levels. Thus, the systolic and diastolic pressures are the highest and lowest pressures measured in the arteries with each heartbeat and are the two pressures that physicians measure when taking someone's blood pressure.

Just as electricity is readily conducted through water, the wave of electrical excitation passing over the heart is

## A. Pressure changes

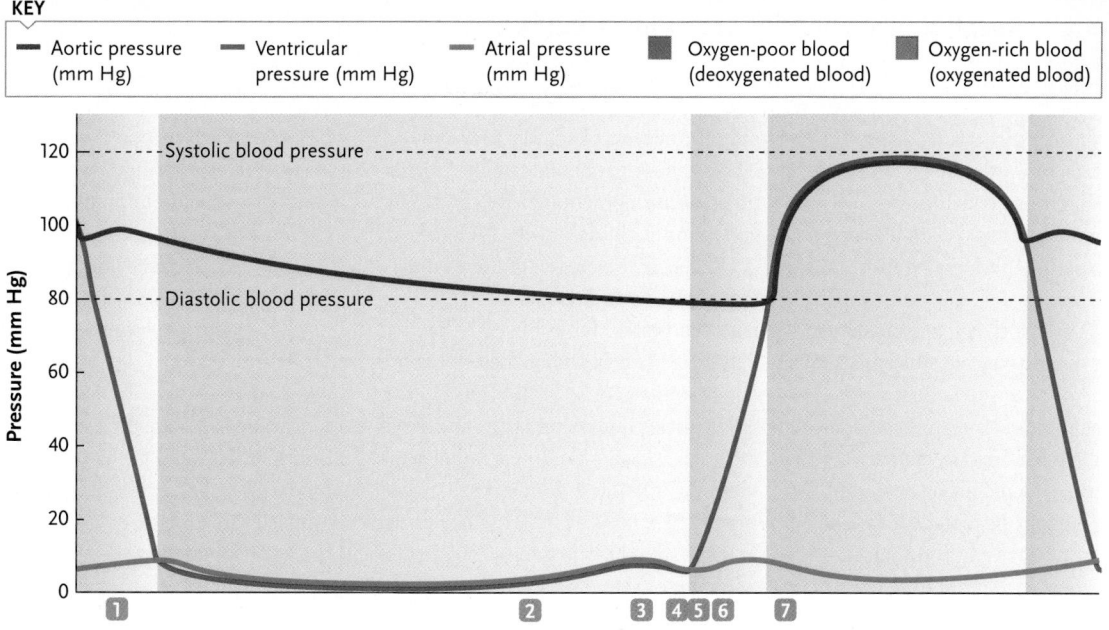

**KEY**

— Aortic pressure (mm Hg)  — Ventricular pressure (mm Hg)  — Atrial pressure (mm Hg)  ■ Oxygen-poor blood (deoxygenated blood)  ■ Oxygen-rich blood (oxygenated blood)

Pressure (mm Hg)

120 — - - - Systolic blood pressure - - - - - - - - - - - - - - - - - - - - -
100
80 — - - - Diastolic blood pressure - - - - - - - - - - - - - - - - - - - - -
60
40
20

1  2  3 4 5 6  7

## B. Muscular events

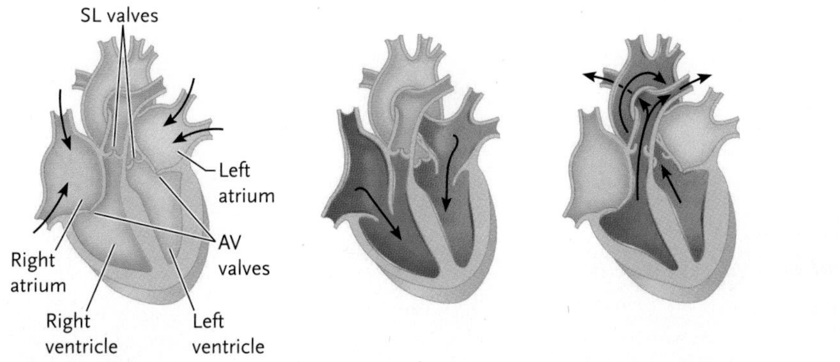

SL valves
Left atrium
Right atrium
AV valves
Right ventricle
Left ventricle

**1** Heart is fully relaxed; begin to fill with blood; AV and SL valves are closed.

**3** Atria contract, filling ventricles completely.

**7** Ventricles contract fully, forcing SL valves open and ejecting blood into arteries.

## C. Electrical events

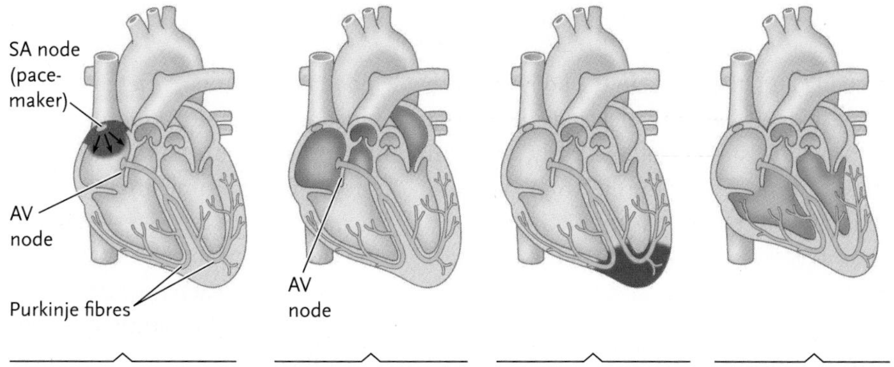

SA node (pace-maker)
AV node
Purkinje fibres

AV node

**2** Pacemaker generates a wave of signals to contract.

**4** Signals are delayed in the region between the atria and ventricles.

**5** AV node cells are stimulated to produce a signal, which travels along Purkinje fibres to the bottom of the heart.

**6** Signals spread from the bottom of the heart upward, causing the ventricles to contract.

*Biology, 2E\**

**FIGURE 24.13** The changes in pressure, muscular contraction, and electrical activity associated with the different phases of the cardiac cycle.

## LIFE ON THE EDGE 24.2
## Small Animals with Large Heart Rates

We began this chapter talking about the tallest animals on earth, the giraffes. To end the chapter, let's consider the smallest endothermic or warm-blooded animals on earth. Although the total metabolic rate, or rate of oxygen consumption of these animals, may appear small in absolute terms (they are small animals), when one considers how much oxygen is being consumed by each gram of tissue (the mass-specific metabolic rate), the rate is incredibly high. In general, the mass-specific metabolic rate of endotherms increases as body mass decreases; thus, each gram of a shrew or a hummingbird consumes roughly 50 times as much oxygen per minute as each gram of you or me **(Figure 1)**. When most birds and mammals go from rest to maximum levels of activity, they can increase their metabolic rate by 7 to 10 times. Amazingly enough, so can shrews and hummingbirds!

To deliver the oxygen to the tissues, these animals must sustain incredibly high heart rates. **Table 1** lists the resting heart rates of a variety of species of birds and mammals.

The heart rate of the Etruscan shrew, the smallest mammal (mean adult body mass 2 grams), is around 800 beats per minute. The maximal heart rate recorded in these animals is just over 1500 beats per minute. The maximal heart rates recorded in hummingbirds are also in the range of 1200 beats per minute. This means that the hearts of these animals must contract and relax again 20 to 25 times each second. These are not the fastest rates of contraction recorded in animals. The sound-producing muscles in the larynx of bats can contract 200 times a second, whereas those associated with sound production in the oyster toadfish, *Opsanus tau*, can contract and relax at a rate of 300 times each second.

There is a trade-off in the design of muscles between the features that make muscles strong and those that enable muscles to contract quickly. The high rates of contraction seen in bats and toadfish are associated with moving air. What makes the rate of contraction of the hearts of shrews and hummingbirds so impressive is that they are associated with moving blood, a denser and more

**FIGURE 1** **(a)** The Etruscan shrew, *Suncus etruscus*. **(b)** A ruby-throated hummingbird, *Archilochus colubris*.

readily conducted through the fluids in the body cavity to the surface of the body. By placing electrodes to detect electrical current on the surface of the body, one can readily record these events. This is the **electrocardiogram** or ECG (sometimes referred to as an EKG, after the German *Electrokardiogramm*). The shape of the electrical signal that is recorded is a function of the number of electrodes used to record the signal and their location on the body. Physicians can use these recordings to detect abnormalities in the conduction of the wave of excitation during the cardiac cycle. The ECG can also tell them whether all of the muscle cells in the heart wall are behaving properly.

The two ventricles each pump the same volume of blood with each heartbeat. However, they do not generate the same pressures. The right ventricle only pumps blood to the lungs, whereas the left ventricle must pump blood throughout the entire body. As a result, the left ventricle is more muscular and generates greater pressures. The volume that is pumped by each ventricle during each beat is referred to as the **stroke volume**, and the cardiac output, the total amount of blood pumped by each ventricle each minute, is equal to the stroke volume multiplied by the number of times the heart beats each minute.

The heart rate of any animal varies with its metabolic rate (Box 24.2). For animals at rest, the metabolic rate varies with body size; thus, so too does heart rate. As a result, heart rates are much higher in small birds and mammals than they are in larger ones, reflecting differences in the mass-specific metabolic rate. As the metabolic rate rises above resting levels, so too will the

| TABLE 1 | Resting Heart Rates and Life Spans for a Variety of Birds and Mammals | | |
|---|---|---|---|
| | Mass (grams) | Heart Rate (beats/minute) | Life Spans (years) |
| **Birds** | | | |
| Ruby-throated hummingbird | 3 | 250 | 9 |
| Canary | 20 | 1000 | 24 |
| Pigeon | 300 | 185 | 10 |
| Crow | 341 | 378 | 17 |
| Buzzard | 658 | 300 | 17 |
| Wild duck | 1100 | 190 | 15 |
| Hen | 2000 | 312 | 8 |
| Domestic duck | 2300 | 240 | 20 |
| Turkey | 8750 | 193 | 12 |
| **Mammals** | | | |
| Etruscan shrew | 2 | 800 | 2 |
| Mouse | 25 | 670 | 4 |
| Rat | 200 | 420 | 7 |
| Guinea pig | 300 | 300 | 15 |
| Rabbit | 2000 | 205 | 10 |
| Small dog | 5000 | 120 | 29 |
| Large dog | 30,000 | 85 | 15 |
| Human | 70,000 | 72 | 122 |
| Horse | 450,000 | 38 | 62 |

viscous fluid. (The fastest muscles in humans are those associated with the eye blink [two to three times per second]). The design of muscles for increased speed requires changes at every step in the contraction pathway (see Chapter 22). Key among these features are the release and uptake rate of $Ca^{2+}$ from the sarcoplasmic reticulum and the rate of myosin–ATPase activity.

It has long been known that larger animals not only have lower mass-specific metabolic rates and heart rates, but they also live longer. Along similar lines, fit humans have lower resting heart rates and also live longer. This has given rise to the "rate of living hypothesis" or the "finite heartbeat hypothesis," a hypothesis that states that all endotherms have a limited number of heartbeats (or breaths for that matter) in their lifetime. Although there is no denying that a strong inverse correlation exists between longevity and resting rates of the mass-specific metabolic rate and the rates of the convective processes required to deliver oxygen to tissues (breathing and heartbeat), this hypothesis failed to consider the fact that animals do not spend all of their time at rest. Thus, although a rough correlation exists, the hypothesis fails in many instances, demonstrating the weakness of basing scientific hypothesis on correlation rather than causation.

heart rate and cardiac output to deliver the increasing levels of oxygen and nutrients required to sustain the elevated metabolism. Most birds and mammals can increase the metabolic rate roughly 10 times from rest to maximum activity. Some species, such as hummingbirds, can increase their metabolism an amazing 20 times, whereas the fittest of we humans can only increase cardiac output in the neighbourhood of seven times. Animals also possess the ability to reduce heart rate and cardiac output, and classic examples of this are the slowing of heart rate associated with breath-hold diving and hibernation, both cases where heart rate may slow to less than five beats per minute. These changes result from the modulation of the activity of the SA node by sympathetic (speeds up) or parasympathetic (slows down) nerves or by hormones.

## STUDY BREAK

1. Which animals have a heart with a pacemaker, and which do not? In animals with a pacemaker, where in the heart is it located?
2. What is systole, and what is diastole? What are systolic and diastolic pressures? Why do physicians monitor these?

## The Variety of Form and Function Seen in Blood Vessels

In the mammalian heart, blood leaves each ventricle through one large blood vessel: either the **aorta** or the **pulmonary artery**. These vessels branch repeatedly into smaller arteries, carrying blood to all the tissues of the

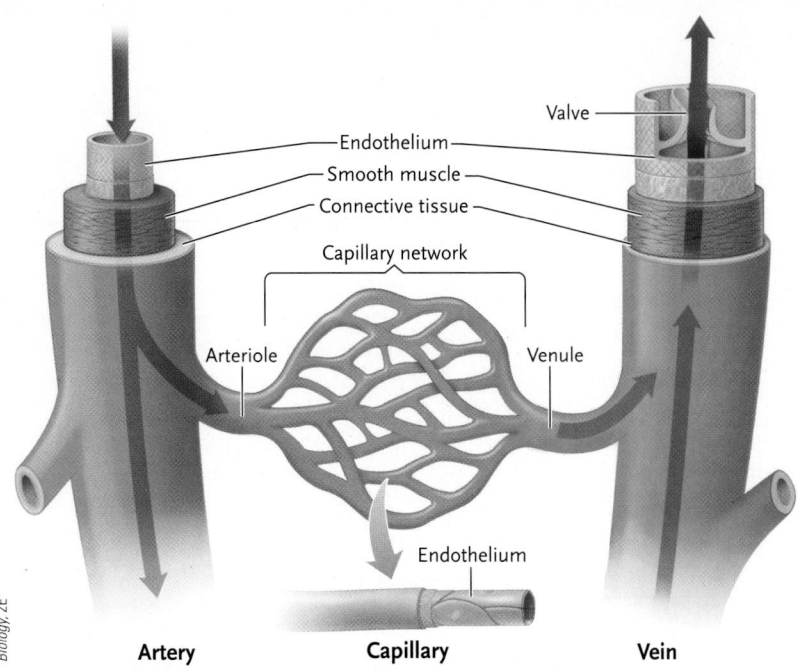

Artery     Capillary     Vein

**FIGURE 24.14** The structure of arteries, capillaries, and veins and their relationship to blood circuits.

*Biology, 2E\**

body. Once they reach a tissue bed, the arteries divide into even smaller arterioles that penetrate the tissue beds, ultimately dividing into capillaries, the smallest of the blood vessels in the circuit **(Figure 24.14)**. These are the sites where substances are exchanged between the blood and the tissues. The capillaries then join to form venules, which join to form small veins. These small veins arising from the different tissues join to form larger veins, which ultimately unite to form the **vena cava** and large pulmonary arteries that enter the atria of the heart.

### Arteries

Arteries are composed of a thin inner endothelial layer of flattened cells surrounded by a thick layer of smooth muscle and an outer elastic layer of connective tissue. The elastic layer allows the arteries to expand and recoil. Each time the heart beats, blood is forced out faster than it can flow into the peripheral blood vessels. As a result, the arteries expand to hold this extra blood, and the pressure of the blood in the arteries rises to its peak. This is the systolic pressure. When the ventricles relax and the semilunar valves close, the walls of the arteries recoil, continuing to push blood into the arterioles. The pressure in the arteries falls continuously to diastolic levels. The result of this expansion and recoil is that blood flows continuously through the blood vessels even though the heart only ejects blood during systole and not during diastole.

In any animal, the normal systolic pressure reflects the pressure required to push blood through all the vessels and back to the heart. The greater the number of vessels and the smaller they are, the higher the pressure

required. In healthy young mice, rats, elephant seals, and humans (i.e., most mammals), this systolic pressure is roughly 120 mm Hg. In most birds, it is slightly higher (around 150 mm Hg), whereas in the giraffe, it would be closer to 250 mm Hg. The diastolic pressure is the lowest the pressure falls to in the system; the vessel walls never relax below this pressure. In most mammals, this is roughly 80 mm Hg.

As the arteries divide into smaller and smaller arterioles, the layers of connective tissue and smooth muscle become thinner.

### Capillaries

By the time the vessels branch into capillaries, all connective tissue and smooth muscle are gone, and the vessel walls consist of only the one cell thick flattened layer of endothelial cells and a basement membrane (Figure 24.14). These vessels, although small, are extensive, penetrating every tissue of the body and bringing blood to within a thousandth of a millimetre of each tissue cell. Because of the large number of capillaries arising from each arteriole, these beds provide an extensive, thin surface for the exchange of gases, nutrients, and wastes with the interstitial fluid. Interstitial fluid (*inter* = between; *stitial* = that which stands) is the fluid that surrounds and bathes the cells. A second feature of the anatomy of capillaries also enhances exchange. Throughout the circulatory system, each time a blood vessel splits in two, the combined cross-sectional area of the two new branches is greater than that of the single vessel from which they arose. As a result, as the system progresses from the large arteries to the very small capillaries, the combined cross-sectional area of the system increases more than a thousand times. Just like the water in a river emerging from a narrow canyon into a wide delta, the blood slows dramatically as it enters the capillary beds. The combination of slow flow through vessels with an enormous surface area maximizes the exchange of substances across the capillary walls.

The exchange of substance between the blood in the capillaries and the interstitial fluid that surrounds them occurs by several processes. The endothelial cells of the capillary wall are loosely connected, and water, gases, ions, and small molecules can squeeze between them. Larger molecules are transported across the endothelial cells, either by transport proteins or by a combination of endocytosis, taking up substances from the blood, and exocytosis, to release them into the interstitial fluid. The red blood cells, platelets, and most proteins in the plasma are too large and remain in the plasma, flowing through the capillaries.

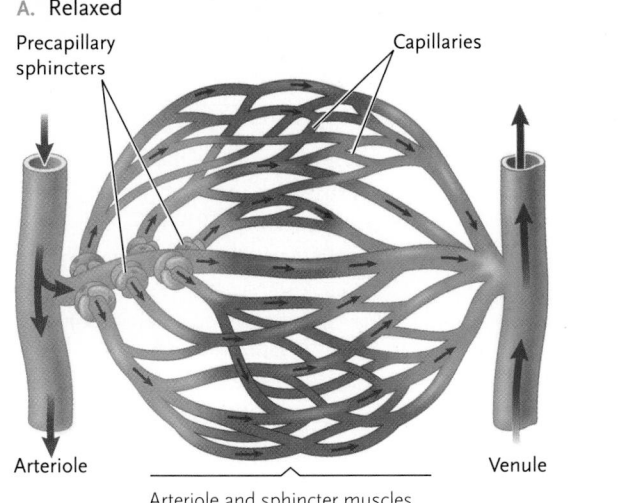
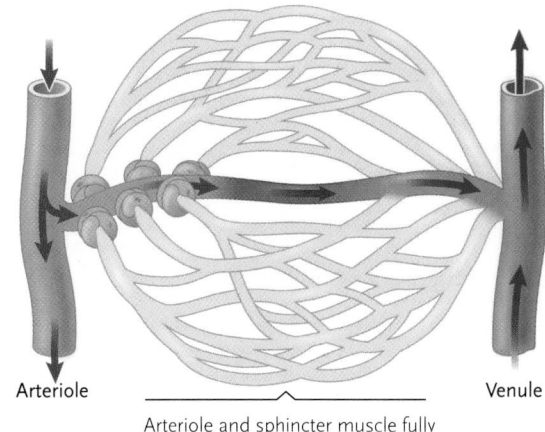

**FIGURE 24.15** Control of blood flow through capillary networks. **(a)** Maximal blood flow when arteriole and sphincter muscles are fully relaxed. **(b)** Minimal blood flow when the arteriole and sphincter muscles are fully contracted.

The junctions between the endothelial cells of the capillary wall vary in different tissues. For instance, in the small intestine, the spaces between endothelial cells are larger, allowing nutrients to pass into the bloodstream. This is also the case in bone marrow, allowing newly synthesized red blood cells to enter the bloodstream. In the brain, on the other hand, the endothelial cells are so tightly connected that only gases, as well as ions and molecules that are specifically transported across the endothelium, can enter.

The amount of blood being delivered to any capillary bed varies as a function of the metabolic demands of the tissue bed, and this changes over time. The flow to each capillary bed is controlled by smooth muscle sphincters (precapillary sphincters) on the arterioles feeding into them. Increasing tone in the sphincter muscles constricts the arterioles and reduces the flow to the capillary bed, whereas relaxing the tone in the sphincter muscles dilates the arterioles and increases blood flow **(Figure 24.15)**. The tone of the sphincter muscles is regulated by the levels of oxygen, carbon dioxide, and various ions in the interstitial fluid, which change with the metabolic activity of the tissues surrounding them. Thus, for instance, if the metabolic rate of a group of cells increases, the oxygen consumption of the tissues will increase, reducing the oxygen levels in the interstitial fluid that surrounds them. This fall in oxygen will cause the sphincter muscle to relax, increasing blood flow to the capillary bed and restoring oxygen to normal levels. A second example where the opening and closing of capillary beds plays an important role is in thermoregulation (described in Chapter 20). When birds and mammals need to cool and lose heat, they can increase blood flow to capillary beds at the body's surface (often at specialized sites designed for this, such as the feet and bills in birds, where the skin is not covered in insulating feathers) or reduce blood flow when they need to conserve

heat. This is why we appear red and flushed on a hot day and pale on a cold day. As another example, if capillaries are damaged due to trauma, the damaged cells release the chemical histamine, which also acts to relax precapillary sphincters to increase blood flow and deliver white blood cells to the area to combat any infection that may result as well as nutrients to aid in the repair process. This gives rise to the redness, warmth, and swelling associated with tissue damage, all results of the increased blood flow.

An important point to remember is that each capillary bed adjusts its own blood flow to meet its own needs. How the body knows what the needs of each bed are and adjusts the total blood flow coming out of the heart will be discussed in the next section.

### Veins

As the capillaries merge together to form venules and the venules merge to form veins, the total cross-sectional area of the system decreases again and the velocity of the blood increases. The pressure in the blood by this point is quite low since the pressure is dissipated in overcoming the resistance to blood flow in the small capillaries. As a result, the walls of the veins are thin compared to those of the arteries, with little connective tissue and less smooth muscle (Figure 24.14). One result of this is that the veins are very extensible and can expand without developing much recoil force. This allows them to act as blood reservoirs; thus, in many animals at rest, from 60% to 80% of the blood may reside in the veins. This would be at a time when the metabolic rate was low and most capillary beds would be shut down. As metabolic demands increase, such as during exercise, and capillary beds open up, the blood required to fill these beds would be recruited from the venous reservoir.

Because the pressure in the venous system is very low, several mechanisms have evolved to assist in the

## Cholesterol

One of the greatest health risks facing North Americans is atherosclerosis, hardening or narrowing of the arteries. This is particularly damaging when the arteries involved are the coronary arteries supplying the heart itself. High levels of fats, especially cholesterol, in the blood circulation are strongly associated with this disease. So how do we reconcile this with the fact that cholesterol is such an important molecule for normal physiological function? It is an essential structural component of animal cell membranes. The model of the cell membrane is the fluid mosaic model, and part of what makes the membrane fluid is the presence of cholesterol. Cholesterol also plays key roles in intracellular transport, cell signalling, and nerve conduction and as a precursor for the biosynthesis of steroid hormones **(Figure 1)**.

Cholesterol is a component of bile salts, which solubilize fats in the digestive tract and aid in the intestinal absorption of fat molecules and the fat-soluble vitamins, A, D, E, and K. The levels of cholesterol in our blood are a balance between cholesterol taken in in our diet and cholesterol produced by our bodies. The absolute levels present and circulating in the blood are normally controlled homeostatically. If the levels in our diets are high, then our bodies make less; if the levels in our diet are low, then our bodies synthesize more. It is such an important molecule that roughly 50% of the cholesterol excreted into the small intestine is reabsorbed back into the bloodstream.

How can a molecule that is so essential for life be so bad? The answer is still not clear but appears to involve the manner in which cholesterol is transported within the blood. Cholesterol is not very water soluble. As a result, it is transported in the blood within lipoproteins, a complex of lipids and proteins whose outward-facing surfaces are water soluble and whose inward-facing surfaces are lipid soluble. The amount of protein in the complex can vary, and, as a result, so too will the density of the complex; the more protein and less lipid in a lipoprotein, the denser it is. The lipoproteins with the least amount of protein are the very-low-density lipoproteins followed by the intermediate-density lipoproteins (IDL), the low-density lipoproteins (LDL), and the high-density lipoproteins (HDL), in order of increasing density. Of significance is that each of these groups of lipoproteins contains different signalling molecules, which determine which cells in the body they will interact with.

LDL particles are the major carriers of cholesterol in the blood. Any cell with the proper receptor will bind with and take up the LDL particle by endocytosis, where the cholesterol can be used for membrane biosynthesis or stored for future use. HDL particles are thought to transport cholesterol back to the liver for excretion or to other tissues for hormone synthesis. Correlation studies have shown that high levels of LDL particles and low levels of HDL particles tend to be associated with atherosclerosis, heart attacks, and stroke. As a result, LDL particles have been termed "bad cholesterol," delivering cholesterol to the cells of the arterial walls and leading to plaque formation, and HDL particles have been termed "good cholesterol" and are believed to remove cholesterol from areas of excess and deliver them to the liver for excretion. It appears to be the levels of these fractions, and their ratio relative to one another, that correlate to the presence of atherosclerosis rather than the total cholesterol level. This balance is largely genetically determined but can be modified by diet, fitness levels, and medications.

This continues to be an area of intensive research but is another example of where both too much or too little of an essential molecule is not a good thing.

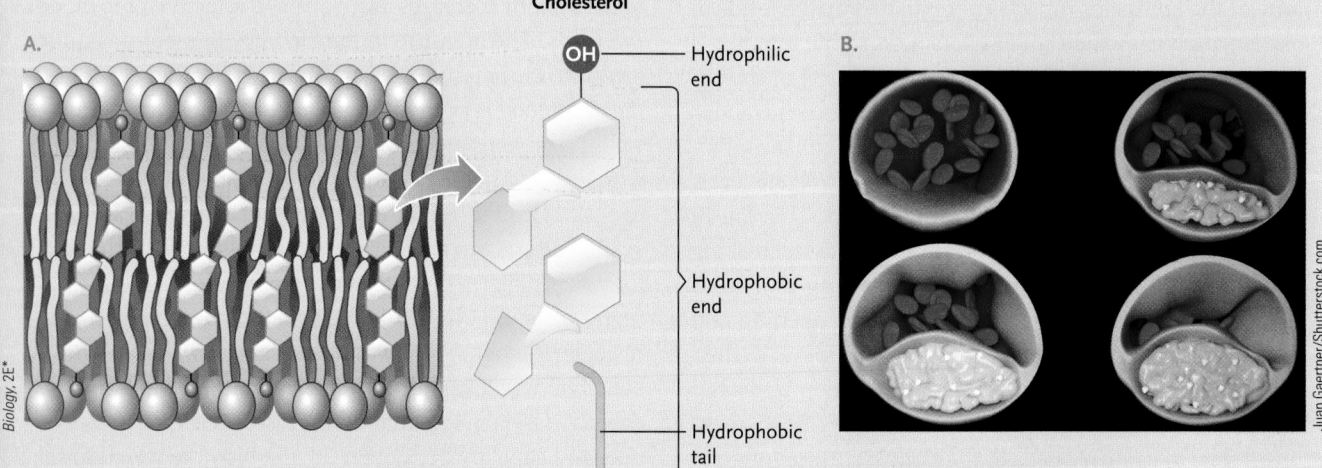

Cholesterol

A.

*Biology, 2E\**

Hydrophilic end

Hydrophobic end

Hydrophobic tail

B.

Juan Gaertner/Shutterstock.com

**FIGURE 1** **(a)** Cholesterol is an important component of the plasma membrane of all animal cells. Cholesterol acts to stabilize membranes if temperatures rise and to maintain fluidity in membranes as temperatures fall. **(b)** Excess levels, however, lead to deposition in arterial walls, forming plaques that restrict blood flow.

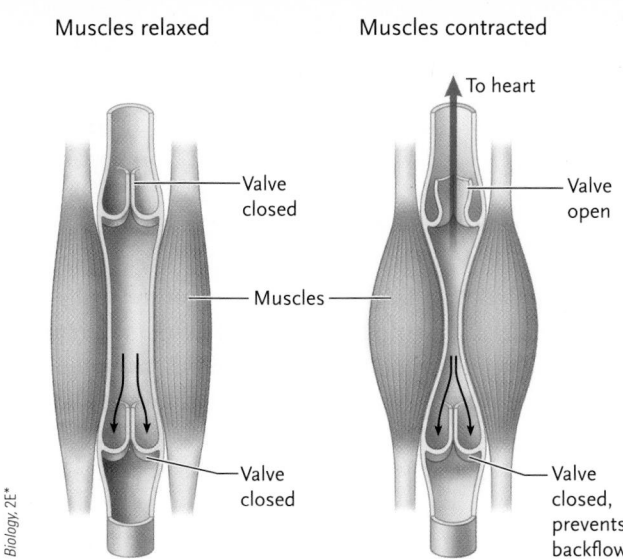

Muscles relaxed | Muscles contracted

To heart

Valve closed

Valve open

Muscles

Valve closed

Valve closed, prevents backflow

Biology, 2E*

**FIGURE 24.16** How skeletal muscle contraction and the valves inside veins help move blood toward the heart.

movement of blood back to the heart. The veins running through large skeletal muscles, such as those in the limbs, will be compressed when the muscles surrounding them contract. Most of these veins contain flap valves on their inner walls that prevent blood from flowing backwards. As a result, every time the muscles contract, blood is pushed toward the heart, and the backward flow of blood is prevented when the muscles relax **(Figure 24.16)**. Expansion and relaxation of the lungs will also have the same effect on the large veins running through the body cavity.

## Blood Flow to Tissues Is Regulated to Match Supply and Demand

We read extensively about the need to control our blood pressure and the negative consequences of a blood pressure that is too high or too low. If blood pressure falls too low, not enough blood flows to the tissues to meet their metabolic demands. This can lead to tissue damage or even the death of cells. If blood pressure rises too high, we run the risk of overworking the heart and of producing ruptured blood vessels (aneurysms), either of which can be deadly (Box 24.3).

There is another key reason for maintaining a constant and proper blood pressure, however. By doing so, the body can ensure that the flow of blood to each capillary bed is adequate to meet the metabolic demands of every cell in the body. This is the answer to the question posed in the previous section. The two main regulators of blood pressure are the **cardiac output** (the total amount of blood pumped by each ventricle per minute) and the degree of constriction of the blood vessels. The total blood vessel resistance is largely controlled by the changes in the tone of the precapillary sphincters.

Put simply: Arterial Blood Pressure = Cardiac Output × Total Blood Vessel Resistance.

This means that if the total blood vessel resistance decreases because several capillary beds open up due to

dilation of the precapillary sphincters, such as might occur at the onset of exercise, the total blood vessel resistance will fall. To keep blood pressure constant, cardiac output must increase. The increase in cardiac output required to hold the blood pressure constant will equal the amount of blood flow required to perfuse the freshly opened capillary beds. The elegance of this control scheme is that every capillary bed acts in an independent manner to control its own blood flow, and the body, simply by keeping blood pressure constant, alters cardiac output so that the total blood flow produced by the heart is exactly what is needed to satisfy the flows required by each capillary bed.

To achieve this, however, blood pressure must be monitored, and when changes are sensed, appropriate changes must be made to cardiac output, primarily by altering heart rate, to return blood pressure to its normal level. Monitoring of blood pressure is achieved by pressure sensors, called **baroreceptors**, in the walls of the heart and of key blood vessels, notably the aorta and the carotid arteries delivering blood to the brain. These receptors sense the stretch of the vessel walls and send information to the medulla in the brain stem, which in turn sends signals to the SA node (in mammals) and muscles of the arterial walls. Activation of the parasympathetic nervous system slows the heart rate and reduces the force of heart contraction when blood pressure is too high, whereas activation of the sympathetic nervous system increases the heart rate and the force of heart contraction when blood pressure is too low.

Several different hormones also regulate heart rate and blood vessel tone. The effects of histamine have already been mentioned, and both **epinephrine** and **norepinephrine** are two other hormones secreted by the adrenal glands that have significant effects on both heart rate and vascular tone. As part of the fight or flight response, epinephrine is released and acts on the heart to increase the heart rate and the strength of cardiac contraction, increasing the stroke volume. Both of these effects lead to a dramatic increase in cardiac output, an increase that is needed to increase blood flow to the skeletal muscles, heart, and lungs, tissue beds where epinephrine causes dilation of the arterioles in anticipation of increased activity. Epinephrine also causes constriction of the arterioles in the gut and kidneys, tissue beds that do not require increased blood flow at that time.

## STUDY BREAK

1. Describe the difference we see in the form and function of arteries and veins.
2. What is the role of the capillaries? Why are they so important?
3. Why is it so important to maintain blood pressure at the proper level?

## PUTTING IT IN PERSPECTIVE

Our societies depend on rapid and efficient transportation systems for moving people and products around. Following any major natural or human-made catastrophe, such as floods, tsunamis, earthquakes, droughts, and wars, the single largest problem is transportation. The need either to deliver water, food, and shelter to affected people or to transport people to locations where their basic needs can be met is crucial.

The bodies of plants and animals also depend on rapid and efficient internal transportation systems. The evolution of multicellular organisms allowed for the development of tissues, organs, and organ systems, as described in Chapter 20. These allow for a division of labour; they allow cells to differentiate and take on specialized roles. The ensuing increase in performance, however, depends on the ability of the organism to transport needed supplies to each organ and to deliver their specialized products to the cells that need them.

Death is defined as the cessation of the biological functions that sustain a living organism. The most common cause of human deaths worldwide is heart disease. When the transportation system fails, everything fails. Failure may take place in the form of constricted arteries (atherosclerosis), constricted coronary arteries restricting oxygen delivery to heart cells (myocardial infarct), or constricted or ruptured arteries restricting oxygen delivery to the brain (stroke).

Similarly, girdling, or ring barking of trees (the complete removal of a strip of bark around the entire circumference of a tree), disrupts the phloem and will lead to the death of the tree above the damage. This can be caused by herbivorous mammals (such as rabbits) feeding on bark during the winter. It can also be caused by boring insects as well as by birds, such as woodpeckers, boring into the trees to feed on the insects. If the holes are close enough together, they will effectively also girdle the tree.

Plants and animals have solved the problem of creating an efficient transport system in very different ways, primarily reflecting differences in lifestyle: organisms that are rooted to the soil versus those that are free to move about. Each system is well suited to the needs of each group.

## KEY CONCEPTS REVIEW AND QUESTIONS

### 24.1 Transport Systems

In single-celled organisms, all exchange with the environment takes place across the cell membrane. Multicellular organisms have evolved specialized organs and organ systems for gas exchange, nutrient uptake, and waste elimination. Although the ways in which plants and animals have solved the problem of internal transport are very different, the fundamental components of each transport system are the same; there are vessels through which fluids and dissolved substances are moved, a means of generating the pressures required to move them, and ways in which to ensure that all cells are able to match the supply and demand for various substances.

1. Internal transport systems are required for which of the following?
   a. The movement of water in plants
   b. The movement of $CO_2$ in plants
   c. The exchange of nutrients by single-celled organisms
   d. The elimination of wastes by plants
   e. The distribution of hormones in both plants and animals
2. The fundamental components of all transport systems (plant and animal) include which of the following?
   a. Vessels through which fluids flow
   b. A muscular pump
   c. Vascular fluids
   d. A means of generating pressure
   e. A means to match supply and demand for different substances by different tissues

### 24.2 Transport in Plants

In plants, water, organic ions, and minerals are taken up by the roots, while $CO_2$ is converted to sugar in the leaves by photosynthesis. Plants move water, dissolved minerals and ions, and sugars from areas of uptake and storage to sites where they are needed in the vascular tissue, the xylem and phloem. There are two principal forces causing water to move: osmosis and pressure. In the roots, water is taken up by osmosis, and the swelling of the cells produces pressure that assists the movement of the water. Ions are taken up actively by ion-specific transport proteins. Water and solutes are transported up through the xylem by root pressure and transpiration. Transpiration is dependent on adhesion, cohesion, and evaporation, three phenomena that combine to draw water to the tops of the tallest trees. The movement of sugars and organic substances in the phloem is by translocation. Translocation is pressure flow due to the establishment of concentration gradients between the source end of each: the phloem sieve tubes and the sink end, where substances are transported out of the phloem and into cells for storage or consumption. The movement of the various substances draws water with it by osmosis, which in turn creates the pressure to move the sap.

3. Which of the following statements are correct?
   a. There are two different routes by which water can enter plant roots.
   b. Water and solutes can enter the stele and pass into the xylem vessels passively.
   c. The tracheids and vessel elements of the xylem are composed of dead cells.

d. Water may move out of the roots and into the soil under certain conditions.

e. Water and solutes may pass directly from cell to cell within the root.

f. The Casparian strip is a barrier to solute movement but not water movement.

4. Which of the following contribute to the movement of water up a plant stem?

a. Pressure generated by the roots

b. Osmosis

c. Active pumping requiring energy

d. Cohesion–tension generated by evaporation in the leaves

e. Transpiration

5. Which of the following statements are true?

a. Most of the water transported to the leaves in the xylem is used for photosynthesis.

b. The opening and closing of the stomata in the leaves are regulated.

c. The guard cells protect the leave from invasion by insects.

d. Opening and closing of the stomata exhibit a circadian rhythm.

e. Opening of the guard cells is due to water uptake by osmosis.

6. Which of the following statements apply to the movement of sugars in the phloem?

a. Companion cells pump sucrose into sieve tube members.

b. The sap moves toward a source as pressure builds up in a sink.

c. Companion cells use energy to load solutes at a source, and the solute then follows their concentration gradients to sinks.

d. Sugars can move either up the plant from roots to leaves or down the plant from leaves to roots depending on the season.

e. Movement of the phloem in any given sieve tube is always in one direction.

## 24.3 Transport in Animals

All animals share certain fundamental features in the design of their circulatory systems; they use a muscular pump to transport vascular fluids through tubular vessels. These systems may be either closed or open. Arthropods, most molluscs, and the ancestors of the vertebrates (urochordates and cephalochordates) use neurogenic hearts to pump a fluid, called hemolymph, into the body cavities, where it percolates between cells before being sucked back into the heart to be pumped again. Annelids, cephalopod molluscs, and all vertebrates pump blood throughout the body enclosed in blood vessels. Exchange of substances with cells takes place across the thin walls of the capillaries that penetrate close to every cell. Their hearts are myogenic, and the number of chambers in the heart and the arrangement of the major blood vessels leaving the heart reflect

evolutionary changes associated with the transition from fish with low metabolic rates to endothermic birds and mammals with high metabolic rates. The latter requires the heart to pump more blood through a larger number of small vessels, requiring much more pressure. All vascular fluids are complex and are considered to be a form of connective tissue. The fluid or plasma contains a variety of proteins and glycoproteins and in all vertebrates and many invertebrates has blood cells suspended in it. In vertebrates, these consist of erythrocytes (red blood cells), leukocytes (white blood cells), and platelets.

7. Which of the following is not transported by the circulatory system?

a. Oxygen

b. Hormones

c. Neurotransmitters

d. Nutrients

e. Lipids

f. Heat

8. Which of the following statements apply to a closed circulatory system versus an open circulatory system?

a. Allows higher rates of blood flow

b. Does not require hearts to generate high pressures

c. Requires hearts to generate higher pressures

d. There is no distinction between interstitial fluid and vascular fluid

e. Allows flow to different capillary beds to be independently regulated

f. Imposes greater resistance to blood flow

9. Which of the following statements is correct?

a. Vertebrate hearts are neurogenic.

b. All vertebrates have a four-chambered heart.

c. All white blood cells have nuclei, whereas red blood cells do not.

d. Blood in the pulmonary artery is high in oxygen and low in carbon dioxide.

e. Veins contain one-way valves to prevent backflow.

10. Insert the following terms into the appropriate sentences below.

systolic pressure          electrocardiogram
diastolic pressure         cardiac output
stroke volume              baroreceptors

a. Blood pressure is monitored by _____.

b. The peak pressure that the blood rises to during each heartbeat is the _____.

c. The vessel walls never relax below the _____.

d. The electrical activity of the heart can be monitored by the _____.

e. The total amount of blood pumped by each chamber of the heart each minute is the _____, which is a function of the _____ multiplied by the frequency with which the heart beats.

# Water, Solutes, and Temperature

## WHY IT MATTERS

What are the most inhospitable environments on Earth? Surely, among these are the hot dry deserts of Africa and Chile and the cold dry deserts of the Arctic and Antarctic **(Figure 25.1)**. Ironically, the middle of the ocean is often also considered a desert, giving rise to the old adage "water, water, everywhere but not a drop to drink" (Figure 25.1). What makes all of these environments challenging for humans are difficulties associated with controlling water balance and body temperature. Animals such as the rattlesnake (*Crotalus* sp.), shown in the opening photograph, must be able to tolerate hot days, cold nights, and very dry environments—a challenge for maintaining both water and heat balance. But although these challenges can be insurmountable for humans, many plants and animals have successfully adapted to them.

Thermal challenges can be constant, daily, or seasonal, and the adaptations required to deal with each will vary. We find organisms living on the edges of deep sea hydrothermal vents where temperatures are close to the boiling point, as well as organisms that reproduce and live at temperatures as low as −20°C. In the Gobi Desert in Mongolia and northern China, daily temperatures can vary by as much as 60°C, and in northern Canada, temperatures can vary seasonally by over 80 to 100°C. Despite this, many species of plants and animals

survive there. Equally varied are the challenges for water balance faced by organisms living in marine, freshwater, and terrestrial environments. Plants and animals living in fresh water have no problems obtaining water, whereas those living in marine and terrestrial environments do. Obtaining adequate amounts of salts and other solutes, however, is much easier for marine plants and animals and relatively difficult for freshwater and terrestrial ones.

When reviewing the section in the book on biomes (see Chapter 30), ask yourselves what challenges are faced by the organisms that live there. Understanding the basis of our own limitations and the adaptations that have allowed other organisms to colonize such extreme habitats is the basis of this chapter.

## 25.1  Water and Solutes

The cells of all organisms, bacteria, fungi, plants, and animals, are composed largely of water containing solutes ranging from ions to complex macromolecules. If water becomes limiting to a cell, it will shrivel and die. If it takes up too much water, it will swell and burst **(Figure 25.2, p. 546)**. Maintaining a proper balance is essentialfor life.

**FIGURE 25.1** Fresh, drinkable water can be absent in **(a)** hot, dry deserts, **(b)** cold, dry deserts, and **(c)** saltwater (marine) environments.

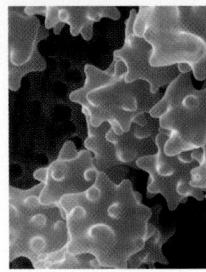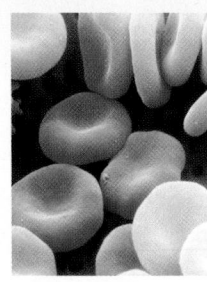

**FIGURE 25.2** A normal red blood cell (right) when placed in saltwater will lose water to its environment and shrivel (centre); whereas one placed in fresh water (left) will gain water and swell until it bursts.

SOURCE: © 1976 M. SHEETZ, R. PAINTER, and S. SINGER. *The Journal of Cell Biology*, Volume 70:193–302. By permission of Rockefeller University Press.

The movement of water into and out of cells is determined by the concentration of solutes inside and outside the cell. Water moves passively by osmosis, all other things being equal, from a solution with a low solute concentration to a solution with a high **solute** concentration (a solute in this case is any substance that dissolves in water; see Chapter 4). As a result, maintaining proper water balance requires maintaining proper solute balance; water and solute balance are tightly linked.

The challenges facing any organism for maintaining proper water and solute balance vary depending on the levels of water and solutes in the environment in which it lives. For single-celled organisms, all exchange is with the external environment. For multicellular organisms, exchange is between the cells and the extracellular fluid that surrounds them. As you will see, these organisms have a choice: to allow the extracellular fluid to equilibrate with the environment and let every cell fend for itself or to maintain an extracellular fluid different from the environment that is more similar to the intracellular fluids of the cell. Let's explore the ways in which different organisms manage this process.

## 25.2 Water and Solute Balance in Plants

The uptake of water and solutes from the environment by plants has been described in Chapters 22 and 24. This reflects the fact that the primary nutrients required for the growth and maintenance of plants are solutes, and the transport of these throughout their bodies is by the movement of water.

To recap briefly, most plants obtain their solutes and water from the soil. Most minerals and ions from the soil enter the roots along with water, penetrating into the non-living spaces between the cells. When

needed by cells, solutes and water must be taken up against their concentration gradients, which means by active transport. Since the root cells contain more dissolved solutes than the soil water, water will be drawn by osmosis into the cells. The water and the solutes in the root cells are then distributed to all other cells within the plant in the phloem and xylem, as described in Chapter 24.

If the soil surrounding terrestrial plants dries out, the solute content of the remaining soil water can increase until it is greater than that in the cytoplasm of the plant cells, and water will leave the cells. This reduces the internal pressure, and the plant wilts. Under these conditions, loss of water from stems and leaves worsens the condition. This problem is solved by several evolutionary adaptations in plants that live in dry environments. These plants usually have a thick cuticle that reduces evaporation, and their leaves tend to be greatly reduced, with much of the photosynthesis now taking place in the stem. In cacti, for instance, the leaflike pads (Figure 25.1a) are thickened parts of the stem and the leaves are reduced to the spines, tremendously reducing the surface area for transpiration. Many of these plants have also evolved the $C_4$ mode of carbon fixation in photosynthesis described in Chapter 5. As you will recall, the $C_4$ cycle occurs in the mesophyll cells close to the surface of the leaves and stems. This pathway allows these plants to close or restrict the opening of stomata, restricting water loss from transpiration, but still allows photosynthesis to occur in the mesophyll cells near the surface, where oxygen is abundant.

Finally, another adaptation in such plants as orchids and succulent plants as well as cacti is a biochemical variation of photosynthesis called Crassulacean acid metabolism (CAM), previously described in Chapter 5. Whereas many plants exhibit the classic Calvin cycle for metabolism or CAM **(Figure 25.3)**, these plants exhibit both. These two cycles operate at different times of the day. The stomata of these plants open at night, allowing $CO_2$ to enter and the $O_2$ produced during the day to leave. The $CO_2$ is fixed (converted to malate) by the $C_4$ pathway and accumulates throughout the night, being stored in vacuoles. Then, during the day, the stomata close, the $CO_2$ is released to be used in the Calvin cycle, and $O_2$ accumulates until the following night, when the process is repeated.

If the soil contains too much water, the excess water per se will not have any deleterious effects because the cell walls of plant cells limit the extent to which they can swell and prevent cell bursting. The excess water will, however, reduce the air space in the soil, restricting oxygen uptake by root cells, which, in turn, can kill the plant. This is what happens when houseplants are overwatered.

**FIGURE 25.3** **(a)** Corn (*Zea mays*) is a plant that uses the C$_4$ cycle for photosynthesis simultaneously with the Calvin cycle, whereas **(b)** the cactus (*Echinocactus grusonii*) and **(c)** the jade plant (*Crassula ovata*) use C$_4$ metabolism at night and operate the Calvin cycle only during the day, a unique strategy that further reduces water loss in hot, dry climates.

## STUDY BREAK

1. What is the primary source of water and solutes for most plants?
2. What is the significance of stomata opening and closing to water balance in plants?
3. What adaptations are seen in plants living in hot, dry climates to reduce water loss?

## 25.3 Water and Solute Balance in Animals

### Osmoregulation: Balancing the Gain and Loss of Water and Solutes

Many marine organisms eliminated the need to actively maintain water balance by maintaining the solute concentration of their extracellular fluids equal to that of the surrounding sea water. This group, which contains most marine invertebrates as well as hagfish, lampreys, sharks, and rays, is called **osmoconformers.** They do not gain or lose water because they are isosmotic: the solute concentrations of their cellular and extracellular fluids are the same as those in sea water. This does not mean that the composition of the solutes is identical in each compartment. The concentration of $K^+$, $Na^+$, and $Ca^{2+}$, for instance, differs from inside to outside cells because of active transport. This is essential for normal cell function. But by keeping the total concentration of all solutes the same, osmoconformers eliminate the need to actively regulate water balance.

Most freshwater and terrestrial animals (invertebrate and vertebrate), as well as the teleost fish and marine tetrapods (such as whales, dolphins, marine iguanas, and sea snakes), are **osmoregulators**. The solute concentration of their extracellular fluids differs from that of the environments around them **(Figure 25.4)**. To maintain water and solute balance, they must actively regulate solute and water uptake in a homeostatic fashion.

Freshwater animals maintain a higher solute concentration in their cells and extracellular fluid than occurs in the water that surrounds them. They

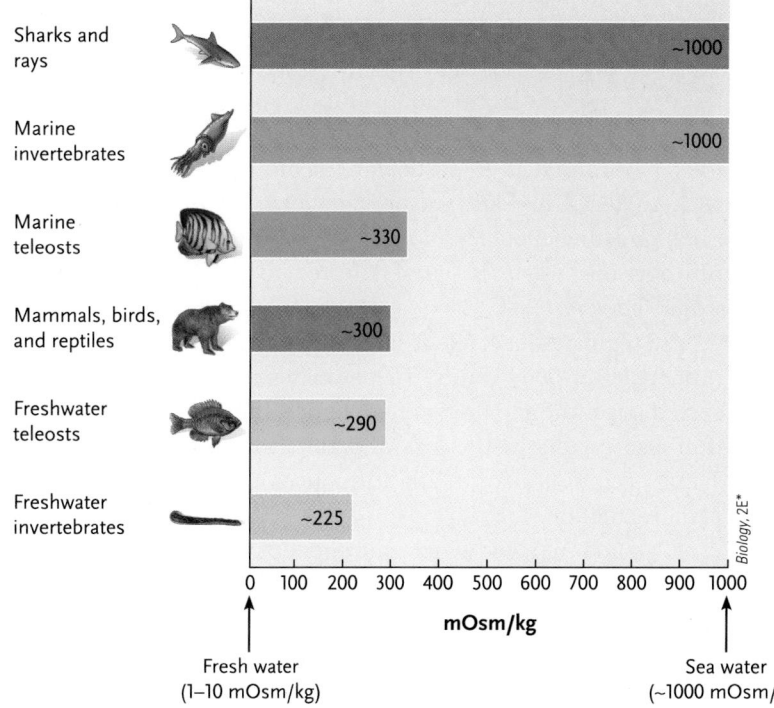

**FIGURE 25.4** Osmolality of body fluids in some animal groups.

constantly gain water by osmosis and lose solutes to the environment. Their challenge is obtaining solutes and eliminating excess water. Osmoregulators living in salt water maintain a lower solute concentration in their cells and extracellular fluid than is present in the waters in which they live. They constantly lose water by osmosis and gain solutes from the environment. Their challenge is to obtain water and eliminate excess solutes. Terrestrial animals cannot exchange water directly with their environment; they must obtain it by drinking or in their food. They must also obtain solutes in this way. They are constantly losing water in urine and feces, as well as by breathing and by evaporation across the skin, and losing some solutes in the urine and through metabolism. The strategies used to face these challenges are described in **Table 25.1**.

| TABLE 25.1 | **Challenges Facing Different Groups of Osmoregulators** | |
| --- | --- | --- |
| | Water | Solutes |
| Freshwater Animals | Gain from the environment and must actively excrete | Lose to the environment and must actively obtain |
| Saltwater Animals | Lose to the environment and must actively obtain | Gain from the environment and must actively excrete |
| Land Animals | Lose to the environment and must actively obtain | Lose to the environment and must actively obtain |

## Excretion: Eliminating Nitrogenous Wastes and Other Unwanted Compounds

There is a strong link between obtaining energy (Chapter 21), osmoregulation, and excretion. We have just discussed the need to balance water and solute levels in the body of animals. Food ingested for energy, growth, and maintenance is metabolized, and this process produces metabolic water and a host of solutes. Thus, for many animals, drinking and eating influence the need for osmoregulation. Although many solutes are needed by the cells, many are waste products that must be eliminated. In particular, the proteins and nuclear material in food are broken down into amino acids and nucleic acids, solutes containing nitrogen (nitrogenous wastes) that if allowed to accumulate would be very toxic. $H^+$ is another ion that must be tightly regulated because it is essential to maintain a proper pH in body fluids. These wastes must be dissolved in solution to be excreted; hence, their elimination also results in the loss of water from the body. Thus, excretion also greatly influences the need for osmoregulation.

The manner in which nitrogenous wastes are excreted largely reflects water availability and, to some extent, reproductive mode (**Figure 25.5**).

Ammonia ($NH_3$) is the simplest way to dispose of nitrogenous wastes. But $NH_3$ is highly toxic and must be diluted by water before it can be eliminated. Thus, aquatic animals (aquatic invertebrates, teleost fishes, larval amphibians) routinely excrete ammonia (Figure 25.5). Most other animals convert ammonia into urea, a compound that is still highly soluble in water but 100,000 times less toxic. Since this compound does not need to be diluted, its excretion requires much less water. It does, however, cost energy to convert from ammonia. Sharks and rays, adult amphibians, turtles, and mammals all excrete urea (Figure 25.5). Ammonia can also be converted into uric acid. Although an acid, it is non-toxic and relatively insoluble. As a result, it can be excreted with very little water. It precipitates as a semi-solid paste (the white substance in bird and reptile droppings). The process of precipitation takes place in the final stage of excretion as water is reabsorbed just before release. Excretion of uric acid occurs in many insects, snakes, and lizards as well as in birds (Figure 25.5). Interestingly, the embryos of reptiles and birds develop within leathery or hard-shelled eggs, where water conservation is essential and uric acid is stored as a harmless solid. It is also stored in the rectum of the pupae of developing insects. It is not clear which was the driving force in the evolution of uric acid excretion: the need to conserve water in the egg or the need to conserve water in the adult (another "chicken or egg" conundrum).

Many animals excrete more than one form of nitrogenous waste. Although humans and most mammals primarily excrete urea, there are also small amounts of ammonia and uric acid in urine. Some toads excrete ammonia when water is abundant but switch to excreting urea when water is scarce. Some terrestrial frogs also excrete uric acid besides ammonia, and insects living in moist environments excrete ammonia besides uric acid. Sharks and rays not only produce urea instead of ammonia, but they also use it as a major solute for maintaining water balance. As a result, there are high levels of urea in their blood and tissues. The meat of the shark and

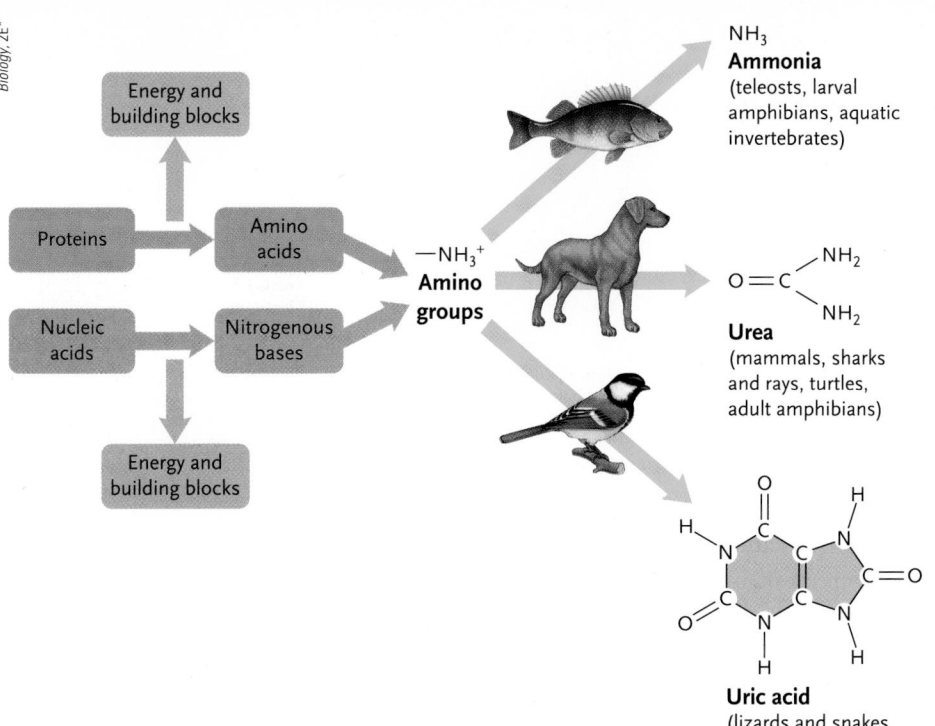

**FIGURE 25.5** Nitrogenous wastes excreted by different animal groups.

$NH_3$
**Ammonia**
(teleosts, larval amphibians, aquatic invertebrates)

**Urea**
(mammals, sharks and rays, turtles, adult amphibians)

**Uric acid**
(lizards and snakes, birds, insects)

the ray is often cut into round pieces with cookie cutters and sold as scallops. Not only can you identify these forgeries by the orientation of the muscle fibres in the meat, but you will also usually be able to identify the mild taste of urea in your dinner.

## Filtration, Reabsorption, Secretion, and Release: The Basis of Excretion

The simple strategy for excretion in most animals is to begin by eliminating almost all solutes by non-selective **filtration**, take back as much of the water as necessary and the important solutes by **reabsorption**, and ensure the elimination of select molecules in high concentration by **secretion**. Everything not needed is then released to the environment. This four-stage process **(Figure 25.6)** generally takes place in microscopic tubules.

Depending on the animal species, blood or body fluids are filtered non-selectively through narrow spaces between loosely connected epithelial cells at the proximal end (origin) of the tubule. Farther along the tubule, the epithelial cells contain abundant transport proteins that reabsorb glucose and other nutrients, ions, and amino acids along with much of the water. The distal end of the tubule is much less permeable, and excess ions and other small molecules can be selectively concentrated in the urine by active transport. The resulting fluid, high in nitrogenous wastes and other unwanted substances, is then released to the outside.

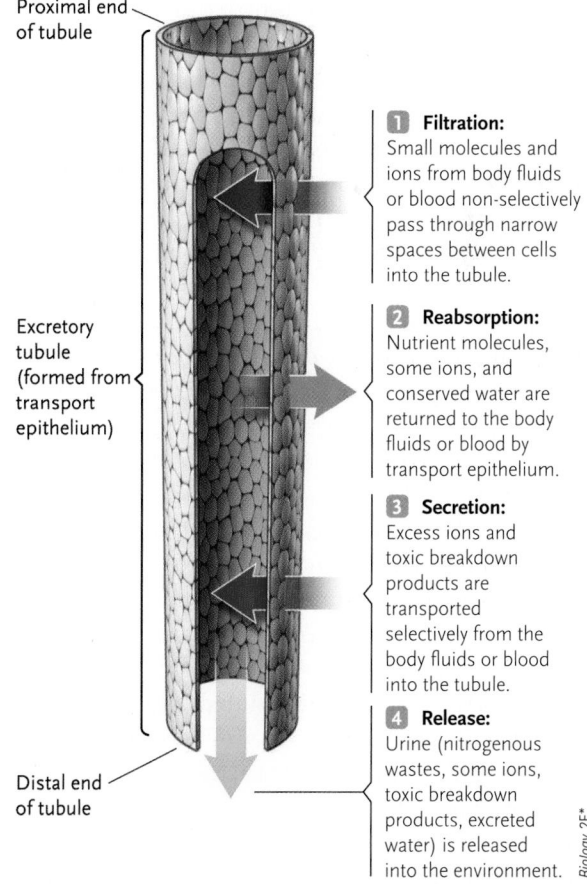

Proximal end of tubule

Excretory tubule (formed from transport epithelium)

Distal end of tubule

**1** **Filtration:** Small molecules and ions from body fluids or blood non-selectively pass through narrow spaces between cells into the tubule.

**2** **Reabsorption:** Nutrient molecules, some ions, and conserved water are returned to the body fluids or blood by transport epithelium.

**3** **Secretion:** Excess ions and toxic breakdown products are transported selectively from the body fluids or blood into the tubule.

**4** **Release:** Urine (nitrogenous wastes, some ions, toxic breakdown products, excreted water) is released into the environment.

**FIGURE 25.6** Common structure and operation of the tubules carrying out osmoregulation and excretion in animals.

The arrangement of these excretory tubules and the fluid that they filter (body fluid in animals with open circulatory systems and blood in animals with closed circulatory systems; see Chapter 24) are usually concentrated in specialized organs and are discussed briefly next.

## Strategies for Osmoregulation and Excretion: Variety in the Animal Kingdom

Most invertebrates possess excretory tubules similar to the general model just discussed. There are several variations on the theme. Three examples are shown in **Figure 25.7**. In some invertebrates, such as the flatworm and the grasshopper, the proximal end of the tube (the origin or beginning of the tube) is closed, and fluid enters by filtration or secretion, whereas in others, such as the earthworm, it is open, and fluid is drawn in by cilia. In both the flatworm and the earthworm, urine is excreted to the outside, whereas in the grasshopper, it drains into the gut, where it passes into the intestine and rectum, where further secretion and reabsorption can occur. In all cases, reabsorption of some solutes and secretion of others occur along the length of the tubule. In most aquatic invertebrates, water and solutes may also be exchanged across the general body wall.

In vertebrates, the specialized excretory tubules, called **nephrons**, are concentrated into a pair of kidneys, specialized organs lying one on each side of the vertebral column in the abdominal cavity. Each nephron receives blood from a complex of capillaries called a glomerulus, from which fluid and solutes are filtered into a capsule (**Bowman's capsule**) at the proximal end of the tubule. Each tubule is very convoluted. The proximal region of this tubule is designed for reabsorption of glucose, amino acids, and other nutrient molecules, and the distal portion is designed to balance key ions through the secretion of $K^+$ and $H^+$ and reabsorption of $Na^+$ and $Cl^-$.

In the non-mammalian vertebrates, the kidneys produce a urine in which the solute concentration is either lower than (**hypo-osmotic**) or equal to (**isosmotic**) that in the body fluids. Some aquatic birds can produce a slightly concentrated urine, but only the mammals can produce a very concentrated urine (**hyperosmotic**). This unique ability arises from special anatomical and physiological features. The convoluted tubules of each nephron loop down into the body of the kidney (the loop of Henle). The permeability of each region of the tubule varies, as do the specific transport proteins that are present. These features result in the production of a solute gradient within the kidney, with solutes becoming highly concentrated in the deepest levels of the kidney. The ducts that collect the urine from the nephrons pass

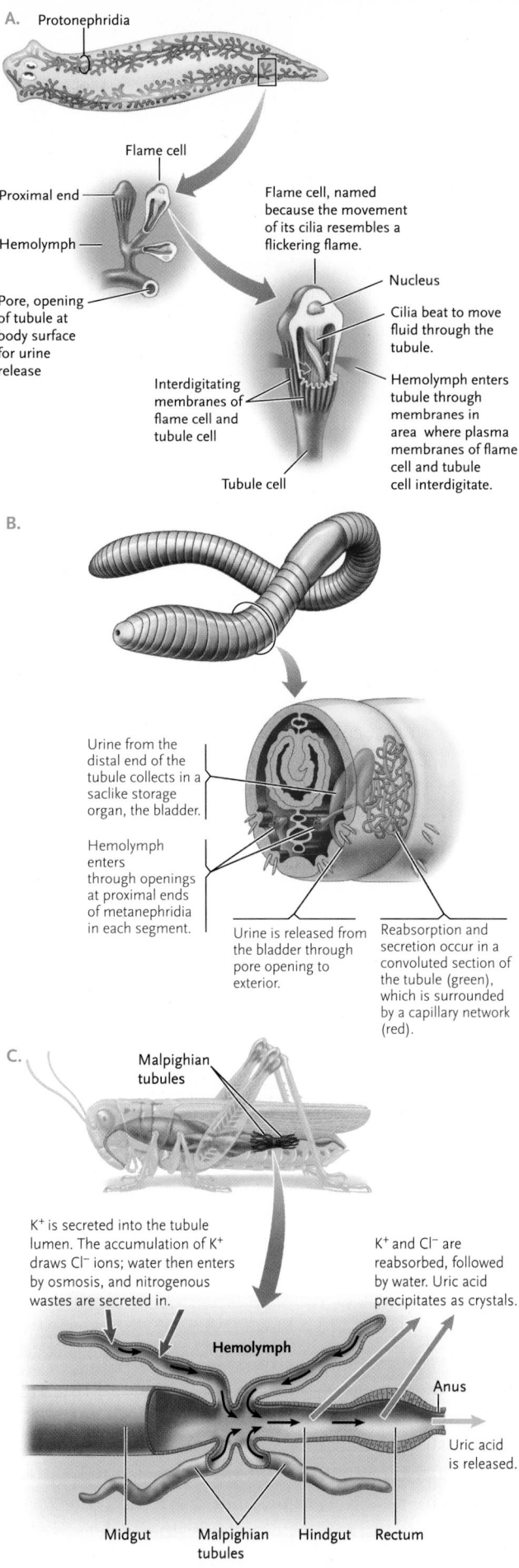

**A.** Protonephridia

Flame cell

Proximal end

Hemolymph

Pore, opening of tubule at body surface for urine release

Flame cell, named because the movement of its cilia resembles a flickering flame.

Nucleus

Cilia beat to move fluid through the tubule.

Interdigitating membranes of flame cell and tubule cell

Hemolymph enters tubule through membranes in area where plasma membranes of flame cell and tubule cell interdigitate.

Tubule cell

**B.**

Urine from the distal end of the tubule collects in a saclike storage organ, the bladder.

Hemolymph enters through openings at proximal ends of metanephridia in each segment.

Urine is released from the bladder through pore opening to exterior.

Reabsorption and secretion occur in a convoluted section of the tubule (green), which is surrounded by a capillary network (red).

**C.**

Malpighian tubules

$K^+$ is secreted into the tubule lumen. The accumulation of $K^+$ draws $Cl^-$ ions; water then enters by osmosis, and nitrogenous wastes are secreted in.

$K^+$ and $Cl^-$ are reabsorbed, followed by water. Uric acid precipitates as crystals.

Hemolymph

Anus

Uric acid is released.

Midgut    Malpighian    Hindgut    Rectum
           tubules

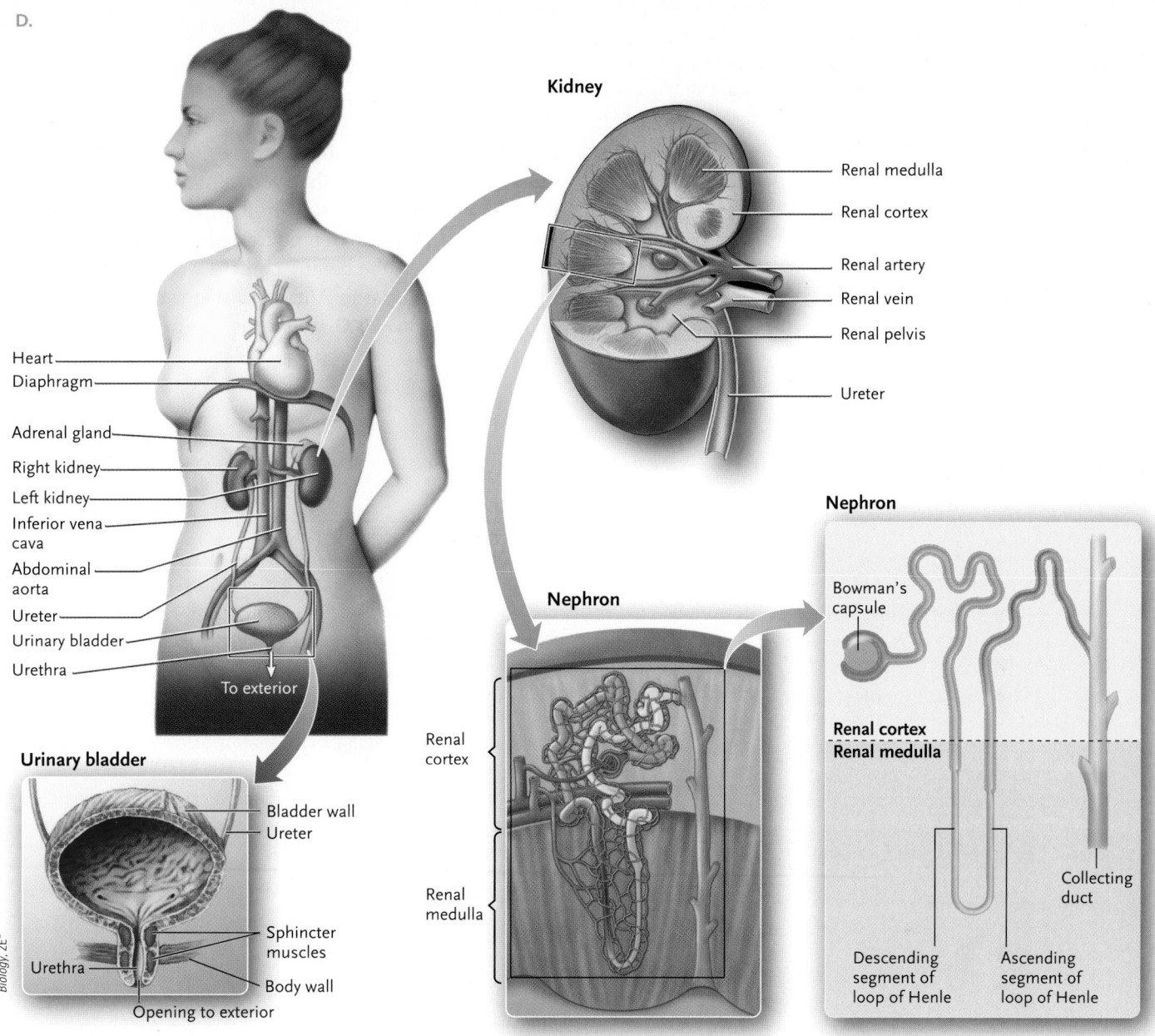

**D.**

Kidney

Renal medulla

Renal cortex

Renal artery

Renal vein

Renal pelvis

Ureter

Heart

Diaphragm

Adrenal gland

Right kidney

Left kidney

Inferior vena cava

Abdominal aorta

Ureter

Urinary bladder

Urethra

To exterior

Nephron

Bowman's capsule

Renal cortex

Renal medulla

Collecting duct

Descending segment of loop of Henle

Ascending segment of loop of Henle

Nephron

Renal cortex

Renal medulla

**Urinary bladder**

Bladder wall

Ureter

Sphincter muscles

Urethra

Body wall

Opening to exterior

*Biology, 2E\**

**FIGURE 25.7** The excretory tubules **(a)** in a flatworm (protonephridia), **(b)** in an earthworm (metanephridia), **(c)** in a grasshopper (Malpighian tubules), and **(d)** in a mammal (nephrons).

through this region, and as they do, water is drawn back into the kidney by osmosis, greatly increasing the concentration of the urine as it enters the ureters, which drain the kidneys into the urinary bladder. The longer and deeper the loops, the greater the concentration gradient that is produced and the more concentrated the urine.

Marine mammals depend on their ability to produce a very concentrated urine. They take in large amounts of salt in the food they eat and the water they ingest in the process. They survive by producing urine that is more concentrated than sea water. Desert rodents are among the most efficient animals at conserving water. In species such as the kangaroo rat, a large proportion of their

nephrons have long loops descending deep into the kidney. This allows them to produce a urine with up to 25 times the solute concentration of body fluids, and, as a result, they excrete very little water. Most of the water in their feces is reabsorbed in the large intestine and rectum. They are nocturnal. They lack sweat glands and reduce evaporative water loss from breathing in specialized passages in their nasal cavities. As a result, they do not need to replace much water. Roughly 10% of the water they need is contained in the food they eat. The other 90% of their water needs is satisfied by the production of metabolic water from the digestion of their foods (metabolizing fat produces a significant amount of water). This species never has to drink water.

1. How are water balance problems different in animals living in freshwater, saltwater, and terrestrial environments?
2. What are the advantages and disadvantages of producing ammonia versus urea or uric acid as a means to eliminate nitrogenous wastes? Name some animals that use each strategy.
3. What is unique about the mammalian kidney compared to the excretory organs of other vertebrates?

## 25.4 Temperature

There are limits to the environmental temperatures compatible with life. These temperatures vary tremendously between simple single-celled microorganisms and complex multicellular plants and animals.

At present, it appears that some single-celled microorganisms harvested from hydrothermal vents on the floor of the Pacific Ocean reproduce and grow at temperatures above 100°C, the boiling point of water, and other microorganisms exist in Antarctica that can reproduce and grow down to −20°C, well below the freezing point

## BIOLOGY IS EVERYWHERE 25.1
### Dialysis Technician

In humans, the kidneys are essential for waste excretion and for maintaining water and solute balance. Kidney failure results in an inability to regulate ion concentrations and pH and leads to a buildup of toxic wastes. The inability to regulate water balance also leads to an inability to regulate blood pressure. Lack of proper kidney function is fatal. Fortunately, our knowledge of how kidneys in general and of how nephrons in particular work has allowed bioengineers to design an artificial kidney called a dialysis machine. This machine works much like the kidney itself **(Figure 1)**. A patient's blood is removed from an artery and pumped through tubes made of selectively permeable membranes. By regulating the composition of the dialyzing solution, urea and excess ions can be removed from the blood and glucose and needed solutes can be added to the blood. The blood is returned to the patient through a vein, and the dialyzing solution is discarded.

Patients usually receive dialysis at a hospital or a clinic. Dialysis technicians (sometimes called hemodialysis technicians) are responsible for preparing the patients, operating and maintaining the dialysis machine and equipment, monitoring the patient's progress (Figure 1), and preparing reports for the medical staff. Training can be obtained from vocational and technical schools, community colleges, and even online programs.

A.

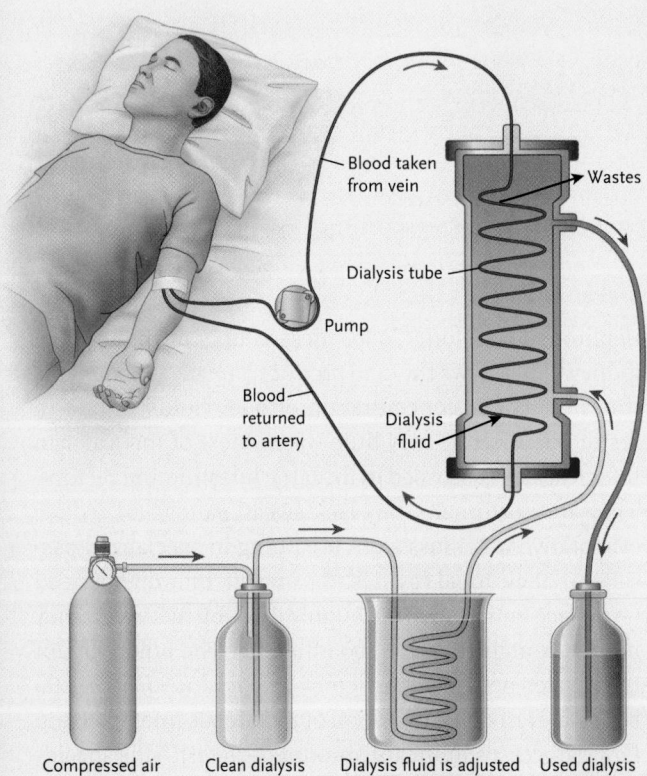

Blood taken from vein
Wastes
Dialysis tube
Pump
Blood returned to artery
Dialysis fluid

Compressed air and carbon dioxide | Clean dialysis fluid | Dialysis fluid is adjusted to body temperature | Used dialysis solution

B.

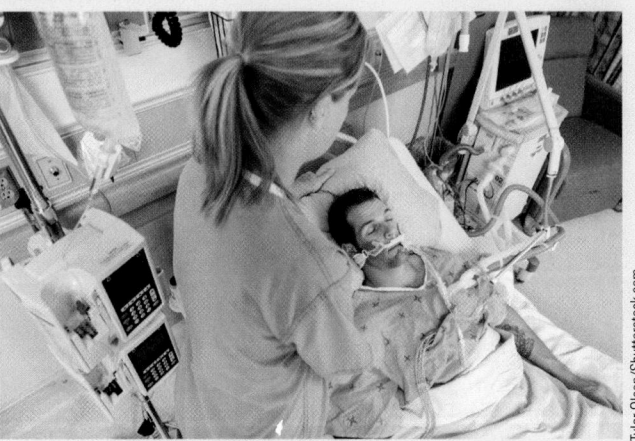

Tyler Olson/Shutterstock.com

**FIGURE 1** **(a)** Schematic of the mechanism behind kidney dialysis. **(b)** A kidney dialysis technician with a patient.

of water. These organisms contain functional proteins (enzymes and membrane transporters) and cell membranes with unique abilities.

But the cells of most multicellular organisms cannot function at temperatures below freezing because at these temperatures, the lipid bilayers of their biological membranes change from a fluid to a frozen gel. Since membranes are dynamic and control what enters and leaves a cell, this prevents their normal function. At lower temperatures, ice crystals begin to form, and these penetrate and destroy cell membranes. Strategies exist that allow some species to survive at very low temperatures (below −40°C), but in a non-functional state. Most cells from multicellular organisms also cannot function at temperatures above 45°C. Their proteins and the nucleic acids in their DNA and RNA begin to unfold (denature), and as they lose their three-dimensional shapes, they lose their ability to function. Most multicellular organisms, therefore, must maintain body temperatures somewhere within the 0 to 45°C range. Some can function normally over this entire range, but most can function properly only over a small portion of it.

Within their functional range, multicellular organisms are also profoundly affected by changes in temperature. Because of its effect on chemical processes, temperature regulates the rate of all biological processes. Most processes increase or decrease in rate by two- to threefold for every 10°C change in temperature. That is, rates will double or triple for every 10°C rise in temperature or fall to one-half to one-third their normal rate with a 10°C fall in temperature.

## Organisms Gain or Lose Heat in One of Four Ways

Any object sitting out in the environment, living or nonliving, will exchange heat with its environment in one of four ways. These are depicted for a mammal in **Figure 25.8** but apply equally to plants and inanimate objects such as rocks. Objects that are cooler than their environment will warm up, whereas those that are warmer than their environment tend to cool down. If two objects are touching, heat will be transferred directly from one object to the other by **conduction**. Thermal energy is transferred directly between the molecules in contact with one another. As air or water flows over the surface of an object, heat will be transferred to or from the object by **convection**. Because the air or water is flowing away from the object and continually being replaced, heat transfer by convection is very efficient. This explains why even light winds in winter make the outside temperature seem much colder than it is (the

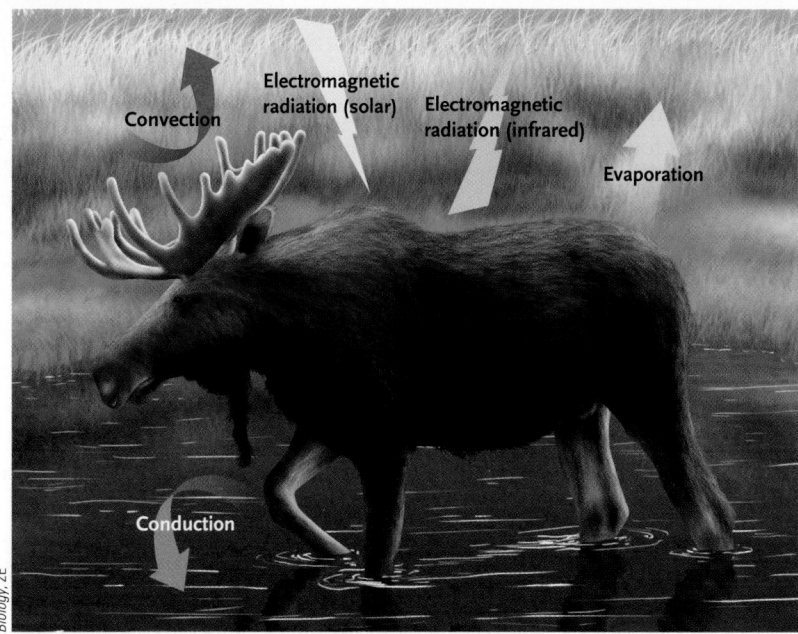

**FIGURE 25.8** Heat flows into and out of a moose (*Alces alces*) on a hot, sunny day.

wind-chill factor). All objects radiate heat by electromagnetic radiation. The direction of flow of heat is from warmer objects to cooler ones. Thus, plants and animals exposed to the sun on a warm day will pick up heat by **radiation** but during a cold night will lose heat to the sky by radiation. Finally, as fluids evaporate into their gas phase, energy is consumed in the form of heat. **Evaporation** occurs in plant leaves (remember that transpiration is the driving force for the movement of xylem in plants) and from the respiratory passages of air-breathing animals. It is the mechanism behind the cooling effects of sweating in mammals. Sweating itself does not cause cooling; cooling occurs only when the sweat evaporates from the skin surface, drawing heat with it. In hot climates with high humidity, the air is already saturated with water vapour and sweat cannot evaporate. As a result, all that sweating achieves is to make us feel even more uncomfortable.

In the following section, we will explore the ways in which plants and animals respond to changes in environmental temperature.

## 25.5 Plant Responses to Temperature Change

### Freeze Avoidance and Freeze Tolerance Are Plant Strategies for Dealing with Extreme Cold

Most plants from tropical regions cannot survive freezing temperatures, whereas perennial plants in temperate regions can. The manner in which plants respond to short-term changes (such as a unseasonable cold snap) and long-term changes (i.e., winter) may be quite different.

In many cold-tolerant plants, the result of a cold snap is the up-regulation of genes encoding for a family of proteins called antifreeze proteins. This is a class of proteins found in bacteria, fungi, plants, and animals. These proteins are produced by cells and act internally to bind to small ice crystals, preventing their growth and crystallization (a process called **freeze avoidance**). They do this by covering the water-accessible surfaces of the ice. The function of these proteins may fail at very low temperatures.

The second strategy for surviving very low temperatures is **freeze tolerance**. Perennial plants in temperate regions must survive not only low temperatures but also the freezing of their tissue water **(Figure 25.9)**. The secret to this (which is also shared by many animals) is to allow the water outside their cells to freeze, but not the water inside their cells. In this way, the ice crystals will not disrupt and damage their cell membranes. They do this by transporting and concentrating solutes outside the cell in the intracellular spaces. The high concentration of solutes (metabolites, sugars, and osmolytes) will draw the water out of the cell by osmosis. This leads to extreme cellular dehydration. In woody plants that survive temperatures below $-40°C$ (some down to $-196°C$), almost all of the water leaves their cells by freeze-induced dehydration.

Studies designed to understand the biochemical and biophysical mechanisms that underlie this phenomenon have given rise to two hypotheses. The water replacement hypothesis maintains that the critical step in resisting dehydration is to replace water in membranes and macromolecules with sugars. Another hypothesis maintains that hydrophilic (water-repellent) molecules enter a glassy state during desiccation, providing an inert protective matrix that immobilizes macromolecules, preventing denaturation and other structural disruptions. These two hypotheses are not mutually exclusive.

Thus, the secret to freeze tolerance is being able to tolerate severe dehydration. Most temperate plants cannot tolerate freezing during the summer, when they are actively growing. Environmental cues in the fall (low temperature and short photoperiod) trigger changes in gene expression, leading to physiological changes at the molecular, cellular, and whole-plant levels, a process referred to as **cold acclimatization**. These are complex adaptations that prevent the cell damage caused by cellular dehydration. Among these are the remodelling of the membrane lipids in both the cell membrane and the membranes of cell organelles, such as the mitochondria and chloroplasts. This requires the synthesis of enzymes that compensate for changes in organelle volume and that stabilize the membranes during freezing.

Despite recent advances in our understanding of cold-induced molecular responses in freeze-tolerant plants, much remains unknown. This is an area of intense investigation as scientists explore ways to bioengineer cold-tolerant crop plants.

## Evaporative Water Loss and Synthesis of Heat Shock Proteins Are Plant Strategies for Dealing with Heat

Plants living in hot environments can do little to prevent warming. The one avenue that is open to them is evaporative cooling. If water is abundant, they can open their stomata to allow transpiration and evaporation to cool their leaves. If water is not abundant, however, the stomata will close, eliminating this possibility. Under these conditions, plants will warm along with the air temperature around them.

**FIGURE 25.9** Freeze tolerance is a strategy employed by many plants (such as the silver birch-*Betula pendula*) **(a)** and insects (such as the goldenrod gall fly-*Eurosta solidaginis*) **(b)**.

Elena Larina/Shutterstock.com

Patrick Coin

Most plants can survive a brief period of heating, but if heating is prolonged, enzymes and functional proteins begin to unfold. Since the proper function of these proteins depends on their three-dimensional shape, unfolding inactivates them, and death quickly ensues. All organisms contain a family of proteins referred to as **heat shock proteins (HSPs)**. These proteins are considered to be molecular chaperones. As temperatures rise, the genes encoding these proteins become active, and as many as 50 different heat shock proteins begin to accumulate within the cells. These proteins bind to and stabilize other proteins, including enzymes, preventing them from denaturing. When temperatures fall again, the HSPs release the proteins to which they were bound so that they can resume their normal functions.

## 25.6 Animal Responses to Temperature Change

There are several ways that animals have been classified based on the manner in which they balance heat loss and heat gain. The most widely used is to classify them based on the primary source of heat gain. If that source is primarily from external sources (the environment), they are referred to as **ectotherms** (*ecto* = outside). When internal sources (metabolism) are the main form of heat, the animals are referred to as **endotherms** (*endo* = inside). For the most part, ectotherms have body temperatures similar to their environment. As a rule, they are cool to the touch (and hence sometimes referred to as cold blooded), and their temperatures vary as the environment warms and cools (thus, they are sometimes referred to as poikilotherms [*poikilo* = variable]). Endotherms, on the other hand, tend to have a high internal temperature (hence, they are sometimes called warm blooded) that is rigorously maintained (thus, they are sometimes called homeotherms [*homeo* = constant]). The alternate terms mentioned here have proven to be problematic because an ectothermic snail basking in the sun will be warm to the touch, whereas an endothermic ground squirrel will have a seasonally variable body temperature and be cold to the touch while in hibernation. For this reason, the terms *endotherm* and *ectotherm* have become the more useful terms.

We tend to think that endothermy is a better strategy than ectothermy because humans are endotherms. In reality, neither is necessarily better than the other. They are just different strategies, each with its costs and benefits. Endotherms can remain functional at optimal physiological levels over a wider range of temperatures, but as temperatures vary from optimal levels, the metabolic cost of maintaining a constant body temperature soars. Indeed, the high metabolic rates of endotherms require that they consume more food, be more active to obtain that food, and lose more water due to higher rates of respiratory gas exchange. This makes them much more prone to dehydration in hot, dry climates and dependent on food availability in cold climates. A 300-g rodent needs 15 to 20 times more food and water per day than a 300-g reptile living in the same habitat. Because ectotherms have lower body temperatures and metabolic rates, they require less food and spend less time foraging and exposing themselves to predators. They can invest a greater percentage of their metabolic rate into growth and reproduction. In the tropics, reptiles outcompete mammals in terms of both the number of species and the number of individuals. Because they are warm and do not have to expend energy to elevate body temperature, they can divert more energy into reproduction. At colder temperatures, however, ectotherms become sluggish and inactive, and endotherms are at an advantage (as long as food and water are available). The further from the equator, the more abundant are terrestrial endotherms. There are only a few terrestrial invertebrates in polar and subpolar regions and no reptiles.

### Ectotherms Primarily Regulate Body Temperature by Behavioural Means

Animals classified as belonging to this group include most invertebrates, fishes, amphibians, and reptiles. Although they do generate some heat from internal metabolic processes, it is small and readily dissipates to the environment. As a result, their body temperatures are generally the same as the environment around them. This is not to say that they do not **thermoregulate**. They do regulate their body temperatures to allow optimal physiological performance, but they do this primarily by behavioural means: they seek out regions of the environment that are most optimal.

This strategy is very limited for aquatic ectotherms (invertebrates, fish, and amphibians), where environmental temperatures tend to be quite uniform. To some extent, they can change location to take advantage of the thermal stratification that occurs in lakes, ponds, and streams between deep and shallow waters or between sunny and shaded areas. There are some marine fish (tunas, mackerels, and some sharks) that retain heat generated by exercising muscle to keep it warm, allowing it to operate more efficiently. They do this by using a countercurrent heat exchange system in the arteries supplying the muscle and the veins returning from them, similar in principle to the countercurrent system employed for gas exchange in the gills (see Chapter 23).

Terrestrial ectotherms generally can take advantage of a much greater range in environmental temperatures, moving from shaded to sunny areas as they need to warm up or cool down. They also exhibit a wider range of physiological adjustments to aid heat exchange. Many bees, moths, butterflies, and dragonflies use a form of shivering to warm flight muscles in cold weather, allowing them to fly. Many amphibians and reptiles adjust blood flow to the skin to speed the distribution of heat from the surface of their bodies to core tissues. Burmese pythons use shivering to produce heat when incubating their eggs.

If the temperature of the environment departs too greatly from optimal levels, especially when temperatures fall, ectotherms cannot sustain optimal levels of physiological performance. Just as with plants, ectotherms living in temperate regions undergo cold acclimatization and exhibit the same strategies of freeze tolerance and freeze avoidance (see Box 25.2) (Figure 25.9).

## Endotherms Primarily Regulate Body Temperature by Physiological Means

The endothermic animals are primarily birds and mammals. They sustain high metabolic rates that generate heat as a waste product. They carefully control the rate at which this heat is lost to the environment and use it to sustain relatively high body temperatures (32 to 39°C for most mammals and 39 to 42°C for most birds). Although the body temperatures of homeotherms can be turned up or down (such as with a fever or during sleep) for the most part, they are regulated around a constant value homeostatically. This requires that they sense and monitor body temperature and employ physiological strategies to maintain their body temperatures at the appropriate level. They have temperature-sensitive receptors in the skin as well as in the spinal cord and the hypothalamus in the brain (see Chapter 26). Information from these receptors is integrated in the hypothalamus, and if body temperature differs from the set point, the core body temperature that the animal wishes to maintain, various physiological mechanisms are activated to return the body temperature to where it should be (Figure 25.10).

When environmental temperatures are high, endotherms need to increase the rate at which they lose heat from their bodies. The immediate response is to increase blood flow to the skin, carrying heat from the body core to the surface, where it can dissipate, and to reduce the thickness of any insulation by flattening fur and feathers to release trapped air. A few species of mammals have sweat glands (humans, cows, horses, and antelopes) that begin to release sweat onto the surface of the skin, where it evaporates, helping to dissipate heat. Other species of mammals and most birds begin to breathe rapidly and shallowly, increasing evaporative water loss from the respiratory passages, a process called panting in mammals and gular fluttering (rapid fluttering of the floor of the mouth pouch) in birds. Many species also use behavioral strategies to cool off (Figure 25.11). Most species splay out, increasing the surface area for heat loss, and if possible do so on cool ground. They will expose the less insulated parts of their body—the belly in dogs, the ears in rabbits, and the legs and feet in birds. Many will wet themselves down in streams and ponds to increase evaporative cooling, and elephants will spray themselves with water.

When environmental temperatures begin to fall, endotherms stay warm by increasing insulation, reducing

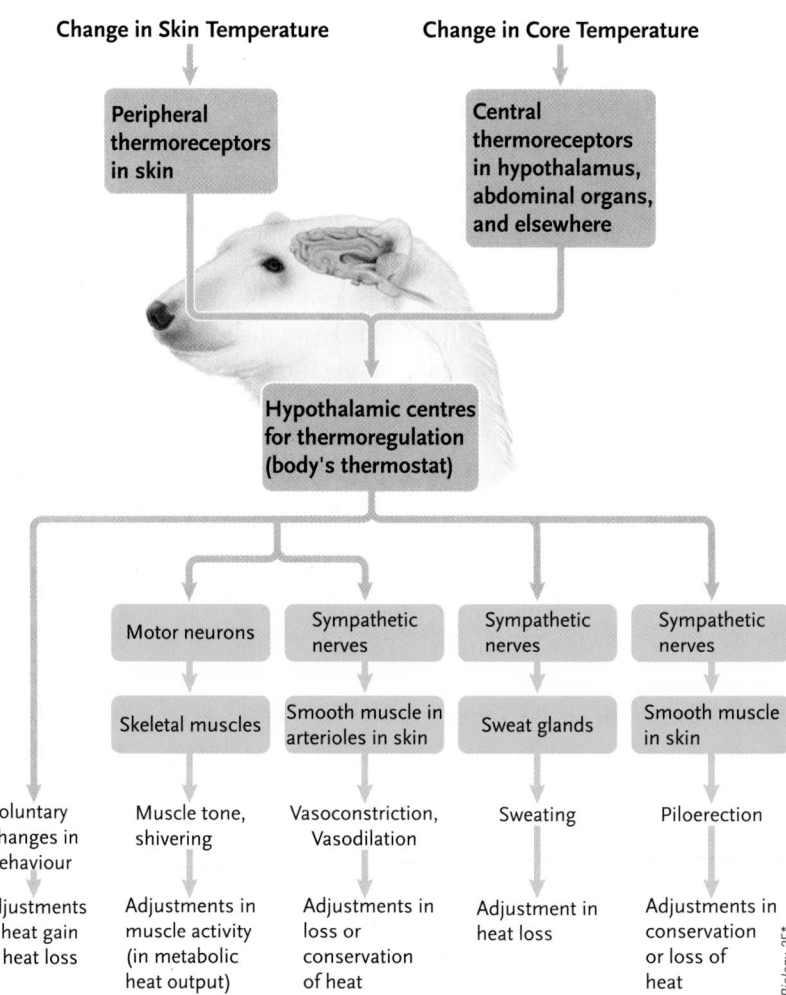

**FIGURE 25.10** The physiological and behavioural responses of birds and mammals to changes in skin and core temperature.

*Biology, 2E*

**FIGURE 25.11** Behavioural adaptations for heat transfer in birds and mammals. **(a)** A husky (*Canis lupus familiaris*) curling up with the limbs under the body and the tail around the nose to conserve heat. **(b)** Penguins (family Spheniscidae) huddling together to conserve heat. **(c)** An elephant (*Elephas maximus*) spraying itself with water to cool off. **(d)** A jackrabbit (*Lepus* sp.) erecting its ears to lose heat on a hot day.

the loss of metabolic heat to their surroundings. This consists of erecting their fur or feathers (**piloerection**), trapping air, and increasing the thickness of the layer of insulation. Species that live in particularly cold environments have an inner layer of guard hair that is particularly well suited for this. Muskox are an excellent example. They also reduce blood flow to the skin so that less heat is lost across this surface. Marine mammals and birds (e.g., polar bears, seals, and penguins) also have a thick layer of fat or blubber below the skin and can control their insulating abilities by controlling the amount of blood that flows through this layer to the skin. Behavioural strategies such as huddling and curling up to reduce exposure to less insulated parts help maintain body temperature (Figure 25.11). These strategies are relatively inexpensive. If temperatures fall sufficiently that these are not adequate to maintain body temperature, then endotherms begin to shiver. Shivering consists of rapid muscle contractions that produce shivering, rhythmic tremors in skeletal muscle. They also stimulate the oxidation of fats and other fuels to produce more metabolic heat. This form of heat production is termed **non-shivering thermogenesis** (the generation of heat by non-shivering means). This form of heat generation is best seen in young mammals and adults of species of mammals capable of hibernating. In both groups, a specialized form of fat called **brown fat** (or brown adipose tissue) is present and can be activated. Remember that the metabolism of all fuels leads to the breaking of chemical bonds and that some of the energy released is ultimately converted to ATP, although much is lost as heat. This form of fat contains mitochondria in which the electron transport chain is uncoupled from ATP production. As a result, fuel is metabolized at a very high rate and very little ATP is produced; almost all the energy is lost as heat.

Just as with plants and ectotherms, endotherms too undergo thermal acclimation, exhibiting seasonal changes in the thickness of fur coats and insulating fat. Many species of mammals also have the ability to hibernate (see Box 25.3). This unique ability does not represent an abandonment of homeostatic temperature regulation, however, but results from a careful resetting of the set point for temperature regulation to extremely low levels.

## STUDY BREAK

1. How do heat shock proteins work, and in what organisms are they found?
2. Why are functional proteins such as enzymes so sensitive to changes in salinity, pH, and temperature?
3. What is thermal acclimation, and in what organisms is it found?
4. How do ectotherms and endotherms differ in their ability to respond to low temperature?

# THE MOLECULE BEHIND THE BIOLOGY 25.2
## Antifreeze Proteins

Antifreeze proteins are a class of proteins that were first discovered in a group of Antarctic fishes. Scientists realized that these fish survived in waters that were colder than the freezing point of their blood. Their research ultimately allowed them to isolate the protein and characterize its physical and chemical properties. They have since been discovered to occur in all living organisms, bacteria, fungi, plants, and animals. These proteins have a three-dimensional structure that gives rise to a flat, rigid surface that allows them to adsorb to ice; that is, it allows the protein molecules to bind to the ice crystals with weak bonds, creating a film that covers the surface of the ice crystals **(Figure 1)**. It does not penetrate the ice crystals but coats them, preventing the crystals from growing.

Recently, these proteins have been renamed as ice-structuring proteins to distinguish them from antifreeze solutions such as automotive antifreeze. Automotive antifreezes work by greatly increasing the solute concentration of solutions, a process that lowers the freezing point of the solutions. These high concentrations of solutes would be disastrous in living systems as they would tremendously dehydrate cells. By binding to ice crystal surfaces, antifreeze proteins work at 1/300th to 1/500th the concentrations of commercial antifreeze solutions, minimizing their osmotic effects. Indeed, antifreeze proteins are now being used industrially to prevent ice crystal formation in ice cream (Figure 1) and frozen yogurt and could potentially lead to synthetic products that could be used for the preservation of transplant organs and tissues.

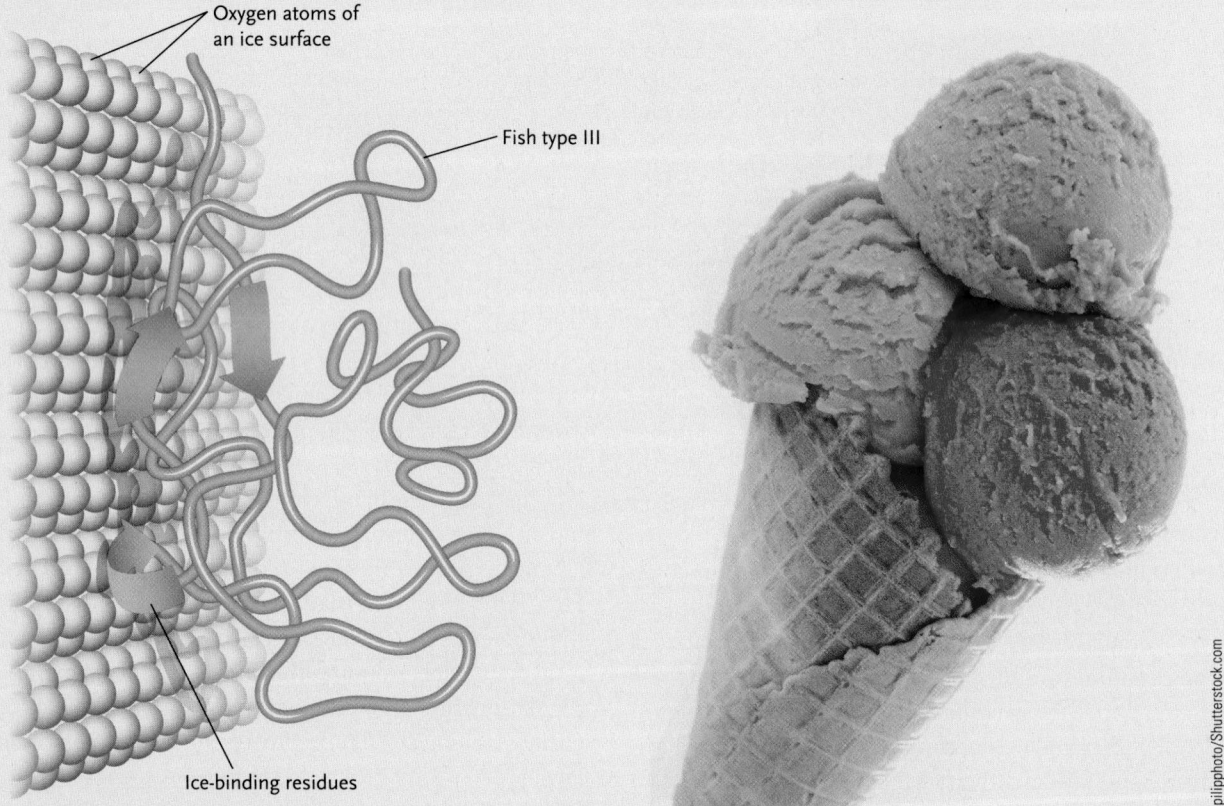

**FIGURE 1** Antifreeze proteins coat the surfaces of ice crystals, preventing them from further growth. These proteins that have been found in bacteria, fungi, plants, and animals are now being used for industrial purposes, such as preventing the formation of ice crystals in ice cream and frozen yogurt.

# LIFE ON THE EDGE 25.3
## Hibernation

Many groups of mammals cope with the long, harsh winter months, when food and water are limited, not by increasing metabolic supplies and remaining warm and active but by reducing metabolic demand **(Figure 1)**. During the summer, when food is plentiful, they fatten up, in some cases more than doubling in body weight. As winter approaches, they retreat into burrows, which, when covered with snow, are insulated and will fall to just below freezing levels, protected from the subzero temperatures experienced above ground. They progressively reduce their set point for body tempera-ture regulation, reduce their metabolic heat production, and actively cool, allowing their body temperature to fall to levels that are only a degree or so above the environmental temperature, stopping just above freezing. This ultimately reduces their metabolism to roughly 2% of their normal summer metabolic rate.

Intriguingly, hibernators remain in this state for up to several weeks but then arouse to a normal body temperature for a short period of roughly one day and then re-enter hibernation. These periodic arousals are metabolically expensive, slowly consuming the fat supplies the animals have stored up over the summer. Why they undergo these expensive excursions remains a mystery, but there are several theories. One suggests that they may be necessary to eliminate nitrogenous wastes (just as we often have to get up to go to the bathroom in the middle of the night). Another suggests that these episodes of rewarm-ing may be required to allow genetic transcription and translation to occur. These processes may be too slow at the greatly reduced temperatures of the hibernating animals to maintain levels of functional proteins.

A.

B.

C.

**FIGURE 1** Hibernation is a common strategy for many mammals in cold regions, such as the **(a)** dormouse (*Glis glis*), **(b)** bats, and **(c)** European hedgehog (*Erinaceus, europaeus*).

# PUTTING IT IN PERSPECTIVE

Water is the single largest component of living cells. Depending on the amount of inorganic matter in supporting structures, the water composition of the bodies of fungi, plants, and animals can range from 50% to 90%. Water is so important to life that most attempts to identify whether there is life on other planets hinges on whether or not there are signs of water on other planets. We cannot imagine life without it. Life is also dependent on the variety of chemical processes that go on inside cells, processes that are highly temperature sensitive. Optimal performance of all living things is dependent on adequate supplies of water and optimal temperatures. Our attempts to fully understand why this is so have not only led to biomedical breakthroughs that help save lives, but they have also led to a tremendous variety of industrial applications. These include everything from air conditioners, desalination plants, and dialysis machines to warmer winter clothing, smoother frozen yogurt, and the production of freeze-tolerant crops. Interestingly, these attempts led to the invention of Gatorade. Gatorade was cre-ated at the request of the head coach of the University of Florida Gators to aid his athletes during strenuous workouts in hot weather. Although water was adequate to prevent dehydration, athletes were losing salts through sweat. A team of researchers from the College of Medicine at the uni-versity experimented with rehydration drinks of different salt compositions and came up with a mixture that the ath-letes felt increased their performance during practice. The team subsequently made it to the Orange Bowl, which was played under sweltering conditions. The Gators won that year and attributed their superior performance to the Gato-rade. Shortly thereafter, Gatorade became a commercial product, and the rest is history.

# KEY CONCEPTS REVIEW AND QUESTIONS

## 25.1 Water and Solutes

The cells of all organisms (bacteria, fungi, plants, and animals) are composed largely of water containing solutes ranging from ions to complex macromolecules. The challenges facing any organism for maintaining the proper levels of water and solutes in their cells vary depending on the levels of water and solutes in the environment in which it lives.

## 25.2 Water and Solute Balance in Plants

Most plants obtain their solutes and water from the soil. Most minerals and ions are taken up by active transport. Water follows by osmosis. Plants that live in dry environments have a thick cuticle and small leaves, with photosynthesis taking place in the stem. Many of these plants also have evolved the C4 mode of carbon fixation in photosynthesis and use Crassulacean acid metabolism (CAM), allowing these plants to close or restrict the opening of stomata, restricting water loss from transpiration.

1. Plants living in hot, dry climates exhibit many adaptations to reduce water loss. What are the disadvantages of these strategies, and why are they not appropriate in moister climates?

## 25.3 Water and Solute Balance in Animals

Many marine animals are osmoconformers, maintaining the solute concentration of their extracellular fluids equal to that of the sea water that surrounds them. They eliminate the need to actively regulate water balance. Most freshwater and terrestrial animals are osmoregulators. The solute concentration of their extracellular fluids differs from that of the environments. They must actively regulate both solute and water uptake in a homeostatic fashion.

2. Match each of the following groups of organisms with their osmoregulatory strategies.

   a. Marine invertebrates    ___ Lose water easily and have trouble obtaining solutes

   b. Marine fish    ___ Lose water easily and have trouble excreting solutes

   c. Freshwater fish    ___ Obtain water easily and have trouble retaining solutes

   d. Terrestrial vertebrates    ___ Have no trouble balancing water and solutes

   e. Terrestrial invertebrates

3. Which of the following statements are true?

   a. The concentrations of individual ions are identical inside and outside the cells of osmoconformers.

   b. Osmoconformers are found in both fresh water and sea water.

   c. All osmoregulators are hypo-osmotic to their environment.

   d. Osmoconformers do not need to expend energy on maintaining water balance.

   e. Osmoregulators do not need to expend energy on maintaining water balance.

Although many solutes are needed by the cells, many are waste products, particularly solutes containing nitrogen (nitrogenous wastes), and must be eliminated. Aquatic animals dispose of nitrogenous wastes as ammonia ($NH_3$), a toxic compound that can only be disposed of with a lot of water. Most other animals convert ammonia into urea, a compound that is much less toxic and can be excreted with less water. Some animals living in dry habitats excrete uric acid, a relatively insoluble substance that can be excreted with very little water. Both urea and uric acid take more energy to produce.

4. Match each of the following groups of organisms with their excretory strategies.

   a. Terrestrial insects    ___ Excrete ammonia

   b. Fish    ___ Excrete urea

   c. Reptiles    ___ Excrete uric acid

   d. Mammals

   e. Birds

The simple strategy for excretion in most animals is to begin by eliminating almost all solutes by non-selective filtration, take back as much of the water as necessary and the important solutes by reabsorption, and ensure the elimination of select molecules in high concentration by secretion. Everything not needed is then released to the environment. This four-stage process generally takes place in microscopic tubules concentrated in specialized organs. In mammals and birds, these are the kidneys.

5. Match each of the following substances that can be found in blood with what happens to them when blood flows through a mammalian kidney.

   a. Water    ___ Almost all excreted in the urine

   b. Water-soluble vitamins    ___ Almost all reabsorbed into the blood

   c. Glucose    ___ Leaves the blood by filtration

   d. Urea    ___ Can be secreted into the urine

## 25.4 Temperature

All objects, living or non-living, exchange heat with their environment by conduction, convection, radiation, or evaporation. There are limits to the environmental temperatures compatible for life. These temperatures vary tremendously between simple single-celled microorganisms and complex multicellular plants and animals. Within their functional range, multicellular organisms are also profoundly affected by changes in temperature.

Because of its effect on chemical processes, temperature regulates the rate of all biological processes.

6. Match each description on the left with the proper term on the right.

a. Drop in temperature due to wind   ___ Radiation

b. Loss of heat in still water   ___ Convection

c. Cooling of the air on a clear, starry night   ___ Evaporation

d. Cooling due to panting   ___ Conduction

## 25.5 Plant Responses to Temperature Change

Most plants from tropical regions cannot survive freezing temperatures, whereas perennial plants in temperate regions can by either freeze avoidance, using antifreeze proteins, or freeze tolerance, a strategy shared by many animals in which the water outside their cells is allowed to freeze, but not the water inside their cells. Environmental cues in the fall (low temperature and short photoperiod) trigger changes in gene expression, leading to physiological changes at the molecular, cellular, and whole-plant levels, a process referred to as cold acclimatization. For plants living in hot environments, there is little they can do to prevent warming. Evaporative water loss and synthesis of heat shock proteins are plant strategies for dealing with heat.

7. Many strategies for dealing with severe temperature change are shared by some plants and some animals. Which of the following is not?

a. Evaporative water loss

b. Freeze tolerance

c. Tolerance of severe dehydration

d. Synthesis of heat shock proteins

e. Shivering

f. Freeze avoidance

g. Cold acclimatization

## 25.6 Animal Responses to Temperature Change

Animals for which the primary source of heat is the environment are referred to as ectotherms, whereas those for which it is primarily from metabolism are referred to as endotherms. These are different strategies for establishing body temperature, each of which can be advantageous in different environments.

8. What are the costs and benefits of being an ectotherm versus an endotherm when living in the tropics versus living in subpolar regions?

Invertebrates, fishes, amphibians, and reptiles are ectotherms. Their body temperatures are generally the same as the environment around them; thus, they regulate their body temperatures by behavioural means: they seek out regions of the environment that are most optimal.

9. Which of the following strategies for temperature regulation in cold environments are seen in some ectotherms?

a. Countercurrent heat exchange

b. Basking

c. Brown fat oxidation

d. Shivering

e. Regulation of skin blood flow

Birds and mammals are endotherms. They maintain high body temperatures by controlling the rate at which metabolic heat is lost to the environment. Their body temperatures are regulated around a constant value homeostatically by sensing body temperature and employing physiological strategies to maintain their body temperatures at the appropriate level. When environmental temperatures are high, they reduce insulation, increase heat flow to the skin, and, in many, use evaporative water loss by sweating or rapid breathing (panting or gular fluttering). When environmental temperatures are low, they increase insulation by erecting their fur or feathers, reducing blood flow to the skin, and may huddle. If temperatures fall sufficiently, they shiver and recruit non-shivering thermogenesis (the generation of heat by fat oxidation).

10. In Figure 25.12, we see a thermal image of a ground squirrel in the process of arousing from hibernation. Heat for arousal is being generated by the oxidation of brown fat. Note that the hottest areas are the brain and the body core. This is because heat is being generated from brown fat surrounding the heart. What is the advantage of storing brown fat in this area?

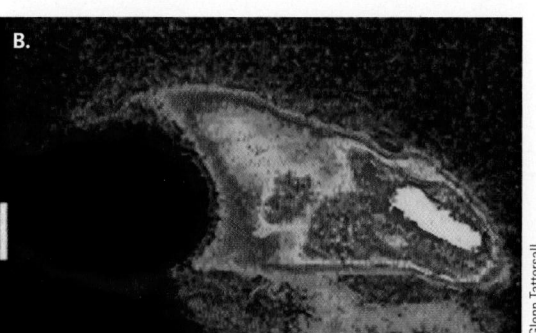

**FIGURE 25.12 (a)** A ground squirrel. **(b)** Thermal image of a ground squirrel arousing from hibernation. The head is on the right, and the hindlimbs are on the left. The brighter the colour, the warmer the tissue is.

# Intercellular Communication

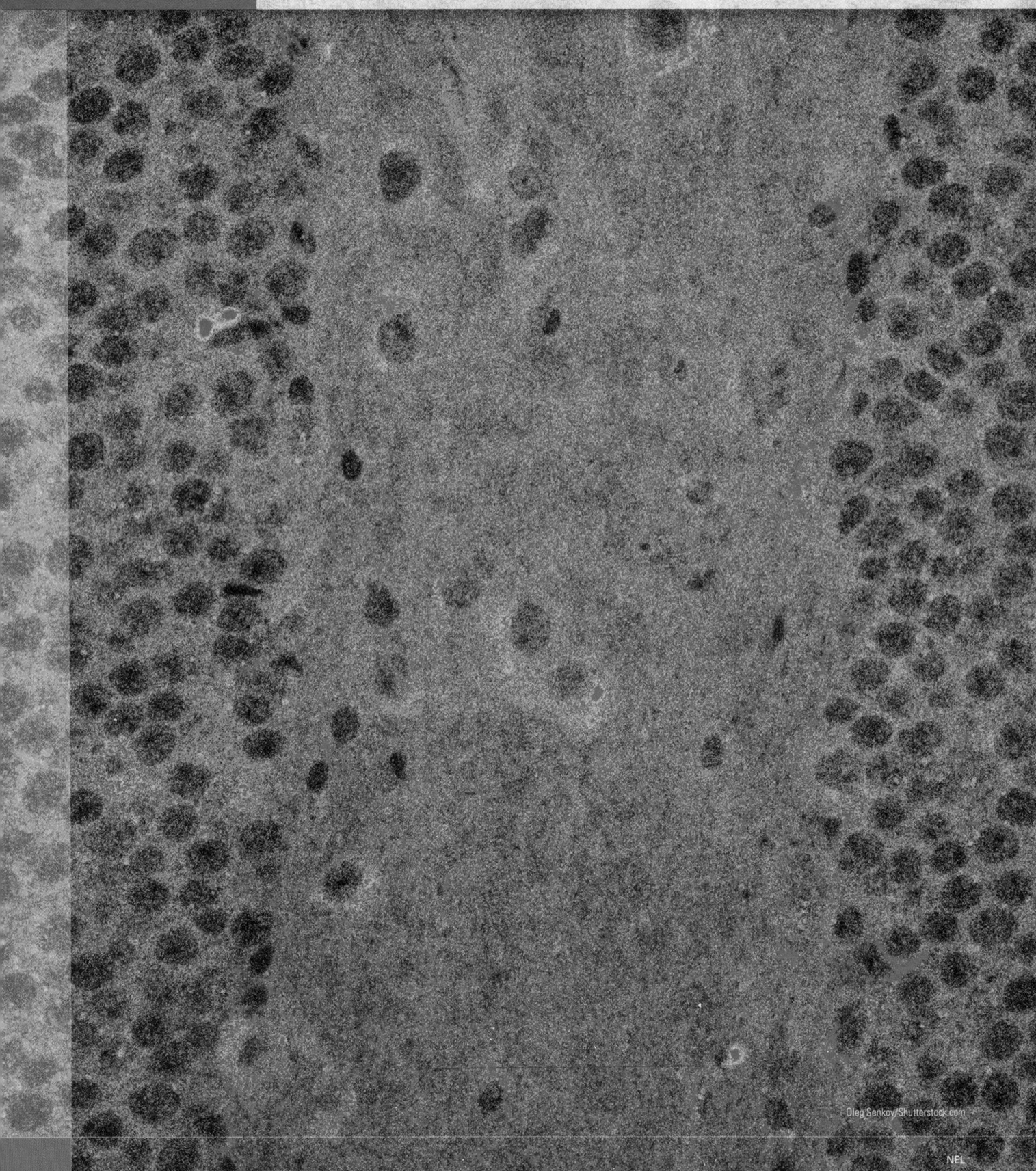

## WHY IT MATTERS

Often when you are hiking in the mountains of western Canada you will hear a sharp trill that echoes throughout the alpine meadow. This is the call of a marmot (*Marmota marmota*) that has spotted you approaching **(Figure 26.1)**. The sound sends every other marmot in the valley scampering back to its burrow. It triggers a complex series of events within each individual—the so-called fight-or-flight response. This response requires careful communication between cells in all parts of the body. The nervous system produces immediate changes in blood flow to muscles, lungs, and heart that prepare the marmot to either flee or defend itself. The hormonal system produces slower but longer-lasting changes in such things as glucose and fat metabolism to sustain the elevated activities of these other systems. It is important that all of these changes be coordinated. The glucose must be released from the liver and the fat from body lipid stores, both to fuel increased activity. The tissues involved will need more oxygen to metabolize these compounds. This will require an increase in breathing to obtain more oxygen, an increase in heart rate to transport it, and changes in blood flow to muscles and other organs to ensure that the extra oxygen is delivered to the right destination. As you can see, this is a well-orchestrated series of events—one that requires perfectly timed interactions and excellent intercellular communication.

This is only one example of the way in which the activities of different organs and organ systems in plants and animals must be coordinated on a minute-by-minute basis. Many other activities are coordinated over different time scales, such as we see in daily cycles of events and with seasonal changes.

In this chapter, we will consider the communication that occurs between cells throughout the bodies of multicellular plants and animals that ensures that coordinated responses to various stimuli occur at the correct time in an efficient and orchestrated manner. We present the material in a slightly different way than most other textbooks by combining the discussion of the hormonal and nervous control systems in one chapter. This allows us to stress the tremendous similarities between the two systems as well as the differences. These are two physiological systems of chemical communication that are structurally and functionally related. Where they differ is primarily in the types of activities they control, and why this is will become apparent when we examine how they work.

## 26.1 Intercellular Communication: An Overview

### The Growth, Survival, and Reproduction of Multicellular Plants and Animals Depend on the Ability of Their Cells to Communicate with One Another

Chapters 17 and 19 describe the different tissues and organ systems that can be found in multicellular plants and animals. This differentiation of cells within the bodies of

**FIGURE 26.1** **(a)** Subalpine habitats are home to marmots throughout western Canada and the United States. **(b)** Marmots live in colonies and **(c)** are preyed on by both large mammals (such as bears [*Ursus arctos*]) and birds. They use alarm calls to warn one another and to prepare to flee or to defend themselves.

SOURCE: (Photos A–C): Johnny Adolphson/Shutterstock.com; Bildagentur Zoonar GmbH/Shutterstock.com; bikemp/Shutterstock.com

plants and animals allows different groups of cells to perform different tasks, leading to a very efficient division of labour. To be truly efficient, however, each tissue, organ, and organ system must know what the others are doing and coordinate their activities. This requires good communication. In plants, this communication is achieved almost exclusively by hormones. In animals, it is achieved by a coordinated effort between hormones and nerves. These are two physiological systems of chemical communication that are structurally and functionally related but that control different types of activities.

**Hormones** are chemicals secreted by specialized cells that generally control and coordinate slow, long-acting responses of multiple tissues or organs. These responses usually involve transcription and translation of DNA, leading to the synthesis of new proteins that remain active for hours, weeks, months, or even years **(Figure 26.2)**.

The nervous system, on the other hand, controls and coordinates activities that are fast and immediate and can selectively act on only one tissue or organ; such activities allow animals to react rapidly to changes in their internal or external environment (Figure 26.2).

Although we usually distinguish between hormonal and neural control, the main differences between these two regulatory systems are the speed and specificity of their actions. Both involve chemical signals that cause cellular responses by interacting with specific receptors on or in their **target cells**. Just as is the case with enzymes and substrates (see Chapter 4), each hormone and neurotransmitter binds only to a specific receptor protein that has the right shape and charge characteristics to produce a chemical bond.

Some hormones act as local regulators to communicate between neighbouring cells. In **autocrine** regulation, a chemical is released that acts on the same cells that release it **(Figure 26.3a)** to either reduce or increase their sensitivity to other stimuli. In **paracrine** regulation, a cell releases a chemical that acts on its neighbours. These are

**FIGURE 26.2** The actions of many hormones are relatively slow because they involve transcription and translation to produce new proteins. Hormones control **(a)** the flowering of plants in an alpine meadow or **(b)** pregnancy and childbirth in fish (sea horse, *Hippocampus* sp.) and **(c)** in mammals. The nervous system controls rapid actions that take place in fractions of a second, such as **(d, e)** the touch-induced movement in mimosa leaves (*Mimosa pudica*) or **(f)** the attack of a leopard (*Panthera pardus*).

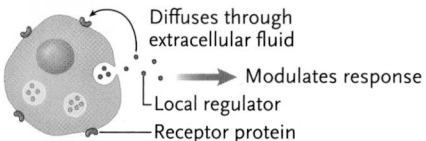

**A. Autocrine regulation**

Diffuses through extracellular fluid

Modulates response

Local regulator

Receptor protein

**B. Paracrine regulation**

Diffuses through extracellular fluid

Receptor protein

Response

Local regulator

Target cell

Receptor protein

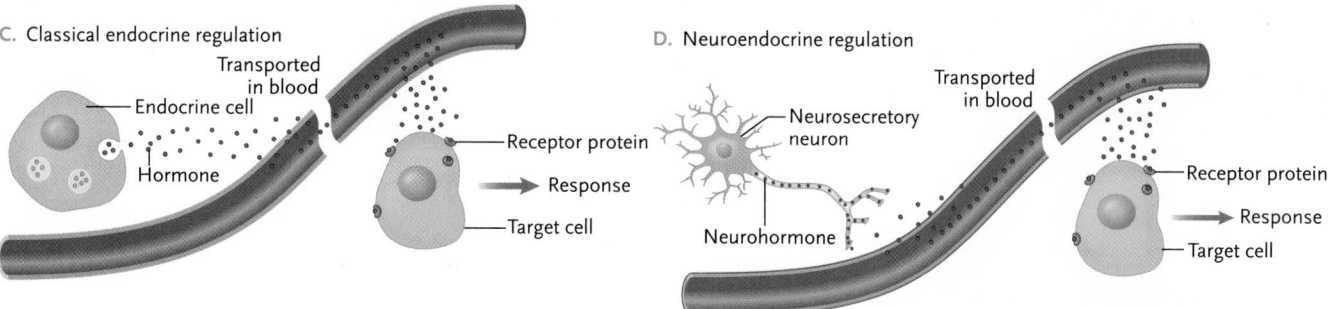

**C. Classical endocrine regulation**

Transported in blood

Endocrine cell

Receptor protein

Hormone

Response

Target cell

**D. Neuroendocrine regulation**

Transported in blood

Neurosecretory neuron

Receptor protein

Response

Neurohormone

Target cell

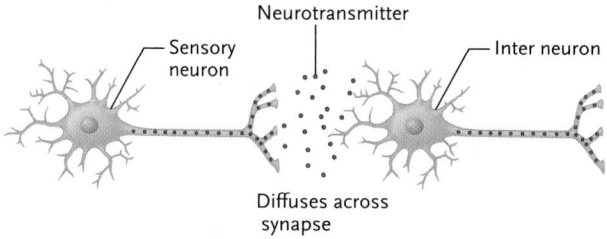

**E. Classical neural regulation**

Neurotransmitter

Sensory neuron

Inter neuron

Diffuses across synapse

*Biology, 2E\**

**FIGURE 26.3** The major types of cell signalling in the hormonal and nervous systems.

examples of local regulation **(Figure 26.3b)**. The growth factors that we will describe shortly are hormones that regulate cell division and differentiation through local regulation.

Other hormones and neurotransmitters are used to communicate with distant cells. Hormones may be secreted into the vascular system (plant or animal) **(Figure 26.3c)** and transported throughout the body. Target cells that possess receptors (Chapter 4) that recognize and bind the hormone will react to them. The hormones from the adrenal glands in animals and the **cytokines** in plants work in this way.

In **neuroendocrine** regulation, specialized nerve cells release a chemical into the circulation when stimulated **(Figure 26.3d)**. This chemical is distributed in blood or other body fluids, just like a regular hormone. Because these hormones are released from nerve cells, they are called **neurohormones**.

By contrast, in neural regulation, nerve cells release neurotransmitters such as noradrenaline and acetylcholine directly onto their target cells **(Figure 26.3e)**.

## STUDY BREAK

1. What are the major types of chemical signalling that occur between cells?
2. How do hormonal control and neural control differ? How are they the same?

## 26.2 Hormones

We will focus first on hormones and how they act in the bodies of plants and vertebrate and invertebrate animals. They control major body systems and processes in several different ways. We will review these before exploring the details of how different kinds of hormones work and what they do.

### Hormones Work to Coordinate Body Functions in Several Ways

Remember that a hormone will not react with a cell if it does not have the specific receptor protein for that hormone. If the cell does have the appropriate receptor, however, a series of chemical events within the cell will begin when the hormone binds to the receptor. These events will produce a response: a change in the activity or behaviour of the cell. This may happen in one of two ways depending on the chemical structure of the hormone (hormones come in several shapes and sizes) **(Figure 26.4, p. 566)**. Remember that chemicals may be charged compounds (in which case, they are water soluble but not lipid soluble) or neutral compounds (in which case, they are lipid soluble but not water soluble).

### Peptide Hormones

Water-soluble hormones include the peptide hormones, which are amino acid–derived hormones ranging in

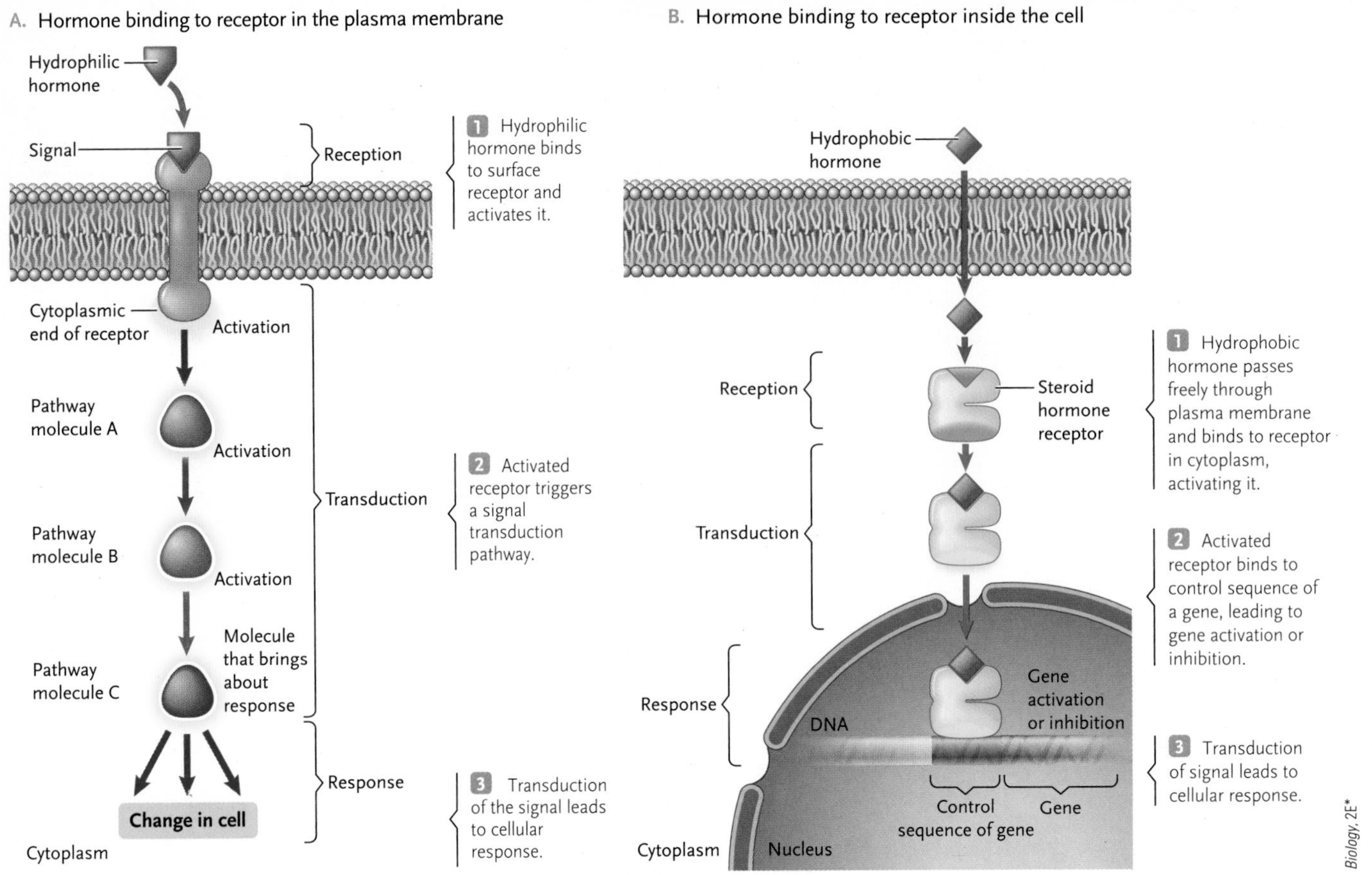

**A.** Hormone binding to receptor in the plasma membrane

Hydrophilic hormone

Signal

Reception

Cytoplasmic end of receptor — Activation

Pathway molecule A — Activation

Pathway molecule B — Activation

Pathway molecule C — Molecule that brings about response

Transduction

Response

**Change in cell**

Cytoplasm

1 Hydrophilic hormone binds to surface receptor and activates it.

2 Activated receptor triggers a signal transduction pathway.

3 Transduction of the signal leads to cellular response.

**B.** Hormone binding to receptor inside the cell

Hydrophobic hormone

Reception — Steroid hormone receptor

Transduction

Response — DNA — Gene activation or inhibition

Control sequence of gene — Gene

Cytoplasm — Nucleus

1 Hydrophobic hormone passes freely through plasma membrane and binds to receptor in cytoplasm, activating it.

2 Activated receptor binds to control sequence of a gene, leading to gene activation or inhibition.

3 Transduction of signal leads to cellular response.

*Biology, 2E*

**FIGURE 26.4** Reaction pathways are activated by hormones that bind to receptor proteins **(a)** in plasma membranes or **(b)** inside cells. In both mechanisms, the signal—the binding of the hormone to its receptor—is transduced to produce the cellular response.

length from as few as 3 amino acids to more than 200. These hormones, such as adrenaline, diffuse readily into extracellular and vascular fluids but do not cross membranes easily. As a result, they act on target cells by binding to receptors at the cell surface on the outside of the membrane. When a surface receptor binds a hormone, it changes shape, and this results in a cascade of chemical events inside the cell **(Figure 26.4a)**. Typically, the cascade (or signal transduction pathway; see Chapter 4) activates or inhibits a functional protein, such as an enzyme, an ion channel, or a transport protein.

### Steroid and Fatty Acid Hormones

The steroid and fatty acid hormones, such as **estrogen** and testosterone, are not water soluble. As a result, they must bind to water-soluble carrier proteins before they can be transported in vascular or other fluids. Once they contact a target cell, the hormone is released from its carrier protein and diffuses readily through the lipid bilayer of the plasma membrane. These hormones bind to receptors within the cytoplasm or nucleus **(Figure 26.4b)**. The hormone–receptor complex that is formed usually either activates or inhibits transcription of specific genes in the nucleus. The net effect of this activity depends on the specific genes controlled by the activated receptors. But,

in general, it leads to synthesis of functional proteins such as enzymes, ion channels, and transport proteins. These hormones are slower acting because their effects depend on the synthesis of new proteins rather than on modulation of existing proteins.

Small quantities of hormones can often produce very large effects. An activated receptor can turn on many enzyme molecules that can in turn activate an even larger number of proteins. If this occurs at each step in a pathway, the final result is quite profound (see Chapter 4). This process is called **amplification**. It has been estimated that a single molecule of the hormone adrenaline, acting on a liver cell in a mammal, can liberate over 100 molecules of glucose from stored glycogen by this process of amplification.

Once a hormone binds to its receptor, it will activate whichever signalling cascade the receptor is linked to. These are genetically programmed in different ways in different cells at different developmental stages in different species. Researchers are working hard to unravel these pathways. The net result is that any individual cell may respond to more than one hormone, and different cells may respond in different ways to the same hormone. For instance, the pancreatic hormone insulin increases glucose uptake and conversion to glycogen by liver cells in vertebrate animals, which decreases blood glucose levels. In contrast, glucagon, another hormone released from the pancreas, stimulates the same cells to breakdown glycogen, which increases blood glucose levels.

In both plants and animals, many processes are affected by more than one hormone. Physiological processes such as oxidative metabolism, growth, sexual development, and reactions to stress are all controlled by multiple hormones. In general, these processes are controlled by the secretion of hormones that have opposing actions. The balance of their effects maintains body homeostasis, the tight regulation of the internal environment of living organisms. The levels of each hormone are controlled by negative feedback, and these systems ensure that essential physiological processes function properly regardless of changes in either the external or the internal environment of the plant or animal (see Chapter 20).

Plant hormones are often synthesized and released widely throughout the body by general body tissues (apical meristems, young shoots and leaves, flowers, fruits, etc.). Many tend to be released and act locally. Animal hormones are usually produced by specialized cells concentrated in secretory organs called **endocrine glands** and tend to act on cells some distance away. Also, many (but not all) of the effects of hormones in animals are integrated and coordinated by the nervous system.

## STUDY BREAK

1. Why do hormones only affect certain cells?
2. Explain how a single cell can respond to many hormones and how the same hormone can have different effects on different cells.
3. Explain how a small amount of hormone can produce very large responses.

## Hormones in Plants

You might be surprised to learn that plants have hormones. I think most of us have heard the word *hormone*, usually in relation to our own bodies. Although there are some key differences between plant and animal hormones, both are chemicals that serve as a form of communication between different organs and tissues that coordinate their physiology and behaviour. Most plant hormones are primarily involved in cell growth, stimulating or inhibiting cell division and elongation. Others are involved in dormancy and aging. These hormones are listed in **Table 26.1**. Recent discoveries have identified several groups of plant defence molecules that have hormonelike properties. Those that are associated with defence against herbivores are discussed in Chapter 30, whereas those involved in defence against microbes and pathogens are discussed in Chapter 27. Bear in mind that many hormones have more than one action.

### Biological Rhythms in Plants: Daily and Seasonal Control of Plant Hormone Release

Many plants exhibit daily and seasonal behaviours. When we think of the word *behaviour*, we usually think of animals—such as the marmot's defence tactics. We rarely think of plants as having behaviours, but they do. Plant behaviours are defined as their daily or seasonal responses to their environment. Daily behaviours include the opening and closing of stomata and the morning opening and evening closing of leaves. Seasonal behaviours include flowering, seed germination, and the onset and ending of dormancy.

| TABLE 26.1 | Major Plant Hormones and Signalling Chemicals | | |
|---|---|---|---|
| **Hormone/Signalling Compound** | **Where Synthesized** | **Tissues Affected** | **Effects** |
| Auxins | Apical meristems, developing leaves and embryos | Growing tissues, buds, roots, leaves, fruits, vascular tissues | Promote growth and elongation of stems; promote formation of lateral roots and dormancy in lateral buds; promote fruit development (see Box 26.1); inhibit leaf abscission; orient plants with respect to light, gravity (see Box 26.2) |
| Gibberellins | Root and shoot tips, young leaves, developing embryos | Stems, developing seeds | Promote cell divisions and growth and elongation of stems; promote seed germination |
| Cytokinins | Mainly in root tips | Shoot apical meristems, leaves, buds | Promote cell division; inhibit senescence of leaves; coordinate growth of roots and shoots (with auxin) |
| Ethylene | Shoot tips, roots, leaf nodes, flowers, fruits | Seeds, buds, seedlings, mature leaves, flowers, fruits | Regulates elongation and division of cells in seedling stems, roots; in mature plants, regulates senescence and abscission of leaves, flowers, and fruits |
| Brassinosteroids | Young seeds, shoots and leaves, pollen | Mainly shoot tips, developing embryos | Stimulate cell division and elongation, differentiation of vascular tissue |
| Abscisic acid | Leaves, roots | Buds, seeds, stomata | Promotes responses to environmental stress, including inhibiting growth/promoting dormancy; stimulates stomata to close in water-stressed plants |

*Biology, 2E\**

## THE MOLECULE BEHIND THE BIOLOGY 26.1
### Auxins

Given the importance of auxins for plant growth, there has been significant research into the use of synthetic auxins for agricultural purposes. Commercial orchardists spray synthetic auxins on fruit trees to promote uniform flowering and to prevent premature fruit drop. This allows all fruit (particularly oranges and grapefruits) to be picked at the same time, reducing labour costs. However, the application of auxins must be done with care, because if too much auxin is applied ethylene production will be stimulated, making the fruit ripen and drop too quickly **(Figure 1a)**. Indeed, this has also been used by orchardists to thin fruit production (particularly apples) so that the remaining fruits grow larger **(Figure 1b)**. In some cases, auxins can also induce fruit development without the need for pollination, making it possible to grow seedless fruit (tomatoes) **(Figure 1c)**.

Some synthetic auxins are also used as herbicides, essentially stimulating plants to "grow themselves to death." The most widely used herbicide in the world is 2,4-D (2,4-dichlorophenoxyacetic acid). Eudicots (broadleaf weeds) are more sensitive to this compound than monocots (cereal crops such as corn); thus, 2,4-D causes the weeds to elongate up to 10 times faster than the monocots—much faster than the plant can support, leading to its death.

**FIGURE 1** Ethylene is used **(a)** to promote uniform and simultaneous fruit ripening in oranges (*Citrus sinensis*) and grapefruits; **(b)** for fruit thinning to promote larger growth in apples (*Malus domestica*); and **(c)** for the development of seedless varieties of fruit, such as tomatoes (*Solanum lycopersicum*).

Daily or 24-hour rhythms are referred to as circadian rhythms (from the Latin *circa*, meaning about, and *dies*, meaning day). What underlies this phenomenon is a biological clock. In the case of plants, the leading hypothesis for the mechanism underlying timekeeping is the synthesis of a protein that regulates its own production through negative feedback control. Through protein synthesis, the protein accumulates until it reaches a level that turns transcription of the gene off. When the concentration of the protein falls sufficiently, transcription restarts. For this to explain circadian rhythms, the time required for one full cycle would be 24 hours. This rhythm can continue in the absence of any environmental cues but generally requires daily signals from the environment to entrain it or keep it exactly timed to

24 hours. The most common environmental cue used to adjust the clock timing is the light/dark cycle of day and night. The clock cannot immediately adjust to changes in the light/dark cycle but adjusts slowly; thus, just like us, if plants are moved rapidly from one location to another, they experience disruptions to their circadian rhythms similar to jet lag.

In the case of seasonal changes, the stimulus plants use most frequently to detect the time of the year is also the photoperiod. A classical example of such a seasonal event is flowering. Many plants flower in late spring or early summer, when days are long and nights are short (long-day plants), whereas others flower in late summer, fall, or even winter, when days are short and nights are long (short-day plants).

BOX 26.2

# Plant Tropisms

If you have ever had houseplants or planted seedlings near a window, you may have noticed them leaning toward the nearest light source. This process is called **phototropism** (from the Greek *photos*, meaning light, and *tropos*, meaning to turn). It is an adaptive response that orients growing seedlings and the shoots and leaves of mature plants toward sunlight, enhancing photosynthesis **(Figure 1a)**. This process was extensively studied by Charles

**A.**

**B.**

Question: Why does a plant stem bend toward the light?

Experiment 1: The Darwins observed that the first shoot of an emerging grass seedling, which is sheathed by a coleoptile, bends toward sunlight shining through a window. They removed the shoot tip from a seedling and illuminated one side of the seedling.

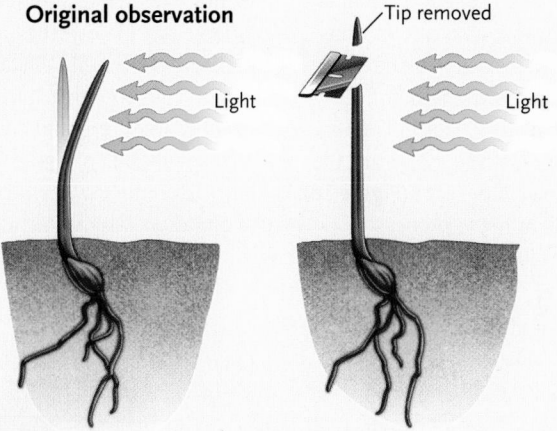

Result: The seedling neither grew nor bent.

**C.**

Experiment 2: The Darwins divided seedlings into two groups. They covered the shoot tips of one group with an opaque cap and the shoot tips of the other group with a translucent cap. All the seedlings were illuminated from the same side.

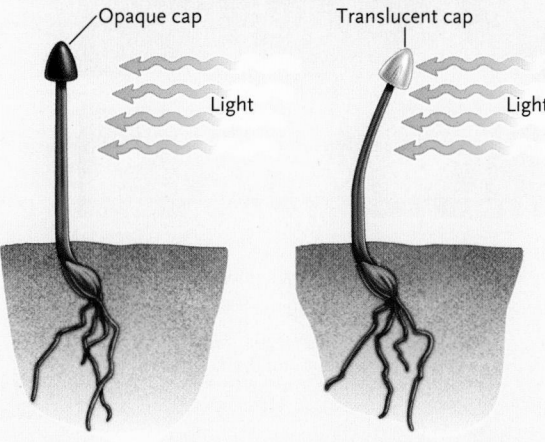

Result: The seedlings with opaque caps grew but did not bend. Those with translucent caps both grew *and* bent toward the light.

Conclusion: When seedlings are illuminated from one side, an unknown factor transmitted from a seedling's tip to the tissue below causes it to bend toward the light.

**D.**

Experiment 3: Frits Went removed the tip of a seedling and placed it on an agar block. He placed the agar block containing auxin on one side of the shoot tip.

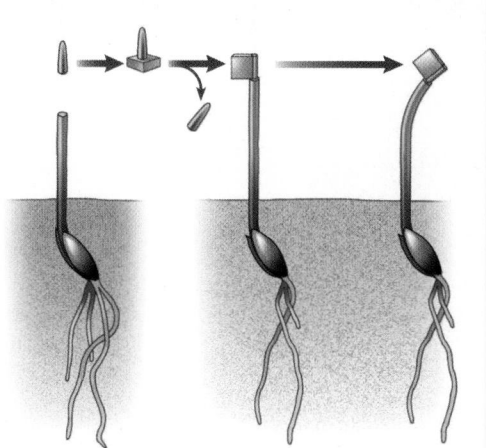

Result: Auxin moved into the shoot tip on that side, causing it to bend away from the hormone.

Conclusion: The unknown factor transmitted from a seedling's tip to the tissue below that causes it to bend toward the light was auxin.

**FIGURE 1** **(a)** Young plant shoots bending toward the light (phototropism). **(b, c)** The Darwins' experiments on phototropism showing that an unknown factor produced in the shoot tip in response to light caused the seedling tip to bend toward the light. **(d)** Frits Went's experiment demonstrating that the unknown factor was auxin.

*(Continued)*

BOX 26.2 *(Continued)*

Darwin and his son, Francis, in the late 19th century **(Figures 1b** and **1c)**. Research into phototropism ultimately led to the discovery of auxin by the Dutch scientist Frits Went. These experiments were the first to suggest that plants possessed mobile chemicals (hormones) involved in growth. Although the mechanisms behind this differential growth are still not totally clear today, protein pigments that detect light are now known to be present in shoot tips and somehow cause auxins to migrate laterally to the shaded side of the plant. The auxins move down the shoot, causing the shaded side to elongate more than the sunny side, and as a result, the shoot grows toward the light **(Figure 1d)**.

**Gravitropism** is the process by which gravity alters plant growth. The shoots of young plants grow upward against the force of gravity, and their roots grow downward. If a seedling is placed on its side so that the shoot and root are horizontal, the shoot will turn to grow upward **(Figure 2a)** and the root will turn and grow downward. How different parts of the plant know up from down and alter their growth patterns accordingly is not clear. It is currently believed that organelles containing dense starch grains are affected by gravity; they move to the bottom of the cell. This appears to signal cells to redistribute auxins, leading to differential growth. In the case of shoots, a high concentration of auxins on the lower side stimulates cell elongation, which causes the shoot to turn upward. In the case of roots, a high concentration of auxin on the lower side inhibits cell elongation and causes the root to curve downward.

**Thigmotropism** describes differential growth in response to touch. This is commonly seen in the tendrils (modified leaves) that many plants produce to anchor and support their growth, such as you see with the growth of grapes on a trellis or ivy on the wall of a house. Tendrils grow straight until they touch an object. Contact stimulates the cells to grow at different rates on opposite sides of the tendril. Cell elongation is inhibited on the side that makes contact but is stimulated on the opposite side. This causes the tendril to coil around the object, anchoring and supporting the plant **(Figure 2b)**.

**FIGURE 2** **(a)** Gravitropism in young shoots. When the pot was turned on its side, negative gravitropism caused the stems to bend so that the shoots grew upright. **(b)** Thigmotopism in a growing shoot. Tendrils making contact with other structures twist around them for support.

It now appears that plants measure photoperiod via **phytochromes**, proteins that can absorb light. Plants synthesize phytochrome in an inactive form that, in daylight, absorbs the light of the red wavelength. This triggers conversion of the phytochrome to an active form. This form of the protein remains active until it encounters light in the far-red wavelength (common in the shade, at sunset, and at night), which converts the protein back into its inactive form. Botanists suspect that phytochrome controls the activity of various proteins that are required for the different functions that are regulated by photoperiod, such as the development of flowers **(Figure 26.5)**.

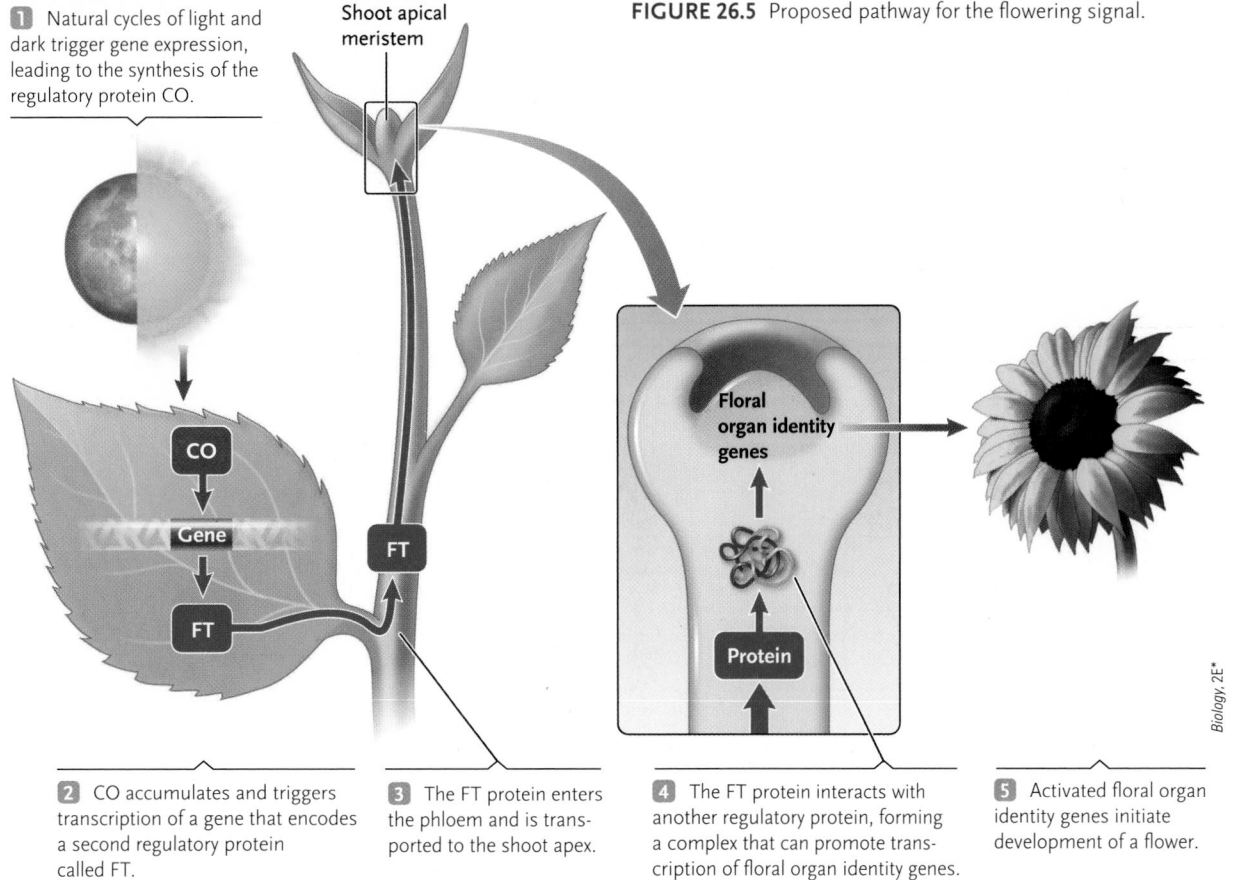

**1** Natural cycles of light and dark trigger gene expression, leading to the synthesis of the regulatory protein CO.

Shoot apical meristem

**FIGURE 26.5** Proposed pathway for the flowering signal.

Floral organ identity genes

Protein

*Biology, 2E\**

**2** CO accumulates and triggers transcription of a gene that encodes a second regulatory protein called FT.

**3** The FT protein enters the phloem and is transported to the shoot apex.

**4** The FT protein interacts with another regulatory protein, forming a complex that can promote transcription of floral organ identity genes.

**5** Activated floral organ identity genes initiate development of a flower.

## STUDY BREAK

1. Which plant hormones promote growth, and which inhibit it?
2. What is the direct stimulus for phototropism, gravitropism, and thigmotropism?
3. Give examples of how the knowledge of the actions of plant hormones has been used in agriculture.

**proteins** that the hormone can recognize and bind to. Our bodies continually clear hormones, either by breaking them down using enzymes in the target cells or by filtering them out in the liver or kidneys and excreting them with our body's waste. Their synthesis and levels in the vascular fluids are tightly controlled.

In vertebrates there are 11 endocrine organs **(Figure 26.7, p. 572)**, each secreting different hormones that have different targets and actions (see **Table 26.2, p. 572**).

## Hormones in Animals

Remember that with plants, hormones are produced by and released from cells that have many functions. This is also true in animals. Organs such as the pancreas and stomach also produce hormones. However, most animal hormones enter the blood or the fluid surrounding a cell from endocrine glands **(Figure 26.6)**. The hormones then move through the body in the blood or other fluids, constantly exposing most of the body's cells to a wide variety of hormones. Cells will respond to the hormone, however, only if they are **target cells** with **receptor**

**A.** Exocrine gland

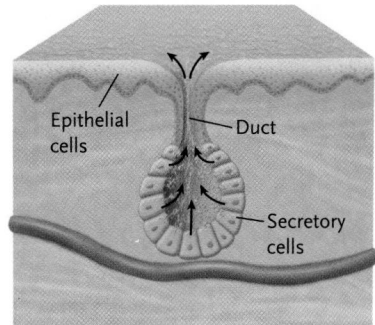

Epithelial cells

Duct

Secretory cells

**B.** Endocrine gland

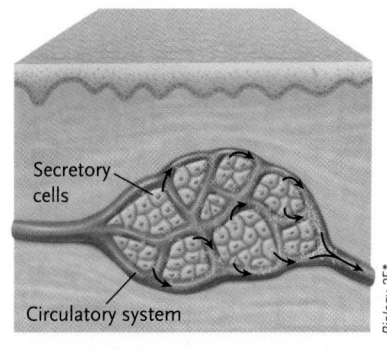

Secretory cells

Circulatory system

*Biology, 2E\**

**FIGURE 26.6** The structure of exocrine and endocrine glands. **(a)** Exocrine glands secrete chemicals into ducts that lead to the surface of the body or the digestive tract. **(b)** Endocrine glands lack ducts and secrete hormones directly into body fluids, especially the circulatory system.

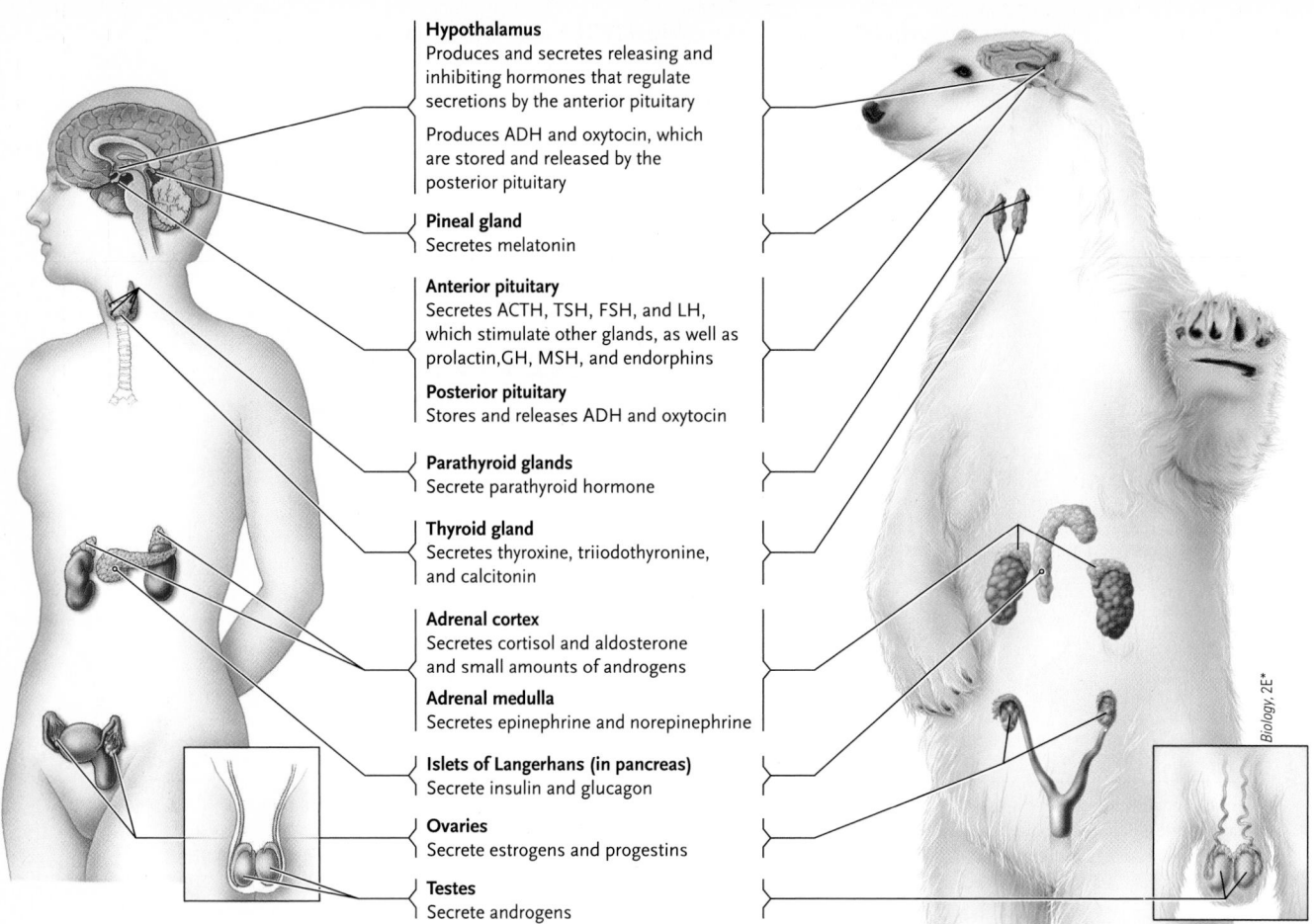

**Hypothalamus**
Produces and secretes releasing and inhibiting hormones that regulate secretions by the anterior pituitary

Produces ADH and oxytocin, which are stored and released by the posterior pituitary

**Pineal gland**
Secretes melatonin

**Anterior pituitary**
Secretes ACTH, TSH, FSH, and LH, which stimulate other glands, as well as prolactin, GH, MSH, and endorphins

**Posterior pituitary**
Stores and releases ADH and oxytocin

**Parathyroid glands**
Secrete parathyroid hormone

**Thyroid gland**
Secretes thyroxine, triiodothyronine, and calcitonin

**Adrenal cortex**
Secretes cortisol and aldosterone and small amounts of androgens

**Adrenal medulla**
Secretes epinephrine and norepinephrine

**Islets of Langerhans (in pancreas)**
Secrete insulin and glucagon

**Ovaries**
Secrete estrogens and progestins

**Testes**
Secrete androgens

*Biology, 2E\**

**FIGURE 26.7** This diagram shows the major endocrine glands in a mammal's body using a human and a bear as models.

**TABLE 26.2** | **The Major Human Endocrine Glands and Hormones**

| Secretory Tissue or Gland | Hormones | Molecular Class | Target Tissue | Principal Actions |
|---|---|---|---|---|
| Hypothalamus | Releasing and inhibiting hormones | Peptide | Anterior pituitary | Regulates secretion of anterior pituitary hormones |
| Anterior pituitary | Thyroid-stimulating hormone (TSH) | Peptide | Thyroid gland | Stimulates secretion of thyroid hormones and growth of thyroid gland |
| | Adrenocorticotropic hormone (ACTH) | Peptide | Adrenal cortex | Stimulates secretion of glucocorticoids by adrenal cortex |
| | Follicle-stimulating hormone (FSH) | Peptide | Ovaries in females, testes in males | Stimulates egg growth and development and secretion of sex hormones in females; stimulates sperm production in males |
| | Luteinizing hormone (LH) | Peptide | Ovaries in females, testes in males | Regulates ovulation in females and secretion of sex hormones in males |
| | Prolactin (PRL) | Peptide | Mammary glands | Stimulates breast development and milk secretion |
| | Growth hormone (GH) | Peptide | Bone, soft tissue | Stimulates growth of bones and soft tissues; helps control metabolism of glucose and other fuel molecules |
| | Melanocyte-stimulating hormone (MSH) | Peptide | Melanocytes in skin of some vertebrates | Promotes darkening of the skin |
| | Endorphins | Peptide | Pain pathways of peripheral nervous system (PNS) | Inhibit perception of pain |
| Posterior pituitary | Antidiuretic hormone (ADH) | Peptide | Kidneys | Raises blood volume and pressure by increasing water reabsorption in kidneys |
| | Oxytocin | Peptide | Uterus, mammary glands | Promotes uterine contractions; stimulates milk ejection from breasts |

*Biology, 2E\**

TABLE 26.2 | The Major Human Endocrine Glands and Hormones (*Continued*)

| Secretory Tissue or Gland | Hormones | Molecular Class | Target Tissue | Principal Actions |
|---|---|---|---|---|
| Thyroid gland | Calcitonin | Peptide | Bone | Lowers calcium concentration in blood |
| | Thyroxine and triiodothyronine | Amine | Most cells | Increases metabolic rate; essential for normal body growth |
| Parathyroid glands | Parathyroid hormone (PTH) | Peptide | Bone, kidneys, intestine | Raises calcium concentration in blood; stimulates vitamin D activation |
| Adrenal medulla | Epinephrine and norepinephrine | Amine | Sympathetic receptor sites throughout body | Reinforce sympathetic nervous system; contribute to responses to stress |
| Adrenal cortex | Aldosterone (mineralocorticoid) | Steroid | Kidney tubules | Helps control body's salt–water balance by increasing $Na^+$ reabsorption and $K^+$ excretion in kidneys |
| | Cortisol (glucocorticoid) | Steroid | Most body cells, particularly muscle, liver, and adipose cells | Increases blood glucose by promoting breakdown of proteins and fats |
| Testes | Androgens, such as testosterone* | Steroid | Various tissues | Control male reproductive system development and maintenance; most androgens are made by the testes |
| | Oxytocin | Peptide | Uterus | Promote uterine contractions when seminal fluid is ejaculated into vagina during sexual intercourse |
| Ovaries | Estrogens, such as estradiol** | Steroid | Breasts, uterus, other tissues | Stimulate maturation of sex organs at puberty and development of secondary sexual characteristics |
| | Progestins, such as progesterone** | Steroid | Uterus | Prepare and maintain uterus for implantation of fertilized eggs and the growth and development of embryos |
| Pancreas (islets of Langerhans) | Glucagon (alpha cells) | Peptide | Liver cells | Raises glucose concentration in blood; promotes release of glucose from glycogen stores and production from non-carbohydrates |
| | Insulin (beta cells) | Peptide | Most cells | Lowers glucose concentration in blood; promotes storage of glucose, fatty acids, and amino acids (see Box 26.3) |
| Pineal gland | Melatonin | Amine | Brain, anterior pituitary, reproductive organs, immune system, possibly others | Helps synchronize body's biological clock with day length; may inhibit gonadotropins and initiation of puberty |
| Many cell types | Growth factors | Peptide | Most cells | Regulate cell division and differentiation |
| | Prostaglandins | Fatty acid | Various tissues | Have many diverse roles |

*Small amounts secreted by ovaries and adrenal cortex.
**Small amounts secreted by testes.

As noted earlier, there is a close association between the endocrine system and the nervous system of animals. In both plants and animals, hormone secretion is regulated, most frequently by feedback loops, to ensure that physiological functions are maintained at appropriate levels. Although this feedback control is exclusively hormonal in plants, in animals, it is often modulated by neural control. The hypothalamus, an endocrine organ in the brain, provides the link between the nervous and endocrine systems through a close association with the pituitary gland, as illustrated in **Figure 26.8 (p. 574).**

## STUDY BREAK

1. What are the hormones controlling calcium ion levels in the blood of vertebrates? Why is it important to control calcium ion levels?
2. Distinguish between the adrenal medulla and the adrenal cortex. What hormones do they secrete, and what are their functions?
3. How are levels of glucose in the blood maintained?
4. It is striking that invertebrate peptide hormones so closely resemble those in vertebrates. What are the possible explanations for this, in evolutionary terms? What research would you do to help you choose among the possibilities?

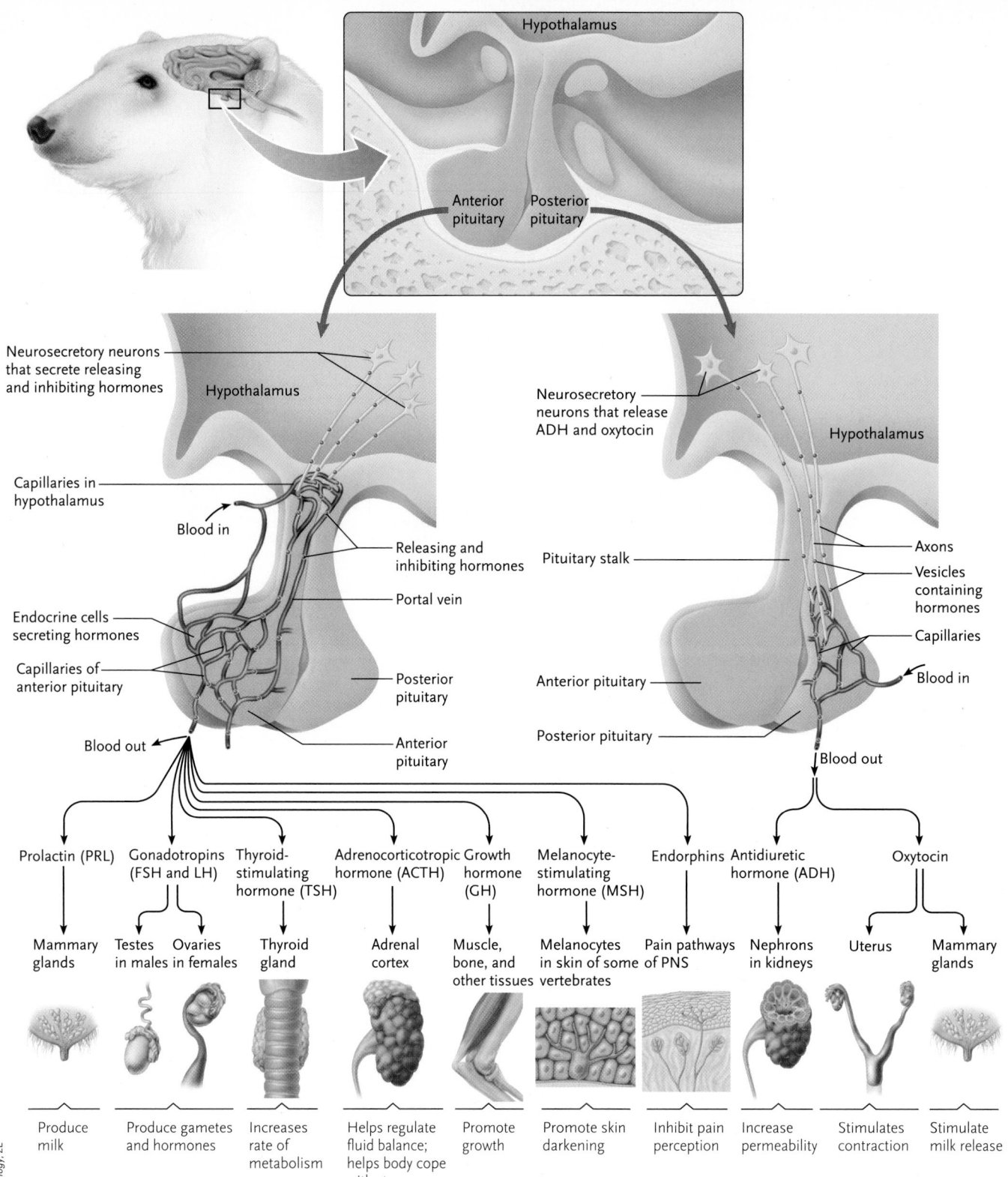

**FIGURE 26.8** The hypothalamus and pituitary. Hormones secreted by the anterior and posterior pituitary are controlled by neurohormones released in the hypothalamus.

*Biology, 2E*

## 26.3 The Nervous System

As mentioned earlier, hormonal systems and nervous systems are both systems of chemical communication. The differences between these two regulatory systems are primarily the speed and the specificity of their actions.

The nervous system acts through high-speed electrical signals to activate or inhibit highly specific localized targets, enabling an organism to react rapidly to changes in its internal or external environment. Hormones, on the other hand, act more slowly to produce widespread changes throughout the body (Figure 26.3).

# BOX 26.3
## Diabetes Mellitus

More than 2 million people in Canada suffer from **diabetes mellitus**, a disease that results from problems with either the production or action of insulin **(Figure 1)**. Type 1 diabetes, which occurs in about 10% of diabetics, is a disease that is caused when the pancreas does not produce enough insulin. Type 2 diabetes, which occurs in the other 90% of diabetics, is due to a reduction in the responsiveness of the body's cells to the hormone. Type 1 diabetes is usually caused by an autoimmune reaction that destroys pancreatic beta cells; consequently, type 1 diabetics must receive regular insulin injections to survive. Type 2 diabetes arises due to an interaction between genetic and lifestyle factors. Treatment consists of diet and weight control, exercising, and taking drugs that increase the production and/or action of insulin.

The word *diabetes* is derived from a Greek word meaning "siphon," referring to the frequent urination that commonly accompanies this disease. *Mellitus* is derived from a Latin word meaning "sweetened with honey," referring to the sweet smell and taste of a diabetic's urine.

If untreated, the cells in the bodies of diabetics are unable to use glucose as an energy source. Consequently, they start to break down fats and proteins to generate energy. As more and more proteins are broken down, diabetics experience many unfortunate symptoms. Blood vessels throughout the body become weaker. Poor circulation causes tissues to degenerate in the arms, legs, and feet. It also leads to bleeding in the retina, which can cause blindness and can lead to kidney failure.

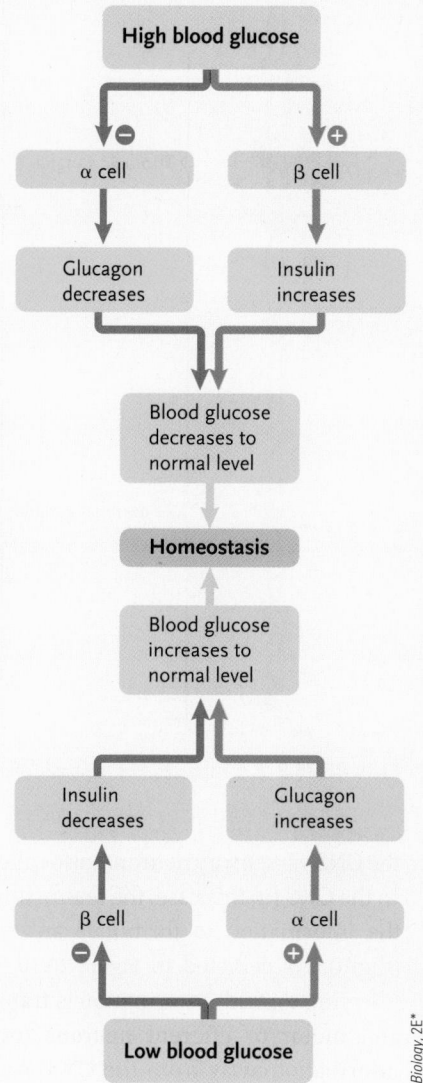

**FIGURE 1** The action of insulin and glucagon in maintaining the concentration of blood glucose at an optimal level.

---

Most multicellular animals have a nervous system. The ability of animals to detect small changes in their environment and to instantaneously analyze and process that information to produce specific behaviours is astounding, even in relatively simple animals. At the base of all of this is one major cell type: the neuron. This is the fundamental nerve cell, and in most animals, the individual neurons are organized into complex networks, or nervous systems. These nervous systems are typically composed of a **central nervous system (CNS)**, where large numbers of neurons are condensed into **ganglia** and often a **brain**, and a **peripheral nervous system (PNS)**, which communicates between the CNS and all parts of the body **(Figure 26.9, p. 576)**. This communication occurs via the long, slender projection of each neuron: the **axon**. The axons are bundled into cable-like projections called nerves.

## Information Flow in Neurons

Communication between cells of the nervous system produces a flow of information between neurons. This typically requires four processes:

1. The information has to be perceived (**reception**).
2. A decision has to be made about what to do (**integration**).
3. Information needs to be sent to the structures that will respond (**transmission**).
4. The **response** must be initiated.

For example, the marmot's flight response to hearing an alarm call (see Why It Matters, at the beginning of this chapter) required it to detect, or receive, a stimulus (hearing the alarm call) and transmit that information to

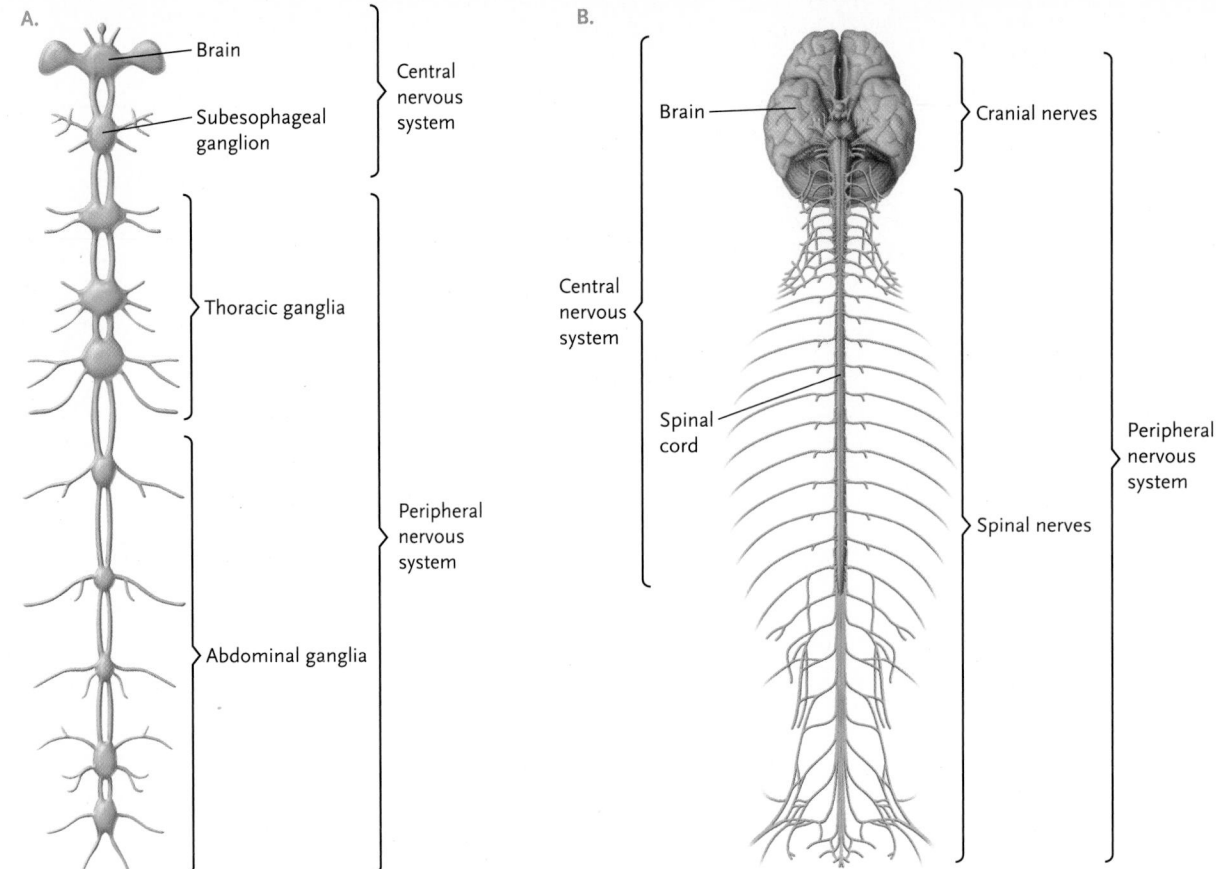

**FIGURE 26.9** A comparison of the basic elements of the nervous systems of **(a)** an invertebrate and **(b)** a vertebrate.

the CNS via sensory neurons (also called **afferent neurons**). In the CNS (in this case, the brain), **interneurons** integrate the information to formulate an appropriate response (flight). As depicted in **Figure 26.10**, sensory or afferent (carrying toward) information is transmitted to the CNS, and motor or **efferent neurons** (carrying away) carry information away from the CNS. Any pathway within a nervous system involving multiple neurons is called a **neural circuit**.

### Neurons Are the Basic Cells of the Nervous System

Although neurons vary widely in shape and size, they do have some features in common. At one end, they have extensions called **dendrites (Figure 26.11, p. 578)**. This is the part of a neuron that receives new information. Dendrites are generally highly branched, forming a treelike structure. **Axons** are another extension of neurons, and these are the structures that conduct information from one neuron to another neuron or to an effector (muscle or gland). Most neurons only have a single axon that branches at its tip and ends in small swellings called axon terminals. Dendrites and axons are highly specialized cell extensions. The nucleus of the neuron and the majority of cell organelles are located in the cell body. The relationship between the cell body and its dendrites

and axons varies in different types of neurons. Note the similarities and differences between sensory neurons, motor neurons, and interneurons in Figure 26.11. Also note that although the figure shows the shapes of typical neurons in each category, there are many exceptions to these descriptions.

### All Cells in the Body Have a Resting Membrane Potential

Understanding how neurons generate and transmit electrical signals is not difficult. What underlies these processes is the movement of ions, the small chemical molecules that carry either a positive or a negative charge (such as sodium or chlorine ions—$Na^+$ or $Cl^-$ that are abundant in every cell). Remember that all cells in the body are surrounded by a plasma membrane and that this membrane allows only some molecules to move across through protein channels. Under normal resting conditions, all animal cells have more negatively charged molecules inside the cell than there are outside the cell. Because of the difference in the balance of charges on either side of the membrane of a resting cell, the cell is said to be **polarized**—it has a negative charge on the inside and a positive charge on the outside. The size of this difference in charge can be measured and is in the range of roughly 70/1000 of a volt (70 millivolts).

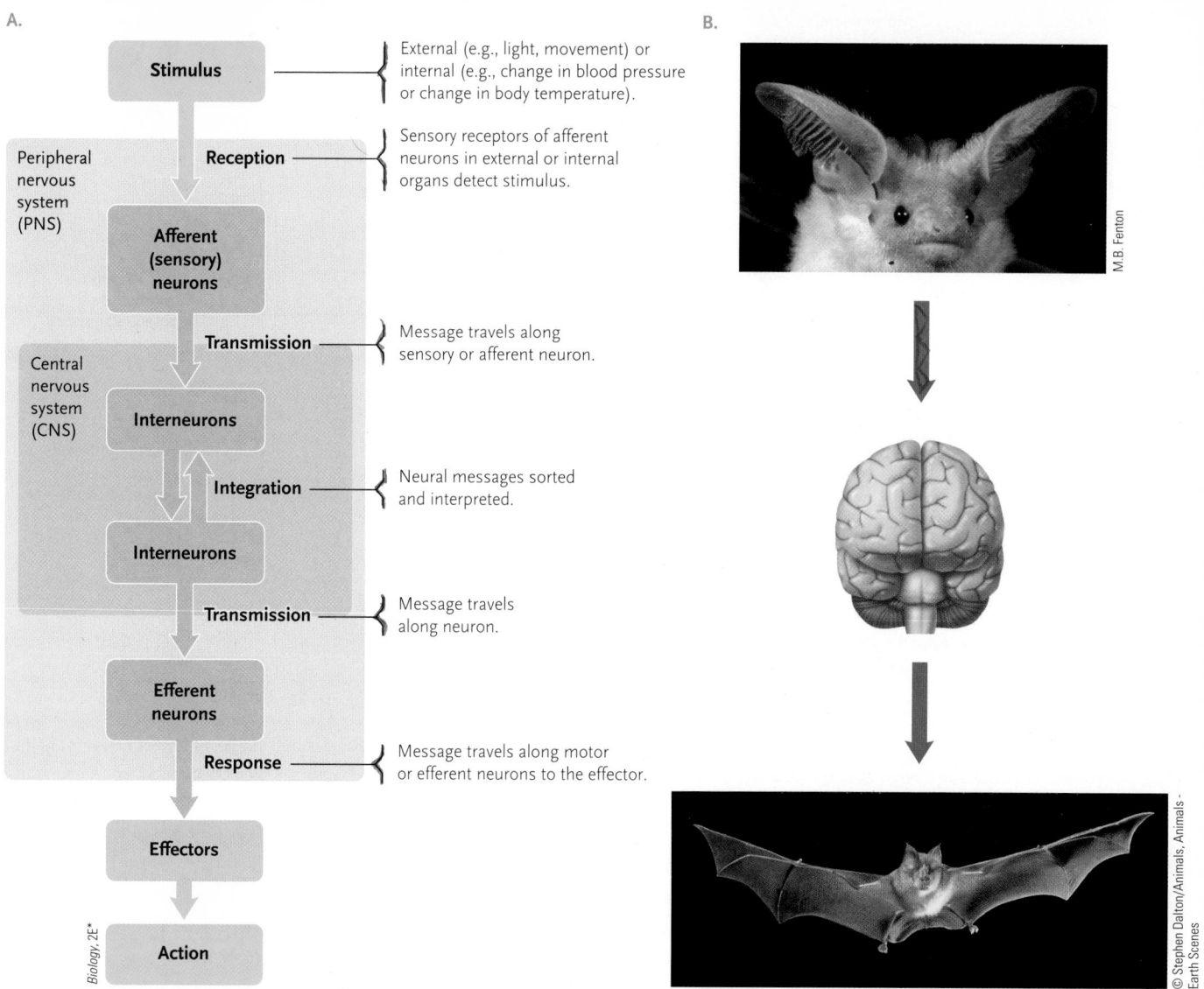

**A.**

External (e.g., light, movement) or internal (e.g., change in blood pressure or change in body temperature).

**Stimulus**

**Reception** — Sensory receptors of afferent neurons in external or internal organs detect stimulus.

Peripheral nervous system (PNS)

**Afferent (sensory) neurons**

**Transmission** — Message travels along sensory or afferent neuron.

Central nervous system (CNS)

**Interneurons**

**Integration** — Neural messages sorted and interpreted.

**Interneurons**

**Transmission** — Message travels along neuron.

**Efferent neurons**

**Response** — Message travels along motor or efferent neurons to the effector.

**Effectors**

*Biology, 2E\**

**Action**

**B.**

M.B. Fenton

© Stephen Dalton/Animals, Animals - Earth Scenes

**FIGURE 26.10 (a)** Neural signalling: the information-processing steps in neural circuits. **(b)** An example of such a pathway. Sound stimulates sensory nerves in the ear of a bat that transmit this information to the brain, where it is integrated, leading to motor output to wing muscles that control the flight pattern of the bat (*Rhinolophus ferrumequinum*).

This is very small. Remember that the voltage of the electricity in the wires in North American homes is 120 volts.

The plasma membranes of cells contain a variety of pores and channels. When a channel opens, the membrane's permeability to that ion changes; that is, the ability of the ion to move through the channel increases. If, as a result, positively charged ions enter the cell (such as $Na^+$) or negatively charged ions leave the cell (such as $Cl^-$), the charge across the membrane will become less negative and the membrane will be less polarized, or **depolarized** **(Figure 26.12, p. 578)**. If positively charged ions leave the cell or negatively charged ions enter, the membrane will become more polarized, or **hyperpolarized**. When the ions are restored to their initial levels, the membrane is **repolarized**, and the cell membrane returns to its resting membrane potential. The extent to which the cell will be

depolarized or hyperpolarized by these movements depends on how many ions move; the changes can be big or small. The significance of this will become clear in a moment.

### An Action Potential Is a Rapid Reversible Event That Occurs Only in Excitable Cells

Neurons and muscle cells possess special channels whose opening and closing is regulated by the difference in charge across the cell membrane. These are the voltage-gated sodium and potassium ion channels (remember, both of these ions have a positive charge). When nerve cells or muscle cells are stimulated, these special channels open very briefly **(Figure 26.13, p. 578)**. Neurons and muscle cells are the only cells in the body that have these channels.

The first thing to happen when a neuron is stimulated is that the membrane begins to depolarize. This

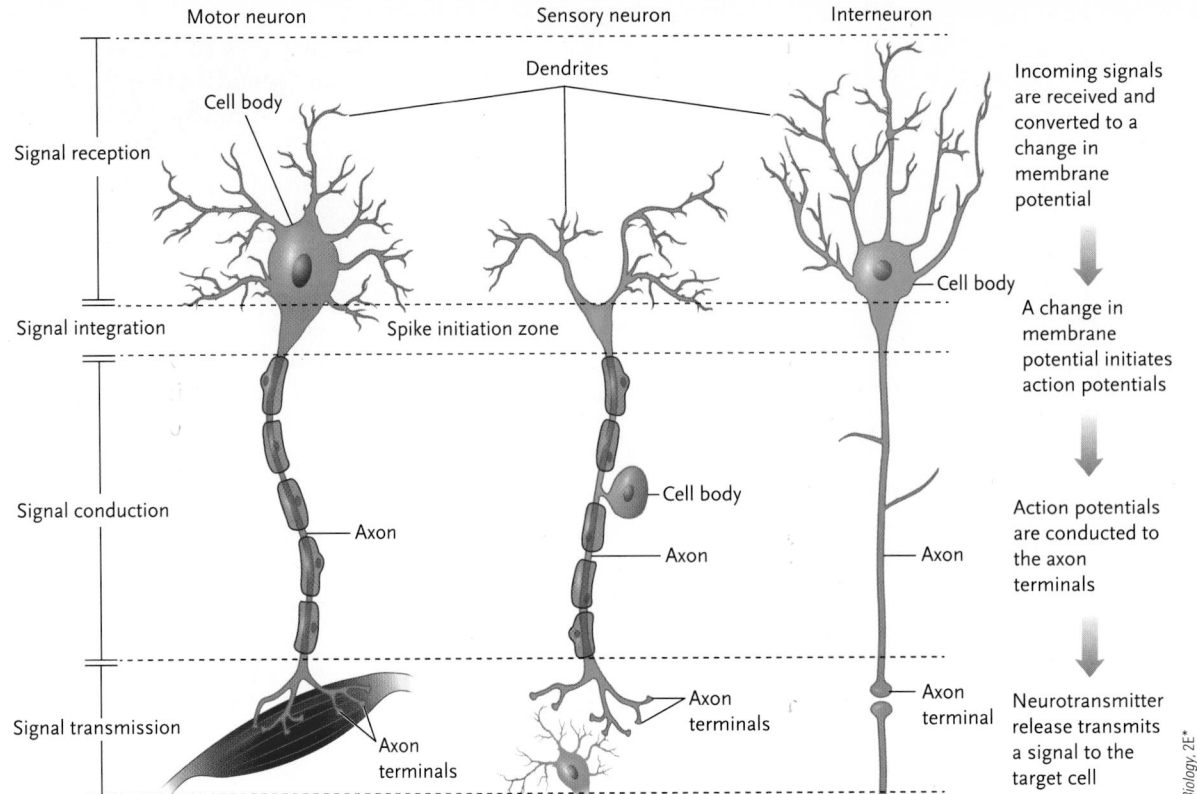

**FIGURE 26.11** Neural signalling: information-processing steps in single neurons. Neurons vary in size and shape, but most neurons are divided into four functional regions, each specialized for a particular task: signal reception, signal integration, signal conduction, and signal transmission to other cells.

change in the charge across the membrane ultimately reaches a level, a **threshold**, at which the voltage-gated sodium ion channels open (1 in Figure 26.13). This allows sodium ions to flow into the axon. The net result is the membrane at that specific site goes from being negative on the inside to being positive on the inside (2 in Figure 26.13). This change in charge at the plasma membrane closes the voltage-gated sodium ion channels and opens the voltage-gated potassium ion channels (2 in Figure 26.13). Now, potassium ions

flow rapidly out of the cell. The movement of positive potassium ions out of the cell returns the membrane to its resting potential (3 in Figure 26.13). As the resting potential re-establishes, all the gates of both the potassium and sodium ion channels return to their resting positions. The gates open and close because of interactions between the charge on the plasma membrane and

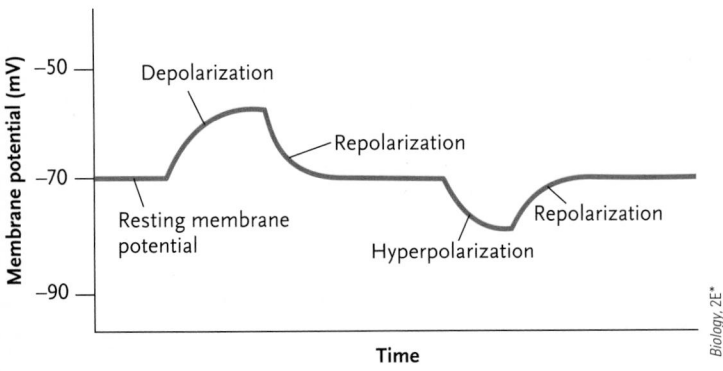

**FIGURE 26.12** Changes in membrane potential in a cell due to changes in ion permeability. The resting membrane potential in this cell is –70 millivolts. During depolarization, the membrane potential becomes less negative. During hyperpolarization, the membrane potential becomes more negative. During repolarization, the membrane potential returns to its resting level.

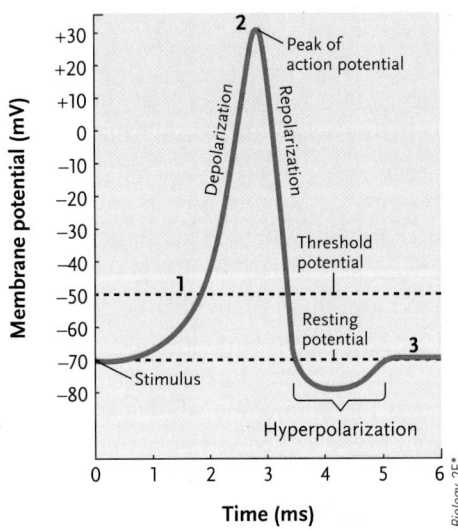

**FIGURE 26.13** Changes in the charge across the nerve cell membrane during an action potential. These changes are very transient and rapid and are due to the opening and closing of the special voltage-gated $Na^+$ and $K^+$ channels.

the charge on the gates themselves. These charges will either pull the gates toward the membrane and open them or push the gates away and close them.

This very rapid, reversible change in membrane potential is an **action potential**. It occurs only at the site where the voltage-gated channels opened and closed; it is very localized. The amount of sodium and potassium ions that flows into and out of the cell is small (ions flow for only 5/1000th of a second, or 5 ms). The sodium/potassium active transport pumps described earlier quickly restore the sodium and potassium ions to their original locations.

No matter how strong the stimulus, the same number of ions will flow and the action potential will always be the same size. If the stimulus is too small to depolarize the cell to threshold, nothing happens. If it is large enough to depolarize the cell to threshold, an action potential is produced. Even larger stimuli have no further effect. Either the voltage-gated channels open, or they don't. Thus, either an action potential of a fixed size is produced, or it is not. This is referred to as the **all-or-nothing principle**.

### Nerve Impulses Move by the Regeneration of Action Potentials

Since the action potential occurs only at the site where the voltage-gated channels opened and closed, how is the stimulus transmitted along the axon to its terminal? It does so through a process called **propagation**, which is the result of two factors:

1. The charge on the membrane at the site where the action potential was generated reverses, causing ions to flow to adjacent areas. This flow of ions makes nearby regions of the axon membrane less positive on the outside and more positive on the inside; this causes the neighbouring membrane to depolarize.
2. Voltage-gated Na$^+$ and K$^+$ channels are present all along the axon. Thus, an action potential at one site pushes the neighbouring voltage-gated Na$^+$ and K$^+$ channels past their threshold, starting an action potential in the adjacent region. In this way, this same sequence of events repeats all along the axon as each segment stimulates the next segment, and the action potential moves rapidly along the axon as a nerve impulse.

The action potential moves in only one direction along an axon, from the dendritic end toward the axon terminal. This is because there is a short period after an action potential is generated at a spot on the membrane when conditions are being restored, and at this time, the membrane is not capable of generating another action potential. Because the action potential is being

regenerated at each voltage-gated channel along the membrane, and because it is an all-or-nothing event, the size of the action potential stays the same as it travels along an axon. Since all action potentials are the same size, the only way to transmit information about the size or intensity of a stimulus is by changes in the frequency of action potentials.

The rate at which an action potential is conducted increases with the diameter of the axon. Some specialized axons with very large diameters, usually those involved in producing escape responses, occur in invertebrates such as lobsters, earthworms, and squids, as well as a few marine fishes. The rate of conduction is also faster along axons insulated with **myelin sheaths**. Gaps in the sheath, called **nodes of Ranvier**, contain voltage-gated channels that allow the action potential to jump or hop rapidly along the axon from node to node (**Figure 26.14, p. 580**). Myelinated nerves transmit action potentials 100 times faster than unmyelinated nerves.

Multiple sclerosis (MS; *sclero* = hard) is a disease in which myelin is progressively lost from axons due to an autoimmune response. The loss of myelin slows or blocks the transmission of action potentials. This reduces sensory input, producing numbness, and reduces motor output, ultimately causing paralysis. The disease arises from both genetic and environmental factors. The incidence of the disease increases with the distance from the equator and in Canada occurs in 2.4 of every 1000 people. This is one of the highest incidences of MS in the world.

### Information Is Transmitted across Synapses by Neurotransmitters

What happens when an action potential arrives at the end of the nerve? Neurons communicate with other neurons, or with muscles and glands. At the site where they meet, there is usually a gap, called a **synapse**. When an action potential arrives at the synapse, it triggers the release of a chemical messenger, a **neurotransmitter**, that crosses the synapse (**Figure 26.15, p. 580**; see also Figure 26.3). Just as with hormones, the neurotransmitter will produce a response only in cells that have receptors for them.

Neurotransmitters are stored in secretory vesicles, called **synaptic vesicles**, in the cytoplasm of an axon terminal. When an action potential arrives at the axon terminal, it causes some of the vesicles to fuse with the terminal membrane and release the neurotransmitter molecules into the synapse by exocytosis. The neurotransmitter diffuses across the gap and binds to receptor proteins in the membrane of the neighbouring cell. Since this cell comes after the synapse, it is referred to as a *postsynaptic* cell. The cell before the synapse is the *presynaptic* cell. The receptor protein either may be

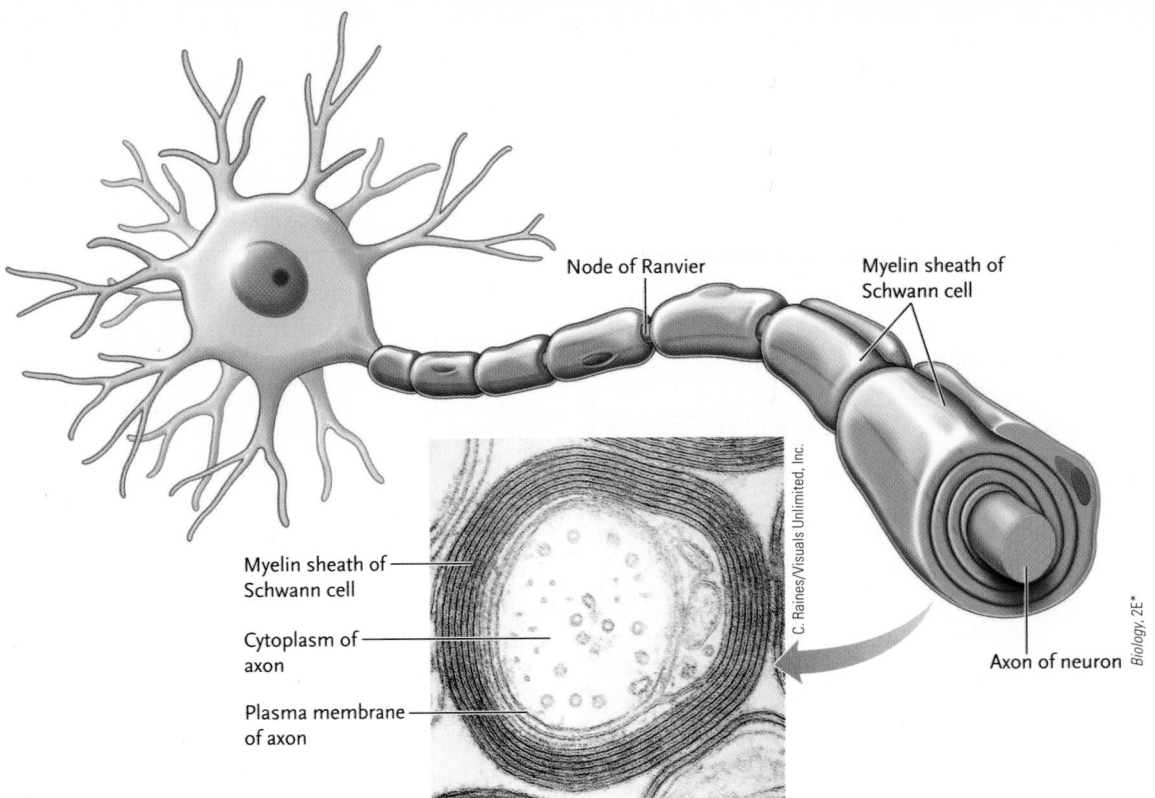

**FIGURE 26.14** Neurons may be myelinated by Schwann cells that wrap the axon in layers of cell membrane like a jelly roll. The layers of membrane contain myelin, which acts as an electrical insulator. Nodes of Ranvier are gaps that occur between Schwann cells, exposing the plasma membrane of the nerve axon. The voltage-gated channels at these sites allow the action potential to "hop" from node to node.

### Chemical synapse

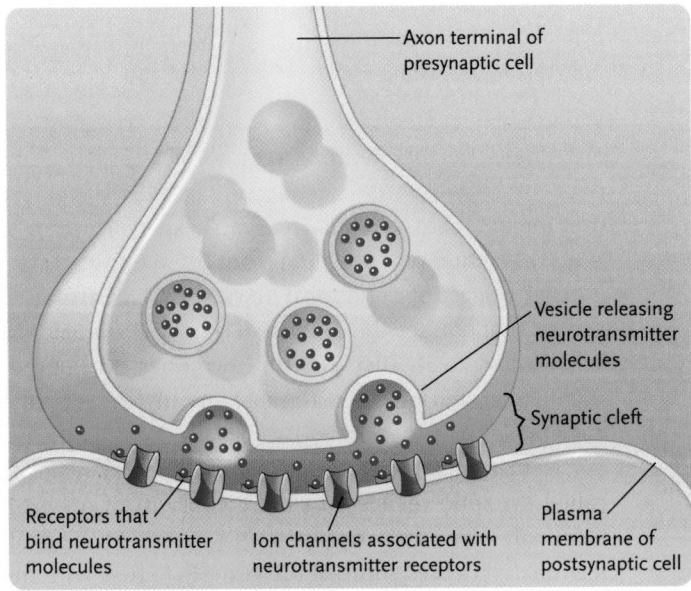

In a chemical synapse, the plasma membranes of the presynaptic and post-synaptic cells are separated by a narrow synaptic cleft. Neurotransmitter molecules diffuse across the cleft and bind to receptors in the plasma membrane of the postsynaptic cell. The binding opens channels to ion flow that may generate an impulse in the postsynaptic cell.

**FIGURE 26.15** A typical synapse by which neurons communicate with other neurons or effectors.

an ion channel or may activate an ion channel, and this alters the flow of ions into the postsynaptic cell.

The result of this alteration in the flow of ions can either inhibit the postsynaptic cell or excite it. This will be a function of the type of ion channel that is opened. The resulting ion flow may depolarize or hyperpolarize the postsynaptic membrane, stimulating or inhibiting the post-synaptic cell, respectively.

There are many different chemicals that act as neurotransmitters. Most are relatively small molecules that diffuse rapidly across the synapse. Some axons release only one of these neurotransmitters, whereas others release several together. Just as with hormones, the net effect will depend on the type of receptor to which the neurotransmitter binds and the ion channels that are activated.

Many diseases are caused by problems associated with the release or reuptake of neurotransmitters atsynapses. Many drugs in common use are designed to target this process. One example is "beta blockers," a group of drugs that block the effects of the neurotransmitter adrenaline (epinephrine) on a specificgroup of receptor proteins (beta-adrenergic receptors). By blocking the ability of adrenaline to bind to these receptors, the effects of adrenaline are reduced on the target cells. Some of the consequences of this action are to reduce the incidence of cardiac arrhythmias, reduce blood pressure, and, in some cases, reduce anxiety disorders.

## STUDY BREAK

1. Information flow involves reception, integration, transmission, and response. Describe this process as it occurs in a single neuron as well as in a neural circuit. Give an example of the latter in an animal of your choice.
2. Distinguish between a neuron, a nerve, a ganglion, and a brain.
3. What is the significance of the myelin sheath?
4. What is the difference between an excitable cell, such as a neuron, and other cells, such as liver or blood cells?

## Sensing

Our ability to sense the world around us is critical. We see, hear, taste, feel, and smell things around us because specialized cells in our nervous systems are able to detect light, colour, sound, touch, odours, etc., and translate this information into signals that are sent to our brains. These specialized neurons are **sensory cells**. These cells are modified to collect information about the internal and external environments of an animal and convert it into neural activity. This process, called transduction, is the first step in the sensory pathway. **Figure 26.16** illustrates three different ways in which neurons can be modified to act as sensors, by modifications to dendrites, to structures surrounding dendrites, or to entire neurons. Transduction occurs when stimuli (such as light, heat, sound waves, mechanical stress, or chemicals) cause changes in the rates at which channels conduct ions (such as $Na^+$, $K^+$, or $Ca^{2+}$) across the plasma membrane of the sensory cell. **Figure 26.17, p. 582** demonstrates how this may occur for each of these stimuli. In all cases, the movement of ions causes the cell membrane to depolarize, which

**A.** **Sensory receptor consisting of free nerve endings—dendrites of an afferent neuron**

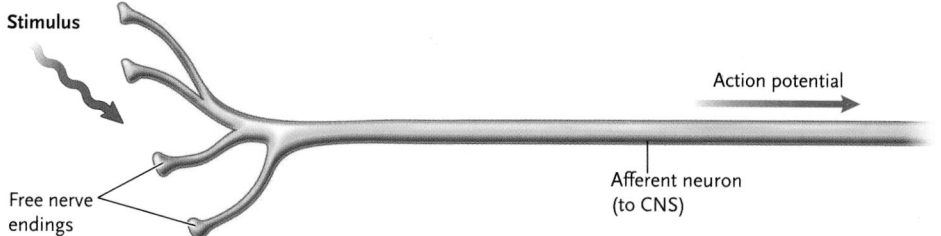

In sensory receptors consisting of the dendrites of afferent neurons, a stimulus causes a change in membrane potential that generates action potentials in the axon of the neuron. Examples are pain receptors and some mechanoreceptors.

**B.** **Sense organ—sensory receptor involving nerve endings of an afferent neuron enclosed in a specialized structure**

In sensory receptors involving nerve endings enclosed in a specialized structure, a stimulus affecting the structure triggers an action potential in the afferent neuron. Some mechanoreceptors are of this type.

**C.** **Sensory receptor formed by a cell that synapses with an afferent neuron**

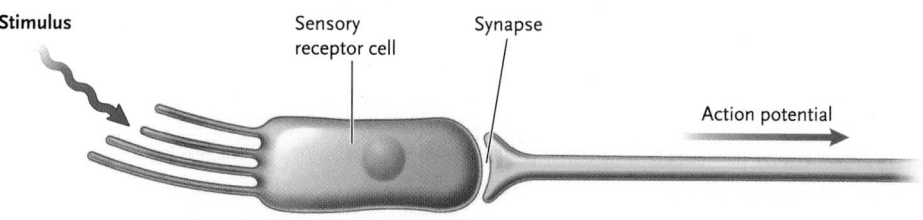

In sensory receptors consisting of separate cells, a stimulus causes a change in membrane potential that releases a neurotransmitter from the cell. The neurotransmitter triggers an action potential in the axon of an afferent neuron to which the sensory receptor cell is synapsed. Examples are photoreceptors, chemoreceptors, and some mechanoreceptors.

*Biology, 2E\**

**FIGURE 26.16** **(a)** Sensory receptor consisting of free nerve endings formed by the dendrites of an afferent neuron. **(b)** Sensory receptor that involves the nerve endings of an afferent neuron enclosed in a specialized structure: a sensory organ. **(c)** Sensory receptor formed by a separate cell or structure that synapses and communicates with an afferent neuron via a neurotransmitter.

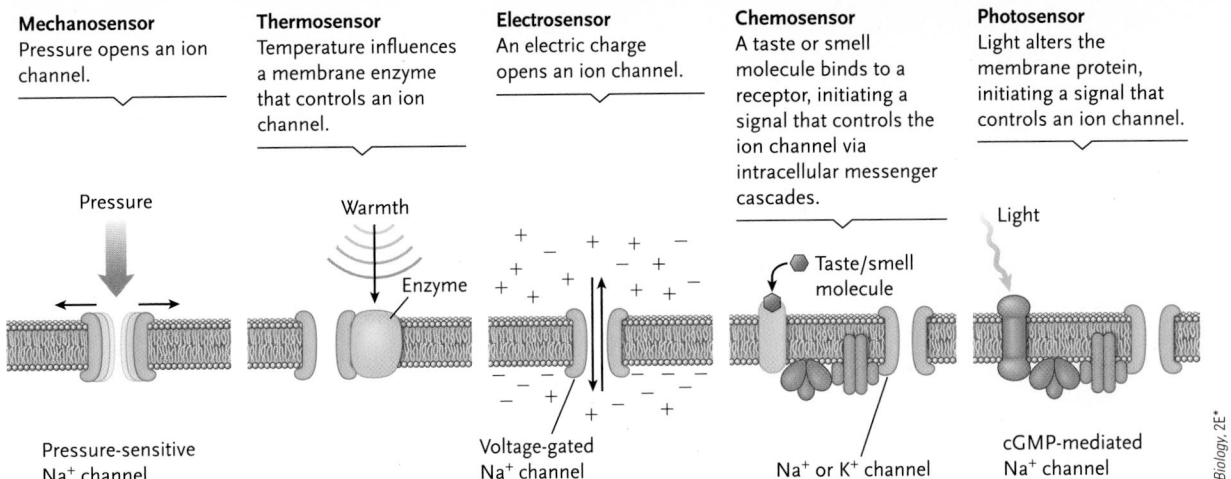

**Mechanosensor**
Pressure opens an ion channel.

**Thermosensor**
Temperature influences a membrane enzyme that controls an ion channel.

**Electrosensor**
An electric charge opens an ion channel.

**Chemosensor**
A taste or smell molecule binds to a receptor, initiating a signal that controls the ion channel via intracellular messenger cascades.

**Photosensor**
Light alters the membrane protein, initiating a signal that controls an ion channel.

Pressure

Warmth

Enzyme

Light

Taste/smell molecule

Pressure-sensitive Na⁺ channel

Voltage-gated Na⁺ channel

Na⁺ or K⁺ channel

cGMP-mediated Na⁺ channel

Biology, 2E*

**FIGURE 26.17** Sensory cell membrane proteins respond to stimuli. Sensory stimuli modify receptor proteins in the membranes of sensors, which in turn modify ion channels. The receptors in mechanoreceptors, thermosensors, and electrosensors are themselves ion channels. In chemosensors and photosensors, activated receptor proteins initiate biochemical cascades that eventually open or close ion channels. cGMP = cyclic guanosine monophosphate.

generates action potentials that travel along the axon of the sensory neuron to reach interneuron networks of the CNS. The number of action potentials produced conveys information about the strength and duration of the stimulus. For instance, a light, brief touch on your leg will produce only a few action potentials in skin sensors that may not even be noticeable, but a strong or longer touch will produce more action potentials, increasing your awareness of the touch.

### Basic Types of Receptors: What Can Animals Sense?

Most sensory organs are relatively complex, such as the eyes or ears of insects and mammals. These organs consist of anatomical structures designed to increase the ability of an animal to sense small changes in stimuli. The fundamental sensory cells, however, are relatively simple.

Sensory cells are classified into five major types, based on the type of energy that each detects. **Mechanoreceptors** detect such things as changes in pressure, body position, or acceleration. **Photoreceptors** detect light energy, **chemoreceptors** detect specific chemical molecules, **thermoreceptors** detect heat energy, and **nociceptors** detect tissue damage or noxious chemicals that give rise to pain (Figure 26.17).

These five classes of receptors, positioned in the appropriate place, allow animals to not only see, hear, taste, smell, and feel touch, but they also allow them to detect changes in temperature (both external and internal temperature), the positions of muscles and joints, movement, and the internal concentrations of substances such as hydrogen ions, oxygen, carbon dioxide, salts, and glucose. Some animals can also sense changes in electrical or magnetic fields.

### Sensory Organs Are Designed to Enhance the Reception of Sensory Information

When we think of sensory structures, we tend to think of the organs that house the sensory cells rather than the sensory cells themselves. These are structures such as our ears, nose, and tongue. The basic mechanisms by which sensory cells detect energy around them—light, sounds, temperature, etc.—are very similar in all animals. However, the organs that house those sensory cells vary immensely. These structures are designed to improve the ability of animals to detect different stimuli. The adaptations we see for detecting stimuli reflect the environments the animals live in and the importance of each stimulus to their lives. In the following sections, we will explore some of these adaptations.

### Mechanoreceptors Detect Touch, Position, Balance, and Sound

Mechanoreceptors provide animals with information on the movement, position, and balance and underlie the sense of hearing. They are also involved in sensing touch and pressure, as well as in sensing blood pressure and the degree of inflation of the lungs. In all mechanoreceptors, the mechanical force of a stimulus causes ion channels to open, allowing ions to flow (Figure 26.17), which depolarizes the sensory cell and generates action potentials in sensory neurons leading to the CNS.

One way animals can detect movement, either through sound waves, touch, or other similar stimuli, is through elongated cells (sensory hairs) that are embedded in fluid-filled chambers. This is very common in many animals. For instance, in fishes and some aquatic amphibians, the chamber is a gelatinous structure, called the little cup or **cupula**. The sensory hairs in the cupola move with pressure changes in the surrounding water, and bending cilia that project from the cell membrane (called **stereocilia**) on the hair cells depolarize the cell membrane, triggering action potentials in sensory neurons that project to the central nervous system **(Figure 26.18)**. This provides information about the fish's orientation with respect to gravity, as well as its swimming velocity.

The organs that sense position and movement in invertebrates such as the lobster and the position of the head with respect to gravity (up versus down), as well as changes in the rate of movement of the human body, work on similar principles (Figure 26.18). In the case of the human ear, **otoliths**, small crystals of calcium carbonate (*oto* = ear; *lithos* = stone), are embedded in the gelatinous cup to help bend the stereocilia within a special chamber in the ear, the vestibular apparatus, when the head moves. Note that although these organs all work in similar ways and serve the same function, they evolved independently through convergent evolution (see Chapter 13 to review convergent evolution).

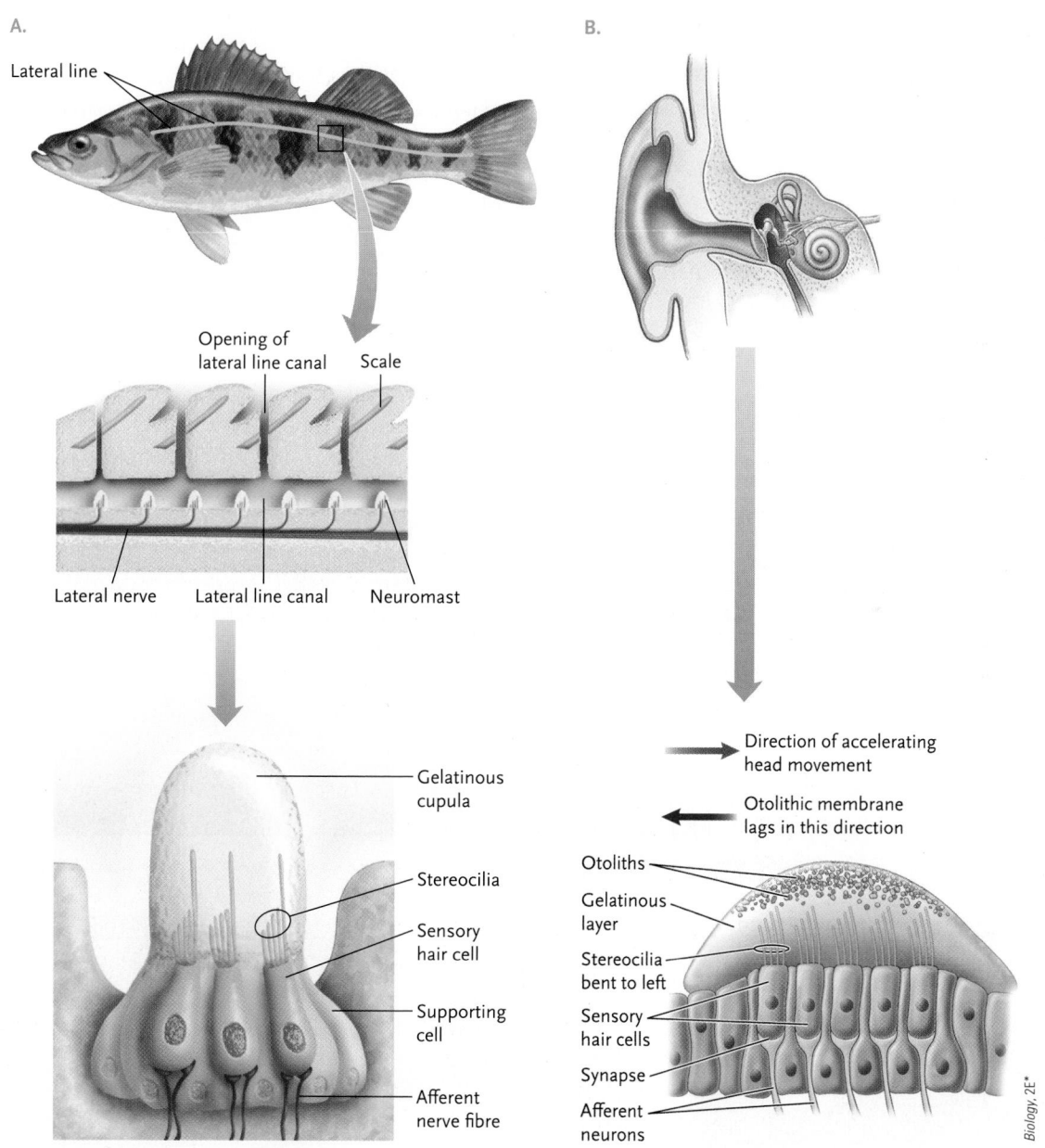

A.

Lateral line

Opening of lateral line canal    Scale

Lateral nerve    Lateral line canal    Neuromast

Gelatinous cupula

Stereocilia

Sensory hair cell

Supporting cell

Afferent nerve fibre

B.

Direction of accelerating head movement

Otolithic membrane lags in this direction

Otoliths

Gelatinous layer

Stereocilia bent to left

Sensory hair cells

Synapse

Afferent neurons

*Biology, 2E*

**FIGURE 26.18 (a)** The lateral line system of fishes. Pores along the side of many fish house sensory receptors in a lateral line. The sensory cells have a gelatinous cupula that is pushed and pulled by vibrations and currents transmitted through the lateral line canal. As the cupula moves, the stereocilia of the sensory hair cells are bent, generating action potentials in sensory neurons that lead to the brain. **(b)** Human ears have a structure (the vestibular apparatus) that detects when we move our head or our body. Otoliths in a gelatinous layer shift with accelerating or decelerating movements and the position of the head relative to gravity, bending the stereocilia and generating action potentials in sensory neurons leading to the brain.

Hearing is based on the same fundamental mechanisms. Most invertebrates detect sound through mechanoreceptors in their skin or on other surface structures. In insects such as grasshoppers and crickets, thinned regions of their exoskeleton form a **tympanum** (*tympanum* = drum) or "ear" over a hollow chamber. Sound makes the membrane vibrate, and mechanoreceptors connected to the tympanum deform and generate nerve impulses. Tympanic membranes can be found on the abdomen, thorax, legs, or the head of different invertebrate species **(Figure 26.19)**. The ears of terrestrial vertebrates are more complex. Ultimately, however, they too transduce sound vibrations to sensory hair cells that respond by triggering action potentials. Many animals have an outer ear or pinna (*pinna* = wing or leaf) that concentrates and focuses sound waves (Figure 26.19).

### Photoreceptors Create Vision

Most animals detect and respond to light. This involves sensory cells called photoreceptors (see Figure 26.17). In all animals, light energy is absorbed by different forms of a lipidlike pigment called **retinal**, which is synthesized from vitamin A. The plasma membranes of the sensory cells depolarize when retinal absorbs light, and this generates action potentials or increases the release of neurotransmitter molecules.

As with mechanoreceptors, photoreceptors are commonly associated with complex structures that enhance their ability to both detect light and distinguish shapes and colours, as well as generate and focus an accurate image of objects. Some invertebrates, such as earthworms, only have photoreceptors in their skin that allows them to sense and respond to light. Other invertebrates have evolved eyes that range from collections of photoreceptors to eyes such as ours, with a lens and the ability to form images.

The compound eyes found in insects, crustaceans, and a few annelids and molluscs consist of hundreds to thousands of visual units called **ommatidia** (*omma* = eye) **(Figure 26.20)**, each of which forms an image of only a small part of the visual field. Although such an eye does not produce a single compound image of the environment, it is extremely sensitive to detecting movement. This is because any motion occurring in the animal's visual field is detected simultaneously by multiple images in many of the ommatidia.

In the single-lens eye seen in cephalopod molluscs and vertebrates, including humans (Figure 26.20), a

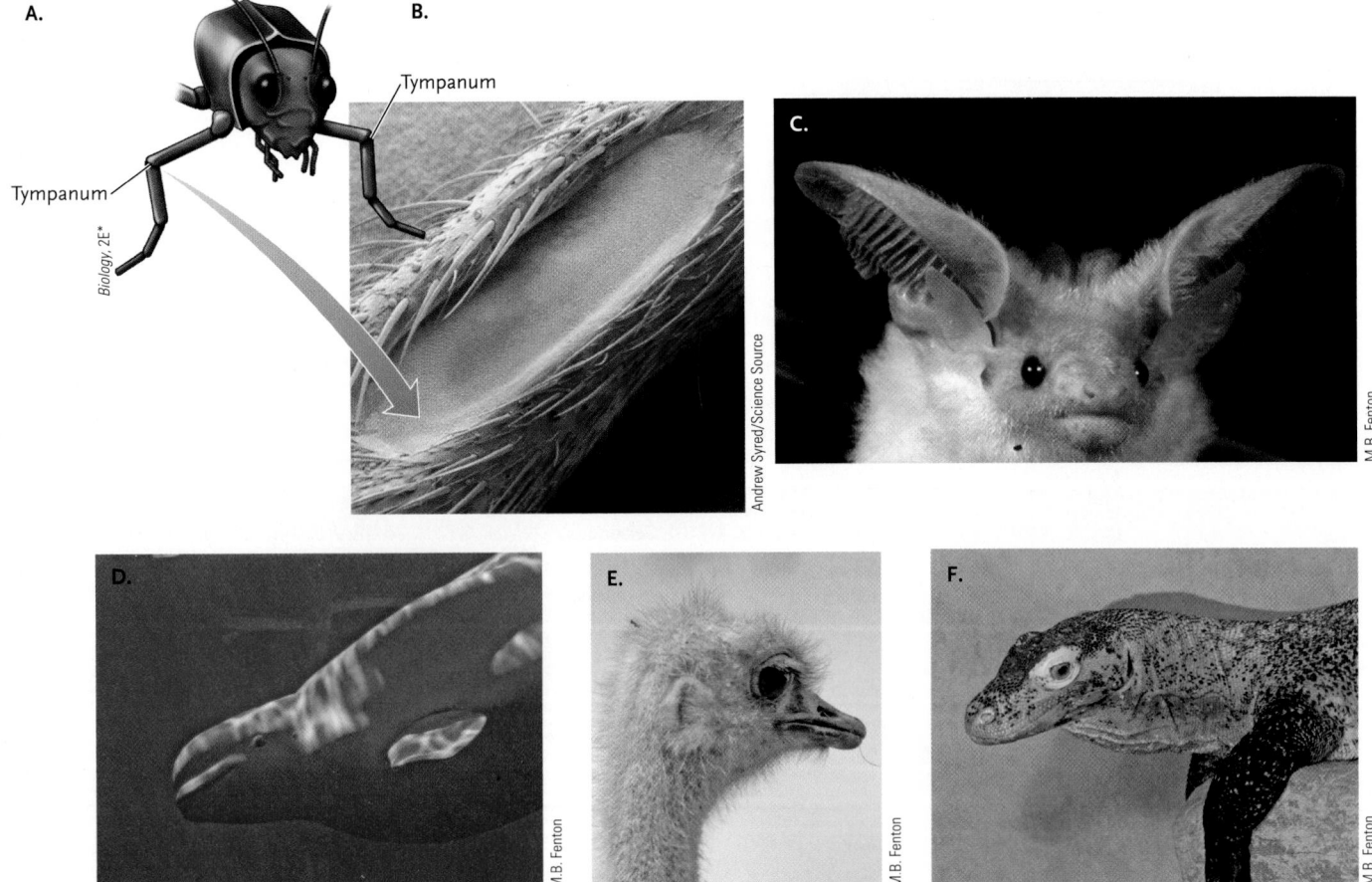

**FIGURE 26.19** The tympanum or eardrum of a cricket **(a)**, is located on the front walking legs **(b)**. Pinnae (external ears) are large and conspicuous in **(c)** a bat (*Otonycteris hemprichii*) but lacking in mammals such as **(d)** the beluga (*Delphinapterus leucas*), **(e)** birds (*Struthio camelus*), and **(f)** reptiles (*Varanus komodoensis*).

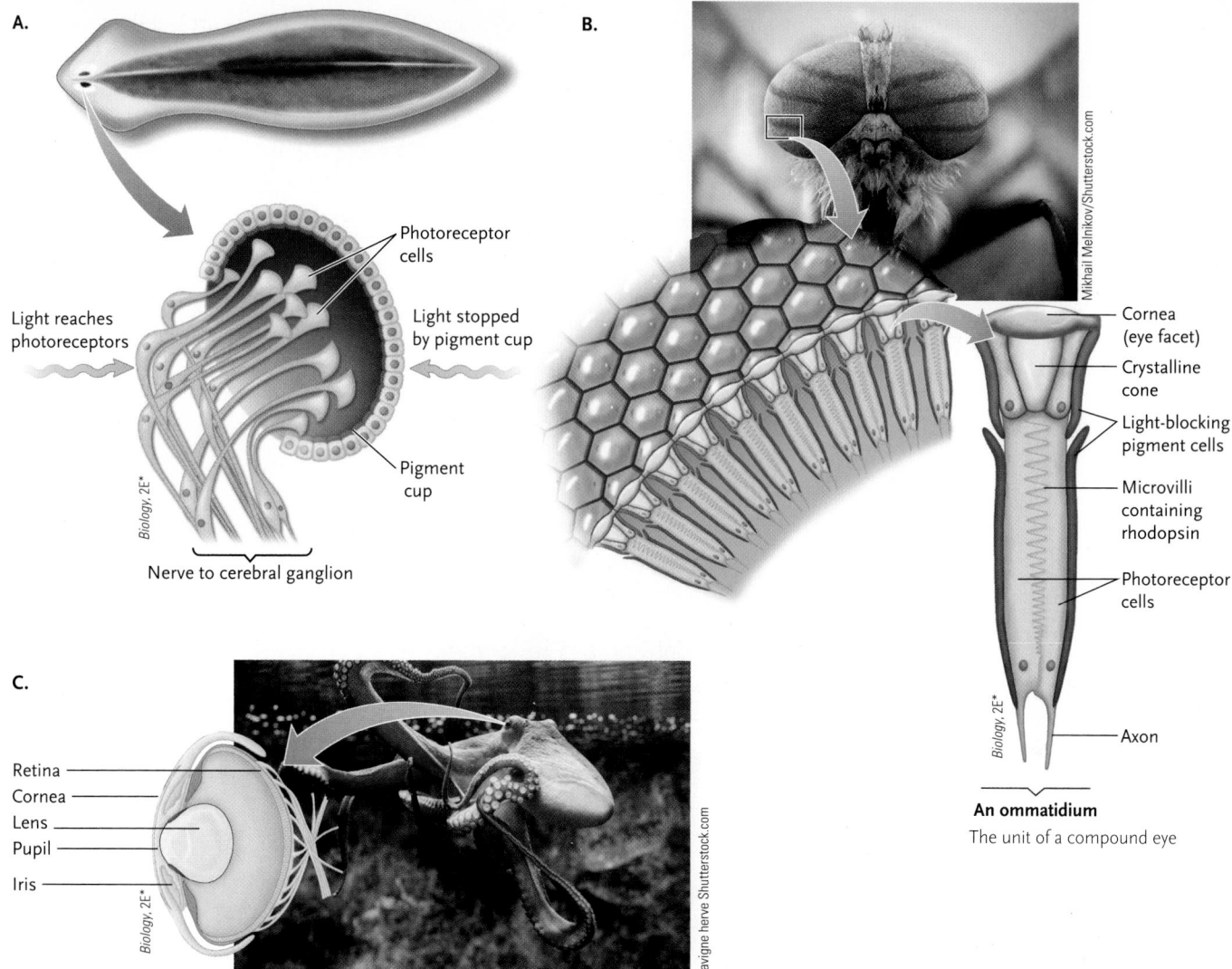

A.

Light reaches photoreceptors

Photoreceptor cells

Light stopped by pigment cup

Pigment cup

*Biology, 2E\**

Nerve to cerebral ganglion

B.

Mikhail Melnikov/Shutterstock.com

Cornea (eye facet)

Crystalline cone

Light-blocking pigment cells

Microvilli containing rhodopsin

Photoreceptor cells

*Biology, 2E\**

Axon

**An ommatidium**
The unit of a compound eye

C.

Retina
Cornea
Lens
Pupil
Iris

*Biology, 2E\**

lavigne herve Shutterstock.com

**FIGURE 26.20 (a)** The ocellus of a planarian flatworm and the arrangement of pigment cells on which its orientation response is based. **(b)** The compound eye of a deer fly (*Chrysops niger*). Each ommatidium has a cornea that directs light into the crystalline cone; in turn, the cone focuses light on the photoreceptor cells. **(c)** The single-lens eye of an octopus (*Octopus dofleini*), a cephalopod mollusc.

single lens focuses light onto a layer of photoreceptors at the back of the eye, the **retina**. In most aquatic animals (cephalopods and fish), the image is focused by moving the lens toward and away from the retina, whereas in most terrestrial vertebrates, the lens is focused by changing its shape (Figure 26.20). Vertebrate eyes also possess two types of photoreceptors: rods, which are specialized to detect light at low intensities, and cones, which are specialized to detect different wavelengths (colours).

## Chemoreceptors Are the Basis of Taste and Smell

Chemoreceptors provide information about the levels of molecules in the body, such as glucose, oxygen, carbon dioxide, and hydrogen ions. They also provide information about levels of molecules that give rise to taste

(gustation) and smell (olfaction). Chemoreceptors have membrane-bound receptor proteins that bind with specific molecules in their environment, leading to ion flows that generate action potentials in sensory nerves leading to the CNS (see Figure 26.17).

Many invertebrates do not distinguish between taste and smell. They use receptors distributed over the body surface to detect chemicals in their external environment. Some terrestrial invertebrates, however, do distinguish between taste and smell, as do all vertebrates.

In insects, taste receptors are inside hollow sensory hairs that protect the delicate sensory cells. Pores in these hairs allow sugars, salts, amino acids, or other chemicals to diffuse into the chemoreceptors. Sensory hairs can be found on the feet, mouthparts, or antennae of different species **(Figure 26.21, p. 586)**.

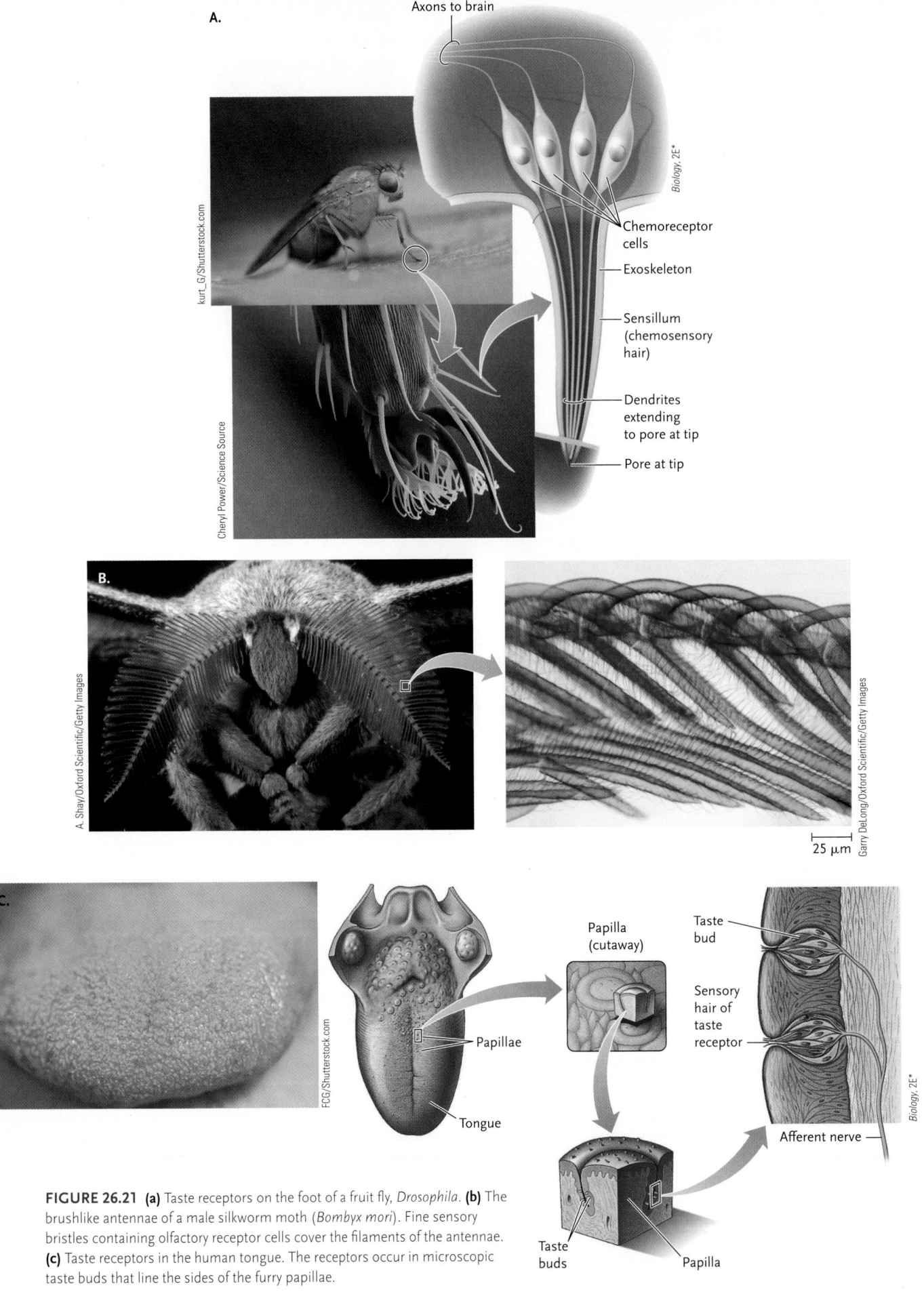

**A.**

Axons to brain

Chemoreceptor cells

Exoskeleton

Sensillum (chemosensory hair)

Dendrites extending to pore at tip

Pore at tip

*Biology, 2E\**

kurt_G/Shutterstock.com

Cheryl Power/Science Source

**B.**

A. Shay/Oxford Scientific/Getty Images

Garry DeLong/Oxford Scientific/Getty Images

25 μm

**C.**

FOG/Shutterstock.com

Papillae

Tongue

Papilla (cutaway)

Taste buds

Papilla

Taste bud

Sensory hair of taste receptor

Afferent nerve

*Biology, 2E\**

**FIGURE 26.21** **(a)** Taste receptors on the foot of a fruit fly, *Drosophila*. **(b)** The brushlike antennae of a male silkworm moth (*Bombyx mori*). Fine sensory bristles containing olfactory receptor cells cover the filaments of the antennae. **(c)** Taste receptors in the human tongue. The receptors occur in microscopic taste buds that line the sides of the furry papillae.

The taste receptors of most vertebrates are also protected—in this case, by a small capsule with a pore at the top opening to the exterior (Figure 26.21). These are the taste buds. Although generally confined to the mouth, in some species of aquatic vertebrates (e.g., fish and amphibian tadpoles), they can be distributed all over the body surface.

Terrestrial invertebrates and all vertebrates smell by detecting chemical molecules in the surrounding environment. Pheromones are one important group of such chemicals. Many invertebrates and vertebrates use pheromones to attract mates (Figure 26.21). Odours are also used to identify members of the same family or colony, to mark territories, and to alert others to danger.

### Thermoreceptors, Nociceptors, and Electroreceptors Detect Heat, Pain, and Electrical Current

There are three other groups of sensory receptors that tend to be widely distributed in the bodies of animals that possess them. Thermoreceptors are designed to detect heat. They are free nerve endings formed by the dendrites of afferent neurons. They are not generally associated with complex secondary structures such as eyes or ears but are loosely distributed over the surface of the body. We can sense temperature over our entire bodies. In some vertebrates, however, they are concentrated in special areas that may be modified to enhance their ability to detect heat. For instance, some snakes, such as rattlesnakes and pythons, use thermoreceptors to detect the body heat of warm-blooded prey animals. These thermoreceptors are located in pits that both increase their sensitivity and allow them to focus the source of the stimulus **(Figure 26.22a)**. Vampire bats that feed on warm-blooded prey have infrared receptors on their nose **(Figure 26.22b)** that allow them to identify the best place to bite—places where blood (their food) flows close to the skin.

Nociceptors are responsible for our response when we are hurt. They respond to stimuli that could damage

A.

Pit organs

**FIGURE 26.22** **(a)** The pit organs of an albino western diamondback rattlesnake (*Crotalus atrox*) are located in depressions on both sides of the head below the eyes. These thermoreceptors detect infrared radiation emitted by warm-blooded prey such as mice and kangaroo rats. **(b)** The noseleaf on the face of a vampire bat (*Desmodus rotundus*) houses an infrared detector, allowing the bat to find places where blood flows close to the skin. The bat then uses razor-sharp teeth to remove a divot of skin and anticlotting chemicals in its saliva to allow it to get a blood meal. **(c)** The electric eel (*Electrophorus electricus*) stuns prey with an electric discharge.

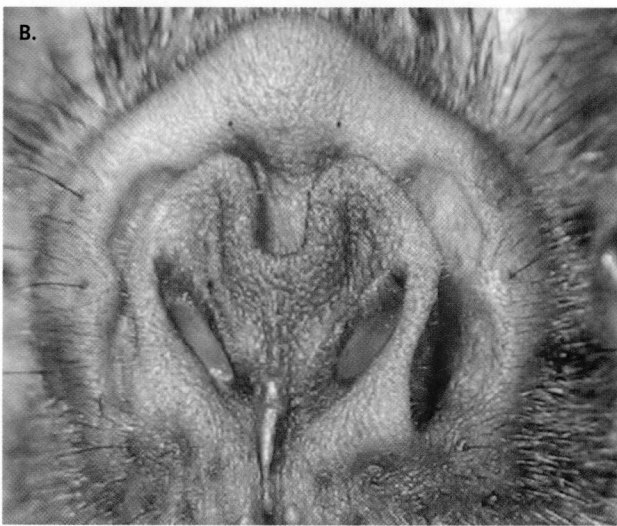

B.

C.

the surrounding tissues. In mammals and possibly other vertebrates, their input is interpreted by the brain as pain. Pain usually elicits a reflex response that removes or decreases the damaging stimulus.

Many vertebrates are able to detect electrical fields. This is true of sharks, bony fishes, some amphibians, and some mammals, such as the star-nosed mole and duck-billed platypus. Some animals use electrical information to locate prey by detecting electrical currents generated by the prey's heartbeat or by their muscle contractions. Others use it to navigate in murky waters and to communicate.

### Perception versus Detection: The Role of Central Integration

The output of sensory receptors is action potentials. That is the form in which all information arrives at the brain. The manner in which this information is processed to provide a conscious awareness of the external and internal environment is called **perception**. On the one hand, an organism's perception of the world depends on the types of receptors it possesses. What can it sense? On the other hand, processing the different forms of sensory input gives those inputs unique characteristics. For instance, all taste receptors generate action potentials, but the action potentials arriving from different receptors can give rise to bitter or sweet sensations. Furthermore, integration of input from different sensory structures and with previous memories adds a tremendous degree of complexity to these fundamental inputs. All of this comes from central processing of the sensory information. We will touch on this in the next section.

### STUDY BREAK

1. How is the strength of a sensory stimulus conveyed to the brain?
2. What are the different roles of primary and secondary sensory structures? What do the secondary structures contribute?
3. Why are compound eyes so adept at detecting motion?
4. What are the similarities and differences between taste and smell?
5. What is the difference between a receptor protein, a receptor cell, and a receptor organ?

### Integration

Integration is the process of combining information from many sources and using that combined information to make a decision. In the case of neurons, the decision will be whether to fire action potentials or not. In animals, the sensory pathways carry information to the central nervous system, where decisions must be made about what to do with this information. Specific areas of the CNS receive different types of sensory input and integrate, store, and retrieve information related to each of the senses. Based on this, the CNS sends commands to muscles and glands and produces such complex activities as behaviour, emotions, learning, reasoning, language, and memory.

### Integration by Individual Neurons

What underlies the ability of the nervous system to integrate information and make decisions is the fact that only certain parts of a neuron can generate action potentials. In most neurons, dendrites and cell bodies cannot. This comes as a surprise to many students, but it is the critical basis of a neuron's ability to integrate information. If it were not for this, every incoming action potential would produce an action potential in the postsynaptic cell. The reason these sites cannot generate action potentials is because they do not have voltage-gated ion channels. In all neurons, the first site where action potentials can be initiated is referred to as the *spike initiation zone*, and this site differs in different types of neurons (see Figure 26.11). As a result of this, some integration takes place at every synapse in a neural circuit. A typical neuron—the postsynaptic neuron (page 579)—receives hundreds to thousands of chemical synapses from the axon terminals of other neurons—the presynaptic neurons **(Figure 26.23)**. Each releases one or many neurotransmitters that act on various ion channels

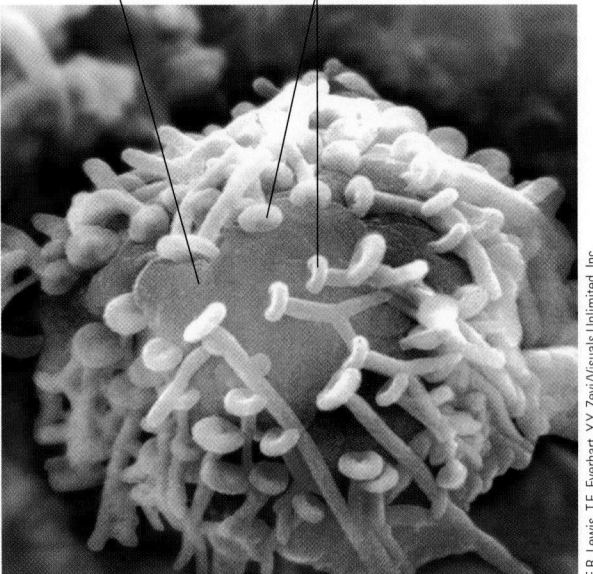

Cell body of postsynaptic neuron

Axon terminals of presynaptic neurons

E.R. Lewis, T.E. Everhart, Y.Y. Zevi/Visuals Unlimited, Inc.

**FIGURE 26.23** The multiple chemical synapses relaying signals to a neuron. The drying process used to prepare the neuron for electron microscopy has toppled the axon terminals and pulled them away from the neuron's surface. Note the abundance of axon terminals from presynaptic neurons terminating on the cell body of the one postsynaptic cell.

# Biomechatronics

It is amazing the extent to which many science fiction creations of the past are becoming reality today. In the 1960s, the term *cyborg* was coined to describe "cybernetic organisms"—organisms that were made of both organic (natural) and mechanical parts. This combination provided the cyborg with enhanced abilities. In the 1970s, these flights of fantasy gave rise to two TV series: "The Six Million Dollar Man" (Steve Austin) and "The Bionic Woman" (Lindsay Wagner). In both series, an individual almost killed in an accident received surgically implanted bionic parts that not only saved their lives but also gave them special powers. Since then, we have seen a host of cyborgs cross the screen: the Borg from Star Trek, Darth Vader from Star Wars, and the Terminator, to say nothing of the wide variety of military cyborgs that appear with inbuilt weapons. These TV series and movies were purely science fiction, but today the field of biomechatronics is beginning to make such things possible.

Biomechatronics is a field that spans many disciplines: biology, neuroscience, engineering mechanics, electronics, and robotics. The focus of the field is on creating prosthetic devices that interact with human muscle, skeleton, and nervous systems to operate artificial limbs **(Figure 1)**. Surgeons can now connect the motor nerves that once controlled the muscles of an amputated limb to a small region of a healthy muscle. Now when the individual thinks about moving the amputated limb, this small patch of muscle contracts instead. Sensors placed over this site can use this information to drive electrical circuits within the prosthetic limb to produce the desired movement. Scientists are now working to find ways to control artificial limbs directly from the nervous system rather than through their actions on muscle and skin.

More recently, Naweed Syed and his colleagues from the Hotchkiss Brain Institute at the University of Calgary have successfully grown neurons on silicon semiconductor chips. This interface of neuronal chemical synapses with semiconductor chips allows him to monitor neuronal activity from many neuronal circuits simultaneously. These chips can be transplanted into animals and humans and may be the next step in driving artificial prosthetic devices.

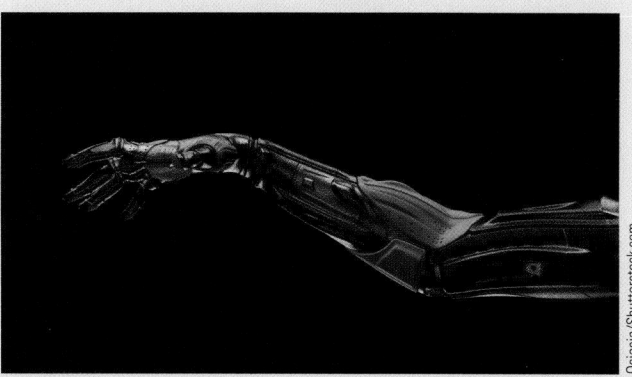

**FIGURE 1** A futuristic prosthetic robotic arm and hand.

to produce ion movements that may depolarize or hyperpolarize their membrane. Whether a cell is excited or inhibited depends on the number, types, and activity of the synapses that the postsynaptic neuron receives from presynaptic neurons at any given time. At each synapse, the sum of the excitatory and inhibitory information is constantly being compared, and only if the excitatory information outweighs the inhibitory information sufficiently is a decision made to produce action potentials and pass information on to the next step in the chain.

## Integration by Networks

The manner in which the central nervous systems of animals produce complex behaviours, emotions, learning, reasoning, language, and memory based on neurons that can either be silent or fire action potentials seems amazing. However, this is exactly how digital computers work as well, based on a mathematical language in which there are only two states (on or off) (see Box 26.4). This kind of higher-level integration takes place in the central nervous system, where interneurons are recruited specifically to integrate information coming in from many different sites in the body.

The kinds of networks used for central integration vary across the animal kingdom in a manner that largely reflects differences in lifestyle and habitat. Radially symmetrical animals such as jellyfish and sea anemones have a nervous system composed of a **nerve net**; they lack a central nervous system. A loose mesh of neurons crisscross the entire organism just beneath the outer surface **(Figure 26.24a, p. 590)**. The neurons have communicating synapses wherever they cross one other. If any part of the animal is stimulated, the nerve net transmits this information in all directions to all other parts of the animal. The response is generally a change in shape. In jellyfish, this may give rise to swimming movements.

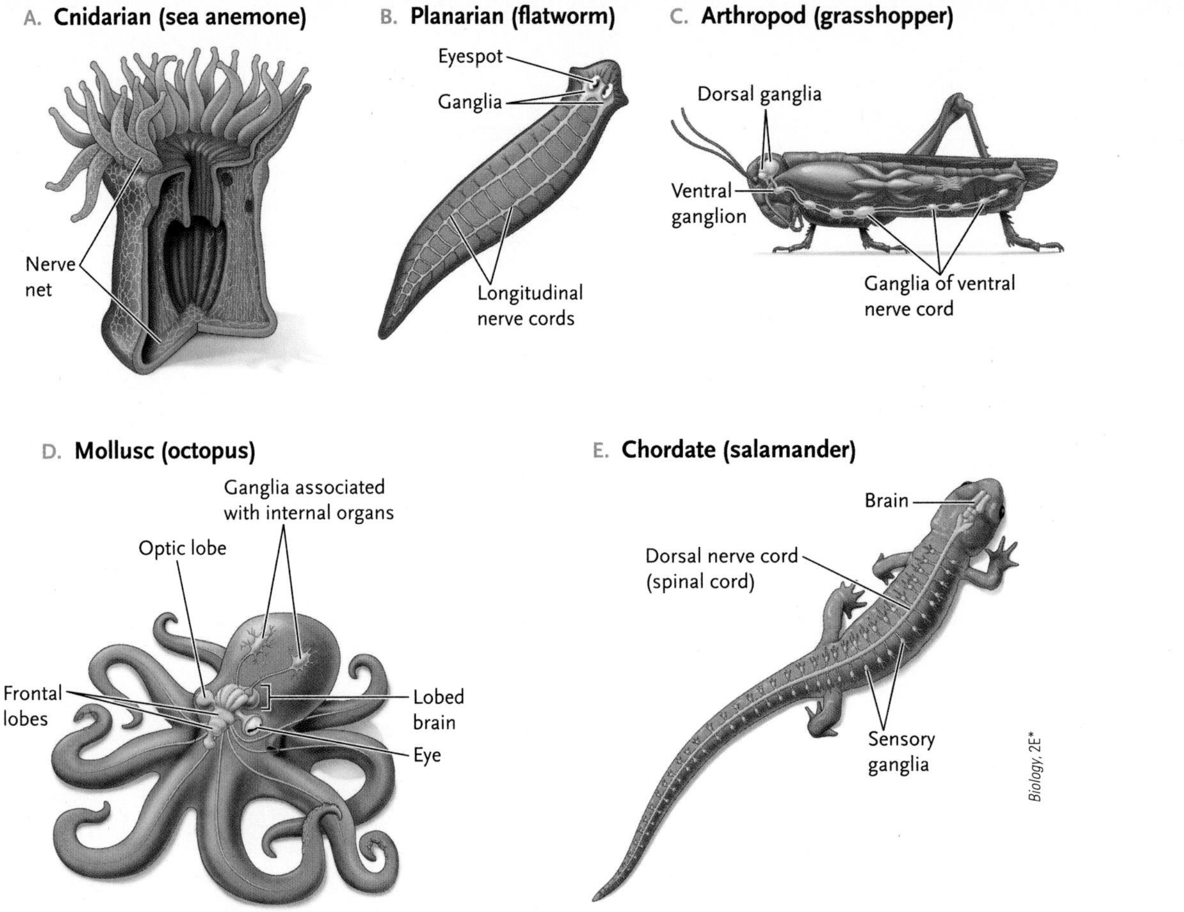

**A. Cnidarian (sea anemone)**

Nerve net

**B. Planarian (flatworm)**

Eyespot
Ganglia
Longitudinal nerve cords

**C. Arthropod (grasshopper)**

Dorsal ganglia
Ventral ganglion
Ganglia of ventral nerve cord

**D. Mollusc (octopus)**

Ganglia associated with internal organs
Optic lobe
Frontal lobes
Lobed brain
Eye

**E. Chordate (salamander)**

Brain
Dorsal nerve cord (spinal cord)
Sensory ganglia

*Biology, 2E\**

**FIGURE 26.24** Invertebrate and vertebrate nervous systems compared, showing increasing cephalization. The diagrams are not drawn to the same scale.

In more complex invertebrates, interneurons are clustered close together to form ganglia (singular = ganglion) **(Figure 26.24b)**. By being clustered together, the distance that information has to travel between the interneurons is reduced to produce rapid integration of sensory information. In segmented organisms (such as flatworms and grasshoppers), each segment has a separate pair of ganglia. The ganglia in individual segments are connected to one another as well as to the ganglia in the segments in front of and behind them. This allows rapid integration of information within each segment and communication between the ganglia in different segments.

The most complex invertebrates have "heads." This region is usually the first part of the animal to encounter new stimuli as it moves through its environment. As a result, it also usually contains key sensory structures. There has been an evolutionary trend to also concentrate ganglia in this region, reducing the distance that the sensory information has to travel and reducing the time required to integrate sensory information and produce a response. This concentration of ganglia to form a brain is well illustrated in flatworms, arthropods, and molluscs **(Figure 26.24b, c, and d)**. Cephalopod molluscs (octopuses

and squid) have the most pronounced development of any invertebrate group. Octopuses are capable of rapid movement to hunt prey and to escape from predators and are excellent at problem solving, suggesting that they are capable of higher levels of integration.

In vertebrates, the central nervous system consists of the brain and spinal cord **(Figure 26.24e)**. All vertebrates have a brain located in the head. Most specialized sensory organs (eyes, ears, etc.) are situated on the head and are connected directly to the brain by nerves. Vertebrates still do have ganglia in other locations, but these are not as common as in invertebrates. Compared to invertebrates, vertebrates have larger brains and fewer ganglia.

Although the general structure of the brain is similar in all vertebrate animals, the specific pattern of brain development varies in different groups of animals, largely reflecting their habitat and lifestyle **(Figure 26.25)**. In sharks, the regions of the brain associated with smell (the olfactory bulbs) are prominent, testifying to the importance of smell in these aquatic predators. Frogs, however, are hunters that rely on vision, so the optic lobes, the area of the brain that receives visual information, are prominent. This is also true of birds. In reptiles, there is also an increase in the relative size of the fore-

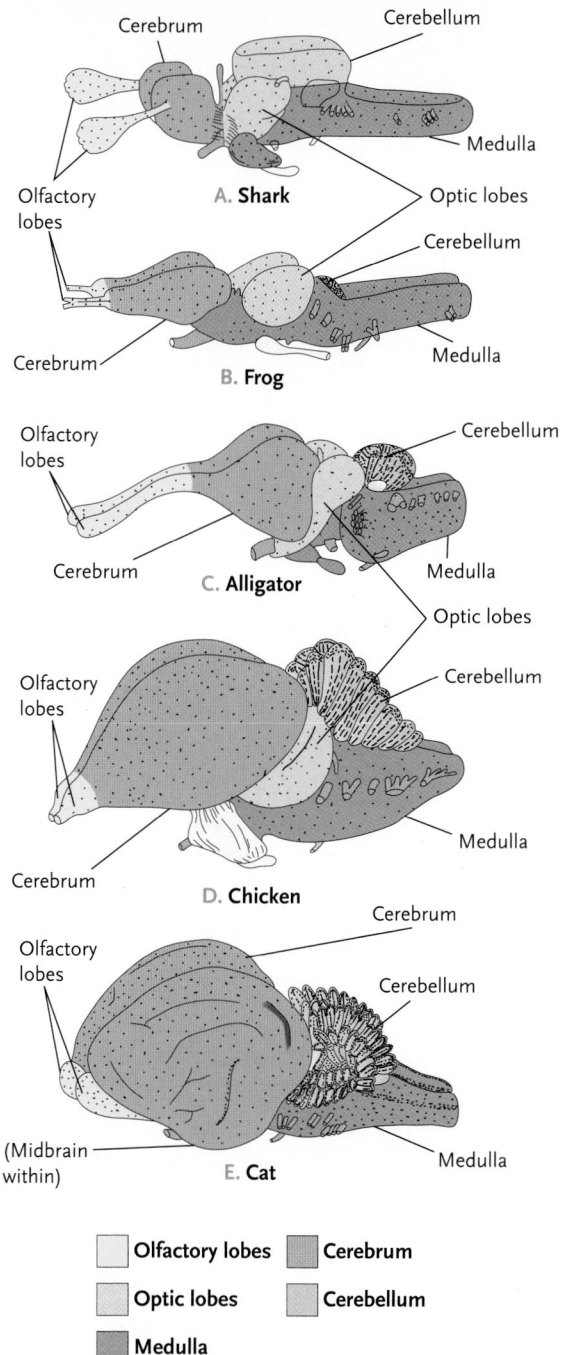

**FIGURE 26.25** A comparison of brain structures in five different groups of vertebrates, illustrating the evolutionary trends described in the text.

Legend labels:
Olfactory lobes
Optic lobes
Medulla
Cerebrum
Cerebellum

Brain labels (A. Shark): Cerebrum, Cerebellum, Medulla, Optic lobes, Olfactory lobes
(B. Frog): Cerebellum, Medulla, Cerebrum
(C. Alligator): Olfactory lobes, Cerebellum, Medulla, Cerebrum, Optic lobes
(D. Chicken): Olfactory lobes, Cerebellum, Medulla, Cerebrum
(E. Cat): Olfactory lobes, Cerebrum, Cerebellum, Medulla, (Midbrain within)

*Biology, 2E\**

brain, the anterior region of the brain associated with locomotion, and the coordination of complex tasks (such as thought, memory, language, and emotions). Birds and mammals also exhibit this increased size of the forebrain as well as an increase in the size of the **cerebellum**, a major coordinating centre for automatic activities.

Our knowledge about the functions of various brain regions comes from studying animals, as well as patients with brain damage from stroke, infection, tumours, and concussion. In recent years, modern imaging techniques such as functional magnetic resonance imaging (fMRI) and positron emission tomography (PET) have allowed researchers to record brain activity during normal behaviours.

The spinal cord is also part of the central nervous system. Part of its role is to carry information between the peripheral nervous system and the brain. But it also contains interneurons that form nerve nets that integrate sensory information and produce motor output, just as the brain does. These reflexes are programmed movements that take place without conscious effort. They include such classic reflexes as the knee-jerk reflex that is produced when a doctor taps the base of your knee cap and the crossed extensor reflex that makes you hop from one foot to the other when you step on a sharp object. Another well-studied reflex is the withdrawal reflex illustrated in **Figure 26.26, p. 592.** The spinal cord does communicate its activities to the brain via interneurons connected to the reflex circuits. This makes you aware of the stimulus causing the reflex slightly after the fact but also allows the brain to modify the reflex if necessary.

## STUDY BREAK

1. Why is the brain stem of such critical importance?
2. Describe a spinal reflex and discuss why such reflexes are important.

### Motor Output

Transmission of sensory input to the brain, as well as transmission of motor commands from the brain to effectors such as muscles and glands, is the domain of the peripheral nervous system (PNS). The motor system is divided into somatic and autonomic systems **(Figure 26.27, p. 592).**

*The Somatic System Controls the Contraction of Skeletal Muscles*

The neurons that make up the **somatic nervous system** carry signals from the CNS to the skeletal muscles to control voluntary (conscious) body movements. The cell bodies of motor neurons are located in the spinal cord, and their axons extend from the spinal cord to the skeletal muscles they control.

*The Autonomic System Is Divided into Sympathetic and Parasympathetic Pathways*

The neurons that make up the **autonomic** nervous system carry information to smooth muscles in all parts of the body, including those of the blood vessels, digestive tract, and reproductive and excretory systems. They

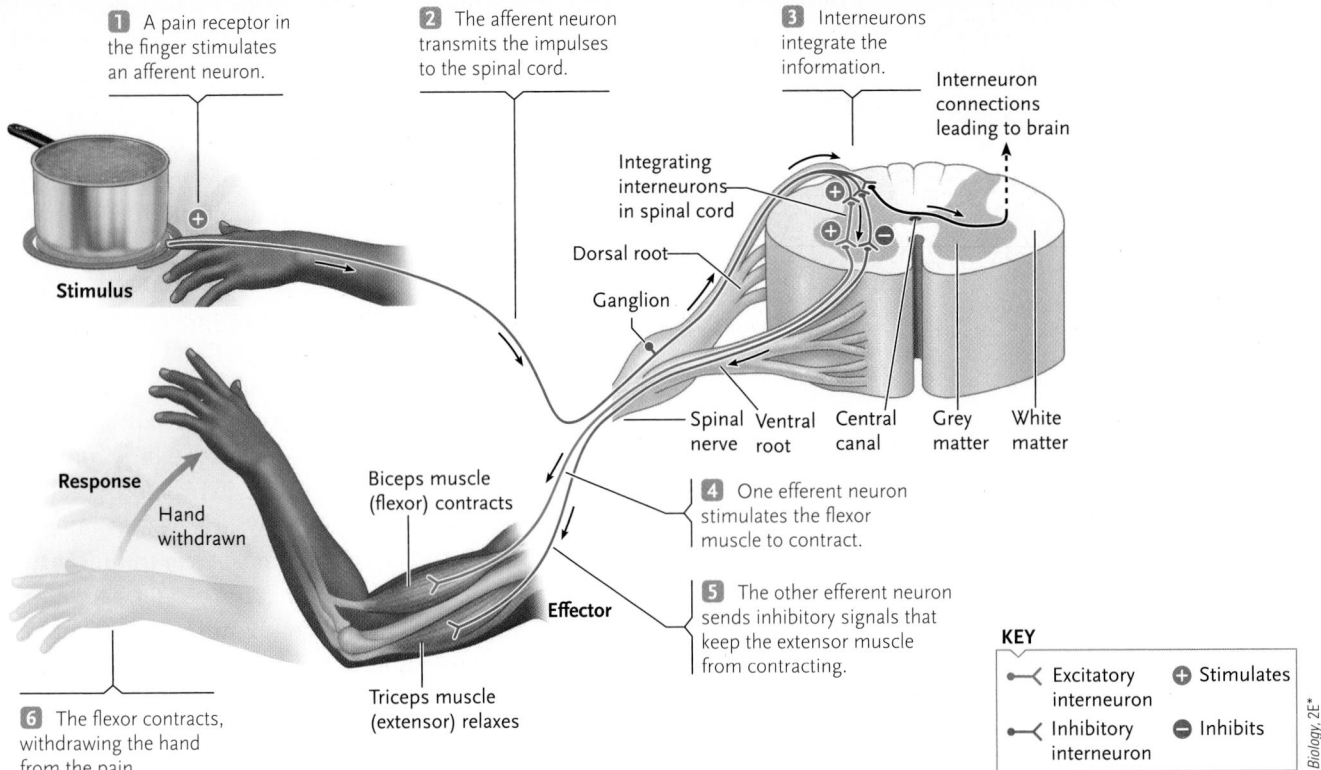

**FIGURE 26.26** Organization of the spinal cord and the withdrawal reflex. The withdrawal reflex is an example of a relatively simple neuron circuit that integrates incoming information to produce an appropriate response. The reflex movement produced by this circuit is so rapid that the hand is withdrawn before the brain recognizes the sensation of pain.

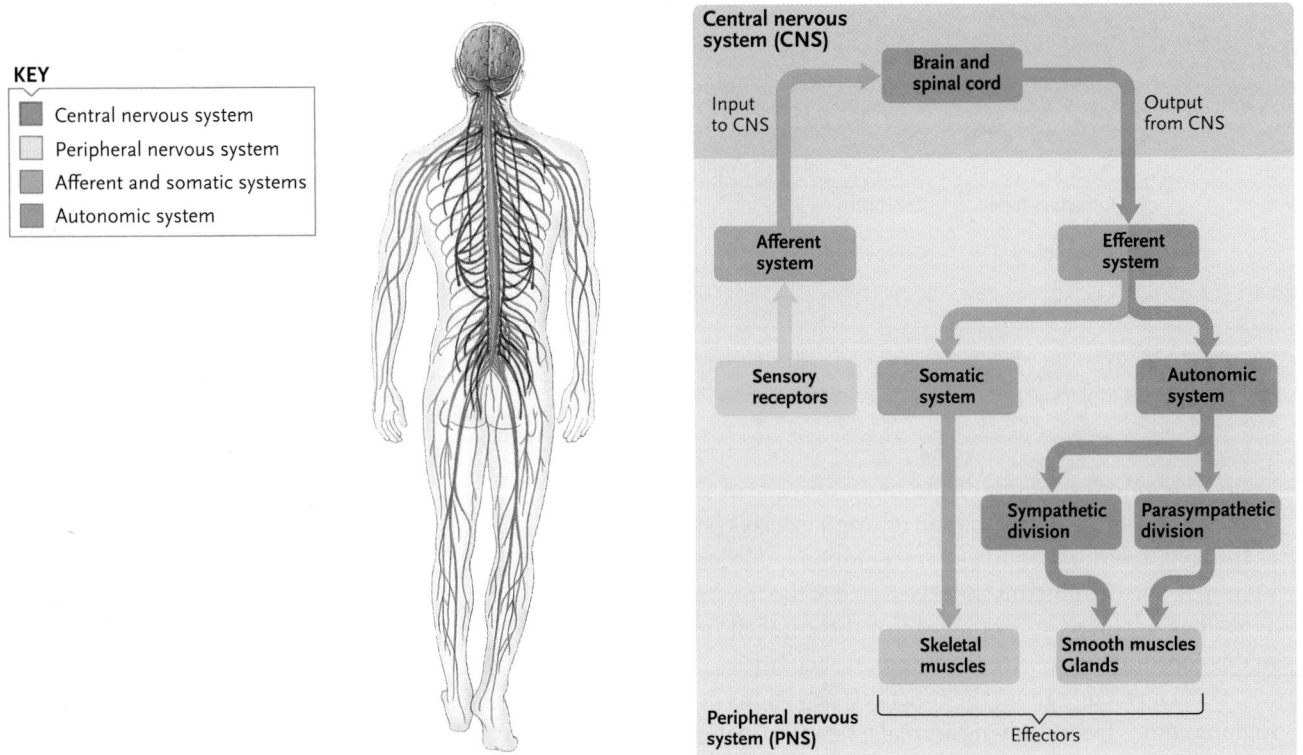

**FIGURE 26.27** The central nervous system (CNS) and the peripheral nervous system (PNS) and their subsystems.

also control the secretion of sweat glands. This system is organized into **sympathetic** and **parasympathetic** divisions. Both divisions are active, even under resting conditions. They have opposite effects on the organs they innervate. This more or less applies an accelerator and brake at the same time, and small changes in the activity of either system allow for very precise control. For example, the heart of most vertebrates at rest receives sympathetic input that stimulates it and parasympathetic input that inhibits it. As an animal begins to exercise, the activity of the sympathetic system increases and the activity of the parasympathetic systems decreases. Such control of these opposing effects allows our bodies to very precisely control involuntary body functions.

Note that the autonomic nervous system also contains sensory, or afferent, neurons that carry sensory information to the central nervous system. All of the cranial nerves that come directly from the brain are part of the autonomic nervous system, and these are the pathways for most sensory information.

## STUDY BREAK

1. What two systems make up the peripheral nervous system, and what do they generally control?
2. What two divisions are there to the autonomic nervous system, and how do they interact?

## PUTTING IT IN PERSPECTIVE

In this chapter, we have explored the way in which the activities of different organs and organ systems in plants and animals are coordinated, on both a minute-by-minute basis and a daily or seasonal basis. This coordination requires good intercellular communication. The major processes in the life of any plant or animal are growth, development, maintenance, and reproduction. All of these are events that require coordination of cells distributed throughout the body, and all are disrupted if the communication between cells fails.

Nothing demonstrates the importance of good communication better than the changes that occur when communication fails. In both plants and animals, disruption of intercellular communication gives rise to a host of endocrine disorders. In animals, it also gives rise to neural dysfunctions. We have discussed one of these that occurs in humans in this chapter—diabetes mellitus. The unregulated cell growth associated with cancer in animals is another classic example of failure in intercellular communication.

Understanding the nature of these systems of communication is essential for developing treatments for these disorders. They can also be used to advantage in other ways. For instance, coordinated growth in plants depends on hormones. Many herbicides are synthetic mimics of plant hormones that act by interfering with plant growth. We have discovered that some plants produce "natural herbicides" that restrict the growth of plants around them, reducing competition for nutrients. Plants also produce compounds that disrupt the endocrine systems of animals. These chemicals have become known as "endocrine disruptors." These are typically chemicals that mimic the sex steroid hormones estrogen and androgen. One such group is the phytoestrogens naturally found in some fruits, vegetables, beans, and grasses. Synthesis of these compounds may help reduce herbivory.

One of the recurring themes of the chapters on structure and function in plants and animals is homeostasis: the need to respond to environmental changes in a manner that establishes and maintains optimal conditions within the bodies of plants and animals. The basis of all homeostatic control systems is good communication.

## KEY CONCEPTS REVIEW AND QUESTIONS

### 26.1 Intercellular Communication: An Overview

The cells in different tissues, organs, and organ systems in plants and animals must communicate with one another to coordinate their functions and to allow plants and animals to respond to changes in their environments. This communication is achieved exclusively by hormones in plants but by both hormones and the nervous system in animals. The difference between the two systems is in the speed and specificity of their actions. Hormones are generally involved in controlling slow, long-acting responses involving many tissues or organs, whereas the nervous system generally controls fast, immediate responses and can selectively act on only one or a few tissues and organs.

1. How are the functions of hormones and nerves similar? How do they differ? What is the significance of this?

2. Match the description of the following systems with the proper term from the list below.

   a. A cell releases a chemical that acts on itself.     ___ Neuroendocrine regulation

   b. A cell releases a chemical that acts on its neighbour.     ___ Hormonal regulation

   c. A cell releases a chemical that acts on cells that are distant at other parts of the body.     ___ Autocrine regulation

   d. A specialized nerve cell releases a chemical into the circulation that acts on cells that are distant at other parts of the body.     ___ Neural regulation

   e. Nerve cells release a chemical that acts directly on its target cell.     ___ Paracrine regulation

## 26.2 Hormones

Hormones that are water soluble circulate in body fluids and interact with receptors on the external surface of the plasma membranes of target cells. In general, they initiate a cascade of events that ultimately activate or inhibit functional proteins such as enzymes, ion channels, and transport proteins. Hormones that are lipid soluble require transporters to carry them in body fluids but pass freely through the lipid bilayer of the cell membrane and interact with receptors in the cytoplasm of cells. Typically. they initiate a sequence of events leading to gene transcription or translation leading to the synthesis of functional proteins such as enzymes, ion channels, and transport proteins. Their effects are generally slower but longer lasting.

In plants, growth, development, and reproduction are all under hormonal control. Several plant hormones are involved in cell growth. Growth is not only a result of development but also includes directed growth as an adaptive response to light, gravity, and touch. Remember, plants can't move, but they can grow into new locations. Other hormones are involved in aging and dormancy as well as in daily and seasonal responses to changes in their environment.

For a deeper look into the roles and mechanisms of action of plant hormones, see MindTap > Chapter 26: Intercellular Communication > Readings.

3. Match the following descriptions with the hormones listed below.

   a. Hormones that stimulate cell growth     ___ Auxins

   b. Hormones associated with termination of seed and bud dormancy     ___ Gibberellins

   c. Hormones that inhibit cell growth     ___ Cytokines

   d. Hormones that cause leaf drop in the fall     ___ Brassinosteroids

   e. Hormones that stimulate fruit ripening     ___ Abscisic acid

       ___ Ethylene

In animals, most hormones are secreted from special ductless glands called endocrine glands. In vertebrates, there are 11 endocrine organs that each secrete different hormones that have different targets and actions. The levels of each hormone are under feedback control. Although this feedback control is exclusively hormonal in plants, in animals, it is often modulated by neural control, largely from the hypothalamus.

For a deeper look into the roles and mechanisms of action of animal hormones, see MindTap > Chapter 26: Intercellular Communication > Readings.

4. Match the following descriptions with the hormones listed below.

   a. Stimulates the kidney to retain more water     ___ Luteinizing hormone

   b. Stimulates the ejection of milk from mammary glands     ___ Antidiuretic hormone

   c. Regulates part of the estrus/menstrual cycle in female mammals     ___ Calcitonin

   d. Inhibits the perception of pain     ___ Endorphin

   e. Stimulates metabolism, development, and maturation     ___ Insulin

   f. Regulates blood glucose levels     ___ Triiodthyronine

   g. Regulates calcium levels     ___ Oxytocin

## 26.3 The Nervous System

Nervous systems in animals are composed of a central nervous system (CNS), where large numbers of neurons are condensed into ganglia and brains, and a peripheral nervous system (PNS) that communicates between the CNS and all parts of the body via nerve cells (neurons) that are bundled into cablelike projections called nerves. Information transfer along nerves involves four processes: reception, integration, transmission, and the production of a response. Information is conducted along the axons of nerve cells by the generation and transmission of action potentials that cause the release of neurotransmitters from the nerve terminals. These in turn cross synapses to produce an effect on the receiving cell.

For a deeper look into the various parts of the vertebrate brain, see MindTap > Chapter 26: Intercellular Communication > Readings.

5. Which of the following statements are true?
   a. Dendrites are the part of a neuron that receives incoming information.
   b. Cells are depolarized when either positively charged ions leave a cell or when negatively charged ions enter the cell.
   c. Voltage-gated $Na^+$ and $K^+$ channels are unique to nerve and muscle cells.
   d. Action potentials are slow, long-lasting events.
   e. Action potentials can be of different sizes.

Sensory cells are nerve cells that are modified to collect information about the internal and external environments of an animal and convert it into neural activity. This process, called transduction, occurs when stimuli (such as light, heat, sound waves, mechanical stress, or chemicals) cause changes in the rates at which channels conduct ions across the plasma membrane of the sensory cell. This leads to depolarization of the cell membrane and the generation of action potentials that travel along the axon of the sensory neuron to reach the CNS. The number of action potentials produced conveys information about the strength and duration of the stimulus. Structures such as our ears, nose, and tongue house the sensory cells and are designed to improve the ability of animals to detect different stimuli. Differences in structure between species reflect adaptations to the environments the animals live in and the importance of each stimulus to their lives.

6. What are the five major types of sensory cells, and what does each transduce information about?

Integration is the process by which decisions are made based on sensory information as well as information stored as memory. To some extent, integration takes place at every synapse in the body, but finer processing of information takes place in ganglia and in brains.

7. The regions of the brain can vary dramatically in size in different species of the same group. This reflects the extent to which each species relies on the information that is processed in that region of the brain. Given this, and knowing what you do of the role of the cerebellum, which group of fish is likely to have a larger cerebellum: those that live in the sand on the bottom of shallow bays or those that live in the open ocean?

The peripheral nervous system is composed of both sensory nerves that carry information to the central nervous system and motor nerves that transmit commands from the brain to muscles and glands. The motor system is divided into the somatic nervous system and the autonomic nervous system. The somatic nervous system carries signals from the CNS to the skeletal muscles to control voluntary (conscious) body movements. The cell bodies of motor neurons are located in the spinal cord, and their axons extend from the spinal cord to the skeletal muscles they control. The autonomic nervous system carries information to smooth muscles of the blood vessels, digestive tract, and the reproductive and excretory systems. They also control the secretion of sweat glands. This system is organized into sympathetic and parasympathetic divisions. Both divisions are active even under resting conditions and have opposing effects on the organs they innervate. This more or less applies an accelerator and brake at the same time, and small changes in the activity of either system allow for very precise control.

8. Reflect back on the fight-or-flight response of the marmot in the opening section of this chapter. Would this involve the somatic, sympathetic, or parasympathetic branches of the peripheral nervous system? Explain your answer.

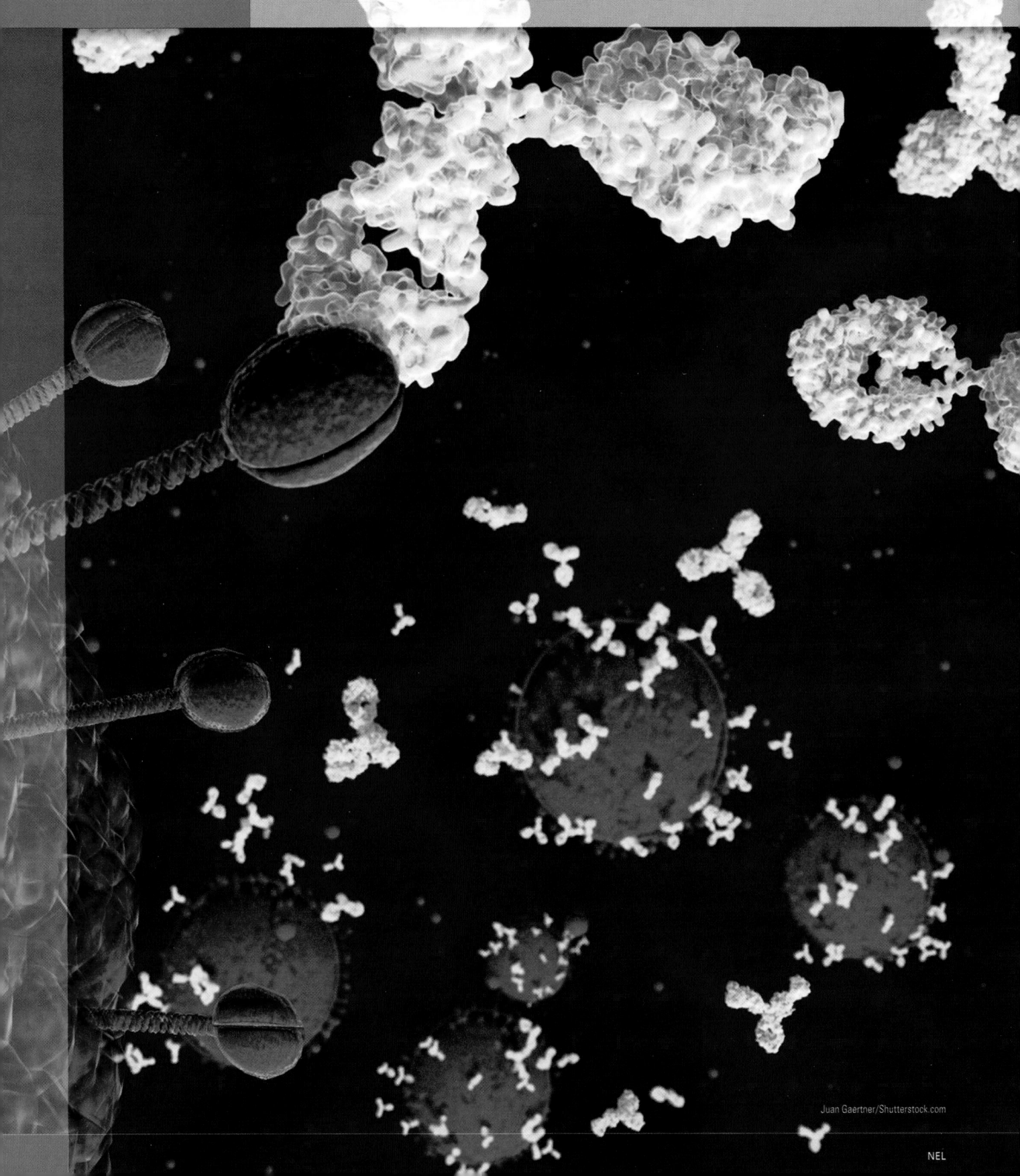

Juan Gaertner/Shutterstock.com

## WHY IT MATTERS

Imagine yourself standing on a bus going to school on a winter morning. As your brain drifts between the demands of the day ahead, you hear a loud sneeze behind you. We have all seen slow-motion video of the tiny droplets of spray that result from a violent sneeze. You hope the person covered his or her face, dreading the idea that some of the droplets might land on you.

Luckily, natural selection has led to the development of strong defence systems to protect us from disease-causing organisms. Over evolutionary time, plants and animals continually interacted with each other and with the bacteria, fungi, and protists that surround us. Although most of these interactions are benign or even mutually beneficial, some can lead to infections, diseases, or parasitic infestations. As a result, living organisms have evolved complex mechanisms to defend themselves. The vertebrate **adaptive immune system** is critical to our survival in a world heavily populated with resource-hungry microbes.

Looking back in human history, there are many examples of the effects on society when a new disease organism arrives to which we have limited immunity. Great plagues periodically swept through the Classical Age Egyptian, Greek, and Roman empires. The European Black Death caused by the bubonic plague during the 1300s killed approximately 50% of the population of Europe. The host of diseases released in North America when the first Europeans arrived almost completely destroyed the pre-Columbian Native American societies in a devastating series of epidemics. One of the most frequently discussed incidents in modern Canada was the pandemic influenza outbreak that swept through the world in 1918, killing approximately 50,000 Canadians.

Modern scientific approaches to disease prevention not only try to develop means to combat disease but also to minimize its spread through populations. Since the severe acute respiratory syndrome (SARS) outbreak in the spring of 2003 **(Figure 27.1)**, the World Health Organization (WHO) and national health ministries around the world, such as the Public Health Agency of Canada, have been on a heightened alert for a viral pandemic. When severe outbreaks of a particular disease occur, national and international health monitoring agencies track how the disease spreads, evaluate how dangerous it is, and warn people in an appropriate manner. If a particular disease is present in a localized population, at a level above that normally found, it can be categorized as an **epidemic**. When the disease spreads beyond the local population and moves across international borders, it is reclassified as a **pandemic**. Although this can be a frightening term, in part because of the role of the news media in keeping us informed, the definition of a pandemic disease depends solely on a large number of individuals being affected across a wide area. A pandemic disease is not necessarily deadly.

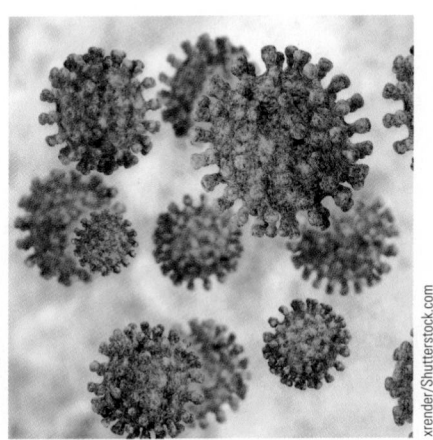

**FIGURE 27.1** At the height of the SARS scare, it was common to see people wearing masks when in close contact with others. The coronavirus that causes SARS interacts with surface receptors on tissues in the airways but can be trapped in mucus and ejected by coughing to infect others.

Avian influenza virus (H5N1), also known as the bird flu, was watched carefully by researchers at the WHO in the fall of 2006. It was followed by "swine flu" (H1N1) in the spring of 2009. The recent emergence of a new variety of the avian influenza virus (H7N9) in 2013, coinciding with an outbreak of a SARS-like virus in the Middle East and Europe called the Middle East respiratory syndrome coronavirus (MERS-CoV), has global health authorities on high alert. The Canadian National Microbiology Laboratory obtained samples of MERS-CoV and began studying the virus before any cases were even reported in Canada. Researchers in the fields of virology, immunology, microbiology, and basic biochemistry are scrambling to understand these viruses and the diseases they cause. Characterizing emerging viruses is a key step in controlling outbreaks and possibly developing vaccines before the disease can become a pandemic.

Since 2009, the WHO has had a new definition of a pandemic influenza. In this specific case, the WHO is concerned about new forms of the influenza A virus, which are genetically distinct from the strains cycling through populations as part of the normal seasonal flu. As a result of the lack of genetic similarity of these viruses, there is expected to be only a base level of immunity in humans. To be dangerous to a large number of humans, a potential pandemic influenza A virus would need to be highly infective—not all viruses are good at infecting humans. It would also need to be easily transmitted from infected to non-infected individuals. Unfortunately, the research done to date has only scratched the surface of understanding what makes some influenza viruses more infectious or more easily transmitted from individual to individual.

## 27.1 Physical and Chemical Deterrents

In a natural ecosystem, the resources available for the inhabitants are limited. This means that there is continuous, intense competition between organisms to obtain the resources they need to grow and reproduce. As discussed in Chapter 13, this is one of the fundamental concepts behind natural selection and evolution.

To protect themselves from competitors and predators, many organisms have evolved sophisticated systems to stop others from taking their resources. These protections are called **defence mechanisms.** Just as in sports, where defence systems are designed to reduce the number of goals or points scored against your team, in nature, defence systems evolve to reduce the impact of other organisms. Some defences are always present, such as the quills of a porcupine **(Figure 27.2a)**. The porcupine's quills stops potential predators such as wolves from biting and killing the porcupine. Increasing one's chances of survival

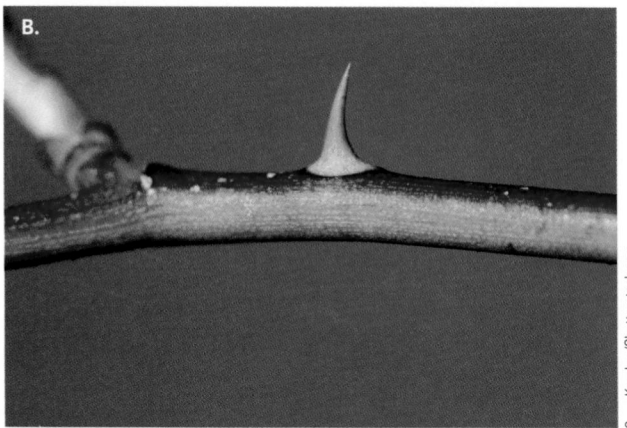

**FIGURE 27.2** Physical defences are quite common and range from the sharp quills of the porcupine (*Hystricomorph hystricidae*) **(a)** and the prickles of a wild rose (*Rosa acicularis*) **(b)** to the hard shell of an eastern painted turtle (*Chrysemys picta*) **(c)**. The octopus, on the other hand, releases a cloud of ink that confuses animals that are chasing it **(d)**. The common theme is to reduce the chances of being attacked by predators.

is the ultimate purpose of a defence mechanism. Other defence mechanisms are activated only when needed, such as the release of ink by a frightened octopus (**Figure 27.2d**).

We are perhaps most familiar with visible physical defence mechanisms such as the aforementioned porcupine, the thorns of a rose bush, or the hard shell of a painted turtle. In these cases, **physical defence mechanisms** place structural barriers between the predator and prey organisms. Each of the structural adaptations listed above reduces the chances that the defended organism will be eaten, attacked, or injured. Living organisms have a vast array of physical defence mechanisms that have evolved to protect them from competitors and predators (**Figure 27.2**).

What we can see with our eyes is only the tip of the iceberg. In addition to physical defences, many organisms also have chemical defences. Rather than a physical barrier, **chemical defence mechanisms** use compounds produced by the organism as a form of protection. The defensive chemicals can be stored in the cells of the organism and released when damage occurs, as we see with the tear-causing compounds in the bulb on an onion, or they can be excreted onto the surface of the organism. Often at a significant metabolic cost, organisms ranging from bacteria to vertebrates produce chemicals that reduce the rate of growth of competitors or render themselves unpalatable or even toxic to predators. The antibiotic penicillin is a chemical produced naturally by fungi of the genus *Penicillium*. Penicillin is a classic example of a chemical defence mechanism. The chemical is produced by the slower-growing fungus to stop the growth of faster-growing bacterial cells, which are competing for the same nutrients. We will discuss the discovery and function of penicillin in greater detail below.

## Physical Defences Use Structural Barriers as Protection

Physical defence mechanisms are the most visible forms of protection. As with all physical defences that have evolved over time, compromises are made between protection and other traits, such as mobility or rate of growth. In biology, we often describe compromises as **evolutionary trade-offs**. When we are attempting to make difficult decisions, it is often suggested that we make a list of pros and cons. Our decision is then made on whether the pros outweigh the cons. Evolution through natural selection works in a similar way—minus the logical thought processes. Any mutation leading to a change in an organism's defence mechanism may have other effects. For example, if we look back at the eastern painted turtle in Figure 27.2, we can see that the upper shell extends further than the bottom shell. This provides protection to the legs while allowing them to extend and move the turtle around. A larger bottom shell might provide more protection for the turtle, and we

might expect to see turtles with larger bottom shells if they live in areas of high predation. However, the larger bottom shell might come with a trade-off: decreased mobility. Which is more important to the survival of the organism? Evolution often leads to a balance between defence and the other needs of the organism. We can also view an evolutionary trade-off as a **cost-benefit ratio**. The larger shell may make the turtle safer from predators, an obvious benefit, but if the cost is decreased locomotion, it may not be able to capture enough food. An impregnable physical defence would be of no use to the turtle if it cannot get enough to eat.

The three-spined stickleback (*Gasterosteus aculeatus*) provides an excellent example of how cost–benefit ratios can dictate natural selection (**Figure 27.3**). This small fish has been a **model organism** for the study of evolutionary processes for many years (see the Purple Pages for an overview of model organisms). The three-spined stickleback is found in both fresh water and salt water across the northern hemisphere. It originated as a marine fish. But with the retreat of the glaciers 30,000 to 10,000 years ago, sticklebacks moved inland to inhabit freshwater ecosystems. Following this migration, the populations inhabiting freshwater evolved to lose their protective armour plating (Figure 27.3). The marine populations of the stickleback normally exhibit 30 or more bony lateral plates on each side of their body. In the photographs of sticklebacks in Figure 27.3, the bony plates are stained with a red dye (Alizarin Red S) so that they can be easily visualized. However, freshwater populations sport far fewer armour

10 mm

**FIGURE 27.3** The heavy armour plating of the three-spined stickleback was no longer as useful after the fish migrated to fresh water. Natural selection favoured fish with less of the metabolically costly armour. The fish on top has a full-plate body type, as we can see from the red-stained bony structures, whereas those below has fewer armour plates. Faster growth and greater agility provided a better defence for the freshwater fish than the cumbersome and energetically costly armour plates.

SOURCE: From Rowan D. H. Barrett, Sean M. Rogers, Dolph Schluter, "Natural Selection on a Major Armor Gene in Threespine Stickleback," *Science* 10 October 2008: Vol. 322 no. 5899 pp. 255–257. Reprinted with permission from AAAS.

plates. One can imagine that the tough bony plates would make it more difficult for a predator to chew and swallow a stickleback that had a full set of armour.

Research suggests that as the sticklebacks adapted to life in fresh water, the cost of armour production to the animal outweighed its benefits. There was an increased metabolic cost to obtain the minerals required to build the bony plates in freshwater ecosystems. This is because in fresh water, there are lower levels of dissolved minerals compared to saltwater environments. Therefore, the cells that form the plates need to work harder to accumulate the necessary minerals. Using controlled experiments, scientists have clearly demonstrated that in freshwater ecosystems, the fully armoured body-type fish grow more slowly. The increased metabolic cost of acquiring the minerals needed to build the armour plates decreased the rate at which the fish grew. At the same time, the benefit of having heavy armour decreased. First, the predators found in freshwater environments are smaller than those in salt water. This means that a smaller set of armour plates could still provide some level of protection. Smaller predator mouths mean that smaller armour plates are needed. In terms of the cost-benefit ratio, we see that as sticklebacks moved to fresh water, the cost of producing armour plates increased and the benefit they provided decreased. Not surprisingly, the presence of heavy armour plates reduced the reproductive fitness of sticklebacks in fresh water. Thus, when random mutations led to reduced armour plate production, the adaptive trait was favoured by natural selection. In a situation such as this, the heavy armour of the marine stickleback became obsolete in the freshwater ecosystems and was selected against. With this example, we can see that the benefits physical defences provide come with associated costs. In the example of the stickleback, we can also see that similar defences do not always work equally well in all circumstances.

Similar types of physical defences can be observed in plants. Spines, thorns, and prickles are all types of cell or organ modifications that help protect plants from herbivores. Spines are modified leaves that are hard and dried out. A thorn is a short, sharp, modified branch. In these cases, entire organs have been modified to act in a defensive role rather than in the plant's growth and reproduction. Prickles are somewhat simpler, being a pointed outgrowth of the epidermal cells. The "thorns" of rose bushes (Figure 27.2b) fall into the category of prickles, whereas cacti are typically covered in spines. Regardless of their origin, these sharp structures reduce grazing by physically damaging the sensitive mouths of herbivores. Spines, thorns, and prickles are examples of convergent evolution, a process described in Chapter 13. They are structures with different structural and genetic origins that have arisen in many unrelated plant lineages, yet they serve a common function.

Recent research demonstrated that many plant thorns and spines carry bacteria. This means that a simple puncture wound inflicted on an herbivore may become infected, making the spine a more severe deterrent to potential herbivores. It is not clear whether the plants attract specific bacteria to their thorns or if their presence is accidental. Regardless, a simple physical defence system has the potential to be much more punishing to herbivores that disregard it.

One final example of a physical defence is the dynamic alteration of an organism's body shape to distract or deter predators. An extreme example of such an animal is the porcupine fish (Figure 27.4). These fish are generally medium sized but are slow swimmers, making them easy targets for larger fish. However, in response to a perceived threat, they swallow enough air or water to more than double their volume. This has the effect of diminishing the number of predators that would be able to eat the porcupine fish. However, the change in size is

**FIGURE 27.4** When frightened, the porcupine fish (*Diodon nicthemerus*) swallows water to more than double its size. In addition to confusing predators, the swelling causes its skin to become tight, and its normally flat spines stand erect. This combination of defensive tactics helps dissuade predators from attacking the fish.

only the first defensive adaptation these fish use. The porcupine fish has rows of sharp spines that normally lie flat against its skin. As the fish swallows water and expands, the skin becomes tight and the spines become erect and point outwards. These spines reduce the risk of predation even further (Figure 27.4). Finally, as an additional predation deterrent, the porcupine fish is poisonous. It accumulates the extremely toxic alkaloid tetrodotoxin. It is not clear whether the fish produce this poison themselves or if it comes from their diet. Regardless, this three-pronged approach to defence is hard to get around. In a strange twist of fate, the porcupine fish feeds on other defensive specialists: hard-shelled molluscs and spiny sea urchins. The porcupine fish has evolved strong, sharp teeth located at the front of its jaws to penetrate the hard shells of its prey. It also has tough, rubbery lips to protect it from puncture damage when eating sea urchins. It is quite ironic that a fish that evolved such impressive physical defences has also evolved mechanisms that allow it to overcome similar defences in its prey.

## Chemical Defences Use Distasteful and Toxic Compounds as a Form of Protection

In addition to the spines, armour, and body shapes that plants and animals use to protect themselves from predators and competitors, many organisms also mount chemical defences. Some, such as the Pacific newt (members of the genus *Taricha*; see Box 27.1) or the porcupine fish, described above, produce toxins to dissuade their foes, whereas others, such as the common milkweed plant (*Asclepias syriaca*), accumulate compounds that make them poisonous and distasteful. Some chemical defences are always present, whereas others are induced by cellular damage or stress. Plants, fungi, and prokaryotes seem to possess more impressive and varied chemical defences. Perhaps they have evolved such impressive chemical defence mechanisms because they are unable to change their location or move away from danger.

A number of fungi produce chemicals that slow the growth of competing prokaryotes. Of these antibacterial compounds, the most famous is penicillin. Discovered by Alexander Fleming in 1928, penicillin is a defensive chemical produced by fungi of the genus *Penicillium*. Fleming served as a medical officer during the First World War and saw first-hand how infected wounds and post-surgical complications greatly decreased the survival of injured soldiers. At the time, it was common medical practice to use antiseptics, such as Dakin's solution (a mixture of bleach and baking soda), to clean wounds. However,

Fleming noticed that in deep wounds, treatment with antiseptics often made recovery more difficult. He hypothesized that the antiseptics were destroying helpful factors that would normally keep the anaerobic bacteria in check.

After the war, Fleming took up a research and teaching position at St. Mary's Hospital and later the University of London, where he continued to look for compounds that stopped the growth of bacteria. It was in 1928 that Fleming noticed that one of his culture plates growing *Staphylococcus* (a genus of gram-positive bacterium) had become contaminated with fungus. Although this might normally be considered an annoyance, leading a scientist to discard the contaminated plate, Fleming noticed that there was a clear zone surrounding the fungus in which no bacteria were growing. He hypothesized that the fungus was producing a chemical that stopped bacterial growth. Fleming was able to grow the fungus on its own and demonstrate that a substance it produced could stop the growth of a number of bacteria. He named the substance penicillin after the genus of fungus he isolated it from, *Penicillium* (**Figure 27.5**).

Unfortunately for *Penicillium* and us, some bacteria have evolved a resistance to penicillin. As mentioned in Chapter 15, the cell wall of bacteria is composed of sugars and amino acids arranged into a macromolecule called **peptidoglycan**. Penicillin acts not by killing bacteria outright but by interfering with the synthesis of peptidoglycan in

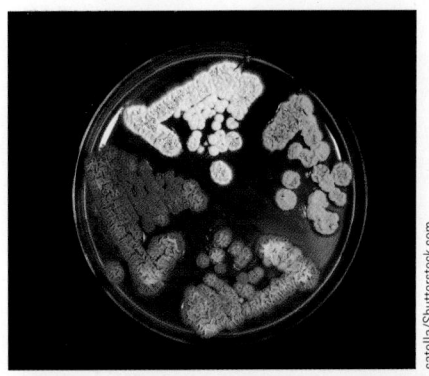
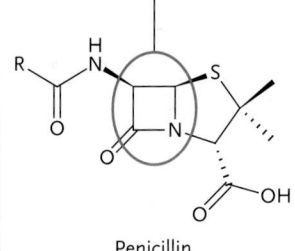

Beta-lactam ring

Penicillin

**FIGURE 27.5** Alexander Fleming's discovery of penicillin was a fundamental breakthrough in modern medicine. It highlights the chemical warfare occurring between microbes. In the Petri dish shown above, the blue-green coloured *Penicillium* fungus inhibits the growth of the pale yellow bacteria. However, the beta-lactamase-producing white bacteria degrade the penicillin molecule, allowing both it and the yellow bacteria to grow next to the penicillin-producing fungus.

# LIFE ON THE EDGE 27.1
## The Adaptive Arms Race

A wide variety of different organisms have evolved the ability to produce chemicals that their predators find distasteful or are even toxic. Fungal species produce a number of antibiotics. Bacteria such as *Clostridium botulinum* (Botox) or *Bacillus anthracis* (anthrax) produce chemicals that can incapacitate an infected host. Toxins produced by these organisms evolve over time as a defence mechanism.

However, we often forget that the predators are also living organisms that can adapt due to natural selective pressures. When toxin-producing prey and their predators apply selective pressure to each other, some incredibly interesting adaptations can occur. In one particular case, the selective pressure placed on the predator and prey animals has led to a chemical arms race, or what evolutionary biologists call **phenotypic exaggeration**. The broadly classed Pacific newt belongs to the genus *Taricha* and can be found across the west coast of North America, from California to Vancouver Island. Generally speaking, all of the *Taricha* species produce a paralytic neurotoxin called tetrodotoxin. Individuals belonging to the species *Taricha granulosa*, the rough-skinned newt, are the most toxic. However, even within this single species, newts found in northern California and Vancouver Island contain very low levels of tetrodotoxin, whereas individuals found in parts of Oregon contain enough neurotoxin to kill humans if ingested. The reason for this huge variation in toxicity within the species was a puzzle until scientists began examining a predator of the rough-skinned newt: the common garter snake (*Thamnophis sirtalis*) **(Figure 1)**. One would assume that if a newt contained enough toxin to incapacitate or kill an adult human, a garter snake would not stand a chance. However, due to a mutation in the gene that encodes the sodium channel protein tetrodotoxin binds to, the snakes are only moderately affected by the toxin. Thus, instead of dying, the snakes are mildly paralyzed while they digest the poisonous newt. Within the populations of newts and snakes there is a wide degree of variation in both toxicity and resistance. The presence of this variation allows for strong selective adaptation.

**FIGURE 1** The common garter snake (left) has become generally immune to the tetrodotoxin (below) produced by the rough-skinned newt (*Taricha granulosa*). Although the newt accumulates the toxin to levels that would kill several humans, a mutation in the garter snake's sodium channel means that it shows little effect after a meal of newt.

Edmund D. Brodie III

the cell wall. A set of enzymes called **transpeptidase** is required to link the amino acids found in peptidoglycan together, but the beta-lactam ring structure of penicillin (Figure 27.5) interferes with this reaction. As a result, bacteria cannot produce an intact cell wall in the presence of penicillin, limiting their ability to grow and divide.

Bacteria can become resistant to penicillin by producing an enzyme called **beta-lactamase** (Figure 27.5). Beta-lactamase catalyzes the breakdown of the penicillin molecule so that it is no longer able to inhibit the transpeptidase enzymes. This allows the bacterium to resume normal growth.

Beta-lactamases are an ancient group of enzymes that arose long before our medicinal use of penicillin. However, since our use of antibiotics has increased, the prevalence of the beta-lactamase gene in bacteria has increased. In essence, we are artificially selecting for antibiotic resistance by overuse and misuse of penicillin-type antibiotics. Although a medical problem for us, the beta-lactamase-containing bacteria are counteracting the

As part of his Ph.D. research project, Charles Hanifin and his research supervisors Dr. Edmund Brodie Jr. from the Department of Biology at Utah State University and Dr. Edmund Brodie III from the Department of Biology at the University of Virginia examined the levels of tetrodotoxin in rough-skinned newts and the level of resistance to tetrodotoxin in garter snakes across the newts' habitat range. They compared newt toxicity to what they knew of garter snake tetrodotoxin resistance in the same areas where the newts were caught. **Figure 2** shows the researchers' plot of these results. Although the level of newt toxicity and garter snake resistance appear to correlate, with areas of high newt toxicity also being areas of high garter snake resistance, when examined carefully, by plotting the data together **(Figure 2c)**, the researchers found areas of divergence, meaning that the arms race had failed and was no longer affecting the newt–snake relationship. In fact, across most of the range, even the most toxic newts did not produce enough tetrodotoxin to kill the local garter snakes. It seems that at this point in the evolutionary arms race, the garter snakes have an edge on the newts. Now we just need to wait a few thousand years to see if the newts evolve an improved defence.

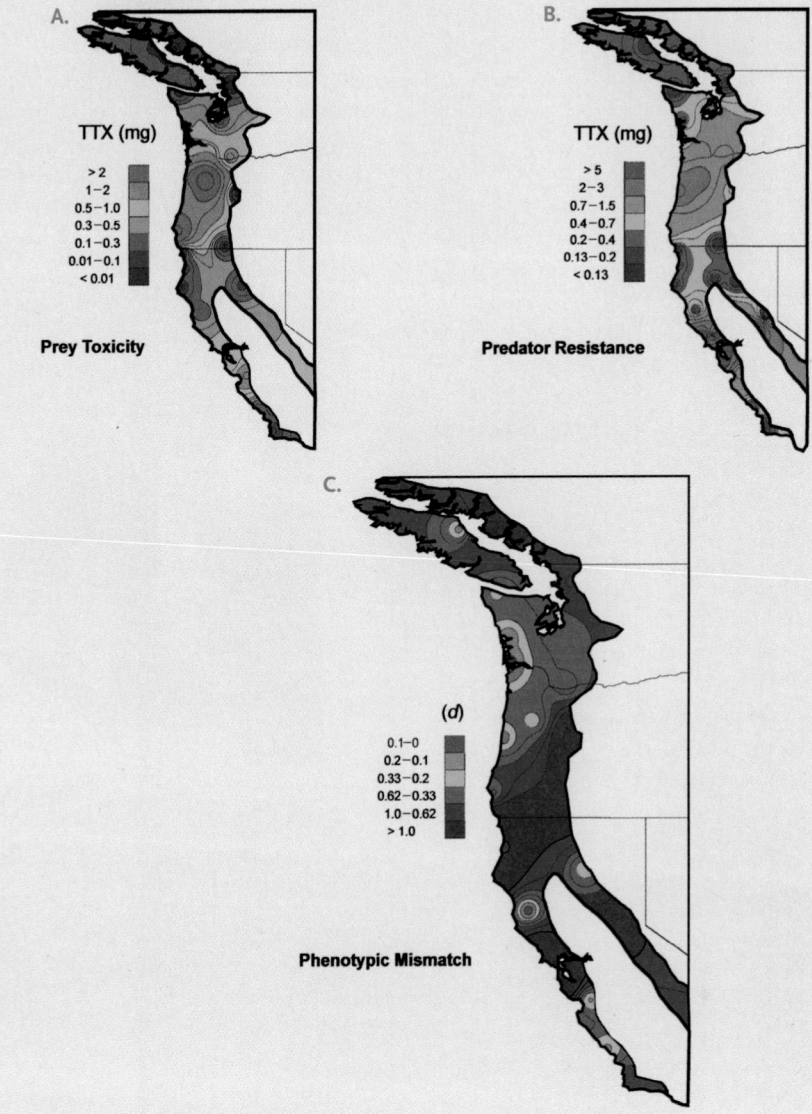

**FIGURE 2** The relationship between rough-skinned newt toxicity **(a)** and garter snake tetrodotoxin (TTX) resistance **(b)** is striking when the two factors are plotted together **(c)** on maps of their distribution. Where newt toxicity is high, so, correspondingly, is garter snake resistance.

SOURCE: Hanifin CT, Brodie ED Jr, Brodie ED III (2008) Phenotypic Mismatches Reveal Escape from Arms-Race Coevolution. *PLoS Biol* 6(3): e60. doi:10.1371/journal.pbio.0060060 © 2008 Hanifin et al.

chemical defence of the *Penicillium* fungi. A number of other antibiotics have been identified from studies of fungal–bacterial interactions. Thus, chemical arms races are continuously under way all around us, with bacteria and fungi fighting for territory and resources.

In an attempt to improve the clinical usefulness of penicillin, researchers such as Dr. Gary Dmitrienko from the Department of Chemistry at the University of Waterloo are searching for inhibitors of the beta-lactamase enzyme (see Box 27.2). Beta-lactamase inhibitors have no antibiotic activity of their own. But when used in conjunction with penicillin-type antibiotics, they decrease the antibiotic resistance of bacteria that produce beta-lactamase enzymes. With this type of approach to pharmacology, researchers are trying to counteract the effects of years of improper use of antibiotics and artificial selection for resistant bacterial strains.

Plants and animals are also able to accumulate toxic or distasteful chemicals to use for defence. Animals that specialize in chemical defence often advertise it. We are

As we discussed in Chapter 15, the rapid rates of evolution that can be observed in bacteria mean that biomedical researchers trying to develop new antibiotics are in a race against time. Depending on the target in the bacterial cell, antibiotic resistance can develop quite quickly. Due to factors such as horizontal gene transfer (see Chapter 7), a gene that confers resistance to an antibiotic can be passed from species to species. Under the extremely strong, artificial selection that antibiotics pose, any misuse can lead to survival of somewhat resistant strains. Repeat this often enough and your drug of choice may no longer work to treat disease.

Through this type of process, misuse and overuse of penicillin have made many bacterial strains resistant. In 2013, it was estimated that 1 in 12 adults in Canadian hospitals were exposed to methicillin-resistant *Staphylococcus aureus* (MRSA). Methicillin is a penicillin-like beta-lactam antibiotic. About 25% of these patients develop an antibiotic-resistant infection.

Because of the difficulty and cost of developing new antibiotics, as we run out of bacterial cell targets, researchers have begun investigating ways to block the bacterial resistance. Dr. Gary Dmitrienko is a professor in the Department of Chemistry at the University of Waterloo. Since the early 1980s, Dr. Dmitrienko's research team has been attempting to develop inhibitors of the bacterial beta-lactamase protein. Funded by the National Sciences and Engineering Research Council of Canada (NSERC) and the Canadian Institutes of Health Research (CIHR), Dr. Dmitrienko's team uses 3D molecular modeling of the

beta-lactamase protein and penicillin antibiotics to determine optimal 3D shapes of molecules that could take the place of penicillin in the beta-lactamase active site and block the enzyme's activity **(Figure 1)**. The team members then use their expertise in synthetic chemistry to build new organic molecules based on their modelling predictions.

Beta-lactamase inhibitors have been in clinical use for over 30 years, but much like the interaction between the newt and

the garter snake described in Box 27.1, the bacteria seem to be winning the arms race. New mutations arise in the beta-lactamase enzyme, which allow them to discriminate between the beta-lactam antibiotics and inhibitors. Thus, work continues to identify new, highly functional beta-lactamase inhibitors. Using the chemical and computational modelling tools at their disposal, Dr. Dmitrienko's team is trying to stay one step ahead of bacterial evolution.

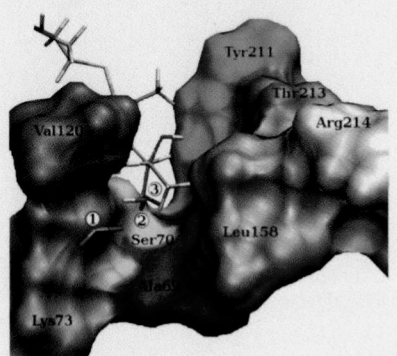

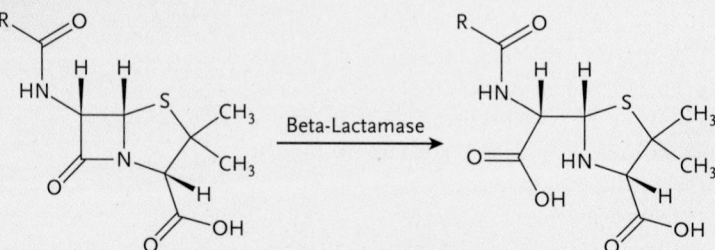

**FIGURE 1** In Dr. Gary Dmitrienko's lab in the Department of Chemistry at the University of Waterloo, the researchers use three-dimensional modelling of the beta-lactamase enzyme to predict what types of chemicals could be used to block the enzyme active site, rendering it inactive. They then develop new methods to make the compounds they want to investigate. This approach to enhancing the activity of drugs we already have available is an alternative to developing new antibiotics from scratch.

SOURCE: Reprinted from *Chemistry & Biology*, Volume 16, Issue 5, Jean-Denis Docquier, Vito Calderone, Filomena De Luca, Manuela Benvenuti, Francesco Giuliani, Luca Bellucci, Andrea Tafi, Patrice Nordmann, Maurizio Botta, Gian Maria Rossolini, Stefano Mangani, "Crystal Structure of the OXA-48 β-Lactamase Reveals Mechanistic Diversity among Class D Carbapenemases," Pages 540–547, Copyright 2009, with permission from Elsevier.

familiar with the brightly coloured poison dart frogs of the Amazon rainforest of South America **(Figure 27.6)**. These highly visible amphibians extract toxic alkaloids from their diet and secrete them onto their skin, much like the Pacific newt (see Box 27.1 for more information about the Pacific newt's chemical defence mechanism). The brightness of the frog's colouration is highly correlated with the amount of toxin it possesses.

The monarch butterfly follows a similar principle (Figure 27.6). While in the larval stage, it eats the leaves of the common milkweed (*Asclepias syriaca*), a plant that produces a suite of foul-tasting and toxic cardiac glycosides. The monarch caterpillars are immune to these chemicals but accumulate the compounds in their tissues. The bright colours of both the caterpillar and the butterfly advertise to potential predators that they do not taste good.

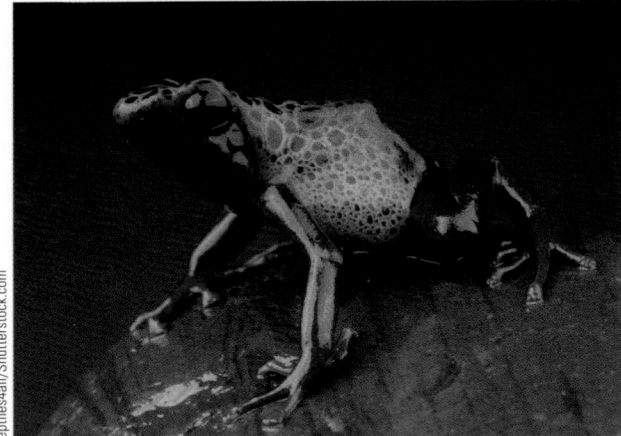

A.

B. **Viceroy butterfly (*Limenitis archippus*)**

*John E Heintz Jr/Shutterstock.com*

C.

*Chris Alcock/Shutterstock.com*

D. **Monarch butterfly (*Danaus plexippus*)**

*csterken/Shutterstock.com*

**FIGURE 27.6** The poison dart frogs of the Amazon rainforest *Dendrobates azureus* **(a)** and *Dendrobates leucomelas* **(c)** accumulate toxic alkaloids in their skin. They advertise this to potential predators with their bright colours. The monarch butterfly **(d)** tastes bad and is mildly toxic due to its diet of cardiac glycoside–containing milkweed plant leaves. The viceroy butterfly **(b)** does not eat the milkweed plant leaves but mimics the monarch's colours, patterning, and body shape to fool possible predators.

In an interesting twist of natural selection, the viceroy butterfly is a mimic of the monarch (Figure 27.6). It looks very similar, tricking potential predators into thinking it is equally foul tasting as the monarch. Here we have both genuine and false forms of chemical defence in animals. This is called **Batesian mimicry**, and it is found in many insects, as well as some fish and reptiles. Batesian mimicry offers a cost-effective alternative to chemical defence as no specialized metabolic pathway is needed. An alternative form of mimicry, **Müllerian mimicry** describes the situation where there are two poisonous (chemically defended) organisms that look similar and have the same predator. The poison dart frogs could be described as Müllerian mimics. In this case, both organisms produce the chemical defence, and the predator learns more rapidly that a particular set of visual cues signals poisonous prey.

## The Epidermis Provides an Outer Layer of Protection

Although many forms of defence are exhibited by plants and animals, the first line of defence in these organisms is their outer layer of protection. In higher plants, this outer layer is the epidermis, and in animals, it is the epithelium. In both groups of organisms, these layers are made up of tightly joined cells forming a continuous sheet, which acts to keep foreign organisms and toxic chemicals on the outside.

Looking at plant leaves **(Figure 27.7, p. 606)**, we can see that the epidermis is composed of relatively flat cells that are tightly connected. The only openings are the stomata, which are present to allow gas exchange. The epidermal cells are also coated in a thick, waxy material called the cuticle, which prevents water loss and helps prevent microbes from infecting the plant.

In vertebrate animals, the epithelium is a complex tissue. It not only covers the outside of the organism, our skin, but also lines interior compartments such as the airways and digestive and reproductive tracts. Our bodies are very highly adapted to exclude pathogens and parasites. The mucus lining our airways traps foreign particles and allows them to be more easily expelled by sneezing or coughing. Similarly, the acidic compartment of the stomach, which also contains a soup of digestive enzymes, prevents most bacteria and viruses from continuing into our intestinal tract.

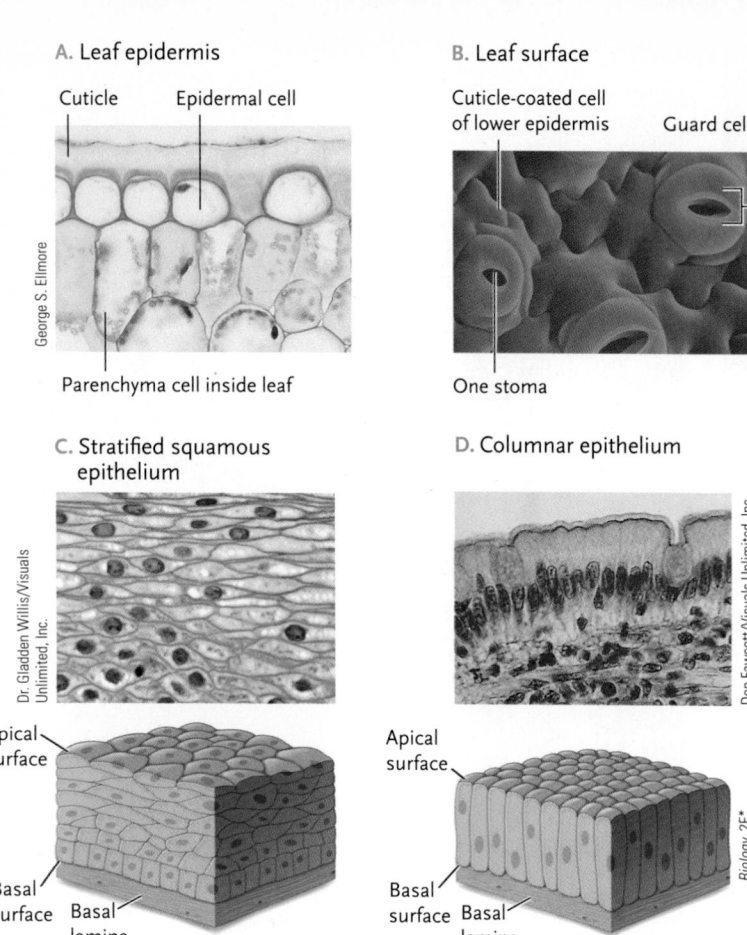

**A. Leaf epidermis**

Cuticle   Epidermal cell

Parenchyma cell inside leaf

George S. Ellmore

**B. Leaf surface**

Cuticle-coated cell of lower epidermis   Guard cells

One stoma

Dr. Jeremy Burgess/Science Source

**C. Stratified squamous epithelium**

Dr. Gladden Willis/Visuals Unlimited, Inc.

Apical surface

Basal surface   Basal lamina

**D. Columnar epithelium**

Don Fawcett/Visuals Unlimited, Inc.

Apical surface

Basal surface   Basal lamina

Biology, 2E*

**FIGURE 27.7** Both plants and animals have protective layers of cells on the outside of their tissues, which play a critical role in keeping pathogens and parasites outside the body. Both the plant epidermis (**a** and **b**) and the animal epithelium (**c** and **d**) are composed of tightly packed cells, limiting access to nutrients and resources stored in the tissues.

One of the best defences vertebrates have against microbial pathogens is the collection of mutualistic microbes in our bodies and on our skin's surface. Scientists estimate that over 100 trillion microbes, from hundreds of different species, inhabit the average adult human's intestinal tract. Our bacterial inhabitants have coevolved with us and provide many health benefits.

In a fascinating medical development, researchers have found that some disease states can be improved following transplantation of fecal material from a healthy individual. Cases of *Clostridium difficile* infection can occur in the intestines of patients who have weakened or suppressed immune systems (as we will discuss later in this chapter). Episodes of *C. difficile* infection are both extremely painful and sometimes fatal. Even extreme antibiotic treatments do not always produce a good outcome. Physicians and researchers who were struggling to find a solution to this difficult infection wondered if a better approach would be to restore a healthy gut microflora to these patients. What started off as a "poop transplantation" has made doctors and researchers think about how our body is protected from a hostile environment.

Think back to Alexander Fleming. In 1915, he suggested that the antiseptic washes used during surgeries led to more severe infections; this type of research is proving him right once again. Now links are being made between gut microflora and ailments ranging from colitis and hypercholesterolemia to obesity and rheumatoid arthritis. There is no doubt that the role of our bacterial partners in our health and defence against disease will be an intriguing area of study for many years to come.

## STUDY BREAK

1. Physical defences often come at a cost to the organism. Can you think of a cost associated with the shell of a turtle?
2. Would you consider human ear wax to be a physical or a chemical defence? Explain your reasoning.
3. Can you develop a hypothesis that would suggest a possible mechanism by which gut microflora could help prevent infection by disease-causing organisms?

## 27.2 The Immune System of Multicellular Organisms

In more complex, multicellular plants, fungi, and animals, the immune system is composed of a number of cell types. These cells work together to help the whole organism fight off pathogens, parasites, cancerous cells, and other foreign objects.

Different organisms have evolved to repel invaders in different ways. The simplest systems operate continuously and act in response to all attacks; we call this **innate immunity**. A limitation of innate immunity is that it does not "learn" from previous exposures to disease. A second immune approach that is found only in vertebrate animals, called **adaptive immunity**, uses specialized cells that can recognize specific pathogens or foreign objects. Following exposure, these specialized cells will become more abundant, meaning that the organism is prepared for the next time it is exposed to the same challenge. This limits the chance that the pathogen or parasite will cause a disease state a second time.

### Some Organisms Have an Innate Base Level of Immunity

Innate immunity is a defensive approach that can be observed across many classes of organisms, such as plants, fungi, arthropods, and vertebrates. It is a programmed response to pathogen attack that happens in the same way each time. Higher plants do not have specialized immune cells, but they do have strong innate immune systems, and their modular style of growth allows them to use different mechanisms to limit the spread of infections. For example, plants often use a "slash and burn" style of defence. If the plant detects an infection, signals can lead to entire leaves being dropped from the plant. Alternatively, cells can send a signal to neighbouring cells telling them to die, again limiting both the pathogen movement within the plant and its access to the plant's nutrients **(Figure 27.8)**.

Because plants are unable to move from one location to another, they are often repeatedly exposed to the same pathogens. For example, the funguslike organism *Phytophthora infestans*, which infects plants belonging to the Solanaceae (potatoes and tomatoes, for example), can survive in the soil as spores year after year.

Normally, natural selection will result in a balance between the level of immunity or disease resistance found in the plants and the infectivity of the pathogens. Agriculture has disturbed this balance in several ways. First, breeding of high-yielding crop plant varieties can unintentionally decrease the plant's innate disease resistance. Both yield and disease resistance are genetic traits, so unless both are tested and selected for by plant breeders, one may be unknowingly sacrificed. Second, when crops are seeded, large fields are normally planted with a single variety of crop plants. This allows disease organisms to easily move from one plant to the next, infecting large numbers of plants and travelling large distances. If farmers do not rotate crops, it can lead to a build-up of spores in the soil, with a devastating effect on crop production.

This was exactly what happened in Ireland during the 1840s Irish potato famine. *P. infestans* was the causative agent of the potato blight. *P. infestans* is currently classified as an Oomycetes, a class of protist (see Chapter 16),

rather than a true fungus. In 2013, scientists from the Sainsbury Laboratory in the United Kingdom, the Max Planck Institutes in Germany, and the United States Department of Agriculture finally identified the strain of *P. infestans* responsible for the Irish potato famine. They demonstrated that the strain originated in Mexico, where wild potatoes originated, and then moved (likely on infected plants) to the northeast United States and southern Canada before being transported to Belgium and then Ireland. This devastating story was caused in part by poor agricultural approaches. The import of contaminated plant material led to about 25% of the population of Ireland perishing or moving to North America.

Modern agricultural plant breeding keeps a close watch on pathogen resistance. Researchers are developing a very thorough understanding of how plant immunity works. Powdery mildew is a fungal pathogen that can infect many types of plants. Of particular concern in western Canada is the sensitivity of some wheat strains to this disease. During wet years, crop losses of up to 35% can occur in sensitive wheat strains. This could lead to severe shortages of flour if outbreaks happen across a large area. Some wheat varieties are more resistant to powdery mildew and can be said to have a higher level of innate immunity. Plant pathologists studying how the powdery mildew fungus infects wheat leaves have discovered that the plant can detect the presence of the fungus on its leaves. This is a common theme in plant immunity. Plant cells have receptor proteins located in their plasma membrane that recognize specific components of the fungal cell wall. The molecules detected are often the polysaccharide- and protein-building blocks of the fungal cell wall. Thus, as the fungus grows on the plant leaf, the plant cells can tell that it is there. The fungal

**FIGURE 27.8** Plant innate immunity attempts to limit disease progression through the plant. The modular growth habit of plants allows them to sacrifice cells or even whole leaves to defend the plant and limit the pathogen's access to the plant's nutrients.

SOURCE: Ministry of Agriculture, Food and Rural Affairs. *Bacterial Diseases of Tomato: Bacterial Spot, Bacterial Speck, Bacterial Canker* (Publication 05-069). © Queen's Printer for Ontario, 2005. Reproduced with permission.

molecules detected by the plant receptors are called **pathogen-associated molecular patterns (PAMPs)**. We will see later in this chapter that vertebrates also detect PAMPs as part of the adaptive immune system. When detected by a plant cell receptor, PAMPs trigger a genetic response in the plant cell, leading to changes in gene expression that allow the plant to mount an immune response.

Through a series of defensive steps, the plant modifies its structure to minimize the spread of the pathogen and protect its resources. One defensive mechanism involves reinforcing the cell wall at the location of a germinating fungal spore **(Figure 27.9)**. Genes required to produce cell wall-strengthening materials such as lignin and callose are upregulated (turned on). As a result, these polymers are deposited at the location on the cell wall, where the fungus is trying to penetrate into the plant cytosol. Some plants also use a mechanism by which extensions of neighbouring cells called **tyloses** grow

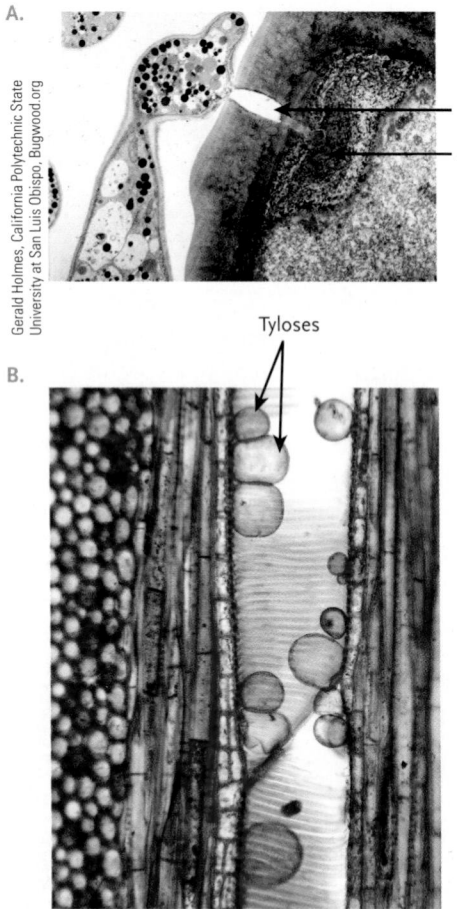

Gerald Holmes, California Polytechnic State University at San Luis Obispo, Bugwood.org

**FIGURE 27.9** When fungal spores germinate on the surface of a plant leaf, they form what is called a penetration peg in an attempt to gain entry into the leaf **(a)**. In defence, the plant detects the penetration peg and thickens the cell wall using cellulose, lignin, and callose. To limit the movement of fungal hyphae, bacteria, and viruses through the open tubes of the xylem, the plant forms tyloses to close off xylem cells and slow movement of the pathogen **(b)**.

SOURCE: Qiang Sun, Thomas L. Rost, and Mark A. Matthews, "Pruning-induced tylose development in stems of current-year shoots of Vitis vinifera (Vitaceae)," *American Journal of Botany* 93(11): 1567–1576. 2006. By permission of the Botanical Society of America.

into the xylem tubes (Figure 27.9). This can block the movement of the pathogen through the open xylem cells and prevent the spread of disease throughout the plant. As mentioned above, in extreme cases, the plant cells will die in an effort to stop the spread of the pathogen. The process of cell death is called apoptosis if it is controlled by the cell (see Chapter 6). In this case, nutrients are removed from the cell before it dies to try to starve the pathogen. When the process of cell death is not controlled by the plant, it is called **necrosis**. In this case, the cell is killed by the pathogen, and nutrients cannot be removed before death. Necrosis can still help protect the plant if it occurs quickly or if the particular pathogen requires a living host cell; otherwise, it leaves the plant cell nutrients for the bacteria or fungus to use for growth and reproduction.

We can see similar types of programmed responses to disease-causing organisms in animals. These responses are an attempt to limit the progression of an infection and limit damage to the host. The process of inflammation, although a temporarily painful situation, has evolved as a mechanism to limit the spread of an infection and kill the invading bacteria **(Figure 27.10)**. Once the bacteria have penetrated the outer defence, the epithelium, their presence elicits an immune response. Cells within the immune system detect the bacteria by the presence of PAMPs through surface receptors on the immune cells. Although we often equate the swelling, redness, and pain of inflammation with a bacterial infection, this response is actually the innate immune system at work.

The blood of vertebrates contains **white blood cells**, also known as leukocytes. The white blood cells help eliminate dead or damaged cells from the body and aid in the immune response **(Figure 27.11, p. 610)**. There are several types of leukocytes, each with a specific function in the overall immune system. **Macrophages** and **neutrophils** are white blood cells that engulf, or phagocytize, and digest both pathogens and damaged tissues, much like the amoeba discussed in Chapter 16. This helps clean up wounds and remove bacterial invaders.

When macrophages engulf bacteria, the process triggers the release of chemical signals called cytokines and **chemokines**. These compounds attract more immune cells to the area, speeding the process of removing the bacteria and damaged cells, thereby reducing the level of infection.

**Histamine** is another chemical signal that is part of the inflammation response. It is released by **mast cells**, immune cells that are present at the site of infection. Histamine dilates the blood vessels in the area. When blood vessels dilate, blood flow increases and the vessel walls become more permeable. This allows circulating immune cells to exit the blood vessel more easily and arrive at the area of infection. The increased blood flow leads to the swelling and redness symptoms associated with inflammation. The swelling associated with the inflammation causes pain and leads to immobilization of

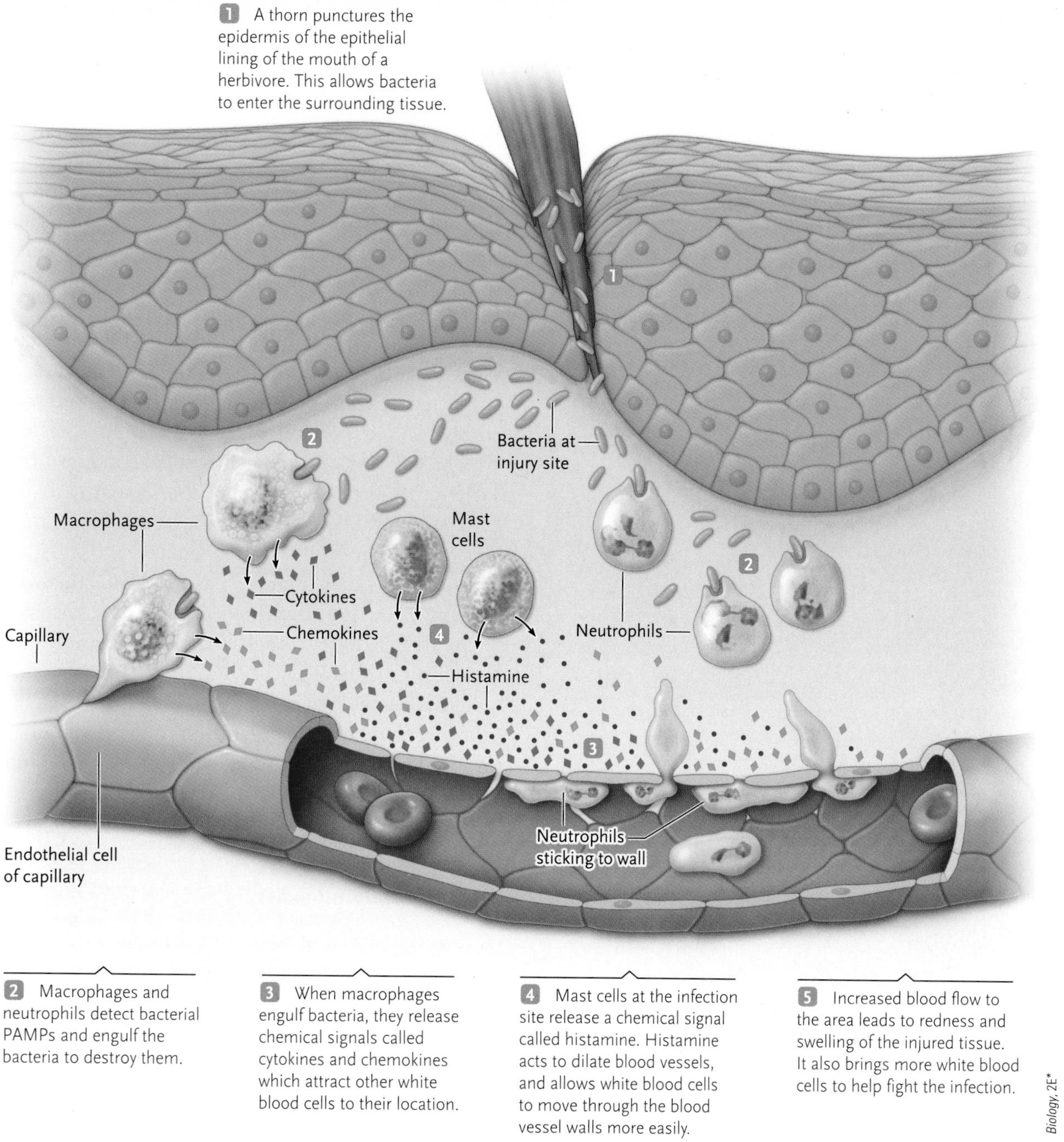

1   A thorn punctures the epidermis of the epithelial lining of the mouth of a herbivore. This allows bacteria to enter the surrounding tissue.

Bacteria at injury site

Macrophages

Mast cells

Cytokines

Chemokines

Capillary

Histamine

Neutrophils

Endothelial cell of capillary

Neutrophils sticking to wall

2   Macrophages and neutrophils detect bacterial PAMPs and engulf the bacteria to destroy them.

3   When macrophages engulf bacteria, they release chemical signals called cytokines and chemokines which attract other white blood cells to their location.

4   Mast cells at the infection site release a chemical signal called histamine. Histamine acts to dilate blood vessels, and allows white blood cells to move through the blood vessel walls more easily.

5   Increased blood flow to the area leads to redness and swelling of the injured tissue. It also brings more white blood cells to help fight the infection.

Biology, 2E*

**FIGURE 27.10** Thorns on plants can cause physical damage to herbivores, and as mentioned in Section 27.1, the presence of bacteria on the thorns can lead to an infection in the mouth of the herbivore. When the outer defensive layer of a vertebrate is compromised, bacteria can enter and begin to reproduce. The damaged skin and presence of bacteria trigger the inflammation response, which recruits cells of the immune system through programmed cellular signalling. In this way, the innate immune response is turned on as it is needed.

the injury. Although a hindrance, this response helps reduce local movement and protects the site of the injury. The inflammation response can occur very rapidly but requires constant stimulation from the immune cells to remain active. Therefore, inflammation will normally diminish quickly once the infection or injury subsides.

We can see from these examples that complex organisms such as plants and vertebrates can defend themselves from infection by viruses, bacteria, and fungi. They make it hard for the infecting organisms to obtain nutrients, and they kill the invaders as quickly as possible. However, the limitation of innate immunity is that it

treats each infection as a new event. In other words, there is no memory of previous similar attacks.

## Adaptive Immunity Is Acquired throughout an Organism's Lifetime

Although the innate immune responses are very effective at protecting injury sites and minor infections, they are general responses that are not tailored to a specific pathogen. Most importantly, they are reactive rather than preparatory, so the immune response can lag behind the spread of a pathogen. In vertebrates, we see an added

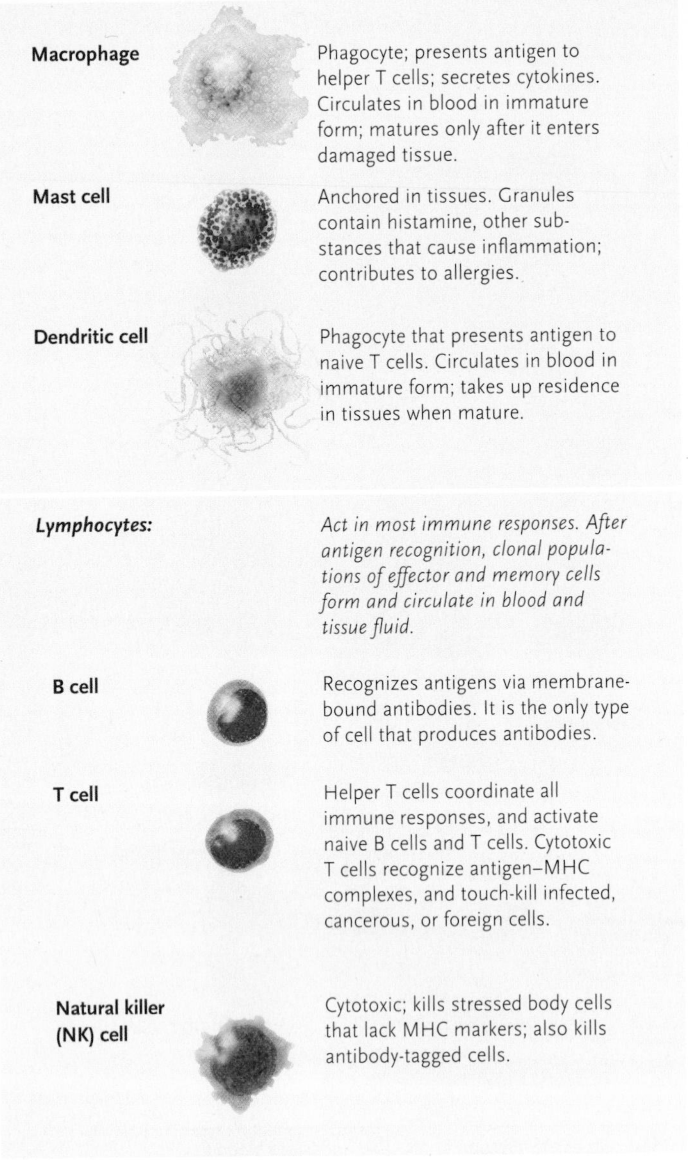

Macrophage
Phagocyte; presents antigen to helper T cells; secretes cytokines. Circulates in blood in immature form; matures only after it enters damaged tissue.
Mast cell
Anchored in tissues. Granules contain histamine, other substances that cause inflammation; contributes to allergies.
Dendritic cell
Phagocyte that presents antigen to naive T cells. Circulates in blood in immature form; takes up residence in tissues when mature.
Lymphocytes:
Act in most immune responses. After antigen recognition, clonal populations of effector and memory cells form and circulate in blood and tissue fluid.
B cell
Recognizes antigens via membrane-bound antibodies. It is the only type of cell that produces antibodies.
T cell
Helper T cells coordinate all immune responses, and activate naive B cells and T cells. Cytotoxic T cells recognize antigen–MHC complexes, and touch-kill infected, cancerous, or foreign cells.
Natural killer (NK) cell
Cytotoxic; kills stressed body cells that lack MHC markers; also kills antibody-tagged cells.


**FIGURE 27.11** The white blood cells (leukocytes) of the immune system. Each cell type plays an important role in defending the body from pathogens, parasites, and environmental toxins.

SOURCE: From STARR/TAGGART/Evers/Starr. *Biology*, 12E. © 2009 Brooks/Cole, a part of Cengage Learning, Inc. Reproduced by permission. www.cengage.com/permissions

component to the immune system—the more complex adaptive immunity. This is a system that targets and "remembers" specific pathogens as targets.

Following an initial exposure, the adaptive immune system can make the host organism immune (highly resistant) to a repeat infection by the same pathogen. Our adaptive immune system is a form of immunological memory, in which our white blood cells recognize past exposures. Hence, immunological memory gives the host organism an advantage—it can better prepare itself against future attacks by similar pathogens. The development of adaptive immunity occurs naturally after initial exposure to pathogens; however, we can also stimulate this type of immunity safely through immunizations. When we are given immunizations as children and boosters as we grow older, we are training our adaptive immune system to fight off severe, life-threatening pathogens without ever getting sick. Diseases such as diphtheria, measles, mumps, and whooping cough (pertussis) used to kill thousands of young children in Canada every year. Polio outbreaks in the 1950s would close public swimming pools and playgrounds. Before immunization began in the 1920s, diphtheria was the leading cause of death in Canadian children age 1 to 4, with about 1000 deaths per year in a population of only 9 million. Now there are fewer than 5 cases per year in a population of over 34 million, mostly in adults with immune deficiencies or inadequate immunization. Similarly, it has been predicted that immunizations against the influenza virus in the United States prevented 5 million illnesses and over 40,000 influenza-related hospitalizations during the 2010–2011 influenza season. Based on similar vaccination patterns and population ratios, one could extrapolate that vaccines prevented approximately 500,000 illnesses and 4000 hospitalizations in Canada during the winter of 2010–2011. Unfortunately, diseases such as measles and polio are making a comeback around the world as vaccination rates have declined. Sometimes this is due to parental choice, but in the case of polio, the inability of non-governmental aid organizations to reach individuals in conflict zones in the Middle East and Africa, combined with the nature of modern global travel, has led to outbreaks of a disease many thought eradicated.

### *Antigens and Antibodies*

A key aspect of the adaptive immune response is the capacity to produce **antibodies** that recognize foreign molecules in the body **(Figure 27.12)**. There are a number of different classes of antibodies produced, each with slightly different shapes and functions. However, all antibodies are a type of protein called **immunoglobulins:** Ig proteins for short. They are called immunoglobins because they are involved in the immune response, and when placed in an electrical field, they migrate in a similar fashion to serum globin proteins. Here we will discuss immunoglobin G (IgG) antibodies, which represent about 75% of serum antibodies in vertebrates.

IgG antibodies are composed of four protein subunits arranged into a Y-shaped structure (Figure 27.12). The constant region of the IgG protein is highly conserved, meaning that it has an almost identical amino acid sequence and three-dimensional folded structure in each vertebrate species. The important part of the IgG, in terms of the adaptive immune system, is the variable region. This portion of the antibody differs depending on which B cell in an organism it is produced by. Thus, different amino acid sequences are found in the variable region of an IgG in a given individual, resulting in differently shaped variable regions. The variable region binds to

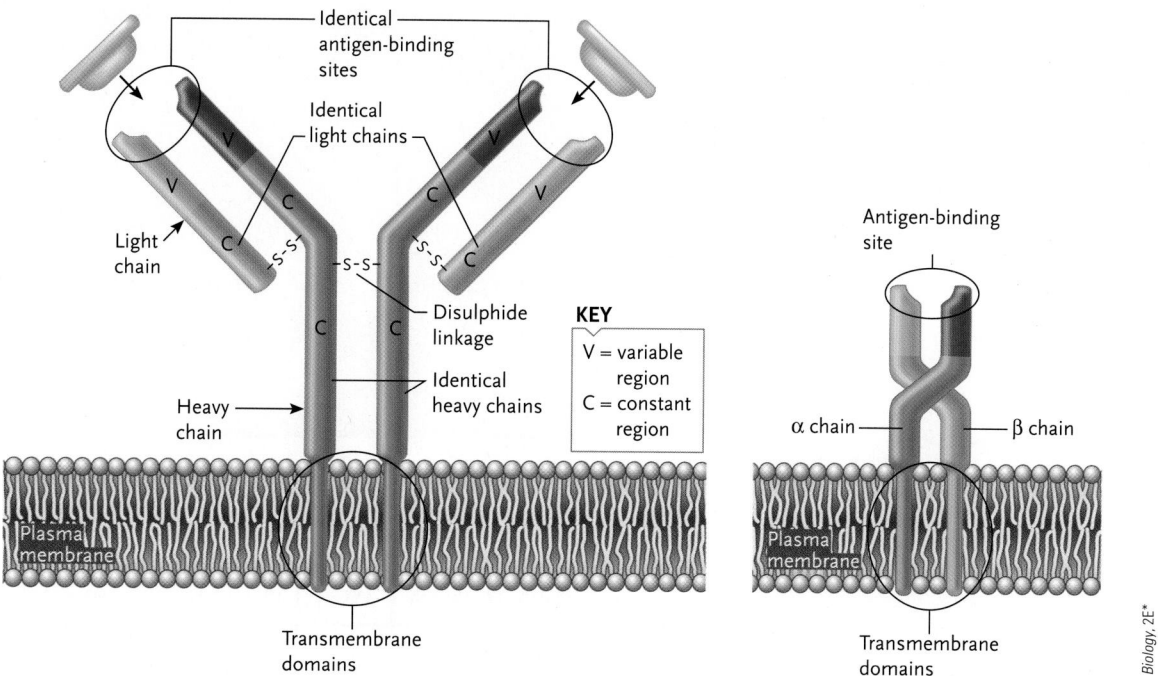

**A.** B cell receptor (BCR)

**B.** T cell receptor (TCR)

Identical antigen-binding sites

Identical light chains

Light chain

Heavy chain

Disulphide linkage

Identical heavy chains

Antigen-binding site

α chain

β chain

**KEY**

V = variable region
C = constant region

Plasma membrane

Plasma membrane

Transmembrane domains

Transmembrane domains

*Biology, 2E\**

**FIGURE 27.12** The B cell IgG antibodies **(a)** are composed of heavy- and light-chain subunits. The variable region (V) interacts with and binds potential antigens. T cell receptors **(b)** have a single-antigen binding site. But, it is formed by two variable regions, thus providing a large number of different receptors.

different foreign structures. Thus, because there are billions of different variable region structures, an equal number of foreign molecules can be recognized. In the study of the immune system, we call these foreign structures **antigens**. Antigens are normally proteins or carbohydrate polymers that are not found in the host organism. The recognition of antigens on the surface of bacteria, viruses, parasites, cancerous cells, or even toxic chemicals by antibodies is one of the essential steps in the adaptive immune system.

Antibody proteins are made by a specific type of white blood cell called **B cells**. B cells are a major cellular component of the adaptive immune system and are produced from stem cells present in the bone marrow (Figure 27.11). As B cells mature and differentiate, they go through a number of genetic rearrangements in the genes required for the variable region of the antibody structure (Figure 27.12). Amazingly, due to the genetic rearrangements that occur in B cells during the life of an individual organism, a vertebrate will have trillions of genetically different B cells, each producing its own unique antibody, capable of recognizing a specific antigen shape.

Antibodies are produced by our immune system as a defence mechanism, but how do antibodies work to defend the vertebrate body? One way is through the molecular interactions of the antibody, binding with the antigen. When antibodies recognize foreign antigens on the exterior of a virus, bacterium, or parasite, they bind to the invader. Having many antibodies bound to their

surface can disrupt the function of the foreign organism **(Figure 27.13, p. 612)**. Similarly, because some viruses, bacteria, and parasites need to interact with surface receptors in the plasma membrane of host cells to gain access to the interior of the cell, coating the exterior of the foreign organism with antibodies will block this mode of entry **(Figure 27.14, p. 612)**. Antibodies, once bound to an antigen, can also act as a signal, attracting macrophages that consume the antibody–antigen complex. At this point, we can see that the macrophages of the innate immune system work in cooperation with the adaptive immune system. Thus, an **antibody-mediated defence** works at both the physical level—blocking vital viral or bacterial function—and as a signal to other immune partners.

Knowledge of how antibodies are produced by a vertebrate host, and how the antibody and the antigen interact, has allowed biomedical researchers to develop antibodies as diagnostic tools. For example, we can determine the ABO blood-type group of an individual with a simple blood sample, using antibodies raised to recognize either the A or the B antigen found on the plasma membrane of red blood cells. A drop of a person's blood is mixed with a sample of the antigen A (anti-A) antibodies and a sample of anti-B antibodies. If agglutination occurs only with the anti-A antibodies, then the donor has type A blood (the anti-A-detecting antibodies react with type A blood). If agglutination occurs only with the anti-B antibodies, the person has type B blood **(Figure 27.15, p. 612)**. If both antibodies lead to agglutination, then the individual's blood cells contain both A and B antigens; hence, the person has

## A. Neutralization

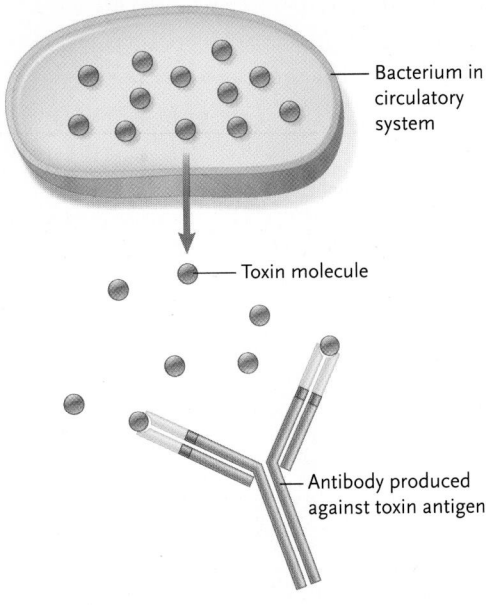

- Bacterium in circulatory system
- Toxin molecule
- Antibody produced against toxin antigen

## B. Agglutination

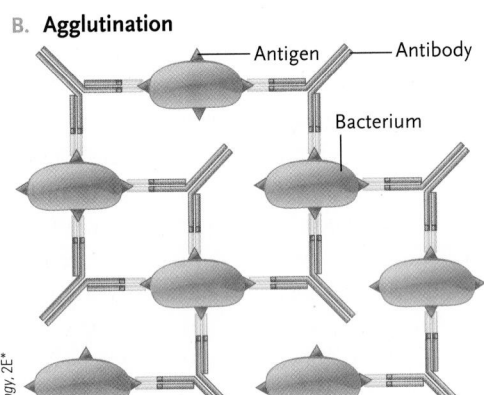

- Antigen
- Antibody
- Bacterium

*Biology, 2E\**

**FIGURE 27.13** Antibodies function by binding to toxins or antigens on the surface of bacteria or viruses. When multiple antibodies bind to the surface of a single object, an agglutination reaction can occur, which clumps the objects into a larger structure that will be targeted by macrophages.

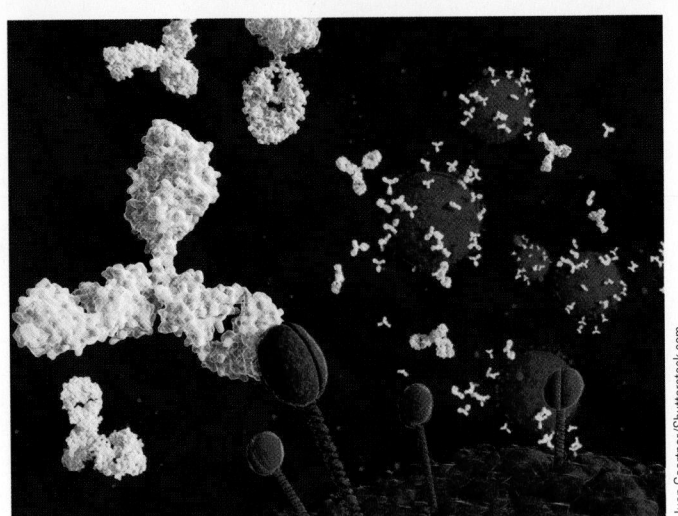

Juan Gaertner/Shutterstock.com

**FIGURE 27.14** By attaching to the surface of virus particles, antibodies can stop viruses from becoming active inside the cell.

| R / N | ANTI-A | ANTI-B | ANTI-A,B | AUTO CONTROL | A-CELLS | B-CELLS |
|---|---|---|---|---|---|---|
| | | | | | | |
| | | | | | | |
| | | | | | | |
| | | | | | | |

enciktat/Shutterstock.com

**FIGURE 27.15** A blood test using antibody reagents. Antibodies that recognize the A or B antigen on human red blood cells are mixed with a droplet of blood. An agglutination reaction indicates the presence of the antigen. Type O blood (second row) does not react with either antibody, so no agglutination occurs.

type AB blood (Figure 27.15). Of course, if agglutination did not occur with either antibody mixture, the tester could conclude that the person tested had type O blood.

Antibody-based assays are used for many types of tests in hospitals and medical diagnostic laboratories around the world. Antibody-based diagnostic tests are frequently used to determine if an individual has or has been exposed to specific pathogens, such as the hepatitis C virus, Lyme disease bacterium, or West Nile virus. Some tests use antibodies that have been generated in animals by exposing them to specific antigens and then harvesting blood samples and isolating the specific antibodies. This can be done using cell cultures (as described in Chapter 11) or even chicken eggs.

A reverse format antibody-based test can be developed using a known antigen to determine whether an individual has been exposed to a particular pathogen. Thus, we test whether the person has produced antibodies that recognize the pathogen. This was the basis for the first human immunodeficiency virus (HIV) tests performed. Medical technicians would take a blood sample from an individual, mix it with an HIV antigen, and examine the response. If agglutination occurred, then the medical technician could conclude that the immune system of the individual whose blood was tested had been activated by exposure to HIV antigens. In 2012, the U.S. Food and Drug Administration approved the first over-the-counter, home HIV test. It works in the same way, testing for the presence of antibodies in the individual that recognize the surface antigens of HIV. However, this test kit is not currently approved for use in Canada.

Home pregnancy tests use an antibody-based test to detect the presence of a hormone called human chorionic gonadotropin (hCG), a glycoprotein that is secreted by the placenta of pregnant women. The hormone is partially removed from the woman's blood by her kidneys; thus, when she urinates on the stick provided in the kit, the antibodies attached to the stick will bind any hCG present and give a positive response if a pregnancy is under way **(Figure 27.16)**.

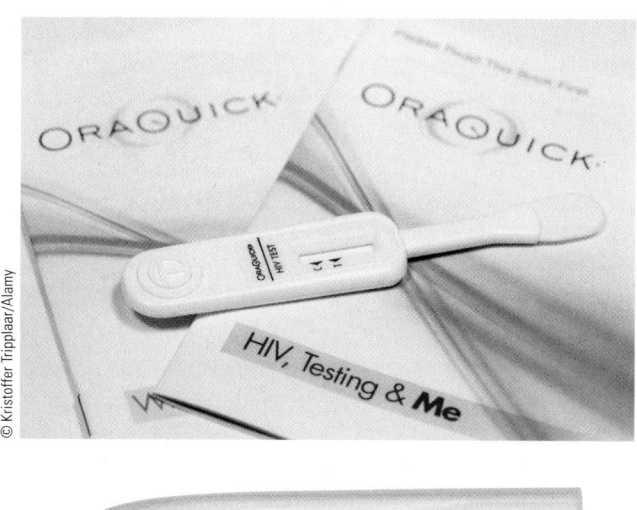

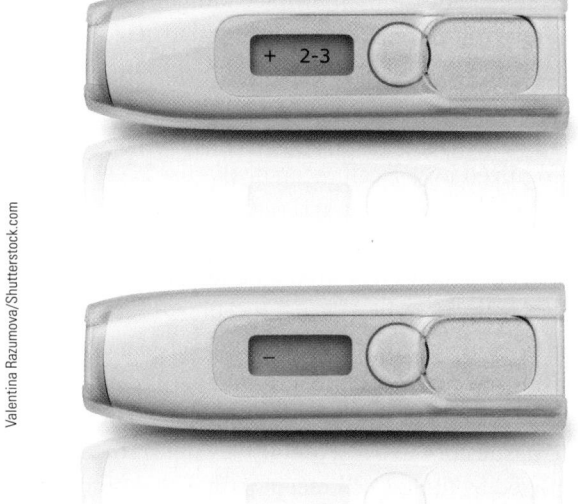

**FIGURE 27.16** Antibody-based home diagnostic kits are reliable and easy to use. Home pregnancy tests were among the first tests developed, but now home HIV tests are available in the United States, and water test kits can be purchased to analyze pools or even drinking water.

## Antibody-Mediated Immunity

The antibody-mediated portion of the adaptive immune system attempts to control foreign objects that are circulating in the blood or lymphatic system. The main objective is to remove antigens from the body. Another type of white blood cell, the **dendritic cell**, or accessory cell, helps macrophages (Figure 27.11). Both dendritic cells and macrophages can engulf foreign objects that they detect **(Figure 27.17, p. 614)**. The foreign object will be captured in an endocytic vesicle—a small vacuole that will form around the engulfed object. The endocytic vesicle will merge with a lysosome to form a digestive vacuole, and

the object will be destroyed (remember lysosomes from Chapter 3). As you can imagine, this is a great way to remove bacteria, virus particles, or small parasites from the host. However, this is still a form of innate immunity. Although the object is degraded by the lysosome, not all of its antigens are destroyed. As the digestive vacuole merges with the plasma membrane to eliminate indigestible materials, some of the remaining antigens from the foreign object will become bound to a cellular protein complex called a **major histocompatibility complex (MHC)**. The antigen–MHC complex will then be located on the surface of the plasma membrane.

The MHC helps identify cells that belong in a particular organism. The MHC is used to define "self" versus "non-self" cells. Once bound to an antigen and located on the exterior of the plasma membrane, the MHC–antigen complex acts as a signal to T cells—white blood cells that specifically aid in the production of antibodies (Figure 27.11). But unlike B cells, they do not recognize free-floating antigens. T cells only recognize MHC-bound antigens that are present on the surface of the dendritic cells (the T-cell helpers). To generate antibodies against the MHC-bound antigen, specific proteins on the surface of the T cells called **T cell receptors** (TCRs) specifically recognize the MHC–antigen complex as a mixture of self and non-self. The TCR will bind to the MHC–antigen complex, attaching the T cell to the dendritic cell hosting the MHC–antigen complex decoration. Once bound to the MHC–antigen complex, the T cell releases chemicals called cytokines, which signal other T cells and B cells containing the same-shaped receptor to divide. This will result in the generation of many identical T cells and B cells capable of detecting the antigen.

If a **B cell receptor**—which, remember, is essentially an antibody that is bound to the B cell plasma membrane—detects a foreign antigen, it will act like a macrophage and engulf the foreign object. During digestion of the foreign object, the B cell will also end up with MHC–antigen decorations that can be detected by T cell receptors. Once detected, the same process occurs: the T cell will release cytokines to induce the B cell to divide until there is a population of identical B cells able to detect and bind the antigen.

Some of these new B cells will differentiate into **effector B cells** that circulate in the blood and lymphatic systems. Effector B cells secrete non-membrane-bound versions of the B cell receptor that detected the foreign antigen; these are the IgG protein antibodies. The remaining B cells are called **memory B cells.** They remain in the lymphatic system and will become active if the same antigen is encountered again. Because there will be a considerable number of these specific memory B cells, if the antigen is encountered again, they will recognize it and initiate a much more rapid immune response. This would result in even more effector and memory cells and more antibodies being produced. When we get booster

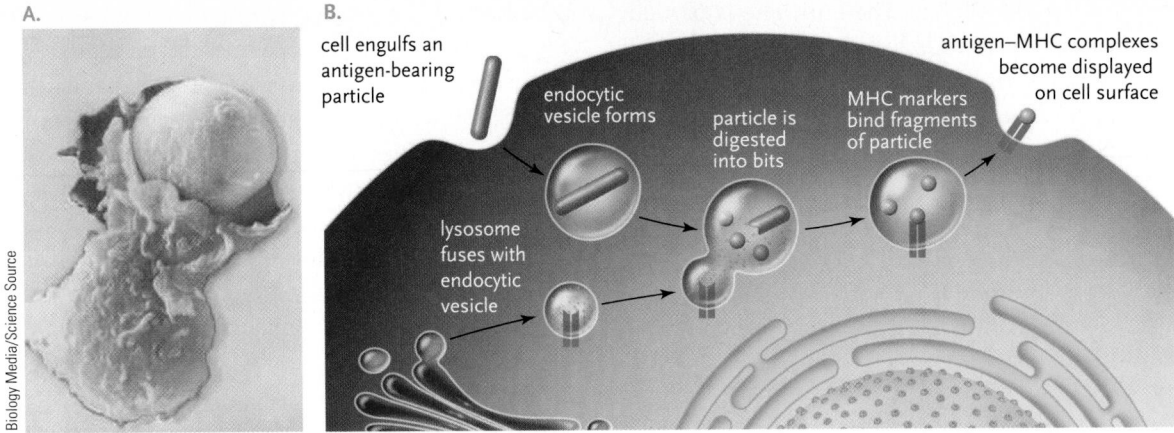

**A.**

**B.**

cell engulfs an antigen-bearing particle

endocytic vesicle forms

particle is digested into bits

MHC markers bind fragments of particle

antigen–MHC complexes become displayed on cell surface

lysosome fuses with endocytic vesicle

Biology Media/Science Source

**FIGURE 27.17** After a dendritic cell engulfs a foreign particle **(a)**, an endocytic vesicle forms around the particle **(b)**. The endocytic vesicle fuses with a lysosome, which contains major histocompatibility complex (MHC) factors (green) to form a digestive vacuole, which degrades the foreign particle. As it is being degraded, some surviving antigens fuse with the MHC markers, which are then left on the surface of the plasma membrane. This leaves a record of the foreign particle on the surface of the dendritic cells so that antibodies can be formed that recognize the foreign particle without it being present in the host.

SOURCE: From STARR/TAGGART/Evers/Starr. *Biology*, 12E. © 2009 Brooks/Cole, a part of Cengage Learning, Inc. Reproduced by permission. www.cengage.com/permissions

immunizations, they work by stimulating the memory B cells that increased in number following the first exposure to the vaccine. This increases the amount of circulating antibodies and the numbers of both effector and memory B cells that recognize the antigen.

## Cell-Mediated Immunity

Although the antibody-mediated response excels at detecting and destroying antigens that are circulating in the blood and lymphatic systems, it is not capable of defending against the bacteria, viruses, and parasites that hide inside host cells. For example, the bacteria of the genus *Rickettsia* are obligate, intracellular parasites, meaning that they can survive only inside host cells. The only time *Rickettsia* cells circulate in the blood or lymphatic system is when they leave one host cell to find another to inhabit. To detect and destroy infected cells, **cytotoxic T cells** are employed. Cytotoxic T cells use their T cell receptors to detect the presence of non-self antigens on the plasma membrane of infected cells. Rather than producing antibodies, cytotoxic T cells will bind to the infected cell and release proteins called **perforins** that enter the infected cell's plasma membrane. Once in the infected cell plasma membrane, the perforins (as their name implies) form holes in the membrane that allow contents to leak out. This will trigger apoptosis, killing the infected cell. This type of immune response is called **cell-mediated immune response** because it uses a living cell to attack and destroy compromised cells rather than just using antibodies.

As its name suggests, the cell-mediated response does not use antibodies but rather the activity of cytotoxic T cells. The process of the cell-mediated response begins in the same fashion as the antibody-mediated response.

A dendritic cell can identify damaged, infected, or cancerous cells because their surface antigens are altered. The faulty cell is engulfed and digested **(Figure 27.18)**. Antigens from the engulfed cell will combine with an MHC and will be displayed on the surface of the dendritic cell as an MHC–antigen complex. This complex can then be recognized by a T cell receptor (Figure 27.18). The T cell will be modified when it is activated by binding to the MHC–antigen complex on the dendritic cell. Once activated, T cells will divide into either **effector T cells** or more **helper T cells**. Both have T cell receptors that recognize the antigen. The effector T cells will release cytokines, triggering cytotoxic T cells to differentiate and divide. The cytotoxic T cells will circulate through the blood and lymphatic tissues of the body, and if they detect the antigen recognized by their T cell receptor, they will bind to and kill the target (Figure 27.18). How the cytotoxic T cells kill infected cells is important. By using perforins to trigger apoptosis, the target cell is destroyed from the inside out. During apoptosis, enzymes are released in the cell that digest proteins and nucleic acids. Thus, if a cell infected by a virus undergoes apoptosis, the viral proteins and nucleic acids would be destroyed. Otherwise, if the cell simply died, it could release functional virus particles and allow the infection to become worse. The memory T cells that are produced will stay in the body until needed to fight off a second attack by the same type of invader, much like memory B cells.

T cells are also an important factor in the body's fight against cancer. When cells become cancerous, they often lose their normal control of gene expression (see Chapter 6). As a result, they can accumulate abnormal proteins and lipids in their plasma membrane. The plasma membranes of cancerous cells are often leaky, meaning that

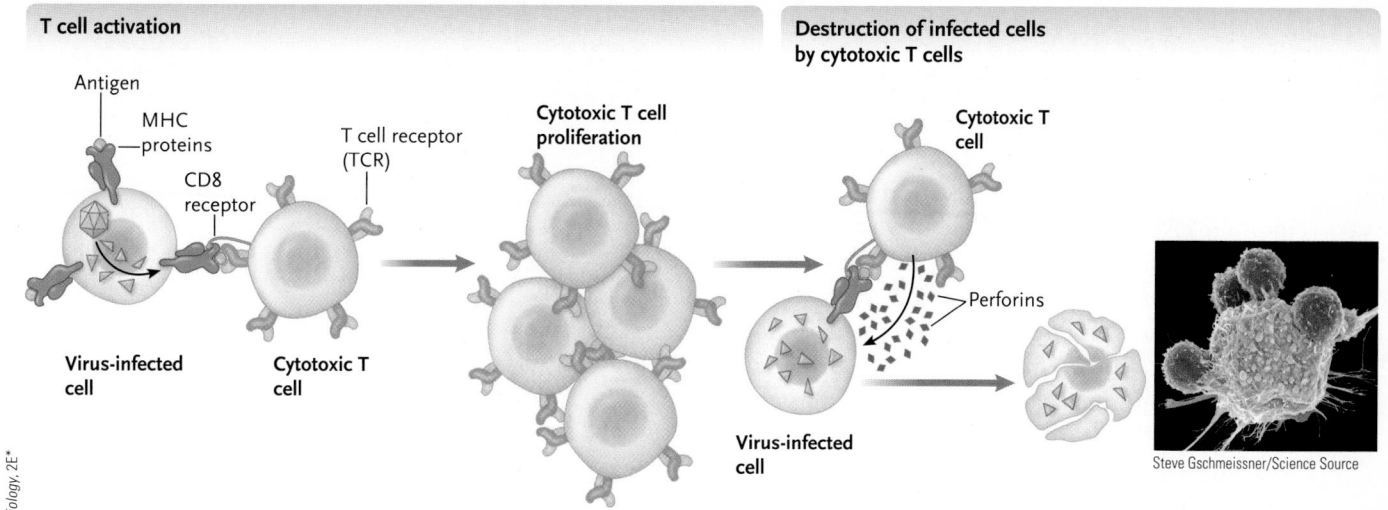

**T cell activation**

Antigen
MHC proteins
CD8 receptor
T cell receptor (TCR)
Cytotoxic T cell proliferation

Virus-infected cell
Cytotoxic T cell

**Destruction of infected cells by cytotoxic T cells**

Cytotoxic T cell
Perforins
Virus-infected cell

Steve Gschmeissner/Science Source

Biology, 2E*

**1** During viral infection, virus components will sometimes be degraded by lysosomes. This can result in viral antigens interacting with MHC factors and being present on the surface of infected cells.

**2** Cytotoxic T cells can detect the viral antigen using their T cell receptor. If the T cell receptor binds to the viral antigen on the surface of the infected cell, it triggers cytotoxic T cell division.

**3** As the cytotoxic T cells divide, some will differentiate into active cytotoxic T cells, which will circulate in the blood and lymph systems. Other cells will differentiate into memory cytotoxic T cells and wait in the lymphatic system until recruited to action by cytokines and chemokines.

**4** While circulating in the blood, if the cytotoxic T cell receptor detects a non-self antigen, it will bind to the infected cell and release a set of proteins called perforins.

**5** Perforins will enter the plasma membrane of the infected cell, forming holes. The holes in the plasma membrane allow cellular contents to leak out, disrupt homeostasis, and induce apoptosis of the infected target cell.

**FIGURE 27.18** The cell-mediated immune response uses cytotoxic T cells to detect and destroy infected host cells. Cytotoxic T cells detect infected cells that express MHC–antigen complexes on their plasma membrane, using their TCRs. When foreign antigens are detected by the TCR of cytotoxic T cells, they release perforins, which destroy the infected cell.

they are not as intact as the plasma membrane of a normal cell. Because the cell surface is not "normal," helper and killer T cells often recognize that cancerous cells do not belong and target them for destruction **(Figure 27.19)**. This is one reason why individuals with compromised immune systems develop cancer more frequently than the general population. We will look at this in more detail in the following section.

The cytotoxic T cells and dendritic cells rely on the presence of MHC–antigen complexes on the cell to activate the cell-mediated immune response. However, this leads to a problem if a damaged or infected cell stops producing the MHC proteins. Although rare, this can occur. Cancerous cells often fall into this category. Lucky for us, evolution has provided another line of defence. **Natural killer cells** (or NK cells) are able to identify and destroy body cells that have been altered due to infection, damage, or mutations but do not produce MHC–antigen complexes on their plasma membrane proteins. NK cells are part of the innate immune system rather than the acquired immune system because they do not have T cell receptors and thus cannot be programmed to detect or proliferate following exposure to specific antigens. Nevertheless, their complex action is more similar to that of cytotoxic T cells, so we will look at NK cells here. The NK cells are able to detect damaged or infected cells without the normal

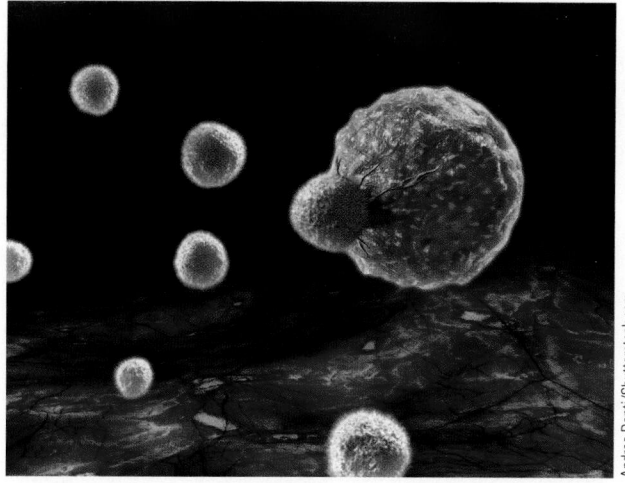

Andrea Danti/Shutterstock.com

**FIGURE 27.19** Cytotoxic T cells can also attack cancerous cells. The cancerous cells do not function normally and will often have abnormal surface antigens. The T cells will recognize the unusual antigens and destroy the cell.

MHC complexes. The NK cells can be recruited to a location in the host body in response to the release of cytokines. Thus, they are recruited to a localized infection during the inflammation response (Figure 27.10). NK cells will attach to body cells that they determine to be "non-self" or damaged. Once attached, the NK cell releases perforins (much like a cytotoxic T cell) to increase the leakiness of the non-self cell membrane.

The leaky membrane leads to apoptosis. This process is similar to the effects of cytotoxic T cells. Again, the fact that the damaged or infected cells goes through apoptosis is important. Apoptosis helps prevent the chance of virus particles being released into the body.

To review what happens during the adaptive immune response, let's think about what happens when you are vaccinated against the influenza virus. In a medical or immunization clinic, you roll up your sleeve and the medical professional injects a small amount of fluid into your arm. The fluid is a specialized mixture called an adjuvant that helps trigger your immune system. Floating in that mixture are protein antigens that medical researchers hope will match those of the coming year's influenza strains. As the adjuvant and antigens enter your tissue, dendritic cells will engulf some of the microscopic particles, and other antigens will bind to B cell receptors, triggering the B cells to engulf the antigen. In both cell types, the engulfed particle will be taken to a lysosome to be degraded. But some of the antigens will combine with the MHC proteins, and as the digested material from the lysosome is released from the cell, some of the MHC–antigen complexes will be left in the plasma membrane, where they are recognized by T cells. Binding of the T cell to the MHC–influenza A antigens on the surface of your dendritic cells triggers the T cell to release cytokines. The cytokines attract other T cells and B cells that have matching T cell or B cell receptors, respectively; those T cells and B cells are triggered to divide. Some of the newly formed T cells and B cells, called effectors, will travel around the body, releasing antibodies and removing the rest of the influenza antigens that were injected into your arm from your body. This is the primary immunological response. If it ended there, it would be of little use other than as a form of innate immunity. However, some of the T cells and B cells that were produced become memory cells. They essentially sit and wait, in case you come into contact with the same influenza virus again. Thus, if a month or two later ou happen to be sitting on the bus and someone next to you sneezes, the influenza viruses you could be exposed to would trigger a secondary immune response. In that case, because you have many memory T cells and B cells already in your body, your adaptive immune system is able to quickly destroy those invading viruses before they get a chance to make you sick.

Of course, the influenza vaccine is only one of many vaccines available to Canadians that reduce the occurrence of human disease. An interesting and relatively new vaccine helps protect individuals against the human papillomavirus (HPV). This virus not only causes genital warts, the most common form of sexually transmitted disease, but if left untreated can also lead to cervical cancer. See Box 27.3 for a more detailed description of the HPV vaccine.

## STUDY BREAK

1. How does the innate immune system protect organisms ranging from plants to humans?
2. What is the difference between a B cell receptor and an IgG antibody?
3. The relationship between an antigen and an antibody is often compared to that of a key and a lock. Explain why this is true.
4. How does the adaptive immune system determine whether a given cell belongs in the host organism? Why is this important for immune function?

## 27.3 Immune Deficiency and Overreaction

The immune system, like your heart or liver, can become diseased or even fail altogether. This causes some obvious problems for individuals and their ability to respond appropriately to pathogens, the development of cancerous cells, and the environment in which they live.

### Immune Failure Can Leave an Individual Vulnerable to Infections

A condition called **immunodeficiency** can occur when one or more components of the immune system fail to function. Immunodeficiency can result from acquired disease or genetic disorders, or it can even be induced on purpose using medications to aid specific medical procedures. Whenever the immune system is compromised, the individual becomes much more sensitive to infections. Often the first signs of immunocompromise are chronic infections by normally harmless disease organisms.

#### Human Immunodeficiency Virus

The most well-known disease affecting the immune system is the human immunodeficiency virus (HIV). It is the virus that causes acquired immune deficiency syndrome (AIDS). HIV infection and the development of AIDS are a slow, progressive loss of immune function. Following initial exposure, HIV infects cells of the immune system such as the dendritic cells and macrophages. As the disease develops, infected leukocytes can die in a number of different ways. For example, internal cellular function may be disrupted due to the presence of the virus, leading to programmed cell death. Or those telltale signs of viral infection that manifest on the surface of the infected cells could recruit T cells to attack and destroy the infected cells. Either way, the number of leukocytes dedicated to the immune system steadily declines. At a certain point, the cell-mediated immune system will be unable to defend the individual, leading to increased prevalence of opportunistic infections.

# Quadrivalent HPV Vaccine (Gardasil)

In 2008, Dr. Harald zur Hausen from the German Cancer Research Centre in Heidelberg, Germany, was awarded a share of the Nobel Prize in Medicine and Physiology for his research leading to the discovery that the human papillomavirus (HPV) can cause cervical cancer. Dr. zur Hausen's research provided the first evidence that cancerous tumours could be caused by the integration of virus DNA into the genome of a host cell. Genital warts and cancers caused by HPV are a significant public health issue. It is estimated that 75% of sexually active men and women will develop at least one HPV infection during their lives. In Canada, about 1350 Canadian women developed cervical cancer in 2012, and 390 deaths were reported. Thanks to screening techniques such as the Papanicolaou test (Pap test or Pap smear), most incidents are detected in the precancerous stage and can be routinely treated. However, not only is this a reactionary approach to cancer prevention, it is estimated that in Canada only about 50% of women have been screened as recommended by Health Canada.

In an effort to reduce the spread of genital HPV, thereby reducing incidents of cervical cancer, a number of research groups attempted to build on the research of Dr. zur Hausen and create a vaccine to immunize people against HPV. There are currently two such vaccines available in Canada. The first goes by the trade name Gardasil. It contains four different viruslike particles that represent four different strains of HPV (HPV-6, HPV-11, HPV-16, and HPV-18). The viruslike particles are designed to mimic the virus surface antigens and thus elicit the production of antibodies as part of an immune response while posing no risk of infection. These four strains of HPV collectively are responsible for approximately 70% of cervical, vulvar, vaginal, mouth, and oropharyngeal cancers and almost all anogenital warts found in both men and women. The second vaccine goes by the name Cervarix. It was developed to immunize people against HPV-16 and HPV-18, two strains of the virus that are more specifically responsible for causing cervical cancer.

Because it helps defend against four different strains of HPV, Gardasil is called a quadrivalent HPV vaccine. It has proven to be between 98% and 100% effective in protecting healthy girls and young women (age 16 to 22) from HPV infections caused by the targeted strains. It is now approved for the vaccination of females age 9 to 45. Gardasil has also been approved for vaccination of boys and young men age 9 to 27. There is an ongoing debate about whether the vaccination of males is necessary from a public health perspective.

In 2007, the Government of Canada set aside $300 million to be given to the provinces to encourage them to implement vaccination programs for girls between the ages of 9 and 13. As an example, in 2010, the Government of Nunavut introduced a school-based program to immunize all girls age 9 and over while in Grade 6. These types of programs have been started in many developed countries around the world. As a result of such a program in Australia, there is a fascinating epidemiological study under way. In 2007, the Australian government started a comprehensive HPV vaccination program for all females between the ages of 12 and 27. A group of researchers has followed the incidence of so-called high-grade cervical abnormalities (a finding that is indicative of cervical cancer) in women of different age groups from before and after the initiation of the HPV vaccination program. They found a significant decrease in cancerous and precancerous abnormalities in women under the age of 18. Thus, within 3 years of starting the vaccination program, the Australian government has scientific evidence supporting its effectiveness.

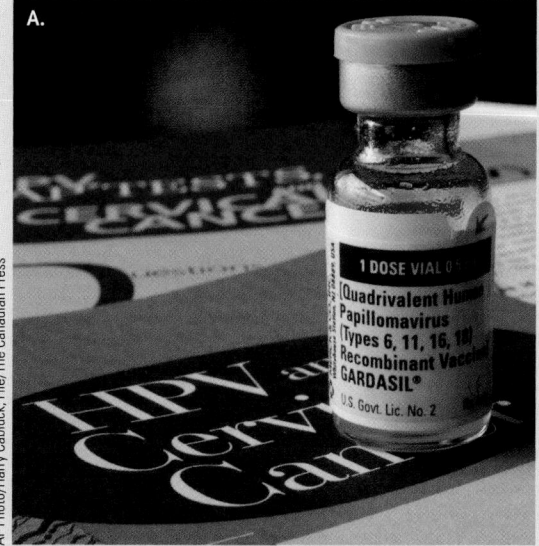

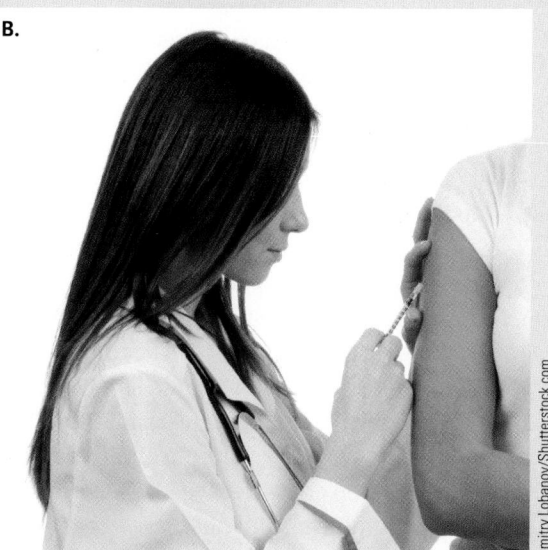

**FIGURE 1** The HPV vaccine is supplied as a liquid solution containing the HPV antigens **(a)**. The vaccine is then injected subcutaneously (below the skin) to elicit the immune response and protect the individual from infection **(b)**.

In 1981, the observations of a cluster of individuals that had developed *Pneumocystis jiroveci* pneumonia, a rare form of pneumonia that develops only in people with extremely weak immune systems, led to investigations by the American Centers for Disease Control and Prevention (CDC). The initial cluster of individuals in Los Angeles, California, included many intravenous drug users and gay men. As the CDC began investigating, it found that the underlying factor leading to diminished immune capacity was not limited to gay men and intravenous drug users but also showed up in a significant number of people who suffer from hemophilia. The disease was formally named the AIDS in July of 1982. HIV was identified by two separate research groups in 1983.

Although there is still no cure for AIDS, its symptoms can be controlled by drugs that stop the virus from reverse transcribing its RNA genome. This stops the virus from infecting new cells and allows the rate of leukocyte production to keep ahead of the rate of cell death. Patients taking the appropriate medication can maintain a relatively healthy immune system and fight off the persistent attacks of microbes in the environment that used to kill all AIDS patients. (See Box 14.2 for a review of anti-HIV medications that target the reverse transcriptase.)

## Immunosuppression Is Required for Organ Transplants

Blood transfusion or the transplantation of organs and tissues from one individual to another can be a life-saving procedure for otherwise terminally ill individuals. Each year in Canada, nearly 2000 organ transplantations are performed, with the limiting factor being the availability of organs. There are a number of reasons why organs are limiting, but one of the main factors is that the donor organ must be a close biochemical match to the intended recipient. As mentioned in Section 27.2, red blood cells have genetically determined surface antigens that will be recognized as non-self if transfused into someone of an incompatible blood type. In the blood typing reactions shown in Figure 27.15, we can observe the agglutination reactions that occur when tissues do not match. People with type A blood produce antibodies that recognize type B blood cells, and vice versa. So if an individual with type A blood received a transfusion of type B blood, the agglutination reaction would occur. Tissues being transplanted also have specific surface antigens that will be recognized by antibodies. Therefore, when performing a tissue match before an organ transplantation, the medical technician must go beyond blood type and examine other antigen markers on the cells of the organ in question. It is critical that the recipient's immune system not immediately recognize the donor organ as a "non-self" structure.

These procedures are becoming relatively routine from a medical and a surgical point of view, with 80% to 95% of transplantations declared successful after 1 year post-operation. However, behind the scenes, a complex process of tissue matching is going on. Despite close matches, recipients must take **immunosuppressive drugs**, which are designed to reduce an individual's immune response. They target the body's production of T cells, NK cells, and B cells. Immunosuppressive drugs can also target cytokine production, which dampens the immune response because fewer T cells and B cells will be recruited and produced. Although immunosuppression is normally a bad thing, during transplantations, it helps prevent the recipient's immune system from recognizing the new donor organ as foreign and attacking it. Colloquially, this is called rejection. However, immunosuppressive drugs are a slowly progressing area of research. Because the drugs are altering such a critical function of the body, they often lead to unwanted and dangerous side effects. The possible complications make it ethically challenging to test new immunosuppressive drugs on humans.

Generally, the immunosuppressive process begins before transplantation and attempts to decrease the number of T cells, circulating antibodies, and antibody-producing B cells. The major risks involved are bacterial or fungal infections that can set in while the body's adaptive immune system is turned off. During this time, patients will often be treated with antibiotics and antiviral drugs to decrease the possibility of them becoming sick. For example, *P. jiroveci* pneumonia, commonly seen in advanced AIDS patients, is also a great risk for immunosuppressed transplant patients.

A secondary effect of transplants is the possibility of the patient developing cancer later in life. Remember that T cells also help destroy cancerous cells. Thus, we see increased rates of cancer in patients who have been on immunosuppressive drugs. Epidemiological studies following kidney transplant patients found that 20 years post-transplantation, about 50% of patients had developed at least one cancer—most often skin cancer. Although this may seem like a great risk, most of the individuals would not have lived those 20 years if they had not received a transplant. As with most aspects of medical treatment, the risks and benefits must be assessed carefully. Additionally, we cannot predict where medical research will take us in 20 years. Research is advancing on drugs that exhibit both immunosuppressive and anti-cancer activities, and treatment for cancer is steadily advancing. Our increasing knowledge of how the immune system works only helps this type of research.

## Immune Malfunction Can Lead to an Overactive Immune System

In the wake of the discovery of HIV–AIDS and the incredible toll the disease has taken, a vast amount of research has focused on immune deficiency and the immune system in general. As a result of this knowledge, researchers began to use techniques developed for AIDS research to explore other areas of immune function. A fascinating area of research is the effect of overactive immune function. Intuitively, one would think that having a strong, active immune system would be a good thing. By extension, if a strong defence is good, a stronger defence should be better. However, this is not always the case.

### Allergies

Allergic reactions are the result of our immune system getting carried away. At the most benign level, allergies result in itchy eyes, a runny nose, and sinus congestion. However, in extreme cases, allergies can lead to anaphylactic shock and death. At a basic level, allergens are antigens that our immune system recognizes as foreign and attempts to remove. In the case of seasonal allergens such as the pollen produced by trees, grasses, and other weeds, the pollen grains are inhaled, and some may bind to the surface receptors of B cells in the lining of the airways. The B cells then begin producing antibodies against the foreign antigen because they have no way of determining if the antigen is hazardous or benign. These antibodies attach to mast cells, which are then stimulated to release histamine, the cell-signalling molecule that triggers an inflammation response.

Remember that the key to the adaptive immune response is training cells to respond to an antigen. A first exposure to an allergen may not lead to much of a response; however, repetitive exposure means that many more antibodies and immune cells will be ready to deal with the invader. As a result, with each subsequent exposure, the mast cells will secrete more histamines and trigger a greater inflammatory response. In the case of pollen, tissues most likely to be exposed to the pollen are those most affected by the inflammation of the immune response: nasal passages, bronchial tubes, and mucous membranes of the eyes. Of course, we are more familiar with the symptoms that are associated with this inflammation—a runny nose, coughing, and watery eyes. Traditional treatments for allergies use drugs that are classified as antihistamines. These medicines interact with histamine receptors and stop the inflammation response from being initiated. Annually in Canada, we spend about $200 million on anti-allergy medication.

Pollen allergies are normally no more than an inconvenience. However, in extreme cases, allergies can be deadly. The immune system of some individuals can overreact to specific antigens, leading to anaphylactic shock. Although such conditions are rare, antigens known to induce such immune overreactions can be found in peanuts, shellfish, bee or wasp venom, latex produced from natural rubber, and penicillin antibiotics. Although a

seemingly diverse set of sources of antigens, they all induce severe allergic reactions in the same way, and individuals can become more sensitive to the antigen following repeated exposures. Just as booster vaccinations keep us protected from diseases, repeated exposure to allergy antigens can make our allergic reactions more severe.

### Autoimmune Diseases

A normal immune response is directed at foreign bodies or chemicals that have invaded the host organism. Bacterial cells, viruses, cancer cells, and even environmental antigens such as pollen or bee venom can elicit an immune response. A different type of problem can arise when the immune system begins to recognize "self" tissues as foreign or "non-self." When this happens, rather than fighting intruders, the immune system begins targeting host cells and tissues for destruction. The condition where the immune system targets its host is called an **autoimmune disorder**.

Autoimmune disorders have received a lot of research focus in the last few years. New theories about the cause of some well-characterized diseases have raised concerns about understanding appropriate immune responses and why they happen. Some diseases that are now thought to be caused by an autoimmune response are systemic lupus erythematosus (lupus), rheumatoid arthritis, multiple sclerosis, and Crohn disease. Another example is type 1 diabetes. Type 1 diabetes is also called insulin-dependent diabetes mellitus because patients must take regular insulin injections. It is also called juvenile diabetes based on the age at onset. Although diabetes has long been known to be caused by a loss of the beta cells of the islet of Langerhans in the pancreas, it was not until the 1970s that biomedical researchers were able to provide a reason as to why these cells disappeared in otherwise healthy individuals. It is now generally accepted that type 1 diabetes is the result of an organ-specific autoimmune disorder that can affect up to 1% of the individuals of some populations. In Canada, the frequency of type 1 diabetes is about 0.4%. Research studies of individuals affected by type 1 diabetes demonstrated that the blood of those individuals contained antibodies that recognized antigens found on the surface of the pancreatic beta cells. Thus, the body had misidentified the beta cells as being foreign and targeted them for destruction. It appears that approximately 70% to 80% of individuals with type 1 diabetes have produced antibodies that target the insulin-producing beta cells. This number increases to over 90% of newly diagnosed patients, suggesting that once the beta cells have been destroyed, the immune system reinforcement decreases.

Research into the causes of other autoimmune diseases has yet to be as successful. Lupus affects approximately 1 in 1000 Canadians. It is a chronic autoimmune disease characterized by inflammation of various organs or tissues. One of the challenging aspects of diagnosing and treating lupus is that it attacks different tissues in different individuals. Inflammation can occur in the joints, circulatory system, heart, skin, brain, or kidneys. The disease normally begins to develop during the late teens, but to date, there is no known distinct cause of the inflammation. Currently, researchers are trying to identify possible triggers for onset and examining treatment options, which include the use of immunosuppressive drugs to decrease this unusual and unproductive immune response.

## STUDY BREAK

1. Why would AIDS patients need to monitor their T cell count?
2. Why do allergens make our eyes water and cause nasal congestion?
3. What aspect of immnosuppressive drugs leads to transplant patients having an increased risk of developing cancer?

## PUTTING IT IN PERSPECTIVE

Perhaps the most amazing aspect of defence systems seen in life on Earth is that they are continually evolving. The arms race we examined between the rough-skinned newt and common garter snake is not a rare event; this same type of process occurs between many different organisms. From one perspective, humans are trapped in several different arms races against influenza, *C. difficile*, and many other microorganisms. Understanding how the defence mechanisms of different organisms function will be a key factor to maintaining the health of not only ourselves but also our agricultural crops and animals and the environment in which we live.

## KEY CONCEPTS REVIEW AND QUESTIONS

### 27.1 Physical and Chemical Deterrents

An enormous variety of chemical and physical deterrents are used by organisms ranging from bacteria and fungi to plants and mammals. The constant struggle for nutrients and resources makes defensive adaptations a necessary part of competition.

1. Why does the porcupine fish need both specialized defensive and feeding adaptations?
2. Which of the following reasons does not help explain why three-spined sticklebacks lost their armour plating following their colonization of freshwater ecosystems?
   a. The acquisition of minerals needed for the bony plates was more energetically costly in fresh water.
   b. Increased mobility was a better defence against freshwater predators.
   c. Freshwater predators were bigger; thus, the armour plates were too small to be helpful.
   d. Random genetic mutations resulting in fewer bony plates were advantageous for survival.

### 27.2 The Immune System of Multicellular Organisms

Innate immunity protects organisms from foreign invaders such as viruses, bacteria, and parasites. PAMPs are recognized by cellular receptors and trigger cellular responses, such as localized cell wall thickening in plants and inflammation responses in vertebrates. Innate immunity is said to provide a basal level of immunity because it does not form a memory of pathogens; it treats every infection as a new event. The adaptive immune system uses two approaches to help defend the host against pathogen attack. Antibody-mediated immunity attempts to remove foreign antigens by the proliferation of specific B cells and secretion of antibodies specific for the particular antigens present in the blood or lymphatic system. Cell-mediated immunity attacks host cells that have been compromised by intracellular parasites or viruses. It does not act to clear the circulatory system; rather, it tries to remove cells that are recognized as non-self.

3. Plant cells may undergo apoptosis following pathogen attack. What advantage does this provide the remaining plant cells in their fight against the pathogen?
4. How does the adaptive immune system remember the antigens of a particular foreign invader?
5. T cells can
   a. Recognize surface antigens on foreign objects using T cell receptors
   b. Stimulate the division of specific B cells by cytokine release
   c. Recognize the lack of MHC proteins on cancer cells and recruit cytotoxic T cells
   d. All of the above
6. Why does a booster shot for a particular immunization better defend the individual against a particular disease?

## 27.3 Immune Deficiency and Overreaction

The immune system is of critical importance to our survival. When it malfunctions, it can lead to debilitating illness and many different secondary effects on the organism. An under-performing immune system leaves an individual susceptible to opportunistic infections, whereas an overactive immune system can lead to severe allergic responses, or it can even attack "self" tissues.

7. Using your knowledge of the adaptive immune system, why do allergies get worse with repeated exposures to the allergen?

8. How would you define an opportunistic infection?

# CHAPTER 28

# Reproduction and Development: Eggs, Sperm, Pollen, Spores, Zygotes, and More

M.B. Fenton

## WHY IT MATTERS

Like the impalas (*Aepyceros melampus*) in **Figure 28.1**, many organisms seem to be preoccupied with reproduction—or at least with sex. But the drive to reproduce can take a great deal of energy and put organisms in harm's way, whether because of competing males (note the horns on the male impala) and females or predators that exploit distracted individuals. So why reproduce sexually when there are alternatives?

On the other hand, mixing up or shuffling genomes appears to be a compelling evolutionary argument in favour of sexual reproduction. Shuffling that occurs through gene recombination and segregation (see Chapter 8) helps maintain genetic variation. But if maintaining genetic diversity is so important, why do some organisms still reproduce without sex?

Some lineages of rotifers (Figure 19.10; phylum Rotifera) have survived for tens of millions of years without sexual reproduction. Others use a mixture of sexual and asexual reproduction. The differences between rotifer lineages provide biologists with an opportunity to study what conditions give rise to sexual or to asexual reproduction. Populations of the rotifer *Brachionus calyciflorus* maintained in an environment that does not vary quickly move to asexual reproduction. But populations living in environments that have a lot of variability show higher rates of sexual reproduction. These observations suggest that in some environments, particularly variable environments, sexual reproduction has enough of an advantage to outweigh the costs associated with it, whereas in others, particularly stable environments, asexual reproduction protects beneficial gene combinations with no reshuffling.

In this chapter, we will examine processes involved with reproduction and development in fungi, plants, and animals. The changes that follow from fertilization through the development of a new adult organism are also considered, along with some of the underlying genetic processes.

**FIGURE 28.1** A male impala attempts to mount and mate with a female.

Courtesy of Naas Rautenbach

## 28.1 Reproduction

The drive to reproduce—to pass one's genes onto the next generation—is one of the most compelling features of living organisms. **Reproduction**, and the structures and behaviours that organisms use to reproduce, provide some of the most intriguing and entertaining stories about life. Meiosis (see Chapter 6) is central to sexual reproduction. Recall that sexually reproducing organisms such as humans have two sets of chromosomes, that is, $2n$ chromosomes, where $n$ is the fundamental number (see Chapter 7). Gametes, such as eggs and sperm, have n chromosomes. In the production of gametes (gametogenesis), meiosis is the process in which cells with $2n$ chromosomes produce cells (eggs or sperm) with $N$ chromosomes. Thus, fertilization, the union of the nuclei of an egg and a sperm, produces a zygote with $2n$ chromosomes.

The life cycles and patterns of reproduction in organisms reflect changes between haploid ($n$) and diploid ($2n$) phases of the life cycle. We use the letter "n" to represent the number of chromosomes in a single set; $2n$ means that there are two sets, or two copies of each chromosome in the cell. Humans have 23 chromosomes in a single set ($n = 23$). Our human gametes (eggs and sperm) are haploid and so have just one copy of each chromosome. All of the rest of our cells are diploid—they have two sets of 23 chromosomes ($2n = 46$).

We are familiar with the mammalian life cycle, which is dominated by diploid cells. Eggs and sperm are the only haploid components, each with $n$ chromosomes produced by meiosis (see page 155) from somatic cells that had had $2n$ chromosomes. This pattern applies to many—perhaps most—other organisms, although in some species, there are more extensive haploid components in the life cycle (**Figure 28.2**). There are other unusual situations as well, such as animals such as honeybees (*Apis mellifera*) or many species of wasps, hornets, and ants. In these **haplodiploid** systems, the males (drones) are haploid and the females (workers and queens) are diploid.

Ultimately, reproductive cycles in organisms are defined by both haploid and diploid phases. For example, the life cycles of seed-bearing plants and animals are almost exclusively diploid, mosses are split between haploid and diploid phases, and most fungi are almost entirely haploid.

## 28.2 Alternation of Generations in Plants (Sporophytes and Gametophytes)

The life cycle of plants has two distinct multicellular phases, or generations: the diploid sporophyte generation ($2n$), during which spores are produced, and the haploid gametophyte generation ($n$), during which gametes are produced. The cycle from one generation to the next is referred to as alternation of generations. The life cycles of most living vascular plants are dominated by the sporophyte generation. But some form of green alga was the likely common ancestor of land plants. The life cycle of many modern green algae is dominated by the gametophyte generation. Only the zygote is diploid (sporophyte), and it quickly divides into haploid spores. There are variations on the theme of alternation of generations.

Mosses, for example, have prominent sporophyte and gametophyte generations (**Figure 28.3**), but they spend the most time as haploid gametophytes. You may have seen these gametophytes as carpets of soft moss in a forest. Structures called gametangia on the gametophytes contain eggs and release sperm. The sperm swim through a film of water to find the egg and fuse with it to begin the sporophyte generation. Successful reproduction by mosses requires water. Stalked sporophytes emerge from the mossy gametophyte carpet. The diploid sporophytes produce haploid spores by meiosis and release spores from a sporangium, the structure you see at the end of the sporophyte's stalk.

Ferns evolved more recently than mosses, and their life cycle is dominated by the sporophyte generation (**Figure 28.4, p. 626**). When (if) we think of ferns, we focus on the fanlike leaves (fronds) of the sporophyte generation. If you turn over a fern frond, you can often see the rows of sporangia that contain haploid spores. This is the fern's sporophyte generation. Fern spores divide by mitosis and grow into small, inconspicuous haploid gametophytes. The gametophytes release male gametes (sperm) that, like those of mosses, require moisture to travel to female plants. Not surprisingly, ferns typically reproduce in moist habitats.

The seed was a major evolutionary innovation. Seed plants have greatly reduced gametophyte generations. Compare the life cycles of a moss (Figure 28.3) and

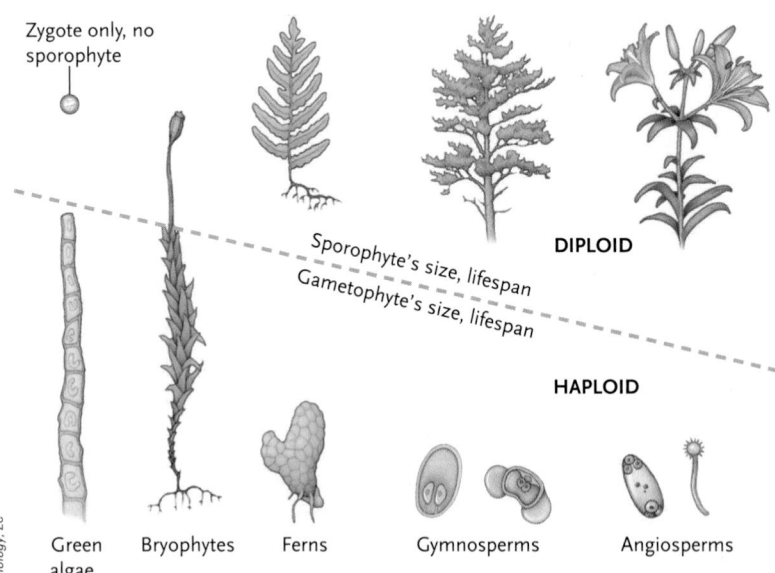

**FIGURE 28.2** From green algae to angiosperms, there is a tendency for the diploid generation (the generation with two sets of chromosomes) to dominate the life cycle. The changes generally coincide with the colonization of land. Sporophytes of vascular plants (ferns, gymnosperms, and angiosperms) are larger and more complex than those of mosses (bryophytes).

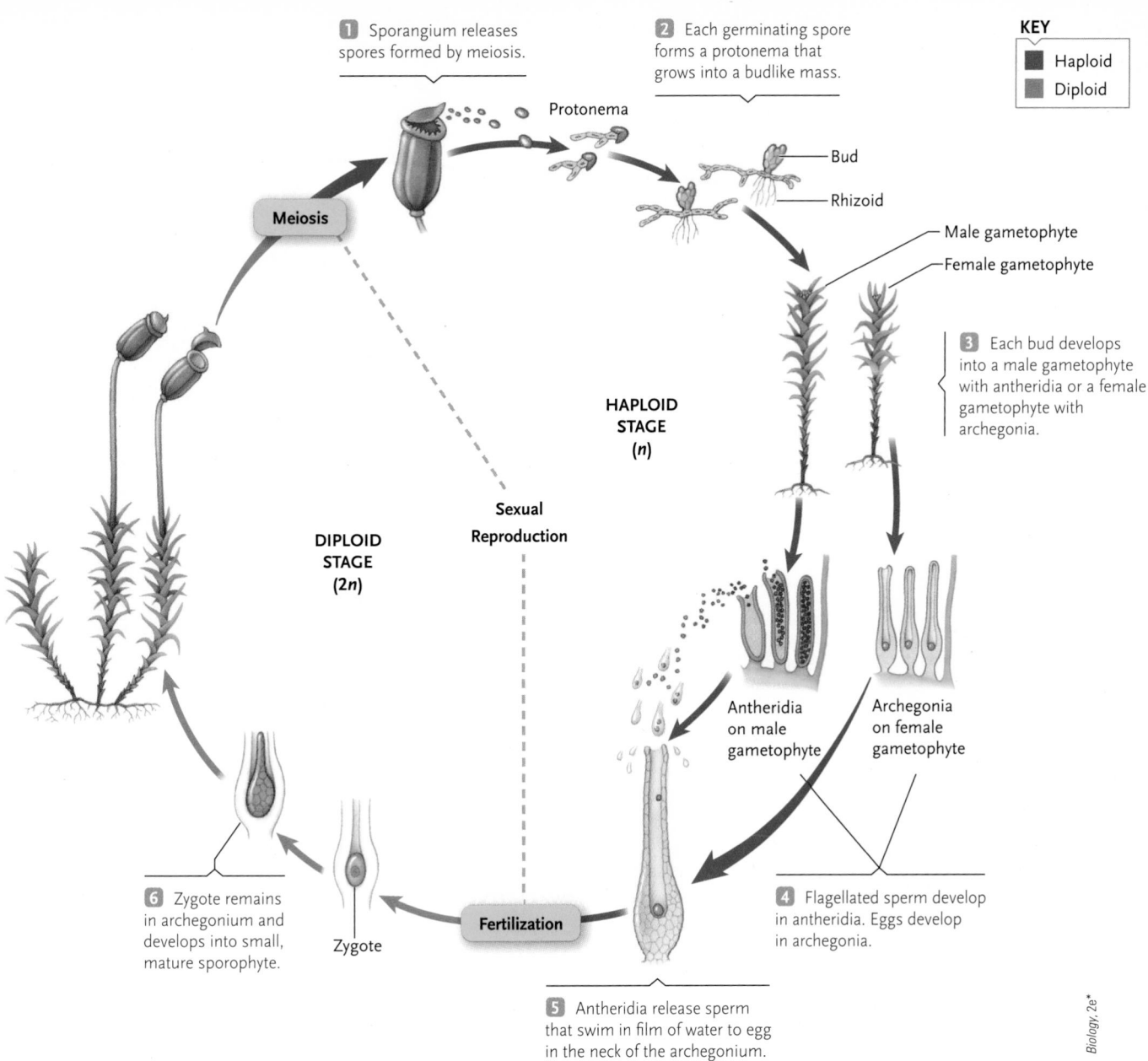

**KEY**

■ Haploid
■ Diploid

Protonema

Bud

Rhizoid

Male gametophyte

Female gametophyte

**Meiosis**

③ Each bud develops into a male gametophyte with antheridia or a female gametophyte with archegonia.

**HAPLOID STAGE (*n*)**

**DIPLOID STAGE (2*n*)**

**Sexual Reproduction**

Antheridia on male gametophyte

Archegonia on female gametophyte

⑥ Zygote remains in archegonium and develops into small, mature sporophyte.

Zygote

**Fertilization**

④ Flagellated sperm develop in antheridia. Eggs develop in archegonia.

⑤ Antheridia release sperm that swim in film of water to egg in the neck of the archegonium.

*Biology, 2e\**

**FIGURE 28.3** Life cycle of a moss showing gametophyte and sporophyte generations.

a pine tree **(Figure 28.5, p. 627)**, a type of gymnosperm. In the pine tree, reproductive structures are contained within the cones. Pine trees have both male and female cones. Male cones produce haploid pollen from microspores, and female cones produce haploid eggs from megaspores, both by meiosis. The gametophyte stage is very reduced. The female gametophyte never leaves the cone. The male gametophyte, as a pollen grain, is released into the environment and transported by wind to a female cone. When the sperm within the pollen fuses with the ovule inside the female gametophyte, the zygote—in this case, a seed—forms and the dominant sporophyte generation begins again.

Angiosperms, or flowering plants, also produce seeds and have greatly reduced gametophyte generations (Figure 28.5). Instead of containing the gametophyte generation within a cone, it is contained within the flower.

The flower contains all of the plant's reproductive machinery. Many plants have evolved elaborate, complex, and sometimes very beautiful floral structures to maximize their chances that pollination will happen. We will discuss types of pollination, and the floral structures that have evolved to support it, later in this chapter.

Pine trees may produce male and female cones and gametes on a single individual (these pine trees are monoecious). Monoecious organisms tend to be **self-incompatible**, or unable to fertilize their own eggs, to minimize the incidence of self-fertilization (inbreeding). The life cycles of most animals are more like that of a pine tree than a fern. But unlike pine trees, many animals are dioecious (one sex per individual). Animals do not have alternation of generations like plants do. It can seem that they do because the life cycles of some animals do have very distinct body forms at

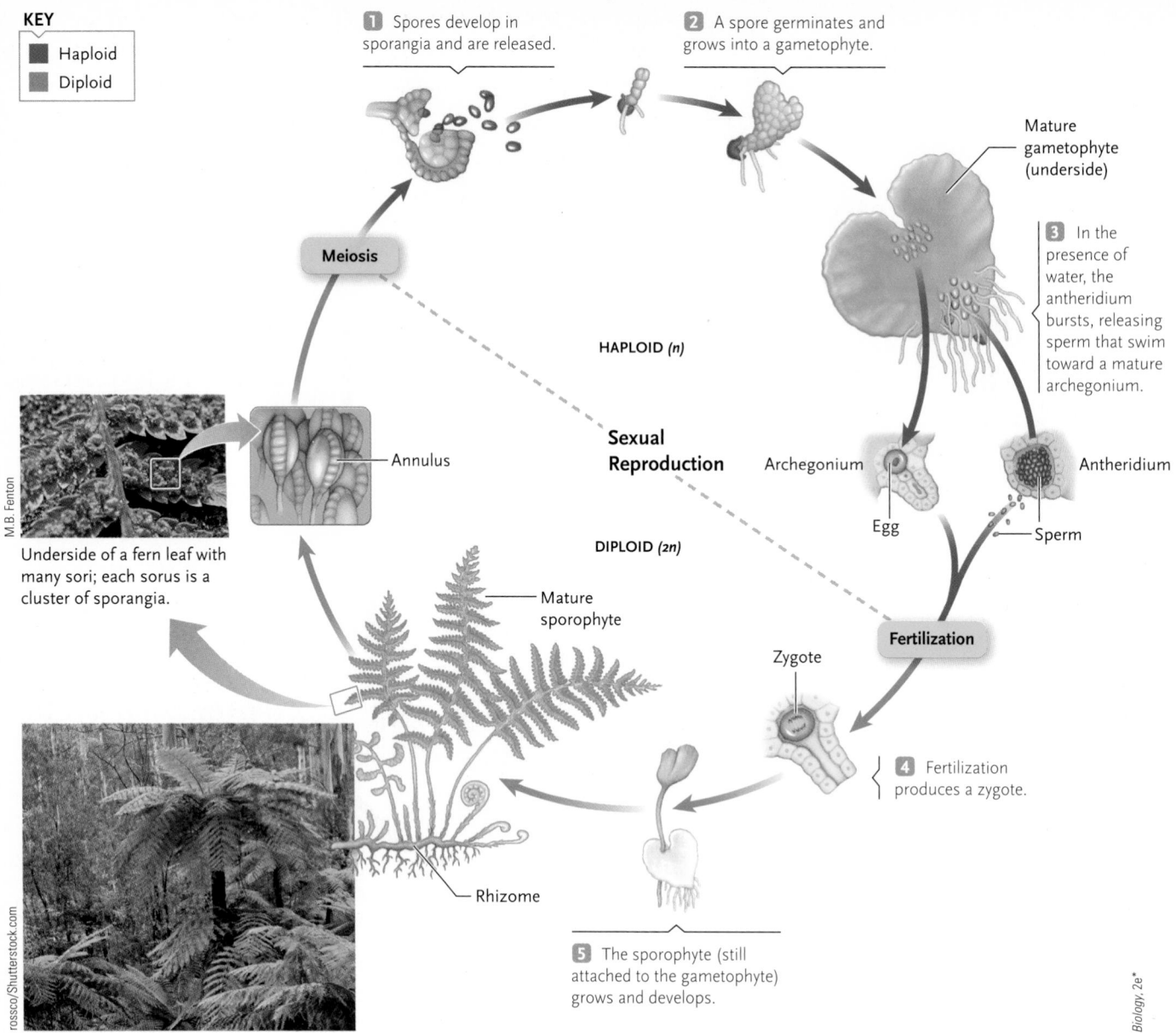

**1** Spores develop in sporangia and are released.

**2** A spore germinates and grows into a gametophyte.

Mature gametophyte (underside)

**3** In the presence of water, the antheridium bursts, releasing sperm that swim toward a mature archegonium.

Meiosis

HAPLOID (*n*)

**Sexual Reproduction**

Archegonium

Antheridium

Egg

Sperm

Annulus

M.B. Fenton

Underside of a fern leaf with many sori; each sorus is a cluster of sporangia.

DIPLOID (*2n*)

Mature sporophyte

Fertilization

Zygote

rossco/Shutterstock.com

**4** Fertilization produces a zygote.

Rhizome

Biology, 2e*

**5** The sporophyte (still attached to the gametophyte) grows and develops.

**FIGURE 28.4** Life cycle of a chain fern (*Woodwardia* spp.). The photograph was taken in Australia's Tarra-Bulga National Park.

different stages of their life cycles—some pass through a larval or other form. But these larva forms are diploids that develop from zygotes; neither larva nor adults are haploid. For example, some colonial cnidarians **(Figure 28.6, p. 629)** have a larval form (planula) as well as two distinct adult forms: the sedentary polyp produces male and female mobile medusae by asexual budding, which in turn produce haploid sperm and eggs by meiosis.

## STUDY BREAK

1. Why is meiosis important in reproduction?
2. What is the difference between haploid and diploid individuals?
3. Compare the alternation of generations in green algae, mosses, and ferns.

## 28.3 Gamete Transfer

Recall that gametes are the haploid cells that join during fertilization. Usually, two gametes unite to form a new organism. Eggs and sperm are the gametes with which we are most familiar. Sperm are generally smaller and lighter than eggs and often are self-propelled. Eggs are larger because, in many cases, they carry resources (such as yolk) that will support development after fertilization. Eggs also contain other cell components, such as mitochondria **(Figure 28.7, p. 629)**. There is considerable variation in egg size among organisms, in part influencing the period of development that occurs in the egg and the size of the hatchlings. Mating is essential for sexually reproducing organisms to transfer their genes to the next generation—a key component of fitness

(Chapter 13). Therefore, organisms invest a great deal of energy and use many approaches to ensure that their gametes have a chance at fertilization.

For fertilization, the fusion of the nuclei of an egg and a sperm occurs after the gametes from two parents come in contact. Fertilization is external when it occurs outside the bodies of males and females or internal when it occurs inside a parent's (usually the female's) body. We will look more closely at how gametes are transferred as we review reproduction in different groups of organisms.

## STUDY BREAK

1. What are gametes? Are they haploid or diploid?

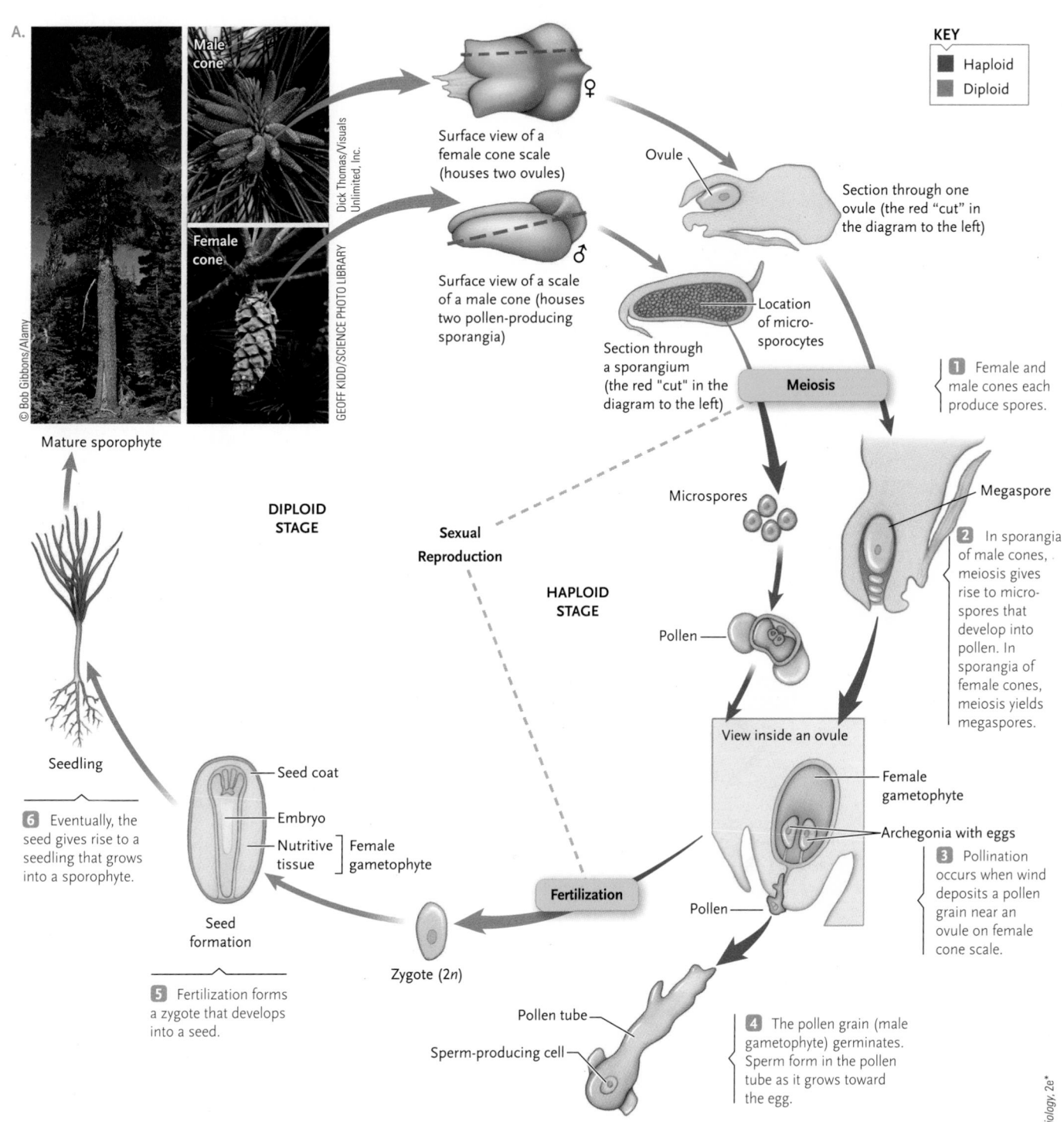

**FIGURE 28.5** *(Continued on page 628.)* A comparison of the life cycles of a gymnosperm (white pine) and an angiosperm. **(a)** The angiosperm shows a flower with four whorls. Anthers of stamens produce haploid pollen from microspores. Stigma of carpel receives pollen. Ovules within ovary contain haploid eggs in an embryo sac. **(b)** Sexual reproduction in a generalized angiosperm. Embryo sporophyte and nutritive endosperm form the seed coat.

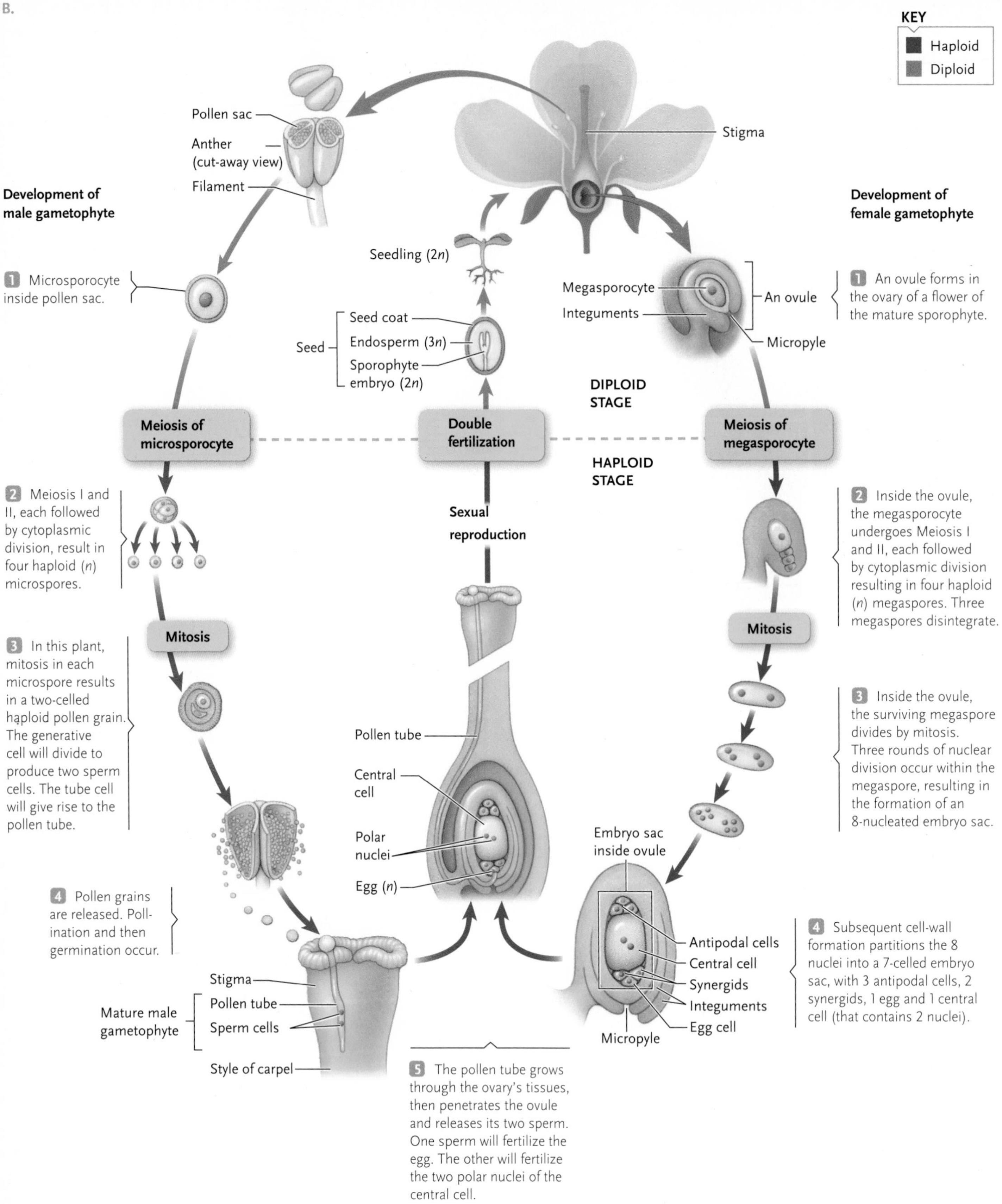

B.

**KEY**
■ Haploid
■ Diploid

■ Haploid
■ Diploid

Pollen sac

Anther (cut-away view)

Filament

Stigma

**Development of male gametophyte**

**Development of female gametophyte**

**1** Microsporocyte inside pollen sac.

Seedling (2n)

Megasporocyte

Integuments

An ovule

**1** An ovule forms in the ovary of a flower of the mature sporophyte.

Seed coat

Endosperm (3n)

Seed

Sporophyte embryo (2n)

Micropyle

**Meiosis of microsporocyte**

**Double fertilization**

**DIPLOID STAGE**

**Meiosis of megasporocyte**

**HAPLOID STAGE**

**2** Meiosis I and II, each followed by cytoplasmic division, result in four haploid (n) microspores.

**Sexual reproduction**

**2** Inside the ovule, the megasporocyte undergoes Meiosis I and II, each followed by cytoplasmic division resulting in four haploid (n) megaspores. Three megaspores disintegrate.

**Mitosis**

**Mitosis**

**3** In this plant, mitosis in each microspore results in a two-celled haploid pollen grain. The generative cell will divide to produce two sperm cells. The tube cell will give rise to the pollen tube.

**3** Inside the ovule, the surviving megaspore divides by mitosis. Three rounds of nuclear division occur within the megaspore, resulting in the formation of an 8-nucleated embryo sac.

Pollen tube

Central cell

Embryo sac inside ovule

Polar nuclei

Egg (n)

**4** Pollen grains are released. Pollination and then germination occur.

Antipodal cells

Central cell

Synergids

Integuments

Egg cell

Micropyle

Stigma

Mature male gametophyte

Pollen tube

Sperm cells

Style of carpel

**4** Subsequent cell-wall formation partitions the 8 nuclei into a 7-celled embryo sac, with 3 antipodal cells, 2 synergids, 1 egg and 1 central cell (that contains 2 nuclei).

**5** The pollen tube grows through the ovary's tissues, then penetrates the ovule and releases its two sperm. One sperm will fertilize the egg. The other will fertilize the two polar nuclei of the central cell.

**FIGURE 28.5** *(Continued)*

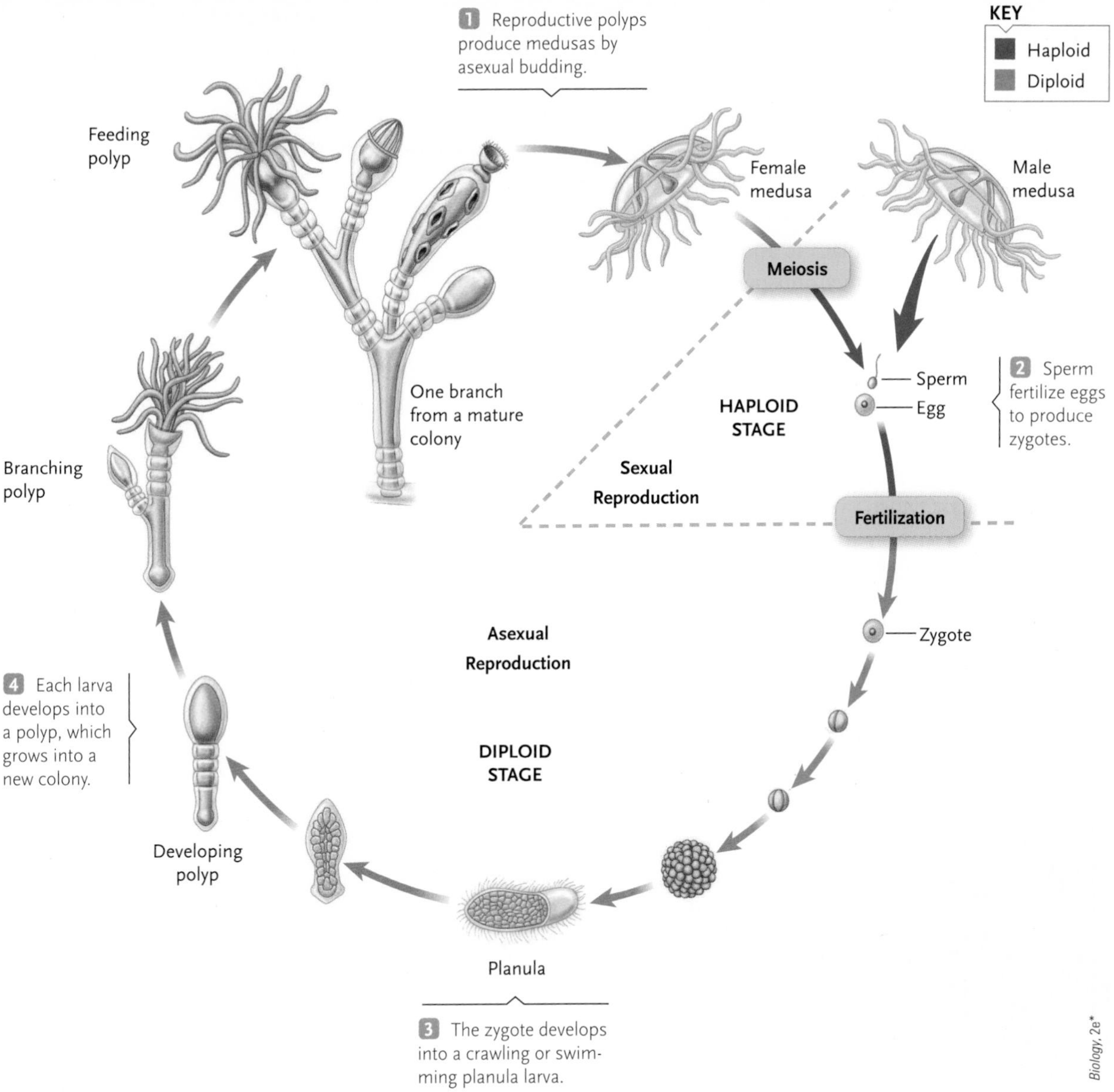

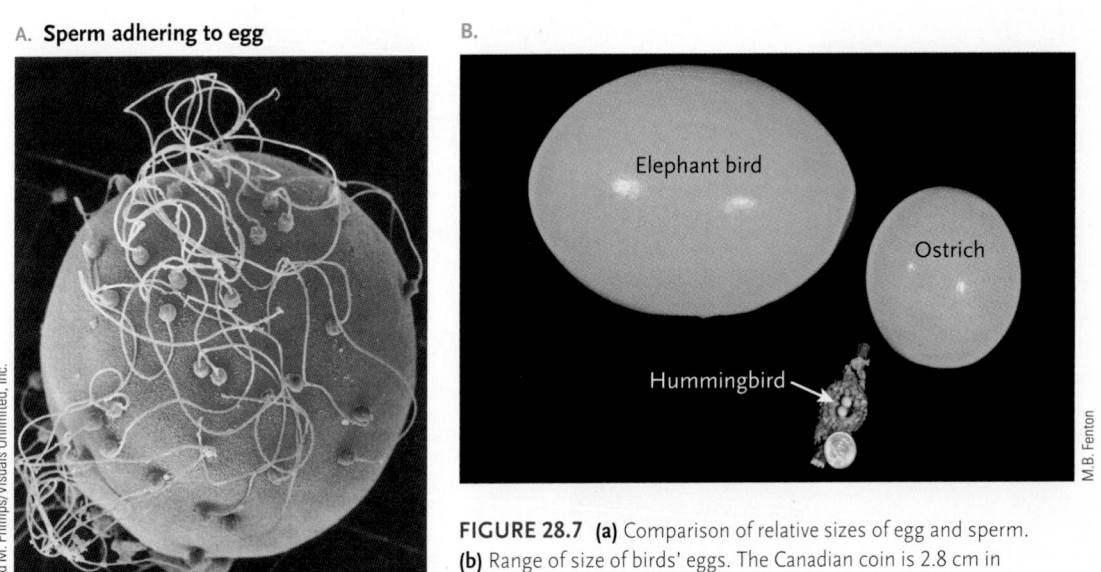

**1** Reproductive polyps produce medusas by asexual budding.

**KEY**

■ Haploid
■ Diploid

Feeding polyp

One branch from a mature colony

Branching polyp

Female medusa

Male medusa

**Meiosis**

Sperm

Egg

**2** Sperm fertilize eggs to produce zygotes.

**HAPLOID STAGE**

**Sexual Reproduction**

**Fertilization**

Zygote

**Asexual Reproduction**

**4** Each larva develops into a polyp, which grows into a new colony.

**DIPLOID STAGE**

Developing polyp

Planula

**3** The zygote develops into a crawling or swimming planula larva.

*Biology, 2e\**

**FIGURE 28.6** The life cycle of *Obelia*, a colonial hydrozoan (phylum Cnidaria). A larval form is evident in both life cycles.

A. **Sperm adhering to egg**

David M. Phillips/Visuals Unlimited, Inc.

B.

Elephant bird

Ostrich

Hummingbird

M.B. Fenton

**FIGURE 28.7 (a)** Comparison of relative sizes of egg and sperm. **(b)** Range of size of birds' eggs. The Canadian coin is 2.8 cm in diameter.

## 28.4 Pollen and Plant Reproduction

Pollen **(Figure 28.8)** is a feature of two main groups of plants, gymnosperms and angiosperms. Gymnosperms, such as evergreen trees, have seeds that are "naked" because they are not encased in a fruit. The seeds of angiosperms are protected in fruit. Pollination, the transfer of pollen from one plant to another, is a central feature of reproduction by gymnosperms and angiosperms. Pollination requires another agent to transfer pollen—typically either wind or animals. But pollination is not the same as fertilization. Pollen itself is not the male gamete (sperm), although it contains the sperm. The gamete is produced by meiosis from microspores contained inside the pollen. The ovules contain the eggs or female gametes. Ovules vary in appearance between angiosperms and gymnosperms (Figure 28.7). Gymnosperms produce pollen in two sporangia housed in the male cones. The female cone produces two ovules (see Figure 28.7a). The female gametophyte provides a food supply for the developing embryo.

Angiosperm flowers can have both male and female structures (**stamen** and **carpel**, respectively) in the same flower, as in **Figure 28.9**. Or there may be separate male and female flowers, either on the same plant or on different plants. The stamen consists of an anther supported on a filament. The carpel consists of a sticky **stigma** that receives pollen, supported by a tube called a **style** that leads down to the ovary. The ovary contains the ovules. Pollen is produced in the anthers of angiosperms from microspores that, in turn, produce sperm (gametes; Figure 28.9). For pollen to reach the ovules, pollen grains land on the stigma (Figure 28.9) and produce tubes that move down the style to access the ovules. The sperm travels through these tubes to fertilize the egg. In angiosperms, more than one sperm is required for fertilization, a process called **double fertilization**. One sperm fuses with the egg to form the embryo, and the other fuses with a special diploid nucleus to form the triploid **endosperm** (it has three sets of chromosomes). The endosperm nourishes the growing embryo.

Pollination is essential to outbreeding—or mixing DNA—in gymnosperms and angiosperms. Associations between angiosperms and specific pollinators provide many examples of parallel and convergent evolution (see Chapter 13, page 297). Note, however, that not all animals that feed at (or on) flowers are pollinators.

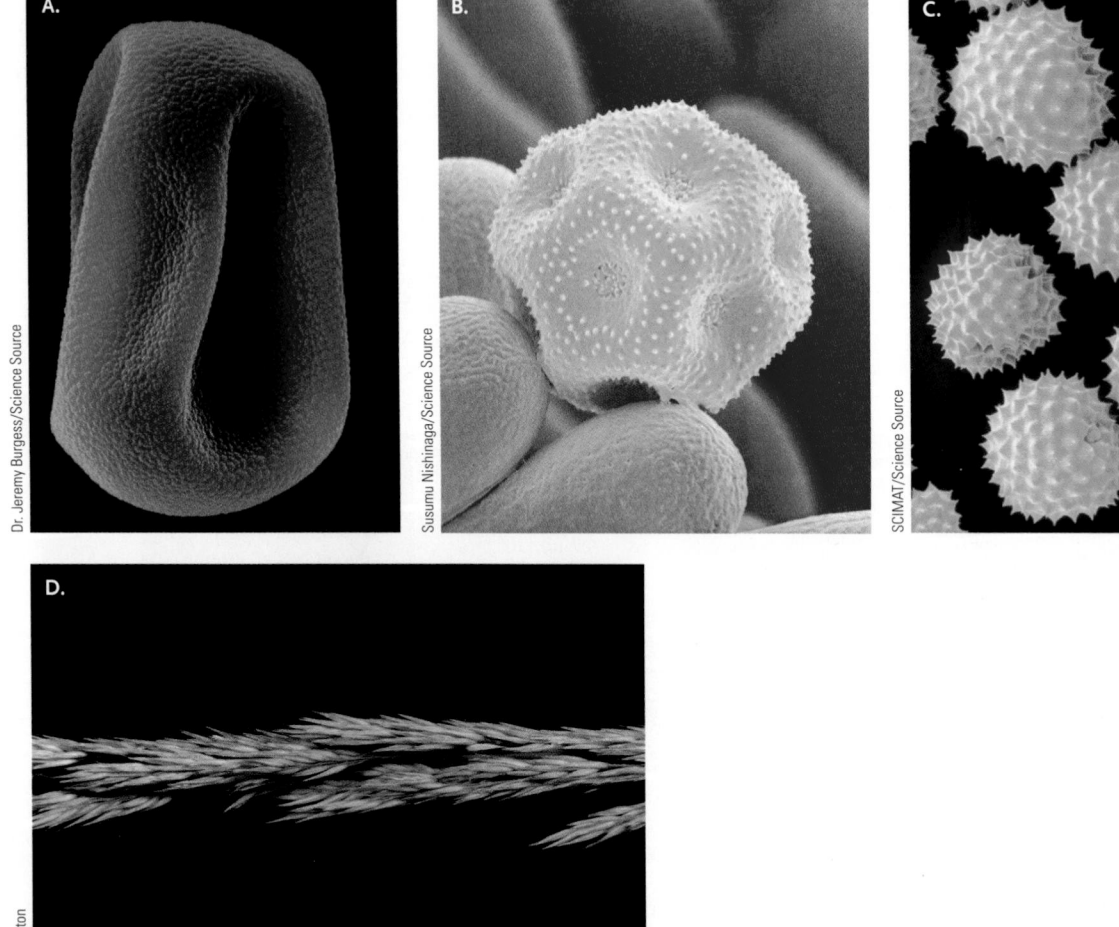

A. *Dr. Jeremy Burgess/Science Source*

B. *Susumu Nishinaga/Science Source*

C. *SCIMAT/Science Source*

D. *M.B. Fenton*

**FIGURE 28.8** Scanning electron micrographs of pollen from a grass **(a)**, chickweed **(b)**, and ragweed **(c)**. Also shown is a grass flower **(d)**.

M.B. Fenton

**FIGURE 28.9** A comparison of two flowers, a bell flower **(a)** and a bee blossom **(b)**, showing male (anther – a) and female (stigma – s) parts.

## Pollen Can Be Transferred by Wind (Anemophily)

People with hay fever are all too familiar with pollen carried on the wind. Wind-pollinated gymnosperms and angiosperms tend to produce vast quantities of pollen, setting up the allergic reactions that cause hay fever. Wind-pollinated ragweed (*Ambrosia artemisiifolia*) is a prime cause of hay fever in many parts of the world. In August and September, in Ontario, ragweed is the main agent causing hay fever. Ragweed pollen (Figure 28.8c) is produced in large quantities and can be carried over 200 km on the wind. Grasses are also windpollinated plants, with pale green (Figure 28.8d), brown, or colourless odourless flowers. Flowering plants with pollen transferred by wind do not need to invest in elaborate, and energetically expensive, flowers to attract animal pollinators.

## Pollen Can Be Transferred by Animals

Three main groups of animals pollinate flowers: birds, bats, and insects. Flower features vary, reflecting the type of pollinator.

Bird-pollinated flowers (ornithophilous) tend to be bright red, white, or orange and odourless. These flowers produce large quantities of nectar that the birds use to fuel their flight. The nectar is an incentive for their pollinators. The nectar is often concealed in funnel-shaped flowers that need to produce relatively little pollen; the structure of the flowers forces the birds to move past the stigma and style to obtain nectar and, in the process, efficiently collect and transfer pollen. The flowers often have a "landing platform" that the birds can rest on while feeding and shapes that maximize the likelihood that the visiting pollinators will be coated with pollen.

Birds in at least 50 families visit flowers of species in over 65 families. Although many species of birds visit flowers and play a role in pollination, relatively few species of birds and plants are closely coevolved around pollination. Birds with special adaptations for feeding at flowers (e.g., long bills and the ability to hover) can be effective pollinators **(Figure 28.10)**.

The combined behaviours and morphologies of both plant and bird pollinators can jointly maximize

M.B. Fenton

**FIGURE 28.10** Flowers of a *Heliconia* spp. **(a)** are pollinated by hummingbirds **(b)**.

outbreeding in the plant. For example, if the plant ensures that the number of open flowers on any single plant is low, it forces pollinators to visit more plants. Individual pollinators with large home ranges are more likely to move pollen among plants than those with small home ranges. This distinction is clear when we consider "hermit" and "non-hermit" species of hummingbirds. Hermit species of hummingbirds have long, curved bills and tend not to defend feeding areas (territories). Hermits move from one flower to the next along straight lines (trap lines). Non-hermit species have short, straight bills and tend to defend a feeding area (they are territorial).

Bat-pollinated flowers bloom at night. They are white, purple, or green; produce large quantities of nectar and pollen; and have a strong, musty odour **(Figure 28.11)**. The combination of colour and odour makes them particularly attractive to flower-visiting bats.

Bat pollinators are found mainly in two families: Old World fruit bats (Pteropodidae) and New World leaf-nosed bats (Phyllostomidae). In the New World tropics, at least two evolutionary lineages of nectar-feeding bats are important as pollinators. In the Old World tropics, there are fewer, mainly nectar-feeding, species of bats that act as pollinators. Throughout the tropics, bats that visit flowers include many that probably eat mostly fruit. One species of trap-lining nectarivorous (nectar-eating) bat, the brown long-tongued bat (*Glossophaga commissarisi*), covers 30 km a night visiting flowers along a 2 km line. The flowers of *Pseudobombax ellipticum* **(Figure 28.11a)** are typical of some bat-pollinated plants in their colour, night opening, and large amounts of pollen. Although *Monophyllus redmani* is a nectar-feeding bat that pollinates plants such as *P. ellipticum*, Jamaican fruit bats (*Artibeus jamaicensis*), even when covered in pollen, appear to be pollen thieves **(Figure 28.11c)** that eat but do not transfer pollen.

Insect-pollinated flowers **(Figure 28.12)** and their insect pollinators, particularly beetles, bees, butterflies, and moths, are most common. Variations in flower colour, odour, and amounts of nectar typically differ among plants pollinated by different insects.

Flowers that are pollinated by flies usually have a putrid odour associated with rotting meat, the site where the flies lay their eggs (or deposit their larvae). Fly-pollinated flowers produce no nectar and have limited amounts of pollen. Fly-pollinated flowers tend to be funnel shaped and have a trap that ensnares the fly. To escape the trap, the flies are forced to pass close to the anther of the flower, maximizing the chances of pollen being transferred to the fly so that it can carry that pollen to the next flower.

Flowers pollinated by beetles tend to be green or white in colour and produce a variable odour (from sweet to foul) and relatively large amounts of pollen.

Moth-pollinated flowers tend to be purple, pink, white, or pale red in colour and have a strong, sweet odour. These flowers are usually nocturnal (like moths) and tubular and produce limited pollen and large supplies of nectar.

Flowers pollinated by butterflies are open by day, are bright red or purple in colour, and produce limited pollen and large amounts of nectar.

Bee-pollinated flowers are usually bright white, yellow, or blue with a pleasant odour. These flowers usually produce nectar that serves as an incentive to bees and limited amounts of sticky pollen. Bees use the pollen and nectar to feed themselves and their larvae. Bee-pollinated flowers tend to have a flat landing surface for the bees (see also Chapter 22, page 490).

Insect-pollinated plants that also consume insects are faced with an interesting conundrum. They depend on the insects they attract as a source of nitrogen. But they also depend on insects to pollinate them. Plants

**FIGURE 28.11** Flowers of *Pseudobombax ellipticum* **(a)** are bat pollinated sometimes by Leach's single-leafed bat (*Monophyllus redmani*) **(b)**. Jamaican fruit bats **(c)** may take pollen, but their role as pollinators may be limited.

**FIGURE 28.12** Insects visiting flowers include a wasp **(a)**, a monarch butterfly **(b)**, and a bumblebee **(c and d)**. Note that the bee leaving the flower (d) is covered with pollen. The mouthparts of the wasp, butterfly (arrow), and bee are evident.

that catch and digest insects must balance the need to attract insects as pollinators and also attract other insects as food. You can imagine that would be a tricky balance. For plants like this, the position of the flower(s) relative to the insect trap that they use to capture food **(Figure 28.13)** may be one way to ensure that meeting their nitrogen requirements does not interfere with pollination.

## STUDY BREAK

1. What role does pollination play in sexual reproduction?
2. What are three specializations of flowers for pollination?
3. What are some differences between wind pollination and animal pollination?

**FIGURE 28.13** In two insectivorous plants, a sundew (*Drosera capensis*) **(a)** and a pitcher plant (*Sarracenia purpurea*) **(b)** flowers are well above the insect traps, whether adhesive traps (*Drosera*) or pitchers (*Sarracenia*). This positioning may minimize capture and consumption of would-be pollinators.

## 28.5 Fungal Reproduction

Fungal reproduction is very different from that of both plants and animals. Fungi of the same species can reproduce sexually and asexually. Unlike animals or plants, fungi do not produce embryos. Most of us are familiar with the reproductive structures or fruiting bodies of fungi. The mushrooms that we eat are fungal fruiting bodies. But fungi are modular organisms, and multicellular reproductive structures such as mushrooms are just appendages of a much larger organism (the mycelium; see Chapter 18 for an overview of fungi).

### Asexual Reproduction

Single-celled yeasts reproduce asexually, either through **budding** or **fission**. In fission, the yeast cell splits into two cells. In budding, a small bud grows on the mother cell. The nucleus of the mother cell divides, and one of the nuclei migrates into the bud. Eventually, this daughter cell grows bigger and splits off from the mother cell. In multicellular fungi, the most common type of asexual reproduction is through spores. Many fungal species can produce spores through mitosis (see Chapter 6 for details on mitosis). These spores can then be dispersed, and if environmental conditions are appropriate, they can establish as a new fungus.

### Sexual Reproduction

There are many variations in the process of fungal reproduction. In general, the sexual life cycle of fungi includes (1) plasmogamy, (2) karyogamy, (3) meiotic spore production, (4) spore dispersal, and (5) establishment of fungal hyphae **(Figure 28.14)**.

Mushrooms produce haploid spores. Fungal spores do not need to combine with another cell to grow, as is required for sexual reproduction in animals. Instead, under the right environmental conditions, hyphae extend from spores that have dispersed into the environment. The cells of the hyphae, like the spores themselves, are haploid. The haploid hyphae of two individuals may encounter each other underground. If these hyphae are compatible, they can then fuse, a process called plasmogamy (from the Greek *plasmo*, meaning plasma or cytoplasm, and *gamy*, meaning marriage or union).

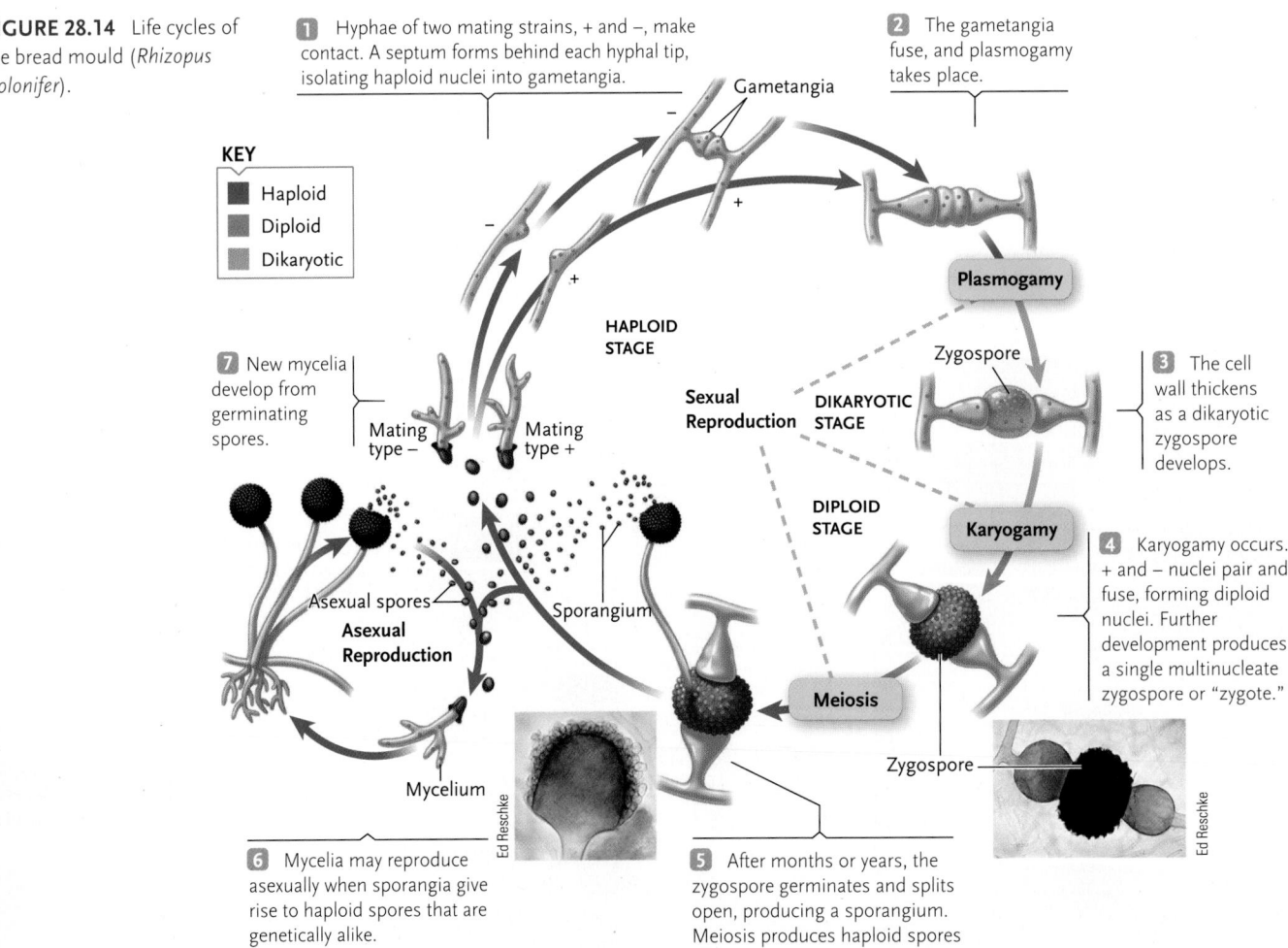

**FIGURE 28.14** Life cycles of the bread mould (*Rhizopus stolonifer*).

**1** Hyphae of two mating strains, + and −, make contact. A septum forms behind each hyphal tip, isolating haploid nuclei into gametangia.

**2** The gametangia fuse, and plasmogamy takes place.

**KEY**
- Haploid
- Diploid
- Dikaryotic

**3** The cell wall thickens as a dikaryotic zygospore develops.

**4** Karyogamy occurs. + and − nuclei pair and fuse, forming diploid nuclei. Further development produces a single multinucleate zygospore or "zygote."

**5** After months or years, the zygospore germinates and splits open, producing a sporangium. Meiosis produces haploid spores of each mating type.

**6** Mycelia may reproduce asexually when sporangia give rise to haploid spores that are genetically alike.

**7** New mycelia develop from germinating spores.

Gametangia

Plasmogamy

Zygospore

HAPLOID STAGE

Sexual Reproduction

DIKARYOTIC STAGE

DIPLOID STAGE

Karyogamy

Meiosis

Zygospore

Mating type −

Mating type +

Asexual spores

Asexual Reproduction

Sporangium

Mycelium

Ed Reschke

Ed Reschke

*Biology, 2E\**

In animals, when a sperm and egg fuse, so do their two nuclei (this process is called karyogamy—*karyon* means nut or nucleus). In fungi, karyogamy occurs, but not always right away. When the cells have fused (plasmogamy) but the nuclei have not (karyogamy), the result is fungal cells with two different haploid nuclei that contain different genetic information. A cell like this with two nuclei is called a dikaryon (in other stages with a single nucleus, the fungus is a monokaryon). Both nuclei divide during growth, maintaining two separate haploid nuclei in old and new cells. Eventually, the fungus produces a fruiting body (a mushroom, for example) that produces spores, and in the spore-producing cells of that fruiting body, the haploid nuclei fuse; karyogamy finally takes place. The nuclei in the spore-producing cells are now diploid, with DNA from both parent cells. Soon afterward, haploid spores are produced by meiosis. These spores are released into the environment, and the process continues.

## STUDY BREAK

1. What is an example of asexual reproduction in fungi?
2. What is plasmogamy?
3. What is a dikaryon?

## 28.6 Animal Reproduction

Most animals reproduce sexually using sperm and eggs. The extent to which individuals maximize the chances of sperm contacting egg varies considerably among species and phyla. The range of approaches varies. Some have no control over mates, leaving sperm (and/or eggs) somewhere in the environment where they may come in contact with other gametes. At the other end of the spectrum, some transfer sperm to a suitable receptacle within another individual, where it may be nourished and stored until the time for fertilization is right.

### Anatomy and Fertilization

The basic anatomical arrangements **(Figure 28.15, p. 636)** of animals include sites for production of gametes (combined **ovotestes** in some individuals, or two genders with ovaries in females, testes in males) and a passage to the outside that may also serve to transfer sperm toward the egg. In females, there can be places to store sperm or chambers (such as a uterus) in which development occurs. Often glandular structures add different components to the eggs and sperm, and other structures may serve for storing gametes (usually

sperm). Some animals, such as earthworms, are **hermaphroditic**—they have both male and female reproductive parts in one individual. Many of the species of animals you are most familiar with, including most vertebrates, have separate individuals with male and female reproductive structures.

Eggs may be fertilized inside (internal fertilization) or outside (external fertilization) a parent's (usually the female's) body. Internal fertilization involves more complex anatomical structures, either to deliver and/or receive sperm. Internal fertilization provides more control over mate choice, usually paternity, and more protection of the offspring. Hermaphroditic organisms can be self-fertilizing but usually exchange sperm, fertilizing each other. Fertilization **(Figure 28.16, p. 637)** may be internal or external depending on the species. The stages involved in fertilization are shown in **Figure 28.17, p. 637**.

Few organisms reproduce all the time because for most there is an optimal time for reproduction. By definition, the optimal time is when most of the young that are produced will survive to reproduce. Extrinsic factors, such as day length, set the stage for reproduction. As days lengthen in spring, the extended hours of daylight stimulate production and release of hormones that in turn stimulate the gonads and lead to gamete production. Often the same hormones affect behaviour, putting males and females "in the mood" for reproduction. Courtship behaviours further synchronize and ready both males and females, setting the stage for mating in many animals. The net result is that young are born when conditions are optimal for their growth, survival, and subsequent reproduction.

### The Timing of Ovulation Is Critical to Fertilization

**Ovulation** is the release of an egg (or eggs) from the ovaries. The steps involved in human ovulation are illustrated in **Figure 28.18, p. 638**. Males that **copulate** (transfer sperm via internal fertilization) close to the time that their female mate ovulates increase the chances of fertilization and getting their genes into the next generation—and therefore their fitness. This may be particularly important when a female mates (copulates) with more than one male. For people who are either trying to ensure pregnancy, or avoid it, the timing of ovulation is a pivotal factor.

Hormones secreted in the hypothalamus, pituitary, and ovaries are central to reproduction in mammals, including the control of ovulation (see Chapter 26 for an overview of hormones). Scientists have demonstrated this in many ways. For example, they have bred mice that lack specific microRNAs that keep luteinizing

## A. Sex organs

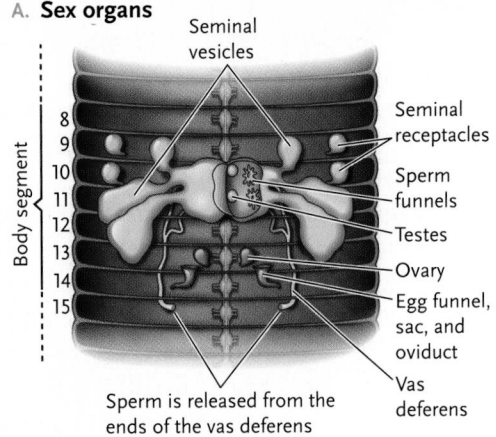

Seminal vesicles

Body segment
8
9
10
11
12
13
14
15

Seminal receptacles

Sperm funnels

Testes

Ovary

Egg funnel, sac, and oviduct

Vas deferens

Sperm is released from the ends of the vas deferens

Biology, 2E*

**FIGURE 28.15** A comparison of the reproductive systems of a hermaphroditic earthworm **(a)** and three species in which each individual has either male or female reproductive structures, including a fruit fly **(b)**, a frog **(c)**, and a cat **(d)**.

## B. Insect (fruit fly)

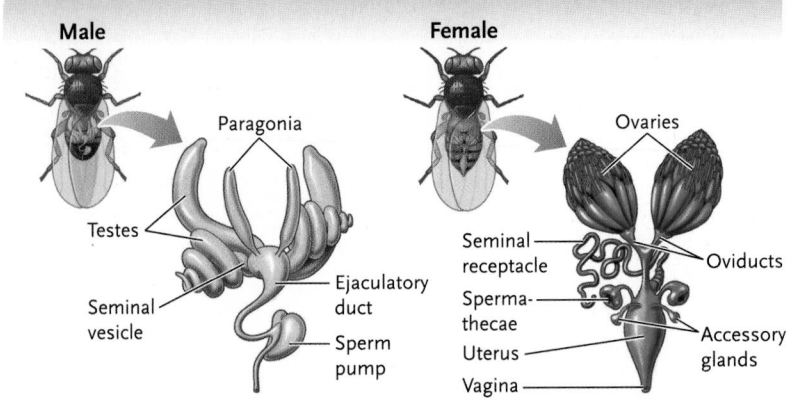

Male

Paragonia

Testes

Seminal vesicle

Ejaculatory duct

Sperm pump

Female

Ovaries

Seminal receptacle

Sperma-thecae

Uterus

Vagina

Oviducts

Accessory glands

## C. Amphibian (frog)

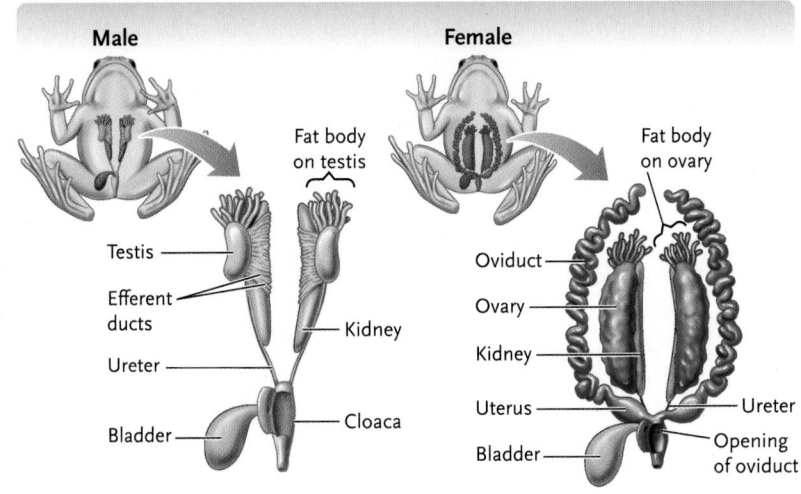

Male

Fat body on testis

Testis

Efferent ducts

Ureter

Bladder

Kidney

Cloaca

Female

Fat body on ovary

Oviduct

Ovary

Kidney

Uterus

Bladder

Ureter

Opening of oviduct

## D. Mammal (cat)

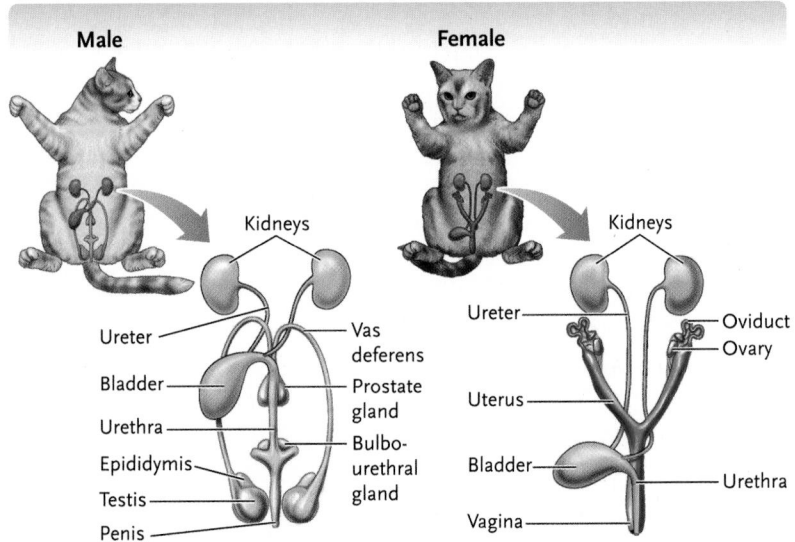

Male

Kidneys

Ureter

Bladder

Urethra

Epididymis

Testis

Penis

Vas deferens

Prostate gland

Bulbo-urethral gland

Female

Kidneys

Ureter

Uterus

Bladder

Vagina

Oviduct

Ovary

Urethra

hormone (LH)—a hormone that triggers ovulation—at appropriate levels for ovulation to occur. These mice do not ovulate and are therefore infertile.

## Behaviour Is Essential for Successful Mating in Many Animal Species

The process of **courtship**—the behaviours animals use to assess and attract mates—is familiar to most of us. Although the specific approaches we use to find partners varies culturally, courtship is a pervasive behaviour. Other animals also use courtship and other mating behaviours that can be quite extreme. These behaviours can stimulate interest in mating and ensure that bodies are aligned correctly when the time comes to transfer gametes. Extensive periods of courtship behaviour can serve to synchronize mating activities, ensuring transfer of sperm when it is most likely to lead to fertilization and so maximize fitness. Together, the costs of reproduction can be high; animals must invest in, for example, producing gametes, appropriate anatomical features (Figure 12.7), behaviours associated with courting and mating, and sometimes parental care.

Animals use a variety of signals in association with mating. The bright colours of male birds are one example (Figure 12.7). Acoustic, or sound, signals can also be important. Strong acoustic signals can travel farther than can visual cues, making the signaller more conspicuous. Small male water boatmen (*Micronecta scholtzi*) produce among the most intense signals known in animals. Scaled to body size, their signals are stronger than those of other animals, including elephants and dolphins. These water boatmen produce their songs by

**FIGURE 28.16** Animals exchanging **(a)** or transferring **(b, c, d)** gametes from one to another. Included are two earthworms (a), two leopard frogs (b), two butterflies (c), and two egrets (d).

**stridulation**, rubbing part of their sperm transfer organ (penis) against a ridge on their abdomen. Many animals use signals (pheromones) to attract mates **(Figure 28.19, p. 638)**.

The process of choosing a mate, and the behaviours that go with it, can be a huge investment for animals. To make that investment worthwhile, males must do what they can to ensure that their sperm produces offspring. Females, in turn, will be motivated to control which male's sperm fertilizes her egg, in an effort to ensure that her offspring are sired by the best possible male. Animals show three basic patterns of mate interactions: monogamy, polygamy, and promiscuity. **Monogamy** is a bond between individuals (typically male and female) that extends over at least one mating season and sometimes through a lifetime. Close association through monogamy may ensure that the couple raises only offspring that carry their own genes. **Polygamy** is a partnership that lasts at least one mating season between one male and several females (**polygyny**) or one female with several males (**polyandry**). Polygamy usually arises when one sex provides virtually

## Steps in fertilization

**1** A sperm contacts the jelly layer of the egg.

**2** The acrosomal reaction begins: enzymes contained in the acrosome are released and dissolve a path through the jelly layer.

**3** Proteins in its plasma membrane bind the sperm to the vitelline coat.

**4** The sperm lyses a hole in the vitelline coat. The sperm and egg plasma membranes fuse.

**5** Membrane depolarization produces the fast block to polyspermy.

**6** The sperm nucleus and centriole enter the egg. The sperm nucleus then fuses with the egg nucleus.

**7** The fusion of egg and sperm triggers the release of $Ca^{2+}$ ions, which trigger the cortical reaction, the fusion of secretory cortical granules with the egg's plasma membrane. The enzymes of the granules released to the outside alter the egg coats, producing the slow block to polyspermy.

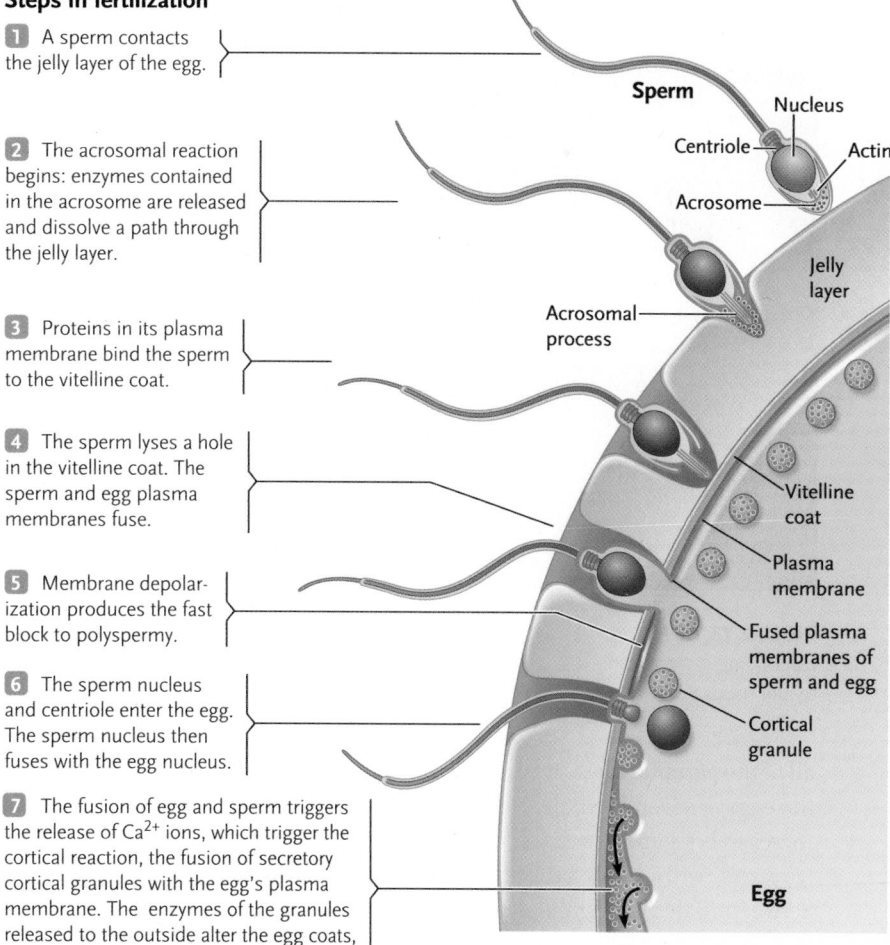

**FIGURE 28.17** Steps leading to fertilization.

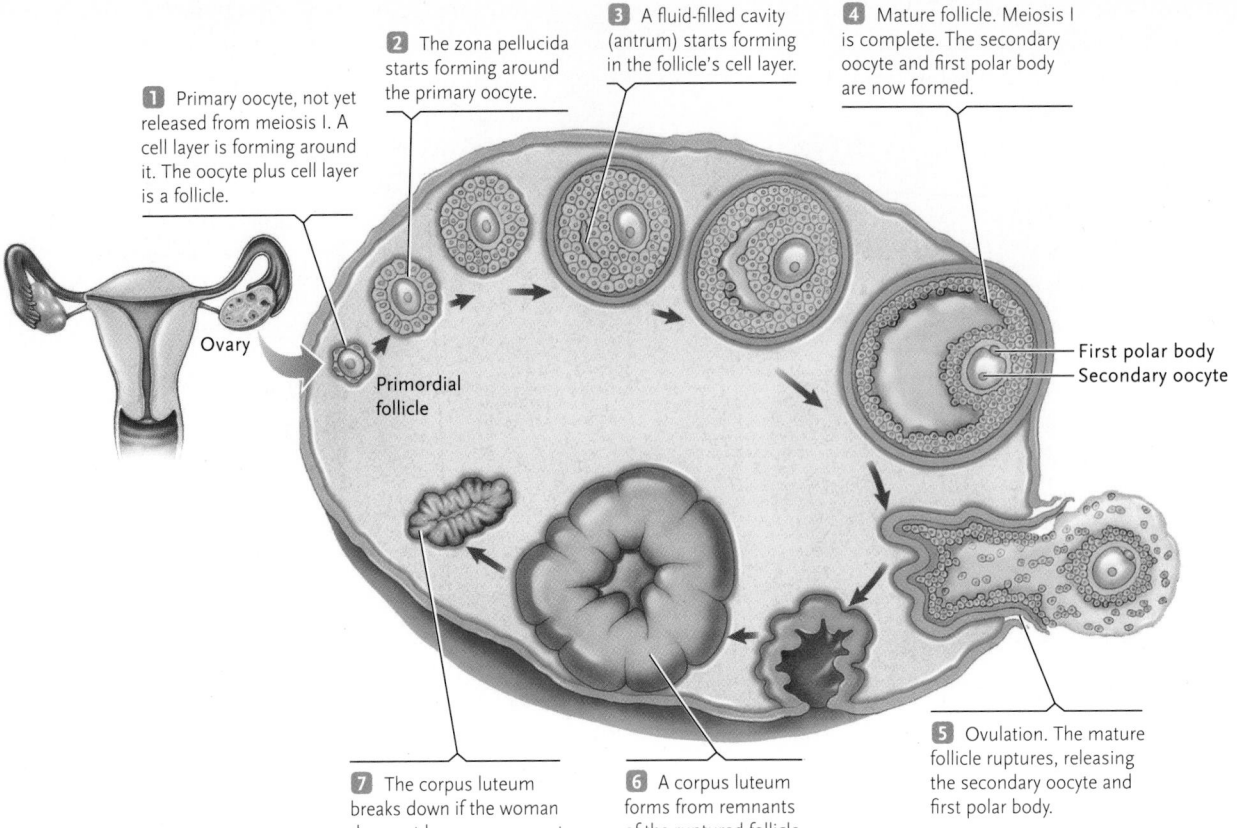

1. Primary oocyte, not yet released from meiosis I. A cell layer is forming around it. The oocyte plus cell layer is a follicle.

2. The zona pellucida starts forming around the primary oocyte.

3. A fluid-filled cavity (antrum) starts forming in the follicle's cell layer.

4. Mature follicle. Meiosis I is complete. The secondary oocyte and first polar body are now formed.

Ovary

Primordial follicle

First polar body
Secondary oocyte

5. Ovulation. The mature follicle ruptures, releasing the secondary oocyte and first polar body.

7. The corpus luteum breaks down if the woman does not become pregnant.

6. A corpus luteum forms from remnants of the ruptured follicle.

*Biology, 2E*

**FIGURE 28.18** Growth of the follicle, ovulation, and formation of the corpus luteum in a human ovary.

M.B. Fenton

**FIGURE 28.19** A flying male gypsy moth (*Lymantria dispar*) responding to a pheromone trap. The female's pheromone is used to lure males to their deaths.

all of the parental care. In polygyny, one male can fertilize the eggs of several females, which care for the young and increase his genetic fitness. In polyandry, the reverse is true. As with monogamy, the long-term association between males and females may provide some certainty to each individual that they are raising their own offspring and therefore using their energy to ensure that their own DNA makes it to the next generation. **Promiscuity** is when

males and females meet only to transfer sperm and there is no long-term association between individuals. Of course, animal species do not always stick to just one approach. There are many species—for example, song-birds—that appear to be mainly monogamous. However, many of these individuals (males and females) "sneak" opportunities to mate with others while remaining in their monogamous pair bond—a phenomenon called **extra-pair mating**. This reality has been revealed by DNA fingerprinting, which has shown that the eggs in a single nest of apparently monogamous songbird species are fre-quently sired by two or more males.

Behaviour after pregnancy can also influence repro-ductive output. Over 50 years ago, Hilda Margaret Bruce reported some interesting findings about the reproductive behaviour of house mice (*Mus musculus*). Specifically, exposure to the urine (or its scent) of a strange male caused pregnant females to miscarry. The "Bruce effect" partly explains the territorial behaviour of the mice and many other species. If males do not protect their territories, they risk losing the offspring they worked hard to sire.

## Homosexual Mating Is Also Common in Animals

Same-sex (homosexual) mating is a recurring phenom-enon among males and females, and it occurs in almost every group of animals. There are many reasons for this:

some are cases of mistaken identity or hormone malfunction, whereas others appear to be adaptive advantages. Whatever the reason, one thing is clear: same-sex pairings are common in nature.

In little brown bats (*Myotis lucifugus*), homosexual matings appear to be cases of mistaken identity—the males confuse other males for females. In other cases, homosexual behaviour is caused by hormonal interference. Pesticides such as DDT cause feminization of males, which has led to gender confusion in species such as Glaucous-Winged Gulls (*Larus glaucescens*) and White Ibises (*Eudocimus albus*). Another example of feminization occurs when hormones from oral contraceptives used by women enter local bodies of water. There the hormones result in feminization of male fish. This reduces reproduction and poses an important challenge for those concerned about conservation of the fish.

Often males that mate with other males also mate with females. In the gynogenetic (see page 274) fish species *Poecilia formosa*, there are no males. Female *P. formosa* must court males of other species to obtain sperm. Female *P. formosa* and females in other species (*Poecilia latipinna*) in the same watersheds tend to pick males that were already chosen by other females. Research with these fish demonstrates that females also prefer males that mate with other males. In this situation, homosexual matings may increase the reproductive output of males that participate in them.

## Study Break

1. Where does fertilization occur in animals?
2. What is ovulation?
3. What is the Bruce effect?
4. What is feminization?

## 28.7 Asexual Reproduction

Among fungi, plants, and animals, many species regularly reproduce asexually. Although many of them have the potential to do so as needed, others do so exclusively.

In flowering plants, asexual reproduction can involve vegetative reproduction through runners (e.g., strawberries) as well as roots and eyes in tubers such as potatoes. In each case, a **callus** develops. This is an unorganized mass of cells, some with the potential to become other types of cells. Cells with the capacity to become other types of cells are **totipotent**, in animals sometimes referred to as stem cells. In plants, totipotent cells can develop into small plants with roots, shoots, and leaves. The same is true of many non-flowering plants, for example, ferns such as the walking fern (*Asplenium rhizophyllum*). There are parallel examples among fungi and animals, demonstrating, as we saw with rotifers, the strategic advantages that can be associated with asexual reproduction.

Asexual reproduction in animals is most common in smaller organisms with less differentiation of tissues and organ systems. Sometimes, however, we discover examples of asexual reproduction in unexpected places. Snakes are animals with **heterogametic sex determination** (see Box 28.1); they have sex chromosomes (X, Y, W, Z; see below) that differ between males and females. In humans, females have two copies of the same sex chromosome (they are XX) and males have two different sex chromosomes (XY). Many species of snakes are the opposite: the females have different sex chromosomes (WZ), and males have two copies of the same (WW). In species of snakes where females have a WZ chromosomal arrangement, WW females might arise through parthenogenesis. Genetic techniques, including microsatellite DNA fingerprinting, have recently revealed evidence that some female boas (*Boa constrictor*) reproduced asexually and produced only WO females. This raises the possibility that parthenogenesis—or asexual reproduction in which haploid offspring develop from unfertilized ova—may be more common in some reptiles than previously expected. Think back to Chapter 13 and our discussion of how genetic tools have changed our view of how organisms are related. This is another example of how genetic tools can change our view of organisms. Genetic testing allowed identification of asexual reproduction by female boa constrictors.

The issue of gender can be complex. For example, in Chapter 7 (Table 7.1), you saw how altered numbers of X and Y chromosomes in humans affect gender.

## Study Break

1. What is parthenogenesis?
2. Why are young boas produced by parthenogenesis always female?

## 28.8 Development

Now that you are familiar with gametes, and how they unite, we will explore what happens next: the development from zygote to adult. This transition involves substantial changes, including increases in the number and size of cells and the diversity of structures and organs. Changes in overall size and appearance come from a combination of cell division, cell differentiation, and growth (see below). Fertilized eggs may contain supplies of nutrients to fuel development: endosperm in flowering plants and yolk in many animals. The amount of stored nutrients is a prime factor in determining how much time passes between fertilization and hatching or germinating. Local environmental conditions (temperature and moisture) can also be important. For example, seeds of angiosperms tend to be dehydrated, which allows them to lie dormant for long periods. Proper hydration is often essential for germination. After 1000 years, the

## Gender Determination

Sexual reproduction requires the participation of two genders: one produces smaller, motile gametes (sperm, male), whereas the other produces larger immobile or less mobile gametes (eggs, female). People tend to be most familiar with gender determined by sex chromosomes that are different in size and the genes they carry. In mammals, gender depends on a group of genes located on the short arm of the Y chromosome. Typically, male mammals have an X and a Y chromosome and females have two X chromosomes. In birds and many reptiles, the sex chromosomes are Z and W, with males being ZZ and females ZW. The gonads are **primary sex characteristics**: either ovaries or testes. **Secondary sex characteristics** are other features that distinguish males from females, including size, colour, and behaviour. In flowering plants, X and Y, as well as Z and W, chromosomes are also quite common.

In mammals, all of the cells in the body contain sex chromosomes, but until activated by sex-determining hormones produced in the gonads, embryos have no gender. The situation differs in birds, where somatic cells and gonadal cells are either male or female, independent of hormonal signals. This accounts for birds that are **gynandromorphs**: individuals that are male on one side of the body and female on the other.

Many animals are dioecious, meaning that individuals are either male or female. Other animals, and many plants, are monoecious, meaning that they have the capacity to produce both eggs and sperm. In hermaphroditic animals, the gonad, an ovotestis, produces male and female hormones as well as eggs and sperm. Flowering plants (angiosperms) are mainly hermaphroditic in sexual expression, with individual plants acting as both male and female parents. Yet dioecy (separate plants with different genders) is a recurring theme among flowering plants and occurs in about half of the families of flowering plants.

Fungi lack sex chromosomes. Here gender is determined by mating types. In some fungi, each sex allele contains a single gene that encodes the protein that determines mating type. This situation suggests that fungi may represent one of the earliest steps in the appearance of sex determination. Even well-known fungi such as *Candida albicans*, a human pathogen studied since 1800, provides surprises. Although long considered to be a diploid species, this pathogen forms haploids that are able to mate, which may account for its versatility as a pathogen of mammals.

In eusocial insects, including many species of bees, ants, and wasps (Hymenoptera), gender is determined genetically. Here the system is called haplodiploid: males are haploid, whereas females are diploid.

In many animals and flowering plants, gender is determined not by genetics and chromosomes but by environmental conditions, often temperature. The list of animals with environmental sex determination includes at least crustaceans, spoonworms, and reptiles such as lizards, turtles, and crocodylians. Environmental conditions determine both primary and secondary sexual characteristics, as well as associated patterns of behaviour. Organisms with environmental gender determination are vulnerable to climate change. Relatively minor changes in temperature could result in the extinction of a species if it no longer produces both genders.

In the final analysis, we know little about sex determination in most organisms. The few that have been studied provide a tantalizing glimpse of diversity in this area.

---

seeds of some plants still have the capacity to germinate. The process of angiosperm germination begins with **imbibition**, when they take on water that is attracted to the hydrophilic seed proteins, causing the seed to swell and rupture. Access to water and oxygen coincides with a burst of metabolism.

## Development in Vascular Plants Begins after Fertilization

The first changes that occur after fertilization in gymnosperms and angiosperms set the stage for the formation of the seed. Further changes occur when the seed germinates and the seedling grows. Initially, the zygote begins to elongate and develop. The example in **Figure 28.23, p. 642** is of a eudicot plant (see Chapter 17 for a review of plant types). The nucleus and most organelles sit in the top half of the cell; most of the rest is filled with an empty vacuole. Mitosis then begins. The first division results in an upper (apical) cell that develops into the embryo and the **suspensor**—a row of cells that forms from the lower (basal) cell and transfers nutrients to the developing embryo. Along the long axis of the plant embryo, there is shoot apical meristem at the top that will grow into the plant and root apical meristem at the bottom that will grow into the root system **(Figure 28.20)**. Cells in the root area are the first to begin to divide. Early in development, three basic plant tissues appear: (1) ground tissues that are responsible for metabolism, storage, and support; (2) vascular tissues (xylem and phloem) that transport water and nutrients; and (3) dermal tissues that form the protective coating on the outside of the plant.

Seeds of angiosperms contain zygotes that are nourished by endosperm. Usually, the seeds are encased in fruits **(Figure 28.21)**, which are ripened ovaries. The wall of the ovary develops into the wall of the fruit **(pericarp)** and may consist of several layers. Hormones in pollen grains and developing seeds may stimulate

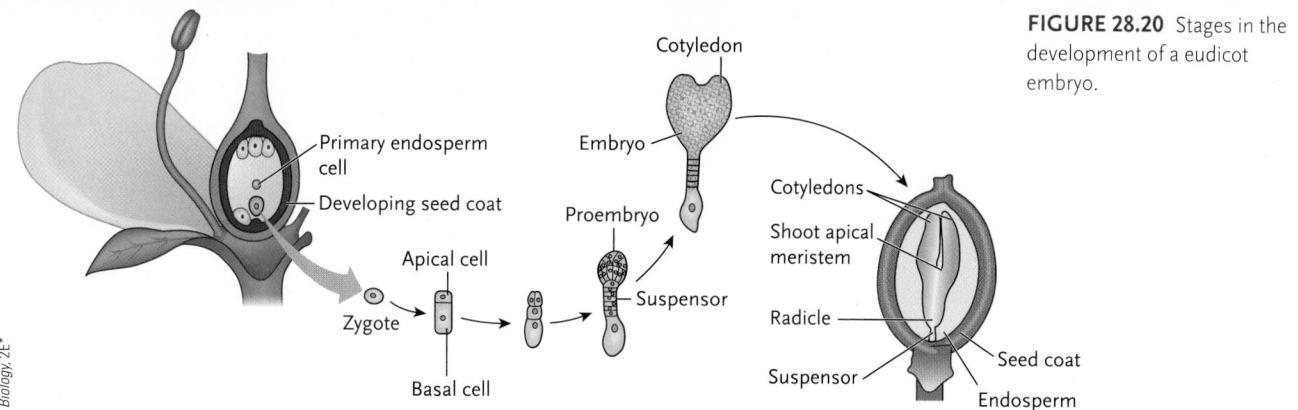

*Biology, 2E\**

**FIGURE 28.20** Stages in the development of a eudicot embryo.

**FIGURE 28.21** Four kinds of fleshy fruits, including both simple fruits (from one ovary) and aggregate fruits (from several ovaries). The blueberries (13), tomatoes (2), and cherries (2) are simple fruits, whereas the blackberries (3) are aggregate fruits.

fruit development. **Simple fruits** develop from a single ovary (such as in peaches and tomatoes) and have at least one fleshy (juicy) layer. Other simple fruits, peas, grains, and nuts have dry pericarp. **Aggregate fruits,**

such as raspberries and strawberries, develop from clusters of ovaries. Pineapples are aggregate fruits that develop from clusters of ovaries and ovaries of more than one flower. Note that some flowering plants produce fruit without fertilization by **parthenocarpy.** Seedless fruit that you buy at the grocery store is produced via parthenocarpy.

Many plants use fruits to attract animals, which serve to disperse seeds. Animals eat fruits, ingesting seeds that are not digestible and pass through the digestive tract. In this way, the animal moves seeds away from the parent plant **(Figure 28.22)** and deposits them in droppings (manure) that may promote germination and growth. In many cases, passage through an animal's digestive tract increases the rate of germination.

## Development in Animals Is Either Determinate or Indeterminate

The change from fertilized egg to adult animal involves huge changes in size and complexity. The details of these changes vary considerably among animals, in part

From Katriona Shea, "How the Wood Moves," *Science,* vol. 315, Mar 2, 2007, pp. 1231–1232. Reprinted with permission from AAAS.

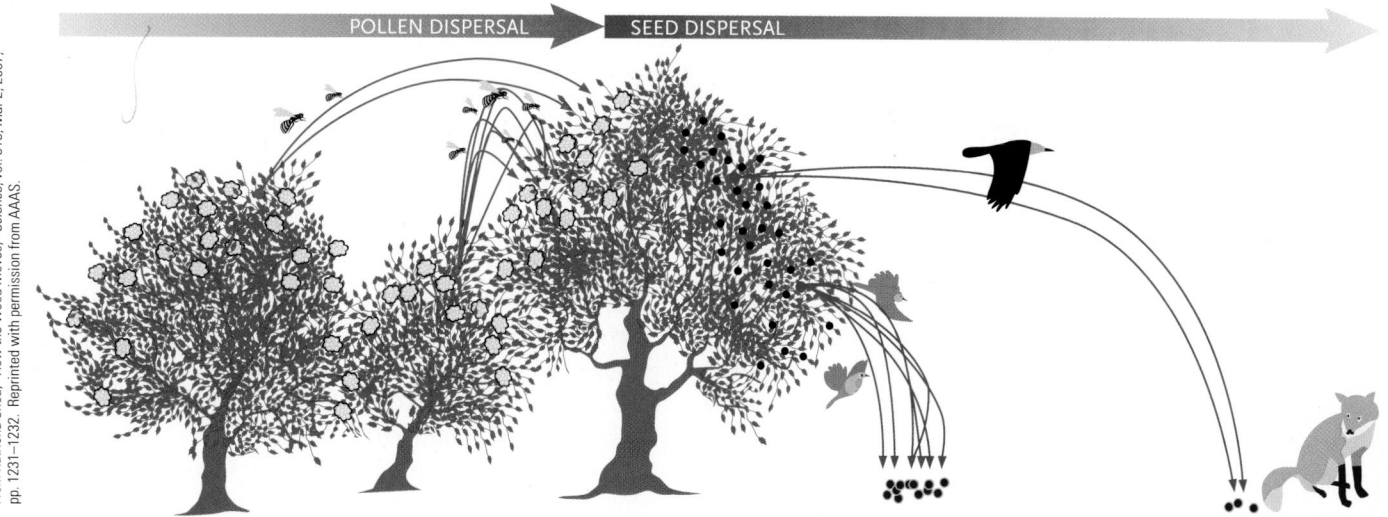

**FIGURE 28.22** Dispersal of pollen and seeds is an important agent in gene flow. This is illustrated by mahaleb cherries (*Prunus mahaleb*), whose seeds are dispersed by birds and mammals. Small songbirds disperse seeds short distances, to about 50 m. Medium-sized birds such as crows (*Corvus corone*) and ravens (*Turdus viscivorus*) move seeds more than 110 m. Mammals, mainly stone martins (*Martes foina*) and red foxes (*Vulpes fulva*), disperse seeds to about 100 m. Plants capable of vegetative (asexual) reproduction are more effective colonists than those that rely on animals for pollination and fruit dispersal.

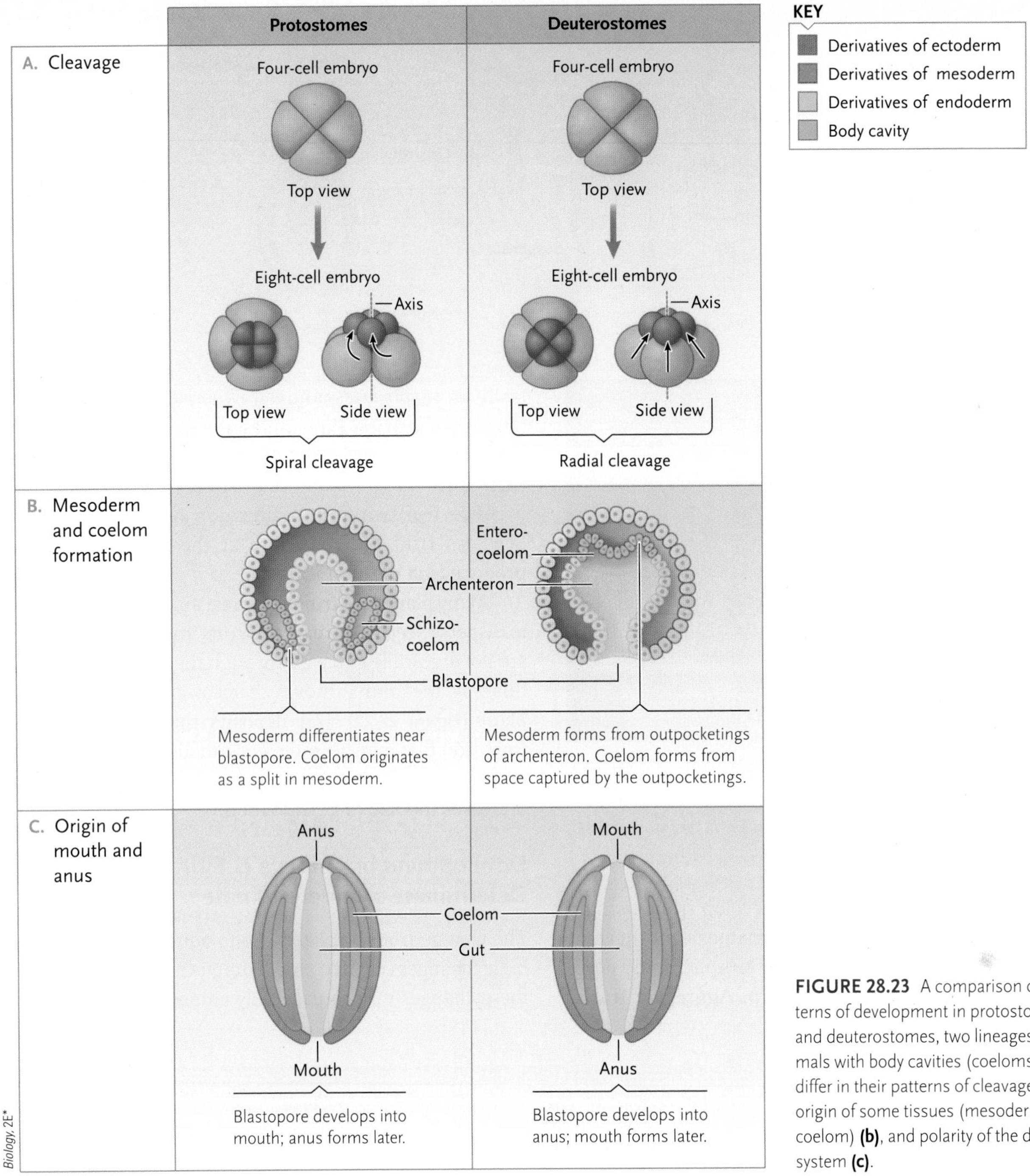

|  | **Protostomes** | **Deuterostomes** |
|---|---|---|
| A. Cleavage | Four-cell embryo<br>Top view<br><br>Eight-cell embryo<br>Top view  Side view<br>Spiral cleavage | Four-cell embryo<br>Top view<br><br>Eight-cell embryo<br>Axis<br>Top view  Side view<br>Radial cleavage |
| B. Mesoderm and coelom formation | Archenteron<br>Schizo-coelom<br>Blastopore<br>Mesoderm differentiates near blastopore. Coelom originates as a split in mesoderm. | Entero-coelom<br>Blastopore<br>Mesoderm forms from outpocketings of archenteron. Coelom forms from space captured by the outpocketings. |
| C. Origin of mouth and anus | Anus<br>Coelom<br>Gut<br>Mouth<br>Blastopore develops into mouth; anus forms later. | Mouth<br>Coelom<br>Gut<br>Anus<br>Blastopore develops into anus; mouth forms later. |

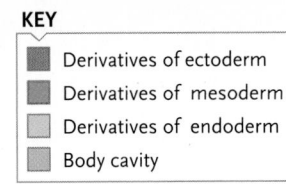

**KEY**
- Derivatives of ectoderm
- Derivatives of mesoderm
- Derivatives of endoderm
- Body cavity

**FIGURE 28.23** A comparison of patterns of development in protostomes and deuterostomes, two lineages of animals with body cavities (coeloms) that differ in their patterns of cleavage **(a)**, origin of some tissues (mesoderm and coelom) **(b)**, and polarity of the digestive system **(c)**.

Biology, 2E*

reflecting their complexity and size. At fertilization, the egg, not the sperm, contains the main cytoplasmic determinants that will be passed on to the offspring, as well as mRNA, proteins, and ribosomes. This means that many features of the developing embryo and then the adult are derived from the mother. The amount of yolk in the egg not only determines how long the embryo will develop within the egg; it also affects the patterns of development. The process of change from zygote to embryo involves both mitotic cell division (cleavage) and the formation of organs (**organogenesis**) **(Figure 28.24)**. Setting aside the influence of yolk, there are two main patterns of development in animals: determinate and indeterminate.

Determinate development typically occurs in **protostomes** (most metazoan animals; see Chapter 19, page 415). In protostome animals, the first opening to develop in the embryo becomes the mouth (from the Greek *protos,* meaning first, and *stoma,* meaning mouth). After the first cell division, the destiny of each subsequently produced cell already has been determined. If you were to remove a single cell, it could not develop into a new offspring. Cleavage proceeds in a spiral pattern.

Indeterminate development typically occurs in **deuterostomes** (Chordates, including humans, and echinoderms). In deuterostomes (from the Greek *deuteron,*

## Cleavage

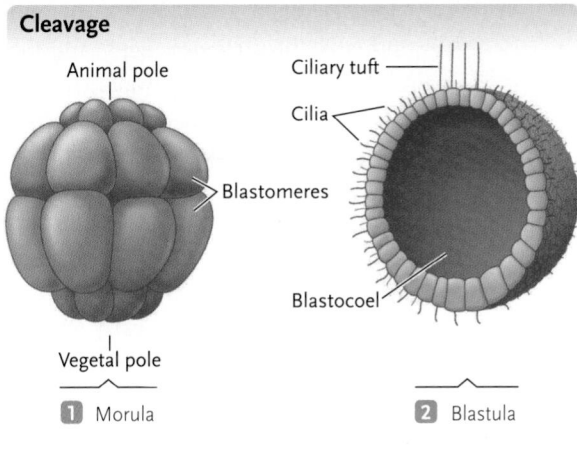

Animal pole

Blastomeres

Vegetal pole

**1** Morula

Ciliary tuft

Cilia

Blastocoel

**2** Blastula

## Gastrulation

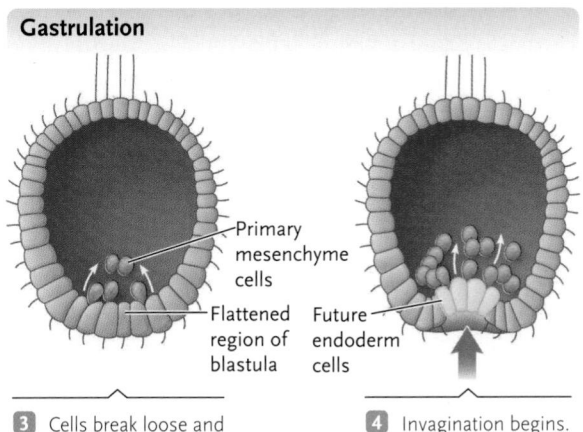

Primary mesenchyme cells

Flattened region of blastula

Future endoderm cells

**3** Cells break loose and migrate into blastocoel.

**4** Invagination begins.

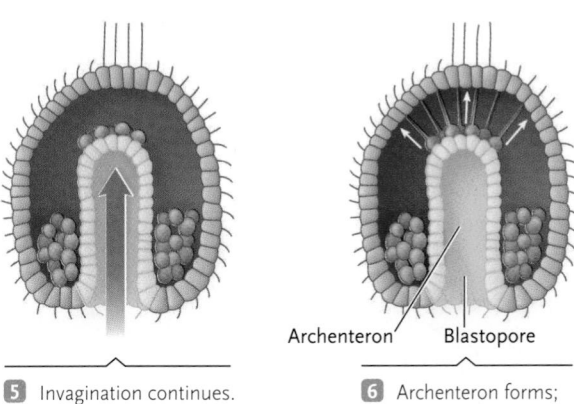

Archenteron    Blastopore

**5** Invagination continues.

**6** Archenteron forms; cells of invagination stretch across blastocoel and adhere to ectoderm.

**KEY**

- ☐ Ectoderm
- ☐ Mesoderm
- ☐ Endoderm

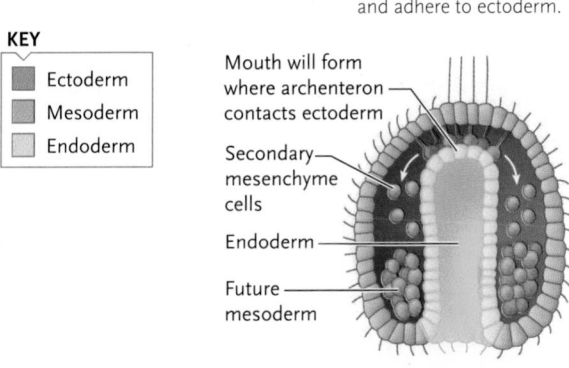

Mouth will form where archenteron contacts ectoderm

Secondary mesenchyme cells

Endoderm

Future mesoderm

**7** Ectoderm and endoderm layers have formed; mesoderm cells are between them.

**FIGURE 28.24** Cleavage and gastrulation in a sea urchin.

Biology, 2E*

meaning second, and *stoma*, meaning mouth), the first opening to develop in the embryo becomes the anus, and the second opening becomes the mouth. At the eight-cell stage in indeterminate development, each cell could be separated and still develop into a new offspring. The function of the cells in the body has not yet been determined. Cleavage proceeds in a radial pattern.

In the rest of this chapter, we will focus mainly on the details of indeterminate development, as it occurs in a selection of deuterostomes.

A sea urchin provides a general overview of the pattern of development following early cell division in deuterostomes that have little yolk. Cells produced by cleavage form a solid ball of cells called a **morula** that, after further cell divisions, forms a hollow ball of cells called a **blastula** (Figure 28.24). When modest amounts of yolk are present, such as in a frog, development occurs around the yolk. When large amounts of yolk are present, such as in birds, the developing embryo develops on top of the yolk. At **gastrulation**, we see the emergence of the three primary tissue layers: ectoderm, mesoderm, and endoderm **(Table 28.1)**. At least five processes are involved in the changes that occur after gastrulation:

1. mitosis
2. movement of cells
3. selective cell adhesions, which often involve the extracellular matrix (ECM)
4. **induction**, which occurs when one group of cells causes or influences another group of cells to follow a particular path of development, setting the stage for development fate
5. **differentiation**, which establishes cell-specific developmental programs (such as whether cells become muscle or nerves or bone, etc.)

| TABLE 28.1 | Origins of Adult Tissues and Organs in the Three Primary Tissue Layers |
|---|---|
| **Primary Tissue Layer** | **Adult Tissues and Organs** |
| Ectoderm | Skin and its derivatives (hair, feathers, scales, nails), nervous system (brain, nerves, lens, retina, cornea of the eye), lining of mouth and anus, seat glands, mammary glands, adrenal medulla, and tooth enamel |
| Mesoderm | Muscles, most of the skeletal systems (bones, cartilage), circulatory system (heart, blood vessels, and blood cells), internal reproductive organs (kidneys, and outer walls of digestive tract) |
| Endoderm | Lining of digestive tract, liver, pancreas, lining of respiratory tract, thyroid gland, lining of urethra and urinary bladder |

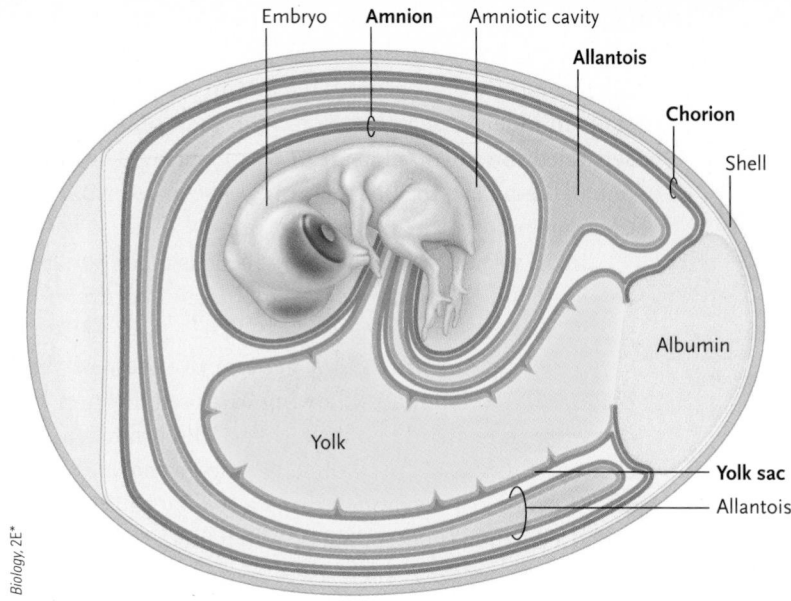

FIGURE 28.25 The four extraembryonic membranes in a bird's egg (shown in bold).

brates). These, the eggs of birds and many reptiles, are called **cleidoic eggs**, and they contain large amounts of water, making them more specialized than other amniote eggs. Embryos developing in cleidoic eggs are less dependent on external sources of water than those developing in other amniote eggs.

Mammals appear to have retained the naked amniotic egg of their early reptilian ancestors. Most mammals use internal fertilization and retain the zygote and developing embryo in the uterus. Among mammals, **monotremes** (spiny anteaters and duck-billed platypus) are the only ones that lay eggs. **Marsupials** give birth to young at early stages of development, whereas **placental mammals** bear well-developed young **(Figure 28.26)**.

The appearance of the **amniotic egg (Figure 28.25)** was pivotal in the evolutionary history of reptiles, birds, and mammals because it did not have to be laid in water. Remember that although most mammals give birth to live young, monotremes (duck-billed platypus and spiny anteaters) lay eggs, as did many early mammals. Animals that produced an amniotic egg could complete their life cycles without returning to the water. Many protostomes, particularly among arthropods, evolved comparable eggs that could be laid on land. This is another example of convergent evolution (see Chapter 13). Amniotic eggs with calcareous shells are rigid, and their shells protect them from organisms living in the soil (e.g., microbes and inverte-

## STUDY BREAK

1. What is gastrulation?
2. What do ectoderm, mesoderm, and endoderm give rise to?
3. What is a meristem?
4. What are the differences between determinate and indeterminate cleavage?

## 28.9 Organogenesis

The next major step in the development of an animal is the appearance of organs. We will see how different processes and cell types are involved in organogenesis.

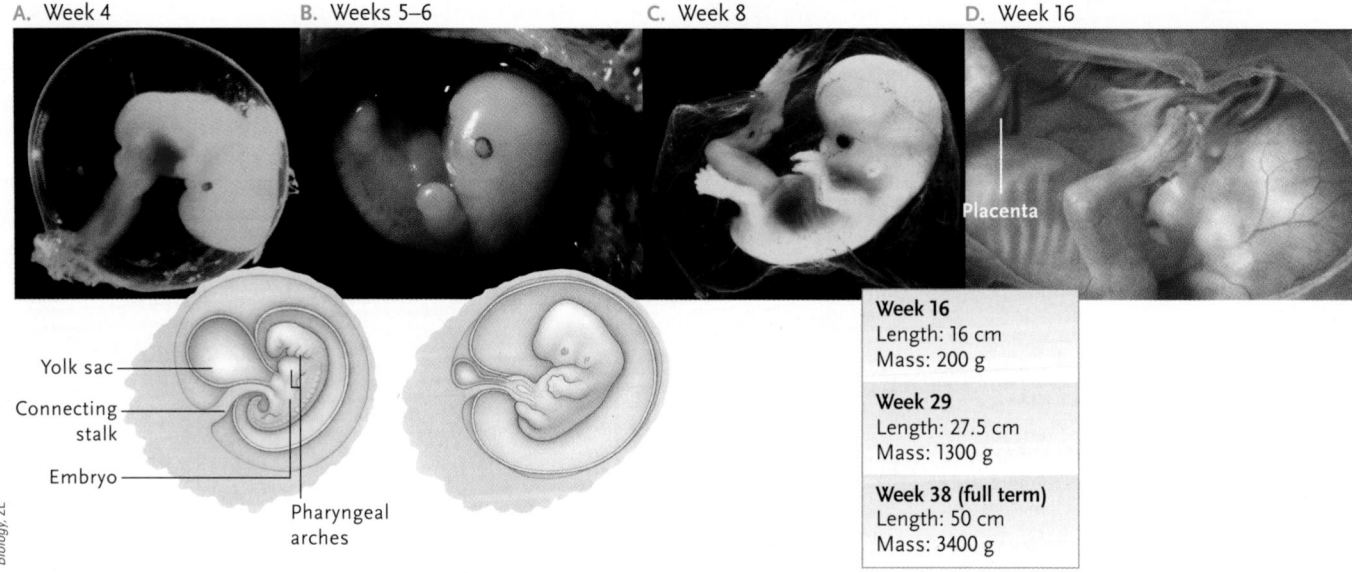

| Week 16 |
| --- |
| Length: 16 cm |
| Mass: 200 g |

| Week 29 |
| --- |
| Length: 27.5 cm |
| Mass: 1300 g |

| Week 38 (full term) |
| --- |
| Length: 50 cm |
| Mass: 3400 g |

FIGURE 28.26 Human embryo at various stages of development beginning from week 4. By moving the chorion aside, we can see the embryo in the amnion at week 8 and week 16, when movements begin as nerves make functional connections with forming muscles.

SOURCE: (Photos A–D): Biophoto Associates/Science Source; Dopamine/Science Source; Biophoto Associates/Science Source. Colorization by: Mary Martin; Petit Format/Science Source

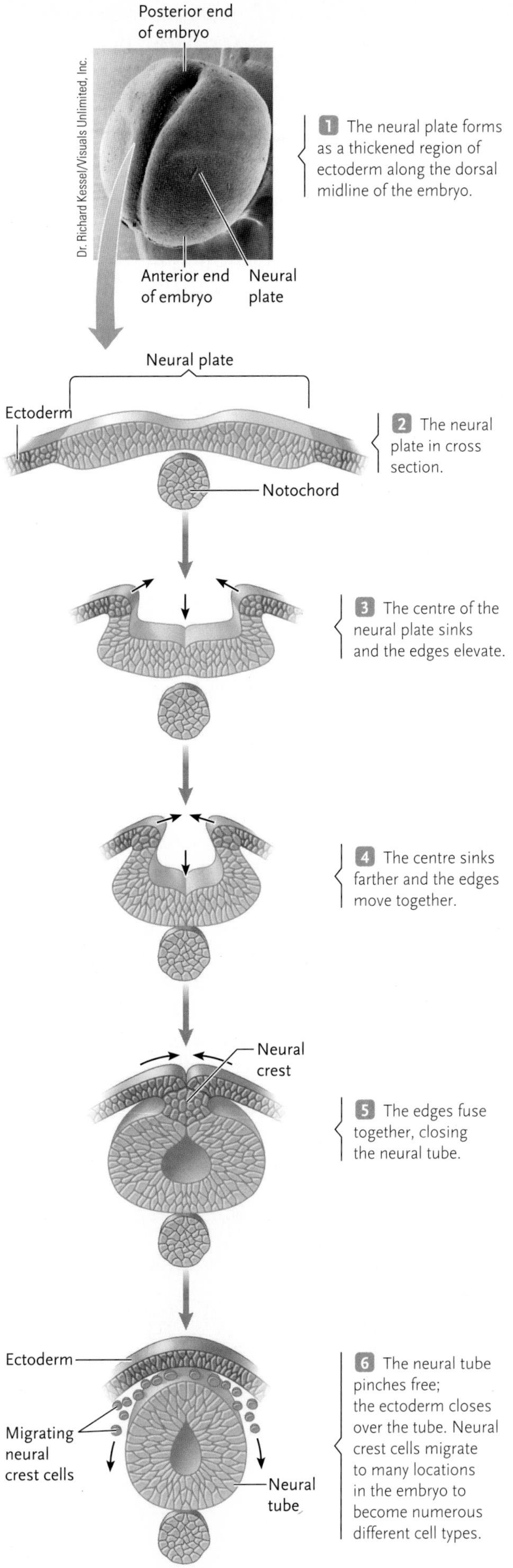

Posterior end of embryo

Anterior end of embryo — Neural plate

**1** The neural plate forms as a thickened region of ectoderm along the dorsal midline of the embryo.

Dr. Richard Kessel/Visuals Unlimited, Inc.

Neural plate

Ectoderm

**2** The neural plate in cross section.

Notochord

**3** The centre of the neural plate sinks and the edges elevate.

**4** The centre sinks farther and the edges move together.

Neural crest

**5** The edges fuse together, closing the neural tube.

Ectoderm

Migrating neural crest cells

Neural tube

**6** The neural tube pinches free; the ectoderm closes over the tube. Neural crest cells migrate to many locations in the embryo to become numerous different cell types.

Biology, 2E*

**FIGURE 28.27** Development of the neural tube and neural crest cells in vertebrates. The photo is of an amphibian embryo, but the drawings show the progression of steps in a bird embryo.

## The Cells of the Early Nervous System Divide, Migrate, and Specialize to Form Many Different Tissues

The development of the nervous system in vertebrates **(Figure 28.27)** involves cell division, cell movements, and interactions among cells. Before the nervous system begins to develop, the notochord forms from mesoderm. This rod of cells extends the length of the embryo near the dorsal surface (the surface of the back). Induction by cells of the notochord causes overlying ectoderm cells to thicken and form the **neural plate**. This flattened band of cube-shaped cells runs the length of the embryo above the notochord. The cells of the neural plate change shape, becoming wedgelike as the plate then sinks along its midline, forming two **neural crests** and a central groove. Changes in cell shape occur as microfilaments within the cells slide over each other, forming a groove that eventually becomes the **neural tube**, which will ultimately become the brain and spinal cord (Figure 28.27).

Two of the defining characteristics of chordate animals (see Chapter 19) are that they have a notochord and a dorsal hollow nerve cord. During formation of the neural tube, neural crest cells migrate to various places in the developing embryo, where they form cranial nerves and the bones of the inner ear and skull, as well as the cartilage of facial features and teeth. Coordinated work by microtubules and microfilaments helps move neural crest cells. Some cells migrate to the skin to form pigment cells, whereas others move elsewhere and give rise to the adrenal glands and the medulla of the kidney. During the development of the neural tube, mesoderm on either side of the tube forms **somites**— or identical, repeated body segments, such as those you might see in many invertebrates **(Figure 28.28, p. 646)**. These somites will give rise to the backbone and limb muscles. At the outer edges of the somites, mesoderm extends around the developing gut, where it splits into two layers: one covering the gut and the other the lining of the inner body wall (creating the coelom, or body cavity).

Movements of cells in the embryo typically occur across the surfaces of other cells as they follow molecules of the extracellular matrix (ECM). ECM tracts are usually molecules of proteins that are released by cells in another part of the embryo. In other migrations, cells follow concentration gradients of certain chemicals, moving either from an area of high concentration to one of low concentration or vice versa. Once again, receptors on the migrating cells are fundamental to the process of directed migrations of cells; they only bind to the correct chemicals so that the cell will migrate where it needs to go.

**Cell adhesion molecules** (CAMs) and **cadherins** (calcium-dependent adhesion molecules) allow cells to

28.9 ORGANOGENESIS

## A. Somites, derived from mesoderm

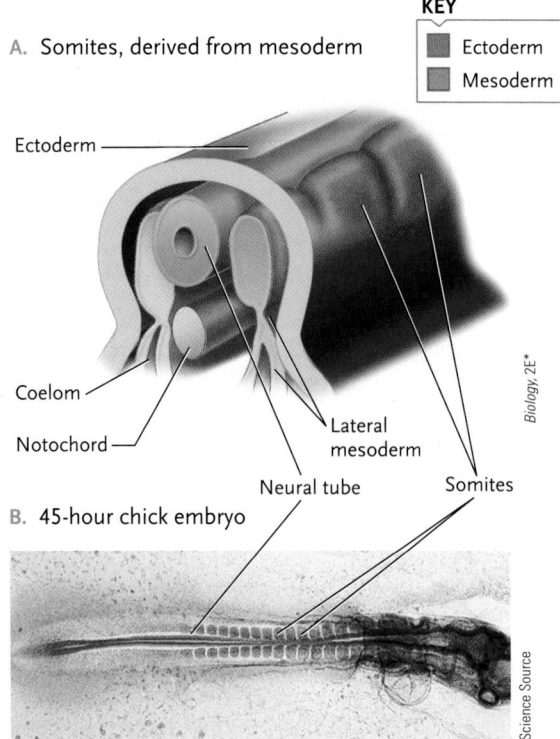

**KEY**
- Ectoderm
- Mesoderm

Ectoderm

Coelom

Notochord

Lateral mesoderm

Neural tube

Somites

*Biology, 2E\**

**B. 45-hour chick embryo**

Neural tube

Somites

*Science Source*

**FIGURE 28.28** Development of somites from mesoderm **(a)** setting the stage for the development of the coelom. Somites form ribs and muscles between them, whereas lateral mesoderm gives rise to the heart and blood vessels. **(b)** The somites are clear in a 45-hour chick embryo.

stick together, or adhere. Cadherins require calcium ions to get cells to stick to one another. The process of adhesion involves different types of CAMs and cadherins that come and go. For example, while the neural plate forms, ectoderm cells are held together by two kinds of cadherins (E- and N-cadherins). Cells that will become the neural tube lose cadherins, and N-CAMs appear on their surfaces. When this happens, cells of the neural tube break away from ectoderm and adhere to one another to form the neural tube.

## Genetically Controlled Cell Death Influences Development of Organs and Structures

During development, it is as important to control when cells die as it is to control how and when cells divide or move. Structures that appear at one stage of development may no longer be needed as development progresses. For example, the wings of bats are "webbed" folds of skin supported by elongated arm, hand, and finger bones. This makes them quite different from the hind feet of bats, which have isolated toes. During development, certain proteins trigger a process of programmed cell death called apoptosis. Both forelimbs and hindlimbs of bats first develop with the skin webs. Apoptosis removes the membranes from between the bats' toes but not their fingers **(Figure 28.29)**. In mice and in humans, selective apoptosis occurs in the same way as in the hindlimbs of bats. If you have ever seen pictures of a human embryo when the limbs first form (between about 6 and 8 weeks), you may have noticed that they also have webbed fingers and toes. These webs are removed through programmed cell death. In these and other situations, apoptosis occurs when genes are activated by molecular signals on the surfaces of marked cells. These signals are effectively "death notices" for the cells that are no longer needed.

## Development in Fruit Flies (*Drosophila*), a Model Organism

Early development in fruit flies such as *Drosophila melanogaster* illustrate another example of how development first proceeds. In fruit flies, fertilization is followed by mitotic divisions of the nucleus that produce a multinucleate (many nucleus) blastoderm **(Figure 28.30)**. The cytoplasm does not divide with the nuclei. Nuclei migrate to the outside of the embryo at the tenth nuclear division. After three more divisions, this

**Forelimbs**                     **Hindlimbs**

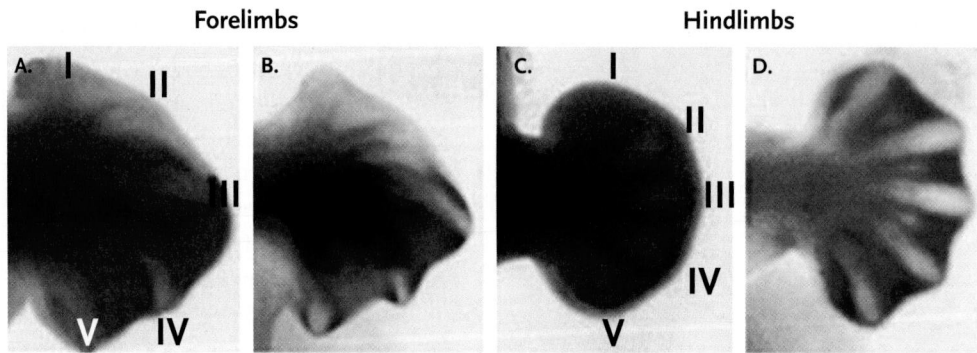

**FIGURE 28.29** Apoptosis triggered by specific proteins removes the webbing from between bats' toes. Inhibition of these proteins prevents apoptosis of the membranes that form bats' wings. Roman numerals indicate digit numbers for forelimbs and hindlimbs, where I on the hand is the thumb and the big toe on the hind foot. Panels **(a)** to **(d)** show different times in the process of development.

SOURCE: "Interdigital webbing retention in bat wings illustrates genetic changes underlying amniote limb diversification," by Weatherbee, Behringer, Rasweiler, and Niswander. *PNAS* October 10, 2006 vol. 103 no. 41, 15103–15107. Copyright 2006 National Academy of Sciences, U.S.A.

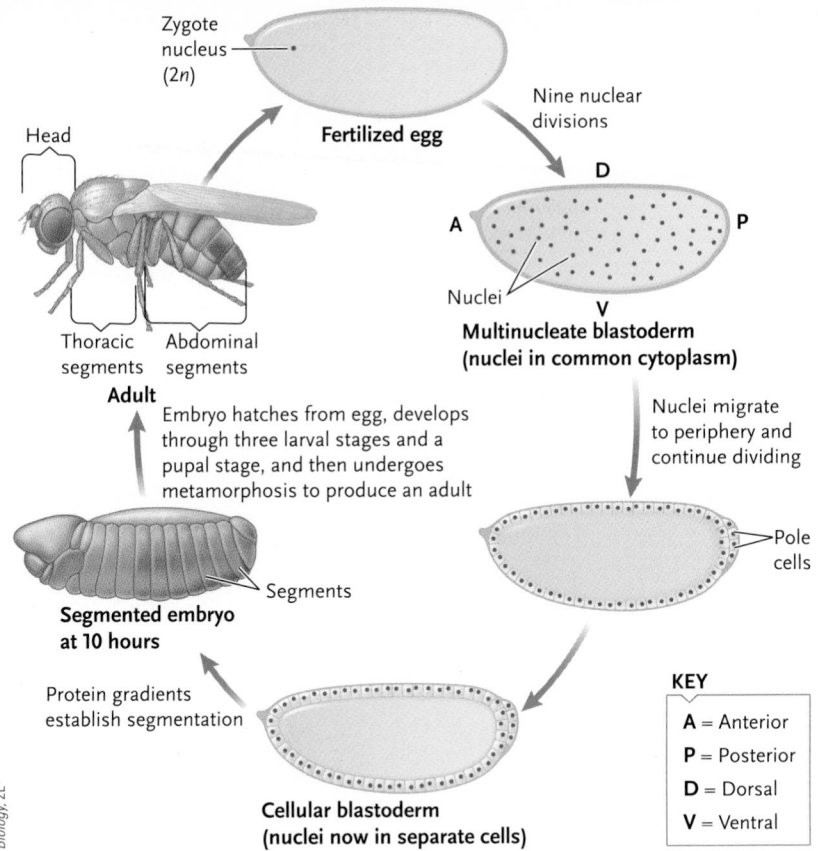

**FIGURE 28.30** Embryogenesis in *Drosophila* shows the relationship among segments of the embryo and segments of the adult.

Labels in figure:

Zygote nucleus (2n)

Fertilized egg

Nine nuclear divisions

D
A — P
V

Nuclei

Multinucleate blastoderm (nuclei in common cytoplasm)

Nuclei migrate to periphery and continue dividing

Pole cells

Head

Thoracic segments    Abdominal segments

**Adult**

Embryo hatches from egg, develops through three larval stages and a pupal stage, and then undergoes metamorphosis to produce an adult

Segments

**Segmented embryo at 10 hours**

Protein gradients establish segmentation

Cellular blastoderm (nuclei now in separate cells)

**KEY**
A = Anterior
P = Posterior
D = Dorsal
V = Ventral

*Biology, 2E*

leads to a cellular blastoderm with what looks like separate cells, each with a nucleus. This is the equivalent of the late blastula stage in deuterostome development.

Different genes work together to regulate the expression of other genes. After the early stages of development, the fruit fly's body segments begin to form. Maternal-effect and segmentation genes work in sequence to regulate expression of other genes. While eggs are forming (oogenesis), many genes that are transferred only through the egg (**maternal-effect genes**) control the polarity of the egg and thus the embryo **(Figure 28.31, p. 648)**; they tell the embryo which end is the head and which is the tail. In the embryo, some maternal-effect genes control formation of anterior structures, whereas others control formation of posterior structures. Still others control the structures at the terminal end. Note the development of somites (segments), reminiscent of the situation in vertebrates and reflecting the same general pattern of genetic control.

Successive division of the developing embryo into segments is in response to the action of at least 24 **segmentation genes**. Gradients of proteins encoded by other maternal-effect genes control the development of different segments. A cascade that activates one type of segmentation gene, the **gap genes**, one after another, establishes the boundaries between segments and the positions of segments along an anterior-posterior axis. Gap genes are so named because if they are experimentally turned off, not all of the body

segments develop, leaving a "gap." There are other kinds of segmentation genes that control how the segments develop. **Pair-rule genes** divide the embryo into pairs of segments. **Segment polarity genes** determine which side of each segment is anterior and which is posterior.

**Homeotic genes (Figure 28.32, p. 648)** are structure-determining genes that are activated once the pattern of segmentation has been established. Homeotic genes determine what each segment will become in the adult fly. These master regulatory genes control the development of structures such as wings and legs. There are eight of these homeotic genes, or *Hox* genes, in *Drosophila* arranged along the chromosome in the same order as they are expressed along the anterior–posterior axis of the adult fly. *Hox* genes are widespread in animals and also occur in plants, where they regulate the development of flowers.

Many different kinds of genes control development. Scientists can prepare *Drosophila* embryos in which there are known mutations in some genes. By looking to see what happens during development, they have revealed key features of development in fruit flies and many other organisms **(Figure 28.33, p. 648)**. This makes *Drosophila* an excellent model system for studying development and many other biological processes (see the Purple Pages for an overview of model systems).

## Epigenetics Is the Interaction between Genes and Their Environment

By definition, identical (monozygotic) twins are derived from one fertilized egg and have the same DNA. Yet often one twin is more susceptible to some diseases than the other, apparently reflecting epigenetic factors. Epigenetic factors also explain why your fingernails differ from the hair on your head when both are made of keratin. In this case, non-genetic cellular memory reflects developmental and environmental conditions. The explanation hinges on the fact that the differences between hair and fingernails reflect the way genes are expressed rather than DNA structure. Epigenetic changes (*epi* = above) reflect modifications to histones, the proteins around which DNA wraps (see Chapter 9 for an overview of DNA structure). **Methylation** more tightly packs DNA around histones, making the genes less accessible and less likely to be transcribed. **Acetylation** loosens DNA packing around histones, making genes more accessible and more likely to be transcribed (see Chapter 10 for an overview of gene expression). In mammals, for

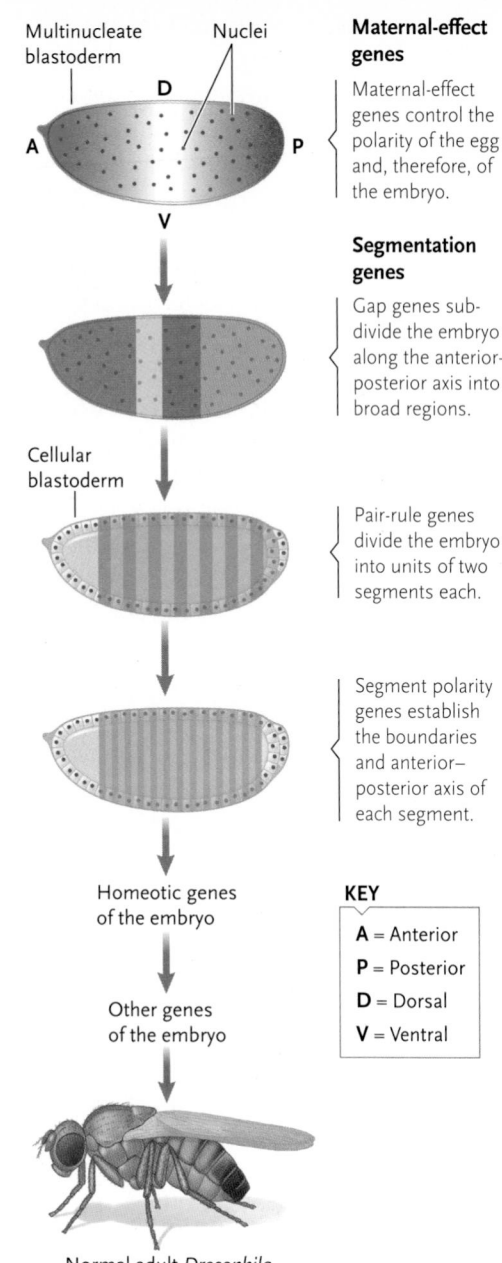

Multinucleate blastoderm

Nuclei

**Maternal-effect genes**

Maternal-effect genes control the polarity of the egg and, therefore, of the embryo.

**Segmentation genes**

Gap genes sub-divide the embryo along the anterior–posterior axis into broad regions.

Cellular blastoderm

Pair-rule genes divide the embryo into units of two segments each.

Segment polarity genes establish the boundaries and anterior–posterior axis of each segment.

Homeotic genes of the embryo

Other genes of the embryo

Normal adult *Drosophila*

**KEY**

**A** = Anterior
**P** = Posterior
**D** = Dorsal
**V** = Ventral

**FIGURE 28.31** Maternal-effect genes and segmentation genes and their role in the embryogenesis of *Drosophila*.

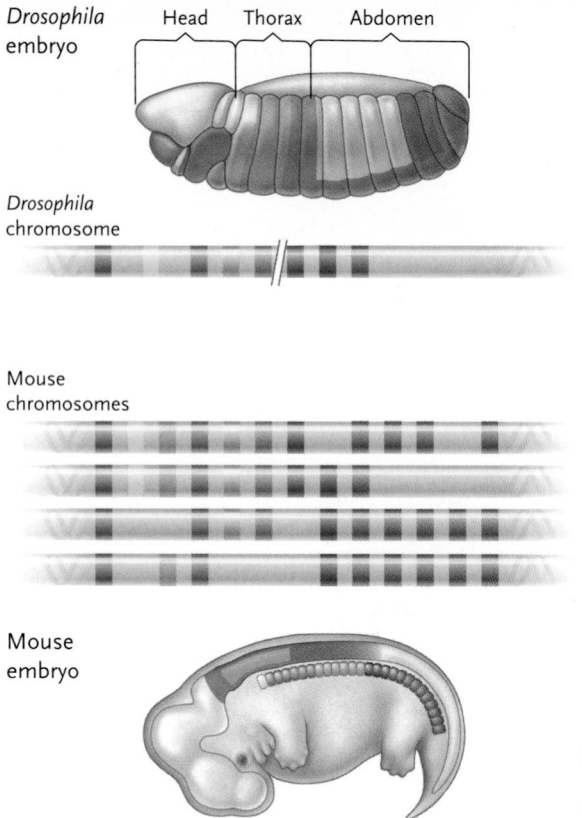

**FIGURE 28.32** *Hox* genes of a fruit fly (*Drosophila*) and a mouse showing the corresponding regions of the embryos that they affect. *Drosophila* have eight *Hox* genes, and mice have four.

example, epigenetic changes are responsible for different patterns of activation of the X chromosome, specifically the activation of one of two X chromosomes in a genetic female.

Epigenetic effects are obvious in honeybees, where there is only one reproductive female: the queen. All of the other females are workers. Remember that bees have a haplodiploid genetic system in which females are diploid (2*n* chromosomes) and the males are haploid (*n* chromosomes). Any female larva has the potential to develop into either a queen or a worker. The post-mitotic changes that

**FIGURE 28.33** Examples of mutations in the different types of segmentation genes of *Drosophila*. Orange highlights indicate wild-type segments that are mutated. **(a)** Gap gene mutants lack one or more segments. **(b)** Pair-rule gene mutants are missing every other segment. **(c)** Segment polarity genes have segments with one part missing and the other part duplicated as a mirror image.

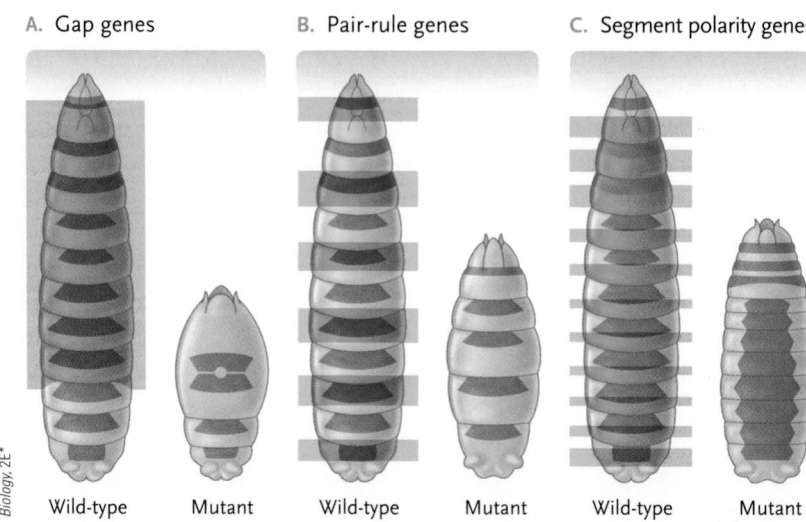

**A. Gap genes**    **B. Pair-rule genes**    **C. Segment polarity genes**

Wild-type    Mutant    Wild-type    Mutant    Wild-type    Mutant

lead to the production of queens, rather than workers, are due to the amount of royal jelly the larva consumes. Royal jelly is relatively homogeneous and composed of water, protein, sugars, lipids, and mineral salts. It is produced by the brood food (hypopharyngeal) gland (hypopharyngeal) of nurse bees and fed immediately to larvae. Larger amounts of royal jelly are fed to larvae that will become queens. These differences in diet act together with patterns of DNA methylation. The brains of queen and worker bees show over 550 genes that have been affected by methylation.

## STUDY BREAK

1. What is apoptosis?
2. What role do *Hox* genes play in development?
3. What is involved in gastrulation?
4. What are homeotic genes?

## 28.10 Pregnancy and Birth

Although some animals in many different phyla lay eggs (**ovipary**), others bear live young (**ovovivipary**, **vivipary**). Bearing live young is not a defining characteristic of mammals. It is also not an exclusively mammalian trait. Other animals, from insects to fish, amphibians, and reptiles, give birth to live young. The terms *ovovivipary* and *vivipary* distinguish the relationship between mother and offspring that develop within her body. See Box 28.2.

Ovoviviparous animals retain developing eggs within the body, where the young may feed on available solutions, eggs, or other embyros. In ovoviviparous animals, the young are protected from the immune system of the mother because the embryos are not directly connected to her circulatory systems.

Viviparous animals develop a direct connection between the circulatory systems of embryo and mother, mediated by a placenta or placentalike structure. A placenta or its equivalent allows a direct connection between parent and embryo that allows efficient exchange of materials between mother and fetus. The placenta also protects the developing young from attack by the parent's immune system. In mammals, successful pregnancy requires sustained immunosuppressive maternal T cells that protect the developing fetus from its mother's immune system (see Chapter 27 for an overview of immune function). Without these cells, the mother's immune system would see the fetus as foreign and would attack.

Although it is usually the female that uses her body to house developing young, in some cases, for example, sea horses (**Figure 28.34**), pipefish, and dragonfish, it is the male. Females transfer fertilized eggs to the males' brood pouches. Male pregnancy in these fish is exceptional

**FIGURE 28.34** A male sea horse giving birth.

Dr. Paul Zahl / Science Source

among animals. It appears to result from sexual selection that happens after copulation and sexual conflict. Specifically, male pipefish selectively resorb some developing young, apparently when they perceive that they are carrying young from lower quality females. Male pregnancy is not restricted to vertebrates but occurs in other animals as well.

The site of development of the young within the parent's body can vary considerably. In the Pacific beetle cockroach (**Figure 28.35, p. 650**; *Diploptera punctata*), fertilization occurs in the reproductive tract of the female, where development takes place in a **brood sac** before the first instar (stage) larvae are born. In cartilaginous fishes, bony fishes, reptiles, and mammals that bear live young, fertilization and development also take place within the female's reproductive tract, usually in a specialized area—a uterus or equivalent. Some fish, the mouth breeders, lay eggs, but then either the female or male scoops them into its mouth, where development occurs until the young hatch. The so-called midwife toads and some insects transfer fertilized eggs to the male's back, where they develop. The fertilized eggs of one species of Australian

## THE MOLECULE BEHIND THE BIOLOGY 28.2
## Testosterone

The **androgen** hormone testosterone is best known as the male sex hormone, although it is produced by both males and females. Among other things, testosterone is responsible for the development of secondary sexual characteristics in males, including behaviour. In women, high levels of testosterone can cause irregular menstrual cycles and the development of secondary sexual characteristics (development of body hair and deepening of the voice) normally associated with males.

Women pregnant with a son are exposed to high levels of circulating testosterone compared to those carrying a daughter. Evidence from records dating to preindustrial Finland showed that women who had borne sons often had shorter lifespans than those who had had daughters. The immunosuppressant impact of testosterone appears to have been responsible for the difference in survival.

According to the folklore of some African peoples, spotted hyenas

(*Crocuta crocuta*) **(Figure 1)** are hermaphroditic because both males and females appear to have male genitalia **(Figure 2)**. In these animals, the clitoris looks like a penis (peniform), and a fat deposit behind it resembles a scrotum. In mammals, female genitalia are the neutral condition. Male genitalia develop from the basic female parts in the presence of a Y chromosome. Females that develop in the presence of circulating testosterone develop masculinized genitalia. This appears to explain the

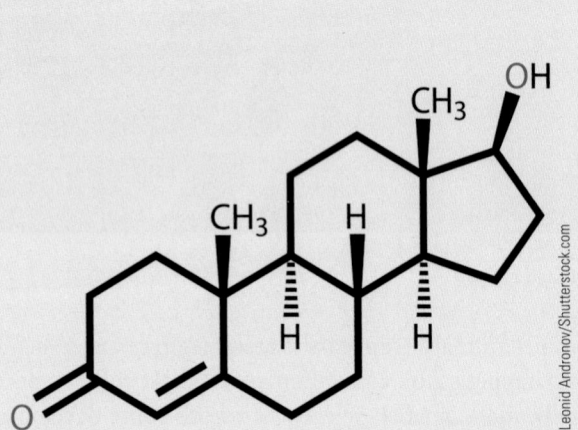

**FIGURE 1** A molecule of testosterone.

**FIGURE 2** A spotted hyena: male or female? How to tell?

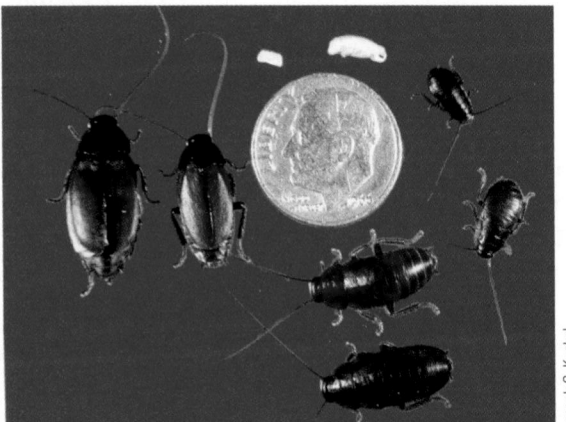

**FIGURE 28.35** Different stages in the life cycle of a Pacific beetle cockroach. This cockroach gives birth to live young. The American dime provides a scale.

frog, *Rheobatrachus silus*, now apparently extinct, developed in the stomach.

Mother mammals feed their young milk, an essentially mammalian food. Milk fosters rapid growth and development of the young while providing antibodies, especially during the first part of lactation. This early milk, known as colostrum, differs from milk produced later in lactation. Other animals also feed their young the equivalent of milk, from the Pacific beetle cockroach to the skin secretions of fish and some types of snakelike amphibians (caecilians). Crop milk is also produced by some birds, including pigeons, which secrete it for about 19 days after the young hatch. Providing high-quality food, although expensive for the mother, is an investment in the future success of the young (and the mother's genes). Among animals that bear live young, female

appearance of the apparently male genitalia of obviously female spotted hyenas, such as female nursing young.

Hyenas belong to the mammalian order Carnivora, and some other members of this group also have females with masculinized genitalia. The fossa (*Cryptoprocta ferox*) of Madagascar is another example **(Figure 3)**. One explanation is that appearing to be male protects females from harassment by both males and other females. In both fossas and spotted hyenas, the way their genitals look influences and reflects their social lives.

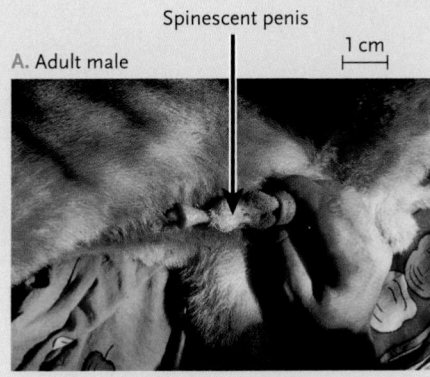

A. Adult male

Spinescent penis

1 cm

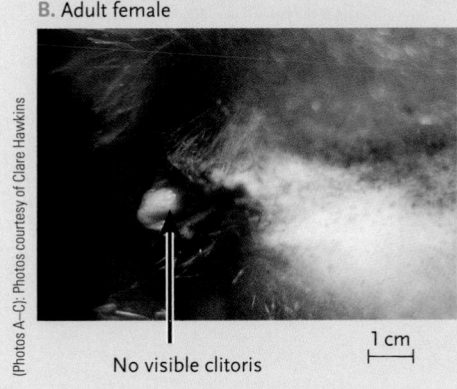

B. Adult female

No visible clitoris

1 cm

(Photos A–C): Photos courtesy of Clare Hawkins

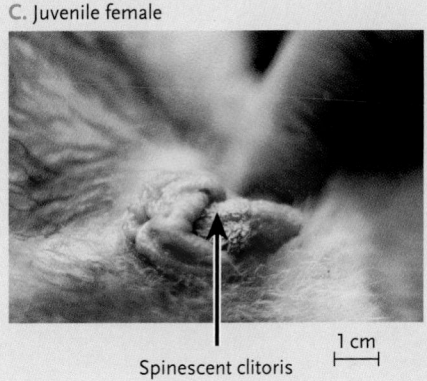

C. Juvenile female

Spinescent clitoris

1 cm

**FIGURE 3** In their external genitalia, subadult female fossas have peniform clitorises that make them appear to be males.

tsetse flies (*Glossina* spp.) are champions. Females ovulate, releasing a single egg, which is fertilized and housed in the equivalent of a mammalian uterus. She then gives birth to a single larva that weighs more than she does.

Newly hatched or newborn young are typically small (the tsetse fly notwithstanding) and relatively defenceless. By providing more food in the egg or longer periods of in-parent development, larger young can be hatched or born, perhaps shortening their period of vulnerability to predators. But large eggs and large newborns can pose a mechanical challenge to the mother. Among mammals, bats are notorious for producing very large young—typically about 30% of the mother's weight. In the case of Brazilian free-tailed bats, the mother's birth canal must expand from 2 mm diameter to 35 mm diameter to allow birth to take place **(Figure 28.36, p. 652)**. Unlike humans and many other mammals, the pubic bones of female bats do not join, and the hormone relaxin stimulates relaxation of the interpubic ligaments during the birth process. Marsupial mammals give birth when the fetus is still at an early stage of development. Then the young moves to the pouch, attaches itself to a nipple, and continues development there. This is one way of solving the birthing problems associated with large fetuses.

In most mammals, young are born head first. There are two exceptions where young are born bottom first (a breech presentation): bats and cetaceans (whales and dolphins). In the case of bats, a breech presentation appears to minimize the chances of the young becoming tangled in the birth canal, probably by the

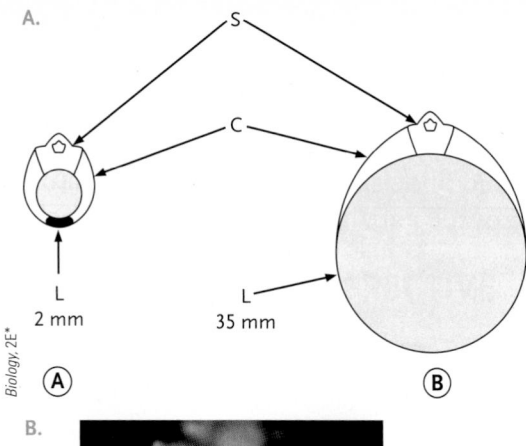

A.

S

C

L
2 mm

L
35 mm

Ⓐ

Ⓑ

Biology, 2E*

**FIGURE 28.36** **(a)** A diagrammatic view of the bony birth canal of a non-pregnant Brazilian free-tailed bat (A) and the bony canal at the time of birth (B). The sacrum (S), coxal bone (C), and interpubic ligament (L) are shown. **(b)** The photograph shows the pelvis in ventral view. **(c)** The inset photograph is a portrait of a Brazilian free-tailed bat.

B.

C.

M.B. Fenton

M.B. Fenton

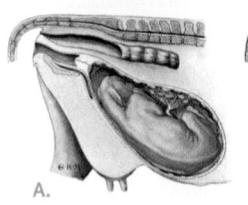 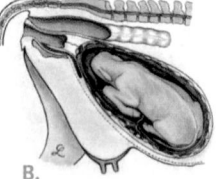 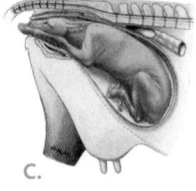

A.   B.   C.

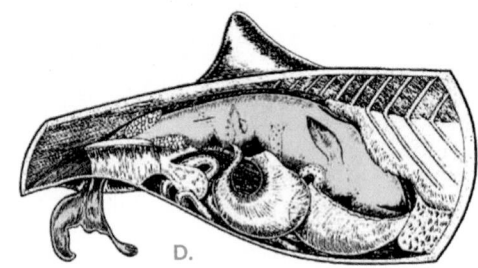

D.

**FIGURE 28.37** A comparison of head versus tail presentation of near- and full-term calves in a domestic cow **(a, b, c)** and a harbour porpoise **(d)**.

SOURCE: Gingerich PD, ul-Haq M, von Koenigswald W, Sanders WJ, Smith BH, et al. (2009) New Protocetid Whale from the Middle Eocene of Pakistan: Birth on Land, Precocial Development, and Sexual Dimorphism. *PLoS ONE* 4(2): e4366. doi:10.1371/journal.pone.0004366. © 2009 Gingerich et al.

long forelimbs that support the wings. In cetaceans, birth occurs in water, where a breech presentation keeps the fetus connected to the mother (and an oxygen supply in her blood) until it clears the birth canal. Young cattle (even-toed ungulates), the closest living relatives of cetaceans, are born head first, giving them access to air from the time the calf's head emerges from the vagina **(Figure 28.37)**.

## STUDY BREAK

1. Compare ovipary, ovovivipary, and vivipary.
2. Why are some mammals born tail first?

## PUTTING IT IN PERSPECTIVE

One important element in the story of reproduction and development is individual fitness, getting one's genes into the next generation. There are several vital components to the story. First is the role of meiosis and the number of chromosomes in different life stages (diploid versus haploid). Fungi are quite different in their life cycles from plants or animals. The advantages of sexual reproduction appear to relate mainly to recombination and shuffling of the genome to maintain genetic diversity. Yet in almost every group of organisms, there is evidence of asexual reproduc-

tion. Sexual reproduction is costly, and there are clearly times when asexual reproduction is a better strategy. Not surprisingly, asexual reproduction is a recurring pattern among organisms. The challenge of getting genes into the next generation involves more than just fertilization, and there is a rich diversity of patterns of parenting that appear to maximize efficiency. Many processes are involved in the transformation from zygote to adult organism, providing examples of processes operating at the genome, cell, and whole organism levels.

# KEY CONCEPTS REVIEW AND QUESTIONS

## 28.1 Reproduction

Living organisms possess a drive to reproduce. Their patterns of reproduction are defined by both haploid and diploid phases of their life cycle. Different species have different proportions of haploid and diploid phases in their life cycles.

1. Why is meiosis crucial to sexual reproduction? How does this relate to haploid and diploid conditions?

## 28.2 Alternation of Generations in Plants (Sporophytes and Gametophytes)

Plant life cycles have a gametophyte and a sporophyte generation. The sporophyte generation dominates most living vascular plants. The dominant generation can be different in other types of plants. The development of seeds was a major evolutionary innovation that greatly reduced gametophyte generations.

2. What are gametophytes and sporophytes? Where do they occur?

## 28.3 Gamete Transfer

Gametes are haploid cells that join during fertilization. They are either sperm or eggs. Fertilization can be internal or external.

3. How are gametes transferred?
4. How do plants and animals differ in this gamete transfer?

## 28.4 Pollen and Plant Reproduction

Gymnosperms and angiosperms have pollen and undergo pollination, a central feature of reproduction that enables outbreeding. However, pollination is not the same as fertilization. Pollen is not the sperm but does contain it. Ovules contain the eggs. Reproductive structures differ between angiosperms and gymnosperms. Pollen can be transferred by various methods, such as wind and animals.

5. What are pollination syndromes?
6. How is ornithophily different from chiropterophily?

## 28.5 Fungal Reproduction

Fungi in the same species can reproduce sexually and asexually. Asexual reproduction can occur through budding or fission. The most common type of asexual reproduction in multicellular fungi is through spores, which are produced through mitosis. Sexual reproduction in fungi displays many variations in the process. There are five phases in the sexual life cycle of fungi.

7. What are the fruiting bodies of fungi? What is plasmogamy?

## 28.6 Animal Reproduction

Most animals reproduce sexually using sperm and eggs. Animals have specific sites for production of gametes. Some species have specific male and female genders, whereas others are hermaphroditic. Many strategies are used to maximize the chances of sperm coming into contact with eggs. Fertilization can be internal or external depending on the species. Most organisms have an optimal time for reproduction, with ovulation timing being critical to fertilization. Behaviour is important to achieve successful mating in many animal species. Homosexual mating among animals is also common in nature.

8. How does internal fertilization differ from external fertilization? Name two animals using external fertilization and two using internal fertilization.
9. What is the Bruce effect?

## 28.7 Asexual Reproduction

Many species of fungi, plants, and animals reproduce asexually. Many plants can reproduce through vegetative reproduction. Asexual reproduction in animals is most common in smaller organisms with less differentiated tissues and organ systems. Some animals can reproduce asexually via parthenogenesis.

10. How is gender determined?

## 28.8 Development

The transition from zygote to adult involves substantial changes. In vascular plants, the first changes after fertilization result in the formation of the seed, and then the seed germinates and the seedling grows. Ground tissues, vascular tissues, and dermal tissues appear early in development. Seeds are usually encased in fruits. Fruits of many plants attract animals so that seeds can be dispersed. In animals, the changes from fertilized egg to adult may involve considerable variation among species, but there are two main patterns of development: determinate and indeterminate. The appearance of the amniotic egg allowed certain animals to complete their life cycles without returning to the water. Most mammals retain the developing embryo in the uterus to differing degrees.

11. Compare development from the zygote in plants and animals.
12. How does determinate cleavage differ from indeterminate cleavage?

## 28.9 Organogenesis

The appearance of organs was the next major developmental step in animals. The nervous system in vertebrates is produced by cell division, cell migration, and interactions among cells. Further cell specialization results in the development of many different tissues and organs. Cell migrations follow extracellular matrix tracts or concentration gradients of certain chemicals. Cells also adhere to each other with the aid of cell adhesion molecules and cadherins. Programmed cell death occurs when certain cells are no longer needed in the development. Many genes control development. There can also be interaction between genes and their environment that affect how genes are expressed.

13. What are somites? Where do they occur?
14. What is organogenesis, and what role(s) does genetics play in this process?
15. What is epigenetics?

# Population Ecology

M.B. Fenton

## CHAPTER OUTLINE



## WHY IT MATTERS

Population biologists need to measure a number of characteristics of populations. These include how long organisms live, how often they reproduce, how many young they have, at what age they first reproduce, and what kills them. Obtaining these measurements requires being able to recognize individuals. Finding and photographing a snapping turtle **(Figure 29.1)**, in itself, does not provide most of the required data.

The tag A-7 on a female snapping turtle **(Figure 29.2)**, combined with other data about this individual and snapping turtles in general, allowed population biologists to determine that A-7 was more than 120 years old in June 2013 when she was photographed at a nest site about to lay her eggs. Imagine any animal becoming a mother again at over 120 years of age. Most organisms do not have this capacity. Many species, such as deer mice, live for a short time and produce many offspring. Others, such as elephants, produce very few offspring over a long lifespan, sometimes putting a great deal of effort into caring for those young. Although snapping turtles lay many eggs over a long period of time, they provide little else in the way of parental care so that most hatchlings do not live to reproduce. Such details of the lives of organisms (their life histories) provide insight into how populations change over time and how readily they can respond to changes in their environments.

A-7 had been caught and tagged in 1972 when she was the same size (shell length 40 cm) as she was 40 years later. At hatching, her shell would have been 3 cm long. We know from reference data that the shells of snapping turtles grow about 0.95 mm a year, so A-7 probably reached sexual maturity in 1907. She would have laid her first eggs (sexual maturity) at age 14 years, when her shell was 24 cm long. She continued to grow after reaching sexual maturity, reaching her maximum body size by 1972.

Snapping turtles are the largest terrestrial or freshwater reptile in Canada. They are omnivorous, opportunistic predators that eat plants and animals. They appear to overwinter by resting on lake bottoms or streambeds. Snapping turtles spend most of their lives in the water and are inconspicuous except when they emerge to bask in the sun or to lay eggs.

Around Lake Sasajewun in Algonquin Park, Ontario, female snapping turtles usually lay about 40 eggs that hatch in 9 to 18 weeks (mid- to late September). They use the same sandy nest sites year after year. The turtles'

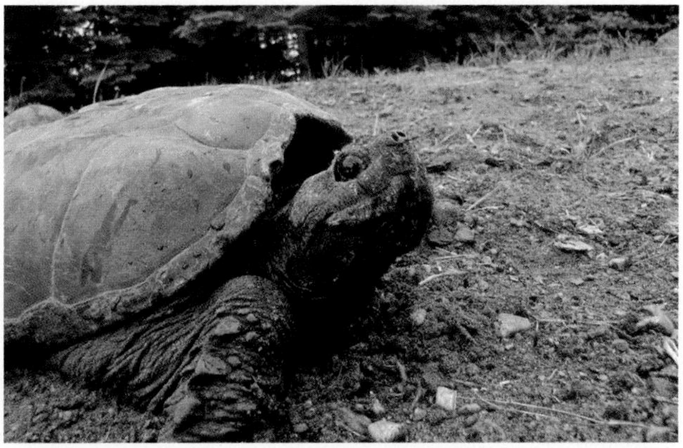

Matt Keevil

**FIGURE 29.1** A snapping turtle (*Chelydra serpentina*) such as this one is a widespread species in North America. Notorious for their bites, these turtles face an uncertain future. Biologists interested in populations of organisms need some way to collect information about individuals.

Matt Keevil

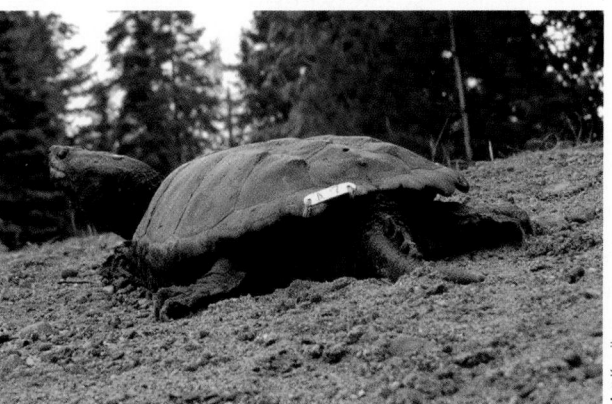

**FIGURE 29.2** A back view of a tagged female snapping turtle (A-7) shows the tag that allowed researchers to recognize her.

repeated use of nest sites provides biologists with an opportunity to tag and follow individuals, providing the kind of details obtained about A-7. Resightings of tagged snapping turtles suggested that individuals do not travel far from nest sites. We believe that adults have few predators other than humans, but many are killed each year when they try to cross roads to get to nesting sites. The work at Sasajewun has provided a different view of mortality of adult snapping turtles. In 1985, there were about 70 adult snapping turtles around Lake Sasajewun. In the winters of 1986–87 and 1987–88, river otters (*Lontra canadensis*) killed many hibernating snapping turtles. After this, the population around Lake Sasajewun dropped to about 30 adults, where it has remained since.

Annual monitoring of nesting sites showed no change in the fecundity of females (number of eggs per clutch). Why then did the populations of snapping turtles not recover after the otter event? At least 20 females each laid about 40 eggs each year, but the population there has not recovered. There can be a 14-year lag between a female hatching and her reaching maturity and coming to lay eggs. If that were the case, the numbers of nesting turtles should have increased by 2004. Just as nest sites that are repeatedly used by turtles are valuable to biologists, they are also a valuable food source for predators such as skunks (*Mephitis mephitis*) and raccoons (*Procyon lotor*). These predators find nest sites and then uncover and eat the eggs. Occasionally, other snapping turtles arrived in the area but typically left about a year later, for reasons that remain unknown.

The basic data about A-7 and other snapping turtles around Lake Sasajewun provide a picture of life history and identify a need for the species to be protected. The numbers (turtles, eggs, age at first reproduction, growth rates) can be used by population biologists to better appreciate the complexities of an organism's life history and population ecology.

In this chapter, we will examine what population biologists measure, how they take these measurements, and why the measures enhance our understanding of populations and our power to predict changes to populations. We will see how numerical data can be used to explain population biology. We will see how an understanding of life histories helps us understand how and why populations of species change. We will see the impact of reproductive options on the potential for populations to increase and how population size is controlled. We will finish by considering how the population biology of humans reflects the same basic principles and features as the population biology of other species.

## 29.1 Ecology

Ecology is the study of the relationships between organisms and their environment. Some ecologists work with theories and mathematical models, whereas others test theories and models in the field and in the laboratory. Different ecologists examine interactions at many levels, from single populations to the entire biosphere (everything on Earth). More and more today, ecology focuses on the impact of humans on the planet.

A central goal of ecologists is to understand the factors affecting variation in the distribution and abundance of species. These are usually some combination of abiotic and biotic factors. Abiotic factors are non-biological things that can affect organisms. They can include temperature and humidity, landscape, and nutrients. Biotic factors are the influences of other living organisms. They can include a range of interactions, from predator–prey interactions to competition, parasitism, and mutualism (see Chapter 13).

Ecologists may focus on interactions at different levels. Some examine the ecology of organisms and collect data about how individuals of a species adapt to their biotic and abiotic environments. Adaptations can be genetic, biochemical, physiological, morphological, or behavioural. Other ecologists work with **populations**, or the individuals of a species of interest that coexist in the same place at the same time. Population ecologists try to determine how these groups of individuals of one species change over time and in changing environments. Still other ecologists focus on communities or ecosystems. **Communities** are the collection of populations that coexist in the same place at the same time. An **ecosystem** consists of one or more communities interacting with their abiotic environment. Each is interconnected by the flow of energy and other materials between organisms and their environment. In coastal British Columbia, ecologists have demonstrated how nutrients in salmon move from river and stream systems into the forest, in part reflecting bears' fondness for salmon. As we saw in Chapter 2, the flow of energy between trophic levels and through food webs is an organizing factor in ecology.

Ecologists recognize that at each ecological level, there are new properties, or **emergent properties**, that arise from the interactions between elements at the lower levels. This concept applies right from the level of a single cell, through to the whole organism, and then through each of these increasingly complex ecological groupings. It is a key principle of biology that new properties emerge from interactions between cells, systems, whole organisms, and, ultimately, the abiotic world.

## STUDY BREAK

1. What is ecology?
2. What are emergent properties?
3. What are biotic and abiotic factors? Think of an example of each that would be relevant to the study of population ecology.

## 29.2 Population Ecology

**Population ecology** is about numbers. How many organisms are there in a population? How often do they reproduce? How many young do they have? How long do they live? How is the population changing over time? What are the consequences of this change? Human populations provide a distressingly good example of the consequences of unrestricted population growth that is approaching or has exceeded the number of people that our planet can sustain. Ecologists study populations using a combination of measurements, experiments, and models. Part of the challenge in understanding the history of any population of interest is knowing what is happening now and how that may influence the future of the population. An ongoing challenge is understanding the nature of interactions that underlie population biology.

## 29.3 What Do Population Ecologists Measure?

Population ecologists document and quantify the changes in the numbers of organisms that make up a population over time and in response to various biotic and abiotic factors. Population biologists use these data to build exponential or logistic models to study and illustrate changes in population size.

An **exponential growth model** describes population growth that is unlimited and that continues to increase indefinitely by a constant factor. For example, the population size might double with every generation. Presented graphically, exponential growth forms a J-shaped curve. Although we consider exponential population growth to be typical of bacteria and prokaryotes, under some circumstances, it can occur in populations of any species, including humans **(Figure 29.3b)**. But few, if any, populations can

**A.**

| Month | Old Population Size | | Net Monthly Increase | | New Population Size |
|---|---|---|---|---|---|
| 1 | 2000 | + | 800 | = | 2800 |
| 2 | 2800 | + | 1120 | = | 3920 |
| 3 | 3920 | + | 1568 | = | 5488 |
| 4 | 5488 | + | 2195 | = | 7683 |
| 5 | 7683 | + | 3073 | = | 10,756 |
| 6 | 10,756 | + | 4302 | = | 15,058 |
| 7 | 15,058 | + | 6023 | = | 21,081 |
| 8 | 21,081 | + | 8432 | = | 29,513 |
| 9 | 29,513 | + | 11,805 | = | 41,318 |
| 10 | 41,318 | + | 16,527 | = | 57,845 |
| 11 | 57,845 | + | 23,138 | = | 80,983 |
| 12 | 80,983 | + | 32,393 | = | 113,376 |
| 13 | 113,376 | + | 45,350 | = | 158,726 |
| 14 | 158,726 | + | 63,490 | = | 222,216 |
| 15 | 222,216 | + | 88,887 | = | 311,103 |
| 16 | 311,103 | + | 124,441 | = | 435,544 |
| 17 | 435,544 | + | 174,218 | = | 609,762 |
| 18 | 609,762 | + | 243,905 | = | 853,667 |
| 19 | 853,677 | + | 341,467 | = | 1,195,134 |

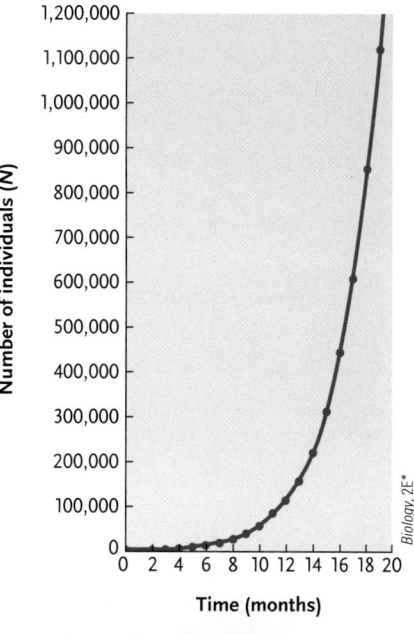

Biology, 2E*

**FIGURE 29.3** Examples of exponential population growth. In **(a)** and **(b)**, we see the typical "J"-shaped curve associated with exponential growth. In both cases, the data used to prepare the graphs are shown. Although the per capita growth rate (r) remains constant, the dramatic increase reflects the number of organisms reproducing. The data in (a) are generated by a model, whereas those in (b) depict the population of humans on Earth.

**B.**

| Estimated Human Population Size | |
|---|---|
| 8000 BCE | 5 million |
| By 1804 | 1 billion |
| By 1927 | 2 billion |
| By 1960 | 3 billion |
| By 1974 | 4 billion |
| By 1987 | 5 billion |
| By 1999 | 6 billion |
| By 2011 | 7 billion |
| Projected for 2050 | 9 billion |

Domestication of plants, animals 9000 BCE (about 11 000 years ago)

Agriculturally based urban societies

Beginning of industrial, scientific revolutions

NASA

Biology, 2E*

continue to grow exponentially forever. Eventually, the population reaches a limit, perhaps because there is not enough food or space to sustain continued growth. But some, like the human population, can experience long periods of exponential growth before they reach that limit.

One fundamental issue here is a population's capacity for increasing in size. This comes down to basic reproductive biology, including how many young are produced in what period and how many of them survive to reproduce. But the size of the initial population is fundamental to predicting its capacity for increase. If we start with 100 cats or oak trees, the total population in 20 years will differ from its size if the starting populations were 1000 individuals. In the equations that follow, rates of immigration and emigration are presumed to be equal.

A **logistic model** describes situations in which something limits exponential growth once a population reaches a certain size. Logistic growth occurs when a population increases in size exponentially for some amount of time until it hits a limit that we call the **carrying capacity**, or the maximum population size that the environment can sustain. At this point, population growth tails off. Presented graphically, logistic growth presents a more S-shaped curve (**Figures 29.4** and **29.5**).

Neither model provides a completely accurate prediction of population growth. This reflects the unpredictable nature of biological systems and the importance of emergent properties. Equation 29.1 shows the mathematical equation that population ecologists can use to calculate exponential growth. Equation 29.2 is the equation for logistic growth.

(Eq. 29.1)     $$\Delta N/\Delta t = r_{max}N$$

(Eq. 29.2)     $$\Delta N/\Delta t = r_{max}N(K-N)/K$$

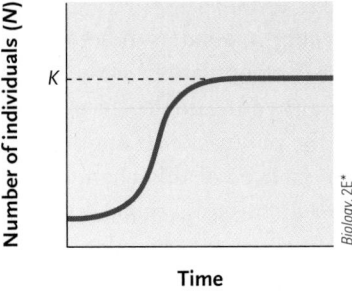

Population size through time

FIGURE 29.4 The logistic model predicts that the population size increases quickly and then slows as the population size approaches some limit to further population growth.

Population ecologists use mathematical models such as these to predict and describe population change over time. The information they need to make their calculations includes the population size ($N$), time ($t$) over which population change will occur, the maximum growth rate ($r_{max}$), and the carrying capacity ($K$). Note that the maximum growth rate is essentially the difference between the birth rate and the death rate. If the death rate is higher than the birth rate, the population will decline unless there is enough immigration to compensate.

In equations 29.1 and 29.2, the delta ($\Delta$) is a function that calculates change—in this case, change in the population size ($\Delta N$) over a period of time ($\Delta t$). In exponential growth, the change in population size over time (or $\Delta N/\Delta t$) is determined by the population size ($N$) and the population growth rate ($r_{max}$) only. In reality, there is usually a carrying capacity ($K$) that limits the maximum size a population can reach. Therefore, in the logistic growth equation, the exponential growth rate is modified by "$K-N/K$"—or how many more individuals could be added to the population

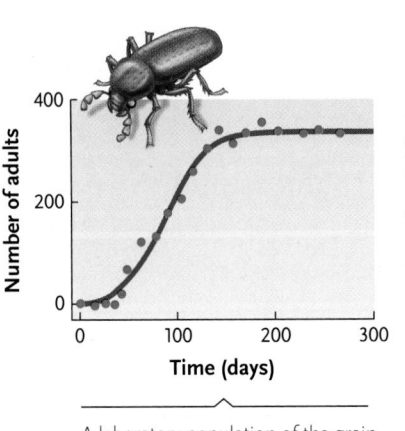

A laboratory population of the grain borer beetle *Rhyzopertha dominica* showed logistic growth when its food was replenished weekly.

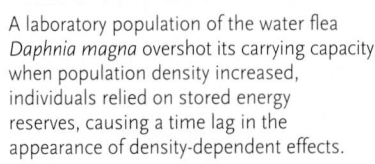

A laboratory population of the water flea *Daphnia magna* overshot its carrying capacity; when population density increased, individuals relied on stored energy reserves, causing a time lag in the appearance of density-dependent effects.

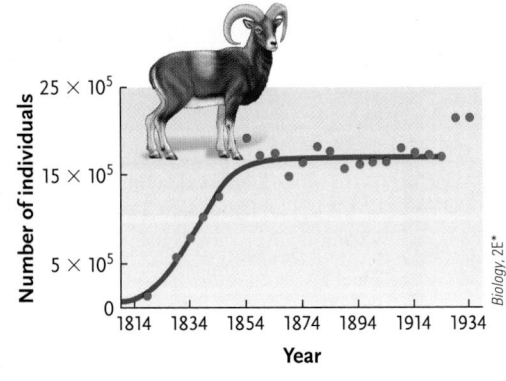

European mouflon sheep (*Ovis musimon*) introduced into Tasmania exhibited logistic population growth; these data represent 5-year averages, smoothing out annual fluctuations in population size.

**KEY**
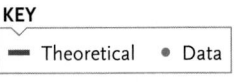
— Theoretical  • Data

**FIGURE 29.5** Examples of logistic population growth.

| N (population size) | (K − N)/K (% of K available) | r = r_max(K − N/K) (per capita growth rate) | ΔN = rN (change in N) |
|---|---|---|---|

**TABLE 29.1** The Effect of *N* on *r* and Δ*N*\* in a Hypothetical Population Exhibiting Logistic Growth in Which *K* = 2000 and $r_{max}$ Is 0.04 per Capita per Year

| N (population size) | (K − N)/K (% of K available) | $r = r_{max}(K − N/K)$ (per capita growth rate) | ΔN = rN (change in N) |
|---|---|---|---|
| 50 | 0.975 | 0.0390 | 2 |
| 100 | 0.950 | 0.0380 | 4 |
| 250 | 0.875 | 0.0350 | 9 |
| 500 | 0.750 | 0.0300 | 15 |
| 750 | 0.625 | 0.0250 | 19 |
| 1000 | 0.500 | 0.0200 | 20 |
| 1250 | 0.375 | 0.0150 | 19 |
| 1500 | 0.250 | 0.0100 | 15 |
| 1750 | 0.125 | 0.0050 | 9 |
| 1900 | 0.050 | 0.0020 | 4 |
| 1950 | 0.025 | 0.0010 | 2 |
| 2000 | 0.000 | 0.0000 | 0 |

*Biology, 2E\**

\*Δ*N* rounded to the nearest whole number.

before it reaches its carrying capacity. This equation also includes the assumption that the population's growth rate (*r*) will slow as the population size (*N*) gets bigger. **Table 29.1** illustrates how *r* varies with population size.

All of these variables will be affected by a species' **life history**. Thus, an organism's mode of reproduction, the energy base on which the population depends, causes of mortality, the environment in which it lives, and its interactions with other organisms all affect $r_{max}$. The way in which populations change over time is partly reflected by birth rates and death rates, and both of these rates can be influenced by rates of emigration and immigration (see Box 29.1).

Equation 29.2, above, identifies *N*, $r_{max}$, and *K* as important features for population biologists to measure.

In the following sections, we will consider how the components of these features can be measured to get the necessary data to assess how populations have been, and will be, changing. Being able to predict the size of a population can be important for humans for many reasons, including growing food, estimating the demand for food, or trying to control outbreaks of pests and/or diseases.

## Population Size (*N*): Counting Organisms

How do we know how many individuals there are in a population? Sometimes we can count them, but, usually, this is simply not possible. More often we sample a small portion of the population and base our estimate on that sample. Several factors can make this difficult. How easy is it to find and see the organisms **(Figure 29.6)**? How dense is the population? How accurately can we count individuals? The accuracy we can achieve is partly human (e.g., how well we see and hear, ) and partly how large the area is that must be surveyed. There are several options.

*Count every individual.* Sometimes we can directly count every organism in a population. To appreciate the challenge of this task, remember that the error margin in the formal census of the human population in Canada is about 1.59%. This means that even though we try to count every individual in the country, the actual population is still only within 1.59% of the survey number. The error value will be much higher in less developed countries, especially during times of turmoil or natural disasters, when it is very difficult to reach every person. You can see

*M.B. Fenton*

**FIGURE 29.6** It is easy to think that large animals such as African elephants would be easy to count from the air **(a)**. This may or may not be true depending on vegetation. But it can be easy to overlook animals, particularly young ones **(b)** in the shade.

# BIOLOGY IS EVERYWHERE 29.1
## Jeffrey A. Hutchings

Population biologists can play a central role in advancing sustainable use of resources and conservation efforts. Dr. Jeffrey Hutchings is a professor of biology and Canada Research Chair in Marine Conservation and Biodiversity at Dalhousie University in Halifax, Nova Scotia. His research has involved various aspects of population biology and life history of fishes, from salmon to cod. He has been extremely active in using basic population ecology information in the context of conservation of biodiversity. His research has ranged from basic population biology to ways in which we can achieve sustained harvest or marine resources. He is a field biologist at heart and has worked in aquatic systems from the area around Kispiox in British Columbia to lakes and rivers around Georgian Bay. He also has extensive field experience in Newfoundland and Labrador. In addition to his research and teaching, Jeffrey has been an active participant in promoting communication about science and effecting conservation. The latter included chairing COSEWIC (Committee on the Status of Endangered Wildlife in Canada) and serving on the board of World Wildlife Fund Canada.

The reality that populations of brook trout (*Salvelinus fontinalis*) living in rivers only 9 km apart had different life history features **(Figure 1)** enhanced our understanding of variations in life histories. The streams are on Cape Race in Newfoundland, and life history traits that differed included size at maturity, proportional allocation of body mass to gonads, fecundity, and egg size. The differences are shown in Figure 1.

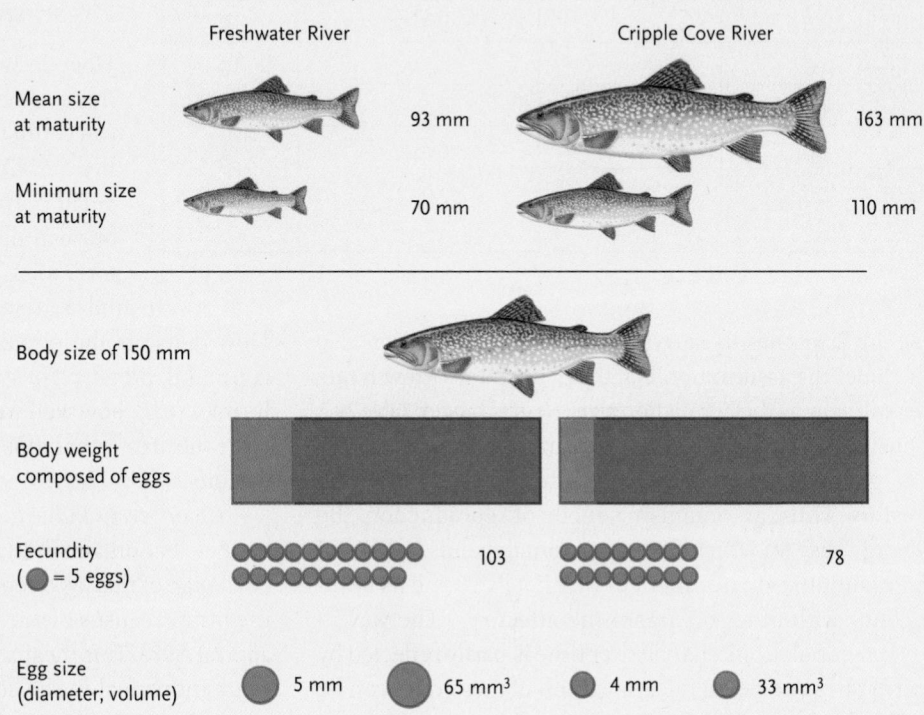

**FIGURE 1** This comparison shows differences in life history traits between neighbouring populations of brook trout.

SOURCE: From FREEDMAN. *Ecology*, 2E. © 2015 Nelson Education Ltd. Reproduced by permission. www.cengage.com/permissions; Photocredit of Fish: Dorling Kindersley/Getty Images

how difficult it is to accurately count every member of a population for yourself. Try having five different people count everyone in a crowded classroom or at a concert. See how closely your numbers match and ask yourself, "Why do the counts vary?" Which one is most accurate?

*Take a sample of organisms in a small area.* Compared to animals, it may be easier to count the numbers of plants because they do not move around **(Figure 29.7)**. But this depends on the habitat, the size of the plants, and the area over which the plants occur. Complicating the count is the question of whether each stalk or stem is a separate individual. Some may be clones. To get a picture of the challenge, imagine trying to do an inventory of the numbers of plants in a park or in your yard. It is easier to count

the trees than the grass. Dandelions are easier to count when they are in bloom. But focus on the numbers of grass plants in your lawn. On hands and knees, you may be able to get a count, but probably it would be easier to count a sample of grass plants in one small area and then extrapolate to the whole lawn. If you count 1000 grass plants in one-tenth of your lawn, and you feel you can assume that the grass is fairly evenly distributed across the whole lawn, you can extrapolate that there are 10,000 grass plants in your yard.

**Mark and recapture** is a sampling method that involves catching, marking, releasing, and recapturing organisms. This approach to sampling provides ecologists with a way to estimate total population size (*N*). The snapping turtle

**FIGURE 29.7** These dwarf lake iris (*Iris palustris*) occurs around the Great Lakes. It is considered to be a species at risk. How many stems can you count in this stand?

A-7 is an example of an animal in a population of organisms being monitored using mark-and-recapture techniques. Sometimes animals are tagged with individually distinct marks (e.g., numbered bird bands or ear tags, such as A-7). Other times, tags will simply indicate that an animal has been caught before, without any individual identification. In the first sample ($n_1$), animals are caught and tagged. In the second sample, the proportion of tagged ($n_{2m}$) to untagged animals ($n_2$) is used to estimate the population. Put another way:

(Eq. 29.3)
$$n_1/N = n_{2m}/n_2$$

Solving this equation allows you to calculate $N$. Imagine that your first sample contained 120 butterflies that were tagged **(Figure 29.8)** and the second sample contained 150 butterflies, of which 30 had been marked in the first sample. Now you can estimate the population: ($N$) = 120*(150/30) = 600. Mark-and-recapture approaches involve a number of assumptions, including, at least, the following: (1) the mark has no effect on survival, (2) marked and unmarked individuals are sampled randomly, (3) there was no migration or immigration of individuals between sampling events, and (4) marked animals are as likely to be sampled as unmarked ones.

**FIGURE 29.8** This butterfly has been captured and marked before release in a capture–recapture experiment.

## *r*, the Per Capita Rate of Increase

For ecologists to calculate the per capita rate of increase in a population, they must know a lot about the population. They must know the rates of reproduction, numbers of individuals in the population that are reproducing, rates of emigration and immigration, and patterns of survival.

We can expect a difference between organisms that reproduce asexually and those that reproduce sexually. Calculating r for asexually reproducing species requires knowing the size of the population and the number of reproducing individuals. For species that reproduce sexually, one needs the same data about the population size and the number of reproducing individuals, as well as the ratio of males to females. In sexually reproducing organisms, it is often possible to calculate rates of fertility and fertilization. Knowing the per capita rate of increase allows biologists to anticipate changes in a population's increase based on population sizes.

## Carrying Capacity (*K*): Hard to Measure

Recall that the carrying capacity in a population ($K$) is the maximum population size that the environment can sustain. Assessing carrying capacity is difficult, but it is possible when there is detailed information about the resources an organism needs to maintain itself **(Figure 29.9)**. These elements of an organism's biotic and abiotic environment that organisms require to survive are called **limiting factors**. To set the stage for considering carrying capacity, how would you determine if you have enough supplies to sustain you and your friends on a camping trip? Whether or not you will have the resources to survive will depend on things such as the number of people in the group, the length of the trip, the amount of water and shelter you have, and what and how much food each camper must eat to survive the trip. This consideration does not extend to having necessary

**FIGURE 29.9** The availability of nest sites can limit reproduction. For example, a male Tree Swallow (*Tachycineta bicolor*) guards the entrance to a nest box in Sackville, New Brunswick.

resources over the longer time period, for example, to permit reproduction and raising young.

For organisms in the wild, carrying capacity may be determined by limiting factors such as the availability of food, water, and physical space. But carrying capacity may be limited by interactions with other species. These factors can change over time and can vary in their impact on a population's carrying capacity. To estimate a population's carrying capacity, we need to know as much as we can about the requirements of life and the limiting factors for a specific organism.

In some cases, access to adequate energy is a limiting factor, one that can halt population growth or trigger an explosion in population growth. For instance, the amount of time a plant is exposed to sunlight can be a limiting factor. This reality will be obvious to the gardener who has tried to grow strawberries in a well-shaded plot. A lack of sunlight means smaller or fewer plants. Access to sunlight can certainly be a limiting factor in plant population growth; as the number of plants in an area, or the **density**, increases, plants will start to shade one another out.

We know that some organisms die from a lack of energy (starve to death). We may know how much exposure to the Sun a photoautotroph needs or how much food a primary or secondary consumer requires to maintain good body condition. Sometimes a shortage of energy causes loss of condition but not death; perhaps it will instead affect reproduction. In other situations, a shortage of mates may limit reproductive output. The bottom line is that determining carrying capacity may be extremely difficult, especially when organisms are part of food webs (Chapter 2) and consume a large variety of resources.

## STUDY BREAK

1. What is the difference between exponential and logistic growth curves?
2. How can you measure N, the number of individuals in a population?
3. What is K? How could you measure it?

## 29.4 Density Dependence and Density Independence in Population Biology

**Density-dependent** and **density-independent** factors both play a role in **population dynamics**—or how populations change over time. Density refers to the number of organisms in an area; a high-density population has many organisms in an area, whereas a comparable low-density population has fewer in the same area. Note that population size and population density are not the same thing. Imagine you have a population of 100 cats. The population density would be low if those 100 cats were all of the cats in Vancouver. Population density would be high if those 100 cats were in a single downtown condominium. Yet the population size of both is the same—100 cats.

Many field and laboratory studies have shown that high densities of organisms can inhibit growth, increase negative interactions, result in smaller adult size, and reduce survival **(Figure 29.10)**. The negative impact of

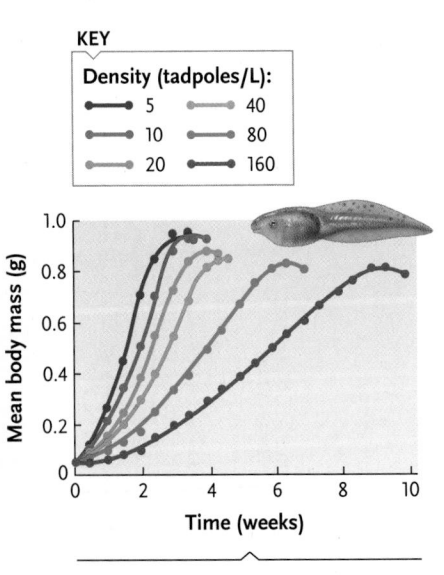

Tadpoles of the frog *Rana tigrina* grew faster and reached larger adult body size at low densities than at high densities.

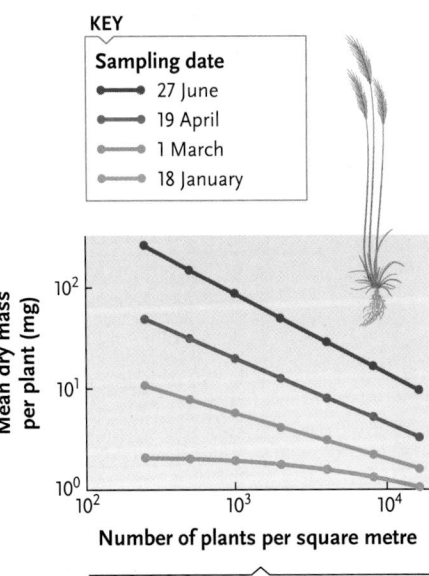

The size of the annual dune grass *Vulpia fasciculata* decreased markedly when plants were grown at high density. Density effects became more accentuated through time as the plants grew larger (indicated by the progressively steeper slopes of the lines).

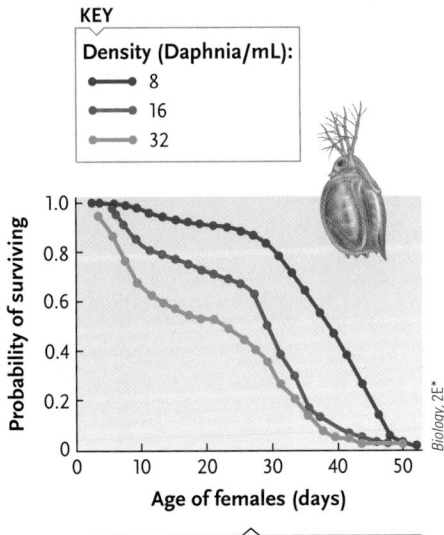

The water flea *Daphnia pulex* had higher survivorship at a density of 8/mL than at densities of 16/mL or 32/mL.

*Biology, 2E\**

**FIGURE 29.10** Effects of crowding on individual growth: size and survival.

density-dependent factors is amplified when essential resources are limited. Think about how you feel when you are in a room with just a few people and a lot of pizza compared to when you are in the same room overflowing with people and a limited number of pizzas. What will be different? In which situation will you be more or less likely to find a slice of pizza? How might you interact with others differently when there are many of you in the room versus when there are few? The effects you experience that depend on how many people and how many pizzas are in the room are density-dependent effects. If a storm caused a fire, ending the party by causing everyone to leave, the effect is the same regardless of the density of people or the density of pizzas. The fire is a density-independent factor.

Small-bodied species generally appear to be more vulnerable to density-independent factors, such as extremes of temperature or availability of moisture. Factors such as these will affect an organism's ability to grow and survive, no matter the population size. Density-independent effects on organisms can result in dramatic changes in population size (e.g., **Figure 29.11**). For example, populations of Australian thrip (*Thrips imaginis*)—a small, feathery-winged insect—grow exponentially during favourable spring weather. But when the hot and dry summer weather sets in, the populations crash.

As we shall see, a population can be affected by both density-dependent or density-independent factors over time. Human populations (page 673) are a classic example. For most of our history, most of our population was limited by density-dependent factors, and only in the last 200 years have human populations become less affected by density-dependent factors. Density-dependent factors would include how many people and how much available food. Density-independent factors could be catastrophes associated with earthquakes or tsunamis.

## 29.5 Population Cycles

There is considerable evidence that populations of a wide range of animals (insects, birds, mammals; **Figure 29.12**) fluctuate in numbers over time, for instance, from day to day or year to year depending on the life cycles of the organisms involved. These are **population cycles**. Over a typical cycle, the population increases in size, reaches a peak, and then declines drastically, and the pattern repeats over time. Populations of some small rodents (lemmings – *Lemmus lemmus*) fluctuate on a four-year cycle. Others, such as snowshoe hares (*Lepus americanus*), Canada lynx (*Lynx canadensis*), and ruffed grouse (*Bonasa umbellus*), have 10-year cycles. Australian thrips, as we saw in the previous section, cycle over a matter of months. So far, there is no simple explanation for why populations cycle, and no one theory explains cycles in different species. Cycles in populations, or population dynamics, could be controlled by something within the organism's body (**intrinsic control**) or an external factor (**extrinsic control**).

### Intrinsic Controls

Sometimes the effects of stress caused by something such as a lack of food or predation pressure can trigger hormonal changes in individuals in growing populations that can cause changes to population growth. Hormonal changes can influence individual aggressiveness, reduce reproduction rates, and foster dispersal. Some scientific evidence suggests that the regular and dramatic population cycles in lemmings are caused at least in part by reduced reproduction rates triggered by the effects of stress from overcrowding. You may have heard of lemmings and the myth that they participate in mass suicide events when their populations grow too large. In reality, what were incorrectly portrayed as mass "suicides" are actually dispersal events that happen when stresses from

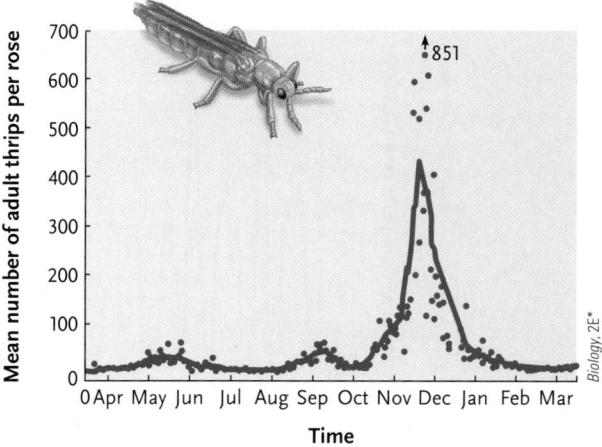

**FIGURE 29.11** Australian thrip populations boom then bust. This is one common life history pattern.

**FIGURE 29.12** A northern collared lemming (*Dicrostonyx groenlandicus*), one species showing population cycles.

high population density trigger hormonal changes that stimulate the lemmings to seek new habitat.

## Extrinsic Controls

Sometimes population dynamics, and regular cycles in population numbers, is controlled by an external force such as food availability or pressure from predators. For example, at its peak, a population of herbivores could overgraze the food supply, causing them to lose body condition, fail to reproduce, and, for many of them, ultimately starve. Interactions between populations of predators and their prey could also cause population cycles. For example, populations of snowshoe hares and lynx **(Figure 29.13)** appear to increase and decrease in cyclical patterns that parallel one another. Long-term (several decades) experiments have been conducted in Kluane National Park in the Yukon in Canada to sort out whether the cycles of these two animals are related. In reality, it appears to be a combination of food source and predation pressure that regulates population cycles in snowshoe hares. Scientists in Kluane demonstrated that adding food to experimental plots resulted in substantial (11-fold) increases in snowshow hare populations. Excluding predators from other experimental plots led to doubling of snowshoe hare populations. It appears that hare populations are most heavily influenced by food availability and that the lynx population cycle is linked to that of its food supply—the hares.

More recently in Europe, other research has demonstrated that, for several species of grass-eating voles (small herbivores), population growth is lower in winter populations. Scientists used shared data provided from vole-monitoring schemes in 11 locations throughout Europe to study vole population cycles. They observed reduced winter population growth in many vole populations. This suggests an influence of climate on vole population dynamics. Scientists continue to share data and use essential tools such as long-term studies to unravel the causes of population cycles in many species.

## Population Collapses and Explosions: Lasting Impacts

Populations of some species of organisms show little evidence of alternating cycles of abundance and scarcity. **Population explosions** occur when population numbers rise quickly and dramatically. **Population crashes** are the opposite: numbers decline quickly and dramatically.

Ed Cesar / Science Source

**FIGURE 29.13** Predator–prey interactions may contribute to density-dependent regulation of both populations. A mathematical model **(a)** predicts cycles in the numbers of predators and prey because of time lags between each species' response to changes in the density of the other. The population size of predators is exaggerated. **(b)** Canada lynx and snowshoe hares had been described as showing a typical cyclical interaction. Lynx abundance (red lines) and snowshoe hare abundance (blue line) were based on counts of pelts trappers sold to the Hudson's Bay Company over 90 years. Recent research has revealed that population cycles in snowshoe hares reflect complex interactions between the hares, its food plants, and its predators.

A. Predictions of a predator–prey model

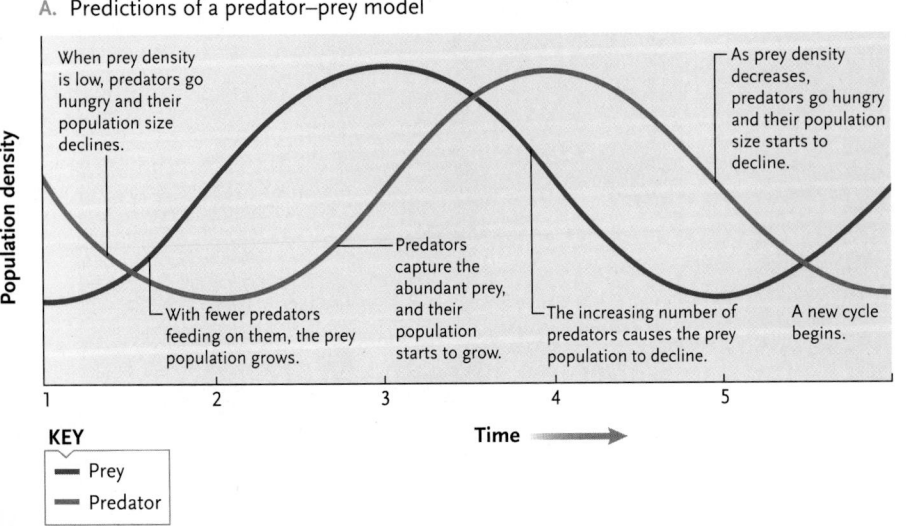

B. Lynx and hare population sizes through time

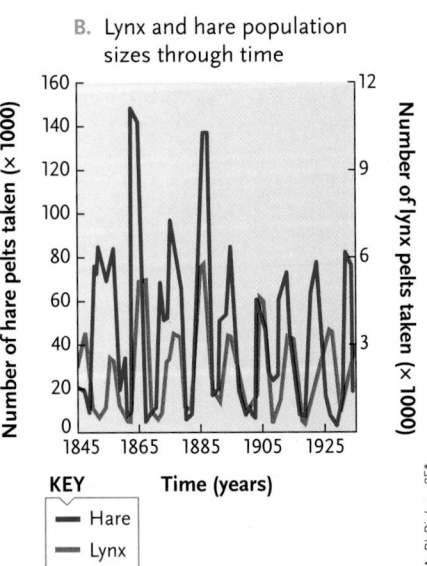

(A–B) *Biology, 2E*

A population cycle is simply a repeated pattern of explosions and crashes, sometimes referred to as "boom and bust." These explosions and crashes could have great economic or environmental implications.

### Population Explosions

Cyclical explosions of pest populations happen in naturally occurring native species. These can have a negative economic impact. Cyclical explosions of insects such as eastern spruce budworm moths (*Choristoneura fumiferana*) or western pine beetles (*Dendroctonus ponderosae*) in Canada have had devastating impacts on the forest industry. There are many other local increases in numbers of individuals, such as the 2014 appearance of many Snowy Owls (*Bubo scandiaca*) **(Figure 29.14)** across southern Canada. These Arctic animals seasonally move south in search of food and often concentrate in open areas, where they have easy access to their prey.

The European corn borer moth (*Ostrinia nubilalis*) in North America is an invasive, introduced species (see Chapter 30 for a discussion of invasive species) that has exhibited uncontrolled population growth (an explosion). It is one of the most widespread pests of corn in the corn belt of the United States. Accidentally introduced in 1917, European corn borer moths spread rapidly and do about 1 billion dollars damage annually in the corn belt. Population explosions of European corn borer moths could be explained by the absence of predators and parasites and a superabundance of food.

Unfortunately, European corn borer moths are just one of literally hundreds of successful invasive species.

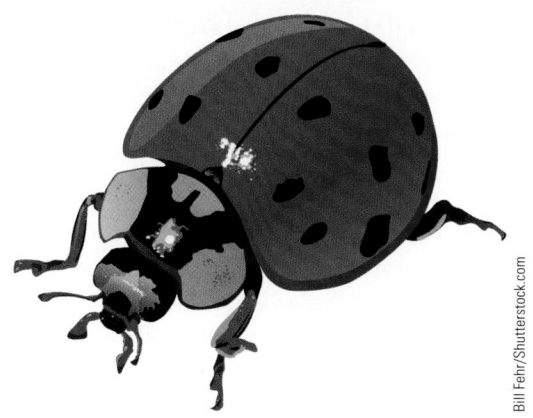

**FIGURE 29.15** Harlequin ladybird (*Harmonia axyridis*).

Although the introduction of European corn borer moths was a mistake, harlequin ladybirds (beetles – *Harmonia axyridis*) were intentionally introduced to North America from eastern Asia as part of a biological pest control program **(Figure 29.15)**, and their populations have been spreading and rising ever since. Ladybird beetles eat aphids, which are devastating agricultural pests. Now the harlequin ladybird has become a conservation concern in its own right as it is very efficiently outcompeting native species in several countries. Spores of an obligate parasitic fungus are common on harlequin ladybirds. Although this parasite does not affect the harlequin ladybird, it is lethal to many other species of native ladybirds, such as *Coccinella septempunctata*. Ladybird beetles are also predators—the reason why they have been used in biological control. The parasitic fungi are spread to native species when they eat contaminated harlequin ladybirds.

### Population Collapses

Population biologists can use model organisms (see the Purple Pages for an overview of model organisms) such as yeast to study population collapses. Experimental populations of yeast collapse because of limits to food supply. Scientists study what happens before the yeast populations collapse to try to predict when a population of other organisms might be at risk for collapse. For example, a yeast population becomes considerably less resilient before a collapse, meaning that the time it takes for the population to recover from any decline increases. Interconnected populations of yeasts were also more resistant to collapse than were isolated populations. These findings identify features that population biologists can study in other species that show cyclical changes in population to see if they show the same properties (such as less resilience with higher density or more vulnerable isolated populations). Collapses of populations could result from a shortage of food or water, failure to reproduce, or an abundance of predators.

Human activities can also cause populations to collapse. Before a population of freshwater molluscs (eastern elliptio – *Elliptio complanata*) in southeastern New York

**FIGURE 29.14** A Snowy Owl (*Bubo scandiaca*) photographed near Regina in the winter of 2013–14. The owls' move south usually reflects food abundance.

State collapsed, the molluscs had stopped reproducing. Several situations could have caused this failure to reproduce. Molluscs such as eastern elliptio have life cycles that depend on a fish host. Therefore, changes in the populations of these molluscs could reflect changes in the local fish community. Scientists checked this, however, and found no relationship between declines in eastern elliptios and their hosts (American eel – *Anguilla americana*) or potential predators (rusty crayfish – *Orconectes rusticus*). But they did find a correlation between the concentration of a pollutant (unionized ammonia in the water) and collapses of populations of eastern elliptios. Unionized ammonia is one by-product of many human industrial activities associated with lands that border watersheds in which the molluscs occur.

Spoon-billed Sandpipers (*Eurynorhynchus pygmeus*) provide another example of human-induced population collapses. As the name implies, Spoon-billed Sandpipers have distinctively spoon-shaped bills. Populations of these sandpipers have been declining rapidly. The known breeding population surveyed in 2010 had declined by about 88% in 8 years. There are many reasons for the decline, including habitat loss, climate change, and, in some cases, hunting. Some of these birds breed on the remote Chukotski Peninsula in Russia and overwinter in the Bay of Martaban in Myanmar. Twenty-six hunters from 15 villages in the overwintering area annually kill about 30,000 shorebirds for human consumption. Most of the hunters interviewed were familiar with the distinctive Spoon-billed Sandpipers. Hunting has almost certainly contributed significantly to the species decline in this particular population.

Population collapses can also be beneficial. In some circumstances, biologists try to cause the collapse of a species' population. Recall the European corn borer moth, which is an invasive pest of agricultural crops in North America. Insecticidal proteins isolated from a bacterium (*Bacillus thuringiensis* or Bt) have been added to the genome of corn, resulting in Bt maize that is relatively resistant to European corn borer moths. Over 14 years, the cumulative benefits associated with Bt maize are estimated at US$3.2 billion in Illinois, Minnesota, and Wisconsin. Some of this benefit is felt by neighbouring farms that do not use Bt maize. There are many opponents to genetically engineered crops in general, but as an approach to population control, it appears to be sustainable.

## STUDY BREAK

1. Compare intrinsic and extrinsic factors in population growth.
2. Why are we more aware of population explosions of pests than of other species?
3. What can cause a population to collapse?
4. Why do populations cycle?

## 29.6 Life Histories

How would you describe the life of an organism? What are the traits you would describe? Biologists typically record such traits as the age at first reproduction, age at maturity, fecundity or fertility (how many offspring a pair have in a lifetime), size of offspring, and the longevity of individuals. These are called life history traits because they define an organism's life history. Life history can be defined as the attributes of an organism's life cycle, particularly those related to survival and reproduction. Life history applies the features of an individual's survival and reproduction to the characteristics of the species to which the organism belongs (see Box 29.2).

Life history traits are closely related to relative fitness. Relative fitness is defined as how much of an individual's genes is represented in the next generation compared to other individuals in the same population. An individual has higher relative fitness when it has more young that survive to reproduce; therefore, more of its genes are represented in future generations. Individuals with lower relative fitness are less likely to be survived by their young. An organism's life history traits together form what we call its life history strategy. Natural selection favours life history strategies that maximize relative fitness.

### *r* and *K* Strategies: Different Patterns of Life History

Some ecologists sort organisms into two main categories of life history: *r* **strategists** and *K* **strategists (Table 29.2)**. But few species fall neatly into one of these two categories. Some distinguishing life history traits of species that are more *r* strategists include small body size, early and

| TABLE 29.2 | Characteristics of *r*- and *K*-Selected Organisms | |
|---|---|---|
| Characteristic | *r*-Selected Species | *K*-Selected Species |
| Maturation time | Short | Long |
| Life span | Short | Long |
| Mortality rate | Usually high | Usually low |
| Reproductive episodes | Usually one | Usually several |
| Time of first reproduction | Early | Late |
| Clutch or brood size | Usually large | Usually small |
| Size of offspring | Small | Large |
| Active parental care | Little or none | Often extensive |
| Population size | Fluctuating | Relatively stable |
| Tolerance of environmental change | Generally poor | Generally good |

*Biology, 2E\**

Birth control pills **(Figure 1)** have had a great impact on the behaviour of people. Compared to non-users, women using "the pill" have more control over their fertility. They are better placed to make active decisions about investing in getting their genes into future. Contraceptive pills allow women to decide between investing in having children at all, having additional children, or providing more support to their own children and others in their lives.

Modification to the molecular structure of **progesterone**, specifically adding a $CH_3$ **(Figure 2a)** group, changed not only the molecular structure but also its effect on women. Specifically, the conversion of progesterone to megestrol prolonged the suppression of ovulation because megestrol was metabolized more slowly. In some ways, megestrol, modified progesterone, was a "miracle drug."

Like most other miracles, megestrol has had both positive and negative effects, on women, society, and other animals. Control of fertility has meant changes in sexual behaviour, which, in turn, have been instrumental in increases in a variety of sexually transmitted diseases. Where the desire to prevent pregnancy was the main reason for not mating, men, but probably mainly women, refrained from having sex. The pill removed this restraint, and the resulting increase in promiscuity resulted in increases in the incidence of sexually transmitted diseases.

There are also environmental impacts arising from the use of the pill. For example, the appearance of megestrol in wastewater caused changes in populations of some fish. Specifically megestrol caused feminization of male fathead minnows (*Pimephales promelas*) and, in some areas, local extirpation of this species.

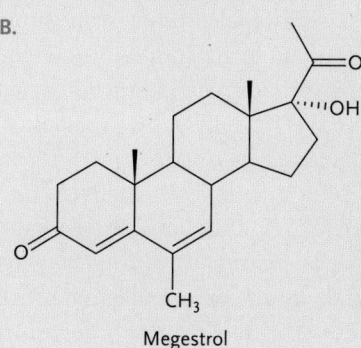

A.

Progesterone

B.

$CH_3$

Megestrol

**FIGURE 2** Progesterone and the synthetic megestrol.

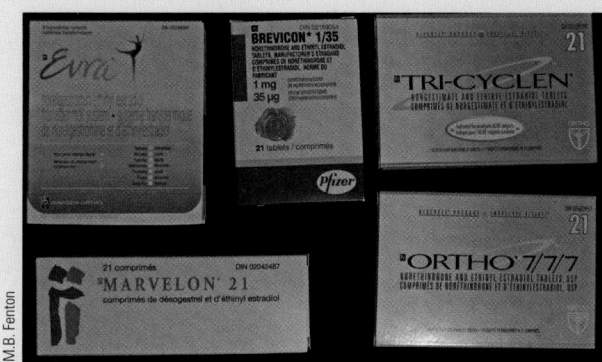

**FIGURE 1** A selection of birth control pills.

frequent reproduction, and minimal investment in parental care. Populations of *r* strategists tend to follow boom-and-bust patterns. Populations of *r* strategists never reach their carrying capacity; their populations grow exponentially until some environmental change causes them to crash (think back to the Australian thrips; Figure 29.11). Thus, we define *r* strategists by their high intrinsic growth rate, or "r." By comparison, *K* strategists tend to be larger bodied and longer lived. They invest a great deal of energy into producing fewer offspring. Populations of *K* strategists tend to settle at or near their carrying capacity (*K*). They are much less influenced by environmental fluctuations. Elephants are a classic example of a *K* strategist.

Coho salmon (Oncorhynchus kisutch) are often used as an example of an *r*-selected species. They spawn at the headwaters of streams. Larval coho salmon hatch and remain at the headwaters for about a year before assuming adult body form and swimming downstream to the ocean. During the next year or two, young coho remain at sea, feeding voraciously and growing rapidly. Then they return to the sites where they hatched. Males prepare nests to which they try to attract females and spawn. Each female lays hundreds to thousands of relatively small eggs, which they defend for a short period. Then males and females lose body condition and die. So coho salmon have a relatively short lifespan and reproduce just once but produce many offspring. They do not care for their offspring, and many die before reaching maturity.

European red deer (Cervus elaphus) are a more *K* selected species. Does (female deer) give birth in spring. The fawns remain with their mothers for almost a year, nursing and growing rapidly. Females reach adult size in year three, when they begin to breed. Adult females produce one or two young each year between when they first start to reproduce and soon before they die. So deer have a relatively long lifespan and produce just one or two young a year, starting when they are 3 years old. They care for their offspring, and a relatively high proportion will survive to adulthood.

Note that it is not possible to divide most organisms neatly into these two life history categories. In reality, organisms fall on a continuum between these two extremes. Even the salmon, which is a commonly used example of an *r* strategist, does not fit all the criteria listed in Table 29.2. Although its lifespan is short relative to that of the red deer, it is quite long compared to that of many other organisms. The young also take a full year to mature. That could be considered a long time. These two categories of life history strategies are useful for exploring the concept of life history evolution and how life history traits relate to one another, but they are an oversimplification and cannot be universally applied.

Distinctions between *r* and *K* strategists focus on body size and reproductive output. If you believe that *K* strategists are large (e.g., an elephant), remember the tsetse fly that produces one young at a time, which is larger than its mother. Now compare two species of small mammals (adult body masses <30 g): the deer mouse (*Peromyscus maniculatus*) and the little brown myotis (*Myotis lucifugus*), a bat. Both species occur widely in the United States and Canada. Adult deer mice weigh 12 to 31 g. Females produce litters that average four young (range two to eight), as often as four or five times a year. Females are sexually mature two months after birth and breed in their first year. Adult little brown bats weigh 8 to 12 g. Females have just one litter a year, each litter with one young. Females sometimes reproduce when they are 1 year old, perhaps bearing a young each year until their deaths, about 30 years after birth.

Note the striking differences in life history between these species. These include age at first reproduction (2 months versus 12 months), litter size (up to 8 versus 1), number of litters a year (4 or 5 versus 1), and maximum age (3 years versus more than 30 years). Over a 3-year lifespan, a female deer mouse could produce 48 young, whereas over 30 years, a little brown bat could produce 29 young. To appreciate the potential for population increase, we also would need to know what percentage of young survive to reproduce. About 75% of deer mice die before reproducing, about 60% of little brown bats. The actual figures will depend on local biotic and abiotic conditions. Which one is an *r* strategist, and which one a *K* strategist? How would either compare to an elephant or to a tsetse fly? If the goal is assessing a population's capacity for increase, then does the deer mouse or the little brown myotis have a greater potential for

explosive increase in population? Why? In 3 years, how many offspring, grand offspring, and great grand offspring could the female deer mouse produce? What about the female bat?

Next we will look more deeply at some of the life history traits that combine to make up an organism's life history strategy. As you will see, these life history traits also influence the intrinsic rate of increase (*r*) in a population, either directly or indirectly through its influence on other traits.

## STUDY BREAK

1. What is relative fitness?
2. What is a life history trait? Compare three life history traits of salmon and deer.
3. What is the difference between an *r* strategist and a *K* strategist?

## Life History Traits

Recall that life history traits can influence patterns of population growth. However, they do so in different ways. We will review some components of life history and discuss how these traits can affect population dynamics.

### Growth

Individual growth is an important component of population growth because it can determine things such as when and how often each individual reproduces or at what age they first reproduce, and therefore the overall growth rate of the population. More *K* strategist species tend to be slower growing and reproduce later in life. Their populations grow more slowly than species that tend toward *r* strategies. We can learn about individual growth rates in a population by taking repeated samples of the same individuals. Some scientists have used a unique sampling approach to determine the growth rate of lichens, which can be very extremely long-lived organisms. By looking at photographs of lichens on tombstones taken over many years or decades, scientists were able measure growth rates **(Figure 29.16)**.

### Reproduction Rate

The average number of offspring produced by each generation, or the **reproduction rate**, partly determines the number of individuals in a population in the next generation. The reproductive rate will be higher if individuals have larger litter sizes (the number of offspring they produce each time they reproduce) or reproduce more often. The more offspring each generation has, the larger the future population will be. *R*-selected species tend to have more offspring each generation, and therefore faster population growth, at least until the population collapses.

A.

B.

**FIGURE 29.16** When lichens grown on rock faces **(a)**, it is unusual to know how long they have been there. But when lichens grow on a tombstone **(b)**, the date on the stone provides a picture of maximum age. Repeated photographs of the same lichens in successive years allow biologists to measure their rates of growth.

Look at **Table 29.3** and see how two populations that start at the same size but that reproduce at different rates grow over three generations. For simplicity, assume that the parents die as soon as they reproduce. In organisms such as humans that live well beyond their reproductive years, the differences between populations with different reproduction rates will become even more extreme over time (all else being equal) because the child, parent, grandparent, and perhaps great-grandparent generations can overlap.

After three generations, the population with a low reproductive rate has 80 individuals and the population with a high reproduction rate has 20,000 individuals.

**Generation time** and the age at first reproduction are also important determinants of future population size. Generation time is the time from the birth of a parent to the average age of birth of all offspring. Generation time is typically shorter when the age at first reproduction is shorter. Generation time varies considerably among organisms, from hours to at least 100 years. The shortest generation times occur in organisms that reproduce asexually **(Figure 29.17)**.

The age at first reproduction and the generation time are the same in species that are classic r strategists, such as the salmon, that only breed once in their lives. They are usually correlated, but not necessary interchangeable, in species that are more like *K* strategists.

Some organisms reproduce at a young age—a matter of minutes in the case of some bacteria or days in insects such as fruit flies (*Drosophila*). Small mammals, such as white-footed mice (*Peromyscus leucopus*), are sexually mature within a few months of birth. Larger mammals, such as humpback whales (*Megaptera novaeangliae*), reach sexual maturity decades after birth. We will look at the effect of generation time, and indirectly age at first reproduction, on population growth.

The shorter the generation time, or the earlier the age at first reproduction, the more offspring that will be produced in a set period of time and the higher the intrinsic rate of growth. Look at **Table 29.4** to compare population growth over 100 years in populations with shorter and longer generation times. In this example, we will assume that the reproduction rate is the same: two new offspring are produced for each individual. Again, for simplicity, let's assume that the parents die once they have reproduced, keeping in mind that the differences would be more extreme in organisms that survive beyond their reproductive years. After 100 years, the population with a short generation time will have just produced its fifth generation. There will be 3200 individuals in that population. The one with a long generation time will have just produced its fourth generation and will have 1600 individuals. As the population is growing, and each generation is larger than the last, the

| TABLE 29.3 | Data on Reproduction Rates of Different Populations | | | | | |
|---|---|---|---|---|---|---|
| | Low Reproduction Rate | | | High Reproduction Rate | | |
| Generation Number | Number of Individuals | Number of Offspring Produced per Individual | Population Size | Number of Individuals | Number of Offspring Produced per Individual | Population Size |
| 1 | 10 | 2 | 20 | 10 | 10 | 200 |
| 2 | 20 | 2 | 40 | 200 | 10 | 2000 |
| 3 | 40 | 2 | **80** | 2000 | 10 | **20,000** |

**FIGURE 29.17** A wide range of organisms provides two views of generation times. In **(a)**, we see that $r_{max}$ tends to increase with increasing body size. In **(b)**, we see that generation time tends to increase with body size.

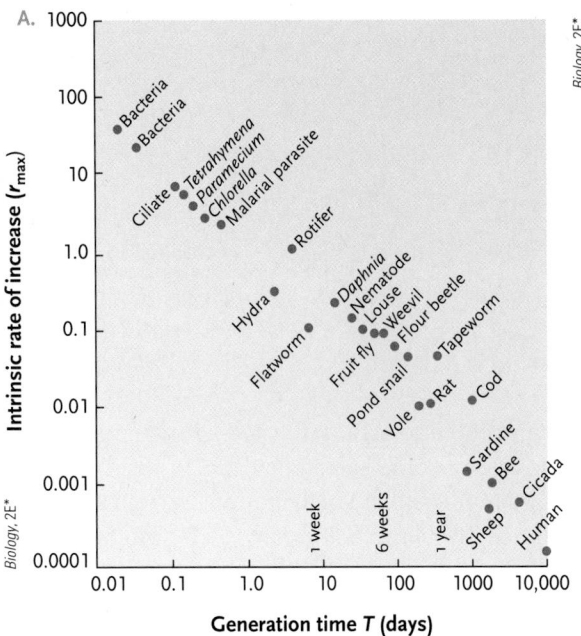

A.

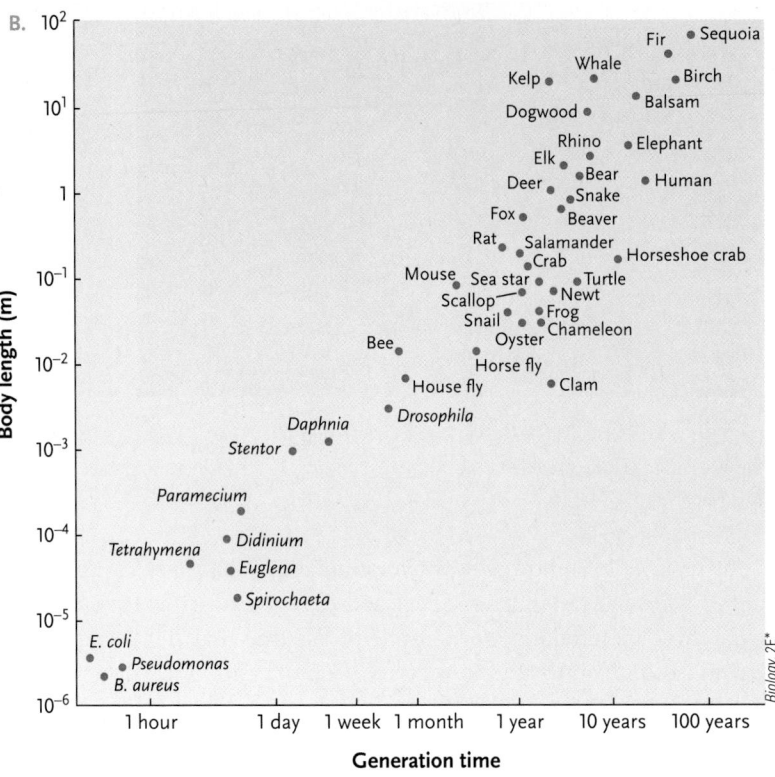

B.

| TABLE 29.4 | Examples of Population Changes of Time | | | |
|---|---|---|---|---|
| | Short Generation Time (20 years) | | Long Generation Time (25 years) | |
| Generation Number | Time (years) | Population Size | Time (years) | Population Size |
| 1 | 20 | 200 | 25 | 200 |
| 2 | 40 | 400 | 50 | 400 |
| 3 | 60 | 800 | 75 | 800 |
| 4 | 80 | 1600 | 100 | 1600 |
| 5 | 100 | 3200 | | |

generation time can have a dramatic impact on the rate of population growth.

## Variability in Life Histories: A Recurring Theme among Organisms

The life history traits of different species can vary considerably, even among some that seem to be very similar. Recall that we mentioned that the generalized life history strategies (*r* and *K*) do not apply neatly to most species. Nature holds an astonishing amount of variation and cannot be so easily categorized. Let's look at some of this astonishing variation **(Figure 29.18)**.

**FIGURE 29.18** Two mother arachnids showing parental care: **(a)** a female scorpion (*Parabuthus* spp.) with her young riding on her back and **(b)** a female wolf spider likewise encumbered. Many animals other than vertebrates invest heavily in parental care.

Parental care is part of the parental investment in offspring. A stereotypical *r* strategist would have a small body size and produce many small offspring. So it is tempting to think that because they are small, insects always produce many young and have a type III survivorship curve. But insects such as tsetse flies (*Glossina morsitans*) and many other flies have low reproductive output; some even produce just one young at a time. The same is true of some species of frogs and toads, even though many other species have a life history that looks much more like the Atlantic cod—producing a lot of offspring and providing little, if any, care. The same general principles apply to plants. Think of the difference between a grain of rice and an avocado, a pear, or a coconut—all seeds of vastly different size. Seed size in plants varies from those of orchids (weight 1 microgram) to the 18-km seeds of coco de mer (*Lodoicea maldivica*), a type of palm from the Seychelles Islands. As a rule of thumb, the larger the individual eggs or young, the fewer are produced.

Body size at maturity is another feature that varies dramatically among organisms. Maturity is defined as the capacity to reproduce. Some organisms, such as oak trees, may grow continuously over their lives (indeterminate growth), alternating growth with reproduction. Many other organisms reach mature body size (determinate growth), start to reproduce, and virtually stop growing. Mammals, birds, and many other organisms stop growing at sexual maturity, whereas others, such as many plants, fish, and reptiles, continue to grow after first reproduction. Deer mice reach adult body size and sexual maturity within months of birth. Little brown bats are about half the size (body mass) of a deer mouse and reach adult size by 18 days. But they are not sexually mature for almost a year. A newborn mouse is less than 10% of its mother's weight, whereas the newborn bat is 30% of its mother's weight. Variability in body size at maturity can differ between males and females.

Adding to the complexity of life history features are patterns of longevity, illustrated by three basic patterns among a wide range of species (**Figure 29.19**). The patterns are illustrated by examining the survival of the group of organisms (a cohort) produced in one breeding season (e.g., 1 month, 1 year, etc., depending on the organism). In Figure 29.19, a type I survivorship pattern is shown by Dall mountain sheep, a type II pattern by five-lined skinks, and a type III pattern by a perennial shrub. The differences reflect the risk of mortality with age. Note that for the Dall mountain sheep, the start date for the cohort is birth.

But these differences are all largely interspecific, or differences between separate species. There is also **intraspecific**, or within-species, variation in life history traits that may or may not be sexual. One spectacular example is an anglerfish (*Photocorynus spiniceps*). Here tiny (6 mm long) adult males are virtually parasitic on the much larger (5 cm long) adult females (**Figure 29.20**). Among Atlantic salmon (*Salmo salar*), the age at sexual maturity is a year for males in some populations but over 10 years for females. In this species, size at sexual maturity ranges from 7 cm in males to >1 m in females. Female Atlantic salmon vary considerably in the numbers and sizes (4.5 to 7 mm) of eggs (tens to tens of thousands) they produce at any reproductive event.

## STUDY BREAK

1. Name five elements of a life history strategy.
2. Compare type I, type II, and type III survivorship curves.
3. What are some ways in which life histories vary?

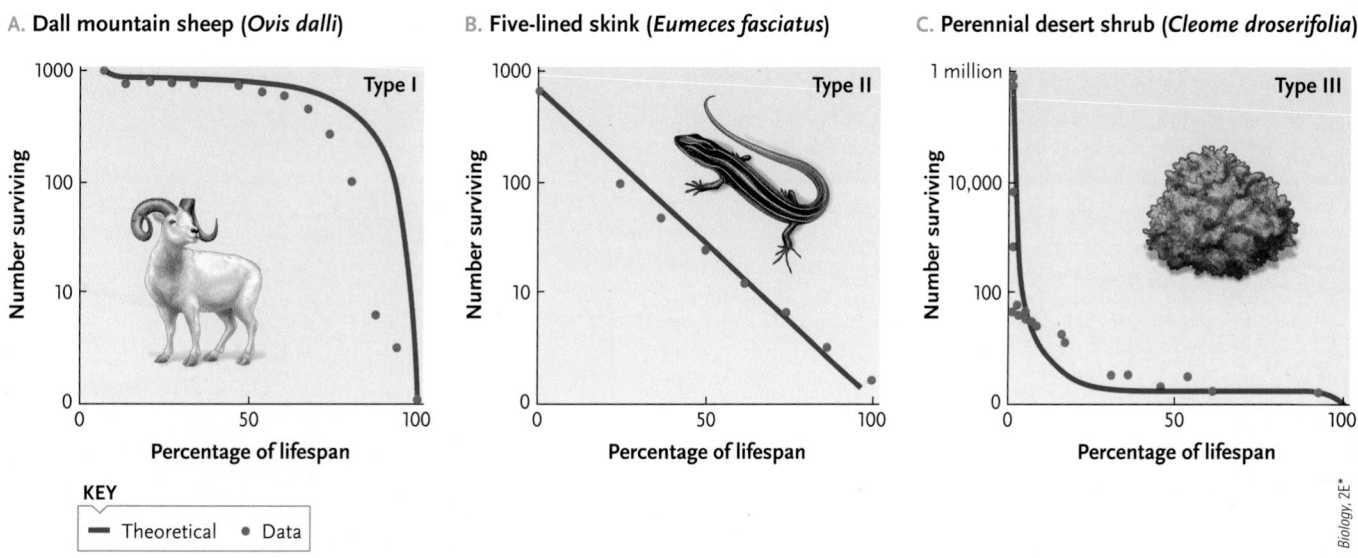

**A.** Dall mountain sheep (*Ovis dalli*)  **B.** Five-lined skink (*Eumeces fasciatus*)  **C.** Perennial desert shrub (*Cleome droserifolia*)

**KEY** — Theoretical  • Data

**FIGURE 29.19** Survivorship curves for three species that roughly match type I, type II, and type III survivorship patterns.

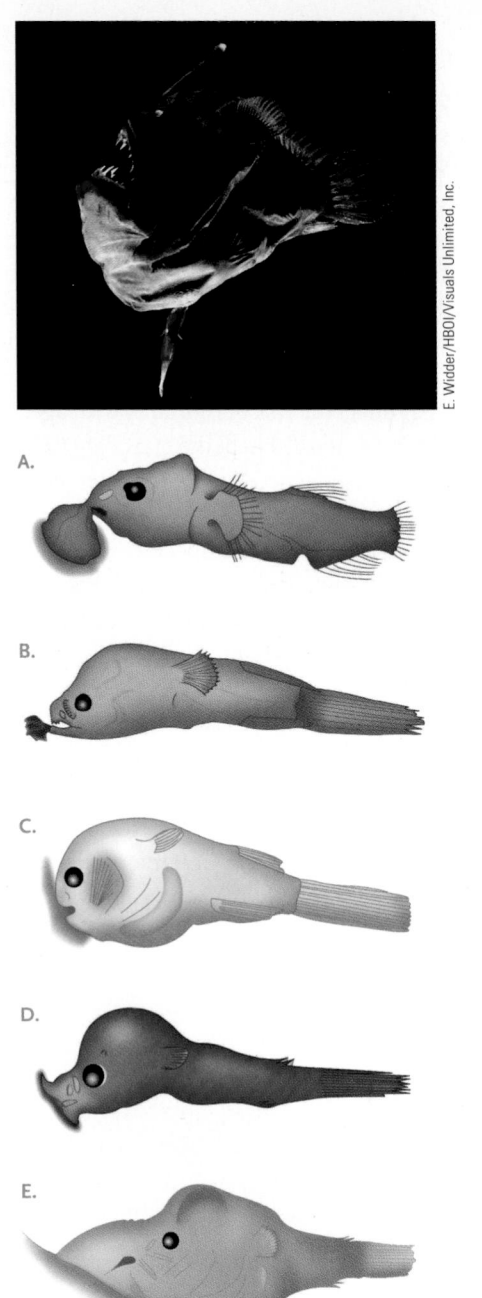

**FIGURE 29.20** Anglerfish (*Melanocetus johnsonii*), a 75-mm-long female with a 23.5 mm long attached male. Also shown are parasitic males of other species as they appear attached to females, including *Caulophryne* **(a)**, *Borophryne apogon* **(b)**, *Haplophryne mollis* **(c)**, *Linophryne agyresca* **(d)**, and *Photocorynus spiniceps* **(e)**.

SOURCE: Based on Pietsch, T.W. 2005. "Dimorphism, parasitism, and sex revisited: modes of reproduction among deep-sea ceratioid anglerfishes (Teleostei: Lophiiformes)," Ichthyological Res. 52: 207–236. From FENTON/DUMONT/OWEN. *Integrative Animal Biology*, 1E. © 2014 Nelson Education Ltd. Reproduced by permission. www.cengage.com/permissions

## 29.7 Trade-Offs and Bet Hedging

There is considerable intraspecific variation in traits relating to life history. This means that not all of the organisms in a population are necessarily the same. This variation could occur when individuals invest their energy in different things. When energy is limited, resources must be allocated among all of the organism's needs. This may mean more energy allocated to growth, more to larger offspring, or more to parental care. These variations are trade-offs. Compromises, such as giving more nutrients to a few larger offspring and less to small offspring, represent **bet hedging**.

A reproductive **trade-off** occurs when an individual invests energy in one aspect of reproduction while reducing the amount of energy available for another. For example, when resources are limited, a female may produce a few larger eggs or many smaller ones. Individuals of a species that grows throughout its life (indeterminant growth) with limited resources might divert energy from growth to reproduction. This might mean that they will reproduce earlier and at a smaller size.

Scientists experimentally tested how land snails **(Figure 29.21**; *Cornu aspersum*) allocate energy to reproduction in different situations. Growing snails store lipids (fats) and use stored carbohydrates for energy. Snails whose diets are poor in lipids increased clutch size (laid more eggs) and allocated more cholesterol to those eggs. Cholesterol is important in functioning of membranes and may be essential for growth, so more of it corresponds to higher rates of hatching and better survival of young. Varying the amount of lipids (fats) in the snails' diet affected their investment in reproduction, explaining why in some situations snails produced larger clutches. This experimental evidence illustrates how diet and environment can affect investment in reproduction and how snails adjust to the conditions they encounter in nature.

Female eastern cottontail rabbits (*Sylvilagus floridanus*) **(Figure 29.22)** have litters of three to six kits. In the northern parts of their range (e.g., in southern Ontario and Manitoba), females can mate and become pregnant in early spring (March) and bear their first litter about 29 days later. In years when the spring is cold and wet, females reabsorb this first litter rather than carrying the pregnancy to term.

**FIGURE 29.21** A brown garden snail (*Cornu aspersum*).

**FIGURE 29.22** Eastern cottontail rabbits (*Sylvilagus floridanus*) showing an adult (**a**) and at least three young in a nest (**b**).

They then mate again when the weather is better, have a second litter, and come into heat just after giving birth. Under favourable conditions, females could produce up to eight litters in a year. They "hedge their bets," or take a chance that the environment will be good enough for them to rear that first litter. If not, they abandon the litter and wait until conditions improve.

## STUDY BREAK

1. How do snails demonstrate trade-offs?
2. How do cottontail rabbits show bet hedging?

## 29.8 Reproductive Senescence

Humans are distinct among primates in that many females typically live well beyond their reproductive years. Women typically do not give birth after age 45 years, and their menstrual cycle disappears after menopause. **Menopause** is when a woman's menstrual cycle stops, and she is no longer able to reproduce. This is an example of **reproductive senescence** (aging). A detailed analysis of long-term data for humans and seven other species of primates showed that reproductive senescence before death was uncommon among other primates; most reproduce until they die. Human women, in contrast, typically live well beyond reproductive senescence.

This life history feature can reflect a relative fitness benefit if the time after reproductive senescence can lead to greater success of offspring. In effect, this is a grandparent explanation of genetically selfish behaviour—grandparents help ensure that their children's genes, and therefore their own, continue into another generation. In the waters off British Columbia and Washington, female resident killer whales (*Orcinus orca*) stop reproducing when they are 30 to 40 years old but may live to 90. Although reproductively senescent mothers have little effect on the reproductive success of their daughters, they increase the survival of their older male offspring. The

data reveal that for a male killer whale about 30 years old, the chances of death are 3.1 times higher in the year after his mother's death. There is no statistical evidence of a difference in this effect between females that are reproductively active and those that are reproductively senescent. Long-term studies of populations in which the animals are individually recognizable have been critical for scientists trying to determine the reason why orca females live so long past their reproductive years.

## STUDY BREAK

1. What is reproductive senescence? Give an example of reproductive senescence and explain why it is a stable evolutionary strategy.
2. Do killer whales show reproductive senescence? If so, how?

## 29.9 Human Populations

Historical patterns of human population growth illustrate many of the complexities of population biology. For over 200 years, the population of *Homo sapiens* (Figure 29.3) continued to grow exponentially, with negative consequences for many humans as well as other species, communities, and ecosystems. This change in population growth patterns is surprising for a species with relatively low reproductive potential, a *K* strategist producing few young per "litter," with relatively high age at first reproduction and early reproductive senescence. Although our population grew slowly for most of our history as a species, over the past 200 years, the pattern changed dramatically. Although human population growth was once limited, something has changed our carrying capacity. Furthermore, humans are a prime example of how population size dramatically affects the potential for explosive population growth. In the following, note how the basic measures of population biology we have seen above are applied to populations of humans.

## Human Population Numbers

Over many hundreds and thousands of years, the global human population size was relatively stable. It reached 1 billion only in about 1804; 123 years later, in 1927, it hit 2 billion. Only 33 years after that, in 1960, it hit 3 billion. By 2011, there were 7 billion people on Earth. The human population had exploded. In spite of predictions to the contrary, our population has continued to increase, albeit at a slowing rate.

Global population growth is not distributed evenly among regions. There is considerable variation in rates of population growth and in age structures among nations. There are three basic patterns **(Figure 29.23)**. Some countries have reached zero population growth (ZPG)—their population numbers are not rising—whereas others have not. In countries with ZPG, there are almost equal numbers of individuals of pre- and post-reproductive ages. Countries with declining populations

(negative population growth) have fewer people of reproductive age than do those with zero or rapid growth (Figure 29.23). Populations with rapid growth have a large proportion of their population at pre-reproductive ages. The large size of this young cohort translates into a **population bomb**—a situation in which the large number of women of reproductive age accounts for the potential for population increase. It is important to remember that immigration and emigration can change the size of a country's population and the population growth rates. This can be further complicated by cultural differences in family structure and size among immigrants.

### Getting Here

To put it simply, the global human population grows when birth rates exceed death rates. For much of human history, both birth and death rates were high, and the difference between them was small. At some points,

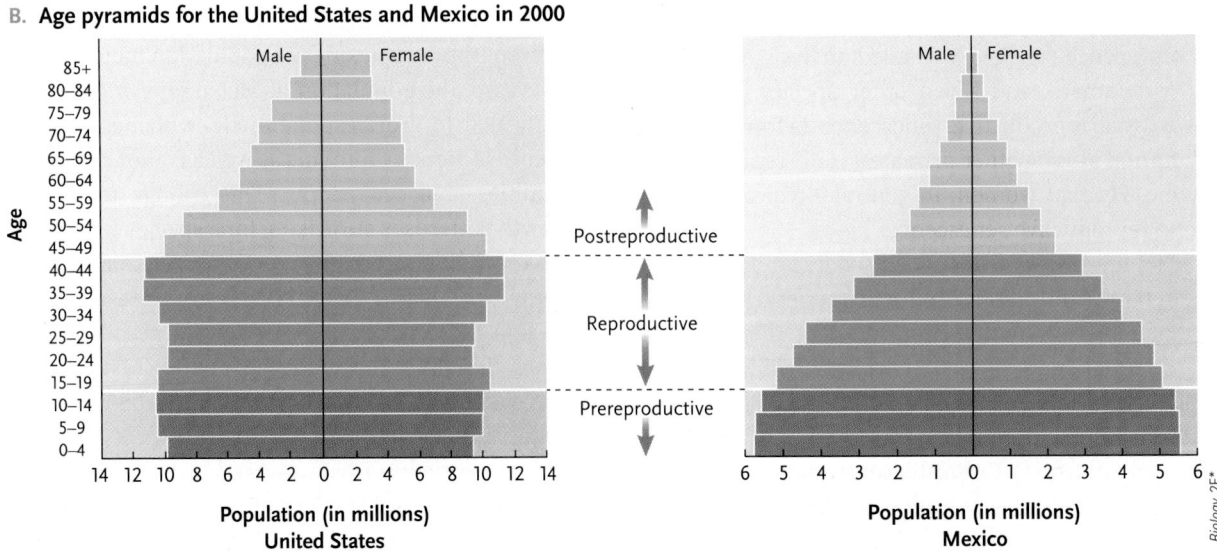

**FIGURE 29.23** Diagrams showing age structures in countries with zero, negative, and rapid rates **(a)** of population growth. The width of each bar represents the proportion of the population in each age class. Age structure diagrams for the United States and Mexico **(b)** are measured in millions of people and suggest that these countries will experience different rates of population growth.

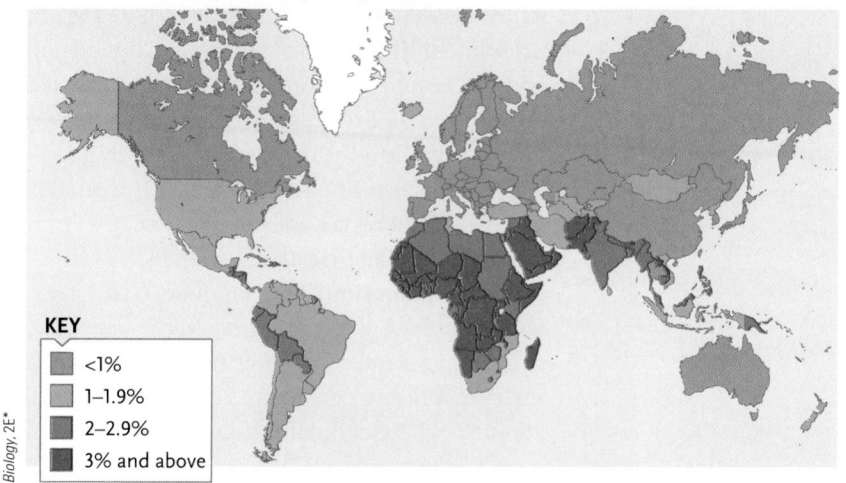

**A. Mean annual population growth rates, 2001**

KEY
- <1%
- 1–1.9%
- 2–2.9%
- 3% and above

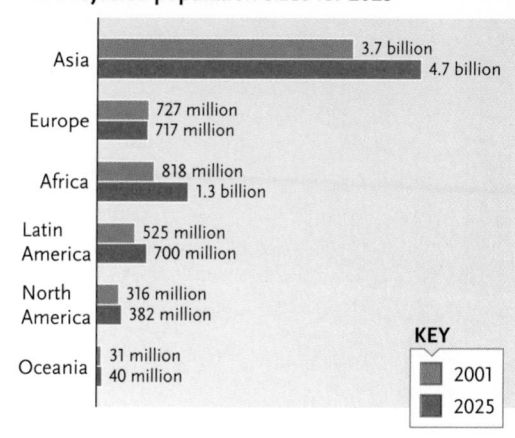

**B. Projected population sizes for 2025**

| Region | 2001 | 2025 |
|---|---|---|
| Asia | 3.7 billion | 4.7 billion |
| Europe | 727 million | 717 million |
| Africa | 818 million | 1.3 billion |
| Latin America | 525 million | 700 million |
| North America | 316 million | 382 million |
| Oceania | 31 million | 40 million |

KEY
- 2001
- 2025

*Biology, 2E\**

**FIGURE 29.24** Local variation in growth rates of human populations. In 2001, **(a)** average annual population growth rates varied among countries and continents. In some regions, **(b)** the human population is projected to increase greatly by 2025 (red) compared to the population size in 2001 (orange). The population of Europeans has declined slightly.

death rates dramatically exceeded birth rates, such as when the Black Death hit in the 1300s, causing the global human population to decline. Typically, however, through most of human history, our population size grew slowly, staying at or near its carrying capacity. So why did the human population suddenly shift to exponential growth? What changed the carrying capacity? At least three factors were important in dramatically extending the carrying capacity of the human population: migration, health improvements, and technology (see **Figure 29.24**).

### Migration

First, between 45,000 and 60,000 years ago, our species expanded its geographic distribution from one centred in Africa to one that is worldwide. This is reflected by genomic evidence, as well as linguistic diversity, data from parasites of humans, and the morphology of humans. This is an example of the serial founder effect. The genetic diversity of humans is much higher in Africa than elsewhere, and some genetically distinct populations of humans persist in Africa. Expansion out of Africa was aided by our ability to build fires, make clothing, work together, and share information. The development of language was central to widespread sharing of ideas and is one aspect of social changes that occurred in humans.

### Improved Health

The second factor was advances in community structure reflected by changes in hygiene and public health. There is no doubt that increasing local populations of humans generated problems associated with both sanitation and disease. More people means that there is more human waste, which carries disease. More people

living in close proximity also makes it easier for many diseases to spread from one to another. Infrastructure that provided clean water and diverted human waste slowed the spread of disease. Improved health care reduced mortality—people began to live longer, and more survived to reproductive age.

### Technology

Although migration and improved health care set the stage for population growth, technology allowed the human population to expand. Without enough food and water to sustain our population, it could not have expanded much further. It is not surprising, then, that the real exponential growth began with the Industrial Revolution—a time characterized by concentrated manufacturing industries that could produce goods quickly and more cheaply and technologies to increase food production. Society shifted its economic approach, relying much less on individual farms and specialized tradespeople and much more on industry and mass production. The technologies that arose during the Industrial Revolution increased the carrying capacity of human habitats, insulating us from some environmental changes.

## Global Population Dynamics in Different Countries and Regions

The patterns of global population growth we see today reflect a complex mixture of demographic patterns in different countries and regions. Overall, global population growth is slowing. In some countries, such as some European countries, populations are in decline. Others are at ZPG, or close to it. Still others continue to grow quite rapidly. Population growth in a particular country is usually linked to economic development. The

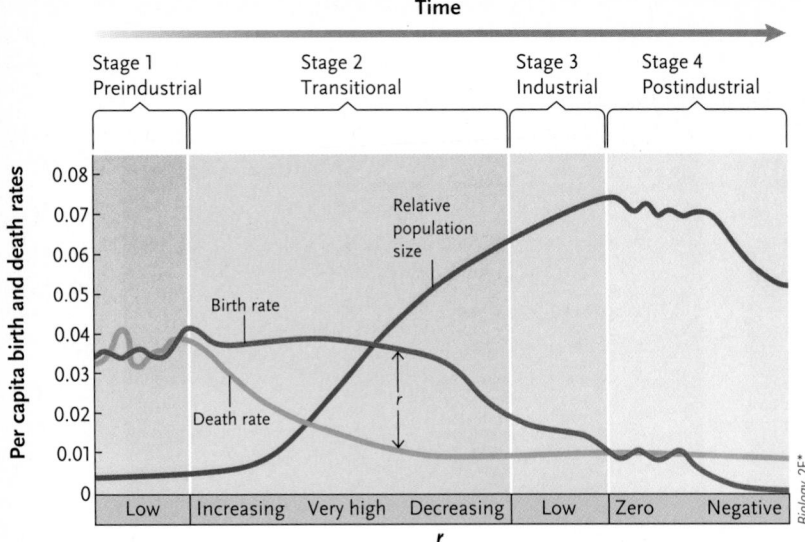

**FIGURE 29.25** The demographic transition model describes changes in the birth and death rates and relative population size as a country passes through four stages of economic development. The bottom bar describes net population growth rate (*r*).

**demographic transition model (Figure 29.25)** describes historical changes in demographic patterns of industrialized countries in Western Europe. In this model, birth and death rates are high during preindustrial stages, so the population grows slowly. During the transitional phase, industrialization begins and the population grows as food production increases and there are improvements in health care and sanitation. Increased rates of population growth mainly reflect declining death rates. Expansion of the industrialization phase coincides with better living conditions and declining birth rates. ZPG arrives in the postindustrial stage, often reflecting the education of women. At this point, any increases in population usually reflect immigration, either from the surrounding countryside or from other nations.

## Population Control: An Important Goal

Limiting reproductive output can benefit an individual or a couple because it may allow them to invest heavily in a few offspring. Extending the limitation of reproductive output to a population is more difficult and walks the boundary between personal freedom and what can benefit society. China's one-child policy (OCP) restricts the number of children that an urban couple can have, with some consideration for ethnic situations and the incidence of severely disabled children. Introduced in 1979, there is no doubt that without this policy, the human population of the world today would be even larger than it is now. Although it has had the desired effect of reducing population growth, there are many repercussions of OCP, ranging from impacts on family interactions to the availability of children and grandchildren to care for their parents and grandparents.

The other side of this coin is situations in which access to fertility control is limited if not prohibited. In 1950, Sri Lanka and Afghanistan had the same population size. At that time, the government of Sri Lanka made strong efforts to encourage family planning in culturally sensitive ways. This did not happen in Afghanistan. By 2050, Afghanistan will have a population four times larger than Sri Lanka. In 2000, the United Nations Millennium Development Goals were widely adopted, committing signatory nations to achieving several goals by 2015. The eight goals included ending poverty and hunger, universal education, gender quality, child health, maternal health, combatting HIV/AIDS, environmental sustainability, and global partnerships.

Control of reproduction is central to achieving these eight goals. In 1994, the United Nations held the International Conference on Population and Development (ICPD) that set targets for investment in family planning. The amount spent on this initiative had fallen to 13% of its target by 2004. As a result, access to family planning is not available to many women in many low-income countries. Recently, Canada withdrew its financial support for initiatives intended to support family planning in developing countries. This kind of political decision can have huge implications on attempts to reduce human population growth. Giving women control over their own reproduction has a powerful impact on birth rates.

Data from the United Nations Development Programme (UNDP) show worldwide variation in fertility rates of humans and highlight the importance of the intrinsic rate of increase (*r*) in the future of our planet. The more countries that have a high intrinsic rate of increase, the more our global population will continue to grow. This coincides with depletion of natural resources and eventually with our capacity to feed everyone in the population. This reality should bring home the fundamental importance of population biology and the components that contribute to increasing the size of a population. The other side of this coin is the impact of the human population on other organisms and the implications of this for our collective future.

## STUDY BREAK

1. What roles have migration, technology, and improved health played in human population biology?
2. Describe three patterns of human population growth.
3. What is China's one-child policy?
4. Why is the population of humans a problem for the inhabitants of Earth?

# PUTTING IT IN PERSPECTIVE

The importance of the impact of human population on the planet and the organisms that live here makes population biology a central topic of concern. In this chapter, we began by looking at populations of other species to review basic features of populations that we can measure to understand processes involved in population biology. We also discussed issues such as those relating to density dependence and density independence. We examined examples of population explosions and crashes, as well as exponential and logistic growth of populations. The life histories of organisms are fundamental to their population dynamics, including populations of humans. Some emerging problems require constant attention and intervention as they continually change with the population. The same measures used in the study of other species also apply to humans. The population of humans provides a stark example of uncontrolled growth and remains one of the most challenging and pervasive problems facing our species.

# KEY CONCEPTS REVIEW AND QUESTIONS

## 29.1 Ecology

Ecology studies the relationships between organisms and their environment. Ecologists seek to understand factors affecting variation in species distribution and abundance. They focus on different levels of interactions. Emergent properties arise at each ecological level from interactions between elements at lower levels.

## 29.2 Population Ecology

Population ecology studies numbers associated with species populations. It considers factors such as how populations reproduce, how long they live, their histories, and how they may change.

1. How does population ecology contribute to the overall field of ecology? Why do emergent properties complicate the picture?

## 29.3 What Do Population Biologists Measure?

Population ecologists collect data on numbers of organisms in a population. They develop models to study and illustrate changes in population size over time. Exponential models show exponential growth in populations that continue to grow by a constant factor. But few (if any) populations can continue to grow exponentially forever. Logistic models demonstrate situations where populations grow until they reach the carrying capacity. Many factors will affect changes in population growth rate and size. Determining carrying capacity is extremely difficult. Since it may not always be possible for all members of a population to be counted, population size is often determined by counting a sample of the population and then making an estimate based on that sample.

2. How does the story of A-7 illustrate some of the data that population ecologists require to appreciate and predict the future of populations?

3. How do biologists determine $N$? What other features of populations are used in logistic and exponential models?

4. List features of individual life histories that are used in population biology.

## 29.4 Density Dependence and Density Independence in Population Biology

Both density-dependent and density-independent factors affect population dynamics. Density-dependent factors include how much food is available. Density-independent factors include temperature extremes of moisture availability.

5. Explain how density-dependent and density-independent factors affect populations and how this relates to $r$ and $K$.

## 29.5 Population Cycles

Populations fluctuate over time in population cycles. These cycles could be controlled by intrinsic or extrinsic control. Population cycles are repeated patterns of population explosions and collapses. Population explosion and population collapses can have great economic and environmental consequences.

6. What are the differences between intrinsic and extrinsic controls of population cycles? How do these relate to explosions and collapses of populations?

## 29.6 Life Histories

The life history traits of an organism are closely related to its relative fitness. Life history strategies that maximize relative fitness are favoured by natural selection. There are two general categories of life history: $r$ strategists, defined by their high intrinsic growth rates, and $K$ strategists, whose populations settle near their carrying capacity. Few species fit neatly into these two categories. Life history traits (e.g., individual growth, reproduction rate, generation time, and age of first reproduction) influence the pattern of population growth in different ways. There is a great deal of variability in the life history traits of different species.

7. How does relative fitness connect to life histories? Consider the consequences of life histories on fitness in three organisms.

### 29.7 Trade-Offs and Bet Hedging

Life history traits vary greatly in individuals of a population. This variation might occur when an organism must make trade-offs when allocating limited energy among all of its needs. Compromises, known as bet hedging, may also occur.

8. What is the difference between a trade-off and bet hedging? How do snails and cottontail rabbits illustrate the differences? What about brook trout?

### 29.8 Reproductive Senescence

Reproductive senescence occurs when a female's menstruation cycle stops and she no longer can reproduce. Although human women live long past their reproductive senescence, this is uncommon among other primates.

9. How is reproductive senescence important in human population biology? How can we balance controlling population growth while recognizing the freedom of individuals?

### 29.9 Human Populations

Human populations grew slowly for most of our history but grew dramatically in the past 200 years. Population continues to grow but at a slowing rate. Global population growth is distributed unevenly among regions. This reflects a mixture of demographic patterns in different regions. Global human population grows when birth rates exceed death rates. Migration, health improvements, and technology dramatically extended human carrying capacity. Population growth in a country is also linked to its economic development. Limiting reproductive output of a population may benefit society but could also have ethical implications.

10. How can we balance controlling population growth while recognizing the freedom of individuals?

11. Think of four ways that human population directly affects populations of other species.

# Community and Ecosystem Ecology

Shelby Riskin

# WHY IT MATTERS

A target-shaped rash is never good news for someone who has been in an area with ticks that carry Lyme disease **(Figure 30.1)**. Accompanying the characteristic rash, early symptoms often include fatigue and headache, but if left untreated, the disease can affect the heart, nerves, and brain. Lyme disease is caused by a bacterial spirochete (*Borrelia burgdorferi*) and is passed to humans through the bite of infected ticks (*Ixodes scapularis* or *I. pacificus*) **(Figure 30.2)**. Both the geographic range in which it is found and its prevalence are increasing. Across the United States between 1992 and 2006, the number of reported cases increased by 101% **(Figure 30.3)**.

Early hypotheses proposed that an increasing deer population over the last century led to the ever-increasing disease frequency. Deer carry adult ticks and can host infected ticks, although they do not serve as host to the disease itself.

Recent evidence, however, suggests that there may be more to the story. Scientists noticed that many deer populations have stabilized or decreased since the 1990s, but the disease has continued to increase dramatically. Scientists hypothesized that the rise in the prevalence of Lyme disease might ultimately be from a decreasing wolf (*Canis lupus*) population; in other words, human culling of the wolf population has led to the increase in human infection rates. But is this possible? Can the absence of an **apex predator**—a consumer at the top of the trophic

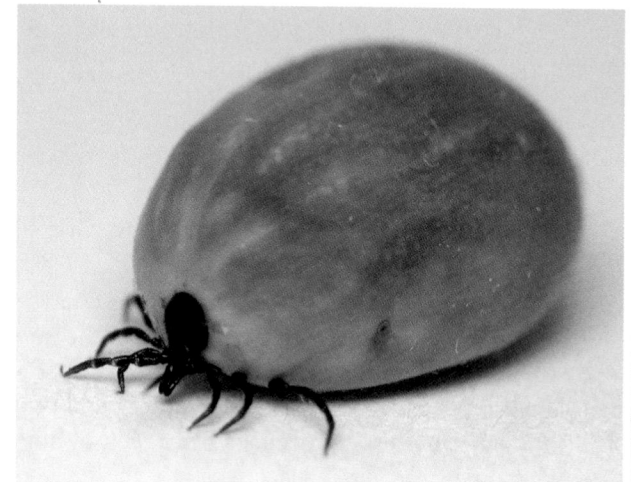

**FIGURE 30.1**  A tick engorged following a blood meal.

pyramid or food chain—impact tick populations and disease infection rates? Understanding how such a phenomenon works means understanding the relationships among the communities of species making up the trophic pyramid. Scientists used data from a variety of sources to examine the relationships in this trophic pyramid. This included data on populations of wolves, coyotes (*Canis latrans*), red foxes (*Vulpes vulpes*), and small mammals; the life history of the pathogenic spirochete; a model of predator–prey populations; and relationships among animal populations and disease.

A.

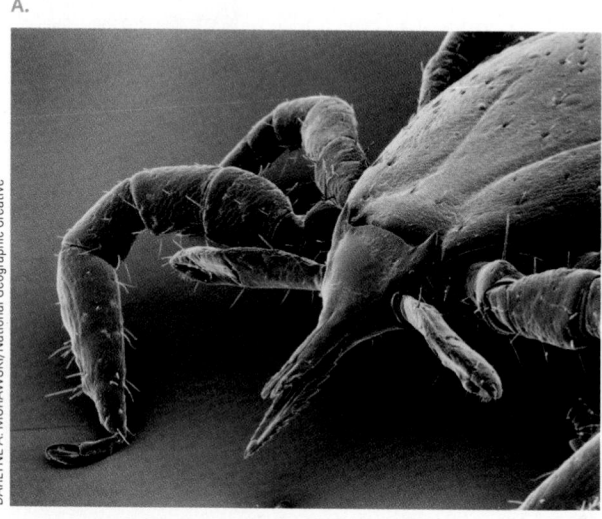

B.

**FIGURE 30.2**  **(a)** A deer tick (magnified approximately 90 times) and **(b)** Borrelia, the type of bacterial spirochete that causes Lyme disease.

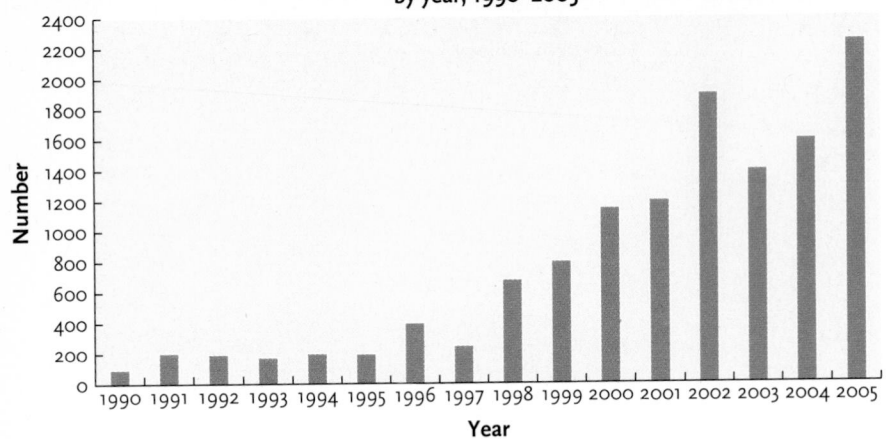

## Number of confirmed Lyme disease cases reported in MA by year, 1990–2005

**FIGURE 30.3** Recorded cases of Lyme disease in Massachusetts, the United States, between 1990 and 2005.

SOURCE: Based on http://lymebook.com/blog/geographic-incidence/lyme-disease-in-massachusetts-counties-county/

Small mammals naturally host the spirochete. Because the spirochete is always present in these animals, they are a continuous source of disease outbreaks. The small mammals are a disease reservoir: a potential source of disease that continuously hosts an infectious pathogen. Juvenile ticks, or nymphs, become infected when they take blood meals from these small mammals. Deer (such as the white-tailed deer, *Odocoileus virginianus*), on the other hand, serve as disease vectors. Rather than being a continuous source of a pathogen, a disease vector transmits the pathogen from one organism to another. Adult ticks take blood meals from deer and are thus carried through ecosystems on these deer hosts. Scientists hypothesize that the number of small mammals, or the size of the disease reservoir itself, might have a larger influence on disease prevalence than the number of disease vectors **(Figure 30.4)**.

Small mammal populations are in part controlled by predation rates (how many are eaten by predators). They are preyed on by a range of carnivores, including red foxes, coyotes, and wolves. The smallest of these carnivores, the fox, depends much more on small mammal prey than does the coyote or wolf, which are able to take much larger animals, such as deer. As humans have decreased wolf populations, populations

of coyote have increased. Coyotes and foxes compete for resources, and fox populations have decreased in response to this **interference competition** (see pages 686–687 for details on competition in general and interference competition in particular). With decreased fox populations have come increased populations of small mammals, and, indeed, with both the model scientists created and state-by-state data, decreasing fox populations are correlated with increased prevalence of Lyme disease **(Figure 30.5)**.

In this chapter, we will look at community ecology. A biological community is the assemblage of species that occurs in a given area, and the study of **community ecology** is the study of these groups of populations. We will explore some of the patterns that allow us to understand community dynamics and structure. We will also move beyond communities and look at how even the abiotic environment shapes biological communities. An ecosystem is a group of biological communities interacting with their shared physical environment. **Ecosystem ecology** is a discipline that explores the interactions between biological communities and their abiotic environment. This includes understanding how nutrients and energy move through ecosystems.

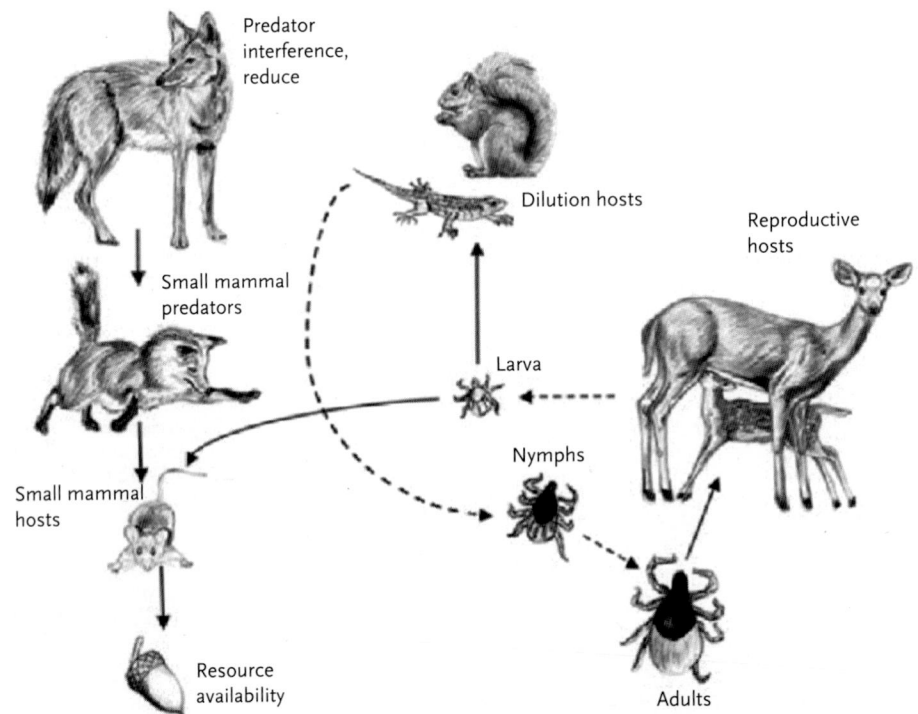

**FIGURE 30.4** Following the removal of an apex predator, the wolf, interference competition between small mammal predators increased the Lyme disease reservoir (small mammals), facilitating the increasing prevalence of Lyme disease.

SOURCE: Levi, T., A. M. Kilpatrick, M. Mangel, and C. C. Wilmers. 2012. "Deer, predators, and the emergence of Lyme disease." *Proceedings of the National Academy of Sciences* 109:10942–10947.

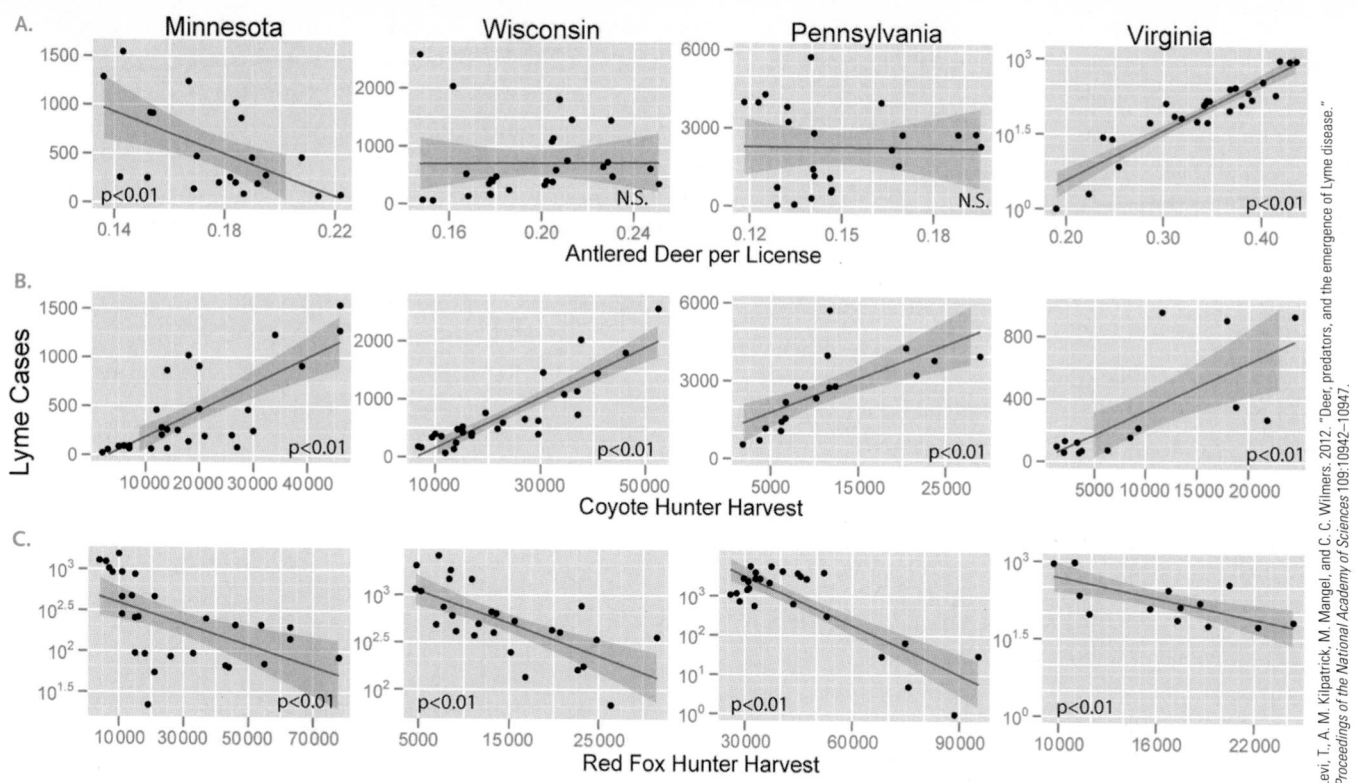

**FIGURE 30.5** Using data from animals harvested by hunters, the prevalence of Lyme disease is not consistently correlated with deer populations **(a)** but is positively correlated with increasing coyote populations **(b)** and decreasing fox populations **(c)** across four states in the United States.

Levi, T., A. M. Kilpatrick, M. Mangel, and C. C. Wilmers. 2012. "Deer, predators, and the emergence of Lyme disease." *Proceedings of the National Academy of Sciences* 109:10942–10947.

The example of Lyme disease and the interactions among the organisms involved highlights the role of humans in shaping communities and ecosystems. This chapter will use a combination of examples from intact ecosystems and human-dominated ecosystems. In this way, you will get a taste for how challenging it is to understand the complexity and to manage our ever-increasing influence on the environments of our planet in our ever-changing world.

# 30.1 Community Ecology

Community ecology focuses on interactions among different groups of organisms in an ecosystem and how they interact. In Chapter 2, you were introduced to some of the ways in which organisms in an ecosystem interact. This included symbioses, close relationships between organisms in which the survival of one organism is dependent on another. Examples of symbioses include parasitism, mutualism, and commensalism. Another fundamental type of interaction among organisms is the act of eating and being eating—trophic dynamics. Ecosystem food webs connect the producers (such as plants), the herbivores (animals that eat plants), the consumers (animals that eat plants or other animals), and the decomposers (organisms that feed on dead organic material). The first half of this chapter focuses on community ecology and the interactions among an ecosystem's organisms. We will begin by looking more in-depth at trophic dynamics.

## Trophic Relationships and Keystone Species Can Alter Species Populations

As you might recall from Chapter 2, the different trophic roles in an ecosystem can be thought of as different trophic levels: producers make up the first level, herbivores the second, and so on. The size of each of these levels is unequal. Consumers are not able to harness all the energy available from the organisms they eat; for example, roots of plants might be left behind by herbivores, or bones might be left behind by carnivores. So a much larger mass of plant material is required to fuel a given mass of herbivore. Because of this incomplete transfer of energy, the mass of organisms, or biomass, decreases with each increase in trophic level. We call this relationship a **trophic pyramid**.

In the Lyme disease example, changes to populations at the highest trophic level have indirect consequences on populations much lower on the trophic pyramid, a phenomenon called a **trophic cascade**. This is just one example of how whole communities of organisms interact and how species influence each other. In the trophic cascade described in the Lyme disease example, the wolves—the top of the trophic pyramid—affect other species' populations many trophic levels below. We think of communities where the top predators ultimately control the populations on lower levels of the trophic pyramid as being under **top-down control**. For example, consider a meadow. The population of rabbits in a meadow, as we have seen, might be controlled by the number of coyotes that live in that meadow. Because the number of rabbits grazing ultimately will constrain the biomass of grass, the coyotes effectively control grass production. There are many examples of communities under top-down control that exhibit cascading effects or even transitions between one ecosystem type and another after an apex predator has been removed (see **Table 30.1**).

In marine environments, sea otters (*Enhydra lutris*) are an essential predator in kelp forest ecosystems. Otter populations feed on sea urchins, and sea urchins are grazers that feed on kelp. In the absence of otters, urchin populations can explode. What were once thick kelp forests can become urchin-dominated barrens.

In freshwater ecosystems, predatory fish such as largemouth bass (*Micropterus salmoides*) indirectly keep phytoplankton populations in check. Largemouth bass are predatory fish that control the populations of fishes that feed on zooplankton. The zooplankton populations are then large enough to maintain phytoplankton densities at levels where water clarity and light penetration into the water remain high. Removing largemouth bass from this type of lake ecosystem, as has been done in an experimental lake, results in a huge bloom of phytoplankton that reduces water clarity and water quality.

In contrast to top-down control, the population of rabbits (and the population of coyotes feeding on these rabbits) in our hypothetical meadow will also depend on the amount of grass that can grow given the available abiotic resources such as light, water, and nutrients. If there is a severe drought and little grass can grow, few rabbits will be supported by the meadow. In this case, the population of rabbits is under **bottom-up control**. In many ecosystems, this is likely not a true dichotomy. Both top-down and bottom-up constraints influence populations

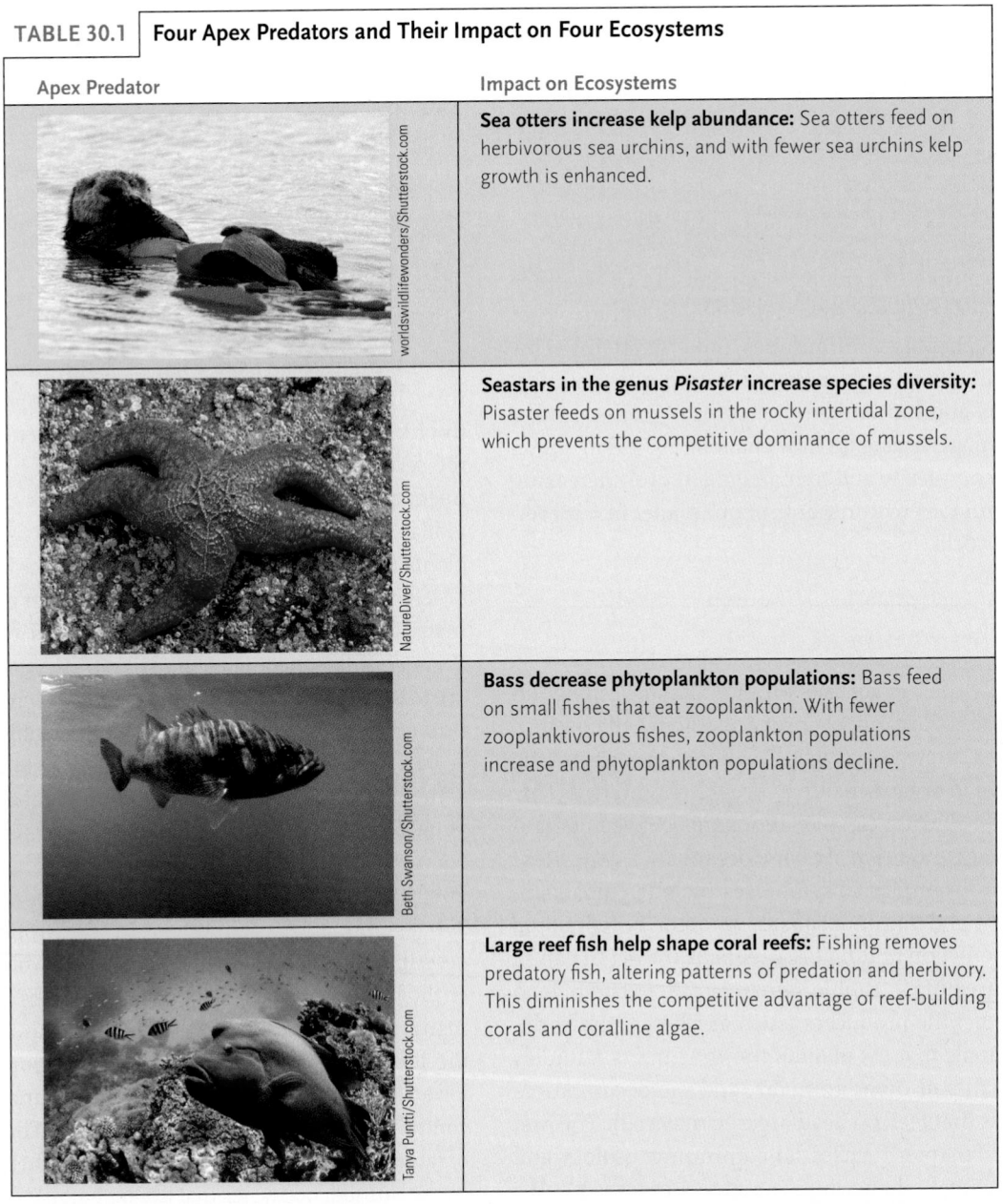

| TABLE 30.1 | Four Apex Predators and Their Impact on Four Ecosystems |
|---|---|
| Apex Predator | Impact on Ecosystems |
| | **Sea otters increase kelp abundance:** Sea otters feed on herbivorous sea urchins, and with fewer sea urchins kelp growth is enhanced. |
| | **Seastars in the genus *Pisaster* increase species diversity:** Pisaster feeds on mussels in the rocky intertidal zone, which prevents the competitive dominance of mussels. |
| | **Bass decrease phytoplankton populations:** Bass feed on small fishes that eat zooplankton. With fewer zooplanktivorous fishes, zooplankton populations increase and phytoplankton populations decline. |
| | **Large reef fish help shape coral reefs:** Fishing removes predatory fish, altering patterns of predation and herbivory. This diminishes the competitive advantage of reef-building corals and coralline algae. |

SOURCE: Based on Estes, J. A., et al., "Trophic Downgrading of Planet Earth," *Science* 15 July 2011: Vol. 333 no. 6040 pp. 301–306.

and community dynamics. Even in examples such as a trophic cascade, the strength of top-down versus bottom-up control can alternate with trophic level. For example, using the system highlighted from a marine environment, otter populations are food limited, whereas urchin populations are limited by predation. Subsequently, kelp populations are food (resource) limited (see Table 30.1).

Both top-down and bottom-up forces play important roles in trophic dynamics. However, their impact on the community is not always equal. If higher trophic levels are removed, lower levels remain intact, whereas removing primary producers leaves no levels at all.

Top-down control such as that seen in a trophic cascade after an apex predator is removed might seem intuitively strange when considered from an energetic point of view: the top level of the trophic pyramid is also the smallest. Organisms with this kind of disproportionate effect, which influence species diversity or species' populations more than their populations would suggest, are called **keystone species (Figure 30.6)**.

The loss of keystone species can be particularly destabilizing to an ecosystem. In fact, the term "keystone" refers to the final and largest stone in the center of an archway. Without this stone, the arch cannot be self-supporting **(Figure 30.7, p. 686)**.

As illustrated by the variety of trophic cascades observed across ecosystem types (Figure 30.5), there are many examples of predators as keystone species. The term was coined by the ecologist Robert Paine to describe the role of a predatory starfish, *Pisaster ochraceus*, in a rocky intertidal marine ecosystem. In this ecosystem, the starfish controls the population of mussels, facilitating a diversity of species to maintain successful populations that would otherwise be outcompeted. Keystone species do not have to be predators, however. Some species, such as beavers (*Castor canadensis*), can be considered keystone species because of the large role they play in altering and establishing habitats; such animals are sometimes called "ecosystem engineers" (Figure 30.6). Other species, such as fig trees (*Ficus* spp.) in tropical forests, are also considered keystone species because they provide important habitat and resources to such a large diversity of species and because they provide food resources when other species do not (Figure 30.6).

## STUDY BREAK

1. What is a keystone species?
2. Consider a trophic pyramid with five levels. If the apex predator is removed, what will likely happen to the herbivore population?
3. Can you think of an example of a species that could be considered an ecosystem engineer?

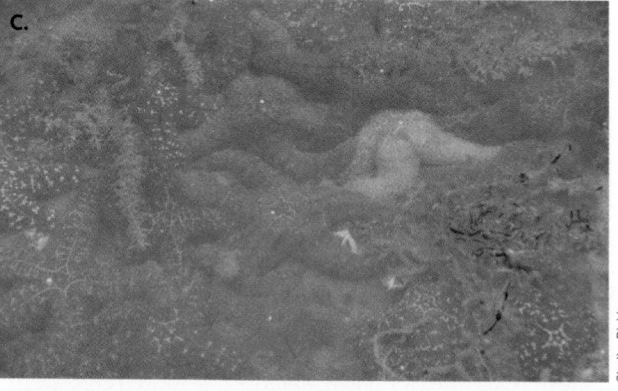

**FIGURE 30.6** Four examples of keystone species: **(a)** a beaver, **(b)** a fig tree, **(c)** a starfish, and **(d)** a sea otter.

**FIGURE 30.7** The keystone is the piece at the height of an arch without which an arch will collapse.

## Competition Influences the Niches Occupied by Organisms

The ecological role inhabited by an organism is its **niche**. This role includes the habitat where the organism makes its home, the nutrients it uses, and the organisms with which it interacts. Different species may fill similar niches in different ecosystems. In many terrestrial ecosystems, there are niches filled by a variety of small mammals. For example, in a temperate forest in southern Manitoba, rodents such as the deer mouse (*Peromyscus maniculatus*), the meadow jumping mouse (*Zapus hudsonius*), and the northern short-tailed shrew (*Blarina brevicauda*) occupy similar niches (**Figure 30.8**).

These mammals forage mostly along the forest floor, are nocturnal, and eat a wide diet that includes a variety of plant material, such as seeds, fungi, or fruit, and a variety of animal material, such as insects, earthworms, or sometimes even other vertebrates. Owls, raptors, and larger omnivorous and carnivorous mammals feed on small mammals such as these.

The islands of New Zealand offer another type of temperate forest ecosystem. However, unlike the forests of Manitoba, for millennia, the forests of New Zealand lacked small terrestrial mammals such as deer mice and shrews and hosted few larger prey animals that might feed on such organisms. This presented an opportunity—an open niche space. And it was filled, amazingly, by an unlikely species: a bat. Just like other small mammals in temperate forest ecosystems, the New Zealand lesser short-tailed bat (*Mystacina tuberculata*) is a small nocturnal mammal with a very wide diet that includes a variety of plant and animal material. Unlike most small mammals and unlike most other bats, however, the New Zealand lesser short-tailed bat has the ability to forage both in the air and on the ground (**Figure 30.9**).

The species is thought to spend between 30% and 40% of its foraging time on the ground, where it behaves like other terrestrial mammals—crawling, sniffing, and

**FIGURE 30.8** The **(a)** deer mouse, **(b)** northern short-tailed shrew, and **(c)** meadow jumping mouse.

SOURCE: (Photo B): Gilles Gonthier, http://commons.wikimedia.org/wiki/File:Blarina_brevicauda.jpg. This file is licensed under the Creative Commons Attribution 2.0 Generic license, http://creativecommons.org/licenses/by/2.0/deed.en

digging among stumps and leaf litter for food. Two species that occupy the same niche space, or two species that have similar morphologies whether or not they are closely

Daniel K. Riskin

Daniel K. Riskin

**FIGURE 30.9** The New Zealand short-tailed bat, up close and on the ground, where it spends a large part of its foraging time.

related, like the New Zealand short-tailed bat and the northern short-tailed shrew, can be thought of as having the same **life form** or of belonging to the same **guild**.

Just as niche space can be open in an ecosystem, it can also be filled, or even overfilled, leading to **competition**. Competition can occur both within a species (intraspecific competition) and between species (interspecific competition). Two plants might compete for the same water and nutrients in the soil, for example, whether or not they are the same species. In interference competition, two species compete directly with each other over a resource, perhaps a territory or a food source. The **competitive exclusion principle**, or Gause's law, states that no two species can occupy the same niche in the same ecosystem with constant environmental conditions. This principle suggests that between two competing species, one will always have a competitive advantage over the other, eventually driving the weaker competitor out of the niche, perhaps even to extinction. In the case of Lyme disease prevalence, although the large coyote with a broader diet can outcompete the smaller fox, both animals have so far been able to coexist as their niches are not completely overlapping. They have different diets, habitats, and behaviours. In other words, they partition the available resources.

## Introduced Species Can Change the Relationships among a Community's Organisms

There are other examples of competition threatening rare species in our highway medians, backyards, ponds, and lakes and especially in relatively isolated island ecosystems. With increasing globalization has come increasing exchange of species between previously isolated ecosystems. Sometimes this exchange, or intro-

duction, of species has been intentional. A fish species, the Nile perch (*Lates niloticus*), was intentionally introduced to Lake Victoria in Africa, for example, when fishing stocks in the lake got too low. Many plant species have been introduced as ornamental plants across the world. The water hyacinth (*Eichhornia crassipes*), native to the Amazon basin, has been introduced as an ornamental aquatic plant across the world. The rosy wolf snail (*Euglandina rosea*), native to the southeastern United States, was introduced to Pacific islands to combat another introduced snail, the African land snail (*Achatina fulica*) **(Figure 30.10, p. 688)**. Species that have been introduced from elsewhere are called exotic, or introduced, species. Not all of these species are problematic in their new environments, and many are unable to even get a foothold. However, in some cases, introduced species can become problematic. When exotic species damage the ecosystems to which they are introduced, they are often called **invasive species**.

Invasive species have affected ecosystems in a variety of ways, all of which involve competition with native species. The rosy wolf snail, through both competition and predation, has now driven the decline of many **endemic** snail species (species specific to a particular region). The Nile perch has been responsible for the extinction of 200 fish species, also through predation and competition. The Nile perch is a voracious predator and has outcompeted and eaten many of the fish in Lake Victoria. The fish is also oilier than other native species in the lake, requiring fisherman and other locals to use more wood to dry the flesh. Logging for this wood has led to increased bank erosion into the lake. The resulting decrease in the water quality of Lake Victoria has been so severe that low levels of dissolved oxygen have caused many more fish deaths.

Water hyacinth is native to the Amazon basin in South America, most likely Brazil. It is an aquatic plant with beautiful lavender flowers that forms floating

**FIGURE 30.10** Three invasive species that have impacted native species populations: the **(a)** Nile perch, **(b)** water hyacinth, and **(c)** rosy wolf snail.

Not all introduced species become invasive pests. In fact, some may have positive ecosystem effects or even conservation value, but it is difficult to predict the effect any species will have on a receiving ecosystem. There has been much debate on the effects of exotic plant species on native species. It has been difficult to document examples of exotic plant species driving native species to extinction. Some communities have simply continued to add species, despite what we expect from what we know about competitive exclusion. So what is going on? Scientists have begun to look at this apparent paradox. In one recent study, scientists compared the competitive ability and susceptibility to herbivores of native and exotic species. They used strandline plant communities in Narragansett Bay, in the northeast of the United States. A strandline plant community occurs along an ocean coast between intertidal and terrestrial ecosystems. This particular strandline plant community has been invaded by exotic species many times over a long period. Surveys beginning in the late 1990s show that whereas the number of exotic species and the area covered by exotics are increasing, the number of native species and the area that they cover are not significantly decreasing. Researchers conducted careful surveys of species and herbivory. They also ran a series of experiments in which herbivory was suppressed in plots with different combinations of native and exotic species. The scientists showed that about twice as much herbivory occurred in exotic species compared to native species **(Figure 30.11b)**. Second, if herbivory is suppressed, the ratio between exotic and native species richness (the number of species) and the ratio between exotic and native cover increased **(Figure 30.11c)**. This means that the exotic species are better competitors and could take over if there were no herbivores. But because they are more susceptible to herbivory, the balance between native and exotic species is maintained.

## Disturbances Can Quickly Change the Makeup of a Community's Organisms

The definition of what constitutes a **disturbance** can vary, but we will think of it as a discrete event that alters resource availability, community structure, or the physical environment of an ecosystem. Disturbances can be catastrophic: a volcanic eruption, a hurricane, or a fire. They can also be smaller and less intrusive: a tree falling in a forest, or a whale carcass dropping to the bottom of the ocean. These disturbances also occur at a variety of time scales—from daily for something such as tree falls to millennially for volcanoes, glaciation, or very large floods **(Figure 30.12)**.

Environmental disturbances disrupt the status quo, changing the balance among species and potentially favouring the success of previously outcompeted species by opening niche space. Many of these disturbances are

vegetative mats and has been introduced across the world as an ornamental plant. You can likely even find water hyacinth–scented soaps and other products in your local grocery store. Across the world, however, it has also become a pest. The plant is fast growing. It quickly covers water surfaces, blocks light from reaching other aquatic plants, limits the space other plants have to grow, and even increases flooding by blocking runoff into streams and lakes. Water hyacinth also serves as an example of how difficult invasive species can be to control. Still a problem today, it was first officially recognized as a serious invasive species in the United States in 1897.

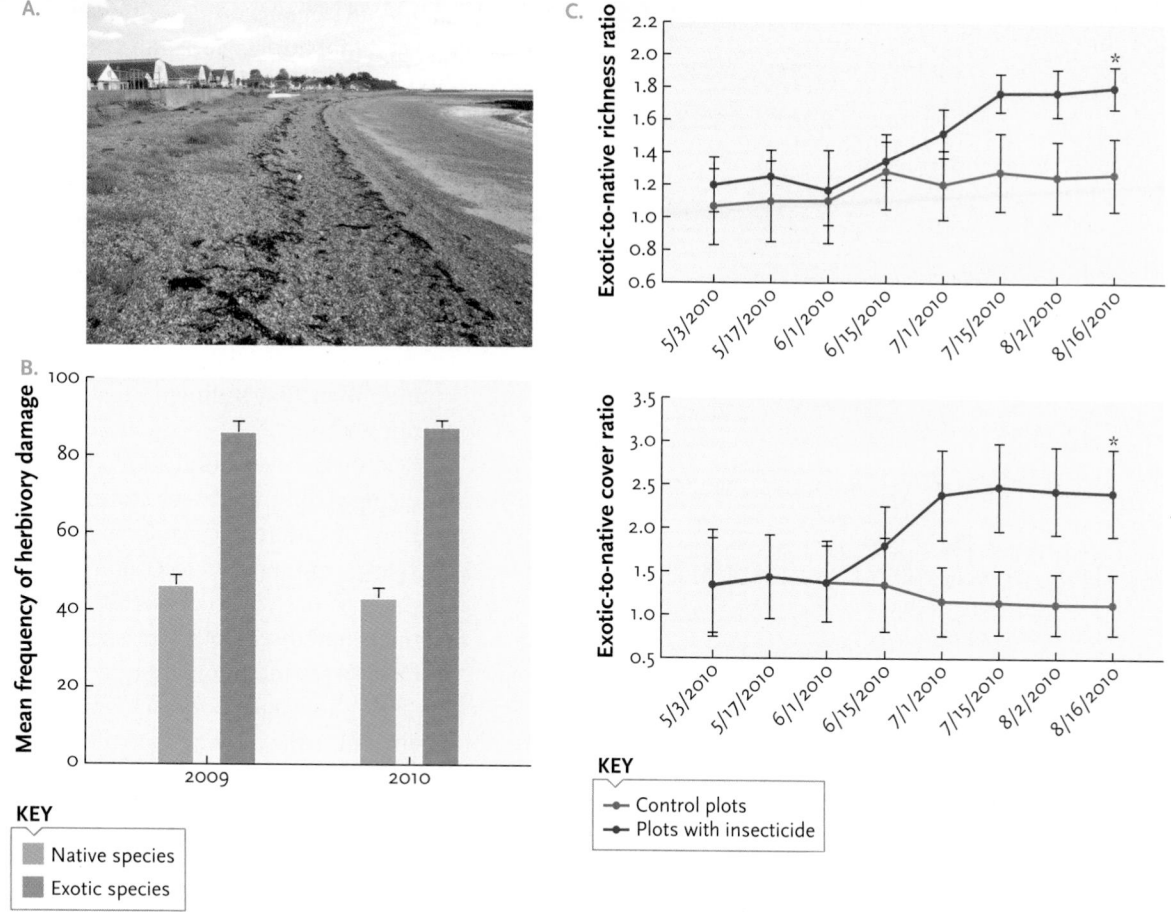

**FIGURE 30.11** In a strandline plant community, **(a)** exotic plants and native plants coexist because of trade-offs between susceptibility to herbivores and competitive ability. Panel **(b)** shows that exotic species are preyed on by herbivores more often than native species, whereas the two graphs in panel **(c)** show that if herbivory is suppressed, the ratio of exotic to native plants changes, with exotic species outcompeting native species.

SOURCE: (Photo A): © Copyright Martin Speck and licensed for reuse under this Creative Commons Licence, http://creativecommons.org/licenses/by-sa/2.0/; (B–C): Heard, M. J. and D. F. Sax, "Coexistence between native and exotic species is facilitated by asymmetries in competitive ability and susceptibility to herbivores," *Ecology Letters*, Volume 16, Issue 2, pages 206–213, February 2013. John Wiley and Sons. © 2012 Blackwell Publishing Ltd/CNRS.

destructive. They can effectively kill many, if not most, of the organisms living in a particular area. This also, however, creates an opportunity. Some plants, for example, grow very quickly and need a lot of direct sunlight. By the time a forest has grown a thick canopy, these plants will no longer be able to access the amount of light they need to grow. After a hurricane, however, or even after the collapse of just one tree, such a plant might be able to colonize.

**FIGURE 30.12** Ecosystem disturbances can be frequent or occur only over long time scales and can be small or large. Pictured here is an example of a dramatic disturbance, the clearing of tropical forest for agriculture in the Brazilian Amazon.

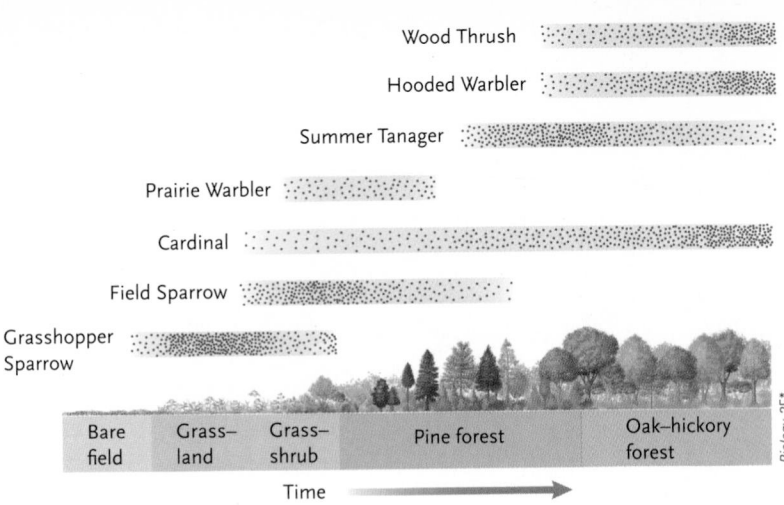

Wood Thrush

Hooded Warbler

Summer Tanager

Prairie Warbler

Cardinal

Field Sparrow

Grasshopper Sparrow

Bare field | Grass-land | Grass-shrub | Pine forest | Oak–hickory forest

Time

*Biology, 2E\**

**FIGURE 30.13** Successional changes in bird species composition in an abandoned agricultural field in eastern North America parallel the changes in plant species composition. The residence times of several representative species are illustrated. The density of stippling inside each bar illustrates the density of each species through time.

## Succession Describes Changes in Community Structure with Time

The community of species that you see following a disturbance will change with time. This process is called **succession (Figure 30.13)**.

Succession often occurs predictably, in terms of both the time scale over which the communities change and the species that make up these communities. Over long time scales, succession may lead to a **climax community**, an ecosystem in steady state, where the proportions of species remain relatively constant, the demand for resources meets the supply, and the major vegetation type does not change. The frequency of disturbances in most places makes this state of equilibrium difficult to attain, and it is likely that any ecosystem you observe is in some stage of active succession.

Succession can even be observed following a disturbance such as a whale fall **(Figure 30.14)**. The deep ocean, with limited light availability and low nutrient availability, is an area with low productivity. Imagine a whale carcass of a large whale species. A blue whale, for instance, can weigh over 150,000 kg, so its carcass might weigh as

much as 15 school buses. Imagine this whale carcass falling to this dark and vast sea floor where any energy source is a limited resource. Does this falling carcass fit our definition of a disturbance? It certainly is a discrete event, and it certainly changes resource availability. The amount of organic matter that enters the ecosystem with this carcass is equivalent to centuries of background levels of organic matter inputs in the deep sea. The carcass can also physically alter the environment by disrupting and moving sediments that host communities of microbes.

Scientists have found that a whale fall also changes community structure, attracting a variety of different organisms. Scientists can track community succession on whale falls by tracking whale carcasses over time. Scientists have used both carcasses found in the deep sea and carcasses intentionally sunk to the sea floor. Scientists visit the whale carcasses over time in piloted submersibles or using remotely operated vehicles (ROVs) to collect time-series data **(Figure 30.15)**.

Following observations of several whale carcasses, scientists have separated the communities congregating on whale carcasses in the deep sea into three phases. During the first phase—the mobile scavenger stage—a number of scavengers, big and small, take advantage of the whale's remaining flesh. This includes hundreds of hagfish (see Chapter 19 for more information on hagfish), sleeper sharks (*Somniosus pacificus*), crabs, amphipods, and copepods (Figure 30.14). These organisms remove an estimated 40 to 60 kg of flesh each day. Depending on the size of the whale carcass, this phase lasts from 4 months to 2 years. The mobile scavenger phase ends when more than 90% of the whale's flesh has been removed and mostly skeleton remains.

During the second phase—the enrichment opportunist stage—many organisms take advantage of the pulse of organic material in the sediments and in and around the skeleton itself. During this phase, the number of individuals colonizing the skeleton and the space just around

**FIGURE 30.14** Stages of succession during decomposition of a whale carcass in the deep sea.

SOURCE: "The Prolific Afterlife of Whales," by Crispin T.S. Little, *Scientific American*, February 2010. JEN CHRISTIANSEN (whale-fall illustration); CATHERINE WILSON (species inset illustrations)

**FIGURE 30.15** A Remotely Operated Vehicle (ROV) visits the deep sea floor.

the skeleton can be incredibly high—between 20,000 and 45,000 individuals per square metre. The community includes polychaetes (marine worms), described as being so thick that they look like sea grass, gastropods (sea snails and slugs), juvenile bivalves (e.g., mussels and clams), cumaceans (small shrimps), and dense congregations of *Vigtorniella* species (marine worms that have only been found in organically enriched areas such as whale falls) (Figure 30.14). All of these organisms are heterotrophs, getting all of their energy from eating other organisms. This phase, like the first phase, lasts less than 2 years.

The third phase is the sulphophilic (sulphur-loving) phase. In this phase, in addition to organisms such as crabs and polychaetes observed in earlier phases, bacterial species, both free living and symbiotic, become important. Whale bones contain a high concentration of lipids (fats), sometimes making up 60% of the fresh weight of the bones. Chemoautotrophic bacteria colonize the anaerobic environment in the core of the bones. These bacteria decompose the lipids in the whale bones using sulphate available from the surrounding sea water to fuel their respiration in the absence of oxygen. This releases large amounts of sulphide (elemental sulphur with a negative charge, $S^{-2}$) into the water surrounding the bones. This means that only organisms that can tolerate high concentrations of sulphur are able to live on the whale skeleton during this phase. This community includes some polychaetes, isopods, gastropods, limpets, galatheid crabs, and mussels (Figure 30.14). Some of these species, including the dominant mussel species (*Idas washingtonia*), host endosymbionts that are chemoautotrophic bacteria. This allows the organisms to harvest energy from the sulphide and hydrogen sulphide released from the whale bones. This unique environment shares several species with hydrothermal vent communities. For example, galatheid crabs, which are actually a type of lobster, are also found on hydrothermal vents in the deep ocean. Others are species that appear to be whale-fall specialists, having never been observed outside this unique

ecosystem (see the discussion of *Osedax* worms in Chapter 19). This extreme sulphophilic stage can be very long lasting. Scientists have observed whale falls more than 50 years old that continued to host this type of community.

## STUDY BREAK

1. What is the competitive exclusion principle?
2. Can you think of an example of intraspecific competition?
3. Describe what succession might be like in an abandoned farm field.

## 30.2 Ecosystem Ecology

At the beginning of the chapter, ecosystem ecology was defined as the study of how ecosystems function. It is a discipline that explores the interactions among biological communities and their physical environments, in large part studying the cycling of nutrients (i.e., chemical elements) through ecosystems. How does studying the chemistry of ecosystems help us understand the biological world? Primary production, and thus all food webs, depends on nutrients (see Chapter 2 for more information on primary production and trophic levels). We can think about this in terms of the gardens we grow in our backyards and the farm fields we cultivate to produce our food. Every plant takes up nutrients and water that it needs from the soil. If this plant is grown in a pot and nothing but sunlight is added to the pot, eventually, the plant will run out of water and die. Likewise, if you take this pot and add only sunlight and water, eventually, the plant will run out of nutrients and its growth will slow, its health will deteriorate, and it will ultimately die. Similarly, you add water and compost or fertilizer to the vegetables and herbs in your garden to maximize their growth potential.

Natural ecosystems function in similar ways: plants need to be able to access nutrients in the soils in which they grow. These nutrients can be recycled within an ecosystem. Plants pull up nutrients from the soil, the plant dies returning the nutrients to the soil, decomposers liberate these nutrients from the dead plant material, and the nutrients are available once again to be taken up by another plant. But how does an ecosystem get nutrient stocks in the first place? And does an ecosystem lose nutrients over time? Are different nutrients more important than others? These are the kinds of questions ecosystem ecology attempts to answer.

### The Elements That Make Up Our Ecosystems Make Up the Universe

You can also take a step even further back and consider this question: where do all of the materials (i.e., elements)

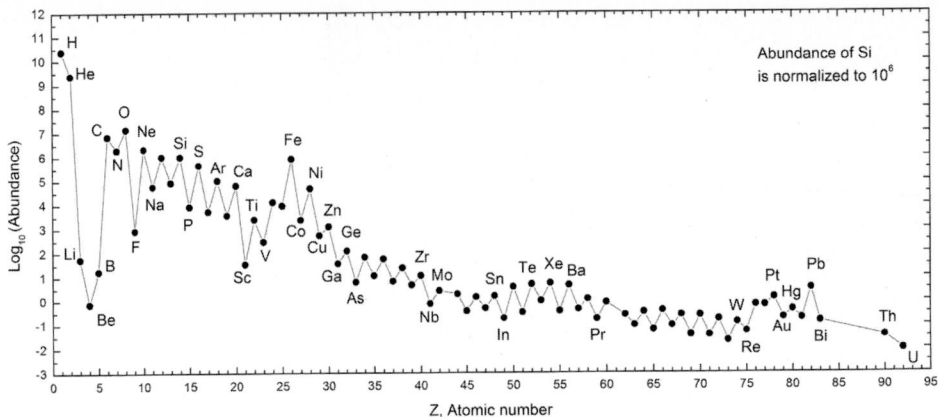

**FIGURE 30.16** The abundance of elements in the universe decreases with increasing atomic number and is higher for even- than for odd-numbered elements.

SOURCE: Orionus, http://commons.wikimedia.org/wiki/File:SolarSystemAbundances.jpg. This file is licensed under the Creative Commons Attribution-Share Alike 3.0 Unported license, http://creativecommons.org/licenses/by-sa/3.0/deed.en

necessary for life come from? Amazingly, we can explain the ratios of elements present on Earth remarkably well by looking at the universe. The universe is thought to have begun with the Big Bang, currently estimated to have occurred close to 14 billion years ago. The Big Bang first brought together particles that made up the most basic of the elements: hydrogen ($^2$H) and helium ($^4$He). The number associated with each of these elements in superscript indicates the number of particles (protons plus neutrons) present in the nucleus of an atom of the element. The universe remained mostly hydrogen and helium until the birth of stars. In a star, the heat and pressure can produce both nuclear fusion (the nuclei, or protons and neutrons, of two atoms coming together to form a new, larger atom) and nuclear fission (the breaking

apart of an atom's protons and neutrons into smaller atoms with fewer protons and neutrons than the original atom). This means that atoms of hydrogen, with one proton and one neutron, can be combined to create atoms of helium, for example, with two protons and two neutrons. This reaction happens a lot. In fact, as a star ages, more and more of the hydrogen present is converted to helium. The star begins to collapse inward on itself, a victim of its own gravity, which further increases the temperature and pressure. This causes the hydrogen to burn, which leads to additional fusion reactions in which $^4$He combines with other $^4$He to form an atom with four protons and four neutrons, or beryllium ($^8$Be). Beryllium ($^8$Be) can then combine with another $^4$He to form carbon ($^{12}$C), the main product of burning helium, or $^8$Be can also

**FIGURE 30.17** The carbon cycle. Marine and terrestrial components of the global carbon cycle are linked through an atmospheric reservoir of carbon dioxide. By far the largest amount of Earth's carbon is found in sediments and rocks. Earth's atmosphere mediates most of the movement of carbon. In this illustration of the carbon cycle, boxes identify major reservoirs and labels on arrows identify the processes that cause carbon to move between reservoirs.

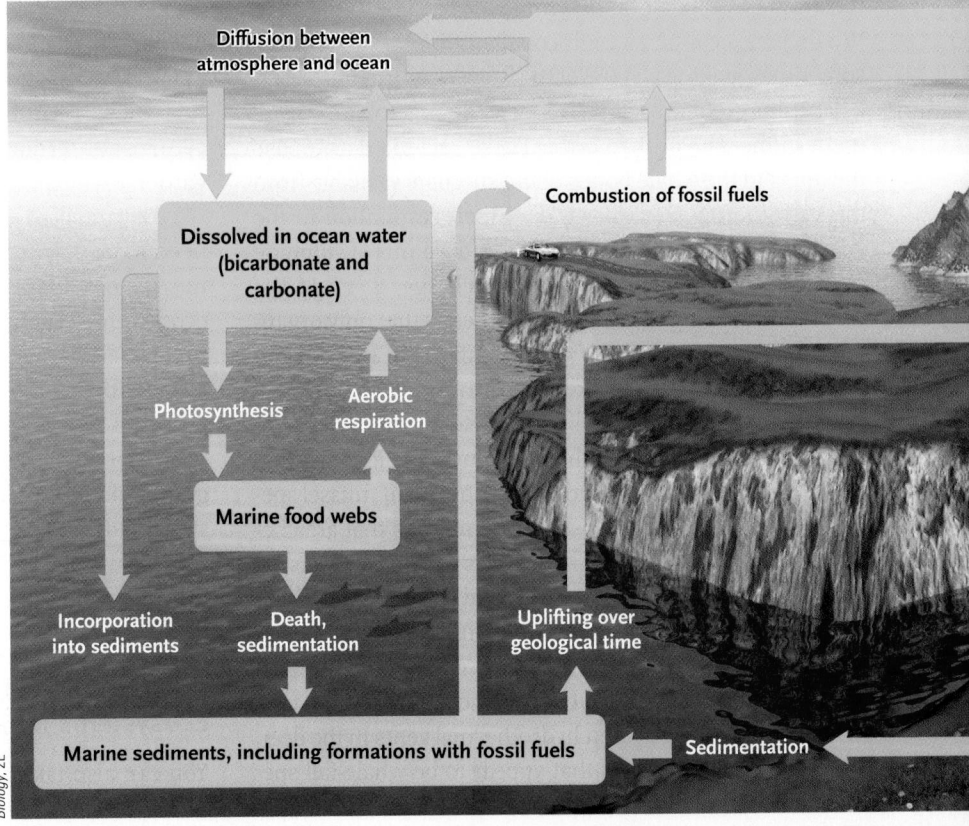

combine with another $^{8}$Be to create oxygen ($^{16}$O). This burning and fusion of elements continues within stars, and these fusion reactions are believed to create all of the even-numbered elements up to iron ($^{26}$Fe).

Most odd-numbered elements are caused by fission reactions, where the nucleus of atoms is split. For these reactions to occur, you need an element with a larger atomic number and, therefore, a nucleus that can lose a proton. For example, to make chlorine ($^{17}$Cl), you need a larger atom with protons to lose, such as argon ($^{18}$Ar). You also need additional energy to split the nucleus. The additional energy requirements make odd-numbered elements both slightly less abundant and slightly less stable than their even-numbered counterparts **(Figure 30.16)**.

These processes can explain a lot about the elemental abundances on Earth and even within the biological world. Hydrogen and helium are the most abundant elements on Earth. The abundance of other elements decreases with increasing atomic weight (i.e., the larger the number of protons and neutrons in the nucleus, the less abundant the element). And life is dominated by these light elements that can be created in stars. No element heavier than $^{26}$Fe is essential to life, nor is any element heavier than $^{26}$Fe present in high concentrations in living tissues.

You are built from the same elements that exist across the universe and in similar proportions. The abundance of these elements is ultimately controlled by imploding stars. Perhaps no less astounding are the ways in which elements cycle through our biosphere today, the ways in which organisms have evolved to exploit the elements essential for life (e.g., nutrients) in different ecosystems, and the ways that humans have harnessed and altered global **biogeochemical cycles** (the cycles of nutrients and other elements through the abiotic and biotic environments on Earth). You will get a brief overview to some of Earth's most essential biogeochemical cycles in the remaining sections of this chapter.

## The Carbon Cycle Influences Organisms and Climate

As you have seen in earlier chapters, carbon is the currency on which biological economies run (see Chapter 2, for example). Plants use light energy to fix atmospheric carbon dioxide ($CO_2$) into carbon sugars (carbohydrates), which then fuel all other trophic levels. Some of this carbon is returned to the atmosphere as organisms break down these organic carbon compounds through respiration, releasing $CO_2$ as a by-product. But what happens to this carbon in the long term, and where are the large pools of carbon on Earth? Is most in the atmosphere? Is most in rocks? How much is in plants?

Carbon is stored in four main reservoirs on Earth: (1) the atmosphere, (2) the land (plants and soils), (3) the oceans, and (4) sediment and rocks **(Figure 30.17)**.

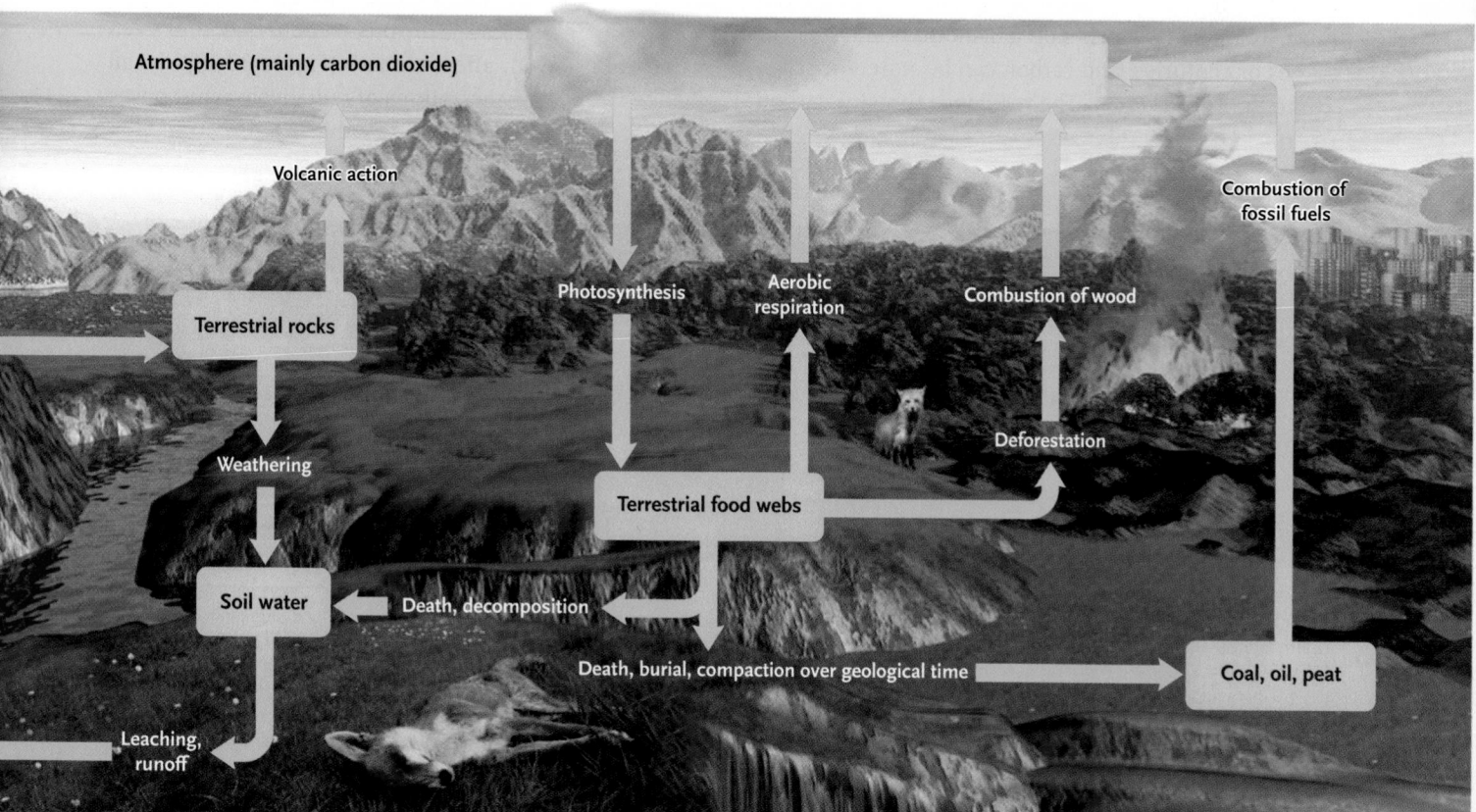

Atmosphere (mainly carbon dioxide)

Volcanic action

Combustion of fossil fuels

Photosynthesis

Aerobic respiration

Combustion of wood

Terrestrial rocks

Deforestation

Weathering

Terrestrial food webs

Soil water

Death, decomposition

Death, burial, compaction over geological time

Coal, oil, peat

Leaching, runoff

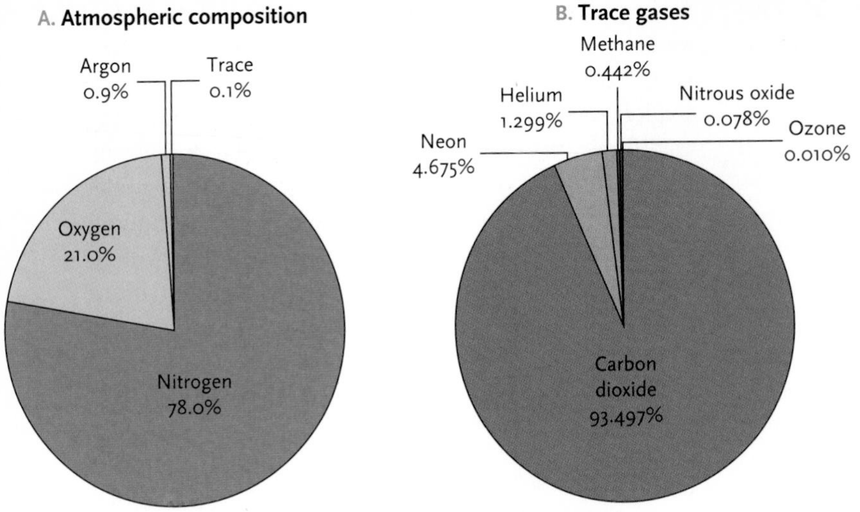

## A. Atmospheric composition

Argon
0.9%

Trace
0.1%

Oxygen
21.0%

Nitrogen
78.0%

## B. Trace gases

Methane
0.442%

Helium
1.299%

Nitrous oxide
0.078%

Neon
4.675%

Ozone
0.010%

Carbon
dioxide
93.497%

**FIGURE 30.18** **(a)** The major constituents of Earth's atmosphere. **(b)** The composition of the trace gases that make up the 0.1% of the atmosphere not accounted for by major gases.

Carbon moves between these four reservoirs all the time. But the time scale—or how rapidly it is exchanged—varies dramatically. The time it takes for carbon (or other substances) to move through one of these reservoirs is called **turnover time**, or **residence time**. It can be calculated by taking the total amount of substance in the reservoir and dividing it by either the flux into the reservoir or the flux out. The residence time over which carbon is taken from the atmosphere by plants for photosynthesis or returned to the atmosphere through respiration is on the scale of seconds or minutes. The relevant time scale for exchanging carbon with the other pools, however, can be much longer. Carbon is stored in biomass and soils for decades or centuries, and carbon can be stored in ocean sediments for millennia. The residence time for carbon in Earth's largest carbon reservoir, that of rock, is even

longer. It turns over through tectonic uplift over millions of years.

The balance between carbon in the atmosphere, carbon in the biotic environment, and carbon dissolved in water and sediments controls the energy that can cycle through our ecosystems. This balance has a huge impact on global climate. However, only a very small fraction of our atmosphere is made up of carbon, and this carbon represents a small fraction of all the carbon on Earth. Most of the atmosphere, about 78%, is nitrogen (in the form of dinitrogen, $N_2$). Another 20% or so of the atmosphere is oxygen, $O_2$. Argon, a noble gas, makes up another almost 1%. Carbon, mainly as carbon dioxide, makes up only about 0.04% (note that this number is rapidly climbing; it was 0.0398%, or 398 parts per million, in February 2014; you might want to check what it is now for yourself) **(Figure 30.18)**.

In the atmosphere, $CO_2$ acts as a greenhouse gas. When light from the Sun hits Earth, some is absorbed by Earth's surface. A lot, however, is reflected back toward space. Radiatively active gases in the atmosphere, such as $CO_2$, are gases that reflect some of this light back toward Earth, effectively trapping the Sun's energy in our atmosphere. We also call these radiatively active gases **greenhouse gases**. This is an important part of how Earth stays warm enough to sustain life **(Figure 30.19)**.

This is the way that $CO_2$ and other greenhouse gases, such as methane ($CH_4$), nitrous oxide ($N_2O$), and even water vapor ($H_2O$), affect climate (Figure 30.19). Small changes in the concentrations of radiatively active gases in the atmosphere can have big impacts on the

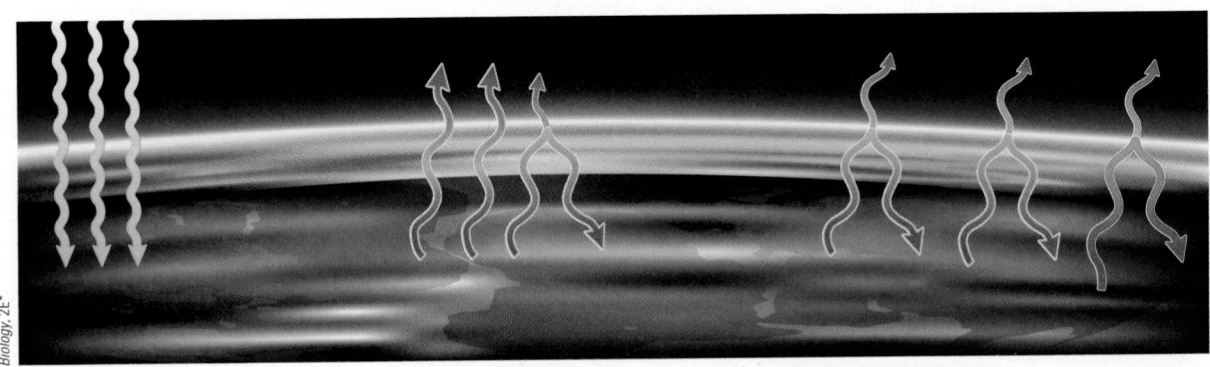

Biology, 2E*

Sunlight penetrates the atmosphere and warms Earth's surface.

Earth's surface radiates heat (infrared wavelengths) to the atmosphere. Some heat escapes into space. Greenhouse gases and water vapour absorb some infrared energy and reradiate the rest of it back toward Earth.

When atmospheric concentrations of greenhouse gases increase, the atmosphere near Earth's surface traps more heat. The warming causes a positive feedback cycle in which rising ocean temperatures cause increased evaporation of water, which further enhances the greenhouse effect.

**FIGURE 30.19** The greenhouse effect.

temperature of the planet. Because even small changes in the concentration of $CO_2$ can make a dramatic difference to global temperatures, scientists pay careful attention to the places on Earth where $CO_2$ is produced—carbon sources—and to the places where $CO_2$ is absorbed—carbon sinks. The balance between sources and sinks determines the amount of $CO_2$ in the atmosphere.

The amount of carbon stored in terrestrial biomass (650 gigatonnes, 109 tonnes) is similar, but slightly less, than the amount of carbon in the atmospheric reservoir (760 gigatonnes). Although it can be difficult to measure, scientists estimate that all of the terrestrial biomass on Earth takes up only slightly more $CO_2$ from the atmosphere (120 gigatonnes) than is returned through respiration from plants and soil (119.6 gigatonnes), making terrestrial vegetation a net sink for carbon.

There is about twice as much carbon in soils (1500 gigatonnes) than in terrestrial biomass or in the atmosphere. In addition to the exchange between the reservoirs of carbon in the atmosphere and on land, every year some carbon is transported through rivers and streams to oceans (0.8 gigatonnes). This carbon flux contains both organic carbon from **detritus** (dead organic matter) and inorganic carbon dissolved from rocks and sediment or soils through **weathering** (dissolution of rocks and sediments through physical and chemical reactions). In the oceans, most of the carbon is in dissolved form in intermediate and deep water (37,100 gigatonnes). Some is in marine biomass (3 gigatonnes). Some, importantly, is used by marine organisms in shells or other hard body parts (carbon used in this way is most often calcium carbonate, $CaCO_3$). Each year some of the organisms die, sinking to the bottom of the deep sea and carrying their calcium carbonate with them. This carbon is then buried in ocean sediments, a process often called the **biological pump**, which is one of the most important ways that carbon is taken out of the shorter-term fluxes in the carbon cycle. The carbon then becomes part of the long-term carbon cycle that cycles over geologic time scales (thousands or millions of years).

By far the largest reservoir of carbon on Earth is that contained in rocks and sediments (60,000,000 gigatonnes). Some of the carbon in this reservoir is originally from organic matter and, under the right geologic conditions, has become the carbon (fossil fuels) we now tap for energy: oil, gas, and coal. By burning these fossil fuels, humans have effectively sped up the global carbon cycle, introducing carbon that would otherwise not have been returned to the rapidly cycling reservoirs of carbon for millions of years. Burning fossil fuels is not the only way that humans have changed the carbon cycle, although this represents about 76% of the carbon emissions that humans release into the atmosphere annually. In addition, deforestation and biomass burning return carbon (about 20%) to the atmosphere each year that

would otherwise be stored for decades or centuries on land. Even cement production for our sidewalks, roads, and buildings influences the carbon cycle, releasing $CO_2$ from rocks containing carbonate ($CO_3^-$) and contributing to carbon emissions (about 4%) each year **(Figure 30.20)**.

The amount of carbon in each of these reservoirs and fluxes cannot be measured directly (can you think of a way to measure the carbon content of all the terrestrial biomass?), and our best estimates are constantly being improved over time. Scientists can, however, measure the components of the atmosphere very accurately and have done so for many decades, creating a long-term data set of concentrations of the different gases that contribute to our current atmosphere. One of these data sets—in fact, the longest available data set—has been recorded at Mauna Loa, a volcano in Hawaii. Observations from Mauna Loa are thought to accurately reflect the background atmosphere. Hawaii's location in the Pacific Ocean makes it the most remote island chain on Earth, far from the cities and industry that can alter local concentrations of atmospheric gases. Even within Hawaii, Mauna Loa is far from cities or industry, making the atmosphere there reflective of global averages. Charles David Keeling,

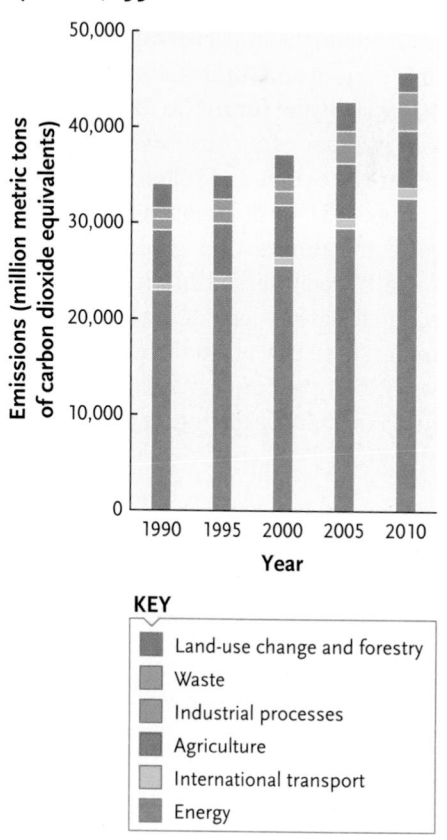

**Global Greenhouse Gas Emissions by Sector, 1990–2010**

**FIGURE 30.20** Greenhouse gas emissions by different economic sectors between 1990 and 2010.

SOURCE: US Environmental Protection Agency, http://www.epa.gov/climatechange/science/indicators/ghg/global-ghg-emissions.html

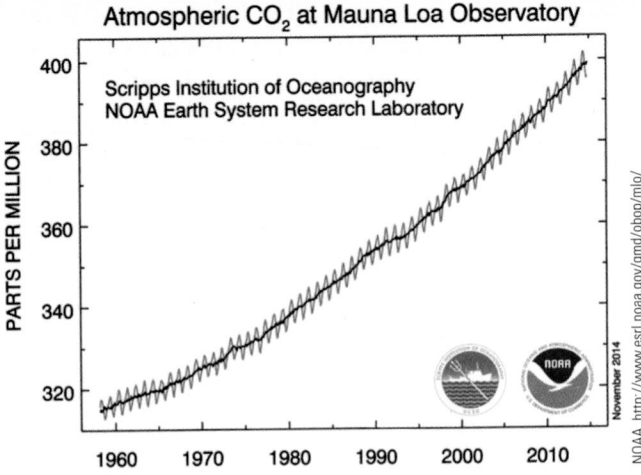

**FIGURE 30.21** The Keeling curve: a plot of atmospheric carbon dioxide concentrations collected continuously beginning in the 1950s on Mauna Loa, Hawaii.

a scientist from Scripps Institution of Oceanography, began recording the concentration of atmospheric $CO_2$ at Mauna Loa in the 1950s. Atmospheric $CO_2$ data have been collected continuously since that time, with the study site now run by his son, Ralph Keeling. A plot of these data, often called the Keeling curve, shows the atmospheric concentration of $CO_2$ increasing dramatically between the 1950s and today **(Figure 30.21)**.

To understand the impact of this rise in atmospheric $CO_2$ on our current and future climate, scientists look to the past as well as the future. To look at the past, scientists use a number of proxies, including the chemical composition of ice cores and pollen grains found in deep lake sediments to look at atmospheric composition and biological communities over geologic time. Scientists have also built models based on what we know about the controls on climate to look at what the effects of continued increases in $CO_2$ and other greenhouse gases will be. We will explore our understanding of climate change and our role in shaping the future climate of our planet in Chapter 31.

## STUDY BREAK

1. Where is carbon stored on Earth?
2. What is residence time?
3. What is the biological pump, and why is it important for the climate?

## Nutrient Limitation Influences Ecosystem Production

Justus von Liebig (1803–1873) was a chemist in the 19th century. Liebig proposed a concept that is now known as Liebig's law of the minimum. This concept suggests that plant growth will be constrained by the least available nutrient. A barrel with staves of different lengths is often used as an analogy to describe this concept. The stave that has the shortest length controls how much water can be held in the barrel. Likewise, if each stave represents a nutrient essential to plant growth, then the nutrient in shortest supply will limit how much a plant is able to grow **(Figure 30.22)**.

Time scales are an important consideration in understanding nutrient limitation. What constrains the productivity of an organism can change over minutes or hours. In the early morning, light availability will limit photosynthesis in a plant, whereas during a hot afternoon, photosynthesis is likely limited by water availability. Over the course of a growing season, however, it might not be light or water but an essential nutrient, such as nitrogen, that limits productivity. But over even longer time scales, say hundreds or thousands or even millions of years, it might not be nitrogen at all but phosphorus that limits productivity. The limitation of these different resources over all of these time scales affects the productivity of ecosystems. The coming sections will describe two important biogeochemical cycles that can influence productivity and the functioning of life on Earth: those of nitrogen and phosphorus.

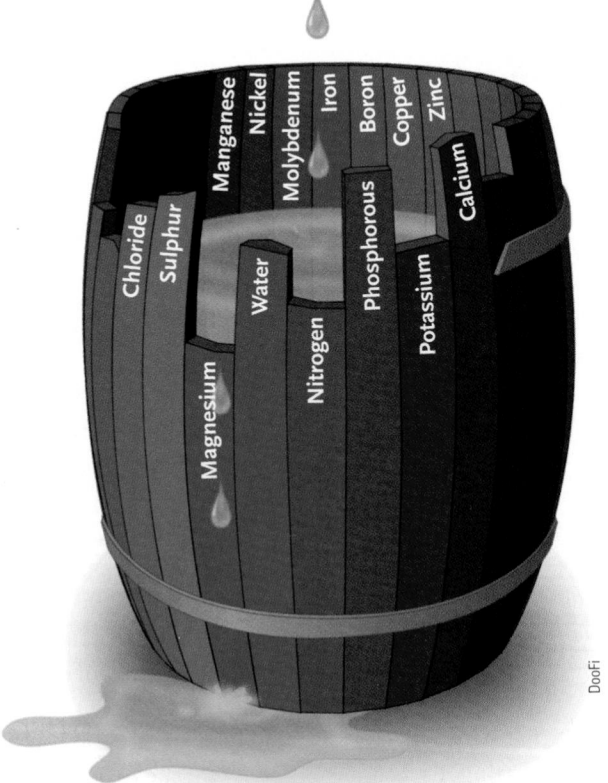

**FIGURE 30.22** A barrel in which each stave represents a nutrient in an ecosystem. The shortest stave controls the level of water in the barrel as the nutrient in shortest supply may limit primary production.

## Nitrogen Is Essential to All Organisms, Including Humans

Nitrogen, like carbon, is essential to all living things. Amino acids, the building blocks of proteins, are rich in nitrogen, as are the nucleic acids DNA and RNA (see Chapter 3 for more information about amino and nucleic acids). We would not exist without it, nor would life as we know it. The nitrogen content of plants can affect how quickly a plant grows, its ability as a competitor, and even the palatability of plants to herbivores. The carbon-rich compounds that are responsible for much of plant structure, lignin and cellulose, are hard or impossible for most animal species to break down (see Chapter 1 or 2 for a discussion of cellulose digestion in some insect species, including ants and termites). Earlier in this chapter, we discussed asymmetry in competitive ability and susceptibility to herbivores between native and exotic plant species. As part of this experiment, scientists additionally found that the amount of nitrogen compared to carbon in plants or the carbon to nitrogen (C:N) ratio explained much of the susceptibility of plants to herbivores. Plants with more nitrogen than carbon—or those with a lower C:N ratio—were more likely to be preyed on by herbivores than plants with leaves that were harder to digest with higher C:N ratios. In closely related species, some native and some exotic, the exotic species were exploited by herbivores more and had lower C:N ratios than their native relatives.

As discussed above, about 78% of the Earth's atmosphere is nitrogen. However, unlike the $CO_2$ that can be taken directly from the atmosphere and used by plants in photosynthesis, dinitrogen ($N_2$), the most common form of nitrogen in the atmosphere, cannot be directly used by most organisms. Instead, atmospheric nitrogen must be "fixed," or converted to a chemical form that can be assimilated by other organisms. Ammonium ($NH_4^+$) and nitrate ($NO_3^-$) are common forms of nitrogen in ecosystems that are considered biologically available.

In the absence of human interference, nitrogen is fixed in two main ways. First, some bacteria are able to fix nitrogen. These include free-living bacteria in soils and also bacteria that are involved in symbioses with plants. Many plants in the family Fabaceae (or Leguminosae), for example, including important agricultural legumes such as peanuts and soybeans, host the symbiotic nitrogen-fixing bacteria rhizobia **(Figure 30.23)**. They fix atmospheric nitrogen that they, the plants, and perhaps neighbouring plants and microbes, can use in exchange for carbon sugars that the plants produce through photosynthesis.

The second way that nitrogen enters ecosystems is through fixation by lightning. The energy in lightning can break the very strong triple bond holding $N_2$ together,

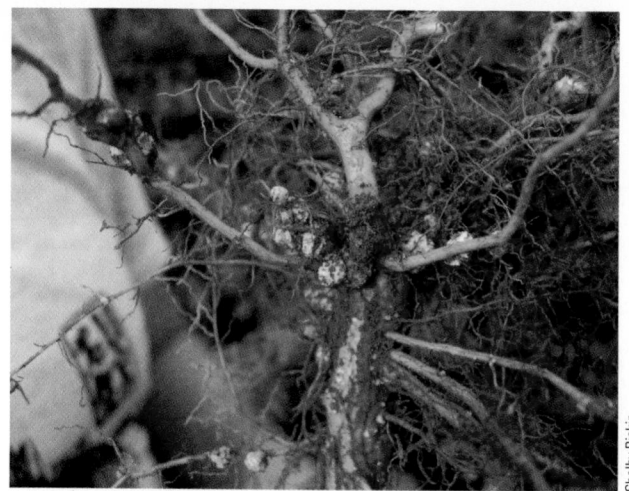

**FIGURE 30.23** The roots of a soybean plant (*Glycine max*) and the nodules that contain nitrogen-fixing bacteria.

which then allows nitrogen to form ammonium or nitrate ions that can be deposited over ecosystems in rain (i.e., wet deposition).

Many terrestrial ecosystems, particularly in the temperate zone, as well as most marine ecosystems, are typically thought of as nitrogen limited. From the discussion of the law of the minimum above, you know that this means that nitrogen is the shortest stave in the barrel of water for these ecosystems; add more nitrogen, and you should see an increase in growth, or more primary production. But why are these ecosystems nitrogen limited and not others? Many factors control nutrient limitation in ecosystems, including age (time), topography, climate, vegetation, soils, and parent material (the rock that underlies an ecosystem). In terms of nitrogen, the age of an ecosystem and the vegetation present will likely be particularly important. Imagine that there has been a large disturbance; for example, a volcano has erupted, and a lava flow has destroyed the life that once existed in the lowland area adjacent to the volcano. Even as plants begin to colonize the area, as the lava is broken down and soils begin to form, there is no large reservoir of nitrogen for these plants to access. Nitrogen must be fixed from the atmosphere, and the stock of nitrogen in soils must be built up. Nitrogen-fixing plants might be particularly successful in such an environment (but see Box 30.1). Over time, stocks of nitrogen in soils will accumulate such that nitrogen is not so scarce.

This is one reason why many temperate terrestrial ecosystems are nitrogen limited. The temperate zones around the globe were glaciated during the last glacial period, which ended some 10,000 years ago. This glaciation was a huge disturbance, just like our hypothetical lava flow, that reset the ecosystem clock in many places. As the ice sheets retreated, old soil surfaces were scraped away, revealing new rocks and surfaces to be colonized. These regions have become the grasslands, forests, and tundra you see today. The recent glaciation makes these ecosystems young compared to other ecosystems on Earth, particularly compared to tropical ecosystems. You will see the importance of these patterns in the discussion of the global phosphorus cycle.

The terrestrial nitrogen cycle is what happens between when $N_2$ is taken from the atmosphere and fixed into an ecosystem and when that nitrogen is returned as a gas to the atmosphere **(Figure 30.24)**.

During the steps in between, nitrogen can be taken up and transformed by microbes, plants, and animals. When fixed nitrogen enters an ecosystem in a biologically available form, there is competition for it between microbes and plants. Microbes, especially soil bacteria, typically win the first round. Some of these bacteria can take ammonium and convert it to nitrate, a process called **nitrification**. Other bacteria can take nitrate and convert it back to a gas. Most of this nitrogen is released as dinitrogen ($N_2$), but some is released as nitrous oxide ($N_2O$) and some is released as nitrogen attached to a variable number of oxygen atoms (gases referred to as $NO_x$). This process of microbial conversion of nitrate to atmospheric nitrogen gases is called **denitrification**. The nitrogen that is assimilated into the bodies of microbes and the nitrogen that is taken up by plants in any form are incorporated into organic matter. This nitrogen can then be cycled through any number of organisms and detritus. You might recall from Chapter 2 that scientists have tracked nitrogen from the bodies of salmon spawning in rivers to the nitrogen in trees that border the rivers' edges, or the example in Chapter 1 of bats using pitcher plants to roost and providing the plant with the nitrogen it needs in the urine and feces they leave behind.

It is often true that the more nitrogen limited the ecosystem, the more efficiently, or conservatively, nitrogen is used. Deciduous trees, for example, can pull nitrogen out of leaves before the leaves drop in the fall, keeping this nitrogen for use in the next season of growth. This process can even contribute to autumnal leaves changing colour. Other plants in nitrogen-limited ecosystems might just put less nitrogen into leaves, such that the C:N ratio of leaves in a nitrogen-limited ecosystem is lower than in a nitrogen-rich ecosystem.

Humans have also figured out how to fix nitrogen from the atmosphere. The Haber–Bosch process, patented in Germany by Fritz Haber in 1908, takes atmospheric dinitrogen and, under high temperature and pressure in combination with hydrogen and iron, converts it to ammonia ($NH_3$). This manufactured ammonia

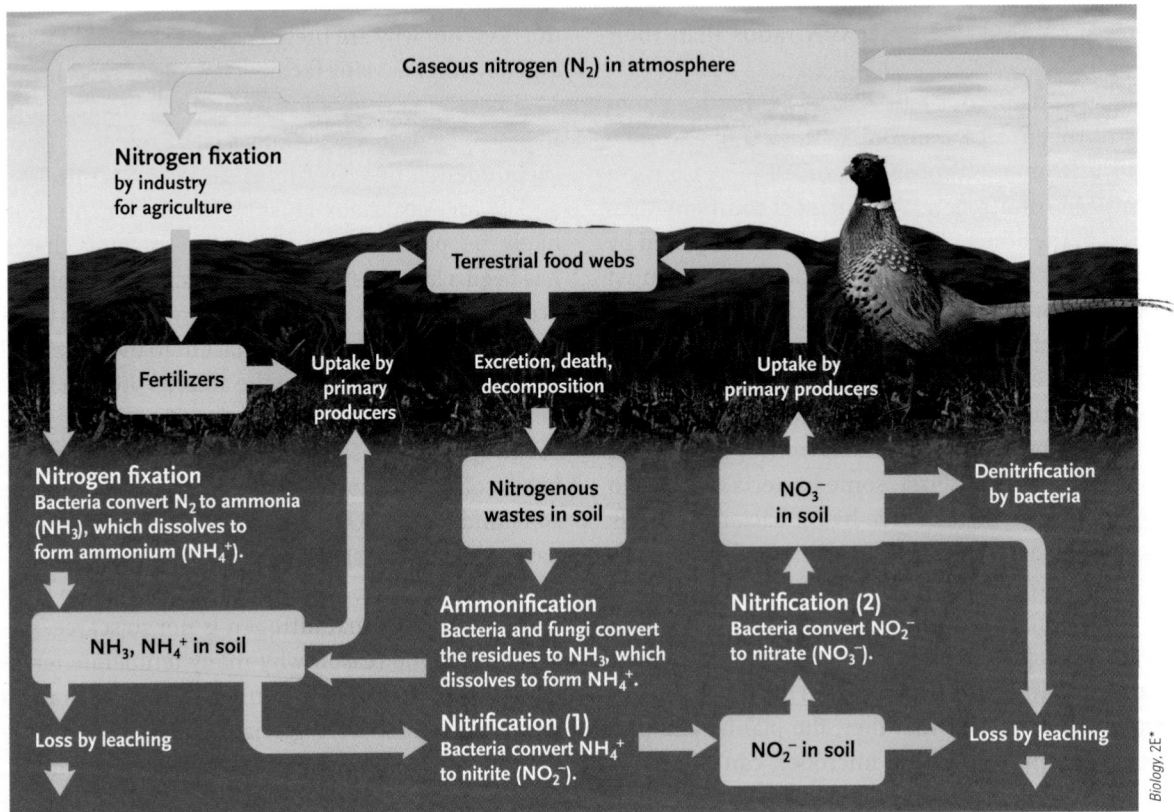

**FIGURE 30.24** The nitrogen cycle in a terrestrial ecosystem. Nitrogen-fixing bacteria make molecular nitrogen available in terrestrial ecosystems. Other bacteria recycle nitrogen within the available organic compartment through ammonification and two types of nitrification, converting organic wastes into ammonium ions and nitrates. Denitrification converts nitrate to molecular nitrogen, which returns to the atmosphere. Runoff carries nitrogen from terrestrial ecosystems into aquatic ecosystems, where it is recycled in freshwater and marine food webs.

was used in explosives in both world wars and still plays an important role in weapons today. Almost 80% of the ammonia manufactured each year, however, is used in nitrogen fertilizers for agriculture. Manufacturing fertilizers on a large scale transformed crop-based agriculture in the 20th century, facilitating an exponential increase in crop production. The Haber–Bosch process has been attributed with feeding 4 billion people in the last century than would have been possible without it. Humans also indirectly fix nitrogen by cultivating nitrogen-fixing crops, particularly soybeans. Additionally, the combustion of fossil fuels can fix atmospheric nitrogen. This happens every time you start your car. By fixing so much nitrogen from the atmosphere, humans have significantly increased the amount of reactive nitrogen cycling through ecosystems. On land, the combination of nitrogen fixed by the Haber–Bosch process, by nitrogen-fixing crops, and by fossil fuel combustion has more than doubled the flux of nitrogen from the atmosphere into reactive forms **(Figure 30.25)**.

This increase in reactive nitrogen has not been without environmental consequences, causing increases in greenhouse gas emissions, decreasing water quality, creating acid rain, and even potentially fertilizing forests.

## The Phosphorus Cycle Is Biologically Essential and Geologically Controlled

Phosphorus is considered by some to be the ultimate limiting nutrient. Like nitrogen and carbon, it is essential for life. Phosphorus is one of the main components in bone, and, similarly to nitrogen, phosphorus is important to the DNA molecule. Unlike nitrogen or carbon, however, phosphorus is not available from the atmosphere. Instead, phosphorus is found in sedimentary rock and enters ecosystems as that rock weathers (primarily through chemical weathering). This means that the amount of phosphorus available to any ecosystem is in large part constrained to what is available in the rock and soils on which that ecosystem establishes.

Phosphorus limitation is most common to ecosystems in the tropics and to freshwater ecosystems such as streams and lakes. In terrestrial ecosystems, all the factors that can control nitrogen limitation—age, topography, climate, vegetation, soils, and parent material—contribute to phosphorus availability as well. For phosphorus, age, topography, and parent material are particularly important. Based on evidence from islands of different ages in Hawaii, phosphorus that is weathered from parent material leaks into an ecosystem over time. In a young ecosystem (hundreds to a few thousand years old), a lot of phosphorus is available in rock but there is not a lot in the soils and biotic communities. In a medium-aged ecosystem (tens of thousands to a few hundred thousand years old), phosphorus is available across the ecosystem in rock, in soil, and in the ecosystem's biotic communities. As an ecosystem gets older and older (approaching millions of years), less and less phosphorus is available from rocks to be weathered, and, thus, less and less phosphorus is available for uptake by organisms.

Phosphorus can be recycled—for example, between plants and leaf litter and microbes— but there are always losses through pathways such as wind and water erosion, herbivory, and animal movement. Eventually, much can be lost, and without new inputs, phosphorus can become the most limiting nutrient in an ecosystem. Many tropical ecosystems, especially lowland tropical ecosystems, are like this. In contrast to temperate ecosystems that experienced glaciation during the last glacial period, as discussed above in terms of nitrogen cycling, tropical regions along the equator were not glaciated during this period. Many of the soils in these regions have been experiencing intense weathering from a hot and humid climate with a lot of rain for millions of years. Here phosphorus is in particularly short supply (see Box 30.1, p. 700).

In some of these tropical ecosystems, the most important source of phosphorus is no longer weathering from rocks and minerals but dust. Across the Hawaiian

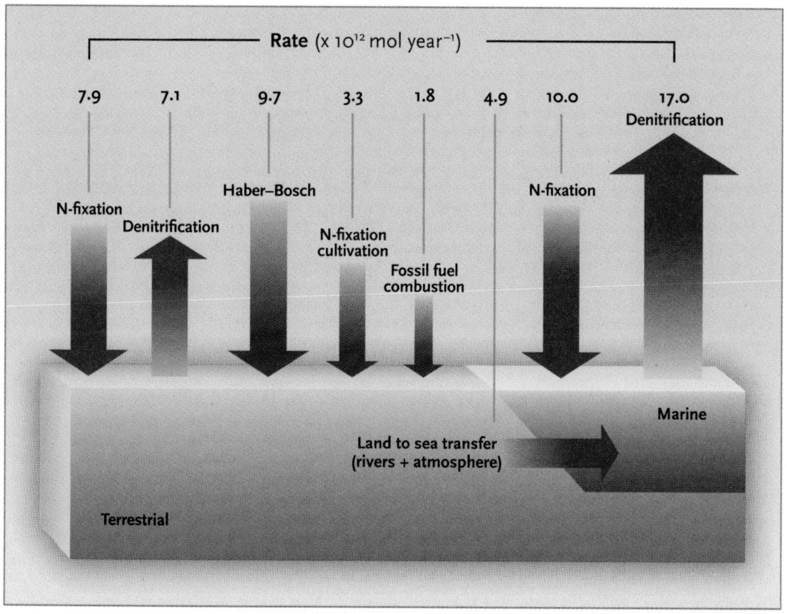

**FIGURE 30.25** Modern global nitrogen flux depends on the efficiency of the transfer of N between reservoirs. The thickness of the arrows indicates the relative size of flux. Anthropogenic inputs are shown as dark brown arrows.

SOURCE: From Canfield, D.E., A.N. Glazer and P.G. Falkowski. "The evolution and future of Earth's nitrogen cycle," *Science* 8 October 2010, Vol. 330 no. 6001 pp. 192–196. Reprinted with permission from AAAS.

# THE MOLECULE BEHIND THE BIOLOGY 30.1
## Nitrogenases and Phosphatases

Plants with symbiotic bacteria that are able to fix atmospheric nitrogen are known as nitrogen fixers. These plants include mostly legumes, such as soybeans, and other larger tree species, such as acacia trees and tamarind, to name a few. Because nitrogen-fixing trees can bring nitrogen into an ecosystem, we might expect that most nitrogen-fixing trees would be found in ecosystems that are nitrogen limited, meaning ecosystems that are most in need of additional nitrogen for primary production. As you saw in the text (page 697), temperate and boreal ecosystems such as those of Canada are generally thought of as nitrogen limited, whereas tropical ecosystems are generally thought of as phosphorus limited. However, nitrogen-fixing plants and trees are much more abundant in tropical ecosystems than temperate or boreal ecosystems. This is a paradox: why are nitrogen-fixing trees more often found in phosphorus-limited ecosystems?

Benjamin Houlton and his colleagues looked at enzyme activity to try to explain the geographic distribution of nitrogen fixers. The symbiotic bacteria that fix atmospheric nitrogen do so with an enzyme: nitrogenase. Nitrogenase is not cheap; the enzyme requires a lot of carbon. There is a trade-off between getting more nitrogen and using more carbon. The balance of this trade-off varies with temperature. Enzyme activity is often more effective at higher temperatures, and Houlton and his colleagues showed this to be true of nitrogenase. Nitrogenase activity peaks at a temperature near 26°C, the average temperature of tropical ecosystems, but much warmer than the average annual temperature of temperate or boreal ecosystems. This suggests that fixing nitrogen in temperate and boreal ecosystems might just be too expensive to be worth it: the carbon costs and the inefficiency of nitrogenase might counteract the effect that any additional nitrogen might have on primary production.

There is another piece to the paradox: why are there so many nitrogen-fixing trees in tropical ecosystems if additional nitrogen alone doesn't increase primary production? Again, enzymes appear to play a role. Plant roots exude enzymes into soil. These enzymes can break the chemical bonds holding important nutrients, allowing those nutrients to be taken up by the plants. Phosphatases are a group of enzymes that are released by plant roots and are able to free phosphates bound in organic matter. Interestingly, phosphatases are rich in nitrogen. Nitrogen makes up about 15% of phosphatase molecules. Nitrogen-fixing trees might facilitate the production of phosphatases in two ways: the additional nitrogen might be used by the nitrogen-fixing plant to produce and exude the enzyme, or the additional nitrogen surrounding the roots of nitrogen-fixing plants might be used by microbes that produce and exude the enzymes. And, indeed, phosphatase activity is higher under tropical nitrogen-fixing trees than under trees that don't fix nitrogen.

These experiments provide mostly circumstantial evidence, but they do shed some light on the paradox of nitrogen fixation in terrestrial ecosystems. A model by Houlton's group supports these data as a way to explain the geographic distribution of nitrogen fixers. There are myriad controls on primary productivity and species distribution, and work continues to be done to learn more about the patterns of the biosphere.

Islands, the main source of phosphorus (and other rock-derived nutrients, such as calcium) switches from rock weathering to atmospheric dust over 4 million years of ecosystem development. Ecosystem dependence on atmospheric nutrient inputs is also true in the Amazon region, where the main phosphorus inputs (in the absence of human disturbance) are from long-range dust that travels all the way from the arid Sahara in Africa. Amazingly, not only does the main source of mineral nutrients to the Amazon come from more than 5,000 km away, but more than half (an estimated 56%) comes from a single source in the Sahara, the Bodélé Depression located to the northeast of Lake Chad. In land area, the Bodélé represents only about 0.2% of the area of the Sahara and only about 0.5% of the area of the Amazon. The Bodélé Depression, located between two mountain regions where wind is funnelled and accelerated, produces as much as 0.7 million tons of dust per day.

For agriculture, we mine phosphorus minerals and then treat this rock with acids to create soluble (easily dissolvable) fertilizer. Our global phosphorus supply, just like the phosphorus supply available for weathering in any ecosystem, is ultimately limited to what we can extract from these mines. It has recently been suggested that we might run out of phosphorus in the next century. Although recent estimates of global reserves suggest that this is unlikely, it is true that the phosphorus deposits that are known and are currently mined are limited to a handful of countries. Canada has some, in places such as northern Ontario and Saskatchewan, but the large majority is in northern Africa in Morocco, the disputed territory of western Sahara, and Jordan or in China. This

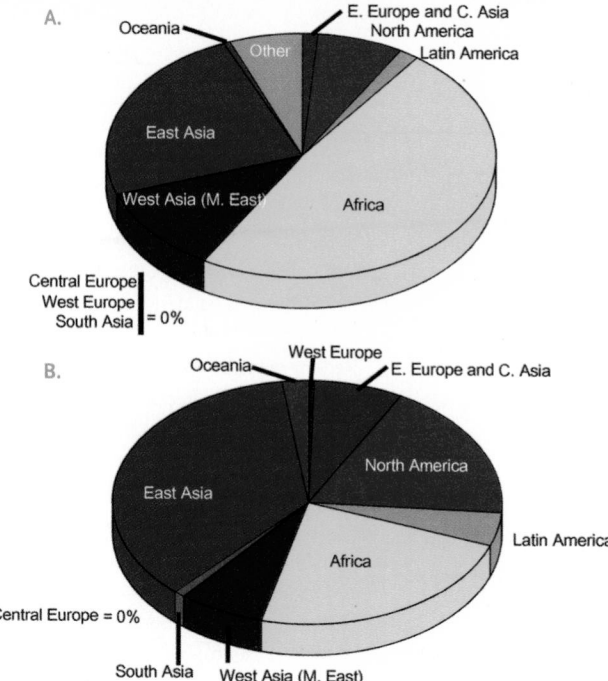

**FIGURE 30.26** Global phosphorus **(a)** reserves and **(b)** production by world region.

SOURCE: From Childers, D. L., J. Corman, M. Edwards, and J. J. Elser, "Sustainability Challenges of Phosphorus and Food: Solutions from Closing the Human Phosphorus Cycle," *BioScience* (2011) 61 (2): 117–124, by permission of Oxford University Press.

means that geopolitical stability is important to global phosphorus supplies and, therefore, global food supply and price **(Figure 30.26)**.

Similar to the carbon cycle, the global phosphorus cycle is renewed over geological time scales **(Figure 30.27)**.

Phosphorus enters ecosystems through weathering, cycling conservatively through the biota and detritus of most ecosystems. Still, some phosphorus is lost and is exported through streams and rivers to the coastal oceans. Here most of the phosphorus settles into the sediments along continental shelves. These phosphorus-rich sediments are then uplifted with tectonic activity, revealing new rocks to undergo weathering from which phosphorus can be used. Through mining, humans have more than tripled the flux of phosphorus compared to background fluxes, and, like nitrogen, this has not been without environmental costs, most notably to the quality of our freshwater ecosystems.

## STUDY BREAK

1. How does nitrogen enter an ecosystem?
2. What is the Haber–Bosch process, and why does it matter?
3. Why is phosphorus considered an ultimately limiting nutrient?

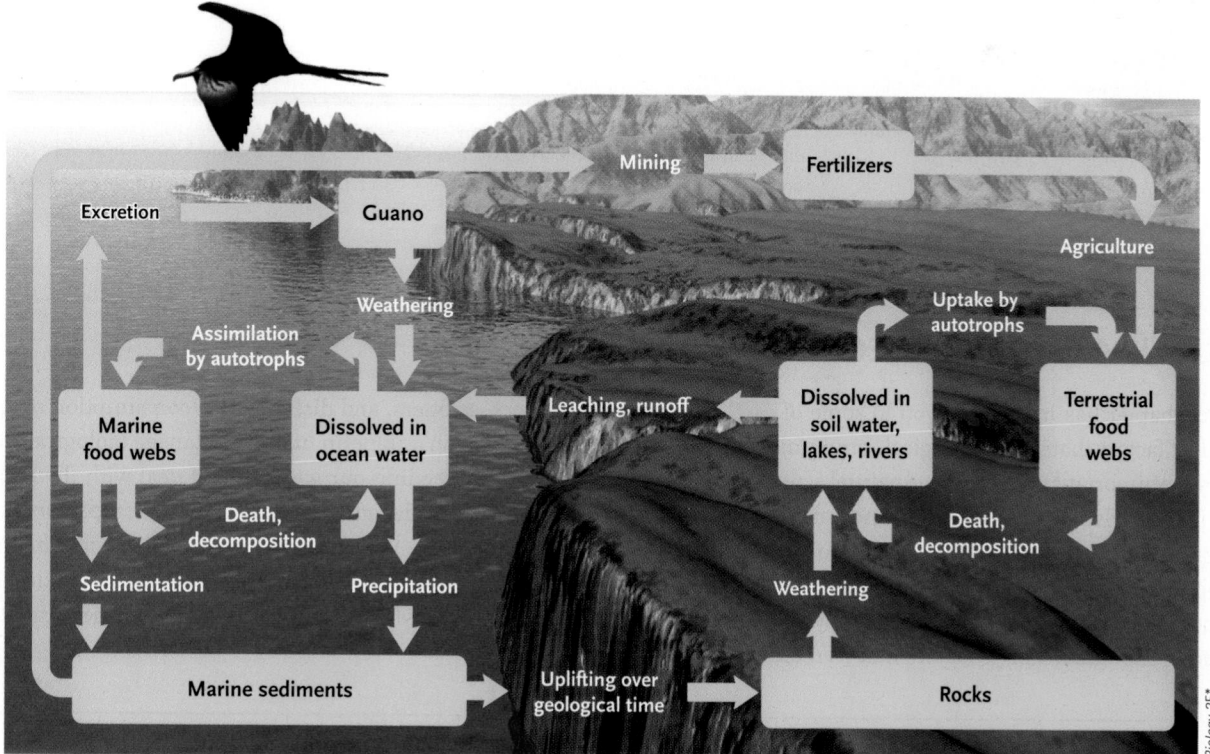

**FIGURE 30.27** The phosphorus cycle. Phosphorus becomes available in biological systems when wind and rainfall dissolve phosphates in rocks and carry them into adjacent soil and freshwater ecosystems. Runoff carries dissolved phosphorus into marine ecosystems, where it is incorporated into marine sediments.

Truffles are gourmet fungal delicacies **(Figure 1)**. They have been eaten since ancient times and continue to be highly sought after and highly priced; some species sell for more than $2000 per kilogram. Truffles are fungal fruiting bodies, structures made of reproductive tissues analogous to mushrooms. Truffles form underground among the mycelium of certain fungal species, mostly of the genus *Tuber*. Truffle-forming fungi are mycorrhizal; that is, they grow in association with the roots of particular tree species. These trees provide the fungus with carbohydrates, whereas the fungi extend the root network of the tree as well as enzymatic action in soil, allowing the tree to take up more water and nutrients.

**FIGURE 1** *Tuber melanosporum*, commonly known as the French black truffle, or Périgord truffle.

Truffles are traditionally thought of as a wild food for which we forage, and most are still collected this way. We cannot find these tasty subterranean nuggets alone and depend on truffle-finding animals, traditionally pigs, but now also some trained dogs, to find them for us. However, truffles can be cultivated, and there is a tradition of cultivation in Europe and more recently in North America. They cannot, however, be cultivated without their tree partners, making truffle farming a balance of species interactions.

Truffle cultivators plant the tree species with which truffles are typically associated—usually oak or hazel. The seeds or seedlings they use are inoculated with the fungal species they hope to harvest. Rather than harvesting every season, however, or even once a year, it takes many years and often a decade or more for truffles to grow, and even then it is not a sure thing. The Duke of Edinburgh, Prince Philip, consort to Queen Elizabeth II, planted a small truffle orchard in the mid-2000s that has still not produced any truffles. Truffles are more likely to grow under specific environmental conditions. They do not grow well with extreme heat or extreme

cold and need well-drained soils and soil with a higher than neutral pH (>7). In Canada, this limits the range of suitable area to southern British Columbia, where some truffle orchards are being established.

Recent research suggests that even more complicated species interactions may help in improving truffle cultivation. By inoculating trees with not only the truffle-producing fungus (in this case, *Tuber melanosporum*, the prized French black truffle) but also with rhizobacteria (*Pseudomonas fluorescens*), researchers saw increased colonization with the truffle-producing fungus.

It may appear that the use of pigs and dogs in the collection of truffles is another species interaction that must be managed as part of truffle cultivation. This is partly true, although the relationship is likely not a trophic one. A chemical produced by the truffles is the same as a chemical produced by the testes of boars. This may explain the propensity of female pigs to find and unearth the truffles. Also, foodies and all lovers of truffles take note: truffle oil does not typically contain any truffles. Instead, it is an oil produced with manufactured truffle essence.

## PUTTING IT IN PERSPECTIVE

This chapter has introduced you to some of the biotic and abiotic factors that shape biological communities. These factors are important to shaping the natural ecosystems around us and are also important in our understanding of human impacts on the natural environment. Humans contribute to trophic interactions (see Box 30.2) and even trophic cascades, both indirectly, through practices such as whaling that reduce populations of predators that feed on keystone species such as otters, and directly, with consumption of apex predators such as bluefin tuna. We manage biological competition by weeding our gardens and deal with the consequences of introduced competitors as we attempt to manage invasive species. We also play a key role in managing biogeochemical cycles. The influence of people on species and ecosystems is what we will focus on in the final two chapters.

## KEY CONCEPTS REVIEW AND QUESTIONS

### 30.1 Community Ecology

The levels of trophic pyramids can be influenced from the top of the pyramid down or from the bottom of the pyramid up. When a change to the population of an upper level affects populations more than one level below, the response is described as a trophic cascade. Species with larger effects on trophic dynamics than their size or populations would suggest are known as keystone species.

1. What might happen to phytoplankton populations if largemouth bass are introduced to a lake for sport fishing?

2. In the absence of wolves or another apex predator, what controls deer populations? What role does hunting play?

Communities are shaped by both intraspecific and interspecific competition. Competition occurs among species for niche space within the environment and among individuals competing for resources.

3. Like the example in the text of small mammals in temperate forests, can you think of a guild of organisms that fill different niches in a single ecosystem?

4. What are two ways that endemic species might be threatened by an invasive species?

Communities are affected by disruptions called disturbances. Communities also change over time. This change, known as succession, is almost always occurring in ecosystems in response to some kind of disturbance.

5. Put the following in order to describe succession in a hypothetical temperate deciduous forest. Assume that the initial ecosystem, the climax community, is a full-canopy deciduous forest with a full understory.

   a. Grass and shrubs
   b. Bare soil
   c. Full-canopy deciduous forest with full understory
   d. Forest fire
   e. Rapidly growing conifers with some understory

## 30.2 Ecosystem Ecology

Ecosystems are affected by constraints posed by nutrient availability. Nutrient availability is shaped by both abiotic and biotic factors. Nutrient limitation to primary production is imposed by the least available nutrient in an ecosystem.

6. In addition to nutrient limitation, what controls primary production in an ecosystem?

7. How are nitrogen and phosphorus introduced to ecosystems?

Now that you have read and reviewed this chapter, we encourage you to attempt to build a concept map using these key concepts and indicate the connections between them. Please see Chapter 5 for examples of concept maps that could be developed for this chapter.

# Conservation

Shelby Riskin

## WHY IT MATTERS

There are two species of orangutan: one living in Borneo (*Pongo pygmaeus*) and the other in Sumatra (*Pongo abelii*). They are the world's largest tree-dwelling animals and are among our closest relatives **(Figure 31.1)**. Orangutans are sometimes referred to as gardeners. They are mainly vegetarian, with a diet of more than 60% fruit, and play an important role in dispersing fruit seeds through the forest. They also eat leaves, insects, and honey and have been observed to eat the meat of another tree-dwelling mammal, the slow loris (species in the genus *Nycticebus*). The populations of these animals and, in fact, of all non-human primates, are currently in dramatic decline.

The Sumatran orangutan is considered critically endangered, with approximately 7300 alive in the wild—80% fewer than there were 75 years ago. The Bornean orangutan is currently considered endangered, with between 45,000 and 69,000 individuals alive in the wild. Orangutans are occasionally hunted for meat or traded as pets. But habitat loss is the primary reason that both species are in decline. The forest habitat available to orangutans is shrinking and becoming more fragmented. Forests are logged for lumber and are converted to crop-based agriculture and to palm plantations to meet growing global demand for palm oil.

Orangutan declines are influenced by choices that we make as consumers here in Canada and in other places far removed from orangutan habitat. Palm oil is in many of the products we eat every day. Palm oil is likely an ingredient in the cookies, crackers, margarine, and any number of other products that you see in the grocery store or that sit in your cupboards. It is also in products such as soap and many cosmetics. Our use of palm oil has increased dramatically in the wake of health concerns over hydrogenated oils in food products and the push to replace them with healthier alternatives. Canada imported 20 times more palm oil in 2011 than in 2000.

If orangutans continue to face increasing pressures on their populations, they could disappear altogether. The orangutan is only one of many organisms whose survival is currently at risk and whose survival depends on a complicated web of economic interactions, management decisions, and human behaviour. **Conservation biology** and **conservation science** focus on understanding the threats that organisms face, particularly due to human activities, and preventing future losses of these organisms.

In this chapter, you will be introduced to the study of conservation biology and conservation science, the challenges that we face in preventing biodiversity loss, and what we can do, even as individuals, to help. Each ecosystem on Earth is complex and dynamic. Each consists of a variety of species that interact in myriad ways. Throughout this book, you have been learning about the biological diversity on Earth, or biodiversity. Earth's biodiversity is currently in trouble, mostly because of human activities. There has been more change in global biodiversity in the past 50 years than in any other period in human history. We drive these changes both directly, through the destruction of habitat and practices such as poaching, and indirectly, through the introduction of invasive species, pollution, and climate change. The study of conservation biology and conservation science focuses on how to prevent or reverse declines in populations of organisms or of biodiversity.

**FIGURE 31.1** Two Sumatran orangutans (*Pongo abelii*). Sumatran orangutans, one of the great apes, currently face extinction because of human activities.

## 31.1 Defining Conservation

The discipline of conservation biology began in the 1970s and defined itself as a crisis discipline, meant to prevent the loss of biodiversity and save species and ecosystems from human activities. Much of this work focused on returning ecosystems to a pristine state and removing the influence of humans from landscapes wherever possible. However, increasingly, we realize that humans have touched every ecosystem on Earth. Words such as "natural" and "pristine" are increasingly difficult to define, as are the environmental baselines to which conservationists once hoped to return. The most remote lakes contain pharmaceutical residues, and animals across world regions accumulate human-produced chemicals in their bodies **(Figure 31.2)**.

The discipline of conservation science expands the original focus of conservation biology. Rather than focusing on maximizing biodiversity alone and removing human activity from our concept of what is natural, conservation science also focuses on human well-being and the ecosystem services provided by biodiversity and the natural world.

The whole world is subject to climate changes such as warming temperatures, changes in precipitation patterns, and rising sea levels. Conservation biology and conservation science now attempt to integrate humans and nature. Humans depend on many services provided by the natural world, including clean air, clean water, and basic resources such as food, fibre, and shelter. Conservation science includes focused efforts, such as breeding programs for critically endangered organisms as well as reintroduction of those organisms into the wild. Conservation science also includes more general efforts, such as improving agricultural yields with fewer environmental consequences or increasing connectivity between patches of habitat. Maximizing human benefits as well as biodiversity and environmental quality is in the best interest of all of Earth's organisms.

## 31.2 Defining Biodiversity

Biodiversity is a measure of the diversity of life in a particular place. The place could be your yard, a national park, an ecosystem such as the boreal forest or the African savanna, or the whole world. There are a number of ways to measure biodiversity, and each can paint a different picture.

One simple metric of biodiversity is the number of species present, or species richness. But this metric does not capture everything that is important about biodiversity. For example, the relative abundance of each species, another metric of biodiversity, is also important and can change our understanding of an ecosystem's diversity. For example, is the diversity of an area with 100 individuals of 10 different species the same as one with 901 individuals of one species and one of the other nine? Species richness is the same in each area, but one area is clearly dominated by a single species. The interactions between species and the way the ecosystem functions will be different in these two areas. Biodiversity also extends to genetic diversity within species and populations. There are many ways to measure and think about the diversity of life in different regions and ecosystems.

As you saw in Chapter 30, different species also occupy different niches in ecosystems. The contribution of many species and their interactions affect the functioning of ecosystems. Some important ecosystem functions, for example the ability to bounce back after a disturbance such as a hurricane, fire, or clear-cut, can depend on the total biodiversity of that ecosystem, the species richness, and the relative abundance of each species. Individual parts of an ecosystem, such as a single species, can also be important to ecosystem functioning and even to human society. Species such as beavers (*Castor canadensis*) are called keystone species because of the large influence they have on ecosystems. Removal of keystone species can affect the functioning of an entire ecosystem. From a human perspective, plants that are important sources of food or medicine are also important components of an ecosystem's biodiversity. But how much do changes in biodiversity matter? If beavers disappeared, would the forests in which they lived be destroyed? Could people die if a medicinal plant went extinct? In other words, should you care about biodiversity? We will explore some of these questions in this chapter.

**FIGURE 31.2** In Pakistan, vultures (*Gyps bengalensis*) have suffered population declines because of the veterinary drug diclofenac. The vultures feed primarily on the carcasses of domesticated animals such as cattle and consume diclofenac from the livestock's tissues. The birds suffer kidney failure and death in response to the drug.

## 31.3 The Value of Biodiversity

You might wonder why any of us should care about biodiversity. After all, as some people argue, the disappearance of species, or extinction, is part of the evolutionary process.

So why worry when one, or even many, species disappears? We live in an ever-changing environment, and more than 99% of species that once lived are now extinct. This is all true, but the concern lies in the differences between the natural extinction rates over Earth's history and those that are happening now. Today, humans are dramatically changing ecosystem dynamics, altering both the way organisms interact and the rate of extinction. Arguably, since the population of *Homo sapiens* exceeded 1 billion, we have shaped the survival of many other species.

Extinction is a common phenomenon in the history of life on Earth. Species are lost due to both gradual and catastrophic events: natural selection in the face of environmental change and large-scale disturbance events can both drive species to extinction. The average rate of extinctions that has occurred throughout the history of life on Earth is called the background extinction rate. Sometimes mass extinction events wipe out huge swaths of life; some have led to the extinction of more than 75% of the species on Earth in a relatively short period. The loss of all non-avian dinosaurs at the end of the Cretaceous, likely due to a catastrophic asteroid impact, is an example of a mass extinction event (see Chapter 2 for more details on mass extinctions through Earth's history). Today's extinction rate is 100 to 1000 times higher than historical background extinction rates. These increased extinction rates are the result of human activities, most notably habitat loss, overexploitation of species, pollution, and climate change. But if Earth has survived mass extinctions before, does it matter now? One argument for halting the current loss of biodiversity is that because the current crisis is our doing, it is also our responsibility to stop it. But even beyond that logic, there are many arguments for the importance of maintaining Earth's biodiversity.

One argument for preserving biodiversity is almost spiritual. All organisms and ecosystems have an innate, unquantifiable value that is independent of humans. In this argument, the use by or value of any species to humans is irrelevant, and it is our duty to conserve them. This ethic drove much of the early work in conservation biology several decades ago and continues to be important today. This idea resonates in some way with most of us. The campaigns of conservation groups such as the World Wildlife Fund often have the most success when they focus on saving charismatic animals such as the giant panda (*Ailuropoda melanoleuca*), sea turtles, gorillas (species in the genus *Gorilla*) or the polar bear (*Ursus maritimus*) (Figure 31.3). Few people look at pandas or sea turtles and say they do not care whether they live or die. Most people want their children and grandchildren to live in a world with wild sea turtles and pandas.

A more pragmatic argument for the value of biodiversity revolves around the services provided by organisms and ecosystems—services essential to our own survival. **Ecosystem services** include services and products provided by mostly wild ecosystems, such as timber, the prevention of erosion by coastal plants, or water filtration

**FIGURE 31.3** World Wildlife Fund Canada runs campaigns dedicated to the conservation of animals that many of us are intrigued by or that we feel a connection to. In 2014, these animals included **(a)** narwhals (*Monodon monoceros*), **(b)** tigers (*Panthera tigris*), **(c)** right whales (*Eubalaena glacialis*), and **(d)** polar bears (*Ursus maritimus*).

and retention by wetlands. Ecosystem services also include services provided by human-modified ecosystems, such as the yields of agricultural crops and cultural services such as recreation or tourism. There is also value in biomolecules produced across the diversity of Earth's organisms. Pharmaceuticals have been developed based on molecules derived from trees (painkillers), fungi (antibiotics), and mammals (anticoagulants), to name only a few. All of these services, from medicines to lakes for swimming, have value. A lot of research has focused on what the monetary or social value of these services is and what we lose by letting them be destroyed. For example, natural predator control of agricultural pests (insects and parasitoids feeding on pest organisms) has been estimated to provide US$4.5 billion of value each year. In Canada, intact wetlands are estimated to provide US$6000 of value per hectare. This value can be compared to what we often replace intact wetlands with, intensive agriculture, which is estimated to provide just over US$2000 of value per hectare.

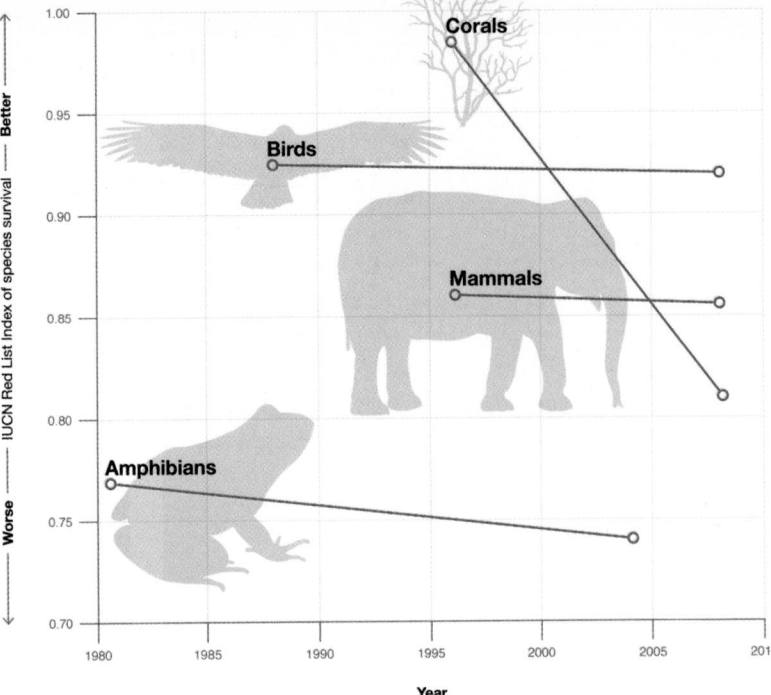

**FIGURE 31.4** The Red List Index (RLI) is used as an index of the status of biodiversity across different groups of organisms. The index uses changes in the threatened status for a number of species within each group to assess changes in the biodiversity of that group over time. RLIs are currently available for amphibians, birds, corals, and mammals. An RLI of 1 would indicate that all assessed species are of least concern, and an RLI of 0 would indicate that all species are extinct. Amphibians are the most threatened group, whereas corals are declining most rapidly. All groups appear to be in decline.

SOURCE: IUCN, The IUCN Red List of Threatened Species™, 2014.2, Summary Statistics, http://www.iucnredlist.org/about/summary-statistics

## STUDY BREAK

1. How might you measure the biodiversity of plants in your yard?
2. What are two ways that your life is improved by ecosystem services?
3. Do you think biodiversity matters? Why or why not?

## 31.4 Tracking Biodiversity and the Status of Species

Many groups across the world keep track of species' populations and biodiversity on a variety of levels, from local to global. One of the most visible and important groups is the International Union for the Conservation of Nature (IUCN). For more than 40 years, the IUCN has maintained a database of the conservation status of many of the world's plants and animals **(Figure 31.4)**.

The IUCN Red List of Threatened Species is a list of plants and animals officially assessed by the IUCN and its affiliated groups. At one time, the list just included species that were of concern for some reason—perhaps a species that was declining or one with low population numbers. The list has now been broadened to include groups that are known not to be at risk. The IUCN has

highlighted plants and animals around the world that should be conservation priorities. The list categorizes organisms into one of seven categories that range from least threatened to extinct. There are also categories for those species for which we lack the data necessary to assess their conservation status. The IUCN Red List of Threatened Species currently lists almost 11,000 species as threatened (those that fall into the IUCN categories vulnerable, endangered, or critically endangered).

In Canada, the Committee on the Status of Endangered Wildlife in Canada (COSEWIC) was established in 1977 to maintain a list like the IUCN Red List of Threatened Species for species in Canada. The list uses categories similar to those of the IUCN, extending from species not at risk, to species now **extirpated** from Canada but living elsewhere, to species that are now extinct. Both federal and provincial programs control the ways in which humans and species at risk interact. Any group, from researchers to construction companies, must apply for permits to work near populations of at-risk organisms in an effort to prevent and control damage to these organisms or their habitats. For example, development projects must consider the effects on local species at risk before they begin construction activity.

The Convention on International Trade in Endangered Species (CITES) was enacted in 1975 in response

**FIGURE 31.5** The Convention on International Trade in Endangered Species of Wild Fauna and Flora (CITES) regulates trade in wildlife to prevent overexploitation of populations. In 2014, in combination with the Chinese government, more than 6 tonnes of ivory confiscated in China under CITES regulations were crushed as a symbol that illegal trade in elephant ivory will not be tolerated in China.

to threats to organisms due to international trade. It is a treaty that controls international trade of species at risk among participating countries **(Figure 31.5)**. CITES currently controls, to varying degrees, the trade of more than 35,000 species of animals and plants. The program is voluntary—179 countries, including Canada, participate—but it is legally binding. Violating countries must pay the appropriate penalties. Participating countries must ensure that national-level policies align with the agreement. CITES does not influence or involve itself with movement of species at risk within a country.

## 31.5 Threats to Species and Biodiversity

The myriad threats to biodiversity at large and to particular species of interest can be overwhelming. Many of the species that we grew up knowing and caring about, whether from books, in zoos, or in the wild, are now perilously close to extinction. It is not, however, hopeless. In this section, you will read about the main drivers of extinction and population declines today. Habitat loss, agriculture, pollution, introduced species, and global climate change are all contributing to species declines. For many species, it is not the impact of only one of these drivers but the effects of many in combination driving population declines. This can make conserving species especially difficult.

Following this section, we will talk about several current conservation efforts and what each of us can do to make a difference. First and foremost, it helps to be a wise consumer. This includes wise consumption of retail products and also of information. The more you know, the more critically you are able to evaluate evidence and new information. With that in mind, what are the main threats to global biodiversity?

## Species Cannot Survive without Their Habitat

Globally, habitat destruction is the leading cause of extinction. Clear-cutting a forest is an obvious example of habitat loss. We also drain wetlands for agriculture or development and build dams along streams and rivers. Cities continue to grow and spread, taking over more and more natural spaces. There are also many less severe encroachments on the size and quality of habitats. In many cases, a piece of habitat might be removed, whereas the rest is left intact, like a cookie cutter removing pieces from a large piece of dough. Often more and more pieces are removed, just like when you are making cookies.

When habitat is fragmented or lost in this way, being rare and having a small geographic range or being sessile (unable to locomote) are disadvantages. Consider a hypothetical circular forested island that can be divided into four equal quadrants. There are four species on the island. One species is found only in the southeastern quadrant. A second species is found only in the two southern quadrants of the circle. A third species is found only in the northwestern quadrant, and the fourth species is found in all four quadrants. As each quadrant is cleared, the extinction risk for each species is different. For two of those hypothetical species, clearing just one quarter of the island's forest is enough to destroy all of the species' habitat. Unless that species can move to another quadrant, it could be wiped out altogether. We see these same patterns on continental scales too. Species that are more widely distributed or that can move more easily do better than patchily distributed or less mobile species.

Migratory species are particularly vulnerable to habitat loss as their reproductive success and survival depend on at least two habitat locations. Monarch butterfly (*Danaus plexippus*) populations are declining because the Mexican forests where they spend their winters are being cleared and less milkweed (species in the genus *Asclepias*), their host plants, is available in the central and northern parts of their range. Similarly, many sea turtle populations are in decline because the beaches they depend on for nesting have been developed, leaving less undisturbed and unlit space for breeding and increasing contact with humans who consume or damage the eggs or hatchlings.

Currently, deforestation has caused the largest habitat losses that affect species diversity. Deforestation, the clearing of forest, is currently happening most rapidly and to the largest extent in the tropics. Tropical ecosystems, in particular tropical rainforests, are also hot spots of biodiversity. More than half of all species on Earth are found in the tropics, and many of these species are endemic (they are found only in that region). In these regions, deforestation can have a particularly detrimental effect on biodiversity and ecosystem functioning. These areas should be conservation priorities: the limited conservation dollars available would save the greatest number of species in

BOX 31.1

# Deforestation in the Brazilian Amazon

Deforestation for agriculture in the Brazilian Amazon shows some of the complicated connections among global markets that influence land use and conservation decisions **(Figure 1)**. Beginning in the 1970s, the main driver of deforestation in the Brazilian Amazon was low-density cattle ranching encouraged by government settlement programs. Ranchers used slash-and-burn practices. Land was cleared of vegetation, burned, and used for a few years, typically supporting an average of one cow per hectare, until the pasture was no longer productive. Then the ranchers moved on to a new patch of forest that was likewise cleared and burned. In the 1990s and early 2000s, a number of forces began to change the face of agriculture and defor-estation **(Figure 2)**. The Brazilian cattle herd was declared free of foot-and-mouth disease. The officially disease-free industry in Brazil, coupled with the outbreak of bovine spongiform encephalopathy (mad cow disease) in the United Kingdom, drove a large increase in the demand and market for Brazilian beef. More land was cleared for pasture, and bigger companies with more productive systems began to move into the industry.

In addition to livestock ranching, new varieties of soybean that tolerated the humid tropical climate of the Amazon became available and complex markets changes increased global demand for soy. The mad cow outbreak in the United Kingdom led the European Union to prohibit the use of animal protein in animal feed, leading many to make soy-based feed. In China, an increasingly wealthy populace led to larger markets for soy-fed animals (particularly chickens). As a result of all of these changes, there was an unprecedented increase in the rate of deforestation in the Brazilian Amazon between 2002 and 2004. This market increase has been economically important for Brazil. Brazil is now second only to the United States in global soybean exports. More than a third of Brazil's gross domestic product comes from the agriculture industry.

However, in 2006, the rates of defor-estation declined dramatically and remained low through 2010. That year, the Brazilian Ministry of the Environ-ment, in combination with a number of international soybean buyers, agreed to institute a two-year moratorium on the purchase of soybeans grown on land deforested following July 24, 2006. There were also new programs to reduce the credit available to deforesters and increase monitoring and enforcement. The effectiveness of these efforts was likely also increased by a decrease in the profitability of soy in 2006. It is difficult to tease apart how much these various and tangled connections influence deforesta-tion decision making. It is clear, however, that international economics and policy can play large roles in driving land use conversion or conservation.

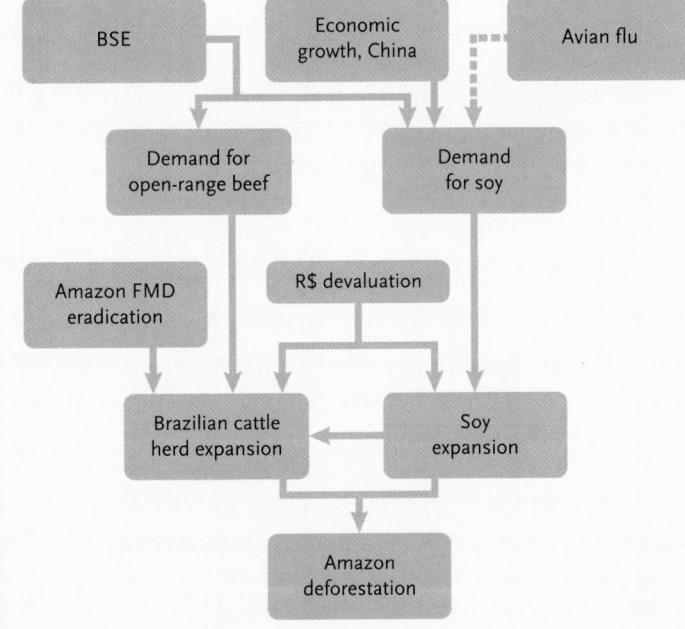

**FIGURE 2** International economic and social drivers of increases in defor-estation in the Brazilian Amazon. BSE = bovine spongiform encephalopathy, or mad cow disease; FMD = foot-and-mouth disease; R$ = Brazilian Real.

SOURCE: DANIEL C. NEPSTAD, CLAUDIA M. STICKLER, ORIANA T. ALMEIDA, "Global-ization of the Amazon soy and beef industries: Opportunities for conservation," *Conservation Biology*, Volume 20, Issue 6, pages 1595–1603, December 2006. John Wiley and Sons. Copyright © 2006, John Wiley and Sons.

**FIGURE 1** Rheas (*Rhea americanus*) walk through a recently harvested soybean field in the Brazilian Amazon.

these areas. Preventing deforestation has proved to be a difficult challenge (see Box 31.1). It is difficult to enforce forest protection initiatives and control deforestation in areas with limited infrastructure such as intact tropical

forest, and in many cases, there are strong economic incen-tives to convert forest to other land uses. Some tropical deforestation is driven by logging and a demand for wood, but the most complete deforestation is for agriculture.

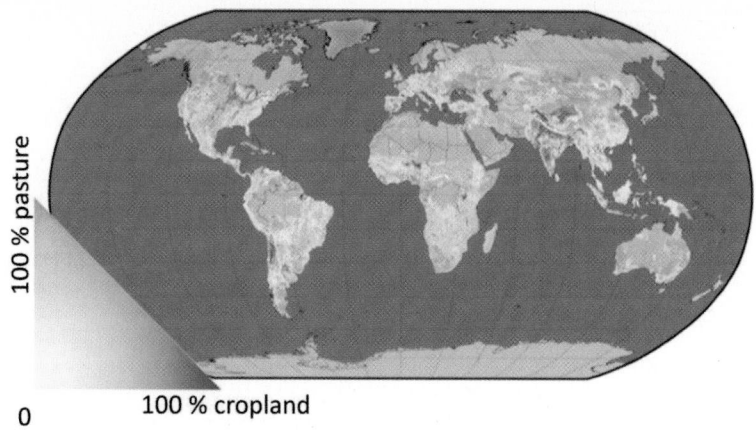

100 % pasture

100 % cropland

0

**FIGURE 31.6** The extent of global agriculture. The areas where agriculture is not occupying the majority of the landscape are tundra, deserts, and tropical forests.

SOURCE: Reprinted by permission from Macmillan Publishers Ltd: *NATURE*, Jonathan A. Foley, Navin Ramankutty, Kate A. Brauman, Emily S. Cassidy, James S. Gerber, Matt Johnston, "Solutions for a cultivated planet," 478, 337–342, copyright 2011.

## Agriculture Is the World's Largest Land Use

Perhaps the largest indirect effect most of us have on habitat loss is through our consumption of foods grown on farms. Humans currently farm almost 40% of the terrestrial Earth surface. This land use occupies by far the largest proportion of land in any land use. As is clear from an image of agriculture around the globe, the only areas that we do not yet cultivate are the tropics, the deserts, and the tundra, and, as is clear from the section above, the last tropical forests are currently being converted to agriculture at a rapid rate **(Figure 31.6)**. This means that 40% of Earth's terrestrial surface is no longer available as habitat for wild populations. Additionally, the demand for agricultural products continues to increase, thus driving more agricultural expansion worldwide.

The Food and Agriculture Organization of the United Nations (FAO) estimates that the human population will exceed 9 billion by 2050. Additionally, as countries become more and more affluent, their appetite for a resource-intensive quality of life also increases. These increases in affluence and population are driving ever-increasing demands for food, feed, biofuels, and fibre. In addition, there are over 1 billion people on Earth who are hungry and who do not receive the food that they need. The FAO estimates that we will have to increase global agricultural production by 70% by 2050 to meet these demands.

There are several ways to increase agricultural production and work toward meeting these demands. We can expand the land area we farm—in other words, expand agriculture further into tropical ecosystems. It will not be possible to meet these demands simply by expanding agriculture, however. We can also intensify agricultural production. In many parts of the world, agricultural production is as high as it can be using the best crop varieties and farming practices currently available. In other parts of the world, most notably parts of Asia and sub-Saharan Africa, there is a gap between the crop yield

farmers attain and what they could attain with better access to water, fertilizer, high-quality seeds, and improved farming practices. Across the world, crops capable of attaining higher yields with fewer inputs can help make our farms more efficient. These might include rice that requires less water or plants that are better at getting nutrients from the soil. Agronomists around the world are working on these issues.

Meat consumption is the third important piece of the puzzle of global agriculture. As you saw in Chapter 2, a great deal of energy is lost between trophic levels. To produce 1 km of cattle takes approximately 8 km of grain. Animal agriculture also occupies large land areas, with relatively inefficient levels of production. By reducing our global consumption of meat, we could decrease the amount of land in agricultural production that could be used to cultivate other foods. Furthermore, we could use more of the crops currently used as animal feed directly as food for ourselves and in food products. These changes will happen only if people are willing to shift their diets and accept foods to which they are not accustomed.

In addition to being the world's largest land use and, therefore, the most important driver of global habitat loss, agriculture influences environmental quality and biodiversity in other ways as well. For example, as you will see in the sections below, agriculture is a driver of nutrient pollution and an important emitter of the greenhouse gases that are driving global climate change. On the other hand, increased agricultural production has also been one of humanity's greatest successes. Over the last century, we have substantially increased the number of people who are able to live on Earth. And agricultural products are an important ecosystem service. Although agricultural ecosystems are managed by people, they are nevertheless ecosystems in which organisms create products of tremendous value. In fact, agricultural production is one of the only ecosystem services that has increased in efficiency, production amount, and value over the past 50 years.

## Pollution Degrades Habitat Quality and Reduces Biodiversity

Sometimes habitat does not have to be completely destroyed or changed to impact biodiversity. Pollution of air, soil, and water degrades habitat. This can affect the species richness and the abundance of different species that can live in a particular area, decreasing local biodiversity. Pollution can come in many forms. Industrial pollution from smoke stacks, for example, can release heavy metals as well as compounds that cause acid rain. Similarly, mining activities can release heavy metals and acidic drainage that can acidify streams such that no organisms can survive.

Nutrient pollution, although not normally directly toxic to organisms, has serious consequences for biodiversity and ecosystem health in aquatic ecosystems. Phosphorus and nitrogen are both nutrients essential to plant growth that are often added as fertilizers to yards, gardens, and farm fields (see Chapter 30 for more on the nitrogen and phosphorus cycles). When added to water bodies, these nutrients also act as fertilizers, driving explosions in algal growth. Large algal blooms can decrease the amount of light that penetrates the water, and these blooms also decrease the amount of oxygen available to other aquatic organisms. Some algal blooms are themselves toxic. Without oxygen, many organisms are unable to live. This can cause fish kills in which hundreds or thousands of fish die simultaneously. This is also what causes the Dead Zone in the Gulf of Mexico—an area in the Gulf almost three times the size of Prince Edward Island that is devoid of life and grows larger every year as more and more nutrients are added from the Mississippi River. This process of overenrichment of water bodies is called **eutrophication**. Eutrophication reduces biodiversity and decreases the ecosystem services provided by water bodies. For example, many eutrophic lakes are not safe to swim in or consume fish from.

Nutrient pollution comes from a variety of sources. A lot of nutrient pollution in North America comes from fertilizer lost from farm fields through leaching or erosion. Nitrogen and phosphorus are also found in manure and excrement (hence the use of manure as fertilizer), so nutrient pollution can also come from untreated sewage, animal agriculture, or other animal waste, such as from pets or high densities of waterfowl, such as geese. Phosphorus was also a central ingredient in detergents for many years. In Canada, it is now illegal to have phosphorus in laundry or dishwasher detergent to reduce nutrient levels in wastewater.

Organisms vary in their ability to survive under different conditions. Many species have very narrow tolerances to pollutants in the environment or to pH or temperature and very specific needs for things such as food and nutrient availability. Sensitive organisms can be used as **bioindicators**, like the proverbial canary in the coal mine. In addition to being sensitive to parameters of environmental quality, bioindicators should be reliable, abundant, and easy to measure. In soils, springtails (invertebrates in the order Collembola) can be used in assessments of soil quality. In freshwater streams, researchers

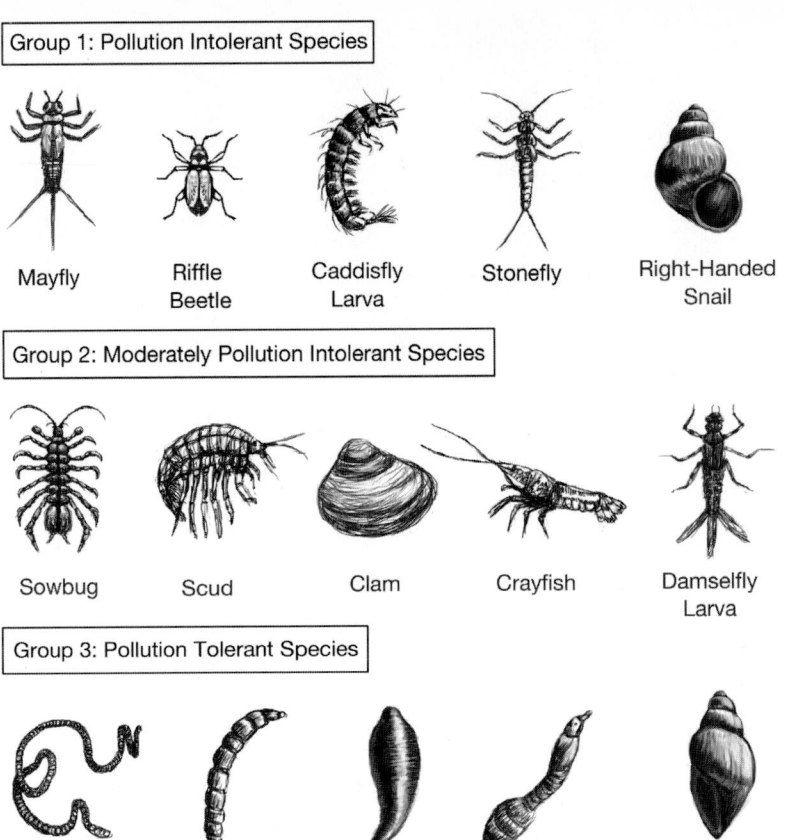

FIGURE 31.7 The diversity of invertebrates in stream sediments can be used as indicators of water quality. The various groups of invertebrates vary in their pollution tolerance. In this example of a key to water quality analysis, the pollution tolerance of organisms increases from group 1 to group 3.

can sample invertebrates along the stream bottom (benthic invertebrates). The presence, absence, and abundance of different species can then be used as indicators of water quality **(Figure 31.7)**.

## STUDY BREAK

1. Diatoms, a group of algae that are typically unicellular, are often used as bioindicators. Diatoms have specific pH ranges at which different species can live. Some are found only in water with a pH < 5.5, some are found only in water with a pH < 7, some are usually found in water with a pH > 7, and some are found only in water with a pH > 7. A group of scientists collected sediment cores from lakes across Canada. They sampled these sediments at measured intervals and sampled the preserved diatoms. What could they infer from their samples?
2. What are three drivers of our increasing demands for agricultural products?
3. What changes could we make to decrease demands for agricultural products?

A.

B.

FIGURE 31.8 (a) Black rhinos (*Diceros bicornis*) were widespread and common in Africa in 1960 (shown in orange on the map in panel b). (b) Today, their range (dark spots in the orange area) is much reduced, reflecting diminished populations.

## Humans Overexploit Many Species

Humans also fish, hunt, and gather animals and plants from the wild, directly affecting biodiversity. Overexploitation of populations by humans, such as catching too many cod in the Atlantic, can drive population declines from which species may never recover.

Overexploitation by humans has led to the extinction of many species. According to the IUCN Red List, 76 species are extinct or extinct in the wild because of intentional use, namely hunting target species. These species include the Passenger Pigeon (*Ectopistes migratorius*), the Dodo (*Raphus cucullatus*), and the Falklands wolf (*Dusicyon australis*). Many other species are now near the brink of extinction because of intentional human hunting.

The black rhinos of Africa are a particularly tragic example (**Figure 31.8**). There are two African rhinoceros species: the white rhino (*Ceratotherium simum*) and the black rhino (*Diceros bicornis*). As of 2010, there were about 20,000 white rhinos remaining in the wild, but only about 5000 black rhinos. The IUCN Red List considers the white rhino to be near-threatened, but the black rhino is considered critically endangered. Since 1960, the population of black rhinos in the wild has

decreased by 98%. Both white and black rhinos face the greatest risks from **poaching**—illegal hunting specifically for their horns.

There were once four identified subspecies of black rhino; three now remain. The western black rhino subspecies (*Diceros bicornis longipes*) was declared extinct in 2011. The western black rhinos once lived in Cameroon, the Central African Republic, Chad, Sudan, and South Sudan. By 1997, only 10 animals were left, and only in Cameroon. When a population gets this small, it is unlikely to be viable. One of the biggest challenges becomes finding a mate. In the case of the western black rhino, 10 were left across approximately 25,000 sq km. The last official sighting was in 2001. The most recent survey for western black rhinos in Cameroon, in 2006, did not find evidence of rhinos and did find widespread evidence of illegal hunting. The survey found traps, poisoned water holes, injured animals, and other evidence that indicated that hunting pressure inside a national park was double the hunting pressure inside official hunting areas.

Most rhinos are killed for their horns (**Figure 31.9**). They are used as dagger handles in the Middle East and

A.          B.          C.

FIGURE 31.9 (a) A horn from a black rhino in Zimbabwe is shown with (b) a rhino horn bowl from China and (c) a jambiya with a rhino horn handle.

in traditional medicines in Asia. The price of rhino horn is increasing, which is driving an increase in poaching. In 1993, rhino horn could bring in $4700 per kilogram. In 2012, it was worth $65,000 per kilogram—more valuable than diamonds, gold, or cocaine. There is a feedback loop that encourages extinction: the more rare a species becomes, the more valuable it becomes. In South Africa, a country that saw a successful decrease in poaching rates in the 1990s, poaching of rhinos doubled every year between 2007 and 2012. Some researchers have suggested that the only way to reduce poaching pressure is to create a legal market for rhino horn, where rhinos are officially farmed and their horns harvested and sold in a tightly controlled market (rhino horns are made of hairlike proteins and can be removed without injury). This suggestion was officially offered to CITES in 2013 but was struck down.

Harvesting and hunting do not just involve large, charismatic animals or even just terrestrial species. Marine creatures are exploited as well, often at unsustainable rates. Many marine species are not killed intentionally but are taken as "by-catch," or accidental capture along with target species during indiscriminate fishing practices. In 2005, scientists estimated that 50% of the world's marine fisheries have been fully exploited, with an additional 25% being actively overexploited. Research in 2001 by scientists at Dalhousie University in Nova Scotia estimated that overfishing has reduced the biomass of predatory fish across the world's oceans by 90%.

## Introduced Species Can Drive Declines in Native Species

Introduced or exotic species are species that have been introduced to an ecosystem where they did not previously exist. Very few introduced species are able to successfully establish in new ecosystems. Of those that do, very few pose threats to the species already living in an ecosystem, the **native species**. However, introduced species can negatively affect populations of native species through competition (see Chapter 30). When this happens, introduced species are called invasive species. Invasive species are another driver of population declines and extinction risk worldwide. The number of introduced species has increased in virtually every corner of the globe as our society becomes increasingly mobile and globalization increases.

Increased trade and tourism directly and indirectly introduce species to new ecosystems. Wildlife trade for the pet industry, for example, directly introduces new animal species to new environments and the diseases that they carry, for example, the case of monkey pox transmitted to humans in North America via African ground squirrels traded as pets (see Chapter 33). The same is true for plants and the introduction of new ornamental and decorative plants for homes and gardens, as in the case of water hyacinth (*Eichhornia crassipes*; see Chapter 30). Indirectly, people can carry seeds or even smaller species such as fungi, bacteria, and viruses between world regions. Large ships use large amounts of water to achieve the right buoyancy to adjust for the weight of the loads they are carrying. The ships pick up many aquatic organisms when they bring on water and then deposit them in other ports when they need to release water, often far from the original source. This is how zebra mussels (*Dreissena polymorpha*), now an invasive species across the Great Lakes, were originally introduced there in the 1980s **(Figure 31.10)**.

One predator that has been introduced by humans around the world is an efficient hunter of birds, rodents, reptiles, and even invertebrates. You may even have a member of this species in your home. Domestic cats (*Felis catus*) kill many animals in urban areas every day and are among the most damaging urban predators. Researchers often rely on reports from cat owners to estimate how many prey items a pet brings home. This is likely an underestimate as cats often consume prey items and abandon carcasses without bringing them home, so no one knows exactly how many animals domestic cats kill. We do know that they have contributed to population declines, especially on islands.

In New Zealand, predation by domestic cats led to the extinction of an endemic bird, Stephens Island Wren (*Traversia lyalli*). Stephens Island is a small island between the two large islands that make up New Zealand. The island was uninhabited until a lighthouse was built in 1892. In 1894, lighthouse keepers and their families moved to the island, bringing at least one cat with them. One of the assistant lighthouse keepers, David Lyall, who was interested in natural history, kept the birds that his cat brought home.

**FIGURE 31.10** **(a)** Zebra mussels (*Dreissena polymorpha*) were introduced to the Great Lakes in North America, where they have spread rapidly. **(b)** They are directly responsible for the declines in eastern pond mussels (*Lampsilis radiata*), a native mussel species.

He gave some of the specimens to traders and a natural history dealer, Henry Travers. One of the birds that the cat brought home was a small, flightless wren that had not previously been identified. In fact, the cat brought home many individuals of this unique bird. Not long after the new species was named (after both Henry Travers and David Lyall), however, it was declared extinct. It appears that in combination with the disturbance of the construction of the lighthouse, the lighthouse keeper's cat caused the extinction of an entire species.

Invasive species compete with native species and, in the absence of their natural predators, can often outcompete native species driving population declines. It is difficult to attribute species declines directly to the introduction of invaders, however. As was the case for Stephens Island Wren and the lighthouse keeper's cat, the introduction of new species is often accompanied by other changes, such as habitat destruction or degradation. It can thus be difficult to tease apart the relative contributions of separate factors to species declines. However, it is clear that invasive species are altering ecosystems in dramatic ways.

## Climate Change Affects All of Us

Today, all life on our planet is affected in some way by climate change. Rapidly rising carbon dioxide levels in the atmosphere are increasing global temperatures, changing precipitation patterns, increasing the frequency of flood and drought, acidifying the oceans, and increasing sea levels across the globe. Our new climate will be unlike what has been experienced on Earth for over 400,000 years. Each change will be problematic for a large number of species. The effects of all of them combined could be catastrophic.

Among the best documented consequences of climate change so far have been mismatches in timing for consumers and their food source, like a butterfly and its host plant, for example, which can drive population declines or even the extirpation of populations. Mismatches between consumers and their food sources occur because climate change can alter the timing of life history events, or **phenology**, of many organisms. Many organisms use environmental cues such as temperature, moisture, or day length for seasonal activities such as flowering, reproductive events, or dormancy. Warming temperatures are changing the timing of many of these environmental cues: spring warming comes earlier, fall cooling comes later, and seasonal temperature extremes, both highs and lows, are increasing. The phenologies of some organisms are changing in response to these environmental changes. But not all organisms depend on the same cues, and organisms differ in how easily they can adjust to changes in their environment. Climate-driven mismatches have been observed between phytoplankton and zooplankton in freshwater lakes and between yellow-bellied marmots (*Marmota flaviventris*) and their food plants.

Temperature itself can affect individual and species survival. Many species have relatively narrow thermal tolerances. Those that already live at or near their limits and cannot acclimate to warmer temperatures will be forced to respond to climate change in one of three ways: move, adapt, or die. We are already seeing species move. The ranges of plant and animal species are moving toward the poles and in some cases up in altitude. Polar animals and those restricted to mountain environments are up against physical boundaries and have been some of the first organisms whose declines can be attributed mainly to climate change. This is true of polar bears (*Ursus maritimus*), Emperor Penguins (*Aptenodytes forsteri*), some butterfly species, and amphibian species restricted to mountain cloud forest environments. Evolutionary adaptation to a changed climate is possible, but scientists worry that the pace of climate change will be faster than evolutionary change, and, thus, species won't evolve tolerances before population declines and extinction. Sessile organisms, such as plants or corals in the oceans, face a particularly large challenge.

The bleaching of coral reefs is a consequence of climate warming (**Figure 31.11**). Coral reefs are the most biodiverse ecosystems in the shallow ocean and are

**FIGURE 31.11** **(a)** Coral polyps with zooxanthellae and **(b)** a bleached coral turns white when the coral polyps expel their zooxanthellae partners in response to stress such as warming water temperatures.

among the most biodiverse ecosystems on Earth. They are important breeding, spawning, and nursery sites for many species. Corals are animals—invertebrates in the class Anthozoa. A coral you see on a reef is made up of many, many coral animals, or polyps, living in a colony. The tiny polyps secrete calcium carbonate exoskeletons that form the coral structures around which you may scuba dive or snorkel. Corals form close associations with algae called zooxanthellae. The corals provide the zooxanthellae with a safe place to live (within the polyps) and some of the compounds necessary for photosynthesis. The zooxanthellae photosynthesize and thus provide the corals with oxygen and energy-rich compounds. The zooxanthellae also provide corals with their colours. Under stress, a coral can expel all of the zooxanthellae that had been partnered with it. The resulting white, or bleached, coral is left vulnerable. Without the zooxanthellae, the coral is more likely to die. Coral bleaching can occur when water temperatures are 0.5 to 1.0°C higher than the average water temperature during the hottest months.

As the levels of carbon dioxide ($CO_2$) in the atmosphere rise, more dissolves from the atmosphere into the ocean. This makes ocean water more acidic. Ocean acidification adds another challenge for coral reefs as it prevents new calcium carbonate from being formed. Warmer temperatures and increases in $CO_2$ can also affect the organisms that live on, in, or around the reef. Recent research has shown that water with increased levels of dissolved $CO_2$ that are likely to be seen in the oceans by the end of the century affects their behaviour. Larval clownfish (*Amphiprion percula*) typically use smell to find appropriate habitat and to avoid predators. A study that introduced larval clownfish into water with increased $CO_2$ found that they were less able to identify habitat cues. They were also either unable to detect predators or appeared to be attracted to, rather than repelled by, the predators' smell. Both of these changes in behaviour are likely to increase the mortality of larval fish. Similar changes were observed in larval damselfish (species in the family Pomacentridae). Their ability to smell predators was similarly affected by increased concentrations of $CO_2$. Warmer ocean temperatures also impaired the swimming ability of damselfish. A water temperature increase of 3°C decreased the maximum speed at which damselfish could swim. This may make the fish unable to swim through the strong currents that are common in their habitat.

## STUDY BREAK

1. What are two ways that invasive species can affect native species?
2. What are three ways that increasing atmospheric carbon dioxide levels are changing habitats?
3. What happens when a coral reef bleaches?

## 31.6 Are There Any Solutions?

Throughout the world, many people are working toward conserving species, conserving biodiversity, and ensuring sustainable use of biological resources. Several international and multilateral groups have defined goals for conserving species and the environment. The combined efforts have been interdisciplinary and have involved individuals and groups from government, non-governmental organizations (NGOs), environmental advocacy groups, and many others. Many efforts have seen some successes. No single conservation effort will be enough to slow or stop the rate of biodiversity loss we are currently experiencing, but even small steps can make a difference.

The Convention on Biological Diversity, a treaty initiated by the United Nations Environment Programme, involves 193 participating countries, including Canada. The United Nations declared the decade from 2011 to 2020 the Decade on Biodiversity. In 2010, the United Nations and the Convention on Biological Diversity adopted a list of five strategic goals for the coming decade, called the Aichi Biodiversity Targets. Within each goal are a number of targets.

The targets include at least halving the rate of habitat loss, protecting 17% of the terrestrial biosphere and 10% of the marine biosphere, and restoring at least 15% of degraded habitats. Another target is to focus on restoring and preserving coral reefs. Still other targets focus on education and outreach, such as the ambitious target of providing everyone with enough knowledge to make choices that promote conservation of biodiversity. Achieving these targets and others like them will not be easy and will require action from many projects, regions, and stakeholders. A few examples of conservation strategies and success stories are featured in the following sections.

### Protected Areas Promote Habitat Conservation

Intact habitat is important for conservation of populations, species, biodiversity, and ecosystems. We use both marine and terrestrial **protected areas**, or areas in which some or all human activities are prohibited, to preserve intact habitat. In general, and especially on land, larger protected areas are better than smaller ones. Many small habitat fragments do not provide the same habitat quality as a single, large protected area. In the oceans, protected areas help increase the number and abundance of species and in many cases have increased the success of fisheries in adjacent, unprotected waters.

Currently, approximately 14% of land area on Earth is contained within official protected areas, making protected areas a substantial global land use. In comparison, urban areas cover about 3% of the terrestrial Earth surface and, as you will recall, agricultural areas almost 40%.

Many protected areas are mostly uninhabited, such as the national parks of the United States and Canada. In other world regions, some are inhabited, and these protected areas also contribute to conservation. Inhabited conservation areas can help preserve not only biodiversity but also the livelihoods and lifestyles of indigenous groups that inhabit these areas. One-fifth of the land area in closed canopy forest in the Brazilian Amazon, for example, is protected as indigenous reserves. Indigenous people live on and use this land. This represents twice as much land area as is protected in uninhabited areas. Both types of protected areas, inhabited and uninhabited, in the Amazon have been shown to prevent deforestation and the conversion of forest to agriculture.

Although protected areas are valuable conservation tools, no single protected area can cover the entire range of all species that live within it. Species that move across great distances can easily move in and out of protected areas. Populations of those that are distributed across large areas can extend across a protected area's boundaries. **Habitat connectivity**—or how well patches of habitat are connected—can have a strong influence on the success of some species. Some organisms, such as large mammals like wolves or bears, require large areas to find food and mates. Others, such as many species of birds, bats, and butterflies, migrate over large distances. Additionally, under climate change, some organisms may need to move—for example, organisms that must move north or to a higher altitude to find cooler temperatures. These organisms need a way to move safely from place to place. It is unlikely that these organisms will have all of the land area that they use within protected areas. Providing a **habitat corridor** to connect habitat fragments can help. You may have seen habitat corridors where you live. They may be bridges or tunnels that animals can use to cross over a highway or thin stretches of trees that connect larger patches of forest. In the Canadian Rockies, a great deal of work has been done to increase habitat connectivity and the safety of habitat corridors, such as wildlife overpasses in national parks, especially where both bears and people use the corridors **(Figure 31.12)**.

## Species-Specific Efforts Protect Species from Extinction

Many conservation efforts focus on a single species. Such programs have had mixed success. There are, however, several notable examples of species-specific programs that have brought species back from the brink of extinction. In some cases, these efforts focus on animals and plants in the wild, making sure that enough habitat is preserved to support a reproducing and viable population of a species that is at risk for extinction. In other cases, conservation efforts include habitat preservation but focus on breeding species at risk in captivity and reintroducing the offspring into wild habitat.

Preserving habitat for a target threatened species also helps provide habitat for the many other organisms

**FIGURE 31.12** To help create better connections between patches of habitat and discourage interactions between wildlife and cars **(a)**, Alberta and British Columbia both have programs that have provided habitat corridors, including vegetated highway overpasses **(b)** and underpasses **(c)**. Estimates show that up to 20% of the grizzly bear (*Ursus arctos*) population and 18% of the black bear population of Banff National Park use these corridors each year.

## DNA in the Blood Meals of Leeches

It can be difficult to find mammals in the wild—particularly species that are shy, rare, or cryptic (cryptic species look very similar to other related species and can be difficult to differentiate by sight alone). It can be particularly difficult to find these species in tropical forests with dense vegetation and thick canopies that limit visibility and make it difficult to navigate through the terrain. In 2012, a group of researchers from the Natural History Museum of Denmark, led by Ida Baerholm Schnell and Philip Francis Thomsen, used an unusual technique to detect difficult-to-find mammalian species.

Many species of leeches eat mammalian blood. Schnell, Thomsen, and colleagues wondered if they could identify the animals leeches feed on by analyzing the DNA in their blood meals. First, in

the lab, they showed that mammalian DNA in the blood meals of leeches could survive for up to four months and that they could identify which mammal the blood came from. Then they collected terrestrial leeches from tropical forest in Vietnam and analyzed the DNA in the leeches' blood meals. From 25 sampled leeches, they found identifiable mammalian DNA in 21 samples **(Figure 1)**.

Each leech contained the DNA from only one mammalian species, suggesting that the scientists were able to see the DNA only from the most recent meal. Seven of the leeches contained cow or pig DNA, both of which are kept as livestock animals in the region. Five of the leeches contained DNA from recently described species: the Truong Son muntjac (*Munti-*

*acus truongsonensis*, described in 1997, found in one leech) and the Ammanite striped rabbit (*Nesolagus timminsi*, described in 2000, found in four leeches). Three contained DNA from serow (*Capricornis maritimus*), a near-threatened mammal. Six contained DNA from the small-toothed ferret-badger (*Melogale moschata*), a species that looks so similar to other species it is impossible to differentiate without handling the animal.

Schnell, Thomsen, and colleagues suggest that this technique could be a cheap and accessible way to collect more data on tropical mammals that are notoriously difficult to track. This, in turn, could help groups such as the IUCN to complete assessments for mammals that are currently listed as being data deficient.

**FIGURE 1** The blood meals of leeches contain DNA from their hosts. This blood can be used to track mammals. **(a)** DNA from goat blood survived for months after it was ingested by a medicinal leech (*Hirudo medicinalis*). **(b)** Leeches sampled from forests in Vietnam revealed DNA from newly discovered, cryptic, and rare mammal species, including the Annamite striped rabbit, small-toothed ferret-badger, Truong Son muntjac (the pattern and colours of the coat are unknown), and serow.

SOURCE: Reprinted from *Current Biology*, Volume 22, Issue 20, Ida Bærholm Schnell, Philip Francis Thomsen, Nicholas Wilkinson, Morten Rasmussen, Lars R.D. Jensen, Eske Willerslev, Mads F. Bertelsen, M. Thomas P. Gilbert, "Screening mammal biodiversity using DNA from leeches," Page 1980, Copyright 2012, with permission from Elsevier.

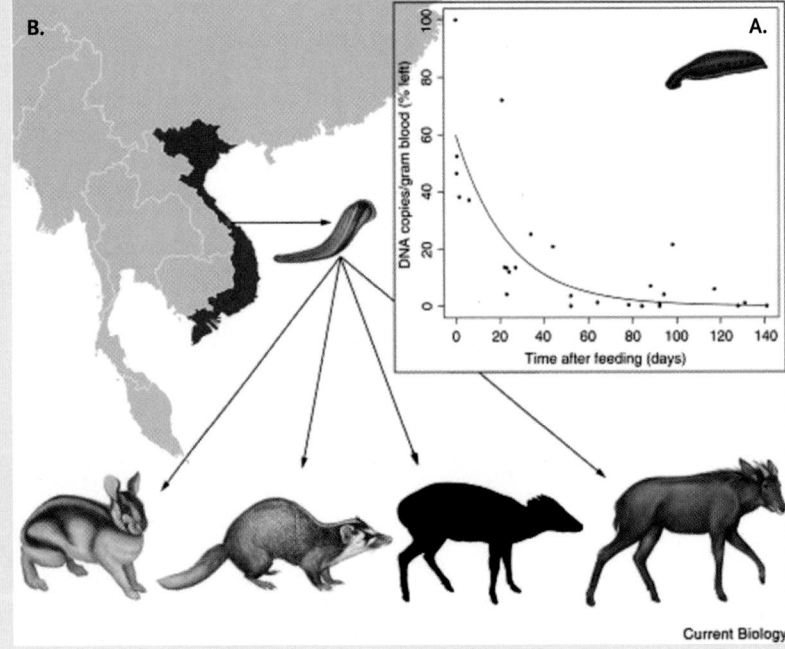

that call that same habitat home. The benefits of single-species habitat conservation to other species are particularly high in areas that are biodiversity hot spots. Setting aside land area to protect a medicinal plant in a tropical rainforest, for example, will likely also set aside land for a number of other potentially endemic or rare plants and animals that coexist with the medicinal plant. Biodiversity hot spots such as tropical rainforest also house a large proportion of the world's biodiversity, including many

species that haven't yet been identified and are difficult to find and track (see Box 31.2).

Captive breeding and reintroduction programs are often undertaken when wild populations are so small that they are experiencing loss of genetic diversity and are not likely to persist. Zoos and aquaria play an important role in captive breeding programs, and there is often international coordination to manage endangered populations and breeding programs. The goals of most of these programs are to grow populations of animals such that they are self-sustaining and stable and avoid problems stemming from a lack of genetic diversity such as inbreeding. In some cases, species' populations are too small or other challenges prevent organisms from being reintroduced in the wild. These organisms will then exist only in captivity. In other cases, individuals from captive breeding programs are reintroduced into the wild. The animals are released into the same regions where they were originally found.

Captive breeding programs have successfully maintained populations of scimitar-horned oryx (*Oryx dammah*), California Condor (*Gymnogyps californicus*), black-footed ferrets (*Mustela nigripes*), and golden lion tamarin (*Leontopithecus rosalia*) **(Figure 31.13)**. All of these species were reintroduced into the wild, although with mixed success.

Wild populations of scimitar-horned oryx have not persisted for more than 15 years; the species is still considered extinct in the wild.

All remaining individual California Condors were taken into captivity in 1987 to begin an intensive attempt to save the species. There is now a small wild population (231 individuals in 2012) that appears to be increasing, but the California Condor is still considered critically endangered.

Intensive conservation efforts were likewise taken to save the black-footed ferret beginning in 1985. After 18 attempts at reintroduction, black-footed ferrets have established three stable and increasing populations in South Dakota and Wyoming. In Canada, where the species once roamed, black-footed ferrets are still considered extirpated (locally extinct). However, groups of black-footed ferrets were reintroduced to Grasslands National Park in Saskatchewan in 2009 and 2011. They appear to be successfully reproducing, marking the first wild reproducing Canadian population in over 70 years.

The golden lion tamarin, a native of eastern Brazil, had only 272 individuals separated into 55 groups that

**FIGURE 31.13** Intensive breeding programs have been undertaken for many critically endangered species, including the scimitar-horned oryx (*Oryx dammah*) **(a)**, black-footed ferret (*Mustela nigripes*) **(b)**, golden lion tamarin (*Leontopithecus rosalia*) **(c)**, and California Condor (*Gymnogyps californicus*) **(d)**.

were mostly isolated from one another in small forest fragments. The golden lion tamarin is still considered endangered but has an increasing wild population. The wild population grew to more than 1000 thanks to a large-scale captive breeding program. Translocation of isolated individuals into larger, continuous, and protected habitat has increased.

Loss of a species from an ecosystem will influence the functioning of that system. For a keystone species, that influence will likely be large (see Chapter 30). Species-specific conservation can not only influence the survival of a species but also may help restoration of ecosystem functions prior to disturbance, whether that disturbance is from habitat destruction, hunting pressure, or something else.

## Ecosystem Restoration Improves Habitat Quality and Ecosystem Services

In practice, many conservation efforts focus on restoring ecosystems. **Restoration ecology** is the discipline that focuses on restoring ecosystems following a disturbance. The disturbance could be natural or anthropogenic (caused by humans). Natural disturbances include floods, fires, volcanic eruptions, and large storms. Anthropogenic disturbances could include pollution, habitat degradation or destruction, resource extraction operations such as mining or oil extraction, and less direct disturbances such as climate change.

Much of restoration ecology focuses on plants and vegetative cover. Native plants could be brought in to restore prairie habitat in fields that had been used for agriculture, or native tree seedlings could be cultivated in deforested areas in the tropics. These restoration efforts can have multiple benefits. Vegetative cover and native plants improve or create habitat for other species, including plants, animals, and microbes. They also improve ecosystem services that may have been impaired by the disturbance. For example, vegetative cover can provide important protection against erosion. Vegetative cover along stream banks protects against erosion of soil and sediment and can also capture and retain nutrients and other pollutants, preventing these pollutants from entering streams.

In some cases, plants or fungi can be used to remove contaminants from a polluted site. This kind of site **remediation** (phytoremediation for plants or mycoremediation for fungi) can be used to break down or remove contaminants. Phytoremediation has been in use for two decades or more. Some plants, such as sunflowers (*Helianthus annuus*), jack pine (*Pinus banksiana*), and even cabbage (*Brassica oleracea*), are particularly good at extracting and accumulating heavy metals. Other plants are particularly good at extracting and accumulating organic contaminants, such as gasoline or diesel. These plants can be

**FIGURE 31.14** Oyster mushrooms (*Pleurotus ostreatus*) growing on a soil contaminated with petroleum products.

planted at polluted sites and subsequently harvested, extracting heavy metal pollution with them. In some cases, the roots of these plants can even be used to remove contaminants from water.

Mycoremediation by fungi as a technique is not yet widely used, but small-scale clean-ups and experiments show great promise **(Figure 31.14)**. Fungi excrete enzymes that are very effective at breaking down cellulose and lignin, the main components that make wood rigid and give it structure. Because petroleum products such as gasoline, diesel, oil—and even other chemicals, such as pesticides—are derived from plant material, many of the chemical bonds that hold these products together are similar to those of cellulose and lignin and can be broken down by fungal digestive enzymes. When fungal mycelium (the filamentous part of the fungus that grows underground) is mixed into contaminated soil, the fungus can break down toxic compounds into smaller, less toxic molecules and in some cases remove them from the soil altogether. In one experiment, fungi reduced the concentration of petroleum-derived pollutants from 20,000 parts per million to 200 parts per million in eight weeks. Although this soil is not nearly as clean as unimpacted soil, this is the same as the difference between the concentration of petroleum-derived pollutants in soil following an oil spill and soil that can be used for landscaping along a highway. Fungi can also take up heavy metals, which are then accumulated in the mushrooms or other fruiting bodies. We can reduce the concentrations of heavy metals such as cadmium, lead, and mercury by inoculating contaminated soil and harvesting fruiting bodies. Many current remediation techniques involve digging up contaminated soil and taking that soil to hazardous waste landfills. Alternatives such as phyto- or mycoremediation may offer cheaper and equally effective ways of turning polluted or unusable landscapes into ones that are safe for use, recreation, and development.

Some aspects of restoration ecology are controversial. For example, the concept of **assisted migration**. In assisted migration, re-searchers would move at-risk species from their current ranges to ecosystems where they have not previously been found. This concept is based on the idea that organisms' most suitable ranges are shifting due to climate change. Some organisms may be unable to move quickly enough to find climatically suitable habitat as the planet continues to warm. Or, in other cases, landscape features may block the movement of species: a city might prevent a plant that reproduces mostly vegetatively from moving north, or a mountain range might make northern migration impossible for a population of salamanders. Scientists argue about the costs and benefits of potentially saving one species with an untested species' introduction that could put others at risk. This idea continues to be debated by many in the conservation community.

The goal of restoration ecology may be to restore an ecosystem, but do we know enough to construct or functionally repair an ecosystem? This unanswered question is particularly important in areas that use land swap techniques, whereby ecosystem damage in one place can be legally compensated for by improving or creating an ecosystem in another place. For example, a wetland might be drained for a company's operations; in exchange, the company pays for constructed wetlands along a nearby highway for erosion and flood control. Despite our best intentions or information, a constructed wetland may simply not provide all of the ecosystem services that the original ecosystem that was damaged or destroyed would have provided.

In most cases, preventing ecosystem damage, when possible, is a cheaper and more reliable alternative for conserving biodiversity than restoration. Consider a eutrophic freshwater lake, for example **(Figure 31.15)**. For many lakes, restoration efforts aim to restore water quality and may include dredging the lake, oxygenating the lake with a bubbler, or adding vegetative buffer strips along the water's edge. All of these efforts are expensive, and none of them guarantee success, particularly in the long term. Effectively preventing nutrient pollution by such means as reducing erosion from farm fields, avoiding storm sewers that bring urban or suburban wastewater directly to water bodies, and reducing fertilizer inputs to lawns and gardens are often cheaper and more effective alternatives.

## Economic Incentives and Agreements Can Encourage Conservation

Economic incentives and partnerships between corporations, environmental groups, and governments can have large positive impacts on conservation goals. In our

**FIGURE 31.15** Eutrophication in Lake Winnipeg. Excess nutrient inputs have driven blooms in algae. Algal blooms reduce oxygen and light in the water. reducing habitat quality and our ability to use the water for swimming, boating, fishing, or other forms of recreation.

globalized world, markets drive many decisions for land use management and, thus, habitat extent and quality. Partnerships between conservation groups, fisheries, and seafood providers, for example, are improving the way consumers make choices about seafood. In Canada, Ocean Wise, a conservation program of the Vancouver Aquarium, is an example of a successful sustainable seafood partnership.

Ocean Wise was developed to educate the public about sustainable seafood. It has developed tools such as a smart phone app that allows consumers to look up different types of seafood (including the source and harvesting method) and make more informed decisions about the seafood they consume. Ocean Wise has four criteria that it recommends are met before we consume seafood: (1) the species are abundant and resilient to current fishing pressure; the species are harvested in ways that (2) do not damage ocean habitats or (3) result in by-catch of other potentially rare species; and (4) the species' fisheries are managed based on current scientific data. Ocean Wise has also partnered with more than 450 groups, including restaurants, food suppliers, universities, and even sports centres. These groups highlight menu items that meet the Ocean Wise criteria for sustainable seafood. Many have also removed menu items that do not meet Ocean Wise criteria. Ocean Wise labelling and food choices might be available from your university campus; they have now partnered with more than 50 Canadian universities and colleges.

Other partnerships have brought the international community together to curb climate change. The United Nations Framework Convention on Climate Change (UNFCCC) is a treaty between 196 different countries to reduce greenhouse gas emissions that contribute to climate change. More than 20% of global greenhouse gas emissions come from the carbon liberated when forest is cleared or degraded through practices such as logging. Although binding and clear policy agreements to reduce emissions have not yet come from the UNFCCC, many countries have agreed to a program that provides financial incentives to reduce deforestation. The partnership provides funding to tropical countries, home of the most intact forest and the site of the highest rates of deforestation, to reduce emissions from deforestation and forest degradation (the program is called REDD+). Both Canada and the United States are among the 75 countries which are current project partners. The program is still in its early stages, and although it has yet to be fully enacted, partner countries have pledged $4 billion to tropical nations. Norway has already begun funding Brazil and Indonesia, pledging each $1 billion in "pay-for-performance" agreements. We will see how these large, multilateral agreements on environmental policy develop. It is becoming increasingly clear that global action must be taken to protect biodiversity and ecosystems.

## Optimizing Agricultural Production Can Minimize Environmental Costs

To slow or stop the expansion of agricultural land, we must increase production on existing agricultural land, reduce food waste, improve infrastructure for growing, and get food into the least developed nations. We also must improve the resiliency of farmers and crops. Solving the challenge of meeting agricultural demands while minimizing environmental costs will involve many trade-offs. It will also require different strategies in different world regions. For example, in a traditional agricultural region such as the Canadian prairies or the American Midwest, there is very little land not in agricultural production. In these regions, some of the biggest challenges for conserving biodiversity are ensuring adequate habitat to maintain populations and enough connectivity between habitats to allow populations to interact and move safely. In this case, lowering the intensity of agriculture in favour of habitat creation and conservation may be the best strategy. In the Amazon, however, one of the planet's biodiversity hot spots and a conservation priority, the biggest challenge will be keeping enough forest intact to maintain the high levels of biodiversity and high habitat quality. Here the best strategy may be intensification of agriculture on already cleared land so that the land area in agriculture is minimized. This means maximizing the yields of crops that are produced. These issues and options remain contentious, and finding solutions will require the work of policy makers, economists, agronomists, ecologists, and many others.

## 31.7 What Can You Do?

If biodiversity matters to you, there are many ways in which you can play an active role in conservation. They cover nearly all of the types of solutions discussed in this chapter. Here are just a few:

1. *Invest in improving the habitat around your home and in your neighbourhood for native wildlife.* This could be planting native species in your yard, including native species that provide habitat or food for native wildlife such as butterflies or birds. It could also be volunteering to plant native trees or remove invasive species or projects in local parks or areas that are undergoing restoration. You could also volunteer or participate in data gathering for citizen science projects (Box 31.3).

2. *Use your money and your votes to support conservation efforts.* Give money to nonprofit groups that focus on conservation efforts you support. Or get involved in politics: write to your representatives when policies and legislation that affect biodiversity and conservation of species are up for debate and vote for representatives who support the policies you do. You could even run for office if you are interested in creating the policies you would like to see in place.

3. *Reduce your contributions to climate change.* There are very real ways that you can commit to reducing your greenhouse gas contributions. For example, switch incandescent light bulbs for compact fluorescent light bulbs. If there are holes in your home where hot or cool air can be lost, fill them. You can also make small commitments to reduce the amount you drive: pledge to walk anywhere less than 1 km from your house 50% of the time or less than 2 km 25% of the time. How challenging these goals are to achieve will, of course, depend on factors such as where you live and whether or not you own your own home, but there are many ways that all of us can make our footprint just a little bit smaller.

4. *Eat less meat.* Reducing your meat consumption decreases demands for agricultural products that are not food crops; remember from Chapter 2 how much energy is lost at each trophic level. The same amount of energy can produce much more plant material than animal. Livestock agriculture is also a contributor of greenhouse gas emissions from both the conversion of forest or other ecosystems to pasture and the methane emissions from the livestock themselves, so eating less meat decreases your carbon footprint.

5. *Stay informed.* If you care about particular areas or species, read critically about the challenges and potential solutions.

## Citizen Scientists

The participation of volunteers in gathering ecological and biological data is becoming more and more common in the study of biodiversity and environmental change **(Figure 1)**. Data collected by the public have been used for many years. In England, for example, flowering times noted by gardeners have been used to document changes in phenology over time. The American naturalist Henry David Thoreau also kept detailed records of flowering times in his native Massachusetts in the 1850s. In combination with records from another naturalist of the same era, scientists showed that flowering times for 43 plant taxa are now an average of seven days earlier than in Thoreau's time.

Citizen science projects, with crowd-sourced data collected over a broad geographic range, allow scientists to examine larger areas than would otherwise be possible and seem to have great success in finding rare species. The Lost Ladybug Project, for example, has citizen scientists send in photos of ladybugs people encounter. The project has engaged children as well as adults, with more than 20,000 photos of ladybugs contributed. The project has identified rare invasive ladybug species and documented their occurrence in new areas. It has also tracked native ladybugs that have recently been increasingly rare with the arrival of the exotic species. Data from the project confirm that native populations are declining.

Long-term bird observations, of both occurrences and abundances, have been particularly well monitored by citizen scientists. With events such as the Christmas Bird Count run by the Audubon Society and programs such as Project FeederWatch run by the Lab of Ornithology at Cornell University, many amateur birders have contributed important data on shifting ranges, migration timing, and egg-laying patterns. Eight of the well-established bird-monitoring projects have led to more than 1000 scientific publications.

Citizen science projects are not typically experimental manipulations, nor do they often address specific hypotheses. However, in an ever-changing global environment, they offer an essential opportunity for looking at changes in the biodiversity of all of our backyards—especially changes that we might not be expecting.

**FIGURE 1** A group of volunteer pollinator monitors counting pollinator visits in a garden of native plants at the Evergreen Brick Works, a restored area in Toronto.

# PUTTING IT IN PERSPECTIVE

The best conservation strategies and the best ways to move forward are still up for debate. There are heated and passionate disagreements among politicians, conservation professionals, scientists, and concerned citizens about what must be done and how to do it. Ultimately, there is no one solution that will solve all of the challenges facing our complicated and dynamic biological world. Do not let this dissuade you from getting involved. Use what you know to make the best decisions you can. Learn more. Teach others.

Think critically about the information you get from all advocacy groups. We cannot leave the fate of our planet in the hands of any one group. And we can all contribute to making a difference. As stated by the Millennium Ecosystem Assessment, a project that brought together more than 1000 scientists to look at ecosystem health and biodiversity worldwide: "Science can help ensure that decisions are made with the best available information, but ultimately the future of biodiversity will be determined by society."

# KEY CONCEPTS REVIEW AND QUESTIONS

## 31.1 Defining Conservation

Conservation biology and conservation science both deal with studying what threatens biodiversity. Both disciplines also focus on finding ways to conserve biodiversity from the genetic to the global level. Conservation biology began several decades ago as a crisis discipline focused on preserving ecosystems and organisms as they exist in the absence of human influence. Today, conservation science continues to strive to protect biodiversity but also recognizes the role of humans in the natural landscape. This includes the pervasive influence humans have on even the most remote ecosystems as well as the value to humans of the biological services provided by Earth's biota.

1. What is a pristine or natural ecosystem? How is it different from a human-controlled ecosystem?

2. What is one way conserving an ecosystem might benefit humans?

## 31.2 Defining Biodiversity

Biodiversity is the biological diversity of an area. The area can be very small, such as a garden, yard, or park, or quite large, such as a country, a continent, or the globe. Biodiversity can also include a number of different measures. Genetic diversity is a measure of biodiversity, as are species richness and species abundance.

3. What is the difference between species richness and species abundance?

4. Can you think of an example in which the loss of a single species affects the functioning of an ecosystem? (Reference Chapter 30 if you need help.)

5. What is a keystone species?

## 31.3 The Value of Biodiversity

The complex and dynamic biological world on our planet is always changing. Throughout the history of life on Earth, species have come and gone. Humans, however, have a larger impact than any other species on species' survival and biodiversity. Biodiversity is currently in trouble, due mainly to the influence of humans. There are many reasons we should all care about biodiversity.

6. What is the background extinction rate?

7. What are two arguments for preserving biodiversity?

8. What is an ecosystem service? What are three examples?

## 31.4 Tracking Biodiversity and the Status of Species

There are many groups worldwide that measure and track the status of species and the movement of species. These groups attempt to track the species that are closest to extinction so that conservation efforts can be focused by organism and region. Tracking the movement of species by humans, particularly across international borders, can also inform the economic drivers of population declines, such as poaching.

9. How do groups such as the IUCN keep track of species? What kind of work does it involve?

10. What does it mean for an organism to be extirpated from a particular region?

11. What is CITES, and what are its major goals?

## 31.5 There are Many Threats to Species and Biodiversity

Humans are decreasing biodiversity directly by overexploiting biological resources, destroying habitat, and appropriating a huge fraction of the planet for agriculture. Humans are indirectly decreasing biodiversity through climate change, pollution, and other forms of habitat degradation.

12. Tropical forests are being cut down for agricultural production in Southeast Asia and South America. How are the diets of people in affluent countries encouraging deforestation in these regions?

13. Diversity matters at a number of levels; it is not simply an accounting of the number of species. Genetic diversity also matters, as does ecosystem diversity. How might habitat loss affect the genetic diversity of populations? How might invasive species affect global ecosystem diversity?

14. What threats to biodiversity facilitate the spread of wildlife diseases?

## 31.6 Are There Any Solutions?

Conservationists are using a number of strategies to preserve biodiversity. There is no single solution that will solve all of the environmental challenges that are currently driving declines in biodiversity. However, researchers use a number of conservation strategies to reduce the rate of biodiversity loss or to help protect particularly vulnerable species. These strategies include the setting aside of protected areas, targeted species programs such as captive breeding or attempts at reintroduction, and habitat restoration.

15. How do campaigns to save target species' habitat benefit other rare species?

16. What is assisted migration? Why is it controversial? What are arguments for or against it?

17. What is phytoremediation?

### 31.7 What Can You Do?

There are many ways that each of us can make a difference to the future biodiversity of our planet.

18. What is citizen science?

19. What are two ways that you can reduce your contribution to climate change?

20. What do you think is your largest contribution to biodiversity loss? Does it matter to you?

Now that you have read and reviewed this chapter, we encourage you to attempt to build a concept map using these key concepts and indicate the connections between them. Please see Chapter 5 for examples of concept maps that could be developed for this chapter.

worldswildlifewonders/Shutterstock.com

## WHY IT MATTERS

Fear is a familiar emotion that can strongly influence behaviour. Humans sometimes openly acknowledge their fear of doing something or going somewhere. But perhaps as often our fear is obvious in our behaviour, body language, and tone of voice. What about other animals? How would you design an experiment in which the results would demonstrate an effect of fear?

When eggs and young are in the nest **(Figure 32.1)**, birds are vulnerable to attacks by predators. Eggs and nestlings are defenceless, depending entirely on one or both parents to protect them from attacks. Parents may be strongly dedicated to protecting their young, ensuring that their genes are passed onto the next generation. Do nesting birds show changes in behaviour associated with fear of attacks on their nests?

Liana Zanette and colleagues from Western University manipulated the situations faced by nesting female Song Sparrows (*Melospiza melodia*). They installed video cameras so that they could monitor what happens at nests. Then, in one manipulation, they eliminated predation by protecting every nest with electrified fences and netting. In their second manipulation, they played back sounds to nesting females, the calls and sounds of predators (e.g., hawks, owls, raccoons, cowbirds). As a control, they also presented playbacks of the sounds of non-predators (e.g., seals, geese, flickers, loons, and hummingbirds).

The results clearly showed that, by itself, the perception of the risk of predation reduced the number of offspring produced per year by Song Sparrows by 40% **(Figure 32.2, p. 728)**. The impact of the threats declined over the nesting period, being highest when eggs were in the nest, lower for hatchlings, and even lower for fledglings. There was also an effect of month on the impact of fear of predators.

This remarkable study revealed that the impact of fear alone was a reduction in the production of young, directly affecting both the fitness of individual birds and their populations. The results illustrate that fear is not unique to humans and that for the determined research

**FIGURE 32.1** Female Song Sparrow on a nest **(a)** and three nestling young begging for food **(b)**. Photographs courtesy of Liana Zanette.

## BIOLOGY IS EVERYWHERE 32.1
## Liana Zanette

Liana Zanette is an associate professor of biology at Western University, where she and her students study some of the dimensions of fear induced by predators. They use Song Sparrows as model prey and look at the topic from various points of view. What impact has the explosion of populations of some predators (e.g., raccoons – *Procyon lotor*) in the wake of extirpation of larger predators (e.g., grey wolves – *Canis lupis*) had in much of North America? In a sense, the work focuses on the equivalent of post-traumatic stress syndrome in animals other than humans. This parallel identifies yet another way in which apparently basic work in biology (behaviour and ecology) could bear on situations facing humans.

Parasites are another recurring challenge for wild animals. For birds such as Song Sparrows, Brown-headed Cowbirds (*Molothrus ater*) are important parasites. Female Brown-headed Cowbirds lay their eggs in the nests of hosts such as Song Sparrows. The behaviour of these cowbirds halves the number of female Song Sparrows that hatch and fledge from parasitized nests, 0.32 versus 0.54 females, respectively. By removing parasitism by Brown-headed Cowbirds, the impact on the number of fledging females was removed.

Professor Zanette and her students are leading the way in terms of how widespread and common species such as Song Sparrows are affected by ongoing changes in their environments. Their work demonstrates how studies of common species will help advance the work and priorities of conservation programs.

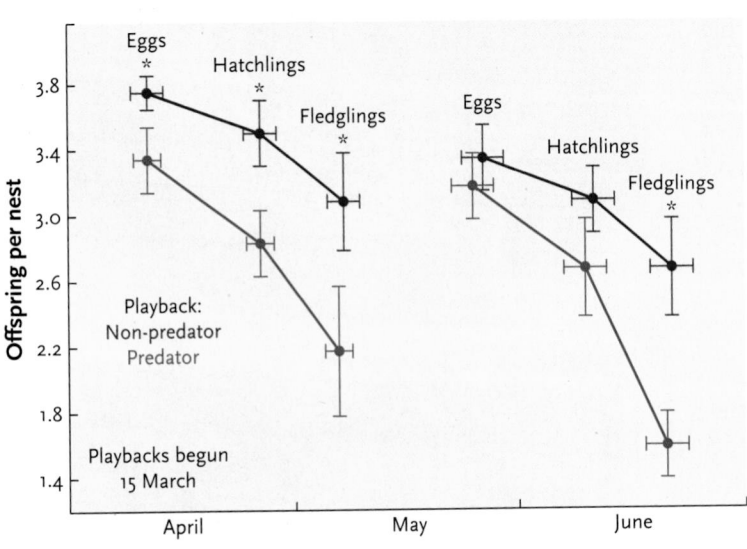

**FIGURE 32.2** The impact of a perceived threat on offspring produced in the nests of Song Sparrows varied by month. Note that playbacks representing threats of predation had a much stronger effect than presentations of other sounds.

SOURCE: From Liana Y. Zanette, Aija F. White, Marek C. Allen, Michael Clinchy, "Perceived predation risk reduces the number of offspring songbirds produce per year," *Science* 9 December 2011: Vol. 334 no. 6061 pp. 1398–1401. Reprinted with permission from AAAS.

team, it is something that can be measured. Read more about this research in Box 32.1.

How does fear influence your behaviour? Can you think of any costs of fear? What would be the benefits of fear?

In this chapter, we will explore selected topics in behaviour, from the link to genetics to various aspects directly affecting survival. These topics range from avoiding predators to being successful as a predator but also extend to sex and social behaviour, communication, language, and tool use. We will finish by considering how some new discoveries about behaviour have opened our eyes to additional possibilities.

## 32.1 Behaviour

Arguably, the study of behaviour is one of the oldest branches of biology. Our ancestors from before *Australopithecus* had to have been acutely aware of behaviour—of prey, of predators. As important was the behaviour of conspecifics (members of the same species), whether part of their group or of another group. As a discipline within biology, behaviour connects directly to anatomy, physiology, and ecology. In the past, some elements of behaviour, such as tool using and language, had been considered unique to humans. As we shall see, our views of these dichotomies have changed.

## 32.2 Behaviour and Genetics

Known as the "nature–nurture" controversy, there has been a long and persistent debate about how much genetic (nature) rather than environmental (nurture) factors influence an organism's behaviour. Research on fruit flies (*Drosophila melanogaster*) revealed two types of larvae: those that move (**rovers**) and those that do not (**sitters**). These are inheritable traits associated with genes, demonstrating a direct relationship between genetics and behaviour. As usual in biology, there are many variations on this theme, and there is a spectrum from behaviours that are fully under genetic control to those that are entirely due to environmental factors.

Colonies (hives) of honeybees **(Figure 32.3 – *Apis mellifera*)** include the queen and several types of worker bees. Worker bees known as "scouts" search for nests, whereas others search for feeding sites. Food scouts comprise 5% to 25% of foraging workers. Gene expression in their

# THE MOLECULE BEHIND THE BIOLOGY 32.2
## Dopamine

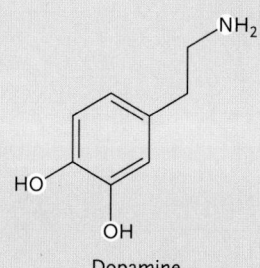

Dopamine **(Figure 1)** is a neurotransmitter, a messenger involved in the transmission of signals in different parts of the body, including the brain. Widely identified as a reward chemical that affects decision-making centres in the brain, dopamine is sometimes identified with addiction. The impact of dopamine on the development of scouting behaviour in bees suggests some interesting parallels to humans with respect to novelty-seeking behaviour. The phylogenetic distance between humans (phylum Chordata) and honeybees (phylum Arthropoda) suggests that dopamine is part of an ancient legacy, likely to be involved repeatedly in behavioural development in animals.

**FIGURE 1** Dopamine molecule.

**FIGURE 32.3** A honeybee.

*Courtesy of Naas Rautenbach*

brains differentiates scouts from other worker bees. Treatment of workers with dopamine increased the incidence of scouting behaviour. Treating workers with two neurochemicals (see Chapter 26) (octopamine and glutamate) that are antagonists to dopamine reduces the incidence of scouting behaviour. Genes influence behaviour, as does the environment; usually, the two act in concert. Read more about dopamine in Box 32.2.

## STUDY BREAK

1. What are rover and sitter genes? Where do they occur? What do they tell us about genetic control of behaviour?
2. How could octopamine and glutamate connect genetics and behaviour in bees?

## 32.3 Struggle for Survival: Defence and Offence

The trophic structure of ecosystems means that plants produce their own food, whereas fungi consume mainly detritus and stationary materials. Animals eat other organisms: plants by primary consumers and other animals by secondary or tertiary consumers. These ecological realities set the stage for a rich array of offensive and defensive behaviours.

### Defensive Ploys

Animals that are predators can also be prey. Furthermore, predators may take a variety of prey species, and prey species have to contend with more than one species of predator. The defence that works against one predator may not work on another—and vice versa.

#### Plants and Animals Can Use Sharp Defences

Plants typically use some combination of mechanical and chemical defences against herbivores. Thorns and spines **(Figure 32.4, p. 730)** are examples of mechanical defences, and chemical defences range from irritating oils (e.g., poison ivy) to alkaloids and other chemicals that cause at least digestive upsets in herbivores. In other situations, plants exploit the behaviour of animals to effect pollination and dispersal of fruits and seeds (Figure 28.22).

Mammals such as porcupines and their relatives also use spines in defence **(Figure 32.5, p. 730)**. This is true of other mammals, such as spiny anteaters, tenrecs, and hedgehogs. Some hedgehogs use toad venom to increase the effectiveness of their sharp quills. They do this by anointing themselves with toad venom. First, they lick a toad's skin and then lick some of its quills. One adventurous researcher stuck himself with hedgehog quills and quickly learned that the ones anointed with toad venom were much more irritating than the unanointed ones.

#### Some Animals Are Eternally Vigilant

Animals use a range of defensive behaviours (Figure 32.5), in part reflecting a variety of situations. Eternal vigilance is a common first line of defence. This means always being on the lookout for predators. On the ground, more eyes

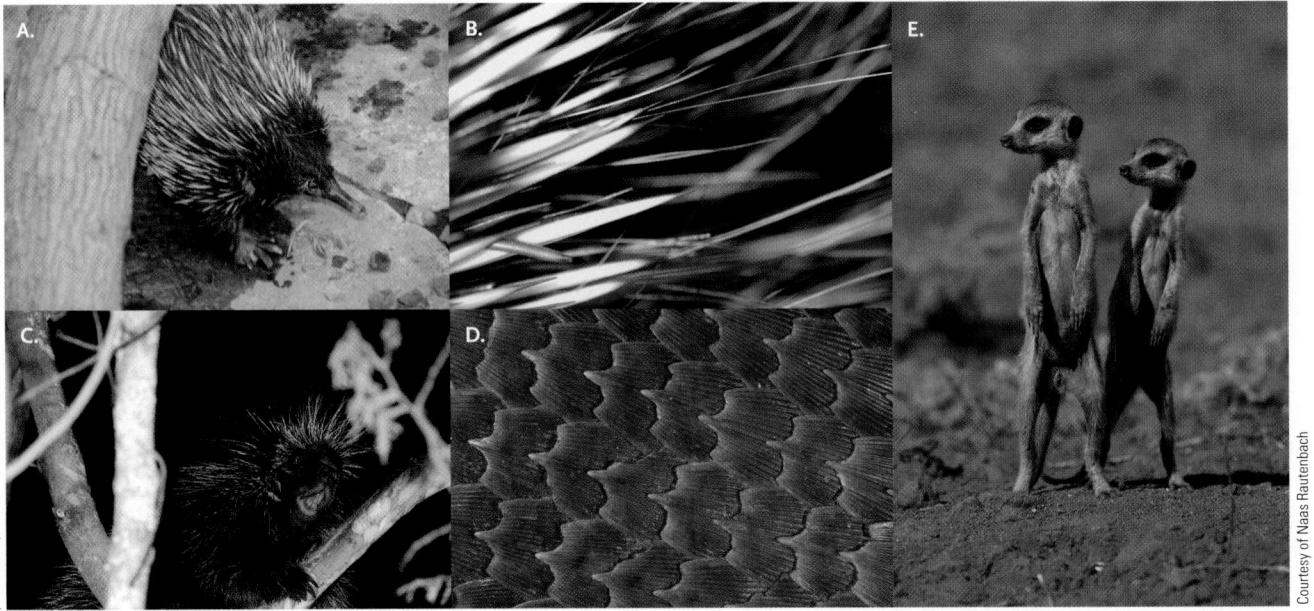

**FIGURE 32.4** Mechanical and chemical defences of plants. Cacti (*Opuntia turpinii* **(a)**; *Cereus peruvianus* **(b)**), and euphorbs (*Euphorbia ingens*) **(c)** have defensive spines. Other plants have chemical protection such as cardenolides in latex sap (*Apocynum androsaemifolium*) **(d)** and irritating oils, such as poison ivy (*Toxicodendron radicans*) **(e)**.

(Photos A–E) M.B. Fenton

(Photos A–D) M.B. Fenton

Courtesy of Naas Rautenbach

**FIGURE 32.5** Mammal defences from spines **(a, b, c)** to armour **(d)** and eternal vigilance **(e)**. The animals include an echidna (a – *Tachyglossus aculeatus*), a Brazilian porcupine (b – *Coendou prehensilis*), a porcupine (c – *Erethizon dorsatum*), a scaly anteater (d – *Manis tricuspis*), and two meerkats (e – *Suricata suricata*).

and ears are more likely to detect danger; thus, vigilance may be enhanced when animals live in groups. A second line of defence is making it clear to the predator that it has been detected and then keeping it in sight and moving away from or even approaching it.

### Other Animals Are Invisible

Camouflage is another common first line of defence, minimizing the chances of being detected by a predator. Camouflage may mean pattern of colouration, combined with not moving because movement attracts attention **(Figure 32.6)**. In some cases, animals closely resemble inedible objects such as sticks, stones, or bird droppings.

### Animals Can Flee from Danger

After the predator has initiated pursuit and an attack, being fast may allow the prey to escape, perhaps by outrunning the predator, getting out of its reach, or climbing a tree. Flight adds another dimension to escape behaviour, unless the predator can also fly.

### Then Animals May Fight Back

Fighting back is one last line of defence. This is usually some combination of biting, kicking, and stinging. An alternative is to play dead. In response to a direct threat, hog-nosed snakes (*Heterodon nasicus*) show an interesting

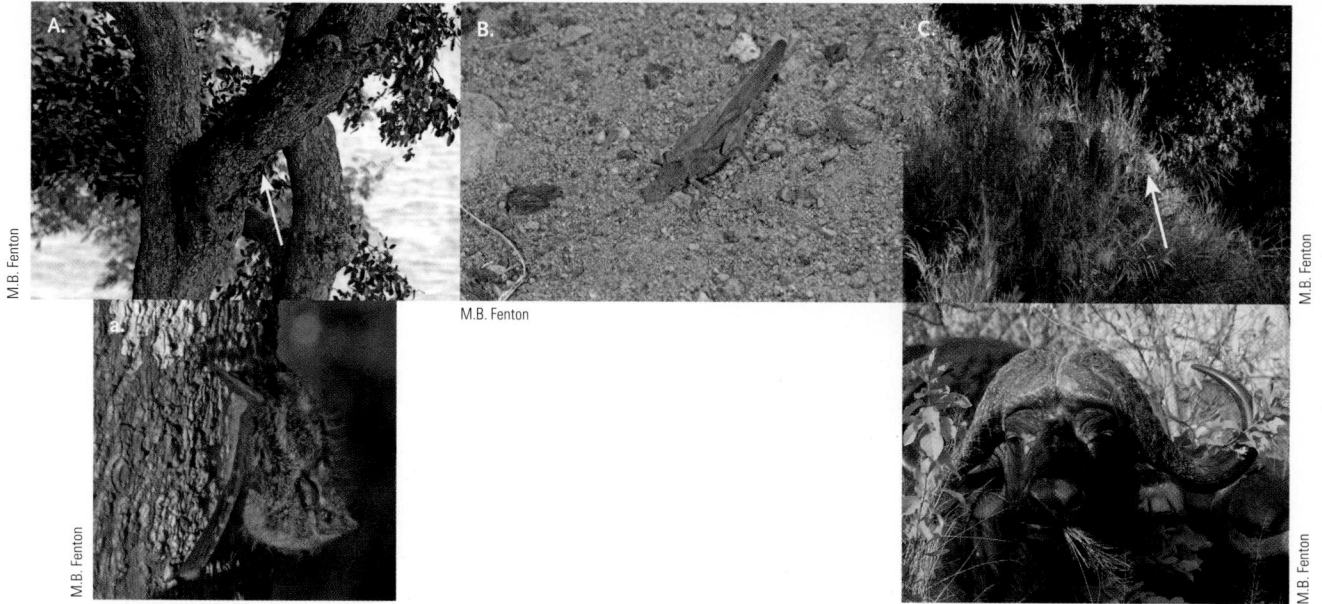

**FIGURE 32.6** This sample illustrates how easy it can be to overlook animals and that size and setting matter. **(a)** A group of proboscis bats (white arrow – *Rhynchonycteris naso*) roost on a tree trunk (the inset shows one bat). **(b)** A grasshopper sitting on the ground. **(c)** A Cape buffalo (white arrow – *Syncerus caffer*) in long grass (the inset shows a buffalo close-up).

**FIGURE 32.7** Three moths vary in appearance. **(a)** A garden tiger moth (*Arctia caja*) shows its warning: coloured hindwings. **(b)** A tissue moth (*Triphosa haesitata*) is easily overlooked (cryptic) depending on the background. **(c)** A herald (*Scoliopteryx libatrix*) is much less colourful than the tiger moth but more conspicuous than the tissue. All three species of moths use specialized ears to detect the echolocation calls of bats.

sequence of behaviour. The snake begins by striking at, but not biting, the attacker. Then the snake defecates all over itself, rolls onto its back, sticks its tongue out, and plays dead. If you turn the snake over on its belly, it turns itself onto its back.

Some tiger moths are the "pessimists of the moth world." In addition to bright, warning colours **(Figure 32.7)**, they have toxins in their bodies and, when pushed, also produce clicking sounds in response to attacks. Grasshopper mice (*Onychomys leucogaster*) eat tiger moths, pay no attention to any of the warning signals the moth produces, and are not affected by their defensive chemicals. The precise strategy or set of strategies used in defence depends on the predator and the prey. Some potential prey, for example, elephants and whales, are too large for most predators. Their sizes are considered a defence.

## Distractions Can Work

Movement attracts the attention of predators. The moving black tip of the tail of an ermine (*Mustela erminea*) often is the target of a predator's attack. In this way, the ermine effectively misdirects the predator and increase its chances of survival. Autotomy **(Figure 32.8, p. 732)** is an extension of this anti-predator behaviour in which body parts break off when grabbed. Many species of lizards and geckoes invite and direct attacks by waving their tails at attacking predators. They break off the tail when the predator grabs it. Some crabs raise autotomy to a higher level, grabbing the attacker with one of their claws, breaking it off, and leaving it attached to the predator. In this case, the pain associated with the crab's pincer persists and further dissuades the predator from continuing its attack.

FIGURE 32.8 This crab has lost its right claw, perhaps through attack autotomy.

Tail flagging is common in some rodents. California ground squirrels (*Spermophilus beecheyi*) flag their tails at snakes poised to attack them **(Figure 32.9)**. They behave this way in response to threats from bull snakes (*Pituophis melanoleucus*) and rattlesnakes (*Crotalus oreganus*). But in response to a rattlesnake, ground squirrels pump blood into their tail so that the distractor is both moving and hot. The heat sensors of rattlesnakes detect the squirrel's tail and its movements, drawing the attack. Bull snakes lack thermal sensors, and the squirrels provide the waved tail as a distraction with no heat.

### Fake Heads Are One Variation on Distraction

Many predators attack the victim's head to maximize their chances of catching and immobilizing it. False heads such as the one on the butterfly in **Figure 32.10** exploit head-directed attacks and often are an effective defence.

### Pain as the Distractor

The venom of bark scorpions (*Centruroides sculpturatus*) causes intense pain in mammals such as humans and rats. Sodium pumps on cell membranes are the targets of the venom. Grasshopper mice regularly eat bark scorpions and are not affected by the venom because their sodium pumps have a different control mechanism.

### Multiple Lures Can Distract

Safety in numbers is a defensive ploy that can extend beyond having more eyes and ears alert to possible danger. Dense aggregations of animals may form around or at a localized resource. Members of the aggregation effectively dilute their risk of attack by predators by swamping the predator with many alternative targets. In these situations, the animals may be superficially similar, making it more difficult for an attacker to focus on one victim. Good examples of this phenomenon **(Figure 32.11)** would be a swarm of locusts, a flock of birds, or a herd of zebras. In the case of zebras, black and white stripes disrupt the outline of the animal, providing a level of camouflage. Closer up, the striped pattern is conspicuous and serves to deter tabanids (biting flies) from biting. Tabanid flies (Figure 19.28) are mainly blood-feeders that use polarized light to find their prey. Light and dark stripes disrupt the tabanids' perception, providing the zebra with some protection from them.

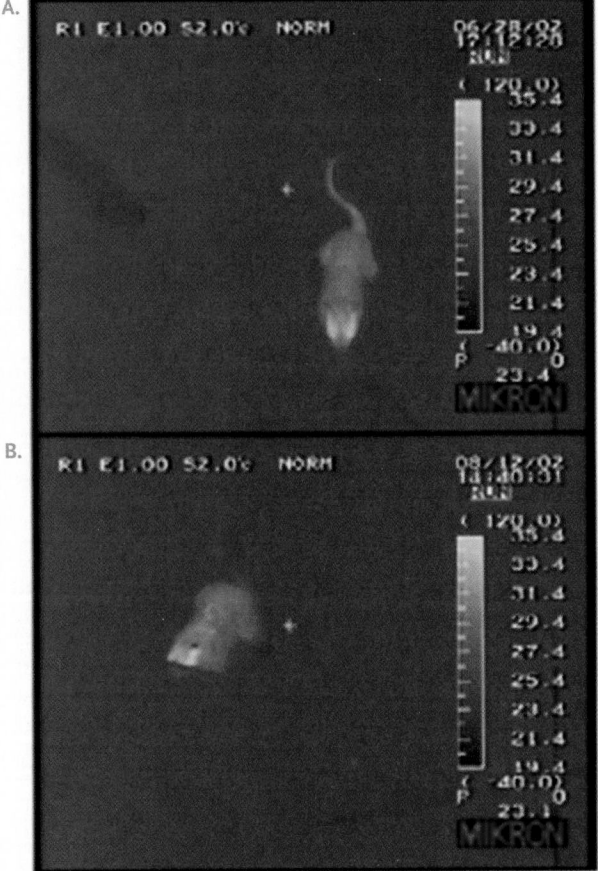

FIGURE 32.9 Two infrared images of a California ground squirrel. **(a)** The squirrel is interacting with a rattlesnake (which has infrared sensors). **(b)** The squirrel interacts with a gopher snake (that lacks infrared sensors).

SOURCE: Rundus et al., "Ground squirrels use an infrared signal to deter rattlesnake predation," *PNAS* September 4, 2007 vol. 104 no. 36 14372–14376. Copyright 2007 National Academy of Sciences, U.S.A.

FIGURE 32.10 Which is the real head on this butterfly?

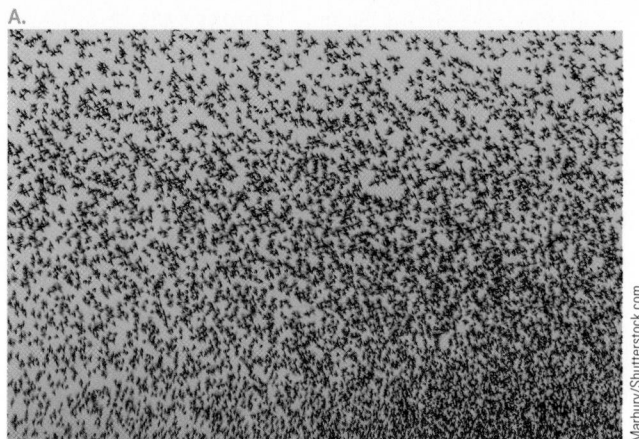

**FIGURE 32.11** Two examples of groups of animals: European Starlings **(a)** and zebras **(b)**.

## False Advertising Can Work

Animals armed with stingers frequently use a combination of behaviour and conspicuous colour patterns to warn predators of the risks involved in attacking them. Bees and wasps are obvious examples, but others include butterflies and caterpillars **(Figure 32.12)**. The warnings, aposematic signals, caution other animals that brightly coloured insects and other animals are dangerous. The results of being stung or getting sick after eating a brightly coloured prey teaches some predators to avoid them. When young insectivorous birds are leaving the nest and learning to hunt, the only wasp- and beelike insects they encounter are bees and wasps, maximizing the chances of their associating the aposematic signals with pain. Earlier and later in the season, harmless mimics of bees and wasps are abundant and benefit from the painful previous experiences of the predators. Dangerous prey are models for mimics. In many cases, several related species that are armed resemble one another in appearance. These two forms of mimicry are referred to as "Müllerian" and "Batesian," named after the biologists who described them. Batesian mimics are harmless but look like dangerous species, the models. Müllerian mimics are as dangerous as the models.

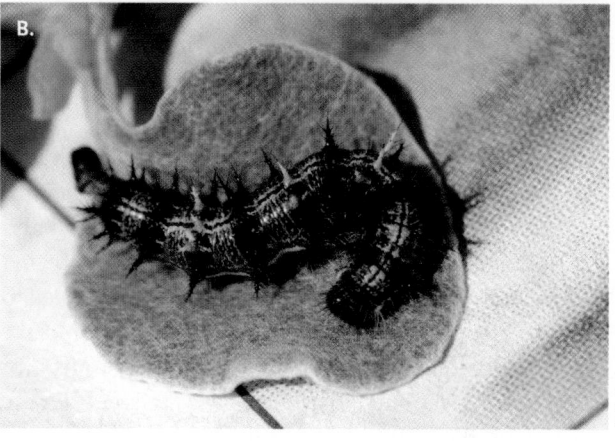

**FIGURE 32.12** Animals with aposematic signals: wasps **(a)** and a colourful caterpillar with spines **(b)**.

Among mammals in the order Carnivora, some species have contrasting coat patterns **(Figure 32.13, p. 734)**, often a variation on black and white stripes or spots. Like many species with these colours, striped skunks (*Mephitis mephitis*) produce noxious secretions in anal glands and can spray attackers. In addition to their coat patterns, the species tend to be stocky in build and live in exposed habitats. Species with white backs tend to be nocturnal sprayers. Horizontal stripes occur in species that spray more accurately, whereas white facial strips usually occur in species that live in burrows.

## Startle Also Works

What startles you? Why do you have a startle reaction? Everyone has been startled by an unexpected sound or sight. The stimulus gives you a "start," which initiates an innate flight reaction. Startle reactions are fundamental defensive behaviours that minimize the chances of your

Sergey Mikhaylov/Shutterstock.com

worldswildlifewonders/Shutterstock.com

Kobie Douglas/Shutterstock.com

KMW Photography/Shutterstock.com

**FIGURE 32.13** The contrasting colour patterns on five carnivores, including a striped skunk (*Mephitis mephitis*) **(a)**, a spotted skunk (*Mephitis* spp.) **(b)**, a honey badger (*Galictis vittata*) **(c)**, and a wolverine (*Mellivora capensis*) **(d)**.

coming to harm. Eye spots **(Figure 32.14)** are stimuli that give animals a start. The sudden, unexpected flash of what appear to be eyes (Figure 32.14) is a common and widespread defensive behaviour apparently directed mainly at insectivorous birds. The "eyes" are perceived to be those of a predator about to turn a would-be predator into prey. The startle reaction puts the insectivorous bird out of harm's way and typically thwarts the attack on the moth (Figure 32.14). Eye spots also occur in the pupae, larvae of Lepidoptera (butterflies and moths), and many other animals.

Literally hundreds of species of insects have eye spots or facelike features. Eye spots may be round or oval, mono- or polychromatic. They do not resemble the eyes of any particular species; rather, they convey the impression that the would-be predator is unexpectedly looking another, larger predator right in the eye. Animals use the startle defence after they have been detected by the predator.

Your startle response is part of your animal ancestry. Startle reactions may be amplified by other stimuli. For example, some termite-eating African snakes have a sharp spine at the tip of their tail. When grabbed, the snake jabs the spine into the grabber. The effect is immediate and reflexive. The predator releases the snake, withdraws, and looks for an expected bite site. Even when the predator is a human who knows the snake is harmless, the defence works.

M.B. Fenton

M.B. Fenton

**FIGURE 32.14** The saturniid moth illustrates the appearance of a pair of eyes where none were visible. One's first glimpse of the moth **(a)** makes it seem bite-sized, but in response to touch, the moth raises its forewings, increasing its size and revealing two eye spots **(b)**.

1. What mechanical defences do animals and plants have in common?
2. What is tail flagging? How does it work?
3. What is the difference between Müllerian and Batesian mimicry?

## Offensive Ploys

Many predators exploit a range of prey, so the predatory behaviour that works against one prey species may be entirely ineffective against another. Observations of hunting spotted hyenas (*Crocuta crocuta*) illustrate the point. When hunting fawns of Thomson's gazelles (*Eudorcas thomsonii*), individual spotted hyenas move through the areas where the females gazelles give birth, looking for and attacking the fawns. When hunting gnu calves, the hyenas operate in pairs. One distracts the mother, while the other goes for the calf. When hunting zebra in herds, groups of hyenas work together. Several individuals attack the stallion, whereas others go around the stallion and attack females and colts.

### Lures Also Work

Many predators use lures to attract prey in organisms, from carnivorous plants to spiders, anglerfish, and snapping turtles. The bolus spider produces a pheromone to attract male moths and applies it to a ball of web. The spider moves the ball of lure around and, when a male moth approaches, catches it in the web. Anglerfish provide a different example **(Figure 32.15)**. Here the first ray of a female anglerfish's dorsal fin is wormlike and moves forward on the fish's body. Wiggling the wormlike fin ray, the anglerfish attracts other fish close enough to catch and swallow them. Some anglerfish have bioluminescent lures on the modified fin ray. Male anglerfish solve the problem of feeding by living as parasites on the female's body. Snapping turtles use the tip of the tongue to lure fish. Sitting on the lake bottom or stream bed, the turtle opens its mouth, wiggles its tongue, and catches and swallows fish that approach too closely.

### Ambushes Work

Other predators rely on camouflage, sitting still, and waiting to ambush prey. This can be effective whether you are a spider, a tiger, or an ambush or assassin bug **(Figure 32.16, a and b, p. 736)**. Cheetahs are ambush predators that rely on stealth and stalking to get close enough

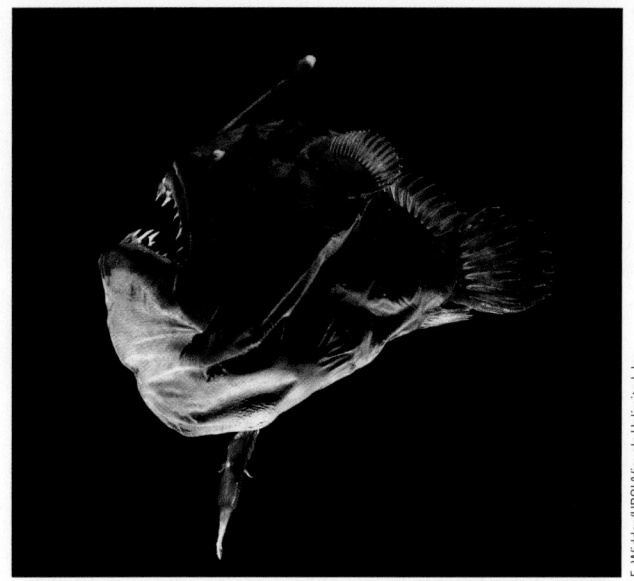

**FIGURE 32.15** Anglerfish (*Melanocetus johnsonii*), a 75-mm long female with a 23.5-mm long attached male.

to make a fast attack. Many birds of prey are ambush hunters that work from above, whether from a perch or from flight. Cursorial or pursuit predators such as wolves (*Canis lupis*), spotted hyenas, and hunting dogs (*Lycaon pictus*) move openly through habitat, making little, if any, effort at concealment **(Figure 32.16, c and d)**. These predators chase prey and wear them down until they are easy to catch. In either situation, a successful attack usually involves the predator fixing on one target. Pursuit predators make short runs toward potential prey to test them and identify individuals that may be vulnerable.

### Filter Feeders Feed by Sifting

Filter-feeding predators (suspension feeders) focus on groups of prey rather than individuals. Sea squirts and mussels are examples of sedentary filter feeders that draw large quantities of water into their bodies and filter out the food items. Scallops and alewives are examples of swimming filter feeders, as are whale sharks, basking sharks, and baleen whales. Remoras **(Figure 32.17, p. 736)** are hitchhiking filter feeders that attach to open ocean animals by a dorsal fin specialized to function as a sucker. At least one species of the Cambrian *Anomalocaris* appears to have been a suspension feeder.

**FIGURE 32.16** Ambush hunters and cursorial hunters. Included are a tiger (*Panthera tigris*) **(a)**, an ambush bug (*Phymata* spp.) **(b)**, a spotted hyena (*Crocuta crocuta*) **(c)**, and hunting dogs (*Lycaon pictus*) **(d)**.

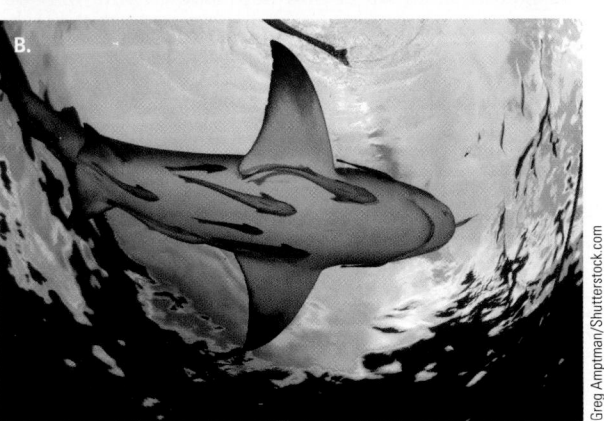

**FIGURE 32.17** Remora (sharksucker – *Echeneis naucrates*) **(a)** showing specialized sucker and several remoras on a lemon shark (*Negaprion brevirostris*) **(b)**.

## 32.4 Sex

Many species of animals live solitary lives, mating or exchanging gametes when the opportunity arises. Some organisms reproduce once and die immediately afterwards (known as **semelparity** or suicidal reproduction). This approach occurs in plants, insects, and some fish, often small and, by definition, short-lived species where high fecundity compensates for a short lifespan. Semelparity is not expected in mammals because females invest heavily in reproduction (pregnancy and lactation). Suicidal reproduction by males has evolved in four lineages of small, insectivorous marsupial (pouched) mammals, three from Australia and Papua New Guinea and one from South America.

This reproductive strategy has appeared in species that live at higher altitudes where the breeding season is brief and there are short peaks in abundance of insect prey. Females' reproductive timing coincides with the peak in food, and ovulation in some populations is synchronized to the day. Suicidal males **(Figure 32.18)** have larger testes relative to body size and shorter mating seasons. These males mate with as many females as possible and experience escalating stress hormones that cause collapse of the immune system and then death. Individual sexual selection explains this pattern of behaviour and reproduction (see Chapters 13 and 28). In this situation, suicidal

**FIGURE 32.18** Suicidal male marsupial mouse (*Antechinus*).

SOURCE: Alan Couch, https://www.flickr.com/photos/couchy/4154587035. This file is licensed under Attribution 2.0 Generic (CC BY 2.0), https://creativecommons.org/licenses/by/2.0/.

reproduction is the best way for these males to ensure representation of their genes in the next generation.

More commonly in animals that reproduce sexually, males and females typically form bonds that result in the production of young (see Chapter 28). In gynogenetic species such as Amazon molly (see Chapter 12), females court and mate with males of another species. The sperm provides mechanical stimulation of the egg and initiates development. More commonly, mating involves transmission (or exchange) and fusion of gametes. The essential part of reproduction is getting your genes into the next generation, and this drive leads to some bizarre patterns of behaviour.

Insects typically deliver sperm in packets. In some species of mayflies (Ephemeroptera), females mate with more than one male. In this species, males have a scoop on their penis, allowing them to remove sperm packets left by males that had mated before. Somewhat more bizarre are acanthocephalan worms, parasites that live in the digestive tract of their hosts, usually mammals. Male worms have a cement gland associated with their genitalia, and after mating with a female, they use glue to seal the opening to her reproductive tract, preventing other males from mating with her. Some males mate with other males and glue their genitalia, rendering them unable to reproduce. In this way, successful males reduce the number of potential competitors for females.

Genetic techniques such as DNA fingerprinting (for a review, see Chapter 11) allow biologists to better understand mating behaviour. Purple Martins (*Progne subis*) **(Figure 32.19)** are insectivorous birds that nest in boxes or natural hollows. Older adult males are aggressive early in the breeding season and attract females to nest sites. One male attracts a female, mates with her, and, when she is laying eggs, attracts other females to other nest boxes and mates with them too. This behaviour increases the representation of his genes in the next generation. Still later in

**FIGURE 32.19** Purple Martin **(a)** and Laysan Albatross **(b)**.

the season, the same aggressive males mate with the mates of younger males and leave these pairs to raise his young. DNA fingerprinting revealed that older, aggressive males produced an average of 8.1 young per breeding season from their mates and from the mates of younger males. Young males sired about 20% of the young hatched in their nets. Note that a single Purple Martin can raise young, unlike some other birds.

In sexually reproducing animals, same-sex pairing appears maladaptive because it may not involve reproduction. Although same-sex pairing is relatively common in the animal kingdom, in most cases, we do not know what benefits it confers. In Laysan Albatrosses (*Phoebastria immutabilis*) **(Figure 32.19b)**, males and females provide parental care through incubating eggs and feeding chicks. Like other albatrosses, a pair produces a single egg in each breeding season, and it takes two parents to raise one chick. In a recently established colony of Laysan Albatrosses on the island of Oahu, Hawaii, two unrelated females raising chicks account for 32% of the breeding pairs. Each breeding pair lays one egg, and, in female–female pairs, the egg layer alternates. The father of the young is an already paired male in the colony. Females comprise 60% of the adults in the Oahu colony.

Compared to male–female pairs in this colony, female–female pairs raised significantly fewer offspring per year than male–female pairs (0.26 versus 0.66 young per year). Over a 10-year period, females in female–female pairs raised about 80% fewer chicks than those produced by male–female pairs. There are two reasons why female–female pairs form. First, even if a female raises only 20% as many chicks as females in male–female pairs, they are reproducing. Second, a single female cannot raise young.

Humans have the same drive to reproduce as other species and face the same decisions about who is the best mate. Like other mammals, pregnancy and lactation mean that females invest more in reproduction than males. Using a sample of 375 male and female volunteers, researchers explored the features that men and women would find attractive in a mate. Although men tended to prioritize facial appearance when selecting mates, women paid more attention to overall cues from the body. The drive to reproduce can explain many aspects of animal behaviour. Further research of this nature will surely reveal many variations in the definition of what is a "good mate" and will remind us that beauty is in the eye of the beholder.

## STUDY BREAK

1. When would female–female pairs be adaptive or advantageous?
2. How does DNA fingerprinting contribute to our knowledge of animal behaviour?
3. What is suicidal reproduction?

## 32.5 Social Organization

Individuals in some species of animals spend most of their lives alone, some alternate between living in groups and living alone, and still others form stable, social groups. Just because there is a group of individuals does not mean that the animals are social. The opposite is also true: just because animals appear to be solitary does not mean that they are not social. A group may be like the people on a subway platform representing nothing more than a group localized around a resource. In many cases, the social unit is two adults and dependent young. In other situations, the group may be much larger and consist mainly of adult males or adult females depending on reproductive realities.

Living with other individuals can make it easier to share resources and learn from the behaviour of other individuals. The closeness of a social unit influences and reflects the ongoing social interactions. When the organisms that form the social unit are genetically closely related, genetic benefits may explain the formation and continued existence of the group. Eusocial organizations are defined by genetic relatedness. The haplodiploid situation (see Chapter 6) means that the worker bees in a hive, for example, are all sisters and are 75% related because males are haploid. Therefore behaviours associated with

**FIGURE 32.20** A vampire bat.

the defence of the colony are genetically selfish. Strongly cohesive social units may involve some genetic component. The adult females in a pride of lions (an adult male and 5 to 15 females) are often closely related (mothers, sisters, aunts, grandmothers). This genetic framework means that communal nursing of young by lions is usually another example of genetically selfish behaviour.

**Altruistic behaviour**, doing something nice or beneficial for someone else who is not genetically related to you, is relatively uncommon in the animal kingdom. Vampire bats (*Desmodus rotundus*) **(Figure 32.20)** are an interesting exception. These bats are colonial, but on any given night, the members of a colony often occupy different roosts. The adult bats eat blood, usually obtained from cattle, chickens, or other mammals or birds. A typical adult bat misses a blood meal once a month, whereas young animals may go hungry two or three nights a week. Neither adult nor young bats can survive two nights without eating.

The vampire bat that returns to its roost without feeding can beg blood from one of the group members, not necessarily a genetic relative. The group member regurgitates some blood at a relatively minor cost compared to the benefits (survival) accruing to the recipient of the blood. This social support means that the hungry vampire survives. These bats regurgitate blood to individuals they know but not to strangers. In this situation, altruistic behaviour (regurgitating blood) benefits the recipient and sets the stage for her or his receiving a reciprocal donation in return. Vampire bats can live to at least 19 years of age in the wild, and their success as individuals and as a species reflects the social support provided by the members of their colony. Social support, in turn, depends on members of the colony knowing and recognizing one another. Social units, like those of vampire bats, where individuals know and recognize one another, have considerable resilience and take us back to the importance of nature (genetics) and nurture (the environment) in which the organisms live.

## STUDY BREAK

1. What is altruistic behaviour?
2. Review three examples of social animals.

## 32.6 Communication

Communication involves three components: the organism that produces the signal (signaller), the signal, and the organisms receiving the signal (receiver). Communication among individuals is a recurring feature of life (see Chapter 26). Signalling systems are prevalent in organisms from bacteria to fungi, plants, and animals. Communication enhances coordination of activities within organisms. At one level, communication occurs between components of cells or among the cells and organs or tissues constituting the organism. At another level, communication occurs among individual organisms.

Signals intended for communication between and among individuals may be transmitted through one medium or a combination of media. Animals' signals may be tactile (touch), acoustic (sound), visual (sight), scent (odour), electrical, or vibrational. For example, a growling dog bares its teeth, perhaps ensuring that the signal inherent in the teeth is received and understood. Many signals are digital in that they are on or off, providing "yes" or "no" information. Other signals are analogue, encoding at least a "yes-maybe-no" message. A Black-capped Chickadee's **(Figure 32.21a)** level of agitation is obvious in the number of syllables in its calls. The signal embodied in the calls is reinforced by the bird's posture and activity while calling. Squirrels, such as red squirrels, flag their tails **(Figure 32.21b)** when agitated. Tail flagging is usually accompanied by scolding calls. Aposematic signals also may be multimedia, the black and yellow colour patterns displayed with the buzzing of bees. Anyone who has taken a dog for a walk (or watched someone else walking a dog) knows about the importance of scent in communication.

In the real world, animals adjust to distractions when they are producing or receiving signals. Examples from human behaviour include cupping your hands around your mouth to increase the directionality of your speech or cupping a hand behind your ear to better hear what someone else is saying. Song birds living in areas with high background noise (e.g., along a busy highway) change the frequencies of sounds and the rates of calling in their songs. This ensures continued communication.

Alarm calls alert group members to an approaching predator. Vervet monkeys are widespread in Africa. As we saw in Chapter 12, they have different signals for leopards and for eagles. Black-capped Chickadees also change their alarm calls in response to different predators.

Animals in stressful situations produce **distress calls**. Although these signals are common, providing a clear definition of a "distress call" is challenging. In some cases, a bird caught by a predator emits a distress call and other birds in the area respond by mobbing the predator, sometimes resulting in the release of the captive. On other occasions, calls produced by a captured individual result in others leaving the immediate area. Playing back the distress call of one species may attract members of the same species or predators apparently looking for a free meal.

One signal can serve more than one function **(Figure 32.22a, p. 740)**. Weakly electric fish, from South America (Gymnotiformes) and from Africa (elephant fishes – Mormyridae), set up an electric field around their bodies. They use **electrolocation**, changes in the electric field to detect objects and prey. Electrolocation signals also serve a communication function, alerting conspecifics to the presence of a signaller. The electric signals may also be associated with courtship and reproduction. Other animals, mainly toothed whales and most species of bats **(Figure 32.22b)**, use echoes of acoustic signals they produce

**FIGURE 32.21** A Black-capped Chickadee (*Poecile atricapillus*) **(a)** and a red squirrel (*Tamiasciurus hudsonicus*) **(b)**.

**FIGURE 32.22** An electric fish (*Gnathonemus petersii*) **(a)** and an echolocating big brown bat (*Eptesicus fuscus*) **(b)**.

to locate objects in their surroundings. This mode of communication is called **echolocation**. The echolocation signals one bat uses to detect, identify, and track an insect are available and may be used by other bats. Electrolocation and echolocation signals reveal the identity (by at least species), gender, and location of the signallers. The same information is also used by potential predators (in the case of electric fish) and many species of insects that might be eaten by bats.

Eavesdropping on the signals of other species and individuals is a recurring pattern of behaviour. Animals that break the communication code of others can exploit the information in the signals. Animals using aposematic signals exploit the behaviour of predators that have experienced painful stings or bouts of sickness after eating something poisonous.

Eavesdropping can be a matter of life or death. In the past in the area of Amboseli National Park in Kenya, Maasai men hunted African elephants with spears, whereas Kamba men did not. Researchers used playback presentations of men speaking Maasai and Kamba (as well as women and children speaking both languages) to demonstrate that African elephants responded differently. The elephants moved away from presentations of men speaking Maasai and did not show this response to the other presentations. The work did not demonstrate that all of the elephants had past experience with the dangers posed by Maasai men with spears, but some surely did and moved to avoid the situation.

Communication between individuals is widespread in biological systems. Language is a specialized form of communication. Although language is always communication, communication is not always language.

## STUDY BREAK

1. What is a digital signal? An analogue signal?
2. What are two examples of multimodal signals?

## 32.7 Language

In language, signals convey symbolism and syntax. "She walked out through the door" includes symbols (she, door) and syntax (walked out through). Many people believe that language is a unique characteristic of humans and that it was an important key to our success because it permitted sharing detailed information. But is language unique to humans? Other animals, usually dogs and parrots, can learn to associate words with the objects they symbolize. Over three years, Chaser, a border collie, learned the proper names of 1022 objects as well as referential information associated with the names. Some parrots not only understand words, they also put them in context. At least some gorillas and chimpanzees can use American Sign Language (AMSLAN) to communicate with humans. These data sets make it more difficult to draw the line between humans' use of language and its use by other animals.

The dance language of honeybees has attracted considerable comment and experimentation. Early experiments provided evidence that, in the hive, the waggle dances of worker bees communicated through a combination of symbols and syntax the locations of flower beds and quality of food there. One convincing demonstration of bee language came from experiments in which one bee "lied" to others. A bee's view of the world was fundamental to the experiment. Bees use simple eyes (ocelli; **Figure 32.23**) to perceive light intensity and compound eyes to form images. Bees with blackened ocelli perceived the position of the "sun" (a light in the hive) in a different but predictable way than untreated workers. The workers that watched the dances of bees with treated ocelli went to the locations to which they were directed by the content of the dances. These were not the locations with food (flowers).

In spring, several thousand worker bees from established hives leave their hive and move to a new site, where

**FIGURE 32.23** On this bee visiting a flower, both compound eyes and ocelli between them are obvious, as are antennae and corbiculae (pollen baskets) laden with pollen.

they establish a new colony. Worker bees that scout new locations for hives (house hunters) use waggle dances to inform other bees about the location and quality of new sites. Typically, several workers dance about different sites before the workers, who decide which new location to pick. To promote making a decision, a dancing bee stops other dancers by using a 150 millisecond long vibrational (350 Hz) signal directed at other dancers. These vibrations are also accompanied by head butts to the other dancers. Stop signals are also used to warn foraging bees away from locations where bees have been attacked by predators.

The behaviour associated with communication continues to intrigue biologists and others. There are many nuances to communication. We use the term *body language* to describe how facial expression **(Figure 32.24)**, posture, and the positioning and movements of arms and hands convey information that may reinforce (or contradict) what we are saying. Observe your body language the next time you are speaking on the telephone. Typically, when we use the telephone, we continue to use body language even when the body language signals we produce are not available to the signal receiver.

## STUDY BREAK

1. What is language? What is body language?
2. What is an example of a stop signal?
3. What stop signal do you use?

## 32.8 Learning

Animals of many species exploit useful social cues, the cues providing some advantage to the individual attending to them. We expect the use of social cues to be more prevalent among animals that live in groups than those that are solitary. But red-footed tortoises (*Geochelone carbonaria*) **(Figure 32.25)** use social learning. Individual captive red-footed tortoises allowed to watch another red-footed tortoise eating food learned to find their way to the food even when this meant initially moving away from the reward. Red-footed tortoises not exposed to the social cue (conspecific feeding) never solved the problem of getting to the reward.

Choices of flowers visited by bumblebees (*Bombus terrestris*) include colour, shape, and scents. But these bees also exhibit social learning, particularly when visiting unfamiliar flowers. Normally, foraging bumblebees join conspecifics at flowers. In this example, access to food rewards reinforces an individual bumblebee's use of social cues—paying attention to the behaviour of other bumblebees. Both red-footed tortoises and bumblebees received food rewards when they observed and emulated the behaviour of others. Neither the tortises nor the bumblebees are usually considered to be "social."

Banded mongooses (*Mungos mungo*) **(Figure 32.26, p. 742)** from Africa live in social groups, and individuals learn forging techniques by watching other mongooses. The social units of banded mongooses consist of 5 to 40 individuals whose composition is biased toward males. Within these groups, small pups form close associations with individual conspecifics known as "escorts" that may or may not be close genetic relatives. By using Kinder containers filled with food, researchers showed how pups

**FIGURE 32.24** Facial expressions are part of body language.

**FIGURE 32.25** Red-footed tortoise (*Geochelone carbonaria*).

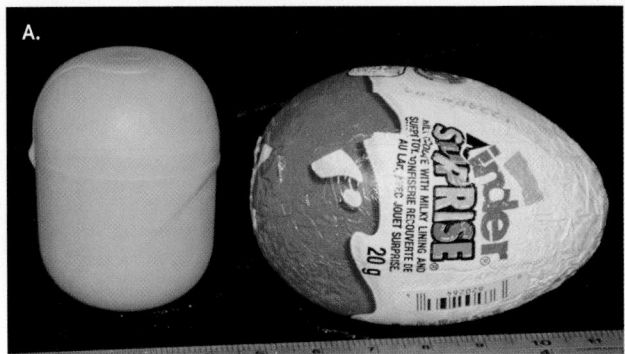

**FIGURE 32.26** The food, a modified Kinder plastic container **(a)**, and two banded mongooses **(b)**.

acquired specific techniques for opening these containers by watching their escorts perform the task (Figure 32.26). In this example, imitation was an important part of the learning process.

## STUDY BREAK

1. How do animals learn?
2. How is animal learning different from human learning?

## 32.9 Using Tools

People used to believe that the ability to make and use tools was a human characteristic. This view was eroded by the discovery of chimps using tools, along with other primates, mammals such as sea otters, then birds, and then insects. Burrowing Owls (*Athene cunicularia*) that collect the dung of mammals and scatter it in the vicinity of their burrows eat more dung beetles than owls without the supply of dung. In virtually every case of animals using tools, the individuals doing so obtained better access to resources such as food, mates, and shelters.

Some ants (*Aphaenogaster*) collect liquid food such as rotting fruit and body fluids on fragments of leaves they carry back to their nets. Other ants (*Dorymyrmex bicolor*) collect soil particles and small stones and use them to block the nest openings of other species of ants. Some male tree crickets (*Oecanthus* spp.) chew a hole in a leaf, position themselves above the leaf, and use it as a baffle to amplify the sounds they use to attract females. Spiders **(Figure 32.27)** emerge as champion tool users, at least the many species that use webs to entrap their insect prey.

Blue-veined octopus (*Amphioctopus marginatus*) use shells as shelters **(Figure 32.28)**. Some individual octopus carry the two halves of a coconut shell stacked under their bodies. When threatened, the octopus stops and assembles its shelter, one half of the coconut shell above and the other below with the octopus in between.

**FIGURE 32.27** An orb-web spider at the hub of its web.

Capuchin monkeys (Figure 18.26) use hammer and anvil tools to crack nuts, in a manner resembling the tools used by some chimpanzees. Flat rocks or tree roosts serve as anvils and stones or sticks as hammers. Capuchins use large, heavy stones as hammers (see Figure 18.27). To be successful, the monkey must place the nut on the anvil in a way that ensures that the nut does not roll away. In West Africa, chimpanzees hunt bush babies (*Galago senegalensis*) **(Figure 32.29)**, nocturnal primates that spend the day in hollows in trees. Chimps hunting bush babies use short sticks sharpened at one end. The chimp holds the dull end and vigorously stabs into hollows with the pointed end. In this way, they impale bush babies, remove them from the hollow, and eat them.

Each passing year brings more and more documented cases of animals such as chimpanzees developing local cultures of tool use. This behaviour reinforces the importance of social learning and information

FIGURE 32.28 *Amphioctopus marginatus*, the veined octopus **(a)**, occupies a coconut shell shelter **(b)**, which it transports by carrying it under its body **(c)**.

FIGURE 32.29 A bush baby, *Galago senegalensis*.

these crows, transfer of information about tools and their use occurs mainly within rather than between social units. This means vertical rather than horizontal transfer of information. New Caledonian Crows are more social than red-footed tortoises but much less so than other corvids (birds in the family Corvidae) and many other animals.

## STUDY BREAK

1. How does tool use by Caledonian Crows differ from tool use by chimps?
2. What are two advantages associated with tool use?

## 32.10 Surprises

Earlier in the chapter, we saw how red-legged tortoises and bumblebees learned by watching the behaviour of conspecifics even though neither was a "social species." Additional work on fruit flies, *Drosophila melanogaster*, has demonstrated that these animals, once thought to be relatively solitary, are strongly influenced by their social environment. A broad range of techniques was necessary to reveal this unexpected side of a common laboratory animal. Specifically, classical genetics, molecular biology, and neuroanatomy were combined with RNA sequencing to assess gene expression. This work, led by Professor Joel Levine (University of Toronto, Mississauga), has involved 12 species of *Drosophila* and has revealed innate determinants of social structure that depend in large measure on chemosensory processing. The importance of chemosensory elements links directly to another unexpected discovery.

In 2006, another report about a much-studied animal further emphasized the importance of new discoveries. In this case, the noses (nasal epithelium) of mice were found to have a new class of chemosensory receptors, known as TAARs (trace amine-associated receptors). TAARs respond to volatile amines in urine, one to a compound linked to stress and two that detect compounds enriched in the urine of males or females. Furthermore, TAARs also occur in humans and in fish. The connection between TAARs and social signals such as pheromones associated with social situations raises interesting questions about their role in humans.

## STUDY BREAK

1. What role do olfactory signals play in the lives of humans?
2. Why do we spend so much money trying to smell good?

sharing. But, in some cases, sophisticated tool use occurs in animals that are not particularly social. New Caledonian Crows (*Corvus moneduloides*) use tools and show individual creativity in making tools, as well as in their use of tools in problem solving. The core social unit in these crows is the immediate family (parents and dependent offspring). Young may remain with parents and continue to be fed by them well into their second year. In

## PUTTING IT IN PERSPECTIVE

Animal behaviour is entirely familiar to us all. We know how to recognize our friends and enemies, and we know how to pick a fight at home and when to give way. Those who have taken courses in self-defence will recognize the basic strategies of survival. When it comes to matters of learning, using tools, and communicating, the continuum between humans and other animals is obvious. We may learn that many animals we thought of as solitary are, in fact, quite social. This is surely the message that emerges from the discovery of the importance of social signals to animals not thought of as social. The results of research on behaviour often open our eyes to other aspects of the diversity of life. Biologists repeatedly discover connections between genetics and behaviour, taking us back to the fundamental nature–nurture conundrum. It is obvious that some behaviours (e.g., camouflage) can be largely genetic, whereas others, such as learning, are more strongly influenced by the environment.

## KEY CONCEPTS REVIEW AND QUESTIONS

### 32.1 Behaviour

The study of behaviour is arguably one of the oldest branches of biology. It is connected to anatomy, physiology, and ecology.

1. What is fear? What effect(s) can it have on animals?

### 32.2 Behaviour and Genetics

Both genes and the environment influence behaviour. Scientists debate what the relative influence of genes and environmental factors is on behaviour.

2. What is the nature–nurture controversy? How do the rover and sitter genes influence our view of the impact of genetics on behaviour?

3. How can animals be "invisible?" How could a predator make them visible?

### 32.3 Struggle for Survival: Defence and Offence

Organisms must use offensive and defensive behaviours to survive. There are many defensive and offensive strategies. These could include mechanical or chemical defences. Similarly, there are many offensive strategies.

4. Review five defensive ploys that animals use in defense. What do they have in common? How many other ploys could be involved? Which defensive ploys do humans use? What accounts for variability in defensive ploys?

5. Now repeat this exercise for offensive ploys. Why do predators have to adjust their hunting behaviour? What implications does this have for our own species?

### 32.4 Sex

Many behavioural approaches exist to mate or exchange gametes. Reproductive strategies have evolved to improve the chances of transmission of genes into the next generation. Genetic techniques are used to improve our understanding of mating behaviour. Same-sex pairing also occurs relatively commonly in the animal kingdom. Many aspects of animal behaviour can be explained by the drive to reproduce.

6. What is suicidal reproduction? Where does it occur?

7. How do genetic techniques such as DNA fingerprinting influence our view of reproductive behaviour?

8. How does reproductive behaviour connect to fitness?

### 32.5 Social Organization

Individuals of a species may be solitary or live in social units of varying organizations. Genetic benefits may explain the formation and existence of a group whose members are closely related. Altruistic behaviour is relatively uncommon in the animal kingdom. There is resilience in social units where individuals are known and recognize each other.

9. What are the differences between social and asocial species?

10. How does social behaviour vary? Why does social behaviour vary?

### 32.6 Communication

Communication involves a signaller, the signal, and the receiver. Communication can occur within organisms or among individual organisms. Signals among organisms can be transmitted by one or more media and can be digital or analogue. They may also be adjusted to compensate for environmental distractions. There are many functions associated with signals, and one signal can serve more than one function.

### 32.7 Language

Language signals convey symbolism and context. Humans use language, and other animals appear to use it also.

11. When is communication language?

### 32.8 Learning

Some animals can learn from social cues. This might occur even when the species is not considered to be social. Imitation can be important for learning.

12. Under what situations do animals exhibit learning behaviour?

13. What could account for the fact that learning behaviour is widespread among animals?

## 32.9 Using Tools

Many animals use tools. Use of tools typically increases an animal's access to resources such as food, mates, and shelters.

14. How does tool use by animals connect to both learning and social organization?

## 32.10 Surprises

There are often new discoveries that shed light on how animals can be influenced by their social environment. Examples include new discoveries about social structure in fruit flies and the relationship to chemosensory processing. Also, research on mice has discovered a new class of chemosensory receptors that detect social signals. These receptors also occur in other animals.

15. Why should we keep an open mind about animal behaviour?

Daniel K. Riskin

## WHY IT MATTERS

Humans manipulate the natural environment. More and more evidence suggests that we have been doing so for thousands of years. Even in what seem like remote wildernesses, we often find evidence that humans have long shaped the environment. For example, although there is a common conception that the Amazon forest is a continuous swath of impenetrable forest sparsely inhabited by small groups of native peoples, archeological evidence presents a different picture. Prior to European contact (circa 1492), many regions of the Amazon were cultivated and settled by large groups of native peoples, some of whom lived in cities as large as any found in the Americas. These groups also left unmistakable marks on the landscape. Many soils of the Amazon are enriched with charcoal, pottery, and other material that together make them more fertile. In some wetland regions, large mounds have been found that appear to have been part of a large society's wetland management system and urban design.

©iStock.com/babyfotothai

**FIGURE 33.1** The Brazil nut tree (*Bertholletia excelsa*) is often found in higher abundances close to known early human settlements in the Amazon region. This practice, in which indigenous people increased the abundance of agriculturally beneficial species, is known as enrichment planting.

In some areas in the Amazon, native people actively manipulated the forest, although the extent of manipulation is still the cause of some debate. In these forests, typically called anthropogenic (caused or created by humans) forests, there is an abundance of agriculturally useful tree species, such as the Brazil nut tree (*Bertholletia excelsa*) **(Figure 33.1)**, or a variety of palms, such as the açai palm (*Euterpe oleracea*). These forests are often associated with visibly enriched soils or other evidence of human activity. They also often appear to be associated with rivers, likely the site of most Amazonian settlements. The abundance of agriculturally useful tree species has been found to be highest along rivers and in the floodplain of rivers and to decrease dramatically with increasing distance from the water. Following European contact came a dramatic population collapse among native peoples. It is still unknown how patchy or widespread human settlement and activity were in the Amazon prior to European contact. It is clear, however, that the extent to which these peoples locally manipulated their environment is much larger than once thought. There are similar data from the highlands of New Guinea on the other side of the world.

Humans have left a footprint on the landscape even in what seem to be the most remote corners of the world. This illustrates how management of our own species and its activity must be part of any global plans for conservation. We are part of the biological world and affect change on our environment, for better or for worse, every day.

In this book, you have been introduced to the many kinds of organisms that make up our biological world. Every day you make decisions that directly relate to this world and the study of biology. A number of these decisions directly affect your health. You decide whether or not to get a flu shot this season, whether you will buy foods that contain genetically modified organisms, and whether or not you will drink expired milk from your refrigerator. A number of your decisions also affect the health of other organisms and ecosystems: whether you live in a city or the country, whether or not you drive a car or air condition your house, whether or not you let your cat outside. Decisions such as these, and decisions made by other organisms, shape our world, sometimes in surprising and unexpected ways (see Box 33.1). In this

Darren Goldstein

**FIGURE 1** Dan Riskin is an evolutionary biologist and presenter of science on TV. He is an adjunct professor of biology at the University of Toronto Mississauga and the co-host of Discovery Canada's daily science show *Daily Planet*.

At first glance, the facts contained in a biology textbook such as this one might seem trivial, with no real applicability to day-to-day decisions. (Who cares that plants have cell walls but animals don't, right?) But nothing could be further from the truth. Because you are a biological organism, this is a book about *you*—where you came from, who you are, and how you fit into the world. By immersing yourself in the study of biology, you can understand yourself more accurately than you otherwise could. And with that knowledge, you are empowered to change your life in ways that would otherwise be impossible.

Let me begin with one of the most mind-bending concepts I know. Imagine a long wall in a museum, on which photos of your ancestors are lined up chronologically. At the right end of the wall, you see your own photo, and then next to it, your mother's photo, then to the left of that, her mother, and so on. Now, imagine what it would be like to explore those photos, one at a time, as you walk to the left. Walking past each frame, you'd see a series of female faces that would slowly become less and less similar to your own. If you prefer, you could do this with male ancestors or alternate between male and female ancestors. What's fun about this imaginary process is that no matter how you did it, no matter what parental lineage you followed back in time, you'd get the same result. At some point, after walking several kilometres down that museum wall, you'd be staring at the photo of a fish. Your great-great-great-great- (etc.) grandparent WAS A FISH. (And what's more, when you got to the picture, you wouldn't even be halfway back to the end of the wall.)

Things such as this are what I love most about biology. You couldn't make something like that up, and yet it's completely true.

But biology isn't just about your origins; it's also about the present. For example, people love to say that life is a "miracle," but I'd argue that it's far more beautiful and amazing than that. Your body is a bag of proteins, carbohydrates, lipids, nucleic acids, and water, and at every scale, those molecules are governed by the same laws of physics and chemistry that rule inanimate objects. Your muscle twitches are controlled by calcium and other ions interacting with specialized proteins. Your cognition is a mixture of chemistry and electricity. Your urges and instincts, even the love you feel for your friends and family, all boil down to hormones, neurotransmitters, blood pressure, and other biological bits—shaped by evolution to help you survive and pass on your DNA. To say life is a "miracle" implies that a living organism somehow transcends the laws of the universe. What makes life so incredible is that it happens in spite of those laws, without breaking a single one of them.

Beyond the big-picture concepts, biology is also useful for the day-to-day decisions you make in your life. Take something as simple as what you'll eat for dinner. You understand that you depend on the living organisms of the planet for 100% of your calories and that those calories were ultimately harnessed from the Sun via photosynthesis. As a result, when you stare down at a menu, you can imagine an invisible "trophic cost" column next to the price list. You know that it takes around 10 times as much land to grow a 16-ounce steak compared to an equivalent weight of rice and beans. If you choose to eat foods from lower trophic levels, you know exactly what the benefits to the planet are. Similarly, you know that extinctions are real and that right now many species of animals we eat are on the brink of that fate, so you can take the conservation status of different kinds of foods, especially seafood, into account when you order.

Some people bemoan the burden of knowing what our negative impacts on Earth are, but that's a silly reason to keep your head in the sand. Knowing a little biology empowers you to make responsible choices and feel good about yourself for doing so.

Food security and threats to biodiversity are just two of the challenges we face in this changing world. That list also includes climate change, water quality, overpopulation, fossil fuel scarcity, clean energy, and others. Every one of those issues touches on the topics covered by this book. Should you choose to take on one of these issues in your lifetime, the knowledge you got from this book will help you get started. And if you want to support other people who are tackling these problems, through donations, volunteer hours, or your votes for political parties, you'll rely on your grounding in biology to help you identify which people and organizations are most deserving of your support.

I know that sometimes when you're making your way through a textbook like this one it's easy to get bogged down by some factoid and throw your hands in the air to ask why that should possibly matter. I urge you to try to see the forest for the trees. I'll concede that knowing what a cell wall does might not pay the bills, but understanding your connection to cell walls, and to everything else that is alive, might be one of the most important things you'll ever learn.

chapter, we will discuss a number of interesting ways in which Earth's organisms affect one another, with a special focus on the human organism and the places where biology intersects with city living, travel, and even video game playing.

## 33.1 Anthromes

A **biome** is defined as an area with similar climate, plants, and animals—for example, tundra, or deserts, or grasslands. Close to 75% of the land on Earth is directly impacted by humans **(Figure 33.2)**. Humans occupy, alter, and in many ways control the majority of Earth's biomes. Some scientists have begun to call these areas under human, or anthropogenic, control **anthromes**. The intensity of the effect of humans varies across these landscapes. Anthromes include, for example, dense urban areas but also preserved parks

crisscrossed by trail systems and frequented by people. This also means that the majority of terrestrial ecosystems are new and that they differ from previously existing ecosystems. As you might expect, anthromes have different biological communities than other, more traditionally defined biomes. Urban environments are the anthromes with the most intensive land use. Although cities occupy only 3% of the terrestrial landscape of the planet, approximately 50% of the world's population lives in cities. This number will increase in the coming decades, particularly in large cities in the developing world. Urban environments consume large amounts of natural resources and generate large amounts of waste that impact cities and surrounding areas as air or water pollution. Urban environments affect the organisms that live in and around them, from soil microbes to people. Urban organisms also exploit urban environments, often in unexpected ways.

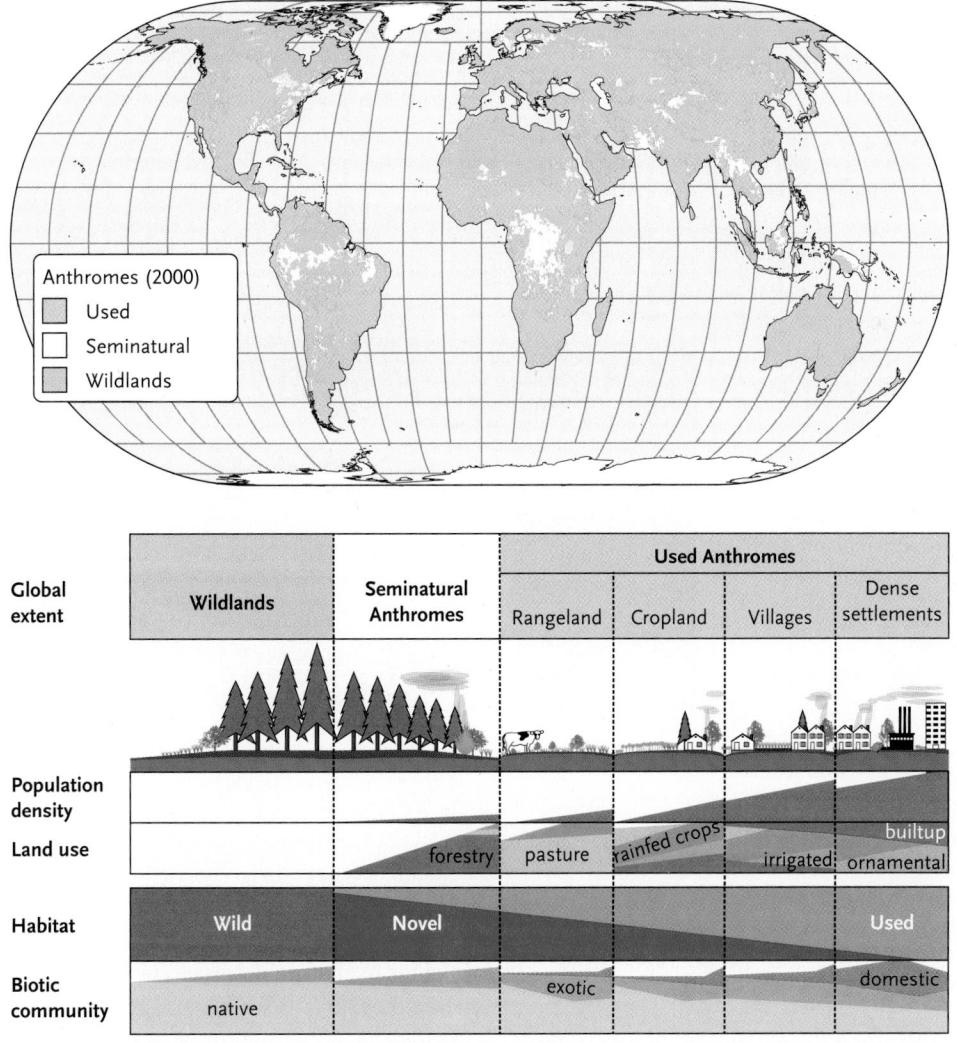

**FIGURE 33.2** Humans use more than 75% of the terrestrial earth surface. These "anthromes," or human-created biomes, vary in their impact on the landscape. They range from sparsely to densely populated and contain a variety of land uses and habitats. The map shows where these anthromes are located. The panel figure shows a qualitative assessment of the different types of anthromes.

SOURCE: Reprinted from *Current Opinion in Environmental Sustainabilit*, Volume 5, Issues 3–4, E. Ellis, "Sustaining biodiversity and people in the world's anthropogenic biomes," Pages 369–372, Copyright 2013, with permission from Elsevier.

## THE MOLECULE BEHIND THE BIOLOGY 33.2
### Light Pollution and Melatonin

In addition to pollution of the air and water, urban areas increase the amount of ambient light in the environment **(Figure 1)**. Light pollution can affect the health of wildlife species and even the health of humans.

For wildlife species, increased light pollution can have detrimental effects on behaviour. For example, bright lights along beaches can deter female sea turtles from approaching the shore to lay their eggs. In addition, after baby sea turtles hatch, they orient to the ocean using light as a guide. Bright lights on or behind the beach serve to disorient the babies, leading them to wander on land, in some cases preventing them from finding water and ending in their deaths. Policy in some beach communities now requires residents and businesses to turn off their lights at night along beaches during nesting periods. Other proposed changes include making the lighting along beaches in different wavelengths that aren't as distracting for turtles.

In humans, one of the clearest health effects of increased lights at night is suppression of the hormone melatonin. Melatonin is a hormone secreted by many organisms, including humans and other mammals, as well as other animals, plants, and even bacteria. In humans, melatonin is secreted by the pineal gland, a pea-sized gland located in the interior of the brain. In plants and in animals, melatonin plays a role in regulating an organism's response to day length, or **photoperiod**, and at the same time photoperiod affects the production of melatonin.

You may have heard recommendations for putting down your electronic devices and turning off the television at least 30 minutes before bed. This practice makes it easier to fall asleep and helps you sleep more soundly. These recommendations are based on melatonin. Melatonin plays an important role in the regulation of sleep and in helping you fall asleep, and increased exposure to light at night reduces melatonin production. In some cases, synthetic melatonin is used as a supplement to help people sleep. People use melatonin to prevent jet lag, for example. Some children with autism or attention-deficit disorders are given melatonin in the evenings to help them overcome sleep challenges.

There may also be long-term health risks associated with increased light pollution and exposure to light at night. Many studies suggest a link between breast cancer and exposure to light at night. Melatonin plays a role in suppressing breast cancer activation, metabolism, and signalling. Reduction of melatonin production associated with increased exposure to light at night, for example, in night shift workers, may increase the risk and spread of breast cancer.

Exposure to light at night affects melatonin production in wildlife species too. Some salamander species, for example, have low levels of melatonin during hours of light and elevated levels in darkness. Melatonin plays a role in metabolism in these animals, lowering their tolerance to high temperatures and their body temperature. In the absence of normal light and dark cycles, some salamanders have been shown to have continuously low levels of melatonin. The metabolisms of salamanders exposed to light at night may have higher metabolisms that require more energy (i.e., more food, more foraging time) to support.

Since the invention of the light bulb in the 1800s, our world has gotten brighter and brighter. In some cases, artificial lighting may increase background nighttime light levels by a million times. We are just beginning to understand the links between light at night, melatonin production, and health. Light pollution appears to be an important human-induced change to the global environment.

NASA Earth Observatory image by Robert Simmon, using Suomi NPP VIIRS data provided courtesy of Chris Elvidge (NOAA National Geophysical Data Center). Suomi NPP is the result of a partnership between NASA, NOAA, and the Department of Defense. Caption by Mike Carlowicz.

**FIGURE 1** A composite image of lights at night across the globe. This image was taken by NASA over nine days in April and 13 days in October 2012. Most of the lights show population centres, although in rural areas, fires as well as operations such as mining and fishing also appear.

## Urban Environments Change Animal Behaviour and Success

Urban environments are substantially different habitats than areas with a lower density of people. Compared to non-urban areas, they are noisier, have fewer and smaller vegetation patches, are hotter, and have more air, water, and even light pollution (see Box 33.2). Many of these changes are altering the behaviour of animals. Songbirds in cities overcome increased noise pollution by changing when they sing as well as the amplitude and frequencies of their songs. Urban European Robins (*Erithacus rubecula*), for example, sing more often at night than European Robins outside urban areas. Other urban birds, such as the Great Tit (*Parus major*) and the Common Blackbird (*Turdus merula*), sing louder and higher songs than rural birds of the same species **(Figure 33.3)**. In forests, lower songs travel

**FIGURE 33.3** The **(a)** European Robin (*Erithacus rubecula*), **(b)** Common Blackbird (*Turdus merula*), and **(c)** Great Tit (*Parus major*) are all examples of birds that have changed their vocalization in response to urban environments. These changes help the birds hear one another and be heard above the increased background noise of cities.

well through dense vegetation. In cities, higher and louder songs can be heard better above lower-pitched traffic noise. In general, urban areas homogenize the diversity of bird species. Rare species or species sensitive to noise, pollution, and the other features of high-density living are driven out. However, more tolerant species and species that can easily alter their behaviour remain and can even thrive in urban environments.

The diversity of other wildlife groups, such as mammals, reptiles, and amphibians, is also reduced in urban areas **(Figure 33.4)**. Notably, the diversity of plant species is sometimes increased in urban environments due to an

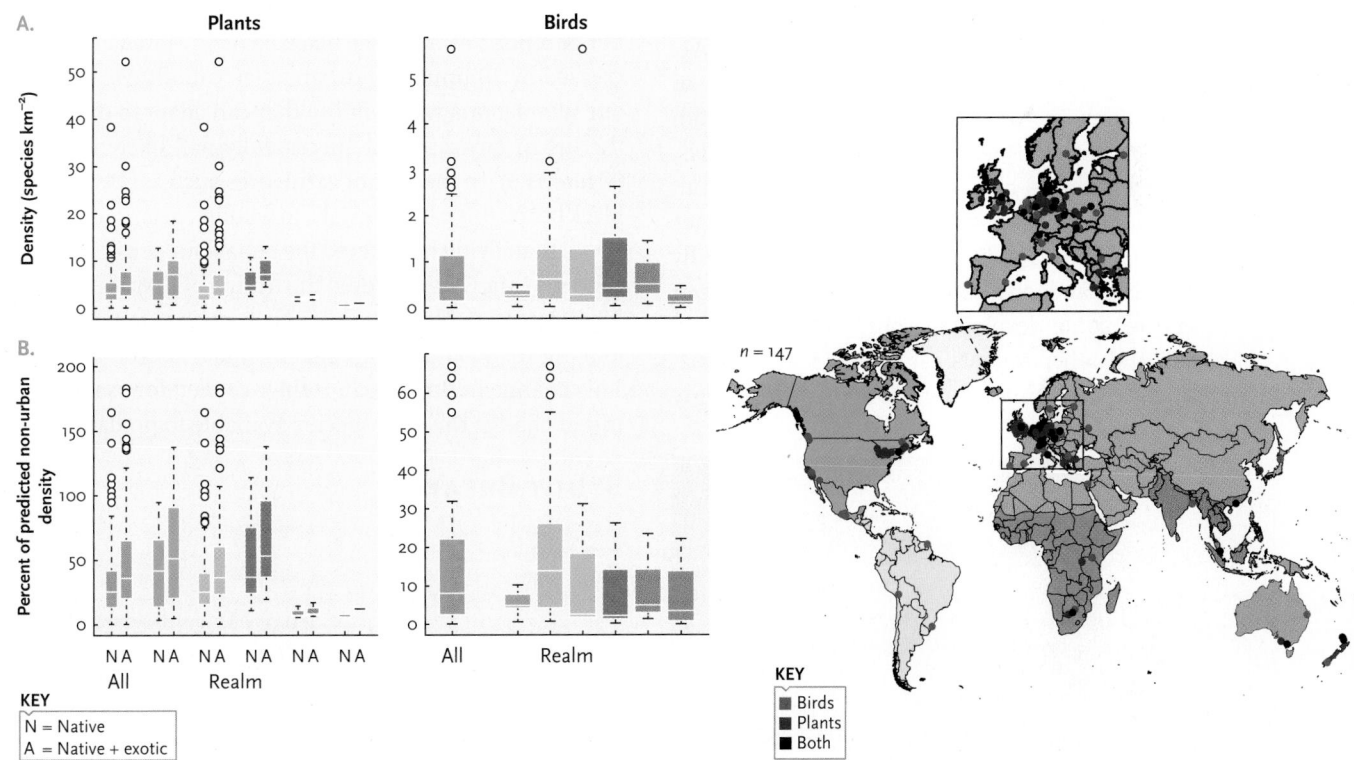

**FIGURE 33.4** Biodiversity can be greatly reduced in cities. In a comparison of 147 cities, the actual density of plant species and bird species in urban areas **(a)** was less than 50% of the density in non-urban areas in the same geographic realm **(b)**. Across all cities, urban birds represented a median of only 8% of non-urban bird species, and urban plants represented a median of 36% of non-urban plant species. The figure shows the values for all cities combined and separates the data by realm. Realms are identified in the map and box plot by colour.

SOURCE: Myla F. J. Aronson, Frank A. La Sorte, Charles H. Nilon, Madhusudan Katti, Mark A. Goddard, Christopher A. Lepczyk, Paige S. Warren, Nicholas S. G. Williams, Sarel Cilliers, Bruce Clarkson, Cynnamon Dobbs, Rebecca Dolan, Marcus Hedblom, Stefan Klotz, Jip Louwe Kooijmans, Ingolf Kühn, Ian MacGregor-Fors, Mark McDonnell, Ulla Mörtberg, Petr Pyšek, Stefan Siebert, Jessica Sushinsky, Peter Werner, Marten Winter, "A global analysis of the impacts of urbanization on bird and plant diversity reveals key anthropogenic drivers," *Proceedings of the Royal Society B*, 2014, 281: 20133330, by permission of the Royal Society.

increase in distinct vegetation patches and because of the introduction of so many plants in yards, gardens, and parks.

Species that are particularly good at adapting to conditions in urban areas and whose survival and reproductive success are improved in urban areas are called **urban adapters** or **urban exploiters**. Urban adapters are defined as animals that are able to cope with urban environments but that continue to depend mostly on natural environmental resources. Urban exploiters are animals that thrive in urban environments and often choose these urban environments. Urban adapters/exploiters include many of the species you likely see regularly, such as the House Sparrow (*Passer domesticus*), the pigeon or Rock Dove (*Columba livia*), grey squirrels (*Sciurus carolinensis*), raccoons (*Procyon lotor*), skunks (*Mephitis mephitis*), woodchucks (*Marmota monax*), and rats (species in the genus *Rattus*).

Rats have been incredibly successful urban adapters for hundreds of years **(Figure 33.5)**. Some people suggest that wherever there are people, there are rats. Others estimate that there are up to four times as many rats as people in New York City. The most common species of rat that live in our urban areas across the globe are the black or roof rat (*Rattus rattus*) and the brown or Norway rat (*Rattus norvegicus*). In many places where rats have been introduced, they have often reduced native biodiversity, particularly on island ecosystems, which often lack native, ground-dwelling predators. Rats have caused local or global extinctions of approximately 35 species from islands. Most affected species are terrestrial animals, including invertebrates and ground-dwelling birds, but even bats and other birds have been impacted by changes in food availability driven by rats. Rats also successfully exploit many human food resources, and not just from our dumpsters. In some developing countries in Asia and Africa, rats and other rodents eat up to 15% of annual grain harvests, preventing calories from reaching hungry

**FIGURE 33.6** Coyotes (*Canis latrans*), once rare in North American cities, are becoming increasingly commonplace. Here a coyote rides the subway in Portland, Oregon.

people who need them. Around the world, almost 280 million people, about 34% of the world's undernourished people, would benefit if rats and other rodents weren't able to get to the grain first.

In recent years, other mammals have increasingly been found in urban or suburban areas, including white-tailed deer (*Odocoileus virginianus*), coyotes (*Canis latrans*), red foxes (*Vulpes vulpes*), and black bears (*Ursus americanus*). In the 1990s, coyote removals from the Chicago metropolitan area increased by 15 times and the number of reports of nuisance black bears in Nevada cities increased by 10 times. As urban areas continue to expand, our interactions with wildlife that can adapt to or exploit the urban environment successfully will likely increase **(Figure 33.6)**. In the case of carnivores such as coyotes and black bears, this can pose risks to wildlife, pets, and people.

Urban living has altered the behaviour of many urban adapters. Many have altered the timing of their daily activities to reduce interactions with humans, for example, looking for food during dawn or dusk or even at night. This change in timing can influence diet; for example, it might change the prey species available to predators.

## STUDY BREAK

1. What is an anthrome?
2. What is an urban adapter?
3. What are two ways an urban environment could increase stresses for wildlife?

## Urban Environments Do Not Always Increase Animal Stress

Urban areas can reduce stresses on some animals. Brazilian free-tailed bats (*Tadarida brasiliensis*), for example, are typically cave-roosting bats **(Figure 33.7)**. More and more often, however, they roost under bridges. You might expect that the increase in traffic noise, air pollution, and the

**FIGURE 33.5** The brown or Norway rat (*Rattus norvegicus*) is an incredibly successful urban exploiter. The rats are native to China but are now found on every continent except Antarctica.

**FIGURE 33.7** Brazilian free-tailed bats (*Tadarida brasiliensis*) typically roost in caves, but more and more bats are making use of human-made bridges. The bats roost in large groups, and their nighttime emergence is amazing to watch. **(a)** These emergences can be observed from caves and caverns and **(b)** from bridges. The Congress Avenue Bridge in Austin, Texas, is the seasonal home to more than 1 million Brazilian free-tailed bats, and the nightly emergence event has become a tourist attraction.

altered roosting environment might cause additional stress in these bats and affect their reproductive success. Interestingly, scientists have found that Brazilian free-tailed bats roosting under bridges have lower levels of stress-related hormones than cave-roosting Brazilian free-tailed bats. Not only that, but their babies are also bigger and grow faster. Certainly, we don't yet know all of the ways in which an increasingly human-occupied planet will affect all wildlife. So far, many of the changes have been surprising, making studies of urban animals as important as studies of their counterparts in unimpacted environments.

Most urban centres do not have large populations of predators, reducing predation pressure for some species, which may also reduce the stress on these prey species. Reduced predation pressure allows animals to spend less energy on being vigilant about predators and more energy doing things such as foraging and mating. People also generate a lot of food and waste, increasing food resources for some animals and reducing the area animals need to use to meet their food needs. The increase in food resources can improve the survival of animals; starvation is very rare among urban animals. This includes starvation during hibernation. In a study of woodchucks (*Marmota monax*), no urban animals died from starvation during hibernation, whereas it was the second most common cause of mortality among rural woodchucks. Many of the benefits to animals of urban environments, however, are accompanied by other costs.

## Urban Environments Can Increase Disease Burden and Vehicular Accidents

The combination of resources such as bird feeders, dumpsters, and road kills often means more food in urban than rural areas, but this impact can be negative **(Figure 33.8)**. Increased access to food resources can increase the density of animals supported in a certain

area. Additionally, many of these food resources are found in distinct areas, for example, a congregation of dumpsters behind a row of restaurants. This makes communal feeding more common in urban animals than their rural counterparts. Increased animal density and increased communal interactions can increase the transmission of disease. In fact, disease is often a leading cause of mortality among urban animals. In several species of urban mammals, urban individuals are more likely to carry the parasite *Toxoplasma gondii* (a protozoan), for example. This parasite, although not usually fatal, can lead to neurological impairment, increased susceptibility to predation, and generally reduced health for infected animals.

*Toxoplasma gondii* is also a parasite of humans that we can contract from undercooked meat or from domestic

**FIGURE 33.8** Increased food is available to animals in many urban settings. Sometimes this is indirect feeding by people, such as when raccoons (*Procyon lotor*) raid your compost bin. Sometimes, as in the case of this group of raccoons at a lookout point on Mount Royal in Montreal, it is direct.

cats. In healthy adult humans, the symptoms of the resulting infection, called toxoplasmosis, are usually subtle. Most people don't experience any symptoms, or they have mild flulike symptoms. Adult infection is also correlated, however, with increased aggression in males and decreased reaction times. In Canada, up to a third of the population is estimated to be infected, although most are likely not aware of it. In fetuses and infants, however, infections with this parasite can be very serious. Some infected babies are born with eye or brain abnormalities. Or, more commonly, people exposed to *T. gondii* in the womb lose their eyesight or suffer mental disabilities later in life. Because accidental ingestion of cat feces can lead to infection, pregnant women are told to avoid cleaning litter boxes so as to avoid contracting the infection and passing it to their unborn babies.

The leading causes of death vary between rural and urban animals of the same species. Predation and starvation are often important in rural populations. For urban wildlife, we have mentioned that disease is a leading cause of death. Urban animals are also killed by cars more often than their rural counterparts. Although there is some variability by region and species, traffic deaths are often the leading cause of death for urban wildlife. Despite all the different costs and benefits, however, existing data suggest that survival rates are, on average, about equal for urban adapters in developed areas compared to rural ones.

### The Urban Environment Has an Ecological Footprint

Cities have environmental footprints beyond their physical footprint on the landscape. Cities are resource intensive, requiring resources from land areas many times larger than the cities themselves. These resources often travel long distances, and many are finite. Cities are also the largest generators of greenhouse gases, contributing to global climate change. In fact, cities themselves alter the climate. The most well-studied example of this is the urban heat island (UHI) effect. Most cities tend to be hotter than the surrounding area. This is due to a number of forces: (1) less vegetative and ground surface cover, which reduces evaporative heat loss; (2) increased surfaces that absorb rather than reflect heat and can store a lot of heat energy (black-topped roads, some roofs, multistory buildings, etc.); and (3) high rises trapping heat similarly to a canyon. The downtown temperature of U.S. cities has risen between 0.14° and 1.1°C per decade since the 1950s due to the UHI effect. Estimates suggest that between 3% and 8% of electricity demand in the United States is to compensate for UHI effects. In contrast to global climate change, however, UHI effects are localized and do not appear to have an impact on climate outside a city's geographic footprint.

Cities also dramatically change natural water cycles. Some cities use more water than can be replaced naturally, for example. Others change the drainage of water from the landscape. A clear example of this is the paving of a parking lot with impervious asphalt. Although the previously exposed soil would absorb some amount of water that falls as precipitation, this same water cannot be absorbed by the parking lot. Instead, the rainwater will flow horizontally across the surface of the parking lot. This makes water flows faster and dirtier. Cities have a lot of impervious surfaces and a lot of pollutants, such as fertilizers, pesticides, and even metals, to be picked up by running water. This increases both the risk of flooding and the pollutant load carried by urban wastewater to streams and estuaries.

Per capita, however, city living can be more efficient than rural living. Living in suburban or rural areas requires an increase in individual driving distances, for example. And many cities have the infrastructure in place to deal with waste and pollution better than rural areas with fewer institutional resources. Cities can also be centres of innovation. Many creative solutions to the many environmental challenges we face are created and implemented in cities. Although cities create many problems, they may also offer paths to many solutions.

### STUDY BREAK

1. What are two ways in which an urban environment might reduce stresses on wildlife?
2. What is the urban heat island effect?
3. What is one reason why the prevalence of wildlife disease is higher in urban environments?

## 33.2 Disease

As described above, urbanization can increase the disease burden of wildlife. Animals live at higher densities and share the same communal food resources, increasing contact among individuals and increasing the spread of disease. Similarly, the globalization and urbanization of human society are also changing disease burden and transmission in humans. The spread of human disease is different today than at any other time in human history. Modern medicine, most notably antibiotics and the development of vaccines, has significantly reduced the burden of disease around the world, in some cases completely eradicating diseases that once killed thousands of people every year (Figure 33.9). At the same time, our increasingly global society has increased the possibility of large disease outbreaks spread across world regions quickly. The outbreaks of swine flu (H1N1), severe acute respiratory syndrome (SARS), and a recent strain of bird flu (H5N1) are all examples of diseases

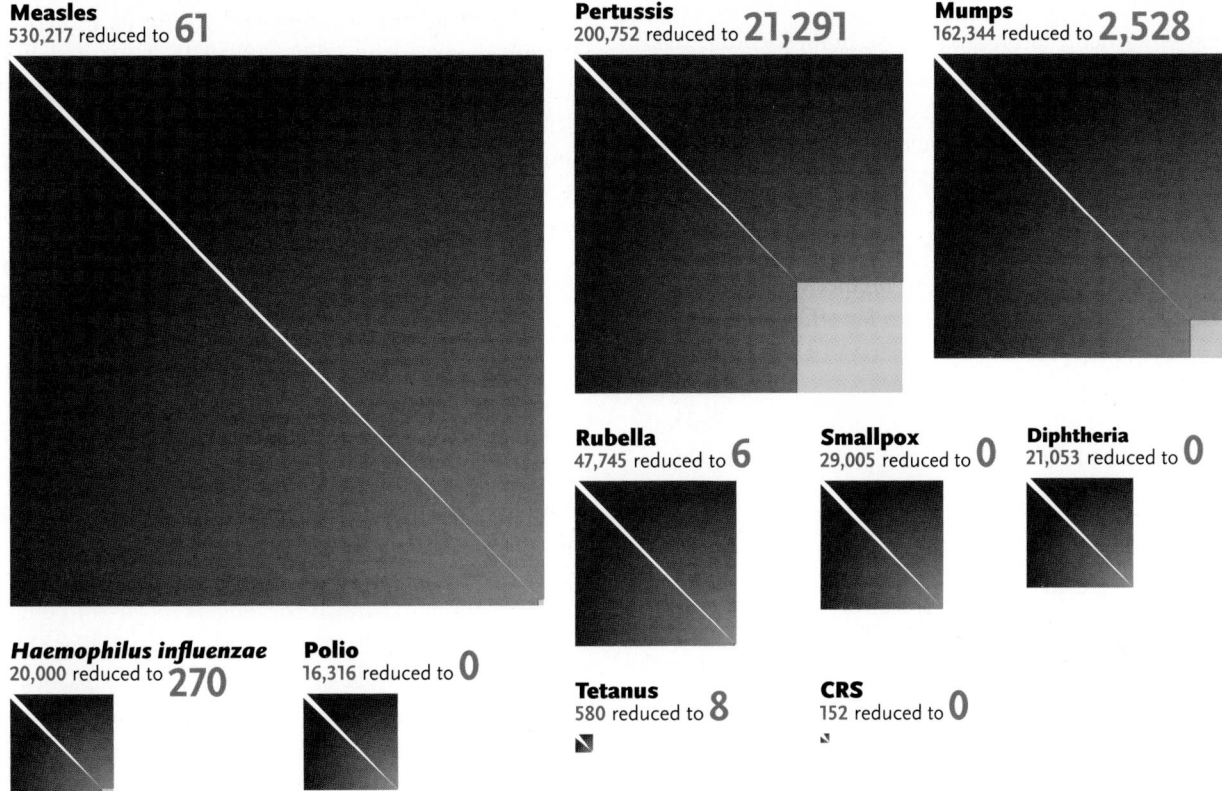

**Annual number of disease cases in the United States** (cases in 1900s compared to cases in 2010)

**Measles**
530,217 reduced to **61**

**Pertussis**
200,752 reduced to **21,291**

**Mumps**
162,344 reduced to **2,528**

**Rubella**
47,745 reduced to **6**

**Smallpox**
29,005 reduced to **0**

**Diphtheria**
21,053 reduced to **0**

**Haemophilus influenzae**
20,000 reduced to **270**

**Polio**
16,316 reduced to **0**

**Tetanus**
580 reduced to **8**

**CRS**
152 reduced to **0**

**FIGURE 33.9** Vaccines are one of the greatest medical advances of the last century. Vaccines have greatly reduced the incidence of deadly diseases.

SOURCE: Based on http://sciencebasedpharmacy.files.wordpress.com/2013/05/vaccine-infographic.gif

that spread rapidly across world regions (see Chapter 14 for more on the naming of influenza viruses). Viruses cause all of these diseases. As discussed in Chapter 14, for most viruses, it is difficult to stop infections once they have taken hold, so prevention is the most effective line of defence against viral disease. Predicting outbreaks and responding quickly, however, can be difficult.

## Globalization Has Increased the Spread of Zoonotic Diseases

The globalization of the pet trade and of biological exchange between regions has increased outbreaks of **zoonotic diseases**, diseases that can spread from animals to humans. These diseases are actually quite common with animals as the source of about 60% of infectious human diseases. In fact, swine flu, bird flu, and SARS are zoonotic diseases that were originally found in animals (originating in pigs, wild and domesticated birds, and bats, respectively). Black rats (*Rattus rattus*) were responsible for spreading plague. In most of these cases, the disease in people originated where the animals live or are raised, but the importation of wildlife has led to outbreaks in humans, even far away from where the animals typically live. In 2003, for example, there was an outbreak of

monkeypox in the United States, a disease previously known from Africa. It was eventually determined that pet prairie dogs (species in the genus *Cynomys*) were the source of the virus **(Figure 33.10)**. The prairie dogs had been exposed to African rodents that carried the disease during their transport and sale in the pet trade.

**FIGURE 33.10** Prairie dogs (species in the genus *Cynomys*) were responsible for a 2003 outbreak of monkeypox in the United States. Interestingly, wild prairie dogs in North America can also be carriers of the bubonic plague and have spread this disease to humans as well, although only in rare and isolated cases.

## Social Networks Reveal Patterns in Disease Transmission

It can be difficult to predict disease outbreaks and their spread. Scientists have tried many techniques to increase their ability to predict when outbreaks will occur and how they will move through a population. Many of these techniques have involved mathematical modelling, for example, but some scientists have also analyzed social networks. This doesn't exactly mean that scientists go on Facebook and use who your friends are to predict who is going to catch your flu next, but it isn't too far off. Researchers at Harvard College, for example, followed a swine flu outbreak in 2009 in hundreds of undergraduate students. The researchers hypothesized that friends of infected individuals, those in the inner circles of a social network, would be more likely to become infected and would become infected sooner than randomly selected individuals in the population. The infection progressed 13.9 days earlier in the friend group than the population as a whole. Studies such as this one motivate mitigation strategies: vaccinations, for example, might be most effective if first given to connected social groups in affected populations.

Another group at the British Columbia Centre for Disease Control used social network analysis to study a tuberculosis outbreak in a community in British Columbia. The community was struggling with alcohol and drug abuse as well as transient housing situations. Researchers were not able to pinpoint the source case of the outbreak using traditional methods. By combining an analysis of social networks within the community with whole genome analysis of the tuberculosis, the researchers made a number of interesting discoveries. First, they identified not one but two distinct outbreaks, both of which had come from a common ancestor present in the community before the outbreaks. Second, they identified the likely source cases of both outbreaks and found that an increase in crack cocaine use likely increased the spread of both strains of the disease (Figure 33.11). In fact, crack cocaine use may have facilitated the spread of disease. Smoking crack cocaine increases the amount you cough, and in a room that isn't well ventilated, this can increase the likelihood of disease transmission.

## Understanding Pandemics Takes More than Microbiologists

Although both of the above examples focus on localized outbreaks, accurately modelling the spread of worldwide, or pandemic, infections is likewise important and challenging. This has become a major challenge for the 21st century. Pandemic disease outbreaks can affect many thousands or millions of people if they are not immediately addressed. Modelling and predicting these outbreaks are difficult: one must decide which factors matter and which do not, an especially tricky challenge considering the speed and patterns of international air travel. Most models are used to address four key questions: (1) Where did the outbreak begin? (2) Where is it going next? (3) How long will it take to get to new and distant locations? and (4) How many people will be affected? Many models are incredibly sophisticated, taking into consideration details of how particular infections spread as well as the movement patterns of many individuals. But models that are dependent on the spread of specific infections may not be able to accurately predict the spread of novel infections. A recent model, however, used a relatively simple idea and accurately predicted the source and spread of both the 2009 swine flu outbreak and the 2003 SARS outbreak.

Instead of considering the specific pathogen or real geographic distance, the model used effective distance. Effective distance was defined in part as the fraction of air-travel passengers between two locations. Consider three international cities: Vancouver, Beijing, and Washington, D.C. The distance between Beijing and Washington is greater than the distance between Beijing and Vancouver. However, if many more air passengers travel from Beijing to Washington, the effective distance between these cities would be more similar to the effective distance between Beijing and Vancouver than measured by geographic distance alone. By using effective distance, the models of disease spread revealed an otherwise hidden geometry. The spread of disease could be modeled by wave propagation—in other words, the way water ripples in concentric circles away from a pebble that has just pierced the surface of the water. The modellers also found that the location closest to the centre of these concentric waves was very close to the source of the infection. Revealing underlying patterns behind phenomena driven by contagions, including phenomena such as gossip or violence, may help us predict and respond better to such situations in our increasingly networked society.

## Gamers Solving Biological Problems

Similar to modelling disease outbreaks, advanced computer simulations are also used to solve biological problems, such as the question of how molecules fold. This is an important technique, for example, for learning about the configurations of macromolecules such as proteins or RNA (see the Purple Pages for an overview of protein folding). Even with sophisticated computer models, however, the structure of some proteins, particularly how they are folded into the most low-energy configurations, continues to elude scientists. The structure of such proteins can be important to disease. For example, a retroviral protease is a protein that plays an important role in the proliferation of viruses. If the structures of these proteins are identified, drugs can be created that target these molecules to make them inactive and thus prevent the virus from reproducing. Scientists have debated the structure of one retroviral protease, of the Mason-Pfizer

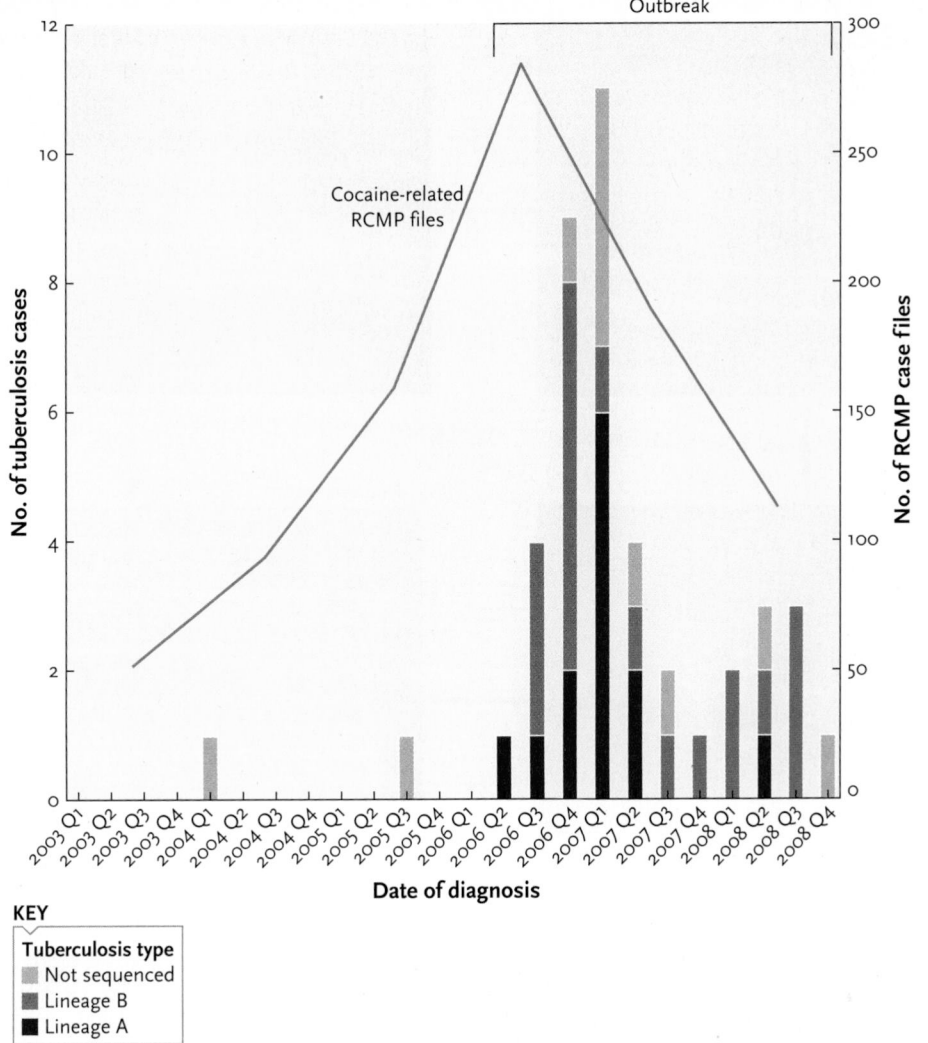

**FIGURE 33.11** A community in British Columbia experienced an outbreak of tuberculosis beginning in 2006. Two strains of tuberculosis were circulating in the community, and the outbreak was correlated with an increase in cocaine-related files reported by the Royal Canadian Mounted Police (RCMP). In total, 41 cases of tuberculosis were recorded in the community.

SOURCE: From *The New England Journal of Medicine*, Jennifer L. Gardy, James C. Johnston, Shannan J. Ho Sui, et al, "Whole-Genome Sequencing and Social-Network Analysis of a Tuberculosis Outbreak," 364:730–739. Copyright © 2011 Massachusetts Medical Society. Reprinted with permission from Massachusetts Medical Society.

monkey virus, an AIDS-causing disease of monkeys, for more than a decade. Scientists decided to pose the challenge of solving the protein's structure not to modellers or biochemists but to video game players. Foldit is an online game challenging players to create the best three-dimensional low-energy configurations of proteins. Players compete against one another individually and in teams to solve posted challenges. Surprisingly, it took only 3 weeks for online gamers to solve the structure of the Mason-Pfizer monkey virus retroviral protease, the same puzzle that had stymied scientists for a decade. Discoveries such as this can be applied to our understanding of pathogens of both humans and wildlife.

A recently published scientific paper had more than 37,000 authors, only 10 of whom are professional scientists. The others are online video game players. The paper describes how players of another online video game similar to Foldit, called EteRNA, are better than the most

advanced computer models in designing biologically active RNA molecules **(Figure 33.12, p. 758)**. The project consisted of several parts. The first phase challenged online players to successfully design biologically active RNA molecules. Scientists synthesized the designs submitted by participants to assess if they were viable. Players could also submit rules for molecule configurations as they found them. At first, players were not very good, and they certainly weren't as good as the computer algorithms previously in use by scientists. However, the players quickly learned from their design failures, and many began to develop successful rules for molecule design. Some of the rules were previously described and used by other computer models, but many were new. Using the rules generated by users, the game developers have created a new computer model to generate RNA molecules. The new model, EteRNAbot, is more successful than previous models but is still not as successful as the players

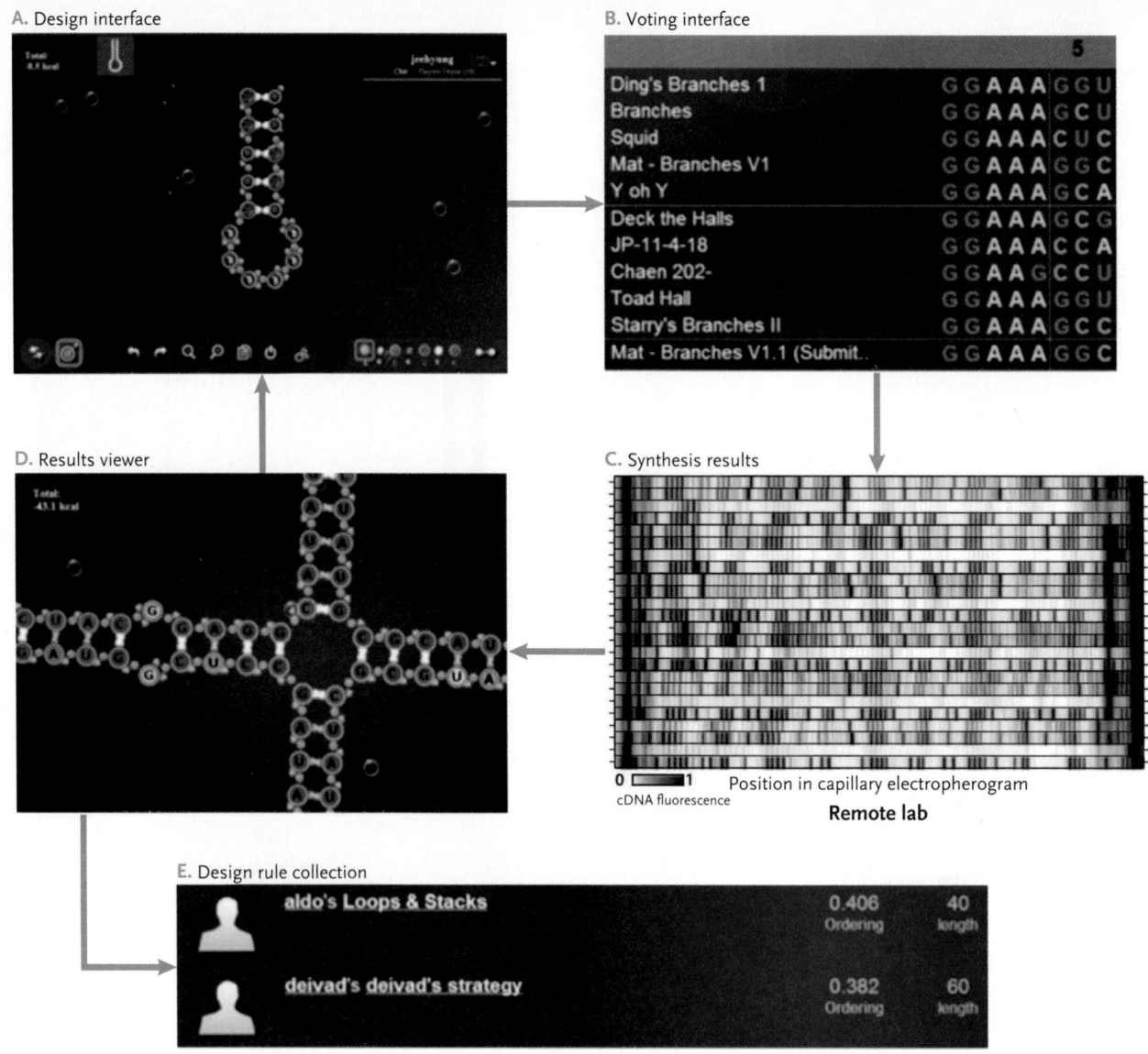

**A. Design interface**

**B. Voting interface**

| | | 5 |
|---|---|---|
| Ding's Branches 1 | G G A A A G G U | |
| Branches | G G A A A G C U | |
| Squid | G G A A A C U C | |
| Mat - Branches V1 | G G A A A G G C | |
| Y oh Y | G G A A A G C A | |
| Deck the Halls | G G A A A G C G | |
| JP-11-4-18 | G G A A A C C A | |
| Chaen 202- | G G A A G C C U | |
| Toad Hall | G G A A A G G U | |
| Starry's Branches II | G G A A A G C C | |
| Mat - Branches V1.1 (Submit.. | G G A A A G G C | |

**D. Results viewer**

**C. Synthesis results**

0 ▭ 1   Position in capillary electropherogram
cDNA fluorescence

**Remote lab**

**E. Design rule collection**

| | | |
|---|---|---|
| aldo's **Loops & Stacks** | 0.406 Ordering | 40 length |
| deivad's **deivad's strategy** | 0.382 Ordering | 60 length |

**FIGURE 33.12** The workflow for EteRNA, an online game in which players compete to design biologically active RNA molecules. **(a)** Players begin by designing molecules. At the end of each week, **(b)** players vote on the best designs. **(c)** The best designs are then synthesized in the lab by scientists, and **(d)** the results are posted publicly. Based on the results, players can (a) design new molecules or **(e)** submit rules for design.

SOURCE: Jeehyung Lee, Wipapat Kladwang, Minjae Lee, Daniel Cantu, Martin Azizyan, Hanjoo Kic, Alex Limpaecher, Sungroh Yoon, Adrien Treuille, Rhiju Das, EteRNA Participants, "RNA design rules from a massive open laboratory," *PNAS*, 2013, vol. 111 no. 6: 2122–2127.

themselves. Games such as EteRNA and Foldit are a new frontier for science. By engaging people's curiosity and ingenuity, they have moved science forward in unexpected ways. We can all contribute to scientific breakthroughs, even through activities such as video games that might look on their surface like the opposite of scientific research.

## STUDY BREAK

1. What is a zoonotic disease?
2. What is Foldit?
3. What is one medical application of understanding the configuration of a retroviral protease?

## 33.3 Biomimicry

There are many ways in which we find inspiration from nature. We exploit natural compounds for medicine and synthesize closely related compounds for drugs (for example, aspirin and related drugs are made from, or inspired by, the salicylic acid of willow trees; see Chapter 17). Another reason people often look to nature is for biologically inspired design ideas, a process called **biomimicry**. The materials and body plans of many organisms have led to innovative inventions and improvements in design. Biomimetic design is another way in which people use our understanding of the living world around us to change and shape the human experience.

**FIGURE 33.13** The design for temperature control at the Eastgate Centre in Harrare, Zimbabwe, is based on the temperature control facilitated by termites in their above-ground mounds.

The water-repellent leaves of plants inspired a very successful example of biomimetic design. A German botanist, Wilhelm Barthlott, noticed that not only were some plants able to repel water from their leaves, but some were also able to self-clean, with dirt particles and other waste particles removed with the repelled water. He conducted experiments comparing the water-repellent properties of leaves with different textures. He found that leaves with rough surfaces, created by microscopic waxes and crystals, demonstrated these self-cleaning properties, whereas smooth leaves did not. The best performing leaf was that of the lotus (*Nelumbo nucifera*); thus, the self-cleaning effect became known as the "lotus effect." Barthlott and others are now applying this idea to surfaces such as exterior paint and sprays to protect things such as furniture, upholstery, and shoes.

Another example of successful biomimetic design is the Eastgate Centre, a building in Zimbabwe. This building was designed based on African termite mounds **(Figure 33.13)**. You may recall from Chapter 1 that termites are fungus farmers. The insects live in colonies and build large mounds in which they live and grow their fungus gardens. The temperature of these gardens must be kept at a constant temperature, a challenge in African desert environments with temperatures that plunge at night and soar during the day. To keep temperatures steady, the termites manipulate the tunnels in their mounds, blocking some and opening others at different times of day to draw air in or out. The Eastgate Centre used these same principles using large fans to draw cool air in or hot air out during different times of the day. The building uses less than 10% of the energy of similarly sized office buildings dependent on traditional heating and cooling methods.

## PUTTING IT IN PERSPECTIVE

This book has introduced you to the biological world of our planet. You have seen examples of the many amazing organisms as well as ways that you interact with these organisms, whether or not you are a biologist. You have also seen how life matters: our own lives depend heavily on other organisms, from the food we eat and the medicine we use to the fossil fuels that run so much of our lives. Humans have the ability to create grave problems for the biological world, but they also have the ability to solve many of them. Biology is important across a variety of scales: understanding biology at the subcellular and cellular levels helps us understand things such as fighting cancer and disease. Understanding how communities of organisms work together helps us understand how to protect ecosystems and biodiversity.

## KEY CONCEPTS REVIEW AND QUESTIONS

### 33.1 Anthromes

Anthromes are biomes whose land use, function, and biology are impacted by the activity of humans. The extent of human influence can vary, with the largest and most intense impacts found in urban environments. Urban environments change the habitat available to many organisms. These changes include increases in food resources, increased noise and other types of pollution, changes to habitat connectivity, and introduced species. Urban environments tend to reduce animal diversity because of these changes and the increased stress they place on organisms. Some animals, however, exploit and adapt to urban environments very successfully.

1. What are two of the leading causes of death for urban wildlife? What are two of the leading causes of death for non-urban wildlife?

2. Describe a way that an urban environment alters the water cycle and another way in which an urban environment alters local climate.

3. Habitat connectivity and exotic species are two challenges that plant species face in urban environments. Why?

## 33.2  Disease

The spread of disease has changed as human society has become increasingly globally connected. Although vaccines and modern medicine are increasingly successfully combatting infectious disease, disease transmission across and among regions is becoming increasingly common. The ways we now study disease have also changed. New breakthroughs have been made possible through multidisciplinary efforts, including genome analysis, social network analysis, and even online video game playing.

4. What is one reason why the prevalence of zoonotic diseases is increasing?

5. Have vaccines been important in reducing the prevalence of infectious diseases? Is it important to continue vaccinating people?

6. What are two techniques that improved our understanding of the spread of infectious disease?

## 33.3  Biomimicry

Biomimetic designs are based on the properties of organisms. Architects, chemists, and many others use biological phenomena to inspire and improve design ideas. Using biomimicry to improve design has led to more energy-efficient buildings, water-resistant and self-cleaning sealant, and even engineered muscle.

7. How do termites control the temperature of the mounds in which they live? How did the design of the Eastgate Centre in Zimbabwe exploit this process?

8. Can you think of a way in which using our understanding of an organism might improve the design of a human-built object?

Now that you have read and reviewed this chapter, think back to what you have learned in this book. Choose an organism and build a concept map connecting the biology of this organism to you (or any human) using key concepts from the cell to ecosystem ecology. Please see the Purple Pages for an example of a concept map that could be developed for this chapter.

# Answers to Key Concepts Review and Questions

## Chapter 1

1. Photosynthesis occurs in both aquatic and terrestrial animals. In vascular plants, chloroplasts are the sites of photosynthesis. The solar sea slug captures chloroplasts from algae and uses them to harvest solar energy.

2. Insectivorous plants obtain nitrogen from their animal (usually insect) prey. Carnivory allows these plants to grow in habitats poor in nitrogen.

3. Humans, leaf-cutter ants, social amoebae, and marine snails.

4. Arguably, some fundamental features are important. They include bipedalism, which allowed the use of forelimbs—hands—for other tasks; a large capacity for learning; and also living in social groups and social transfer of information. Ultimately, technological prowess is associated with such features and increases our potential to affect our surroundings.

5. The highest diversity is in the gut. Organisms there contribute to our overall well-being, including access to otherwise indigestible food.

6. Global warming refers to the overall increase in the Earth's temperature over the last several decades. Climate change reflects global warming, in addition to other changes in climate, including severe winters and strong storms.

7. These topics are front and centre in almost any conversation about politics, including at the local, provincial, national, and international level. Pay attention to the rhetoric and learn that there are strong opinions about most of these topics.

8. This is central to discussion about conservation, the balance between our species' need for resources, and the impact of this need on biodiversity.

9. Use the electronic library to find a recent publication (e.g., a paper or an editorial) about the impact of food prices on our society. What about its effect on people living in poverty?

## Chapter 2

1. Example: The level of a cell, a tissue system, and a body.

2. Artificial intelligence can display order, harness and utilize energy (though not metabolize), and respond to stimuli. It could be argued that some technology can develop or evolve in the sense of learning and adjusting behaviour. However, according to the biological definition of the terms, no technology can maintain homeostasis, grow and develop, or evolve. Human technology can exhibit between three and five characteristics of life.

3.

- Chimpanzee
- Gorilla
- Lion
- Nile crocodile
- Ostrich

4. These organisms are not necessarily any more related than other less morphologically similar species, and this may be misinterpreted when only morphological analysis is used.

5. They would need to (1) display order, (2) harness and utilize energy, (3) respond to stimuli, (4) exhibit homeostasis, (5) grow and develop, and (6) evolve.

6. The food chain, or a food web, needs a place to begin. Without primary production, there would be no food for herbivores, which would leave no food for carnivores.

7. The current rate of extinction is much higher than the background rate of extinction, and we do not fully understand the role of different organisms in ecosystems. Losing one critical species could affect the way ecosystems function.

8. Large extinction events are likely to be driven by large catastrophic disturbances. These catastrophic disturbances can impact more organisms over a much shorter time period.

9. 
| | |
|---|---|
| c | Primary producer |
| b | Primary consumer |
| d | Secondary consumer |
| a, d | Tertiary consumer |

10. $0.5 \text{ km}^2$

11. Cattle, because some energy is lost at each trophic level.

12. Soybeans

13. Examples: (1) mutualism—clownfish and sea anemone; (2) parasitism—Bot fly larva and host.

14. Parasitic fungi are exploited by humans as food and medicine, for example.

## Chapter 3

1. 
- All organisms are composed of one or more cells.
- The cell is the basic structural and functional unit of all living organisms.
- Cells arise only from the division of pre-existing cells.

2. The light microscope uses light to illuminate a specimen, and the electron microscope uses electrons to illuminate a specimen.

3. Cellular membranes act as selectively permeable barriers, and the fluid mosaic model describes membranes as fluid structures composed of two layers of phospholipids (phospholipid bilayer) that contain a mosaic array of membrane proteins. The phospholipid bilayer is arranged so that the hydrophobic tails are sandwiched between the hydrophilic heads. Diverse proteins reside within (integral) or on (peripheral) the membrane; their functions include transport, attachment, recognition, and enzymatic activity.

4. 
| | |
|---|---|
| d | ribosome |
| b | chloroplast |
| g | nucleus |
| i | lysosome |
| h | rough ER |
| e | plasma membrane |
| a | mitochondria |
| c | smooth ER |
| f | Golgi complex |

5. c
6. Nucleoid, circular, cell wall, flagella
7. True. It is believed that prokaryotic cells evolved about 1 to 1.5 billion years before eukaryotic cells. Eukaryotic cells are believed to have evolved from a symbiotic association of prokaryotic cells as described by the theory of endosymbiosis.
8. d
9. False. Although all eukaryotic cells have mitochondria, or remnants of mitochondria, not all eukaryotic cells have chloroplasts.
10. In animals, the ECM is composed of fibrous proteins, polysaccharides, and glycoproteins—namely collagen—that are produced and secreted by the cells. The ECM in plant cells is arranged as a cell wall composed primarily as cellulose that provides protection, support, and shape to the plant.
11. c

## Chapter 4

1. a. True
   b. False. The total amount of energy in the universe remains constant (first law of thermodynamics). It is the disorder of the universe that is always increasing (second law of thermodynamics).
   c. False. Cells display order by releasing energy and decreasing the entropy inside the cell.
   d. True
   e. False. An exergonic reaction releases energy.
2. Most of the energy is stored in the covalent bonds that hold the three phosphate molecules together. During hydrolysis, a phosphate molecule is removed, thereby releasing this energy.
3. In this cycle, the ATP is regenerated using the energy released by exergonic reactions that occur within the cell.
4. Competitive inhibitors and enzyme substrates both bind the active site of an enzyme.
5. a
6. In the cytoplasm, the activity of cathepsin B will be decreased because its optimal pH is more acidic (lower than 7.0).
7. catabolic
8. False
9. b
10. Pinocytosis is the endocytosis of small amounts of liquid and small solutes contained within the liquid into a cell. Receptor-mediated endocytosis involves membrane receptors that bind specific molecules. The receptors are located on the membrane in specific regions that are lined with coat proteins called clathrin.

## Chapter 5

1. ATP and NADPH
2. Electrons go from water to PSII, to electron carriers, to PSI, to electron carriers, to NADP+
3. NADPH
4. Loss of carbon in the form of carbon dioxide
5. | a, b | pyruvate |
   | e | ATP synthase |

| b, c | carbon dioxide |
| a, b, c, d | NADH |
| c, d | FADH$_2$ |
| d, e | proton gradient |
| b, c, d, e | mitochondria |
| b, c | acetyl CoA |
| d | oxygen |

6. The electron transport chain would be uncoupled from chemiosmosis, causing a loss in ATP production.
7. a
8. b
9. d

## Chapter 6

1. True
2. False
3. a
4. c
5. c
6. | b | cells can stay in this phase for an indefinite amount of time |
   | d | DNA replication |
   | g | separation of sister chromatids |
   | f | mitotic spindle is completely formed |
   | h | nuclear envelop reappears |
   | i | cytoplasmic division |
   | a | cell cycle arrest |
   | e | chromatin condenses |
7. b
8. c
9. c
10. a
11. False
12. d

## Chapter 7

1. locus
2. Chromosomes that carry similar genes arranged in a similar physical order.
3. | a | aanaphase I |
   | b | metaphase II |
   | c | telophase I |
   | d | prophase I |
   | e | metaphase I |
4. False
5. b
6. The number of chromosomes in a cell prior to meiosis is double the number of chromosomes in daughter cells generated by meiosis.
7. True
8. c
9. Yes
10. a

11. Increased genetic diversity within a species increases the chances of survival and reproductive success of future generations.

## Chapter 8

1. c
2. e
3. c
4. a
5. d
6. c
7. a
8. a
9. The B gene is closer to the C gene because the recombination frequency is lower thus indicating that the chance of recombination occurring between them is less.
10. Autosomal recessive. The pattern of inheritance cannot be X-linked because one son in the first generation is unaffected, and it cannot be autosomal dominant because two of the children in the first generation are unaffected.

## Chapter 9

1. Looking back to the Purple Pages we can see that proteins do not contain phosphorous in their basic chemical structure. Thus, very little radioactive phosphorous would be attached to the protein fraction isolated from the cells. On the other hand, looking at the chemical structure of DNA, we know that the sugar backbone of the molecule is connected through phosphate bonds. Therefore, large amounts of radioactive phosphorous would be incorporated into the *E. coli* chromosome.
2. c
3. Chargaff's rule states that the amount of pyrimidines is equal to the amount of purines in a DNA molecule. This allowed Watson and Crick to devise the double helix model where A hydrogen bonds with T and G hydrogen bonds with C.
4. Based on Chargaff's rule, we know that purines are connected to pyrimidines by hydrogen bonds that are present between the two strands. This phenomenon helps hold the two strands together. Along the strands, the nucleotides are held together by the 5'–3' connections between the sugar-phosphate molecules. As the DNA molecule assumes its helical structure, a combination of hydrogen bonds and van der Waals forces hold the nucleotides in place with respect to each other.
5. Helicase
6. When cells divide, each daughter cell needs a full complement of chromosomes. If the cell's DNA was not copied before division, each daughter cell would get only half of the necessary DNA.
7. As a cell accumulates damage to its DNA molecules. replication errors can increase. This results in changes to the base pair sequences, which we call mutations. If mutations occur in genes that are important for growth or metabolism, the cell grows more slowly. Cells also contain genes that stop growth when required. When a growth-slowing gene is damaged, the cell may continue to grow and divide even though it should not. This type of uncontrolled cell growth can lead to cancer.
8. The presence of a C-T or T-T dimer alters the shape of the DNA molecule. It will not be able to bend the way it normally does. This can cause the DNA polymerase to make mistakes.

## Chapter 10

1. Key structural differences are the presence of an enhancer, introns, and a polyadenylation signal in the eukaryotic gene.
2. c
3. In an operon, a series of genes, whose proteins often function together, are transcribed as a single unit. This simplifies the regulation of gene expression because the genes encoding the necessary proteins would be transcribed in equal amounts.
4. Because eukaryotes do not transcribe genes in operons, they must use other ways to ensure that the proteins needed for the same task are expressed at the same time. We find that eukaryotic genes have short, conserved DNA sequences in the regulatory area of genes. These short sequences bind proteins called transcription factors. All the genes that encode the proteins needed for the same process will have the same short sequence and hence bind the same transcription factors. The presence of the transcription factor bound to the genes' regulatory area ensures they are transcribed at the same time and so each protein will be present when needed.
5. First the gene must be transcribed, and then the RNA transcript must be processed. If it is a eukaryotic gene this will involve splicing, the addition of a poly-A tail and a 5' tail. The mature mRNA will then be exported from the nucleus to a ribosome where it can be translated.. For a prokaryotic gene, translation of the transcript can begin before transcription is complete. Different genes on the same operon can be translated at the same time.
6. Initiation, elongation, and termination.
7. i) Transcription. Faster rates of transcription result in greater numbers of transcripts.
   ii) Transcript maturation and export. The mature transcript must be present in the cytosol for translation to be performed.
   iii) The rate of translation can be controlled by the cell, altering the amount of a given protein that is produced.
   iv) Following translation, the protein must be folded to become active.
   v) Similarly, the protein must be moved to the correct location to do its job.
   vi) Some proteins need to have additional changes made to become active.
8. All cells of an organism have the same genes, but the function of the cell determines which genes are expressed. For example, a leaf cell will need proteins responsible for photosynthesis to be expressed. This is done by triggering specific transcription factors that turn on transcription of specific genes, and leave other genes turned off. Thus, the proteins present in a given cell are the result of which genes are expressed, not which genes are present.
9. Developmental control of gene expression occurs as a result of signals telling the cells when to activate specific transcription factors. In the leaf of a plant, when the leaf cell is exposed to light, it triggers the transcription of genes whose proteins are needed for photosynthesis and chlorophyll biosynthesis. This process will occur the same way in the plant's

offspring generation after generation. The process is controlled by the presence of specific genes. Epigenetics is an added level of control that can turn off genes even if they are present. Epigenetic regulation results from reversible changes in the chemical and three-dimensional structure of the chromosome, which are often due to changes in environmental conditions. This differs from the developmental regulation in both when and how gene expression is altered.

## Chapter 11

1. Recombinant human insulin is a good example.

2. Bacteria are easy to manipulate at the molecular level, they grow very quickly, and they normally do not require complex chemicals in their growth media. The opposite traits make an organism a bad choice: if it is slow growing, hard to manipulate, or requires complex growth media. Human cells fall into the bad choice category.

3. A restriction endonuclease that produces blunt ends will leave the two strands of the DNA molecule with an equal number of bases. The term *sticky ends* refers to a situation where the enzyme leaves an overhang of between one and four nucleotides that do not have a match on the other strand. It is called sticky because the unpaired bases could hydrogen bond with a complementary sequence of bases on another DNA molecule.

4. If a transgene is expressed using a leaf-specific promoter, the protein would be made only in leaf tissues. Similarly, some genes in Drosophila are only expressed in the eye. By using an eye-specific promoter, one could study how the transgene affects Drosophila eye development. The expression of the transgene in both cases would rely on the presence of cell- or tissue-specific transcription factors.

5. An algorithm is a procedure for making a calculation or decision. They are primarily used in mathematics and computer programming.

6. We can define the term *single nucleotide polymorphism* by looking at each word independently: *single* meaning one, *nucleotide* meaning a DNA base, and *polymorphism* meaning more than one alternative. Thus, an SNP is a single base difference in the DNA strand.

7. Small tandem repeats (STRs) are present in the DNA sequence. Because these repeats are inherited, half of a parent's STRs are found in the DNA of their child. Because there are so many in a typical individual's DNA, STRs provide a unique profile for that individual. Therefore, by looking at the child's DNA, we can see aspects of their STR profile that match the mother's DNA and some that match the father's DNA.

8. A transcriptomic study tells us the steady state level of transcript abundance in the cells or tissues tested. Therefore, we can know which mRNAs are being produced. A proteomic study on the same sample would tell us which proteins are present. If we compared the two sets of data, and saw differences in the level of a particular mRNA compared to the amount of the protein it encoded, we could suggest that there is a translational control mechanism in effect. For example, if a mRNA was present at a high level, but none of its corresponding protein was detected, we could conclude that the mRNA was not being translated due to a separate regulatory control mechanism.

9. This would be a personal response, and I would bring back the Dodo bird. While I like the name, my argument to a regulatory agency would start like this: The Dodo is a large, flightless bird; if it were raised in captivity it would be unlikely to escape into the wild. Apparently, it was quite a tasty

bird, because it became a prime target for sailors visiting Mauritius. With the current popularity of healthy meat production, it could rival turkey and chicken for market share.

## Chapter 12

1. *Eptesicus fuscus* is the correct presentation. *Eptesicus* is the genus, and *fuscus* is the trivial name. The species name is *Eptesicus fuscus*.

2. When you are deciding what food to eat, or what plants to put in your garden, you expect to know (from the label), the species. If you are picking and eating mushrooms, knowing the species can make a difference between life and death. Biologists must know what species they study. Due to the diversity of life styles and life cycles, one definition of species does not work for all species. For example, the concept of species that applies to birds is different from the one that applies to viruses.

3. Bird watchers are more apt to study a bird's appearance and perhaps plumage colour, rather than the bird's genes or chromosomes. The alarm calls of Black-capped Chickadees or vervet monkeys identify different kinds of predators.

4. The array of organisms presented in a field guide directly illustrates biodiversity. The diversity of field guides is an excellent reflection of biodiversity.

5. DNA barcoding allows biologists to quickly distinguish among species that are genetically different. One could use DNA barcode analysis to be sure that the fish you purchase at a market is what is claimed on the label. DNA barcoding will allow conservation officers to confirm that the meat or body parts sold to consumers are correctly labelled.

6. Gene flow, the exchange of genetic information among members of a species, partly accounts for the general similarity among members of a species. Genetic drift occurs when an isolated population changes genetically from the genotype of the founding population. Mutations, inheritable changes, arise in a population and, when they confer an advantage to individuals that possess them, they will spread by gene flow through the interbreeding population.

7. Resident killer whales hunt and eat mainly salmon, exploiting local abundances of these fish. Transient killer whales hunt and eat mainly marine mammals. They cover larger distances than the resident killer whales. Open-ocean killer whales appear to eat mainly sharks. Differences in hunting and killing behaviour and social interactions that promote such differences could account for the three "types" of killer whales.

8. Polyploidy individuals have more than two full sets of chromosomes. Changes in the numbers of chromosomes arise because of interference with meiosis.

9. Ring species illustrate how gene flow occurs among adjacent populations and how local conditions affect phenotypes. Populations at the end of the rings may not be able to breed and produce fertile offspring.

10. Lateral and horizontal gene transfer are mechanisms for allelic exchange among prokaryotes. Neither applies directly to gynogenetic or androdioecious species.

## Chapter 13

1. Natural selection favours some heritable variations over others, as illustrated by Australian sheep blowflies. Flies that are not affected by insecticides are the ones that reproduce and, by definition, their offspring also are resistant.

2. Lamarck, in particular, thought that individual traits were heritable. Darwin noted how natural selection acted on

populations of organisms and favoured some individuals over others.

3. Aging is a natural process; the changes are not the result of natural selection.

4. 2,4-D is a weed killer. Some grasshoppers use a metabolite of 2,4-D as an ant repellent. Individuals that can use 2,4-D in this fashion are protected from attacks by ants. The trait of using a metabolite of 2,4-D is heritable.

5. Pollination is the movement of pollen from one flower to another. Plants pollinated by animals depend on the animal to move pollen (and allow outbreeding). Animals that pollinate are rewarded with nectar and pollen (both can serve as food).

6. A parasite is an organism that lives on/from another organism (the host). Parasites benefit from the interaction, hosts do not. Behaviour, such as social contact, that promotes the movement of a parasite from one host to another can benefit the parasite, but not the host. Australian sheep blowflies are predators more than parasites, but the line between the two is not always clear. Some parasites complete their life cycles in/on the host. Others do not.

7. When one species we know as a fossil is older than another (which is younger). In some cases, we know that the rock layers in which a fossil occurs are 10 million years old. Other fossils occur in rocks that are 20 million years old.

8. A family tree shows the relationships among individuals in a family. A phylogeny shows the relationships among species in a group.

9. In parallel evolution, two closely related groups of organisms independently develop features (e.g., the wings of birds, bats, and pterosaurs). In convergent evolution, two distantly related organisms develop structures that serve similar functions (e.g., the wings of insects and the wings of vertebrates).

10. The appearance of photosynthesis in five modern lineages of bacteria (green nonsulfur bacteria, cyanobacteria, green sulfur bacteria and purple bacteria) is an example of a fundamental change that results in the development of new lineages.

11. Organisms living in environments that have been consistently present for long periods of time may show little change over time. This reflects the persistence of their adaptations and the constancy of their habitat(s).

## Chapter 14

1. The progressive theory of virus evolution suggests that viruses may have started off as simpler structures. Thus, they could be examples of protobionts: simple, non-living structures made out of biological molecules.

2. This is a challenging ethical question and an example of the types of problems facing scientists, the public, and our governments. There is no correct answer for this question, but some points to consider come from both sides of the discussion. Some will argue that the creation of viruses that could infect humans, especially viruses based on the 1918 pandemic virus, is too dangerous. The viruses could be accidentally released and kill millions of people. A similar suggestion is that releasing information about virus production and infectivity could allow terrorist groups to develop their own viruses for use in biological attacks. These arguments were successfully used to block the public release of research into the avian flu virus. On the other hand, the only way we can learn about viruses and prepare for

possible future pandemics is to perform basic research. To do this we need realistic viruses that exhibit varying levels of infectivity. As we have discussed elsewhere in the text, scientific research is difficult if not impossible to do without building upon the results of others. As scientists, we need to share our results so that others can verify our results and think of clever new experiments. Thus, forbidding virus research or its communication would hinder our understanding of a type of pathogen to which we are especially vulnerable. These types of difficult choices must be thoroughly discussed by scientists and governments so that the best overall choices can be made. Thinking about what we would do given such a question is a great place to start.

3. The membrane surrounding animal viruses comes from the host cell in which the virus was produced. The membrane ends up surrounding the virus after it leaves the cell.

4. Because the reverse transcriptase enzyme makes lots of mistakes, it generates a large amount of diversity in the new virus particles being produced. This can provide an advantage by generating new virus strains that are not recognized by the host immune system. Although some of the altered virus strains may be less successful, so many new viruses are produced during an infection that it does not matter. The poor fidelity of the reverse transcriptase helps the viruses elude the immune system of their hosts. Therefore, if a virus strain were made that had greater reverse transcriptase fidelity, its hosts would quickly become immune to it and its progeny.

5. A retrovirus is an RNA virus whose genome undergoes reverse transcription into a DNA copy that can then be transcribed to produce both viral genomes and the virally encoded proteins. A second aspect of a retrovirus is the incorporation of the DNA copy of its genome into the DNA of its host cell.

6. The lawn of bacteria present on the agar plate is disrupted where bacteria have been infected by lambda phage. The reason for the blank spot or plaque is the activation of the lytic cycle. As the virus replicates via the lytic cycle, it kills the bacterial host cell. Thus, the plaque indicates the absence of living bacteria.

7. In each case, animals that are not affected by the virus insert their mouth parts into a viral host and drink fluids that contain the virus. The insects drink phloem sap from the plant or blood from the animal. The insect now contains the virus either on its mouth parts or in its own bodily fluids. When it goes to drink from another plant or animal, the insect inserts its mouth parts a second time, exposing the new source of fluids to the virus. In the case of the mosquito, it actually releases fluids containing anticoagulants into the blood of its meal provider to stop the blood from clotting. This helps the mosquito get a better meal, but increases the chance of the blood provider being infected by viruses.

8. Because HIV is a retrovirus, a copy of its genome will be inserted into one of the human host cell's chromosomes. Therefore, as that host cell grows and divides, it will copy the viral genome at the same time. Unless all the infected cells are destroyed, the individual will never be truly cured of the HIV infection.

## Chapter 15

1. The tree of life attempts to use gene sequence data to determine how closely related different species are to each other. However, if genes are transferred from species to species

through a horizontal process, there will be little change in their DNA sequence. This would be interpreted to suggest the species are highly related even when they are not. Because bacteria and archaea are very efficient at taking up foreign DNA and incorporating it into their genomes, horizontal gene transfer can make it difficult to determine relatedness.

2.

|  | Bacteria | Archaea | Eukaryotes |
| --- | --- | --- | --- |
| **Organelles** | no | no | yes |
| **Membrane lipids** | linear fatty acids | branched and ring-shaped fatty acids; some fatty acids span the membrane | linear fatty acids; contain steroids |
| **Ribosomes** | 70S prokaryotic | 70S prokaryotic or 80S eukaryotic | 80S eukaryotic, but 70S prokaryotic in mitochondria and chloroplasts |
| **Cell wall** | peptidoglycan | some have peptidoglycan | no peptidoglycan; other materials such as proteins, cellulose, chitin |
| **DNA packaging** | normally a single circular chromosome (some linear and some multiple chromosomes) | normally single circular chromosome; wound around histonelike proteins | Linear, wound around histones; have smaller, circular or linear chromosomes in their mitochondria and chloroplasts |

3. Gram-negative cells are more resistant to antibiotics due to the presence of the outer membrane. This lipid layer, located outside the peptidoglycan layer, helps exclude antibiotics from the cell. Because the peptidoglycan layer is located inside the outer membrane, the enzymes that produce it are also located inside the outer membrane. In this way the outer membrane keeps penicillin-type antibiotics, which inhibit peptidoglycan synthesis, away from their target. Thus, the peptidoglycan synthesis enzymes that are affected by the beta-lactam antibiotic are physically separated from the drug by the outer membrane.

4. An autotroph is an organism that can obtain the energy it needs to fix carbon directly from its environment. Generally, autotrophs get their energy from sunlight or inorganic chemicals in their environment. Photoautotrophs are a subset of the autotrophs; they obtain the energy they need to fix carbon from sunlight. Heterotrophs obtain energy by consuming fixed carbon and other nutrients.

5. The sex pillus forms a hollow tube that allows the internal cellular compartments of two neighbouring cells to connect. DNA can then pass from one cell to the other.

6. The structure of the Gram-negative cell wall is distinctive and sets this group apart from all other classes of bacteria. This classification is done in much the same way as all cyanobacteria are placed into the same group, despite other structural and DNA sequence differences.

7. Branched-chain fatty acids help archaea cells maintain their plasma membranes in a fluid state. They work in much the same way as cholesterol does in animal cells.

8. Each of these environmental conditions affects the fluidity of the cell's plasma membrane. To adapt, the cell must alter the membrane lipid content and structure.

## Chapter 16

1. Euglena's combination of chloroplasts and flagellum led to confusion over its placement in the two kingdom model. Its ability to survive by photoautotrophy or heterotrophy also added to the confusion.

2. b

3. convergent

4. Each of these three types of protists is encased in hard silica-based cell walls. In addition, the shape of the cell walls is species dependent. Thus, as these cells die and their remains sink to the sediment of the lake, they remain there. This allows scientists to take cores from the lake sediment and determine what types of diatoms, radiolarians and foraminiferans were present in the lake at a given time in history. The types and numbers of these protists can then be compared to local climate data.

5. The biggest difference is the lack of a vascular transport system in algae. This makes water access more of a challenge for macro-algae.

6. a

7. The chloroplast of the red algae is thought to have come from cyanobacteria. They share the use of phycobilisomes. The presence of only two membranes suggests that the red algae are the result of a primary endosymbiosis.

## Chapter 17

1. They exude enzymes and form associations with mycorrhizal fungi.

2. Stomata are pores in leaves and sometimes elsewhere on the aboveground plant body that control the exchange of gas and water between the plant and the atmosphere.

3. They might be stored in vacuoles so that the acids are contained and separated from the rest of the cell contents.

4. Green vegetables, such as cucumber, broccoli, and celery contain chloroplasts. Tomatoes and carrots contain chromoplasts. Leucoplasts are found in white vegetables such as cauliflower and the white portions of vegetables such as radishes and celery stalks.

5. Epidermal tissue is analogous to epithelial (skin) tissue. The vascular tissue system is similar to the circulatory system in animals.

6. Parenchyma, collenchyma, schlerenchyma.

7. The gametophyte generation photosynthesizes in the bryophytes.

8. Tree trunk cells are diploid; moss cells are haploid.

9. a. Monocots

   b. Eudicots

   c. Eudicots

   d. Monocots

   e. Eudicots

10. Coevolution is the evolution of genetically based, reciprocal adaptations in two or more species that interact closely in the same ecological setting. Coevolution has influenced both plants and animals that interact as pollen producers and pollinators.

## Chapter 18

1. Any two of the following: Fungi are eukaryotic, have cell walls, are sessile, are heterotrophs, and absorb their food.

2. Yeast are unicellular fungi that reproduce asexually.

3. Heterotrophs

4. **A.**

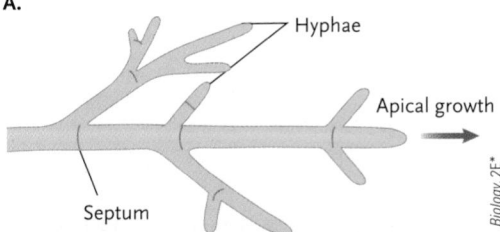

*Biology, 2E\**

**B. Mycelium on leaf litter**

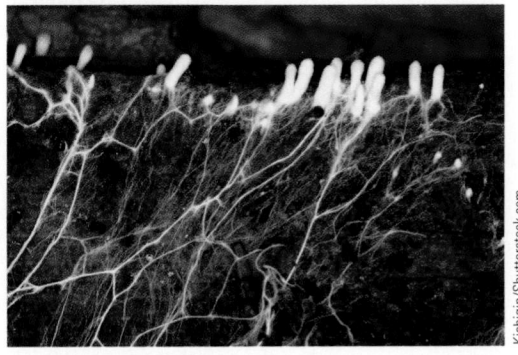

*Kichigin/Shutterstock.com*

5. A polysaccharide that contains nitrogen and is present in the cell walls of fungi and the exoskeletons of arthropods.

6. Absorption

7. __b__ The fusion of nuclei
   __d__ Containing one set of chromosomes
   __c__ A fungus with two dissimilar nuclei
   __a__ The fusion of hyphae

8. For example, fungi live most of their lives as haploid organisms; by contrast, in animals, only the egg and sperm cells are haploid. Fungi delay karyogamy, whereas this occurs immediately in animal reproduction.

9. Basidia are club-shaped and each produces four spores; asci are longer and saclike, and each produces eight spores.

10. In ascomycetes.

11. The fungal hyphae of ectomycorrhizal fungi wrap themselves around the cells inside plant roots but do not penetrate the cells. In endomycorrhizal fungi, the hyphae do penetrate the roots directly.

12. Two examples: thrush, an infection caused by yeast in the body, and ring worm, a fungal skin infection characterized by red rings that grow from the site of the infection.

13. Some examples include preventing erosion, fixing nitrogen, providing a food source in harsh environments, and indicating atmospheric pollution.

14. Some examples include the use of fungi as food, medicines, and in cleaning up polluted environments.

15. Some examples include mould and mildew that affect our homes and health; fungi, such as yeast, that infect our bodies; and other fungi, such as rusts and smuts, that infect our agricultural crops, thereby reducing productivity.

## Chapter 19

1. Limbs are conspicuous and well-developed in Annelida, Arthropoda, Mollusca, and Chordata. Limbs have been lost in some species of annelids, arthropods, and chordates.

2. The main organ systems include nervous, digestive, endocrine, skeletal-muscular, and excretory. Cnidarians and platyhelminths have one opening to their digestive tract. All other multicellular animals have two openings: anus and mouth.

3. The cells of sponges lack cell walls. The cells of sponges are differentiated more like animals than plants, fungi, or bacteria.

4. Radial symmetry is common in *Cnidaria* and *Echinodermata*.

5. First fossil metazoans are *Ediacaran*.

## Chapter 20

1. __b__ A group of cells with a common function
   __c__ Stomach, leaves, hearts, and stems are at this level.
   __d__ The highest functional level of organization
   __a__ The highest functional level of organization

2. False. Dead cells play key roles in both plants and animals. In plants, both xylem and schlerenchma are tissues that are composed of dead cells that have roles in transport (xylem) and support (schlerenchyma). In animals, keratinized cells are dead cells in the epidermis, and they form scales, feathers, hair, nails, claws, hooves, and horns in vertebrates. Dead cells also form the exoskeleton of invertebrates.

3. (a) Ground tissue produces sugars; (b) vascular tissue transports the sugars to the roots; (c) vascular tissue transports water to the leaves; (d) dermal tissue protects the leaves from desiccation.

4. __a, d__ Site of photosynthesis
   __f__ Regulate gas exchange and water loss
   __c__ Transports sugars
   __a__ Protects against infestation and water loss
   __b__ Transports minerals and water
   __e__ Largely consists of dead cells that form fibres for support

5. a. Root and sometimes stem and leaves
   b. Stem
   c. Leaf and often stem
   d. Root and/or stem
   e. Root

6. a. Muscle
   b. Epidermis
   c. Nervous tissue

7. a. Thick and keratinized
   b. Thin with no keratin
   c. Thin with no keratin
   d. Thick and keratinized

8. Endocrine and nervous systems.

9. c

10. Sensor, integrator, effector. There are hundreds of possible examples. What's key here is a description of a circuit that acts to return a controlled variable back to normal following a perturbation. Figures 19.9 and 19.10 are two examples. Your example should have similar detail.

## Chapter 21

1. Micronutrients are nutrients required in small amounts by plants and animals. These include minerals such as chlorine, iron, manganese, boron, zinc, copper, nickel, and molybdenum. These minerals act primarily as cofactors in enzymes: they take the place of an amino acid and give an enzyme the unique shape and binding properties that allows it to catalyze specific chemical reactions. Since enzymes and their cofactors are not consumed in the reactions they catalyze but are used over and over again, the cofactors need only be replaced infrequently as enzymes age and degrade. As a result these cofactors are needed only in very small amounts.

2. This is a nutrient that cannot be manufactured by a plant or animal from other substances but must be obtained in the diet.

3. While sunlight is essential for the health of most plants, it is not an organic compound and is not considered a nutrient.

4. a

5. 
   | c | Glycerol |
   |---|---|
   | d | Nucleic acids |
   | a | Monosaccharides |
   | b | Amino acids |
   | c | Fatty acids |

6. f

7. 
   | b | Membrane phospholipids |
   |---|---|
   | a | Amino acids |
   | c, d | Osmolyte |
   | d | Plant intracellular matrix |
   | a | Chlorophyll |
   | b | ATP |
   | a, b | Nucleic acids |

8. The amount of each essential nutrient that a given plant requires is very species-specific. In fact, the amount essential for one species may be toxic to another. This reflects differences in metabolic processes in each species, and it is why the nutrient content of soils is so important in determining which plants will and won't grow in a given area. It explains why certain plants can settle as pioneering species in one area following a catastrophic event—for example, the volcanic eruption on Krakatoa—, while other species can not.

9. a, b, and e

10. d

11. Both are extracellular. The primary difference is that mammals possess a complete digestive tract with a mouth and an anus, whereas the sea anemone has a gastrovascular cavity with a single opening through which food enters and wastes are expelled.

12. To distinguish differences along the length of the GI tract, to know what each structure is and what it does, and to interpret these in terms of the diets of the two animals, please see Figure 20.13. Start with the esophagus and finish with the anus. Describe every difference you see, what each labelled part of the GI tract does, and, why there are differences between these two animals. For instance, the esophagus is similar in each. It is involved in the transport of food from the mouth to the stomach and plays identical roles in carnivores and herbivores. All other parts except the anus are different between the two animals.

## Chapter 22

1. Fungi are the largest organisms known to date. The very large (huge) ones live in soil, a medium that provides support.

2. Biomineralization is the incorporation of proteins into a matrix such as bone. The spicules of sponges, the exoskeletons of arthropods, and the bones of vertebrates are examples.

3. For a cylinder, we calculate strength by dividing rigidity by the external radius. Toughness is the ability to absorb energy without fracturing. Rigidity of a cylinder can be calculated using a formula that considers the thickness of the cylinder's walls and the radius.

4. Cells of fungi and plants have cell walls that provide rigidity and support. Although capable of some flexibility, the supporting structures of plants are more rigid than those of some animals. Consequently, in comparing fungi and plants with most animals an important difference is the capacity for active movement.

5. Both use calcium phosphate as a major structural component.

6. For the most part, plants are not capable of active movement, whereas most animals are. This means that the supporting systems of most animals include joints, which are points of flexion and movement.

7. Muscle contraction underlies movement: one end of the muscle, the origin, is attached to a part that does not move when the muscle contracts; the other end of the muscle, the insertion, moves when the muscle contracts. Muscles typically occur in pairs, with one contracting while the other relaxes. A direct effect of contraction is the movement, for example, of a limb. An indirect effect could be an increase in internal pressure.

8. The pattern of footfall distinguishes richotetal locomotion (hopping when both hind feet hit the ground simultaneously) from other patterns of running, such as bipedal.

9. Muscle contraction is the main cost of locomotion for most animals. This requires timely delivery of oxygen and fuel to permit respiration.

10. Friction allows an animal to anchor one part of its body, and this provides a point for attachment. Muscle contraction can then push or pull the organism, depending on whether the front or the hind end is attached.

11. Some flatworms, snakes, and eels are examples of animals that move by undulation. Waves of muscle contraction allow the animal to push against the water or substrate.

12. Flippers on whales and penguins and turtles, or fins in fish are used to push against the water.

## Chapter 23

1. b, c, and d

2. a and b

3. A creative way of designing an experiment can be found on the Internet. Either of the two experiments shown in the following video clips would be correct:

   http://www.galaxy.net/~k12/weather/weighair.shtml

   http://www.youtube.com/watch?v=Bv_tS6-qCJ4

4. b and c

5. a. air

   b. water

c. water

d. air

e. water

6. __b, c__    Gases diffuse directly from the atmosphere to individual cells.

   __d__    Gases diffuse into blood moving in the opposite direction.

   __d, e__    Requires muscular pumps for adequate gas exchange

   __a, d, e__    Gas exchange is enhanced by blood perfusion.

   __d__    Produces the most effective gas exchange mechanism

7. a, b, and c

8. This can be tested in a variety of ways. One would be to determine whether the spiracular opening was affected by air humidity. If the hypothesis is correct, what would you expect? How would this test the hypothesis? Another test would be to see if there is a correlation between weight loss and the amount of spiracular opening in different environments. If the hypothesis is correct, what would you expect to happen to weight loss with more or less opening in hot, dry versus cooler, moister environments? How would this test the hypothesis?

9. __b__    Helps support the high metabolic rates required for flight in birds

   __a__    Produces exchange of 80% to 90% of the available oxygen

   __c__    Is associated with tidal, back and forth, movement of air

10. b.

11. e.

12. If the ability is based on genotype, then all members of a species will share it to some extent, regardless of whether they are born at sea level or at altitude. If, on the other hand, the ability is a result of the environment in which the animals were raised, then one will see differences between populations depending on where they were born and raised. Classic experiments to examine the basis of such abilities usually involve transposing animals shortly after birth to a different environment (in this case high to low elevation and low to high elevation) so that where they were born and where they were raised differ.

## Chapter 24

1. a and e

2. a, c, d, and e

3. a, c, d, e, and f

4. a, b, d, and e

5. b, d, and e

6. a, d, and e

7. c

8. a, c, e, and f.

9. e

10. a. baroreceptors

   b. systolic pressure

   c. diastolic pressure

   d. electrocardiogram

   e. cardiac output, stroke volume

## Chapter 25

1. These plants usually have a thick cuticle that reduces evaporation, and their leaves tend to be greatly reduced, with much of the photosynthesis now taking place in the stem. Many of these plants have evolved the $C_4$ mode of carbon fixation in photosynthesis. This pathway allows these plants to close or restrict the opening of stomata, restricting water loss from transpiration; however, it still allows photosynthesis to occur in the mesophyll cells near the surface, where oxygen is abundant. The disadvantage is that these strategies reduce the surface area available for gas exchange.

2. __d, e__    Lose water easily and have trouble obtaining solutes

   __b__    Lose water easily and have trouble excreting solutes

   __c__    Obtain water easily and have trouble obtaining solutes

   __a__    Have no trouble balancing water and solutes

3. d.

4. __b__    Excrete ammonia

   __c, d__    Excrete urea

   __a, c, e__    Excrete uric acid

5. __b__    Almost all excreted in the urine

   __c__    Almost all reabsorbed into the blood

   __a, b, c, d__    Leaves the blood by filtration

   __d__    Can be secreted into the urine

6. __c__    Radiation

   __a__    Convection

   __d__    Evaporation

   __b__    Conduction

7. e

8. In the tropics. Because ectotherms have lower body temperatures and metabolic rates, they require less food and spend less time foraging and exposing themselves to predators. They can invest a greater percent of their metabolic rate into growth and reproduction. In the tropics, reptiles outcompete mammals in terms of both number of species and numbers of individuals. Because they are warm and do not have to expend energy to elevate body temperature, they can divert more energy into reproduction.

In subpolar regions. At colder temperatures, ectotherms become sluggish and inactive, and endotherms are at an advantage (as long as food and water are available). The further from the equator, the more abundant are terrestrial endotherms. There are only a few terrestrial invertebrates in polar and subpolar regions and no reptiles.

9. b and d

10. The heart is warmed first, and blood leaving the heart distributes heat initially to the brain and more slowly to other tissues. Because they warm from the inside out, they do not loose heat to the environment.

## Chapter 26

1. Give a good summary of all the information in section 25.1a.

2. __d__    Neuroendocrine regulation

   __c__    Hormonal regulation

   __a__    Autocrine regulation

   __e__    Neural regulation

   __b__    Paracrine regulation

3. __a__ Auxins

__a, b__ Gibberellins

__a__ Cytokines

__a__ Brassinosteroids

__c__ Abscisic acid

__d, e__ Ethylene

4. __c__ Luteinizing hormone

__a__ Antidiuretic hormone

__g__ Calcitonin

__d__ Endorphin

__f__ Insulin

__e__ Triiodthyronine

__b__ Oxytocin

5. a and c

6. Give a good summary of all the information in section 25.5a

7. Those that live in the open ocean.

8. The underlying mechanism is dependent on the autonomic nervous system, both the sympathetic and parasympathetic branches. However, in readying the animal to fight or flee, the somatic nervous system is also activated to engage the skeletal muscles.

## Chapter 27

1. The porcupine fish's defensive adaptations protect it from being eaten by larger fish. It is generally a medium-sized, slow-moving fish. Without its spines and inflation it would be an easy target for larger predators. It also has a number of feeding adaptations that allow it to eat organisms that have their own defensive adaptations. To eat sea urchins and shellfish, the porcupine fish has evolved rubbery lips that are not damaged by the spines of the sea urchins and sharp, pointed teeth that can effectively break through the hard exteriors of shell fish. These adaptations allow porcupine fish to protect itself and bypass the protections of its prey.

2. c

3. Apoptosis is the controlled death of the cell. It allows cellular contents to be broken down and nutrients removed to neighbouring cells. This means that the nutrients are not available for the pathogen to use for its growth and reproduction.

4. The T cell and B cell receptors that recognize the foreign invader will trigger the growth and division of the cell that contains them. Following exposure to a foreign particle, the organism will have many more T cells and B cells that recognize the foreign particle. In this way the organism is ready to respond rapidly if exposed to the same foreign object another time.

5. d

6. Following a single immunization, the body mobilizes T cells and B cells, and memory cells are produced in case of subsequent exposure to the antigen. When someone receives a booster shot, those T cells and B cells become active. They are signalled to divide and grow, resulting in an even larger supply of memory cells waiting for another exposure to occur. The greater the supply of memory cells, the better the protection against a foreign antigen.

7. Allergies get worse following repeated exposure for the same reason that booster shots help improve your immunity. With repeated exposure, a larger number of memory cells are present to attack the foreign antigen. In the case of allergies, the immune system is overreacting to a harmless antigen, rather than providing protection from a harmful pathogen.

8. An opportunistic infection is caused by a weak pathogen that would normally not cause an infection. The innate and adaptive immune systems of healthy individuals limit the infection and destroy the invading organism. However, individuals with weakened immune systems, such as AIDS sufferers, are unable to mount an effective immune response. This means that the normally ineffective pathogen is able to cause an infection.

## Chapter 28

1. Meiosis is the reduction of chromosome numbers from 2n (diploid) to n (haploid).

2. Meiosis reduces the numbers of chromosomes. Gametophyte generations are haploid, and sporophyte generations are diploid.

3. Gametes are transferred from one organism to another, sometimes by contact, sometimes by placing eggs and sperm together.

4. Vascular plants depend upon wind or animals to transfer gametes, whereas animals use some form of mating behaviour. Pollination syndromes describe the use of wind or animals to transfer pollen. Ornithophily is pollination by birds, chiropterophily is pollination by bats.

5. Pollination by wind (anemophily), by animals (zoophily), by birds (ornithophily), by bats (chiropterophily), by insects (entomophily).

6. Bird-pollinated flowers tend to be red in colour and bloom by day. Bat-pollinated flowers tend to be pale in colour and produce a strong odour.

7. The fruiting bodies of fungi are mushrooms. Plasmogamy is fusion of fungal hyphae.

8. Internal fertilization occurs when sperm meets egg within the body of a parent, usually a female. External fertilization occurs when egg meets sperm outside the parents' bodies. Amphibians and some fish tend to use external fertilization; mammals and guppies use internal fertilization.

9. If a pregnant female mouse is exposed to the urine of a strange male (not the father of her unborn offspring), she miscarries. This is known as the Bruce effect.

10. Gender may be determined genetically or environmentally.

11. Use a tabular display to compare these patterns of development, drawing on the information provided in the text.

12. In determinate cleavage, each cell produced by division of the zygote is preprogrammed to develop into specific tissues or organs. This means that from the first cell division, an individual cell cannot develop into a complete organism. In indeterminate cleavage, for at least the first cell divisions, each cell can develop into a complete organism.

13. Somites are body segments. They occur in annelids, arthropods, and chordates.

14. Organogenesis is the development of organs. These developments are controlled by genes, typically through the production of enzymes. Hox genes are central to development in many animals.

15. Epigenetics occurs through interactions between genes and environment. For example, human hair and fingernails are made from chitin, and epigenetics accounts for the difference in their texture and appearance.

## Chapter 29

1. Population ecology allows biologists to understand the dynamics and components involved in determining the size and extent of populations. The emergent parties component repeatedly reminds us how complex interactions among organisms can be. This alerts us to the challenge of interpreting phenomena based on simple models.

2. A-7 illustrates the importance of having individually tagged organisms whose history you can follow and document.

3. Biologists use direct counts to measure population in some situations. In other situations they rely on capture-recapture to estimate population numbers. They also measure reproductive features such as litter size and time between litters, as well as age at reproductive maturity.

4. Biologists consider the age at first reproduction, the number of young produced at any time, and also the ratio of males to females. Age at first reproduction can be affected by resources (e.g., food), and survival of young can reflect food availability and the incidence of predators.

5. Density, the numbers of organisms per unit area, is an important measure. The amount of food presented at a party, and whether there is enough for all of the guests, is a density-dependent effect. A storm that occurs during the party is a density-independent phenomenon. The carrying capacity (K) reflects the amount of resources used by each individual. The intrinsic rate of increase of the population (r) reflects population density, condition of individuals, and resource availability (K).

6. Intrinsic controls usually derive from the reproductive systems of the organisms (how many young they can produce). Extrinsic controls can be more environmental, reflecting weather and length of growing season (how these affect the young that have been produced).

7. Fitness is usually measured as the number of young surviving to reproduce. This measure applies to individuals. More fit individuals produce more children and grandchildren compared to less fit individuals. Compare the life history features of a deer mouse, a little brown bat, and an apple maggot.

8. A trade-off is illustrated by a female snail that produces fewer larger eggs or many smaller ones, according to the availability of resources. For snails, the amounts of lipids (fats) in the diet may trigger trade-offs. Female cottontail rabbits get pregnant in the early spring. Under conditions of bad weather females hedge their bets by resorbing the litter from the uterus and reproducing again later. The behaviour of brook trout illustrates how populations living only a few kilometres apart can have quite different life history traits.

9. Reproductive senescence (such as menopause) occurs when an individual lives a long time after it has stopped reproducing. Female killer whales continue to care for their young long after they have stopped reproducing. The same can be true of humans, both males and females. Technology makes it relatively easy for some humans to postpone or extend their reproductive production.

10. Some people would say that obligatory birth control (family planning) is not compatible with the freedom of individuals. Others would hold the opposite view.

11. A large human population consumes more resources and destroys more habitat than a smaller one. Habitat disruption—for example, contamination of waters by chemicals in oral contraceptives—can feminize fish and reduce their reproductive output. Overharvesting of resources such as food and water can limit the availability of these resources to other organisms. Urban sprawl often accommodates humans but makes large tracts of land unavailable to other species.

## Chapter 30

1. Largemouth bass might increase predation on planktivorous fish species, allowing phytoplankton species to bloom.

2. Deer populations in the absence of an apex predator are controlled by disease, food availability, and accidental deaths, such as by traffic accidents. Hunting can replace the role of the apex predator.

3. This could have a variety of answers, such as songbirds or spiders.

4. Competition for resources or disease introduction.

5. d, b, a, e, c.

6. Limitation of resources such as sunlight or water, as well as biotic pressure from herbivores.

7. Nitrogen enters an ecosystem through nitrogen fixation. The majority of fixation comes from organisms that fix atmospheric nitrogen and introduce it to an ecosystem. The majority of phosphorus comes from the weathering of rock and liberation of phosphorus from that rock.

## Chapter 31

1. A pristine or natural ecosystem is typically defined as one that has no human influence or development. Compared to human-controlled environments, humans do not interact with pristine or natural ecosystems.

2. Humans benefit from many ecosystem services, including flood control and erosion prevention, and also services such as exploitable plants and animals for food and medicine.

3. Species richness refers to the number of unique species in a given area. Species abundance considers the number of species as well as the population size of each species in a given area.

4. The beaver is one example of a species whose loss would affect many others.

5. A keystone species has more impact on a community than its numbers might suggest.

6. The average rate of extinction of organismal groups through time.

7. Two example arguments are as follows: (1) There is intrinsic value in each organism and each organismal species; and (2) species provide many ecosystem services, many of which we may not know so we cannot replicate.

8. Ecosystem services are services and products provided by ecosystems. Three examples are (1) wetlands providing water filtration capacity, (2) lichens preventing erosion, and (3) maple trees providing sap for maple syrup.

9. IUCN tracks species by conducting population surveys and collecting on-the-ground data for different organisms. This involves teams of scientists all over the world searching for species and counting individuals. Species that have not been assessed directly are not included in the list.

10. Extirpation is local extinction.

11. CITES is the Convention on International Trade in Endangered Species. It is a treaty that controls international trade of species at risk among participating countries.

12. Appetite for crops and crop products from these countries, particularly palm oil in recent years, drives deforestation and palm plantation development.

13. Habitat loss might fragment formerly connected populations, creating barriers to mating and reducing genetic diversity in the newly isolated populations. Invasive species may increase the number of species in a local area; however, as rare species are lost and more ubiquitous invasive species are found in more places, global diversity may decrease.

14. Invasive species can spread wildlife disease; so can species that are commercially exchanged as in the pet industry.

15. Habitat left intact for one species benefits all species that call that habitat home.

16. Assisted migration is a practice in which researchers would move at-risk species from their current ranges to ecosystems where they have not previously been found. This practice is controversial as it essentially introduces exotic species into novel environments. This might have unintended consequences for the ecosystem, but may also serve to maintain populations of the threatened species.

17. Phytoremediation refers to treatment of environmental contamination. Specifically, it refers to the removal of pollutants by plants that can mitigate the problem by taking up target pollutants, thereby removing them from the ecosystem.

18. Citizen science is scientific data collection and analysis by people who may or may not have a formal background in science.

19. Some examples include (1) switching from incandescent light bulbs to compact fluorescent light bulbs; (2) filling any holes in your house where hot or cool air can be lost; (3) making small commitments to reduce the amount you drive, for example, pledge to walk anywhere less than 1 km from your house 50% of the time or less than 2 km 25% of the time.

20. Perhaps you see your largest contribution to the loss of biodiversity as your meat consumption, the carbon footprint of your vehicle, or your daily commute. Whatever your contribution, whether or not you care about the loss of biodiversity can only be answered by you.

## Chapter 32

1. Among Song Sparrows, the sounds associated with predators are a stimulus that evokes fear and interferes with reproductive output.

2. The nature side contends that an individual inherits their traits. The nurture side contends that environment is more important. The discovery of rover and sitter genes is one demonstration that some behaviours are inherited.

3. Camouflaged animals may be invisible as long as they do not move. Predators can get close enough to scare the prey into moving.

4. Animals may taste bad, often because of what they eat. Animals may be dangerous because they bite, scratch, or have poison glands. Animals may stop moving (freeze) to avoid detection by predators. Animals may run or fly away from danger.

5. Predators may lie in ambush and surprise prey that do not detect them. Predators may inject poison into prey and wait for them to die. Predators may run down and catch their prey. Predators may lure prey close enough to attack.

6. Suicidal reproduction involves situations in which males and/or females die immediately after reproducing (semelparity).

7. DNA fingerprinting allows biologists to determine parentage. This revealed that many species thought to have been monogamous are, in fact, promiscuous. Both males and females engage in mating outside their pair bonds.

8. In some cases—for example, male marsupial mice—copulation with many females ensures that the male passes his genes to the next generation. In this situation, semelparity confers a high level of fitness.

9. Social species often live in groups and individually recognize other members of their groups. Asocial species may live in aggregations, but do not individually recognize other members of the aggregation.

10. Social animals tend to live in groups. Group members are highly social when they tailor their behaviour to the animal they interact with. Asocial animals tend to live alone, but even some of them have social interactions with their neighbours. The social organization usually reflects the overall biology of the organism.

11. Communication involving symbols and syntax is usually called language.

12. It has become increasingly clear that many animals learn, often in relation to getting food or interacting with others. In some, perhaps many, species, individuals learn by observing others.

13. Animals from chimps to ants, crows to parrots, and other birds use tools. Tool users typically learn by observing and interacting with others.

14. Tool use by animals illustrates how animals learn to take advantage of situations that increase their reward. In some cases this is an energetic benefit through access to food. In other cases it is a genetic benefit, getting genes into the next generation: tool use thereby influences social organization.

15. It is too easy to assume that "dumb" animals are not as adept as we are. The more we learn about animals and their behaviour, the more we appreciate our animal ancestry.

## Chapter 33

1. The two leading causes of death for urban wildlife are disease and traffic accidents. The two leading causes of death for non-urban wildlife are predation and starvation.

2. One example of an alteration to the water cycle is the increase in impervious surfaces, which leads to changes in the flood regime as well as the loading of pollutants and other materials. Another example is that cities use a lot of

water, sometimes more than can be replaced naturally. Urban environments alter local climate, for example, by increasing the area of the landscape covered with dark surfaces, which increases the amount of heat absorbed, thereby increasing local temperatures.

3. Plant species are not motile, so any fragmenting of habitat can prevent populations from interacting with each other. Exotic species can compete with native species, and this can lead to declines in native species.

4. Increasing globalization increases biotic exchange both directly, through the pet industry and other trade, and indirectly, through accidental biological introductions.

5. Yes and yes.

6. Social network analysis and modelling using geographic analysis can both help predict the spread of infectious disease.

7. To keep temperatures steady, the termites manipulate the tunnels in their mounds, blocking some and opening others at different times of day to draw air in or out. The Eastgate Centre applied these same principles, using large fans to draw cool air in or hot air out during different times of the day.

8. This question can be answered in a variety of ways, using existing examples and speculative ones. For example, scientists have known that the saliva of vampire bats contains anticoagulants that prevent blood clotting. Scientists have exploited the chemistry of this saliva to create anticoagulant drugs used to treat people.

**abiotic factors** Physical factors such as temperature, climate, and weather and chemical and geological factors such as rocks and minerals; factors not usually directly affected by organisms. p. 282

**abscisic acid** A plant hormone involved in the abscission of leaves, flowers, and fruits; dormancy of buds and seeds; and closing of stomata. p. 526

**accessory pigments** Non-chlorophyll pigments that absorb light and transfer the energy to the photosystem chlorophyll. p. 103

**acetylation** The enzymatic addition of an acetyl functional group to a target molecule. In epigenetics, the target is often a nucleotide or histone protein, making genes more accessible. p. 204

**acidophilic** Conditions under which acidophiles grow best; low pH (acidic) conditions. p. 340

**acoelomate** A body plan of bilaterally symmetrical animals that lack a body cavity (coelom) between the gut and the body wall. p. 413

**actin** A globular or G protein. p. 412

**actin filaments** Filaments formed from actin G proteins. p. 70

**action potential** The abrupt and transient change in membrane potential that occurs when a neuron is depolarized past its threshold. p. 579

**activation energy** The initial input of energy required to start a reaction. p. 86

**active site** The region of an enzyme that recognizes and combines with a substrate molecule. p. 86

**active transport** The mechanism by which ions and molecules move against the concentration gradient across a membrane, from the side with the lower concentration to the side with the higher concentration. p. 94

**adaptive immune system** The cells and processes that adjust following exposure to an antigen and thus provides increased protection in case of a second exposure to that antigen. p. 597

**adaptive immunity** A specific line of defence against invasion of the body in which individual pathogens are recognized and attacked to neutralize and eliminate them. Adaptive immunity is limited to vertebrates. p. 606

**adenosine diphosphate (ADP)** An organic compound that consists of a ribose sugar backbone, which is attached to a molecule of adenine and two phosphate groups bonded to the 5' carbon atom of ribose. It is essential for the flow of energy in a cell. p. 85

**adenosine triphosphate (ATP)** The primary agent that couples exergonic and endergonic reactions and serves as the main energy transfer agent in cells. p. 67

**adhesion** The adherence of molecules to the walls of conducting tubes, as in plants. p. 524

**adrenal cortex** The outer region of the adrenal glands, which contains endocrine cells that secrete two major types of steroid hormones: the glucocorticoids and the mineralocorticoids. Online Ch. 26

**adrenal medulla** The central region of the adrenal glands, which contains neurosecretory neurons that secrete the catecholamine hormones epinephrine and norepinphrine. Online Ch. 26

**adrenocorticotropic hormone (ACTH)** Produced by the anterior pituitary gland and stimulates the adrenal glands to secrete cortisol and steroid hormones such as adrenaline and noradrenaline. Online Ch. 26

**adventitious root** A root that develops from the stem or leaves of a plant. p. 372

**aerial** Existing or occurring in the air. p. 440

**aerial shoot system** The stems and leaves of a plant that occur in the air. p. 438

**aerobes** Organisms that require oxygen for cellular respiration. p. 121

**aerobic respiration** The process by which molecules are oxidized to produce ATP via an electron transport chain and ATP synthase, where oxygen is the final electron acceptor. p. 121

**afferent neurons** Carry information to the CNS. They are sensory neurons. p. 576

**aggregate fruits** Fruits developed from discrete ovules (e.g., raspberries). p. 641

**alarm call** A signal used to alert other animals to danger. p. 259

**alcoholic fermentation** Reaction in which pyruvate is converted into ethyl alcohol and $CO_2$ in a two-step series that also converts NADH back into $NAD^+$. p. 122

**aldosterone** A mineralocorticoid hormone released from the adrenal cortex. It increases the amount of Na and water reabsorbed from the urine in the kidneys and absorbed from foods in the intestine; reduces the amount of Na secreted by salivary and sweat glands; and increases the rate of K excretion by the kidneys, keeping Na and K balanced at the levels required for normal cellular function and retaining water at adequate levels to maintain blood pressure. Online Ch. 26

**algorithm** A procedure used to perform a calculation. In the design of computer programs, algorithms are used to make decisions. p. 249

**allele** One of two or more versions of a gene. p. 151

**allopatric** Two allopatric species do not occur in the same area. p. 269

**allopolyploid** Polyploid individuals produced by hybridization of two other species. p. 271

**all-or-nothing principle** Refers to the fact that all action potentials are the same size. If a stimulus is too small to depolarize a neuron to threshold, nothing happens. If it is large enough to depolarize the cell to threshold, an action potential is produced. Even larger stimuli have no further effect. Either the voltage-gated channels open, or they don't. Thus, either an action potential of a fixed size is produced, or it is not. p. 579

**alternation of generations** The regular alternation of mode of reproduction in the life cycle of an organism, such as the alternation between diploid (sporophyte) and haploid (gametophyte) phases in plants. p. 377

**altruistic behaviour** Behaviour that increases the fitness of one individual (the receiver) at the cost of the individual that behaved (e.g., feeding young not genetically related). p. 738

**alveoli** Millions of tiny air pockets in mammalian lungs, each surrounded by dense capillary networks. p. 509

**amniocentesis** Technique of prenatal diagnosis in which cells are obtained from the amniotic fluid. p. 191

**amniotic egg** Amniotic eggs are surrounded by membranes (amnion) that contain water in which the embryo develops. p. 426

**amphipathic** Describes molecules that are partly hydrophilic and partly hydrophobic. Membrane lipids fall into this category. p. 339

**amplification** An increase in the magnitude of each step as a signal transduction pathway proceeds. p. 566

**anabolic pathway** Type of metabolic pathway in which energy is consumed to build complicated molecules from simpler ones; often called a biosynthetic pathway. p. 91

**anaerobe** An organism that does not require oxygen to live. p. 121

**anaerobic respiration** The process by which molecules are oxidized to produce ATP via an electron transport chain and ATP synthase, but unlike aerobic respiration, oxygen is not the final electron acceptor. p. 121

**anaphase I, anaphase II** The phases of mitosis, meiosis I and meiosis II, respectively, during which the spindle separates chromosomes and pulls them to opposite spindle poles. p. 156, 157

**anchoring junctions** Junctions that anchor cells to one another or to components of the extracellular matrix by means of proteins that extend through the plasma membrane to link cytoskeletal proteins in one cell to cytoskeletal proteins in neighbouring cells, or to proteins in the extracellular matrix. p. 73

**androdioecy** Having male and female flowers on the same plant. p. 273

**androgens** A family of hormones that promotes the development and maintenance of sex characteristics. p. 650

**aneuploidy** The condition of having extra or missing chromosomes. p. 163

**angiosperm** A flowering plant. Its egg-containing ovules mature into seeds within protected chambers called ovaries. p. 382

**ankle** The joint between the lower leg bones (tibia, fibula) and the foot bones. p. 3

**annual** A herbaceous plant that completes its life cycle in one growing season and then dies. p. 373

**antheridium** In plants, a structure in which sperm are produced. (Plural, antheridia.) p. 379

**anthromes** Biomes altered, occupied, or under the control of humans. p. 749

**antibodies** Highly specific soluble proteins that circulate in the blood and lymph. They recognize and bind to foreign objects, clearing them from the blood. p. 610

**antibody-mediated defence** Adaptive immune response in which cells secrete antibodies. p. 611

**anticodon** The three nucleotide segment in tRNAs that pairs with a codon in an mRNA molecule. p. 219

**antidiuretic hormone (ADH)** A hormone secreted by the posterior pituitary that increases water absorption in the kidneys, thereby increasing the volume of the blood. Online Ch. 26

**antigen** A foreign molecule that triggers an adaptive immune response. p. 611

**anus** The opening at the end of the digestive tract through which wastes are passed. p. 415

**aorta** The largest artery; arises from the heart and branches into arteries that lead to all body regions except the lungs. p. 537

**apex predator** A consumer at the top of the trophic pyramid or food chain. p. 681

**apical dominance** Inhibition of the growth of lateral buds in plants due to auxin diffusing down a shoot tip from the terminal bud. p. 370

**apical meristem** A region of unspecialized, dividing cells at the shoot tips and root tips of a plant. p. 370

**apoptosis** Programmed cell death. p. 141

**aquaporin** A specialized protein channel that facilitates diffusion of water through cell membranes. p. 92

**aquatic** Existing or occurring in water. p. 440

**arbuscular mycorrhizae** Mycorrhizae that produce highly branched hyphae within the root cells in the roots of a wide range of plants. p. 401

**archegonium** The flask-shaped structure in which bryophyte eggs form. (Plural, archegonia.) p. 379

**armillaria** A disease of trees caused by fungal infection. p. 473

**artificial selection** Selective breeding of organisms to ensure that certain desirable traits appear at higher frequency in successive generations. p. 281

**ascocarp** A reproductive body that bears or contains asci. p. 396

**ascospores** Spore formed by meiosis in ascus, a saclike cell produced by ascomycete fungi. p. 396

**asci** Saclike cells in ascomycetes (sac fungi) in which meiosis gives rise to haploid sexual spores (meiospores). (Singular, ascus.) p. 396

**asexual reproduction** A mode of reproduction in which a single individual gives rise to offspring without fusion of gametes or genetic input from another individual. p. 129

**assisted migration** A practice in which researchers would move at-risk species from their current ranges to ecosystems where they have not previously been found. p. 721

**asymmetrical** Organism with no obvious symmetry. p. 415

**atavism** A trait, lost during evolution, that re-emerges periodically due to mutations. The presence of teeth in chickens or a small tail in humans are examples of atavisms. p. 226

**ATP synthase** A membrane-spanning enzyme that uses the energetically favourable transport of protons across a membrane tosynthesize ATP. p. 108

**ATP/ADP cycle** Continued breakdown and resynthesis of ATP. p. 85

**atrioventricular (AV) node** A second specialized node of muscle cells that behave more like neurons in the nervous system than like muscle cells. The cell bodies in this node are located between the right atrium and the right ventricle, and they receive signals from the sinoartial node and conduct them to the ventricle. p. 534

**autoclave** A laboratory instrument used to sterilize tools, instruments, and growth media. p. 335

**autocrine** Cell signalling in which the cell secretes a chemical messenger that results in reception and response in the same cell. p. 564

**autoimmune disorder** A condition where the individual produces antibodies that recognize and try to destroy molecules of the body. p. 619

**autonomic** Involuntary or unconscious. p. 591

**autophagosome** Large double-membrane vesicle that encloses cytoplasmic components formed from phagophores during autophagy and transports them to lysosomes for digestion. p. 66

**autophagy** Digestion of damaged organelles within a cell. p. 64

**autopolyploid** An individual with two sets of chromosomes from one species. p. 271

**autosomal dominant inheritance** Pattern in which the allele that causes a trait is dominant, and only homozygous recessives are unaffected. p. 181

**autosomal recessive inheritance** Pattern in which individuals with a trait are homozygous for a recessive allele. p. 181

**autosome** Chromosome other than a sex chromosome. p. 181

**autotrophs** Organisms that produce their own food using $CO_2$ and other simple inorganic compounds from their environment and energy from the sun or from oxidation of inorganic substances. p. 36

**auxins** Any of a family of plant hormones that stimulate growth by promoting cell elongation in stems and coleoptiles, inhibit abscission, govern responses to light and gravity, and have other developmental effects. p. 232

**axillary bud** Embryonic shoot that develops where a leaf meets the stem. p. 373

**axon** The single, elongated extension of a neuron that conducts signals away from the cell body to another neuron or an effector. p. 575

**B cell receptor** A type of antibody that is embedded in the plasma membrane of a B cell. They detect foreign antigens in the body. p. 613

**B cells** Lymphocytes that recognize antigens in the body; they have antibodies embedded in their plasma membrane (B cell receptors). p. 611

**background extinction rate** The average rate of extinction of organismal groups through time. p. 34

**bacterial conjugation** In bacteria, the process by which a copy of part of the DNA of a donor cell moves through the cytoplasmic bridge into the recipient cell, where genetic recombination can occur. In ciliate protozoans, a process of sexual reproduction in which individuals of the same species temporarily couple and exchange genetic material. p. 166

**bacteriophage** A virus that infects bacteria, also simply called a phage. p. 315

**baroreceptors** Pressure sensors that monitor blood pressure in the walls of the heart and key blood vessels, notably the aorta and the carotid arteries that deliver blood to the brain. p. 541

**basal body** A cylindrical organelle that contains microtubules and forms the base of cilium or flagellum. p. 70

**basidia** A small, club-shaped structure in which sexual spores of basidiomycetes arise. (Singular, basidium.) p. 397

**basidiocarp** A fruiting body of a basidiomycete; mushrooms are examples. p. 397

**Batesian mimicry** Mimicry in which a palatable or harmless species resembes an unpalatable or poisonous one. p. 605

**bathypelagic** Deep sea, 1000 to 3000 m deep in the ocean. p. 264

**benign tumour** Tumours that remain localized within their environment. p. 139

**bet hedging** A situation where, depending upon nutrient levels, for example, organisms may produce fewer large organisms or more smaller ones. p. 672

**beta-lactamase** An enzyme that breaks down penicillin. It is produced naturally in some bacteria, and a gene that encodes the protein can move to other bacterial species through horizontal gene transfer. This is one way that resistance to penicillin-type antibiotics has spread to many different bacterial species. p. 602

**biennial** A plant that completes its life cycle in two growing seasons and then dies; limited secondary growth occurs in some biennials. p. 373

**bilaterally symmetrical** Animals in which one side of the body is a mirror image of the other. p. 415

**binary fission** Prokaryotic cell division—splitting or dividing into two parts. p. 131

**biodiversity** The richness of living systems as reflected in genetic variability within and among species, the number of species living on Earth, and the variety of communities and ecosystems. p. 38

**biogeochemical cycles** Any of several processes in which a nutrient circulates between the abiotic environment and living organisms. p. 693

**biogeographic realms** Zones based on representation of the biota occurring together found in different parts of the world. p. 298

**bioindicators** Organisms that are sensitive to environmental degradation (pollution of water or soils, for example) and that can be used as indicators of environmental quality. p. 712

**bioinformatics** A field of study that fuses biology with mathematics and computer science. It is especially important for the study of genome sequences and other large data sets. p. 241

**biological pump** An important carbon sink; a process in which marine organisms with calcium carbonate shells die, fall to the deep sea, and are buried in sediments, becoming part of the long-term carbon cycle. p. 695

**biological species concept** A population of organisms capable of interbreeding and producing fertile offspring. p. 260

**biomass** The dry weight of biological material per unit area or volume of habitat. p. 36

**biome** A large-scale vegetation type and its associated microorganisms, fungi, and animals. p. 749

**biomimicry** A process in which people look to nature for biologically inspired design ideas. p. 758

**biomineralization** Production of partly or wholly mineralized support structures (e.g., shells, bones). p. 474

**biotechnology** The use and manipulation of living organisms or biological materials for the production of useful products. p. 238

**biotic factors** Biological factors affecting organisms (e.g., interactions with others). p. 282

**biotrophs** Parasitic fungi that feed continuously from the resources of the living tissue of their host. p. 399

**bipedal** Walking (or running) on two legs (e.g., humans and birds). p. 4

**blade** The expanded part of a leaf that provides a large surface area for absorbing sunlight and carbon dioxide p. 374

**blastula** The hollow ball of cells formed as the embryo develops. p. 643

**blunt ends** Describes the ends of a DNA molecule cut by an endonuclease. In the case of blunt ends, both strands end at the same point. p. 245

**bottom-up control** The control of populations in a community by the bottom of the trophic pyramid, the primary producers. The control is by resource limitation. p. 684

**Bouligand structures** Structures that confer flexibility, in part because of biomineralization of fibres and proteins. p. 474

**Bowman's capsule** An infolded region at the proximal end of a nephron that cups around the glomerulus and collects the water and solutes filtered out of the blood. p. 550

**bract** A modified leaf often located near a flower. p. 23

**brain** A single, organized collection of nervous tissue in an organism's head. It forms the control centre of the nervous system and major sensory structures. p. 575

**brassinosteroids** Any of a family of plant hormones that stimulate cell division, elongation, and differentiation of vascular tissue. Online Ch. 26

**brood sac** Sac in which fertilized eggs develop (e.g., male sea horse). p. 649

**brown fat** A specialized tissue in which the most intense heat generation by non-shivering thermogenesis takes place. p. 557

**buccal cavity** The portion of the oral cavity bounded by the lips and cheeks. p. 510

**budding** Proliferation of cells by budding (mitotic division) can increase the size of an embryo. p. 634

**bulk feeders** Animals that consume sizable food items whole or in large chunks. p. 459

**C$_3$ pathway** See Calvin cycle. p. 109

**C$_4$ pathway** A metabolic pathway where inorganic CO$_2$ is first added to phosphoenolpyruvate, which produces the four-carbon compound intermediate that is later released to the Calvin cycle. p. 111

**C$_4$ plant** A plant that uses the C$_4$ pathway. p. 111

**cadherins** Cell adhesion molecules. p. 645

**calcitonin** A nontropic peptide hormone that lowers the level of Ca$_2$ in the blood by inhibiting the ongoing dissolution of calcium from bone. Online Ch. 26

**callus** A small, hard outgrowth on plants or a mass of undifferentiated cells. p. 639

**Calvin cycle** The second stage of photosynthesis, in which electrons are used as a source of energy to convert inorganic CO$_2$ to an organic form. Also referred to as the Calvin-Benson-Bassham cycle, light-independent reactions, and C$_3$ pathway. p. 105

**cancellous bone** Also known as spongy bone; invariably covered with compact bone. p. 478

**cancer stem cell hypothesis** A theory that proposes that among all cancerous cells, a few act as stem cells that reproduce themselves and sustain the cancer, much like normal stem cells normally renew and sustain our organs and tissues. p. 144

**cancer stem cells** Cancerous cells that act as stem cells, reproducing themselves and fostering the continued survival of the cancer. p. 144

**capsid** The protective layer of protein surrounding the viral genome. It can also be called a viral coat. p. 314

**capsule** An external layer of sticky or slimy polysaccharides coating the cell wall in many prokaryotes. p. 61

**carbon fixation** Reaction in which inorganic carbon (carbon dioxide) is converted to organic carbon molecules. p. 109

**carcinomas** Cancers that originate from cells that line the inner or outer surfaces of the body. p. 140

**cardiac output** The total amount of blood pumped by each ventricle of the heart per minute. p. 541

**carnivores** Animals that primarily eat other animals. p. 40

**carotenoid** Molecule of yellow-orange pigment by which light is absorbed in photosynthesis. p. 103

**carotid body** A small cluster of chemoreceptors, baroreceptors, and supporting cells located near the bifurcation of the carotid artery. It measures changes in the gas composition of arterial blood flowing through it as well as the blood pressure in the carotid artery. p. 512

**carpel** Female reproductive structure in angiosperm plants. p. 630

**carrier** An individual who carries a mutant allele and could pass it on to offspring, but does not display its symptoms. p. 182

**carrying capacity** The maximum population size of a species that the resources present in an environment can sustain indefinitely. p. 658

**cartilage** Firm, elastic, skeletal tissue. p. 72

**Casparian strip** A thin, waxy, impermeable band that seals abutting cell walls in roots. The strip helps control the type and amount of solutes that enter the stele by blocking the apoplastic pathway at the endodermis and forcing substances to pass through cells (the symplast). p. 523

**catabolic pathway** Type of metabolic pathway in which energy is released by the breakdown of complex molecules to simpler compounds. p. 91

**catastrophism** The theory that Earth has been affected by sudden, violent events that were sometimes worldwide. p. 282

**cell adhesion molecules** Cell-surface proteins that are responsible for selectively binding cells together. p. 645

**cell biology** A branch of biology that studies all aspects of cells, including their structural and physiological properties, life cycles, interactions with their environments, and even their death. p. 49

**cell communication** Molecular mechanisms in which cells communicate or signal one another by direct contact or by using chemical signals such as peptides, hormones, or neurotransmitters. p. 59

**cell cycle** The sequence of events during which a cell experiences a period of growth followed by nuclear division and cytokinesis. p. 131

**cell differentiation** A process in which changes in gene expression establish cells with specialized structure and function. p. 138

**cell division** The process in which one cell divides into two new cells p. 131

**cell plate** A new cell wall that forms during cytokinesis in plants. It forms between the daughter nuclei and grows laterally until it divides the cytoplasm. p. 136

**cell theory** Three generalizations yielded by microscopic observations: all organisms are composed of one or more cells; the cell is the smallest unit that has the properties of life; and cells arise only from the growth and division of pre-existing cells. p. 50

**cell wall** A rigid, external layer of material surrounding the plasma membrane of cells in plants, fungi, bacteria, and some protists; provides cell protection and support. p. 61

**cell-mediated immune response** An adaptive immune response in which a subclass of T cells—cytotoxic T cells—becomes activated and, with other cells of the immune system, attacks host cells infected by pathogens, particularly those infected by a virus. p. 614

**cellular respiration** The process by which energy-rich molecules are broken down to produce energy in the form of ATP. p. 67

**cellular senescence** Loss of proliferative ability over time. p. 142

**cellulose** One of the primary constituents of plant cell walls, formed by chains of carbohydrate subunits. p. 368

**central dogma of molecular biology** A description of the movement of information that occurs during gene expression: from gene to mRNA to protein. p. 216

**central nervous system (CNS)** Consists of large numbers of neurons condensed into ganglia and brains. In vertebrates, it consists of the brain and spinal cord. p. 575

**central vacuole** A large, water-filled organelle in plant cells that maintains the turgor of the cell and controls movement of molecules between the cytosol and sap. p. 66

**centromeres** A specialized chromosomal region that connects sister chromatids and attaches them to the mitotic spindle. p. 133

**centrosome** The main microtubule organizing centre of a cell, which organizes the microtubule cytoskeleton during interphase and positions many of the cytoplasmic organelles. p. 70

**cerebellum** The portion of the brain that plays an important role in motor control. It receives sensory input from receptors in muscles and joints, from balance receptors in the inner ear, and from the receptors of touch, vision, and hearing. It does not initiate movement, but contributes to coordination, precision, and accurate timing of movement. p. 591

**cerebral cortex** A thin outer shell of grey matter covering a thick core of white matter within each hemisphere of the brain; the part of the forebrain responsible for information processing and learning. p. 9

**cerebrospinal fluid** Fluid that circulates through the central canal of the spinal cord and the ventricles of the brain, cushioning the brain and spinal cord from jarring movements and impacts, as well as nourishing the CNS and protecting it from toxic substances. p. 512

**character** A heritable characteristic. p. 174

**chemical defence mechanisms** Systems that organisms use to defend themselves that involve the production of distasteful or toxic chemicals. p. 599

**chemical reaction** A reaction that occurs when atoms or molecules interact to form new chemical bonds or break old ones. p. 83

**chemiosmosis** Ability of cells to use the proton-motive force to do work. p. 116

**chemoautotrophs** Organisms that obtain energy by oxidizing inorganic substances such as hydrogen, iron, sulfur, ammonia, nitrites, and nitrates and that use carbon dioxide as a carbon source. p. 334

**chemokines** Proteins secreted by activated macrophages that attract other cells such as neutorphils. p. 608

**chemoreceptors** Detect specific chemical molecules. p. 582

**chitin** A polysaccharide that contains nitrogen and is present in the cell walls of fungi and the exoskeletons of arthropods. p. 394

**chlorophyll** Molecule of green pigment that absorbs photons of light during photosynthesis. p. 6

**chloroplast** An organelle in eukaryotic cells that is the site of photosynthesis. p. 67

**choanocytes** Collar cells found in some algae and in sponges. p. 416

**chorionic villus sampling** Technique of prenatal diagnosis in which cells are obtained from portions of the placenta that develop from tissues of the embryo. p. 191

**chromatin** The structural building block of a chromosome, which includes the complex of DNA and its associated proteins. p. 62

**chromoplast** Plant organelles that contain red, orange, and yellow pigments. p. 370

**chromosome** The nuclear unit of genetic information, consisting of a DNA molecule and associated proteins. p. 54

**chronospecies** A species characterized by the timing of its appearance in the fossil record. p. 260

**cilia** Motile structures that extend from a cell surface and that move a cell through fluid or fluid over a cell. p. 350

**circulatory system** An organ system consisting of a fluid, a heart, and vessels for moving important molecules, and often cells, from one tissue to another. p. 410

**CITES** Convention on the International Trade in Endangered Species. p. 268

**citric acid cycle** Series of reactions in which acetyl groups are oxidized completely to carbon dioxide and some ATP molecules are synthesized. Also referred to as Krebs cycle and tricarboxylic acid cycle. p. 112

**clades** A monophyletic group of organisms that share homologous features derived from a common ancestor. p. 31

**cleavage furrow** A groove that forms in the membrane of a dividing cell and wraps around the cell's midpoint in between the two newly formed nuclei. p. 136

**cleidoic eggs** Amniote eggs that have a hard shell. p. 644

**climate warming** Large-scale warming of climate that may be anthropogenic or natural. p. 14

**climax community** A relatively stable, late successional stage in which the dominant vegetation replaces itself and persists until an environmental disturbance eliminates it, allowing other species to invade. p. 690

**closed circulatory system** System in which the fluid (blood) is confined to blood vessels and circulates throughout the body. p. 529

*Clostridium difficile* **(C difficile)** A bacterium that is naturally part of our gut biota, but when out of balance the impact on patients can be fatal. p. 6

**clotting factors** Substances in the blood plasma that are involved in clotting the blood. p. 529

**coding region** The portion of a gene or mRNA that contains the information to translate a protein. p. 217

**codominance** Condition in which alleles have approximately equal effects in individuals, making the alleles equally detectable in heterozygotes. p. 185

**codon** The three-base segment of an mRNA molecule that is read by the anticodon of the tRNA during translation. p. 219

**coelomate** A body plan of bilaterally symmetrical animals that have a body cavity (coelom). p. 413

**coenzymes** Organic cofactors that include complex chemical groups of various kinds. p. 88

**coevolution** The evolution of genetically based, reciprocal adaptations in two or more species that interact closely in the same ecological setting. p. 285

**cofactor** An inorganic or organic non-protein group that is necessary for catalysis to take place. p. 88

**cohesion** The high resistance of water molecules to separation. p. 524

**cold acclimatization** A set of physiological changes in ectotherms in response to seasonal cooling of environmental temperature, allowing the animals to attain good physiological performance in winter. p. 554

**collagen** Fibrous glycoprotein—very rich in carbohydrates—embedded in a network of proteoglycans. p. 71

**collenchyma** One of three simple plant tissues. It flexibly supports rapidly growing plant parts. Its elongated cells are alive at maturity and collectively often form strands or a sheathlike cylinder under the dermal tissue of growing shoot regions and leaf stalks. p. 375

**common name** The name(s) by which a species is commonly known. p. 259

**communities** Collections of populations of all species that occupy the same area. p. 656

**community ecology** The ecological discipline that examines groups of populations occurring together in one area. p. 682

**companion cell** A specialized parenchyma cell that is connected to a mature sieve tube member by plasmodesmata and assists sieve tube members with both the uptake of sugars and the unloading of sugars in tissues. p. 376

**competition** In ecology, an interaction between organisms in which the organisms compete over a resource (e.g., food, space, water, etc.). The interaction favours one organism at the expense of the other. p. 687

**competitive exclusion principle** The ecological principle stating that populations of two or more species cannot coexist indefinitely if they rely on the same limiting resources and exploit them in the same way. p. 687

**competitive inhibition** Inhibition of an enzyme reaction by an inhibitor molecule that resembles the normal substrate closely enough so that it fits into the active site of the enzyme. p. 89

**complementary DNA (cDNA)** A DNA molecule synthesized by a reverse transcriptase, which is complementary to an mRNA transcript. p. 315

**concertina locomotion** Movement by sine-wave undulations of the body (e.g., in snakes and some fish). p. 490

**conduction** The flow of heat between atoms or molecules that are in direct contact. p. 553

**conidia** Asexually produced fungal spores. (Singular, conidium.) p. 396

**connective tissue** Supporting tissues of the body, such as bone and cartilage. p. 411

**conservation biology** An interdisciplinary science that focuses on the maintenance and preservation of biodiversity. p. 705

**conservation science** An interdisciplinary science that focuses on maximizing biodiversity, human well-being, and the ecosystem services provided by biodiversity and the natural world. p. 705

**conservative replication** Conservative replication describes an early theory of DNA replication, in which the old strands stayed together and the new DNA molecule contained two new strands. p. 206

**consumer** An organism that consumes other organisms in a community or ecosystem. p. 33

**contractile vacuole** A membrane-bound vesicle found in some microorgansims that expands by filling with water and contracts by expelling water and its contents to the exterior of the cell. p. 67

**convection** The transfer of heat to or from an object due to air or water passing over its surface. p. 553

**convergent evolution** The evolution of similar adaptations in distantly related organisms to overcome similar problems (e.g., wings in insects and wings in birds). See also parallel evolution. p. 297

**copulate** Transfer of sperm from one individual to another. p. 635

**cortex** Generally, an outer, rindlike layer. In mammals, the outer layer of the brain, the kidneys, or the adrenal glands. In plants, the outer region of tissue in a root or stem lying between the epidermis and the vascular tissue andcomposed mainly of parenchyma. p. 402

**cortisol** The major glucocorticoid steroid hormone secreted by the adrenal cortex. It increases blood glucose by promoting breakdown of proteins and fats. Online Ch. 26

**COSEWIC** Committee on the Status of Endangered Wildlife in Canada. p. 17

**cost-benefit ratio** In evolutionary terms, the balance between the cost to the organism in terms or resources or mobility and the benefit that the adaptation provides. p. 599

**cotyledon** A leaf of a seed plant embryo; also known as a seed leaf. p. 383

**countercurrent exchange** A mechanism in which the water flowing over the gills moves in a direction opposite to the flow of blood under the respiratory surface, producing very efficient exchange of gases (can also apply to transfer of heat). p. 513

**courtship** Behaviour that preceeds mating. p. 636

**Crassulaceae (CAM) plants** A $C_4$ plant that runs the Calvin and $C_4$ cycles at different times to circumvent photorespiration. p. 111

**Crassulacean acid metabolism (CAM)** A biochemical variation of photosynthesis that was discovered in a member of the plant family Crassulaceae. Carbon dioxide is taken up and stored during the night to allow the stomata to remain closed during the daytime, decreasing water loss. p. 111

**cristae** Folds that expand the surface area of the inner mitochondrial membrane. (Singular, crista.) p. 67

**cross-current exchange** A mechanism in which the blood flowing through the capillaries moves in a direction across the flow of air in the respiratory passages (the parabraonchial tubes) of birds and produces very efficient exchange of gases. p. 513

**crossing over** The recombination process in meiosis, in which chromatids exchange segments. p. 156

**cupula** In certain mechanoreceptors, a gelatinous structure with stereocilia extending into it that moves with pressure changes in the surrounding water; movement of the cupula bends the stereocilia, which trigger release of neurotransmitters. p. 583

**cuticle** The outer layer of plants and some animals. It helps prevent desiccation by slowing water loss. p. 376

**cyclin-dependent kinase (CDK)** A protein kinase that controls the cell cycle in eukaryotes. p. 138

**cytokines** Molecules secreted by one cell type that bind to receptors on other cells and, through signal transduction pathways, triggers a response. In innate immunity, cytokines are secreted by activated macrophages. p. 565

**cytokinesis** Division of the cytoplasm into two daughter cells following the nuclear division stage of mitosis. p. 136

**cytoplasm** A gel-like substance that contains all parts of the cell that surround the central nuclear or nucleoid region. p. 54

**cytoskeleton** The interconnected system of protein fibres and tubes that extends throughout the cytoplasm of a eukaryotic cell. p. 69

**cytotoxic T cells** T lymphocytes that functions in cell-mediated immunity to kill body cells that have been infected by viruses or parasites or transformed by cancer. p. 614

**decarboxylation** A reaction where a carboxyl group is removed and carbon dioxide is released. p. 115

**defence mechanisms** Evolutionary adaptations that confer a level of protection to the organism. They can be chemical or physical in nature. p. 66

**deforestation** The clearing of forest. p. 112

**deletion** Chromosomal alteration that occurs if a broken segment is lost from a chromosome. p. 161

**demographic transition model** Describes changes in birth and death rates and relative population size through stages of economic development. p. 676

**dendrites** Extensions of a neuron that receive incoming information. Dendrites are usually not capable of generating action potentials, but integrate incoming signals and pass the information along to the spike initiation zone of the neuron. p. 576

**dendritic cell** A type of phagocyte, so called because it hasmany surface projections that resemble dendrites of neurons. p. 613

**denitrification** A metabolic process in which certain bacteria convert nitrites or nitrates into nitrous oxide and then into molecular nitrogen, which enters the atmosphere. p. 698

**density** Number of individuals per unit area. p. 662

**density-dependent** Factors that limit the size of a population, depending directly on the current size of the population. p. 662

**density-independent** Factors that limit the size of a population, but not reflecting the current size of the population. p. 662

**deoxyribonucleic acid (DNA)** Double-stranded helical molecule that contains the genetic material of all living organisms. p. 54

**depolarized** The reduced state of polarization of a cell membrane (cell membranes are polarized at rest); the membrane potential becomes less negative. p. 577

**deposit feeders** Animals that consume particles of organic matter from the solid substrate on whichthey live. p. 458

**dermal tissue** Skin and related epitheilum. p. 375

**determinate growth** Growth that stops when the organism reaches a predetermined size. p. 371

**detritivore** An organism that extracts energy from the organic detritus (refuse) produced at other trophic levels. p. 40

**detritus** Dead organic matter. p. 695

**deuterostomes** Animals (echinoderms and chordates) in which the anus forms from the blastopore and the mouth forms from a new opening in the embryo. Development is indeterminant, and cleavage is radial. p. 642

**diabetes mellitus** A disease that results from problems with insulin production or action. p. 575

**diaphragm** The sheet of muscle that extends across the bottom of the rib cage and separates the abdominal cavity from the thoracic cavity. When it contracts, it expands the volume of the thoracic cavity, drawing air into the lungs. p. 506

**diastole** The period of relaxation and filling of the heart between contractions. p. 534

**diastolic pressure** The lowest the pressure falls to in the cardiovascular system between heart beats. The vessel walls never relax below this pressure. p. 534

**dideoxynucleotide triphosphate (ddNTPs)** The monomeric building blocks of DNA. p. 240

**differentiation** The process by which cells in a developing embryo transform into the cells of different tissues. p. 643

**diffusion** The net movement of ions or molecules from a region of higher energy to a region of lower energy. Differences in energy may be due to differences in the concentration of ions, as well as to differences in temperature, pressure, or electrical charge. p. 92

**digestive system** System where food is digested. p. 410

**dihybrid crosses** Cross-fertilizations between two individuals that are heterozygous for two pairs of alleles. p. 179

**dikaryon** The life stage in certain fungi in which a cell contains two genetically distinct haploid nuclei. p. 395

**dioecious** Having male flowers and female flowers on different plants of the same species. p. 382

**diphyletic** Organisms that evolved in two different lineages. p. 296

**diploblastic** Organisms with two cell layers. p. 413

**diploid** An organism or cell with two copies of each type of chromosome in its nucleus. p. 155

**disperse** Movement of an organism away from its place of origin. p. 481

**disruptive selection** Factors that destabilize obvious selective advantages. p. 270

**distress calls** Calls given by animals in distress. p. 739

**disturbance** A stochastic event that alters environmental conditions and results in ecological change. p. 688

**divergent selection** Situations in which natural selection favours different individuals based on their characteristics. p. 270

**DNA barcode** Use of a genetic barcode to identify species from small fragments of tissue. p. 266

**DNA cloning** A process used in molecular biology to assemble fragments of DNA into a new DNA molecule designed by the investigator. p. 246

**DNA oligonucleotide** Short DNA molecule made of several (oligo) nucleotides; can act as a primer for the polymerase chain reaction. p. 240

**DNA polymerase** An enzyme that assembles complementary nucleotide chains during DNA replication. p. 207

**domesticated** Organisms that humans keep and selectively breed for preferred characteristics. p. 11

**double fertilization** Characteristic of flowering plants in which one haploid male nucleus fuses with polar nuclei to form triploid endosperm, and another haploid nucleus fuses with the egg to form the zygote. p. 630

**duplication** Chromosomal alteration that occurs if a segment is broken from one chromosome and inserted into its homologue. p. 161

**dynein** A motor protein that uses ATP for the cellular movements of organelles and cells. p. 70

**echolocation** An orientation behaviour in which animals use the echoes of sounds they produce to locate objects. p. 297

**ecological niches** The resources a population uses and the environmental conditions it requires over its lifetime. p. 425

**ecosystem** A group of biological communities interacting with their shared physical environment. p. 656

**ecosystem ecology** An ecological discipline that explores the cycling of nutrients and the flow of energy between the biotic components of an ecological community and the abiotic environment. p. 682

**ecosystem services** Services and products provided by ecosystems. p. 707

**ectoderm** Primary germ layer that gives rise to the epidermis and nervous system. p. 413

**ectomycorrhizae** Mycorrhizae that grow between and around the young roots of trees and shrubs but do not enter root cells. p. 401

**ectotherms** An animal that obtains its body heat primarily from the external enviroment. p. 555

**effector B cells** B cells involved in effecting—bringing about—a specific immune response to an antigen. p. 613

**effector T cells** T cells involved in effecting—bringing about—a specific immune response to an antigen. p. 614

**efferent neurons** Carry information away from the CNS. They are motor neurons. p. 576

**electrocardiogram** Graphic representation of the electrical activity within the heart, detected by electrodes placed on the body. p. 536

**electrolocation** An orientation behaviour in which an animal (electric fish) uses changes in the electric field it generates to assess its surroundings. p. 739

**electromagnetic radiation** Radiation that consists of electromagnatic waves extending from gamma rays to the longest radio waves and including visible light. p. 102

**electron transport chain** A series of compounds that are used to pass electrons from one to another through a series of redox reactions. p. 107

**embryophyte** The land plants, including hornworts, liverworts, mosses, ferns, gymnosperms, and angiosperms. p. 378

**emergent properties** Properties that arise from interactions among elements (components) in different ecological levels. p. 656

**endemic** A species that occurs in only one place on Earth. p. 687

**endergonic reaction** Reaction that can proceed only if free energy is supplied. p. 83

**endocrine glands** Any of several ductless secretory organs that secrete hormones into the blood or extracellular fluid. p. 567

**endocrine system** Endocrine glands produce hormones that influence every aspect of an animal's life. p. 410

**endocytic vesicle** Vesicle that carries proteins and other molecules from the plasma membrane to destinations within the cell. p. 65

**endocytosis** In eukaryotes, the process by which molecules are brought into the cell from the exterior; involves a bulging in of the plasma membrane, which pinches off to form an endocytic vesicle. p. 66

**endoderm** The innermost layer of the root cortex; a selectively permeable barrier that helps control the movement of water and dissolved minerals into the stele. p. 413

**endodermis** In eukaryotes, a collection of interrelated internal membranous sacs that divide a cell into functional and structural compartments. p. 523

**endomembrane system** In eukaryotes, an extensive interconnected network of cisternae that is responsible for the synthesis, transport, and initial modification of proteins and lipids. p. 63

**endomycorrhizae** Mycorrhizae that grow in association with plant roots and enter root cells. p. 401

**endoplasmic reticulum** An organelle in the cells of eukaryotic organisms that forms an interconnected network of flattened, membrane-enclosed sacs or tubes. The rough endoplasmic reticulum contains ribosomes that are the sites of protein synthesis. Smooth endoplasmic reticulum lacks ribosomes and functions in lipid metabolism, carbohydrate metabolism, and detoxification. p. 63

**endoskeleton** An internal skeleton. p. 415

**endosperm** The tissue that surrounds and nourishes the embryo in the seed of angiosperm plants. p. 630

**endosymbiont** An organism living within another organism in a symbiotic association, such as the biota of the gut. p. 13

**endotherms** An animal that obtains most of its body heat from internal physiological sources. p. 555

**energy coupling** The process by which ATP is brought in close contact with a reactant molecule involved in an endergonic reaction. When the ATP is hydrolyzed, the terminal phosphate group is transferred to the reactant molecule. p. 84

**energy investment phase** The first five reactions of glycolysis where ATP is consumed. p. 113

**energy payoff phase** The last five reactions of glycolysis where ATP is produced. p. 113

**enhancer** In eukaryotes, a region of a gene containing regulatory sequences that determine whether the gene is transcribed at its maximum possible rate. p. 217

**enterobacteria phage lambda** A bacterial virus that specifically infects *E. coli*. p. 317

**entropy** Disorder, in thermodynamics. p. 80

**enzyme** Protein that accelerates the rate of a cellular reaction. p. 86

**epidemic** The situation where a disease is affecting a large number of individuals and being rapidly transmitted through the population. p. 597

**epigenetic inheritance** Inheritance of changes in gene expression that do not arise from changes in the DNA sequence. p. 187

**epinephrine** A hormone secreted by the adrenal medulla. p. 541

**epistasis** Interaction of genes, whereby one or more alleles of a gene at one locus inhibits or masks the effects of one or more alleles of a gene at a different locus. p. 185

**epithelial tissue** One of the four basic tissues found in animals. It lines the outer surface of the body and cavities. p. 410

**erythrocytes** Red blood cells that contain hemoglobin, a protein that transports $O_2$ in blood. p. 529

**estradiol** A form of estrogen. Online Ch. 26

**estrogen** Any of the group of female steroid sex hormones. p. 566

**ethylene** A plant hormone that helps regulate seedling growth, stem elongation, the ripening of fruit, and the abscission of fruits, leaves, and flowers. p. 216

**eudicots** Plants belonging to the Eudicotyledons, one of the two major classes of angiosperms. Their embryos generally have two seed leaves (cotyledons), and their pollen grains have three grooves. p. 383

**eukaryotic** Organisms characterized by the presence of subcellular organelles and, in particular, a nucleus. p. 391

**eutrophication** A process in which excess nutrients added to a water body drive excessive growth of algae, decreasing water quality. p. 712

**evaporation** Heat transfer through the energy required to change a liquid to a gas. p. 553

**evolutionary trade-offs** Similar to the cost-benefit ratio, evolutionary adaptations will, at times, sacrifice one trait for the sake of another. p. 599

**exergonic reaction** Reaction that releases free energy. p. 83

**exocytosis** In eukaryotes, the process by which a secretory vesicle fuses with the plasma membrane and releases the vesicle contents to the exterior of the cell. p. 66

**exonuclease** An enzyme that removes bases from a nucleic acid, beginning at either end of the molecule. p. 221

**exoskeleton** A hard external covering of an animal's body that blocks the passage of water and provides support and protection. p. 415

**exponential growth model** A model of population growth in which the numberof individuals increases by a fixed percentage of the total population. p. 657

**expressed** A term used to say whether a gene product is being made by the cell. p. 215

**external gill** A gill that extends out from the body and lacks a protective covering. p. 506

**extinction** The death of the last individual in a species in a localized areor region. p. 290

**extirpated** Destroyed, wiped out, eradicated, eliminated. p. 708

**extracellular matrix (ECM)** A molecular system that supports and protects cells and provides mechanical linkages. p. 59

**extreme environments** Locations where weather or geological conditions normally preclude the growth of biological organisms. They can be characterized by cold, extreme pH, heat, etc. p. 339

**extremophiles** Organisms capable of surviving extreme conditions. p. 340

**extrinsic control** Control from outside the organism. p. 663

**$F_1$ generation** The first generation of offspring from a genetic cross. p. 175

**$F_2$ generation** The second generation of offspring from a genetic cross. p. 175

**facilitated diffusion** Mechanism by which polar and charged molecules diffuse across membranes with the help of transport proteins. p. 92

**facultative aerobes** Organisms or cells that can live in the presence or absence of oxygen. p. 121

**facultative anaerobes** Organisms that can live in the presence or absence of oxygen, using oxygen when it is present and living by fermentation under anaerobic conditions. p. 121

**FAD** A coenzyme composed of riboflavin 5′-phosphate and adenosine 5′-phosphate in pyrophosphate linkage. It serves as an electron carrier during respiration and is the oxidized form of $FADH_2$. p. 115

**$FADH_2$** Reduced form of FAD. p. 115

**feedback inhibition** In enzyme reactions, a form of regulation in which the product of a reaction acts as a regulator of the reaction. Also referred to as end-product inhibition. p. 90

**fermentation** Process in which electrons carried by NADH are transferred to an organic acceptor molecule, rather than to the electron transfer system. It is a metabolic process that converts sugar to acids, gases, and/or alcohol. p. 121

**fertilization** The fusion of the nuclei of an egg and sperm cell, which initiates development of a new individual. p. 156

**fibrin** A protein necessary for blood clotting; forms a weblike mesh that traps platelets and red blood cells and holds a clot together. p. 529

**fibrinogen** A plasma protein that plays a central role in the blood-clotting mechanism. p. 529

**fibrous root** A type of root that consists of branching roots, rather than a main taproot; roots tend to spread laterally from the base of the stem. p. 372

**filter feeders** Animals that ingest small food items suspended in water; also known as suspension feeders. p. 458

**filtration** The nonselective movement of water and some solutes (ions and small molecules), but not large molecules (such as proteins), into the proximal end of the renal tubules in the kidneys through spaces between the cells. p. 549

**fission** The dividing of cells that can result in growth. p. 634

**fixing nitrogen** Conversion of gaseous nitrogen to ammonia ($N_2$ to $NH_3$). p. 457

**flagella** Long, threadlike, cellular appendages responsible for movement; found in both prokaryotes and eukaryotes, but with different structures and modes of locomotion. (Singular, flagellum.) p. 61

**flagellin** A structural protein of prokaryotic flagella. p. 70

**fluid feeders** Animals that obtain nourishment by ingesting liquids that contain organic molecules in solution. p. 458

**fluid mosaic model** Model proposing that the membrane consists of a fluid phospholipid bilayer in which proteins are embedded and float freely. p. 56

**follicle stimulating hormone (FSH)** The pituitary hormone that stimulates oocytes in the ovaries to continue meiosis and become follicles. During follicle enlargement, FSH interacts with luteinizing hormone to stimulate follicular cells to secrete estogens. Online Ch. 26

**food vacuole** A type of vesicle that contains and digests phagocytized food. p. 66

**fossils** Evidence of former life. p. 290

**fossorial** Animals that live underground in burrows. p. 492

**founder effect** An evolutionary phenomenon in which a population that was established by just a few colonizing individuals has only a fraction of the genetic diversity seen in the population from which it was derived. p. 269

**free energy** The energy in a system that is available to do work. p. 83

**freeze avoidance** A physiological strategy for coping with a freezing environment. The animal prevents tissues from freezing by supercooling internal fluids and removing ice nucleators. p. 554

**freeze tolerance** A physiological strategy for coping with a freezing environment. The animal allows tissues to freeze in a controlled manner. p. 554

**fruiting body** In some fungi, a stalked, spore-producing structure such as a mushroom. p. 8

**functional genomics** An area of research that examines transcript levels, protein levels, and protein functions to help explain how a cell is working. p. 249

**fusion protein** A fusion protein is made by cloning a gene of interest together with the coding sequence of a second protein, often a marker protein such as the green flourescent protein. In this state, the marker protein can be used to determine the amount of the protein of interest and where it is located in the cell. p. 247

**$G_0$ phase** The phase of the cell cycle in eukaryotes in which many cell types stop dividing. p. 133

**$G_1$ phase** The initial growth stage of the cell cycle in eukaryotes, during which the cell makes proteins and other types of cellular molecules, but not nuclear DNA. p. 132

**$G_2$ phase** The phase of the cell cycle in eukaryotes during which the cell continues to synthesize proteins and grow, completing interphase. p. 133

**gametangia** The cells or organs in which gametes are produced. (Singular, gametangium.) p. 379

**gamete** A haploid cell, an egg or sperm. Haploid cells fuse during sexual reproduction to form a diploid zygote. p. 153

**gametophyte** An individual of the haploid generation produced when a spore germinates and grows directly by mitotic divisions in organisms that undergo alternation of generations. p. 378

**ganglia** Functional concentrations of nervous system tissue composed principally of nerve cell bodies; usually lying outside the central nervous system. p. 575

**gap genes** Genes that control development in fruit flies by subdividing the embryo into regions. p. 646

**gap junction** Junction that opens direct channels, allowing ions and small molecules to pass directly from one cell to another. p. 73

**gastrovascular cavity** A saclike body cavity with a single opening, a mouth; serves both digestive and circulatory functions. p. 413

**gastrulation** Early stage in development of animal embryo. p. 642

**Genbank** An online, public bioinformatics database run by the National Center for Biotechnology Information in the United States. p. 248

**gene** A unit containing the code for a protein molecule or one of its parts, or for functioning RNA molecules, such as tRNA and rRNA. p. 5

**gene expression** The process of transforming the information stored in a gene to the active product in a cell (normally a protein). p. 204

**gene flow** Outbreeding moves genes among individuals in a population. p. 268

**gene of interest** A specific gene that a scientist is studying or interested in. p. 247

**generation time** Average time from birth of parents to birth of their young. p. 669

**genetic drift** Interruption of gene flow can lead to isolation of populations from one another and thus to genetic drift. p. 269

**genetic linkage** The phenomenon of genes being located on the same chromosome. p. 188

**genetic species concept** The definition of a species based on the ability of individuals to interbreed and produce fertile offspring. p. 260

**genome** The entire collection of DNA sequences for a given organism. p. 215

**germ cell** An animal cell that is set aside early in embryonic development and gives rise to the gametes. p. 155

**gibberellins** Any of a large family of plant hormones that regulate aspects of growth, including cell elongation. Online Ch. 26

**gills** Respiratory organ formed by evagination of the body; extends outward into the respiratory medium. p. 505

**glottis** The opening to the trachea. p. 510

**glucagon** A pancreatic hormone with effects opposite to those of insulin. It stimulates glycogen, fat, and protein degradation. p. 120

**glucosinolates** Compounds found in some plants that contain sulphur (e.g., cabbages and their relatives). p. 5

**glycolysis** Stage of cellular respiration in which sugars such as glucose are partially oxidized and broken down into smaller molecules. p. 112

**GMO (genetically modified organism)** A living organism whose genetic makeup has been altered by means of molecular biology techniques. It may contain mutated versions of its own genes or genes introduced from other organisms. p. 6

**Golgi complex** In eukaryotes, the organelle responsible for the final modification, sorting, and distribution of proteins and lipids. p. 63

**gonadotropins** Hormones that regulate the activity of the gonads (ovaries and testes). Online Ch. 26

**GPS** Global positioning system p. 267

**Gram negative** Describes bacteria that do not retain the stain used in the Gram stain procedure. p. 332

**Gram positive** Describes bacteria that do retain the stain used in the Gram stain procedure. p. 332

**granum** A stack of thylakoids in chloroplasts within plants and green algae. (Plural, grana.) p. 67

**gravitropism** A directional growth reponse to Earth's gravitational pull, induced by mechanical and hormonal influences. p. 570

**green fluorescent protein (GFP)** A protein isolated from the jellyfish *Aequorea victoria* that gives off green light whan it is exposed to blue light. p. 247

**greenhouse gases** Gases that reflect some incoming solar radiation back toward Earth, effectively trapping the sun's energy in our atmosphere. p. 694

**grip** The ability of an organism to hang on to something. p. 5

**ground tissue** In plants, the parencheyma, collenchyma, and schleronchyma—all of the tissues except those formed from the epidermis. p. 375

**guard cells** A pair of specialized crescent-shaped cells that control the opening and closing of stomata in plant tissue. p. 376

**guild** A group of organisms, not necessarily closely related, that exploit similar resources or niche-space in similar ways in an ecosystem. p. 687

**gymnosperm** A seed plant that produces "naked" seeds, that is, not enclosed in an ovary. p. 382

**gynandromorphic** A characteristic of animals that individually exhibit both male and female characters. Often one side is male, the other side female. p. 640

**gynogenetic** Species with only females. p. 273

**Haber–Bosch process** A commercial process widely used in fixing nitrogen. p. 7

**habitat connectivity** The extent of connection among patches of intact habitat to facilitate movement of organisms. p. 717

**habitat corridor** An area of intact habitat that connects habitat patches and increases habitat connectivity. p. 717

**halophiles** Organisms that grow best in the presence of high salt concentrations. p. 340

**halteres** In flies (Diptera), hind wings modified as sensory receptors. p. 496

**haplodiploid** In haplodiploid species (e.g., honey bees), females are diploid and males are haploid. p. 624

**haploid** An organism or cell with only one copy of each type of chromosome in its nuclei. p. 155

**heartwood** The inner core of a woody stem; composed of dry tissue and non-living cells that no longer transport water and solutes and may store resins, tannins, and other defensive compounds. p. 365

**heat shock proteins (HSPs)** A class of chaperone proteins expressed in response to heat. They help prevent heat damage in other proteins by controlling their folding and unfolding. p. 555

**helicase** An enzyme that unwinds the DNA double helix during replication, so that DNA polymerase has access to both strands. p. 207

**helper T Cells** A clonal cell that assists with the activation of B cells. p. 614

**hemocyanin** A cyanide-containing pigment molecule used to transport oxygen in blood. p. 513

**hemoglobin** An iron-containing pigment molecule that binds and transports oxygen in the blood. p. 513

**hemolymph** The circulatory fluid of invertebrates with open circulatory systems, including molluscs and arthropods; also called interstitial fluid. p. 529

**herbaceous plant** Plant with non-woody stems. p. 438

**herbivore** Animals that obtain energy and nutrients by eating plants. p. 33

**hermaphroditic** Organism that has both male and female gonads and is thus capable of producing eggs and sperm. p. 635

**heterocysts** Specialized cells—in some cyanobacteria—that do not perform photosynthesis but rather convert atmospheric nitrogen into an organic form of nitrogen. p. 337

**heterogametic sex determination** Sex chromosomes (e.g., X and Y) determine gender. In diploid animals, female or males may have the same two chromosomes (XX, female mammals; ZZ, male reptiles and birds; XY, male mammals; ZW, female birds). In other cases (e.g., honey bees), females are diploid, and males are haploid. p. 639

**heterotrophs** Organisms that acquire energy and nutrients by eating other organisms or their remains. p. 39

**histamine** A chemical released by mast cells. It acts to dilate nearby blood vessels, allowing more white blood cells to arrive at an area of infection or damage. It is a key part of the inflammation response. p. 608

**histone** A small positively charged protein that interacts with DNA in eukaryotes to aid chromosome packaging. p. 232

**homeostasis** A steady internal condition maintained by responses that compensate for changes in the external environment. p. 29

**homeothermic** Organisms that maintain a constant body temperature. p. 427

**homeotic genes** *Hox* genes, ancient genes involved in many aspects of development. p. 647

**homologous chromosomes** Chromosomes that carry similar genes arranged in a similar physical order; also called homologues. p. 155

**horizontal gene transfer** The transfer of DNA from one existing cell to another. p. 166

**hormones** Signalling molecules secreted by cells that alter the activity of any cell that has receptors for them; in animals, typically a molecule produced by one tissue and transported via the bloodstream to another specific tissue to alter its physiological activity. p. 564

**horns** Protuberances of keratin (sometimes over a bone core). Unlike antlers, horns are not shed annually. p. 288

**huntingtin** Protein involved in animal development and implicated in Huntington disease. p. 182

**hybrid** Any individual resulting from interbreeding of two species. p. 268

**hybrid zone** The area of contact between two species where hybridization occurs. p. 272

**hybridization** Occurs when two species interbreed and produce fertile offspring. p. 271

**hydrophilic** Polar molecules that interact readily with water. p. 204

**hyperosmotic** Containing a higher concentration of solutes; a more concentrated solution. p. 550

**hyperpolarized** The changed condition of a neuron so that its membrane potential is more negative than the resting value. p. 577

**hyperthermophiles** Organisms, typically archaeans, that can survive very high temperatures, sometimes above the boiling point of water. p. 340

**hyphae** Any of the threadlike filaments that form the mycelium of a fungus. (Singular, hypha.) p. 40

**hypo-osmotic** Containing a lower concentration of solutes; a more dilute solution. p. 550

**hypothalamus** The portion of the brain that contains centres that regulate basic homeostatic functions of the body and contribute to the release of hormones. p. 444

**imbibition** Passive uptake of water. p. 640

**immune system** A system of biological structures and processes within an organism that protects against disease. p. 410

**immunodeficiency** A disease or disorder that limits a person's capacity to mount an effective immune response. p. 616

**immunoglobins** The proteins that form antibodies, key factors in fighting disease; also called **Ig proteins.** p. 610

**immunosuppressive drugs** Drugs given to individuals prior to and following an organ transplant to reduce the chance that the new organ will be determined to be non-self and rejected. p. 618

**in silico** A term that describes a computer-based simulation; refers to the silicon wafers used to build computer processor chips. p. 249

**incomplete dominance** Condition in which the effects of recessive alleles can be detected to some extent in heterozygotes. p. 183

**indeterminate growth** Continued growth of an organism in size over its lifespan. p. 371

**induction** Interactions between different groups of cells during development, specifically, where one type of cells induces changes in another type. p. 643

**inhibiting hormones (IH)** Hormones released by the hypothalamus that inhibit the secretion of a particular anterior pituitary hormone. Online Ch. 26

**innate immunity** A non-specific line of defence against pathogens that inculdes inflammation, which creates internal conditions that inhibit or kill many pathognes. It also includes many types of cells that engulf or kill pathogens and infected body cells. p. 606

**insectivorous plants** Plants that catch and digest insects. p. 7

**insertion of a muscle** Refers to the part of the body that moves when the muscle contracts. Compare with origin of a muscle. p. 486

**insulin** A hormone secreted by beta cells in the islets of the pancreas. It acts mainly on cells of non-working skeletal muscles, liver cells, and adipose tissue (fat) to lower blood glucose, fatty acid, and amino acid levels and to promote the storage of those molecules. p. 237

**insulinlike growth factor (IGF)** A peptide that directly stimulates growth processes. p. 288

**integral membrane protein** Protein embedded in a phospholipid bilayer. p. 59

**integration** The sorting and interpretation of neural messages and the determination of the appropriate responses. p. 575

**integrin** Transmembrane receptors that connect cells to cells or cells to the extracellular matrix. p. 72

**integumentary system** The skin and related structures. p. 410

**interference competition** Form of competition in which individuals fight over resources or otherwise harm each other directly. p. 682

**interkinesis** A brief interphase that separates the two meiotic divisions. p. 156

**intermediate filaments** A cytoskeletal filament about 10 nm in diameter that provides mechanical strength to cells in tissues. p. 70

**intermembrane compartment** Space between the inner and outer membrane of a mitochondrion or chloroplast. p. 105

**intermembrane space** Region between inner and outer membrane of a chloroplast or a mitochondrion. p. 67

**internal gill** A gill located within the body and having a cover that provides physical protection for the gills. Water must be brought to internal gills. p. 507

**interneurons** Integrate information from various sources to formulate an appropriate response. p. 576

**internode** The region between two nodes on a plant stem. p. 374

**interphase** The first stage of the mitotic cell cycle, during which the cell grows and replicates its DNA before undergoing mitosis and cytokinesis. p. 132

**interspecific competition** Competition for resources between species. p. 283

**intraspecific** Between members of the same species. p. 671

**intraspecific competition** Competition for resourcse among members of the same species. p. 283

**intrinsic control** Control from inside the organism. p. 663

**intron** A non-protein coding region of a gene that interrupts the protein coding sequence. Introns must be removed by splicing prior to translation. p. 218

**invasive species** Exotic species that damage the ecosystems to which they are introduced. p. 687

**inversion** Chromosomal alteration that occurs if a broken segment reattaches to the same chromosome from which it was lost, but in reversed orientation, so that the order of genes in the segment is reversed with respect to the other genes of the chromosome. p. 161

**isidia** Structures of lichens that contain both the fungal and the photosynthetic partner and that extend from the thallus. (Singular, isidium.) p. 402

**islets of Langerhans** Endocrine cells of the pancreas that secrete the peptide hormones insulin and glucagon into the bloodstream. Online Ch. 26

**isosmotic** Containing an equal concentration of solutes. p. 550

*K* **strategists** Tend to be larger, longer-lived species living at densities close to carrying capacity. They invest more heavily in fewer offspring, each of which has a relatively high probability of surviving to adulthood. p. 666

**karyogamy** In plants, the fusion of two sexually compatible haploid nuclei after cell fusion (plasmogamy). p. 394

**karyotype** A species characteristic that consists of the shapes and sizes of all of the chromosomes at metaphase. p. 162

**keratin** A fibrous protein that forms the structure of hair, feathers, hoofs, claws, horns, nails, and epidermal scales. p. 442

**keratinized** Formed of or containing keratin. p. 442

**keystone species** A species that has a greater effect on community structure than its numbers might suggest. p. 685

**kinetic energy** The energy of motion. p. 79

**kinetochore** A specialized structure consisting of proteins attached to a centromere that mediates the attachment and movement of chromosomes along the mitotic spindle. p. 134

**kinetochore microtubules** Microtubules of the spindle that connect to kinetochores and direct movement of chromosomes during mitosis and meiosis. p. 134

**lactate fermentation** Reaction in which pyruvate is converted into lactate. p. 122

**lagging strand** During DNA replication, the strand assembled discontinuously in the direction opposite to DNA unwinding. p. 207

**lateral gene transfer** Also called horizontal gene transfer, it is the uptake and incorporation of genetic material from the environment. p. 273

**lateral meristem** A plant meristem that gives rise to secondary tissue growth. p. 371

**lateral undulation** Swimming behaviour that often involves animals moving parts of their bodies from side to side. p. 490

**law of independent assortment** Mendel's principle that the alleles of the genes that govern two characters segregate independently during formation of gametes. p. 175

**law of segregation** Mendel's principle that the pairs of alleles that control a character segregate as gametes are formed, and

half the gametes carry one allele and the other half carry the other allele. p. 175

**leading strand** During DNA replication, the strand assembled in one continuous piece in the direction of DNA unwinding. p. 207

**leaves** In vascular plants, the organ most often specialized for photosynthesis. p. 368

**lenticels** One of the small openings on the surface of the stems of woody plants that allow the exchange of gases between the interior tissue and the surrounding air. p. 507

**leucoplast** Plant organelles that primarily serve to store sugars, but may serve a variety of other functions as well. p. 370

**leukemia** Cancers of the blood-forming tissues. p. 140

**leukocytes** White blood cells. They eliminate dead and dying cells from the body, remove cellular debris, and participate in defending the body against invading organisms. p. 529

**life form** Organisms that exploit a similar niche-space and may have similar morphologies, whether or not they are closely related. p. 687

**life history** Characteristic features of longevity, reproductive capacity, and reproductive output. p. 659

**light-dependent reactions** The first stage of photosynthesis, in which the energy of sunlight is absorbed and converted into chemical energy in the form of ATP and NADPH. p. 105

**light-harvesting complex** Complex of protein subunits that make up a larger supercomplex of a photosystem. p. 106

**light-independent reactions** The second stage of photosynthesis, in which electrons are used as a source of energy to convert inorganic $CO_2$ to an organic form. Also referred to as the Calvin cycle. p. 105

**lignin** A tough, rather inert polymer that strengthens the secondary walls of various plant cells and thus helps vascular plants grow taller and stay erect on land. p. 370

**limbic system** A functional network within the brain that controls emotional behaviour; responsible for the production of feelings of anger, anxiety, fear, satisfaction, pleasure, and sexual arousal; gives rise to such behaviours as smiling, blushing, or laughing. Online Ch. 26

**limiting factors** Factors, such as food or space, that limit the size of a population. p. 661

**lipoteichoic acid** A component of the cell wall of Gram positive bacteria. p. 332

**locomot** Movement of animals. p. 488

**locus** The particular site on a chromosome at which a gene is located. p. 155

**logistic model** S-shaped graph pattern showing an initial fast rate of growth that levels off. p. 658

**lungs** Respiratory organ that is formed as an invagination of the body and extends into the thoracic cavity of vertebrates. p. 505

**luteinizing hormone (LH)** A hormone secreted by the pituitary gland that stimulates the growth and maturation of eggs in females and the secretion of testosterone in males. Online Ch. 26

**lymphatic system** The network of vessels in vertebrates that operates in parallel with the circulatory system to return excess fluid from extracellular spaces. p. 410

**lymphomas** Cancers of the white blood cells of the immune system, including the lymph nodes. p. 140

**lysogenic cycle** A reproductive cycle of viruses in which the genome of the virus is inserted into the host cell and replicated along with the host DNA during cell division. p. 317

**lysosome** Membrane-bound vesicle containing the hydrolytic enzymes involved in digestion of many complex molecules. p. 64

**lysozyme** An enzyme that digests bacterial cell walls. p. 317

**lytic cycle** A reproductive cycle of viruses in which the virus parts are produced by the host cell until the host cell ruptures and releases the viral progeny. p. 317

**macrophages** A phagocyte that takes part in non-specific defences and adaptive immunity. p. 608

**magnification** The ratio of an object as viewed to its real size. p. 52

**major histocompatibility complex (MHC)** A large cluster of genes encoding proteins, which allow the body to determine self from non-self cells. p. 613

**malignant tumour** Tumour that has spread to nearby or distant organs. p. 139

**mark and recapture** Method of estimating the size of populations of organisms. p. 660

**marker protein** A protein such as GFP that can be easily detected in a cell or organism. It can then be used to assess protein expression in specific locations in response to external cues. p. 247

**marsupials** Mammals such as kangaroo and opposums that give birth to young at an early stage of development. After birth, development continues in the pouch (or marsupium). p. 644

**mast cell** A type of cell dispersed through the body that releases histamine when activated by the death of neighbouring cells due to a pathogen or tissue damage. They help trigger the inflammation response by releasing histamine. p. 608

**maternal-effect genes** Genes that specify the RNA and proteins laid down in the egg. p. 647

**matter** Anything that occupies space and has mass. p. 80

**mechanoreceptors** Detect such things as changes in pressure, body position, or acceleration. p. 582

**medusa** Jellyfish-like body plan; a stage in the life cycle of a cnidarian. p. 416

**meiosis** The division of diploid cells into haploid progeny, consisting of two sequential rounds of nuclear and cellular division. p. 132

**melatonin** Produced by the pineal gland most actively during periods of darkness. It acts on cells in the hypothalamus to produce daily cycles in body activities (such as sleep). In some fishes, amphibians, and reptiles, melatonin stimulates the secretion of melanocyte stimulating hormone by the anterior pituitary to produce changes in skin colour. Online Ch. 26

**membrane nanotubes** Thin membranous filaments suspended between cells. p. 72

**membrane potential** The difference in charge (or potential) between the inside and outside of a cell membrane; it is negative under resting conditions and becomes positive during an action potential. p. 95

**memory B cells** In antibody-mediated immunity, a long-lived cell that expresses an antibody on its surface and can bind to a specific antigen. A memory B cell is activated the next time the antigen is encountered, producing a rapid secondary immune response. p. 613

**menopause** Reproductive senescence, usually in reference to women. p. 673

**meristem** An undifferentiated, permanently embryonic plant tissue that gives rise to new cells, forming tissues and organs. p. 370

**mesoderm** Embryonic cell layer that gives rise to muscle and connective tissue, as well as blood, kidneys, and dermis of the skin. p. 413

**metabolic pathway** A chain of enzyme-catalyzed reactions within a cell that converts one biological material into another. p. 91

**metabolism** The biochemical reactions that allow a cell or organism to extract energy from its surroundings and use that energy to maintain itself, grow, and reproduce. p. 91

**metamorphosis** A biological process by which some animals undergo a dramatic and abrupt change in body shape, and often changes in behaviour. p. 390

**metaphase I, metaphase II** The phases of mitosis, during meiosis I and meiosis II, respectively, when the spindle reaches its final form and the spindle microtubules move the chromosomes into alignment at the spindle midpoint. p. 156, 157

**metastasis** The spread of cancer cells from their original site to other parts of the body p. 140

**methylation** The enzymatic addition of a methyl functional group to a target molecule. In epigenetics, the target is often a nucleotide or histone protein. p. 647

**microbiota** The organisms living in the digestive tracts of others. p. 13

**microfilaments** A cytoskeletal filament composed of actin. p. 70

**microscope** Instrument of microscopy that allows different magnifications and resolutions of specimens. p. 51

**microscopy** Technique for producing visible images of objects that are too small to be seen by the human eye. p. 51

**microtubule** A cytoskeletal component formed by the polymerization of tubulin into rigid, hollow rods about 25 nm in diameter. p. 69

**mitochondria** Membrane-bound organelles responsible for synthesis of most of the ATP in eukaryotic cells. (Singular, mitochondrium.) p. 67

**mitochondrial matrix** The innermost compartment of the mitochondrion. p. 67

**mitosis** Nuclear division that produces daughter nuclei that are exact genetic copies of the parental nucleus. p. 132

**mitotic cell cycle** The cell cycle that includes the growth of a cell, DNA replication, mitosis, and cytokinesis. p. 132

**mitotic spindle** The complex of microtubules that orchestrate the separation of chromosomes during mitosis. p. 134

**mixotrophic** Describes organisms that can obtain their energy from various sources, often by a combination of photosynthesis and consumption of organic material. p. 346

**model organism** An organism with characteristics that make it a particularly useful subject of research. p. 599

**molecular biotechnology** The use of molecular biology techniques, such as cloning, to genetically alter organisms so that they can produce different useful products. p. 239

**monocots** Plants belonging to the Monocotyledons, one of the two major classes of angiosperms. Monocot embryos have a single seed leaf (cotyledon) and pollen grains with a single groove. p. 383

**monoecious** Having both "male" flowers (which possess only stamens) and "female" flowers (which possess only carpels) on the same plant. p. 382

**monogamy** A pair bond between a male and a female that may last for a breeding season or for the lives of the partners. p. 637

**monohybrid cross** A genetic cross between two individuals that are each heterozygous for the same pair of alleles. p. 175

**monokaryon** Fungal hyphae with one nucleus. p. 395

**monophyletic** Lineage of organisms that evolved from one ancestor. p. 296

**monotremes** Mammals that lay eggs—the duck-billed platypus and spiny anteater. p. 644

**morphological species concept** Species recognized (defined) by their morphological features. p. 260

**morula** Solid, globular mass of cells that develops after fertilization and cell division. p. 643

**moult** Shedding of the skin covering. p. 477

**mouth** Opening to the digestive tract. p. 415

**mRNA (messenger RNA)** An RNA molecule that serves as a template for protein synthesis; also called messenger RNA. p. 219

**Müllerian mimicry** Being similar in appearance and/or behaviour to an aposematic species; a species with shape or colour that warns others of defensive mechanisms. Compare with Batesian mimicry. p. 605

**multiple alleles** More than two different alleles of a gene. p. 185

**multiple cloning site** A DNA sequence engineered into a plasmid that allows the DNA strand to be cut by a number of different restriction endonucleases. p. 246

**multiple lures** When animals that live in flocks resemble one another, making it difficult for a predator to focus on an individual. p. 732

**muscle tissue** Contractile tissue involved in movement (of individuals and fluids). p. 412

**muscular system** System that produces movement. p. 410

**mushroom** The fruiting body of some fungi. p. 394

**mutation** A spontaneous and heritable change in a DNA sequence. p. 269

**mycelium** A mutualistic symbiosis in which fungal hyphae associate intimately with plant roots. p. 40

**mycorrhizal fungi** The fungal partner in a mutualistic symbiosis in which fungal hyphae associate intimately with plant roots. p. 373

**myelin sheaths** Produced by Schwann cells, they wrap axons in layers of cell membrane that contain myelin, which acts as an electrical insulator, speeding up the rate at which action potentials are conducted along nerves. p. 579

**myogenic** Cardiac cells in which the contraction rhythm is within the muscle cells themselves and does not require input from the nervous system. p. 530

**myosin** Motor protein of eukaryotic cells. p. 412

**NAD⁺** Coenzyme that contains two nucleotides—adenine base and nicotinamide—joined through their phosphate groups. NAD serves as an electron carrier during respiration. It is the oxidized form of NADH. p. 113

**NADH** Reduced form of NAD⁺. p. 113

**NADPH** Reduced form of NADP⁺. p. 105

**native species** A species that has evolved and is still found in a particular ecological setting and region. p. 714

**natural killer cells** Lymphocytes that pathogen-infected cells; also called NK cells. p. 615

**natural selection** The evolutionary process by which alleles that increase the likelihood of survival and the reproductive output of the individuals that carry them become more common in subsequent generations. p. 280

**necrosis** The uncontrolled death of a cell or tissue. p. 608

**necrotrophs** Parasitic fungi that kill all or some of their host and feed off the dead tissue. p. 399

**negative feedback control** The primary mechanism of homeostasis, in which a stimulus—a change in the external or internal environment—triggers a response that compensates for an environmental change. p. 443

**nematocysts** Stinging cells of cnidarians used in offence and in defence. p. 417

**neoplasm** An abnormal mass of tissue that results from uncontrolled and excessive cell division. Also called a tumor. p. 139

**nephrons** Functional unit that is the site of filtration in the vertebrate kidney. p. 550

**nerve** A bundle of axons enclosed in connective tissue and all following the same pathway. p. 413

**nerve net** A simple nervous system that coordinates responses to stimuli but has no central control organ or brain. p. 589

**nervous system** The system of nerve cells that communicates via electrical impulses. p. 410

**neural circuits** Any pathway within a nervous system involving multiple neurons. p. 576

**neural crests** Ridges of neural ectoderm that close together to form the dorsal hollow nerve chord in chordates. p. 645

**neural plate** Ectoderm cells that give rise to the neural crests. p. 645

**neural tube** The neural tube forms when the neural cests meet and close together. p. 645

**neuroendocrine** Cell signalling in which a nerve cell secretes a chemical messenger into the blood for reception and response by other cells. p. 565

**neurogenic** Cardiac cells that maintain their contraction rhythm by means of input from the nervous system. p. 530

**neurohormones** Hormones produced by nerve cells. p. 565

**neuron** A single nerve cell. p. 411

**neurosecretory neurons** Neurons that release or secrete neurohormones or neurotransmitters. Online Ch. 26

**neurotransmitters** Chemical messengers, released at synapses, that cross the synapse to produce a response in cells (nerve, muscle, or endocrine) that have receptors for them. p. 514

**neutrophils** The type of white blood cells that help fight off infections. p. 608

**niche** The resources a population uses and the environmental conditions it requires over its lifetime. p. 686

**nitrification** A metabolic process in which certain soil bacteria convert ammonia or ammonium ions into nitrites that are then converted by other bacteria to nitrates, a form usable by plants. p. 698

**nociceptors** A sensory receptor that detects tissue damage or noxious chemicals; their activity registers as pain. p. 582

**node** The point on a stem where one or more leaves are attached. p. 374

**nodes of Ranvier** The gap between two Schwann cells, which exposes the axon membrane directly to extracellular fluids. p. 579

**non-competitive inhibition** Inhibition of an enzyme reaction by an inhibitor molecule that binds to the enzyme at a site other than the active site and, therefore, does not compete directly with the substrate for binding to the active site. p. 89

**non-kinetochore microtubules** Microtubules of the spindle that do not connect to kinetochores but instead overlap each other and elongate cells during mitosis and meiosis. p. 134

**non-Mendelian inheritance** A form of genetic inheritance that does not follow Mendel's laws of inheritance. p. 187

**non-shivering thermogenesis** The generation of heat by oxidative mechanisms in non-muscle tissue. p. 557

**nondisjunction** The failure of homologous pairs to separate during the first meiotic division or of chromatids to separate during the second meiotic division. p. 162

**norepinephrine** A nontropic amine hormone secreted by the adrenal medulla. Same compound as noradrenaline. p. 541

**nuclear envelope** In eukaryotes, membranes that separate the nucleus from the cytoplasm. p. 62

**nuclear pores** Opening in the membrane of the nuclear envelope through which large molecules, such as RNA and proteins, move between the nucleus and the cytoplasm. p. 62

**nucleoid** The central region of a prokaryotic cell—with no boundary membrane separating it from the cytoplasm—where DNA replication and RNA transcription occur. p. 61

**nucleolus** The nuclear site of rRNA transcription, processing, and ribosome assembly in eukaryotes. p. 62

**nucleomorph** A small vestigial nucleus found between the inner and outer pairs of membranes in some protists. It provides evidence for the concept of secondary endosymbiosis. p. 354

**nucleoplasm** The liquid or semiliquid substance within the nucleus. p. 62

**nucleus** The central region of eukaryotic cells. It is separated by membranes from the surrounding cytoplasm, contains DNA, and is the site of DNA replication and transcription. p. 62

**obligate aerobes** A microorganism or cell that must use oxygen and grows only in the presence of oxygen. p. 121

**obligate anaerobe** A microorganism that cannot use oxygen and grows only in the absence of oxygen. p. 121

**obligate parasite** An organism with an essential parasitc phase in its life cycle. p. 313

**Occam's razor** An expression that refers to using the simplest explanation. p. 295

**Okazaki fragments** Relatively short sequences of DNA synthesized on the lagging strand at a replication fork. p. 207

**ommatidia** Faceted visual units of a compound eye. p. 584

**omnivore** Animals that feed at several trophic levels, consuming plants, animals, and other sources of organic matter. p. 40

**oncogene** A gene that, when deregulated, is capable of inducing one or more characteristics of cancer cells. p. 140

**open circulatory system** One in which fluid is pumped by the heart into vessels that open directly into the body cavities surrounding the various organs. p. 420

**operculum** The covering of the gills in some fishes. p. 507

**operon** In prokaryotes and eukaryotic organelles, a cluster of genes that are normally involved in the same cellular function and are transcribed as a single unit. p. 218

**organ systems** Systems of two or more organs that carry out a major body function, such as movement, digestion, or reproduction. p. 437

**organelles** The nucleus and other specialized internal structures and compartments of eukaryotic cells. p. 6

**organogenesis** Processes in development that generate organs. p. 642

**origin of a muscle** Place of attachment of muscle, which does not move when the muscle contracts. Compare with insertion of a muscle. p. 486

**origin of replication** A short DNA sequence that determines where the replication of a plasmid or chromosome will begin. p. 244

**osmoconformers** Animals in which the osmolarity of the cellular and extracellular solutions match the osmolarity of the environment. p. 547

**osmoregulation** The regulation of water and ion balance. p. 94

**osmoregulators** Animals that use control mechanisms to keep the osmolarity of cellular and extracellular fluids the same, but at levels that may differ from the osmolarity of the surroundings. p. 547

**osmosis** The passive transport of water across a selectively permeable membrane in response to solute concentration gradients, pressure gradients, or both. p. 92

**otolith** One of many small crystals of calcium carbonate embedded in the otolithic membrane of the hair cells. p. 583

**outer membrane** A second membrane found on the exterior of the cell wall of Gram negative bacteria. p. 105

**ovaries** Female gonads that produce eggs. (Singular, ovary.) p. 153

**ovipary** Giving birth to live young that are supported in the parent's body by a placenta or placenta-like structure. p. 649

**oviposition** Laying eggs. p. 5

**ovotestes** Gonads in some animals that serve as both ovaries and testes (can produce eggs and sperm). p. 635

**ovovivipary** Giving birth to live young that develop initially as eggs within a parent's body, where they rely on resources within the developing embryo. p. 649

**ovulation** Release of egg(s) in preparation for fertilization. p. 635

**oxidation** The removal of electrons from a substance. p. 91

**oxidative phosphorylation** Synthesis of ATP in which ATP synthase uses an H+ gradient built by the electron transfer system as the energy source to make the ATP. p. 112

**oxygen evolving complex** Enzyme complex that splits water molecules into hydrogen and oxygen, and releases electrons. p. 107

**oxytocin** A hormone that stimulates the ejection of milk from the mammary glands of a nursing mother. Online Ch. 26

**P generation** The parental individuals involved in an initial cross. p. 175

**pacemaker** A specialized cardiac muscle cell in the upper wall of the right atrium that sets the rate of contraction in the heart. p. 534

**pair-rule genes** Genes that delimit parasegments in developing fruit fly embryos. p. 647

**pancreas** Glandular organ found along the digestive tract in vertebrates. p. 120

**pandemic** The situation where an epidemic spreads beyond a single location. p. 597

**parabronchial tubes** One of the millions of tiny air tubes in bird lungs, each surrounded by dense capillary networks. p. 509

**paracrine** Cell signalling in which the cell secretes a chemical messenger locally for reception and response by other cells in the same area of the body. p. 564

**parallel evolution** Development of features in more closely related organisms (e.g., wings in birds and bats). See also convergent evolution. p. 297

**parapatric** Two (or more) species that meet in a very narrow zone. p. 272

**parasitism** A symbiotic interaction in which one species, the parasite, uses another, the host, in a way that is harmful to the host (involves parasites). p. 42

**parasympathetic** The division of the autonomic nervous system that predominates during quiet, low-stress situations, such as while relaxing. p. 593

**parathyroid glands** A gland next to the thyroid gland that regulates calcium levels. Online Ch. 26

**parathyroid hormone (PTH)** Secreted by the parathyroid glands when calcium ion levels fall in the blood. It has the opposite effect to calcitonin. It stimulates bone cells to release both calcium and phosphate ions into the blood. Online Ch. 26

**parenchyma** One of three simple plant tissues. It makes up a large portion of the volume of a plant, is always living, and is not often elongated. p. 375

**parsimonious** The simplest explanation of a phenomenon. p. 295

**parthenocarpy** Fruit lacking seeds. p. 641

**parthenogenesis** A mode of asexual reproduction in which animals produce offspring by the growth and development of an egg without fertilization. p. 166

**partial pressure** The individual pressure exerted by each gas within a mixture of gases such as air. p. 503

**passive transport** The transport of substances across cell membranes without expenditure of energy, as in diffusion. p. 92

**pathogen-associated molecular patterns (PAMPs)** Proteins and carbohydrates produced by pathogens that are recognized by cell surface receptors of a plant; one way that a plant knows when a pathogen is present. p. 608

**pedigrees** Charts that show all parents and offspring for as many generations as possible, the sex of individuals in the different generations, and the presence or absence of a trait of interest. p. 190

**peptidoglycan** An amino acid-carbohydrate polymer produced by bacteria to form the cell wall. Its synthesis is the target of penicillin-type antibiotic drugs. p. 601

**perception** The conscious mental registration of a sensory stimulus. p. 588

**perennial** A plant in which vegetative growth and reproduction continue year after year. p. 373

**perforin** A group of proteins used by natural killer cells and cytotoxic T cells to make the plasma membrane of target cells permeable. p. 614

**perfusion** The flow of blood through blood vessels in tissues. p. 506

**pericarp** Tissues in fruit that develop from the ovary. p. 640

**peripheral membrane protein** Protein that's held to membrane surfaces by noncovalent bonds formed with the polar parts of integral membrane proteins or membrane lipids. p. 59

**peripheral nervous system (PNS)** Communicates between the CNS and all parts of the body via nerves. p. 575

**phagocytosis** Process in which some types of cells engulf bacteria or other cellular debris to break them down. p. 97

**phagophore** Small double-membrane structure that encloses cytoplasmic components formed during the initial stages of autophagy. p. 66

**phenology** The timing of life history events. p. 715

**phenotypic exaggeration** During evolutionary processes, some phenotypes are strongly favoured by selective pressures. Sometimes this leads to extreme phenotypes, such as very toxic newts or birds with very long tails. p. 602

**phloem** The food-conducting tissue of a vascular plant. p. 365

**phloem sap** The solution of water and organic compounds that flows rapidly through the sieve tubes in the phloem of flowering plants. p. 526

**phosphoenolpyruvate (PEP) carboxylase** Enzyme found in plants and some bacteria that catalyzes the addition of $CO_2$ to phosphoenolpyruvate (PEP) to form the four-carbon compound. p. 111

**phosphorylation** The addition of a phosphate group to a molecule. p. 85

**photoautotrophs** Photosynthetic organisms that use light as their energy source and carbon dioxide as their carbon source. p. 6

**photolyase** Enzyme that catalyzes repair in tissues damaged by ultraviolet radiation. p. 212

**photomicrograph** Digital image or photograph taken through a microscope. p. 52

**photoperiod** The length of time organisms are exposed to light each day. p. 750

**photophosphorylation** The synthesis of ATP coupled to the transfer of electrons energized by photons of light. p. 108

**photoreceptors** Detect light energy. p. 582

**photorespiration** A process that metabolizes a by-product of photosynthesis. p. 110

**photosynthesis** The conversion of light energy to chemical energy in the form of sugar and other organic molecules. p. 6

**photosystems** A large complex into which the light-absorbing pigments for photosynthesis are organized with proteins and other molecules. p. 106

**photosystem I (PSI), photosystem II (PSII)** The two photosystems used in the light-dependent reactions of photosynthesis, numbered in the order of discovery. p. 106

**phototropism** The growth of a plant in response to light, either toward or away from the light source. p. 569

**phylogenetic species concept** Defines a species as a group having a shared and unique evolutionary history. p. 260

**phylogeny** The family tree showing the evolutionary relationships among a group of organisms. p. 293

**physical defence mechanisms** Structural defences that protect an organism by placing a physical barrier between it and a predator. Examples include thorns on plants and the shell of a turtle. p. 599

**phytochromes** A blue-green pigmented plant chromoprotein involved in the regulation of a light-dependent growth processes. p. 570

**pigments** A molecule that can absorb photons of light. p. 103

**pili** Hair or hairlike appendages on the surface of a prokaryote. (Singular, pilus.) p. 61

**piloerection** A reaction of the sympathetic nervous system in response to cold and/or stress in which the hair or feathers are made erect by muscles. p. 557

**pinocytosis** Mechanism by which extracellular water is taken into a cell along with any molecules that happen to be in solution in the water. p. 97

**placental mammals** Animals that give birth to well-developed live young that are nurtured through a placenta during development. Compare with marsupials and monotremes. p. 644

**plasma** The clear, yellowish fluid portion of the blood in which cells are suspended. Plasma consists of water, glucose, and other sugars, amino acids, plasma proteins, dissolved gases, ions, lipids, vitamins, hormones and other signal molecules, and metabolic wastes. p. 529

**plasma membrane** The membrane forming the outer limit of the cytoplasm; responsible for the regulation of substances moving into and out of cells. p. 54

**plasmid** A DNA molecule in the cytoplasm of certain prokaryotes; often contains genes with functions that supplement those in the nucleoid and that can replicate independently of the nucleoid DNA and be passed along during cell division. p. 61

**plasmodesmata** A minute channel that perforates a cell wall and contains extensions of the cytoplasm that directly connect adjacent plant cells. p. 73

**plasmogamy** The sexual stage of fungi during which the cytoplasms of two genetically different partners fuse. p. 394

**plastid** A family of plant organelles. p. 67

**platelets** Found in the blood, an oval or rounded cell fragment enclosed in its own plasma membrane. They are produced in red bone marrow by the division of stem cells and contain

enzymes and other factors that take part in blood clotting. p. 529

**pleiotropy** Condition in which single genes affect more than one character of an organism. p. 186

**poaching** Illeagal hunting. p. 713

**poikilohydry** Having little control over internal water content. p. 379

**poison** A chemical that kills or may severely interrupt normal life processes. p. 257

**polarized** A state in which the cell membrane has an electrical gradient maintained across it, so that one side of the membrane is more negative than the other. p. 576

**pollen** The male gametophyte of a seed plant. p. 377

**pollinate** The transfer of pollen from one flower to another. p. 22

**poly-A tail** A string of adenosine nucleotides found at the 3' end of an mRNA molecule. They are thought to protect the mRNA molecule from degradation by exonucleases. p. 221

**polyandry** A social unit consisting of one female and several males. p. 637

**polygamy** A social unit consisting of either one female and several males (polyandry) or one male and several females (polygyny). p. 637

**polygenic inheritance** Inheritance in which several to many different genes contribute to the same character. p. 185

**polygyny** A social unit consisting of one male and several females. p. 637

**polymerase chain reaction (PCR)** A technique that uses a thermostable DNA polymerase and DNA primers to amplify a targeted DNA sequence. p. 241

**polymorphism** One or more morphologically distinct forms. p. 5

**polyploidy** The condition of having one or more extra copies of the entire haploid complement of chromosomes. p. 163

**populations** The numbers of individuals of a species (may be global, national or regional). p. 656

**population bomb** Uncontrolled increases in populations over time. p. 674

**population crash** Results when the population declines dramatically. p. 664

**population cycle** Occurs when populations vary systematically over time. p. 663

**population dynamics** Changes in populations. p. 662

**population explosion** Occurs when population increases dramatically. p. 664

**postzygotic** Something that happens after fertilization and the formation of the zygote. p. 268

**potential energy** Stored energy. p. 79

**predators** Animals that prey on and consume other animals. p. 40

**prezygotic** Something that happens before fertilization. p. 268

**primary cell wall** The initial cell wall laid down by a plant cell. p. 73

**primary electron acceptor** Molecule that accepts a high-energy electron from the reaction centre chlorophyll. p. 106

**primary growth** The growth of plant tissues derived from apical meristems. Compare with secondary growth. p. 365

**primary producers** Autotrophs, usually photosynthetic organisms and members of the first trophic level. p. 33

**primary sex characteristics** Morphological features such as sex organs that are necessary for reproduction. p. 640

**primer** In DNA replication, a short nucleotide chain made of RNA; it is laid down as the first series of nucleotides in a new DNA strand and acts as the substrate for the DNA polymerase. In biotechnology, a short nucleotide chain made of DNA that's used in the polymerase chain reaction (PCR). p. 207

**product** An atom or molecule leaving a chemical reaction. p. 83

**progesterone** A female sex hormone that stimulates growth of the uterine lining and inhibits contractions of the uterus. p. 667

**progestins** A class of sex hormones synthesized by the gonads of vertebrates and active predominately in females. Online Ch. 26

**progressive theory** A possible explanation for the origin of viruses that suggests viruses started off as simple, mobile genetic elements that became more complex and capable of targeted infections. p. 328

**prokaryote** An organism in which the DNA is supended in the cytoplasm, rather than packaged in a discrete compartment. Such organisms do not contain subcellular organelles. p. 338

**prokaryotic chromosome (bacterial chromosome)** A single, typically circular DNA molecule. p. 61

**promiscuity** A mating system in which individuals do not form close pair bonds, and both males and females mate with multiple partners. p. 638

**promoter** The location at the beginning of a gene where the RNA polymerase binds prior to the start of transcription. p. 216

**propagation** In animal nervous systems, the conduction of an action potential along a neuron. p. 579

**prophase I, prophase II** The beginning phases of mitosis, meiosis I and meiosis II, respectively, during which the duplicated chromosomes within the nucleus condense from a greatly extended state into compact, rodlike structures. p. 156

**protected areas** Areas in which some or all human activities are prohibited. p. 716

**protein epitopes** Epitopes are three-dimensional, structural characteristics of proteins. p. 315

**proteome** All of the proteins found in a given cell or organism. p. 250

**proteomics** The study of the proteins found in a given cell or organism. p. 249

**Protista** A large and diverse group of eukaryotes. Most are unicellular. p. 346

**protistologist** A scientist who studies protists. p. 346

**proto-oncogene** Any gene in the cell that has the potential to become a cancer-causing gene (oncogene) if it is mutated or altered. p. 140

**protobionts** A term given to a group of abiotically produced organic molecules that are surrounded by a membrane or membranelike structure. p. 313

**protocells** A proposed precursor to living cells. Similar to a protobiont, but surrounded by a lipid membrane. p. 313

**protostomes** Animals in which the blastopore becomes the mouth and the anus develops separately. These animals have determinant (spiral) cleavage. p. 642

**pseudocoelomate** A body plan of bilaterally symmetrical animals with a body cavity that lacks a complete lining derived from mesoderm. p. 413

**psychrophiles** Organisms that grow and reproduce best in a cold environment; typically unable to grow above 16°C. p. 340

**pulmonary artery** The artery that conducts blood from the heart to the lungs. p. 537

**Punnett square** Method for determining the genotypes and phenotypes of offspring and their expected proportions. p. 175

**quantitative characters** Variation that is measured on a continuum (such as height in human beings) rather than in discrete units or categories. p. 185

**r strategists** Smaller species with high reproductive output and short generation time. p. 666

**radially symmetrical** Animals with a clear centre and several matching parts radiating out from the centre; the Radiata, for example, starfish. p. 415

**radiation** The transfer of heat energy as electromagnetic radiation. p. 553

**reabsorption** The process in which some molecules (e.g., glucose and amino acids) and ions are transported by the transport epithelium back into the body fluid (animals with open circulatory systems) or into the blood in capillaries surrounding the tubules (animals with closed circulatory systems) as the filtered solution moves through the excretory tubule. p. 549

**reactants** The atoms or molecules entering a chemical reaction. p. 83

**reaction centre** Part of photosystems I and II in chloroplasts of plants. In the light-dependent reactions of photosynthesis, the reaction centre receives light energy absorbed by the antenna complex in the same photosystem. p. 106

**receptor proteins** Proteins that recognize and bind molecules from other cells that act as chemical signals. p. 59

**receptor-mediated endocytosis** The selective uptake of macromolecules that bind to cell surface receptors concentrated in clathrin-coated pits. p. 97

**recognition protein** Protein in the plasma membrane that identifies a cell as part of the same individual or as a member of a foreign species. p. 59

**recombinant DNA** A DNA molecule made by joining together DNA fragments from two or more different sources. p. 246

**recombinant insulin** A form of insulin protein produced in bacteria or yeast cells using a gene cloned from another source. To produce human insulin in bacteria, a copy of the human insulin gene is expressed in the bacterial cells. p. 238

**recombination** The physical exchange of segments between the chromatids of homologous chromosomes or between the chromosomes of prokaryotic cells or viruses. p. 273

**recombination frequency** In the construction of linkage maps of diploid eukaryotic organisms, the percentage of testcross progeny that are recombinants. p. 190

**redox reaction** Coupled oxidation–reduction reaction in which electrons are removed from a donor molecule and simultaneously added to an acceptor molecule. p. 91

**reduction** The addition of electrons to a substance. p. 91

**regressive theory** A possible explanation for the origin of viruses that suggests they developed from obligate parasitic bacteria that lost even more of their self-sustaining properties. p. 313

**regulation of gene expression** The control exerted by cellular components over how much of a protein accumulates in the cell. Control can occur at the level of transcription, translation, or post-translation. p. 227

**releasing hormones (RH)** A peptide neurohormone that controls the secretion of hormones from the anterior pituitary. Online Ch. 26

**remediation** Applications of chemical and biological knowledge to decontaminate polluted environments. p. 720

**replication bubble** A structure resulting from the opening of a DNA strand by helicase. It allows bi-directional DNA replication to occur. p. 207

**repolarized** The condition of a depolarized cell after returning to its resting polarized state. p. 577

**reproduction** Proliferation of organisms by sexual or asexual means. p. 623

**reproduction rate** The rate at which an organism reproduces. p. 668

**reproductive senescence** Occurs when an organism lives beyond its ability to reproduce. p. 673

**reproductive system** System in an organism responsible for reproduction. p. 410

**residence time** The time it takes for a substance to move through a storage reservoir. p. 694

**resolution** The minimum distance that two points in a specimen can be separated and still be seen as two points. p. 52

**respiratory surface** A layer of epithelial cells that provides the interface between the body and the respiratory medium. p. 505

**restoration ecology** A discipline that focuses on restoring ecosystems after either a natural or anthropogenic disturbance. p. 720

**restriction endonuclease** An enzyme that cuts DNA at a specific sequence. p. 245

**retina** A layer of neurons on the back of the eye that sense light stimulus and convey impulses to the brain to create an image. p. 585

**retrovirus** A virus with an RNA genome that replicates through a DNA intermediate. p. 315

**reverse transcriptase** The enzyme used by retroviruses to produce a DNA copy of their RNA genome. The name originated because this process is essentially the reverse of transcription of DNA to make an RNA copy of a gene. p. 315

**Reynolds number (Re)** A calculation used to predict patterns of flow in fluids. p. 485

**rhinovirus** A group of common viruses that infect humans, causing the common cold. p. 321

**rhizoid** Simple, single-cell growths on non-vascular land plants that serve a similar structural function as roots in vascular plants. p. 379

**ribosomal RNA (rRNA)** The RNA component of ribosomes. p. 62

**ribosome** A ribonucleoprotein particle that carries out protein synthesis by translating mRNA into chains of amino acids. p. 56

**riboswitch** An RNA structure that changes shape and alters gene expression when it binds specific metabolites in the cell. p. 230

**ribulose-1-5-bisphophate (RuBP)** An organic substance and substrate of the enzyme rubisco that is involved in the Calvin cycle of photosynthesis. p. 109

**ricochetal locomotion** Moving by hopping on two legs that strike the ground simultaneouisly. p. 490

**ring species** Two species that cannot interbreed where they meet at one end of a ring; however, gene flow occurs between the populations that connect them. p. 272

**RNA** A polymer formed from nucleotide monomers containing ribose as their five-carbon sugar. RNA is a mobile form of genetic information in eukaryotes, bacteria, and archaea. It can form the genetic material of some viruses, such as retro viruses. p. 315

**RNA polymerase** An enzyme that links ribonucleotides together to form an RNA polymer. p. 219

**RNA-dependent RNA polymerase** An enzyme that makes an RNA copy of an RNA molecule. Found in some RNA viruses and used to duplicate their genomes. p. 315

**root cap** A dome-shaped cell mass that forms a protective covering over the apical meristem in the tip of a plant root. p. 370

**roots** An anchoring structure in land plants that also absorbs water and nutrients and (in some plant species) stores food. p. 370

**rough ER (RER)** Endoplasmic reticulum with many ribosomes studding its outer surface. p. 63

**rovers** Insect (fruit fly) larvae that move about, and their behaviour is under genetic control. p. 728

**rubisco** An enzyme that catalyzes the key reaction of the Calvin cycle, carbon fixation, in which $CO_2$ combines with RuBP (ribulose 1,5-bisphosphate) to form 3-phosphoglycerate. p. 109

**S phase** The phase of the cell cycle during which DNA replication occurs. p. 132

**saprotrophic** Organism nourished by dead or decaying organic matter. p. 398

**sapwood** The newly formed outer wood located between heartwood and the vascular cambium. Compared with heartwood, it is wet, lighter in colour, and not as strong. p. 365

**sarcomas** Cancers that originate from supportive or connective tissue. p. 140

**sarcomeres** Striated muscle fibres between Z lines. p. 486

**scientific names** Latinized binomials used to formally recognize species. p. 257

**sclerenchyma** A ground tissue in which cells develop thick secondary walls, which commonly are lignified and perforated by pits through which water can pass. p. 375

**second law of thermodynamics** Principle that for any process in which a system changes from an initial to a final state, the total disorder of the system and its surroundings always increases. p. 81

**secondary cell wall** A layer added to the cell wall of plants that is more rigid and may become many times thicker than the primary cell wall. p. 73

**secondary endosymbiotic theory** The theory developed to explain the origin of the diverse types of plastids present in the protists. p. 360

**secondary growth** Plant growth that originates at lateral meristems and increases the diameter of older roots and stems. Compare with primary growth. p. 365

**secondary phloem** Phloem cells that grow outside the vascular cambium and face the outside of a tree trunk. p. 365

**secondary sex characteristics** Morphological or behavioural features associated with gender. p. 640

**secretion** A selective process in which specific small molecules and ions are transported from the body fluid (in animals with open circulatory systems) or blood (in animals with closed circulatory systems) into the excretory tubules. p. 549

**secretory vesicle** Vesicle that transports proteins to the plasma membrane. p. 64

**seed** The structure that forms when an ovule matures after a pollen grain reaches it and a sperm fertilizes the egg. p. 373

**segment polarity genes** Developmental genes in fruit flies. p. 647

**segmentation genes** Genes that work in sequence to regulate the expression of other genes. p. 647

**self-incompatible** Organisms that produce eggs and sperm that are not able to effect fertilization. p. 625

**semelparity** Reproduction in one burst. p. 736

**semi-conservative replication** The process of DNA replication in which the two parental strands separate and each serves as the template for the synthesis of new double-stranded DNA molecules. p. 206

**sensory cells** Specialized cells that detect various stimuli. They are classified into five major types, based on the type of energy that each detects. p. 581

**septa** Separations in fungal cells that separate hyphae into compartments. p. 393

**sessile** Unable to move on its own from one place to another. p. 366

**setae** Chitin-reinforced bristles that protrude outward from the body wall in some annelid worms. (Singular, seta.) p. 490

**sex pilus** Structure on the cell surface that allows a donor bacterial cell to attach to a recipient bacterial cell. p. 167

**sexual dimorphism** Differences in appearance (morphology) between males and females. p. 261

**sexual reproduction** Mode of reproduction in which male and female gametes fuse to produce a new individual. p. 129

**sexual selection** A form of natural selection established by male competition for access to females and by females' choice of mates. p. 286

**shoots** The stems and leaves of a plant. p. 370

**simple fruits** Fruits that develop from a single carpel or several united carpels (e.g., cherries, apples). p. 641

**single-stranded DNA (ssDNA)** A DNA molecule that is composed of only one strand, rather than the normal two strands. It can be found in some viruses as the genomic information. p. 315

**sinoatrial (SA) node** A small node of specialized cardiac myocytes that is evolutionarily derived from the sinus venosus and that sits where the systemic veins enter the right atrium;

controls the rate and timing of cardiac muscle cell contraction. p. 534

**sinus venosus** Venous sinus just outside the heart. In fish, the region with the fastest intrinsic rhythm. p. 534

**sister chromatid** One of two exact copies of a chromosome duplicated during replication. p. 133

**sister species** Two species in a genus that are more closely related than either is to any other species. p. 271

**site-directed mutagenesis** A molecular biology technique used to change the nucleotide sequence in a specific location on a DNA molecule. p. 244

**sitters** Insect (fruit fly) larvae that do not move very much, and their behaviour is under genetic control. p. 728

**skeletal system** Supporting system (e.g., bones) in organism's body. p. 410

**sliding filament theory** The theory that explains how muscles contract. p. 486

**smooth ER (SER)** Endoplasmic reticulum with no ribosomes attached to its membrane surfaces. Smooth ER has various functions, including synthesis of lipids that become part of cell membranes. p. 63

**social amoeba** Social, single-celled animals. p. 8

**solute** The molecules of a substance dissolved in water. p. 546

**somatic cells** Any of the cells of an organism's body other than reproductive cells. p. 155

**somites** Segments in an animal's body. p. 645

**soredia** Specialized cell clusters produced by lichens, consisting of a mass of algal cells surrounded by fungal hyphae. Soredia function like reproductive spores and can give rise to a new lichen. (Singular, soredium.) p. 402

**specialized chlorophyll a** The chlorophyll located in the reaction centre of a photosystem. p. 106

**speciation** The processes by which species form. p. 268

**species** A group of populations in which the individuals are so closely related in structure, biochemistry, and behaviour that they can successfully interbreed. p. 271

**species concept** The diversity of definitions of a species reflects the variety of living organisms. p. 260

**species richness** The number of species that live within an ecological community. p. 339

**spicules** Skeletal elements in sponges. p. 416

**spiracles** In insects, the openings to the tracheal system used in gaseous exchange. p. 508

**spliceosome** An RNA-protein complex that promotes the removal of introns from unspliced mRNA molecules prior to their export from the nucleus. p. 221

**splicing** The process of removing introns from mRNA molecules prior to their export from the nucleus. p. 221

**sporangia** In fungi and plants, single-celled or multicellular structures in which spores are produced. (Singular, sporangium.) p. 379

**spore** A haploid reproductive structure, usually a single cell, that can develop into a new individual without fusing with another cell; found in plants, fungi, and certain protists. p. 377

**sporophyte** Diploid or asexual phase of a plant's life cycle. p. 378

**stamen** Male reproductive organ in a flower. p. 630

**start codon** The first codon of an mRNA molecule that is read by the ribosome. Its sequence is AUG. p. 222

**stele** The central core of vascular tissue in roots and shoots of vascular plants. It consists of the xylem and phloem together with supporting tissues. p. 523

**stem cells** In most multicellular organisms, undifferentiated cells that can divide without differentiating and also divide and differentiate into specialized cell types. p. 144

**stereocilia** Non-motile projections (cilia), for example, in the inner ear of vertebrates. p. 583

**stereom** The skeleton of echinoderms. p. 423

**sticky ends** Describes the ends of a DNA molecule cut by an endonuclease. Because one DNA strand is longer than the other, base pairing can occur between complementary sticky ends of different DNA fragments. p. 245

**stigma** Female part of a flower that includes the upper part of carpel that receives pollen. p. 630

**stomata** The opening between a pair of guard cells in the epidermis of a plant leaf or stem, through which gases and water vapour pass. (Singular, stoma.) p. 374

**stop codon** The final codon of an mRNA molecule that is read by the ribosome. Its sequence can be UAG, UAA, and UGA. Also called a termination codon or nonsense condon. p. 222

**stridulation** The process of making sound by rubbing one body part against another (e.g., cricket). p. 637

**stroke volume** The volume that is pumped by each ventricle during each heart beat. p. 536

**stroma** An inner compartment of a chloroplast, enclosed by two boundary membranes and containing a third membrane system. p. 67

**style** The slender stalk of a carpel situated between the ovary and the stigma in plants. p. 630

**substrate** The particular reacting molecule or molecular group that an enzyme catalyzes. p. 86

**substrate-level phosphorylation** An enzyme-catalyzed reaction that transfers a phosphate group from a substrate to ADP. p. 114

**subterranean root system** An underground (or submerged) network of roots with a large surface area that favours the rapid uptake of soil water and dissolved mineral ions. p. 438

**succession** The change from one community type to another. p. 690

**suprachiasmatic nucleus** Small nuclei in the hypothalamus that are thought to regulate circadian rhythms. Online Ch. 26

**suspension feeders** Animals that ingest small food items suspended in water. p. 458

**symbionts** Two or more species whose ecological relations are intimately tied together (symbiosis). p. 6

**sympathetic** The division of the autonomic nervous system that predominates in situations involving stress, danger, excitement, or strenuous physical activity. p. 593

**sympatric** Two species that live in the same area are sympatric. See also parapatric. p. 269

**synapse** A site where a neuron makes a communicating connection with another neuron or an effector, such as a muscle fibre or gland. p. 579

**synapsis** Process in meiosis in which homologous chromosomes come together and pair. p. 156

**synaptic vesicle** Small, intracellular, membrane-bound vesicles containing neurotransmitters that are released into the synapse to signal the receiving cell. p. 579

**systole** The period during which the heart is contracting and ejecting blood. p. 534

**systolic pressure** The blood pressure measured during contraction of the left ventricle. p. 534

**T cell** A lymphocyte produced by the division of stem cells in the bone marrow and then released into the blood and carried to the thymus grand. T cells participate in adaptive immunity. p. 315

**T cell receptor (TCR)** A protein found on the plasma membrane of T cells that can detect a specific antigen. p. 613

**taproot** A type of root consisting of a single main root from which lateral roots can extend; often stores starch. p. 372

**Taq polymerase** A heat stable DNA polymerase enzyme isolated from the thermophilic bacterium *Thermus aquaticus*. It is the key component of the PCR reaction. p. 243

**target cells** A cell with receptors for a certain chemical signalling molecule. p. 564

**teichoic acid** A component of the cell wall of Gram positive bacteria. p. 332

**telomerase** An enzyme that adds telomere repeats to the end of a chromosome. p. 209

**telomere theory of aging** A theory that suggests cells lose telomere length as they divide, eventually reaching a point where they can no longer accurately replicate their chromosomes. At this point the cell enters into a terminal phase where it will not divide again. p. 210

**telophase I, telophase II** The final phases of mitosis, meiosis I and meiosos II, respectively, during which the spindle disassembles, the chromosomes decondense, and the nuclei re-form. p. 156 , 157

**tendons** The connective tissue connecting muscles to bone. p. 480

**terminal bud** A bud that develops at the apex of a shoot. p. 374

**termination signal** A specific DNA sequence that signals the end of transcription. p. 217

**terrestrial** Existing or occurring on land. p. 440

**testcross** A genetic cross between an individual with the dominant phenotype and a homozygous recessive individual. p. 178

**testes** Male gonads that produce sperm. Online Ch. 26

**testosterone** A hormone produced by the testes; responsible for the development of male secondary sex characteristics and the functioning of the male reproductive organs. Online Ch. 26

**tetrad** Homologous pair consisting of four chromatids. p. 156

**tetrapod** A group of animals that includes all land-living vertebrates, amphibians, reptiles, birds, and mammals. Most species have four legs, and several have secondarily lost their limbs (such as snakes). p. 425

**thallus** A plant or lichen body not differentiated into stems, roots, or leaves. (Plural, thalli.) p. 402

**theory of endosymbiosis** A theory that hypothesizes that mitochondria and plastids are descendants of prokaryotic cells that were engulfed by, and formed a symbiotic relationship with, a larger host cell. p. 68

**thermocycler** A laboratory instrument used to perform the PCR reaction. p. 241

**thermodynamics** The study of the energy flow during chemical and physical reactions. p. 80

**thermoreceptors** Detect heat energy. p. 582

**thermoregulate** The homeostatic maintanence of the internal body temperature to a certain set point. p. 555

**thigmotropism** Growth in response to contact with a solid object. p. 570

**threshold** In a neuron, the voltage level at which the voltage-gated sodium ion channels open, leading to the production of an action potential. p. 578

**thylakoid lumen** The space in the closed sacs that make up a membrane system within the stroma of a chloroplast. p. 67

**thylakoid membranes** The outer surfaces of closed sacs that make up a membrane system within the stroma of a chloroplast. p. 105

**thylakoids** Closed sacs that make up a membrane system within the stroma of a chloroplast. p. 67

**thymine** A pyrimidine nucleotide that base pairs with adenine in DNA molecules. p. 200

**thyroid gland** Produces the thyroid hormones thyroxine (T4) and triiodothyronine (T3), hormones that help regulate the heart rate, blood pressure, body temperature, and the rate at which food is converted into energy. Online Ch. 26

**thyroid stimulating hormone (TSH)** A hormone that stimulates the thyroid gland to grow in size and secrete thyroid hormones. Online Ch. 26

**thyroxine** The main hormone of the thyroid gland, also called T4; responsible for controlling the rate of metabolism in the body. Online Ch. 26

**tight junctions** Region of tight connection between membranes of adjacent cells. p. 73

**tissues** A group of cells and intercellular substances with the same structure and that function as a unit to carry out one or more specialized tasks. p. 437

**tokogenetic** Features such as hair colour, size, and facial features that permit the recognition of individuals. p. 260

**tonicity** The measure of osmotic pressure against a membrane. p. 92

**top-down control** Control of communities in which the top predators ultimately control the populations on lower levels of the trophic pyramid. p. 683

**totipotent** Cells that can change into any other type of cell in an animal's body. p. 639

**tracheae** In insects, the extensively branched series of air-conducting tubes formed by invaginations of the outer epidermis of the animal and reinforced by rings of chitin. In vertebrates, this is the windpipe, which branches to the bronchi. p. 508

**tracheal system** A branching network of tubes that carries air from small openings in the exoskeleton of an insect to tissues throughout its body. p. 508

**tracheids** Conducting cells of xylem, usually elongated and tapered. p. 523

**tracheoles** The small branches of the tracheal system in insects that penetrate between all the cells of the body. p. 508

**trade-offs** Occur when organisms put energy into one aspect of reproduction, thereby reducing the energy available for other activities. p. 672

**trait** A particular variation in a genetic or phenotypic character. p. 174

**transcription** The mechanism by which the information encoded in DNA is made into a complementary RNA copy. p. 56

**transcription factors** Proteins that bind to the promoter region of a gene and recruit the RNA polymerase to begin transcription. p. 227

**transcription initiation site** A specific DNA sequence that signals where to begin transcription. p. 217

**transcriptome** A term used to discribe all the transcripts present in a cell or organism. p. 250

**transcriptomics** The study of all of the transcripts present in a cell or organism. p. 250

**transduction** In cell signalling, the process of changing a signal into the form necessary to cause the cellular response. In prokaryotes, it is the process in which DNA is transferred from donor to recipient bacterial cells by an infecting bacteriophage. p. 330

**transfer RNA (tRNA)** A small RNA molecule that translates the nucleic acid codons of the mRNA molecule into the amino acid sequence of a protein. p. 219

**transformation** The uptake and incorporation of foreign DNA by a bacterium. This can lead to horizontal gene transfer. p. 330

**transgene** A gene that has been cloned and incorporated into the genome of a different organism. p. 247

**transgenic organism** An organism that contains a gene that has been cloned and incorporated from a different organism. p. 248

**transition state** An intermediate arrangement of atoms and bonds that both the reactants and the products of a reaction can assume. p. 86

**translation** In genetics, a chromosomal alteration that occurs if a broken segment is attached to a different, non-homologous chromosome. In vascular plants, the long-distance transport of substances by xylem and phloem. p. 56

**translation start site** The first codon of an mRNA molecule that is read by the ribosome. Its sequence is AUG. Also called a start codon. p. 222

**translocation** Directional flow in the living sieve-tube member cells of the phloem vessels. p. 161

**transmembrane proteins** Membrane proteins that interact with the hydrophobic core of membranes and completely span the membrane. p. 59

**transpeptidase** An enzyme used by bacteria in the cross-linking of peptidogylcan. p. 602

**transpiration** The evaporation of water from a plant, principally from the leaves. p. 365

**transport protein** A protein embedded in the cell membrane. It forms a channel that allows selected polar molecules and ions to pass across the membrane. p. 60

**transposable element (TE)** A sequence of DNA that can move from one place to another within the genome of a cell. p. 167

**transposon** A short sequence of DNA that can move from one location to another within the genome of a cell. p. 313

**trichome** A single-celled or multicellular outgrowth from the epidermis of a plant; provides protection and shade and often gives the stems or leaves a hairy appearance (transposon). p. 376

**triiodothyronine** A hormone secreted by the thyroid gland and that regulates metabolism. Online Ch. 26

**trophic cascade** The effects of predator–prey interactions that reverberate through other population interactions at two or more trophic levels in an ecosystem. p. 683

**trophic pyramid** The relationship among trophic levels. Because there is an incomplete transfer of energy between two trophic levels biomass decreases as trophic level increases. p. 683

**true breeders** Individual that passes traits without change from one generation to the next. p. 174

**tumour** An abnormal mass of tissue that results from uncontrolled and excessive cell division. Also called a neoplasm. p. 139

**turgor** The internal hydrostatic pressure within plant cells; the normal fullness or tension produced by the fluid content of plant and animal cells p. 94

**turnover time** The time it takes for a substance to move through a storage reservoir. p. 694

**tyloses** In plants, outgrowths of xylem cells that block the movement of viruses and bacteria through the plant vascular system. p. 608

**tympanum** A thin membrane in the auditory canal that vibrates back and forth when struck by sound waves. p. 584

**type specimen** The original specimen on which the description of a species is based. p. 265

**uniform (mixed pool) flow** The tidal movement of air in and out of the lungs of mammals. p. 512

**uniparental inheritance** Inheritiance of genes from only one parent to all offspring. p. 187

**urban adapters** Organisms that are able to cope in urban environments. p. 752

**urban exploiters** Organisms that thrive in urban environments. p. 752

**urinary system** Excretory system in vertebrates; includes kidneys, ureters, bladder, and urethra. p. 410

**USFWS** United States Fish and Wildlife Service p. 17

**vacuoles** Membrane-enclosed spaces or vesicles in the cytoplasm of a cell. p. 66

**vascular cambium** A lateral meristem that produces secondary vascular tissues in plants. p. 365

**vascular fluids** The extracellular fluid that circulates water and nutrients through the vessels of the circulatory system. p. 528

**vascular tissue** In plants and animals, the tissue that transports water and nutrients around the body. p. 375

**vaults** Cytoplasmic ribonucleoprotein organelles found in the cytoplasm of some eukaryotic cells. p. 72

**vena cava** A large vein that carries deoxygenated blood from the body into the right side of the heart. p. 538

**ventilation** The movement of air between the environment and the lungs via inhalation and exhalation. p. 506

**vertical gene transfer** The transfer of heritable factors from one generation to the next. p. 273

**vesicle** A small, membrane-bound compartment that transfers substances between parts of the endomembrane system. p. 63

**vessel elements** A cell type found in xylem tissue that conducts water from the root of the plant to the stem and leaves. p. 523

**viral RNA (vRNA)** The RNA genome of a virus. p. 315

**vivipary** Gives birth to live young that were nourished via a placenta or placenta-like structure. p. 649

**Wallace's line** A line separating the Australasian and Oriental biotas. p. 298

**wavelength** The distance between two successive peaks of electromagnetic radiation. p. 102

**weathering** Dissolution of rocks and sediments through physical and chemical reactions. p. 695

**white blood cells** Important components of the vertebrate immune systems. Also called leucocytes. p. 608

**woody plant** A plant with hard, woody parts or stems, usually containing the tough protein lignin. p. 438

**wound healing** A process in which tissue repairs itself after injury. p. 132

**X-linked gene** Gene located on the X chromosome p. 187

**X-linked recessive disorders** Diseases caused by the expression of recessive alleles located on the X chromosome. p. 187

**X-ray crystallography** A method used to determine the location of specific atoms within a larger molecule. Franklin, Watson, and Crick used this method to help deduce the molecular structure of DNA. p. 202

**xenoestrogen** One of a class of human-produced molecules that mimic the biological effects of estrogen. p. 230

**xylem** The plant vascular tissue that distributes water and nutrients. p. 365

**Z line** Dark line separating sarcomeres in vertebrate muscles. p. 486

**zoonotic disease** Diseases that can spread from animals to humans. p. 755

**zygote** A fertilized egg. p. 154

# Index

*The letter f designates illustration; t designates table;* **bold** *designates defined or introduced term.*

*2,4-D (2,4-dichlorophenoxyacetic acid),* 283, 568
3-phosphoglycerate (3-PGA), 109
3' poly-A-tail, 221
5' cap, 221
23andMe, 172
1000 Genomes Project, 249

Abiotic factors, **282**, 283, 656
ABO blood typing, 185, 185f
Abscisic acid, 567t
Açai palm, 747
Acanthocephalan worms, 737
Acetylation, **204**, 647
Acetylsalicylic acid (Aspirin), 365
Acid, F-19
Acidic solution, F-19
Acidophilic archaea, **340**, 341f
Acoelomate animals, 414f
Acquired immune deficiency syndrome (AIDS), 618–620
ACTH. *See* Adrenocorticotropic hormone (ACTH)
Actin filaments, **70**
Action potential, 577–**579**
Activation energy, **86**
Active site, **86**, 87f
Active transport, **94**–95
Adaptive arms race, 602–603
Adaptive immunity, 609–616
Adenine, 202f
Adenosine diphosphate (ADP), **85**
Adenosine triphosphate. *See* ATP
ADH. *See* Antidiuretic hormone (ADH)
Adhesion, **524**
Adiabatic cooling, F-43, F-45
Adipose tissue, 412f
Adjuvant, 616
ADP. *See* Adenosine diphosphate (ADP)
Adrenal cortex, 572f, 573t
Adrenal medulla, 572f, 573t
Adrenaline, 566, 581
Adrenocorticotropic hormone (ACTH), 572t, 574f
Adventitious roots, 372, 373f
Aerial root system, 438
Aerobes, **121**
Aerobic respiration, **121**
Afferent neurons, 576, 577f
African sleeping sickness, 350
*Agaricus bisporus,* 398f
Age pyramids, 674f
Agglutination, 611, 612f
Aggregate fruits, **641**
Agnatha, 413
Agouti mouse model, 232–233, 232f
Agriculture/agricultural production, 711, 720
Aichi Biodiversity Targets, 716
AIDS. *See* Acquired immune deficiency syndrome (AIDS)

Air circulation (wind patterns), F-42
Alanine, F-28
Alarm call, 739
Alcohol overconsumption, 124
Alcoholic fermentation, 101, **122f**, 123–124
Aldosterone, 573t
Algal biotechnology, 254
Algal blooms, 327, 712, 721f
Alkaline solution, F-19
All-or-nothing principle, **579**
Allele, 152–154
Allergies, 619
Allopatric, **269**, 272
Allopolyploid, **271**
Allosteric activation, 90f
Allosteric inhibition, 90f
α helix, F-31
Altered chromosomal structure, 161–162
Alternation of generations, 378, 378f, 624–626
Altitude (thin air), 503t, 516
Altruistic behaviour, **738**
Alveolates, 350
Alveolus (alveoli), **509**, 509f
Amazon molly, 274
Amazon region, 710, 717, 722, 747
Ambrosia beetles, 9
Ambush hunters, 735, 736f
American wigeon, 31, 31f
Amino acid residues, F-27
Amino acids, 451–452, F-27–F-28
Amino group, F-23
Ammonia, 548, 549f
Ammonites, 430
Amniocentesis, **191**, 192f
Amniotic eggs, **426**, 644
Amoebozoa, 354–356
Amphibians, 425–426, 533f
Amphipathic molecules, F-18, F-38
Amplification, **566**
Amylose, F-26
*Anabaena,* 337, 337f
Anabolic pathway, **91**, 91f
Anaerobes, **121**
Anaerobic respiration, **121**–122
Analogue signals, 739
Anaphase, 135, 135f
Anaphase I, **156**, 159f
Anaphase II, **156**, 159f
Anaphylactic shock, 619
Anatomical adaptations, 439, 439f, 445
Anchoring junction, **73**, 74f
Androdioecy, **273**
Anemophily, 631
Aneuploidy, **163**
Angiosperms, **382**–383, 438, 438f, 625, 627f, 630
Anglerfish, 464–465, 464f, 671, 672f, 735, 735f
Animal farmers, 8–9
Animal hormones, 571–574
Animal life cycle, 155f
Animal skeletons, 441
Animals, 408–432
   amphibians, 425–426
   annelida, 419–420

appendages, 413–415
arthropoda, 421–422
behaviour. *See* Behaviour
birds. *See* Birds
body plans, 413–415
chordata, 424–428
cnidaria, 416–417, 417f
development, 641–644
echinodermata, 423
fish, 424–425, 425f
fossil record, 428–431
hemichordata, 424, 424f
hormones, 571–574
mollusca, 420–421
movement, 482–487
nutrient requirements, 451–452
obtaining nutrients, 457–463, 464–465
organ systems, 410
organs and systems, 440–441
orientation and symmetry, 415, 415f
phyla, 416t
platyhelminths, 418–419
porifera, 415–416, 417f
reproduction, 635–639
reptiles, 426–427, 426f
syndermata, 419
temperature change, 555–557
tissue types, 410–413
transport, 528–541
water and solute balance, 547–551
Anion, 456, F-11
Annelids, 419–420, 420f, 478
Annual plants, **373**, 374f
*Anomalocaris,* 429, 429f
Anterior pituitary, 572f, 572t
Antheridium, **379**, 379f
Anthrome, **749**
Anthropogenic disturbances, 720
Anthropogenic forest, 747
Antibiotics, 14, 168
Antibodies, 611, 612f, F-27
Antibody-based diagnostic tests, 612, 613f
Antibody-mediated immunity, 611, 613–614
Anticodon, **219**
Antidiuretic hormone (ADH), 572t, 574f
Antifreeze proteins, 558
Antigen-MHC complex, 613, 614f
Antigens, **611**
Antihistamines, 619
Aorta, **537**
Apex predator, **681**, 684t
Apical dominance, **370**
Apical meristem, **370**, 371f
Apicomplexa, 350
Apolipoproteins, F-27
Apoptosis, **141**, 144–145, 146f, 608, 614, 616, 646
Aposematic signals, 737, 739
Apple maggots, 270–271
Apple tree, 215–216
Aquaporin/aquaporins, **92**, 93f, F-27
Arbuscular mycorrhizae, **401**
Archaea, 329f, 339–341. *See also* Bacteria and archaea
Archaeplastida, 356–359

Stroma, **67**, 68f
Stromatolites, 307, 307f
Strong acid/base, F-20
Structural biological composites, 476t
Structural formula, F-12
Structural proteins, F-27
Structure-function relationships, 436–437
Style, **630**
Substrate, **86**, 87f
Substrate-phosphorylation, 114
Subterranean root system, **438**
Succession, **690–691**
Sucrose, F-25
Suction feeding, 464–465
Suicidal reproduction, 736–737
Sulfhydryl group, F-23
Sulphophilic stage, 690f, 691
Sulphur, 451
Sumatran orangutan, 705, 705f
Sundew plant, 464
Sunflowers, 451, 473f, 490, 490f
Sunlight, 102
Superb fairywren, 44, 45f
Superbugs, 168
Support and movement, 470–499
  biomineralization, 473–476
  bones, 478–481
  burrowing, 493
  cell walls, 477
  control over locomotion, 488
  costs of movement, 483–486
  flight, 494–496
  hydraulic movement, 497
  jet propulsion, 496–497
  joints and flexibility, 487
  movement, 481–497
  muscle contraction, 486
  shells, 478
  size and density (support), 472–473
  spicules, 477–478
  stereoms, 478
  supporting structures, 477–481
  swimming, 493
  tubes, 478
  undulations, 490–492
Surface area-to-volume ratio, 60
Surface tension, F-16
Survival and prosperity, 434–447
  animal organs and systems, 440–441
  control systems, 443–444
  integrated body systems, 441–445
  plant organs and systems, 438–439
  roots and shoots, 438–439
  structure-function relationships, 436–437
  tissues, organs, and systems, 437–438
Survivorship curves, 671, 671f
Suspension feeders, **458**, 735
Suspensor, 640, 641f
Svalbard archipelago, 481, 482f
Swallow-tailed bee eater, 427f
Sweating, 553
Swimming, 493
Swine flu, 598, 754, 755
Symbioses, 40, 683
Symmetrical animal, 415
Sympathetic system, 592f, 593
Sympatric, 72, **269**
Synapse, **579**, 580f
Synapsis, **156**, 158f
Syndermata, 419
Synovial joint, 487, 487f

System, 81, 81f
Systemic lupus erythematosus (lupus), 619–620
Systole, **534**
Systolic pressure, **534**

*T. aquaticus (Thermus aquaticus)*, 243, 335
*T. gondii (Toxoplasma gondii)*, 345, 753–754
T cell, **315**, 610f, 613, 614, 618
T cell receptor (TCR), 611f, **613**, 615f
T-T dimer, 211
TAARs. *See* Trace amine-associated receptors (TAARs)
Tail flagging, 732, 739
Tapeworm, 418f, 419, 464f
Taproots, **372**, 373f
*Taq* polymerase, **243**
Target cells, **564**, 571
Taste, 585–587
Taxonomy, 30
TCA cycle, 115
Technology and population growth, 675
Teichoic acid, **332**, 333f
Telomerase, **209**, 210, 211f
Telomere theory of aging, **210**
Telophase, 135, 135f
Telophase I, **156**, 159f
Telophase II, **156**, 159f
Temperate forest ecosystem, 686
Temperature/temperature change, 552–557
  animals, 555–557
  ecotherms, 555–556
  endotherms, 556–557
  freeze tolerance/freeze avoidance, 554, 554f
  heat gain/loss, 553
  heat shock proteins (HSPs), 555
  plants, 553–555
Tendons, **480–481**
Tendrils, 439f, 570
Terminal bud, **374**
Termination signal, **217**, 217f
Termite gut protists, 348
Termites, 9, 12f, 280, 759
Terrestrial ecoregions, F-46
Terrestrial forest ecosystem, 33, 37f
Tertiary structure (proteins), F-30, F-32
Testcross, **178**, 178f
Testes, 572f, 573t
Testosterone, 566, 573t, 650
Tetrad, **156**
Tetrodotoxin, 602, 602f, 603f
*Teuthidodrilus samae*, 420, 420f
Thallus, **402**
Theory of endosymbiosis, **68**, 69f
Therapeutic enzymes, 88
Thermal acclimation, 554, 557
Thermocycler, **241**
Thermodynamics, 80–82
Thermoreceptors, **582f**, 587
Thermoregulation, 539, **555**
Thiamine, 453t
Thigmotropism, **569**
Thorns, 600, 609f, 729
Three-spined stickleback, 599–600, 600f
Threonine, F-28
Threshold, **578**
Thrips, 384–385
Thrush, 393
Thylakoid lumen, **67**, 105
Thylakoid membrane, **105**, 105f
Thylakoids, **67**, 105, 105f

Thymine, 202f
Thymine dimers, 212f
Thyroid gland, 572f, 573t
Thyroid-stimulating hormone (TSH), 572t, 574f
Thyropterid bats, 490, 491f
Thyroxine, 573t
Tiger moth, 731, 731f
Tight junction, **73**, 74f
Time-lapse microscopy, 52–53, 53f
Time scales, 696
Tobacco hornworm, 497
Tocopherol, 452t
Tokogenetic, **260**
Tomato, 104, 104f
Tongue, 586f
Tonicity, **92–93**, 93f
Tool use, 742–743
Top-down control, **683–684**, 685
Topiary, 372
Topography, F-45
Torricelli, Evangelista, 504
Tortoise, 442f
Totipotent, **639**
Toucan, 442f
Touch, 582
Toughness, 475
Toxins, F-27
*TP53* gene, 141
Trabeculae, 480
Trace amine-associated receptors (TAARs), 743
Trace gases, 694f
Tracheal system, **508**, 509f
Tracheids, **523**
Trade winds, F-42, F-44
Transcription, **56**, 218–219
Transcription factors, 219, 220f, **227**
Transcription start site, 217, 217f
Transcriptional regulation, 227–230, 227f
Transcriptomics, 250
Transduction, 167, 167f, **330**
Transfer RNA (tRNA), **219**
Transformation, 167, 167f, 199, 199f, 245, **330**
Transgene, **247**
Transgenic maize, 88
Transgenic organisms, **248**
Translation, **56**
Translation start site, **222**
Translational regulation, 227f, 230–231
Translocation, 161f, 162, 526, 526f
Transmembrane protein, **59**
Transpeptidase, **602**
Transpiration, **365**, 524, 525f, 553
Transplantation of organs, 618
Transport, 520–543
  animals, 528–541
  arteries, 538, 538f
  blood pressure, 541
  capillaries, 538–539, 538f
  cardiac cycle, 534–537
  cardiac output, 541
  extracellular/intracellular pathway, 522f
  guard cells, 524–526
  muscular pumps, 530–533
  open/closed tubular systems, 529–530, 531f
  plants, 522–527
  rhythmic heartbeat, 534
  root pressure, 524
  translocation, 526, 526f
  transpiration, 524, 525f